Musicians' Union National Directory of Members 1999/2000

First Edition

■

Musicians' Union
60/62 Clapham Road
London
SW9 0JJ

Tel : 020 7582 5566
Fax : 020 7582 9805
Email : info@musiciansunion.org.uk
Website : www.musiciansunion.org.uk

D0493597

First published 1999 in Great Britain by the
Musicians' Union, 60/62 Clapham Road, London SW9 0JJ
Tel : 020 7582 5566

Produced by Rhinegold Publishing Ltd,
241 Shaftesbury Avenue, London WC2H 8EH
Tel : 020 7333 1721

British Library Cataloguing in Publication Data.
A catalogue record for this book is available from the British
Library.

ISBN 0 946890 82 X
ISSN 1466-643X

Printed in Great Britain by Perfectaprint, Byfleet, Surrey.

Contents

BAKERS *Diary service*

IS NOW UNDER NEW MANAGEMENT!

BIG IS NOT NECESSARILY BEST!

After spending the last 12 years working closely with both our clients and fixers, Sandy has now taken over the responsibility of continuing, and improving, the professional and reliable service "Bakers" is renowned for.

Our small, but highly trained, team is always ready to assist you - 7 days a week. Their combined knowledge and expertise is '2nd to none'.

Why not let us prove to you the value of our experience - move into the new Millennium with the people who care. Let us take the stress out of managing your diary, leaving you free to concentrate on "making Sweet Music"

Freedom of choice is everyone's right - make sure you use it wisely!!

If you have any questions that need answering, or want to talk about your diary requirements in more detail to help you decide if "BAKERS" could indeed make your life easier, do nor hesitate to call Sandy on any of these numbers. We are waiting for your call.

BAKERS *Diary service*

The ORIGINAL Diary Service

TELEPHONE	01483-723644
MESSAGE FACILITY	01483 723687
EMERGENCY TEL.	01483-723647
FACSIMILE	01483-723662

MUSICIANS' UNION

National Office
60/62 Clapham Road,
London SW9 0JJ

Tel: 020 7582 5566
Fax: 020 7582 9805

e-mail:
info@musiciansunion.org.uk
web site:
www.musiciansunion.org.uk

Subscription and Membership
Enquiries
020 7582 5566

General Secretary
Dennis Scard

**Assistant General
Secretaries**

Andy Knight
(Administration)

John Smith
(Media)

Bob Wearn
(Live Engagements)

Media Official
Marilyn Stoddart

Session Organiser
Howard Evans

Music Business Adviser
Nigel McCune

TONY GAMBLE

A Message from the General Secretary

Just a quick glance at the number of names listed in this new National Directory, together with the range of instruments shown, will convince you of my claim that the Musicians' Union is "the representative organisation for all musicians". One of the main strengths of the MU, nationally and internationally, is that we are a single organisation covering music teachers, performers and music writers in all areas of the music profession. It is only through our collective strength that the rates and conditions application to musicians will be improved, and it is only through a democratic organisation such as ours that any member can have a say, not only in the running of the Union, but in formulating our policies. Whilst the Union is recognised for its strengths, this reputation depends on recruiting and retaining our membership in all areas of the profession. We need you to keep up to date with your subscriptions so that the MU has sufficient income to provide the services that musicians so badly need. Remember that your strength is our strength, so let's maintain our influence by ensuring that all musicians with whom you work are in membership of the MU.

Dennis Scard

EXECUTIVE COMMITTEE

To February 2000

DISTRICT ORGANISERS

Scottish Office
11 Sandyford Place, Glasgow G3 7NB
Tel: 0141 248 3723 Fax: 0141 204 3510
Ian Smith, Scottish Organiser & Glasgow Branch Secretary
(Mobile: 0411 457944)

North West Office
40 Canal Street, Manchester M1 3WD
Tel: 0161 236 1764 Fax: 0161 236 0159
Bill Kerr, District Organiser & Manchester Branch Secretary
(Mobile: 0585 521332)

North East Office
40 Canal Street, Manchester M1 3WD
Tel: 0161 236 1764 Fax: 0161 236 0159
Elaine Rogers, District Organiser & Leeds Branch Secretary
(Mobile: 0777 5895141)

Midlands Office
Benson House, Lombard Street,
Birmingham B12 0QN
Tel: 0121 622 3870 Fax: 0121 622 5361
Bob Bennett, District Organiser & Birmingham Branch Secretary
(Mobile: 0410 889793)

East/South East Office
60/62 Clapham Road, London SW9 0JJ
Tel: 020 7840 5536 Fax: 020 7840 5599
Alfred Clarke, District Organiser
(Mobile: 0589 435444)

South West Office
131 St Georges Road, Bristol BS1 5UW
Tel: 0117 926 5438 Fax: 0117 925 3729
Paul Westwell, District Organiser & Avon Branch Secretary
(Mobile: 0421 532155)

London Office
60/62 Clapham Road London SW9 0JJ
Tel: 020 7840 5533 Fax: 020 7840 5599
Horace Trubridge, District Organiser & Central London Branch Secretary
(Mobile: 0860 507536)

BRANCHES

SCOTLAND

Aberdeen
Sarah Walsh - 48 North Deeside Road,
Aberdeen AB15 7PL
01224 322 353

Edinburgh
Bill Martin - 1 Seafield Road East,
Edinburgh EH15 1EB
0131 669 8807

Forth Valley
Peter Petrie - 7 Langour, Devonside,
Tillicoultry, Clackmannanshire FK13 6JG
01259 752 350

Glasgow
Ian Smith - 11 Sandyford Place,
Sauchiehall Street,
Glasgow G3 7NB 01412 483 723
(fax: 0141 204 3510)

Highlands/Islands
Archie Gillies - 17 Crown Circus,
Inverness IV2 3NU 01463 232 646

South West Scotland
Tom McMurdo - 12 Leslie Road,
Kilmarnock, Ayrshire KA3 7RR 01563 535 638

Strathtay
Kevin Murray - East Byres Cottage,
Balmerino, Fyfe DD6 8SB 01382 330 567

NORTH WEST DISTRICT

Cumbria
Gordon Sear - 11 Cliffe Lane,
Barrow-in-Furness, Cumbria LA14 4HU
01229 824 898

Blackpool/Lancaster/Morecambe
Len France - 44 St Georges Avenue,
Cleveleys, Blackpool FY5 3JW
01253 854 844

Central Lancashire
Harold Salisbury - 4 Grosvenor Place,
Preston, Lancashire PR2 1ED
01772 726 397

Isle of Man
c/o Bill Kerr - District Organiser

Liverpool
Martin Taggart - 53 Penkett Road,
Wallasey, Merseyside L45 7QG 0151 637 0211

Manchester
Bill Kerr - Musicians' Union, 40 Canal Street,
Manchester M1 3WD 0161 236 1764

North Wales Coast
Morgan Borthwick - 14 Patrick Avenue, Rhyl
Clywd, North Wales LL18 4TU 01745 353 264

NORTH EAST DISTRICT

Barnsley
Doug Fellowes - 3 North Close, Kirkfield Way,
Royston, Barnsley, Yorkshire S71 4NS
01226 723 297

Bradford
Walter Rathmell - Bradford Tradesmen Homes,
45 Lily Croft, Heaton Road, Bradford BD8 8QY
01274 548 364

Doncaster
Barry Wootton - 7 Clifton Court, Fieldside Thorne
Doncaster CN8 4BH 01325 359157

Durham
Keith Smith - 14 Mitford Drive, Chase Park,
Sherburn, Durham DH6 1QS 0191 372 0749

Hull/Grimsby
Eric Taylor - 15 Westhill Road,
Grimsby, South Humberside DN34 4SG
01472 343 392

Leeds
Elaine Rogers - 40 Canal Street,
Manchester M1 3WD 0161 236 1764

Lincoln
Dan McCaughern - 30 Victoria Street,
West Parade, Lincoln LN1 1HY 01522 539 730

Newcastle
Ian Heslop - 1 Fergusons Lane,
Newcastle-upon-Tyne NE15 7PL 0191 274 6104

Scarborough
Stan Wright - 51 Seamer Road, East Ayton,
Scarborough YO13 9HN 01723 864 210

Sheffield & Rotherham
Peter Piper - 18 Autumn Drive,
Maltby, Rotherham S66 7DZ 01709 816 298

South Tyne
George Hastings - 35 Chillingham Drive,
Southridge, Chester-le-Street DH2 3TJ
0191 388 2953

Teesside
c/o Elaine Rogers - District Organiser

Wearside
John Allen - 13 Emmbrook Close, East Rainton,
Houghton-le-Spring DH5 9SQ
0191 584 1071

York
Martin Boyd - 3 Grove Terrace Lane,
The Groves, York YO3 7PL
01904 635 759

EAST DISTRICT

Cambridge
Antony Teale - 71 Blinco Grove,
Cambridge CB1 4TX
01223 246 026

Clacton/Colchester
Mick Hodgson - 7 Hampstead Avenue,
Clacton-on-Sea, Essex CO16 7HE
01255 428 974

Ipswich
Paul Burrows - 20 Wharfedale Road,
Ipswich IP1 4JP
01473 400 380 (mobile: 0860 852990)

Luton
Ron Franks - 39 Chard Drive, Luton,
Bedfordshire LU3 4EQ
01582 580 736 (fax: 01582 593 207)

Mid Herts
Terry Vincent - 22 Windridge Close,
St Albans, Hertfordshire AL3 4JP
01727 862 727

Norfolk & North Suffolk
Tony Young - 103 Beccles Road,
Bungay, Suffolk NR35 1HU
01986 894 854

Peterborough
Mark Haley - 12 Admiral House, Rivergate,
Peterborough PE1 1ES
01733 897 065 (mobile: 0966 451 528)

Southend
Peter Morris - 226 Thorpe Hall Avenue,
Thorpe Bay, Essex SS1 3SE
01702 588 304

South Herts
Eddy Clayton - 3 Goodwood Avenue,
Watford, Hertfordshire WD2 5LA 01923 236 616

MIDLANDS DISTRICT

Birmingham
Bob Bennett - MU, Benson House,
Lombard Street, Birmingham B12 0QN
0121 622 3870 (fax: 0121 622 5361)

Coventry/Rugby
c/o Bob Bennett - District Organiser

Derby
Peter Wilkins - 20 Ferrers Avenue, Tutbury,
Burton-on-Trent DE13 9JR
01283 812 423

Leamington Spa
Les Spreckley - 43 Villiers Street,
Leamington Spa, Warwickshire CV32 5YA
01926 428 625

Leicester
Don Payne - 38 Waterfield Road,
Cropston, Leicester LE7 7HN
01162 364 507

Northampton
Paul Manser - 5 Coleridge Walk, Daventry,
Northants NN11 5AU 01327 878 328

Nottingham
Nev Cheetham - 15 Victoria Road, Draycott,
Derbyshire DE72 3PS 01332 874 234

Stoke
Graham Simpson - 20 The Avenue, Harpfield,
Stoke-on-Trent ST4 6BJ 01782 614 374

SOUTH EAST DISTRICT

Bognor Regis
c/o Alfred Clarke - District Organiser

Bournemouth
Grahame Laurence - 1803 Wimborne Road,
Bear Cross, Bournemouth BH11 9AY
01202 574 144

Brighton
Eddie Hurcombe - 4 Highdown Avenue,
Worthing, Sussex BN13 1PU 01903 690 542

East & South Kent
Michael Davis - 17 Nash Court Gardens,
Margate, Kent CT9 4DG 01843 293 669
Medway
Doug Young - 71 Brewer Street, Maidstone,
Kent ME14 1RZ 01622 755 085(day)
01622 200 439 (evening)

Milton Keynes
John Eastcott - 29 Eagle Gardens,
Bedford MK41 7FE 01234 215 634
Mobile 0378 283144

Oxford
Roger Woodley - 1 Melton Drive,
Didcot, Oxon OX11 7JP 01235 813 410

Portsmouth/IoW
Derek Dod - 36 Brougham Road,
Southsea, Hampshire PO5 4PA 023 9282 9819

Reading
Dorian Kelly - 11 Hill Brow, Reading,
Berkshire RG2 8JD 0118 967 3461

Southampton
Paul Mckenna - 71 Millais Road, Southampton,
Hampshire SO19 2FX 023 9244 0835
(fax: 023 9234 6326)

Surrey & N.E. Hampshire
Glenn Weston - PO Box 243,
Guildford GU2 6WQ 01483 236 632 (& fax)
(mobile: 0973 230123)

Wealden Downs
Tony Akehurst - "Homelands",
Winchelsea Road, Guestling, Hastings
TN35 4LW 01424 813 215

SOUTH WEST DISTRICT

Avon
Paul Westwell - 131 St Georges Road, Bristol
BS1 5UW 0117 926 5438 (fax: 0117 925 3729)

Cardiff
Tom Edwards - 199 Carlisle Street,
Splott, Cardiff CF2 2PE 029 2046 1205

Channel Islands
James Harrison - 1 Belle Vue Court,
Longueville Road, St Saviours, Jersey JE2 7WG
01534 852 430

Cornwall
Margaret Thomas - 38 Tresawls Avenue,
Truro, Cornwall TR1 3LA 01872 277 173

Exeter
Colin Harris - 20 Summerway,
Whipton, Exeter EX4 8DA
01392 467 562

Mid Glamorgan
Keith Stuckey - 2 Cwmneol Place,
Cwmaman, Aberdare CF44 6PA 01685 870 497

Newport
Simon Linton - 2a Gibbs Road,
Newport, Gwent NP9 8AR 01633 271 456

Plymouth
Mick Paine - 282 Tavy House, Duke St,
Devonport, Plymouth, Devon PL1 4HL
01752 568 269

Torbay
Julian Howe - 391 Teignmouth Road,
Torquay, Devon TQ1 4SW 01803 325 424

Wessex
Tim Rose - 68 Field Barn Drive, Southill,
Weymouth, Dorset DT4 0EE 01305 774 678

West Wales
Gary Martin - Melin Court P.O. 10 Hill Street,
Melin Court, West Glamorgan SA11 4AT 01639
710 204

LONDON DISTRICT

Central London
Horace Trubridge - 60/62 Clapham Road,
London SW9 0JJ 020 7840 5533
(fax: 020 7840 5599)

East & North London
Terry Childs - 60/62 Clapham Road,
London SW9 0JJ 020 7840 5530
(fax: 020 7840 5599)

South & South East London
Gary Hyde - 60/62 Clapham Road,
London SW9 0JJ 020 7840 5532
(fax: 020 7840 5599)

West & South West London
Keith Ames - 60/62 Clapham Road,
London SW9 0JJ 020 7840 5531
(fax: 020 7840 5599)

MUSICIANS' UNION SECTIONS

In addition to the geographically based Branch structure, the Union also recognises the diversity within the music profession and the Sections below have been established to facilitate representation of concerns specific to members working within these groups.

BRITISH MUSIC WRITERS' COUNCIL

Secretary: Marilyn Stoddart
(National Office - 020 7840 5558)

The British Music Writers' Council is concerned with all matters that directly or indirectly affect music writers, i.e. composers, songwriters, arrangers and copyists. Membership of the BMWC gives direct access to rates information, contract advice, and collective individual representation.

The work of the BMWC is directed by a Committee which is elected biennially and meets regularly.

Fees
The BMWC establishes the General Rate for arranging and copying and recommends fees for electro and conventional composers. These should be applied to all commissions.

Contracts
A specimen Composer's Contract, a general Arranging Contract and a Copying Contract are available free of charge from the MU office, and these contracts can be used for all commissions.

Collective and individual advice is given on all contracts that affect music writers, including complex commissioning and publishing contracts which are vetted by the Union's lawyers.

Representation
The BMWC Committee is involved in and makes representations on all matters that affect music writers. These include negotiations and discussions with media and other users. This representation is both at a collective level and also on behalf of individual members of the BMWC. Action is undertaken by Union Officials and through the legal process on behalf of members to secure payment for invoices, claims for breach of contract and similar problems. Contact Marilyn Stoddart in the Media Department for further information.

FOLK, ROOTS & TRADITIONAL MUSIC SECTION

Section Organiser: Ian Smith (Scottish Office - 0141 248 3723)

The newest Section within the Musicians' Union arose from our 1997 Biennial Delegate Conference and was created to address the specific needs of those members working in this highly specialised field. No longer seen as a 'minority' interest, the Section will be the Union's voice in this growth area within the music industry. We already have close ties with organisations such as the AFO (Association of Festival Organisers) and publications such as the 'Living Tradition'. The Section will provide a direct channel of communication to the Union's Executive Committee. The Section Committee will meet at least twice a year and a newsletter will be regularly distributed to members of the Section.

Members wishing to register should contact Ian Smith stating their name and membership number, together with a brief précis of where they would place themselves within the 'folk, roots & traditional' heading. It would also be helpful to Ian Smith if members would provide some background on where they have played i.e. venues, festivals etc. and, if they are in a band, the name of the band and the names of other band members.

FREELANCE ORCHESTRAL SECTION

Section Organiser: Bill Kerr
(Manchester Office - 0161 236 1764)

The Section is restricted to casually employed musicians in order to create a direct line of communication and facilitate closer links between the Executive Committee and members working casually in the orchestral field. The Section Committee meets regularly and a newsletter is mailed to all Section members. Members who undertake casual work in the orchestral field can register with the Freelance Orchestral Section by writing to the Membership/Subscriptions Department at National Office stating your name and membership number.

JAZZ SECTION

Section Organiser: Bob Bennett (Birmingham Office - 0121 622 3870)

The particular interests of the Union's jazz constituency are represented by the Jazz Section. The Section's elected committee meets twice a year to address matters of concern to jazz musicians, and provides a direct line of communication with the Executive Committee. The Section also maintains a regular liaison with the Association of British Jazz Musicians and Jazz Services Ltd. Members of the Jazz Section are kept informed through their own quarterly newsletter. To register with the Jazz Section, simply apply in writing to the Membership/Subscriptions Department at National Office stating your name and membership number.

SESSION SECTION

Section Organiser: Howard Evans (National Office - 020 7840 5559)

Musicians having a substantial involvement with media engagements (television, radio, commercial audio recording, library music, feature/television film and video recording) may apply for inclusion. At present the Section is restricted to members paying on 'C' and 'D' rates of subscription.

The Section Committee meets on a quarterly basis and acts as a channel of consultation and communication with the Executive Committee. An Annual General Meeting is held, usually in December. Members also receive a copy of the Section Newsletter. To register with the Session Section, apply in writing to Howard Evans at National Office stating your name and membership number.

THEATRE SECTION

Section Organiser: Paul Westwell (Bristol Office - 0117 926 5438)

The Section is primarily concerned with members working under the Union's Agreement with TMA and is intended to create direct access to theatre musicians around the country. The Section Committee meets regularly and a newsletter is mailed to all Section members. Members who undertake engagements in theatres can register with the Theatre Section by writing to the Membership/Subscriptions Department at National Office stating your name and membership number.

TEACHERS' REGISTER

Secretary: Bob Wearn (National Office - 020 7582 5566)

The Union maintains an active role in music education. All members on the Teachers' Register are kept informed on relevant issues by means of MU publications. Members involved in instrumental teaching can be included on the Teachers' Register by writing to the Membership/Subscriptions Department at National Office stating your name, membership number and the instrument(s) you teach.

GENERAL ADVICE

INFORMATION FOR MEMBERS UNDERTAKING RECORDING ENGAGEMENTS

Members should, in their own interest and as an obligation of Union membership, accept broadcasting and recording engagements only from companies and organisations with which the Union has collective agreements. Such agreements exist with the BBC, ITV Companies, and Independent Producers; also with the British Phonographic Industry on behalf of the major record producers and with a large number of independent record producers who have signed a standard agreement with the Union. These independent recording companies form the Union's "Fair List". Where engagements are not entered into directly with the above companies and organisations, they should only be accepted from "Approved Contractors", i.e. contractors who have entered into an agreement with the Union.

Information on the Fair List and the Approved Contractors' List is published periodically in Musician and Branch Newsletters, and further information can be obtained from District offices.

It is particularly important that any offers of engagements for recording, filming or broadcasting made by or on behalf of foreign companies should be immediately reported to the Union so that a satisfactory agreement can be concluded. Only in this way can members be assured of receiving the correct fees for the various uses to which their performances may be put.

PROCEDURE FOR AUDIO RECORDINGS UNDER THE BPI/MU AGREEMENT

Both as a matter of law and under Union Agreements and procedures it is necessary for the consent of musicians to be obtained before their performances are recorded. The form in which this consent is given is very important since it forms the basis for Union negotiations on such matters as payment for 'promo videos', use of commercial records in films, backing tracks and other secondary uses.

The standard agreement signed by all Union Approved Contractors includes an undertaking that the contractor will ensure that the consent of performers required by the Copyright, Designs & Patents Act 1988 (as amended) is of the type and form approved by the Union. The form of consent, included as a standard condition of all commercial audio recording engagements, has been for many years agreed with the British Phonographic Industry for commercial audio recording. Members should ensure that they sign the BPI/MU Consent Form AND NO OTHER for all commercial audio recording engagements. When completing the Consent Form members are advised to require payment via the Musicians' Union and not to give their home address for payment.

AUDIO VISUAL RECORDING ENGAGEMENTS

The Union has TV Agreements with the BBC, ITV Companies and the Producers' Alliance for Cinema and Television (PACT). The PACT/MU Agreement also covers film soundtrack sessions. Members who undertake work for PACT producers must complete a Musicians' Payment Voucher which ensures that the correct consent, required by Part II of the Copyright, Designs and Patents Act 1988 (as amended), is acquired by the producer.

INFORMATION FOR MEMBERS UNDERTAKING LIVE ENGAGEMENTS

MU members are under an obligation to observe not less than the minimum rates and conditions established by the Union. The Union's Executive Committee is responsible for fixing national minimum rates and conditions.

Rates for live engagements can be obtained from your Branch Secretary. For TV & recording rates contact the media rates department on 020 7840 5555.

Members are strongly advised to obtain written confirmation of all engagements. The Union produces printed standard contracts for many types of engagements and these can be obtained free from Branch Secretaries. The present range is as follows:

Contract 2: for the engagement of a band/group for a holiday centre engagement (to be used between holiday camp proprietor and bandleader/contractor)

Contract 2A: for the engagement of a musician for a holiday centre engagement (to be used between bandleader/contractor and musician)

Contract 3: for the engagement of a band/group for a single casual 'gig' engagement (to be used between engager and bandleader)

Contract 4: for the engagement of an orchestra/band for a theatre engagement (excluding West End of London) (to be used between management and contractor/leader)

Contract 4A: for the engagement of a musician for a theatre engagement (excluding West End of London) (to be used between contractor/leader and musician)

Contract 5: for the engagement of a band/group for a continuing engagement. Intended mainly for use in social/working men's clubs, night clubs, hotels, restaurants and similar venues (to be used between engager and bandleader)

Contract 7: for the engagement of a musical act/group/band for a specified period in clubs, cabaret rooms and similar venues (to be used between engager and leader)

Contract 8A: for the engagement of a musician for Amateur Operatic productions in venues other than theatres and cinemas (to be used between contractor and musician)

Contract 9A: for the engagement of a musician for Casual Orchestral Concerts (to be used between orchestra management and musician)

Contract 10: for private teaching (to be used between teacher and student/parent/guardian)

Contract 11: for the engagement of a solo musician for a casual engagement (to be used between engager and musician)

Contract 12: for the engagement of a solo musician for a continuing engagement (to be used between engager and musician)

Contract 13: for teaching in independent schools (to be used between teacher and school)

Contract 14: for the engagement of a band or group on a profit sharing basis.

It is in members' own interests to use the above contracts, since they provide clear evidence of the conditions of an engagement if a dispute should arise. In general, the Executive Committee is reluctant to grant legal assistance in cases where a claim arises from an engagement to which an MU standard contract applies but was not used.

In cases where standard MU contracts are not used, written evidence of engagements is still desirable. A letter or note should specify the date, time and place of the engagement, the fee, and the fact that the engagement is subject to Union rates and conditions. Such a letter or note should be signed by someone fully authorised to be responsible for payment.

It is particularly important that contracts for engagements abroad should be approved by the Union before they are entered into. In addition to ensuring that the rates and conditions are satisfactory (e.g. provision of adequate subsistence payments, fares and insurances), such notification will, in some countries, avoid difficulties arising with the national unions of those countries.

MUSIC BUSINESS, CONTRACT AND CAREER ADVICE

Throughout their professional lives, many musicians are required to enter into complex and often long-term agreements for such things as their recording and song writing services, the engagement of management, and contracts for touring and merchandising. It is vital that the musician receives expert advice on the terms and implications of such contracts and this can be obtained from one of the many solicitors who specialise in music business matters.

In the early stages of a musical career members may be invited to enter into an agreement whilst not having the means to pay for legal advice. To cater for such circumstances, the MU offers to its members a contract advisory service which, in the majority of cases, is available at no cost to the member. Expert advice can be given on how to negotiate the best deal in any given situation.

Career advice is also available to members seeking to increase employment opportunities in all areas of the music business. Marketing advice and information is available to enable performers to raise their profile through constructive use of the live gig circuit.
A range of information leaflets and fact files is available, aimed at making the business side of a musician's career easier to run. Assistance is also provided in the form of regularly up-dated lists of music industry contacts within record companies,

publishing companies, agents, managers, promoters, etc.

Members wishing to make use of these services should contact the Music Business Adviser, Nigel McCune, at National Office where a personal appointment can be arranged.

PR/COMMUNICATIONS

The Union has various ways of communicating with members, including the quarterly Musician magazine and Branch newsletters. Enquiries should be addressed in writing to: PR/Communications, National Office, or via your Branch Secretary. Information about the MU is also available on the web site: www.musiciansunion.org.uk.

MUSIC PROMOTION ACTIVITIES

Over the years the MU has achieved increasing recognition for our significant role in the actual promotion of music, both by compensating for deficiencies in funding from public sources, which regrettably continues to decline, and by stimulating entirely new initiatives. The MU has been responsible for assisting many musicians to earn their livelihood through a wide range of music activity. It is certain that we are called upon to help promote a wider range of music than probably any other funding organisation in the UK.

These activities are decided by the Music Promotion Committee, a panel of wide musical experience elected from the ranks of the Executive Committee and comprising half its membership. In any typical year, direct financial assistance will be granted to around 400 different music organisation, with the consequent creation of jobs for thousands of MU members.

Where major financial assistance has been given to other organisations, this has been the result of fuller discussion by the full EC.

Guidelines for funding applications and application forms can be obtained from the Music Promotion Officer at National Office, telephone 020 7840 5513.

LEGAL ASSISTANCE

The Union's legal assistance is mainly intended to help in obtaining outstanding sums of money owed to members for non-payment of fees for engagements, breaches of contract, or dismissals without the requisite notice.

Requests for legal assistance should be made in writing to your Branch Secretary but the following points should be borne in mind:

1. Although the Union will take all practicable steps to assist members in the recovery of fees, the provision of solicitors' services remains at the discretion of the Executive Committee.
2. The amount owing must be more than £20.
3. All correspondence and documents (contracts if possible) should be sent with the request to the Branch Secretary.
4. Your membership must be up-to-date (see Rule XV.4.b) and your subscription must have been paid at the correct rate.
5. If there is an appropriate MU Standard Contract it must have been used for the engagement (the current range of MU Standard Contracts is shown elsewhere in the Diary and can be obtained from your Branch Secretary).

Other cases will be considered on their merits.

Please remember casual engagements cannot be cancelled, and, if an engager attempts to do so, the full fees should be claimed. However, every effort should be made by the musician to get other employment on the date and, if successful, the amount earned must be deducted from that claimed.

An engagement on a continuing contract is subject to at least two weeks' notice or payment in lieu of this notice. This applies whether the engagement is for one or more nights a week.

It is in your interests that all contracts including those with managers, agents, recording and publishing companies are submitted for approval by the Music Business Advice department (020 7840 5514).

TAXATION NOTES

The processing of a return by the Inland Revenue and their calculation of the tax etc due based on the return (or agreement/correction of tax calculated by the tax payer) does not constitute agreement or acceptance of the tax return. The Inland Revenue have, if the tax return is filed on time, a year from the filing date to raise queries or start an investigation - and they do not need to give reasons.

Employees

Employees are taxed under PAYE through a tax code reflecting entitlement to personal allowances and any allowable expenses/deductions. The self-assessment rules relating to completion and submission of tax returns, payment of tax due not collected through PAYE, keeping records relating to tax returns and the need to notify the Inland Revenue of new sources of income also apply to employees as well as to the self-employed. From 6th April 1998 there were new rules for employees regarding tax relief on travel and subsistence expenses which may be particularly advantageous to 'site based' employees.

Tax Returns

The tax return must now be fully as well as accurately completed. If you do not receive a tax return or receive the right supplementary schedules, and you have income that needs to be declared, then you must request a return and/or the supplementary schedules. If you have untaxed income for 1998/99 and you haven't requested a tax return by 6th October 1999 then you can be liable to a penalty up to the amount of tax unpaid at 31st January 2000. Even if the self-employed decide to submit accounts (no longer necessary), relevant details must still be extracted from the accounts, summarised and included on the tax return. Failure will incur fixed automatic penalties starting at £100. Penalties not paid within 28 days will also attract interest. Tax returns for the year ended 5th April 2000 must be received by 30th September 2000 if the Inland Revenue are to calculate the tax due (tax returns must be completed in all other respects) or by 31st January 2001 if you calculate the tax due.

Current Basis of Assessment

From 6th April 1998 all self-employed, irrespective of when they started self-employment, are on a current year basis (i.e. taxed on the accounts that ended in the current tax year). It may be appropriate for them to review their financial year end date to see if a change appears potentially advantageous.

Tax and Class 4 NIC Payments

'Payments on account' are required twice a year with a third 'balancing' payment. For the 1999/2000 tax year, the first 'on account' payment will be due on 31st January 2000 with the second on 31st July 2000. The balancing payment is due on 31st January 2001 (the balancing payment is the difference between the liability for the year and the payments already made on account). Each payment on account is 50% of the previous year's net tax liability, subject to a total £500 de minimis

provision. Applications may be made to reduce the payments on account but penalties apply to negligent and fraudulent applications. Additionally, interest will be charged on 'over-reduced' payments, whatever the reason.

Interest is charged on late payments of tax though interest (at a lower rate) is payable on over payments. Furthermore, surcharges additionally apply to balancing payments made more than 28 days late. Late payment of surcharges also attracts interest.

Don't forget Class 2 NI Contributions are payable in addition to Class 4.

Keeping Records

Since 6th April 1996 it has been a legal requirement to keep records to support all entries on the tax return. This means employees need to keep P60s, P45s, P11Ds, interest certificates, dividend vouchers etc. In addition the self-employed must keep full and proper records detailing all monies received and spent in connection with the business; also records of all goods sold and bought are required. A detailed mileage log must be kept so that motor expenses can be accurately apportioned between business and private usage.

From the date on which the tax return was filed or, if filed early, from the filing deadline, employees must keep records for one year and the self-employed for five years. If there is an investigation, records may have to be kept longer. Failure to keep proper records can incur penalties of up to £3,000 per year.

Conclusion

The above notes, which were believed to be accurate at the time of preparation (15th March 1999) but give no more than a brief introduction to certain key implications, were prepared by John Seeley & Co, accountants specialising in the accountancy and taxation affairs of musicians and others involved in the music and entertainment industries throughout the UK. For a copy of their free 'Financial Guide for Musicians' contact them on 0121 429 1504.

PERSONAL FINANCIAL ADVICE

If you are in difficulties with the Inland Revenue, National Insurance contributions, VAT, your "band" finances, or just in need of some financial advice, the MU can help. Our Music Business Advice Department has a list of specialist accountants used to dealing with musicians' problems. For local firms contact your Branch Secretary or District Organiser.

MUSICIANS' UNION BENEFITS ADMINISTRATION

There are a number of further benefits available to members whose subscriptions are fully paid up at the correct rate. MUBA is administered on the Union's behalf by AON Risk Services.

Aon Risk Services is the Union's only recommended insurance broker. They provide all the insurance for the MU and offer specialist insurance for musicians on instruments, studios, equipment, travel, motor, house and events as well as the benefits listed below. Telephone free on 0800 387 250 or write to Aon Risk Services, FREEPOST, PO Box 1012, Caterham CR3 5XF.

INSTRUMENT BENEFIT

As a member who is registered with the MUBA Scheme, you are able to claim if you lose or suffer damage to your instruments.

Am I automatically covered?
No, you must register your instrument(s) with the MUBA Scheme.

Where do I get a registration form?
From your Branch Secretary.

What is the amount of the Instrument Benefit?
It is limited to £500 in any 12-month period.

How does the scheme work?
Firstly you must arrange insurance bearing a voluntary excess of £500 and then complete the MUBA registration form and return it to MU Benefits Administration. You must register to qualify for this scheme.

What is meant by an excess?
It is the first part of a claim which is not covered by the insurance.

What is a voluntary excess?
It is an excess additional to any imposed by an insurer in certain specified circumstances.

Are there any points I should bear in mind when I am arranging my insurance?
Yes, two especially:
(1) You should ensure that, in the event of a claim for more than £500, your insurer will co-operate

with the MU Benefits Administration if requested.
(2) As your entitlement to benefit in the event of a claim could be reduced or used up completely during an 12-month period, your insurance should be arranged so that on payment of an additional premium the excess can be reduced or waived until the anniversary date of the claim.

Are there any insurances available which fit these requirements?
Yes - Aon is the recommended insurance broker for the MU and provides specialist insurance for musicians. You can telephone Aon direct on 0800 387 250.

What if my instruments are not worth £500?
Use the same enrolment form, but additionally give details of the instruments you wish to cover. There is a special section on the form for members who do not own instruments together valued at more than £500, or who do, but do not wish more protection than £500 annually.

Would my instruments be covered if I left them in a vehicle at night for more than half an hour?
No benefit would be paid: if you wish such cover you should arrange your insurance accordingly.

Can any instrument or equipment be covered under this scheme?
Yes, provided it is owned personally and exclusively by the member and used for the member's professional purposes.

What about geographical scope?
Anywhere within the EU and on ships where the member is musically employed under a contract, the terms and conditions of which have been approved by the Musicians' Union.
Can cover be extended beyond the EU?
Yes, on a contract for an engagement abroad approved by the Union, the geographical scope may be extended on application to MUBA.

VEHICLE INSURANCE

The Union has arranged with AON to provide at competitive prices tailored vehicle insurance cover (cars and vans) for musicians. For further details telephone AON Risk Services on 0845 603 0606.

MATERNITY, SICKNESS OR ACCIDENT BENEFIT

Am I automatically covered?
Yes, there is no need to do anything until you want to claim benefit.

Is there a qualifying period of Union membership?
Yes, it is necessary for you to have been a member for at least six months prior to your accident or the start of your illness.

How do I claim?
Simply complete a claim form obtainable from MU Benefits Administration or from your Branch Secretary.

How much can I get?
For any period of four weeks' continuous total unemployment due to pregnancy, illness or accident the benefit provides for a payment of £40. This may be increased for periods of incapacity longer than four weeks but in no case may benefit exceeding £80 be paid in any calendar year. The maximum benefit payable in any period of three consecutive years may not exceed £160.

Benefit payments cannot be made to members who owed subscriptions to the Union at the time of pregnancy, injury or illness. To avoid any difficulties members should ensure that their subscriptions are paid at the correct rate and on time. (The actual dates are printed on the membership card.)

PUBLIC LIABILITY INSURANCE

Public Liability Insurance protects the member against liability for bodily injury and/or loss of or damage to a third person's property whilst playing, performing and teaching music. The MU currently pays for each member to have this cover and this insurance cover is available to all members. The current level of indemnity is £5million per member. No registration is needed. Details are printed on your MU membership card.

BENEVOLENT ASSISTANCE

MU BENEVOLENT FUNDS
One of the objects of the Union, as defined in the Rules, is to provide benevolent assistance for members and their dependants in times of need. To this end the Union's Branches maintain Branch Benevolent Funds from which grants may be authorised by the Branch Committee. In addition the Union nationally maintains a Benevolent Fund from which the Executive Committee may authorise grants of a suitable level of assistance to members who find themselves in need through illness, old age, or some misfortune. Applications for such assistance should be made to the Branch Secretary in the first instance and the Branch Committee may refer cases for further assistance to the EC for consideration.

Other sources of financial assistance include that provided by the Musicians' Benevolent Fund, the Royal Society of Musicians, and the PRS Members' Benevolent Fund. Further details are shown below.

MBF
Spending around £1million each year supporting over a thousand people, the Musicians' Benevolent Fund provides help for all professional musicians covering a wide range of needs. Help ranges from assistance with items such as basic household expenditure right through to substantial grants or loans. The MBF also runs its own residential home for retired musicians, Ivor Newton House in Bromley, Kent, and provides 'top up' funding for residential and nursing home fees.

For further information write to the MBF, 16 Ogle Street, London W1P 8JB. Telephone: 020 7636 4481.

RSM
The Royal Society of Musicians of Great Britain was founded in 1738 by Handel and over 200 other musicians to meet those needs arising from 'age, infirmity or disease'. Membership of the Society is £5 per annum. Grants are voted by the 48 Members elected to the RSM Court of Assistants from which are elected the 12 Governors who consider applications every month.

Each year the Society makes available over a quarter of a million pounds to musicians and their dependants. Assistance is also given to non-members.

For further information write to the RSM, 10 Stratford Place, London W1N 9AE. Telephone: 020 7629 6137.

PRS
Founded in 1934 and registered as a Charity in 1962 the PRS Members' Fund exists to help all members, ex-members and the dependants of deceased members.

The type of help offered includes short term loans to cover unexpected financial crisis, one off payments in cases of hardship or illness, or regular assistance to enable elderly members to maintain a decent standard of living.

For further information write to The Secretary, PRS Members' Fund, Copyright House, 29/33 Berners Street, London W1P 3DB. Telephone: 020 7306 4067.

MU FUNERAL GRANT
A Funeral Grant is payable to the next of kin of members who at their time of death have completed ten years continuous MU membership. Further details about obtaining the grant of £125 and an application form are available from the member's Branch Secretary.

OTHER ASSISTANCE

MEDICAL ASSISTANCE - BPAMT
Help is available to members for performance related problems which could include overuse/misuse syndrome, alcohol/drugs related problems, injuries and psychological problems.

Free assessment clinics are held at the Trust's consulting rooms in London and a number of other clinics will be opening around the UK in the coming year. Assessment clinics at the consulting rooms are free to members as a result of the considerable financial assistance given by the MU to the British Performing Arts Medicine Trust (BPAMT). Further assessments outside the Trust's premises may incur charges, but the Trust is normally able to negotiate reduced fees for such consultation.

In the first instance ring BPAMT on 020 7240 4500 (London) 0845 602 0235 (all other UK areas - local rates apply) 12pm - 5.45pm extended to 7.45pm on Monday and Thursday.

TUC LAW SCHEME
This TUC scheme expands the legal services available to members of the Union and aims to encourage members to seek help for personal and domestic matters, so ensuring greater protection of your legal rights and more use of solicitors' services. The Union Law scheme should help to remove some of the barriers that prevent people from seeing a solicitor, such as the uncertainty about how to find one or fear of the cost.

The scheme is designed to offer advice only on problems not connected with musical employment. Work related matters are not covered by the Union Law Scheme. Participating solicitors agree to provide the following services:

i) A free initial diagnostic interview on any legal problem (except work-related matters which are dealt with elsewhere under the heading **LEGAL ASSISTANCE**)

ii) A written estimate for the cost of further work or a legal aid assessment where appropriate. If a firm estimate is not possible an indication of the hourly rate for that type of work and of the likely number of hours of work required should be given.

iii) A fixed price conveyance, with the overall cost being notified at the outset of the matter on the Law Society's domestic conveyancing estimate form.

iv) A fixed price for drawing up a will, to be agreed in advance with the client.

v) Providing a free Personal Assets Log after drawing up a will. (This is a Law Society document for recording the nature and location of the will and of other important personal and financial documents, e.g. title deeds and insurance policies).

A list of solicitors participating in the Scheme is held by your District Organiser who can also give further details.

MUSICIANS' UNION PENSION SCHEME

Union members can participate in an MU Pension Scheme negotiated through Abbey Life. The arrangement involves members setting up a personal scheme and then contributing 5% of qualifying earnings through Agreements with employers - at this stage the BBC and ITV companies. A further 71-72% of the musicians' fees are added to the scheme by the employer. All of the 121-122% paid into the scheme is tax deductible.

Details from The Administrator, Musicians' Union Pension Scheme, 4 Hilgay Court, Cross Lanes, Guildford GU1 2ED.

UNITY FINANCIAL SERVICES

A package of membership benefits has been negotiated with Unity Financial Services to provide affordable financial services exclusively to Union members and their families. Unity Financial Services, part of the Unity Trust Bank plc has, with the full support of the TUC and the Union, negotiated special deals with reputable financial institutions. As a result of this collaboration members will have the opportunity to make considerable savings on mortgages and loans. For further details telephone 0800 600 999.

UNITY FIRST MASTERCARD

All members are eligible to apply for a credit card specially negotiated by the Union and the TUC.

There are two cards which offer a unique range of benefits with no annual fee. One card attracts a lower interest rate and is designed for members who tend not to pay off the balance at the end of the month as it has no 'free days' of interest. The second is like the 'traditional' credit card and offers up to 50 free interest free days, but has a higher interest rate after that. Application forms from MU Mastercard, FREEPOST ANG4191, D8 Pinetrees Road, Norwich NR7 9BR (telephone 0800 783 2833).

VEHICLE BREAKDOWN

MU arrangements with Green Flag National Breakdown provide excellent value and high quality car breakdown services to members with a range of specially negotiated rates. Full details on Green Flag services are available on 0345 670 345 at local rates.

For professional musicians there is always help at
hand from the Musicians Benevolent Fund.

Help with stress and health problems.

Help and advice on financial problems.

Help that's given in absolute confidence.

If you have a problem, or know of any professional
musicians who have, call us on 0171-636 4481.

MUSICIANS
BENEVOLENT FUND

HELP!

(DO YOU NEED SOMEBODY?)

Musicians Benevolent Fund, RM MU2, 16 Ogle Street, London W1P 8JB
Registered Charity No. 228089

TELEPHONE NUMBER CHANGES

Due to the increasing demand for telephone numbers, Oftel, the UK telecommunications regulator, is to introduce changes to some area codes and local numbers.

In six geographic areas, telephone numbers will consist of a three digit area code (the first two digits of which are 02) followed by an eight digit local number. Those areas affected are Cardiff, Coventry, London, Northern Ireland, Portsmouth and Southampton.

Area	Old Number	New Number
Cardiff	(01222) XXX XXX	(029) 20XX XXXX
Coventry	(01203) XXX XXX	(024) 76XX XXXX
London	(0171) XXX XXXX	(020) 7XXX XXXX
London	(0181) XXX XXXX	(020) 8XXX XXXX
Northern Ireland	(01XXX) XXXXX	(028) XXXX XXXX*
Portsmouth	(01705) XXX XXX	(023) 92XX XXXX
Southampton	(01703) XXX XXX	(023) 80XX XXXX

*Whilst the area code 028 will apply for the whole of Northern Ireland, local telephone numbers will be afforded prefixes according to their region. A list of these particulars can be obtained either by visiting www.numberchange.org on the internet, or by calling Cable & Wireless on 0800 096 2696.

To facilitate these changes, there is to be a period during which the old and new telephone numbers will both be recognised - indeed you may already use the new area codes with the new local numbers. As from the autumn of 2000, however, only the new area codes with the new eight digit local numbers will work when calling into one of the six areas.

With regards to making a local call within one of these areas, until 22 April 2000 you will be required to dial the old local number. After this date only the new local number will be recognised.

These changes to telephone numbers within the six areas have been accounted for in the listings of the Directory. Oftel has also set out plans to change mobile telephone numbers, so that they all carry the prefix 07. These changes, however, are to be implemented at a later date and will be accounted for in the next edition of the Musicians' Union National Directory of Members.

Key and Abbreviations

General. The geographical scope of this book covers England, Scotland, Wales, Isle of Man and the Channel Islands.

Addresses. Postal listing is followed by the telephone and fax numbers. *& fax* after a telephone number indicates that the number can also be used as a fax line, *(fax)* indicates that the number is exclusively a fax line, *(mob)* indicates that the number is that of a mobile telephone. Conventional address abbreviations are given in all listings and are not included below.

Instruments. The following abbreviations are used for instruments.

A Clt	Alto Clarinet	Bq Gtr	Baroque Guitar	Crum	Crumhorn
A Flt	Alto Flute	Bq Hrn	Baroque Horn	Ctna	Concertina (including
A Sax	Alto Sax	Bq Man	Baroque Mandolin		English Concertina)
A Tbn	Alto Trombone	Bq Ob	Baroque Oboe	Cuatro	Cuatro
AK 1	Akai Ewi 1000	Bq Rec	Baroque Recorder	Cuica	Cuica
Ac Gtr	Acoustic Guitar	Bq Tpt	Baroque Trumpet	Darab	Darabouka
Acc	Accordion	Bq Tym	Baroque Tympani	Db	Double Bass
Accom	Accompanist	Bq Vla	Baroque Viola	Dholak	Dholak
Af Dms	African Drums	Bq Vln	Baroque Violin	Didj	Didjeridu
Alp Hrn	Alpine Horn	Bq Wnd	Baroque Wind	Dilruba	Dilruba
App Dulc	Appalachian Dulcimer	Br Hrn	Baritone Horn	Dms	Drums
Arab Dms	Arabic Drums	Br Sax	Baritone Sax	Dobro	Dobro
Arr	Arranger	Brass	Brass	Dom	Domra
Aural	Aural Training	Bsn	Bassoon	Dsc Hrn	Descant Horn
Auto Hrp	Auto Harp	Bt Hrn	Bassett Horn	Dulc	Dulcimer
B Bsn	Contra Bassoon	Bugle	Bugle	E Acc	Electric Accordion
B Clarinet	Bass Clarinet	Bzk	Bouzouki	E Bjolin	Electric Banjolin
B Flt	Bass Flute	C B Clt	Contra Bass Clarinet	E Flt	Electric Flute
B Gtr	Bass Guitar	Cabassa	Cabassa	E Gtr	Electric Guitar
B Ldr	Bandleader	Canon	Canon	E Hmca	Electric Harmonica
B Ob	Bass Oboe	Cast	Castanets	E Hpsd	Electric Harpsichord
B Reb	Bass Rebec	Cauld Wp	Cauld Wind Pipes	E PF	Electric Piano
B Sack	Bass Sackbut	Cav	Cavaquinho	E Sax	Electric Saxophone
B Sax	Bass Sax	Cel	Cello	E Tbn	Electric Trombone
B Tba	Bass Tuba	Cel Hrp	Celtic Harp	E Tpt	Electric Trumpet
B Tbn	Bass Trombone	Ch Per	Chinese Percussion	E Vln	Electric Violin
B Tpt	Bass Trumpet	Charango	Charango	E Vox	Electrovox
B Viol	Bass Viol	Cheng	Cheng	EE Bass	Double E Flat Bass
BB Bass	Double B Flat Bass	Cho Mstr	Chorus Master	Ea Stg	Early Strings
Bach Tpt	Bach Trumpet	Cimb	Cimbalon	Ea Wnd	Early Wind
Bag	Bagpipes	Citole	Citole	Efl Bass	E Flat Bass
Bal	Balalaika	Citt	Cittern	Efl Clt	E Flat Clarinet
Balafon	Balafon	Cl Gtr	Classical Guitar	Erhu	Erhu
Bando	Bandoneon	Clars	Clarsach	Eth Flts	Ethnic Flutes
Bansuri	Bansuri	Clav	Clavichord	Eth Obs	Ethnic Oboes
Battaria	Battaria	Clrno	Clarino	Eth P	Ethnic Pipes
Bendir	Bendir	Clst	Celesta	Eup	Euphonium
Berimbau	Berimbau	Clt	Clarinet	Fl Gtr	Flamenco Guitar
Bjo	Banjo	Cnt	Cornet	Flag	Flageolet
Bjolin	Banjolin	Cntrc	Contractor	Flex	Flexatone
Bod	Bodhran	Cntt	Cornett	Flgl	Flugel Horn
Bombos	Bombos Legueros	Cntt Zin	Cornett Cornetto (Zink)	Flt	Flute
Bong	Bongos	Com	Composer	Fo Fdl	Folk Fiddle
Bottles	Bottles	Con	Conductor	Fo Gtr	Folk Guitar
Bq Bsn	Baroque Bassoon	Cong	Conga Drums	Gal	Galoubet
Bq Cel	Baroque Cello	Cop	Copyist	Gedulka	Gedulka
Bq Clt	Baroque Clarinet	Cor	Cor Anglais	Glck	Glockenspiel
Bq Flt	Baroque Flute	Cord	Cordovox	Gtr	Guitar

Gtr Bah	Guittarra Bahiana	Naal	Naal	Stgs	Strings
Gtrr	Guitarron	Nai	Nai	Surb	Surbahar
Guiro	Guiro	Nak	Nakers	Surm	Surmandal
H Bag	Highland Bagpipes	Nor P	Northumbrian Pipes	Syn Dms	Syndrums
H Gtr	Hawaian Guitar	Nov	Novachord	Synth	Synthesiser
H Gurd	Hurdy-Gurdy	Npm	Non Playing Member	T Hrn	Tenor Horn
Handb	Handbells	Ob	Oboe	T Sax	Tenor Saxophone
Harm	Harmonium	Obdac	Oboe Da Caccia	T Tba	Tenor Tuba
Harmony	Harmony	Obdam	Oboe D'Amore	T Viol	Tenor Viol
Heck	Hecklephone	Oca	Ocarina	Tab	Tabor
Hel	Helion	Ondmar	Ondes Martinot	Tabla	Tabla
Hmca	Harmonica (including Bass Harmonica)	One M B	One Man Band	Tam	Tam Tam
		Oph	Ophicleide	Tamb	Tambourine
Hnd Hrn	Hand Horn	Or Dms	Oriental Drums	Tamboor	Tamboor
Hpsd	Harpsichord	Or Flt	Oriental Flute	Tamp	Tampura
Hrn	Horn	Org	Organ	Tar	Taragatte
Hrp	Harp	Oud	Oud	Tba	Tuba
Impro	Improvisation	P Tab	Pipe & Tabor	Tbn	Trombone
Ind Flt	Indian Flute	Pan P	Pan Pipes	Theorbo	Theorbo
Ind Per	Indian Percussion	Pd Gtr	Pedal Guitar	Theory	Theory
Ir P	Irish Pipes	Per	Percussion	Timb	Timbales
Iron	Iron	Pf	Pianoforte	Tin Wh	Tin Whistle
Jap Stg	Japanese Strings	Ph Fid	Phono Fiddle	Tiple	Tiple
Jav Gam	Javanese Gamelan	Pic	Piccolo	Tnd Per	Tuned Percussion
Jaw H	Jaw's Harp	Pic Tpt	Piccolo Trumpet	Tpt	Trumpet
Jz Gtr	Jazz Guitar	Pl Gtr	Plectrum Guitar	Tr Kan	Turkish Kanun
Kaz	Kazoo	Psal	Psaltery	Tr Viol	Treble Viol
Kbds	Keyboards	Pst H	Post Horn	Tran	Transichord
Kora	Kora	Quena	Quena	Trans	Transcription
Koto	Koto	R Inst	Renaissance Instruments	Triangle	Triangle
LA Per	Latin American Percussion	R Stg	Renaissance Strings	Tym	Tympani
		R Wnd	Renaissance Wind	Ud	Ud
Lam	Lamellophone	Reb	Rebec	Uill	Uilleann
Ld Gtr	Lead Guitar	Rec	Recorder	Uke	Ukelele
Lireone	Lirone	Regal	Regal	V Tbn	Valve Trombone
Lute	Lute	Rep	Repetiteur	Vadag	Viola Da Gamba
Lyric	Lyricon	Rh Gtr	Rhythm Guitar	Vadam	Viola D'Amore
M Bow	Mouth Bow	Rq Tiple	Requinto Tiple	Veena	Veena
M Fid	Medieval Fiddle	Rudi	Rudiments	Vib	Vibraphone
M Flts	Medieval Flutes	S Cnt	Soprano Cornet	Vielle	Vielle
M Hist	Musical History	S Sax	Soprano Saxophone	Vih	Viheula
M Hrp	Medieval Harp	Sack	Sackbut	Viol	Viol
M Inst	Medieval Instruments	Santoor	Santoor	Virg	Virginals
M Per	Medieval Percussion	Sarangi	Sarangi	Vla	Viola
M Saw	Musical Saw	Sarod	Sarod	Vln	Violin
MD	Music Director	Saxes	Saxophone	Vlne	Violone
Man	Mandolin	Saxes	Saxophones	Voc	Vocalist
Man Cel	Mando Cello	Saz	Saz	Voice	Voice
Man Ha	Mandol Harmon	Serp	Serpent	W Bd	Washboard
Mando	Mandola	Sh	Shakrhachi	Wcap	Windcaps
Manje	Manjeera	Shawm	Shawm	Wg Tba	Wagner Tuba
Mar	Maraccas	Sheh	Shehanai	Wh	Whistle
Mel	Melophone	Shoz	Shozygs	Wood W	Woodwind
Metall	Metallophone	Sight	Sight Reading	Xyl	Xylophone
Mex Hrp	Mexican Harp	Sitar	Sitar	Zip Hrp	Zither Harp
Mldca	Melodica	So Sax	Sopranino Saxophone	Zit	Zither
Mldn	Melodeon	Song W	Songwriter	Zurna	Zurna
Mrba	Marimba	Sou	Sousaphone		
Muh	Muharsing	Sp Gtr	Spanish Guitar		
Multi	Multi Instrumental	Spoones	Spoons		
N Hrn	Natural Horn	St Gtr	Steel Guitar		
N Tpt	Natural Trumpet	St Pan	Steel Pan		

All Flutes Plus

5 Dorset Street, London W1H 3FE
Tel: 0171 935 3339 Fax: 0171 224 2053
Email: afp@allflutesplus.co.uk http://www.allflutesplus.co.uk

Europe's favourite flute specialist

telephone: 0171 401 8787
facsimile: 0171 401 8788
email: topwind@topwind.com
website: **www.topwind.com**

flutes
repairs
music
cd's
recordings
accessories

TOP WIND

We are now collecting entries for our six annual sales of Musical Instruments, which attract buyers from all over the world.

If you are considering selling an instrument, we would be delighted to provide **Free Auction Valuations**.
(Members of the M.U. will receive reduced commission when selling at Bonhams)

For further information about buying or selling at Bonhams, please call:
Peter Horner, Elisabeth Tölken or Camilla McCreery on 0171 393 3958

or visit our Internet Site (www.bonhams.com) for more information

A very fine Italian Violin by C. Camilli, Mantova 1739. Sold on behalf of The Musicas Fund for £78,500

AUCTIONEERS & VALUERS SINCE 1793

Montpelier Street, London SW7 1HH
Tel: 0171 393 3900 Fax: 0171 393 3959
Internet: www.bonhams.com

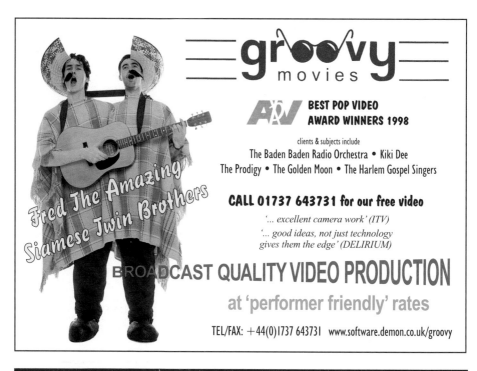
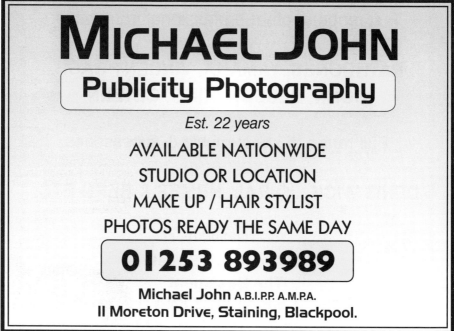

FINANCIAL SERVICES GUIDE

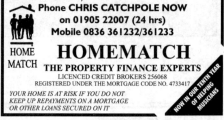

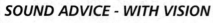

RECORDING
FACILITIES
GUIDE

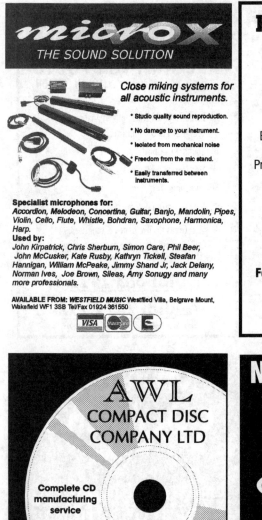

National Directory of Members

The following pages comprise a list of members of the Musicians' Union ordered by instrument and district. For an alphabetical list of members, please refer to the index beginning on page 457 of this Directory.

ACCOMPANIST

NORTH EAST

GRANT Cilla (*Pf*): 59 Hookstone Drive, Harrogate, North Yorkshire HG2 8PR ☎ 01423 883777

SOUTH WEST

MCCLURE Paul (*Per*): Flat 3, 7 Old Tiverton Road, Exeter EX4 6LD ☎ 01392 439029

LONDON

BROWN Stephen (*Pf, Md, Con, Org*): Address Unknown ☎ 0958 409267 mob, 020 8675 0180

SAMMONS Tony (*Pf, E Pf*): 48 Ashgrove Road, Bromley, Kent BR1 4JW ☎ 020 8460 6744

SULLIVAN Edel (*Vla, Pf, Wh, Gtr*): Flat 1, 60 Southwood Lane, London N6 5DY ☎ 020 8342 8081

ACCORDION

SCOTLAND

ADAMSON Deirdre (*Pf*): 22 Westfield Drive, Forfar, Angus DD8 1EQ ☎ 01307 464324

AINSLIE John: 12 Hawthorn Place, Perth PH1 1ET ☎ 01738 637460

ANDERSON Billy (*Pf*): 4 Kingsloan Court, Largoward, Fife, Scotland KY9 1JH ☎ 01334 840469

ANDERSON Marian: Eaglehall, Whitsome, Duns, Berwickshire TD11 3ND ☎ 0403 471540

ANDERSON Stuart: 1 Crawford Park, Springfield, Cupar, Fife KY15 5SW ☎ 01334 652418, 0374 438702 mob

BARBOUR Freeland (*Kbds*): 6 The Steils, Edinburgh EH10 5XD ☎ 0131 447 0991 & fax, 0831 779920 mob

BARNETT George: 5 Burnbank Terrace, Perth PH2 7ER ☎ 01738 627591

BENNETT Gordon: 1 Sherwood Loan, Bonnyrigg, Midlothian EH19 3NF ☎ 0131 663 1003

BRECHIN Sandy: 5 The Square, Kirkliston, West Lothian, Scotland EH29 9AX ☎ 0131 554 7806, 0131 555 3303 fax

BROADBRIDGE Nicolas: Linnmill, Kirkfieldbank ML11 9UP ☎ 01555 662212

BROGAN Shane (*Pf, Kbds*): 28 Belmont Crescent, Ayrshire, Scotland KA7 2NT ☎ 01292 269832, 0402 544121 mob

BRYSON Una (*Pf*): 4 Station Road, Lesmahagow, Lanarkshire, Scotland ML11 0DG ☎ 01555 894978

CAMPBELL Colin: Feorlin, Longsdale Road, Oban, Argyll PA34 5DZ ☎ 01631 562930

CAMPBELL James (*E Acc, Pf*): 75 Castlehill Road, Glasgow G61 4DY ☎ 0141 942 5455 & fax

CARMICHAEL George (*Kbds*): 35 Coupar Angus Road, Dundee, Scotland DD2 3HX ☎ 01382 611256

CARMICHAEL John: 2 Brora Drive, Giffnock, Glasgow G46 6NR ☎ 0141 638 0344

CONLON Gerry (*Pf*): 19 Birkhill Avenue, Bishopbriggs, Glasgow G64 2LD ☎ 0141 772 6774

COPLAND Neil (*Pf*): 108 Cedar Place, Perth, Scotland PN1 1RJ ☎ 01382 641854

COUPLAND Gary (*Pf, Tbn*): Feirfield, 11 Hawthorn Gardens, Loanhead, Midlothian EH20 9EQ ☎ 0131 440 4744 & fax

CRUICKSHANK Jennifer (*Pf*): Morven, Main Road, Lumphanan, Kincardineshire AB31 4PX ☎ 013398 83582

CUNNINGHAM Philip (*Wh, Kbds, Voc*): Craig Cottage, Crask Of Aigas, Beauly, Invernesshire ☎ 01463 782364, 01463 782525

CURRIE James (*Kbds*): 21 Garvel Road, Milngavie, Glasgow G62 7JD ☎ 0141 956 3891

CURRIE Thomas (*E Acc, Vln*): 21 Garvel Road, Milngavie, Glasgow G62 7JD ☎ 0141 956 3891

CURRIE William (*E Acc, Gtr, Clt, Bjo*): 21 Garvel Road, Milngavie, Glasgow G62 7JD ☎ 0141 956 3891

DAVIE Peter (*Pf, Kbds*): 8 Miller Place, Stirling FK8 1XD ☎ 01786 475360

DELANEY Jack: 47 Grange Road, Alloa, Clackmannanshire FK10 1LT ☎ 01259 723741

DEWAR Colin: 4 Broomfield Place, Freuchie, Fife KY15 7EN ☎ 01337 857476

DUNCAN Archibald: 43 Deveron Road, Bearsden, Glasgow G61 1LN ☎ 0141 942 3305

EDMOND Edward: 28 Kinnairdy Terrace, Torphins, Banchory AB31 4HH ☎ 013398 82458

ESSON Charles: Waterside, Pitcaple, Inverurie, Aberdeenshire AB51 5HN ☎ 01467 681269

FAGERVOLD Ragnar (*Gtr*): 1B Knipoch Place, Glencruitten, Oban, Argyll PA34 4ED ☎ 01631 570 280

FORD Tommy: 9 Pelstream Avenue, St Ninians, Stirling FK7 0BE ☎ 01786 475082

GALLEY Edward: 23 Mcculloch Drive, Forfar, Angus DD8 2EB ☎ 01307 462286

GORDON Scott (*Dms, Kbds, Pf*): 1 Church Lane, Galston, Ayrshire, Scotland KA4 8HE ☎ 01563 820 507

HARKIN Treasa (*Wh*): 1F3, 4 St Leonard's Bank, Newington, Edinburgh EH8 9SQ ☎ 0131 662 4584

HOLMES Ian (*B Ldr*): 11 Averill Crescent, Dumfrieshire DG2 7RY ☎ 01387 254 484 eve, 01387 262 063 day

HOWITT Charles: 66 Henderson Drive, Kintore, Inverurie, Aberdeenshire AB51 0FB

HUTCHEON Jim (*Kbds*): 1 Montgomerie Terrace, Ayr KA7 1JL ☎ 01292 264313

HUTCHEON Kevin: Keithfield Smithy, Tarves, Ellon, Aberdeenshire AB41 7NU

KEITH Lex: 59 Woodside Avenue, Lenzie G66 4NG ☎ 0141 775 0412

KELLY John: 34 Logan Street, Blantyre,

MAILEY Thomas: 24C Shore Street, Gourock, Renfrewshire PA19 1RQ ☎ 01475 630 747

MCKENZIE James: 12 Peatville Terrace, Edinbugh EH14 2EB ☎ 0131 443 5418

MCLAREN Nicol (*B Ldr*): 9 Sheila Road, Blairgowrie, Perthshire PH10 6RP ☎ 01250 874526

MELLISH Margaret (*Clt, Man*)

MILLWARD Dave: An Torr, Kilmelford, By Oban, Argyll PA34 4XA ☎ 01852 2220

MITCHELL Graeme: Inchlonaig, Huntly, Aberdeenshire AB54 4SJ

MOIR Sandy: 27 South Mains Road, Milngavie, Glasgow G62 6DD ☎ 0141 956 2894

MUIR Ian (*Kbds*): 24B Ardayre Road, Prestwick, Ayrshire KA9 1QL ☎ 01292 477053

MURDOCH Donald (*Hmca*): 5 Rowan Brae, Plock Road, Kyle Of Lochalsh, Ross-Shire IV40 8BL ☎ 01599 534980

O'SULLIVAN Seamus (*Pf*): 7 Westerton Avenue, Westerton, Glasgow G61 1HW ☎ 0141 942 5020

OSWALD David: 58 Claymore Drive, Wallace Glen, Stirling FK7 7UP ☎ 01786 818752

PATTULLO Gordon (*Acc*): Hill Cottage, Tullybaccart Farm, Coupar, Angus, Blairgowrie PH13 9LA ☎ 01382 581265

RAE Derek: 1 Dundee Court, Carrongate, New Carron, Falkirk FK2 7SL ☎ 01324 633194

ROSS David: 8 Manse Street, Kilmarnock, Ayrshire KA1 3BB ☎ 01563 528642

RUTHERFORD Walter: Ardimannoch, Keith, Banffshire AB55 3NS ☎ 01542 882716

SHAW Michael (*Pf*): Newton Villa, Strathpeffer, Ross-Shire IV14 9DH ☎ 01997 421248

SINCLAIR Neil (*Pf*): Gleanndaloch, Connel, By Oban, Argyll PA34 5TX ☎ Connel 201

STUART William: 29 Spey Road, Aberdeen AB16 6SH ☎ 01224 690593

THOMSON Kenny: 20 Walker Court, Cumnock KA18 1TF ☎ 01290 422404

THOMSON Stuart: 79 Coylebank Prestwick, Prestwick, Ayrshire KA9 2DJ ☎ 01292 470439

TURNER George *(Pf)*: 3 Ryehill Grove, Edinburgh EH6 8ET ☎ 0131 554 1035

WATSON George *(Voc)*: 11 Rose Bank, Glasgow Road, Perth PH2 0SY ☎ 01738 624554

WATSON Thomas *(Org)*: 47 Dumyat Drive, Falkirk FK1 5PA ☎ 01324 629381

WILSON C Callum: 23 Cardon Drive, Biggar, Lanarkshire ML12 6EZ ☎ 01899 220233

NORTH WEST

BALL Ian *(Ac Gtr)*: Springfield House, Micklehurst Road, Mossley, Ashton-U-Lyne, Lancs OL5 9JF ☎ 01457 835990

BEAUTEMONT Wendy: 3 Guilden Green, Guilden Sutton, Chester CH3 7SP ☎ 01244 301937

CONNOR Paul: 196 Church Street, Eccles, Manchester M30 0LZ ☎ 0161 707 3969

DUMAS Andre: 151 Hillock Lane, Woolston, Warrington, Cheshire WA1 4PJ ☎ 01925 822087

HARTLEY Kenneth *(Pf, Org)*: 100 Beach Road, Cleveleys, Blackpool, Lancashire FY5 1EH ☎ 01523 826337

HINDLEY Aileen: 32 Tuxford Road, Ansdell, Lytham, St. Annes, Lancs FY8 4BH ☎ 01253 737832

HINDLEY Guy *(B Tbn)*: 32 Tuxford Road, Ansdell, Lytham, Lancs FY8 4BH ☎ 01253 737832

LYRICAL LORD LEO *(Tbn, Per, Tin Wh, Gtr)*: 57 Exchange Street, Accrington, Lancs BB5 0LE ☎ 01254 381848

MCGREGOR Frank: 13 Burntbarrow, Storth, Milnthorpe, Lancs LA7 7JW ☎ 01524 762090

MURRAY Ben: 2 Grassfield Cottages, Nenthead, Alston, Cumbria CA9 3LW ☎ 01434 381170

VINCENT Reuben *(Org, Kbds)*: 44 Wood Lane, Pen-Y-Maes, Holywell, Clwyd CH8 7HU ☎ 01352 710441

WAITT Deryn *(Voc)*: Orchard Cottage, Canonbie, Dumfrieshire DG14 0RZ ☎ 013873 71423

WAITT Robert: Orchard Cottage, Canonbie, Dumfrieshire DG14 0RZ ☎ 013873 71423

WALSH Tom *(Gtr, Uill, Flag)*: 10 Summertrees Avenue, Lea, Preston PR2 1SA ☎ 01772 729715

WESSON Rees *(Mldn, Mldca, Gtr)*: Penllwyn, Castell Caereinion, Welshpool, Powys SY21 9AS ☎ 01938 850425

NORTH EAST

BRADFORD Colin *(Nor P)*: Quarry Byre, Ellingham, Chathill, Northumberland NE67 5HF ☎ 01665 589008, 0410 305407

BULMER David *(Fo Fdl)*: 2 High Street, Starbeck, Harrogate, North Yorkshire HG2 7AY

CAMPBELL Brian *(Ctna, Pf, Kbds)*: 235 Western Road, Crookes, Sheffield S10 1LE ☎ 0114 2660319

COWING Thomas *(B Ldr)*: 19 Leazes Crescent, Hexham, Northumberland NE46 3JZ ☎ 01434 604838

DALLING Tim *(Voc, Pf)*: 7 Sidney Grove, Fenham, Newcastle -upon-Tyne, Tyne & Wear NE4 5PD

HANDLE Johnny *(Nor P, Pf, Tpt, Bjo)*: 15-16 Wood Terrace, High Spen, Rowlands Gill, Tyne & Wear NE39 2AP ☎ 01207 543873

HARTNELL Roy: 18 Thornhill Road, Ponteland, Newcastle-upon-Tyne NE20 9QA ☎ 01661 824073

HOLLAND Alf *(Pf)*: 4 New Villas, Hunters Road, Spital Tongues, Newcastle-upon-Tyne NE2 4NH ☎ 0191 261 1690

MILLER Glenn: 10 Springfield Close, Stockton Lane, York YO3 ILD ☎ 01904 410 038, 0191 372 0173, 01904 410 038

OLIVER David: 9A Tynedale Terrace, Hexham, Northumberland NE46 3JE ☎ 01434 607432

STOPPARD Jon *(Ac Gtr, Rec)*: c/o Moonshine Music, Westwinds, 31 Somersall Park Road, Brampton, Chesterfield, Derbys S40 3LD ☎ 01246 566521

STOREY E: 133 Compass Road, Beverley High Road, Hull HU6 7AW ☎ 01482 3804962

WRIGHT Geoffrey: 10 Woodside Road, Scawthorpe, Doncaster, South Yorks DN5 9LE ☎ 01302 784561

EAST

ADCOCK Michael *(Pf, Gtr)*: 6 Ramsbury Road, St Albans, Herts AL1 1SL ☎ 01727 835989

FOX Garney *(Pf)*: 63, Gleneagles Drive, Ipswich, Suffolk IP4 5SF ☎ 01473 724631

GAME Martin *(Saxes, Clt)*: 12 Lisle Road, Colchester, Essex CO2 7SB ☎ 01206760480, 01585 513559

GREEN Martin *(Pf, Bod)*: 62 Blinco Grove, Cambridge CB1 4TS ☎ 01223 561289, 01223 248970, 01223 248970

HEYWOOD Alison *(Sax, Kbds)*: 2 Borough Road, Dunstable, Beds LU5 4BZ ☎ 01582 662467

HUSSEY Harry *(E Acc)*: c/o 44 Shepherds Way, Rickmansworth, Herts WD3 2NL ☎ 0976 529575

KATIE *(Kbds, Pf, Voc)*: 53 Main Road, Dyke, Nr Bourne, South Lincs PE10 0AF ☎ 01778 393803, 0468 921092 mob

MAYES Jerry: 19 Colchester Road, Southend, Essex SS2 6HW ☎ 01702 340909

MILES George *(Pf)*: 20 Johnston Close, Halstead, Essex CO9 1NG ☎ 01787 474919

ROMERO John *(Kbds)*: 26 Pevensey Drive, Clacton-on-Sea, Essex CO15 1XR ☎ 01255 423387

SANTILLY Bert: 29 Abbots Way, Horningsea, Cambridge CB5 9JN ☎ 01223 861261

WILLOUGHBY Robert *(B Gtr, Gtr, Voc, Dms)*: 5 Park Road, Westcliff-on-Sea, Essex SS0 7PE ☎ 01702 342975

MIDLANDS

ADAMS Michael: 8 Sycamore Road, Bournville, Birmingham B30 2AD ☎ 0121 472 7352

BRYAN Joseph *(Gtr, Voc)*: 7 Langdale Close, Lillington, Leamington Spa CV32 7QB ☎ 01926 315391

DOWNES John: 3 Gorse Meadow, Higher Heath, Whitchurch SY13 2JF ☎ 01948 840773

ELLIS John: 484 Streetsbrook Road, Solihull, West Midlands B91 1RN ☎ 0121 705 1684

GARWOOD David: 17 Tudor Court, Hucknall, Nottingham NG15 6RU ☎ 0115 963 6988

HABERMACHER Anne *(Vln, Voc, Per)*: 165 Oak Farm Road, Kings Norton, Birmingham B30 1ET ☎ 0121 458 5535

HAWTHORN Heather: 88 Clifton Road, Ruddington, Nottingham NG11 6DE ☎ 0115 9845052

KIRKPATRICK John *(Ctna, Mldn)*: Cowpasture Gate, Mainstone, Bishops Castle, Shropshire SY9 5LG ☎ 01588 638531

MIDDLETON Tracey: 16 Norgrave Road, Solihull, West Midlands B92 9JH ☎ 0121 743 6637

OSBORNE Jim: Reservoir Cottage, Brewood, Staffs ST19 9LX ☎ 01902 850554

RODGERS Phillip *(B Ldr)*: 20 Ebrington Avenue, Solihull, West Midlands B92 8HU ☎ 0121 742 3192

SOCCI Antoine *(B Ldr)*: 6 Brylan Croft, Birmingham B44 8DW ☎ 0121 356 0995

STELLING Roy *(B Ldr)*: 12 Woodrow Close, Catshill, Bromsgrove B61 0NY ☎ 01527 877236

TRENTHAM Tony *(E Acc, Qrg)*: 19 High Meadow Road, Kings Norton, Birmingham, West Midlands B38 9AP ☎ 0121 458 3426

TWEED Karen *(Vln)*: 21 Chapel Lane, Chaddesden, Derby, Derbyshire DE21 4QT ☎ 01332 853804

SOUTH EAST

ASHTON Kenneth: 47 Stratfield Road, Kidlington, Oxford OX5 1DJ

BREADSTILL John *(B Gtr)*: 166 High Street, Swanage, Dorset BH19 2PE ☎ 01929 421077

BURBIDGE David: 21 Marsh Lane, Upton, Poole, Dorset BH16 5NH ☎ 01202 625136

CORBETT Guy *(Gtr, B Gtr, Per)*: 1 Warren Crest, Froxfield, Petersfield, Hants GU32 1RL ☎ 01730 827265

CRUTCHER Johnny *(B Ldr)*: Units 7 & 8 The Parade, 147 Wareham Road, Corfe Mullen, Wimborne, Dorset BH21 3LA ☎ 01202 601153

DANIELS Luke (*Ctna, Pf, Gtr, Bod*): 4 Lea Road, Sonning Common, Nr Reading, Berks RG4 9LJ ☎ 01734 722657

DUNCOMBE Leslie: 4 Foxholes Road, Southbourne, Bournemouth, Dorset BH6 3AS ☎ 01202 420798

FIONDELLA Gennard (*Kbds, Pf*): 24 Gannon Road, Worthing, Sussex BN11 2DT ☎ 01903 202590

HAGUE Andrew (*E Acc, Kbds, Cnt*): 69 Branksome Hill Road, Bournemouth, Dorset BH4 9LF ☎ 01202 752572, 01589 134861

HARVEY Shirley (*Pf*): 18 Heene Terrace, Marine Parade, Worthing BN11 3NW ☎ 01903 238785, 0973 103424

JOHNSON Tina (*Pf, Org*): 12, Baldslow Road, Hastings, Sussex TN34 2EZ ☎ Hastings 427785

LAVER Keith (*E Pf*): 33 Wellington Road, Binstead, Ryde, Isle Of Wight PO33 3QH ☎ 01983 617048

LETLEY Roger (*E Acc*): 92 Bloors Lane, Gillingham, Kent ME8 7DS ☎ 01634 230434

MAY Peter (*Ctna, Fo Fdl, Kbds, Voc*): 29 Grange Road, Deal, Kent CT14 9TT ☎ 01304 360669, 01304 201714

PERKINS William: 7 Arun Close, Durrington, Worthing, West Sussex BN13 3HT ☎ 01903 693258

SOUTH WEST

ALLEN Mark (*Pf, Kbds*): 3 March Hywel, Cilfrew, Neath, South Wales SA10 8ND

COPPARD Sue: 6 Huntingdon Street, Bradford-on-Avon, Wiltshire BA15 1RE ☎ 01225 866679

DINGLE Kenneth: 3 Sunnycroft, North Road, West Looe, Cornwall PL13 2EL ☎ 01503 3103

SANDERS Anthony (*Clt*): 45 Broadwalk, Wearde Estate, Saltash, Cornwall PL12 4NP ☎ 01752 854467

SHUTLER Peter (*Ctna, Wh, Mldn*): Maybank, Marston Road, Sherborne, Dorset DT9 4BJ ☎ 01935 814667

SIMMONS Jacob: 34 Euston Grove, Ringwood, Hants BH24 1FB

STUBBS Tish (*Pf*): Woodlands, Brixham Road, Paignton, Devon TQ4 7BA ☎ 01803 528004

THIBODEAUX Pete (*Hmca, Kbds*): 11 Bodmin Hill, Lostwithiel, Cornwall PL22 0AH ☎ 01208 872960

TOMKINS Margaret: 8 St. Johns Crescent, Canton, Cardiff CF5 1NX ☎ 029 2034 2138

TOWLER Gideon (*Kbds, Bjo*): 20 Two Chimneys, (Residential Site), Praa Sands, Penzance, Cornwall TR20 9SP ☎ 01736 762785

WILSON John (*Acc*): Meadow View, Cheriton, Fitzpaine, Crediton EX17 4BB

LONDON

ALLODI Claudio (*Synth*): 36 Park Road, High Barnet, London EN5 5SQ ☎ 020 8441 1500

BINELLI Mickey: 28 Beverley Drive, Edgware, Middx HA8 5NG ☎ 020 8204 3918

BIRKINSHAW Roy (*Gtr, Voc*): 2 Field Park, Holly Spring Lane, Bracknell, Berks RG12 2DZ ☎ 01344 486338

BOUSIE Mark (*Pf, Kbds, Md*): 19 Dunford Road, London N7 6EP ☎ 020 7609 8880, 0103 945 466 mob

BRUCE Nichola (*Pf, Gtr*): West Hill Villa, Coburg Place, Old Town, Hastings TN34 3HY

BUCK Stanley (*Org, Pf*): Palomares, 18 Lavorrick Orchards, Mevagissey, St Austell Cornwall PL26 6TL ☎ 01726 843840

CROSSMAN Gerald (*Pf, Kbds, Clst, Md*): 22 Willow Way, Church End, Finchley, London N3 2PL ☎ 020 8346 3170

CURRIE Pete (*Bag*): The Wheatsheaf, Hever Road, Bough Beech, Kent TN8 7NU ☎ 01732 700254

DAWSON Barry (*Voc, Tpt, Pf*): Hill Cottage, 4 Bourne Way, Cheam, Surrey SM1 2EN ☎ 020 8661 0931

DECICCO Vincent (*Pf*): 510 Brixton Road, London SW9 8EN

DESTEFANO Don: Address Unknown

DEXTER Brian (*Pf*): 2 Brookfield Terrace, Pyrles Lane, Loughton, Essex IG10 2NR ☎ 020 8508 2022

DUNN Alan (*Kbds, Tin Wh*): 10 Holden Hse, Deptford Church Street, London SE8 4SQ ☎ 020 8691 3698

EMBLOW Jack: Captive Oak, Magpie Lane, Coleshill, Nr Amersham Bucks HP7 0LU ☎ 01494 724075

EMILIO (*Cord*): Indio Pond, 1 Paddock Flat, Bovey Tracey, Newton Abbot S Devon TQ13 9DY ☎ 01626 832963

FORBES Alistair (*Pf, Sax*): 25 Coleshill Road, Teddington, Middlesex TW11 0LL

GILLINGHAM Phyllis (*Pf*): Mill Cottage, West Chiltington Road, Pulborough, West Sussex RH20 2PR ☎ 01798 812688, 020 8942 3810

GOLDSMITH Tracey (*Kbds*): 47 Witham Road, Anerley, London SE20 7YB ☎ 020 8778 2837, 04325 209854

GUARARE Grupo: 14 Hansler Road, London SE22 9DJ ☎ 020 8693 4718

HADLEY Nicola (*Pf*): 47 Davenant Road, London N19 3NW ☎ 020 7281 5340

HERBERT Royston (*Arr, Com*): 9 All Saints Way, Churchfields, Mundesley, Norfolk NR11 8BY

HESSION Edward (*Pf, Kbds*): 17 Westbury Road, London N11 2DB ☎ 020 8881 7278

HETHERINGTON Edward (*Pf, Org*): 131A London Road, Ewell, Surrey KT17 2BS ☎ 020 8393 9549

HOLLINGTON Donald (*Pf*): 143 Woodside, Leigh-on-Sea, Essex SS9 4RD ☎ 01702 524458

HOLT Helen: Beachway, 19 Ulwell Road, Swanage, Dorset BH19 1LF ☎ 0929 423077

JACQUES Martyn (*Voc, Kbds, Stgs, Pf*): 020 7821 9457, 0410 799028, 020 7821 9457

JENKINS Peter (*Bod*): 20 Charles Street, Hillingdon Heath, Middlesex UB10 0SY ☎ 020 8581 2921

LEGH Peter (*Pf, Sax, Clt*): 5 Branton Road, Horns Cross, Greenhithe, Kent DA9 9JU ☎ 01322 383481

LESLIE John: 17 Cricklewood Lane, London NW2 1HN ☎ 020 8452 8668, 0831 424444

MERRICK Stephen: 34 Horn Lane, Woodford Green, Essex IG8 9AD ☎ 020 8504 3475

MILETIC Dragan: 22 Highworth Road, London N11 2SJ ☎ 020 8368 0158 & fax, 0956 696888 mob

MOLONEY John (*Tin Wh, Bod, Man, Gtr*): 158 Hydethorpe Road, Balham, London SW12 0JD

MONTY (*Hmca, B Gtr*): 39 Ermine Road, South Tottenham, London N15 6DD ☎ 020 8800 6899, 0976 296 505

MOORE Billy (*Voc*): 43 Collingwood Close, Langney Point, Eastbourne, E. Sussex BN23 6HW ☎ 01323 646452

MURPHY Joe (*Synth*): 12 Anna Close, Brownlow Road, Hackney, London E8 4NW ☎ 020 7241 2581

MURPHY William (*Pf*): 17 Yerbury Road, Upper Holloway, London N19 4RN ☎ 020 7272 0644

ORABY Moustafa (*Org*): 2 Priinces Alice House, Danlgarno Way, London W10 5EN ☎ 020 8968 5022

OUTKINE Igor (*Voc, Gtr, Kbds*): 12A Turle Road, London N4 3LZ ☎ 020 7561 1450

PACHNINE Serguei (*Dms, Voc*): 35 Westway, East Acton, London W12 0PT ☎ 07970 160306

PARKER John (*B Gtr, Db*): 38 Effingham Road, Reigate, Surrey RH2 7JH ☎ 01737 245641

READ Geoffrey: 2 Stormont Way, Chesington, Surrey KT9 2QN ☎ 020 8397 3933

ROSE Saul: 74 Southwark Park Road, London SE16 3RS ☎ 020 7231 5171, 0468 874807

RUFF Michael (*Rec*): 25 Alexandra Road, Chalvey, Slough SL1 2NQ ☎ 0175 352 0632

SCHWARZ Martina: 56 Belgrade Road, London N16 8DG ☎ 020 7249 6211

SELBY Peter (*E Acc, Voc, Arr*): 1 South Hall Close, Eynsford Road, Farningham, Kent DA4 0BP ☎ 01322 862794

SLIM: Slim@Cyder.Demon.Co.Uk

STREET Kevin (*Kbds, Md, Tpt, Arr*): 221 Kent House Road, Beckenham, Kent BR3 1JZ ☎ 020 8776 6431, 0956 537802 mob

TREVANI: 14 Mapledale Avenue, Croydon, Surrey CR0 5TB ☎ 020 8656 1450

TROUP David (*Voc, Kbds*): 47 Heston House, Tannershill, Deptford, London SE8 4PX ☎ 020 8691 3635

AFRICAN DRUMS

SCOTLAND

AMU-LOGOTSE Gift (*Af Dms*): Flat 2/2, 2 Nimmo Drive, Glasgow G51 3SX ☎ 0141 440 1207
CRUICKSHANK David Rowland (*Af Dms, Cong*): 3/1, 9 Arthur Street, Glasgow G3 8QZ ☎ 0141 339 5813
HUGHES Allan (*Af Dms, Gtr, Wh*): 157E Monteith Row, Weavers Court, Calton, Glasgow G40 1AZ ☎ 0141 554 8879, 0141 211 2792

NORTH WEST

ABIODUN (*Af Dms*): Flat 5, 2B Gloucester Drive, Finsbury Park, London N4 2LW ☎ 020 8802 3911
HOUFE David (*Af Dms, Cong*): 1 Avon Street, Shaw Heath, Stockport, Manchester SK3 8DP ☎ 0161 477 2761

NORTH EAST

JACKMAN Keith (*Af Dms, Didj, Hmca*): 3 Scarcroft Road, York YO23 1ND ☎ 01904 632073

MIDLANDS

MBOOB Yusupha (*Tkg Dms, Djembe, Eth Per*): 35 Sandon Street, New Basford, Nottingham NG7 7AL ☎ 0115 9708149, 07970 967601

SOUTH EAST

MOON Simon (*Af Dms, Per*): 1 Oakleigh Road, Bexhill-on-Sea, East Sussex TN39 4PY ☎ 01424 844041, 0498 634976 mob, 01424 846624

LONDON

AYANDOSU (*Tkg Dms, Cong, Cabassa, Tamb,*): 6B Brunswick Park, Camberwell, London SE5 7RH ☎ 0956 482418
BLAGROVE Stephen (*Af Dms, Per*): 13 Lockwood House, Kennington Park Estate, London SE11 5SZ ☎ 0956 347 302
BLAND Bill (*Af Dms, Cong, La Per*): 33 Macbeth House, Ivy Street, Hoxton, London N1 5JG ☎ 020 7729 2099
FUSTER Francis (*Af Dms*): 98 Addison Road, Enfield, Middx EN3 5LA ☎ 020 8805 3485
HLELA Betty (*Af Dms, Per*): 27 Crondall Court, St Johns Estate, London N1 6TZ ☎ 020 7613 0774
LAWAL Gasper (*Af, Tkg Dms, Per, La Per*): 47 Sheriff Road, West Hampstead, London NW6 2AS ☎ 020 7624 0784

AKAI EWI 1000

LONDON

FITZGERALD David (*Saxes, Flt*): 48 Avenue Road, Norwich, Norfolk NR2 3HN ☎ 01603 632444 & fax, 0468 573284 mob

ALTO CLARINET

SOUTH EAST

HAWKES Claire (*Clt, Pf, Sax, Flt*): The Old Orchard, Ellesboro Road, Butlers Cross, Aylesbury, Buckinghamshire HP17 0XH ☎ 01844 343222 eve, 020 8749 9359

ALTO FLUTE

LONDON

WYVER Andrew (*Flt, Pic, Clt, Sax*): Hilltop, Gravel Hill, Chartham Hatch, Canterbury Kent CT4 7NH ☎ 01227 730923

ALTO TROMBONE

NORTH WEST

TEAGUE John (*Tbn, Sack, T Tba*): Cherry Trees, Tilstock, Shropshire SY13 3NR ☎ 01948 880 679

LONDON

WHITEHOUSE David (*Tbn, B Tbn, Eup, B Tpt*): 28 First Avenue, Bush Hill Park, Enfield, Middx EN1 1BL ☎ 020 8482 3753, 0973 295261 mob, 01306 880669 day

APPALACHIAN DULCIMER

NORTH EAST

LAW Elizabeth: 40 The Grove, Hartlepool, Cleveland TS26 9LZ ☎ 01429 273203

ARC

LONDON

EASTLEY Max: Flat B, 551, Finchley Road, London NW3 7BJ ☎ 020 7794 3502

ARRANGER

SCOTLAND

ESDAILE Sarah (*Com*): 6 Raglan Terrace, Mill Road, Nairn, Scotland IV12 4AL
MATHIESON Ken (*Dms, Zit, B Ldr*): 20 Kylepark Crescent, Uddingston G71 7DQ ☎ 01698 814475

NORTH WEST

MCLEAN Morris (*Md*): 36 London Road, Buxton, Derbys SK17 9NX ☎ 01298 23879

NORTH EAST

BELLWOOD Derek (*Org, Kbds*): 58 Chatsworth Road, Pudsey, West Yorkshire LS28 8JX ☎ 01274 664475

MIDLANDS

FRANCIS Gregor (*Con, B Ldr*): 72 Davids Drive, Wingerworth, Chesterfield, Derbyshire S42 6PS ☎ 01246 231 746
LUND Eric (*Flt, Kbds, Cop*): 15 Jasmine Road, Great Bridgeford, Stafford ST18 9PT ☎ 01785 282366
PATRICK John (*Pf, Md, Com, Kbds*): c/o Musicians Union, Benson House, Lombard Street, Birmingham B12 0QN ☎ 01564 784029 & fax

SOUTH EAST

ALLWOOD Ralph (*Com, Md*): Ballards, Keates Lane, Eton, Berks SL4 6EL ☎ 01753 671169 day, 01753 671005 eve, 01753 671005
COLLETT-SIMPSON Reginald (*Cop, Kbds, Org, Md*): 1 Chessington Court, 5 Durley Chine Road, Bournemouth, Dorset BH2 5JR ☎ 01202 761125
DUNKLEY Matthew (*Cop*): Slapps Cottage, Pickhurst Lane, Pulborough, W Sussex RH20 1DA ☎ 01798 875515, 0973 317209, 01798 875865
HOLLAMBY Stephen (*Cop, Tpt, Bugle*): 17 Albany Road, St Leonards-on-Sea, East Sussex TN38 0LP ☎ 01424 442187

SOUTH WEST

WHITE Ted (*Cop*): Chycara Farm, Carnon Valley, Carnon Downs, Truro, Cornwall TR3 6LG ☎ 020 8997 4730

LONDON

ARTHEY Johnny (*Com, Cop, Pf*): 36 Pine Walk, Carshalton Beeches, Surrey SM5 4HD ☎ 020 8642 7444
ASHMORE Larry (*Md, Db, Com*): 20 Drayson Mews, Kensington, London W8 4LY ☎ 020 7938 1628, 020 7938 1728 fax
BAMFORD George (*Cop*): 18 Gatesden, Cromer Street, London WC1H 8LX ☎ 020 7837 0850
BARHAM John (*Com, Md*): Flat 3, 14 Clorane Gardens, London NW3 7PR ☎ 020 7435 1249
BAXTER Bruce (*Pf, Gtr*): 8 Dorchester Court, Chalk Hill, Watford, Hertfordshire WD1 4DB ☎ 01923 231413
BELL John (*Com, Md, Pf*): 132 Brondesbury Villas, London NW6 6AE ☎ 020 7328 0060, 020 7372 3860 fax
BENNETT Malcolm (*Com, Cop, Tpt, Flgl*): Spennythorne, Cokes Lane, Little Chalfont, Bucks HP8 4UD ☎ 01494 762637
BOLTON Cecil (*Md, Com*): 4 Camberley Close, North Cheam, Sutton, Surrey SM3 9BH ☎ 020 8644 3248
BRADEN Alan (*Com, Con*): 56 St Marys Mead, Witan Way, Witney, Oxon OX8 6EZ ☎ 01993 779415 & fax

BREMNER Tony (*Con, Com*): 3 Dukes Avenue, Finchley, London N3 2DE ☎ 020 8346 0459

BRENNAN Ted (*Tpt*): 153 Botwell Lane, Hayes, Middx UB3 2AQ ☎ 020 8573 2576

BRISTOW Alan (*Md*): Dusun Lama, Sandy Lane, Kingswood, Surrey KT20 6ND ☎ 01737 832844

BROUGH Harvey (*Com, Voc*): 68 Clissold Cres., London N16 9AT ☎ 020 7241 0317

BROWN Richard (*Md, Pf*): 1 Winterfold Court, Barhatch Lane, Cranleigh, Surrey GU6 7NH ☎ 01483 274346

BURTON Jonathan (*Com, Cop, Bsn*): 12 Corner Green, Blackheath, London SE3 9JJ ☎ 020 8852 7399, 020 7836 0111 ext.435

BYE Peter (*Pf, Gtr, B Gtr*): Flat A, 14 Avenue Elmers, Surbiton, Surrey KT6 4SF ☎ 020 8390 5896

CLOUT Tony (*Cop, B Gtr, Gtr*): 36 Shirley Gardens, Hornchurch, Essex RM12 4NH ☎ 01708 472718

CULLEN David (*Com, Pf, Synth*): Chiddinghurst, Scrapers Hill, Chiddingly, East Sussex BN8 6HJ ☎ 01825 872 206, 01825 872423 fax

DODGE (*Com, Kbds, Per*): 14 Stanthorpe Road, Streatham, London SW16 2DY ☎ 020 8677 6364

DOUGLAS Johnny: 39 Tadorne Road, Tadworth, Surrey KT20 5TF ☎ 0173781 2922

ELLERBY Geoff (*Kbds, Hrn*): 6 Glencoe Way, Orton Southgate, Peterborough PE2 6SJ ☎ 01733 361761, 0370 637751, 01733 361744

ELLIOTT Christopher (*Com, Pf*): Flat 2, 6 Exeter Road, London NW2 4SP ☎ 020 8830 6470

ELMES Baz (*Cop*): 40 Ruskin Road, Belvedere, Kent DA17 5BB ☎ 013224 39826

EVANS John (*Cop, Pf, Flt*): 41 Saxon Way, Saffron Walden, Essex CB11 4EQ ☎ 01799 527618

FIELD Bobbie (*Com, Cop*): 81 Uffington Road, West Norwood, London SE27 0NE ☎ 020 8670 0597 & fax, 0976 943923 mob

FORGIE Barry (*Con, Tbn*): 29 Elgin Road, Croydon, Surrey CR0 6XD ☎ 020 8656 9699

FOX John (*Com, Md, Pf*): Coniston, 26 Garratts Lane, Banstead, Surrey SM7 2EA ☎ 017373 60005 & fax

FRENCH Paul (*Kbds, Com*): 23 Ladbroke Cresc, London W11 1PS ☎ 020 7221 3206

GASCOIGNE Brian (*Md, Kbds, Synth, Vib*): 25 Parliament Hill, London NW3 2TA ☎ 020 7435 6703

GOULD Alec: 51 Cannon Lane, Pinner, Middx HA5 1HN ☎ 020 8866 3401

HARTLEY Richard (*Com, Pf*): 6 Frithville Gardens, London W12 7JN

HAWKINS John (*Pf, Md*): 19 Montpelier Court, Montpelier Road, Ealing, London W5 2QN ☎ 020 8810 6853, 0850 918066 mob, 020 8810 7619 fax

HAZLEHURST Ronnie (*Com, Md*): Testa Rossa, Ville Baudu, Valle, Guernsey GY3 5AB ☎ 01481 48608, 04481 148608, 01481 48638 fax

HERMAN Thomas (*Gtr*): 12 Wornum House, 298 Kilburn Lane, London W10 4BW

HUNTER Len (*Tpt*): 46 Ibsley Way, Cockfosters, Herts EN4 9EY ☎ 020 8449 4138

KING Tony (*Com, Pf*): 48 Hale Grove Gardens, Mill Hill, London NW7 3LP ☎ 020 8906 0292

MACPHERSON Ian (*Md, Con, Pf*): 101 Lauderdale Mansions, Lauderdale Road, London W9 1LY ☎ 020 7286 2969

MALONE Wil (*Pf*): 13 Lyndhurst Gardens, Finchley, London N3 1TA ☎ 020 8346 8352

MATTEN Douglas (*Cop*): 65 Crescent West, Hadley Wood, Barnet, Herts EN4 0EQ ☎ 020 8449 3701

MONK Raymond (*Md, Synth, Pf*): Orchard Way, Chartridge Lane, Chesham, Bucks HP5 2RG ☎ 01494 776255

MOORE Roy (*Com, Con, Md, Pf*): 52 Waddington Way, Upper Norwood, London SE19 3XJ ☎ 020 8771 1948, 020 8771 6115

NEWMAN Del (*Com, Md, Cntrc*): Penbryn, Bangor Teifi, Ceredigion, Dyfed SA44 5BJ ☎ 01559 362619, 0402 480826 mob

OSTERDAHL Marcus (*Con*): Mallow, Priory Road, Sunningdale, Berks SL5 9RH ☎ Ascot 22611

PAYNE Cy (*Com, Md, Con*): Tacet, 2 The Poplars, Ten Mile Bank, Downham Market, Norfolk PE38 0EJ ☎ 01366 378822

PEBERDY Jack (*Md*): 26 Ratcliffe Road, Sileby, Loughborough, Leics LE12 7PZ ☎ 0150981 6808

PROLETARSKI Valery (*Com, Kbds*): 24 Albany Road, Ealing, London W13 8PG ☎ 020 8248 0610

ROBERTS Harry (*Cop*): 29 Eden Road, Croydon, Surrey CR0 1BB ☎ 020 8680 3361

ROGERS Brian (*Md, Pf*): Mulberry, 117 Abbotts Road, Abbotts Langley, Nr Watford Herts WD5 0BJ ☎ 01923 263505 & fax

SEGAL Marianne (*Gtr*): 39 Frinton Road, Tooting, London SW17 9EH ☎ 020 8769 6820

SHAW Roland (*Com*): Coppers, Furze Field, Oxshott, Surrey KT22 0UR ☎ 01372 843124 & fax

SMITH Jonathan (*Cop*): 6 Lismore Close, Isleworth, Middlesex TW7 6QX ☎ 020 8568 6705, 07957 45603

SMITH Robin (*Kbds*): Ketton, 9 Rutland Road, Maidenhead, Berkshire SL6 4HZ ☎ 01628 20011 & fax

STOKES Bart (*Com, Md, Saxes, Flt*): 41 Southern Cross Road, Kohi, Auckland 1005, New Zealand ☎ NZ 09 528 0671, NZ 09 521 3075 fax

SURMAN John (*Com*): Knowle House, Warren Street, Charing, Kent TN27 0HJ ☎ 0123 371 2746

TOWNEND Kevin (*Com, Gtr*): Ridings, Bridle Lane, Loudwater, Rickmansworth Herts WD3 4JB ☎ 01923 775376

TOWNEND Mike (*Com, Md*): 44 Eastwick Crescent, Rickmansworth, Herts WD3 2YJ ☎ 01923 720083, 0976 713660, 01923 710587 & fax

VINALL Leslie: 8 Ingleboro Drive, Purley, Surrey CR8 1EE ☎ 020 8660 3772

VYE-PARMINTER Arthur (*Cop, Con*): Address Unknown

WAKEFIELD Tony (*Com, Cop*): 115 Village Way, Ashford, Middx TW15 2JY ☎ 01784 252958 & fax

WALKER Chris (*Com, Pf*): 24 Coborn Road, London E3 2DA ☎ 020 8980 0480, 020 8980 6043

WALTERS John (*Com, Flt, Lyric, Md*): 108 Shenley Road, Camberwell, London SE5 8NF ☎ 020 7703 9309

WILLIAMS Leslie (*Com, Con*): 15 Falconry Court, Fairfield South, Kingston-upon-Thames KT1 2UR ☎ 020 8541 0255

WILSON John (*Con, Pf, Cntrc*): 62 Bowman Mews, Standen Road, London SW18 5TN ☎ 020 8875 1824 & fax

WOODMAN Ken (*Com, Md*): 74 Lilliput Avenue, Northolt, Middx UB5 5PZ ☎ 020 8845 3630

BAGPIPES

SCOTLAND

CAMPBELL Rory (*Wh*): 3 Laundry Cottage, Gorebridge, Midlothian EH23 4AH ☎ 01875 823 676

GRACE Annie (*Wh, Voc, Flt*): 1/2, 92 Park Road, Kelvinbridge, Glasgow G4 9HB ☎ 0141 357 4822

INNES Neil: The Bungalow, Bush Nursery, By Roslin, Midlothian EH25 9RE ☎ 0131 445 3233

MACDONALD Allan (*Tin Wh, Jaw H, Voc, Com*): 13 Greenbank Drive, Morningside, Edinburgh EH10 5RE ☎ 0131 4476641

MCLAUGHLIN William (*Wh, Gtr, Man, Clars*): Clunie Cottage, Moulinearn, Pitlochry, Perthshire PH9 0NB ☎ 01796 482373

METHVEN David (*Wh*): 'Cladich', Station Road, Gargunnock, Stirling, Scotland FK8 3DA ☎ 01786 860302

PINCOCK Douglas (*Flt, Wh, Sax, Per*): 313 Main Street, Renton, Alexandria G82 4PZ ☎ 01389 759878

WALLACE Robert: 36 Mount Harriet Drive, Stepps, Glasgow G33 6DN ☎ 0141 779 1750

NORTH WEST

CARR Terry (*Ir P, Tin Wh, Voc*): 21 Whitecar Avenue, New Moston, Manchester M40 3GW ☎ 0161 681 7187

SWINDELLS Malcolm: 109 Wigan Road, Atherton, Manchester M46 0LW ☎ 01942 892356

WALSH Phil: 48 Empress Way, Euxton, Nr Chorley, Lancs PR7 6QB ☎ 01257 249033

NORTH EAST

SUMMERS Anne (*H Gurd, Rec, Shawm, Wood W*): Brancepeth Castle, Brancepeth, Co. Durham DH7 8DF ☎ 0191 378 9321

EAST

LAWTHER Ian (*Nor P, Uill*): 38 Manor View, Stevenage, Herts SG2 8PF ☎ 01438 725660

MIDLANDS

BARKER Stuart Christopher (*Uill, H Gurd, Clt, Tbn*): 4A Colston Parade, Redcliffe, Bristol BS1 6RA ☎ 0117 927 6643
SAUNDERS Paul (*Nor P*): 1 Passev's Barn, Church Farmhouse, Buildwas, Shropshire TF8 7DA ☎ 01952 433636
SIMPSON Lester (*Mldn, Voc*): 4 Golf Lane, Duffield, Derby DE6 4EE ☎ 01332 840758
WARD Donald: 80 Witherford Way, Selly Oak, Birmingham B29 4AS ☎ 0121 472 1555

SOUTH EAST

FAGAN Kevin: 97 Holcroft Road, Thornhill, Southampton, Hants SO2 6GZ ☎ 023 8040 3132
HUTH Roger: 58 Scotland Farm Road, Ash Vale, Aldershot, Herts GU12 5JB ☎ 01252 25241, 01276 452837
WILLIAMS Philip (*Mando, Ctna, Gtr*): Califonrnia Farm, Priests Way, Swanage, Dorset BH19 2RS ☎ 01929 426091 & fax, 0421 000936 mob

SOUTH WEST

CLACK Leslie: Heather Bank, Westfield, Bradninch, Exeter EX5 4QO ☎ 01392 851735
MOR Calum: 8 Elm Park, Filton, Bristol BS34 7PW ☎ 0117 9753579

LONDON

BABBINGTON Roy (*Db, B Gtr, Sitar*): 7 Sinclair Road, London W14 0NS ☎ 020 7602 3018
BROOKS David (*Saxes, Flt*): 9 Grove Place, London NW3 1JR ☎ 020 7431 8972
CAUTION James (*Voc*): 'The Roost', 67 York Road, New Barnet, Herts EN5 1LN ☎ 020 8449 5778
COCHRANE Willie: 53 Galliard Road, Edmonton, London N9 7PA ☎ 020 8805 0912
DUNSMORE Allan: 3 Cleveland Park Avenue, Walthamstow, London E17 7BP ☎ 020 8521 6479
FLEMING Ian: 29 Downsview Road, Upper Norwood, London SE19 3XD ☎ 020 8653 9330
GALLOWAY Charles: 76 Cuckoo Hill Road, Pinner, Middx HA5 1AX ☎ 020 8866 2616
MACLEOD Donald: 20 Parsonage Lane, North Cray, Sidcup, Kent DA14 5HD ☎ 020 8302 3081, 0941 113723 pager
MCCLINTOCK Robert (*Gtr*): 6 Catelowes Road, London NW1 9XJ ☎ 020 7485 3495
MURPHY Robert (*Acc*): 97 Erskine Road, Sutton, Surrey SM1 3AT ☎ 020 8644 4744
REID George: 52 Poplar Road, Sutton, Surrey SM3 9JX ☎ 020 8644 4195
STEWART Iain: Flat 14, 9 Queensbridge Road, London E2 8NP ☎ 020 7739 2110
VAUGHAN Michael ☎ 01707 650868

NORTH WEST

BORIS (*Gtr, Synth, Per, Voc*): 98 Park Road, Hindley, Wigan, Lancs WN2 3RX ☎ 01942 522946

LONDON

EKKEL Bibs: 115 Green Lane, Sunbury-on-Thames, Middlesex TW16 7NY ☎ 01932 711906 & fax, 07970 161002 mob

NISSEN David (*Bsn*): 54 Morshead Mansions, Maida Vale, London W9 1LF ☎ 020 8723 5384, 0961 123155 mob, 020 8932 2501 fax

SCOTLAND

MATHIESON Ken (*Dms, Zit, Arr*): 20 Kylepark Crescent, Uddingston G71 7DQ ☎ 01698 814475
MCLAREN Nicol (*Acc*): 9 Sheila Road, Blairgowrie, Perthshire PH10 6RP ☎ 01250 874526

NORTH WEST

TAYLOR Raymond (*Org, Pf*): Flat 32, Sandown Court, Lord Street, Southport, Merseyside PR9 0HE ☎ 01704 541401

NORTH EAST

ASHFORTH S (*Clt, Cel, Saxes*): 235 Queensgate Extension, Bridlington, East Yorkshire YO16 5RG ☎ 01262 675307
BRENNAN Dave (*Bjo, Voc*): Tanglewood, Marcliffe Lane, Listerdale, Rotherham S66 0AZ ☎ 01709 700440
CHESTER Ray (*Pf, Org, Tpt, Tbn*): 10 Roker Park Terrace, Sunderland, Tyne & Wear SR6 9LY ☎ 0191 567 3013
GARVEY Edward (*Tpt, Org*): 12 Low Haugh, Ponteland, Newcastle-upon-Tyne NE20 9XN ☎ 01661 871481, 0976 872786 mob
HALLAM John Carstairs (*Tba, Db, Arr, Bjo*): 46 Belsay Avenue, Whitley Bay, Tyne & Wear NE25 8PZ ☎ 0191 252 3512
MOWAT Arthur (*Sax, Clt, Flt, Org*): 49, Ingleside Road, North Shields, Northumberland NE29 9PB ☎ 0191 257 5284
TAWS Johnny (*Pf, Org, Acc, Vib*): 63 Beech Road, Tynemouth, North Shields, Tyne & Wear NE30 2TW ☎ 0191 258 0788
WATSON William (*Md, Tpt*): Jutland Cottage, Fir Tree, Crook, Co Durham DL15 8BN ☎ 01388 767208, 01388 767208

EAST

ANTHONY Phil (*Dms, Tpt, Voc, Gtr*): 3 Rye Mill Lane, Feering, Colchester, Essex CO5 9SA ☎ 01376 570385
BAKER Joe (*Md*): 84 Stanford Road, Luton, Beds LU2 0QA ☎ 01582 612588
MACLEAN Alexander (*Gtr*): 21 Chilburn Road, Great Clacton, Clacton-on-Sea, Essex CO15 4NX ☎ 01255 429388
MCVAY Ray (*Md*): Courtyard Cottage, High Canons, Shenley, Herts WD6 5PL ☎ 020 8207 2474, 0410 202711, 020 8207 4473
THORBY George: 81 Mowbray Crescent, Stotfold, Hitchin, Herts SG5 4DY

MIDLANDS

ALLCOCK Garry (*Dms*): 617 Bristol Road South, Birmingham B31 2JS ☎ 0121 475 7524
BARRETTO Ben (*Per*): 2 Oakham Road, Somerby, Melton Mowbray, Leics LE14 2QF ☎ 01664 454888
BURCHELL Anthony (*Pf, E Pf, Org, Acc*): 100 St Gerrards Road, Solihull, West Midlands B91 1UD ☎ 0121 705 5062
CAMPBELL Colin (*Pf, Org, Arr, Cop*): 16 Clarry Drive, Four Oaks, Sutton Coldfield, West Midlands B74 2RA ☎ 0121 308 6518
CROSBY Roy (*Tpt, Flgl*): 20 Norgetts Lane, Melbourn, Cambs SG8 6HS ☎ 01763 261283
DENE (*Voc*): 2 Greswolde Park Road, Birmingham B27 6QD ☎ 0121 707 3062
DOVEY Norman (*A Sax, T Sax, Clt, Flt*): 10 Pear Tree Road, Great Barr, Birmingham B43 6HY ☎ 0121 357 3622
ENTWISTLE Eric (*A Sax, Clt*): 195 Damson Lane, Solihull, West Midlands B92 9LD ☎ 0121 705 1612
FISHER John (*Dms, Vib*): 14 Clayton Drive, Castle Bromwich, Birmingham B36 0AN ☎ 0121 747 2601
FRANCIS Gregor (*Arr, Con*): 72 Davids Drive, Wingerworth, Chesterfield, Derbyshire S42 6PS ☎ 01246 231 746
GOUGH Geoff (*A Sax, Clt, Flt*): 2 South Street, Sheepwash, Beaworthy, Devon EX21 5NA ☎ 0140 923 421

GREGORY Alfred *(A Sax, Clt, Db)*: Abbeyfield, 39 Silverbirch Road, Birmingham B24 0AE ☎ 0121 350 4166

HEMUS Alan *(Voc, Arr, Com, Cop)*: 4 Rowallan Road, Four Oaks, Sutton Coldfield, Warks B75 6RJ ☎ 0121 308 6294, 0121 429 5603

KETCH Gordon *(Dms, Voc)*: 7 Winsford Close, Newhall, Sutton Coldfield, West Midlands B76 8EU ☎ 0121 329 3318

MATHER Don *(T Sax, A Sax)*: 68 Dillotford Avenue, Styvechale, Coventry, West Midlands CV3 5DT ☎ 024 7641 2366

MERCER Frederick *(Tbn, Eup, Arr, Com)*: 61 Charles Road, Solihull, Warks B91 1TT ☎ 0121 705 0550

NEWTON Robert *(Tbn)*: 23 Windmill Avenue, Blisworth, Northants NN7 3EQ ☎ 01604 858549

O'LOUGHLIN William *(Saxes, Clt, St Pan, Flt)*: 133 Boyne Road, Sheldon, Birmingham B26 2QG ☎ 0121 628 9931

PEATE Andrew *(Tpt, Flgl, Kbds)*: 40, Poole Crescent, Harborne, Birmingham B17 0PB ☎ 0121 472 4483

RAE Roger *(Tbn, B Tbn, B Gtr, Md)*: 45 Grange Crescent, Halesowen, West Midlands B63 3ED ☎ 0121 550 6515

RODGERS Phillip *(Acc)*: 20 Ebrington Avenue, Solihull, West Midlands B92 8HU ☎ 0121 742 3192

ROYAL Jos *(Tpt, Flgl, Eup, Voc)*: 76 Valley Road, Solihull, Warks B92 9AX ☎ 0121 743 4337

SHIRLEY Robert *(Dms)*: 47 Shirburn Road, Leek, Staffs ST13 6LD ☎ 01538 384403

SOCCI Antoine *(Acc)*: 6 Brylan Croft, Birmingham B44 8DW ☎ 0121 356 0995

ST CLARE Avis *(Voc, Kbds)*: 13 Walmley Ash Road, Sutton Coldfield, West Midlands B76 1HY ☎ 0121 351 1513

VALENTINE Art *(Dms, Voc)*: Belvedere, 17 Lancing Avenue, Leicester LE3 6HF ☎ 0116 2857730

WILLETS Colin *(Vib, Pf)*: 32 Marsh Lane, Hampton In Arden, Solihull, West Midlands B92 0AJ ☎ 01675 442585

SOUTH EAST

GARNHAM Phil *(Dms)*: Sunflower House., Haglands Lane, West Chiltington, West Sussex RH20 2QS ☎ 01798 815222

HYDE Paul *(Tbn, Voc, Flt, Md)*: 10 Norton Terrace, East Side, Newhaven, East Sussex BN9 0BT ☎ 01273 516632

JENNER Derek *(Hrn)*: 19 Gloucester Road, Parkstone, Poole, Dorset BH12 2AW ☎ 01202 721383

LIGHT Amber *(Voc)*: 75 Swanfield Drive, Chichester, West Sussex PO19 4TQ ☎ 01243 785203

PEARSON Dave: 8 Westbrooke Court, Crescent Road, Worthing, West Sussex BN11 1RG ☎ 01903 230126

SOUTH WEST

BRITTON Jack *(Dms, Voc)*: 8 Field Road, Kingswood, Bristol BS15 1HU ☎ 0117 9674529

KILMISTER James *(Arr, A Sax, Clt, Flt)*: Stratford, Liberty Lane, Blagdon, Somerset BS40 7TJ ☎ 01761 462305

LEAVEY Graham *(Tpt, Flgl)*: 20 Glenarm Road, Brislington, Bristol BS4 4LW ☎ 0117 9771431

PHILLIPS Nigel: 95 Heol Tawe, Abercrave, Swansea SA9 1XR ☎ 01639 730179

LONDON

BAILEY Paul *(Kbds)*: 22 Wolsey Road, East Molesey, Surrey KT8 9EL ☎ 020 8941 2034

BARRIE Brian *(Dms)*: 2A Gordon Road, Hounslow, Middlesex TW3 1XP ☎ 020 8570 1608

BINGLEY Del *(Voc)*: Tall Pines, 10 Pinetree Close, Chalfont St Peter, Bucks SL9 8TS ☎ 01753 885402

BROOKS Colin: 40 Lichfield Drive, East Hunsbury, Northampton NN4 0QU ☎ 01604 760765

BUNCE Martin *(Tpt, Flgl)*: 18 State Farm Avenue, Farnborough, Kent BR6 7TN ☎ 01689 861627, 0956 224492

COOPER Douglas *(Per)*: 119A Ashley Gardens, London SW1P 1HL ☎ 020 7834 7796

FIORENTINI Mario *(Acc, Pf, Voc)*: 20 Pytchley Crescent, Beulah Hill, London SE19 3QT ☎ 020 8653 1090

GOLD Harry *(Sax, Clt, Arr)*: Flat 26, 53 Foxham Road, London N19 4RR ☎ 020 7281 5471

HAYWARD Dennis *(Per, Arr)*: 148 Church Road, Shoeburyness, Essex SS3 9EZ ☎ 01702 292695 & fax

HOWARD Johnny *(Md)*: 2 Oxford House, Parkside, Wimbledon Common, London SW19 5NE ☎ 020 8944 6432

HUNTER Gerry *(Dms)*: 50 Dromey Gardens, Kenton Lane, Harrow Weald, Middx HA3 6AX ☎ 020 8954 0771

JANES Eric *(Per)*: 53 Cannon Lane, Pinner, Middlesex HA5 1HN ☎ 020 8868 5723

JOHNSON Val *(Voc)*: 59 Moring Road, London SW17 8DN ☎ 020 7767 9831, 0802 887876 mob, 020 8767 9844 fax

MILLER Bob *(Sax)*: Address Unknown

PHILLIPS Len: 16 Camden Road, Bexley, Kent DA5 3NR ☎ 01322 521515

RICARDO Peter *(Voc, Gtr)*: 48 Alexandra Road, Hounslow, Middlesex TW3 4UH ☎ 020 8570 8794

ROGERS Victor *(Gtr, Bjo, Voc)*: 69 Crown Woods Way, London SE9 2NL ☎ 020 8850 4955

ROS Edmundo *(Per)*: El Escondite De Eros, A Cuesta San Antonio 21, Javea, Alicante 03730, Espana ☎ Javea 5790281

SOLO Judd *(Gtr, Voc)*: 24 Ashdown Drive, Boreham Wood, Herts WD6 4LZ ☎ 020 8207 5552

SPROUD Billy *(Clt, Sax, Pf, Org)*: Address Unknown ☎ 01446 741677

STORER Duncan *(Kbds)*: 116 Westleigh Avenue, Putney, London SW15 6UZ ☎ 020 8789 6645, 0411 258339, 020 8785 7533

TATE Phil *(Com, Sax, Clt, Vln)*: 24 Badgers Walk, Cedars Village, Chorley Wood, Rickmansworth, Hertfordshire WD3 5GA ☎ 01923 496613 & fax

TEMPLE Nat *(Clt, Sax)*: Frenat, Forest Rd, Pyrford, West Byfleet, Surrey GU22 8NA ☎ 019323 43348

TODD Wilfred *(Md, Arr, B Gtr, Voc)*: 88 Broadway, Bournemouth, Dorset BH6 4EQ ☎ 01202 432485

VAN-EMDEN Henry *(Sax, Clt, Pf)*: 18 Park Farm Close, Finchley, London N2 N2 0PU ☎ 020 8883 2715

WEB Billy *(Dms)*: 27 Brodie Road, Enfield, Middx EN2 0EU ☎ 020 8245 0733

WISE Denny *(Md)*: 65 Shawley Way, Epsom Downs, Surrey KT18 5PD ☎ 017373 61077

BANDONEON

LONDON

PEIRO Teddy: 64 Rosslyn Crescent, Wembley, Middlesex HA9 7PA ☎ 020 8902 5077

BANJO

SCOTLAND

KNIGHT Beverley *(Bjo, Tba, Eup)*: 27 Halmyre Street, Edinburgh EH6 8QE ☎ 0131 554 5885

MACKINTOSH Iain *(Bjo, Ctna)*: 27 Strowan Crescent, Glasgow G32 9DW ☎ 0141 778 1609

MACLEOD Kevin *(Bjo)*: 37 Lauriston Gardens, Edinburgh EH3 9HJ ☎ 0131 228 6777

WALKER Ian *(Bjo, Gtr, Hrp, Bod)*: 51 Chestnut Grove, Kinneil, Boness, West Lothian EH51 0PJ ☎ 01506 824868

WILSON David *(Bjo, Gtr, Pf)*: 19 Kensington Gate, Glasgow G12 9LQ ☎ 0141 334 1790

NORTH WEST

BALDWIN Kenneth *(Bjo, Gtr)*: 59 Caithness Road, Allerton, Liverpool L18 9JJ ☎ 0151 427 0745

BROWN John *(Bjo)*: 2 Ilkley Drive, Davyhulme, Urmston M41 8DB ☎ 0161 748 8519

DEXTER Michael *(Bjo, Gtr, B Gtr, Db)*: 1 Meadow Street, New Mills, High Peak, Stockport Ches SK22 4AY ☎ 01663 743610

HARRISON Dennis *(Bjo)*: 14 Salacre Crescent, Upton, Wirral L49 6LN ☎ 0151 678 5575

HINDLEY Ann *(Bjo, Voc)*: 151 Sefton Street, Southport, Merseyside PR8 5DA

HORNE Malcolm (*Bjo, Gtr*): 7, Station Road, Roby, Huyton, Merseyside L36 4HU ☎ 0151 489 3047

HOWARTH John (*Bjo*): 13 Verney Road, Royton, Oldham, Lancs OL2 6AZ ☎ 0161 624 0008

JENKINSON Wilfred (*Bjo*): 7 Rookwood, 2 Norwood Avenue, Southport, Merseyside PR9 7DT ☎ 01704 28563

MCCANN Ian (*Bjo, Gtr*): 7 Gibb Lane, Mellor, Stockport, Cheshire SK6 5LZ ☎ 0161 449 7317

MOORE Les (*Bjo, Sou*): 100 Burnage Lane, Manchester M19 2NG ☎ 0161 225 4558

SHEPHERD Howard 'Shep' (*Bjo*): 7 Aldwick Avenue, Didsbury, Manchester M20 6JL ☎ 0161 445 2254

SULLIVAN Anthony (*Bjo, Bzk, Hmca, Voc*): 37 Catherine Street, Macclesfield, Cheshire SK11 6ET ☎ 01625 610849

TAYLOR Keith (*Bjo, Tba*): 3 Mellings Wood, St Annes, Lytham St Annes FY8 3DW ☎ 01253 781828

WILLIAMS Stuart (*Bjo, Gtr, Fo Fdl*): 1 Swireford Road, Helsby, Cheshire WA6 9BA ☎ 0928 723256

NORTH EAST

BELTON Gavin (*Bjo*): 1 Walker Lane, Middridge, Newton Aycliffe, Co. Durham DL5 7JN ☎ 01325 315029

BURTON Patrick (*Bjo, Per, Uke, Acc, Gtr*): 43/44 Gladstone Terrace, Sunniside, Bishop Auckland DL13 4LS ☎ 01388 730574

INESON Richard (*Bjo, Man, Gtr*): 66 Main Road, Ridgeway, Nr. Sheffield S12 3KR ☎ 0114 248 5698

KIRK Nicholas (*Bjo, Gtr*): 36 Kilpin Hill Lane, Staincliffe, Nr Dewsbury, West Yorkshire WF13 4BH ☎ 01924 402931

NAPPER Tom (*Bjo, Man*): Flat 2, 2 Woodland View, Leeds LS7 4QJ ☎ 0113 2680963

RICHARDSON John (*Bjo, Gtr*): 19 Whiteley Croft Rise, Otley, Leeds LS21 3NR ☎ 01943 463817, 0973 779262 mob

RUSBY Stephen (*Bjo, Man, Gtr*): 17 Darton Road, Cawthorne, Nr Barnsley S75 4HR ☎ 01226 770536, 01226 790536

STEPHEN Ian Keith (*Bjo, Gtr, Man, Uke*): 3 Palmer Terrace, Widdrington Station, Northumberland NE61 5RF ☎ 01670 79130893

THOMPSON David (*Bjo*): 36 Fairway, Snydale Road, Normanton, Yorks WF6 1SE ☎ 01924 890676

EAST

COX Melville (*Bjo, Gtr*): 39 Timperleys, Hintlesham, Nr Ipswich, Suffolk IP8 3PS ☎ 01473 652466

DIPLOCK Owen (*Bjo, Pf, Db*): North Lodge, Messing Park, Colchester, Essex CO5 9TD ☎ 01621 816265

FAWCETT David (*Bjo*): 83 Lalleford Road, Luton, Beds LU2 9JH ☎ 01582 415079

GYFORD William (*Bjo, Voc*): 1 Wheatsheaf Cottages, Alconbury Hill, Huntingdon, Cambs PE17 5JH ☎ 01480 458973

HOWLETT Roger (*Bjo*): 65 Teversham Drift, Cherryhinton, Cambridge CB1 3JZ ☎ 01223 240822

JONES Stephen (*Bjo, Gtr, Man*): 32 Wynchlands Crescent, St. Albans, Herts AL4 0XL ☎ 01727 766171, 01727 766170 fax

LINCE Louis (*Bjo, Gtr, Dms*): 28 Stortford Hall Park, Bishops Stortford, Herts CM23 5AL ☎ 01279 653525

PARLE Mike (*Bjo, Gtr, Vln*): 73 City Road, Norwich NR1 3AS ☎ 01603 618109

ROSE Gerry (*Bjo, Db, Voc*): 99 Hurst Park Avenue, Cambridge CB4 2AB ☎ 01223 365107

SMITH John (*Bjo, E Gtr*): 12 Whitefriars Crescent, Westcliff-on-Sea, Essex SS0 8EU ☎ 01702 345989

SOUTHEND BOB (*Bjo, Voc*): 1 Crowstone Close, Westcliffe-on-Sea, Essex SS0 8BB ☎ 01702 346506

VOUSDEN Edwin (*Bjo, Rh Gtr*): West Meadows, 15 Shepreth Road, Foxton, Cambridge CB2 6SU ☎ 01223 870380

WHIPP Freddie (*Bjo*): 'The Briars', 18 Overcote Road, Over, Cambs CB4 5NS ☎ 01954 231256, 0860 540965 mob

MIDLANDS

BOWERS Geoffrey (*Bjo, Man, Gtr, Vln, B Gtr*): 49 Claremont Avenue, Hucknall, Nottingham NG15 6EE ☎ 0115 953 7272, 0589 495479

BROWN John (*Bjo, Ac Gtr, Man, Dul*): 94 Middleton Hall Road, Kings Norton, Birmingham B30 1DG ☎ 0121 624 0409

HOSKIN Brian (*Bjo*): 74, Berwick Road, Shrewsbury, Salop SY1 2NF ☎ 01743 366243

JONGMAN Bruce (*Bjo*): Brookhill Cottage, Ravensthorpe Road, Barn Acre, East Haddon, Northampton NN6 8BY ☎ 01604 770617

MELLOR Brian (*Bjo, Gtr*): 12 Ellesboro Road, Harborne, Birmingham B17 8PT ☎ 0121 427 9096

MOWATT Dennis (*Bjo, B Gtr*): 6 Selbourne Road, Dudley, West Midlands DY2 8LA ☎ 01384 459839

SCOTT Bill (*Bjo*): 47 Knapp Way, Malvern Link, Worcs WR14 1SG ☎ 01684 562152

SIDHU Amarjit (*Bjo, Kbds*): 86 Harborne Road, Edgbaston, Birmingham B15 3HN ☎ 0121 553 3258, 0121 553 3258

SOUTH EAST

BISHOP Paul (*Bjo, B Gtr, Gtr, Citt*): 30 Cambridge Road, Bexhill-on-Sea, East Sussex TN40 2BU ☎ 01424 217323

BROOMFIELD David (*Bjo*): Misty Summer Lane, Burton, Christchurch, Dorset BH23 7JB ☎ 01202 485034

DENNIS Maurice (*Bjo, Gtr, Ph Fid*): Porlock House, Hambledon Road, Denmead, Hants PO7 6LR ☎ 023 9225 5028

MARTIN Roy (*Bjo, Gtr, Hmca, Dms*): 61 Victoria Road, Polegate, East Sussex BN26 6BY ☎ 01323 485330

MAYNARD Andrew (*Bjo, Gtr*): Manor House, Goudhurst Road, Marden, Tonbridge Kent TN12 9JE ☎ 01622 831655

MCKINNON Bill (*Bjo, Gtr, Man, Ctna*): 26 Roxburgh Drive, Didcot, Oxon OX11 7HF ☎ 01235 810794

MITCHELL Brian (*Bjo*): 7 Padwell Road, Southampton, Hampshire SO2 0QY ☎ 023 8022 8950

PERKINS Andrew (*Bjo*): 21 Stone Street, Faversham, Kent ME13 8PU ☎ 01795 533864

STRAKER David (*Bjo, Gtr*): 16 Holcombe Road, Rochester, Kent ME1 2HU ☎ 01634 402799

TOWNEND Richard (*Bjo, Vln, Gtr, Man, Db*): 2 Fairview Cottages, Balaclava Lane, Wadhurst, East Sussex TN5 6EQ ☎ 01892 882412

VINCENT Julian (*Bjo, Gtr, Nor P*): 93 Redhatch Drive, Earley, Reading RG6 2QN ☎ 01734 875759

WALKER George (*Bjo, Gtr*): 186 Brighton Road, Lancing BN15 8LL ☎ 01903 752948

WEBSTER Eric (*Bjo, Rh Gtr*): 14 The Cherries, Barming, Nr Maidstone, Kent ME16 9DJ ☎ 01622 727275

WILLETT Nobby (*Bjo, Gtr*): 23 Cerne Road, Gravesend, Kent DA12 4BL ☎ 01474 363784

SOUTH WEST

CURRIE John (*Bjo, Gtr*): 49 Morestone Road, Wooton Bassett, Swindon, Wilts SN4 7DH ☎ 01793 8507612

EDWARDS Hilary (*Bjo*): 13 Parkfield Road, Topsham, Devon EX3 0DR ☎ 01392 873890

FRISBY Sid (*Bjo, Gtr*): 4 Station Terrace, Dowlais Top, Merthyr, Tydfil CF48 3PU ☎ 01685 371567

HAWKINS John (*Bjo*): 56 Sandringham Road, Brislington, Bristol 4 BS4 3PP ☎ 0117 977 7610

LANGHAM Thomas (*Bjo, Ac Gtr, Man, Uke, Per*): 24A Stockwells, Moreton In Marsh, Glos GL56 0HQ ☎ 01608 652411

LONG Pete (*Bjo*): 7 Pinetree Rise, Swindon, Wilts SN2 3BY ☎ 01793 526422

MACDONALD Mac (*Bjo*): 1 Winsham Terrace, Ilfracombe, Devon EX34 8HA ☎ 01271 6485

MURRAY Geraldine (*Bjo, Voc, Auto Hrp*): 4 Station Terrace, Dowlais Top, Merthyr, Tydfil CF48 3PU ☎ 01685 371547 & fax, 0385 575648 mob

ROOFE Sarah (*Bjo, Pf*): 1 Bath Street, Newport, South Wales NP9 7BD ☎ 01633 251043

BANJO - SOUTH WEST

SIMS Sam (*Bjo, Man, Dobro, Gtr*): 2 Graig Park Circle, Malpas, Newport, Gwent NP9 6HE ☎ 854748

SUMNER Peter (*Bjo*): Lentney House, Longlands Drive, Heybrook Bay, Plymouth PL9 0BL ☎ 01752 863044, 01752 482510

WHITLOCK John (*Bjo, Pf*): 8 Higher Brimley, Teignmouth, Devon TQ14 8JS ☎ 01626 774710

WHITTINGHAM Jill (*Bjo*): 16 Queens Road, St George, Bristol BS5 8HR ☎ 0117 9551976

LONDON

COX James (*Bjo, Gtr*): 18 Curlew Close, High Wycombe, Bucks HP13 5JY ☎ 01494 532823

FORD Andrew (*Bjo*): 5 Clarence Road, Wallington, Surrey SM6 0EW ☎ 020 8647 5745, 020 8395 5606, 0973 267529 mob

HEAD John (*Bjo*): 2 Claremont Gardens, Upminster, Essex RM14 1DN ☎ 01708 221474

LINDSAY David (*Bjo*): 23 Park Road, East Twickenham, Middx TW1 2QD ☎ 020 8892 2956

MEADOWS Colin (*Bjo*): 12 Kenlor Road, Tooting, London SW17 0DF ☎ 020 8767 7083

OVER Geoffrey (*Bjo*): 67 Whitehall Park Road, Chiswick, London W4 3NB ☎ 020 8995 9058

PICK Kenneth J (*Bjo, Gtr*): 78 Harley Street, London W1N 1AE

ROBERTS Kevan (*Bjo, Bzk, Gtr*): 260 Park Road, London N8 8JY ☎ 020 8341 3400

SADLER Albert (*Bjo*): 65 Clements Road, East Ham, London E6 2DR ☎ 020 8470 2898

SINGER Nicholas (*Bjo, Gtr*): 11 Langley Road, Beckenham, Kent BR3 4AE ☎ 020 8650 8843

SMITH Richard (*Bjo, Man, Gtr*): 180 Broomwood Road, Battersea, London SW11 6JY ☎ 020 7585 2958

SOFTLEY John (*Bjo, Gtr*): 1 Ashendene Road, Bayford, Herts SG13 8PX ☎ 01992 511254

STAGG Bill (*Bjo, Gtr*): Oak Cottage, Eliot Bank, Forest Hill, London SE23 3XE ☎ 020 8291 4513

THOMPSON Christopher (*Bjo, Gtr*): 27 Hawley Street, London NW1 8BY ☎ 020 7482 2241

WATSON John (*Bjo*): 14, St Albans Gardens, Teddington, Middlesex TW11 8AE ☎ 020 8977 6547

BARITONE HORN
NORTH EAST

HOPES Clifford (*Eup, Efl Bass, Tba*): 128 Merrill Road, Thurnscoe, Rotherham, S Yorks S63 0PP

BASS CLARINET
SCOTLAND

FOLLAN James (*Bt Hrn*): 10/1 St Leonards Crag, Edinburgh EH8 9SP ☎ 0131 667 7092

LEE Dick (*Sax, Rec, Com, Arr*): 32 Regent Street, Edinburgh EH15 2AX ☎ 0131 669 2440 & fax

NORTH WEST

BROWNE Dennis (*Efl Clt, A Sax*): 1, Barway Road, Chorlton, Manchester M21 1JZ ☎ 0161 860 7442, 0161 881 6297 day, 041 038 4742

POWNALL Colin (*Clt, Efl Clt, Bt Hrn*): 10 Kenilworth Road, Neston, South Wirral L64 0SP ☎ 0151 336 2421

EAST

ROWE Charles (*Sax, E Flt, Clt, Flt*): 8 Hamels Mansion, Knights Hill, Buntingford, Herts SG9 9NA ☎ 01920 821774

SOUTH WEST

BUCKLEY Jack (*A Sax*): 13 Mead Close, Shirehampton, Bristol BS11 0EQ ☎ 0117 9821989

LONDON

BUCKINGHAM Mark (*A Sax, Clt, T Sax*): 13 Bury Grove, Morden, Surrey SM4 5NG ☎ 020 8646 4361

CHAMBERLAIN Ian (*Clt, Saxes*): 34 Woodway Crescent, Harrow, Middlesex HA1 2NQ ☎ 020 8907 3096

FOWLER Emma (*Efl Clt, Clt, Saxes, Flt*): 18 Ardleigh Road, Walthamstow, London E17 5BU ☎ 020 8531 5064

WEBSTER Andrew (*Efl Clt, Bt Hrn*): 73 Dallinger Road, London SE12 0TQ ☎ 020 8857 0847, 0976 357375 mob

BASS GUITAR
SCOTLAND

ADAMS John (*Bjo, Ac Gtr, Jaw H*): Schiehallion, Cromwell Road, Kirkwall, Orkney ☎ 0185 687 2677

AGNEW Peter (*Gtr*): 27 Munro Street, Kirkcaldy, Fife, Scotland KY1 1PY ☎ 01592 64177817

BAIRD William: 40 Ferrier Crescent, Armadale, West Lothian, Scotland EH48 2PJ ☎ 01501 730454

BARRY Adrian: 53 Hazel Avenue, Johnstone, Renfrewshire PA5 0BQ

BOYLE James (*Tpt*): 114 Mansel Street, Glasgow G21 4HW ☎ 0141 558 7476

CHALMERS Bryan: 45 Mains Circle, Westhill, Aberdeenshire AB32 6HD ☎ 01224 744650, 0850 506098, 01224 745501

CHAPMAN Ian (*Kbds, Ac Gtr*): 45 Ash Grove, Blackburn, West Lothian EH4 7 7QJ ☎ 01506 636541, 0850 953000, 01506 858208

CLARK Graeme (*Gtr, Kbds, Hmca*): 1 Park Gate, Glasgow G3 6DL ☎ 0141 353 1515

CLARK John: Tarratit, Laxo, Vidlin, Shetland ZE2 9QD ☎ 01806 8251

CLARKE Timothy: 26 Banavie Road, Partickhill, Glasgow G11 5AN

COTTRELL Simon (*Didj*): 22 Willowbank Crescent, Woodlands, Glasgow G3 6NB ☎ 0141 331 0322

COWAN David: 16 Luss Brae, Earnock, Hamilton ML3 9UW ☎ 01698 424003

CROZIER Archibald (*Voc*): Flat 4 B, 195 Fernbank Street, Glasgow G22 6BQ ☎ 0141 558 7425

DAVIDSON Colin (*Ac Gtr, Pf, Voc*): 30 Bonnethill Place, Dundee DD1 2AD ☎ 01382 871681

DE-LUXE Alain: c/o Richard Gordon Mgmt, 3 Berkley Grove, London NW1 8XY ☎ 020 7483 4945

DUBOIS Lewis (*Gtr, Cel*): Southcore, Bridge Street, Halkirk, Caithness KW12 6YG ☎ 01847 831507

DUNBAR Edward (*Db*): 20A Cedar Avenue, Johnstone, Renfrewshire PA5 9TH ☎ 01505 21832

EVANS Paul (*Gtr, Pf, Dms, Kbds*): 8 Trent Street, Townhead, Coatbridge, Scotland ML5 2NT ☎ 01236 437225

FAGAN John (*Voc*): 145 Arbroath Road, Dundee DD2 1BB ☎ 01382 453465

FALCONER Mark: Flat 2, 6 Montague Street, Kelvinbridge, Glasgow G4 9HX ☎ 0141 564 1832

FARNAN Peter (*Acc*): 26 Parkhill Avenue, Dyce, Aberdeen AB21 7FP ☎ 01224 724310

FORBES Derek: Davidson & Workman, 16 Royal Terrace, Glasgow G3 7NY ☎ 0141 332 8038, 0141 332 3736

FULLERTON Henry: 42 Merkland Road, Alloway, Ayr KA7 4UN ☎ 01292 443465

GILBODY Paul (*Gtr, Voc, Kbds*): If2 37 Gillespie Crescent, Toll Cross, Edinburgh EH10 4HX ☎ 0131 229 7235

GIZZI Dante: c/o Gun, Parkline Studios, 974 Pollokshaws Road, Glasgow G41 2HA ☎ 0141 632 1111

GRAHAM Elaine: 170 Menzies Road, Balornock, Glasgow, Scotland G21 3NF ☎ 0141 558 6376

GRIMES Ged (*Kbds, Per, Dms, Db*): Jack's Hoose, c/o Radio Tay, 6 North Isla Street, Dundee DD3 7JQ ☎ 01382 817741

HAMILTON Laurie (*Gtr, Pf*): 19 Park Drive, Bannockburn, Stirling FK7 0EQ ☎ 01786 811871

HAMILTON Ross (*Gtr, Pf, Dms*): 27 Park Avenue, Bishopbriggs, Glasgow G64 2SN ☎ 0141 772 0219, 0385 523 383

HARKNESS Iain (*Acc*): 2 Moss Haw, Moscow, Galston, Ayrshire KA4 8PU ☎ 01560 700211

HENDERSON Stuart *(Rh Gtr, Kbds)*: Flat 2/1, 138 Burnhouse Street, Maryhill, Glasgow G20 8AR

HILL Matt *(Gtr)*: Easter Blawloan Cottage, Blackness, Scotland EH49 7NP ☎ 01324 635627

IVITSKY *(Db, Gtr, Dms)*: 23 St Leonards Bank, Edinburgh EH8 9SQ ☎ 0131 667 4484

JACK Cy *(Db)*: The Coach House, 12 Sydenham Lane, Glasgow G12 9EU ☎ 0141 339 4367

JACK David *(Voc, Gtr)*: Address Unknown ☎ 0131 228 8348

KELLY Daniel *(Ld Gtr, Kbds)*: 134 Arbroath Road, Dundee, Tayside DD4 7HR ☎ 01382 461732

MACARTHUR Quee *(Voc, Per)*: 18 (3F1) Waverley Park, Edinburgh EH8 8ET ☎ 0131 620 1513

MACDONALD Rory: c/o Marilyn Ross, Runrig, 1 York Street, Aberdeen AB11 5DL ☎ 01224 573100, 01224 572598

MAKOS Tony *(Gtr)*: Flat 5, 2 Glenogle Road, Edinburgh EH3 5HW ☎ 0131 558 1198

MANSON Kenneth *(Gtr)*: 68/3 Great Junction Street, Leith, Edinburgh EH6 5LD ☎ 0131 554 1836

MANSON Paul: 15 Cargil Terrace, Trinity, Edinburgh EH5 3ND ☎ 0131 551 3395

MCANDREW Alex: 90 Tay Street, Tayport, Fife DD6 9DB ☎ 01382 552039

MCDONALD Donald *(Ac Gtr)*: 11F Hughenden Gardens, Glasgow G12 9XW ☎ 0141 334 7413

MCELHONE John: c/o T Whitelaw, Park Lane Studios, 974 Pollokshaws Road, Glasgow G41 2HA

MCFARLANE Ed *(Db)*: 245 Peat Road, Glasgow G53 6RRZ ☎ 0141 881 8694, 0402 562814

MCGARRIGLE John: 29 Millcroft Road, South Carbrain, Cumbernauld, Scotland G67 2QE ☎ 01236 615 771

MCHUGH Michael *(Kbds)*: 30 Tweed Street, Ayr KA8 9JD ☎ 01292 268926

MCPHERSON John *(E Gtr)*: 43 Kilmuir Crescent, Arden, Glasgow G46 8DU ☎ 0141 6210344, 0374 147988 mob

MILLER Gary: 16 Nevis Place, Hallglen, Falkirk FK1 2QE ☎ 01324 636833

MILLER Robert *(Db)*: 14 Stewart Avenue, Currie, Midlothian EH14 5SD ☎ 0131 449 4865, 0131 343 4651

MITCHELL Andy *(Db)*: 7 Clairinch Way, Drymen, Glasgow G63 0DL ☎ 01360 660279

MORISON George *(Db)*: 126 Brediland Road, Linwood, Renfrewshire PA3 3RR ☎ 01505 322484

MOUAT W *(Didj)*: T.F.R., 228 King Street, Aberdeen, Scotland AB24 5BU ☎ 01224 630 152, 01224 630 152

MULRINE Jonathan: 132 Kingswood Drive, Glasgow G44 4RE ☎ 0141 649 2183, 0411 803 208

MURDOCH Stuart: Blanchory Management, No. 374 Central Chambers, 93 Hope Street, Glasgow G2 6LD ☎ 0141 227 2751

MURRAY Kieran: Craighaed Cottage, Braco, Dunblane FK15 9LP ☎ 01786 880353

MURRAY Mark: 106 Linghope Place, Gowkthrapple, Wishaw, Lanarkshire ML2 0LL ☎ 01698 290127, 01698 373724

ODDOYE Winston *(Rh Gtr)*: 64 Polwarth Gardens, Edinburgh EH11 1LL ☎ 0131 229 6639

OWENS Campbell *(Gtr)*: Address Unknown ☎ 0141 337 6572

PATON David *(Ac Gtr, Voc)*: 80 Morningside Drive, Edinburgh EH10 5NU ☎ 0131 447 7062

PINSKY Philip *(Kbds)*: 23 St Leonards Bank, Edinburgh EH8 9SQ ☎ 0131 668 4405

RODEN Paul: Flat 1/1, 348 Dumbarton Road, Partick, Glasgow G11 6TG ☎ 0141 334 0871

ROSS Billy *(Gtr)*: 244 Elizabeth Drive, Bathgate, West Lothian, Scotland EH48 1HU ☎ 01506 634755 & fax, 0410 461656

SHARKEY Andrew: 62 Reservoir Road, Gourock, Renfrewshire PA19 1YQ ☎ 01475 631570, 0141 576 0464

SIMPSON David *(Gtr, Voc, Pf, Man)*: 27 Fenwick Road, Kilmaurs, Ayrshire KA3 2TE ☎ 01543 529075

SINCLAIR George *(Gtr)*: Dolphin House, 179 Croftfoot Road, Croftfoot, Glasgow G44 5JY ☎ 0141 569 4323

SMITH Joe: 12 Falkland View, Kirkcaldy, Fife KY1 3JD ☎ 01592 592899

SOAVE Roberto: 76A Dartnell Road, Dartnell Road, Croydon CR0 6JA ☎ 020 8655 2358

TETTEH-LARTEY Benny *(Ac Gtr, Pf, Kbds, Voc)*: 50 Paradykes Avenue, Loanhead, Mid Lothian EH20 9LD ☎ 0131 440 0076

THOMSON Brian *(Voc)*

TURNER Nicholas *(E Gtr, Kbds)*: Watercolour Music, Ardgour, Lochaber, Scotland PH33 7AH ☎ 01855 841259

TYRE Grant *(Db)*: 138 Main Street, Thornton, Kirklady, Fife KY1 4AQ ☎ 01592 774280, 0441 077743

VERNAL Ewen *(Db, Gtr)*: 3 Coyle Park, Troon, Ayrshire KA10 7LB ☎ 01292 311987, 0802 486995 mob

WATSON-JONES Mark: 49 Kelvin Street, Grangemouth, Stirlingshire, Scotland FK3 8EX ☎ 01324 483501, 0411 596650 mob

WELLS William *(Gtr)*: 9 Wolfe Road, Falkirk FK1 1SL ☎ 01324 624120

WHITE Jeremy: 51 Millwood St, Shawlands, Glasgow, Scotland G41 3JS ☎ 0141 649 2933

WOODSIDE James *(Dms)*: 21 Seventh Ave, Birkenshaw, Uddingston, Glasgow G71 6DQ ☎ 01698 321320

NORTH WEST

ARMSTRONG David: 13 Ellerbank, Harrington, Workington, Cumbria CA14 5LA ☎ 01228 47790, 01946 832829

BARLEY Michael *(Gtr)*: 27 Pippins Close, Sutton, Deeside, Flintshire CH5 1PE ☎ 01244 836627

BARNETT Carl *(Db, Arr, Cop)*: 11 Countess Street, Stockport, Cheshire SK2 6HB ☎ 0161 456 7894

BARTON Richard: 5 Valley View, Fulwood, Preston PR2 8HA ☎ 01772 718703

BEESLEY Adrian *(Gtr, Kbds, Tba)*: 1 Malton Avenue, Chorlton-Cum-Hardy, Manchester M21 8AT ☎ 0161 881 8556, 07970 183298

BLOOMFIELD Damian: 9 Jimmy Mc Mullen Walk, Fallowfield, Manchester M14 4JG ☎ 0161 226 2127

BONWICK Michael: 22 Raglan Road, Sale, Cheshire M33 4AQ ☎ 0860 456064

BRADDOCK Phil *(E Gtr)*: 22 Quernmore Avenue, Marton, Blackpool, Lancs FY3 9SU ☎ 01253 791456

BREWER David: 68 Petteril Street, Carlisle, Cumbria CA1 2AJ ☎ 01228 515474

BROUGHTON Ben *(Gtr, Db)*: 46 Sealand Road, Chester CH1 4LB ☎ 01244 372083

CAMPBELL Martyn *(Voc, Gtr)*: 33 Annesley Road, Liverpool L17 9QR ☎ 0151 726 9406

CHIPPENDALE Mick *(Rh Gtr)*: 4 Bute Avenue, Blackpool, Lancs FY1 2HR ☎ 01253 751683

CLARK Stephen: 68 Rannerdale Drive, Whitehaven, Cumbria CA28 6LA

COWX Timothy *(Gtr, Cnt)*: Glan Llyn, Glan Llyn Road, Bradley, Wrexham LL11 4BB ☎ 01978 757 332

CROOKES Allan: 84 Gorsey Lane, Warrington, Cheshire WA2 7SH ☎ 01925 650610

CULSHAW Gary *(B Viol)*: 180 Tulketh Road, Preston, Lancs PR2 1ER ☎ 01772 724284

CUNLIFFE Paul: 1 Turnstone Avenue, Newton Le Willows, Warrington WA12 9SD ☎ 01925 291839

DANSON William *(Synth, Gtr)*: 55 Beech Lane, Macclesfield, Cheshire SK10 2DS ☎ 01625 615558

DAY Martyn *(Gtr, Acc)*: 117 Haliburton Road, St. Margarets, Middlesex TW1 1PE ☎ 020 8892 5211

DIXON Mark *(Rh Gtr)*: 32 Atherton Street, St Helens, Merseyside WA10 2DT ☎ 01744 739164

DUNCAN Philip: 58 Tan Yard Brow, Gorton, Manchester M18 8UJ ☎ 0161 202 2418

EASTHAM Stuart *(Man, Mando, Gtr)*: 68 Huxley Street, Oldham, Lancs OL4 5JZ ☎ 0161 624 7493

EDDIE *(Gtr, Dms, Per, Voc)*: 237 Sutton Way, Great Sutton, South Wirral L65 7BE ☎ 0956 220 811

FOLEY Gregory (*Voc, Gtr, Kbds*): R.S.P.C.A. Animal Centre, Bryn-Y-Maen, Colwyn Bay, Clwyd LL28 5EJ ☎ 01492 534282

FRIZELL Andy (*Flt, A Sax, Gtr, Tbn*): Flat 3, 2 Hartington Road, Liverpool L8 0SG ☎ 0151 733 6657

FROST Karen (*Voc, Per*): 6 Malton Avenue, Manchester M21 8AT ☎ 0161 861 8971

GENIC

GIBBS Nathan (*Per*): 1 Back Gladstone Buildings, Rawtenstall, Rossendale, Lancs BB4 8SE

GILBERT Nicholas: 17 Brownsville Road, Heaton Moor, Stockport, Cheshire SK4 4PE

GLENNIE James: C Young & Co, Chesham House, 150 Regent Street, London W1R 5FA ☎ 020 7432 0337, 020 7432 0338

GODFREY Phillip: 6A Bold Street, Southport, Merseyside PR9 0DD ☎ 01704 533690, 01704 544817, 01704 544817

GRIFFITH Barrie (*Gtr*): 33 Somerset Road, West Kirby, Merseyside L48 ☎ 0151 625 7512

GRIME Frank (*La Per*): 40 Albert Road, Levenshulme, Manchester M19 2AB ☎ 0161 224 1550

GUNSON Keith (*Gtr, Kbds, Voc*): 4 Milbrook Crescent, Old Hall Estate, Kirkby, Liverpool, Merseyside L32 1TJ ☎ 0151 548 2282

HALL Christopher (*Kbds, Gtr*): 140 Stanley Street, Atherton, Manchester M46 0AH ☎ 01942 791547

HAMMOND Graham (*Voc*): 29 Brandreth Drive, Parbold, Wigan, Lancs WN8 7HB ☎ 01257 464398

HARTLEY Faron: 11 Claxheugh Road, South Hylton, Sunderland SR4 0RE ☎ 0191 534 6129

HESKETH George (*Gtr, Org*): 95 Wilkinson Avenue, Little Lever, Bolton, Lancs BL3 1QP ☎ 01204 77377

HEYWOOD Barrington (*Synth*): 15 Mayfield Road, Grappenhall, Warrington, Cheshire WA4 2NP ☎ 01925 268114

HODGKINSON Stephen: 42 Broadhill Road, Stalybridge, Cheshire SK15 1HQ ☎ 0161 338 3076

HOOK Peter: Gamewest Ltd, 11/13 Whitworth Street, Manchester. M1 5WG ☎ 0161 445 5415

HUGHES James (*Gtr*): 1 Mount Pleasant, Pontyblyddyn, Mold, Flintshire CH7 4HX ☎ 01352 771474

ISAAC Michael: 35 Exmouth Road, Sale, Cheshire M33 5HT ☎ 0161 905 3271

JACKSON Carol (*Voc, Rh Gtr*): 34 George Street, Sedgley Park, Prestwich, Manchester M25 8WS ☎ 0161 773 3351

JACOB Huw: Flat 4, 84 Palatine Road, Withington, Manchester M20 3JW ☎ 0161 448 7310

JENKINSON Derek (*Tpt*): Barne House, Broad Dale, Ulverston, Cumbria LA12 7SE ☎ 01229 585305, 0421 620282, 01229 588089

JONES Graham: 27 Conway Drive, Leeds LS8 5JG

KEETON Dylan (*Gtr*): 49 Farm Lane, Worsley, Manchester M28 2PG ☎ 0161 288 5928

KEMP Rick (*Gtr*): The Steppings, Roweltown, Carlisle, Cumbria CA6 6PW ☎ 01697 748642 & fax

KRAWIECKI Jim (*Per, Db*): 36 Torbay Road, Chorlton, Manchester M21 8XD ☎ 0161 282 9789

LAMB Steve: 4 Serpentine Road, Kendal, Cumbria LA9 4PE ☎ 01539 725996

LARKEY Glenn Edward (*Pf*): 22 Bull Lane, Walton, Liverpool L9 8DB ☎ 0151 523 3284

LEATHER Craig: 30 Glendale Road, Boothstown, Manchester M28 1AZ ☎ 0161 357 0106

LEE Bo: 25 Thornleigh Road, Fallowfield, Manchester M14 7AH ☎ 0161 225 6197

LIVESEY Chris: 49 Bankmouse Road, Bury, Lancashire BL8 1DS ☎ 0161 763 1806, 0421 483108

LORENZO Jimmy (*Ac Gtr, Kbds, Bjo, Flt*): Flat 3, 48 West Parade, Rhyl, Clwyd LL18 1HH ☎ 01745 331346

LOWE Gary (*Hmca, Dms*): 13 Hope Park Rd, Prestwich, Manchester M25 1GE ☎ 0161 773 8164

LYNCH Dan (*Gtr, Kbds, Dms, Hmca*): 11 Tynwald Road, West Kirby, Wirral L48 4DA ☎ 0151 625 1606

MACNAGHTEN Alex

MARSLAND Andrew (*Gtr*): 35 Ash Drive, Wardley, Swinton, Manchester M27 9QP ☎ 0161 281 0542, 0467 244296, 0161 281 0542

MATTHEW Howard (*Hmca, Sl Gtr*): 98 Old Road, Tintwistle, Glossop, Derbyshire SK13 1JY ☎ 01457 862025

MAWDSLEY Stephen ☎ 01704 213068, 01704 567640

MCNEICE Francis (*Gtr, Pf*): 88 Vine Lane, Hillingdon, Middlesex UB10 0BE ☎ 01895 34330

MITCHELL-DAVIDSON Paul (*Com, Gtr, Man, Arr*): 25 Bannerman Avenue, Prestwich, Manchester M25 1DZ ☎ 0161 798 9604 & fax, 0797 9883516

MORAN Pauline: 43 Blackpool Road, Bispham, Blackpool, Lancs FY2 0HT ☎ 01253 53932

MORRISON Dom: 20 Throstle Hall Court, Middleton, Manchester M24 3SF ☎ 0161 653 2260

MORRISON Rob: 9 Hornby St, Crosby, Liverpool L23 5TL ☎ 0151 924 3257

MWYN Rhys: 5 Gorllewin Twthill, Caernarfon, Gwynedd LL55 1PE ☎ 01286 672539

NAHAJSKI Michael: 99 Harwood Street, Darwen, Lancs BB3 1PA ☎ 01254 704214

NICHOLAS Christopher (*Voc*) ☎ 0161 929 4183, 0468 843859 mob

PERCY Michael: c/o Freedom Management, Suite 4, 19 Brunswick Terrace, Brighton BN3 1HL ☎ 01273 748599

PIKE Tim (*Ob*): 37 Seafield Drive, Wallasey, Merseyside L45 0LN ☎ 0151 639 3845

POOLE Ronald (*Voc*): Address Unknown ☎ 0161 434 2802

QUARTEY Jeffery: 36 Charles Berrington Road, Wavertree, Liverpool L15 9HQ ☎ 020 8722 4031, 020 8734 4753

READ Tom (*Db, Arr*): 37 Cross Street, Macclesfield, Cheshire SK11 7PG ☎ 01625 612916

RELTON John S (*Pf*): 141 Moss Road, Birkdale, Southport, Merseyside PR8 4JA

REYNOLDS Ambrose (*Per*): c/o USL PO Box 223, Liverpool L69 8LR ☎ 0151 709 7562, 0151 707 2325

RIGBY John (*E Gtr*): 19A Waterloo Road, Birkdale, Southport PR8 2HL ☎ 01704 566429

ROGERS Geoffrey: 5 Crescent Drive, Furness Vale, High Peak, Derbyshire SK23 7PE ☎ 01663 733973

ROTHWELL Tony (*Gtr, Kbds*): Old Fallbarrow Cottage, Fallbarrow Road, Windermere, Cumbria LA23 3DJ ☎ 015394 88241

RUBBA (*Gtr, Per, Voc*): 5 Bembridge Close, Rusholme, Manchester M14 5WX ☎ 0161 225 8675

RYAN Timothy: 8A Victoria Street, Denton, Manchester M34 3JQ ☎ 07887 683923

SARKO Richard: 15 Broomville Avenue, Sale, Cheshire M33 3DD ☎ 0161 976 2578

SEFTON David (*E Gtr, Ac Gtr, Db*): 18 Ainsford Road, Withington, Manchester M20 4ST ☎ 0161 445 1006

SEIFFERT Graeme (*Gtr, Kbds*): 38 Ann Moss Way, Rotherhithe, London SE16 2TL

SHIPWAY Robert (*Gtr, Man*): 6 Copperfields, Chew Moor, Bolton BL6 4HZ ☎ 01942 840249

SINNOTT Kevin (*Gtr*) ☎ 0151 523 7480, 0151 261 1442 fax

SLATER Alan: 1 Slaters Yard, Station Road, Wigton, Cumbria CA7 9BA ☎ 016973 44680

SOMERVILLE Peter: Flat 4 Hoyle Court, Trinity Road, Hoylake, Wirral, Merseyside L47 2RS ☎ 0151 632 5897

SOULED AS SEEN (*Pf*): 45 Stamford Road, Mossley, Lancs OL5 0BG ☎ 01457 833334

STELNICKI Craig (*Rh Gtr*): 17 Campion Way, Shawclough, Rochdale, Lancs OL12 7UL ☎ 01706 712069

STOLOFF Paul (*Db*): 17 Fairway, Milnrow, Rochdale, Lancs OL16 3DU ☎ 01706 633573

STRATTON Lynda

SUDDERS Nathan (*Kbds, Gtr*): 936 Rochdale Road, Blackley, Manchester M9 7EP, 07970 446112 mob, 0161 281 5733

SWEENEY John: 49 Clarence Road, Grappenhall, Warrington, Cheshire WA4 2PH ☎ 01925 265564

THOMPSON Charles: 79 Sylvancroft, Preston, Lancs PR2 7BW

TOMPKINS David (*Db*): 72 Nicolas Road, Chorlton, Manchester M21 9LR ☎ 0161 881 0670

TREMAYNE John (*Kbds*): 11 Raven Street, Bury BL9 5AU ☎ 0161 797 9925

TURNER David (*Db*): 34 Riverside Drive, Flixton, Manchester M41 9FL ☎ 0161 748 1245

WALSH Neil: 30 Squires Court, Salford, Manchester M5 2AD ☎ 0161 707 0014

WALTON Pete (*Per, Bjo*): 10 Mount Pleasant, Ruabon, Wrexham LL14 6DT ☎ 01978 810084

WARBURTON Gareth (*Kbds, Gtr*): 6 Ashfield Square, Droylsden, Manchester M43 6PZ ☎ 0161 371 7925

WARBURTON Stephen: Brookwood, Old Hall Mill Lane, Atherton, Manchester M46 0RG ☎ 01942 671777

WHITEHEAD Peter (*B Tba*): Old Hey Farm, Millcroft Lane, Delph, Oldham, Lancs OL3 5UX ☎ 01457 874508

WHITFIELD Andrew: 5 Yale Grove, Rhosnesni, Wrexham

WILLIAMS Christopher: 20 Shaw Street, Glossop, Derbyshire SK13 8DW ☎ 01457 866458

WILLIAMS Steven

WIMMERA Spencer (*Dms*): Flat 1, 76 Nicolas Road, Chorlton, Manchester M21 9LR ☎ 0161 860 6965

NORTH EAST

ABBOTT Lee (*Db, Gtr*): 18 Birchwood Avenue, Shadwell, Leeds, W. Yorks LS17 8PL ☎ 0113 269 3236

ADAMS Craig (*Kbds*): 38 Wellington Road, Ilkley, West Yorks LS29 8HR ☎ 01943 603782

ADDISON John (*Ac Gtr*): Squirrels Haunt, Main Road, Sibsey, Boston, Lincs PE22 0TN ☎ 01205 750753

AGBAKOBA Paul (*Gtr, Kbds*): 44 Townhead Street, Sheffield S1 2ED ☎ 0114 2817436

ALLAN Simon (*E Gtr, Ac Gtr*): 7 Norwood Avenue, Shipley, Bradford BD18 2AX ☎ 01274 590 607

AVERY Clement (*Tpt, Db*): 9 Herd Close, Blaydon-on-Tyne, Tyne & Wear NE21 6EG ☎ 0191 414 4479

BACON Kevin: 10 Edgefield Road, Nether Edge, Sheffield S7 2BT ☎ 0114 255 7345

BAINES Trevor (*Cel, Gtr, Dms*): 51 Keswick Close, Siddal, Halifax, West Yorkshire HX3 9BP ☎ 01422 323178

BALL Mark (*Kbds, Per, Flt, Tpt*): 1st Floor Flat, 11 Goldsmid Road, Hove, Sussex BN3 1QA ☎ 020 7737 6497, 020 7924 0890 fax

BALLARD Roland (*Db, Acc*): 3 Woodhall Drive, Leeds LS5 3LQ ☎ 0113 2588729

BOWEN Andrew (*Pf*): 26 Springfield Close, Stockton Lane, York YO31 1LD ☎ 01904 423741

BOYES Derrick (*Kbds, Gtr*): 4 Church Rest House, Westgate, Driffield, East Yorkshire YO25 6TE ☎ 01377 256216

BROOKES Richard (*Ac Gtr, Voc, Hmca*): 45 West Park Close, Roundhay, Leeds LS8 2ED ☎ 0113 217 1232, 0113 2697669

BROWN Michael (*Ac Gtr*): Appletree Cottage, Doncaster Road, Wragby, Wakefield, West Yorkshire WF4 1QX

BUCKTON Malcolm: 22 Marlborough Avenue, Marske By The Sea, Redcar, Cleveland TS11 6AS ☎ 01642 471331, 01642 433091

BULL Christopher (*Gtr*): 39 Castlegate, Malton, North Yorkshire YO17 0EA ☎ 01653 694038

BUNT (*Db, Hmca*): Havelock House, 5 Havelock Place, Whitby, N Yorkshire YO21 3EY ☎ 01947 606361

BUNTING Darren (*Gtr*): 5 Pretoria Villas, Degrey Street, Hull HU5 2RT ☎ 01482 444734

BUTLER Anthony: Bath Cottage, Dinsdale Park, Middleton St George, Co Durham DL2 1DJ ☎ 01325 332723

CARTER Tim Nibbs (*Gtr, Dms, Kbds*): 17 Swinhope Road, Brookenby, Lincolnshire LN3 6EN ☎ 01472 398544

CHAMBERLAIN Paul (*Pf, Tbn*): 68 Greenhead Lane, Dalton, Huddersfield HD5 8EB ☎ 01484 304956

CLAYTON Malcolm (*Db, Pf, Gtr*): 42 Lansdowne Crescent, Darton, Barnsley S75 5PP ☎ 01226 383262

CLIFFE Marcus (*Kbds, Gtr, Dms*): 1211 London Road, Norbury, London SW16 4UY

CLOUGH Allison (*Flt, Gtr, Pf, Voc*): 21 Mitford Street, Fulwell, Sunderland SR6 8HT ☎ 020 8548 2854

COULSON Lindsay (*Db*): 13 Alexandra Terrace, Lincoln LN1 1JF ☎ 01522 549243

CROSSLAND Barry (*Vib*): Archway House, 27 West Bank, Scarborough, Yorks YO12 4DX ☎ 01723 369337

DAWES Len: 27 Thornsett Road, Sheffield S7 1NB

DAY John (*Pf*): 11 Newport Road, Headingley, Leeds LS6 3BZ ☎ 0113 274 7126

DODD Richard: 6, Westwick Crescent, Sheffield S8 7DG ☎ 0114 2377967

EDMONDSON Stephen: 35 Rowantree Drive, Thorpe Edge, Bradford, West Yorkshire BD10 8DJ ☎ 01274 617635

FISCHER Jessica: 19 De Lacy Mount, Leeds LS5 3JF ☎ 0113 2754759

FORD Kenneth (*Gtr*): 1 Richmond Street, Hull HU5 3JY ☎ 01482 3492868

FRANCE Phil: 54 Union Street, Kindley, Huddersfield, West Yorkshire HD3 3EW ☎ 01484 850823, 0374 900848

FRENCH Paul: 8 Windmill Road, Bramham, Wetherby, West Yorkshire LS23 6QP ☎ 01937 845266

FROGGATT Ian: 11 Borrowdale Avenue, Halfway, Sheffield S20 4HH ☎ 0114 247 8409, 0831267881

GANNEY Paul (*Ac Gtr, E Gtr*): 31 Ferry Lane, Woodmansey, N. Humberside HU17 0SE

GARTHWAITE Paul (*Cl Gtr, Db, Voc*): 25 Beckwith Road, Harrogate HG2 0BG ☎ 01423 568143

GIBBON Frank (*E Gtr, Pf*): 6 Bowes Farm Cottages, Lambton Park Est, Chester Le Street, Co Durham DH3 4PG ☎ 0191 385 4249

GIBSON Richard: Bushblades Farm, Tantobie, Stanley, Co Durham DH9 9UA ☎ 01207 232722

GLADWIN Thomas (*E Gtr, Pf*): Flat 2, 17 Walmgate, York YO1 9TX ☎ 01904 628896

GREGORY Michael (*Db, Kbds*): 28 Queen Street, Clifton, Rotherham S65 2SR ☎ 01709 369847, 0370 733121 mob

HALL Donald: 439 Doncaster Road, Ardsley, Barnsley S71 5EN ☎ 01226 286919

HAMILTON Ian (*Gtr, Dms, Pf*): 5 Rochford Crescent, Boston, Lincs PE21 9AE ☎ 01205 365442

HARLAND Neil (*Db*): 92 Cardigan Terrace, Heaton, Newcastle-upon-Tyne, Tyne & Wear NE6 5NY ☎ 0191 265 9139

HIBBS Colin (*Db*): Farndon House, Main Street, Scothern, Lincoln LN2 2UG ☎ 01673 862503

HILL Richard (*Voc*): 17 Westwood Court, Huddersfield Road, Barnsley S70 2LT ☎ 01226 245747

HOBSON Andy: 76 Acre Lane, Brixton, London SW2 5QN

HOLMES Nigel (*Gtr, Kbds*): 50 Rowntree Wharf, Navigation Road, York YO1 9XA ☎ 01904 635962, 0421 595548 mob, 01964 535521

HOUGHTON John (*Gtr*): 85 Whirlowdale Road, Sheffield, South Yorks S7 2NF ☎ 0114 296 2097

HUDSON Kristian (*Kbds, Clt*): 3 Raven Meadows, Swinton, Mexborough, South Yorkshire S64 8EN ☎ 01709 588363

IBBERTSON Colin (*Pl Gtr, B Ldr*): 5 Highfield Crescent, Chester Le Street, Durham DH3 3UJ ☎ 0191 388 9466

JACKSON Michael: 164A Doncaster Road, Conisbrough, Doncaster, S. Yorks DN12 3AE ☎ 01709 863718

JOLLY Warren (*Ac Gtr*): 14 Crampin Road, Cleethorpes DN35 7LA ☎ 01472 897811

JORDAN Craig (*Voc*): 3 Wodburn Close, Burnmoor, Houghton Le Spring, Tyne & Wear DH4 6DH ☎ 0191 385 2395

KAEMPF Tony (*Clt*): 3 Woodhouse Close, East Ardsley, Nr Wakefield, West Yorkshire WF3 2JX ☎ 01924 824420

KAMPEN Philip: 15 Holt Gardens, Idle, Bradford, West Yorkshire BD10 8UG ☎ 01274 622418

KEECH Robin: 92 Cundy Street, Walkley, Sheffield S6 2WN ☎ 0114 249 7913

LAING Micha (*E Gtr*): 73 Beechwood View, Burley, Leeds LS4 2LS ☎ 0113 2177749

LAUGHLIN Philip (*Tba*): 109 Pateley Close, Newton Aycliffe, Co. Durham DL7 7NG

LAWRENCE Aidan: 69 St. John's Road, Scarborough YO12 5ES ☎ 01723 862839

LEACH Christopher *(Gtr)*: 77 Caledonia Street, Scarborough, N Yorks YO12 7DP ☎ 01723 368608, 0976 859402

LEAKE Steven *(Db)*: Woddhill Cottage, Calverley Lane, Calverley, Pudsey, Leeds LS28 5QQ ☎ 0113 2363357

LEESE Ian: 95 Newmarket, Louth, Lincolnshire LN11 9EG ☎ 01507 607902

LEWIS David *(Db)*: 8 Mount Pleasant Avenue, Leeds, West Yorks LS8 4EF ☎ 01132 937077

LOCKWOOD Nicholas *(Synth, Rh Gtr)*: 206 Alexandra Park Road, Alexandra Park, London N22 4UQ

LOFTY James: 56 Walton Road, Chesterfield S40 3BY ☎ 01246 34326

LUTON Hamlet *(Kbds)*: 6A St Chads Drive, Leeds LS6 7QD ☎ 0113 278 1965

MACKEY Steven: Pru Harris, Rough Trade, 66 Golborne Road, London W10 5PS ☎ 020 8960 9888, 020 7424 9189

MANNING Mervyn: 78 Kedleston Road, Leeds LS8 2AU ☎ 0113 293 7585, 0973 113585, 0113 237 0747

MCLOCKLAN Adam ☎ 01274 681349

MCPHERSON Ken: 11A Gifford Street, Middlesbrough, Cleveland TS5 6BP ☎ 01642 821485

MCQUEEN David: 1 Dick Street, Crawcrook, Tyne & Wear NE40 4DL ☎ 0191 413 1705, 0831 731395

MONTROSE Emmy-Kate *(Tpt, Voc, Kbds)* ☎ 01661 822140

MUSGRAVE Gerard *(Kbds)*: 23 Woodend Court, West Bowling, Bradford, West Yorkshire BD5 8QL ☎ 01274 783891

NAYLOR Phillip *(Kbds)*: 8 First Avenue, Leeds LS12 1LD ☎ 0113 246 9239, 0973 375414 mob, 0113 243 9328

NIXON John *(Gtr, Man, Kbds)*: 68 Almshouse Lane, New Millerdam, Wakefield WF2 7ST ☎ 01924 254722, 0860 122821 mob, 01977 704576

O'HERN Paul *(Gtr, Dms, Kbds, Voc)*: Black Cat Barn, Main Street, Fulford Village, York YO10 4PN ☎ 01904 673610

PADDISON James *(Tbn, Pf, Kbds)*: 184 Beverley Road, Hessle, East Yorkshire HU13 9AT ☎ 01482 649007

PALMER Jeff *(Gtr, Club Dj)*: 4 Langley Road, Newton Hall, Durham DH1 5LR ☎ 0191 386 1540

PEBERDY Keith: 37 Mendip Drive, Redcar, Cleveland TS10 4HE ☎ 01642 480765

PEDDER John *(Gtr, Voc, Rec, Vln)*: 87 South View Crescent, Sheffield S7 1DG ☎ 01142 586 702

RAILTON Trevor: 40 Victoria Avenue, Whitley Bay, Tyne & Wear NE26 2AZ ☎ 0191 251 0669

RICKARBY Barry *(Db, Gtr)*: 38 Parkstone Avenue, West Park, Leeds LS16 6EN ☎ 0113 2611795

ROBERTS John: 32 Olivers Mount, High Hazels, Sheffield S9 4PB ☎ 0114 244 2323

RUTHERFORD Richard *(Pf, Gtr)*: 240A Chillingham Road, Heaton, Newcastle NE6 5LP ☎ 0191 265 6301, 0191 266 3342

SALISBURY Simon: 9 Yews Green, Clayton, Bradford, W Yorkshire BD14 6PX ☎ 01274 884 727, 0498 632789

SANDS Ian Anthony *(Gtr, Voc)*: 30 Highfield Road, Pudsey, W. Yorkshire LS28 7JN ☎ 0113 256 2921

SCOTT Robert: 7 Rushley Avenue, Dore, Sheffield S17 3EP ☎ 0114 236 0319

SHAND Peter: Chilvers Coton, 1 Belmont Terrace, The Green, Ossett, West Yorkshire WF5 0AL ☎ 01924 264046

SHEPHERD Johann *(Gtr)*: Blue Jay Way, 3 Birkshead, Wilsden, Bradford, West Yorkshire BD15 0DH ☎ 0958 596633

SHIPTON Christopher: 16 Park Lodge Lane, Wakefield, West Yorkshire WF1 4NL ☎ 01924 200346, 07930 0443048

SHORT David: 1 Fountains Way, North Cave, North Humberside HU15 2NW

SIMONS Gary *(Ac Gtr, Db)*: 5 Armley Ridge Terrace, Armley, Leeds LS12 2QU ☎ 0113 263 5894, 0976 933917 mob

SMITH Simon *(E Gtr, Ac Gtr)*: 25 Evesham Road, Park End, Middlesbrough, Cleveland TS3 7EX ☎ 01642 310102

STAFFORD Simon *(Gtr, Dms, Kbds, Cnt)*: 283 Chesterfield Road, Sheffield S8 0RT ☎ 0114 250 7673

STUART Shaun *(Gtr, Tpt)*: 15A Patterdale Road, Blyth, Northumberland NE24 5JU ☎ 01670 365030

SWINDELLS Christopher: 5 Pasture Grove, Chapel Allerton, Leeds LS7 4QP ☎ 0113 2690145

THOMAS Courtny *(Gtr, Dms)*: 44 Bayswater Row, Harehills, Leeds LS8 5LF ☎ 0113 225 3489

THOMPSON Jonathan *(Gtr, Kbds, Sax, Per)*: 33 Old Lansdowne Road, West Didsbury, Manchester M20 2PA ☎ 0161 448 1953

THOMSON Ian *(Dms, Gtr)*: 99 Holystone Crescent, Heaton, Newcastle-upon-Tyne, Tyne & Wear NE7 7EY ☎ 0191 266 7802

THORP Bernard *(Gtr, Pf)*: 46 Low Carrs, Framwellgate Moor, Durham DH1 5HG

TILLOTSON Liz: 31B Hanover Square, Leeds LS3 1AW ☎ 0113 243 1001

TURNER Anthony *(Tbn)*: Low Hall Cottage, 67 Garth End Road, W. Ayton, Scarborough YO13 9JJ ☎ 01723 862788

UDEN Paul *(Per, Kbds)*: 16 Lincoln Road, Saxilby, Lincoln LN1 2NF ☎ 01522 702948

UTTLEY Terence: The Beeches, Curly Hill, Middleton, Ilkley, West Yorkshire LS29 0BA ☎ 01943 603155, 0467 435830

WALKER Kevin *(Db, Voc)*: 162 Oakbrook Road, Sheffield S11 7ED ☎ 0114 2307262

WALKER Robert *(Kbds)*: 28 Newlands Park Road, Scarborough, North Yorkshire YO12 6PX ☎ 01723 371848

WALLER Duncan: 8 Chapel Street, Birdwell, Barnsley, South Yorkshire S70 5UW ☎ 01226 744444

WELLS Gary *(Ac Gtr)*: 61 Avenue Road, Wath-upon-Dearne, Rotherham, South Yorkshire S63 7AG ☎ 01709 878361

WESTON Steve *(Gtr)*: 8 Southlea, Rillington, Malton, North Yorkshire YO17 8LR ☎ 01944 758982

WHITE Paul *(Gtr)*: 9 Hotspur Street, Heaton, Newcastle-upon-Tyne NE6 5BE ☎ 0191 240 3248, 0191 240 3248

WILES Andrew: 33 Nunthorpe Grove, York YO23 1DT ☎ 01904 610663

WRIGHT Anthony *(Cel, Com, Per)*: 13 Lunan Terrace, Leeds LS4 4ER ☎ 0113 294 9976, 0468 972650 mob

WRIGHT Jim *(Bjo, Rh Gtr)*: 37 Drummond Avenue, Leeds LS16 5JZ ☎ 0113 2753251

EAST

ADAMIK Milan *(Dms)*: 24B Kirkstall Ave, London N17 69H ☎ 020 8808 2189

ALANCROFT Rick *(Arr, Com, Song W)*: 31 Stains Close, Cheshunt, Herts EN8 9JJ ☎ 01992 638168

ALLEN Edward: 14 St Leonards Road, Ipswich, Suffolk IP3 4AU ☎ 01473 712504

ANTOINE *(Kbds, Voc)*: 25 Gullet Wood Road, Watford, Herts WD2 6RH ☎ 0956 428265 mob

ASH Stephen: 1 Twyford Mill, Pig Lane, Bishops Stortford, Herts CM22 7PA ☎ 01279 659773

AYLING Luke *(Gtr, Dms)*: 72A Waverley Crescent, Wickford, Essex SS11 7LW ☎ 01285 753209

BALCH Colin *(Db)*: 'San Michele', Felden Lane, Hemel Hempstead, Herts HP3 0BA ☎ 01273 691537

BAMFORTH Jon: 162 Alexandra Road, Millfied, Peterborough PE1 3DL ☎ 01733 310968

BEDFORD Max: 39 Lords Lane, Bradwell, Great Yarmouth, Norfolk NR31 8NY ☎ 01493 661577

BERNARD Neil: 2 Park Farm Cottages, North Lopham, Diss, Norfolk IP22 2NN ☎ 01379 688284

BERRIMAN Michael: 11 Kirtle Road, Chesham, Bucks HP5 1AD ☎ 01494 786236

BISHOP Anthony *(Gtr, Man)*: 8 Orchard Close, Wingrave, Bucks HP22 4PP ☎ 01296 681803

BLACK Jim *(Rh Gtr)*: New Hope House, 69 Queen's Road, Watford, Herts WD1 2QN, 01923 0411 555865 mob

BREWER Neil: 7 Bushells Wharf, Tring, Hertfordshire HP23 5HS ☎ 01442 825751

BROOKE Philip *(Cl Gtr, Lute, Citt)*: 9 Well Green, Frettenham, Norwich NR12 7LS

BURROW Richard: 141 Cavendish Street, Ipswich, Suffolk IP3 8BG ☎ 01473 250956

BURROWS Paul: 20 Wharfedale Road, Ipswich, Suffolk IP1 4JP
☎ 01473 400380, 0860 852990, 01473 400810

CASTELLANO Michael: 22 Campbell Drive, Gunthorpe, Peterborough, Cambs PE4 7ZJ ☎ 01733 320154, 01733 555529

CHILDS Christopher: 7 Broad Green, Bayford, Nr Hertford, Hertfordshire SG13 8PT ☎ 0199 286 442

COLE Jonathan: 24 Fisher Road, Diss, Norfolk IP22 3JS ☎ 01379 644293

COOK John (*Gtr*): 140 Inskip Crescent, Stevenage, Herts SG1 1JZ ☎ 0438 229855

CROCKETT Gary: 109 Clifton Avenue, South Benfleet, Essex SS7 5QU

CUTTING Chris (*Gtr, Voc*): 10 Inverness Close, Chesterton, Cambridge CB4 1RB ☎ 01223 360080

DALLING August (*Gtr, Kbds*): 75 Moffats Lane, Brookmans Park, Hatfield, Herts AL9 7RT ☎ 01707 655212, 0973 432074 mob

DANCE Andrew: 7 Allen Close, Deeping St James, Peterborough PE6 8EZ ☎ 01775 724816

DE LA CRUZ Vincente (*Ld Gtr*): 45 Belvoir Road, Cambridge CB4 1JH

DICE (*Voc*): Wheatsheaf Cottage, Shop Road, Little Bromley, Manningtree, Essex CO11 2PY ☎ 01206 396559

DRE: c/o 43 Mousehold Lane, Norwich, Norfolk NR7 8HL ☎ 01603 424574

DYER Billy: 2 School Hill Cottages, Birch Road, Birch, Nr Colchester, Essex CO2 0NA ☎ 01206 330157

EDWARDS John: 47 Farm Way, Bushey, Herts WD2 3TA ☎ 020 8950 5188

ELMES James (*Db*): 466 Broadwater Crescent, Stevenage, Herts SG2 8HE ☎ 01438 225668

EVANS Stephen: 7 Lambsale Meadow, North Entrance, Saxmundham, Suffolk IP17 1AS ☎ 01728 604199, 0850 946261, 01394 380622

FLETCHER Tim (*Voc, Db, Gtr*): 58 Taranto Road, Canvey Island, Essex SS8 7LH ☎ 01268 512182, 0378 644612 mob

FRANCIS Paul (*E Gtr*): 97 Sycamore Road, Croxley Green, Herts WD3 3TE ☎ 01923 233 161, 0956 424821

GAUNT Stephen: 14 Gower Road, Romston, Hertfordshire SG8 5DU ☎ 01763 244576, 0973 907164, 01763 245134

GIDDENS Richard (*Gtr*): 17 Whitestone Walk, Hemel Hempstead, Herts HP1 3NB ☎ 01442 262638

GILL Wayne (*Rh Gtr, Voc*): 18 Hamsworth Court, The Ridgeway, Hertford, Hertfordshire SG14 2JH ☎ 01992 420811, 07775 974719

GOODWIN Peter: 105 St Johns Road, Clacton-on-Sea, Essex CO16 8DB ☎ 01255 428042

HANBY Chris: Cavendish House, 2 Moorfield, Harston, Cambridge CB2 5TP ☎ 01223 871771

HARRIS Brian (*Gtr, Kbds, Voc*): 1 Old Barn, West Street, Stamford, Lincolnshire PE9 2PS ☎ 01780 481353

HARRIS Michael: 34 Eastgate Street, North Elmham, Norfolk NR20 5AB ☎ 01362 668 498

HARVEY Brian (*Db*): 76 Spinney Road, Thorpe St Andrew, Norwich, Norfolk NR7 0PJ ☎ 01603 434722

HAWKETTS Nigel (*Ld Gtr*): 81 Jubilee Avenue, Fakenham, Norfolk NR21 8DQ ☎ 01328 855555

HAYE Brian: 13 Maryport Road, Luton, Bedfordshire LU4 8EA ☎ 01582 573476

HEWERDINE Boo (*Voc*): 8 Edward Street, Cambridge CB1 2LS ☎ 01223 366850

HEWITT Edwin (*Gtr*): 01268 456567, 0402 447792 mob

HILL Brian: 2 Edward Avenue, Brightlingsea, Colchester, Essex CO7 0LZ ☎ 01206 304804

HINDES Richard (*Gtr*): Elvina, Ormesby Road, Hemsby, Gt Yarmouth, Norfolk NR29 4LA ☎ 01493 732139

HOCKRIDGE Stephen: The White Cottage, 22 Thorpe Avenue, Peterborough PE3 6LA ☎ 01733 54635

HOLDER Peter: 33 James Avenue, Lake Sandown, Isle Of Wight PO36 9NH ☎ 01983 406072

HOWARD Don (*Db, Org*): 4 Linnet Dene, Cullompton, Devon EX15 1UF ☎ 01884 34243

HUGHES John: 9 Woodlands Road, Hertford, Herts SG13 7JE ☎ 01992 582932

ING George (*Dms, Kbds*): 48 Sprowston Road, Norwich, Norfolk NR3 4QN ☎ 01603 413509

JACKMAN Neil (*Db, Gtr*): 8 Anchor Court, South Town, Great Yarmouth, Norfolk NR31 0QJ ☎ 01493 300485

JAKINS Robert: 38 Monkswell, Trumpington, Cambridge CB2 2JU ☎ 01223 842939

KELLY Robin (*Cel, Pf, E Gtr*): 59 Glendale Gardens, Leigh-on-Sea, Essex SS9 2BG ☎ 01702 713584

KEMI: Address Unknown ☎ 01438 310139, 01438 310001 fax

LANDYMORE Charles (*Tpt, Flgl*): 11 Montford Close, Chesterton, Burwell, Cambridgeshire CB5 0RF ☎ 01638 743406

LARKIN Ian (*Gtr, Uke, Bjo*): Kupitz, 107 High Road, Wisbech, Cambs PE13 4PJ ☎ 01945 870021, 01945 870670

LAVELLE Tom: 3 Meadow Road, Oulton, Lowestoft, Suffolk NR32 3AZ ☎ 01502 589096

LE HER Thomas (*Tbn*): 58 Gilberd Road, Colchester, Essex CO2 7LR ☎ 01206 798377

LEVY David: 18 Titian Avenue, Bushey Heath, Herts WD2 1LU ☎ 020 8950 3669

LILLIE Paul (*Cl Gtr, Bsn, Voc*): 3 Rookery Close, Great Chesterford, Nr Saffron Walden, Essex CB10 1QA ☎ 01799 531099

LINDLEY John (*Db, Tba*): Walnut Barn, Upper Street, Baylham, Nr Ipswich IP6 8LE ☎ 01473 832885

MARCHINGTON Simon: 49 Parr Drive, Kexden, Colchester, Essex CO3 5EW ☎ 01206 571211

MARTIN Rob (*Db, Tbn*): 40, King George Road, Colchester, Essex CO2 7PG ☎ 01206 577740

MCLAUGHLAN Anthony: 9 Stanley Street, Luton, Beds LU1 5AL ☎ 01582 453408, 0958 370703

MCNAUGHT Paul: 53 Maynewater Lane, Bury St Edmunds, Suffolk IP33 2AB ☎ 01284 703444

MERCEL Robert (*Voc*): 120 Langdale Road, Dunstable, Beds LU6 3BT ☎ 01582 608222

MULRAIN Gordon: 105 Hawthorn Drive, Ipswich, Suffolk IP2 0PD ☎ 01473 423884, 01473 688142

MYATT Peter: 52 Kings Road, Hitchin, Herts SG5 1RD ☎ 01462 436152

NEISH Martin: Flat 3, 2 Victor Road, Bradford BD9 4QL ☎ 01236 729603, 0831 222098 mob

NEWMAN Ian: 292 High Street, London Colney, St. Albans, Herts AL2 1HW ☎ 01727 763259

NICHOLLS Jon: 64 Wooton Drive, Hemel Hempstead, Herts HP2 6LB ☎ 01442 258021

PATTERSON Martin: 41 Falkland Way, Bradwell, Great Yarmouth, Norfolk NR31 8RW ☎ 01493 604176

PAYNE Mike: 143, Trident Drive, Houghton Regis, Nr. Dunstable, Beds LU5 5QQ ☎ 01582 862179

POOLE Edward: 12 Wivels Field, Wallace Drive, Eaton Bray, Beds LU6 2JQ ☎ 01525 222022

RAMSAY Richard: Barningham Cottage, Wyatts Road, Chorleywood, Herts WD3 5TE ☎ 01923 333504 & fax, 0958 288838 mob

READMAN Peter: 26 Jersey Way, Braintree, Essex CM7 2FA ☎ 01376 326088

REEVE Eric: 7 Mill Lane, Alwalton, Peterborough PE7 3UZ ☎ 01733 233225

REEVES Anthony: Fordhouse, 58 Cross Road, Bushey, Herts WD1 4DQ ☎ 01923 234050

RICKARDS Charles (*Gtr, Man*): 2 Moores Close, Debenham, Suffolk IP14 6RU ☎ 01728 860433

RODFORD Jim: 2 Gurneycourt Road, St Albans, Hertfordshire AL1 4RL ☎ 01727 869316

ROLLASON Mark (*Pf, Cl Gtr, Chap Stk, Rec*): 22 Curlew Way, Bradwell, Gt Yarmouth, Norfolk NR31 8QX ☎ 01493 662681

ROSE Philip (*Db, Gtr, Man*) ☎ 01223 563294, 0402 820086

RUSHBROOK Simon (*Db, Voc*): Flat 4, Duddery Court, Haverhill, Suffolk CB9 8EA ☎ 01440 703452

SAUNDERS Duncan

SAYER Ron James (*Voc, Ld Gtr, Rh Gtr, Dms*): 27 Morris Road, N Walsham, Norfolk NR28 0EJ ☎ 01692 407795

SCHOLES CORBETT Stuart (*Gtr, Kbds*): 24 Bridport Way, Braintree, Essex CM7 9FJ ☎ 01376 585288, 0850 363070

SELBY Philip (*E Gtr*): 2 Ganners Hill, Taverham, Norwich NR8 6XL ☎ 01603 262856

SHARKEY Grant (*Db, Voc, Rh Gtr*): 4 Nettlecroft, Welwyn Garden City AL7 2DW ☎ 023 8089 4947, 0958 710718 mob

SHARP Allan: 40 Wrights Way, Leavenheath, Colchester CO6 4NR

SHARP Garry (*Org, Kbds*): 57 Delgate Bank, Weston, Spalding, Lincolnshire PE12 6JB ☎ 01406 371411, 0378 259108

SHARPLES Jonothan: 38 Gaping Lane, Hitchin, Hertfordshire SG5 2JQ ☎ 01462 450007, 01438 840015

SIMMONDS Ronald: 66 Brian Road, Harlington, Bedfordshire LU5 6NH

START Doug: 198 Fairview Road, Stevenage, Herts SG1 2NA ☎ 01438 351071

STEVENS Tony: 2 Stanborough Cottages, Great North Road, Stanborough, Nr Hatfield, Herts AL8 7TE ☎ 01707 257 802, 01707 257 802

SUBRATI Shakeel (*E Gtr, Kbds*): 71 Rosemary Road, Waterbeach, Cambridge CB5 9NB ☎ 01223 860688

SUTTON Colin (*Db*): 80 Broome Grove, Wivenhoe, Essex CO7 9QT ☎ 01206 826585

TYLER Damian (*Ld Gtr, Rh Gtr, Ac Gtr, Dms*): 16 Hereford Road, Riverside Estate, Colchester, Essex CO1 2RD ☎ 01206 501247

WAISSMAN Brad (*Dms, Gtr*): 71 Sedley Grove, Harefield, Middlesex UB9 6JD

WALKER Nicholas (*Voc*): 35 Gordon Avenue, Thorpe, St Andrew, Norwich NR7 0DP ☎ 01603 300148, 0402 582050

WEBSTER Darren (*Gtr*): 01525 379926, 04325 164620

WHEATLEY Daniel (*Sax, Dms, Pf, E Gtr*): Highdown, 44 Beacon Way, Rickmansworth, Herts WD3 2PE ☎ 01923 774752, 0378 118375, 01923 775292

WIGGS Josephine (*Cel, Db, Pf, Gtr*): Fairfield House, Biggleswade, Beds SG18 0AA

WILLIAMS Peter: 25 Wynchlands Crescent, St Albans, Herts AL4 0XW ☎ 01727 839443, 0802 887940

WILSON Neil (*Kbds, Gtr*): 32 Primrose Hill, Chelmsford, Essex CM1 2RH ☎ 01245 256277

WOOD Anthony (*Gtr, Voc*): 43 Sutton Lane, Hornchurch, Essex RM12 6RJ ☎ 01708 437251

WORT Adrian (*Mldn*): 2 Oakdene, Church Road, Gt. Yeldham, Halstead, Essex CO9 4PS ☎ 01787 237910

WORTLEY Paul: 12 Magnay Road, Drayton, Norwich NR8 6BT ☎ 01603 487580

MIDLANDS

ADAMSON Mark (*Gtr, Kbds*): 5 Dayhouse Bank, Romsley, Halesowen, West Midlands B62 0EU

ADLEY Carlos (*Kbds, Per*): ☎ 0121 440 7654

ALLSOPP David: 15 Greenfield Avenue, Stourbridge, West Midlands DY8 1SX ☎ 01384 372157

ASHTON David (*Gtr*): 59 Assarts Road, Malvern Wells, Worcs WR14 4HW ☎ 01684 893108

BADHAMS Brian (*Pf, Kbds*): 32 Salop Close, Hateley Heath, West Bromwich, West Midlands B71 2SB ☎ 0121 553 7524

BALCON David (*Voc*): 16 Ise Vale Avenue, Desborough, Northants NN14 2PU ☎ 01536 761409, 0973 166136, 01536 762891

BAXTER Richard (*E Gtr, Dms, Per*): 503 Burton Road, Midway, Burton-on-Trent DE11 0DQ

BAYLISS Simon (*Rh Gtr, Kbds*): 25 Minitoba Croft, Kings Norton, Birmingham B38 9QJ ☎ 0121 680 6716

BEARD Donald (*Db*): 6 Crosbie Road, Chapelfields, Coventry CV5 8FY ☎ 024 7667 7538

BLACKWELL Mark (*Db, Tpt, Tbn, Tba*): 27 Darnel Hurst Road, Four Oaks, Sutton Coldfield, West Midlands B75 5NE ☎ 0121 308 0761, 0973 187 933

BLOMBERG Philip Suen (*Gtr, Vln, Kbds, Dms*): 24 Hockett Street, Coventry CV3 5FR ☎ 024 7650 2540

BOOTHBY Hannah (*Vln, Pf*): 52 Hornyold Road, Malvern, Worcester WR14 1QH ☎ 01684 565402, 04325 110941 pager, 020 8558 9013

BRAMLEY Simon: Flat 2, Sparrow Lodge, 356-360 Humberstone Road, Leicester, Leics LE5 0SA ☎ 0116 2627838

BROWN Derrick (*Gtr*): 68 Beaumont Road, Bournville, Birmingham B30 2DY ☎ 0121 459 0862

BROWN Ronnie (*Kbds*): ☎ 01952 261727, 0374 979232 mob

BUCKINGHAM Paul (*Gtr*): 24 Oak Tree Avenue, Cambridge CV4 1BA ☎ 020 8752 0948

CADWALLADER Neil (*Ac Gtr, Bjo*): 19 Danvers Road, Mountsorrel, Loughborough, Leicestershire LE12 7JG ☎ 0116 237 6052

CAMPBELL Andrew (*Synth*): ☎ 0121 682 2213, 0958 757 749

CANAAN Danny (*Kbds*): 97 Catherine Road, Bearwood, West Midlands B67 5QY ☎ 0121 558 9353

CARLIN John (*Gtr*): 49 Kneeton Road, East Bridgford, Nottingham NG13 8PG

CARVALHO Robert (*Flt, Kbds, Per*): Flat 2, 30 Haughton Road, Perry Barr, Birmingham B21 3LD ☎ 0121 356 0224

CASWELL Dave: 12 Thakeray Road, Leyfields, Tamworth, Staffs B79 8HZ ☎ 01827 705999

CHAPLIN M J (*Db, Ac Gtr, Tin Wh*): 91 Claremont Road, Rugby, Warks CV21 3LX ☎ 01788 579763

CLARK Louis (*Arr, Com, Cop*): 421 Whitman Boulevard, Elyria, OH 44035, USA

CLEWS Martyn: 18 Elm Tree Way, Cradley Heath, West Midlands B65 6EN ☎ 01384 347895, 09556 145703

COLE Michael (*Kbds, Dms*): 70 Peartree Crescent, Derby DE23 8RQ ☎ 01332 770939, 0976 677157

COOMBES Joel: 17 Woodhall Close, Leicester LE3 6PZ ☎ 0116 287 6530

DALE Martin (*Gtr, Voc*): 6 Badger, Nr.Burnhill Green, Shropshire WV6 7JP ☎ 01746 783617

DARBY Thomas (*Gtr*): 109 Glebe Road, Thringstone, Leicestershire LE67 8NU ☎ 01530 222887

DAVIES John: 16 St. Annes Road, Rugby, Warwickshire CV22 4NP ☎ 01788 576722

DEEMING Philip: 40 Vincent Road, Sutton Coldfield, West Midlands B75 6AN ☎ 0121 378 0574

DEMICK Rod (*Gtr, Hmca, Voc*): 340 Tessall Lane, Northfield, Birmingham B31 5EN ☎ 0121 476 9334

DOLAN Stephen (*Db*): 31 Albany Road, Harborne, Birmingham B17 9JX ☎ 0121 244 4826

DUNN Peter J (*Per*): 31. Silvercroft Avenue, Handsworth Wood, Birmingham B20 1LN ☎ 0121 551 5378

EASTAUGH Martin (*Gtr, Pf*): 36A Slade Gardens, Erith, Kent DA8 2HT ☎ 01322 342995

EDWARDS Darren Paul (*Db*): 3 Field Close, Thringstone, Coalville, Leicestershire LE67 8PU ☎ 01530 223616, 01822 852274, 01822 854332 fax

EVANS Steven (*Ld Gtr*) ☎ 01922 58694

EWEN Alvin: c/o 42 Upper Dean Street, Digbeth, Birmingham B5 4SG ☎ 0121 551 1165

FELGATE Robert: Address Unknown ☎ 01785 604973

FOXWORTHY Jane (*Pf, Gtr, Mldn*): 9 Belgrave Avenue, Leicester LE4 5PB ☎ 0116 2682730

GAFFNEY Stephen: 81 Franklyn Avenue, Crews, Cheshire CW2 7NE ☎ 01270 661561

GALLAGHER James (*Voc, Cl Gtr*): 22 Westland Road, Compton, Wolverhampton, West Midlands WV3 9NZ ☎ 01902 25325

GARRISON John (*Gtr, Dms, Kbds*): Flat 1A, 25 Warwick Place, Leamington Spa CV32 5BS ☎ 01926 337619

GILBERT William (*Gtr*): Flat 1, 9 Kidderminster Road, Bewdley, Worcestershire DY12 1AQ ☎ 01299 400895

GILCHRIST Adam: 18A Augusta Road, Moseley, Birmingham B13 8AE ☎ 0121 449 1052

GILES Steve A (*Tpt*): 18 Granby Avenue, Mansfield Notts, Notts NG19 7BT ☎ 01246 827406

GILL Roger (*Synth*): 22 Rectory Lane, Rock, Kidderminster, Worcs DY14 9RS ☎ 01299 832596

GRANT Ray (*Db*): 29 Rood End Road, Oldbury, Warley, West Midlands B68 8SJ ☎ 0121 454 8264

GREAVES Mark (*Gtr*): 19 Waterways Drive, Oldbury, Warley, West Midlands B69 2EX ☎ 0121 544 6617

GRIFFIN Dirk: 125 Clare Street, Northampton NN1 3JA ☎ 01604 633 501

HAMMOND Stan: 20, Ireton Close, Tanyards Farm Estate, Tile Hill, Coventry, West Midlands CV4 9UA ☎ 024 7646 0089

HENLEY John (*E Gtr*): 28 South Avenue, Norton, Stourbridge, Worcs DY8 3XY ☎ 01384 377321

HERRING Duncan: 8 Orchard Close, Wooton, Northampton NN5 6HF ☎ 01604 73537, 0402 616899

HEY Peter (*Gtr, Kbds*): 91 Middleborough Road, Coventry CV1 4DG ☎ 024 7652 0643

HILL Ian: c/o Mcbride & Partners, Brook House, Wood Lane, Uttoxeter, Staffs ST14 8BD ☎ 01889 567813

HILL Thomas (*Per*): 49, Flat 2, Grafton Road, Handsworth, Birmingham B21 8PN ☎ 0121 515 3571

HILLARD Ross (*Kbds, Pf*) ☎ 0116 2781040, 07775 617527

HOLT Derek: 3 Shawns Crescent, Radford Rise, Stafford ST17 4PT ☎ 01785 49370

HOWARD Adrian (*Db*): 2 Tryon Place, Bilston, West Midlands WV14 7NY ☎ 0956 836006

HOWARD Nathan (*Saxes*): 9 Sandringham Drive, Rowley Regis, W Midlands B63 9RS ☎ 0121 559 2379

HOWES Colin: 1 Wharrage Road, Alcester, Warwickshire B49 6QY ☎ 01789 762201

HUDSON Gary (*Voc*): 12 Greenfield Road, Spinney Hill, Northampton NN3 2LH ☎ 01604 492875

HUGHES Richard (*Rh Gtr, Voc, Pf*): Meadow Cottage, Mansfield Road, Farnsfield NG22 8NG ☎ 01623 682 450

HULL Geoff: 33 Prince Of Wales Road, Coventry, Warwickshire CV5 8GR ☎ 024 7671 2251

JARVIS Jonathan (*Kbds, Gtr*): 83 Buxton Road, Chaddesden, Derby DE21 4JL ☎ 01332 603157, 0802 716741, 01332 603157

JENKINS Brian: 58 Kelvin Road, Leamington Spa CV32 7TQ

JONES Richard (*Pf, Md*): 12 Ormsby Grove, Acocks Green, Birmingham B27 7JW ☎ 0121 777 0040, 0956 200 209, 0121 777 1453

KING Paul (*Gtr*): 024 7638 6155, 0421 472725 mob

KING Paul: 3 Minster Crescent, Leicester LE4 0JB ☎ 0116 235 3927

KINGSLEY Loz (*Rh Gtr, Man*): 131A Alcester Road, Moseley, Birmingham B13 8JP ☎ 0121 443 5620, 0121 449 8122 day

KINTON Robert (*Per*): 221 Big Barn Lane, Mansfield, Notts NG18 3LB ☎ 01623 647052, 01623 414114 ext 4653

KIRKHAM Gareth (*Voc*): 4 Redwing Drive, Biddulph, Stoke-on-Trent, Staffs ST8 7UA ☎ 01782 523950

KNIGHT Stephen (*Gtr*): 26 Shaftesbury Avenue, Pedmore, Stourbridge, West Midlands DY9 0YP ☎ 01384 393998, 0976 763532

KOPINSKI Stefan: 22 Nelson Road, Daybrook, Nottingham NG5 6JE ☎ 0115 9265484

LAZZARI Stephen: 5 Park Drive, Barlaston, Stoke-on-Trent ST12 9DW ☎ 01782 372526

LEATHER Stephen (*Voc, Per, Kbds, Gtr*): c/o PO Box 3413, Moseley, Birmingham B13 9EQ

LEE David: Three Springs, Stanford Bishop, Worcestershire WR6 5UA ☎ 01886 884545, 0973 195771

LETMAN Mark: 13 Howe Crescent, Short Heath, Willenhall, West Midlands WV12 5RW ☎ 01922 409565, 0411 357146

LLEWELLYN Aids (*Gtr, Voc*): 28 Thames Close, Medway Park, Worcester WR5 1ND ☎ 01905 351961

LUNN Philip (*E Gtr, Ac Gtr, Hmca*): 78 Ardath Road, Kings Norton, Birmingham B38 9YH

MAGUIRE Gordon (*Pf*): 4 Lynwood Walk, Harborne, Birmingham B17 0LS ☎ 0121 605 0690

MARKLAND Ben (*T Sax, Flt, Db*): 1 Malt Close, Harborne, Birmingham B17 0HX ☎ 0121 426 4618

MARTIN Matthew (*Gtr*): Hillcrest, Lutterworth Road, Ullesthorpe, Leics LE17 5DR ☎ 01455 209329

MASON Robert (*B Gtr*): 64 Mill Hayes Road, Knypersley, Stoke-on-Trent, Staffs ST8 7PR ☎ 3029

MCCULLOCH John: 52 Arnside Court, North Park Road, Erdington, Birmingham, B23 7YG ☎ 0121 681 4611

MELLANBY Ian (*Gtr, Voc*): 20 Rue Mayet, Paris, France, F75006

MINCHELLA Damon: c/o Suite 17, Jago House, 692 Warwick Road, Solihull, W. Mids B91 3DA ☎ 0121 605 8448

MONAGHAN Gavin (*Kbds, Dms, Per, Hmca*): 309 Stafford Road, Wolverhampton, West Midlands WV10 6DQ ☎ 01902 429148

MOORE Jennifer (*Vln*): Bcm Material, London WC1N 3XX ☎ 0115 9706502

MURRAY Glynn: 15 Gable Close, Daventry, Northants NN11 4EX ☎ 01327 872294

NASON Andy: 35 Rock Road, Olton, Solihull, West Midlands B92 7LB ☎ 0121 706 8440, 0370 998332

NICHOLLS Dave (*Gtr, Voc*): 29 Northumberland Road, Coundon, Coventry, West Midlands CV1 3AP ☎ 024 7622 4773

NILO David (*Gtr, Dms*): 52 The Heathers, Cheltenham Road, Evesham, Worcestershire WR11 6PF ☎ 01386 443925

NUTTER Stephen (*Db, Multi, Bjo, Kbds*): 10 Grange Drive, Glen Parva, Leicester LE2 9PF ☎ 0116 2786695

OLIVER Dave (*Gtr, Bjo*): 114 Rowanberry Avenue, Braunstone, Frith, Leicester LE3 6PQ ☎ 0116 2875502, 0850 070 887 mob

PEARCE Geoffrey (*Gtr*): 8 Botteville Road, Acocks Green, Birmingham B27 7YD ☎ 0121 708 1349

PEGG Dave (*Man*): PO Box 37, Banbury, Oxon OX16 8YN

PLANT Mark (*Gtr*): 28 Greenland Walk, Danesholme Estate, Corby, Northants NN18 9DH ☎ 01536 744317

PORTAS Andrew: 14 Honeycroft Close, Belper, Derbyshire DE56 1RL ☎ 01773 827674

PORTER John (*Db*): 6 Edward Avenue, Newark, Nottinghamshire NG24 4UZ ☎ 01636 700481, 0850 588138

PRYOR Paul (*Voc*): 24 Oval Road, Erdington, Birmingham B24 8PL ☎ 0121 373 3361, 0378 324416 mob

RADLEY Christopher (*E Gtr*): 14 Northcote Street, Leamington Spa, Warks CV31 1DX ☎ 01926 421830

RAVEN Daniel (*Gtr, Db, Dms, Man*): 68 Limes Road, Tettenhall, Wolverhampton, West Midlands WV6 8RB ☎ 01902 753047, 01902 747173

REA Alistair: 112 Summerfield Road, Solihull, Warks B92 8PZ ☎ 01604 601319

RICHARDS Paul (*Ld Gtr*): 1 Clare Street, Northampton NN1 3JG ☎ 01604 601319

ROBB Frank (*Tpt*): 36 Gregory Avenue, Green Lane, Coventry, West Midlands CV3 6DL ☎ 024 7641 0258

ROSS John (*Kbds*): 393 Stourbridge Road, Kidderminster, Worcs DY10 2PP ☎ 01562 515744

ROWE Alan (*Dms, Synth, Kbds*): 8 Barley Croft, Whittington, Lichfield, Herts WS14 9LY ☎ 01543 432 750, 0976 585678

ROWLEY Ted (*Db*): 136 Blackhalve Lane, Wednesfield, West Midlands WV11 1AA ☎ 01902 732002

ROWSON Mark (*Kbds, Voc, Dms*): 72 Salisbury Road, Moseley, Birmingham B13 8JU ☎ 0121 449 1711

SCHNEIDER Phil (*E Gtr*): 23 Browning Road, Coventry CV2 5HR ☎ 024 7645 6411

SCRIVENS Michael (*Mldn, Gtr, Man, Pf*): 73A Bradgate Road, Anstey, Leicester LE7 7FE ☎ 0116 2363757

SEGROTT Neil (*Gtr*): 59 Wyngate Drive, Leicester LE3 0UU ☎ 0116 255 7554

SHEPHERD Stuart (*E Gtr, Rh Gtr, Ld Gtr, Kbds*): 21 Radnor Drive, Shepshed, Leicester LE12 9SA ☎ 01509 651095

SHORTEN Daniel (*Kbds, Voc*): 1 Radford Road, Cliffe Vale, Stoke-on-Trent, Staffs ST4 7DA ☎ 01782 250318

SILVER Tony (*Db, Per*): 2 St Johns Avenue, Trent Vale, Stoke-on-Trent ST4 6SS ☎ 01782 749138

SLATER Harry: 110 Draycott Road, Longeaton, Notts NG10 3BZ

SMITH Benjamin: Sibson Mill, Sibson, Nr Nuneaton, Leicester CV13 6LR ☎ 01827 880506, 0976 362513 mob, 01827 880563

SMITH Jamie: Flat 4, 46 Fosse Road South, Westcotes, Leicester LE3 0QD ☎ 0116 254 0982

SMITH Ric (*Kbds*): 16 Glen Close, Walsall, West Midlands WS4 2EL ☎ 01922 35094

SOLMAN Philip: 89 Lord Lytton Avenue, Wyken, Coventry CV2 5JJ ☎ 024 7663 1946

STEELE David: Clement Keys, Nettleton House, Calthorpe Road, Edgbaston, Birmingham B15 1RL

STONE Jed *(Ac Gtr, Pd Gtr)*: 107 Cannock Road, Corby, Northants NN17 1YQ ☎ 01536 400937

STORM D J Peter *(Dms, Gtr, Kbds)*

STURT David: 36 Hillside Rise, Belter, Derby DE56 1NH ☎ 01773 820459

SWEET Adam *(Gtr)*: 14 Bransdale Close, Farndale Estate, Whitmore Reans, Wolverhampton WV6 0TN ☎ 01902 755978

TAFARI Amlak *(Gtr)*: 40, Wilnecote Grove, Perry Barr, Birmingham B42 1SJ ☎ 0121 356 9688, 0121 551 0832

TODD Alan: 9 Bank Street, Kings Heath, Birmingham B14 7RH ☎ 0121 443 2857

TODDINGTON Mike *(Db)*: 3, Fabian Crescent, Shirley, Solihull, West Midlands, B90 2AA ☎ 0121 744 3539

TONGE Andrew: 6 Coplow Cottages, Coplow Street, Edgbaston, Birmingham B16 0DG ☎ 0121 455 9331, 07971 521 973

TUCKER Nicholas: 28 Carlyle Road, Rowley Regis, W Midlands B65 9BQ ☎ 0121 5593684

TWIGG Gary: Kates Cottage, Broad Street, Long Compton, Warks CV36 5JH ☎ 01608 684458

TWO-NAMES *(Voc)*: 80 Foster Rd, Radford, Coventry CV6 3BG ☎ 024 7659 5871

VAUGHAN Ronald *(T Sax)*: 5 Coalway Gardens, Merry Hill, Wolverhampton WV3 7NL ☎ 01902 338720

WALL Stephen *(Ac Gtr)*: 125 Allesley Old Road, Chapelfields, Coventry, Warwickshire CV5 8FJ ☎ 024 7667 0034

WARE Gareth *(Per)*: 4 The Larches, Newport, Shropshire TF10 7SQ ☎ 01952 813888, 07970 345481, 01952 825715

WEST James: 28 Riverside Walk, Bottesford, Nottingham NG13 0AT ☎ 01949 843778, 0966 173021

WIDDOWSON Jeffrey *(Flt, Sax)*: 14 Alton Close, Allestree, Derby DE22 2LJ ☎ 01332 558350

WILLIS Mark *(Synth, Dms)*: 82 Deyncourt Road, Wednesfield, Wolverhampton WV10 0SY ☎ 01902 304572

WOOD Stanley Gordon Davis: 32 Cambria Road, Evesham, Worcs WR11 4QD ☎ 01386 446793

YOUNG Locksley: 108 Lancaster House, Oldbury Road, Rowley Regis, Worcs B65 0QE ☎ 0121 561 5153

SOUTH EAST

ABBOTT Michael: 16 Wind Rush Tower, Knights Road, Cowley, Oxford OX4 5HX ☎ 01865 433369, 0402 44753

ADAMS David *(Gtr)*: Titians, Banbury Road, Bicester, Oxon OX6 8HH ☎ 01869 240126

ADKINS Robert *(Gtr)*: 91 Springfield Avenue, Banbury, Oxon OX16 9JF ☎ 01295 262683

ALFORD Derek *(B Gtr, Voc)*: 22 Pendennis Close, Basingstoke, Hants RG23 8JD ☎ Basingstoke 274

ALLEN Dennis: Flat 2, 830 Wimborne Road, Bournemouth, Dorset BH9 2DT ☎ 01202 528314

ANTHONY David *(Db, Pf, Vln)*: The Cottage, Parklands Farm, Snailing Lane, Greatham, Liss, Hants GU3 6HQ ☎ 01420 538 741, 0370 591033

ATKINSON Paul *(B Tbn, Tba, Eup)*: 36 Yorke Way, Hamble, Southampton, Hants SO31 4LQ ☎ 023 8045 7478

BAKER Dan *(Vln, Ld Gtr, Pf)*: The Old Red Lion, Market Place, Blandford, Dorset DT11 7EB ☎ 01258 459669

BAKER Nigel: 81 Five Heads Rd, Horndean, Hampshire PO8 9NZ ☎ 023 9259 2649

BANYARD Peter *(Voc, B Ldr)*: 5 Alington Road, Bournemouth, Dorset BH3 7JX ☎ 01202 551703

BARR James: Periwinkle Cottage, Cox Green, Rudgwick, West Sussex RH12 3DE ☎ 01403 822685

BAVIN Jon *(Ld Gtr, Kbds)*: 2 Blackbird Way, Bransgore, Christchurch, Dorset BH23 8LG ☎ 01425 673674

BECKETT Nigel: 94 Parkfield Road, Rainham, Kent ME8 7TA ☎ 01634 365574

BEGG Alistair *(Voc)*: 50A Saxon Way, Romsey, Hants SO51 5QY ☎ 0966 363967

BELL Peter: 334 Minster Road, Minster-on-Sea, Sheerness, Kent ME12 3PE ☎ 01795 875849

BENNETT Phillip: 2 Heatherlea Road, Bournemouth, Dorset BH6 3HN ☎ 01202 426201

BEST Steve *(Voc)*: 14 Exeter Close, Tonbridge, Kent TN10 4NS ☎ 01732 353937, 0976 295630

BETTS Paul *(Kbds, Gtr)*: 180B Dunstons Road, East Dulwich, London SE22 0ES ☎ 020 8693 8781

BIRZNIEKS Robert: 40 Chetwynd Road, Southsea, Portsmouth PO4 0NB ☎ 023 9282 8503

BOWDEN Thomas: Field End House, Glebe Lane, Abinger Common, Dorking RH5 6JQ ☎ 01306 731 337

BOWER Nick *(Gtr)*: 8 Stirling Close, Maidenbower, Crawley, West Sussex RH10 7UZ ☎ 01293 889515

CARRERA-WEATHERLEY David: 7A Queens Gardens, Louisa Bay, Broadstairs, Kent CT10 1QE ☎ 01843 868511 & fax

CARTER Daniel: 4 Magnolia Close, Dibden, Southampton SO45 5HF ☎ 023 8084 7322

CASCARINO Lidia: 19 Wheelers Lane, Bearwood, Bournemouth, Dorset BH11 9RR ☎ 01202 576743

CHAPMAN Jackie: 15 Wenrise Drive, Minster Lovell, Oxon OX8 5SP ☎ 01993 774981

CLARKE Dean *(E Gtr)*: 69 Warren Avenue, Southsea, Portsmouth PO4 8PX ☎ 023 9286 2509, 023 9281 5528, 023 9221 4126

CLARKE Ian *(Gtr)*: 17 Aldworth Avenue, Wantage, Oxon OX12 7EJ ☎ 01235 764171

CLEWS Karl *(Cl Gtr, E Gtr)*: 7 Home Close, Wolvercote Road, Oxford OX2 8PS ☎ 01865 556770, 01865 556767 ext.4444

COLLEN James: 18 The Hollow, Haywards Heath, West Sussex RH16 2SX ☎ 01444 458997, 0411 325092 mob

COOK Norman *(Kbds, Gtr)*: 11 Western Esplanade, Brighton, Sussex BN41 1NE, 0860 466204

COOPER Mark *(Efl Bass)*: 9 Western Avenue, Bournemouth BH10 5BA ☎ 01202 534499

COURTIE Gavin *(Db, E Gtr, Com)*: 23 Griffin Court, Station Road, Wimborne Minster, Dorset BH21 1RQ ☎ 01202 842109

COX Rob *(Ld Gtr, Kbds)*: 39 Bramble Gardens, Burgess Hill, West Sussex RH15 8UQ ☎ 01444 239280

CROMPTON Paul: Flat 1, 201 Kingsway, Brighton, East Sussex BN3 4FD ☎ 01273 747124, 0402 600048 mob

CULLING James *(Gtr, Pf)*: 2 Temple Road, Temple Cowley, Oxford, Oxfordshire OX4 2HD ☎ 01865 775162

DARVILL Peter: 71 Pelham Road, Cowes, Isle Of Wight PO31 7DN ☎ 01983 293823

DAVIS Peter *(Gtr, Pf)*: 74 Holmcroft, Southgate, Crawley, West Sussex RH10 6TP

DEBRIAE David *(Per, Kbds, Voc)*: 44 Bonfield, Hook, Hants RG27 9SA ☎ 01256 765753, 0468 421426

DI FRANCO Anthony *(Gtr, Synth)*: 44 South Hill, Godalming, Surrey GU7 7JT ☎ 01483 416540

DIMARCO Michael: 1 Alderbury Close, Benlease, Swanage, Dorset BH19 2SN ☎ 01929 424464

DOMAY Michael *(Pf)*: 20 Argyll Road, Poole, Dorset BH12 2DR ☎ 01202 721329

DURANT Bob *(Tpt, B Ldr)*: 17, Copse Hill, Withdean, Brighton, East Sussex BN1 5GA ☎ 01273 541941

EDWARDS David: 60 Mill Rise, Westdene, Brighton, Sussex BN1 5GH ☎ Brighton 558815

EDWARDS Steven *(Kbds)*: 60 Mill Rise, Westdene, Brighton, Sussex BN1 5GH ☎ 01273 558815, 0411 319600

ELTON Mark: 16 Fremantle Road, Aylesbury, Bucks HP21 8EJ ☎ 01923 237435

EVANS Philip *(Tbn)*: 77 West Street, Bere Regis, Wareham, Dorset BH20 7HL ☎ 01929 471088

FADLALLA Mohamed *(Per)*: 68 Spencer Crescent, Rose Hill, Oxford OX4 4SW ☎ 01865 434772

FLAVELL Roger B *(Gtr)*: 14 Willowmead Gardens, Marlow, Bucks SL7 1HW ☎ 01628 485397

FLETCHER Colin *(Gtr, Kbds)*: c/o 70 South Street, Reading, Berks RG1 4RA ☎ 0421 362800

FORRESTER John *(Voc)*: 51 Barkham Road, Wokingham, Berkshire RG41 2RG ☎ 01734 785565

FRY Peter: 2 Wilson Close, Compton, Berks RG20 6NA ☎ 01635 578736

GAYLE Roy *(Per, Kbds)*: Linlea Croft, Cowpitts Lane, Ringwood, Hampshire BH24 3JX ☎ 01425 475288

GIBSON Will *(Gtr, Voc, Dms)*: Coombe End, Whitchurch Hill, Reading, Berks RG8 7TE ☎ 01189 842128, 0370 621 715

GIFFORD Jason *(Pf, Kbds)*: 26A Preston Road, Brighton, Sussex BN1 4QF ☎ 01273 231740, 0973 138688

GISBY Steve: 6 Elizabethan Way, Maidenbower, Crawley, West Sussex RH10 7GU ☎ 01293 887 027

GLOVER Dave *(E Gtr, Voc)*: 33 Windmill Close, Clanfield, Hants PO8 0NA ☎ 023 9279 7760, 0374 254929 mob, 023 9279 7760

GOSS Robert: The Red Lion, Thame Road, Longwick, Princes Risborough Bucks HP17 1SG ☎ 018444 4180

GREEN Gus *(Spoons)*: 4 Newland Street, Worthing, West Sussex BN11 1JU ☎ 01903 520449, 01273 462440

HARRIES Mark *(Ac Gtr, Voc)*: 4 Newfield Road, Liss Forest, Hampshire GU33 7BW ☎ 01730 895943

HARRIOTT Thomas: Flat 48, Milward Court, Wilmot Road, Shoreham By Sea, Sussex BN43 6BU ☎ 01273 591264

HARRISON David: 207 Orts Road, Reading RG1 3JS

HART Iain *(Gtr)*: 20 Zambra Way, Seal, Sevenoaks, Kent TN15 0DJ ☎ 01732 763825, 07771 887941 mob

HENDERSON Colin: 63 Mead Avenue, Langley, Slough SL3 8HS ☎ 01753 542671

HERBERT Vincent: 9 Mill Crescent, Tonbridge, Kent TN9 1PE ☎ 01732 354701

HIGGS David: 53 Wharfdedale Road, Margate, Kent CT9 2TA ☎ 01843 293039

HIGGS Lindsay *(Bal)*: 34 Reginald Road, Maidstone, Kent ME16 8HA ☎ 01622 759831

HOLT Carl *(Gtr, Dms)*: 18 Tylehurst Hill Road, Chesham, Bucks HP5 1XH ☎ 01494 783628

HOOPER Frederick: 28 Lockwood Crescent, Woodindean, Brighton, Sussex BN2 6UG ☎ Brighton 31256

HOPPER Hugh: Flat 5, 29 Castle Road, Whitstable, Kent CT5 2DZ

HORNE Jeffrey *(Gtr, Man)*: Kingsdown, Warmlake Road, Chart Sutton, Maidstone, Kent ME17 3RP ☎ 01622 842638

HOUSDEN Jeremy: 73 Mullion Place, Fishermead, Milton Keynes, Bucks MK6 2DW ☎ 020 8960 9888, 020 8968 6715

HURDLE Lez *(Tpt, Pf, Gtr)*: 19420 Lorne St, Reseda, CA 91335 ☎ +1 818 998 4948

INCHLEY Simon: 14 Pear Tree Close, Bransgore, Christchurch, Dorset BH23 8NH ☎ 01425 674053

JEBBITT Stuart *(Voc, Pf)*: 7 Cherry Tree Avenue, Guilford, Surrey GU2 5XB ☎ 01483 578573, 0468 457454, 01483 448606

JONES Alan *(Gtr)*: 4A Mercury Close, Bampton OX18 2AH ☎ 01993 851546

JONES Garry: 32 Brunswick Hill, Reading, Berkshire RG1 7YU

JOYCE Nathan: Address Unknown

KARAR Abdul *(Cong, Gtr)*: 50A Ashurst Way, Rosehill, Oxford OX4 4RE ☎ 01865 773816

KEAREY Ian *(Gtr)*: 88 Roundhill Crescent, Brighton, Sussex BN2 3FR ☎ 01273 624986

KEMP Daniel: 11 Western Road, Oxford OX1 4LF

KEYNES Nicholas *(Gtr)*: 7 White Hill Close, Chesham, Bucks HP5 1AS ☎ 01494 784676, 0961 127478 mob

KINCH Stephen: 174 Hughenden Road, Hastings, East Sussex TN34 3TA ☎ 01424 715230

KING Anthony *(Kbds, Gtr)*: 14 Queen Street, Stony, Stratford, Milton Keynes MK11 1ES ☎ 01908 262447

KING Ian: 5 Argyll Street, Ryde, Isle Of Wight PO33 3BZ ☎ 01983 617307

KING Steve *(Voc)*: 39 Ellison Way, Rainham, Gillingham, Kent ME8 7PG ☎ 01634 387804

KITCHER Martin *(Ac Gtr)*: 29 Broad Avenue, Bournemouth, Dorset BH8 9LX ☎ 01202 302566

LAIRD Peter: 32 Hobart Drive, Hythe, Southampton SO4 6FH ☎ 023 8084 8593

LANG Brad: 19 Walnut Close, Yateley, Hants GU46 6DA ☎ 01252 873206

LAWES Peter: Melton, 93 Bursledon Road, Hedge End, Southampton Hants S030 0BU ☎ 01489 783171

LE BAIGUE Paul *(Gtr)*: 13 Addington Street, Margate, Kent CT9 1PN ☎ 01843 299615

LEWIS Paul: F5 Charter House, Dover, Kent CT16 1LE ☎ 01304 241701

LISHEEN: 14 Garstons Road, Titchfield, Fareham, Hampshire PO14 4EG ☎ 01329 841455

MARGETTS Tristram: 17 Barbers Piles, The Quay, Poole, Dorset BH15 1JJ ☎ 01202 670283

MARSHALL Timothy: Oakdene, Rookley, Ventor, Isle Of Wight PO38 3NH ☎ 01983 721201

MAY John *(Gtr, Pf)*: 66 Cherry Gardens, Herne Bay, Kent CT6 5QZ ☎ Herne Bay 74175

MCLAREN Robert: 3 Vale Road, Parkstone, Poole, Dorset BH14 9AT ☎ 01202 259622

MCNAMEE John *(Db)*: The Old Pumping Station, Nr Hart Leisure Centre, Hitches Lane, Fleet, Hants GU13 8HZ ☎ 01252 819619, 0468 175488

MILNER Robert A: 8 Kassassin Street, Southsea, Portsmouth, Hants PO4 9PS ☎ 023 9234 6731

MITCHELL John *(Voc)*: 2 Dart Close, Durrington, Worthing, Sussex BN13 3LH ☎ Worthing 63434

MOIR Leslie *(Kbds, Ac Gtr)*: 60 Ringwood Road, Eastbourne, East Sussex BN22 8TB ☎ 01323 72008

MOORE Iain: 30 Star Lane, Ash, Aldershot GU12 6RH ☎ 01252 679142

MOORE Julian: 149 Slough Road, Datchet, Berks SL3 9AE ☎ 01753 541702

MOWLEM Matt: 1 Cecil Villas, Osborne Road North, Portswood, Southampton SO17 2UQ ☎ 023 8055 3257

MURRAY Steven ☎ 023 9286 1507

MYER Matthew *(Db, Gtr)*: 25 East Drive, Brighton, East Sussex BN2 2BQ ☎ 01273 622 182

NICHOLLS Barry: 24 Suffolk Avenue, Westgate-on-Sea, Kent CT8 8JG ☎ Thanet 32277

NICHOLLS Victor: 8 Slaidburn Green, Forest Park, Brackenell, Berkshire RG12 0GG ☎ 01344 56098

O'DONNELL Michael: 5 Lowfield Close, Lightwater, Surrey GU18 5QT ☎ 01276 72924

O'SHEA Franc: 22A Newark Place, Brighton, E Sussex BN2 2NT ☎ 01273 697730

ORFORD Lloyd: 362 Priory Road, St Denys, Southampton, Hants SO17 2LQ ☎ 023 8032 1903

PALMER Maurice *(Db, Pf)*: 16A Willow Gardens, North Baddesley, Southampton SO52 9FY ☎ 023 8073 5230

PARKER Timothy *(Gtr, Dms)*: The Cabins, Stokefield Farm, Knightsbridge Lane, Oxon OX9 5AT ☎ 01491 613266, 01491 613304

PEARCE Richard: 10A St Augustines Road, Bournemouth BH2 6NX ☎ 01202 265684

PEARSON Nigel *(Gtr, Voc)*: 3 Harvesters, Horsham, West Sussex RH12 5TJ ☎ 01403 64571

PECKHAM Geoffrey *(Gtr, Acc, Db)*: 2 Mill Close, Poynings, Sussex BN45 7AF ☎ 01273 857599

PEDLEY Chris *(Gtr, Club Dj)*: 64 Leybourne Avenue, Ensbury Park, Bournemouth, Dorset BH10 6HF ☎ 01202 252416, 07971 226 176

PENNECK Anthony *(Gtr, Man)*: 1 Hemdean Hill, Caversham, Reading, Berkshire RG4 7SB ☎ 0118 954 3017

PORTER Ian: Flat 5, 13 Chesham Place, Kemptown, Brighton BN2 1FB ☎ 676607

PROSSER Alan *(Gtr, Vln)*: 18 Seymour Place, Canterbury, Kent CT1 3SF ☎ Canterbury 5617

PULLEN Dave *(Tpt, Voc)*: 34 Charnock Close, The Orchards, Hordle, Lymington, Hants SO41 0GU ☎ 01425 620048, 0378 787342 mob

PYKE Alan *(Kbds)*: 52 Forton Road, Gosport, Hants PO12 4TP ☎ 023 9258 0816, 0836 329240

QUEST John: 8 Sunnyside Residential Park, St. Ives, Ringwood, Hampshire BH24 2NW ☎ 01425 480338

RIDDLE Michael: 27 Whitedown, Alton Hants GU34 1LX ☎ 01420 86709

RIEGER Paul *(Gtr, Pf)*: 16 Victoria Court, Victoria Street, Maidstone, Kent ME16 8JZ ☎ 01622 663264

ROBERTS David *(Kbds, Per, Voc)*: 69 Waverley Road, Reading, Berks RG30 2QB ☎ 01734 591709

ROBSON Neil *(Db, Pf, Kbds)*: 20 Dereham Way, Branksome, Poole, Dorset BH12 1LZ ☎ 01282 740741

ROSARIO Rafeal *(Gtr, Kbds, Per)*

SARGENT Christopher *(Pf)*: 6 Pentland Road, Aylesbury, Bucks HP21 7NB ☎ 01296 420 485

SARGENT Frederick: 122 George V Avenue, West Worthing, West Sussex BN11 5RX ☎ 01903 506019

SHAUGHNESSY Jack *(Voc)*: 11 Culliford Crescent, Poole, Dorset BH17 9DY ☎ 01202 690033

SHAW Pete: Dingley Dell, Rhododendron Avenue, Culverstone, Meopham, Kent DA13 0TT ☎ 01732 823209, 01732 823127

SHELDON Nick *(E Gtr, Kbds)*: Flat 5, Commonside, Common Road, Redhill, Surrey RH1 6HQ ☎ 01737 761006

SINCLAIR Douglas *(Com)*: 188 Winston Avenue, Branksome, Poole, Dorset BH12 1PH ☎ 01202 723866

SMITH Alan *(Kbds, Org, Dms)*: 16 Middlewall, Whistable, Kent CT5 1BJ ☎ 01227 762718, 0370 887 587, 01227 780045

SMITH Clive: 19 The Poles, Upchurch, Nr Sittingbourne, Kent ME9 7EX ☎ 01634 235776

SMITH Harvey *(Tbn)*: 21 Coleman Road, Bournemouth, Dorset BH11 8EQ ☎ 01202 570473

SPOLIA Rajan *(Gtr)*: 41 Hemwood Road, St. Leonards Hill, Windsor, Berks SL4 4YX ☎ 01753 867271

STAPLES I G: Narrowboat Lichfield, The Old Wharf, Appletree Lane, Gropredy Oxfordshire OX17 1PZ ☎ 01295 758438

STARES Steve: 74 Calmore Road, Totton, Southampton SO40 8GN ☎ 023 8086 4416

STEAR Geoff *(Tba, Db)*: 2 Manor Villas, Taylors Lane, Bosham, West Sussex PO18 8QQ ☎ 01243 574027

STEELE Luke: 13 Salegate Lane, Temple, Cowley, Oxford OX4 2HQ ☎ 01865 770272 & fax

STOW Pete *(Gtr)*: 79A Fawcett Road, Southsea, Hants PO4 0DB ☎ 023 9287 6401

TATE George *(Db, Tba)*: 1 Japonica Way, Havant, Hants PO9 2FP ☎ 023 9248 1909

TAYLOR Lou *(Voc, Kbds)*: 124 Church Road, Woolston, Southampton, Hants SO19 9FX ☎ 023 8044 7462, 0836 631485 mob

TAYLOR Scott *(Voc, Gtr)*: 14 Grafton Street, Sandown, Isle Of Wight PO36 8JJ ☎ 01983 404949

TEAH Haizi *(Kbds, Voc)*

THOMAS Peter: Padmore Farm, Whippmonam, East Cowes, Isle Of Wight PO32 6LY ☎ 01983 291984

THOMSON Rhuraidh *(Db, Kbds)*: 37 Woking Road, Guilfrod, Surrey GU1 1QD ☎ 01483 822233, 0403 578172

THORNE Mike: 35 Windsor Way, Alderholt, Nr Fordingbridge, Hants SP6 3BN ☎ 01425 655265

TRIBBLE *(Kbds)*: Basement Flat 1, 28 Ashburton Road, Southsea, Hants PO5 3JT

TUNBRIDGE Grant: 10 Orchard Road, East Peckham, Tonbridge, Kent TN12 5AN ☎ 01622 872137

VIRGOE Duncan: Rownas, 51 Piers Lane, Lingfield, Surrey RH7 6PM ☎ 01343 835129

WAGSTAFF Stuart: 3 Hawth Valley Court, Surrey Road, Seaford, East Sussex BN25 2NF ☎ 01323 895450

WALL Andrew *(Db, Tba, Cel)*: 1St Band Squadron, Royal Guard Of Oman, PO Box 1193, Code 211, Salalah, Oman

WATKINS Chris *(Gtr, Pf, Kbds)*: 15 The Dene, Manor Park, Uckfield, East Sussex TN22 1LA ☎ 01825 769836

WATSON Saul: 35 Bloors Lane, Rainham, Kent ME8 7EJ ☎ 01634 377483

WEBB Alan *(Kbds)*: 25 Tideway, Littlehampton, West Sussex BN17 6PP ☎ 01903 725014

WHITE Veronica *(Rh Gtr)*: Wood Lodge, Yalding, Kent ME18 6EB ☎ 01622 814229

WILLMENT Mark *(Kbds, Com, Arr, Md)*: 13 Kibbles Lane, Southborough, Tunbridge Wells, Kent TN4 0LN ☎ 01892 680487

WOODWARD John *(Voc, Tba)*: The Shambles, 2 Badgers Walk, Angmering, West Sussex BN16 4DJ ☎ 01903 775382

SOUTH WEST

ALLEN Thomas *(Ac Gtr, Hmca)*: End Cottage, Frampton, End Road, Frampton Cotterell, South Glos BS36 2JY ☎ 01454 774208

AMES Kenneth *(Gtr)*: 108 Kings Road, Kingston-upon-Thames, Surrey ST2 5HT ☎ 020 8546 0125

APPLEBY Richard *(Gtr)*: Harmony Cottage, 1 The Square, Petrockstowe, Devon EX20 3HN ☎ 01837 810752

ATKINSON Richard *(Dms)*: 48 Belle Vue Road, Salisbury, Wiltshire SP1 3YG ☎ 01722 333345

BAILEY Ronald *(Org)*: 10 Isambard Court, Moor Lane, Torquay TQ2 8PP ☎ 01803 313843

BAKER Jeff: 82 Long View Road, Port Talbot, Glam SA12 7EH ☎ 01639 888750

BALL Dave: c/o 16 Park Crescent, Barry, South Glamorgan CF62 6HD ☎ 01446 741779

BANTING John *(Kbds, Gtr)*: 109 Victoria Drive, Lyneham, Swindon, Wiltshire SN15 4TE ☎ 01249 891504

BARNARD David: 6 Jewel Close, Grange Park, Swindon, Wilts SN5 6HP ☎ 01273 420625

BARRINGTON Guy: Kielder, Y Parc, Groes-Faen, Pontyclun, Mid Glamorgan CF7 8NP ☎ 029 2089 0564

BEST Andrew *(Kbds)*: 41 Blenheim Park, Bowerhill, Melksham, Wiltshire SN12 6TA ☎ 01225 700435

BLAND Richard: 43 Northmoore Road, Dulverton, Somerset TA22 9PW ☎ 01398 324394

BUCKLEY Gary *(Voc, Db)*: 4 Collingwood Close, Worle, Weston Super Mare, North Somerset BS22 9PQ ☎ 01934 516786

BURGE Richard: 83 Church Rd, Cinderford, Glos GL14 3EL ☎ 01594 826714

BUSHELL Julian *(Mando, Man)*: Barn Cottage, 1 Rackfield, Westford, Wellington, Somerset TA21 0EA ☎ 01823 666813

CADBURY Richard *(Vln)*: Hilcot House, Stanley Road, Battledown, Cheltenham, Glos GL52 6PF ☎ 01242 233555

CADDLE Tony: 23 Landsdown Road, Easton, Bristol BS5 0PB

CAULFIELD John: First Floor Flat, 69 Claire Road, Grangetown, Cardiff CF1 7QQ ☎ 029 2039 6626, 07970 071203

CHILVERS Jonathan: 3 Penrice Street, Morriston, Swansea SA6 6HQ ☎ 01792 790608

CLUTTERBUCK Carl *(Db, Pf, Kbds, Gtr)*: 8 Victoria Drive, Eastington, Stonehouse, Glos GL10 3AW ☎ 01453 82 4278

COLE Kevin: 9 Tennyson Street, Swindon SN1 5DT ☎ 01793 338975, 0468 332696

COLLINSON Christopher: 36 Gelligaled Road, Ystrad Pentre, Rhondda, Cynon Taff CF41 7RH ☎ 01443 442562

COOK Sean: 38 Greenbank Road, Southville, Bristol BS3 1RJ ☎ 0117 9669171

COOL Johnny Ace *(Gtr, Man, Didj, Triangle)*: c/o Ann Hamilton, Rosedene, Limehead, St Breward, Bodmin, Cornwall PL30 4LU ☎ 01208 851447

DANIELS Jonathan: Top Flat, Ingleside Way, Lower High Street, Newnham-on- Severn GL14 1BX ☎ 01594 510261

DAVID Neil *(Gtr, Kbds)*

DAVIES Marc *(Gtr, Voc, Kbds, Dms)*: 38 Springfield Close, The Reddings, Cheltenham, Glos GL51 6SE ☎ 01452 548605, 0421 784132

DERRICK Stuart: Flat 2, 11 Broad Street, Launceston, Cornwall PL15 8AA ☎ 01566 776538

DINGLE Juanita: 3 Sunnycroft, North Road, West Looe, Cornwall PL13 2EL ☎ 01503 3103

DIXON K Michael (*Gtr*): c/o 3 Orchard Lea Villas, Dedworth Green, Windsor, Berks SL4 4LD ☎ 01753 860091, 0468 301873

DOYLE Andrew (*Db*): Basement Flat, 18 London Road, Cheltenham, Glos GL52 6DX ☎ 01242 581902, 01242 221311

DUNFORD Philip (*Saxes, Clt, Vla, Rh Gtr*): 4 Higher Town Park, Landrake, Saltash, Cornwall PL12 5DQ ☎ 01752 851744

DUXBURY Mark (*Kbds, Voc*): 1 Lynmoor Road, Weymouth, Dorset DT4 7TW ☎ 01305 784053

ENGLAND John (*Gtr*): 9 Chiltern Close, Warmley, Bristol BS15 5UH ☎ 0117 909 4573

EVANS-JONES Peter (*Dms*): 38 Purbeck Close, Weymouth, Dorset DT4 9QU ☎ 01305 783585

FITZSIMONS Gerard: 13 West Ave, Sticklepath, Barnstaple, N Devon EX31 2EE ☎ 01271 346487

FRYER Dave (*Ac Gtr, Kbds*): 20 Bayer Road, Amesbury, Wiltshire SP4 7XG

GENDALL Luke: 25 Queensway, Chelston, Torquay, Devon TQ2 6BP

GOODIER David (*Db*): 68 Somerset Road, Knowle, Bristol BS4 2HY ☎ 0117 971 6785

GRAY Paul (*Kbds*): 45 Alfred Street, Roath, Cardiff CF2 4TZ ☎ 029 2040 5902 & fax

GWILLIAM Michael: 54 Nibletts Hill, St George, Bristol BS5 8TR ☎ 0117 961 2326

HADDON William: 4 Dylan Close, Llandough, Penarth, Glamorgan CF6 1PA ☎ 029 2070 1386

HARRIES Alun (*Kbds*): 3 Heol Pwll-Y-Pant, Caerphilly, South Wales CF83 2ND ☎ 029 2088 4417

HARRIS Christopher: 4 Pavilion Place, Exeter, Devon EX2 4HR ☎ 01392 436377

HARRIS Paul (*Chap Stk*): 2 Wells Street, Swindon, Wiltshire SN1 2JJ

HARRIS Sydney (*Fo Fdl, Cel*): Brookvilla, Blakes Hill Road, Landkey, Barnstaple, Devon EX32 0NE ☎ 01271 830267

HEEL Christopher (*Gtr*): 88 North Road, Newbridge, Gwent, S. Wales NP1 4AF ☎ 01495 249075

HENNING Martin (*Db, Man*): 1 Pittford Cottages, Wembworthy, Chulmleigh, Devon EX18 7QA ☎ 01837 83347

HILLMAN Paul (*Db*): 6 The Fairway, Cyncoed, Cardiff CF2 6RE ☎ 029 2075 8561

HODGE Andrew (*Db, Kbds, Per*): 26 The Reddings, Red Road, Boreham Wood, Herts WD6 4SS ☎ 020 8207 5088

HOWE John (*Rh Gtr, Db*): 17 Park Crescent, Lonlas, Skewen, Neath SA10 6SH ☎ 01792 815054

HOWE Julian (*Gtr*): 391 Teignmouth Road, Torquay, South Devon TQ1 4SW ☎ 01803 325424

HOWELL Terry (*Db*): 8 Garth Road, Tairgwaith, Ammanford, Dyfed SA18 1UY ☎ 01269 822651

HUMPHRIS Neil: 6 Beaumont Road, Longlevens, Gloucester GL2 0EJ ☎ 01452 504967, 0402 628318

HUNT Alan: 15 South Burrow Road, Ilfracombe, N Devon EX34 8JE ☎ 01271 862137

ILES Robert (*Br Sax*): 7 Long Street, Galhampton, Yeovil, Somerset BA22 7AZ ☎ 01963 440464, 0402 353831, 01963 440464

JOACHIM Ian (*Db*): 60 The Dormers, Highworth, Swindon SN6 7NZ ☎ 01793 764970

JOHN Simon (*Tpt, Kbds*): 45 Green Street, Totterdown, Bristol BS3 4UB ☎ 0117 942 4638

JONES Nicholas: Greenfield Park Terrace, Woodfieldside, Blackwood, Gwent NP2 0PE ☎ 020 8740 6288

JONES Paul: 5 Preswyfla Street, Canton, Cardiff CF5 1FS ☎ 029 2066 8703

JONES Wyn (*Pf, Gtr*): Llys-Y-Coed, Heol Dinbych-Y-Pysgod, Aberteifi, Ceredigion SA43 3AH ☎ 01239 614691, 04325 273343, 01239 614680

KENNEDY Sean (*Synth, Dms*): Leasbrook Bungalow, Leasbrook Lane, Monmouth NP5 3SN ☎ 01600 715049, 0410 419166

KEYS Ronnie (*Gtr*) ☎ 01225 743178

KIDD Steven: Garden Flat, 24 Sydenham Road, Bristol BS6 5SJ ☎ 0117 942 1120

KILBRIDE Daniel (*E Gtr, Ac Gtr, Man, Pf*): 75 Llandaff Road, Canton, Cardiff CF1 9NG ☎ 029 2021 4897

KING Patsy (*Bjo, Man, Gtr*): Tanglewood, Drakewalls, Gunnislake, Cornwall PL18 9EJ ☎ 01822 833800

KINGSTON Duncan: 55 North Street, Oldland Common, Bristol BS30 8TT ☎ 0117 9326045

LEASE Michael (*Gtr, Pf*): 194 Oaksford, Coedeva, Cwmbran, Gwent NP44 6UQ ☎ 01633 871838

LEWIS Anthony: West Ways, Bank Road, Pilning, Bristol BS12 3JG

LEWIS Colin (*Voc, Dms, Gtr, Kbds*): Llwyn, Beaufort Road, Ebbw Vale, Gwent NP3 5NJ ☎ 01495 305875

LEWIS Kevin: 141 Pencoed Road, Burry Port, Carmarthenshire SA16 0PS ☎ 01554 835319

LOCKE Robert (*Db, Kbds*): 30 Clarendon Road, Redland, Bristol BS6 7EU ☎ 0117 924 0151

MARTIN Robert (*Tbn*): 14 Woodloge Close, South Brent, Devon TQ10 9BN ☎ 01364 72359

MATTHEWS Paul (*Clt, Flt, Sax*): 11 Sudbury Close, Worle, Weston-Super-Mare, Nr Somerset BS22 7QP ☎ 01934 521 667

MCGOWAN Sean: 18 Wyefield Court, Monmouth, Gwent NP5 3TN ☎ 01600 716237

MEACHAM John (*Ac Gtr, Kbds*): Keeper Cottage, East End, Nr Newbury RG15 0AB ☎ 01635 253650

MOCKRIDGE Christopher (*Gtr*): 5 Holway Hill, Taunton, Somerset TA1 2HB ☎ 0182 3321 357

MOULDING Colin (*Voc*): St Annes Foxhill, Wanborough, Swindon SN4 0DS

NEWELL Roger: 2 Hawthorn Road, Frome, Somerset BA11 2LP ☎ 01373 465165

OSBORNE Michael (*Gtr, Kbds, Pf, Dms*): 28 Meadow Close, Kingskerwell TQ12 5AS

PAGE W: 2 Arfyn Road, Sketty, Swansea SA2 0YJ ☎ 01792 203652

PARSONS Bernard (*Tbn*): 11 Glasllwch View, Newport, Gwent NP9 3RJ ☎ 01633 892591

PERRY Christian (*Gtr, Dms*): 2 Packers Road, Porth, Rhondda, Mid Glam, Sth Wales CF39 0LW ☎ 01443 687693

PRITCHARD Alan (*Voc*): 8 Worcester Walk, Broadwell, Coleford, Glos GL16 7PL ☎ 01594 810782

RICHARDS Dylan: 58 Swiss Valley, Llanelli, Carmarthenshire, South Wales SA14 8DT

RICK (*Gtr*): 7A William Street, Truro, Cornwall TR1 2ED

SCADDING James (*Tbn, Voc, Gtr*): 6 Chesham Road North, Milton, Weston Super Mare BS22 8AD ☎ 01934 416836

SEDDON Colin (*Dms, Per*): 2 Sunnycroft, North Road, West Looe, Cornwall PL13 2EL ☎ 01503 265214, 01523 122525 pager

SIMPSON Ian: 52 Selborne Road, Ashley Down, Bristol BS7 9PH ☎ 0117 942 3356

SMITH Ian (*Pf, Kbds*): 5 Windmill Court, Windmill Hill, Brixham TQ5 9HG ☎ 01803 858995

STARKS Elliott: Flagstone Cottage, Condicote, Stow-on-The Wold, Gloucestershire GL54 1ER

TAYLOR John (*Gtr, Db, Kbds*): 19 Bernard Street, Uplands, Swansea SA2 0HU ☎ 01792 290835

TEAGUE Rodney: 12 Fourgates Road, Dorchester, Dorset DT1 2NL ☎ 01305 263361

THORNE David (*St Gtr*): Greenlands, Luppitt, Honiton, Devon EX14 0SX ☎ 01404 891604

WAITE Andrew: Flat 2, Yarn Barton, Fleet Street, Beaminster, Dorset DT8 3DR ☎ 01308 861137

WARD Steven (*Gtr, Kbds*): Leckford, Crookes Lane, Kewstoke, Weston Super Mare BS22 9XB ☎ 01934 625 936

WEST Richard (*Voc*): 221B London Road, Shippenham, Wiltshire SN15 3AP ☎ 01249 446792, 07970 472781

WILLIAMS Gareth (*Vln, Gtr*): Serene, Rehoboth Road, Five Roads, Llanelli, Carmarthenshire, South Wales SA15 5EX ☎ 01269 861438

WILLIAMS Owen ☎ 01242 227257, 0498 796202 mob, 01242 227328

WILSON Leonard: 28 Southwood Drive East, Coombe Dingle, Bristol BS9 2QS ☎ 0117 9687209

WILTSHIRE Stephen: 161 Goddard Avenue, Swindon, Wiltshire SN1 4HX ☎ 01793 486745

LONDON

ADAMSON Maurice: 106 George Crescent, Muswell Hill, London N10 1AJ ☎ 020 8444 9386

ADDISON Lawrence: 14 Rockhampton Road, South Croydon, Surrey CR2 7AQ ☎ 020 8686 7126

ADSHEAD Christopher (*Db*): 42 Clarkes Drive, Uxbridge, Middx UB8 3UJ ☎ 01895 442314, 0966 286933

ALEXANDER (*Ld Gtr, Pf*): c/o C.M.O., 35-37 Parkgate Road, London SW11 4NP

ALLEN Sebastian (*Dms, Kbds*): 68 Whitton, King Henry's Road, London NW3 3AG ☎ 020 7209 3162

AMMAR Morris (*Gtr, Kbds, Hmca, Per*): 187 Charlemont Road, London E6 4AG ☎ 020 8472 9252

ANDERSON Alicia: 2 Eveline Court, Connaught Gardens, London N10 3LA ☎ 01781 252 3581

ANDERSON George: Woodplace Farmhouse, Woodplace Lane, Coulsdon, Surrey CR3 1NE ☎ 01737 557480

ANGIAMA Oroh (*Db, Voc, Kbds*): Flat 1, 91 Cranfield Road, Brockley, London SE4 1TR ☎ 0958 297 077

ANGUS Colin (*Gtr, Kbds*): Address Unknown ☎ 020 8555 5423, 020 8519 6834 fax

ANTONIADES Loucas (*Dms*): 201 Albion Road, Stoke Newington, London N16 9JU ☎ 0956 500927

AP GWYNEDD Rheinallt (*Gtr, Dms*): Flat 5, 23-25 Brecknock Road, London N7 0BL ☎ 020 7485 2734

APTAKER Randolph: 151A Fordwych Road, London NW2 3NG ☎ 020 8452 0933

ARMSTRONG Steve (*Voc*): 83 Dallinger Road, Lee, London SE12 0TQ ☎ 020 8851 6068

ASTROVIBE (*Gtr, Synth*): 26 Burrow Road, East Dulwich, London SE22 8DW ☎ 020 8693 4859

AUGUSTE-ETIENNE Patrick (*Gtr*): Flat 5, 40 Lambert Road, Brixton Hill, London SW2 5BE ☎ 020 7274 7700

AUKER Brian (*Db*): 19 The Close, Copyhold Road, East Grinstead, Sussex RH19 1DQ ☎ 01342 326843

AUSTEN Kenneth: 54 Woodcote Valley Road, Purley, Surrey CR2 3AJ ☎ 020 8660 1562

AYRE Ian (*Pf, Gtr, Voc*): 129 Lower Richmond Road, Putney, London SW15 1EZ ☎ 020 8789 9644

BAILEY Michael (*Db*): 194 Grasmere Ave, Wembley, Middlesex HA9 8TH ☎ 020 8904 3164

BAKER Laurence (*Com*): 47 Abdale Road, London W12 7ER ☎ 020 8743 4084

BALL Daryl (*Ac Gtr*): 37 Mount Satreet, Ballymena, Co Antrim, North Ireland BT43 6BW ☎ 01266 42039

BALL Denny: 5 Chetwynd Heights, 123 Chetwynd Road, London NW5 1DB ☎ 020 7267 2372

BARNACLE Steven (*Gtr, Kbds, Sax*): 65 Natal Road, Streatham, London SW16 6JA ☎ 020 8677 2407, 0956 672264

BARRETT James: 43 Vineyard Hill Road, Wimbledon Park, London SW19 7JL ☎ 020 8946 1389

BARRY Trevor: Chestnut Cottage, Station Road, Tilbrook, Huntingdon PE18 0JT ☎ 01480 860824

BARTELL Paul: 44 Birch Avenue, Caterham, Surrey CR5 5RU ☎ 01883 343712, 01883 343712

BARTON Paul: 39 Grey House, White City, London W12 ☎ 020 8749 8475

BASS Adrien (*Gtr*): 30 Geoffrey House, Pardoner Street, Borough, London SE1 4DW ☎ 020 7357 6056 & fax

BATT Bill: 6 Balmoral Road, Brentwood, Essex CM15 9PN ☎ 01277 218204

BAXTER Derek: 2 Margetson House, Stamford Hill, London N16 5LE ☎ 020 8800 2224

BEABLE Mathew: 25 Blundel Lane, Cobham, Surrey KT11 2SU ☎ 01372 843380

BEACON Ronnie (*Gtr*): 128 Telford Avenue, London SW2 4XQ ☎ 020 8671 8247, 020 7306 8528

BEDBROOK James (*Db, Kbds*): 47 Claremont Road, Teddington, Middlesex TW11 8DH ☎ 020 8977 6817

BEEF (*Gtr, Hmca, Pf, Voc*): J.P.R Management, 4E Westpoint, 33-34 Warple Way, London W3 0RG ☎ 020 8742 0052

BEGGS Nicholas (*Chap Stk, Voc*): 1 Aslett Street, London SW18 2BE ☎ 020 8877 3149

BENSON Phil (*Db, Voc*): 44 Addison Road, Caterham, Surrey CR3 5LR ☎ 01883 340057

BENTHAM Dominic: 80 Leighton Road, Kentish Town, London NW5 2QE ☎ 020 7482 3317

BENTLEY Johnny (*Db*): 32 Ham Road, Worthing, West Sussex BN11 2QX ☎ 01903 232387

BERGELODT Rune (*Gtr, Kbds*): Harrow Hall Of Residence, c/o T Lind Flat 76C, PO Box 853, Harrow, Middlesex HA1 3YU ☎ 020 7911 5000 ext 4825

BERRY David (*Db, Tba*): 33 South Villas, London NW1 9BT ☎ 020 7267 6135

BERRY John (*Voc, Gtr*): 78 Longfellow Road, Gillingham, Kent ME7 5QQ ☎ 01634 230454

BETHELL Brian (*Gtr*): 4 Napier Court, Lovelace Gardens, Surbiton, Surrey KT6 6SJ ☎ 020 8399 6520

BEZER Terry (*Dms*): 6 Winifred Road, Erith, Kent DA8 1AJ ☎ 01322 435935

BINGHAM Steve: 32 Quadrant House, Burrell Street, London SE1 0UW ☎ 020 7633 9576, 0421 065618 mob

BISWAS Kingusk (*Synth, Per*): 9 Northwick Avenue, Kenton, Harrow, Middlesex HA3 0AA ☎ 020 8907 8278, 020 8909 2933

BLAKE Jerome: 58 Wedgwood House, Lambeth Walk, London SE11 6LN ☎ 0973 846 278, 020 7497 8239

BLANCHARD Mark (*Tbn*): 10A Bensham Manor Road, Thornton Heath, Surrey CR7 7AA ☎ 020 8683 4941

BLISSETT Winston: 22 Lochaber Road, London SE13 5QU ☎ 020 8318 6013

BLUE Barry (*Per*): 20 Woodlands Road, Bushey, Herts WD2 2LR ☎ 01923 229 630, 01923 244693 fax

BLYTH Terry: 19 Tadlow, Washington Road, Kingston, Surrey KT1 3JL ☎ 020 8546 1260, 0958 653491

BOATENG Danny (*Kbds, Dms*): 4 Samuel Johnson Close, Streatham, London SW16 3TB

BODNAR Andrew (*Gtr, Kbds*): 8, Block B, Peabody Buildings, Horseferry Road, London SW1P 2ET ☎ 020 7233 2773

BOND Gordon (*Voc*): 30 Great Elms Road, Bromley, Kent BR2 9NF ☎ 020 8466 5223 & fax

BOWER Jon: 37 Barbrook Way, Bicknacre, Chelmsford, Essex CM3 4HP ☎ 01245 222247

BOWLEY Martin (*Voc*): 33B Grantbridge Street, Islington, London N1 8JL ☎ 020 7704 0629, 0956 249738 mob

BRADLEY Stuart (*Db*): 65 Spring Road, Lower Feltham, Middlesex TW13 7JA ☎ 020 8893 7089, 0421 898013 mob

BRANCH Philip (*Gtr*): 18 Rowney Wood, Sawbridgeworth, Herts CM21 0HR ☎ 01279 722527

BRETT Martin (*Synth, Voc*): 13 Prince Georges Avenue, London SW20 8BQ ☎ 020 8542 5827

BRIQUETTE Pete (*Kbds*): 74 Grafton Road, Acton, London W3 6PF ☎ 020 8896 0520, 020 8896 3472 fax

BROLAN David: 36 Priory Grove, Stockwell, London SW8 2PH ☎ 020 7720 7744

BRONZE David: 21 Seaview Road, Leigh-on-Sea, Essex SS9 1AT ☎ 01702 715113

BROOKS Michael: 8 Brentvale Avenue, Southall, Middlesex UB1 3ER ☎ 020 8574 5043

BROUGHTON Ian (*Gtr, Pf*): 105 Ankerdine Crescent, Shooters Hill, London SE18 3LD ☎ 020 8244 1089

BROWN Andy (*Cong, Md*): 72 Cromwell Avenue, Cheshunt, Herts EN7 5DW ☎ 01992 24961

BROWN Len (*Kbds*): 2 Latimer Drive, Suttons Lane, Hornchurch, Essex RM12 6TQ ☎ 0802 721540

BROWN Livingstone (*Kbds, Gtr, Dms, Tbn*): 13 Hillside Grove, London NW7 2LS

BROWN Mark William: 15A Khartoum Road, Tooting, London SW17 0JA ☎ 020 8672 0595

BROWN Pete *(Sax)*: 18 Naylor House, Albion Avenue, London SW8 2AJ ☎ 020 7622 1561

BROWN Robin *(E Gtr, Synth)*: 37B Billington Road, New Cross Gate, London SE14 5QH ☎ 020 7732 8459

BROWNE Kevin *(Dms, Gtr, Kbds)*: 12 Elers Road, Northfields, Ealing, London W13 9QD ☎ 020 8579 4925

BRUCE Paul *(Db, Pf)*: 82B Florence Road, Finsbury Park, London N4 4DP ☎ 020 8968 9571

BRYANT Mike *(Clt, Pf)*: c/o Fluke, Rear Court Yard, Sagaland, 326 Kensal Road, London W10 5BZ ☎ 020 8964 4623

BUCHANAN Robert *(Vln)*: 62 Malden Avenue, South Norwood, London SE25 4HS ☎ 020 8656 9107

BULPITT John: 8 Claremont Avenue, Hersham, Surrey KT12 4NR ☎ 01932 248214

BURDEN Martin *(Voc, Gtr)*: Flat 1, 314 Alexandra Park Road, London N22 7BD ☎ 07971 101874

BURNS Robert *(Man)*: 15 Berkshire Gardens, London N13 6AA ☎ 020 8888 2215

BURRELL Alvin *(Db)*: Flat 2, 8 Windmill Road, Croydon CR0 2XN ☎ 020 8684 4876, 0468 696533

BURTON Tigger *(Gtr)*: Hunters Lodge, Potter Street Hill, Pinner, Middlesex HA5 3YH ☎ 020 8866 3647

BUSH Marcus D *(Gtr, Man)*: 326A West End Lane, London NW6 1LN ☎ 020 7794 0674

BUSHBY Adrian *(Per)*: 17 Brookside, Hoddesdon, Herts EN11 8AA ☎ 01992 466431, 0956 217194 mob

BUTTON Ian *(Voc)*: 33, Davenport Road, Sidcup, Kent DA14 4PN

C-LEX *(Pf, Kbds, Gtr, Voc)* ☎ 020 7221 1001 & fax, 0956 492528 mob

CAIRD Alexander *(Gtr)*: 2A High Street, New Malden, Surrey KT3 4HE ☎ 020 8949 6109, 020 8540 5646

CANTY Laurence: 23 St. Mary's Parade, Lancaster LA1 1YX ☎ 01524 33077

CAREY Patrick: 3 Griffith Ave, Dublin 9, Ireland ☎ 833 0732

CARMICHAEL Paul *(Com, Arr)*: 26 Vallis Way, Ealing, London W13 0DD ☎ 020 8810 9800

CARR Julian: The Basement Flat, 45A Drayton Park, Highbury, London N5 1NT ☎ 020 7686 1678, 0956 259673, 020 7686 1678

CARROLL Andy *(Kbds)*: 104 Chevening Road, London NW6 6DY

CARROLL Colin: 18 Cumberland Park, Acton, London W3 6SX ☎ 020 8992 5321

CARTWRIGHT Bernice: 109 Kneller Road, Twickenham, Middlesex TW2 7DT ☎ 020 8286 9830

CATT Ian: 14 Rickman Hill, Coulsdon, Surrey CR5 3DN ☎ 020 8679 7536 & fax

CHAI Derek *(Voc)*: 26 Castell House, Crossfields Estate, Deptford, London SE8 4SD ☎ 020 8488 6734

CHAN Wun *(Db)*: 78A Evershot Road, Finsbury Park, London N4 3BU ☎ 020 7263 3130

CHARLES Yolande: 96 Greyhound Road, London N17 6XN ☎ 020 8808 5377, 0976 919004 mob

CHICK Mark: Flat 3, No 6 Highbury Park, London N5 2AB ☎ 020 7226 2171

CHILDS Phil: 36 Stanford Road, London SW16 4QA ☎ 020 8764 8835

CLAIR Laura *(Cel)*: 120 Hermon Hill, South Woodford, London E18 1QB ☎ 020 8989 7640, 09611 44475

CLARK Peter: 29 Galba Court, Brentford Dock, Brentford, Middlesex TW8 8QT ☎ 020 8847 0587

CLARKE David *(Tpt)*: 13 Blythwood Road, London N4 4EU ☎ 020 7561 1583

CLARKE Peter Andrew: First Floor Flat, 192 Archway Road, Heringey, London N6 5BB ☎ 0956 522506

CLAYDEN Mark: c/o Knightmare Mngmt Ltd, Friars House, Suite 118, 1st Floor, 157- 168 Blackfriars Road, London SE1 8EZ ☎ 020 7928 6755

CLAYTON Adam: Not Us Limited (U2), 30/32 Sir John Rogersons Quay, Dublin 2., Ireland ☎ Dublin 677 7330

CLAYTON Robin: 50 Oxberry Ave, Fulham, London SW6 5SS ☎ 020 7736 5422, 020 7384 1708

CLEMENTS Rod *(Gtr, Man, Vln)*: Whitton Cottage, Rothbury, Morpeth, Northumberland NE65 7RL ☎ 01669 20435

CLIFFORD Bob *(Gtr, Voc)*: 4 Ashcombe Gardens, Edgware, Middlesex HA8 8HS ☎ 020 8958 9947

COHEN Nicholas *(Md)*: Flat 2, 12 Guilford Street, London WC1N 1DT ☎ 020 7405 0269 & fax

COLLINS Michael *(Clt)*: 48 Daneby Road, London SE6 2QH ☎ 020 8461 2615

COMER Tex: 21 Lime Grove, New Malden, Surrey KT3 3TW ☎ 020 8942 0919

CONDON Paul *(Gtr, Voc)*: 16 Quail Gardens, Selsdon Vale, South Croydon CR2 8TF ☎ 020 8651 5408

CONLON John *(Gtr, Kbds)*: 112 Gunners Bury Avenue, Ealing W5 4HB ☎ 020 8993 7441, 020 8992 9993 fax

COOMBES Jacqueline *(Pf)*: 2 Huntingdon Street, London SW11 1PQ ☎ 020 7223 8741, 0956 924819

COOPER Clive *(Db, Gtr, Vib, Synth)*: 59A Kenyon Street, Fulham, London SW6 6LA ☎ 020 7385 3019

COOPER Ray *(Cel, Voc, Arr)*: 11 Kelross Road, London N5 2QS ☎ 020 7226 6412

CORBETT Ben *(Gtr, Kbds)*: 129B Stoke Newington Road, London N16 8BT ☎ 020 7241 3869

CORDELL John *(Gtr)*: May Cottage, 7 Old Lane Gardens, Cobham, Surrey KT11 1NN ☎ 01483 3993

CORPE David: PO Box 244, Ilford, Essex IG6 2PG ☎ 020 8518 1881, 0973 131662 mob, 020 8518 1095

COTTAM Jon *(Db)*: 259A Wick Road, Hackney, London E9 5DG ☎ 020 8985 9402, 04325 324494 pager

COTTLE Laurence *(Tbn, Kbds)*: 1 Harriet Walker Way, Rickmansworth, Hertfordshire WD3 2RT ☎ 01923 710230

COUNTOURIS Alexis: Flat 3, 42 Leamington Road Villas, London W11 1HT ☎ 020 7221 4583

COWAN Robert *(Gtr, Kbds)*: 28/30 Wood Wharf, Horseferry Place, Greenwich, London SE10 9BT ☎ 020 8293 4909

CRAMPTON Julian *(Kbds)*: 5A Wroughton Road, London SW11 6BE ☎ 020 7924 3706

CRANHAM Philip: 9 Torbridge Close, Edgware, Middx HA8 6NF ☎ 020 8952 7617

CRIBB Garry: 11 Boarley House, Massinger Street, London SE17 1TE ☎ 020 7703 3698, 0973 693204

CRIPPIN Dick *(Kbds, Ld Gtr, Per)*: 5 Doods Road, Reigate, Surrey RH2 0NT ☎ 01737 241893, 01737 210848 fax

CROFT David: 6 Weston Close, Ballfield Road, Godalming, Surrey GU7 2EY ☎ 01483 420766

CROFTS Tony *(Db)*: Cairnryan, Harrow Park, Harrow, Middx HA1 3JE ☎ 020 8869 1216

CROMAR Tim *(Db)*: 180 The Broadway, Muswell Hill, London N10 3SA ☎ 020 8883 8400, 020 7437 5794

CRONK Chas *(Ac Gtr)*: 15 South Road, Hampton, Middlesex TW12 3PE ☎ 020 8941 0586

CROOKE Oliver *(Kbds)*: 46 Shacklewell Lane, London E8 2EY ☎ 020 7254 0849, 020 7739 5600

CUCKSON Michael *(Ac Gtr)*: Flat 2, 20 Elmbourne Road, London SW17 8JR ☎ 020 8675 4033

CULBERTSON (Samuel) *(Kbds, Voc)*: 242 Windyhill Road, Ballinrees, Coleraine, N Ireland BT57 4JN ☎ 01265 43054

CUNNINGHAM Jerry: 3 Sackville Gardens, Buckhurst Way, East Grinstead, West Sussex RH19 2AH ☎ 01342 313374

CURRIE John: 100 Framfield Road, Hanwell, London W7 1NJ ☎ 020 8840 0718

CUSICK Michael *(Pf)*: c/o Qmm Ltd, Saga Centre, Suite 216, 326 Kensal Road, London W10 5BZ ☎ 020 7565 4711, 020 7565 4712

DAMARELL Lee: Flat 2, 105 York Way, Camden, London N7 9QF ☎ 020 7267 4702

DANIELS Matthew *(Gtr, Kbds)*: 42 Victoria Road, London NW6 6PX ☎ 020 7625 6759

DAPERIS Nicholas: 53 Buckingham Road, South Woodford, London E18 2NH ☎ 020 8504 9721

DAS Aniruddha *(Per)*: 12 Petherton Court, Gayton Road, Harrow, Middx HA1 2HE ☎ 020 8424 0714, 020 7490 2891

DATTA Robin

DAVIES Gareth Huw (*Db, Cel, Arr*): 31 Vineyard Hill Road, Wimbledon Park, London SW19 7JL ☎ 020 8241 4080, 0973 430852

DAVIS Dale: 71A Uxbridge Road, London W12 8RN ☎ 020 8746 11983

DAVIS Gordon (*Db*): Flat 4, 32 Veronica Road, London SW17 8QL ☎ 020 8673 0087

DAVIS Steve: 17 Hartley Down, Purley, Surrey CR8 4EF ☎ 020 8660 5456, 0956 660379, 020 8660 5456

DE ROSA Fabio (*Pf, Db, Gtr*): 3 Hambledon Gardens, London SE25 6BJ ☎ 020 8771 3057

DE SPIG Nick (*Gtr*): Basement, 39 Sutherland Place, London W2 5BZ ☎ 020 7284 0335

DE-NIRO Chris (*Voc, Gtr, Flt*): 327B City Road, London EC1 1LJ ☎ 020 7690 6771, 0956 549937

DEACON John: The Mill, Mill Lane, Cookham, Berkshire SL6 9QT

DEGNAN (*Voc, Kbds*): 392B Harrow Road, Westbourne Park, London W9 2HU ☎ 020 7289 3813

DELANO (*Sax, Voc*): Flat 13, 97 Southwark Street, London SE1 0JE ☎ 020 7261 0083

DENHAM James (*Cnt*): 65 Powis Square, Notting Hill, London W11 2BN ☎ 020 7229 0108

DENIM Sue (*Vln*): Address Unknown ☎ 0187 964 2535, 04325 228932

DICK Nigel: c/o 56 Wigmore Street, London W1H 9DG ☎ 020 7935 5133

DINGLEY John: 138 Harborough Road, Streatham, London SW16 2XW ☎ 020 8677 6232

DINWOODIE Stephen: 23 Handley Court, Off Riversdale Road, Aigburth, Liverpool L19 3QS ☎ 0151 427 9884

DODD Chris (*Dms, Kbds*): 74 Milner Street, Newark, Notts NG24 4AA ☎ 01636 676 889, 0958 760770

DONALDSON Pat: 5195 Rue Chambord, Montreal, Quebec, Canada H2J 3N4 ☎ +1 514 522 3824

DONNELLY John (*Db*): 104 Hornsey Park Road, Crouch End, London N8 0JY ☎ 020 8889 5462

DONNELLY Paul: 107 College Road, London NW10 5EY ☎ 020 8969 8007

DOWN Jeremy: 33A Annandale Road, Chiswick, London W4 2HE ☎ 020 8742 1098

DOWNING Paul (*Cel, Com, Arr*): 14 Randolph Road, Walthamstow, London E17 9NR ☎ 020 8520 3701

DOYNE-DITMAS Nicholas: 229B Queens Road, London SE15 2NG ☎ 020 7277 7017

DUFFY Keith: 48 Killarden Heights, Tallaght, Dublin 24 ☎ +323 1 4599136

DUNCAN Pete (*Gtr*): Flat 2, 22 Cambridge Road, East Twickenham, Middlesex TW1 2HL ☎ 020 8892 4277, 0802 817170

DUNNING Steve (*Gtr*): 4 Surrey Road, London SE15 3AU ☎ 020 8291 7734

DURELL Matthew (*Dms, Gtr*): 33 Melford Road, Leytonstone, London E11 4PR ☎ 020 8558 4699

DWORNIAK Joseph (*Kbds, Gtr, Db*): 19A Oxford Gardens, London W10 5UE

DWYER Paul: 12B Maude Road, Camberwell, London SE5 8NY ☎ 020 7708 4575

EAGLESTONE Robin: c/o One Fifteen, The Gallery, 28-30 Wood Wharf, Horseferry Place, Greenwich, London SE10 9BT ☎ 020 8293 0999, 01473 463657, 020 8293 9525

EARL (*Ac Gtr, Kbds, Per*): 184A Leander Road, Brixton, London SW2 2LL ☎ 020 8244 6849

EASTABROOK Cliff (*Voc*): 4A Redcar Close, Northolt, Middlesex UB5 4EE ☎ 020 8422 3857, 07050 114670

EDMONDS Michael (*Db*): 4 Eric Road, Forest Gate, London E7 0AZ ☎ 020 8555 9127

EDWARDS Ian (*Kbds*): 23 Lucas Court, Strasburg Road, Battersea, London SW11 5JF ☎ 020 7978 2196

EDWARDS James (*Voc*): 20 Dering Road, Croydon CR0 1DS ☎ 020 8688 5812, 020 7265 0284

EDWARDS John (*Gtr, Dms*): c/o The Handle Group, Pinewood Studios, Pinewood Road, Iver Heath, Buckinghamshire SL0 0NH ☎ 01753 651 001, 01753 630 555/633

EDWARDS Reginald (*Db*): 5 Caxton Road, Southall, Middlesex UB2 5LR ☎ 020 8571 2616

EDWARDS Simon: Flat 1, 83 Dartmouth Park Road, London NW5 1SL ☎ 020 7267 3876

EL-SALAHI Sam (*Per*): 7A Clissold Road, London N16 9EX ☎ 020 7249 8359

ELLER James: Huge & Jolly, 27 Buspace, London W10 5AP ☎ 020 7565 0044, 020 7792 3323

ELLIOTT Martin: 20 Daniels Court, Island Wall, Whitstable, Kent CT5 1ET ☎ 01227 771533

ELLIS Wayne (*Voc*): 2 Helena Place, Frimont Street, Hackney, London E9 7NJ ☎ 020 8533 2557 & fax

ELSDON Alan (*Gtr*): 20 Ribblesdale Road, Hornsey, London N8 7EP

ELTON Sophie (*Kbds, Db, Sax*): 28 St Marks Crescent, London NW1 7TU ☎ 020 7428 0712

ELVIN Mark (*Arr*): 10 Heath Way, Horsham, West Sussex RH12 5XN ☎ 01403 241711

ENIFER Tony (*Kbds, Voc*): 6 Foxbury Road, Bromley, Kent BR1 4DQ ☎ 020 8466 8929, 020 7702 9995 day, 020 7626 6331

ENTWISTLE John (*Tpt, Hrn, Tbn*): Whistle Rhymes Ltd, Quarwood Fosseway, Stow-on-The Wold, Cheltenham Glos GL54 1JU ☎ 01451 31073

ESTUS Deon (*Com*): c/o Negus Fancey Company, 78 Portland Road, London W11 4LQ ☎ 020 7727 2063, 020 7229 4188 fax

EVANS Glynn: 6 Oriel Court, 47 Lansdowne Road, Croydon, Surrey CR0 2BE ☎ 020 8667 1063, 0976 431447

EVANS Neil (*Vln, Vla*): 38 Grena Road, Richmond, Surrey TW9 1XS ☎ 020 8332 6045

FAIRWEATHER Robert (*Gtr*): 53 Holsworthy Square, Elm Street, London WC1X 0BG ☎ 020 7278 4691

FELIX Frank (*Kbds, Gtr*): 71 Church Street, Stratford, London E15 3EH ☎ 020 8519 0590

FELSKI Uwe (*Voc*): 7 Leconfield Avenue, London SW13 0LD ☎ 020 8878 8847

FERNANDES Ray (*Gtr*): 10 Willowdene Court, 1498 High Road, London N20 9QB ☎ 020 8445 7453

FIELD Stephen (*E Gtr, Ac Gtr, Kbds, Pf*): 3 Lawn Close, Sundridge Park, Bromley, Kent BR1 3NA ☎ 020 8464 3941, 020 8313 1296

FIRTH Scott (*Gtr*): 27B Crouch Hill, London N4 4AP ☎ 020 7281 5470

FISHER Jonty (*Db, Pf*): 33 Westcott Crescent, Hanwell, London W7 1PL ☎ 020 8578 1313

FISHER Judith (*Gtr, Ac Gtr, Voc*): 39 Croham Road, South Croydon, Surrey CR2 7HD ☎ 020 8680 1466

FISHER Stephen (*Cl Gtr*): 5 Culvers Avenue, Carshalton, Surrey SM5 2BN ☎ 020 8647 9115

FLAVIUS Terrince (*Vln, Bjo, Dms, Kbds*): 8 Brill House, Aylesbury Street, London Nw10 0AP ☎ 020 8450 4135, 020 8795 3462

FLEMMING Peter (*Gtr, Dms, Kbds*): 65 Station Road, Maghera, Co Derry, Northern Ireland BT46 5EY ☎ 01648 45803

FLETCHER Gary (*Com, Arr*): 18 Heath Gardens, Twickenham, Middlesex TW1 4LZ ☎ 020 8892 6175

FLINT Mathew (*Gtr, Kbds*): 115A Evering Road, London N16 7SL ☎ 020 8806 0514

FLOWERS Herbie (*Db, Tba*): 15 High St, Ditchling, Hassocks, Sussex BN6 8SY ☎ 01273 845928

FORDHAM Ian (*Db*): 24 Warren Park Road, Sutton, Surrey SM1 4PA ☎ 020 8395 2241

FOREMAN Brian (*Kbds, Dms, Voc*): 1 Bottlehouse Cottages, Coldharbour Road, Penshurst, Kent TN11 8EU ☎ 01892 870517

FOSTER Kevin: 8 Farndale House, West End Lane, London NW6 4QS ☎ 020 7372 4117

FOSTER Malcolm: 12 Stuart Avenue, Walton-on-Thames, Surrey KT12 2AA

FOSTER Mo: 6 Princess Mews, Belsize Village, London NW3 5AP ☎ 020 7794 7757

FOSTER Nick (*Kbds, Pf*): 25 Coombe Gardens, New Malden, Surrey KT3 4AB ☎ 020 8949 4580

FOSTER Stephen (*Pf, Voc*): 45 Girdlestone Walk, Bredgar Road, London N19 5DN ☎ 020 7272 9008

FOX Marcus (*Voc*): 4 Winton Ave, London N11 2AT ☎ 020 8888 6017

FOXTON Bruce (*Rh Gtr*): Three Gables, The Drive, Wonersh Park, Wonersh, Guildford, Surrey GU5 0QW ☎ 01483 898441 day

FRANCIS Charles: Garden Flat, 13 Burghley Road, London NW5 1UG ☎ 020 7284 3167

FRANCIS Sedley: 2/4 The Broadway, Crouch Hill, London N8 9SN ☎ 020 8348 3923

FRANGOS Marco (*Voc, E Gtr, Dms, Kbds*): 10C Victoria Road, London N4 3SQ ☎ 020 7281 0442

FRIEND Alistair (*Db, Bong*): 7 Ickburgh Road, London E5 8AF ☎ 020 8806 5817

FRITH Mark (*Gtr, Kbds*): 29 Elsie Road, London SE22 8DX ☎ 020 8299 6132

FUGE Charles: 16 Eastlake Road, Camberwell, London SE5 9QL ☎ 020 7274 9295

FUGE Christopher (*Voc, Alp Hrn*): 23 Rembrandt Road, London SE13 5QM ☎ 0976 232448

FYFFE Nicholas: 1E Portnall Road, London W9 3BA ☎ 020 8969 4633, 0973 663967

GAISBURGH-WATKYN Dean (*Gtr*): 35 Casella Road, New Cross, London SE14 5QN ☎ 020 7358 9857

GALLAGHER Julian (*Dms, Kbds, Voc*): 18 Hayeswood Avenue, Hayes, Kent BR2 7BL ☎ 020 8462 7844

GALLUP Simon: c/o Fiction Records, 4 Tottenham Mews, London W1P 9PJ ☎ 020 7323 5555

GARCIA Dean: 167 Ferme Park Road, Crouch End, London N8 ☎ 020 8340 8890

GARRETY Hugh (*Gtr, Kbds*): 109 Clifford Gardens, Kensal Green, London NW10 5JG ☎ 020 8964 1008

GEE Steve (*E Gtr, Ac Gtr*): 27 Chadwell Avenue, Chadwell Heath, Essex RM6 4QN ☎ 020 8590 4097

GIBBINS Christopher: 326A West End Lane, London NW6 1LN ☎ 020 7916 2711

GIBBS Karen: 2 Finsen Road, London SE5 9AX

GIBLIN John (*Voc*): Barwell Court, Chessington, Surrey KT9 2LZ ☎ 01372 462735

GIBSON Colin (*Dms, Per, Voc*): 25 Vale Road, Battle, East Sussex TN33 0HE ☎ 01424 774835 & fax

GILL Richard: 70A Acton Lane, Harlesden, London NW10 8TU

GITA Salman (*Gtr, Tpt*): 2 Brook Road South, Brentford, Middlesex TW8 5NG ☎ 020 8568 6932

GLOVER Martin (*Kbds, Gtr, Dms*): 34 Wandsworth Common, Northside, London SW18 2SL

GLOVER Roger: c/o Thames Talent, 45 East Putnam Ave, Greenwich, Conn, 06830 USA

GOAD Gus (*Gtr*): 2Vine Cottages, The Street, Walsham Le Willows, Nr Bury St Edmunds, Suffolk IP31 3AZ ☎ 01359 258 336

GOMEZ Nico: 345 Brewster Gardens, London W10 6AQ ☎ 020 8960 8339

GOODMAN Kevin (*E Gtr, Kbds, Voc*): Flat 3, Bank Chambers, 120 Hornsey High Street, London N8 7NN

GOODWIN Karen (*Db*): 2 Clifton Road, London N22 4XN ☎ 020 8888 2289, 020 8881 2303

GOODWIN Kevin (*Voc*): 12 Mount Road, Mitcham, Surrey CR4 3EY ☎ 020 8687 1711, 020 8241 6199

GORDON Leigh (*Gtr, Voc*): 219 Manor Way, Mitcham, Surrey CR4 1EN ☎ 020 8764 9182

GORDON Steven (*Bag*): 20 Consort House, 26 Queensway, London W2 3RX ☎ 020 7229 8512, 0961 131816

GOULD High (*Voc, Gtr*): Flat No 5 Glys Court, 199 Leighamcourt Road, Streatham, London SW16 2SF ☎ 020 8677 1592

GOULD Rowland (*Sax*): c/o O J Kilkenny & Co., 6 Landswowne Mews, London W11 3BH ☎ 020 5792 9494

GRAHAM Andrew (*Db, Tbn*): 53 Hardington, Belmont Place, Camden, London NW1 8HN ☎ 020 7267 7687

GRANT Peter: 2 Roseneath Walk, Enfield, Middx EN1 2AH ☎ 020 8367 9642

GREEN David (*Gtr*): Flat 32 4Th Floor, No 10 Caldecott Road, Kowloon, Hong Kong

GREGORY Terrence: 2 Spriggs Court, Palmers Hill, Epping, Essex CM16 6SD ☎ 01992 577086

GROOVES T.C. (*Synth, Voc*): 7 Highstone Court, New Wanstead, Snearsbrook, London E11 2SE ☎ 020 8471 2665

GROSSART Andy (*Voc*): 43 Seaforth Gardens, Stoneleigh, Ewell, Surrey KT19 0LR ☎ 020 8393 1970

GROVE Neil: 10 Aldborough Court, 69 Chingford Avenue, London E4 6RW ☎ 020 8524 3078

GRUNER Alan (*Pf*): 79 Gordon Road, London N3 1ER ☎ 020 8346 0159

GUNNARSSON Jonas (*Pf*): Grundtjrrnsu 39, 921 34, Lycksele, Sweden, 0967 694 4742

GWIZDALA Janek (*Dms, Pf, Cl Gtr, Stgs*): 40 Worcester Close, Mitcham, Surrey CR4 1SP ☎ 020 8648 8830, 0956 626356 mob

HAGE David: 7 Arthur Road, New Malden, Surrey KT3 6LX ☎ 020 8336 0999, 0850 221830, 020 8336 1232

HAIMES John: 2 Newlyn Close, Hillingdon, Middlesex UB8 3PA ☎ 01895 52605

HAINE Frank: 22 Larkbere Road, Sydenham, London SE26 4HB ☎ 020 8778 7936

HALEY Richard (*Tba*): 2 Kingswood Close, Orpington, Kent BR6 8PA ☎ 01689 872935

HALL Jason: 16 Highfield Road, Hornchurch, Essex RM12 6PT ☎ 01708 508472

HANDS Tim (*Gtr*): 137 Melrose Avenue, Willesden Green, London NW2 4LY ☎ 020 8459 0896

HANNAFORD Richard (*Flt*): 48 Altenburg Gardnes, Battersea, London SW11 1JL ☎ 020 8940 7322

HANNAM David (*Per, Gtr, Kbds, Dms*): 95 Clissold Crescent, London N16 ☎ 020 7249 2480, 020 7407 1123

HARADA Kuma: 28/30 Coronet Street, London N1 6HD ☎ 020 7613 2135

HAREWOOD Greg: 59 Bedford Road, Walthamstow, London E17 4PU ☎ 020 8531 2971

HARRIS James (*Ld Gtr*): Flat 2, 114 Lady Margaret Road, London N19 5EX ☎ 020 7700 0813

HARRIS Steve: c/o Iron Maiden, The Colonnades, 82 Bishopsbridge Road, London W2 6BB

HARRISON Thomas (*Gtr, Pf*): 60 Shepherds Bush Road, Hammersmith, London W6 7PH ☎ 020 7602 4385

HART Paul (*Pf, Vln, Vla, Com*): 59 Dean Street, London W1V 5HH

HARTLEY Peter (*Vln*): 38 Lindsay Court, Battersea High Street, London SW11 3HZ ☎ 020 7223 1641, 020 8344 5513, 020 8344 5621

HARVEY David: 9 Ashdown Chase, Nutley, East Sussex TN22 3LY ☎ 0958 936546

HASTINGS David (*Db*): 168 Moselle Avenue, London N22 6EX ☎ 020 8881 3423

HAYES Tony (*Arr*): 94 Heath Street, London NW3 1DP ☎ 020 7794 6380

HEART Andrew (*Voc, Gtr, Kbds*): 34 Greenbank Avenue, Sudbury, Wembley, Middlesex HA0 2TF ☎ 020 8900 0183

HECTOR Timothy (*Sax*): ☎ 020 8586 9269, 0973 714824

HENNING Douglas: 23 Downs View, London Road, Holybourne, Alton, Hants. GU3 4HY ☎ 01420 541703

HENSON Joe: 2nd Floor Flat, 6 Charlotte Street, London W1P 1HE ☎ 020 7523 9358

HICKSON Robert: 60 Coleman Road, London SE5 7TG ☎ 020 7703 8988

HIGGINS Andy: 35 Binyon Crescent, Stanmore, Middlesex HA7 3ND ☎ 020 8954 7946

HILL Anthony (*E Gtr*): Flat 3, 35 Chatsworth Road, Brighton BN1 5DA ☎ 01273 566329

HILLS John (*Db, Sl Gtr*): 1 Worslade Road, Tooting, London SW17 0BT ☎ 020 8672 0307

HILTON Michael (*E Gtr, Gtr*): 45 Eaton Road, Enfield, Middlesex EN1 1NJ ☎ 020 8364 4967, 0976 204194 mob

HINDS Camelle (*Voc, Per*): 59A Furness Road, London NW10 5UJ ☎ 020 8838 1794

HINSON Amanda: 12 The Holt, London Road, Morden, Surrey SM4 5AP ☎ 020 8646 1089

HIROSE Taka: 83 Wakeman Road, London NW10 5VH ☎ 020 8968 6038

HOBSON Lee (*Ac Gtr*): 58 Church Hill Road, Cheam, Surrey SM3 8LJ ☎ 020 7543 3004

HODGSON Brian (*Gtr, Voc*): 10 Horsley Rd, North Chingford, London E4 7HX ☎ 020 8524 7650

HOLLIDAY John: Flat 2, 57 Kenninghall Road, Clapton, London E5 8BS ☎ 020 8986 2362

HOLMEN David

HOOPER Matt: 40 Chancelot Road, Abbey Wood, London SE2 0ND ☎ 020 8473 8332

HOPE-TAYLOR Randy: 9 Moreland Street, London EC1 8BE ☎ 020 8451 4512

HOSKIN Allon

HOUGHTON Richard (*Synth, Kbds*): 53 Chart Lane, Reigate, Surrey RH2 7DZ ☎ 01737 221982

HOWARD Dominic: 139 Kingston Road, Ewell, Epsom, Surrey KT17 2HA ☎ 020 8224 2498

HOWARD Felix (*Gtr, Db, Voc*): 166 Ifield Road, London SW10 9AF ☎ 0973 660 421

HOWE Timothy (*Voc*): 3 Priory Court, Tower Hill, Dorking, Surrey RH4 2BB ☎ 01306 877692

HOWELL Toby: 31 East Sheen Avenue, London SW14 8AR ☎ 020 8876 5921

HOWLETT Michael (*Gtr, Kbds*): 57 Holland Park, London W11 3RS ☎ 020 7727 3314

HOYLE Nigel (*Voc, Hmca, Kbds*): Flat 4, 15 Vaughan Road, Camberwell, London SE5 9NZ ☎ 020 7978 8557

HUMPHRIES Roland: 52 Ruisilip Road, Greenford, Middlesex UB6 9QJ ☎ 020 8578 5909

HUNT (*Gtr*): 37 Prospect Road, Woodford Green, Essex IG8 7NA ☎ 020 8505 4702, 0956 468634

HUNT Darryl (*Gtr, Dms*): 24 Charlton Kings Road, Kentish Town, London NW5 2SA ☎ 020 7267 2308

HUNTER Kieron (*Gtr*): 64.5 Englefield Rd, Islington, London N1 3LG ☎ 020 7354 8843

HUNTLEY Rob: 124 Sackville Court, Harold Wood, Romford, Essex RM3 0ED ☎ 01708 348860

HURFORD Paul: 38 Hylands Road, Walthamstow, London E17 4AJ

HUTCHINGS Ashley: Flat 1, 9 Rainmoor Park Road, Sheffield S10 3GX ☎ 0114 2308197

HUTCHINSON Stephen: 57 Holly Park Road, London N11 3EY ☎ 0956 487813

HYLTON Francis (*St Pan*): 42 Stilecroft Gardens, North Wembley, Middlesex HA0 3HD ☎ 0973 219224

ILHAN Adem (*Db, Gtr, Per*): 1 Ringwood Gardens, Roehampton, London SW15 4UP ☎ 020 8789 9796

INSTONE Michael: 44 Priory Crescent, Norwood, London SE19 3EE ☎ 020 8771 2296

JACKSON David (*E Gtr*): 21 Tall Elms Close, Bromley, London BR2 0TT ☎ 020 8325 1972

JAMES Brad (*Kbds, Pf, Gtr, Dms*): 4 Allenby Close, Greenford, Middx UB6 9SA ☎ 020 8576 9758

JAMES Carl (*Gtr*): 285B Stanstead Road, Forest Hill, London SE23 1JB ☎ 020 8852 0973

JAMES Marcus: 9663 Yardarm Terrace, The Harbour At Hobe Sound, Martin County, USA Fl 3345S ☎ 407 546 3217

JAMES Tony: 17 Nightingale Lodge, Admiral Walk, Carlton Gate, London W9 3TW ☎ 020 7289 5618, 020 7289 5808

JAY (*Gtr*): 39 Copse Road, Cobham, Surrey KT11 2TW ☎ 01932 865452, 0777 571 5949, 01932 867337

JAY Cee (*Voc*): 64 Maple Avenue, Chingford, London E4 8RR ☎ 020 8523 3453, 0958 217269 mob

JAZ (*Pf, Gtr*) ☎ 020 7738 5470

JENKING Brian: Meadow View, 5 Davenport, Church Langley, Essex CM17 9TF ☎ 01279 830 972

JENNINGS John (*Voc*): 14 Arkwright House, Streatham Place, London SW2 4QE

JINGLES (*Voc, Md*): 107 Lewis Trust Estate, Vanston Place, Fulham, London SW6 1UB ☎ 020 8248 9074, 0973 198621 fax

JOBSON Jeremy (*Kbds, Tpt*): 149C Breakspears Road, London SE4 1TY ☎ 020 8692 5105 & fax

JOE (*Gtr, Db, Kbds*): 14 Clifton Road, London N8 8HY ☎ 020 8341 7896

JOHANNESSON Chris (*Gtr, T Sax*) ☎ 07775 686540

JOHNSTONE Douglas (*Voc, Man, Gtr*): 39 Halsbury Road East, Northolt, Middlesex UB5 4PX ☎ 020 8422 7803

JONES Dave (*Ac Gtr*): Flat 2, 13 Minster Road, London NW2 3SE ☎ 020 8452 3834, 0976 294804 mob

JONES Michael (*Cl Gtr*): 29 Greenacres, Oxted, Surrey RH8 0PA ☎ 01883 714280

JONO (*Per*): 369A Cranbrook Road, Ilford, Essex IG1 4UQ ☎ 0374 623485 mob

KARN Mick (*Voc*): 100A Christchurch Road, Brixton, London SW2 3DF

KATZ Dill (*Gtr, Db*): Flat B, 20 Avenue Road, Highgate, London N6 5DW ☎ 020 8340 7273

KAY Derek (*Db*): 9 Blenheim Road, Stratford, London E15 1UF ☎ 020 8519 7709

KEITH THA MISSILE (*Gtr*): 34 Hichisson Road, London SE15 3AL ☎ 020 7732 7008

KELLY Patrick (*Kbds, Gtr, Voc*): 56, Potter Street, Pinner, Middlesex HA5 3XE ☎ 020 8866 0061

KEMP Leonard (*Gtr*): 35 Boulton Road, Dagenham, Essex RM8 3DD ☎ 020 8595 2076, 0973 528663 mob, 020 8970 8065

KEMP Martin: Dagger Entertainment, 14 Lambton Place, Notting Hill, London W11 2SH ☎ 020 7792 1040, 020 7221 7625 fax

KENDALL Tony (*Gtr, Voc, Vln*): 18 Edward Avenue, Chingford, London E4 9DN ☎ 020 8527 0574

KENNY Clare: Middle Flat, 68 Highbury Hill, London N5 1AP ☎ 020 7354 5394

KENT Piers (*Rh Gtr, Voc, Kbds*): Flat 2 Monkridge, 81 Crouch End Hill, London N8 8DE ☎ 020 8341 5969

KHAN Kameel: 21A Glenluce Road, Blackheath, London SE3 7SD ☎ 020 8853 0663

KIDD David (*Kbds*): 90 Roll Gardens, Gants Hill, Ilford, Essex IG2 6TL ☎ 020 8551 3698

KING Nathan (*Dms, Kbds*): 1 White Hart Road, London SE18 1DF ☎ 020 8473 9397, 0467 338162

KINGS Michael: 47 Ross Road, South Norwood, London SE25 6SB ☎ 020 8653 0402

KIRBY John (*Db*): Liddington Hall South, Lliddington Hall Drive, Guilford, Surrey GU3 3AD ☎ 020 8898 6464

KIRKBY Paul (*Rh Gtr*): 5 Stephenson Road, Twickenham, Middlesex TW2 7EH ☎ 020 8894 3765

KIVIAHO Heikki (*Gtr, Kbds, Voc*): Arkovagen 36, 121 55 Johanneshov, Sweden ☎ + 46 8 6486828, + 46 708667693

KOOZIE Jer (*Gtr, Voc*): 253 Pirton Lane, Sugar Loaf View, Churchdown, Gloucester GL3 2QJ

KOVADLOFF Diego: 34 Gerridge Court, Gerridge Street, London SE1 7AF ☎ 020 7928 8440, 0956 261861

KREMER Andy (*Db, Gtr, Per*): 95A Belsize Lane, London NW3 5AU ☎ 020 7722 6430, 0973 419142

KRISH Felix: Homeside House, Dargate, Nr Faversham, Kent ME13 9HQ ☎ 01227 750408

LADBURY Julian: 30 Woodside Road, South Norwood, London SE25 5DY ☎ 020 8656 5800

LAFONE Andy: 19 Furzedown Drive, London SW17 9BL ☎ 020 8677 1677

LANDI Francesco (*Gtr, Synth*): Flat C, 8 Sharples Hall Street, London NW1 8YN ☎ 020 7586 8160

LATI (*Gtr, Kbds*): Black Plastic Magick, 481 8Th Avenue, 1552 (Box G-16), New York, USA, NY 10001 ☎ +1 212 736 636, +1 212 736 6361

LAWES Wayne: Flat 5, 23 Calendine Drive, London E8 3XB ☎ 020 8985 5262, 020 7249 6983

LAWRENCE Steve (*Db, Voc, Gtr, Kbds*): 36 Great Russell Street, London WC1B 3PP ☎ 020 7636 4390

LEA James (*Voc, Pf*): c/o Newman & Co, Regent House, 1 Pratt Mews, London NW1 0AD ☎ 020 7267 6899, 020 7267 6746

LEE Lushi: 29 Holmdale Road, Chislehurst, Kent BR7 6BY

LEGGETT Dave: 36 Fairlands Avenue, Sutton, Surrey SM1 3JE ☎ 020 8408 0231

LEISSLE: 15B Weston Park, London N8 9SY

LEVY Andrew (*Dms, Per*): Sedley Richard Laurence, 23 Bridford Mews, Off Devonshire Street, London W1N 1LQ ☎ 020 7275 9594

LEWINSON Steve (*Dms, Kbds*): c/o Timeless Music Ltd, 38 Coolhurst Road, London N8 8EU ☎ 020 8372 2045

LEWIS Andy (*Voc, Db, Gtr, Kbds*): 36 Chatworth Road, London E5 0LP ☎ 020 8533 6408

LEWIS Cass (*Voc*): c/o 8 Belgrave Mansions, Belgrave Gardens, London NW8 0RA

LILLYWHITE Stephen: c/o Bright Grahame Murray, 124/130 Seymour Place, London W1H 6AA ☎ 020 7402 5201

LINDEMERE Peter (*Db*): 20 Potters Grove, New Malden, Surrey KT3 5DE ☎ 020 8286 9615, 0421 358 945

LINKE Paul: 2 Richmond Road, London N11 2QR ☎ 020 8361 8976

LIVESEY Warne (*Gtr*): c/o Jpr Management Ltd, The Power House, 70 Chiswick High Road, London W4 1SY ☎ 020 8742 0052

LLEWELLYN John: 10 Cherry Tree Walk, Beckenham, Kent BR3 3PG ☎ 020 8658 0750

LOCHRIE Jaz (*Voc*): 78 Norfolk House Road, Streatham, London SW16 1JH ☎ 020 8769 8602

LODGE John: The Threshold Record Co Ltd, 53 High Street, Cobham, Surrey KT11 3DP ☎ 01932 864142/3

LONGDEN Anthony (*Kbds, Gtr*): Flat 3, Grundy House, 8 Chiltern View Road, Uxbridge, Middx UB8 2PA ☎ 01895 33220

LOWE Nick: 30 The Butts, Brentford, Middlesex TW8 8BL ☎ 020 8847 2481

LOWE Steven: 22 Chequers House, Lisson Grove, London NW8 8JE ☎ 020 7706 2189

LUCAS Rob ☎ 07971 233 145

LUNDY Mark: 34 Millhaven, Sion Mills, County Tyrone, N.Ireland BT82 ☎ 016626 58748

LUPINO Angela: 141Whiteleas Way, South Shields, Tyne & Wear NE34 8HB ☎ 020 8994 9756

LUSHER Phil (*Voc, Gtr, Kbds, Dms*): 42 Hillcross Avenue, Morden, Surrey SM4 4EB ☎ 020 8542 8579

MACE Charles (*Kbds*): 11A Grantham Road, Chiswick, London W4 2RT ☎ 020 8747 1802

MACINTOSH Felix (*Voc*): 107 Kings Avenue, London SW4 8EL ☎ 020 8678 0474

MACMANUS Ruairi (*Voc, Gtr, Dms*): 24 River Way, Twickenham, Middlesex TW2 5JP ☎ 020 8241 3363, 020 8894 3590

MAIDMAN Ian (*Gtr, Dms, Pf*): 22 Richford Road, Stratford, London E15 3PQ ☎ 020 8519 1398

MALTBY David: 31 Waltham Close, Dartford, Kent DA1 3LT ☎ 01322 71917

MAMBO Johnny

MANINGTON David (*Db, Gtr*): 16 Spencer Road, Upton Park, London E6 1HH ☎ 020 8503 4072

MANN Paul (*Voc*)

MANTOVANI Davide (*Db, Synth, Gtr*): 22 Parkside, Dollis Hill, London NW2 6RH ☎ 020 8452 5227

MARHEINEKE Stuart: 6 Wallers Close, Woodford Bridge, Essex IG8 8BL ☎ 020 8505 5934

MARK Dean (*Gtr*): 11 Graces Road, Camberwell, London SE5 8PF ☎ 020 7701 70174

MARKS Andrew (*Rh Gtr*): 25A Whittingstall Road, Parsons Green, London SW6 4EA ☎ 020 7371 0288 & fax

MARTIN Joseph: 92 Mill Hill Road, Acton, London W3 8JJ ☎ 020 8993 3734

MATHIS Alan (*Gtr, Kbds*): 72 Portland Ave, New Malden, Surrey KT3 6BA ☎ 020 8942 3346

MAYNES Malcolm (*Gtr*): 159 Dames Road, London E7 0DZ ☎ 020 8926 6995, 0411 004 577 mob

MC'TEAGLE: 58A Boston Road, Hanwell, London W7 3TR ☎ 020 8579 0778

MCCORMICK-SMITH Giles (*E Gtr*): 329B City Road, Islington, London EC1V 1LJ ☎ 020 7278 7622, 0973 697 757

MCCRACKEN Charlie: 66 Garrick Close, Ealing, London W5 W5 1AT ☎ 020 8998 4209

MCDONALD Frank: 62 Falkland Park Avenue, South Norwood, London SE25 6SH ☎ 020 8653 0755

MCFARLANE George (*Gtr*): 9 Alfred Road, Sutton, Surrey SM1 4RR ☎ 020 8642 7954

MCFARLANE Rory (*Db*): 167 Elsenham Street, London SW18 5NZ ☎ 020 8870 1529

MCGARVEY Pat (*Gtr*): 108A Acton Lane, Harlesden, London NW10 8TX ☎ 020 8838 0804

MCKINNA Robert (*Db*): 122 Crofton Road, Camberwell, London SE5 8NA ☎ 020 7277 4707

MCKINNEY Andrew: Top Flat, 60 South Ealing Road, Ealing, London W5 4QA ☎ 020 8840 8357, 01403 259805

MCKONE Ernest: 14 Inderwick Road, Hornsey, London N8 9LD ☎ 020 8348 4697

MCLAUGHLIN Larry (*Db*): 5 Cedar Avenue, East Barnet, Hertfordshire EN4 8DY ☎ 020 8361 8841

MCLEOD David John (*Pf*): 387 Westhorne Avenue, Lee, London SE12 9AB ☎ 020 8852 4143

MCMANUS John (*Voc*): c/o 9 Thornton Place, London W1H 1FG ☎ 020 7935 9719

MCNEISH Colin (*Ld Gtr, Kbds*): 89 Elderfield Road, Hackney, London E5 0LE ☎ 0956 571640 mob

MCQUATER Thomas (*Voc*): 23 Rosecroft Road, Southall, Middlesex UB1 2XH ☎ 020 8578 4624

MEADE Lennox: 80 Blenheim Gardens, Willesden Green, London NW2 4NT ☎ 020 8450 2466

MEADOWS Alex: 48 Hadley Road, New Barnet, Herts EN5 5QS ☎ 020 8440 2257

MEDHURST Trevor (*Tba*): Old School House, 5 West Street, Hothfield, Nr Ashford, Kent TN26 1ET ☎ 01233 625594

MEDWIN Steven: 83 Woodmere Avenue, Shirley, Surrey CR0 7PH ☎ 020 8240 8576, 0589 486590

MEEHAN Jeremy (*Bsn*): 41 Chipperfield Road, Bovingdon, Hertfordshire HP3 0JN ☎ 0144 283 3134, 0973 383 942

MELBOURNE Carrie (*Voc*): 2 Bryantwood Road, London N7 7BE ☎ 020 7609 1316

MELLOR Jon (*Voc*): 113 Old Ford Road, London E2 9QD ☎ 020 8983 5865

MERCER James (*Db*): 42 Colebrook Close, West Hill, London SW15 3HZ ☎ 020 8788 4865

MIDUS: 4 Carden Road, Nunhead, London SE15 3UD ☎ 020 7635 0052

MILES Kevin (*Gtr*): c/o Jerry Smith, Automatic, 3 Wansdown Place, London SW6 1DN ☎ 020 7386 7172, 020 7610 1250 fax

MILLER Kevin (*Synth, Voc*): 8 Northcross Road, Dulwich, London SE22 9EU ☎ 020 8693 8176

MILLS Bryan (*Gtr*): 5 Brook View Rise, Enniskillen, Co Fermanagh, Northen Ireland ☎ 028 6632 7842

MIZRAKI Raf (*Per, Cel, Oud*): 136 Manor Road, Banbury, Oxon OX16 7JW ☎ 01295 266 506, 01295 255 427

MOLE John (*Db*): 9 Waterman Way, Wapping, London E1 9QN ☎ 020 7488 0527

MONDESIR Michael: 97A Hamlets Way, London E3 4TL ☎ 020 8980 5851

MONTEIRO Isabel: 14 Commodore House, Poplar High Street, London E14 0BA ☎ 0961 189878

MOORE Alex: 9 Fountains Crescent, Southgate, London N14 6BG ☎ 020 8886 1609, 0966 147763 mob

MOORE Malcolm (*Db, Kbds, Gtr, Voc*): 116 Skitts Hill, Braintree, Essex CM7 1AS ☎ 01376 346520, 0378 552666

MOORE Patrick (*Voc, Cel*): 17 Freemasons Road, Croydon, Surrey CR0 6PB ☎ 020 8654 8002

MORGAN Gareth (*Voc*): 191 Earlham Grove, Forest Gate, London E7 9AB ☎ 020 8534 3549

MOUTHFULL Mike (*Gtr, Pf, Koto*): Upper Flat, 91 Dalyell Road, Brixton SW9 9UR ☎ 020 7274 9524, 01426 182419

MULFORD Phillip: 37 Salisbury Road, Banstead, Surrey SM7 2DP ☎ 020 8661 9554

MULVEY St: 12B Queensdown Road, Hackney, London E5 8NN ☎ 020 8533 3429

MURRAY Neil: 51 Old Oak Lane, London NW10 6UB ☎ 020 8453 0124

MURRAY Peter (*Voc*): 9 Carlton Court, Craven Gardens, Barkingside, Essex IG6 1TL ☎ 020 7918 2812 & fax, 0958 356649 mob

MYERS Justin (*Db*): 14 Thurlby Road, West Norwood, London SE27 0RL ☎ 020 8670 8297

NELSON Steven: 19 Vaughan Road, Stratford, London E15 4AA ☎ 020 8257 8716

NEW Bryan Chuck: 73 Fearnley Street, Watford, Herts WD1 7DB ☎ 020 7371 1672

NEWMAN/T-BONE.FRETLESS Eric (*Gtr*): 15 Elmfield Mansions, Elmfield Road, London SW17 8AA ☎ 020 8675 4277

NEWNHAM Paul (*Gtr, Voc*)

NEWTON Tony (*E Gtr*): 75 Dendridge Close, Enfield, Middx EN1 4PN

NICHOLS Michael (*Kbds*): 93 Alderbrook Road, Balham, London SW12 8AD ☎ 020 8673 6043

NOBLE Duncan (*Per*): 21A Navarino Road, London E8 1AD ☎ 020 7254 2829

NUNES Wayne (*Kbds*): 52 Teasel Way, Stratford, London E15 3AA ☎ 0836 339967, 020 7473 6478

NUNN Aubrey (*Gtr, Voc*): 81 Ludham, Lismore Circus, London NW5 4SF ☎ 020 7482 0172

O'BRYAN Jason Daniel: 96 Thames Street, Weybridge, Surrey KT13 8NH ☎ 01932 843072

O'DONNELL Howard: 39A Linden Gardens, Notting Hill Gate, London W2 4HQ ☎ 020 7221 6533, 0973 912259

O'KEEFE Laurence: c/o Sanctuary Music Mgmt, The Colonnades, 82 Bishops Bridge Road, London W2 6BB ☎ 020 7243 0640, 020 7243 0470

O'LOCHLAINN Fionn (*Pf, Saxes, Gtr, Man*): 16 Narcissus Road, London NW6 1TH ☎ 020 7431 5864

O'NEILL Bernard (*Db, Pf, Cel*): 43 Queens Road, Leytonstone, London E11 1BA ☎ 020 8532 8413, 0378 282839 mob

O'TOOLE Brian: 114 Petherton Road, Islington, London N5 2RT ☎ 020 7359 1764

OAKMAN Peter: 18 Heath Park Road, Romford, Essex RM2 5UB ☎ 01708 701203

ODELL Rodney (*Pf, Gtr, Dms*): 21 Calderon Road, Leytonstone, London E11 4ET ☎ 020 8556 2848

OGAWA James: 127 Thanet House, Thanet Street, London WC1H 9QE ☎ 020 7388 4732

OLIVER Rowan (*Dms, La Per, Vla, Pf*): Flat 3, 18 Alexandra Grove, Finsbury Park, London N4 2LF ☎ 020 8802 6750, 07666 707335

OLSDAL Stefan (*Gtr, Pf*): c/o Elevator Lady Ltd, The Colonnades, 82 Bishops Bridge Road, London W2 6BB ☎ 020 7243 0640, 020 7727 2226

ORAKWUE Orefo: 92 Arthur Court, Charlotte Despard Avenue, London SW11 5JB ☎ 020 7498 7578

ORIORDAN Caitlain: C/0 By Eleven, 12 Tideway Yard, Mortlake, London SW14 8SN ☎ 020 8847 2481

OSMAN Matthew: c/o Interceptor Enterprises, First Floor, 98 White Lion Street, London N1 9PF ☎ 020 7278 8001, 020 7713 6298 fax

OSRIN Adrian David: 55 Love Lane, Pinner, Middlesex HA5 3EY ☎ 020 8868 0459 & fax, 0589 978803

OWEN Nick: 100D Hervey Road, Blackheath, London SE3 8BX ☎ 020 8319 0196

PAGE Ken (*Gtr*): 42 Hadley Grove, Barnet, Herts EN5 4PH ☎ 020 8449 6195

PAINTER Ian (*Gtr, Kbds*): Garden Flat, 48 Burghley Road, Kentish Town, London NW6 7UG ☎ 020 7284 0927

PALLADINO Pino (*Gtr, Kbds, Dms*): 22 St James Avenue, Hampton, Middlesex TW12 1HH ☎ 020 8979 3920, 020 8797 1706

PALLETT Bill: 42 Holly Park Road, London N11 3HD ☎ 020 8368 4049

PALMER Del (*Gtr, Per*): 15 Glenalvon Way, Morris Walk Estate, London SE18 5HX ☎ 020 8854 5285

PALMER Dominic: 27 Downs Court Road, Purley, Surrey CR8 1BE ☎ 020 8660 0874

PAMPHILLE Ishmael (*E Gtr, Dms*): 19 Thornsett Road, Anerly, London SE20 7XB ☎ 020 8697 0665, 0956 323619

PARKER Peter (*Kbds, Per, Voc*): Metro Music Ltd, P.O Box 75, Shepperton, Middlesex TW17 9NA ☎ 01932 221796

PARKIN Matthew (*Gtr, Sax*): 40 Essendine Mansions, Essendine Road, Maida Vale, London W9 2LU ☎ 0958 546339

PARSONS Jacqueline: 99 The Avenue, London N10 2QG ☎ 020 8883 8625

PASK Andrew (*Cel*): The Corner House, 52 Cecil Road, London N10 2BU ☎ 020 8883 4774

PAUL Michael (*Gtr, Kbds*): 537A Barking Road, Plaistow, London E13 9EZ ☎ 020 8470 1557

PAYNE Douglas: Unit F, 21 Heathmans Rd, Parsons Green, London SW6 4TJ ☎ 020 7371 7008, 020 7371 7708

PEACOCK Joanna (*Kbds, Ob*): 71B Villiers Road, Willesden Green, London NW2 5PG ☎ 020 8830 2845, 020 7405 7641

PEACOCK Mike: 94 Baker Street, Enfield, Middlesex EN1 3EZ ☎ 020 8342 0623

PEAKER Terry (*Db*): 20A Angel Walk, London W6 9HX ☎ 020 8748 7195

PEARCE Steve: 20 Gresham Avenue, Whetstone, London N20 0XL ☎ 020 8368 6579, 0976 406399 mob

PEARS Les (*Tbn*): 30 Clarendon Road, Shanklin, Isle Of Wight PO37 7AG ☎ 0198 386 4376

PENDA Hilaire: 185A Haverstock Hill, London NW3 4QG ☎ 020 7431 4652, 0961 341747

PENNANT Trevor (*Gtr, Dms, Kbds, Per*): 9 Louisville Road, Tooting Bec, London SW17 8RL ☎ 020 8672 4675, 0374 858871

PEPPE Daniel: 15 Conway Street, London W1P 5HD ☎ 020 7631 1532

PERCIVAL Don: 9 Holbrook House, St Pauls Cray Road, Chislehurst, Kent BR7 6QE ☎ 020 8295 0310

PHILLIPS Don: 44 Glenbldon Road, Streatham, London SW16 2BD ☎ 020 8677 3602, 0956 416261 mob

PHILLIPS Dudley (*Gtr*): 64 Weston Park, London N8 9TD ☎ 020 8340 7636

PHILLIPS Pj (*Voc*): Address Unknown ☎ 020 8749 4159, 020 8749 4159 fax, 0468 770825 mob

PHILPOT Rufus (*Db*): Flat 2, 301 Liverpool Road, London N1 1NF ☎ 020 7607 7496

PIERCE Nigel: 24 Portland Road, London SE9 ☎ 020 8857 9640

PIRIE Michael: Flat 2, 10 Boutflower Road, London SW11 1RE ☎ 020 7924 7992

PIVA Anna (*E Gtr, Cl Gtr, Voc*): 59 Bassett Road, London W10 ☎ 020 8968 0141

POMEROY Lee (*Chap Stk, Gtr, Kbds, Voc*): 3 Tamworth Place, Croydon, Surrey CR0 1RL ☎ 020 8680 4211

POOLE Adrian (*Db, Ac Gtr*): Flat 7 Wyndham Lodge, 57 Elmsdale Road, Walthamstow, London E17 6PN ☎ 020 8509 1354

POOLE Matthew (*Gtr, Kbds*): Flat 4, 14A Lake Avenue, Bromley, Kent BR1 4EN ☎ 020 8464 0315

PORTCH Kevin: 107 Cooling Road, Frindsbury, Rochester, Kent ME2 4RT ☎ 01634 714476

PORTER Anthony (*Vln*): Gorse View Cottage, 115 Queens Road, Bisley, Woking, Surrey GU24 9AT ☎ 01483 480193 & fax

POTTER Roger: 56 Gloucester Gardens, Cockfosters, Herts EN4 0QP ☎ 020 8441 9260

POWELL Kevin (*Tbn*): 10 West Hill Drive, Dartford, Kent DA1 3DU ☎ 01322 224728, 0836 692043 mob

POWER Paul: c/o 60B Hazlewell Road, Putney, London SW15 6LR ☎ 020 8785 9499, 020 8788 7660

PRATT Guy (*Kbds*): 8A Garlinge Road, London NW2 3TR ☎ 020 7435 0278, 020 7435 0582 fax

PRESS Stephen (*Db*): Flat 4, 361 Clapham Road, London SW9 9BT ☎ 020 7738 3319

PRICE Steve (*Cntrc*): Appt 7, 32 St Marys Road, Peckham, London SE15 2DW ☎ 020 7652 0869

PRITCHARD Peter (*Db, Gtr, Pf*): 56 King Edward Road, Edmonton, London N9 N9 7RP ☎ 020 8804 6443

PROSSER Alan (*Clt, Voc, Arr, Com*): Rose Cottage, High Street, Henham, Nr. Bishops Stortford, Herts CM22 6AR ☎ 01279 850912

PRYOR Dave: Flat 13, Silks Court, 612 Leytonstone High Road, London E11 3BZ ☎ 0976 667630

QUATRO Suzi: Hyde Hall, Great Waltham, Nr Chelmsford, Essex CM3 1BY

RAJA Shez: 44 Inwood Avenue, Hounslow, West Middlesex TW3 1XG ☎ 020 8570 3468, 0958 693004

RAMSAY James (*Gtr*): 79 Ernest Grove, Beckenham, Kent BR3 3HZ ☎ 020 8663 6098, 0850 408926 mob

RANKINE Ken (*Db*): 293 Greenford Avenue, Hanwell, London W7 1AD ☎ 020 8578 7360

RASITES: 49 Broke Walk, Regent Estate, Hackney, London E8 4SH ☎ 020 7254 4179

RAYNER Alison (*Db*): 76 Hawksley Road, London N16 0TJ ☎ 020 7254 8935 & fax, 0973 799415 mob

READ John (*Gtr, Kbds*): 51 Wolseley Avenue, Wimbledon Park, London SW19 8BG ☎ 020 8946 5237

REDGRAVE Constance (*W Bd*): 65 Makepeace Mansions, Makepeace Avenue, London N6 6HB ☎ 020 7681 0085

REEMAN Mike (*Dms*): 21 Palermo Road, College Park, London NW10 5YR ☎ 020 8838 1521

REES Paul Rapsey: Mayfield, 13 Holcombe Drive, Llandrindod Wells, Powys LD1 6DN

REID Roy: 92 Amesbury Road, Dagenham, Essex RM9 6AD ☎ 020 8594 5288

RELF Jason (*Kbds, Gtr*): 126A Upper Tooting Road, London SW17 7EN ☎ 020 8672 1817

RICHARDS Dewi John: 160 Stroud Crescent, Putney Vale, London SW15 3EH ☎ 0589 618817 mob, 020 8788 5815

RICHARDSON Stephen (*Chap Stk, Cl Gtr*): 4 Canons Court, Cannon Grove, Fetcham, Leatherhead, Surrey KT22 9LH ☎ 01372 376852, 0976 796268

RICHMOND Dave (*Db, Com*): 112 Thames Side, Staines, Middx TW18 2HQ ☎ 01784 455733

RIORDAN John: 2B Brantwood Road, Barnehurst, Kent DA7 6LQ ☎ 01322 400523

RITSON William (*Voc*): 125 Danson Road, Bexley, Kent DA5 1DG ☎ 020 8304 5218

RIVE Iain: 255 Devonshire Road, Honor Oak, London SE23 3NS ☎ 020 8699 9352, 020 8699 9352

RIXON Steven: 22 Killierer Ave, London SW2 4NT ☎ 020 8678 6775, 0976 936641 mob

ROBERTS Christopher (*Pf*): 87 Dartford Road, Dartford, Kent DA1 3EQ ☎ 01322 228318

ROBERTS Geraint (*Db*): 96 Salterford Road, Tooting, London SW17 9TF ☎ 020 8767 5322, 0374 261181 mob

ROBERTS Martine (*Voc*): 315A Finchley Road, London NW3 6EH ☎ 020 7431 2009 & fax

ROBERTSON Keith (*E Gtr*): 26 Walsingham Way, Billericay, Essex CM12 0YE ☎ 020 7721 2485 day

ROBINSON Neil: 16 Lynfield Court, Devonshire Road, Forest Hill, London SE23 3ND ☎ 020 8291 1809

RODRIGUEZ-DURAN Cesar (*Ac Gtr, Gtrr, Tiple, Cuatro*): 9 Temple Fortune Court, Temple Fortune Lane, London NW11 7TR ☎ 020 8455 0257 & fax, 0973 787662 mob

ROGAN Michael (*Db, Voc*): 48A Darwin Road, Ealing, London W5 4BD ☎ 020 8568 4659

ROGERS Peter: 74 Pinewood Avenue, Sidcup, Kent DA15 8BD ☎ 020 8302 3414

ROMERO Ricardo (*Gtrr*): 23 West Avenue, Hendon, London NW4 2LL ☎ 020 8203 4185

ROSE David (*Db*): Westwood, Lorraine Park, Harrow Weald, Middx HA3 6BX ☎ 020 8954 9431

ROSEMBERT Nixon: 101A Sheridan Road, Manor Park, London E12 6QY ☎ 020 8471 3728

ROSS Alyn (*Gtr, Db*): 37 Sutherland Avenue, London W9 2HE ☎ 020 7286 3765

ROUND Matthew: 120 Shakespeare Road, Hanwell, London W7 1LX

ROUTCLIFFE Kim (*Pf, Voc, Db, Ob*): 10 Lymington Road, West Hampstead, London NW6 1HY ☎ 07957 350038, 04325 245915

ROWLES Patrick (*Gtr*): Flat 2, 72 Brixton Water Lane, London SW2 1QB ☎ 020 7207 0821

RUPAL Sanjeve (*Kbds*): 89 Canterbury Avenue, Ilford, Essex IG1 3NG ☎ 020 8554 5687, 0956 473795

RUSSELL Simon (*Gtr*): Flat 4, 206 Brixton Road, London SW9 6AP ☎ 020 7326 4290

RUTHERFORD Michael (*Gtr*): c/o Hit & Run Music Ltd, 25 Ives Street, London SW3 2ND ☎ 020 7581 0261

SAID Mario (*Db*): 1 Wesley Close, Bierton Park, Aylesbury, Bucks HP20 1DL ☎ 0410 505540

SALLISS David (*Voc, Kbds, Cop*): 53 York Gardens, Walton-on-Thames, Surrey KT12 3EW ☎ 01932 227347

SALMONS Richard (*Gtr, Voc*): 15 Heston House, 30 Wellesley Road, London W4 4BN ☎ 020 8995 2545

SANDERS Stephen (*Kbds, Gtr*): Flat 10, Yellow Hammer Court, Eagle Drive, London NW9 ☎ 020 8202 3929

SARGEANT Benjamin: 21 Minshull Place, Park Road, Beckenham, Kent BR3 1QF ☎ 020 8650 0468, 0958 705093

SARGEANT Rex: Flat B, 110 Osbaldeston Rd, Stamford Hill, London N16 6NL ☎ 020 8806 7049 & fax, 0973 834788 mob

SARICI Sedat (*Cl Gtr*): 6 Fitzgerald House, Stockwell Park Estate, London SW9 0UG ☎ 020 7737 0028

SAUNDERSON Matthew: 21A Macfarland Road, London W12 7JY ☎ 020 8742 9170

SAVAGE Richard: c/o Prager & Fenton, Midway House, 27/29 Cursitor Street, London EC4A 1LT ☎ 020 7831 4200

SCOTT Gavin (*Db, Kbds*): 113 Manhattan Building, Bow Quarter, Fairfield Road, London E3 2UG ☎ 020 8981 1646

SCOTT Paul (*Db*): 13 Ranelagh Gardens, Ilford, Essex IG1 3JR ☎ 020 8554 0976, 0802 768206 mob, 020 8554 0975 fax

SCRAGG Phil (*Gtr*): 28 Manwood Road, London SE4 1AD ☎ 020 8690 2337

SEABROOK Ronnie (*Db*): 7 Oxford Road, Enfield, Middlesex EN3 4BA ☎ 020 8804 5801

SEAR Brian: 46 Compton Place, Carpenders Park, Herts WD1 5HG ☎ 020 8421 3120

SEDGWICK Simon (*Gtr, Man*): 19 Stowting Road, Orpington, Kent BR6 9SJ ☎ 01689 858625

SEEGER Justin (*Gtr, Pf*): 373A Walworth Road, London SE17 2AL ☎ 020 7701 5154

SELIGMAN Matthew: 29 Legard Road, London N5 1DE ☎ 020 7354 3281

SELLAR Gordon (*Gtr*): 2 Clewer Court Road, Windsor, Berks SL4 5JD ☎ 01753 621026

SETCHFIELD David (*Kbds*): 13A Wedmore Road, Greenford, Middlesex UB6 8SB ☎ 020 8566 6149

SHAH Syed (*Dms, Ld Gtr, Rh Gtr*): 1 Byegrove Court, Byegrove Road, Colliers Wood, London SW19 2BA ☎ 020 8543 1931, 020 7373 2222 day, 020 7373 0559

SHEARER Kenny (*Db*) ☎ 0589 058900 mob

SHEARER Orlando (*Gtr*): 6 College Road, London NW10 5EN ☎ 020 8960 1969, 0403 331444

SHIELDS Chris (*Gtr, Voc*): 103 Spar Hill, Upper Norwood, London SE19 3TT ☎ 020 8653 8529

SILCOCK Bill (*Arr, Cop*): 17 Richfield Road, Bushey Heath, Herts WD2 3LB ☎ 020 8950 6508

SILLS Roger: 53 Connaught Crescent, Brookwood, Woking, Surrey GU24 0AW ☎ 01483 481416

SIMKINS Ted (*Db, Arr, Com*): 120 Moreland Avenue, South Benfleet, Essex SS7 4JW ☎ 01268 753672

SIMMONDS Ian (*Kbds, Per*): 9 Bartholemew House, Denmark Road, London SE5 2LP ☎ 020 7274 5822

SINISTER (*Dms, Club Dj*): 183 Lambeth Walk, Kennington, London SE11 6EJ ☎ 0956 244088

SKEAT Robert: 25 Mountfield Road, Ealing, London W5 2NG ☎ 020 8997 3979

SKIPSEY Andrew (*Dms, Gtr*): 34 Forest Side, Worcester Park, Surrey KT4 7PB ☎ 020 8337 8189, 0468 362131 mob

SKIVINGTON Peter (*Db*): 25 Churchgate, Cheshunt, Herts EN8 9NB ☎ 01992 634329

SMITH Alan (*Pf*): 12 Elm Road, Green Street Green, Orpington, Kent BR6 6BA ☎ 01689 855739

SMITH Kerin (*Voc, Gtr*): 43 Pepys Road, West Wimbledon, London SW20 8NL ☎ 020 8946 3879

SMITH Mark (*Gtr, Kbds*): Suite 501, International House, 223 Regent Street, London W1R 8QD ☎ 01523 762366 pager

SMITH Mark (*Kbds, Gtr*): 5 Fineran Court, St Johns Hill, London SW11 1SG ☎ 020 7228 1100

SMITH Martin: 89 St. James' Road, Sutton, Surrey SM1 2TJ ☎ 020 8643 8381

SMITH Nigel (*Db, Pf*): 26 Kendrey Gardens, Twickenham, Middx TW2 7PA ☎ 020 8892 0437

SMITH Stephen (*Db, Synth*): 23 Westbury Crescent, Oxford OX4 3RZ ☎ 01865 777610, 0860 888620

SNELL Frazer (*Db*): 47 Woodfield Road, Radlett, Herts WD7 8JD ☎ 01923 858187, 0973 196498

SPELLER John: 15 Billings Hill Shaw, Hartley, Longfeild, Kent DA3 8EU ☎ 0147 470 7565

SPRINGATE John (*Gtr, Kbds, Voc, Per*): 61 Lansdowne Lane, London SE7 8TN ☎ 020 8853 0728

SPURLING John (*Voc, Kbds, Per*): Rosedene, Oak Hill Road, Stapleford Abbotts, Essex RM4 1JJ ☎ 01708 725319

SPY (*Gtr, Dms, Kbds*): 37 Glycena Road, Battersea, London SW11 5TP ☎ 020 7586 5367

STAPLES Andy: 73 Glovers Field, Kelvedon Hatch, Brentwood, Essex CM15 0BD ☎ 01277 372912/37

STATHAM Rob: 35B North End Road, Golders Green, London NW11 7RJ ☎ 020 8458 4375

STEIN David: 38 Danehurst Gardens, Redbridge, Essex IG4 5HQ ☎ 020 8550 2712

STEVENSON Tony: 358 Avenell Road, Highbury, London N5 1DN ☎ 020 7226 7998

STEWART Dan (*Gtr, Pf, Per*): 436 Honeypot Lane, Stanmore, Middlesex HA7 1JW ☎ 020 8206 0993, 07970 417985

STEWART Jimmy (*Pf*): 27 By The Wood, Carpenders Park, Watford, Herts WD1 5AG ☎ 020 8428 8020

STIEVET Sophie (*E Gtr*): 30 Glenwood Road, London N15 3JU ☎ 020 8880 2064

STOBBART Wayne (*Gtr*): 10 Herbert Gardens, Kensal Green, London NW10 3BU ☎ 020 8960 3942, 0410 483 214

STOCK Mike: 83 Silvermere Road, Catford, London SE6 4QX ☎ 020 8690 3705

STONE Tony (*Db*): Address Unknown

STONER Michael: 163B Mitcham Rd, Tooting, London SW17 9PG ☎ 020 8767 7232

STRANIS Marcel (*Gtr, Per*): Flat D, 15 Fitzjohns Avenue, London NW3 5JY ☎ 020 7433 1994

STREET Stephen (*Kbds*): Sheen Mount Lodge, 12 West Temple Sheen, Sheen, London SW14 7RT ☎ 020 8876 7489 & fax

STROUD Stephen (*Gtr*): The Oast House, Chart Farm, Seal Chart, Nr Sevenoaks, Kent TN15 0ES ☎ 01732 763118

STRUTTON George (*Db, Voc*): 3, Fairlands Avenue, Buckhurst Hill, Essex IG9 5TF ☎ 020 8504 2741

SUMNER Gordon: Estate House, 921A Fulham Road, London SW6 5HU ☎ 020 7602 5566

SWAIN Martyn: 22 Rydal Water, Robert Street, London NW1 3QT

SWIFT Dave (*E Gtr*): 52A Ommaney Road, New Cross, London SE14 5NT ☎ 020 8692 8953

SWIFT David (*Db*): Top Flat, 23 Bennett Park, Blackheath Village, London SE3 9RA ☎ 020 8297 2901

SYKES Nico: 17 Lyme Grove, London W12 8EE ☎ 020 8723 8477, 020 8743 2362 fax

T.J. (*Gtr*) ☎ 020 7585 1928

TADMAN Paul: 2 Eldertree Way, Mitcham, Surrey CR4 1AG ☎ 020 8715 1384, 0956 364962 mob

TAIT Christopher (*Gtr, Hmca*): 29B Queens Avenue, Muswell Hill, London N10 3PE ☎ 020 8444 2438, 0978 776227

TARANTINO T. J (*Gtr*): 12 Crescent Road, London N15 3LL ☎ 020 8889 6431

TAYLOR Chris: 201 Hainault Road, Leytonstone, London E11 1EU

TAYLOR Clovis (*Gtr*): 63 Derby Road, South Woodford, London E18 2PY ☎ 020 8504 3152

TAYLOR Jeffrey (*Voc*): 2A Friary Road, Wraysbury, Staines Middx TW19 5JP ☎ 01784 483170

TAYLOR Jonathan: c/o Mr N Payn, 85 Jamestown Road, London NW1 7PB

TAYLOR Julian (*Voc, Tpt*): 5 Tile Kiln Lane, London N6 5LG ☎ 020 8347 7959

TECKKAM Christopher (*Kbds, Voc, Dms, Sax*): 116 Old Street, London EC1V 9BD

TEDDER Michael: 88D Lady Margaret Road, London N19 5ES ☎ 020 7607 7101

THOMAS Henry (*Pf, Vln*): 129 Sheldon Road, Edmonton, London N18 1RL ☎ 020 8807 6860

THOMAS Richard (*Db, Voc*): 200 Mayplace Road East, Barnehurst, Kent DA7 6EJ ☎ 01322 522012

THOMPSON Christopher (*Voc, Gtr*): 4 Wickham Road, Brockley, London SE4 1PB ☎ 020 8692 5670

THOMPSON Freddie (*Kbds, Dms, Gtr, Per*): 45 Thackeray Avenue, Tilbury, Essex RM18 8HS ☎ 01375 84 6972

THOMPSON John (*Pf*): 38 Grove Way, Wembley, Middlesex HA9 6JT ☎ 020 8795 3508

THOMPSON John (*Gtr*): 6 Winslow House, Smedley Street, Stockwell, London SW8 2QS ☎ 020 7627 3531, 020 7627 3531

THORN Mike (*Db*): Matthews Hall, Fore Street, Topsham, Devon EX3 0HF ☎ 01392 877065, 0378 784318

THORNALLEY Philip (*Gtr, Kbds, Dms, Voc*): Basement Flat, 27 Priory Rd, London NW6 4NN ☎ 020 7625 8447, 020 7328 8875 fax

TIBBS Gary: 32 Harlyn Drive, Northwood Hills, Middlesex ☎ 020 8977 8198

TOSTI Gabriele (*Gtr*): 24 Fenton Place, Pollens Estate, Kennington, London SE17 3JT ☎ 020 7735 2548

TOWNSEND Paul (*Com*): 39 Grange Park Road, Thornton Heath, Surrey CR7 8QE ☎ 020 8771 0938, 0973 184158 mob

TRUMAN Roy (*Gtr*): 14 Nevilles Court, Dollis Hill Lane, London NW2 6HG ☎ 020 8208 1981

TURNER Neil (*Dms, Pf, Gtr, Voc*): 19 Eyebright Close, Shirley, Croydon, Surrey CR0 8XR

TURNER Nigel (*Tpt*): 36 Grange Park Drive, Leigh-on-Sea, Essex SS9 3JZ

TURNER Paul: 73 Valetta Road, Acton, London W3 7TG ☎ 0973 745871, 020 8749 4737

ULLAH Anrul ☎ 020 8933 6173

UNDERHILL Justin (*Gtr, Kbds*): 59 Cecile Park, Crouch End, London N8 9AX ☎ 020 8348 1653

VAN LEER Jon (*Gtr*): 250A Blackfen Road, Sidcup, Kent DA15 8PW ☎ 020 8303 0639, 020 7915 0202

VERMA Ranvir (*Tabla, Gtr, Kbds, Voc*): 256 Croxted Road, Herne Hill, Briston, London SE24 9DA

VESPA Guseppina: 34 East India Dock Road, Lime House, London E14 6JJ ☎ 020 7515 9135

WAIN Phil (*Per*): 68 Treaty Street, London N1 0TE ☎ 020 7837 7365

WAKEFIELD Graham: 56 Hansol Road, Bexleyheath, Kent DA6 8JG

WALKER Bo (*Gtr, Voc*): 158A Northview Road, Crouch End, London N8 7NB ☎ 020 8348 9081

WALKER Jeffrey (*Db*): 13 Beechwood Avenue, Ruislip, Middx HA4 6EG ☎ 01895 638375

WATERS Daniel (*Gtr, Pf, Sax*): 41A Station Road, Edgware, Middx HA8 7HX ☎ 020 8952 1901

WATERS George: 31 Ruvigny Gardens, London SW15 1JR ☎ 020 8785 6262

WEIGHT Alan: 34, Winchester Road, Walton-on-Thames, Surrey KT12 2RH ☎ 01932 886579

WESTCOTT Stephen (*Gtr, Per*): 12 Glmerside Road, Beckenham, Kent BR3 4AJ ☎ 020 8658 5910

WESTWOOD Paul: 52 Arnold Crescent, Isleworth, Middlesex TW7 7NU ☎ 020 8898 5769 & fax

WHELAN John (*Hrm*): 660A Hanworth Road, Hounslow, Middlesex TW4 5NP ☎ 020 8755 2348

WHITE Carlton (*Gtr, Kbds, Per*): 5 Goldsmith Road, Acton, Ealing, London W3 6PX ☎ 020 8992 8094, 0973 443 864

WHITE Simon (*Voc, Gtr*): 30 Dewberry Street, Poplar, London E14 0RN ☎ 020 7538 4207, 07957 322031

WHITMORE Iain (*Gtr*): 14 Fairlawn Court, Acton Lane, London W4 5EE ☎ 020 8994 4059

WILKINSON Keith: Donkey Hall, Risborough Road, Little Kimble, Bucks HP17 0UE

WILLETTS Carey (*Gtr*): 16 Foxbury Road, London SE4 2SP ☎ 020 8692 5202, 0961 998055

WILLIAMS Clifford: Prager & Fenton, 27/29 Cursitor Street, London EC4A 1LT ☎ 020 7831 4200

WILLIAMS Danny (*Db, Gtr, Voc*): 56 Bond Road, Tolworth, Surrey KT6 7SG ☎ 020 8241 4231

WILLIAMS Marcus: Croft Head Barn, Prickshaw Village, Knacks Lane, Rochdale, Lancs OL12 6BD ☎ 01706 355201

WILLIAMS Mark: 44 Eleanor Road, London E8 1DN ☎ 020 7254 1161

WILLIAMS Peter ☎ 020 8985 1326

WILLIAMS Philip (*Ac Gtr*): 62 New Road, Staines, Middlesex TW18 3DA ☎ 01784 469461

WILLIAMSON David (*Voc, Bag*): 33A Hoyle Road, Tooting, London SW17 0RS ☎ 020 8767 3759

WILSON Peter: 8 Basing Hill, Golders Green, London NW11 8TH ☎ 020 8458 7745

WINFIELD Stephen (*Dms, Gtr, Serp*): Outwood, Woodfield, Ashtead, Surrey KT21 2RL ☎ 01372 276504

WISH Stephen (*Kbds, Gtr, Per*): 56 Teignmouth Road, London NW2 4DX ☎ 0956 151891 mob

WONG Anthony: Flat 1, 1 Cromwell Place, London N6 5HR ☎ 020 8292 6301

WYKES Deborah (*Voc*): 79 Turnpike House, Goswell Road, London EC1V 7PD

WYMAN Bill: c/o Ripple Productions Ltd, 344 Kings Road, London SW3 5UR ☎ 020 7352 5628

YATES Rowdy: 16 Andover Way, Aldershot, Hants GU11 3RJ ☎ 01252 29137

ZAPATA Lisandro (*Voc, Ac Gtr*): 42 Droop Street, London W10 4DH ☎ 020 8960 4747

ZEPHANIAH Benjamin (*Voc*): P.O.Box 673, East Ham, London E6 3QD

ZORN Peter (*Gtr, Man, Per*): 123 Gipsy Hill, London SE19 1QS ☎ 020 8761 0244

BASS OBOE

SCOTLAND

BELL Morven (*Ob, Cor, Obdam*): 39/1 Bryson Road, Edinburgh EH11 1DY ☎ 0131 313 1298

LONDON

EVANS Jane (*Ob, Cor, Obdam*), "Stretton", Manor Close, East Horsley, Surrey KT24 6SB, 01483 281839, 0973 75 0973 mob

BASS TROMBONE

SCOTLAND

BONE David: 6/3E Buccleuch Street, Garnethill, Glasgow G3 6SL ☎ 0141 332 2164, 0370 590484

BOWEN Colin (*Tbn, Tba*): 38 Durward Avenue, Glasgow G41 3UE ☎ 0141 632 3326

DROVER Adrian (*Tba, Arr, Com, Md*): 130C Southbrae Drive, Glasgow G13 1TZ ☎ 0141 954 8983

MCDONALD Lorna (*Sack*): 15 Strathblane Road, Milngavie, Glasgow G62 8DL ☎ 0141 956 7636, 0961 747 399

PETRIE Peter: 7 Langour, Devonside Tillicoultry, Clackmannanshire FK13 6JG ☎ 01259 752350, 0370 898553 mob

SINCLAIR Alistair: 9 Calderwood Road, Newlands, Glasgow G43 2RP ☎ 0141 637 3939

STEARN Christopher (*C B Tbn, Tib Tpt*): Endrick Cottage, Main Street, Fintry, Stirlingshire G63 0XF ☎ 01360 860220

NORTH WEST

ALLISON Jack (*Tba, Cimbasso*): 147 Higher Lane, Lymm, Cheshire WA13 0BU ☎ 01925 753804

BATES Mark (*Eup, B Tpt*): 2 Leaden Knowle, Chinley, Derbyshire SK23 6DA ☎ 01663 750733, 04325 165684 pager

BOULTER Ian: 31 South Philpingstone Lane, Bo'Ness, West Lothian, Scotland EH51 9JZ ☎ 01506 826105

CHAPPELL Simon: 9 Highlands Road, High Crompton Shaw, Oldham, Lancs OL2 7RD ☎ 01706 846619

FROST Mark (*Eup*): 8 Corporation Street, Stalybridge, Cheshire SK15 2JL ☎ 0161 304 9561

LANGFORD John: 12 Hallville Road, Liverpool L18 0HR ☎ 0151 475 1361

LITTLE David (*Dms*): 26 Hoghton Road, Longridge, Preston, Lancashire PR3 3UA ☎ 01772 783998

MANSFIELD Simon: 46 Station Road, Shepley, Huddersfield, West Yorks HD8 8DS ☎ 01484 602401

MATHISON Frank: Moorcroft, Wadsworth Lane, Hebden Bridge, West Yorkshire HX7 8PP ☎ 01422 842246

MCLAUGHLIN Mark (*Eup*): 29 Freshfield Road, Wavertree, Liverpool L15 5BR ☎ 0151 733 2507, 0976 356 776 mob

PAYNE Michael (*Vln*): 65 Broomhall Road, Irlams O The Heights, Pendlebury, Manchester M27 2XR ☎ 0161 736 1613

ROBINSON Timothy (*Sack, Tba*): 109 Brookdale Avenue, South Greasby, Wirral, Merseyside L49 1SP ☎ 0151 606 0413

STOREY Leslie: 35 Hartington Road, Disley, Stockport, Cheshire SK12 2NB ☎ 01663 763241

TAYLOR Russell: 5 Fishers Bridge, Hayfield, Stockport, Cheshire SK12 5JZ ☎ 01663 741196

NORTH EAST

DAVIES Ian: 38 Farnley Road, Menston, Ilkley, Yorkshire LS29 6JN ☎ 01943 878581

ETHRIDGE Stephen (*Tbn*): Flat One, 10 Blenheim Avenue, Leeds, West Yorks LS2 9AX ☎ 09617 43777

GREENFIELD Alexander (*Clt, Pf, Voc, Sax*): Honeyholes South Farm, Hackthorn, Lincoln, Lincolnshire LN2 3PW ☎ 01673 861868, 0411 572874, 01873 861368

HAIRSINE William (*Tbn*): 89 Woodhall Way, Beverley, East Yorkshire HU17 7JR ☎ 01482 862705

INGMAN John: 7 Gainsborough Close, Whitley Bay, Tyne & Wear NE25 9XA ☎ 0191 252 1675, 07803 125504

MILNER Paul E (*Eup*): 5 Blakestones, Slaithwaite, Huddersfield HD7 5UF ☎ 01484 846460

PRITCHARD David (*Tbn, Eup*): 1 Ash Grove, Greengates, Bradford BD10 0BP ☎ 01274 616080, 0378 912505

SNELL Andrew: 2 Whitehouse Farm Cottage, Village Road, Sunk Island, E Yorkshire HU12 0ED ☎ 01964 631307, 0421 663640

WARHAM Clive (*Tbn, Sack*): 6 Cornfield Road, Middlesbrough, Cleveland TS5 5QL ☎ 01642 821682

BASS TROMBONE - EAST

EAST

HOLDING Christopher (*Tbn*): 3 Mariner Way, Hemel Hempstead, Hertfordshire HP2 4RN ☎ 01442 233982, 0973 458427

JARVIS Adrian (*Tbn, Tba, Eup*): 89 Church Hill, Cheddington, Leighton Buzzard, Bedfordshire LU7 0SX ☎ 01378 301759 mob

WATSON Nicholas: 18 Tudor Drive, Watford, Herts WD2 4NT ☎ 01923 231192

MIDLANDS

BROOMHEAD Richard: Beech Farm, Upper Holloway, Matlock, Derbyshire DE4 5AW ☎ 01629 534426, 0976 829447

BRUCE Mike: 193 Barton Road, Barton Seagrave, Kettring, Northants NN16 6RU ☎ 01536 724939

DEVEREUX Frederick (*Tba*): 78 Briarley, Beacon View Road, West Bromwich B71 3PQ ☎ 0121 588 7581

GREEN Alwyn (*Tba, Eup*): 72 Stanbrook Road, Monkspath, Solihull, West Midlands B90 4US ☎ 0121 247 0576, 0956 414109 mob

HALL Simon T (*Pf, Gtr*): 272 Frankley Beeches Road, Northfield, Birmingham B31 5LZ ☎ 0121 476 0546, 0976 301414

JONES Christian (*Pf*): Spring Bank Cottage, 273 Eaves Lane, Bucknall, Stoke-on-Trent, Staffordshire ST2 8LY ☎ 01782 303016

KIMBERLEY Ian (*Eup*): 49 Brookfield Road, Hockley, Birmingham B18 7JA ☎ 0121 551 6469

STEWART Alex: Flat 2, 73 Fountain Road, Edgbaston, Birmingham B17 8NP ☎ 0121 429 8281, 0966 499789 mob

TEARNAN Gregory (*Eup, B Tpt, Com, Arr*): 27 Scott Street, Derby DE23 8QT ☎ 01332 721057

WARBURTON Jonathan (*Pf, Clt*): 484 Hagley Road West, Oldbury, Birmingham B68 0DJ ☎ 0121 422 7244

SOUTH EAST

KENYON John (*Cop*): 12 Lockeridge Close, Blanford, Dorset DT11 7TT ☎ 01258 455101

MASLEN Andrew (*Gtr, Tba, Db*): 9 Drake Close, Horsham, West Sussex RH12 5UB ☎ 01403 274144, 01523 418693 pager

NIBLETT Christopher (*Tbn, Eup*): 48 Coxwell Street, Faringdon, Oxon SN7 7HA ☎ 01895 810709

PARKER Michael: 23 Arundel Court, 18/19 South Parade, Southsea, Hants PO5 2JE ☎ 023 9282 9938, 0850 664402

SOUTH WEST

DAVIES Ian (*Tba, Tbn, T Tba*): April Cottage, Bowden, Stratton, Bude, Cornwall EX23 9BH ☎ 01288 3199

HAMMOND Ian (*Tbn*): 9 Hapsburg Close, Worle, Weston Super Mare BS22 0UH ☎ 01934 513430

HENDY Peter: 37 Llantrisant Road, Pontyclun, Rhondda Cynon Taff, Mid Glamorgan CF72 9DP

JAMES Aneurin: 2 Oakleafe Drive, Oakleigh Park, Pentwyn, Cardiff CF2 7AL ☎ 029 2073 4403

POWELL John (*Tbn*): Cuming Farm, Colston Road, Luscombe, Buckfastleigh Devon TQ11 0LP ☎ 01364 643204

RAVENOR Terence: Gabrieli, Greenway Lane, Lower Henlade, Taunton TA3 5NA ☎ 01823 442786

WILLIAMS Andrew: 5 Lon-Y-Deri, Lon-Y-Llyn, Caefphilly, Mid Glam CF83 1DS ☎ 029 2086 9047

LONDON

AITKEN Stephen (*Eup*): 63 Gordon Road, London E11 2RA ☎ 020 8989 1452

ARGENTE Roger (*Tbn, T Tba*): 41A Gabriel Street, Forest Hill, London SE23 1DW ☎ 020 8291 7674

ASHMORE Richard (*Tbn*): 168 Squires Lane, Finchley, London N3 2QT ☎ 020 8343 3291, 07050 164266, 020 8533 1372 day

BARR Nigel (*Eup, Tba*): 10 Huntley Close, High Wycombe, Bucks HP13 5PQ ☎ 01494 437265, 01494 437619 fax

BEAN Bernard (*Tbn, Eup*): 90 Oakley Road, Luton, Beds LU4 9QD ☎ 01582 571884

BELL John: 29 Park View House, Hurst Street, London SE24 0EQ ☎ 020 7733 9307

BROOKES Arthur: 121 Glenview, Abbey Wood, London SE2 0SB ☎ 020 8310 6362

BROWNING Stephen (*B Sack*): 28 Lawrence Close, Basingstoke, Hampshire RG24 9DP ☎ 01256 461507, 07970 774508

BRYANS Ronald (*Sack, Eup, Tba*): 7 Dorchester Court, Leigham Court Road, London SW16 2PH ☎ 020 8769 6953

BURGESS Rob (*Sack, Eup*): 193 Bellenden Road, London SE15 4DG ☎ 020 7252 8361, 07970 874988

CLARKE Marcus: 180 Waller Road, New Cross, London SE14 5LU ☎ 020 7732 9457, 07899 678162

DOUGLAS Bruce: Flat 2A, 12 Tankerton Road, Whitstable, Kent CT5 2AB ☎ 01227 280 164, 0860 173882 mob

ECCOTT David (*Tbn, A Tbn*): 66 Fleet Road, Dartford, Kent DA2 6JF ☎ 01322 226379

FASHAM Ian (*C B Tbn*): 22 Southview Road, Loughton, Essex IG10 3LG ☎ 020 8508 2904, 020 8549 1706

FOWER Chris (*Tba, Eup*): 3 Eskdale Avenue, Chesham, Buckinghamshire HP5 3AX ☎ 01494 776769, 0973 146397 mob, 07970 505485

FRANCE Adrian (*B Sack, C B Tbn, Tba, N Tpt*): 80 Carslake Road, Putney Heath, London SW15 3DP ☎ 020 8780 9512

GOODHEW Robert: 52A Garthorne Road, Forest Hill, London SE23 1EW ☎ 0976 438727 mob, 020 8776 4588

GORDON David (*Eup*): 17 Holders Hill Drive, London NW4 1NL ☎ 020 8203 2592

GREEN Bob: 34 Chalcroft Road, London SE13 5RF ☎ 020 8318 9966

HALLOWELL Adrian (*Eup, Tba*): 82A Harrow View, Harrow, Middx HA1 4TE ☎ 020 8930 5383, 0777 5626620

HARTMANN Tibor: 2 Manorside, Barnet, Herts EN5 2LD ☎ 020 8440 3376

HARVEY Peter (*B Sack*): 2 Sloe Cottages, Polhills, Arlington, Polegate, East Sussex BN26 6SB ☎ 01323 870271, 01306 880669

HAVELL Nicholas: 6 Glaserton Rd, Stoke Newington, London N16 5QX ☎ 020 8800 9734

HENRY Richard: 40 Church Hill Road, Walthamstow, London E17 9RX ☎ 020 8520 7075, 0374 988330 mob, 020 8533 1372 day

HIGGINBOTHAM John (*Tba, Eup*): 5 Old Street, Plaistow, London E13 9EG ☎ 020 8503 5707, 0973 189663

HUGHES Robert: Windmills, Devonshire Avenue, Amersham, Buckinghamshire HP6 5JF ☎ 01494 433722

JACKMAN Patrick: 35 Northcroft Road, London W13 9SR ☎ 020 8567 5666

JANSSON Bo: The Flat, Dilton Court, Westbury, Wiltshire BA13 4DE ☎ 01373 825185

KHOKHER Omar: Flat 4, Sankey House, St James Avenue, Bethnal Green, London E2 9JE ☎ 020 8981 9527, 0585 490651

KNIGHT Alison (*Tbn, Eup*): 23 Elm Road, New Malden, Surrey KT3 3HB ☎ 020 8949 1836, 0973 262001

LAKE Leslie (*Tbn, Eup, B Tpt*): 55 Heather Road, Grove Park, London SE12 0UG ☎ 020 8857 4152

LEGGETT Tony (*B Sack, C B Tbn, Eup*): 18A Holmwood Gardens, Finchley, London N3 3NS ☎ 020 8371 0179, 0973 615 718

LESTER Andrew (*B Sack, Eup, Tba*): 19 Whitehorn Gardens, Enfield, Middlesex EN2 6HF ☎ 020 8363 1133

LYNN Brian (*Com, Arr*): 204 Hatch Road, Pilgrims Hatch, Brentwood, Essex CM15 9QN ☎ 01277 220315

MASLIN Robert (*Tbn*): 75 Wellington Avenue, Blackfen, Sidcup, Kent DA15 9HF ☎ 020 8304 1723

MCELHONE Gerard: 6 Spinney Close, Westbury Road, New Malden, Surrey KT3 5BQ ☎ 020 8395 7496

MCNICOLL Keith: 13 St. Faith's Road, West Dulwich, London SE21 8JD ☎ 020 8244 5057

MEE William (*Eup, Tba*): 46 Broomleys Road, Coalville, Leicester LE67 4DA ☎ 01530 835938, 0421 671533 mob

NICHOLLS Martin: Daneby Hall, Fordcombe, Tunbridge Wells, Kent TN3 0RP ☎ 01892 740235

PETKEN David: Echo Cottage, 31 Parrock Road, Gravesend, Kent DA12 1QE ☎ 01474 352148, 0802 274391

PREMRU Raymond (*B Tpt, Con, Arr, Com*): 36 Petherton Road, London, N5 2RE ☎ 216 774 4412

ROSS Andrew: 29 Fitzjohn Avenue, Chipping Barnet, Herts EN5 2HH ☎ 020 8449 4237

SAUNDERS Steve (*B Sack, Eup, Tba*): Holly Cottage, Nutley, East Sussex TN22 3LL ☎ 01825 712397, 01825 712103 fax

SINCLAIR Robert: 80 Gloucester Road, Kingston-Upon-Thames, Surrey KT1 3RA ☎ 020 8546 2559

STEWART David (*Sack, Eup*): Flat 2, 33 Betterton Street, London WC2H 9BP ☎ 020 7240 7543

STUBBINGS Richard: 41 Ryecroft Gardens, Blackwater, Camberley, Surrey GU17 0JA ☎ 01276 32743

TATT Mike (*Tba, Db, B Gtr*): 41B Coningsby Road, High Wycombe, Buckinghamshire HP13 5NY ☎ 01494 462072, 0374 715007

THOMPSON (*Eup, Tba, B Sack*): 32 Benskin Road, Watford, Herts WD1 8HW ☎ 01923 246062, 0956 566007, 020 8549 1706 day

TYACK Richard: 12 Normandy Avenue, High Barnet, Herts EN5 2JA ☎ 020 8449 1746

WALL Richard (*B Sack, Eup*): 6 Park Hill Road, Wallington, Surrey SM6 0SB ☎ 020 8647 7577

WILLIAMS Roger (*Tba, Eup, Sack*): 63 Brouncker Road, Acton, London W3 8AF ☎ 020 8992 8932, 020 8533 1372 day, 0183 533 1372 mob

WILLIAMS Sarah (*B Sack, Eup, Ea Wnd*): 47 Whymark Avenue, London N22 6DJ ☎ 020 8365 8364, 0976 298509 mob

BASS TUBA

NORTH WEST

WASSON Barry (*T Tba*): 1 Turnfield Rd, Cheadle, Cheshire SK8 1JQ ☎ 0161 428 2366

MIDLANDS

SINCLAIR Alan (*Tba*): 31 Kennerley Road, S Yardley, Birmingham B25 8LS ☎ 0121 603 1936

SOUTH EAST

LOACH James (*Tba, Pf*): 108 Orchard Way, Barnham, Bognor Regis, West Sussex PO22 0HY ☎ 01243 555 162, 0441 082942 mob

LONDON

GRAPPY Andy (*Sou*): 79 Olinda Road, London N16 6TS ☎ 020 8880 2979, 01306 500022, 0973 165621

TRELOAR Dennis (*B Tbn, Sou*): 22 Wickham Avenue, Shirley, Croydon CR0 8TY ☎ 020 8654 0802

BASSOON

SCOTLAND

ALCOCK Helen (*Bsn*): 2 Midlothian Drive, Shawlands, Glasgow G41 3RE ☎ 0141 649 1521

BLOXWICH Janet (*Bsn*): 91 Fotheringay Road, Pollokshields, Glasgow G41 4LH ☎ 0141 423 2303

DAVIDSON David (*Bsn*): 25 Darlington View, Stewarton, Ayrshire KA3 5PP ☎ 01560 483119

GEDDES Allan (*Bsn*): 12 Kirklee Terrace, Glasgow G12 0TH ☎ 0141 334 9911

GORDON Andrew (*Bsn*): 17 Langside Drive, Glasgow G43 2EP ☎ 0141 569 5659

GOURLAY Caireen (*Bsn, C Bsn, Bq Bsn*): Avalon, Bishop Kinkell, Cononbridge, Dingwall, Ross-Shire, Scotland IV7 8AW ☎ 01349 861106 & fax

GREEN Alison (*Bsn, C Bsn*): 32 Randolph Road, Glasgow G11 7LG ☎ 0141 334 4533 & fax

HAGUE Karen Michelle (*Bsn*): 1st Floor Flat, 2 Athole Gardens, Glasgow G12 9AY ☎ 0141 400 2928, 01426 215035 pager

HILL Gavin (*Bsn*): 4 Kiltrochan Drive, Balfron G63 0QJ ☎ 01360 440200

HUNTER Andrew (*Bsn*): 29 Queen Mary Ave, Glasgow G42 G42 8DS ☎ 0141 423 3325

MUNRO Julian (*Bsn*): 13 Murrayfield Place, Edinburgh EH12 6AA ☎ 0131 337 0810

ROBERTS Julian (*Bsn*): 77 Ormonde Crescent, Netherlee, Glasgow G44 3SW ☎ 0141 637 1939

STEWART Jennifer (*Bsn, C Bsn*): 2/G Garnet Court, Shamrock Street, Glasgow G4 9NT ☎ 0141 332 3415, 01426 299662 pager

WARHURST Alan (*Bsn, C Bsn*): 91 Fotheringay Road, Pollokshields, Glasgow G41 4LH ☎ 0141 423 2303

WATERSTON Eileen (*Bsn*): 35 Buchan Drive, Perth PH1 1NQ ☎ 01738 631615, 01738 561204 fax, 0467 888904 mob

WATSON Kathryn (*Bsn, C Bsn*): 51 West Graham Street 2/1, Garnethill, Glasgow G4 9LJ ☎ 0141 564 3822

WAY Alan (*Bsn, Heck*): 56, Garvock Hill, Dunfermline, Fife KY12 7UU ☎ 01383 723830

WILSON Lesley (*Bsn, Bq Ob*): 226 Bankhead Road, Aberdeen, Aberdeen AB21 9HR ☎ 01224 716418, 0421 366020

NORTH WEST

ARLAN F (*Bsn, C Bsn*): 36 Corbridge Road, Liverpool L16 7QW ☎ 0151 280 8692

AUSTIN Peter (*Bsn*): 27 Ollerbarrow Road, Hale, Altrincham, Cheshire WA15 9PP ☎ 0161 928 9345, 0161 926 9633

BAKER Catherine (*Bsn, Pf*): Station View, St Marys Street, Penistone, Sheffield S36 6AD ☎ 01226 767759

BARRETT Hazel (*Bsn*): 13 Mill Grove, Bulkeley, Nr Malpas, Cheshire SY14 8BJ ☎ 01829 720193, 0403 538739

BURNELL Carol (*Bsn, C Bsn, Flt, Pf*): 84 Townfield Lane, Oxton, Birkenhead L43 2LH ☎ 0151 653 9264

CHATWIN David (*Bsn, Con*): Rose Bank, Kinder Road, Hayfield, Stockport SK12 5LE ☎ 01663 744929

CONNOLLY Robert (*Bsn*): 24 Knowsley Road, Liverpool L19 0PG ☎ 0151 427 1632

DURNFORD Simon (*Bsn*): 67 Adelaide Road, Bramhall, Stockport, Cheshire SK7 1NR ☎ 0161 440 0603

ENTWISTLE Albert (*Bsn*): 23 Corringham Road, Levenshulme, Manchester M19 2RG ☎ 0161 432 5900

GAINFORD Claire (*Bsn*): 12 Mulberry Mews, Heaton Norris, Stockport SK4 1HX ☎ 0161 476 6213, 0374 723698 mob

GIBSON Roger (*Bsn, C Bsn*): Bank Head, Bulkeley, Malpas, Cheshire SY14 8BQ ☎ 01829 720283

GROVE John (*Bsn, C Bsn*): 2 North Road, Liverpool L19 0LR ☎ 0151 427 1158

HINDE Bob (*Bsn, Br Sax, Clt*): 14 St John's Road, Queen's Park, Chester CH4 7AL ☎ 01244 677214

HOOSON James (*Bsn*): 15 Thornton Crescent, Gayton, Wirral, Merseyside L60 3RR ☎ 0151 342 4649

LEE-BROWNE Alison (*Bsn*): 3 The Grove, Sale, Cheshire M33 3WD ☎ 0161 972 0039

MAGEE Steven (*Bsn, C Bsn*): 11 Lingards Terrace, Marsden, Huddersfield, West Yorks HD7 6LT ☎ 01484 845182

OWEN Aled (*Bsn*): The Lodge, 98 Llanelian Road, Old Colwyn, Clwyd LL29 9UH ☎ 01492 515563

PELLER Helen (*Bsn*): 2 Clayton Avenue, Didsbury, Manchester M20 6BN ☎ 0161 448 0991, 0973 392 648

PENDLEBURY Alan (*Bsn*): 53 Baxter Road, Sale, Cheshire M33 3AJ ☎ 0161 969 2820

PERKINS Laurence (*Bsn, Pf*): 10 Adria Road, Didsbury, Manchester M20 6SG ☎ 0161 434 6182

POLLARD Mark (*Bsn*): 30 Wyverne Road, Chorlton, Manchester M21 0ZN ☎ 0161 881 4314, 0976 772735

POOLE Vanessa (*Bsn*): 9 Kings Close, Fairfield, Buxton, Derbyshire SK17 7NT ☎ 01298 70329, 01934 712349

POTTER Amanda (*Bsn*): 15 Exchange Street, Edenfield, Ramsbottom, Lancs BL0 0LA ☎ 01706 828 301, 0421 902381 mob

RACE Zoe (*Bsn*): 5 Blakestones, Slaithwaite, Huddersfield, W Yorks HD7 5UF ☎ 01484 846460

SALVAGE Graham (*Bsn*): Thorngate, 54 Ack Lane East, Bramhall, Stockport, Cheshire SK7 2BY ☎ 0161 439 8251

TAYLOR Tracey (*Bsn*): 49 Post Street, Padfield, Glossop, Derbyshire SK13 1EF ☎ 01457 869742

THOMAS David (*Bsn*): 92 Ruabon Road, Wrexham, Clwyd LL13 7PH ☎ 01978 358 558

WARREN Edward (*Bsn, Con*): 7 Manor Close, Parkgate, S. Wirral, Cheshire L64 6TE ☎ 0151 336 4039

WARREN Julian (*Bsn*): 2 Manor Close, Parkgate, South Wirral L64 6TE ☎ 0151 336 4039

WESLEY Peter (*Bsn, C Bsn, Bq Bsn*): 83 Primrose Terrace, Glossop, Derbyshire SK13 8EJ ☎ 01457 862636

WHITTICK Tim (*Bsn, C Bsn*): 26 Scott Avenue, Chorlton Cum Hardy, Manchester M21 9QW ☎ 0161 881 7736

WIGLEY Richard (*Bsn*): 128 Cavendish Road, West Didsbury, Manchester M20 8JY ☎ 0161 283 9642

WRIGHT Malcolm (*Bsn*): 42 Chelmsford Avenue, Aston, Sheffield S31 0AU ☎ 01142 872490

NORTH EAST

BAKER David (*Bsn*): Richmond House, 49 Cowpasture Road, Ilkley, W Yorkshire LS29 8SY ☎ 01943 430135

BARLOW Arthur (*Bsn*): 15 Banberry Court, The Butts, Gloucester, Gloucestershire GL4 6NX ☎ 01452 302885

BISHOP Ann (*Bsn*): 21 Linden Avenue, Darlington, Co Durham DL3 8PS ☎ 01325 487145

BLACKWELL Susan (*Bsn*): Pogstone House, 19 Cuckstool Road, Denby Dale, Huddersfield HD8 8RF

CATCHPOLE Jackie (*Bsn, Clt*): 21 Cornfield Road, Linthorpe, Middlesbrough, Cleveland TS5 5QJ ☎ 01642 813236

EMERSON June (*Bsn, C Bsn*): Windmill Farm, High Street, York YO62 4HF ☎ 014393 324

GURNEY Samantha (*Bsn, Flt*): 10 First Ave, Heworth, York YO31 7YQ ☎ 01904 423806

HARDWICK Sheila (*Bsn*): 33 Newlay Wood Rise, Horsforth, Leeds LS18 4LY ☎ 0113 2591391

JAKOB Andrew (*Bsn, Saxes, Clt, Flt, Ob*): 90 Station Road, Epworth, Nr Doncaster, Yorkshire DN9 1JZ ☎ 01427 875248

JOHNSON David (*Bsn, C Bsn, Ob*): 22 Dragon View, Harrogate, N. Yorks HG1 4DG ☎ 01423 522885

JUDSON Paul (*Bsn*): 72 Coptleigh, Houghton Le Spring, Tyne & Wear DH5 8JE ☎ 0191 512 0189

LYONS Graham (*Bsn, Clt, Sax*): West Flat/Whitwell Hall, Whitwell-on-The Hill, Yorks YO60 7JJ ☎ 01653 618 085

PROCTOR Andrew (*Bsn*): 75 Hansom Place, York YO31 8FQ ☎ 01904 622054

REAY Stephen (*Bsn*): 42 Queens Road, Jesmond, Newcastle/Tyne 2, Tyne & Wear NE2 2PQ ☎ 0191 281 8974

THORNDYCRAFT Ron (*Bsn*): 11 Kingsland, Jesmond, Newcastle NE2 3AL ☎ 0191 281 5573

WALKER Geoffrey (*Bsn, Sax*): 29 Colwyn Street, Marsh, Huddersfield HD1 4PQ ☎ 01484 428341

EAST

BETTS Robert (*Bsn*): Scoth Brook Cottage, Broad Drove East, Tydd St Giles, Nr Wisbech, Cambs PE13 5UN ☎ 01945 870443

BOYES Paul (*Bsn, C Bsn, Pf*): 66 Fergus Drive, Glasgow G20 6AW ☎ 01582 600525

GOOD Michael (*Bsn*): 11 Australia Court, Cambridge CB3 0JA ☎ 01223 316382

MCKEE David (*Bsn*): 11 Beech Row, Hildersham, Cambridge CB1 6BT ☎ 01223 890969

TATE Alison (*Bsn*): 8 Wickery Dene, Wooton, Northampton NN4 6BE ☎ 01604 763610

MIDLANDS

BARNELL Andrew (*Bsn*): 72 Park Hill Road, Harborne, Birmingham B17 9HJ ☎ 0121 427 5149

BASSEY Andrew (*Bsn*): 36 Lindsy Ave, Abington, Northampton NN3 2SJ ☎ 01604 414315

BRIERLEY Alison (*Bsn, C Bsn*): 14 Hampton Court Road, Harborne, Birmingham B17 9AE ☎ 0121 428 3619

BROOKES Philip (*Bsn, C Bsn*): 2 Station Road, Kings Heath, Birmingham B14 7SR ☎ 0121 444 5655

BUCKLEY Ronald (*Bsn*): 37 Meremore Drive, Waterhays Village, Chesterton, Newcastle-U-Lyme, Staffs ST5 7SE ☎ 01782 560139

CAFFELLE Anja (*Bsn, Voc, Pf, Flt*): The Boundary, Lugwardine, Hereford HR1 4AB ☎ 01432 850358

CALDERBANK Merle (*Bsn, C Bsn*): 10 Larks Mill, Foxglove Meadows, Pelsall, Walsall, West Midlands WS3 4QX ☎ 01922 691832

CHAPPLE Sara (*Bsn*): 52 Westfield Road, Kings Heath, Birmingham B14 7ST ☎ 0121 444 4624, 04325 342184

COOKHORN Margaret (*Bsn, C Bsn*): 25, Grove Avenue, Moseley, Birmingham B13 9RU ☎ 0121 449 4677

ESSEX Sarah (*Bsn*): 11 Oriel Drive, Syston, Leicester LE7 2AR ☎ 0116 2607273

GIBBON Westerby (*Bsn, C Bsn*): 77 Bardney, Orton Goldhay, Peterborough PE2 5QQ ☎ 01733 232468

HARGREAVES John (*Bsn, C Bsn, Pf*): Trenwyth, Mill Street, Aston-on-Clun, Shropshire SY7 8EN ☎ 01588 660 422, 0973 774704

MEALEY Maria (*Bsn, C Bsn*): 60 Albany Road, Stratford-upon-Avon, Warwickshire CV37 6PQ ☎ 01789 295752

PERCIVAL Robert (*Bsn, C Bsn*): Flat 1A, 37 Stanmore Road, Edgbaston, Birmingham B16 9ST ☎ 0121 429 8517

POYNER Jo (*Bsn, C Bsn*): 22, Cramlington Road, Great Barr, Birmingham B42 2EB ☎ 0121 357 6988

PREDOTA Christine (*Bsn*): 72 Park Hill Road, Birmingham B17 9HJ ☎ 0121 427 5149

RUBACH Keith (*Bsn, Pf*): Tollgate Cottage, Willslock, Uttoxeter, Staffs ST14 8RJ ☎ 01889 566608

SCHRODER John (*Bsn*): 42 Billesley Lane, Moseley, Birmingham B13 9QS ☎ 0121 449 2407

SYRETT Michael (*Bsn*): 26 Hill Street, Kings Hill, Wednesbury, West Midlands WS10 9LB ☎ 0121 526 5391, 0378 478340 mob, 0121 568 6607

THEOBALD Felicity (*Bsn*): Birch Tree Farm, Knightley, Stafford, Staffs ST20 0JN ☎ 01785 74 279

TURLINGTON Maurice (*Bsn*): Royal Oman Symphony Orch, PO Box 18, Seeb Code 121, Sultanate Of Oman

SOUTH EAST

BARTHOLOMEW Sally-Anne (*Bsn*): 1 The Cottages, Chamber House, Mill Lane, Thatcham, Berkshire RG19 4NU ☎ 01635 865128

BENNETT Elizabeth (*Bsn, Pf*): Queens Acre, Solent Avenue, Lymington, Hants SO41 3SD ☎ 01590 673955

BRASINGTON Damian (*Bsn*): ☎ 01306 500022 day

BUTT Eric (*Bsn, C Bsn*): 7 Alton Road, Parkstone, Poole, Dorset BH14 8SJ ☎ 01202 744027

DOWNS Nicholas (*Bsn, Rec, Sax*): 56 Raphael Road, Gravesend, Kent DA12 2PW ☎ 0467 480723 mob, 01474 321683

EWART John (*Bsn*): 10 Hungerford Road, Broadway Lane, Bournemouth, Dorset BH8 0EH ☎ 01202 511649

FIDLER Aoileann (*Bsn, C Bsn*): Emmern, Folkestone Road, Charing, Ashford, Kent TN27 0JD ☎ 01233 713833

GALE Christopher (*Bsn*): 45 New Road, Lower Bryanston, Blandford, Dorset DT11 0DR ☎ 01258 455809

HARRISON Nathaniel (*Bsn, Bq Bsn*): 120 London Road, Sevenoaks, Kent TN13 1BA ☎ 01732 464324, 0589 271870

LAMBOURNE Philip (*Bsn*): 4 Churchill Avenue, Hastings, East Sussex TN35 4LB ☎ 01424 443316

LLOYD Donald (*Bsn*): 6 Sapphire Ridge, Waterlooville, Hampshire PO7 8NY ☎ 023 9264 7613

LOCKETT Julian (*Bsn*): 9 Lewens Close, Wimborne, Dorset BH21 1JT ☎ 01202 840695

MAYBURY Tess (*Bsn, Flt, Pf*): 9 Lewens Close, Wimborne BH21 1JJ ☎ 01258 450874

MILLAR Catherine (*Bsn, Pf, Flt, Clt, Sax*): 90 Park Lane, Tilehurst, Reading, Berks RG31 5DT ☎ 0118 942 2269

MILNE Patrick (*Bsn*): 19 Beaconsfield Road, Poole BH12 2NH ☎ 01202 733010

POTTER Warwick (*Bsn, Con, C Bsn, B Sax*): ☎ 01424 440929, 0973 734572, 01424 729064

RANCE Jessica (*Bsn, Ob, Pf*): Holly Lodge, 114 Clifton Road, Shefford, Beds SG17 5AN ☎ 01462 851590, 0802 720909

RENNIE Jane *(Bsn)*: Abbots House, Church Street, Winslow, Bucks MK18 3AN ☎ 0129671 2326

SALAVAGE Neil *(Bsn)*: 20 Cissbury Road, Hove, East Sussexx BN3 6EN ☎ 01273 777752

THOMAS Veronica *(Bsn)*: 143 Aylesbury Road, Wendover, Bucks HP22 6LJ ☎ 01753 38589

WALKER Robert *(Bsn)*: 8 Elmsway, Bournemouth, Dorset BH6 3HU ☎ 01202 421783

WHITE Eve *(Bsn, Clt, Ob)*: 69 Fairfield Road, Salisbury, Wilts SP1 3NY ☎ 01722 412856

WILSON Colin *(Bsn)*: 38 Brockhurst Road, Gosport, Hants PO12 3DE ☎ 023 9279 1480

SOUTH WEST

BOWEN Martin *(Bsn)*: 34 Tymawr Road, Llandaff, Cardiff CF4 2FN ☎ 029 2056 7720

BRUCE Jo *(Bsn)*: 14 Brookfield, Highworth, Wiltshire SN6 7HY ☎ 01793 766129

BUCKLAND David *(Bsn, C Bsn)*: 4 Penylan Court, Penylan Road, St Brides Major, Mid Glamorgan CF32 0SB ☎ 01656 880300

CODD Robert *(Bsn, Clt)*: 40 Highfields, Llandaff, Cardiff CF5 2QB ☎ 029 2056 2962

COWLES Colin *(Bsn, Sax, Pf, Com)*: Keens Barn Cottage, Keens Lane, Othery, Somerset TA7 0PU ☎ 01823 698162

DAVIES Timothy *(Bsn, C Bsn, Kbds, Synth)*: 17 Wimmerfield Avenue, Killay, Swansea, West Glamorgan SA2 7BT ☎ 01792 204082

FOSTER Dominic *(Bsn, Clt, Flt, Ob, Rec)*: Savoy Suite, 16 Causewayhead, Penzance, Cornwall TR18 2SN ☎ 01736 331177, 01736 333500, 01736 333500

HIGGINS Andrea *(Bsn, Pf, Ob)*: 11 Woolsery Avenue, Exeter, Devon EX4 8BJ ☎ 01392 468459

JOHNSON David *(Bsn, C Bsn)*: 27 Knightley Road, St Leonards, Exeter EX2 4SR

JOHNSTONE Michael *(Bsn)*: 13 Oakbourne Road, Brentry, Bristol BS10 6RE ☎ 0117 9503861

JONES Paul *(Bsn, C Bsn, Org)*: 274 North Road West, Plymouth PL1 5DQ ☎ 01752 661477

KINGSLAKE Clara *(Bsn, Pf)*: The Lodge, 64 Campbell Road, Salisbury, Wilts SP1 3BG, 0850 040 954

MARSDEN Stephen *(Bsn)*: 2 White House, Barry, South Glamorgan, Cardiff CF62 6FB ☎ 01664 744261

MERRYWEATHER Michael *(Bsn)*: The White House, St Katherines Road, Torquay, Devon TQ1 4DE

MORGAN Adele *(Bsn, C Bsn)*: 2 Cleddau Close, Otterbrook Village, St Melons, Cardiff CF3 0SG ☎ 029 2036 3185

MORGAN Sian *(Bsn, C Bsn)*: The Vicarage, Heol S.O. Davies, Georgetown, Merthyr Tydfil, Mid Glamorgan ☎ 01685 371995

NEATE Michael *(Bsn)*: 17 Richmond Gardens, Longlevens, Gloucester GL2 0DT ☎ 01452 523454

PALMER Elizabeth *(Bsn)*: 32 Downs Cote Park, Bristol BS9 3JT ☎ 0117 9629882 eve

SECKER John *(Bsn, Flt, Clt)*: 24 Manor Road, Wheathampstead, St. Albans, Hertfordshire AL4 8JD ☎ 01727 843275, 0973 629118 mob

SNEYD Peter *(Bsn, Bq Bsn, Sax, Flt, Clt)*: 55 Bradford Road, Trowbridge, Wilts BA14 9AN ☎ 01225 755439

SOULSBY Katherine *(Bsn)*: 37 Hampton Park Road, Hereford HR1 1TH ☎ 01432 270592

SUMMERS Isolde *(Bsn)*: Sarum House, Union Road, Crediton, Devon EX17 3AL

WALKER Clare *(Bsn, Vln, Clt)*: 80 Pontwillim, Pendre, Brecon LD3 9BS ☎ 01874 611151

LONDON

ALEXANDER Meyrick *(Bsn)*: 25 Nursery Road, Godalming, Surrey GU7 3JU ☎ 01483 416620 & fax, 0973 312299, 01306 880669 day

ANDREWS Julie *(Bsn)*: Address Unknown ☎ 020 8693 2993

ANTCLIFF Catherine *(Bsn)*: Nightingale Old Farm, Wood Street Green, Guildford, Surrey GU3 3DU ☎ 01483 234320

BENNETT Peter *(Bsn, Rec, C Bsn)*: 38B Nova Road, Croydon CRO 2TL ☎ 020 8686 3697, 07970 210498

BENTLEY Anne *(Bsn, C Bsn)*: 7 Trefusis Road, Flushing, Falmouth, Cornwall TR11 5TY ☎ 0370 623442 mob, 01689 853809

BERENT Fritz *(Bsn, C Bsn)*: 22 Latchett Road, South Woodford, London E18 1DJ ☎ 020 8504 3001

BIRKINSHAW Celia *(Bsn)*: April Cottage, Anvil Road, Pimperne, Dorset DT11 8UQ ☎ 01258 454795

BIRNSTINGL Roger *(Bsn)*: 12 Chemin Kermely, 1206 Geneva, Switzerland ☎ +41 22 347 4425 & fax

BLAKE Anna *(Bsn)*: 9 Pandora Road, West Hampstead, London NW6 1TS ☎ 020 7435 4778, 0973 512921 mob

BOURTON Robert *(Bsn)*: 32 Vallance Road, London N22 4UB ☎ 020 8888 2677

BOYLE Michael *(Bsn)*: 55 Monkhams Avenue, Woodford Green, Essex IG8 0EX ☎ 020 8504 1216

BRYAN Fiona *(Bsn)*: 41 Wing Road, Linslade, Leighton Buzzard, Beds LU7 7NG ☎ 01525 853720

BURNETT Sarah *(Bsn)*: 67 Crescent West, Barnet, Herts EN4 0EQ ☎ 020 8449 2014, 020 8533 1372

CAMDEN Kerry *(Bsn)*: Willowdown, Megg Lane, Chipperfield, Herts WD4 9JN ☎ 01923 263715

CARBEN Barry *(Bsn)*: 32 Station Road, Hopton-on-Sea, Norfolk NR31 9DE ☎ 01502 732236

CARPOS Francesca *(Bsn, Bq Bsn)*: 18 Churchfield Avenue, North Finchley, London N12 0NT ☎ 020 8446 5394

CARTER Ruth *(Bsn, Clt)*: 10 Forster Road, Walthamstow, London E17 8AU ☎ 020 8521 4364

CHAPMAN Michael *(Bsn)*: 24 High Road, Waterford, Hertfordshire SG14 2PR ☎ 01992 558643, 01306 880669 day

CHAPPELL Suzanne *(Bsn)*: 101 Windsor Road, Leyton, London E10 5LP ☎ 020 8723 7046, 0836 371762, 01306 880669 day

CHATTERTON David *(Bsn, C Bsn, Sarru)*: 238 Pinner Road, North Harrow, Middx HA1 4JU ☎ 020 8427 4304, 01306 880669

CHISWELL Simon *(Bsn, Gtr, Cl Gtr)*: 25 Postmill Drive, Tovil Mill, Maidstone, Kent ME15 6FY ☎ 01622 672799

CLARKE Brynly *(Bsn, C Bsn, Con)*: 565 Dorpstraat, B-3061 Leefdaal, Belgium

COHEN Susanna *(Bsn, Pf)*: 3 Lawrence Court, Mill Hill, London NW7 3QP ☎ 020 8959 7177, 01306 880669

COLE Michael *(Bsn)*: 21 Desenfans Road, London SE21 7DN ☎ 020 8299 1746

COOPER Lindsay *(Bsn, Ob, S Sax, Com)*: 6B Burton Place, London WC1H 9AH ☎ 020 7388 3539, 020 7383 7582

COTT David *(Bsn, C Bsn)*: Millcroft, Mill Road, Banham, Norwich, Norfolk NR16 2HU ☎ 01953 887209

COUZENS Simon *(Bsn, C Bsn, Kbds, Com)*: 63 The Cloisters, 145 Commercial Street, London E1 6EB ☎ 020 7247 1523, 0973 134215

CUTHILL Ian *(Bsn, C Bsn, Dul, Bq Bsn)*: 2 Vulcan Gate, Enfield, Middx EN2 7PP ☎ 020 8366 5097, 01306 500022

DE FLAMMINEIS Andrea *(Bsn)*: 2 Ringmer Avenue, London SW6 5LW ☎ 020 7731 2084

DE HAAN Stefan *(Bsn)*: 96 Highgate Hill, London N6 5HE

DUCKETT Catherine *(Bsn, C Bsn)*: 55 Longton Grove, Sydenham, London SE26 6QQ ☎ 020 8778 9475, 01306 880669 day

DUNDAS-GRANT Deirdre *(Bsn)*: 24 Dora Road, London SW19 7HH ☎ 020 8946 6875

EDMONDS Rachel *(Bsn)*: 30 Weatherbury, 90 Talbot Road, London W2 5LF ☎ 020 7727 5365, 0976 754294 mob

ELLIOTT Lizbeth *(Bsn)*: 28 Braidwood Road, London SE6 1QX ☎ 020 8333 1050, 020 8698 6352 & fax

ESTELL Simon *(Bsn, C Bsn)*: 15 Conifer Way, Sudburymeadows, Wembley, Middlesex HA0 3QP ☎ 020 8908 5526, 0958 930764

EVERSDEN Susan *(Bsn)*: 43 Cowley Road, Ilford, Essex IG1 3JL ☎ 020 8518 2304

FAIRBANK Anne *(Bsn)*: 36 Argyle Road, North Harrow, Middlesex HA2 7AJ ☎ 020 8863 4208

FARMERY Emma *(Bsn)*: 432 Waterside, Chesham, Buckinghamshire HP5 1QE ☎ 01494 774723, 0370 394937

FITZGERALD Brendan *(Bsn)*: 37 Kilmorie Road, London SE23 2SS ☎ 020 8699 6161

FORBES Ian *(Bsn)*: 174 Amherst Drive, Orpington, Kent BR5 2HL ☎ 01689 818424, 0973 693620 mob, 020 8533 1372

FORD Michael (*Bsn, Saxes, Br Sax, Flt, Clt*): 8 Spenser Road, Herne Hill, London SE24 0NR ☎ 020 7733 9890, 020 7652 0687 fax

FORSHAW Alec (*Bsn, Hpsd, Pf*): 49 Great Ormond Street, London WC1N 3HZ ☎ 020 7405 9848

FRANCIS Peter (*Bsn, C Bsn*): 29 Orchard Avenue, New Malden, Surrey KT3 4JU ☎ 020 8942 6174

FULLER Stephen (*Bsn, C Bsn*): 13 Spencer Close, Orpington, Kent BR6 9QZ ☎ 01689 827995, 0860 273331 mob

GATT Martin (*Bsn*): 20 Kingston Deverill, Nr Warminster, Wilts BA12 7HE ☎ 01985 844787

GILCHRIST Neil (*Bsn, C Bsn*): 15 Oakfield Road, Ashtead, Surrey KT21 2RE ☎ 01372 276949

GLENISTER Clare (*Bsn*): 141 Bramley Close, London E17 6EG ☎ 020 8523 1723 day

GOUGH Rachel (*Bsn*): 89 Streathbourne Road, London SW17 8RA ☎ 020 8672 0072

GRAHAM Joanna (*Bsn*): Flat 4, 4 Northumberland Road, New Barnet, Herts EN5 1ED ☎ 020 8447 0504, 097 3781144 mob, 01306 880669 day

GUNIA Christopher (*Bsn*): 104 St Marys Road, London SE15 2DU ☎ 020 7732 9100

HADFIELD Sarah (*Bsn*): 47 Homecroft Road, Sydenham, London SE26 5QN ☎ 020 8778 2415

HAGGER Roger (*Bsn*): 11 Sherwood Close, Fetcham, Nr. Leatherhead, Surrey KT22 9QT ☎ 013724 50452

HAMMOND Alan (*Bsn, C Bsn*): 6 Mandinan, Gower Road, Swansea, South Wales SA2 7AA ☎ 01792 203185

HARRIS Paul (*Bsn, C Bsn, Bq Bsn*): 411 Manhattan Buildings, Bow Quarter, Fairfield Road, London E3 2UQ ☎ 020 8981 7913 & fax, 020 8533 1372 day

HARRISON Peter (*Bsn*): 124A Swaby Road, Earlsfield, London SW18 3QZ ☎ 020 8946 5463

HELLYER Roger (*Bsn, Kbds*): 60 Albany Road, Stratford-upon-Avon, Warks CV37 6PQ ☎ 01789 295752

HESTER Dieter (*Bsn, C Bsn*): 561 Kenton Lane, Harrow, Middlesex HA3 7LB ☎ 020 8427 5918, 020 8863 7826 fax

HOLLAND Simon (*Bsn, Clt, Flt, Pic, Saxes*): 46 Blackthorn Avenue, Tunbridge Wells, Kent TN4 9YG ☎ 01892 549205

HUNKA Nicholas (*Bsn, C Bsn*): 61 Erpingham Road, London SW15 1BH ☎ 020 8788 1031

JACKSON Sally (*Bsn*): 16 Three Crowns Road, Colchester, Essex CO4 5AD ☎ 01206 854830

JONES Christopher (*Bsn*): Kirkview, 26 High Road, Soulbury, Leighton Buzzard LU7 0BX ☎ 01525 270385

JORDAN Robert (*Bsn, C Bsn*): 91 Brands Hill Avenue, High Wycombe, Bucks HP13 5PX ☎ 01494 527826

JUDD Anthony (*Bsn*): 94 Christchurch Avenue, London NW6 7PE ☎ 020 8459 3289

KENNARD Robin (*Bsn*): Green Gables, Bepton, Midhurst, W.Sussex GU29 0JB ☎ 01730 813464

KENNEDY Valentine (*Bsn, C Bsn*): Address Unknown ☎ 020 8904 5132

KERSHAW Julian (*Bsn*): 141 Shipbourne Road, Tonbridge, Kent TN10 3EJ ☎ 01732 357619

KING Conrad (*Bsn, C Bsn, Sax, Clt, Flt*): 25 Newdigate Road, Harefield, Middlesex UB9 6EH ☎ 01895 823778

LAING Gordon (*Bsn, C Bsn*): 64 Montem Road, Forest Hill, London SE23 1SJ ☎ 020 8690 8661

LEGGE Howard (*Bsn, C Bsn*): Flat 4, 11 Gunnersbury Avenue, Ealing Common, London W5 3NJ ☎ 020 8993 3939, 0860 242860 mob

LEVEAUX Ursula (*Bsn, Bq Bsn*): Flat 6, 138 Calton Road, Edinburgh EH8 8DP ☎ 0131 557 6071 & fax, 0374 103567 mob

LEVESLEY Neil (*Bsn, C Bsn*): Bryony, School Lane, Barcombe, Lewes, East Sussex BN8 5DS ☎ 01273 400827

LOCK David (*Bsn, C Bsn*): Bay Tree Farm, Stutton, Ipswich, Suffolk IP9 2SQ ☎ 01473 327738, 0850 815415

MACKIE Melbon (*Bsn, Heck*): 8 Crouch Hall Road, Crouch End, London N8 8HU ☎ 020 8340 6112

MACKINDER Neville (*Bsn, Clt, Con*): 15 Wodehouse Road, Old Hunstanton, Norfolk PE36 6JD ☎ 01485 534010

MALLETT Timothy (*Bsn, C Bsn*): 49 Heather Park Drive, Wembley, Middlesex HA0 1SP ☎ 020 8902 2052, 020 8533 1372, 0378 794706 mob

MASKELL Jane (*Bsn, Pf*): Midwood, 31 Ashley Road, Farnborough, Hants GU14 7EZ ☎ 0252 543134/299

MASON Elizabeth (*Bsn*): 37B Waldegrave Road, Upper Norwood, London SE19 2AL ☎ 020 8771 9914, 0973 515645

MAW Stephen (*Bsn, C Bsn, Md*): 24 Bousfield Road, London SE14 5TR ☎ 020 7639 8529

MCDOUGALL John (*Bsn*): 79 Wakefield Street, London E6 1NR ☎ 020 8470 0305, 0973 343640, 01306 880669

MCNAUGHTON Gavin (*Bsn*): 206B Devonshire Road, Forest Hill, London SE23 3TQ ☎ 020 8291 5077, 01306 880 669 day, 0973 660701 mob

MEADOWS Anna (*Bsn*): 25 Old Cross Tree Way, Ash Green, Nr Aldershot, Hants GU12 6BT ☎ 01252 314680

MENDAY Rebecca (*Bsn, C Bsn*): 132 Osidge Lane, Southgate, London N14 5DN ☎ 020 8368 5899, 01306 880669

MILES David (*Bsn*): 20 Church Lane, Toppesfield, Essex CO9 4DS ☎ 01787 238045, 01306 880669

MILNE Hilary (*Bsn*): Flat 4, Ashborne, 82 Honor Oak Road, London SE23 3RR ☎ 020 8291 3390

MITCHELL Alastair (*Bsn, Bq Bsn*): 35 Hawkenbury Way, Lewes, E Sussex BN7 1LT ☎ 01273 477383

MOORE Richard (*Bsn, C Bsn, Dulc, Sarru*): Stockleigh, Catherington Hill, Catherington, Waterlooville, Hants PO8 0TU ☎ 023 9259 1058

MORGAN Dominic (*Bsn, C Bsn*): 55 Homecroft Road, Sydenham, London SE26 5QN ☎ 020 8659 1075, 0973 821489 mob, 01306 880669 day

MORRELL Joanne (*Bsn, C Bsn*): 32 Valley Road, Uxbridge, Middlesex UB10 0RP ☎ 01895 237147, 07050 648249

MURPHY Kim (*Bsn, C Bsn*): 15 Jackson Road, East Barnet, Herts EN4 8UT ☎ 020 8364 8241, 020 7354 2711 day

NEALGROVE Lynda (*Bsn*): Clare Cottage, Swan Lane, The Lee, Gt.Missenden, Bucks HP16 9NU ☎ 01494 837445

NEWMAN Gareth (*Bsn, C Bsn*): 29 Alston Road, Barnet, Herts EN5 4EU ☎ 020 8441 1107, 01306 880669 day

NISSEN David (*Bsn, Bal*): 54 Morshead Mansions, Maida Vale, London W9 1LF ☎ 020 8723 5384, 0961 123155 mob, 020 8932 2501 fax

ORFORD John (*Bsn, C Bsn, Heck, Sarru*): 6 Park Road, Chesham, Bucks HP5 2JE ☎ 01494 786315, 01306 880669

OWEN Jean (*Bsn*): La Demeure, Clos Des Goddards, Vazon Castel, Guernsey, C.I. GY5 7JD ☎ 01481 55742 & fax, 0585 237135 mob

PENN Alfred (*Bsn*): Address Unknown

PHILLIPS Wendy (*Bsn*): Kiln, Dawes Road, Dunkirk, Faversham, Kent ME13 9TP ☎ 01227 751621, 01306 880669, 0402 954309

POLLOCK Margaret (*Bsn, Pf*): 3 Queens Road, Chesham, Bucks HP5 3AE ☎ 01494 785666

PORTER Bob (*Bsn, C Bsn, Cntrc*): 57 Kingswood Road, Merton Park, London SW19 3ND ☎ 020 8542 1661

PRICE John (*Bsn*): Birchwood, Birchwood Lane, Chaldon, Surrey CR3 5DQ ☎ 01883 346306

PRICE Jonathan (*Bsn*): Flat B, 39 Felday Road, London SE13 7HQ ☎ 020 8314 0825, 0976 725513, 01306 880669

PRICE Julie (*Bsn*): 19 Miswell Lane, Tring, Hertfordshire HP23 4DD ☎ 01442 826 901, 0976 446 428 mob, 01442 826 901

PRICE Sarah (*Bsn*): 77 Chesterfield Road, Ashford, Middlesex TW15 3PF ☎ 01784 240807, 0973 795060 mob

READER Nicholas (*Bsn, C Bsn, Sarru*): 19 Warrender Park Crescent, Edinburgh EH9 1EA ☎ 0131 229 7740

REAR Michael (*Bsn, Bq Bsn*): 34 Landcroft Road, London SE22 9LH ☎ 020 8299 2150, 0958 393078

REID Donald (*Bsn, C Bsn*): 4 Penton Hall, Penton Hall Road, Staines, Middlesex TW18 2HR ☎ 01784 459901

ROWLINSON Tamsin (*Bsn*): 17 Fairfield Road, London E17 6EW ☎ 020 8527 8398, 01306 880669 day

SEWELL Brian (*Bsn, C Bsn*): 49 Fairway, Raynes Park, London SW20 9DN ☎ 01306 880669 day, 0410 023 324 mob, 020 8241 1280 fax

BASSOON - LONDON

SHEEN Graham *(Bsn)*: 13 Radlett Ave, London SE26 4BZ ☎ 020 8699 9030

SHEVLIN Zoe *(Bsn)*: 27 Aynhoe Road, London W14 0QA ☎ 020 7602 0563, 01426 123967 pager

SIBLEY Jane *(Bsn, C Bsn, Pf)*: 41 Brockhurst Road, Chesham, Bucks HP5 3JB ☎ 01494 792684

SIMMS Rachel *(Bsn, C Bsn, Sax, Flt, Kbds)*: Flat 174, 29 Abercorn Place, St Johns Wood, London SW8 9DU ☎ 020 7372 5487, 01306 880669

SIMONS Helen *(Bsn)*: 35 Bonnington Square, Vauxhall, London SW8 1TF ☎ 020 7582 6578, 0976 820127

SKINNER Richard *(Bsn, C Bsn, Wi Synth)*: 260 Friern Road, London SE22 0BB ☎ 020 8693 2993

SMITH Daniel *(Bsn)*: 138 Abbey Road, Flat 4, London NW6 4SR ☎ 020 7624 7485

SMITH Helen *(Bsn)*: 12 Millins Close, Owlsmoor, Sandhurst, Berks GU47 0TL ☎ 01344 774905

STANIFORTH Julia *(Bsn)*: 1 Roxley Road, London SE13 6HG ☎ 020 8265 7689, 0976 739403, 020 8244 5386

STOWELL Andrew *(Bsn)*: Middleton Stables, Golford, Cranbrook, Kent TN17 3PA ☎ 01580 714821

TARLTON Philip *(Bsn)*: 31 Green Lane, Chislehurst, Kent BR7 6AG ☎ 020 8467 7089, 0976 278498

TUMELTY Helen *(Bsn, Flt, Pf, Rec)*: 222 Park Road, London N8 8JX ☎ 020 8340 2641

TURNER Joanne *(Bsn)*: 40 Firs Close, Mitcham, Surrey CR4 1AY ☎ 020 8646 7792, 0378 462815 mob

VALE Christopher *(Bsn, C Bsn, Pf)*: 50 Parc-Y-Coed, Creigiau, Nr Cardiff CF4 8LY ☎ 029 2089 2388 & fax

WADSWORTH Claire *(Bsn, C Bsn)*: 42 Arthurdon Road, Brockley, London SE4 1JU ☎ 020 8690 5957, 0966 213603 mob

WALLER Ronald *(Bsn, C Bsn)*: 8 St Marys Avenue, London N3 1SN ☎ 020 8346 5834

WARD Jeremy *(Bsn, Bq Bsn)*: 38 Llwyn-Y-Pia Road, Lisvane, Cardiff CF4 5SY ☎ 029 2076 4086

WARNER Kay *(Bsn, C Bsn)*: 84 Bridge Road, Uxbridge, Middx UB8 2QW ☎ 01895 236326

WARNOCK Felix *(Bsn)*: 5 Kingsbridge Road, London W10 6PU ☎ 020 8969 5738

WATERHOUSE William *(Bsn, Bq Bsn, C Bsn)*: 86 Cromwell Avenue, London N6 5HQ ☎ 020 8340 8362

WATTS Valerie *(Bsn, C Bsn, Tbn)*: 18 Kirbymills, Kirkbymoorside, North Yorkshire YO6 6NR ☎ 01751 432543

WEDDLE Susan *(Bsn, C Bsn)*: 38B Nova Road, Croydon CR0 2TL ☎ 020 8686 3697, 07970 865705 mob

WHITFIELD John *(Bsn, Cop, Arr, Con)*: A24 Peabody Estate, Old Pye Street, Westminster, London SW1P 2JU ☎ 020 7976 7650, 01306 880669

WHITTAKER Peter *(Bsn)*: 69 Aintree Road, Parklands, Northampton NN3 6EA ☎ 01604 646780

WIGHTMAN Brian *(Bsn)*: 20 Park Avenue, London N3 2EJ ☎ 020 8349 2868

WILLIAMS Edgar *(Bsn, Vln)*: 34 Crofters Close, Northampton NN4 0BJ ☎ 01604 766095

WILLIAMS Glyn *(Bsn)*: Flat C, 93 Priory Road, London N8 8LY ☎ 020 8341 3556

WINCHESTER Judith *(Bsn)*: 11 Rusholme Road, London SW15 3JX ☎ 020 8788 7340

WISEMAN Howard *(Bsn, C Bsn)*: 7 Genoa Road, London SE20 8ES ☎ 020 8778 0752

BERIMBAU

LONDON

HOBAN Christopher *(Gtr, Pf, Cel, Per)*: 26 Dora Road, Wimbledon Park, London SW19 7HH ☎ 020 8946 8852

MILLAR Jhalib *(Tabla, Ind Per, Jaw H, Djembe)*: 65 Bayham Street, London NW1 0AA ☎ 020 7388 8205

BODHRAN

NORTH EAST

MACPHERSON Cluny *(Darab, Acc, Wh)*: 7 Conway Avenue, Harehills, Leeds LS8 5JE ☎ 0113 2405318

EAST

GLADWELL Kevin: 21 Hilltop Road, Berhampstead, Herts HP4 2HL ☎ 01442 875808

MIDLANDS

DAVIES Wally *(Per, Gtr)*: Koinonia, Cheddleton Heath Road, Cheddleton, Staffs ST13 7DX ☎ 01538 360256

GRUNDY David *(Dms, Man, Uke, E Gtr)*: 25 Albert Street, Bignall End, Audley, Stoke-on-Trent ST7 8QB ☎ 01270 584721

HARRIS David: 35 St Michaels Close, Madeley, Telford, Salop TF7 5SD ☎ 01952 680249

ROGERS Marie: 16 Caledon Road, Sherwood, Nottngham NG5 2NG ☎ 0115 9109153

SOUTH EAST

ROSE Brian *(Cong, Dms)*: Chapel Cottage, Pulliam, Dorchester, Dorset ST2 7DY ☎ 01258 817572

SOUTH WEST

HANKS Nicholas *(Voc)*: 89 Coronation Road, Southville, Bristol BS3 1AX ☎ 0117 908 5055

MAY Andy *(Voc, Wh)*: 52 Winchester Street, Taunton, Somerset TA1 1QF ☎ 01823 336626

LONDON

CONNEFF Kevin: Carothann, Lugglass, Hollywood, Co Wicklow, N Ireland ☎ 0074171, 6673910

INCE Austin *(Wh)*: 40 Pentland Street, London SW18 2AL ☎ 020 8874 3399

BONES

LONDON

CLINCH David *(Bod, Tin Wh, Wh)*: 14 Winsford Road, Catford, London SE6 4LX ☎ 020 8699 3460, 020 8690 1114 day

BOUZOUKI

SCOTLAND

LAWRENCE Steven *(Citt, Man, Ac Gtr, Dul)*: Flat 2/2, 1012 Crow Road, Anniesland, Glasgow G13 1JW ☎ 0141 579 5846

LUNNY Manus *(Gtr)*: c/o Secret Music, 5 Newton Terrace Lane, Glasgow G3 7PB ☎ 0141 564 1161, 0141 564 1221 fax

STEELE David *(Gtr, Bod)*: Midfield House, Lasswade, Midlothian, Scotland EH15 1ED ☎ 0131 660 5559

NORTH WEST

MANDELSON Benjamin *(Vln, Gtr, Bjo, Man)*: 89 Clissold Crescent, London N16 9AS

NORTH EAST

COE Pete *(Bjo, Dul, Mldn)*: 103 Oldham Road, Ripponden Sowerby Bridge, West Yorks HX6 4EB ☎ 01422 822569

MIDLANDS

MORAITIS George *(Gtr, Voc)*: 28 Western Road, Sutton Coldfield, West Midlands B73 5SP ☎ 0121 354 6690

PARADISSIS Stavros *(Gtr)*: 26 Rawlings Road, Smethwick, Warley, West Midlands B67 5AA ☎ 0121 429 1130, 0850 210194

TAKIS: 246 Tennal Road, Birmingham B32 2HJ ☎ 0121 682 2333, 0789 9917373

LONDON

BARNES Ted *(Gtr, Man)*: 36 Middleton Road, Dalston, London E8 4BS ☎ 020 7254 0431

COSTA Lenios: 43 Nightingale Lane, Hornsey, London N8 7RA ☎ 020 8341 9739, 020 8340 6321

HADJINEOPHYTOU George *(Saz, Darab, Ud)*: 41 Burlington Rise, East Barnet, Herts EN4 8NH ☎ 020 8368 3684

HAJISHACALLI Zacharia *(Per)*: 7 Bulwer Road, Edmonton, London N18 1QL ☎ 020 8803 2058, 803 1923

MARKIDES Andreas *(Kbds, Sax)*: 167 Valley Drive, London NW9 9NT ☎ 020 8204 8641

PELAS G *(Gtr)* ☎ 020 8989 2560

RIALAS Costa: 4 Covert Way, Hadley Wood, Barnet, Herts EN4 0LT ☎ 020 8449 8795

BRASS

SCOTLAND

HOOK Heather *(Wood W)*: 55 Millbank Road, Dingwall, Ross-Shire IV15 9UH ☎ 01349 862200

NORTH EAST

WALKER Norman: 24 Thornton Lea, Pelton, Chester-Le-Street, Co Durham DH2 1UN ☎ 0191 370 3863

WIGHAM Carolyn: Morland, Kepier Gardens, South Hylton, Sunderland SR4 0PS ☎ 0191 534 4159

WILSON Paul *(Clt, Flt, Sax)*: Royal Air Force, College Band, Cranwell, Lincolnshire NG34 8HB ☎ 01400 261204

WOOD Stephen *(Eup)* ☎ 0114 233 6384

EAST

ECCLESTONE Malcolm *(Stgs, Wood W, Pf, Voc)*: The Old Station, Kimberley, Wymondham, Norfolk NR18 0NU ☎ 01953 850711

MIDLANDS

CHAPLIN Maggie *(Pf, Gtr, Voc)*: 1 Ambleside Close, Loughborough, Leics LE11 3SH ☎ 01509 215890

VENISON Timothy *(Kbds)*: 1 Peak View Drive, Ashbourne, Derbyshire DE6 1BR ☎ 01335 343347

SOUTH EAST

YOUNG Colin: 17 Harland Road, Southbourne, Bournemouth, Dorset BH6 4DN ☎ 01202 425923

LONDON

WHITE Robert *(R Wnd, Ea Wnd, Bag, Eth Flts)*: 38 Castle Road, Isleworth, Middlesex TW7 6QS ☎ 020 8400 9747, 0973 332027

CAULD WIND PIPES

SCOTLAND

SEATTLE Matt *(Fo Fdl, Gtr)*: PO Box 13772, Peebles, Scotland EH45 8YE ☎ 01721 724707

CELLO

SCOTLAND

ADAM Stephen *(Pf)*: 3/L 35 Camphill Avenue, Langside, Glasgow G41 3AX ☎ 0141 632 9115

ARMOUR Lynn *(Bq Cel)*: The Steading, Pictfield, Rattray, Blairgowrie, Perthshire PH10 7HQ ☎ 01250 876334

BEAN Rebecca *(Pf)*: 2/2 Glassford Court, 83 Wilson Street, Merchant City, Glasgow G1 1UZ ☎ 0141 552 375, 0976 512875 mob

BEAUCHAMP Ruth: 48 Spottiswoode Road, Edinburgh EH9 1DB ☎ 0131 447 5210

BINNIE Anne *(Pf)*: Mansewood, 31 Adelaide Street, Helensburgh, Dunbartonshire G84 7RD ☎ 01426 673061

BOHONEK Judith *(Vln)*: 23 Dunellan Road, Milngavie, Glasgow G62 7RE ☎ 0141 956 6288

BOYD Marian: 73 Waverley Gardens, Shawlands, Glasgow G41 2DP ☎ 0141 636 5775

BROOK Elaine: c/o Huntriss, 8 Glebe Road, Newton Mearns, Glasgow G77 6DU ☎ 0141 616 0800

BROWN Alison: 13 East Trinity Road, Top Centre Flat, Edinburgh EH5 3DZ ☎ 0131 551 4531

CAMPBEL Isobel *(Voc, Gtr, Pf)*: 12 Northland Drive, Scotstoun, Glasgow G14 9BA ☎ 0141 950 1225

CHAHIN Myra: 5 Chapelton Avenue, Bearsden, Glasgow G61 2RE ☎ 0141 942 1356

CONNELL Marie: 109 Whitehill Street, Dennistoun, Glasgow G31 2LS ☎ 0141 550 2180

CONWAY William *(Con)*: 24 Granby Road, Edinburgh EH16 5NL ☎ 0131 667 4630 & fax

COPP Gillian *(Pf)*: 10 Dudley Drive, Hyndland, Glasgow G12 9SB ☎ 0141 339 7082

DANCE Susan: 30 Oxford Road, Renfrew PA4 0SJ ☎ 0141 886 7446, 0411 923 555 mob

DAVIDSON Anne: 25F Taylors Lane, Dundee, Tayside DD2 1AP ☎ 01382 644613

DAVIDSON John: 5 Rodger Drive, Burnside, Rutherglen, Glasgow G73 3QZ ☎ 0141 647 5047, 0585 560200 mob

DE GROOTE Rudi *(Pf)*: Flat 3/1, 38A Kingston High Street, Glasgow G5 8BP ☎ 0141 418 0575, 0411 349596 mob

DOWSE Pauline *(Pf)*: 38 Hallydown Drive, Jordanhill, Glasgow G13 1UF ☎ 0141 954 9346

DUNCAN Helen: 37 Earlbank Ave, Scotstoun, Glasgow G14 9HE ☎ 0141 958 0532

DUNCAN Paul *(Vln)* ☎ 0141 632 8416 & fax

EDWARDS David: 3 Marchhall Road, Edinburgh EH16 5HR ☎ 0131 667 8802

EICKHORST-SQUIRE Katrin *(Bq Cel, Rec)*: 42 Duddingston Park, Edinburgh EH15 1JY ☎ 0131 669 2123

FLETCHER C Jeremy: The Steading Pictfield, Blairgowrie, Perthshire PH10 7HQ ☎ 0410 566 877, 01250 876334

GARDEN Malcolm: 9 Roseneath Street, Edinburgh EH9 1JH ☎ 0131 229 8801

GIFFORD Gerald *(Pf)*: 150 Fergus Drive, Glasgow G20 6AX ☎ 0141 946 3714

GOUGH Christopher: 9 Chester Street, Edinburgh EH3 7RF ☎ 0131 220 4754

GOW Aline: 227 Glasgow Road, Longcroft, By Bonnybridge, Stirlingshire FK4 1QY ☎ 01324 841368

HADEN Joseph *(Pf)*: Address Unknown

HALE Helen: 71 Morningside Drive, Edinburgh EH10 5NJ ☎ 0131 466 0305

HARRINGTON Sarah: 17 Antonyne Road, Glasgow G61 4DP ☎ 0141 942 9375, 0802 703685 mob

HARRIS Harold: 1 Trefoil Place, North Street, Houston, Renfrewshire PA6 7HG ☎ 01505 612260

HOLMES Marie: 20 Marlborough Avenue, Glasgow G11 7BW ☎ 0141 339 1922

HUNT Peter: Wilden Moor, Main Street, Gartmore, Nr Aberfoyle FK8 3RW ☎ 01877 582594

HUTTUNEN Katri: 20 Holly Drive, Springburn, Glasgow G21 4EQ ☎ 0141 5582705

IRVINE Robert: Forth House, Gartmore, Stirlingshire FK8 3RW ☎ 01877 382646

JOHN Gareth *(Con)*: Awel-Y-Mor, Alvah Terrace], Banff, Aberdeenshire AB45 1BG ☎ 01261 815121

JOHNSON David *(Rec, Pf, Arr)*: 8 Shandon Crescent, Edinburgh EH11 1QE ☎ 0131 337 4621

KENNY Irene *(Pf)*: 69 Spottiswoode Street, Edinburgh EH9 1DL ☎ 0131 447 3707

LAWRANCE Alison *(Pf)*: 92 Kirkcaldy Road, Pollokshields, Glasgow G41 4LD ☎ 0141 423 8149, 0374 873 599 mob

LAY Robert *(Bq Cel, B Vln, B Viol, Vlne)*: Hillview, Cochno Road, Hardgate, Clydebank, Dunbartonshire G81 6PT ☎ 01389 875996, 01426 977225 pager

LEE Rachael: 1/R 53 Landerdale Gardens, Hyndland, Glasgow G12 9QT ☎ 0141 400 0987, 07775 854354

LEITCH John: Kingsdown, Kirkmichael, Maybole KA7 2RQ ☎ 01655 750509

LINKLATER William: 5 Hutcheonlow Drive, Persley, Aberdeen AB21 9WH ☎ 01224 685229

LUSHER Richmond: South Teavarran, Foxhole, Kiltarlity, Inverness IV4 7HT ☎ 01463 741 439

MASON Robin: 5 Newton Farm Cottages, Millerhill, Dalkeith, Midlothian EH22 0AS

MCCOSH Hilary: 51 Murray Terrace, Aberdeen AB1 2SA

MORTON Claire (Pf): 57 Laxton Drive, Lenzie, Glasgow G66 5LX ☎ 0141 777 8506

MUSTARD John M: Tarradale, Cloves, Alves, By Forres, Moray IV36 0RA ☎ 0134 385 402

NICHOLLS Julianna (Db): Talla Lan, Arinagour, Isle Of Coll, Argyll PA78 6SY ☎ 01786 833099

NORRIS Philip (Pf): Lyall Cliff, 141 Alexandra Parade, Dunoon, Argyll PA23 8AW ☎ 01369 702041

PARRY Frederick: 48 Duncan Avenue, Scotstoun, Glasgow G14 9HS ☎ 0141 954 4442

PATERSON William: 21 Main Street, Fintry, Glasgow G63 0XA ☎ 01360 860429

PAXTON Timothy: 15 Woodburn Terrace, Edinburgh EH10 4SJ ☎ 0131 4476751

PHYTHIAN-ADAMS Miranda: G/Lift, 38 Thornwood Drive, Glasgow G11 7UE ☎ 0141 337 2518

ROUTLEY Priscilla (Pf): 198 Braehead Road, Paisley PA2 8QF ☎ 0141 884 4423

ROWLANDS Ruth (Pf): 3/L, 139 Marlborough Avenue, Broomhill, Glasgow G11 7JE ☎ 0141 339 9373

RYCROFT Marjorie (T Viol, B Viol, Vielle, Bq Ce): 29 Airthrey Avenue, Glasgow G14 9LJ ☎ 0141 954 5020

SAYER Anthony: 3 Sanda Street, Glasgow G20 8PU ☎ 0141 946 2933

SCORDIA Geoffrey: 10 Montrose Drive, Bearsden, Glasgow G61 3JZ ☎ 0141 942 8174

SHEARMAN Amanda: 33/2 43 Walton Street, Top Right, Shawlands, Glasgow G41 3LR ☎ 0141 632 6215

SILVER Noreen: 4 May Terrace, Mount Florida, Glasgow G42 9XF ☎ 0141 569 6319

TAIT Alasdair (Pf): 18 Polmont Park, Polmont, Stirlingshire FK2 0XT ☎ 01324 713746, 0370 755318 mob

TURNER Angela: 17 St Marys Drive, Perth PH2 7BY ☎ 01738 621827

WEATHERBY Wendy (Voc): 1 Seafield Road East, Edinburgh EH15 1EB ☎ 0131 669 9667

WELSH Angela: 8 Milngavie Road, Bearsden, Glasgow G61 2HX ☎ 0141 942 2796

NORTH WEST

ALDERSEA Rebecca: Flat 2, 550 Wilbraham Road, Chorlton, Manchester M21 9LB

BENNET Andrew (Db): 50A Albion Hill, Brighton, East Sussex BN2 2NW ☎ 01273 570678

BILLS Heather: Bod Feddau, Llaniestyn, Beaumaris, Anglesey LL58 8YG ☎ 01248 811433

BINGHAM Ruth: 'Ty Hir', Caerwys, Mold, Flintshire CH7 5BG ☎ 01352 720387, 0370 723786 mob

BODDIS Walter

BRACKEN Ian: 25 Birch Road, Bebington, Wirral, Merseyside L63 7RJ ☎ 0151 645 6403

BRADSHAW Julia: 109 Kinder Road, Hayfield, High Peak SK22 2LE ☎ 01663 747690

BRIERLEY Elizabeth: 29 Harefield Drive, Didsbury, Manchester M20 2SZ ☎ 0161 445 9591

BROOKS Jean: 2, Turrocks Close, Little Neston, Cheshire. L64 0UD ☎ 0151 336 4325

BROWNING Hilary: 25 Birch Road, Bebington, Wirral, Merseyside L63 7RJ ☎ 0151 645 6403

BUNTING Catherine: 20 Princes Court, Croxteth Road, Liverpool L8 3UJ ☎ 0151 727 1894

CALLOW Steven: Roselle, Buxton Road, High Peak, Derby SK23 6BR ☎ 01663 750 368

COOK John (Acc): Conway Cottage, Thurstaston Road, Heswall Wirral, Merseyside L60 6SA ☎ 0151 342 4073

COSTELLO Sharon: 2 Stanley Court, Off Stanley Road, Old Trafford, Manchester M16 9DL ☎ 0161 848 7104

CULLIFORD Dale: 4 Rock Bank, Whaley Bridge, Cheshire SK12 7LE ☎ 01663 733073

DAVIES Arthur: 78 Cardiff Road, Llandaff, Cardiff CF5 2DT

DENNERLY Melanie: 7 Ashbourne Road, Denton, Manchester M34 2ED ☎ 0161 320 9371, 0958 465089 mob

DIXON Peter: 8 Hey Cliff Road, Holmfirth, W. Yorks HD7 1XD ☎ 01484 689489

EDWARDS Rebecca: 13 Catterick Road, Didsbury, Manchester M20 6HN ☎ 0161 445 0274

FAIRHURST Zoe: 53 Whitechapel Street, Didsbury, Manchester M20 6TX ☎ 0161 434 5997

FISTEIN Jonathan: 112 Claremont Road, Salford M6 8NL ☎ 0973 753902

GLENTON Robert (Bq Cel, Con): 16 Broomville Ave, Sale, Cheshire M33 3DD ☎ 0161 969 7098

GOOD: Flat 1 20 Brighton Grove, Fallowfield, Manchester M14 5JR ☎ 0161 257 2753, 0961 391311

GORDON Wendy (Clt, Pf, Rec, Flt): 8 Greenhowe Avenue, West Kirby, Wirral, Merseyside L48 ☎ 0151 722 7630

GRIMM Nigel: Ballamoar, Shore Road, Gansey, Port St Mary, Isle Of Man IM9 5LZ ☎ 01624 835026

GRUNTHAL Barbara: 92 Henwood Road, Withington, Manchester M20 4XG ☎ 0161 445 5544

HAGGARTY Gaynor (B Gtr, Kbds): ☎ 0161 225 7402

HALL Dorothy: 115 Atwood Road, Didsbury, Manchester M20 6JW ☎ 0161 434 6916

HALLETT Jane: The Bungalow, West Lane, High Legh, Knutsford, Cheshire WA16 6NE ☎ 01925 757339

HARRIS Kathryn (Pf): 30 Belfield Road, Didsbury, Manchester M20 6BH ☎ 0161 434 3522, 0802 449 773

HAYWARD Valerie: 59 Hill Top Avenue, Cheadle Hulme, Cheadle, Cheshire SK8 7HZ ☎ 0161 485 1458

HEWITT Stephanie (Pf, Rec): 54 Chestnut Street, Chadderton, Oldham, Lancs OL9 8HH ☎ 0161 688 6580

HEXT Joanna: 12, Urban Road, Sale, Cheshire M33 1TX ☎ 0161 905 3213

HOYLE Christopher: Mill View, Old Mill Farm, Wilshaw Mill Road, Meltham, Huddersfield HD7 3EB ☎ 01484 854736

HUNT Annie: 2 Hendre Bach, Llanelidan, Ruthin, Clwyd LL15 2PU ☎ 01824 750 399

JOHNSON Alan (Pf): 22 Croxteth Road, Liverpool L8 3SQ ☎ 0151 733 7363

JOHNSON Gerald: 55 Greyhound Lane, Norton, Stourbridge, West Midlands DY8 3AD

JONES Caroline: 4 Goosebrook Close, Comberbach, Northwich, Cheshire CW9 6BX ☎ 01606 891395

JONES Gethyn: 4 Oakland Vale, Wallasey, Merseyside L45 1LQ ☎ 0151 630 1884

KITCHEN Rayford: 73 Dalston Drive, Didsbury, Manchester M20 5LQ ☎ 0161 445 7658

LANGRIDGE Jennifer (Bq Cel): 39 Woodlawn Court, Whalley Range, Manchester M16 9RJ ☎ 0161 881 6852

LOVELL Sara: 90 High Street, Banwell, Weston-Super-Mare, North Somerset BS29 6AQ ☎ 01934 823321

MANN Stephen (Org): 24 Ashburne House, 100 Oxford Place, Victoria Park, Manchester M14 5SF ☎ 0161 224 0982

MARSHALL Mark: 3 Madeley Gardens, Spotland, Rochdale, Lancs OL12 7BZ ☎ 01706 654951

MCILWAINE Elizabeth: 129 Stamfordham Drive, Liverpool L19 6PY

MILNER Dorothy: Park View, Staffield, Kirkoswald, Penrith, Cumbria CA10 1EU ☎ 01768 898578

MORTON Greg (Kbds, Voc): 4 Mayfield Road, Whalley Range, Manchester M16 8FT ☎ 07970 807667

MURDIN Geoffrey: 131 Church Road, Rainford, St Helens, Merseyside WA11 8QH ☎ 01744 882919

NELSON Becca: 25 King Street, Middlewich CW10 9EJ ☎ 01606 738327

NEVILLE Elizabeth *(Pf)*: Flat 5 8 Clyde Road, West Didsbury, Manchester M20 2WH ☎ 0976 722674

PARROTT M: 26 Elgin Avenue, Garswood, Lancs WN4 0RH ☎ 01942 712941

PAUL Daniel: 10 Cresswell Grove, West Didsbury, Manchester M20 2NH ☎ 0161 446 1053

PENDLEBURY Sally: 32 Woolstone Road, Forest Hill, London SE23 2SG

PETRI David: 8 Moorland Road, Didsbury, Manchester M20 6BD ☎ 0161 445 4393

PRICE Jonathan: 6 Raynham Avenue, Didsbury, Manchester M20 6BW ☎ 0161 445 4053

QUINN Susan: 267 Chester Road, Little Sutton, South Wirral L66 1QG ☎ 0151 339 7269

ROBERTS Hannah: 37 Moorland Road, Didsbury, Manchester M20 6BB ☎ 0161 224 4651

ROBERTS Paul *(Db, B Gtr, Pf)*: 7 Lon Ganol, Menai Bridge, Gwynedd LL59 5LU ☎ 01248 717015

SAYERS Caroline: 97 Lyndhurst Avenue, Mossley Hill, Liverpool L18 8AR ☎ 0151 724 2082

SIDDALL Roger: 11 Ashlands, Hixon, Stafford, Staffs ST18 0NQ ☎ 01889 270774

SKINNER Miriam: 12 Bridgeholme Mill, Charley Lane, Chinley SK23 6DX ☎ 01663 751808

SMITH Anne *(Vadag)*: 11 Vernon Avenue, Stretford, Manchester M32 8JD ☎ 0161 865 6740

STEAD Sidney *(Db)*

STEER Caroline: Willow Dene, Moss Lane, Hebden Bridge, W Yorks HX7 7DS ☎ 01422 844470

STEWART Diane *(Pf)*: The Gatehouse, Barker's Lane, Snainton, Scarborough YO13 9BG ☎ 01723 859362

TASKER John: 26 West Bond Street, Macclesfield, Cheshire SK11 8EQ ☎ 01625 502586

TURNER Amanda: 105 Wigshaw Lane, Culcheth, Warrington WA3 4AD ☎ 01925 767098

VELLA Fiona: 22 Croxteth Road, Liverpool L8 3SQ ☎ 0151 733 7363

WALLACE E: Address Unknown ☎ 0151 733 3456

WARDALE Andrew *(Pf)*: 109 Lord Street, Crewe, Cheshire CW2 7DP ☎ 01270 212249

WESLING David: Flat 5, 46 Atwood Road, Didsbury, Manchester M20 6TD ☎ 0161 445 3707, 0976 774942

WHETTAM Rebecca: 9 Ivy Road, Poynton, Chesire SK12 1PE ☎ 01625 858878

WHITE Peter: 55 New Road, Holymoorside, Chesterfield S42 7EW ☎ 01246 568101

WILCOCK Carol: 43 Radnor Drive, Wallasey, Merseyside L45 7PJ ☎ 0151 637 0250

WILLIAMS John: 17 Ranford Road, Manchester M19 2QN ☎ 0161 224 9662

WOOD Frances: 10 Cresswell Grove, West Didsbury, Manchester M20 2NH ☎ 0161 446 1053

WOOD Laurence: 26 Larkhill Cottages, Old Langho, Blackburn BB6 8AR ☎ 01254 248923

WORRALL Peter: 442 Parrswood Road, Didsbury, Manchester M20 5GP ☎ 0161 445 9409

NORTH EAST

BEALL David: 62 Rook Lane, Norton, Stockton-on-Tees, Cleveland TS20 1SB ☎ 01642 555030

BENNETT Ruth: 25 Regent Road, Gosforth, Newcastle 3 NE3 1ED ☎ 0191 284 1655

BERRIDGE Cara *(Pf)*: 61 Wensley Drive, Chapel Allerton, Leeds LS7 3QP ☎ 0113 2693940, 0410 505432

BISHOP Charlotte *(Pf)*: 7 Burns Hill, Addingham, Ikley, West Yorkshire LS29 0JQ ☎ 01943 830857

BOWELL Mary: 63 Walkley Road, Sheffield S6 2XL ☎ 0114 232 5701

BRISSENDEN Elizabeth: The Coach House, 16 Barton Road, Wrawby, Brigg, N.Lincs DN20 8SH ☎ 01652 656058

BRYAN Margaret: 21 St Clements Grove, York YO23 1JZ ☎ 01904 644528

BURGIN Judith: Westfield House, 2 Newfield Drive, Menston, Leeds LS29 6JQ ☎ 01943.870598

CALLOW Penelope: 13 Bassington Cose, Newcastle-upon-Tyne, Tyne & Wear NE4 5BW

CAWOOD Elizabeth: 182 The Heights, Linthwaite, Huddersfield, Yorks HD7 5SS ☎ 01484 844643, 0411 260833

COOPER Frank *(Sax, Clt)*: Flat 21, Richmond House, Street Lane, Leeds LS8 1BW ☎ 0113 2681017

CORMACK James: 114 Vale House, Lansdowne Gdns, Jesmond, Newcastle-upon-Tyne, Tyne & Wear NE2 1HG ☎ 0191 281 0912

CRAIG James: North Farmhouse, Killing North Village, Newcastle-upon-Tyne NE12 0BL ☎ 2321207

EDMUNDS David *(Pf, Db)*: 12 Wordsworth Vale, Acklam, Middlesbrough, Cleveland TS5 8PL

FAIRLEY Andrew: 45 West Park Drive East, Leeds LS8 2EE ☎ 0113 293 4399

FARNON Nicola *(Db, Kbds, Voc)*: 71 Burcot Road, Sheffield S8 9FD ☎ 0114 255 3581

FERGUSON Penelope *(Pf)*: 2 Minster Court, York YO1 7JJ ☎ 01904 624965

FOX Margaret: 38 Fords Avenue, Healing, Grimsby, N.E Lincs DN37 7RP ☎ 01472 882461

GIVAN Curtis: PO Box 311, Durham, Hampshire, NH 03824 0311, USA

GRAY Rachel: The Point, 11 Beadle Garth, Copmanthorpe, York YO23 3YJ ☎ 01904 707145

GREENSMITH Brian *(Md, Con, Arr, B Ldr)*: Torridon House, 104 Bradford Road, Wrenthorpe, Wakefield West Yorkshire WF1 2AH ☎ 01924 371496

GREGOR-SMITH Bernard: 16, Silver Birch Avenue, Fulwood, Sheffield, Yorks S10 3TA ☎ 0114 2305531

HEYES Nicola *(Db)*: 18 Eve Gardens, Washingborough, Lincoln LN4 1QU ☎ 01522 792021

HOTTON Jean *(Pf)*: 1 Riverside Mews, Millgate, Thirsk, North Yorkshire YO7 1AE ☎ 01845 525207, 01262 850269

IRVINE Benedict: 36 Rue Renier Chalon, 1050 Ixelles, Brusssels, Belgium ☎ +32 23472665

KENNAWAY George *(Bq Cel)*: 23 Ingledew Crescent, Leeds LS8 1BP ☎ 0113 2663966 & fax, 0378 615957 mob

LADDS Roger: 34 Stainburn Crescent, Leeds LS17 6NS ☎ 0113 2660602, 0860 192166 mob

LADDS Sally J: 34 Stainburn Crescent, Leeds LS17 6NS ☎ 0113 2660602

LLOYD Elizabeth: 3 Lingerfield Terrace, Scotton, Knaresborough, North Yorkshire HG5 9HJ ☎ 01423 869503

LOCKER Aileen: 540 West Road, Denton Bank, Newcastle-on-Tyne 3, Northumberland NE5 2JL

MCEWEN Kathryn: 38 Colleridge Grove, Beverley, North Humberside HU17 8XD ☎ 01482 864834

MORRIS Anne: Wike Croft, Avon Garth, Linton, West Yorkshire LS22 6HH ☎ 01937 585068

MOSCROP YOUNG Ann: 38 Wayside Avenue, Harrogate, N Yorks HG2 8NP ☎ 01423 884133

ROBINSON Elizabeth *(Pf)*: 45 Spitalfields, Yarm, Stockton Tees TS15 9HN ☎ 01642 898072

ROULSON Michele *(Pf, Acc, Fo Fdl, Cl Gtr)*: 2 Gordon Willas, Carr Road, Ulceby, Lincs DN39 6TX ☎ 01469 588362, 01469 588911

ROYCROFT Miriam: 23 Ingledew Crescent, Leeds LS8 1BP ☎ 0113 2663966

SAVILLE Deborah *(Flt, Pf)*: Bridge Cottage, Baslow Road, Bakewell, Derbyshire DE45 1AA

THIN William: 81 Greystones Road, Sheffield S11 7BP ☎ 0114 267 8005

THORNTON Barrie: 24 Smawthorne Grove, Castleford, W Yorks WF10 5AS ☎ 01977 731688

TILER Jeffrey *(Db, Md)*: 2 Haise Mount, Darton, Barnsley S75 5LU ☎ 01226 383003

WANT Judith: Sorrel Bank, Park Avenue, Wortley, Sheffield S30 7DR ☎ 0114 2882348

WAREHAM Patricia: Plum Tree Cottage, 15 Wood Lane, Wickersley, Rotherham S66 0JT

WARHAM Christine *(Viol)*: 6 Cornfield Road, Middlesbrough TS5 5QL ☎ 01642 821 682

WELLS Jackie *(Db)*: 24 Hockley Lane, Wingerworth, Chesterfield, Derbyshire S42 6QG ☎ 01246 234965

WICKHAM Antonia: 1 The Square, Farnley, Otley, West Yorkshire LS21 2QG ☎ 01943 851072

YEADON Carol *(Db)*: 13 Huby Park, Strait Lane, Huby, Leeds LS17 0EE ☎ 01423 734361, 0802 713707 mob

EAST

APPLETON Anna: 15 Cowper Street, Ipswich IP4 5JB ☎ 01473 710172

BAINES Kathryn *(Pf)*: 154 The Avenue, Bengeo, Hertford, Hertfordshire SG14 3DX ☎ 01992 552999

BAUR Jane: 20 Battlefield Road, St Albans, Herts AL1 4DD

BENCSIK Deirdre: 38 Crosshill, Cotgrave, Nottingham NE12 3NB ☎ 0115 9894308

BENNETT Harriet *(Db, Pf, Org)*: Marsh Cottage, The Ferry, Felixstowe, Suffolk IP11 9RZ ☎ 01394 670633, 0378 153155

BROADHEAD Mark: 22 House Lane, Sandridge, St Albans, Herts AL4 9ET ☎ 01727 841451

COX Joanne: 26 Chadwick Road, Leytonstone, London E11 1NF ☎ 020 8530 7988

DAVIS Louise *(Pf)*: 82 Lindsey Way, Stowmarket, Suffolk IP14 2PD ☎ 01449 774892

DRINKALL Hilary: 13 Purwell Lane, Hitchin, Herts SG4 0NE ☎ 01462 459897

GILL Timothy: 48 Surrey Road, London SE15 3AT ☎ 020 7732 6231, 01306 880669

GRAHAM Julia: 38 Broadwater, Birkhamsted, Herts HP4 2AH ☎ 01442 874765, 0467 370 722 mob

HARDING Kate: 125 Starling Place, Boundary Way, Watford, Herts WD2 7SP ☎ 01923 679336 & fax

HARMER Marjorie *(B Viol, T Viol, Tr Viol, Bq C)*: The Auberies, Stonham Aspal, Stowmarket, Suffolk IP14 6AQ ☎ 01449 711571

HENDERSON Veronica: 33 Romsey Road, Cambridge CB1 3DD ☎ 01223 413234

HEYWOOD Susan: 6 Gurney Lane, Cringleford, Norfolk NR4 7SB ☎ 01603 454568

HOPGOOD Andrea *(Eup, Voc)*: 71 Prince Thorpe Road, Ipswich, Suffolk IP3 8NU ☎ 01473 727778

HUGHES Jeremy *(Con)*: 5 Chapel Street, Woodbridge, Suffolk IP12 4NF ☎ 01394 384 248

LILLEY Janet: 63 Church Road, Rayleigh, Essex SS6 8PL ☎ 01268 771026

LOCKE Kathryn *(Voc, Com)*: 28 Beeliegh Road, Maldon, Essex CM9 7QH ☎ 01621 852234

LOVERDIDGE Dury *(Db, Gtr, Clt, B Gtr)*: 31 Covehite Court, Haverhill, Suffolk CB9 8NE ☎ 0121 4466516, 01440 763211

OGDEN Nicola *(Pf)*: Fair Rig, Lt Thurlow Green, Nr Haverhill, Suffolk CB9 7JH ☎ 01440 783260

PASSCHIER Maja: 77 Gipsy Lane, Norwich NR5 8AX ☎ 01603 507934

PELLS Mary *(Pf, Vadag, Bq Cel)*: 36 Chaplin Road, East Bergholt, Colchester, Essex CO7 6SR ☎ 01206 298256

SUMMERS Mark *(Vadag, Hpsd)*: 1 St Clements Hill, Norwich NR3 4DE ☎ 01603 412714, 01603 462181 fax, 01523 120291

WHITEHOUSE Kathy: 49 Cliveden Close, Cambridge CB4 3LX

MIDLANDS

ARDAGH-WALTER Catherine: 53 Russell Road, Hall Green, Birmingham B28 8SF ☎ 0121 777 6643

BAILEY Joyce: 168 Station Road, Wylde Green, Sutton Coldfield, Warks B73 5LE ☎ 0121 354 1335

BATES Jasmine: 6 Jasmin Road, Malvern, Worcs WR14 4XD ☎ 01684 569981

BEAN John *(Pf)*: 184 Ratcliffe Road, Sileby, Leicestershire LE12 7QB ☎ 01509 814856

BOLGER Lorraine: 1 Windmill Lane, Belper, Derbys DE56 1GN

BOOLE-MASTERSON Naomi: 44 Alderminster, Stratford-upon-Avon, Warwickshire CV37 5NX ☎ 01789 450239, 0956 618949 mob

BOSHER Edward: 59, Braemar Road, Olton, Solihull, West Midlands B92 8BS ☎ 0121 706 7398

BOUND Andrew *(Eup)*: 10 Bambrook Close, Desford, Leicester LE9 9FY ☎ 01455 824 114

BROOKES Oliver *(Vadag)*: Waye House, Alston Cross, Ashburton, South Devon TQ13 7ET ☎ 01364 52114

BROWN Graham *(Pf, Tbn)*: Yew Tree, Uttoxeter Road, Lower Tean, Staffs ST10 4LN ☎ 01538 723896

BROWN Moira: Levesley House, 14 City Road, Stathern, Nr Melton Mowbray, Leics LE14 4HE ☎ 01949 860829, 0374 11880, 01949 860829

CALVERLEY Anthony: 8 Cornel, Amington, Tamworth, Staffs B77 4EF ☎ 01827 64149

CALVERLEY Rachael: 8 Cornel, Amington, Tamworth, Staffs B77 4EF ☎ 01827 64149, 0402 591864 mob

CAREY Jadie *(E Cel)*: 24 Hobson Road, Birmingham B29 7QH ☎ 0121 471 3093

CARUS-WILSON Alan: 4 Mews Cottage, 81 Albert Road South, Malvern, Worcs WR14 3DX

COLLARBONE Winifred: 40, Tamworth Stubb, Walnut Tree, Milton Keynes MK7 7DD ☎ 01908 671440

COX Elspeth: 46 Moorcroft Road, Moseley, Birmingham B13 8LX ☎ 0121 449 2383

CRACKNELL Robert: 610 Parkfield Road, Wolverhampton, W. Midlands WV4 6EH ☎ 01902 408704

DAVIS Russell: Wilcroft, Bartestree, Hereford HR1 4BB ☎ 01432 850409

FITZGERALD Helen *(Rec)*: 30 Sir Johns Road, Selly Park, Birmingham B29 7ER ☎ 0121 604 7537, 0374 435502 mob

FROST Corinne: Oak Cottage, Clifton-upon-Teme, Worcestershire WR6 6EN ☎ 01886 812659

GILDE Sean Karsten *(Voc)*: Flat 30, Hamstead Court, Hamstead Road, Hockley, Birmingham B19 1BU ☎ 0121 551 6518

GOODBORN Olive *(Db)*: 247 Hay Green Lane, Bournville, Birmingham B30 1SH ☎ 0121 475 7817

GUBBINS Jean *(Vadag, Bq Cel)*: 22 Trafalgar Road, Moseley, Birmingham B13 8BX ☎ 0121 449 2352

GWILT Dawn: 41 Franche Road, Wolverley, Kidearminster, Worcs DY11 5TP ☎ 01562 851630

HARPER Alison: c/o J S Lloyd, Young & Lee, No.6 The Wharf, Bridge Street, Birmingham B1 2JS ☎ 0121 633 3233, 0956 581 059 mob, 0121 632 5292

HEARTFIELD Jill: 46, Hazelmere Road, Hall Green, Birmingham B28 8HZ ☎ 0121 604 5488

HEINEN Elaine: 52 Harborne Park Road, Harborne, Birmingham B17 0DH ☎ 0121 427 1270

HEINEN Ulrich: 52 Harborne Park Road, Harborne, Birmingham B17 0DH ☎ 0121 427 1270

HOWELL Christopher: 3 Brackenfield Road, Hasbury, Halesowen, West Midlands B63 1AH ☎ 0121 550 8442

JOUBERT Anna: 21 Austin Road, Handsworth, Birmingham B21 8NU ☎ 0121 554 4151

KNUSSEN Sylvia: 61 Somers Road, Malvern, Link, Worcs WR14 1JA ☎ 01684 576538

KRISTY Nikki: Cream Cottage, 4 Church Lane, Martin Hussingtree, Worcs WR3 8TQ ☎ 01905 755421

LEADBEATER Sonia: 8, Keynsham Bank, Cheltenham, Glos. GL52 6ER ☎ 01242 514256

LEWIS Keith: 23 Victoria Road, Malvern, Worcs WR14 2TE ☎ 01684 568848

LUDFORD Ian: 98 Northfield Road, Kings Norton, Birmingham B30 1JG ☎ 0121 459 0557

LUDFORD Janet: 98 Northfield Road, Kings Norton, Birmingham B30 1JG ☎ 0121 459 0557

CELLO - MIDLANDS

MACCARTHY Ian: 2 Blythefield Avenue, Off Longleat, Great Barr, Birmingham B43 6QG ☎ 0121 358 7779, 0410 770872

MAINARD Amanda: 32A Oaks Road, Great Glen, Leicestershire LE8 9EG ☎ 0116 259 3095, 0589 238183

MCGINNES Maxine: 33 Granville Avenue, Long Eaton, Nottingham NG10 4HA ☎ 0115 973 2363, 07970 014715

NEWTON Erica (Pf): 9 Dunsmore Road, Hall Green, Birmingham B28 8EA ☎ 0121 777 9005

PARKIN Victoria: 5 Sherwood Hse, Sherwood Road, Smethwick, West Midlands B67 5DE ☎ 0121 420 1962, 0403 219092

POWELL David: 21 Clarence Square, Cheltenham, Glos. GL50 4JP ☎ 01242 510425

ROBB Susan: 131 Great Charles Street, Brownhills, Walsall, West Midlands WS8 6AF ☎ 01543 821094

ROTHWELL Ellen (Pf): 77 Fruitlands, Malvern Wells, Worcestershire WR14 4XQ ☎ 01684 569129, 07771 608 132

RUSSELL David: 14, Broadfields Road, Birmingham B23 5TL ☎ 0121 373 7849

SETTERFIELD Katharine: 26 Wighorn Road, Bearwood, Birmingham, West Midlands B67 5HQ ☎ 0121 434. 4480, 0966 253 762 mob

SHILLING George (Pf, Kbds, Gtr, B Gtr): Bank Cottage, Great Wolford, Nr. Shipston-on-Stour, Warwickshire CV36 5NQ ☎ 01608 674491, 0410 200203

SMART Shirley (Pf, Rec): 63 Lutterworth Road, Blaby, Leicester LE8 4DW ☎ 0116 2772751

SPEAR Elizabeth: The Court, Vicarage Drive, Stramshall, Nr Uttoxeter, Staffs ST14 5DL ☎ 01889 566998

SPENCER-SMITH Clare: 289 St Pauls Road, Smethwick, Warley, West Midlands B66 1HF ☎ 0121 532 3152

STEPHENSON Karen (Pf): 57 Ingleton Road, Edgeley, Stockport, Cheshire SK3 9NN ☎ 0161 480 5922, 0973 661003

STUBBS Julie (Pf): 8, Antler Drive, Etching Hill, Rugeley, Staffs WS15 2XS ☎ 01889 576010

TUSTAIN Sarah: Loth Lorien, The Compa, Kinver, Stourbridge DY7 6HS ☎ 01384 878 340

TYLER Jacqueline: 69 The Hurst, Moseley, Birmingham, West Midlands B13 0DA ☎ 0121 604 6181

VASSALLO Eduardo: 21 Ashfield Road, Kings Heath, Birmingham B14 7AS ☎ 0121 449 1171

VOWLES Thomas (Sax): c/o 2 Lynton Gardens, Arnold, Nottingham NG5 7HA

WALDEN Suzanne: 2 The Drive, Colletts Green, Powick, Worcs WR2 4SA ☎ 01905 830592

WALDOCK Wendy (Pf, Db): 68 Fairview Way, Stafford ST17 0AX ☎ 01785 222789

WALKER Kathleen: 9 Orchard Place, Deer Park, Ledbury, Herefordshire HR8 2XD ☎ 01531 2590

WHITING Gillian: 207 St Bernards Road, Solihull, West Midlands B92 7DL ☎ 0121 706 1840

SOUTH EAST

ALEXANDER Drusilla: 7 Edward Road, Parkstone, Poole, Dorset BH14 9ES ☎ 01202 746469

ASHBY Rhiannon: 189 Divinity Road, Oxford OX4 1LP ☎ 01865 245248

BAXTER Nicola: 'Woodside', 151 Amersham Road, Beaconsfield, Buckinghamshire HP9 2EH ☎ 01494 675668

BEVAN Catriona: 9 Bailey Close, Windsor, Berkshire SL4 3ND ☎ 01753 833726

BLANCHARD John (Gtr, Pf) ☎ 01865 875507

BROOKS Hilary (Bq Cel): 63 St Johns Street, Winchester, Hants SO23 8HF ☎ 01962 69843

BRUNDAN Amanda: 17 Bury Road, Branksome Park, Poole, Dorset BH13 7DE ☎ 01202 707726

BURDETT Bryan: York House, 39 The Avenue, Fareham, Hants PO14 1PF ☎ Fareham 235474

BUSER Felix: 110 Springfield Road, Southborough, Tunbridge Wells, Kent TN4 0RA ☎ 01892 548483

CHARLTON Neil (Pf): 93 Oldstead, Crown Wood, Bracknell, Berks RG12 0UF ☎ 01344 487271

CHILCOTT Polly: Champs Folly, Frilford, Nr Abingdon, Oxon OX13 5NX ☎ 01865 391397, 01865 391080

CHILD Angela: 14 Hillbrow Road, Pokesdown, Bournemouth, Dorset BH6 5NT ☎ 01202 433561

CLAYDEN Roger (B Tbn): 26 The Bramblings, Rustington, West Sussex BN16 2DA ☎ 01903 782811

CLEAL Carol (Pf): 23 Chandlers, Sherborne, Dorset DT9 3RT ☎ 01935 814494

CLUNIES-ROSS Andrew (Vln): Burley Moor House, Forest Road, Burley, Ringwood, Hants BH24 4DQ

COE Jane (Bq Cel): 38 Coombe Avenue, Ensbury Park, Bournemouth, Dorset BH10 5AE ☎ 01202 859247 & fax

COLLIER J Jayne (Pf): 1 Carfax Villas, Pattenden Lane, Marden, Kent TN12 9QS ☎ 01622 831097

COX Paul: 17 Western Avenue, Woodley, Reading, Berks RG5 3BJ ☎ 01734 692818

CRANHAM Lynden (Bq Cel): 15 South Leigh Road, Warblington, Havanat, Hants PO9 2RR

CREIGHTON Bernard: 2 Llandewi Court, Abergavenny, Gwent NP7 8AW

DEACON Lorraine: 18 Mountbatten Close, Slough SL1 2BG ☎ 01753 570897

EGGINGTON Phillippa: 3 Tarrant Rushton, Nr Blandford, Dorset DT11 8DS ☎ 01258 455720

EMERY Nigel: North House, Itton Court, Itton Chepstow, Gwent NP6 6BW

FILMER David: 5 Durley Chine Court, 36 West Fliff Road, Bournemouth, Dorset BH2 5HJ ☎ 01202 551270, 0468 572153 mob

FINDLAY Valerie: 9 St Peters Road, Abingdon, Oxon OX14 3SJ ☎ 01235 525502

FISH Christopher: 105 Wellington Street, Thame, Oxon OX9 3BW ☎ 01844 260851, 0966 165953 mob

FRAZER Anna: 34 Richmond Street, Kings Sutton, Banbury, Oxon OX17 3RT ☎ 01295 812192

GARBUTT Christopher: 53 Austin Avenue, Lilliput, Poole, Dorset BH14 8HD ☎ 01202 701326

GILLETT Fiona (B Viol, Pf, Flt): 40 Salts Avenue, Loose, Maidstone, Kent ME15 0AZ ☎ 0973 442839 mob

HANDY Lionel: Tullagh, 3 Fernhill Road, New Milton, Hampshire BH25 5JZ ☎ 01425 638682

HANESWORTH Walter: 1019 Christchurch Road, Bournemouth, Dorset BH7 6BD ☎ 01202 423563

HARWOOD Richard (Pf, Com): 77 Highfield Avenue, Waterlooville, Hampshire PO7 7QP ☎ 023 9226 5831

JAMES J (Tbn): 7 Woodland Mews, West End, Southampton SO3 3DF ☎ 023 8088 3913

JOHNSON Jacqueline: 32 Bartlemas Road, Oxford OX4 1XX ☎ 01865 240481

KENNEDY Laurien: 30 Byron Road, Twyford, Reading, Berks RG10 0AE ☎ 0118 934 0107

KOOS Joseph: 45A Portchester Road, Bournemouth, Dorset BH8 8JU ☎ 01202 552483

KUHLES Theresa (Pf): 2 Mill Lane, Amersham, Bucks HP7 0EH ☎ 01494 438044

LOCKYER Simon (Kbds, Com): 45 Radipole Lane, Poole, Dorset BH17 8BZ ☎ 01202 658153

LOWES Clare: Tangley, 15 Salisbury Road, Blandford, Dorset DT11 7HL ☎ 01258 453232

LOWREY Ray: 19 Navarino Road, Worthing, West Sussex BN11 2NE ☎ 01273 463591

MAGNUS Ian: 18 Grove Road, Wimborne, Dorset BH21 1BW

MANDEVILLE Marion: 6 Waterworks Cottages, Hillbarn Lane, Worthing, Sussex BN14 9QQ ☎ 01903 202783

MASON Susan: 3 Blackmans Lane, Hadlow, Tonbridge, Kent TN11 0AX

MCMURTRIE Virginia: The Shealing, Backsideans, Wargrave, Berks RG10 8JP ☎ 0118 940 3321, 0118 940 1131 fax

MORTER Thomas (Db, Pf): 27 St Johns Road, Abingdon, Oxon OX14 2HA ☎ 01235 554315

MYERS Alison: Peppercorn Cottage, 58 Wainsford Road, Everton, Lymington, Hampshire SO41 0UD ☎ 01590 45918

44

NORTON David: 23 Dorset Street, Blandford, Dorset DT11 7RF ☎ 01258 459347

PRESTON Roger: 84 Nortoft Road, Charminster, Bournemouth, Dorset BH8 8PZ ☎ 01202 467001

REYNOLDS Helen: 11 Osborne Road, Parkstone, Poole, Dorset BH14 8SD ☎ 01202 747707

ROWE Samantha: The Cottage, Nine Elms, Jordans Way, Jordans Beaconsfield, Bucks HP9 2SP ☎ 01494 875074

SIM Janet: 4 Nursery Road, Blandford, Dorset DT11 4EZ ☎ 01258 454747

STEVENS Gary: 43 Barnes Road, Farncombe, Surrey GU7 3RG ☎ 0148 687398

STILWELL John: 12 Rowlands Road, Roffey, Horsham, Sussex RH12 4LH ☎ Horsham 52914

STUART-PENNINK Ms S (*Bq Cel, Acc, Con*): 25 Holden Road, Tunbridge Wells TN4 0QG ☎ 01892 527253, 07771 790750

TAYLOR Lorna: Avenue Villa, 43, Eastern Avenue, Reading RG1 5RX ☎ 01734 663912

THOMPSON Caroline (*Voc*): 9 Jealott's Hill, Warfield, Bracknell, Berkshire RG42 6ES ☎ 01344 450065, 0589 275268 mob

TOLLERVEY Mary (*Pf*): 6A High Street, Burnham, South Bucks SL1 7JH ☎ 01628 669024

TUCKER Kay: 8 Nelson Road, Horsham, West Sussex RH12 2JE ☎ 01403 256226

WARDELL Joanna (*Pf*): 19 Windsor Road, Poole, Dorset BH14 8SF ☎ 01202 723567

WEBB Simon: 29 Hawden Road, Tonbridge, Kent TN9 1JN ☎ 01732 362322

WHITEHEAD Diana: Stags Lodge, Main Street, West Hagbourne, Oxon OX11 0NJ ☎ 0836 773303 mob, 01235 850781 fax

WILSON Spike: 53 Stapleton Road, Headington, Oxford OX3 7LX ☎ 01865 66565

SOUTH WEST

AIRD Liza Ellen: 3 Llanbedr Road, Fairwater, Cardiff CF5 3BU ☎ 029 2057 6338, 0378 017276

BEARD Nick (*B Gtr*): 7 Meadow Park, Burton, Milford Haven, Pembrokeshire SA61 1NZ ☎ 01646 601826

BOYCE Charlotte: The Music Box, 1 Bramley Way, Ashill, Cullompton, Devon EX15 3NG ☎ 01884 841753

BRETWYN Wolfe: 4 Queensberry House, Friars Lane, Richmond, Surrey TW9 1NT

BREWER Emmeline (*Pf, Voc, Rec*): Top Flat, 18 Bellevue, Clifton, Bristol BS8 1DB ☎ 0117 973 7018, 0117 973 7018

BUNE Margaret: 88 Parc Y Fro, Creigiau, Cardiff CF8 8SB ☎ 029 2089 0045

CASSIDY Claudine (*Bq Cel*): 22 Clos Powys, York Dale Estate, Beddau, Ponty Pewys CF38 2SY ☎ 01443 201204

CORCOS Nadia: 167 Berrow Road, Burnham-on-Sea TA8 2JE ☎ 01278 785 242, 01934 647 069 day

COX Rosalind: Lower Hayne Barton, Ashill, Cullompton, Devon EX15 3NL ☎ 01884 84168

CREASER Sandra: 43 Henley Drive, Highworth, Swindon SN6 7JU ☎ 01793 413041 day, 01793 762528 eve

CRUMP Ursula: Flat 3, 25 East Street, Weymouth, Dorset DT4 8BN, 01305 780658

DAVID Stephen: 112 Alexandra Road, Six Bells, Abertillery, Gwent NP3 2LH ☎ 99323132

DAVISON Simon: 72 Heol Isaf, Radyr, Cardiff, S Glam CF4 8DZ ☎ 029 2084 3442

DE-LLOYD Rose-Marie (*Db*): 3 Wingfield Road, Whitchurch, Cardiff CF4 4NJ ☎ 029 2061 5459, 0973 789316

DEBBONAIRE Thangham: 89 Mina Road, St Werburghs, Bristol BS2 9XP ☎ 0117 935 0402, 0370 924389

DICKIE Charles (*Db, Kbds, Impro*): 2 Ropers Buildings, Upwey, Weymouth, Dorset DT3 5LR ☎ 01305 816151

DOWNIE Margaret (*Pf*): 30 Windsor Road, Radyr, Cardiff CF4 8BQ ☎ 029 2056 8392

DURHAM Catherine (*Bq Cel*): 49 Hawthorne Street, Totterdown, Bristol BS4 3DA ☎ 0117 972 3993

EARDLEY Aidan: 67 St Fagans Rise, 91 Cathedral Rd, Cardiff CF5 3EZ ☎ 029 2055 4547

ELLIOTT Andrew: Brynawel, Trerhyngyll, Cowbridge, S.Glamorgan CF7 7TN ☎ 01446 773824

EVANS Michael: Lakemead, Totnes, Devon TQ9 5EX ☎ 01803 863677, 01803 868771

EVANS Vicky: Lakemead, Maudlin Road, Totnes, Devon TQ9 5EX ☎ 01803 863677

FARNON Margaret (*Pf*): 32 High Street, Market Levington, Nr Devizes, Wilts SN10 4AG ☎ 0138 081 2237

GLYN-WILKINSON George: Pontymeddyg, Dinas Cross, Fishguard, Dyfed SA42 0XL ☎ 01348 811247

GREENWOOD Jane: The Holt, Fluxton, Ottery St Mary, Devon EX11 1RL ☎ 01404 815 596

HAIME David: 17 Clos Brynderi, Rhiwbina, Cardiff CF4 6NN ☎ 029 2062 7678

HAIME Helen: 17 Clos Brynderi, Rhiwbina, Cardiff CF4 6NN ☎ 029 2062 7678

HALL Herbert: 15 Summerfield, Sidmouth, Devon EX10 9RY ☎ 01395 514593

HAMES Robin (*Db, B Gtr*): Tay Lodge, 70 Preston Avenue, Newport, Gwent NP9 4JD ☎ 01633 257618

HARRHY Emma (*Db, Pf*): 26 Llanthewy Road, Newport, Gwent NP9 4LD ☎ 01633 252079

HEWITT Keith: 169 Fairwood Road, Fairwater, Cardiff CF5 3QH ☎ 029 2055 2354

HIER Philip: 9 Flatholme Way, Nottage, Portcowl CF36 3TW

HIGGINSON Victoria L (*Vadag*): 56 Cathedral Road, Cardiff CF1 9LL ☎ 029 2066 6968

HODGES Christopher (*Pf*): Derlwyn, Ynyshir Road, Ynyshir, Mid Glamorgan CF39 0DY ☎ 01443 682340

HOWARD Jennifer: 321 Western Avenue, Llandaff, Cardiff CF5 2BA ☎ 029 2056 1077

ISTANCE Jennifer: The Beeches, 45 Pentwyn, Radyr, Cardiff CF4 8RE ☎ 029 2084 2435

JOHNSTONE Christine: 13 Okebourne Road, Brentry, Bristol, Avon BS10 6RE ☎ 0117 9503861

KHOO Christine (*Db*): 76 Campion Drive, Bradley Stoke, Bristol BS32 0BH ☎ 01454 625 737, 07957 277 142 mob

LACEY Helen: Koskikatu. 21B. 18, 80100. Joensuu. 10, Finland

LASS Ruth: Sunnyhill, Littledown Lane, Newton Poppleford, Sidmouth / Devon EX10 0BG ☎ 01395 68786

LEWIS Roger: 47A Eversley Road, Sketty, Swansea, West Glamorgan SA2 9DE ☎ 207018

LONERGAN Terence: 11 Cwrt Cefn, Mill Road, Lisvane, Cardiff CF4 5US

LUNT Helen (*Pf, Flt*): 188 High Street, Street, Somerset BA16 0NH ☎ 01458 447374

MAY John: 17 Claverton Road West, Saltford, Bristol BS31 3AL ☎ 01225 872763

MILLER Raymond: 3 Laurence Court, Ludgershall, Andover, Hampshire SP11 9QN

MORRIS Gwyn: Penstead, Higher Furzeham Road, Brixham TQ5 8QP ☎ 01803 51721

NEWLAND Barry (*Db, Cl Gtr*): Holly Cottage, Barge Lane, Honey Street, Pewsey, Wiltshire SN9 5PS ☎ 01672 851344

PARKES Arthur: 5 The Tudors, Melrose Avenue, Penylan, Cardiff CF3 7BA ☎ 029 2048 1970

PEGNA Shirley (*Acc, Pf, Gtr*): 3 Fairlawn Road, Montpelier, Bristol BS6 5JR ☎ 0117 9240612

POWER Shena (*Voc*): 13 Grosvenor Terrace, St Saviours Road, Larkhall, Bath BA1 6SR ☎ 01225 319603

RICHARDS Carolyn (*Pf*): 67 Saint Fagans Rise, Fairwater, Cardiff, South Glamorgan CF5 3EZ ☎ 029 2055 4547

RUMP Avril: Churchill Hall, Stoke Park Road, Bristol BS9 1JG ☎ 0117 9684219

SENTER John: 18 St Michaels Road, Llandaff, Cardiff CF5 2AP ☎ 029 2055 5908

SPEAK Eric (*Db*): 186 St Mary Church Road, Babbacombe, Torquay TQ1 3JT ☎ 01803 314613

Early music today

Britain's brightest early music news and listings magazine

STAPLES Ann *(Vln, Vla)*: 7 Hensley Road, Bath BA2 2DR ☎ 01225 314905

STEVENS Gillian *(Bq Cel, Vadag, Com)*: Mill House, Ross Road, Abergavenny, Gwent NP7 5RF ☎ 01873 850968

STOCKS Linda: 48 First Avenue, Oldfield Park, Bath BA2 3NW

TEMPEST Keith: 122 Locksbrook Road, Lower Weston, Bath ☎ 01225 338538

THOMAS Kay: 7 Collingwood Road, Redland, Bristol BS6 6PB ☎ 0117 9738107

THOMAS Nicola: 13 Maes Hafren, Eglwyswrw, Pembrokeshire SA41 3SH ☎ 01239 891258

TOMLINSON Joanna: 2 The White House, The Cathedral Green, Llandaff, Cardiff CF5 2EB

TOMLINSON Juliet *(Tr Viol)*: Cinder Tump, Pennywill Lane, Littledean, Glos GL14 3JX ☎ 01594 824549 & fax, 0468 870235

TREHARNE Gwen *(Hrn, Pf)*: 22 Geraints Way, Cowbridge, Vale Of Glamorgan CF71 7AY ☎ 01446 773049

TYLER Anne *(Db)*: 14 Woodhurst Road, Weston Super Mare, North Somerset BS23 3JR ☎ 01934 626249

WALDEN Timothy: 1 Boywood Cottages, Mappowder, Sturminster Newton DT10 2EQ ☎ 01258 817135

WATKINS Dewi *(Db, Gtr)*: 127 Cardiff Road, Taffs Well, Cardiff CF4 7PP ☎ 029 2081 0687

WEBB Daphne: Northolt, The Glen, Saltford, Bristol BS18 3JW ☎ 012217 3272

WIEGOLD Richard: 131 Heol-Y-Deri, Rhiwbina, Cardiff CF4 6UH ☎ 029 2062 0469

WILKINS Richard: Hillside House, 17 Lyall Close, Blunsdon St Andrew, Swindon, Wilts SN2 4EH ☎ 01793 706 775

WILLS Margaret *(Db)*: 28 Cleeve Wood Road, Downend, Bristol BS16 2SS ☎ 0117 9568093

WILSON-DICKSON Rachel *(Flt, Per)*: Mill House, Ross Road, Abergavenny, Gwent NP7 5RF ☎ 01873 850 968, 020 7790 4844

WRIGHT Adrian: 2 Lancaster Way, Chepstow NP6 5SI ☎ 01291 628852

ZAGNI Ruth: 11 Prior Park Cottages, Widcombe, Bath BA2 4NR ☎ 01225 314613, 07970 797216

LONDON

ABBOTT Josephine: 34 Milman Road, London NW6 6EG ☎ 020 8960 7322

ADAMS Peter *(Vadag, Pf)*: 22 Crouch Street, Banbury, Oxfordshire OX16 9PP ☎ 01295 277976 & fax

ADAMS Raymond: 48 Brooklands Park, Blackheath, London SE3 9BL ☎ 020 8297 2076

ADEJAYAN Jennifer: 27 St Georges Road, Forest Gate, London E7 8HT ☎ 020 8548 4951

ADLER Stanley *(B Gtr)*: 148B Westcombe Hill, Blackheath, London SE3 7DT ☎ 020 8858 6382

ALBERTS Lionel: 54 Culverden Park, Tunbridge Wells, Kent TN4 9QR ☎ 01892 513008

ALFORD Ruth *(Bq Cel)*: The Westleton, Old London Road, Knockholt, Kent TN14 7JR ☎ 01959 532360

ALLAN Christopher: 16A Brooke Road, London N16 7LS ☎ 020 7249 5879 & fax

AMHERST Gabriel *(Bq Cel)*: 37 Chalfont Road, Oxford OX2 6TL ☎ 01865 558503

ANDREWS Elizabeth *(Bq Cel)*: 86 Park Hill, Carshalton Beeches, Surrey SM5 3RZ ☎ 020 8669 4358

ANGEL Elizabeth *(Pf)*: 120 Belmont Rise, Belmont, Sutton, Surrey SM2 6EE ☎ 020 8642 5714

ANSTEE Stephen *(Man, Gtr)*: 4 Eagle Court, 69 High Street, Hornsey, London N8 7QG ☎ 020 8342 9426, 0973 502066 mob, 01306 500011 day

ASHTON Ann *(Hrp, Pf, Voc)*: 96A Camberwell Grove, London SE5 8RF ☎ 020 7703 9102

ASLANGUL Philip *(Pf, Con)*: 35 Haddon Road, Sutton, Surrey SM1 1RN ☎ 020 8643 6009

ATTWOOD Elspeth: 59 Ecton Park Road, Ecton Brook, Northampton NN3 5LF ☎ 01604 414828

AUPHAN Aude: 4 Tetherdown, London N10 1NB ☎ 020 8374 7662, 0411 749122

AYRES Marvin *(Pf, Vln)*: 27 Kings Avenue, Clpaham, London SW4 8DX ☎ 020 7733 5763, 0836 648083

BAILEY Diana *(Clt, Pf)*: 111 Kings Road, Biggin Hill, Westerham, Kent BR6 6DA

BAILEY Lucy *(Pf)*: 30 Ravenscourt Road, London W6 0UG ☎ 020 8846 9704

BAILEY Robert: Wentworth, 19 Kirkstall Road, Streatham, London SW2 4HD ☎ 020 8671 0018

BAILEY Sarah: 93 Burnt Ash Road, Lee, London SE12 8RF ☎ 020 8852 4413, 01306 880669

BAIRD Ben *(Db, B Gtr, E Gtr)*: 134 Beechcroft Road, Wandsworth Common, London SW17 7DA ☎ 020 8672 0423, 020 7586 1271

BAIRD-SMITH Georgina: 36 Middleton Road, London E8 4BS ☎ 020 7254 0431, 0410 764 811

BAKER Anne: 6 Ophelia Gardens, Hamlet Square, The Vale, Golders Green London NW2 1ST ☎ 020 8452 8747

BALDWIN Kelly *(Pf)*: 10 Dorchester Court, Buckingham Road, South Woodford, London E18 2NG ☎ 020 8504 4799

BALKWILL Maryan: 8 Rodney Place, Wimbledon, London SW19 2LQ ☎ 020 8542 7275

BANBURY James *(Theramin)*: 7 Spezia Road, London NW10 4QJ ☎ 020 8961 3463

BANDA Pal *(Bq Cel)*: 19 Holden Road, North Finchley, London N12 8HP ☎ 020 8343 8935

BARBER Ann: 76 Babington Road, London SW16 6AH ☎ 020 8769 1061

BEAMISH Dinah *(Arr)*: Ground Floor, 2 Oak Lane, London N2 8LP ☎ 020 8349 3967, 0976 262515 mob, 020 8533 1372 day

BEARE Kate: 2 Sheen Wood, Christ Church Road, London SW14 7AG ☎ 020 8878 0821

BEAVAN Peter: Address Unknown ☎ Ashburton 52366

BEKOVA Alfia: 7A Cleveland Road, Islington, London N1 3ES ☎ 020 7226 8412 & fax

BELCHER Barrie: 27 Shelvers Way, Tadworth, Surrey KT20 5QJ ☎ 01737 351591

BELL Sian: 120 Amyand Park Road, Twickenham, Middlesex TW1 3HP ☎ 020 8744 1066, 01306 880669

BERGIN Mary: 48A Messina Avenue, West Hampstead, London NW6 4LD ☎ 020 7372 3963

BERSEY William *(Pf, Db)*: 411 Upper Richmond Road, Putney, London SW15 5QX ☎ 020 8878 9593, 0701 0709742

BETHEL Mark: 10 Melrose Place, Watford, Hertfordshire WD1 3LN ☎ 01923 255920

BETHGE Deitrich: 11 Ravenscroft Park, High Barnet, Herts EN5 4ND ☎ 020 8440 4695

BINNEY Helena: 44 High Street, Seal, Sevenoaks, Kent TN15 0AP ☎ 01732 762994

BIRTCHNELL Una *(Pf)*: 19 Cranhurst Road, Wilsden Green, London NW2 4LJ ☎ 020 8450 3513

BISWAS Anup: 93B Cambridge Gdns, North Kensington, London W10 6JE ☎ 020 8960 5889

BLACK Catherine: 83 Smallwood Rd, Tooting, London SW17 0TN ☎ 020 8767 0633 & fax, 0956 614530 mob

BLACK Emma: 16 Wilton Crescent, Wimbledon, London SW19 3QZ ☎ 020 8542 4178, 0973 780490, 020 8533 1372 day

BLAYDEN Alastair: Flat 2, 6 Saltoun Road, London SW2 1EP

BLOMILEY Nigel: 6 The Crescent, Friern Barnet, London N11 3HN ☎ 020 8368 1526

BODNAR Emese: 12A South Approach, Moor Park, Northwood, Middlesex HA6 2ET ☎ 01923 836873, 0585 763590

BOOTH Elizabeth: 20A Whitehall Road, Harrow, Middlesex HA1 3AJ ☎ 020 8423 6851

BOOTHROYD Nicholas: Flat 5, 132 Battersea Church Road, London SW11 3NA ☎ 020 7924 1448, 01306 880669

BRADBURY Adrian: 89 Waller Road, London SE14 5LB ☎ 020 7639 1382

BRADSHAW Graham: 152 Alexandra Park Road, London N22 4UJ ☎ 020 8889 5798

BRADSHAW Martin: 3 Tachbrook Court, Tachbrook Street, London SW1V 2JT ☎ 020 7821 9530

BRADSHAW Noel: 64 Casewick Road, London SE27 0SY ☎ 020 8766 7073

BRADSHAW Penny: 82 Salcott Road, London SW11 6DF ☎ 020 7738 9479, 020 7207 9969 fax

BRIDGER Mary (*Pf, Voc, Gtr*): 13 Farm Lane, Southgate, London N14 4RP ☎ 020 8441 7091

BRIDGMONT Richard: 12 Kingsdown Avenue, Ealing, London W13 9PR ☎ 020 8579 7790

BRIGDEN Jonathan: Flat A, 40 Manville Road, Balham, London SW17 8JN ☎ 020 8682 0575, 04111 3115, 020 7483 4699

BRODIE Janice: 152 Alexandra Park Road, London N22 4UJ ☎ 020 8889 5798

BROTHERS Philip: 21 Street Farm Lane, Ixworth, Suffolk IP31 2JE ☎ 01359 232168

BROWN Gabrielle: 22 Canonbie Road, Forest Hill, London SE23 3AP ☎ 020 8699 6128, 0860 105004 mob

BROWN Jennifer: Beech House, 6 Sydenham Park Road, London SE26 4ED ☎ 020 8291 5939

BRUCE William: 12 Pierrepoint Road, London W3 9JH ☎ 020 8248 9067

BRUCE-MITFORD Myrtle: 50A Underhill Road, East Dulwich, London SE22 0QT ☎ 020 8693 1695

BRUNNER Paul: 1 Roxley Road, Lewisham, London SE13 6HG ☎ 020 8265 7689

BUCKNALL David: 20 Cassland Road, London E9 7AN ☎ 020 8986 7452 & fax, 01306 880669 day, 0973 722181 mob

BUCKNALL Francis: 28 Fernbrook Drive, North Harrow, Middlesex HA2 7EB ☎ 020 8933 9291, 07970 631321

BURDGE Ian (*Db*): 151 Leander Road, London SW2 2LP ☎ 020 8674 0728, 0958 625070

BURLEY Imogen: 48 Craven Gardens, Wimbledon, London SW19 8LU ☎ 020 8543 2439

BURLEY Trevor: 104 Valley Road, London SW16 2XR ☎ 020 8677 1500

BURROWES David: Loxley Cottage, Stonehouse Road, Halstead, Kent TN14 7HW ☎ 01689 850770

BUTCHER Sarah: 48 Sunnyside Road, Chesham, Bucks HP5 2AR ☎ 01494 786791, 0585 875977 mob

BUTTERWORTH Naomi (*Pf*): 64 Park Hall Road, West Dulwich, London SE21 8DW ☎ 020 8761 4397, 020 8670 7842

CALDER Ronald: 8 Wilton Crescent, Wimbledon, London SW19 3QZ ☎ 020 8540 4900

CAMERON Alexander: 1 Willow Drive, Seaford, East Sussex BN25 4BZ ☎ 01323 891718

CARVALHO Santiago: 4 Croxton Lane, Lindfield, Haywards Heath, West Sussex RH16 2SD ☎ 01444 483853

CATLOW John: 24 Surrey Road, North Harrow, Middx HA1 4NH ☎ 020 8427 9688

CHALMERS Geraldine: 100A Weston Park, Hornsey, London N8 9PP ☎ 020 8348 9358

CHAPPELL Ben: 18C Cheverton Road, Archway, London N19 3AY ☎ 020 7272 5480, 01306 50001

CHERNAIK David (*Con*): 43 Clifden Road, London E5 0LL ☎ 020 8986 4101

CHEW Walija: 28 Dalmore Avenue, Claygate, Surrey KT10 0HQ ☎ 01372 462 463

CHILLINGWORTH John (*Org*): 17 South Cottage Gardens, Chorleywood, Herts WD3 5EH ☎ 01923 282412

CHRISTIE Michael (*Vadag*): Basement Flat, 16D Hampstead Hill Gardens, London NW3 2PL ☎ 020 7435 0914, 020 7794 3610 & fax

CIVVAL Sally (*Vadag, Bq Cel*): c/o Music Management (UK) Ltd., PO Box 1105, London SW1V 2DE ☎ 020 7823 1111

CLIFF Penelope: 83 Oriel Road, London E9 5SG

CLUTTON Christine: 62 Danziger Way, Borehamwood, Herts WD6 5DD ☎ 020 8953 6576, 01306 880669

COLE Joanne: Gate Cottage, High Street, Hinxworth, Herts SG7 5HQ ☎ 01462 743052, 01306 880669

COLES Janet: 53 Crescent Wood Road, London SE26 6SA ☎ 020 8693 5741

COMBERTI Sebastian: 38 Chandos Road, London N2 9AP ☎ 020 8444 6358 & fax, 020 8533 1372 day

CONSTABLE Claire: 1 New Church Court, Waldegrave Road, Crystal Palace, London SE19 2AU ☎ 020 8653 0411, 0973 915476, 01306 500011 day

COOPER Deirdre: 7 Allenby Road, Forset Hill, London SE23 2RQ ☎ 020 8291 6544

COOPER Nicholas: 75 Byne Road, Sydenham, London SE26 5JG ☎ 020 8244 2045

COOPER Susan: 34 Tennyson Avenue, Wanstead, London E11 2QN ☎ 020 8989 7319

COOTE Nicholas: 1 Blacksole Cottages, Pilgrims Way, Wrotham, Kent TN15 7DF ☎ 01732 780310

COSSACK Malka: 11 Park Chase, Wembley Park, Middx HA9 8EQ ☎ 020 8902 2073

COUCHMAN Humphrey (*Man*): 93C Elgin Avenue, London W9 2DA ☎ 020 7266 1177

CROMWELL Laurence: 16 Merewood Road, Barnehurst, Bexleyheath, Kent DA7 6PG ☎ 01322 332421

CROUCH Janet: Address Unknown ☎ 01420 472206, 01420 478690 fax

CULLIS John: 25 The Marina, Deal, Kent ☎ 01304 373160

CUMMINGS Douglas: 11 St Marks Road, Ealing Common, London W5 3JS ☎ 020 8579 4963

CUNDY Margaret: 12 The Grange, Worcester Park, Surrey KT4 7DJ ☎ 020 8337 6026

DALE Caroline: 9 Hollymount, Hampstead, London NW3 6SG ☎ 020 7435 4489, 020 8549 1706 day

DANIELS David: 49 Lynton Mead, Totteridge, London N20 8DG ☎ 020 8445 1970

DANIELS Muriel: 22 Belle Vue Road, Salisbury, Wiltshire SP1 3YG ☎ 01722 320072

DAVIES Benjamin: 17 Cecilia Road, Dalston, London E8 2EP ☎ 020 7249 6519 & fax, 0976 723381 mob

DAVIES Huw (*Pf, Arr*): 25 Lytton Avenue, London N13 4EH ☎ 020 8886 3067 & fax

DAVIS Benjamin: 14 Fairmount Road, London SW2 2BL ☎ 020 8674 9573

DAWKINS Tanera (*Pf, Com, Arr*): Basement Flat, 116 Tachbrook Street, London SW1V 2ND ☎ 020 7233 8132

DE GROOTE Philip: 43 Turney Road, West Dulwich, London SE21 7JA ☎ 020 7733 4352, 0410 179925 mob

DEARNLEY Caroline: 86 Stanley Road, London N11 2LG ☎ 020 8368 6441, 020 8549 1706 day

DEL-MAR Pauline: 8 Campden Hill Gate, Duchess Of Bedfords Walk, London W8 7QH ☎ 020 7937 7346 & fax

DENBIN Sid: 8 Hendon Hall Court, Parson Street, Hendon, London NW4 1QY ☎ 020 8203 3045

DENT Robert: Ground Floor Flat, 33 Carlingford Road, London NW3 1RY ☎ 020 7794 6749

DESBRUSLAIS Julia: 46 Harold Road, London SE19 3PL ☎ 020 8653 9446

DINITZEN Kim Bak: Flat 1, 3 Randolph Place, Edinburgh EH3 7TQ ☎ 0131 225 5143

DOLTON Maria (*Db*): Flat 2, 146 Coldharbour Lane, Camberwell, London SE5 9QH ☎ 020 7738 6242

DONOGHUE Laura: 68 Deanery Close, East Finchley, London N2 8NT ☎ 020 8362 2676, 0589 073 279 mob

DOREY Sue: 163 Elms Crescent, London SW4 8QQ ☎ 020 8675 6163, 020 8533 1372

EAGLES Harvey (*Con*): 11 Chestnut Close, London SW16 2SH ☎ 020 8677 9537

EAST Angela: 34 Fernwood Avenue, London SW16 1RD ☎ 020 8769 4168, 01749 675941

EAST Ruth: 84 Whitmore Gardens, London NW10 5HJ ☎ 020 8969 8999

EBBUTT Lucinda (*Pf, Org, Voc*): 13 Ardross Avenue, Northwood, Middlesex HA6 3DS ☎ 01923 824944, 0958 547018 mob

EDGAR Helen: 32 Dukes Avenue, Chiswick, London W4 2AE ☎ 020 8742 8940, 0976 205794 mob, 020 8878 1345

EDWARDS Rosemary: 5 Hillside Gardens, Wallington, Surrey SM6 9NX ☎ 020 8647 3143

EKSTEEN Charlotte: 5 Milburn House, Coombe Lane, Raynes Park, London SW20 0BX ☎ 020 8241 7555, 0956 252486

ELLIOTT Deirdre: 25 Glenhouse Road, Eltham, London SE9 1JH ☎ 020 8859 3473

ELLIOTT Naomi: 12 Field End Road, Eastcote, Pinner, Middlesex HA5 2QL ☎ 020 8866 6317, 0976 553142

ELLIOTT Rosemary: 6 St Pauls Place, London N1 2QD ☎ 020 7359 7584

EVANS Bridget (*Pf*): Flat 3, 2 Bloemfontein Road, Shepherds Bush, London W12 7BX ☎ 020 8740 6293

FAIRHURST Laura: 78 Dynevor Road, Stoke Newington, London N16 0DX ☎ 020 7241 5562, 0402 469736 mob

FAUX Kevin: 51 Greenvale Road, Eltham, London SE9 1PB ☎ 020 8850 4614

FEILE Matthias: 180 South Park Road, London SW19 8TA ☎ 020 8947 4065, 01306 880669, 020 8540 5522

FENTON Jane: 26 Sutcliffe Road, Plumstead Common, London SE18 2NG ☎ 020 8316 4865, 01306 880669 day

FERRAND Emma: Ings Cottage, Berrier, Greystoke, Penrith, Cumbria CA11 0XD ☎ 017684 83443

FEW Jonathan: Ground Floor Flat, 75 Bovill Road, Forest Hill, London SE23 1EL ☎ 020 8291 0116, 0389 486 169 pager

FIRMAN Robin: Little Linton, 54 Burkes Road, Beaconsfield, S Bucks HP9 1EE ☎ 01494 671802

FISHER Susannah (*Pf*): 61 Essex Park, Finchley, London N3 1ND ☎ 020 8346 8296

FITZGERALD David (*Gtr, Vln*): 1 Rosslyn House, Rushcroft Road, London SW2 1LG ☎ 020 7738 7795

FITZGERALD Josephine: 32 Harbury Road, Carshalton Beeches, Surrey SM5 4LA ☎ 020 8643 5487

FLEET Judith: 6 Alma Crescent, Cheam, Surrey SM1 2LN ☎ 020 8641 2702, 0973 241620

FOLCH Laura: Address Unknown ☎ 020 7249 4612

FORD Allen: 28 Flag Court, Courtenay Terrace, Hove BN3 2WG ☎ 01273 205975

FORD Charles: 3 Warren Lodge, Warren Road, Kingston, Surrey KT2 7HY ☎ 020 8549 4041

FORD Rachel: Flat 2, 48 Canning Road, Croydon CR0 6QF ☎ 020 8656 1558, 0976 734026

FREYHAN Peter: 56 Wood Vale, London N10 3DN ☎ 020 8883 3735

FULLER Andrew: 121 Casewick Road, West Norwood, London SE27 0TA ☎ 020 8670 3651, 01483 451700 day

FULLER Michael: 2 Meadow Walk, Harpenden, Herts AL5 5TG ☎ 01582 461657, 01306 880669

GALE Jocelyn: 54 Grange Gardens, Pinner, Middx HA5 5QF ☎ 020 8868 3308

GARDNER Thomas: 15 Nightingale Lane, London N8 7RA ☎ 020 8340 6535

GASKIN Barbara: 5 Wolseley Ave., Wimbledon Park, London SW19 8BG

GEDDES Helen: 24 Avondale Road, Palmers Green, London N13 4DU ☎ 020 8447 8101, 0958 531080 mob

GETHIN Nicholas: 35 Claremont Road, Teddington, Middlesex TW11 8DH ☎ 020 8977 5845

GILCHRIST Elizabeth: 15 Oakfield Road, Ashstead, Surrey KT21 2RE ☎ 01372 276949

GILES Cathy: 11 Queens Road, London E11 1BA ☎ 020 8558 4000

GILFORD Sara: 56 Reighton Avenue, Rawcliffe, York YO3 6QN ☎ 01904 692366

GILLIVER Rebecca (*Pf*): 46 Whitehall Park, London N19 3TN ☎ 020 7686 5189

GLEDHILL Oliver: 528 Finchley Rd, London NW11 8DD ☎ 020 8455 7211

GLOSSOP Keith: 55 Ruskin Walk, Herne Hill, London SE24 9NA ☎ 020 7274 5287

GOODALL Amanda: 1 Ardlui Road, West Norwood, London SE27 9HB ☎ 020 8766 8794

GOUGH Caroline: 74 Carlton Park Avenue, Raynes Park, London SW20 8BL ☎ 020 8543 1731

GRAHAM Mary-Louise (*Pf*): 23 Leslie Road, East Finchley, London N2 8BN ☎ 020 8444 0487

GREAVES Ernest: 1 Castle House, 46 - 48 Old Bath Road, Speen, Newbury, Berks RG14 1QL ☎ 01635 38136

GREEN Christopher: The Cottage, Oxhey Drive South, Northwood, Middx HA6 3ET ☎ 01923 825891

GREENING William (*Gtr, Bjo, Db*): Address Unknown

GREENSMITH Clive: 37 Dryden Road, London SW19 8SQ ☎ 020 8543 0994

GRITTON Robin (*Con, Voc*): Heath Farm, Reigate Heath, Reigate RH2 8QP ☎ 01737 43058

GROGAN Sheila: 105 Woodcock Hill, Harrow, Middx HA3 0JJ ☎ 020 8907 2112

GUNN Andrew: Flat 2, 3 Suffolk Road, South Norwood, London SE25 6EY ☎ 020 8771 5219, 0973 889745

GUNNING Shelley (*Vadag*): 39 Birkbeck Road, Mill Hill, London NW7 4BP ☎ 020 8959 7129

HALSEY James: 16 Grangeside, Ventnor, Isle Of Wight PO38 1RW ☎ 01983 852201

HARRIES Nia (*Pf*): 139 Churchill Road, London NW2 5EH ☎ 020 8459 6462

HARRIOTT Esther: 347 Ivydale Road, London SE15 3ED ☎ 020 7640 2172

HARRIS Eve: Flat 6, 46 Onslow Square, London SW7 3NX ☎ 020 7584 9845

HARRIS Gina: 16A Burnt Ash Lane, Bromley, Kent BR1 4DH ☎ 020 8325 8016

HARRIS Sophie: 50 Londesborough Road, London N16 8RP ☎ 020 7254 4930

HARRISON Heather: 276 London Road, Wokingham, Berks RG40 1RD ☎ 01734 786186

HARRISON James (*Com*): 17 Hugo Road, London N19 5EU ☎ 020 7700 7327

HARTLEY Moira (*Kbds, Voc*): 32 Grundy St, Poplar, London E14 6DR ☎ 020 7987 2996

HARVEY Keith: 23 St Johns Wood Terrace, London NW8 6JL ☎ 020 7722 8435

HAVERS Angus (*Pf, Voc, B Gtr*): 153 Dalling Road, Ravens Court Park, London W6 0ES ☎ 07957 740635

HAWLEY Joy: 106B Clova Road, Forest Gate, London E7 9AF ☎ 020 8555 0898, 0410 095 395 mob

HEATH Martin: 60 Esmond Road, Chiswick, London W4 1JF ☎ 020 8994 3046

HEDLEY-MILLER Sarah: 85 St Albans Road, Kingston-upon-Thames, Surrey KT2 5HH ☎ 020 8546 6393

HEGEDUS Olga: 8 Kensington Place, London W8 7PT ☎ 020 7727 4463

HEGGART William (*B Viol*): 17 Canbury Avenue, Kingston, Surrey KT2 6JP ☎ 020 8546 3657

HELEY John: The Old Lamb, Potter Row, Great Missenden, Bucks HP16 9LT ☎ 01494 862727 & fax

HENRY Frank: 21 Marine Close, Leigh-on-Sea, Essex SS9 2RD ☎ 01702 558081

HERBERT Judith: 8 Park Ave South, London N8 8LT ☎ 020 8341 0754, 0976 362890 mob

HESS Andrea: 10 Belsize Park, London NW3 4ES ☎ 020 7794 1485

HESS Benjamin (*Com*): c/o 10 Belsize Park, London NW3 4ES ☎ 0958 661558, 020 8533 1372

HESS Ursula: 17 The Vale, Golders Green, London NW11 8SE ☎ 020 8458 1949

HEWETT Polly Jane (*Pf, Kbds, Voc, Hrp*): 12 Hamilton House, Devonshire Road, London W4 2AJ ☎ 020 8994 7027 eve, 020 7284 3999 day

HEWITT-JONES Timothy: 38 Carson Road, West Dulwich, London SE21 8HU ☎ 020 8670 3687

HINNIGAN Anthony ☎ 020 8473 8823, 020 8766 6966

HINTON Clare (*Flt*): 53 Salisbury Road, Banstead, Surrey SM7 2DP ☎ 01737 362 906

HOLM Jane: 46 Mayfield Road, North Chingford, London E4 7JA ☎ 020 8529 4257, 020 8529 4257

HOLMES Anna *(Bq Cel)*: 5 Cowley Road, London SW14 8QD ☎ 020 8876 9149

HOLMES Edward: 22 Courtnell Street, London W2 5BX ☎ 020 7727 4374

HOLMES John: 9 Beech Court, Teddington, Middx TW11 9QW ☎ 020 8977 3811

HOLT Sian: 337 Carterhatch Lane, Enfield EN1 4AW ☎ 020 8366 8155, 07971 847112 mob

HOPKINS Louise *(Pf)*: 322 Earlsfield Road, London SW18 3EJ ☎ 020 8871 2652

HOWARD-LUCY Alison: Highfields, 104 Kingsmead Avenue, Worcester Park, Surrey KT4 8UT ☎ 020 8330 3696

HURWITZ Michael: 44 Church Crescent, Finchley Central, London N3 1BJ ☎ 020 8349 4067

HUSSEY Ivan: 26C Fordwych Road, London NW2 3TG ☎ 020 8452 5381, 0976 558001

IRBY Chris: 2 Ravens Court, 23 Uxbridge Road, Kingston-upon-Thames, Surrey KT1 2LS ☎ 020 8549 9899, 0777 5531641, 020 8533 1372 day

ISAAC Emily: 80C Palmerston Road, Wood Green, London N22 4RF ☎ 020 8889 6442, 0839 456593 pager, 01306 880669 day

ISAACSON Rhian: 8 Rosedew Road, London W6 9ET ☎ 020 8748 4757, 020 8533 1372 day

IVES George: Old Meads Cottage, Church Road, Weald, Sevenoaks Kent TN14 6LU ☎ 01732 451951

IVES Paul: Ty Newydd, Sarnau, Llanymynech, Powys SY22 6QJ ☎ 01938 590215

JACKSON Christine: 48 Albatross Street, London SE18 2SA ☎ 020 8854 4748

JACKSON Colin: Lakefields Farm House, Idehill Road, Bough Beech, Kent TN8 7PW ☎ 01732 700339

JANSE Jennifer *(Bq Cel)*: 146 Iffley Road, London W6 0PE ☎ 020 8741 5390

JARY Catherine *(Org, Pf)*: 76 Oakfield Road, London N4 4LB ☎ 0114 266 6672

JEFFERIES Edward: 1 Grovefield House, Coppice Grove, New Southgate, London N11 1NS ☎ 020 8361 1349, 0973 825901

JENKINSON Richard *(Con, Pf)*: 110 Longtree Close, Tetbury, Glos GL8 8LW ☎ 01666 502875 & fax, 0402 183493 mob

JOHNSTON Deborah: 63A Bedford Avenue, Barnet, Herts EN5 2ES ☎ 020 8441 7334

JOHNSTON Philip: 136 Erlanger Road, New Cross, London SE14 5TJ ☎ 020 7639 2806

JOHNSTONE David: c/o 89 Chapel Hill, Tilehurst, Reading, Berks RG3 5BX ☎ 01734 427069, 020 7354 2711

JONES David: 10 Cromwell Close, Bromley, Kent BR2 9AH ☎ 020 8460 2739

JONES Hilary: 8 Hertford Road, Tewin, Herts AL6 0JY ☎ 01438 717386, 01438 717386

JONES Jenny *(Pf, B Gtr, Voc)*: Flat 3, 54 Stoke Newington High Street, London N16 7PB ☎ 020 7241 1509

JONES Norman: 14 Silverdale Road, Bushey, Herts WD2 2LZ ☎ 01923 465565

JONES Stuart *(Tpt, Zit)*: 20 Cleveleys Road, London E5 9JN ☎ 020 8806 7808 fax

JOSEPH Vivian: Flat 35, Vernon Court, Hendon Way, London NW2 2PE ☎ 020 7435 8934

KANER Tamsy: 20 Garthorne Road, London SE23 1EW ☎ 020 8699 6068, 01306 880669

KANTROVITCH Ula/Ursula: 3 Verity House, Hamilton Terrace, London NW8 9YB ☎ 020 7328 0426

KAZNOWSKI Michal: 85 St Albans Road, Kingston-on-Thames, Surrey KT2 5HH ☎ 020 8546 6393

KEANE Helen: Borovere, The Chase, Pinner, Middlesex HA5 5QP ☎ 020 8868 3647

KEARS Paul *(Pf, Vla, Vln)*: 15 Bolton Road, Stratford, London E15 4JY ☎ 020 8555 1199, 0956 577438 mob

KEGG Paul: Rockcliff, Broomfield Hill, Great Missenden, Buckinghamshire HP16 9HT ☎ 01494 864184

KELLETT Paul *(Com)*: 401 Mountjoy House, Barbican, London EC2Y 8BP ☎ 020 7628 5298, 0839 632 366 pager

KENNARD Benjamin: The Old School House, Radstone, Brackley, Northants NN13 5TZ ☎ 01280 702529

KERR Felicity: 35, Tannsfeld Road, London SE26 5DQ ☎ 020 8778 2634

KIRBY Joseph: 55 Southbrook Road, Lee, London SE12 8LJ ☎ 020 8318 3238

KITCHEN Jonathan *(B Gtr, Pf)*: 578 Downham Way, Bromley, Kent BR1 5HW ☎ 020 8461 5481, 0973 204642 mob, 020 8533 1372 day

KOK Bobby: 62 Warwick Gardens, London W14 8PP

KONII Yuki: 103 Elm Tree Court, Elm Tree Road, London NW8 9JT ☎ 020 7289 0158

KOOS Joely *(Pf, Voc)*: 48 Surrey Road, Nunhead, London SE15 3AT ☎ 020 7732 6231, 01306 880669 day

KRAEMER Timothy *(Bq Cel, Com)*: 24 Elm Park Road, London N3 1EB ☎ 020 8346 4175

KRAUS Oliver *(Pf)*: Elmview, Farley Green, Albury, Surrey GU5 9DN ☎ 01483 202047

LANMAN Nadia: 6 Fitzroy Terrace, Redland, Bristol BS6 6TF ☎ 020 8455 5386, 020 8201 9952

LANNIGAN Brendan: 6C Rutland Park, Catford, London SE6 4LH ☎ 020 8291 4301

LASKER Anita: 27 Chelmsford Square, London NW10 3AP ☎ 020 8459 3151

LAVELLE Caroline *(Voc)* ☎ 01435 830003

LAVERICK Samantha: 12 Hill Court, St Marks Hill, Surbiton KT6 4LW ☎ 020 8390 0290

LAWRENCE Bettina: 11 Woolstone Road, Forest Hill, London SE23 2TR ☎ 020 8699 8856

LE FEUVRE Gerard: 19 Cross Way, Harpenden, Herts AL5 4RA ☎ 01582 462668

LEBON Christopher: 9 Orchard Close, Calne, Wiltshire SN11 8HA

LEE Matthew: 45 York Terrace East, Regents Park, London NW1 4PT ☎ 020 7487 3213

LEHWALDER Julie *(Bq Cel)*: 5 Kingsbridge Road, London W10 6PU ☎ 020 8969 5738

LENTON Judith: 15 Marriott Road, Barnet, Herts EN5 4NJ ☎ 020 8449 7324

LESTER Richard: 65 Oakwood Road, London NW11 6RJ ☎ 020 8455 3538 & fax

LEVINE Joanna *(Vadag, Vlne)*: 46 Uplands Road, London N8 9NL ☎ 020 8348 4295, 020 8292 7125 fax

LEWIS Anthony: 23 Watermill Close, Ham, Richmond, Surrey TW10 7UJ ☎ 020 8948 0154

LICHTENSTEIN Babette: 69 Rodenhurst Road, London SW4 8AE ☎ 020 8674 4804

LIEBMANN Helen: Hallfield House, Chardleigh Green, Wadeford, Chard, Somerset TA20 3AJ ☎ 01460 68463

LINES Ann: 16 Cypress Gardens, Crofton Park, London SE4 2FB ☎ 020 8533 1372, 0831 344078, 020 8699 8650

LIVINGSTONE Christine: 8A Guildford Road, London SW8 2BX ☎ 020 7627 8776

LLOYD-WEBBER Julian: 18A Sussex Mansions, Old Brompton Road, South Kensington, London SW7 3JZ ☎ 020 7581 1218, 020 7581 3911

LOESER Brigitte: 6 Bromwich Avenue, London N6 6QH ☎ 020 8340 2864

LOVEDAY Martin: 171 Haliburton Road, St.Margarets, Twickenham, Middlesex TW1 1PE ☎ 020 8744 0347

LOVELL Maureen: 1 Glovers Road, Reigate, Surrey RH2 7LA ☎ 01737 243996

LOWBURY Miriam *(Bq Cel)*: 51 Salisbury Road, London E17 9JW ☎ 020 8521 5398, 01306 880669

LOWDELL John: Lupitsch 87, 8992 Altaussee, Austria ☎ +43 3622 72126

LUKOSZEVIEZE Anton: 43 Grove Avenue, Twickenham, Middlesex TW1 4HX ☎ 020 8892 4201, 020 8892 4201

LUNN Roger *(Vadag)*: 46 William Allen Lane, Lindfield, Haywards Heath, West Sussex RH16 2SU ☎ 01444 454878

MACFARLANE Jane: 52 Fortis Green Road, Muswell Hill, London N10 3HN ☎ 020 8444 4778, 0976 434 994

MACKRELL Kim: 1 Friern Road, East Dulwich, London SE22 0AT ☎ 020 8693 5416

MACRAE Christina: 35 Fisherbeck Park, Ambleside, Cumbria LA22 0AJ ☎ 015394 31326

MANN Sylvia: 5 Warwick Court, Alderton Close, Felstead, Essex CM6 3EL ☎ 01371 821212, 0937 222711

MANSELL Christopher: 20 West Park, Mottingham, London SE9 4RQ ☎ 0973 361748

MARTIN Charles: Cavendish Manse, 39 South Eastern Road, Ramsgate, Kent CT11 9QF ☎ 01843 592391

MARTIN Matthew: 151 Edgwarebury Lane, Edgware, Middx HA8 8ND ☎ 020 8958 8293

MARTINDALE Margaret: 44 Dalyell Road, Stockwell, London SW9 9QR ☎ 020 7274 7039

MARTLEW Zoe: Flat 7, Christchurch Court, 171 Willesden Lane, London NW6 7XS ☎ 020 8451 1657, 0956 369338 mob

MATTHEWS Victoria: 17A Gowan Road, Willesden Green, London NW10 2SH ☎ 020 8451 9317, 0966 496412

MATTHEY Clemence: 13 Carlingford Road, London N15 3ED ☎ 020 8888 3353

MAX Robert: 5 Asmuns Hill, London NW11 6ES ☎ 020 8458 2839

MCCARTHY Eileen: Flat 5, 93 Elm Park Gardens, London SW10 9QE ☎ 020 7351 3655

MCCARTHY Juliet: 45 Elliston Road, Redland, Bristol BS6 6QQ ☎ 0117 973 0593, 0973 305 335

MCCREADY Ivan: 78 Astbury Road, London SE15 2NW ☎ 020 7732 1170, 0777 5635918 mob

MCDOWELL Hugh (*Com, Arr*): 29A Mulkern Road, London N19 3HQ ☎ 020 7272 7482

MCGILLIVRAY Alison (*Pf*): 10 Hamilton Road, Dollis Hill, London NW10 1NY

MCKEE Susan (*Pf*): 112 The Grove, West Wickham, Kent BR4 9JZ ☎ 020 8777 2055, 0403 648 928

MCKENZIE Sheena (*Pf*): Flat 4, 57 Aberdare Gardens, West Hampstead, London NW6 3AL ☎ 020 7209 1040

MCKINLEY Sharon: 12 Belgrave Court, 25 Cowbridge Road East, Cardiff CF1 9BJ ☎ 029 2023 2342

MCLEOD Mary: 90 Emmanual Road, London SW12 0HR ☎ 020 8674 0475

MCVEIGH Alice (*Bq Cel*): 13 Oakwood Road, Orpington, Kent BR6 8JH ☎ 01689 861594

MEDDEMMEN Brian: 40 Jacksons Place, Cross Road, East Croydon, Surrey CR0 6TA ☎ 020 8680 4608

MEYER Anne-Isabel: 20 Harmood Street, London NW1 8DJ ☎ 020 7284 0443, 01306 880669

MILBOURN Gwenda: 1A The Uplands, Gerrards Cross, Bucks SL9 7JQ ☎ 01753 886951

MILES Claire (*Pf*): 26 Walwyn Avenue, Bromley, Kent BR1 2RD ☎ 020 8464 9952, 0976 547028 mob

MILHOLLAND Joanna: 17 York Avenue, East Sheen, London SW14 7LQ ☎ 020 8876 5066

MILLER Rose: 40 Portland Road, London W11 4LG ☎ 020 7727 4722

MILLETT Sebastian: 79A Linden Gardens, London W2 4EU ☎ 020 7727 9527 & fax

MILNE Stephen: 1 Ardlui Road, West Norwood, London SE27 9HB ☎ 020 8766 8794, 0976 946857 mob

MITCHELL Judith: 38 Denman Rd, London SE15 5NR ☎ 020 7701 6438 & fax

MONKS Susan: 60 Port Vale, Bengeo, Hertford SG14 3AF ☎ 01992 501557

MORAN John (*Bq Cel*): 814 N. Daniel Street, Arlington, VA 22201, USA

MORRIS Simon: Yew Tree Cottage, Poundsbridge Hill, Penshurst, Kent TN11 8AL ☎ 01892 862515, 020 7928 5683 fax

MOULTON Duncan: 6 Alma Crescent, Cheam, Surrey SM1 2LN ☎ 020 8641 2702, 020 8641 2702

MULLAN Brian (*Pf, Com, Arr*): Flat 4, Simons Court, 2B Stamford Hill, London N16 6YD ☎ 020 8806 7720

MUNDY Mary: 26 Sycamore Grove, New Malden, Surrey KT3 3DQ ☎ 020 8949 7750

NARVEY Mayda: 84 Pirbright Road, London SW18 5NA ☎ 020 8870 8028

NEBE Michael: 24 Thornton Avenue, Streatham Hill, London SW2 4HG ☎ 020 8671 4408, 020 8671 2848 fax

NEWBY David: 64 Oakhurst Grove, East Dulwich, London SE22 9AQ ☎ 020 8693 7432

NICE Andrew (*Sax*): 69 Onslow Gardens, Muswell Hill, London N10 3JY ☎ 020 8883 9438

NORMAN David (*Gtr, B Gtr, Voc*): 45 York Street, London W1H 1PW ☎ 020 7738 2213

NORRIS Robert: 25 Gateside Road, London SW17 7NB ☎ 020 8672 1402

O'DELL Dominic (*Bq Cel*): 93 Claude Road, Leyton, London E10 6NF ☎ 020 8558 4592, 020 8533 1372 day

OAKES Sonia (*Pf*): 324A New Cross Road, New Cross, London SE14 6AG ☎ 020 8694 0029

ORTON Stephen: 5 Bullocks Hill, St Pauls Walden, Hitchin, Herts SG4 8DG ☎ 01438 871361, 01306 880669

PACEY Sara: 11 Ravenscroft Park, High Barnet, Herts EN5 4ND ☎ 020 8440 4695

PARK Vanessa: 316 Kings Road, Kingston, Surrey KT2 5JL ☎ 020 8541 3671, 0976 691 580

PARKER Elizabeth (*Pf*): Flat 5, 47 Anerley Park, London SE20 8NQ ☎ 020 8778 0029, 01306 880669

PARSONS Mike (*Gtr, B Gtr*): 96 Salmen Road, Plaistow, London E13 0DT ☎ 020 8472 0094

PAYNE Lars: 40 Durand Gardens, London SW9 0PP ☎ 020 7735 7948

PEARSON Justin: 23 Beechfield Road, Catford, London SE6 4NG ☎ 020 8690 1768, 0973 705197 mob

PERETTI Jacques: Address Unknown

PERKS David: 27D Clifton Villas, Maida Vale, London W9 2PH ☎ 020 7289 5674

PERRIN Ingrid: 3 Arbuthnot Road, London SE14 5LS ☎ 020 7732 4590

PHELPS Melissa: Quincefold, Rusper, Horsham, Sussex RH12 4PR ☎ 01293 871242

PHILLIPS Jaqueline: Flat 2, 42 Hermon Hill, Wanstead, London E11 2AP ☎ 020 8530 3506

PHILLIPS Ruth: Flat 5, 28 Sussex Square, Brighton, Sussex BN2 5AB ☎ 01273 670462 & fax, 020 8549 1706 day

PINKETT Nigel: 24 Park Avenue, Enfield, Middx EN1 2HP ☎ 020 8360 6358

PLEETH Anthony (*Bq Cel*): 3 Bells Hill, Barnet, Herts EN5 2SE ☎ 020 8449 1160

POND Celia: Fermain House, Dolphin Street, Colyton, Devon EX13 6LU ☎ 01297 52272

POPLE Ross (*Vadag*): Sellet Hall, Stainton, Kendal, Cumbria CA8 0LE

PORTEOUS Diane: Upper Flat, 100 Adelaide Avenue, Ladywell, London SE4 1YR ☎ 020 8469 3353

POTTER James: Wing Flat, New House, Hale Lane, Wendover, Nr Aylesbury, Bucks HP22 6NQ ☎ 01296 696783, 020 8549 1706

POWELL Margaret: 2 Morecambe Gardens, Stanmore, Middlesex HA7 4SP ☎ 020 8958 6983 & fax

PRESSLAND Ian: 10 Vyner Court, Rossington Street, London E5 8SF ☎ 020 8806 8520

PRICE Janie (*Dms, Voc*): Flat 7, Frithville Court, Frithville Gardens, Shepherds Bush, London W12 7JH ☎ 020 8743 6057, 0956 255723

PRITCHARD Emma: 50 Dollis Ave, Finchley, London N3 1BU ☎ 020 8343 2264, 0966 518 123, 01306 500011

RAINEY Jane: 337 Carterhatch Lane, Enfield, Middlesex EN1 4AW ☎ 020 8373 8756, 07971 008337

RAYNER Peter: 53A Elmsdale Road, Walthamstow, London E17 6PN ☎ 020 8509 2026

REED Janet: 12 Manor Road, Barnet, Herts EN5 2LH ☎ 020 8440 1032

RICHARDS Margaret (*Bq Cel*, *Vadag*): The Grove, The Ridgeway, Mill Hill Village, London NW7 1QX ☎ 020 8959 1006

RIDDELL Susanna: 44 Bromley Gdns, Bromley, Kent BR2 0ET ☎ 020 8290 5797

RILEY Audrey (*Arr*): Ground Floor Flat, 25B Hermon Hill, Wanstead, London E11 2AR ☎ 020 8530 5402

RIMER Catherine: 206 Tufnell Park Road, London N7 0PZ ☎ 020 7263 2555 & fax

RIST Marianne: 83 Annandale Road, London SE10 0DE ☎ 020 8305 0147

RIVE Francois: 80C Palmerston Road, London N22 8RF ☎ 020 8889 6442

RIVERS Ben: 6 Fishersdene, Claygate, Esher, Surrey KT10 0HT ☎ 01372 464948

ROBERTS Nicholas: 21 Strauss Road, London W4 1DL ☎ 020 8995 1913

ROBINSON David (*Pf*): 73 Brondesbury Road, London NW6 6BP ☎ 020 7328 2476

ROBINSON Martin: 68 Puller Road, High Barnet, Herts EN5 4HD ☎ 020 8449 3009

RONAYNE Michael: 44 Vineyard Hill Road, Wimbledon Park, London SW19 7JH ☎ 020 8879 0088

ROOSE Helen: 50 Meadway, Hampstead Garden Suburb, London NW11 6PS ☎ 020 8458 4793

ROPER Amaryllis: 80 Alleyn Road, Dulwich, London SE21 8AH ☎ 020 8670 0300

ROSEBERRY Catherine: 77 Delafield Road, Charlton, London SE7 7NW ☎ 020 8858 8597

ROSKELLY William: 147 Elgin Crescent, London W11 2JH ☎ 020 7727 5707

ROTH George: 6 Snowdon Mansions, Gondar Gardens, London NW6 1ES ☎ 020 7435 2895

ROTT Reynard: 17 Astra House, Alfred Street, London E3 2BA ☎ 020 8981 1951, 0958 208752 mob

ROUTLEDGE William: 5 Aplin Way, Isleworth, Middx TW7 4RJ ☎ 020 8847 2170, 0958 511 673 mob

ROWNTREE Louise: Cedar House, Philpot Lane, Chobham, Nr Woking, Surrey GU24 8HE ☎ 01276 857157 fax

RUDALL Stephen (*Pf*): 39 Worsley Road, Leytonstone, London E11 3JL

SALMON Jane: 5B Colinette Road, Putney, London SW15 6QG ☎ 020 8246 6674, 020 8246 6827 fax

SANSOM Marilyn: Gorewell, Old Wives Lees, Chilham, Nr Canterbury, Kent CT4 8BD ☎ 01227 752275

SAUNDERS Francis: 79 Foyle Road, London SE3 7RQ ☎ 020 8858 2543

SAWYER Helen (*Clt*, *Pf*, *Rec*): 4 Orlestone Gardens, Orpington, Kent BR6 6HB ☎ 01689 822453

SCHAEFER Frank (*Gtr*): 141B Southwood Lane, Highgate, London N6 5TA, 01306 880669

SCHOFIELD Phillippa: 11 Dellafield Close, Berkhamsted, Herts HP4 1DS ☎ 01442 864040

SCHOFIELD William: 11 Dellfield Close, Berkhampstead, Herts HP4 2JG ☎ 01442 864040, 01442 385960

SCOTT Phoebe (*Pf*): 78 Duke's Ave, London W4 2AF ☎ 020 8994 5387

SHARMAN Katherine: 136 Manor Road, Banbury, Oxon OX16 7JW ☎ 01295 266 506, 020 8533 1372 day, 01295 255 427

SHARP John: 126B Arthur Road, Wimbledon Park, London SW19 8AA ☎ 020 8947 4065, 01306 500011 day

SHARP Matthew: 7 Princes Road, Wimbledon, London SW19 8RQ ☎ 020 8542 2791

SHAVE Peter (*Db*): 48 Richardson Road, East Bergholt, Colchester CO7 6RR ☎ 01206 298795

SHAXSON Rhydian: 45 Burghill Road, London SE26 4HJ ☎ 020 8778 6196

SHEPPARD Susan: 35 Redston Road, London N8 7HL ☎ 020 8348 5757

SHERIDAN Mark: 4 Belmont Avenue, New Malden, Surrey KT3 6QD ☎ 020 8942 2954

SHILLITO Christina: 16 Beresford Road, New Malden, Surrey KT3 3RQ ☎ 020 8949 7425

SHRIGLEY-JONES Lesley (*Bq Cel*, *Vadag*): 182 Broom Road, Teddington, Middlesex TW11 9PQ ☎ 020 8977 9690/9207

SHULMAN Andrew: Fir Cottage, Kingsley Common, Kingsley, Hampshire GU35 9NH ☎ 01420 472206, 0973 312224

SHUTTLEWORTH Anna: 1 Buckingham Road, Leeds LS6 1BP ☎ 0113 2758509, 01227 261975

SIMPSON Derek: 97 North Bersted Street, Bognor Regis, West Sussex PO22 9AF ☎ 01243 829802

SIMPSON Erica: 32 Clairview Road, London SW16 6TX ☎ 020 8677 1787 & fax, 0973 386059 mob, 01306 880669 day

SMITH David: Address Unknown ☎ 01920 469839

SMITH Richard: Tattlebury Lodge, Cranbrook Road, Goudhurst, Cranbrook, Kent TN17 1BT ☎ 01580 212491

SMITH Roger: The Fountain, Tidebrook, Wadhurst, East Sussex TN5 6PF ☎ 01892 782220, 01306 880669

SMITH Sonya: Tattlebury Lodge, Cranbrook Road, Goudhurst, Cranbrook, Kent TN17 1BT ☎ 01580 212324

SMITH Ursula: Flat 1, 3 Randolph Place, Edinburgh EH3 7TQ ☎ 0131 225 5143

SOUTHARD Dennis: Address Unknown

SPENCER Jayne: Foxley, Tilthams Green, Godalming, Surrey GU7 3BT ☎ 01483 424773

SPENCER Kirstin: Garden Flat, 23 St Johns Road, Golders Green, London NW11 0PE ☎ 020 8209 0792, 0976 754195

SPOONER Joseph: 85B Pepys Road, New Cross, London SE14 5SE ☎ 020 7732 4062

STARK Anthony: 2 Allenby Road, Forest Hill, London SE23 2RQ ☎ 020 8699 3249

STEHN Leonard: 25 Marsden Road, London SE15 4EE ☎ 020 7277 6130

STIRLING Michael (*E Gtr*): 69 Landscroft Rd, London SE22 9JS ☎ 020 8693 7414, 020 8299 0750 fax

STRANGE David: 35 Durand Gardens, Stockwell, London SW9 0PS ☎ 020 7735 8965

STREVENS Anita: Loxley Cottage, Stonehouse Road, Halstead, Kent TN14 7HW ☎ 01689 850770

STROM Marie: 20 Bradbourne Vale Rd, Sevenoaks, Kent TN13 3QJ ☎ 01732 741890

SUTHERLEY Susan: 57 Lincoln Road, London N2 9DJ ☎ 020 8444 7648, 01306 880669

SZUCS Ferenc: 13B St. Marys Avenue, Finchley, London N3 1SN ☎ 020 8349 3125, 01483 451 700 day

TAYLOR Josephine: 3 Percy Place, Datchet, Slough SL3 9EU ☎ 01753 582218, 0802 819319

TAYLOR Philip: Flat 4, 42 Elmbourne Road, Tooting Bec, London SW17 8JJ ☎ 020 8767 4078 & fax

THODAY Gillian: 55 The Drive, High Barnet, Herts EN5 4JG ☎ 020 8447 0858, 01306 880 669

THOMAS Helen (*Pf*): 92 East Dulwich Road, London SE22 9AT ☎ 020 8299 4730, 0956 813633 mob

THOMAS Jacqueline: 31 Park Avenue South, London N8 8LU ☎ 020 8348 2603

THOMAS Martin: 14 Dunheved Rd. Sth, Thornton Heath, Surrey CR4 6AD ☎ 020 8684 6208

THOMPSON-CLARKE Robin: 3 Halford Road, Leyton, London E10 6DR ☎ 020 8558 4179

THORNER Madeleine (*Bq Cel*): 39 Erskine Hill, London NW11 6EY ☎ 020 8458 1832, 01306 880669

THULBORN Katherine: Well Cottage, Chapel Lane, Enstone, Oxfordshire OX7 4LY ☎ 01608 677404

TODD John: The Red Barn, Cryfield Grange Road, Kenilworth, Coventry CV8 2JV ☎ 024 7669 7389, 024 7641 7219 fax

TRAVERSE Eleanor: 2 Effra Court, Homelands Drive, London SE19 2NS ☎ 020 8768 0611, 0370 338135

TRUELOVE Amanda (*Pf*): 33 Stile Hall Gardens, Chiswick, London W4 3BS ☎ 020 8747 1009

TRUMAN Robert: 79 Deacon Road, Kingston-upon-Thames, Surrey KT2 6LS ☎ 020 8549 7066

TRUNDLE Abigail (*Pf*): 41B Gellatley Road, London SE14 5TU ☎ 020 7252 9442, 0973 858591

TRZEBIATOWSKI Philip: 278 Kew Road, Kew, Richmond, Surrey TW9 3EE ☎ 020 8948 6140

TUNNELL Charles: 4 Marble Hill Close, Twickenham, Middlesex TW1 3AY ☎ 020 8892 6837

TUNNELL Jonathan: 191 Lincoln Avenue, Twickenham, Middlesex TW2 6NL ☎ 020 8894 6173, 020 880669

TUNNICLIFFE Richard (*Vadag*): Egton Cottage, Kidd Lane, Clun, Shropshire SY7 8JB ☎ 01588 640361 & fax

TURNER Haydn (*T Sax*): Address Unknown

TURPIN Sean: 62 King Edward Road, Walthamstow, London E17 6HZ ☎ 020 8531 3749

TYLER Marianne: 9 Tudor Road, New Barnet, Herts EN5 5NL ☎ 020 8440 2791, 0966 456586 mob

URQUHART Wayne (*B Gtr, Pf, Dms*): 15A Dean Drive, Stanmore, Middlesex HA7 1HB ☎ 020 8621 4448, 0976 743 827 mob

VAN DER TANG Rachel: Ground Floor Flat, 5 Hurstbourne Road, Forest Hill, London SE23 2AA ☎ 020 8699 7589, 0306 880669 day

VANDERSPAR Christopher: 26 Grand Ave, Muswell Hill, London N10 3BB ☎ 020 8444 8887

VEL Peter (*Vadag*): 164 Camden Road, London NW1 9HJ ☎ 020 7813 7981, 01306 880669

VERNEY Helen: Mulberry Lodge, 14A Liverpool Road, Kingston-upon-Thames, Surrey KT2 7SZ ☎ 020 8546 6218

VIDGEON Emma: 48B Boscombe Road, London W12 9HU ☎ 020 8749 4021

VIGAY Denis: 12 Chesterfield Road, London N3 1PR ☎ 020 8346 3670

VINCENT Felicity: 112 Chetwynd Road, London NW5 1DH ☎ 020 7485 1211

VOCADLO R. Bernard: 1A The Uplands, Gerrards Cross, Bucks SL9 7JQ ☎ 01753 886951

VOHRALIK Julia (*Pf*): 2 Horton Manor, Canterbury, Kent CT4 7LG ☎ 01227 730 843, 020 8533 1372

VOLKARD Timothy (*Gtr, Kbds*): 5 Portland House Mews, Ashley Road, Epsom, Surrey KT18 5BB ☎ 01372 748255

VUKOTIC Bozidar: 27 Kitson Road, Barnes, London SW13 ☎ 020 8748 0145, 0976 246086, 01306 880669

WAGLAND Simon: 23 Chadwick Road, Peckham Rye, London SE15 4RA ☎ 020 7771 6983, 0966 134962 mob

WALKER Colin: 31 Littlebury Road, London SW4 6DW ☎ 020 7627 0085

WALKER Julia (*Bq Cel, Cheng*): 127 Lee Park, Blackheath, London SE3 9HE ☎ 020 8852 2982

WALTHAM Rachel: 5 Ashford Road, Tenterden, Kent TN30 6AB ☎ 01580 766316

WARD Charlotte (*Tbn*): October House, Glaziers Lane, Normandy, Guildford, Surrey GU3 2DQ ☎ 01483 811547

WARD Tony (*Kbds*): 16 Charteris Road, Kilburn, London NW6 7ET ☎ 020 7328 1579

WARD-CLARKE Jennifer: 23 Honeywell Road, London SW11 6EQ ☎ 020 7228 7059

WARD-RODEN Richard: 1 Norlington Road, Leytonstone, London E11 4BE ☎ 020 8728 0612, 0976 355916

WATERMAN David: Flat 4, 27 Lancaster Grove, London NW3 4EX ☎ 020 7435 7345

WATKIN David (*Bq Cel*): 5 Oakthorpe Road, Oxford OX2 7BD ☎ 01865 54258

WATKINS Paul: 67 Hutton Grove, North Finchley, London N12 8DS ☎ 020 8446 5316, 01306 4465316

WATSON Andrea: 8 Farm Lane, Shirley, Croydon CR0 8AQ ☎ 020 8777 8371, 020 8777 7975 fax

WEAVER Paul (*Tba*): 20 Foresters Close, Wallington, Surrey SM6 9DH ☎ 020 8647 8993

WELCHMAN Juliet: Address Unknown ☎ 020 8556 6348

WELSH Moray: 28 Summerfield Ave, Queens Park, London NW6 6JY ☎ 020 8960 9122

WESTERHOFF Gay-Yee (*Db, Pf*): 1541A London Road, Norbury, London SW16 4AD ☎ 020 8679 2195

WETTERS Rosemary (*Cntrc*): Flat 3, 43 Upper Park Road, Belsize Park, London NW3 2UL ☎ 020 7722 5970

WHIPPLE Eleanor: 49 Warham Road, London N4 1AR ☎ 020 8348 0930, 01306 880669

WILDE Libby: 154 Turney Road, Dulwich, London SE21 7JJ ☎ 020 7733 5965

WILDING Lucy: 1 Pottery Road, Brentford TW8 0SE ☎ 020 8568 3597

WILLIAMS Jonathan: 33 Whittingstall Road, London SW6 4EA ☎ 020 7736 7316, 020 7371 7396 fax

WILLIAMS Quentin (*Cntrc*): 17 Elmwood Avenue, Kenton, Middx HA3 8AJ ☎ 020 8907 2455

WILLISON Peter: Pigeon House, 27 Grove Road, Beaconsfield, Bucks HP9 1UR ☎ 014946 77934

WILLSON Sarah: 282 Muswell Hill Broadway, Muswell Hill, London N10 2QR ☎ 020 8444 8208

WILMERS Catherine: The Brew House, Radwell, Baldock, Hertfordshire SG7 5ES ☎ 01462 730490 & fax, 01306 880669 day

WILSON Sally: Flat 59B, Southend Crescent, Eltham, London SE9 2SD ☎ 020 8859 2077, 0973 791689 mob

WILSON Shuna: 8 The Quadrangle, Welwyn Garden City, Herts AL8 6SG ☎ 01707 336 422, 01707 323961

WILSON Susanna (*Voc*): 109 Pulborough Road, Southfields, London SW18 5UL ☎ 020 8874 2125

WILTSHIRE Harriet (*Bq Cel*): 61 China Court, Asher Way, Wapping, London E1 9JF ☎ 01747 820327, 0958 764522

WOODCOCK Melanie (*Bq Cel*): 16 Yewtree Rise, Ipswich IP8 3RJ ☎ 01473 688957, 09665 513943

WOODFORD Charles: 5 Woodslands Road, Pewsey, Wilts SN9 5HR

WOODHOUSE Chantal (*Pf*): 48 Rothschild Road, Chiswick, London W4 5HT ☎ 020 8563 7538

WOOLLARD Anthony (*Pf, Kbds*): 62 Rope Street, Surrey Quays, London SE15 1TF ☎ 0973 657503 mob

WOOLLARD Robert: 57 Sunnyside Road, Chesham, Bucks HP5 2AR ☎ 01494 792572, 0370 766146 mob

WORSEY Christopher (*Pf*): 87 Cassiot Road, London SW17 8LB ☎ 020 8682 3533, 0973 473 976

YEADON Daniel: 53 Tresco Road, London SE15 3PY ☎ 020 7358 1170

ZIMBLER Maurice: 11B Oseney Crescent, London NW5 2AT ☎ 020 7485 3522

ZOOB Naomi: 8 Sycamore Close, Fetcham, Surrey KT22 9EX ☎ 01372 379813, 0802 485263 mob

CELTIC HARP

SCOTLAND

DAVIDSON Fiona (*Voc*): Duncauld Cottage, Cauldhame, Kippen, Stirlingshire FK8 3HL ☎ 01786 870626, 0410107654

NORTH EAST

KAY Julie-Ann (*Pf, Wh, Per, Voc*): 8 Cardigan Terrace, Heaton, Newcastle-upon-Tyne, Tyne & Wear NE6 5NU ☎ 0191 265 4925

EAST

MONGER Eileen (*Wh*): Mill House, Lockington Road, Stow Market, Suffolk IP14 1BQ ☎ 01449 674803

MIDLANDS

HIDSON Jean (*Pf*): 6 Springfield Avenue, Ashbourne, Derbyshire DE6 1BJ ☎ 01335 343026

SHIRRA Fiona (*Voc*): 312 Broad Street, Coppenhall, Cheshire CW1 4JH ☎ 01270 584934

SOUTH EAST

CLARKE Owain (*Pf, Gtr*): 77 Newlands Avenue, Shirley, Southampton SO15 5EQ ☎ 023 8078 1191

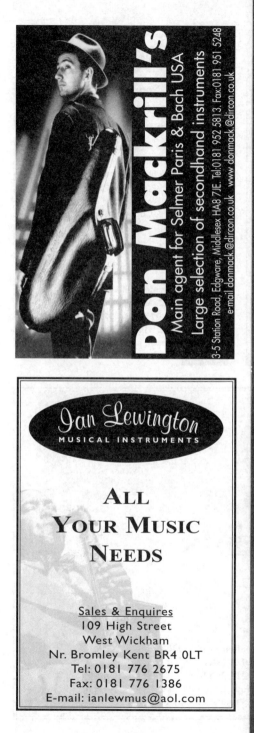

SOUTH WEST

CROOK Jennifer *(Voc, Gtr)*: Garden Flat, 7A Walcot Buildings, London Road, Bath BA1 6AD ☎ 01225 483254

EVANS Delyth *(Pf)*: 124 Overland Road, Mumbles, Swansea, West Glamorgan SA3 4EU ☎ 01792 360150

LONDON

SMITH Paula *(Bod, Gtr)*: 398 Hanworth Road, Hounslow, Middlesex TW3 3SN ☎ 0956 955464 mob

CHARANGO

SCOTLAND

MUNOZ Fernando *(Pan P, Quena, Flt, Gtr)*: 30 Polwarth Crescent, Edinburgh EH11 1HN ☎ 0131 229 2183 & fax

MIDLANDS

MUNOZ Carlos *(Gtr, Man, Tiple)*: 8 Woodville Road, Kings Heath, Birmingham B14 7AH ☎ 0121 444 7773

CIMBALON

SCOTLAND

CORBETT Heather *(Per, Tym, Pf)*: 33 Faskally Avenue, Bishopbriggs, Glasgow G64 3PJ ☎ 0141 772 3152, 07050 168772 mob

CIMBASSO

LONDON

ANDERSON Jim *(Tba)*: 34 Lytton Road, New Barnet, Herts EN5 5BY ☎ 020 8449 5670, 020 8549 1706

WICK Stephen *(Tba, Oph, Serp)*: 22 Methuen Park, Muswell Hill, London N10 2JS ☎ 020 8442 0589, 0973 119762 mob, 020 8482 5399 fax

CITTERN

SCOTLAND

ARMSTRONG-WILSON Robert *(Bzk, Gtr, Man, Wh)*: Harelan Hill Cottage, Canonbie, Dumfriesshire DG14 0RX ☎ 013873 71557

SOUTH EAST

ESPLIN Alexander *(Gtr, H Gurd)*: Stags Lodge, Main Street, West Hagobourne, Oxon OX11 0NJ ☎ 01235 850781

CLARINET

SCOTLAND

ALEXANDER Philip *(Sax)*: 1 Wellgate Street, Newport-on-Tay, Fife DD6 8HS ☎ 01382 542042

BECKETT Seren *(Sax, Pf, Flt, Ob)*: 10 Grosvenor Crescent, Dowanhill, Glasgow G12 9AF

BENEDICT David *(B Clt, Flt, A Sax)*: Top Left, 3 Queens Park Ave, Glasgow G42 8BX ☎ 0141 423 0352

BLACKWOOD William *(Saxes, Flt, Theory, Com)*: 4 Cambridge Gardens, Edinburgh EH6 5DJ ☎ 0131 554 6183

BRODIE Andy *(Sax, Flt)*: 47 Woodhead Crescent, Thornwood, Uddingston G71 6LR ☎ 01698 817686

CAIRNS Forrest *(Sax)*: Chalenstr. 29, 8123 Ebmatingen, Switzerland ☎ 020 8980 4361, 079 448 2085 mob, 020 8980 4637

CLENNON Ornette *(Saxes)*: 57 2F2 Prince Regent Street, Leith, Edinburgh EH6 4AP ☎ 0131 554 1721, 020 8667 7938

CONSIDINE Rachel *(Bsn, Pf, T Sax)*: 45 Raeswood Drive, Crookston, Glasgow G53 7LB ☎ 0141 883 8099, 0973 773215

CUSHING John: 1 Ibert Road, Killearn, Glasgow G63 9PX ☎ 01360 550166

DUNSMORE John *(Pf)*: 16 Braehead Terrace, Kilmaurs, Ayrshire KA3 2TP ☎ 01563 539238, 0797 0490502

ELLIS Ruth *(B Clt)*: Grooms Cottage, 5 Markle Steading, East Linton, East Lothian EH40 3EB ☎ 01620 861018

FAIRLEY Douglas *(B Clt, Sax)*: 4/5 Advocate's Close, 375 High Street, Edinburgh EH1 1PS ☎ 0131 225 9117

FAIRLEY Robert *(B Clt, T Sax, A Sax, Efl Clt)*: 5 Mellock Gardens, Falkirk, Scotland FK1 5NU ☎ 01324 633559

FOLEY John *(Sax, Flt)*: 2 Perth Street, Edinburgh EH3 5DP ☎ 0131 557 8562

FORBES Ann E J *(Sax)*: 35 Underwood Cottages, Cambusbarron, Stirling FK7 9PA ☎ 01786 448842

FREELAND Joanne *(B Clt, Rec, Efl Clt)*: 84 Iona Way, Kirkintilloch G66 3PY ☎ 0141 776 3336

GHIRO Yann *(B Clt, Efl Clt)*: Top Right, 98 Raeberry Street, North Kelvinside, Glasgow G20 6EG ☎ 0141 946 5683

GILL Lawrence *(B Clt, Sax)*: 32 Randolph Road, Broomhill, Glasgow G11 7LG ☎ 0141 334 4533 & fax

GRAY John: 27 Oxford Street, Edinburgh EH8 9PQ ☎ 0131 667 0850

GREENE Philip: 16 Learmonth Terrace, Edinburgh EH4 1PG ☎ 0131 332 0481

HAGGART Alison: 41 Burnett Place, Aberdeen AB24 4QD ☎ 01224 492502

HASTIE James *(Saxes, Flt, Pic, Ob)*: 70 Archerhill Road, Knightswood, Glasgow G13 3NH ☎ 0141 959 0715

HAY Tom *(Saxes)*: 1A St Leonard's Road, Ayr KA7 2PR ☎ 0292 265298

HAYDOCK Geoffrey *(Efl Clt, B Clt, Sax)*: 17 Douglas Muir Drive, Milngavie, Glasgow G62 7RS ☎ 0141 956 4685

MCGREGOR Hamish *(A Sax, Br Sax, S Sax)*: Waterbeck, 49 Cramond Glebe Road, Edinburgh EH4 6NT ☎ 0131 336 3635

MCLEAN Philip *(B Clt)*: Address Unknown

MITCHELL Timothy *(Sax)*: 20 Soutar Crescent, Perth, Perthshire, Scotland PH1 1QB ☎ 01738 622054

MOSSMAN Jenny *(Pf, Rec, Sax, Flt)*: Address Unknown ☎ 0141 942 9714

NAIRN Duncan *(B Clt, Saxes)*: 11 Esmond Street, Glasgow G3 8SL ☎ 0141 334 3880

NEIL Robert *(A Sax, T Sax, B Clt)*: 36 Tanton Road, Stokesley, North Yorkshire TS9 5HR ☎ 01642 710823

PAXTON Edward *(Sax)*: 59 Bellwood Street, Glasgow G41 3EX ☎ 0141 649 1481

ROSS James *(Rec, Ea Wnd)*: Cullaggan, 18 Sunnyside, Culloden Moor, Inverness IV1 2ES ☎ 01463 790666

ROSS Nicholas: 59 Neilston Road, Uplawmoor, Glasgow G78 4AF ☎ 01505 850 318, 07050 325710 mob

SMITH George *(Sax)*: 67A Busby Road, Clarkston G76 7BW ☎ 0141 644 3011

SUTHERLAND Elise *(Pf)*: Clashbuie Cottage, Dalchalm Brora, Sutherland, Scotland KW9 6LP ☎ 01408 621543

SWEENEY William *(Com)*: 49 Lawrence Street, Glasgow G11 5HD ☎ 0141 334 9987

TUCKER Alison *(Efl Clt, Sax, Pf, Kbds)*: Flat 2/2 22 Hotspur Street, North Kelvinside, Glasgow G20 8NN ☎ 0141 576 5477, 07971 923323

TURLEY Pamela: 30A Inverleith Place, Edinburgh EH3 5QB ☎ 0131 552 2410

WALLER Alison: 21 Morningside Grdns, Edinburgh EH10 5LE ☎ 0131 447 6565

WALLER George *(Sax)*: 10, Foxes Grove, Lenzie, Near Glasgow, Scotland G66 5BN ☎ 0141 776 6609

WALSH Sarah *(B Clt, A Sax, Br Sax, Flt)*: 48 North Deeside Road, Aberdeen AB15 7PL ☎ 01224 322353

WIMHURST Karen *(Saxes, Flt, Acc)*: The Garden Cottage, 89 Church Lawn, Stourton, Warminster, Wilts BA12 6QE ☎ 01747 841 232

NORTH WEST

ANDERSON Molly *(Sax, Flt)*: 2 Lynton Grove, Bradshaw, Halifax, W Yorks HX2 9XN ☎ 01422 247162

ARMITAGE David *(Bt Hrn)*: Mount View, Church Road, Tilston, Cheshire SY14 7HB ☎ 01829 250323

ASQUITH Alan *(Efl Clt, B Clt, Bsn)*: 70 Kenilworth Road, Cheadle Heath, Stockport, Cheshire SK3 0QN ☎ 0161282 1696

BENN Max: 2 Vienna Road, Edgley, Stockport SK3 9QH ☎ 0161 480 0858

British & International Music Yearbook

Britain's most accurate and comprehensive directory of the classical music industry

18,000 Contacts – artists, agents, orchestras, ensembles, opera companies, choirs, venues, promoters, music festivals, record companies, music publishers, musician services and education.

PLUS International listings of orchestras, agents, publishers, competitions and festivals.

Published each December
650 pages

HOW TO ORDER

Please send a cheque for **£27.45** (inc. p&p) payable to *Rhinegold Publishing Ltd* to: **BMYB Sales, Rhinegold Publishing, FREEPOST, London WC2H 8BR**.

TELEPHONE:	**0171 333 1721** (or 020 7333 1721 after 22 Apr 2000)
FAX:	**0171 333 1769** (or 020 7333 1769 after 22 Apr 2000)
EMAIL:	**sales@rhinegold.co.uk**
WEBSITE:	**www.rhinegold.co.uk**

BRADBURY John

BRUNTON John (*T Sax, A Sax*): 52 Crow Wood Avenue, Burnley, Lancs BB12 0JG ☎ 01282 432690

BURKE David (*T Sax*): 23 St Georges Avenue, Windle, St Helens, Merseyside WA10 6EU ☎ 01744 22919

BUSHNELL-WYE Mairearad: Woodgarth, 102 Townfield Lane, Barnton, Northwich, Cheshire CW8 4QL ☎ 01606 784816

CATON Elizabeth (*Efl Clt, B Clt, Bt Hrn, S Sax*): 1 Oldfield Road, Sale, Cheshire M33 2AP ☎ 0161 976 2392

COE Debbie (*Pf, Sax, Flt*) ☎ 0161 440 7713, 0378 2702008

COX Nicholas: 33 Sandy Lane, Lymm, Cheshire WA13 9HP ☎ 01925 756 281, 020 8533 1372 day

DAVIES Heidi (*Sax, Flt*): 3 Hareswood Close, Winsford, Cheshire CW7 2TP ☎ 01606 558 787, 09661 34284

DICKINSON Andrew (*A Sax, S Sax*): 108 Shuttle Street, Tyldesley, Greater Manchester M29 8BS ☎ 0797 1226845

FAIRHURST Lynne (*Voc, Cl Gtr, Pf, A Sax*): 8 Ward Street, St Helens, Merseyside WA10 2RX ☎ 01744 757089, 0378 442667

FOSTER Leonard (*Pf*): 9 Sandbrook Rd, Ainsdale, Southport, Merseyside PR8 3JH ☎ 01704 573370

FOSTER Nicholas: 38 Lingard Road, Northenden, Manchester M22 4EN ☎ 0161 902 0964

FUEST John: 41 Reading Drive, Sale, Cheshire M33 5DJ ☎ 0161 905 2144

GOULD Emily (*Pf, Vln*): 42 Vancouver Quay, Salford Quays, Salford, Lancs M5 2TU ☎ 0161 877 3072

GREGSON James: 25, New City Road, Mosley Common, Worsley, Manchester M28 1XZ ☎ 0161 790 3655

HAWLEY Rosalind: Flat B, 92 Boundary Lane, Manchester M15 6FD ☎ 0161 232 1584

HAYDOCK Alan (*Sax*): 55 Victoria Road, Elland, West Yorkshire HX5 0QA ☎ 01422 379575

HEYWOOD David: 106 Ballaquark Estate, Braddan, Isle Of Man IM2 2EN ☎ 01624 629964

HILL Peter (*B Clt, Bt Hrn, A Sax, Br Sax*): 41 Derby Road, Southport, Merseyside PR9 0TZ ☎ 01704 544956

HILTON Janet: Holly House, 2 East Downs Road, Bowden, Altrincham, Cheshire WA14 2LH ☎ 0161 928 3471

HOUGHTON Anthony (*B Clt, Sax*): 17 Abington Road, Sale, Cheshire M33 3DL ☎ 0161 969 3301

JACOBS Howard (*B Gtr, Per, Pf*): Flat 3, 60 Old Landsdowne Road, West Didsbury, Manchester M20 2WU ☎ 0161 448 0897

JONES Helen (*Pf, Voc*): 9 Bryn Road, Flint, Clwyd CH6 5HU ☎ 01352 732712

KIRBY Dawn: 112 Cambridge Road, Liverpool L21 1EZ ☎ 0151 920 5022

KIRKPATRICK Dennis (*S Sax, A Sax*): 30 Lyndhurst, Ashurst, Skelmersdale, Lancs WN8 6UH ☎ 01695 722875

LYDIATT J (*T Sax*): 17 Court Hey Road, Liverpool L16 2LY ☎ 0151 489 5218

MANNION Joanne: 159 Grant Road, Dovecot, Liverpool L14 OL6 ☎ 0151 283 1309, 0961 935 388

MARSHALL Barrie (*A Sax*): 112 Aldrens Lane, Skerton, Lancaster LA1 2DT ☎ 01524 37381

MELLOR John (*B Clt, Efl Clt, A Sax*): Flat 14, Kennerley Lodge, 140-144 Bramhall Lane, Stockport, Cheshire SK3 8SB ☎ 0161 487 4246, 0966 179680 mob

MILLER David (*Sax, Efcb Clt, B Clt*): 45 Ashworth Park, Knutsford, Cheshire WA16 9DG ☎ 01565 651665

MILNER Edward (*Sax, Flt*): 'Avalon', 1 Rydal Grove, Lache Lane, Chester CH4 8HJ ☎ 01244 682105

MUIRHEAD James (*Saxes, Flt*): Hillstead, 68 Thorley Lane, Timperley, Altrincham, Cheshire WA15 7AN ☎ 0161 980 3061

NEWHILL John (*B Clt, Bt Hrn*): 25 Amberley Road, Sale, Cheshire M33 6QP ☎ 0161 973 2796

PATTON Joanna: 32 Broadlake, Willaston, South Wirral, Cheshire L64 2XB ☎ 0151 327 6408, 0161 227 9640 day

PROUDMAN Robin: 8 Hob Lane, Edgworth, Tulton, Bolton, Lancs BL7 0PS ☎ 01204 853776

PURCELL Roger (*Saxes*): 10 The Sands, Whalley, Clitheroe, Lancs BB7 9TL ☎ 0125 482 2294

QUINN Jennifer (*Pf*): Address Unknown ☎ 0161 256 0454

RACZ Lynne (*Efl Clt, A Sax, Pf*): 4 Ellendale Grange, Worsley, Manchester M28 7UX ☎ 0161 703 9007

REBBECK Janet (*Sax, Flt*): 1 Grosvenor Crescent, Rosset, Wrexham LL12 0HX ☎ 01244 571003, 0973 674449 mob

REDPATH Timothy (*Sax*): 5 Littler Grange Court, Littler Lane, Winsford, Cheshire CW7 2TJ ☎ 01606 861005 & fax

RICHARDS Paul: 10 Dunsmure Road, Stoke Newington, London N16 5PW

ROBERTS Andrew (*B Clt, Efl Clt, Bt Hrn*): 36 Nicander Road, Liverpool L18 1HY ☎ 0151 734 3283, 0976 264275, 0151 734 3202

ROBSON Leo (*Sax, Org*): 17 Aintree Road, Blackpool, Lancashire FY4 3BD ☎ 01253 41649

SELLERS Brian E (*Sax*): 7 Valley View, Grindleton, Clitheroe, Lancs BB7 4RP ☎ 01200 441031

SELLORS Bob (*Br Sax, Con*): 27 High View Road, Douglas, Isle Of Man IM2 5BH ☎ 01624 622121

SHOTTON Stephen (*B Clt, A Sax, T Sax, S Sax*): 17 Jubilee Road, Wrexham, N. Wales LL13 7NN ☎ 01978 355167, 0860 147027

SLACK Karen (*B Clt*): 21 Elmsett Close, Great Sankey, Warrington WA5 3RX ☎ 01925 729996

SMITH Geoffrey: 1 The Mere, Cheadle Hulme, Cheadle, Cheshire SK8 5LA ☎ 0161 485 8006

STAFFORD Gordon: Shudehill, Hayfield, High Peak, Derbyshire SK22 2EP ☎ 01663 742784, 01523 120811 pager, 0966 496751 mob

STARK Valerie (*B Clt, Sax*): 21 Allanson Road, Northenden, Manchester M22 4HN ☎ 0161 998 2524

SWANN Christopher (*Sax*): 24 Gladstone Road, Neston, South Wirral L64 9PJ ☎ 0151 336 4078

TENNANT Sarah (*B Clt*): 27 Coronation Street, Macclesfield, Cheshire SK11 7PQ ☎ 01625 424267

TOLLEY Warren (*A Sax*): Cherokee, 23 Napier Avenue, Blackpool, Lancs FY4 1PA ☎ 01253 403781

TROUGHTON Harold (*T Sax, A Sax*): 18 Morreway, Prescot, Merseyside L35 6PD ☎ 0151 426 2324

TURNER Karen (*B Clt*): 107 Tyldesley Road, Atherton, Manchester M46 9AA ☎ 01942 799259, 0370 934855

WALKER Ann: 17 Mossgrove Road, Timperley, Altrincham, Cheshire WA15 6LF ☎ 0161 980 2767

WARR Valerie: Leaway, Dunstan Lane, Burton, South Wirral L64 8TJ ☎ 0151 336 3618

WILDE Gail: 13 Hazel Grove, Irby, Wirral, Merseyside L61 4UY ☎ 0151 648 7764

WILKINSON Adrian (*Saxes*): 51 Newhouse Road, Hopwood, Heywood, Lancs OL10 2NU ☎ 01706 365556

WOONTON David: 19 Collier Avenue, Milnrow, Rochdale, Lancs OL16 3UY ☎ 01706 524594, 0161 273 6283

NORTH EAST

ALLEN John (*A Sax, Dms, Per*): 13 Emmbrook Close, East Rainton, Houghton Le Spring, Tyne & Wear DH5 9SQ ☎ 0191 584 1071

BARTLETT Peter (*T Sax, B Clt, A Sax, Flt*): Mill House, Reeth, N Yorks DL11 6SL ☎ 01325 356125

BASS Rodney (*S Sax, A Sax, T Sax, Flt*): 292 Thornhills Lane, Clifton, Brighouse, Yorks HD6 4JQ ☎ 01484 713733

BEESTON Martin: 13 Station Court, Easingwold, Yorks YO61 3JW ☎ 01347 822945

BROWN Rachel: 49 Craigs Road, Edinburgh, Scotland EH12 8EW ☎ 0131 339 3299

CARRICK Brian (*T Sax*): 18 Gladstone Terrace, New Penshaw, Tyne & Wear DH4 7PJ ☎ 0191 385 3358

CHALLIS Dave (*Sax*): Chapel House, Arkendale, Knaresbrough, North Yorkshire HG5 0QU ☎ 01423 340560

CHILTON Catherine (*Sax, Voc*): 3 Crossley Place, Skipton, North Yorkshire BD23 1PZ ☎ 01756 797634, 01756 700096 fax

CLEGG Eric (*A Sax, S Sax, T Sax*): Tanfield, Durham Road, Annfield Plain, Stanley Co. Durham DH9 7UF ☎ 01207 239977

DENFORD Sharon (*Sax, Flt*): 1 Compton Drive, Grimsby, N. E. Lincs DN34 4PB ☎ 01472 320721

DORR Julie (*Sax, Flt*): 26 Meadow Road, West Monkseaton, Whitley Bay, Tyne & Wear NE25 8NB ☎ 0191 252 1473

DYLAK Anthony (*B Clt, A Sax, T Sax, Pf*): 34 Altar Drive, Heaton, Bradford, West Yorkshire BD9 5QD ☎ 01274 542328

FENWICK Terry (*T Sax, S Sax*): 21 Kingswell, Morpeth, Northumberland NE61 2TY ☎ 01670 510369

FLECK Derek (*Saxes, Gtr, Bjo, B Gtr*): 261 Broadway, Cullercoats, North Sheilds, Tyne & Wear NE30 3DG ☎ 0191 297 0792

FROST Brian (*Sax*): 2A Western Street, Barnsley, South Yorkshire S70 2BP

GIBSON Daniel (*B Clt*): 90 Town Street, Farsley, Leeds LS28 5LF ☎ 0113 270 4992

GOFFIN Alison (*Hrn, Pf*): 22 Hallcroft Lane, Copmanthorpe, York YO23 3UG ☎ 01904 702777

HAIGH Willie (*A Sax, T Sax, S Sax*): High Fleets, Fleets Lane, Rylstone, Nr Skipton North Yorkshire BD23 6NA ☎ 01756 730202

HALL Julian (*Saxes, B Gtr, Gtr*): 10, Castle Road, Sandal, Wakefield WF2 7LY ☎ 01924 253003

HONOUR Colin (*Efl Clt, B Clt*): 22 Sandhurst Street, Calverley, Leeds LS28 5RN ☎ 0113 2559567

HOWE Robert (*Saxes, Per*): 94 Parkside, Spennymoor, Co Durham DL16 6RX ☎ 01388 816575

HURRELL Susan (*B Clt*): 76 Simonside Terrace, Heaton, Newcastle-upon-Tyne NE6 5JY ☎ 0191 265 8910

JINSKI Steve (*Pf, Gtr, Clt*): 198 Jesmond Dene Road, Jesmond, Newcastle-upon-Tyne, Tyne Wear NE2 2NL ☎ 0191 281 5074

JOSEPH James (*A Sax, S Sax, Kbds*): 28 Holly Avenue, Jesmond, Newcastle-upon-Tyne NE2 2PY ☎ 0191212 0312 & fax, 0976 274833 mob

KENNY Brian (*S Sax, T Sax, B Sax*): 8 Durlastone Close, Gleadless, Sheffield S12 2TR ☎ 0114 239 4893

KIRK Philip (*B Clt*): Michaelmas Cottage, Leavening, Malton, North Yorkshire YO17 ☎ 0165385 279

LAWSON Sarah A (*Sax*): 2 New Houses, Newton Morrell, Richmond, North Yorkshire DL10 6HL ☎ 01642 780844

LE-GRAND John (*Sax, Pic, Flt, Ob*): 64 Otley Road, Eldwick, Bingley, West Yorks BD16 3EE ☎ 01274 569104

MACKENZIE John (*Saxes, Con, Pf*): 15 Springwell, Ingleton, Darlington, Co. Durham DL2 3JJ ☎ 01325 730072

MALONE Anthony (*Flt, Sax*): 53 South Parade, Northallerton, North Yorkshire DL7 8SL ☎ 01609 776229

MATTHEWS Colin (*Sax*): Address Unknown ☎ 01423 507057

MCBRIARTY Jim (*A Sax, T Sax, Br Sax, Voc*): 39 Nilverton Avenue, Ashbrooke, Sunderland, Tyne & Wear SR2 7TS ☎ 0191 522 5196, 0191 222 1325

MCDONALD George (*Saxes*): 24 Lansdowne Gardens, Jesmond, Newcastle-upon-Tyne 2 NE2 1HE ☎ 0191 281 0496

MOORE Malcolm (*B Clt, A Sax, T Sax, Flt*): 4 Blanchland Avenue, Woodlands Park, Wideopen, North Tyneside NE13 6JR ☎ 0191 236 7523

MOORE Norman (*A Sax, T Sax, Flt, Bsn*): 30 Cotswold Gardens, Newcastle-on-Tyne, Tyne & Wear NE7 7AE ☎ 0191 281 1325, 0402 357405 mob

MORE Andrew (*Sax, Flt, Pf*): 20 The Glade, Abbey Farm, North Warbottle, Newcastle-upon-Tyne NE15 9XJ ☎ 0191 267 9943

MORRISON Terrence (*Sax, Flt, Kbds*): 19 Simon Place, Brunswick Green, Wideopen, Newcastle-upon-Tyne 3 NE13 7HT ☎ 0191 236 4895

MYERSCOUGH Roger (*B Sax*): Underhill, Langthwaite, Nr Richmond, North Yorks DL11 6RE ☎ 01748 884721

OADES Debbie (*Sax, Flt*): 63 Faraday Street, Hull, East Yorkshire HU9 3EF ☎ 01482 376042

PLUMB Mary (*Saxes*): 96 Bankside Street, Leeds LS8 5AD ☎ 0113 2496808

POWER James (*Flt, Ob, Saxes*): 1 Station Cottages, Harecroft, Wilsden, Bradford, Yorks BD15 0BS

ROBERTS Kathryn (*Flt, Saxes*): Salters Croft, 2 High Street, Dodworth, Barnsley S Yorks S75 3RF ☎ 01226 203816

ROBERTS Michael (*Saxes, Flt, Pic, Arr*): 2 High Street, Dodworth, Barnsley S75 3RF ☎ 01226 203816

ROBINSON John (*Efl Clt*): 3 Heather Road, Meltham, Huddersfield HD7 3EY ☎ 01484 850457

ROBINSON Leslie (*Saxes*): 3, Dingle Dell, Plantation Road, Leighton Buzzard, Beds LU7 7JL ☎ 01525 3477

ROGERSON Howard (*Con*): Four Winds, The Mains, Giggleswick, Settle, North Yorkshire BD24 0AX ☎ 01729 822195

SANDER Adrian (*B Clt, S Sax, A Sax, T Sax*): 59 Fern Avenue, Jesmond, Newcastle/Tyne 2, Tyne & Wear NE2 2QU ☎ 0191 281 6802, 0191 265 5977

SANDER Hilary: 12 Mount Pleasant, Stocksfield, Northumberland NE43 7LP

STAMP Roger (*A Sax, T Sax*): 12 Darrington Drive, Warmsworth, Nr Doncaster DN4 9LF ☎ 01302 854487

THREADGOLD Helena (*Rec, T Sax, Pf*): 31 Herril Ings, Tickhill, Doncaster, South Yorks DN11 9UE ☎ 01302 742552

TODD Liane (*A Sax, T Sax, Flt, Pf*): 7 The Crest, Willow Grange, Bedlington, Northumberland NE22 6HH ☎ 01670 822626

TURNER Nicholas: 23 Manor House Road, Wilsden, Bradford BD15 0EB ☎ 01535 273033

VAUGHAN Caroline (*Sax*): 103 Carr Lane, Acomb, York YO26 5HN ☎ 01904 788773

WEARE Michael (*B Clt*): 10 First Ave, Heworth, York YO31 7YQ ☎ 01904 423806

WIXEY Jayne (*Saxes, Flt, Pf*): 123 Westgarth, Whorlton Grange, Westerhope, Newcastle-upon-Tyne NE5 4NX ☎ 0191 286 8065

YATES Simeon (*B Clt, Sax, Flt, Pf*): Coatham Cottage, 30 Armitage Road, Armitage Bridge, Huddersfield HD4 7PD ☎ 01484 665470, 0836 601497

EAST

BOMBER Ray (*Acc, Kbds*): 14 Talbot Street, Hertford SG13 7BX ☎ 01992 553 249

BRINKLEY Sarah (*A Sax, T Sax, Br Sax, Flt*): 25 Osprey Close, Off Flacon Way, Garston, Watford, Herts WD2 4XR ☎ 01923 682443

CAMERON Sarah: Fox Corner, High Street, Rampton, Cambs CB4 8QX ☎ 01954 252493

CAMPBELL Lucy (*Sax, Flt*): 56 Millstream Close, Hitchin, Hertfordshire SG4 0DA ☎ 01462 440216

CARTER David S (*Saxes, Gtr, B Gtr*): 30 Greens Road, Cambridge CB4 3EF ☎ 01223 722909

CLARKE Ken (*Arr*): 6 Great Ley, Welwyn Garden City, Herts AL7 4TS ☎ 01707 328644

DENSHAM Timothy (*S Sax, A Sax, Br Sax*): 28 The Paddocks, Hill Farm Road, Halesworth, Suffolk IP19 8RR ☎ 01986 875909 & fax

DEXTER-MILLS Suzanne (*B Clt, Sax, Flt*): 123 Nowton Road, Bury St Edmunds, Suffolk IP33 2NH ☎ 01284 703238

DRINKALL Spencer (*Saxes*): 13 Purwell Lane, Hitchin, Herts SG4 0NE ☎ 01462 459897

FORD Julia: Hillside Cottage, Stoke By Nayland, Nr Colchester CO6 4QD ☎ 01206 262407

GEORGIE Esther (*Pf*): Rua Conde Moserr 115, Monte Estoril, 2765 Estoril, Portugal

HALL Robert (*Sax*): c/o 12 Church End, Rampton, Cambs CB4 8QA ☎ 01954 251820, 0973 145976 mob

HARLAN Ben (*B Clt, Efl Clt, A Sax*): 46 Lemsford Road, St. Albans, Herts AL1 3PR ☎ 01727 832851

HEMMINGS Diana (*B Clt, Efl Clt, Sax*): Ashe Cottage, Lower Hacheston, Woodbridge, Suffolk IP13 0PB ☎ 01728 746002

LIGHTFOOT Terry (*A Sax, T Sax, So Sax*): 26 Hollow Wood, Olney, Bucks MK46 5LY ☎ 01234 241293 fax, 0860 643120 mob

LINDSELL Robert (*Saxes*): 267 London Road, Black Notley, Braintree, Essex CM7 8QQ ☎ 01376 331760, 01376 331760 fax

LUMB Rachel (*A Sax, B Clt, Flt, T Sax*): 89 Church Hill, Cheddington, Nr Leighton Buzzard, Beds LU7 0SX ☎ 01296 660324

LYONS Lorna (*A Sax, Flt*): 41 Broom Grove, Knebworth, Hertfordshire SG3 6BZ ☎ 01438 215519, 0585 81 2957

MANNING Gary: 11 Northcotts, Hatfield, Herts AL9 5ES ☎ 01707 269418

MOORE-ORTON Donald *(Sax, Pf, Db)*: 27 Main Road, Colly Weston, Stamford, Lincs PE9 3PF ☎ 01780 444 681

NEALE, L.R.A.M. Clive *(Dms, A Sax, T Sax, So Sax)*: 393 Main Road, Dovercourt, Harwich, Essex CO12 4ET ☎ 01255 504931

PRITCHARD Malcolm *(B Clt, Sax, Pf)*: 88 Lawn Lane, Hemel Hempstead, Herts HP3 9HS ☎ 01442 268 362

RODGERS John *(A Sax)*: 29 Lyndhurst Gardens, Enfield, Middlesex EN1 2AP ☎ 020 8367 7167

ROGERS Zoe *(Pf)*: 2 The Spinney, Roundwood Park, Harpenden, Hertsfordshire AL5 3AZ ☎ 01582 622253

SECLUNA Clive *(Flt, A Sax)*: 12A Mildmay Road, Chelmsford, Essex CM2 0DX ☎ 01245 265312

SMITH David *(Flt)*: 17 Church Meadow Cottages, Great Gaddesden, Nr Hemel Hemptstead, Herts HP1 3BJ ☎ 01442 243354

SPOTSWOOD Janet: 76 St Annes Road, London Colney, Herts AL2 1LJ ☎ 01727 821386

STUART Gareth: Croeso Church Lane, Hilton, Huntingdon, Cambridge PE18 9NH ☎ 01480 830882

TEALE Antony *(T Sax, A Sax, B Clt)*: 71 Blinco Grove, Cambridge CB1 4TX ☎ 01223 246026

THURGOOD John *(Pf)*: Elms Farmhouse, Gt Barton, Bury St Edmunds, Suffolk IP31 2MP ☎ 01284 87792

TREBBLE Ceri *(Rec)*: 15 Upper Tail, Carpenders Park, Watford, Herts WD1 5DF ☎ 020 8386 2749

WYBROW Clifford *(B Clt, Sax)*: 10 Constable Road, Felixstowe, Suffolk IP11 7HL

MIDLANDS

ALLEN Frank *(B Clt, Efl Clt)*: 799 Chester Road, Erdington, Birmingham B24 0BX ☎ 0121 373 0420

ALLISON Christopher *(B Clt)*: 18 Birch Lane, Oldbury, Warley, West Midlands B68 0NZ ☎ 0121 421 7998

BATEMAN Marie *(Pf, Flt)*: 19 Westcliffe Avenue, Westbury Park, Newcastle-Under-Lyme, Staffordshire ST5 4JS ☎ 01782 638352

CARTWRIGHT Sarah *(Sax, Voc)*: 25 Falmouth Avenue, Weeping Cross, Stafford ST17 0JQ ☎ 01785 603616, 0378 871680 mob

CARUANA Nicholas *(A Sax)*: 16 Peverels Way, Weedon Road, Northampton NN5 5DD ☎ 01604 582610

CAWDREY Leslie *(B Clt, A Sax, S Sax, Flt)*: 8 Brook End Close, Henley In Arden, Warks B95 5JE ☎ 01564 793394

CHAMBERLAIN Sarah *(A Sax, Pf, Rec, Gtr)*: Ground Floor Flat, 43 Preston Road, Brighton BN1 4QE ☎ 01273 571940, 0966 138281 mob

CHAMBERS Rod *(Sax)*: 53 Fairfield Road, Bournheath, Bromsgrove, Worcs B61 9JL ☎ 01527 878611, 0370 472530 mob

CONDLIFFE Jacqueline *(Sax)*: 4 Marsh Close, Werrington, Stoke-on-Trent, Staffordshire ST9 0LP ☎ 01782 305063

CURRY-PEACE Sarah *(A Sax, B Clt, T Sax, Pf)*: 51 Jonathon Road, New Park, Trentham, Stoke-on-Trent, Staffs ST4 8LP ☎ 01782 644170, 0976 369084

DAVEY Eric *(A Sax)*: 97 Kamloops Crescent, Leicester LE1 2HX

DAVIES Martyn: 26 Falstaff Avenue, Hollywood, Birmingham B47 5EP ☎ 01564 822309

DAVIES Sally *(Pf, Rec)*: 3 Blackhill, Upper Welland, Malvern, Worcs WR14 4JT ☎ 01684 564090

DAVIES Stephen *(Sax, Flt)*: 12 Vienna Grove, Blue Bridge, Milton Keynes MK13 0LG ☎ 01908 322696

EDWARDS Alfred *(A Sax)*: 31, Fairway, Nuneaton, Warwickshire CV11 6NP ☎ 024 7638 4552

FIELD Norman *(A Sax, T Sax, Saxes)*: 14 Regent Road, Harborne, Birmingham B17 9JU ☎ 0121 426 3663

FORD Luan: 115 Selsey Road, Edgbaston, Birmingham B17 8JP ☎ 0121 434 5440

GOSLING Peter: 1075 Bristol Road, Selly Oak, Birmingham B29 6LX ☎ 0121 472 6587

GRAY Paul *(Sax, Flt)*: 7 Byfield Drive, Wigston Meadows, Leicester LE18 3PY ☎ 0116 2888042

GREENLEES Robert *(B Clt, Saxes)*: 14 St Denys Road, Evington, Leicester LE5 6DT ☎ 0116 2736247

GRIFFITHS Richard: 9 Kings Avenue, Wolstanton, Newcastle, Staffs ST5 8DA ☎ 01782 626833

HARROP Sally *(Sax)*: 48 Ashfield Drive, Moria, Derbyshire DE12 6HQ ☎ 01530 411315

HAWKES Gillian *(Pf)*: 24 Shanklin Drive, Stoneygate, Leicester LE2 3RG ☎ 0116 2703524

HIBBERT Ian *(Flt, Pic, Saxes, Md)*: 18 Diamond Avenue, Sherwood Park, Rainworth, Nottingham NG21 0FF ☎ 01623 795399

HOOD Victoria: 25 Shardlow Close, Fenton, Stoke-on-Trent, Staffs ST4 2NZ ☎ 01782 313238

HOPKINSON Christopher *(S Sax, A Sax, T Sax, B Sax)*: 1 Byron Grove, Stone Broom, Alfreton, Derbyshire DE55 6JL ☎ 01773 873379

HUBBARD Roy: 12 Berkeley Crescent, Stourport-on-Severn, Worcs DY13 0HJ ☎ 01299 871585

HUXLEY George *(S Sax)*: 56 Broadfern Road, Knowle, Solihull, West Midlands B93 9DD ☎ 01564 730 098

JACK Tony *(A Sax, T Sax)*: 23 Saxon Rise, Old Duston, Northampton NN5 6HP ☎ 01604 753750

JONES Dave *(Br Sax)*: 71 Westfield Avenue, Deanshanger, Milton Keynes MK19 6LH ☎ 01908 56 3037

LUXMOORE Kate *(B Clt)*: 24 Grove Avenue, Moseley, Birmingham B13 9RU ☎ 0121 449 4668, 04325 170648 pager

LYCETT Jonathan *(Pf, Sax, Gtr)*: 25 Chester Crescent, Westlands, Newcastle ST5 3RT ☎ 01782 616852

MEADOWS John *(B Clt, Sax)*: Church House, Maurice Road, Smethwick B67 5LR ☎ 0121 429 1192

MELLOR Steve *(S Sax, A Sax, Br Sax, Cnt)*: 46A West Malvern Road, Malvern, Worcs WR14 4NA ☎ 01684 565105

MEREDITH Daniel *(Br Sax, T Sax)*: 20 Radway Close, Church Hill North, Redditch, Worcs B98 8RZ ☎ 01527 65348

MORAN John *(Sax)*: 74 Oaklands Ave, Wolstanton, Stoke-on-Trent, Staffordshire ST5 0DS ☎ 01782 628226

NEWMAN Peter *(Br Sax, T Sax, Bjo)*: 140 Cambridge Road, Great Shelford, Cambridge CB2 5JU

NEWTON Eric: 6 Linley Road, Alsager, Stoke-on-Trent ST7 2QD ☎ 01270 877885

NEWTON Selwyn: 12 Rowan Close, Kingsbury, Staffs B78 2JR ☎ 01827 872661

O'BRIEN Mark *(B Clt, Efl Clt)*: 17, Whitehead Drive, Minworth, Sutton Coldfield, West Midlands. B76 9AN ☎ 0121 351 5868

OLDLAND Marie *(T Sax, A Sax)*: 65 Byfield Rise, Tallow Mill, Hillsborough, Worcester WR5 1BA ☎ 01905 26113, 0468 586698

OSBORNE John *(A Sax, Br Sax, T Sax, Bjo)*: Castle Despair, 1042 Chester Road, Erdington, Birmingham B24 0LJ ☎ 0121 382 6836

PALMER Matt *(T Sax, S Sax)*: 12 Brookside Road, Ruddington, Nottingham NG11 6AW

PARR Colin: 20 Parkfield Road, Stourbridge, West Midlands DY8 1HD ☎ 01384 390047

PERCY Richard *(B Clt, A Sax, T Sax)*: Old Elm Cottage, 93 Guarlford Road, Malvern WR14 3QU ☎ 016845 67501

RANDLE Mac *(S Sax)*: Beech Lawn, Mill Lane, Kineton, Warwickshire CV35 0LA ☎ 01926 640078

REYNOLDS Gillian *(Flt)*: 493, Warwick Road, Solihull, West Midlands B91 1AN ☎ 0121 705 1239

RODGERS Claudia *(A Sax)*: Gate Farmhouse, 2 Main Road, Smalley, Derbys DE7 6EE ☎ 01332 781270

SAGI Zoltan *(Saxes, Pf, Gtr)*: 109 Aston Cantlow Road, Wilmcote, Stratford-on-Avon CV37 9XH ☎ 01789 267303

SHAW Robert *(B Clt, Efl Clt, Sax, Flt)*: 45, Grendon Drive, Avon Park, Brownsover, Rugby, Warwickshire CV21 1UA ☎ 01788 565363

SIMPSON Georgina *(T Sax, Pf)*: 20 The Avenue, Harpfields, Stoke-on-Trent, Staffs ST4 6BJ ☎ 01782 614374

SMITH Joanna *(Pf)*: 12 Reservoir Retreat, Edgbaston, Birmingham B16 9EH ☎ 0121 242 0400 & fax

SMITHYMAN Ernest *(Sax, Pf, Voc)*: 313 Littleworth Road, Hednesford, Staffs WS12 5HY ☎ 01543 871874

SPROSTON Diane *(Sax)*: 65 High Street, Alsagers Bank, Stoke-on-Trent ST7 8BQ ☎ 01782 720956

STOWELL Christopher (*B Clt, A Sax, T Sax*): Clayfoot Farm, Linley Green Road, Whitbourne, Worcester WR6 5RE ☎ 01886 21088

TAYLOR David: 37 Gregory Avenue, Green Lane, Coventry, Warwickshire CV3 6DJ ☎ 024 7641 2590

THOMPSON Terence (*Saxes, Com, Arr, Bt Hrn*): 58 Willenhall Road, Bilston, West Midlands WV14 6NW ☎ 01902 495646

WAITE Nicola: 132 Streetly Lane, Sutton Coldfield, West Midlands B74 4TD ☎ 0121 353 0827

WALL Sharon (*B Clt, Efl Clt, A Sax*): 54 Greenhill Road, Moseley, Birmingham B13 9SS ☎ 0121 449 4423

WATSON Ted (*A Sax, S Sax, Efl Clt, B Clt*): Jasmine Cottage, Front Street, Pebworth, Nr Stratford-upon-Avon CV37 8XQ ☎ 01789 721197

WHITHAM Frank (*T Sax, A Sax*): Woodlands, 16 Avenue Road, Wolverhampton WV3 9JR ☎ 01902 24644, 01902 28019 fax

WOODLAND Caroline (*A Sax, S Sax, T Sax*): 55 Balmoral View, Milking Bank, Dudley, West Midlands DY1 2TP ☎ 01384 459394

WYATT Sally (*Efl Clt, B Clt, S Sax*): 241 Station Road, Kings Heath, Birmingham B14 7TF ☎ 0121 441 5807

SOUTH EAST

BANKS Kevin: 86 Parkstone Avenue, Parkstone, Poole, Dorset BH14 9LS ☎ 01202 730281

BARLOW Caroline (*A Sax, B Clt, S Sax*): 36 Durler Avenue, Kempston, Bedford MK42 7DG ☎ 01234 301236

BETTS Michael (*T Sax*): 18 Hayward Crescent, Verwood, Wimborne, Dorset BH21 6JT ☎ 01202 827632

BLAKE Brian (*Sax*): No. 1 Oceania, West Parade, Bexhill-on-Sea, East Sussex TN39 3DZ ☎ 01424 225520

BLANKEN Robert: 11 Gurnard Road, Cosham, Hants PO6 3HM ☎ 023 9238 9164

BREWSTER Walter: Minstrels' Cottage, 3 The Old Grange, Litton Cheney, Dorchester, Dorset DT2 9AR ☎ 01308 482593

BYROM Reginald (*A Sax, Br Sax, Vln, B Gtr*): 15 Wildown Road, Bournemouth, Dorset BH6 4DR ☎ 01202 428071

CARPENTER Raymond: 38 Richmond Park Avenue, Bournemouth, Dorset BH8 9DP ☎ 01202 515412

CARTWRIGHT Sally (*B Clt*): 12 Mill Lane, Trotton, Petersfield, Hants GU31 5JS ☎ 01730 814997

CHAPMAN Dick (*A Sax, T Sax*): 15 Wenrisc Drive, Minster Lovell, Witney, Oxon OX8 5SP ☎ 01993 774981

COLVILLE Randolph (*A Sax, S Sax, Con, Arr*): 28 Childscroft Road, Rainham, Kent ME8 7SS ☎ 01634 366698

CONIBEAR Peter (*A Sax, S Sax*): 9 Havant Farm Close, Havant, Hants PO9 2DH ☎ 023 9247 2935

CORNET Victoria (*Efl Clt, B Clt, Pf*): Flat 1, 51 Waterloo Street, Hove, East Sussex BN3 1AH ☎ 01273 725469, 0802 956751

COULBER Dunstan (*T Sax, Dms*): 1 Coneycroft Cottages, Down Lane, Compton, Guildford, Surrey GU3 1DN ☎ 01483 810748

DE LA MOTHE Peter (*B Clt, A Sax*): 35 Brookside, Wokingham, Berks RG11 2ST ☎ 01734 784048

DENLEY Jane (*T Sax, A Sax, S Sax*): Firwood, Victoria Road, Bishops Waltham, Hants SO32 1DJ ☎ 01489 892730

DINGLE Patrick: 2 Cream Cottages, Emery Down, Lyndhurst SO43 7DY ☎ 023 8028 3358

DOBBYN Pamela (*B Clt, Pf*): Greenacres Kilmacomb, Dunmore East, Co.Waterford, Ireland ☎ 010353 51 83178

DOWSE Edward (*A Sax, T Sax, Gtr, Kbds*): Christmas Cottage, Little Wittenham, Abingdon, S Oxon OX14 4QU ☎ 01865 407562

DREW Elizabeth: 2 Diamond Villas, High Street, Hurst, Berks RG10 0DG ☎ 01189 508736

ELDRIDGE Richard (*Sax, Org, Pf, Kbds*): 3 Amherst Close, Hastings, E Sussex TN34 1TY ☎ 01424 712314, 01424 719233

FINNAMORE Marina (*B Clt, Efl Clt*): 27 Foxglove Close, Burgess Hill, W Sussex RH15 8UY ☎ 01444 23968

FISH Rosalind: The Warren, 31 Dashwood Close, Sturminster Newton, Dorset DT10 1PF ☎ 01258 473360

FOSTER Geoffrey (*Efl Clt, T Sax*): 18 Pavilion Road, Folkeston, Kent CT19 5RW ☎ 01303 246660

GARDNER Christopher (*A Sax, T Sax, Pf, Md*): 65 Basingstoke Road, Alton, Hants GU34 1QJ ☎ 01420 89408, 0378 284554 mob

GARFIELD Laurence (*A Sax*): 17 Rozelle Close, Littleton, Nr Winchester, Hants SO22 6QP ☎ 01962 882022

HALLAM Norman (*Saxes, Arr, Com*): 29 Hawthorne Drive, Creekmoor, Poole, Dorset BH17 7YG ☎ 01202 381598

HILL Lisa (*Sax, Pf, Flt*): 9 Poplar Avenue, Hove, East Sussex BN3 8PU ☎ 01273 321929, 0831 108029

HORNER Herbert (*B Clt, Saxes, Flt, Pic*): 11 Roeshot Crescent, Highcliffe, Christchurch, Dorset BH23 4QH ☎ 01425 273107

HUGHES Alison (*B Clt, Pf, T Sax*): 34 Westwood Road, Portswood, Southampton SO17 1DP ☎ 023 8058 2688

JENKINS Robert (*Gtr*): 217 Tangier Road, Lopnor, Portsmouth, Hampshire PO3 6PQ ☎ 023 9269 3857

JOHNSTON Edward (*T Sax, Pf, Gtr*): 17 Stevenson Crescent, Lower Parkstone, Poole, Dorset BH14 9NU ☎ 01202 746775

JOYCE Lucy (*Sax*): 37 New Road, Wonersh, Guildford, Surrey GU5 0SF ☎ 01483 892540, 07887 565459

KNIBB Robin: 11 Browning Road, Worthing, West Sussex BN11 4NS ☎ 01903 204971

KRIWACZEK Rohan (*Fo Fdl, Bag, Flt, Sax*): 45 Lincoln Street, Brighton BN2 2UG ☎ 01273 689325

LANGTON Derek (*A Sax, T Sax*): 9 St Christophers Green, St Peters Road, Broadstairs, Kent CT10 2SS ☎ Thanet 64560

LAYTON Teddy (*A Sax, T Sax*): 1 Little Green Orchard, Little Green, Gosport, Hants PO12 2EY ☎ 023 9258 0043

LEWIS Malcolm (*T Sax, A Sax, Flt*): Flat 4, 140 West Wycombe Road, High Wycombe, Bucks HP12 3AA ☎ 01494 437904

LITTLE Derek (*S Sax, T Sax*): 36 Brooklyn Avenue, Worthing, Sussex BN11 5QJ ☎ 01903 249900

LONG Jim (*S Sax, A Sax, Hmca*): Poste Restante, Post Office, High Street, Braunston, Daventry, Northants ☎ 0973 776841

MADDOCKS John (*Saxes*): 18 Orchard Avenue, Poole, Dorset BH14 8AJ ☎ 01202 742368

MASON Roy (*T Sax*): 40 Plantation Road, Faversham, Kent ME13 8QY ☎ Faversham 2481

MCGOVERN Clare (*Sax, Pf, Flt*): Woodstock House Hotel, Charlton, Nr Chichester, West Sussex PO18 0HU ☎ 01243 811666, 0421 904752

MOORE Sarah: 7 Somerton Gardens, Reading RG6 5XG ☎ 01734 861502

MORGAN Sarah (*Sax, Flt, Pf*): 52 Brassey Road, Winton, Bournemouth, Dorset BH9 1PT ☎ 01202 460579, 0780 3425648

MUNSCH Melanie-Jane (*Sax, Kbds, Flt*): 10 Farlaine Road, Eastbourne, East Sussex BN21 1XG ☎ 01323 430704

MURRAY Michael (*Saxes, Vln*): 40 Dover Road, Deal, Kent CT14 7JW ☎ Deal 64431

MUSKETT Michael (*Rec, Bag, R Wnd*): The Old Mill, Duntish, Dorchester, Dorset DT2 7DR ☎ 01300 345412

PALMER Tim (*Pf, Gtr*): Penn Beacon, Woodland Close, New Barn, Longfield, Kent DA3 7HA ☎ 01474 703304

PAYNE Lawrence (*Sax*): 5 Moorland Crescent, Upton, Poole, Dorset BH16 5LA ☎ 01202 625375

PETERS Ian (*Efl Clt, B Clt, A Sax*): Appledrift, Burnetts Lane, Horton Heath, Eastleigh, Hants SO50 7DG ☎ 023 8069 5724

PICKERING Gillian (*Pf, Rec, Gtr*): 33 Echo Barn Lane, Farnham, Surrey GU10 4NG ☎ 01252 733225

PINKERTON John (*S Sax*): 16 Station Terrace, Great Linford, Nr Milton Keynes, Bucks MK14 5AP ☎ 01908 672819

PRANGNELL Barnaby (*Efl Clt, B Clt*): 41 Clifton Road, Regents Park, Southampton SO15 4GY ☎ 023 8077 1206

RAYSON (*Bt Hrn*): Julia's Cottage, The Ridings, Shotover, Headington, Oxford OX3 8TB

RUDD Hilary (*Rec*): 10 Park Road, Faversham, Kent ME13 8ET ☎ 01795 532062, 01227 764000 day

RUMBOL Ronald (*A Sax, T Sax*): 11 Lakeside, Bracknell, Berks RG42 2LE ☎ 01344 429629

SHILHAM Brian: 3 Brooklyn Avenue, Worthing, West Sussex BN11 5QH ☎ 01903 248924

STORR Josephine (*Sax*): 178 Upper Grosvenor Road, Tunbridge Wells, Kent TN1 2EH ☎ 01892 533450

SUTTON Andrew (*B Clt, Sax, Con*): 1 Hillmead, Gossors Green, Crawley, West Sussex RH11 8RP ☎ 01293 546762

SWATMAN Ian (*Sax*): 79 Cedar Road, Sturry, Canterbury CT2 0JG

TELLICK Linda: 5 Hobart Close, Durrington, West Sussex BN13 3HL ☎ Worthing 68914

THORP Reginald: 13 Pinewood Way, Midhurst, W. Sussex GU29 9LN ☎ 01730 814782

TIPLADY Malcolm (*Sax*): 78 Tavistock Road, Fleet, Hampshire GU13 8EZ ☎ Fleet 628423

VICKERS Stan (*Sax*): 53 Elizabeth Avenue, Hove, Sussex BN3 6WA ☎ Brighton 553010

WALKER Christopher (*A Sax, Br Sax*): Greenfield, Presseys Corner, Alderholt, Fordingbridge, Hants SP6 3BB ☎ 01425 655631

WARD Elizabeth (*Sax, Pf, Voc*): 5 Rillington Gardens, Emerson Valley North, Milton Keynes, Bucks MK4 2EB ☎ 01908 501406

WEATHERALL Ted (*T Sax*): 28 Western Avenue, Bridge, Nr Canterbury, Kent CT4 5LS ☎ Bridge 830786

WELLER Karen (*Sax, Pf, Efl Clt*): 25 Juniper Court, Ock Street, Abingdon, Oxon OX14 5UB ☎ 01235 555079

WEST Paul (*Sax, Flt*): 4 Old Cottages, Horsham Road, Findon, Worthing, West Sussex BN14 0TQ ☎ 01903 873918, 0467 826896

WHITE Brian (*Sax, Flt*): 4 Clifton Road, Bognor Regis, Sussex PO21 2HH ☎ 01243 821281

WHITING Trevor (*So Sax, T Sax, Ac Gtr*): 7 Ironsbottom, Sidlow, Reigate, Surrey RH2 8PT ☎ 01293 863603

SOUTH WEST

ALLEN Pete (*S Sax, Br Sax*): 22 Rumble Dene, Chippenham, Wiltshire SN15 3XE ☎ 01249 652 965

ARMSTRONG Ann: 9 Coombe Rocke, West Rocke Avenue, Coombe Dingle, Bristol BS9 2AN ☎ 0117 9681658

BOORER Jeffrey (*B Clt*): 4 Allerton Walk, Mayflower Walk, Eggbuckland, Plymouth PL6 5RZ ☎ 01752 703233

BOWEN David (*T Sax, A Sax*): Ivy House, Piddletrenthide, Nr Dorchester, Dorset DT2 7QF ☎ 01300 348255

BRIDGEWATER Paul (*Flt, Sax, Com, Md*): Flat 3, Bythorn, Bronshill Road, Torquay TQ1 3HD ☎ 01803 326246

BRIMFIELD Terence (*B Clt, S Sax, A Sax, Flt*): 23 Springfield, Bradford-on-Avon, Wiltshire BA15 1BA ☎ 01225 863651

BROWNE Jacqueline: Pengribyn, Cilrhedyn, Llanfyrnach, Pembs SA35 0AA ☎ 01239 698602, 0402 234209, 01239 612200

BURNELL Donald (*T Sax, A Sax*): 49 Westbury Road, Westbury-on-Trym, Bristol BS9 3AU ☎ 0117 9621187

BUSBY Terry (*Saxes, Flt*): Beech House, 45 Draycott Road, Chiseldon, Wiltshire SN4 0LT ☎ 01793 741076

BUTLER Verity (*Efl Clt, B Clt, Bt Hrn*): 11 Balmoral Court, King George Close, Cheltenham, Glos GL53 7RW ☎ 01242 252885

BUTT Raymond (*A Sax, T Sax, Kbds, Vln*): 33 Chestnut Springs, Lydiard Millicent, Swindon SN5 9NA ☎ 01793 770929

BUTTERWORTH Roy (*Sax, Tba*): 17 Tangmere Drive, Llandaff, Cardiff CF5 2PP ☎ 029 2055 2834, 029 2025 0080

COLEMAN Hilary (*Voc*): Ferndale, Tregajorran, Carn Brea, Redruth, Cornwall TR15 3YX ☎ 01209 219011

COLVILLE Donna (*T Sax, Flt*): 15 Elm Grove Close, Dawlish, Devon EX7 0DB

COOPER John (*Sax*): 67 Heol Penlan, Whitchurch, Cardiff CF4 2BZ ☎ 029 2069 2949, 0385 986078 mob

COOTE Heather (*Sax, Flt, Pf*): 40 Ferndale Road, Church Crookham, Fleet, Hants GU13 0LN ☎ 01252 627296, 0410 918171

CRAIG Richard (*Saxes, B Clt*): 34 Bridge Street, Chepstow, Monmouthshire NP6 5EY ☎ 01291 620746, 07970 942553 mob

DE LA RUE Richard (*Sax*): 21 Highcliffe Close, Lympstone, Exmouth, Devon EX8 5HF ☎ 01395 274099

FIELDING Peter (*Sax*): 23 Augusta Crescent, Penarth, S Glam CF64 5RL ☎ 029 2070 7605

FIELDING Verity Fay (*B Clt, Efl Clt, Pf*): 23 Augusta Crescent, Penarth, S Glam CF64 5RL ☎ 029 2070 7605

FULCHER Harry (*Sax, Pf*): Lulworth, Grenville Road, Salcombe, S Devon TQ8 8BJ ☎ 0154 884 2869

GREENWOOD Michael (*Sax*): The Holt, Fluxton, Ottery St Mary, Devon EX11 1RL ☎ 01404 815 596

HEARNSHAW Charles (*Sax, Pf*): 89 Shelly Road, Exmouth, Devon EX8 1DX ☎ 01395 268868

HODGES Valerie (*B Clt, T Sax*): 23 Stafford Road, St Werburghs, Bristol BS2 9UR ☎ 0117 9557509

JONES Paula (*Pf, Hpsd*): Serai, 43 Hospital Road, Builth Wells, Powys LD2 3HE ☎ 01982 552109

JONES Sara (*Pf*): 80 Heol Hir, Llanishen, Cardiff, S Glam CF4 5AB

JONES William: Llwyn Ial, Llanbedrog, Pwllhelli, Gwynedd LL53 7TG ☎ 01758 740209

KELLEHER Frank (*Db*): 35 Palace Road, Llandaff, Cardiff CF5 2AG ☎ 029 2056 1821

LATHAM Dr John (*S Sax, A Sax*): 2 Church Meadow, Reynoldston, Swansea SA3 1AA ☎ 01792 390055

LAURENS Elizabeth (*Sax, Pf*): Sunnydale, La Rue de la Haut l'Orme, Mont A L'Abbe, Trinity, Jersey, C.I. JE3 5FG ☎ 01534 62493

LE FEUVRE Phillipa (*Sax, Pf*): La Brise, St Lawrence, Jersey, C.I JE3 1FA ☎ 01534 879055

LE SUEUR Jane (*Saxes*): 17 Le Clos Orange, La Moye, St Brelade, Jersey JE3 8GU ☎ 01534 499528

LEE Brian: 2 Phillip Street, Craig, Ponty Pridd, Mid Glamorgan CF37 1LY ☎ 01443 405039

LINTON Simon (*T Sax*): 2A Gibbs Road, Newport, Gwent NP9 8AR ☎ 01633 271 456, 0402 896601 mob

LOCK Kate (*Pf*): 45 Boness Road, Wroughton, Swindon, Wiltshire SN4 9DY ☎ 01793 812201

LODWICK Wynfoed (*Vib*): Y Pinwydd, Heol Yr Ysgol, Pwll Llanelli, Dyfed SA15 4AL ☎ 015542 52636

MAINWARING James (*Sax*): 12 Waun Road, Morriston, Swansea, West Glamorgan SA6 6JY ☎ 01792 310090

MANWARING Roger (*T Sax, S Sax*): Nutshells, Link End Road, Corse Lawn, Gloucestershire GL19 4NN ☎ 01452 780496

MAYER Michael: Ivy Cottage, Cheriton Fitzpaine, Devon EX17 4JA

MERRICK Linda (*B Clt, Efl Clt, Sax*): 6 Bostonthorpe Road, London W7 2HA ☎ 020 8840 2957 & fax

MULCAHY Beth (*A Sax, T Sax*): 19 Medway Road, Bettws, Newport, Gwent NP9 6XA ☎ 01633 858292

NODEN Paul: Plot 24, Nant Celyn, Efail Isaf, Pontypridd, Mid Glam CF38 1AN

PAGETT David (*B Clt, Sax*): 116 Clayfield, Brimsham Park, Yate, Bristol BS17 5HU ☎ 0145 432 3261

PASSMORE Rhianon (*Pf, Sax, Flt*): Tallis House, 42 Sycamore Crescent, Ty Sign, Risca, Gwent NP1 6AP ☎ 01633 614453, 0378 899275

PELLETT Roy: 97 Durnford Street, Stonehouse, Plymouth, Devon PL1 3QP ☎ 01752 28722

PYSANCZYN Helen (*Pf, Sax*): 129 Goddard Avenue, Swindon, Wilts SN1 4HX ☎ 01793 497142

REECE Robin (*A Sax, T Sax, Voc*): Newlands Cottage, Corn Worthy, Nr Totnes, Devon TQ9 7ES ☎ 01803 732654

REES Ceri (*Sax, Per*): 12 Plassey Square, Penarth, Vale Of Glamorgan CF64 1HD ☎ 029 2025 9371, 0976 901608 mob

RICHARDS Jack (*B Clt, Sax*): 52 Downs Park West, Bristol, Avon BS6 7QL ☎ 0117 9622077

ROBERTS Anthony (*Flt, Sax*): Dodpen Cottage, Wooton Fitzpaine, Bridport, Dorset DT6 6NW ☎ 01297 678462

ROBERTS Hugh (*Sax, Pf*): 19 Egerton Road, Bishopston, Bristol BS7 8HN ☎ 0117 942 1493

RONCHETTI Martin: 20 Alfreda Road, Whitechurch, Cardiff, South Glamorgan CF4 2EH ☎ 01222 66312

SAUNDERS Helen: Coleford House, Coleford, Bath, Somerset BA3 5LU ☎ 01373 812203

SAXTON Michael (*B Clt, Hrn, Sax*): Flat 3, Blue Cedar Court, Cyprus Road, Exmouth, Devon EX8 2DZ ☎ 01395 223720

SIMMONS Mark (*Efl Clt*): 8 Wellington Street, Tongwynlais, Nr Cardiff, S. Glamorgan CF4 7LP ☎ 029 2081 1275

SMITH Justin (*Arr, Com, Con*): 10 Stefan Close, Hooe, Plymouth PL9 9RS ☎ 01752 404585

THOMPSON Julie (*Kbds*): 25 Garrett Drive, Bradley Stoke, Bristol BS32 8GD ☎ 01454 619773

TILLEY Jennifer (*Efl Clt, B Clt, Saxes*) ☎ 0973 720303 mob, 020 8533 1372 day

WALL Philip: Bramble Cottage, Lower Stoney Road, Pontypool, Gwent NP4 8QH ☎ 01495 774150

WALTHEW John: 66 Mount Pleasant Avenue, Exmouth Devon EX8 4QR ☎ 01395 271757

WATKINSON Peter (*Sax*): Chalumeau, Gretton Fields, Cheltenham, Glos GL54 5HH ☎ 01242 620327

WATT Ruth: 17 Coryton Crescent, Whitchurch, Cardiff CF4 7EQ ☎ 029 2069 1811

WHEELER Ian (*Sax*): April Cottage, The Coombes, Polperro, Cornwall PL13 2RH

WOODHOUSE Lynne (*A Sax, Br Sax, Flt*): 2 Church Street, Kingsbury Episcopi, Martock, Somerset TA12 6AU ☎ 01935 822755

LONDON

ADDISON Richard (*Efl Clt, B Clt, C B Clt, Saxe*): 60 Eastern Road, Fortis Green, London N2 9LA ☎ 020 8444 5487

ALCOCK Susan: Flat 119, Samuel Lewis Estate, Liverpool Road, London N1 1LH ☎ 020 7609 8830

ALLEN Alexander (*Pf*): 298 Nelson Road, Twickenham TW2 7BW ☎ 020 8893 3172

ALLEN Geraldine: 18 Hillfield Park, Muswell Hill, London N10 3QS ☎ 020 8444 8587

ALLEN Leslie (*S Sax*): Rosery, Dirtham Lane, Effingham, Surrey KT24 5SD ☎ 01483 283477

ALLEN Paul (*B Clt, Bt Hrn*): 68 Kilmorie Road, Forest Hill, London SE23 2ST ☎ 020 8699 5802, 0374 127920, 020 8699 5302

ALLEN Peter (*B Clt*): 25 Victor Road, Harrow, Middlesex HA2 6PT ☎ 020 8863 2117

ALLEN Stuart: 31 Beresford Road, East Finchley, London N2 8AT ☎ 020 8883 9768

ANDERSON Jill (*Bq Clt, Bt Hrn, Saxes*): 96 Highworth Road, London N11 2SH ☎ 020 8361 9646

ANDREWS Alan (*Efl Clt, Bt Hrn, B Clt, C B C*): 9 Moorland Gardens, Luton, Beds LU2 7QF ☎ 0973 208401, 01306 500022

ANDREWS Michelle (*B Clt, Bt Hrn*): 41 Cordrey Gardens, Coulsdon Woods, Coulsdon, Surrey CR5 2SP ☎ 020 8668 5914 & fax

ANGRESS Michael (*Efl Clt, B Clt, Saxes*): 28 Willesden Lane, Kilburn, London NW6 7ST ☎ 020 7625 5985

ARAJS Hazel: 10 Reeve Road, Reigate, Surrey RH2 7PH ☎ 017372 47176

ARCHIBALD Margaret (*B Clt, Efl Clt, Bt Hrn*): 17 Hayesford Park Drive, Bromley, Kent BR2 9DA ☎ 020 8464 1645

ASHBY Duncan (*B Clt, C B Clt, Saxes, Flt*): 57 Staveley Gardens, Chiswick, London W4 2SA ☎ 020 8994 9647, 01306 880669

ASHWORTH Neyire

ATKINSON Christopher: Pigotts, North Dean, High Wycombe, Bucks HP14 4NF ☎ 01494 565871

AULT Robert (*B Clt, Efl Clt, Bt Hrn*): The Cannings, 2 Struan Gardens, Woking, Surrey GU21 4DJ ☎ 020 8533 1372

BACKHURST Don: 21 Mead Way, Burpham, Guildford, Surrey GU4 7LG ☎ 01483 60389

BAIGENT Nicola (*Sax*): 28B Heddington Grove, Off Stock Orchard Cres, London N7 9SY ☎ 020 7700 5431

BAKER Robert (*B Clt*): Tickerage Castle, Pound Lane, Framfield, Uckfield Sussex TN22 5RT ☎ 01825 890348

BAUGHAN Claire (*Pf*): 16 Steele Road, London W4 5AF ☎ 020 8994 6603

BEAMAN Julie (*Efl Clt, B Clt, Sax*): Angel Cottage, High Street, Redbourn, Herts AL3 7LN ☎ 01582 792123, 0976 446473 mob

BELDOM Tamara (*B Clt, Bt Hrn*): 40 Markland House, Darfielddway, London W10 6UA ☎ 020 8455 6415, 0976 982371 mob

BENNETT Stephen: 47 Hambalt Road, Clapham, London SW4 9EQ ☎ 020 8675 3877

BENNETTO Peter (*T Sax, Flt*): 19 Broadmead, Hitchin, Herts SG4 9LU ☎ 01462 459713

BILK Acker: F.A.O. Ms J Bilk, 21 The Avenue, Potters Bar, Herts EN6 1EG ☎ 020 7978 5885/6, 020 7978 5882 fax

BISHOP Helen (*B Clt, Efl Clt*): 38 Fearnley Street, Watford, Herts WD1 7DD ☎ 01923 230235

BISHOP Susan (*Efl Clt*): 204 Livingstone Road, Thornton Heath, Surrey CR7 8JW ☎ 020 8653 8987, 0441 188012

BONDONNO Alessandro (*Sax, S Sax, A Sax, T Sax*): 175R Langham Road, South Tottenham, London N15 3LP ☎ 01293 410830, 0956 353 337 mob

BOOTH Jane (*Bq Clt, B Clt, Efl Clt, A Sax*): 38 Alric Avenue, New Malden, Surrey KT3 4JN ☎ 020 8942 1519

BOSTON Jonny (*T Sax, B Gtr*): 181 Portnall Road, West Kilburn, London W9 3BN ☎ 020 8968 9132

BOWLES Thomas (*B Clt*): 112 Warner Road, London E17 7DZ ☎ 020 8521 6281, 0986 938547 mob

BOWRING Sarah: 12A Calton Avenue, Dulwich, London SE21 7DQ ☎ 020 8299 0945

BRADBURY Colin: 56 Castlebar Road, London W5 2DD ☎ 020 8997 4300, 020 8991 5982 fax

BRADY Gareth (*Saxes, B Clt, Flt, Pic*): 150A Upland Road, London SE22 0DQ ☎ 020 8299 6456 & fax, 0850 452448 mob, 01306 880669 day

BRAMPTON Harry (*A Sax*): Kedleston, 194 Queens Road, Wimbledon, London SW19 8LY ☎ 020 8540 2765

BROWN Aletha (*Pf, Kbds, Dms*)

BROWN Stewart: 14 Tootswood Road, Bromley, Kent BR2 0PD ☎ 020 8464 5947

BRYMER Jack: 31 Sycamore Court, Hoskins Road, Oxted, Surrey RH8 9JQ ☎ 01883 712843

BUCKNALL Juliet (*Efl Clt, B Clt*): 8A Dalmore Road, London SE21 8HB ☎ 020 8761 2944, 01306 880669

BUCKNALL Nicholas (*Efl Clt, Bt Hrn, B Clt, Sax*): Monkswood, 76 Warminster Road, Norwood, London SE25 4DQ ☎ 020 8771 0390, 020 8768 1800 fax

BURVILL Mandy (*Efl Clt, Bt Hrn*): 204A Ferme Park Road, London N8 9BN ☎ 020 8341 9302

BUXTON Ruth: 75 Overhill Road, East Dulwich, London SE22 0PQ ☎ 020 8693 5906, 0973 775289

CALE Mavis: 6 Strathearn Road, Wimbledon, London SW19 7LH ☎ 020 8947 0547

CAMPBELL David: 83 Woodwarde Road, London SE22 8UL ☎ 020 8693 5696, 020 8533 1372 day, 0850 014495 mob

CANAVAN Emma (*Efl Clt, B Clt*): 2 Farley Drive, Seven Kings, Ilford, Essex IG3 8LT ☎ 020 8597 1659, 0958 629656 mob

CANNON Rachel (*Efl Clt, B Clt*): 32 Brittain Road, Walton-on-Thames, Surrey KT12 4LR ☎ 01932 226769

CARNAC Jon (*B Clt*): 29A Preston Road, London E11 1NL ☎ 020 8530 8110, 01306 880669

CARPENTER Nicholas: 71 De Montfort Road, Lewes, East Sussex BN7 1SS ☎ 01273 475653

CASEY Graham: Cornubia, 16 Edenfield, Orton Longueville, Peterborough, Cambs PE2 7HY ☎ 01733 235888

CASSIDY Carl (*Sax, Flt, Pf, B Gtr*): 2 Mazenod Ave, West Hampstead, London NW6 4LR ☎ 020 7625 7938, 0973 741194 mob

CHAPPELL John (*B Clt*): 36 Queens Road, Whitstable, Kent CT5 2JF ☎ 01227 263576

CHARD Rebecca (*Efl Clt, Saxes*): 35 Caversham Avenue, Palmers Green, London N13 4LL ☎ 020 8882 9631, 01850 683669

CHARLESWORTH Dick (*T Sax*): 28 Basing Way, Thames Ditton, Surrey KT7 0NX ☎ 020 8398 8189

CHEESMAN Valerie (*Bt Hrn*): 48 Basils Road, Stevenage, Herts SG1 3PX ☎ 01438 315965

CHRISTOU Francis (*Efl Clt, B Clt, Bt Hrn, A Sax*): 19 Darwin Road, Welling, Kent DA16 2EQ ☎ 020 8306 7699

CLARK Geoff: 18 Jasmine Court, Alexandra Road, Wimbledon, London SW19 7JY ☎ 020 8946 4702

CLARKE Sarah (*Efl Clt, B Clt, Saxes, Flt*): 16 Clacton Road, London E17 8AR ☎ 020 8503 7098, 0956 269352 mob

CLEMENT-EVANS Peryn (*B Clt, Efl Clt*): 97 Hinds Road, Harrow, Middx HA1 1RX ☎ 07970 680819, 020 8861 4052

COCKS Elaine (*B Clt, Efl Clt*): Flat 1, 157 High Road, Willesden Green, London NW10 2SG ☎ 020 8451 6187, 0385 740470 mob

CODY Maurice: 7 Cambray Road, Orpington, Kent BR6 0EE ☎ 01689 825736

COE Anthony (*B Clt, Saxes, Com*): 22 Glenton Road, London SE13 5RS ☎ 020 8318 0256

COLES Derren (*B Gtr*): 10 St. Annes Road, Leytonstone, London E11 4BP ☎ 020 8558 5617 & fax, 0973 156047 mob

COLLARD Esther: 88A Cambridge Gardens, London W10 6HS ☎ 020 8969 8864, 020 8969 8864

COOK Dick (*Efl Clt, T Sax, A Sax, Br Sax*): 15 Tentelow Lane, Norwood Green, Southall, Middx UB2 4LQ ☎ 020 8571 3043

COOK Natasha (*Vln, Pf*): 5 Collingtree Road, Sydenham, London SE26 4QG ☎ 020 8244 9297

COOMBES Nigel (*B Clt*): 25 Limerick Close, Blaham, London SW12 0BE

COOPER Gordon (*Clt*): Twr-Y-Capel, Oxford Road, Hay-on-Wye, Powys HR3 5DG ☎ 01497 820808

COOPER Jonathan (*Kbds*): 6B Richmond Crescent, London N1 0LZ ☎ 020 7609 4475, 0802 429271 mob

COPAS Paul: 248 Priests Lane, Shenfield, Brentwood, Essex CM14 8LD ☎ 01277 222335

COURTNEY Colin (*B Clt*): 1 Arkwright Mansions, 206 Finchley Road, London NW3 6DE ☎ 0956 908820, 01306 880669 day

COWLEY Guy (*Efl Clt, B Clt*): 35 Panmuir Road, Raynes Park, London SW20 0PZ ☎ 020 8947 2666, 024 7641 6142

CRAVEN Leslie (*Efl Clt, B Clt*): The Beeches, St Thomas Road, Overmonnow, Monmouth, Gwent NP5 4FA ☎ 01600 714169, 01306 880669

CRISPE Angela (*B Clt, Bt Hrn, Efl Clt*): 20 Spencer Gate, St Albans, Herts AL1 4AD ☎ 01727 839516

CROCKER John (*A Sax, T Sax*): 70 Fountains Crescent, Southgate, London N14 6BE ☎ 020 8886 0459

CROSS Fiona (*B Clt*): Flat A, 3 Milton Road, London N6 5QD ☎ 020 8340 6950

CURTIS George (*B Clt, A Sax, T Sax, Br Sax*): Address Unknown

DAVIS Peter (*Sax*): 22 Elton Court, Elton Road, Bengeo, Hertford, Herts SG14 3EJ ☎ 01992 534037, 01973 378836

DAVISON Martin (*S Sax*): 89 Ashleigh Road, Mortlake, London SW14 8PY ☎ 020 8876 6026

DEACON Barry (*Sax*): Flat 1, 5 Venner Road, Sydenham, London SE26 5EQ ☎ 020 8659 9140, 0966 508471

DELL Peter (*Sax*): 2 Abbotsbury Road, Hayes, Bromley, Kent BR2 7HQ ☎ 020 8462 5582

DENMAN John: 1542 E Lester, Tucson, Arizona 85719, U.S.A. ☎ 520 795 5591, +1 520 327 8874 fax

DIAKOW Tamara (*B Clt*)

DOBREE Georgina (*Bt Hrn*): 6 The Grange, Grangewood Gardens, Leeds LS16 6EY ☎ 0113 230 0532

DOUGLAS Terry (*T Sax*): Dellwood, 164 Pembroke Close, Banstead, Surrey SM7 2BH ☎ 01737 357226

DOUTHWAITE Richard (*B Clt, Sax, Flt, Arr*): ☎ 01689 837633

DOWN Daphne: Min-Y-Don, Minffordd, Penrhyndeudraeth, N.Wales LL48 6EH ☎ 01766 771007

DRAIN Pauline (*Efl Clt*): 17 Avenue Road, London W3 8NH ☎ 020 8992 6372

DRAKE Ronald (*S Sax, T Sax*): 50 Langley Park Road, Iver, Bucks SL0 9QR ☎ 01753 652065, 0370 731399

DRYSDALE Dainty (*Pf*) ☎ 020 8341 7140

DUBBER Godfrey (*T Sax, S Sax*): 29 Selsdon Road, South Croydon CR2 6PY ☎ 020 8680 7960

EDGAR Ronald (*B Clt, Sax*): 49B Eton Avenue, London NW3 3EP ☎ 020 7794 4373

EDWARDS Bryan (*Sax*): 30 Gordon Road, Sidcup, Kent DA15 8SX ☎ 020 8859 3206

EDWARDS Felicity (*B Clt*): 3 Elliswick Road, Harpenden, Herts AL5 4TP ☎ 01582 762905

EDWARDS Phillip (*Efl Clt*): 15 Market Square, Battle, East Sussex TN33 0XB ☎ 01424 773038

ELKAN Geoffrey: 31 Coleridge Walk, London NW11 6AT ☎ 020 8455 8845

ELLIOTT Rosalynd: 62 Bingley Road, Sunbury-on-Thames, Middlesex TW16 7RB

ELLIS C Nigel (*B Clt, Saxes, Flt*): 75 Kilravock Street, London W10 4HY ☎ 020 8968 1583, 04325 225201 pager, 020 8960 6250

EMMOTT Geoffrey (*B Clt*): 12 Brook Drive, Ruislip, Middx HA4 8AG ☎ 01895 639811

ESTALL Joanna (*Efl Clt*): Woodside, Orestan Lane, Effingham, Surrey KT24 5SN ☎ 01372 452513

EVANS John (*S Sax, Dms*): 68 Mill Hill Road, London W3 8JJ ☎ 020 8992 5133

EVANS John: 70C Belsize Park Gardens, London NW3 4NE ☎ 020 7722 8317

FAIRBAIRN Zoe: 103 Whitehall Gardens, London E4 6EJ ☎ 020 8524 3898

FANTONI Barry (*Saxes, Db*): 3 Franconia Road, London SW4 9NB ☎ 020 7720 4154

FARNHAM Michael (*Efl Clt, B Clt*): 6 Heathfield South, Twickenham, Middx TW2 7SS ☎ 020 8892 0085

FARRALL Joy: 26 Haddon Court, Milton Road, Harpenden, Herts AL5 5NA ☎ 01582 460140

FARRELL Julian (*B Clt, Efl Clt, Bt Hrn*): 41 Egmont Road, Sutton, Surrey SM2 5JR ☎ 020 8643 7766

FERER Lionel (*S Sax, A Sax, B Sax*): 2 Market Place, London N2 8BB ☎ 020 8883 3276, 0956 428257

FIELDING Leslie (*B Clt*): Belclare, 6 Harefield Place, Jersey Farm, St Albans Herts AL4 9JQ ☎ 01727 835667

FOX Oliver (*Pf, A Sax*): 20 Burrows Road, Kensal Rise, London NW10 5SG ☎ 020 8960 3063

FUEST David (*Efl Clt, B Clt, Bt Hrn*): 25 Fournier Street, London E1 6QE ☎ 020 7247 7219, 01306 880669 day, 0374 842389 mob

FULKER Nicola: 86 Lower Barn Road, Riddlesdown, Purley CR8 1HR ☎ 01737 358740, 01523 186724, 01202 317331

FUSSELL Angela (*Efl Clt, Bt Hrn, B Clt, Sax*): 90 Becmead Avenue, Kenton, Middx HA3 8HB ☎ 020 8907 8428

GALE David (*Sax, B Gtr*): 29 Chaucer Road, Welling, Kent DA16 3NH ☎ 020 8854 0247

GILL Susan (*Efl Clt, B Clt*): 66 Cambridge Gardens, Muswell Hill, London N10 2LN ☎ 020 8444 1729

GITTINS Kate (*Sax, Per, Pf, M Saw*): 4B Ashmore Road, London W9 3DF ☎ 020 8525 0252

GODDARD Wilfred (*B Clt, Bt Hrn*): 14 Lytton Road, London E11 1JH ☎ 020 8556 8294

GODSELL Edward (*Efl Clt, B Clt, Saxes, Bt Hrn*): 89 Leigham Court Road, London SW16 2NR ☎ 020 8769 4118

GRADWELL Christopher (*B Clt, A Sax, Flt, Pic*): 76 The Avenue, Ealing, London W13 8LB ☎ 020 8997 3642

GRAHAM Barry (*B Clt, A Sax, Flt, Pic*): 24 Chesham Crescent, Anerley, London SE20 7RL ☎ 020 8778 5543

GRAHAM Neville (*B Clt, Efl Clt*): Flat C, 13 Bloom Grove, West Norwood, London SE27 0HZ ☎ 020 8761 7538, 01306 880669 day

GRAY Margaret (*Sax, Flt*): 35 Havelock Road, Addiscombe, Croydon CR0 6QQ ☎ 020 8656 1751, 0956 392435

GREEN Malcolm: 8 Swan Court, Olney, Bucks MK46 4JP ☎ 01234 712330

HACKER Alan: Hindlea, Broughton, Malton, N. Yorkshire Y017 6QJ ☎ 01653 696163

HAMBLETON Hale (*Sax*): 49 Lowther Hill, London SE23 1PZ ☎ 020 8690 5518

HANNIGAN Derek: 52 Boveney Road, Forest Hill, London SE23 3NN ☎ 020 8699 8895, 020 7354 2711

HARRIS Michael (*Efl Clt, B Clt, Bt Hrn*): 60 Westfields Avenue, Barnes, London SW13 0AU ☎ 020 8876 0911, 01306 880669

HARVEY Paul (*B Clt, Bt Hrn, Efl Clt, Saxes*): 36 Alton Gardens, Twickenham, Middlesex TW2 7PD ☎ 020 8898 4869

HASTIE William (*Sax*): Flat 13 Brookgate, 97 Lordship Park, London N16 5UR ☎ 020 8802 2425

HAYES Nicholas: 11C Oakley Gardnes, Hornsey, London N8 9PB

HAYSTED Ian (*Efl Clt*): Hanworth House Cottage, Main Street, Hanworth, Middlesex TW13 6SU ☎ 020 8384 5748

HERBERT Ian (*Sax*): 27 South Hill Park, London NW3 2ST ☎ 020 7435 6823

HERSON Janet (*Efl Clt*): 15 Thorn Lane, Four Marks, Alton, Hampshire GU34 5BX ☎ 01420 562074

HIER Carolyn (*T Sax, A Sax, B Clt*): 17 Gowlett Road, Peckham, London SE15 ☎ 020 8314 5110, 07957 932249

HILL Robert: 35 Oakwood Park Road, London N14 6QD ☎ 020 8886 3887

HILL Steve (*Saxes, Flt, Pic*): 63 Shrewsbury Lane, Shooters Hill, Woolwich, London SE18 3JJ ☎ 020 8854 7309

HINE Charles: 8 Beverley Road, Colchester CO3 3NG ☎ 01206 546666, 01206 545453

HOLDEN Bernard: 24 Squarey Street, London SW17 0AB

HOLDSWORTH Gary (*B Clt, Efl Clt, Sax*): 30 The Heights, Charlton, London SE7 8JH ☎ 020 8853 0826, 020 8533 1372

HOLMAN-FOX Lynn (*Saxes, Flt*): 4 Winton Avenue, New Southgate, London N11 2AT ☎ 020 8888 6017

HOMER Sarah (*B Clt*): 31 Riversdale Road, Highbury, Islington, London N5 2ST ☎ 020 7226 6935

HOOK Teddie (*T Sax, Flt, Voc*): 1 Broomfield House, Broomwood Road, St Pauls Cray, Kent BR5 2JL ☎ 01689 872261

HOSFORD Richard: 1 Court Lane Gardens, London SE21 7DZ ☎ 020 8693 3973, 020 8693 3973

HOUGHTON James (*Sax, Flt, Pf*): 302 Woolwich Church Street, Woolwich, London SE18 5ND ☎ 020 8317 1336

HOWES Peter (*B Clt*): 53 Station Rd., Teddington, Middx TW19AA ☎ 020 8943 1532

HOWLETT Steve (*A Sax*): 73 Brian Road, Chadwell Heath, Romford, Essex RM6 5BX ☎ 020 8590 3740

HUNT Matthew: 264 Kirkdale, Sydenham, London SE26 4RS ☎ 020 8778 9407 & fax

HURD James (*S Sax*): 47 Windmore Avenue, Potters Bar, Herts EN6 3BE ☎ 01707 657470

HYAMS Derek (*Sax*): 12 Courtlands Avenue, Hayes, Bromley, Kent BR2 7HZ ☎ 020 8462 2727

HYLAND Julie (*Pf*): 187C Devonshire Road, Forest Hill, London SE23 3NJ ☎ 020 8291 2510

HYLAND Terry (*B Clt, Sax, Flt, Arr*): 34 Cloisters Avenue, Bickley, Kent BR2 8AW ☎ 020 8467 2705

JACKMAN Bill (*Sax*): 53 Mallard Way, London NW9 8JJ ☎ 020 8205 2704

JENNINGS Anthony (*B Clt, Efl Clt*): 44B Hopefield Avenue, London NW6 6LH ☎ 020 8968 8921, 01491 651371

JONES Leslie (*A Sax*): 26 Aschurch Road, Croydon, Surrey CR0 6JS ☎ 020 8656 2259

JOWITT Roy (*B Clt*): 25 Monivea Road, Beckenham, Kent BR3 1HJ ☎ 020 8658 5398, 0973 146620, 01306 880669 day

JOYCE Norman (*B Clt, A Sax*): 41 Raisins Hill, Pinner, Middx HA5 2BU ☎ 020 8866 6848

KAYE Sally (*Sax, Pf, Voc*): 305 Lonsdale Road, Barnes, London SW13 9PY ☎ 020 8876 0564

KEAN Bret (*B Clt, Saxes, Flt, Pic*): 51 Caversham Avenue, London N13 4LL ☎ 020 8351 8082, 0378 504012

KEENAN Andy (*S Sax, A Sax, Br Sax, Efl Clt*): Flat D, 219 Underhill Road, London SE22 0PB ☎ 020 8516 2587 & fax, 07050 127577

KELLY Thomas: 56 Potter Street, Pinner, Middx HA5 3XE ☎ 020 8866 0061

KEMPTON Karina (*B Clt*): 73 Holden Close, Goodmayes, Essex RM8 2QT ☎ 020 8597 0361

KILLORAN Ian (*Sax, Flt*): 46 Borough Way, Potters Bar, Herts EN6 3HB ☎ 01707 850398

KING Stuart (*Efl Clt, B Clt*): 64 Castletown Road, West Kensington, London W14 9HG ☎ 020 7381 8158, 07970 276472, 020 7381 8158

KING Thea: 16 Milverton Road, London NW6 7AS ☎ 020 8459 3453, 020 8830 2631 fax

KIRBY David (*Efl Clt, B Clt, Sax, Flt*): 183 Tenniswood Road, Enfield, Middlesex EN1 3LU ☎ 020 8342 1261 & fax, 0973 562004 mob

KIRKPATRICK William (*Arr, Com*): 70 Oldfield Lane South, Greenford, Middlesex UB6 9LD ☎ 020 8575 0388

LACEY Mark: 11 Baden Road, London N8 7RJ ☎ 020 8348 0128

LAFONTAINE Bernie (*Sax, Flt, B Clt, Pf*): 6 East View, Pursers Lane, Peaslake, Surrey GU5 9RG ☎ 01306 730087, 0973 655763

LAING Gregor (*B Clt, Saxes*): 8 Milestone Road, Knebworth, Herts SG3 6DA ☎ 01438 814052

LAMB Tony (*Efl Clt, B Clt*): 37 Bolton Gardens, Teddington, Middx TW11 9AX ☎ 020 8977 2051

LAURIE Cyril: Lyngs Farm, Stapleford, Abbotts, Essex RM4 1JR ☎ 01708 346032

LAURIE Richard: 27, Clarendon Drive, Putney, London SW15 1AW ☎ 020 8780 1939

LAWRENCE David (*Sax*): 109 Rowtown, Addlestone, Weybridge, Surrey KT15 1HQ ☎ 01932 848600

LAWSON Colin: 46 Clitheroe Avenue, Harrow, Middx HA2 9UX ☎ 020 8866 3557

LEAVER Roger (*Pf, Sax*): 21 Snowdrop Way, Widmer End, High Wycombe, Buckinghamshire HP15 6BL ☎ 01494 714266, 0468 922945

LEDINGHAM David (*Sax, Flt*): 6 Beaconsfield Court, Beaconsfield Road, New Southgate, London N11 3AF ☎ 020 8361 1860

LEE Sara: 34 Clarence Road, Walthamstow, London E17 6AQ ☎ 020 8531 7117

LEVY Shelley: 27 Princes Avenue, London N1 2DA ☎ 020 8346 6963

LEWIN Gordon (*B Clt, Sax*): 11 Park Chase, Wembley Park, Middx HA9 8EQ ☎ 020 8902 2073

LEWINGTON Sarah: 8 Lorne Road, London E17 7PX ☎ 020 8509 1419, 0966 235 089

LINES Timothy (*Efl Clt, B Clt*): 12 Epsom Close, Northolt, Middx UB5 4BH ☎ 020 8422 9535

LLOYD Marie (*B Clt*): 76 Lynton Road, Acton, London W3 9HW ☎ 020 8992 6139

LLUNA Joan-Enric: 64 Gracefield Gardens, London SW16 2TT ☎ 0370 623 423 mob, 020 8533 1372 day

LOGAN Alistair (*Efl Clt, B Clt, Bt Hrn*): 115 Ealing Road, Brentford, Middx TW8 0LF ☎ 020 8847 0539, 01306 880669

LOWE Frederick (*B Clt, Bt Hrn*): Moase Hames, Wadhurst, East Sussex TN5 6NA, 01892 782593

LOWE Jeremy (*Bt Hrn, B Clt, Efl Clt*): 102A Greenwich South Street, London SE10 8UN ☎ 020 8691 6944, 020 8691 6868

LUCY Laura: 1 Giggs Hill Villas, Portsmouth Road, Thames Ditton, Surrey KT7 0TF ☎ 020 8398 9300

LYLE Andrew: 26 St James Avenue, West Ealing, London W13 9DJ ☎ 020 8567 6901

MALSBURY Angela: 40 Greenford Avenue, Hanwell, London W7 3QP ☎ 020 8579 0420

MARPLES Gillian (*B Clt, Sax, Flt*): 54 Greenwood Close, Morden, Surrey SM4 4HZ ☎ 020 8542 0693

MARRINER Andrew: 67 Cornwall Gardens, London SW7 4BA ☎ 020 7937 3237

MARSH Lynsey (*B Clt*): 51 Cannon Street, St Albans, Herts AL3 5JR ☎ 01727 851091, 01306 500022 day, 01727 851008

MARSHALL Roger (*B Clt*): 5 Pine Grove, Maidstone, Kent ME14 2AJ ☎ 01622 673853 & fax, 0973 340182 mob

MARTIN Celetia: 3B Herschell Road, Brockley Rise, London SE23 1EG ☎ 020 8291 6828, 0956 708061, 020 8291 6828

MARTIN Glenn (*Flt, Sax*): 7 Mallards Way, Lightwater, Surrey GU18 5ND ☎ 01276 452998

MAUNDER Peter (*B Clt*): 86 Lakenheath, Southgate, London N14 4RS ☎ 020 8882 2415

MCALLISTER Kenneth: Woodyard Cottage, Vicarage Lane, Podington, Northants NN29 7HP ☎ 01933 413137

MCCAW John (*B Clt*): 15 Leinster Avenue, London SW14 7JW ☎ 020 8876 4840

MCCULLOUGH Andrew (*B Clt*): 36 Bolton Crescent, Windsor, Berks SL4 3JQ ☎ 01753 861541

MCDOWALL Ruth (*B Clt, Bt Hrn*): 41A Gabriel Street, Forest Hill, London SE23 1DW ☎ 020 8291 7674, 01306 880669

MCGUIRE Colin (*B Clt*): 10 Shirley Road, Enfield, Middx EN2 6SB ☎ 020 8367 0212

MCKAY Patricia (*Voc*): 450 Lady Margaret Road, Southall, Middx UB1 2NN ☎ 020 8575 0755

MCLAREN Jennifer (*Efl Clt, B Clt, A Sax*): 15 Shipman Road, Forest Hill, London SE23 2DY ☎ 020 8244 5823, 07970 016168 mob, 01306 500022 day

MCMILLAN Malcolm (*B Clt, Efl Clt, Sax*): The Hawthorns, 21 South Eastern Road, Ramsgate, Kent CT11 9TR ☎ 019843 587732

MEDCALF Victoria (*Bt Hrn, B Gtr, Pf*): 44 Richmond Park Road, Kingston, Surrey KT2 6AH ☎ 020 8549 7964, 0402 502 899

MEPHAM Rachel (*B Clt*): 89A Westminster Bridge Road, London SE1 7HR ☎ 020 7401 9927, 0378 987719

MILLARD James (*Vln*): 2 Friends Road, Purley, Surrey CR8 1BL ☎ 020 8660 8079

MITCHELL Douglas (*Efl Clt, B Clt*): 29A Dartmouth Road, Forest Hill, London SE23 3HN ☎ 020 8473 9925

MITCHELL Ian (*Bt Hrn, B Clt, Sax*): 137 Upland Road, East Dulwich, London SE22 0DF ☎ 020 8693 4694

MO Chi-Yu: Flat 2 Bishopsbourne, 134-6 Westbourne Terrace, London W2 6QB ☎ 020 7402 9239, 0973 887532 mob

MOORE Keith (*Gtr*): 7 St Olaves Gardens, Walnut Tree Walk, Kennington, London SE11 6DR ☎ 020 7735 8104

MORGANS Avril (*A Sax, T Sax, S Sax, Flt*): 33 Jubliee Way, Sidcup, Kent DA14 4JP ☎ 020 8308 9236

MORPHETT Catherine: 25 Downside Crescent, Hampstead, London NW3 2AN ☎ 020 7794 4621

MORRIS Steve (*B Clt, Efl Clt, Saxes*): 51A Clarendon Gardens, Wembley, Middlesex HA9 7QW ☎ 020 8902 2954, 0966 494674

MORRISON Fergus (*B Clt, Efl Clt, Saxes*): 19 Burghill Road, Sydenham, London SE26 4HJ ☎ 020 8244 3172

MOSS Susan (*Saxes*): 167 Ellerton Road, Tolworth, Surbiton, Surrey KT6 7UB ☎ 020 8390 8307

MUNDAY Jason (*Saxes, Pf, Rec, Flt*): 77 Churchfield, Harlow, Essex CM20 3DB ☎ 01279 420415, 0976 679739 mob

MUNN Julia: 21 Allendale Close, Camberwell, London SE5 8SG ☎ 020 7703 7372

MURPHY Kevin: Address Unknown ☎ 020 8656 9212, 020 8656 9212

MYATT John (*B Clt, Sax, Bsn, Flt*): Belvedere, Harrisons Lane, Halesworth, Suffolk IP19 8HU ☎ 01462 420057, 0896 874813

NEEDHAM Joseph (*Sax*): PO Box 4700, Station E, Ottawa, Ontario, Canada, K1S 5H8

NEIGHBOUR Peter (*A Sax, T Sax*): 16 Wynndale Road, South Woodford, London E18 1DX ☎ 020 8505 6877, 0468 870881 mob

NEWIS Carlos: 1 Onslow Drive, Sidcup, Kent DA14 4PB ☎ 020 8302 4843

NICHOLS Peter (*B Clt, Saxes, Flt, Wi Synth*): 171 Elm Road, New Malden, Surrey KT3 3HX ☎ 020 8942 6177, 01306 880669 day

ORCHARD Eric (*A Sax, Flt*): 70A Victoria Road, Ruislip Manor, Middlesex HA4 0AG ☎ 01895 638745

PARRIS Janet: Southfield House, Wangford Road, Reydon, Southwold, Suffolk IP18 6BP ☎ 01502 723493

PAY Antony: 79 Southmoor Road, Oxford OX2 6RE ☎ 01865 553339 & fax

PAYNE John: 16 Malden Hill, New Malden, Surrey KT3 4DR ☎ 020 8942 6055

PAYNE Timothy (*Efl Clt, Bt Hrn, C B Clt, Sax*): Severn Cottage, Barrow Lane, Harwell, Oxfordshire OX11 0EA ☎ 01235 832902

PEARCE Michael: 2 Dorset Court, 25-27 Cumberland Park, London W3 6SY ☎ 020 8993 3613, 0976 922281 mob

PETERSON Soozy: Flat 1, 3 Nelgarde Road, Catford, London SE6 4TA ☎ 020 8314 0097, 0831 395916 mob, 020 8244 8527

PETTER Jonathon (*T Sax, Kbds*): 47 Glenarm Road, London E5 0LY ☎ 020 8985 7608

PHILLIPS Jane (*Pf*): 61 Bellclose Road, West Drayton, Middlesex UB7 9DF ☎ 01895 421673

PIERCE Stephen (*B Clt, Saxes*): 6 Swallows Court, Somerville Road, London SE20 7NS ☎ 020 8659 7779

PIKE Anthony (*Efl Clt*): 27 Birchington Road, London NW6 4LL ☎ 020 7372 1237

PLANE Robert (*B Clt, Efl Clt, Bt Hrn*): 8A Burners Road, Wood Green, London N22 5NE ☎ 020 8881 7584, 09662 06634 mob

PRITCHARD Dai (*B Clt, Saxes, Flt*): 101 Windsor Road, Leyton, London E10 5LP ☎ 020 8923 7046, 0973 760199

PUDDY Keith: 20 Courtnell Street, London W2 5BX ☎ 020 7229 4185, 020 7727 2036 fax

PUGSLEY David (*A Sax, Rec, Flt, Pan P*): The Lady Val, Benbow Way Moorings, Cowley, Uxbridge Middx UB8 4HD ☎ 01895 59341

PUMMELL Andrew (*A Sax*): Fern Cottage, Drury Lane, Hundson, Herts SG12 8NU ☎ 0127984 2786

QUILTER Graham (*Efl Clt, B Clt, Saxes*): 24 Fletcher Lane, Leyton, London E10 6JE ☎ 020 8539 0348, 020 8533 1372 day, 0831 260924 mob

RAE James (*B Clt, Saxes, Flt, Arr*): 85 Gordon Road, Carshalton Beeches, Surrey SM5 3RG ☎ 020 8773 8744

RIX David (*B Clt*): 129 Oakhill Road, Putney, London SW15 2QL ☎ 020 8874 4113

ROBERTS Christine (*Sax, Efl Clt, B Clt*): 6 Lingfield House, Park Court, Crystal Palace Park Road, Sydenham SE26 6ES ☎ 020 8908 3681, 0976 694333, 01306 500022 diary

ROBSON Barnaby (*Rec*): 127 Troughton Road, London SE7 7QF ☎ 020 8333 5947 fax, 0973 33 44 20 mob, 020 8533 1372 diary

RODWELL Nicholas: 30 Avenue Rise, Bushey, Herts WD2 3AS ☎ 020 8386 6692 & fax

ROY Alvin: 19 Vincent Square, Wood Green, London N22 6NB ☎ 020 8888 8062

ROYLE Jeremy (*Sax, Flt*): 7 Kent Avenue, Welling, Kent DA16 2LP ☎ 020 8303 2975

RYE Daniel (*B Clt*): 20 8533 1372, 07803 007561

RYSER Terry: 16 Heathfield, Chislehurst, Kent BR7 6AE ☎ 020 8467 8147

SADLER Jill (*B Clt*): 117 Holmwood Road, Cheam, Surrey SM2 7JS ☎ 020 8393 6385

SAGOO Ranjit (*Sax*): Flat 4, 32 Lovelace Gardens, Surbiton, Surrey KT6 6SD ☎ 020 8399 8701

SARGEANT Paul (*Saxes, Bt Hrn, Db, Bag*): 26 Molescroft Way, Tonbridge, Kent TN9 2QW ☎ 01732 364171

SAUNDERS Emily (*Flt*): 11 Werter Road, London SW15 2LL ☎ 020 8789 8150, 0956 137061

SAUNDERS Patrick (*Efl Clt, A Sax, B Clt*): 29 Passage Street, Fowey, Cornwall PL23 1DE ☎ 01726 83 3415

SAUNDERS Paul (*Sax, Flt*): 46 Whitworth Road, London SE18 3QB ☎ 020 8854 0381, 0956 599693 mob

SCHATZBERGER Lesley (*B Clt, Bt Hrn, Bq Clt*): 10 Bootham Terrace, York YO30 7DH ☎ 01904 658189 & fax, 020 8558 4421

SCHECHTER Gregory (*Sax*): 26 Thistlecroft Gardens, Stanmore, Middlesex HA7 1PN ☎ 020 8952 2902

SCHULMAN Lorraine (*B Clt, Efl Clt*): 21 Hewitt Road, London N8 0BS ☎ 020 8347 8174, 0976 642943

SCOTT Ian (*Efl Clt*): 35 Bury Road, Old Harlow, Essex CM17 0EE ☎ 01279 635848, 020 8533 1372 day

SCRIVENER Graham (*B Clt*): 12 Holmbush Road, London SW15 3LE ☎ 020 8785 6996

SEAGO Peter (*Sax*): 65 Bradgate Road, Catford, London SE6 4TT ☎ 020 8690 9459

SENFLUK Jerry (*A Sax, Rec*): 105 Kirkdale, Sydenham, London SE26 4QJ ☎ 020 8699 5584

SHEPHERD Dave (*A Sax, B Ldr*): 13 Royston Place, Barton-on-Sea, New Milton, Hampshire BH25 7AJ ☎ 01425 627107

SHEPHERD Merlin (*Sax, Flt, Kl Clt*): ☎ 020 7642 9806, 0795 7416364

SHEPPARD Alan (*Flt, Pic, A Flt, Saxes*): 70 Willow Park, Otford, Sevenoaks, Kent TN14 5NG ☎ 01959 524566, 0411 672605

SHIPP Alison (*Sax*): 12 Broadwood Close, Horsham, West Sussex RH12 4JX

SIBTHORP Philip (*B Clt, Saxes, B Sax*): 58 Bullingdon Road, Oxford OX4 1QJ ☎ 01865 241040, 0370 812 475

SKINNER Stephen: 154 Choumert Road, London SE15 4AA ☎ 020 7635 8379

SLACK Frank (*Sax*): 9 Geneva Road, Kingson-upon-Thames, Surrey KT1 2TW ☎ 020 8549 9975

SLAYMARK Victor (*B Clt*): 14 Exford Road, London SE12 9HD ☎ 020 8857 6583

SMITH Chris (*Sax, Gtr, Pf*): Penshurst, 18 Brooklands Park, London SE3 9BL

SOAMES Victoria (*B Clt*): 77 St Albans Ave, East Ham, London E6 4HH ☎ 020 8472 2057 & fax

SPARLING Andrew (*B Clt, Efl Clt*): 411 Forest Road, Walthamstow, London E17 5LD ☎ 020 8503 2364, 020 8533 1372 day

STAFFORD Joe (*Sax*): 167 Green Lane, New Eltham, London SE9 3SZ ☎ 020 8850 1449

STAGG Kathryn (*Saxes*): 74 Townholm Crescent, Hanwell, London W7 2NA ☎ 020 8536 1997, 0370 631544

STANTON Bernard (*Pf*): The Beacon, 71 Burkes Road, Beaconsfield, Bucks HP9 1PW ☎ 01494 673965

STENHOUSE John (*B Clt, Sax*): 43 Lessar Avenue, London SW4 9HW ☎ 020 8673 0063, 01306 880669 day

STEPHENSON Lee (*Sax*): 90 Emmanuel Road, Balham, London SW12 0HR ☎ 020 8674 0475

STRINGLE Julian (*Saxes*): Nyn Park Cottage, Northaw Road West, Northaw, Hertfordshire EN6 4NS ☎ 01707 661874

STUART Ian (*Bt Hrn, B Clt, S Sax*): 13 Sandringham Road, Brent Cross, London NW11 9DR ☎ 020 8455 4084

SUNSHINE Monty (*B Ldr*): 6 Cox Close, Shenley, Herts WD7 9JQ ☎ 01923 857533

SWALE Trevor (*Br Sax*): 17 Fairmile Avenue, London SW16 6AG ☎ 020 8769 4956

SWINDELLS Duncan (*B Clt, Efl Clt*): 73 Headstone Gardens, Harrow, Middlesex HA2 6PJ ☎ 01459 122876 pager, 01306 880669 day

THOMPSON Peter (*B Clt, Efl Clt*): Address Unknown ☎ 020 8291 2510

THOMPSON Shaun (*B Clt, A Sax, T Sax, Efl Clt*): 23C Maple Road, Anerley, London SE20 0LA ☎ 020 8659 0230, 07930 631075

THURLOW Sarah (*B Clt, Bt Hrn, Efl Clt*): 64A South Eden Park Road, Beckenham, Kent BR3 3BG ☎ 020 8776 2628, 0956 458977 mob

THURLOW Tracey (*Efl Clt, B Clt, Saxes*): 64A South Eden Park Road, Beckenham, Kent BR3 3BG ☎ 020 8776 2628, 0956 591048 mob

TODD Roger: 12 Palace Road, East Molesey, Surrey KT8 9DL ☎ 020 8979 1302

TRIER Stephen (*Bt Hrn, B Clt, C B Clt, A Sax*): 6 Carthew Villas, London W6 0BS ☎ 020 8748 4711

TROMANS Mark (*Efl Clt, Bt Hrn, B Clt, Saxes*): Summerleaze, North Cadbury, Yeovil, Somerset BA22 7DB ☎ 01963 40502

TSCHAIKOV Basil (*Efl Clt, B Clt*): Hillside Cottage, Hill Brow, Liss, Hants GU33 7PS ☎ 01730 892148, 01730 894264 fax

TUDGE Cyril (*Sax*): Address Unknown

TUFF Jane (*B Clt, Br Sax, Flt*): 58 Lodge Road, Feltwell, Thetford, Norfolk IP26 4DL ☎ 01842 828717

TURBETT Philip (*Bsn*): Redwings, Linden Chase, Uckfield, East Sussex TN22 1EE ☎ 01825 760046 & fax

UNDERWOOD James (*A Sax, T Sax, Flt*): 22 Vandyke Close, Putney, London SW15 3JQ ☎ 020 8780 3983

VAN DE WIEL Mark: 31N Rodin Court, 25 Essex Road, London N1 2SD ☎ 020 7704 8079 & fax

VASSALLO Antonino: 18 Comeragh Road, London W14 9HP ☎ 020 7381 8335

VINALL Graeme (*Efl Bass, Saxes, Com*): 53 Hillary Road, Maidstone, Kent ME14 2JT

VINE Jacky (*Sax*): 41 Beechfield, Hoddesdon, Herts EN11 9QG ☎ 01992 467783

WALKER Kate (*Pf, Voc*): 7 Downing Avenue, Guildford, Surrey GU2 5SY ☎ 01483 33801

WALKLIN Leslie (*B Clt, Efl Clt*): 29 Parbury Road, Stondon Park, London SE23 1NZ ☎ 020 8699 3650

WALLBANK Alfred (*Sax, Bt Hrn, B Clt, C B Clt*): 6 Stock Field Close, Hazlemere, Bucks HP15 7LA ☎ 01494 814059

WARREN Susanna (*Pf*): 103 Halliford Road, Sunbury, Middx TW16 6DN ☎ 0956 886 222

WASSERMAN Clare (*B Clt, Saxes, Flt*): 4 Vallentin Road, London E17 3JH ☎ 020 8520 8682

WATERS Stephen: Address Unknown

WATSON Donald: 33 Sarre Road, London NW2 3SN ☎ 020 7431 1741, 0973 758097 mob

WATSON Ruth: Owens Cottage, 1A Wilfred Owen Close, Wimbledon, London SW19 8SW ☎ 020 8540 9126

WEBB Niall: 13 Ashton Hall, 70 Golbe Road, Morningside, Durban 4001, South Africa

WEINBERG Anton: 32 Cromer Road, Tooting, London SW17 9JN ☎ 020 8672 5903

WELLS Billy (*Sax, B Ldr*): Flat 2, Sovereign Court, Wannock Road, Eastbourne, East Sussex BN22 7JQ ☎ 01323 642212

WEST Richard (*Bt Hrn*): Moorgaurds, West Hall, Brampton, Carlisle CA8 8NY ☎ 01702 465683, 01306 889537

WHELAN Larry (*Sax*): 47 Grove Road, Acton, London W3 6AN ☎ 020 8992 4091

WHENNELL Tony (*Sax, Flt, Cop*): 38 Lily Hill Road, Bracknell, Berkshire RG12 2SD ☎ 01344 53804

WHIGHT Michael (*B Clt, Efl Clt*): 29A Dartmouth Road, Forset Hill, London SE26 7HN ☎ 020 8244 3180

WHITE Brian (*Sax*): 12 Newborough Green, New Malden, Surrey KT3 5HS ☎ 020 8949 0776

WHITE David (*Sax*): Cedar House, Vine Lane, Hillingdon, Middlesex UB10 0BX ☎ 01872 241731, 01306 500022 day

WHITESTONE Tom: 3 Wimpole Street, London W1M 7AB ☎ 020 7636 8410

WHITTAKER Prudence: 14 Homersham Road, Kingston-upon-Thames, Surrey KT1 3PN ☎ 020 8546 8135

WILLIAMS Glenn (*Sax, Flt*): 49 Boscombe Road, Shepherd Bush, London W12 9HT ☎ 020 8749 4916

WOLLEN Damaris (*B Clt, Efl Bass*): 70 Studley Grange Road, Hanwell, London W7 2LX ☎ 020 8840 6139

WOODIN Paul (*A Sax, T Sax, Br Sax*): 31 Kershaws Hill, Hitchin, Herts SG4 9AQ ☎ 01462 453187

WURR John (*A Sax, S Sax, Br Sax*): 26 Roe Lane, Roe Green Village, Kingsbury, London NW9 9BJ ☎ 020 8204 2809

WYLLIE Barbara (*S Sax*): 11 Callcott Court, Callcott Road, London NW6 7ED ☎ 020 7372 2686

CLARSACH
SCOTLAND

GOW Phamie (*Pf, Acc*): 10 Garnet Court, Shamrock Street, Concaddens, Glasgow G4 9NT ☎ 0141 332 2481, 07801 540740

KINNAIRD Alison: Shillinghill, Temple, Midlothian EH23 4SH ☎ 01875 328

NAPIER Marie Louise (*Pf, Voc*): Cherrygrove, Old Spey Bridge, Grantown-on-Spey, Moray PH26 3NQ ☎ 01479 872832

NORTH WEST

MAWSON Annie (*Hrp, Voc*): Old Post Office, Tirril, Penrith, Cumbria CA10 2JE ☎ 01768 67806

CLUB DJ
NORTH WEST

BAGGALEY Benjamin (*Kbds, Pf*)

DJ FUNK BOUTIQUE (*Kbds*)

ELLIS Richard: The Boot Inn, Whittington, Oswestry, Shropshire SY11 4DG ☎ 01691 680739, 0802 521398

MATHEWS Nicholas (*Kbds*): 1 St Mary's Close, Appleton, Warrington WA4 5DD ☎ 01925 262510, 04325 168366, 01925 262510

NELSON Craig: Shangri-La, North Scale, Barrow In Furness, Cumbria LA14 3RP ☎ 01229 473404

NORTH EAST

MCDONALD Wayne: 324 Waterloo Street, Newcastle NE1 4DJ ☎ 0966 398396 mob

EAST

WINK Christopher *(Kbds, Gtr)* ☎ 01603 749243, 0374 490963

MIDLANDS

BLAK SPICE
DANGERFIELD Bernard: 11 The Woodlands, Waden Hill, Cradley Heath, West Midlands B64 7JY ☎ 0121 501 1211
MATTU Satinder *(Kbds, Dholak, Sarangi)*: 74 Jacklin Drive, Rushey Mead, Leicester LE4 7SU ☎ 0116 2667428, 0860 148177
MYNARD Marc ☎ 01327 876669, 0976 747873

SOUTH EAST

DJ TRIGGER ☎ 023 8063 6883
NAPTHINE Guy
SPACEMAN: 26 Herons Rise, Andover, Hampshire SP10 2DY ☎ 01264 396778, 0468 650604, 01264 366965
TRISH: 188 Church Street, Wolverton, Milton Keynes MK12 5JS ☎ 01908 312847

SOUTH WEST

WHITELAW Edward *(Kbds)*: 2 Habershon Street, Splott, Cardiff CF2 2DX ☎ 029 2031 8422
WILSON Jennifer *(Gtr, Kbds)*: 2 The Mead, Holcombe, Bath, Banes BA3 5EQ ☎ 01761 232699, 0831 630783

LONDON

DJ IMPULSE : 18 Armstrong Avenue, Woodford Green, Essex IG8 9PT ☎ 020 8527 4984
DJ INSPIRATION (Kbds) ☎ 020 8657 3051, 0802 816765, 020 8657 3051
DJ PERKS: 44 Bankmore Road, Omagh, Co Tyrone, Northern Ireland BT79 0EU ☎ 028 8224 5736, 0410 503586, 028 8224 1131
DJ SHAMPEZ: 37 Bryne Road, Balham, London SW12 9HZ ☎ 020 8673 2585, 0958 559 584
DUVOISIN Patrick *(Kbds, Gtr)*: 2C St Mark's Rise, London E8 2NJ, 020 7690 4432
JAMES Barry ☎ 020 8800 9551, 0956 208074 mob
K. Harry *(B Gtr, Voc)*: Unit 5, 51 Tudor Road, Homerton, London E9 7SN ☎ 020 8525 9838
PARIKH Rajan *(Arr)* ☎ 020 7737 3734
RAY Rita *(Voc)*: 46 Broomwood Rd, London SW11 6HT ☎ 020 7228 1161, 0956 359841, 020 7350 1983
REED Stewart: 207 Beck, Shepherds Bush, London W12 9HA ☎ 020 8746 2147, 0410 549693
WILLIAMS Barry

COMPOSER

SCOTLAND

BEAT Janet: Address Unknown ☎ 0141 637 1952
BRYCE James *(Md, B Gtr, Kbds)*: 50C Huntersfield Road, Gorebridge, Midlothian EH23 4TT ☎ 01875 820511
CHERNS Richard *(Md, Kbds)*: 21 Lockharton Avenue, Edinburgh EH14 1AY ☎ 0131 443 1541
CLARK Gerry *(B Gtr, Kbds, Gtr, Hmca)*: Flat 1/R, 69 Albert Avenue, Crosshill, Glasgow G42 8RA ☎ 0141 423 2899
DON Nigel *(Pf, Arr)*: 12 Kelso Place, Dundee DD2 1SL ☎ 01382 667251
FOWLER Tommy: 60 Maryhill Rd, Glasgow G20 7QB ☎ 0141 353 0927
GEDDES John *(Ob, Arr)*: 20 Baronald Drive, Glasgow G12 0HZ ☎ 0141 357 2941
HARRISON Dan *(Flt, Pic, Gtr, Pf)*: 1 Lennel Avenue, Edinburgh EH12 6DW ☎ 0131 337 6632
HILL Richard *(Arr)*: 19 Huggincraig Road, New Milns, Ayrshire KA16 9EW ☎ 01560 320881
LEONARD-MORGAN Paul *(Pf, Rec, Cntrc)*: Rage Music, Cava House, 30 Bentinck Street, Glasgow G3 7TU ☎ 0141 357 3795, 0378 039976, 0141 357 0338
MACDONALD Allan *(Bag, Tin Wh, Jaw H, Voc)*: 13 Greenbank Drive, Morningside, Edinburgh EH10 5RE ☎ 0131 4476641

MCGUIRE Edward *(Flt)*: 13 Lawrence Street, Glasgow G11 5HH ☎ 0141 334 8580
MORYKIT Dmytro *(Pf, Kbds)*: 13 Carlton Terrace, Edinburgh EH7 5DD ☎ 0131 556 1250
MURRICANE David *(Con, Kbds, Md, Arr)*: Kensington House, 227 Sauchiehall Street, Glasgow G2 3EX ☎ 0141 332 7282, 0141 332 6517 fax
O'HANLON Frank: 26 Borthwick Drive, East Kilbride, Near Glasgow, Scotland G75 8YW ☎ 01355 245076
SILVER Ronald *(Md, Arr, Gtr, Db)*: 6 Dean Place, Crosshouse, Kilmarnock, Ayrshire KA2 0JZ ☎ 0411 348832
VAN DER WALT J Simon *(Tpt, Tbn, Flgl, Gtr)*: 124 Dumbarton Road, Glasgow G11 6NY ☎ 0141 357 5743

NORTH WEST

BAINES Andy *(Arr, Sitar, Db, Per)*: 1 Langley Road, Prestwich, Manchester M25 1NF ☎ 0421 592117
BIGGIN Tony *(Kbds)*: 38 Manchester Road, Southport, Merseyside ☎ 01704 535 740
CONNOR Bill *(Con)*: Bod Feddau, Llaniestyn, Beaumaris, Anglesey LL58 8YG ☎ 01248 811433
DAVIES Simeon: Flat 1, 21 Old Lansdowne Road, W Didsbury, Manchester M20 2PD ☎ 0161 445 8304
DEWHURST Robin *(Arr, Kbds, Tbn)*: 17 Crossfield Grove, Woodsmoor, Stockport, Cheshire SK2 7EQ ☎ 0161 456 0097
HILTON Derek *(Md, Con, Arr, Pf)*: 54 Brownlow Court, Cooper Street, Horwich, Bolton, Lancs. BL6 7AT ☎ 01204 669128
HUGHES Brian *(Con)*: Noddfa, Chester Road, Gresford, Clwyd LL12 8TN ☎ 01978 853836
KIMPTON Geoffrey *(Vla)*: 52 Hillingdon Road, Stretford, Manchester M32 8PJ ☎ 0161 865 1201
LEWIS Anwen: 112 Horton Road, Fallowfield, Manchester M14 7GD ☎ 0161 224 7602, 0589 161514
MACKAY Paul *(Cl Gtr, Org, B Gtr, Dms)*: The Nursary Gardens, 20 Laithwaite Close, Cockermouth, Cumbria CA13 0AQ ☎ 01900 822851
MITCHELL-DAVIDSON Paul *(Gtr, B Gtr, Man, Arr)*: 25 Bannerman Avenue, Prestwich, Manchester M25 1DZ ☎ 0161 798 9604 & fax, 0797 9883516
MORGAN-WILLIAMS Ian *(Arr, Pf, Db, B Gtr)*: Hafgan, Llandyssil, Montgomery, Powys. SY15 6LQ ☎ 01686 668400
ROYLE Roger *(B Gtr, Rh Gtr, Voc)*: 70 Sharples Avenue, Astley Bridge, Bolton BL1 7HF ☎ 01204 308074
SULLIVAN John *(Kbds)*: 1 Godley Hill Road, Godley, Hyde, Cheshire SK14 3BW ☎ 0161 368 8363
VIBRANS Mark *(Md, Pf, Synth, Arr)*: 116Longford Rod, Chorlton Cum Hardy, Manchester M21 9NP ☎ 0161 881 2638, 0161 374 9673
WALLFISCH Benjamin *(Pf, Con, Md, Arr)*: 8 St Brendans Close, Withington, Manchester M20 3GH ☎ 0956 128793, 0161 434 5812

NORTH EAST

FREEMAN Michael *(Arr, Pf, Man, Per)*: Risemoor Cottage, Lownewton By The Sea, Alnwick, Northumberland NE66 3EP ☎ 01665 576365, 01665 576117 day
PYWELL Jim *(Bsn, Con, Pf, Kbds)*: 19 Moss Street, Newsome, Huddersfield, West Yorkshire HD4 6NL ☎ 01484 513242, 01484 305 199, 01484 305199
STONE Richard *(Md, Kbds)*: 194 Cobden View Road, Crookes, Sheffield S10 1HT ☎ 0114 268 2055
UNDERWOOD Maria *(Pf, Voc)*: 11 East Avenue, Rawmarsh, Rotherham, South Yorkshire S62 7AA ☎ 01709 325267

EAST

FACE Angel: Grafton House, 1 Hart Road, Old Harrow, Essex CM17 0HY ☎ 01279 305717, 0410 327349, 01279 305717
FLATAU David *(Song W)*: 6 St. Michaels Court, Fishpool Street, St. Albans, Herts AL3 4SD
GODDARD Jonathan *(Gtr, Kbds)*: Sunnyville, Brundish, Woodbridge, Suffolk IP13 8BE ☎ 01728 628795
JUDD Garry: 30 Kingsway, Ware, Herts SG12 0QT ☎ 01920 487823

COMPOSER - EAST

LOMAX Oliver (PKA Shogun): 94 Oxney Avenue, Oxney, Herts, Watford WD1 4HA ☎ 01923 239778

MOORE Timothy (Pf): 86 Chesterton Road, Cambridge CB4 1ER ☎ 01223 564933, 01223 363731

PHILIPS Julian: The Granary, 19 Green End, Comberton, Cambs CB3 7DY ☎ 01223 264210 & fax

SEGGER Jill (Clt, Flt, Org): 32 Holland Park, Cheveley, Newmarket, Suffolk CB8 9DL ☎ 01638 730006, 0411 031837 mob

STAFFORD Duncan (Vln, Kbds): 38 Lingholme Close, Cambridge CB4 3HW ☎ 01223 360798

WEBB Bruce (Md, Pf, Arr): Abbots Manor, Kirby Cane, Nr Bungay, Suffolk NR35 2HP ☎ 01508 518703

WELLS Jane (Pf, Kbds, Saxes): Lion Cottage, 2 High Street, Wughton, Wells-Next-The-Sea, Norfolk NR23 1AL ☎ 01328 820917

MIDLANDS

BURT Nicholas (Arr, Org, Pf, Con): 1 Keyes Drive, Bilton, Rugby CV22 7ST ☎ 01788 521222, 01788 810217, 01788 816922

CARLTON Malcolm (Arr, Kbds, Pf): 12, Yeadon Close, Webheath, Redditch, Worcs B97 5TG ☎ 01527 43141

EASTBURY Jonathan (Multi): 65 Cotton Lane, Moseley, Birmingham B13 9SE ☎ 0121 449 3148

LEDDINGTON WRIGHT Paul (Arr, Con, Org, Pf): 11 Styvechale Avenue, Earlston, Coventry CV5 6DW ☎ 024 7667 3633

PATRICK John (Pf, Md, Arr, Kbds): c/o Musicians Union, Benson House, Lombard Street, Birmingham B12 0QN ☎ 01564 784029 & fax

POPOV David: 67 Station Road, Mickleover, Derby, Derbyshire DE3 5GJ ☎ 01332 519020

RAMSKILL Robert (Arr): 142 Woodside Avenue South, Green Lane, Coventry, West Midlands CV3 6BE ☎ 024 7641 0325

RILEY Martin (Arr, Pf, Kbds): 93 Brook Lane, Kings Heath, Birmingham B13 0AB ☎ 0121 422 6382

SKEMPTON Howard: Flat 11, 11 Warwick Place, Leamington Spa, Warwickshire CV32 5BS ☎ 01926 316595

SPENCER Nyah: 52 Flat 1 Gladstone Road, Parkbrook, Birmingham B11 1LW ☎ 0121 689 7168, 0958 930297, 0121 689 7168

SPENCER Timothy (Arr, Kbds, Pf): 27 Thickthorn Close, Kenilworth, Warwickshire CV8 2AF ☎ 01926 512392, 024 7655 0704

STYLER Richard: Finham Green Farm, St. Martins Road, Coventry CV3 6PQ ☎ 024 7641 5720, 024 7641 4959

SUDLOW Paul (Vla, Pf, Vln): 48 Price Road, Cubbington, Leamington Spa, Warks CV32 7LQ ☎ 01926 429607

SOUTH EAST

CLARK Jonathan (Clt, Pf): 35 The Warren, Burgess Hill, West Sussex RH15 0DU ☎ 01444 257549

CORK Peter: 39 Alder Road, Folkestone, Kent CT19 5DA ☎ 01303 253994

CREMONA Robert (Pf, Gtr, B Gtr, Per): The Cremona School of Ballet, 81 High Street, Horsell Village, Woking, Surrey GU21 4UA ☎ 01483 851212/8

DALY Michael (Arr): Chapel School House, Station Road, Launton, Oxon OX6 0DS ☎ 01869 243133

EWINS Frank (Gtr): 51 St Lukes Road, Bournemouth BH3 7LR ☎ 01202 512204

HENDERSON Keith (Arr): 25 Rydal Avenue, Nethercourt, Ramsgate, Kent CT11 0PU

KING Jamie: Flat 3, 24 Browning Avenue, Bournemouth BH5 1NN ☎ 01202 392783

MALCOMSON Hettie: Flat 4, 65-66 Regency Square, Brighton, East Sussex BN1 2FF ☎ 01273 321546, 0976 713272 mob

NEWMAN Adam: 35 Stert Street, Abbingdon, Oxford OX14 3JF ☎ 01235 525 732

PRATLEY Susie: Easter Cottage, Church Enstone, Chipping Norton, Oxon OX7 4NN ☎ 01608 677345

PRITCHARD Fiona (Song W, Arr, Voc): 17B Willow Way, Christchurch, Dorset BH23 1JJ ☎ 01202 481963 & fax, 0973 344139 mob

SANDFORD Christopher (Song W): Flat 2, 14 Gratwicke Road, Worthing, Sussex BN11 4BH ☎ 01903 239458

THORNLEY Steve (Dms, Pf, Voc): 38 Chantryfield Road, Angmering, Littlehampton, West Sussex BN16 4LZ ☎ 01903 775144 & fax, 0858 368159 mob

SOUTH WEST

BARBER Charles (Con): 62 Arran Street, Roath, Cardiff, South Glamorgan CF2 3HT ☎ 029 2049 7157

CLIFF Tony (Arr, Pf, Kbds): Tremar, Trescobeas Manor, Trescobeas Road, Falmouth, Cornwall TR11 4JB ☎ 01326 314423 & fax, 07970 921993 mob

EDWARDS Nicola (Voice, Pf, Vln): 5A Vicars Close, Wells, Somerset BA5 2UH ☎ 01749 671423

HARDY John (Kbds, Cnt, Tpt): Ael Y Garth, 3 Iron Bridge Road, Tongwynlais, Cardiff CF4 7NJ ☎ 029 2081 0653

HINTON Alistair: Easton Dene, Bailbrook Lane, Bath BA1 7AA ☎ 01225 852323 & fax

KISZKO Martin: 29 Wellington Park, Clifton, Bristol BS8 2UW ☎ 0117 9731267

KYRKE-SMITH Peter (Voc, Pf, Clt): 65 Park Lane, Pinhoe, Exeter, Devon EX4 9HP ☎ 01392 469838

NICHOLLS Jonathan (Pf): 23 Bowbridge Lane, Stroud, Glos GL5 2JP ☎ 01453 765033 & fax

OTTAWAY Helen (Pf, Synth): 38 Alexandra Road, Frome, Somerset BA11 1LX ☎ 01373 467201 fax

PAINTER Christopher (Cop): 33 Southminster Road, Penylan, Cardiff CF2 5AT ☎ 029 2049 9970

REYNOLDS Peter (Con): 46 Richmond Road, Roath, Cardiff CF2 3AT ☎ 029 2048 2183

STEER Maxwell (Arr, Kbds, Cntrc): Maxwell Steer, 125 Duck Street, Tisbury SP3 6LJ ☎ 01747 870070

WILLIAMS Christopher (Con, Pf): 11 Great Bridge Cottages, Headborough Road, Ashburton, Devon TQ13 7QW

WILLIAMS Edward: 10 Cornwallis Crescent, Bristol BS8 4PL ☎ 0117 9738024

LONDON

ALBERGA Eleanor (Pf): 166 Bethnal Green Road, London E2 6DL ☎ 020 7729 8362

ALLISON Ralph: 37 The Drive, Morden, Surrey SM4 6DH ☎ 020 8646 5551

ANDRE Eric: 3 Alvis Avenue, Herne Bay, Kent CT6 8AR ☎ 01227 373337

ANTHONY Monica: 43 Gomm Road, London SE16 2TY ☎ 020 7232 2562

ARDEN Jeremy: 83 Albion Road, London N16 9PL ☎ 020 7241 6296

ARDLEY Neil (Arr): 13A Priory Avenue, Chiswick, London W4 1TX ☎ 020 8994 6513 & fax, 020 8994 6513

ARLIDGE Victoria (Vln, Pf): 9A Church Row, Hampstead, London NW3 6UT ☎ 020 7435 9952

ARNOLD, CBE, FRCM, RARAM Malcolm (Con, Tpt): 26 Springfields, Attleborough, Norfolk NR17 2PA ☎ 01953 455420

AYRES Mark (Kbds, Flt): 165 Old Church Road, London E4 6RD ☎ 020 8529 4736, 020 8529 4090 fax

BAILEY Keith (Arr, Pf, Song W): 194A Straight Road, Harold Hill, Romford, Essex RM3 8XR ☎ 01708 371936

BALL Christopher (Arr, Con, Rec, Ea Wnd): Top Flat, 122 Wigmore Street, London W1H 9FE ☎ 020 7935 1270

BARNARD Keith (Pf): Thirty Four Longberrys, Cricklewood Lane, London NW2 2TE ☎ 07970 971513

BAULD Alison (Voc, Pf): 6 Dungarvon Avenue, Putney, London SW15 5QU ☎ 020 8876 3008

BELL Garry (Kbds, Gtr): 34 Foster Road, Chiswick, London W4 4NY ☎ 020 8994 8301

BELO Ola (Kbds, Voc): ☎ 020 7460 9228

BENSTEAD Christopher *(Per)*: Flat 1, 155 Eglinton Hill, London SE18 3DU ☎ 020 8854 0668

BERSEY, DIP, TCL James *(Db)*: Flat 7 Surrey Court, Broughton Avenue, Finchley, London N3 3EP ☎ 020 8343 1531

BLAIKLEY Alan: Flat 2, 31 Willow Road, London NW3 1TL ☎ 020 7431 2029

BREWSTER Susan *(Pf, Kbds, Per, Voc)*: 9-11 Chenies Street, Flat 13, London WC1E 7ET ☎ 020 7436 2315

BROADLEY Robert *(E Gtr, Cl Gtr)*: 18 Bedford Court, Mowbray Road, Upper Norwood, London SE19 2RW ☎ 020 8771 9793, 0966 473211

BROOKS Nigel *(Md, Arr, Pf)*: 115 East Street, Epsom, Surrey KT17 1EJ ☎ 01372 729207

BROWN Steven *(Kbds, Voc, Gtr)*: 5 Eleanor Grove, Barnes, London SW13 0JN

BURN Christopher *(Pf, Tpt)*: Field View, 11 Marks Avenue, Chipping Ongar, Essex CM5 9AY ☎ 01277 362 416

BUSH Kate *(Voc, Song W)*: c/o Sheridans, 14 Red Lion Square, London WC1R 4QL

CAIRN Steve: Bassetts Yard, Lostwithiel, Cornwall PL22 0EL ☎ 01208 873492

CAMERON John *(Md)*: The Studio, 35 Ragged Hall Lane, Chiswell Green, St Albans Herts AL2 3LB ☎ 01727 851199

CARSAN Paul *(Arr, Con, Md, Cop)*: 78 Boreham Holt, Elstree, Herts WD6 3QL ☎ 020 8953 3894

CASTRO Anthony *(Md)*: 55 Canadian Avenue, London SE6 3AX ☎ 020 8314 0136, 020 8690 1764 fax

CES John *(Synth)*: 7 Ericcson Close, London SW18 1SQ ☎ 020 8870 0523, 0860 916974 mob, 020 8944 0391

CLAXTON Andrew *(Kbds, Tba)*: Ivony, Hurst Lane, Cumnor Hill, Oxford OX2 9JA ☎ 01865 865 654, 01865 865 653

COHEN Alan *(Arr, Saxes)*: 6 Observatory Road, London SW14 7QD ☎ 020 8876 1974

COLLIER Graham *(Arr, Md)*: 38 Shell Road, Lewisham, London SE13 7TW ☎ 020 8692 6250

COULTER Phil *(Arr, Md)*: Killarney House, Killarney Road, Bray, Co.Wicklow, Ireland ☎ Dublin 286 9944, Dublin 286 9945 fax

CREES Kathleen *(Pf, Hpsd, Clav)*: PO Box 3020, Victoria Point West, Queensland 4165, Australia ☎ +61 73206 3969 & fax

CRISP Michael: 13 York Road, Worthing, West Sussex BN11 3EN ☎ 020 8567 6168

DALTRY Stephen *(Pf, Acc, Org)*: 8 Tavistock Avenue, Walthamstow, London E17 6HR ☎ 020 8531 5362

DAVIDSON Howard: 15 Chancellors Street, London W6 9RN ☎ 020 8748 5453

DAVIES Ray *(Arr, Con)*: 10 Princess Mews, Hampstead, London NW3 5AP ☎ 020 7431 1771, 020 7431 8422 fax

DAVIES Terry *(Arr, Md)*: 8 Heyford Ave, London SW8 1ED ☎ 020 7735 8950

DAVIS Carl: c/o Paul Wing, 16 Highland Road, Amersham, Bucks HP7 9AU ☎ 020 8348 6604, 020 8340 8434 fax

DAVISON Simon *(Kbds)*: Address Unknown

DE CARLO Nicholas *(Arr, Gtr)*: Flat 2, 31 Castletown Road, London W14 9HF

DE WILDE Graham: The Annexe, 3 Beeching Close, Upton, Oxon OX11 9JR ☎ 01235 851500

DEAN Ian *(Con, Arr, Ea Wnd, Kbds)*: 23 Canonbury Lane, Islington, London N1 2AS ☎ 020 7359 0406

DEMIANIUK Rob *(Pf, Kbds)*: 98 Havelock Road, London SW19 8HB ☎ 020 8542 6121

DEMPSEY Michael *(B Gtr, Kbds)*: Herstmonceux Place, Church Road, Hestmonceux, East Sussex BN27 1RL ☎ 01323 833619 & fax

EDWARDS Genene *(Song W, Vla, Pf, Arr)*: 54 Barnsbury Grove, London N7 8BP ☎ 020 7700 7967

EMNEY Mark *(Tpt)*: 10 Vicarage Street, Frome, Somerset BA11 1PX ☎ 01373 451839

ENGLISH Virgil *(Gtr)*: 254A Chiswick High Rd, Chiswick, London W4 1PD ☎ 020 8747 8010

ETCHELL Simon *(Kbds)*: 34 Upland Drive, Brookmans Park, Herts AL9 6PT ☎ 01707 647025, 01707 647026

FIDDY John *(Arr, B Gtr)*: Fruit Farm House, Foxton, Cambridge CB2 6RT ☎ 01763 208610

FINCH Flora *(Song W, Vln, Voc)*: Ground Floor Flat, 5 Richborne Terrace, Oval, London SW8 1AS ☎ 0941 100200 ext152275

FINDLEY Andi *(E Gtr, B Gtr, Kbds, Per)*: 26 Lydden Grove, Wandsworth, London SW18 4LL ☎ 020 8871 3659

FLOWERS Mike *(Arr)*: 2-3 Fovant Mews, 12A Noyna Road, London SW17 ☎ 020 8682 9950, 020 8682 9959 fax

FRIBBINS Peter *(Arr)*: 44 Rosecroft Drive, Watford, Hertfordshire WD1 3JQ ☎ 01923 223581, 01923 334696 fax

GILL David *(Arr, Org, Pf)*: 73 Chandos Road, Stratford, London E15 1TT ☎ 020 8534 5443

GLASSER Stanley *(Md)*: 46 Weigall Road, Lee, London SE12 8HE ☎ 020 8852 1997

GOODWIN Ron *(Con, Arr)*: Blacknest Cottage, Brimpton Common, Reading, Berkshire RG7 4RP ☎ 01734 815147

GOWERS Patrick *(Pf, Arr, Tba)*: 29 Gauden Road, London SW4 6LR ☎ 020 7622 1107

GREENSLADE David *(Song W, Synth, Kbds)*: 16 Queens Road, Berkhamsted, Herts HP4 3IIU ☎ 01442 863956

GREGORY John *(Arr, Md, Vln)*: 25 Latchmoor Way, Gerrards Cross, Bucks SL9 8LS ☎ 01753 884810

GREGORY Sean *(Pf, Flt, Gtr)*: 83 Elia Street, London N1 8DF ☎ 020 7278 1160

GULLAND Brian *(Voc, Bsn, Rec, Sax)*: 10 Greenside Road, London W12 9JG ☎ 020 8932 0494, 020 8932 0334

GUNNING Christopher *(Con, Pf)*: 24 Ranelagh Road, Ealing, London W5 5RJ ☎ 020 8810 0559, 020 8840 5899

HAINES Francis *(Kbds)*: 28 Riverway, London N13 5LJ ☎ 020 8886 9485

HANDY Allen *(Tpt, Cnt, Arr)*: 20 Eton Road, Datchet, Berkshire SL3 9AY ☎ 01753 542990, 020 8549 1706 day, 01753 544222 fax

HARVEY Richard: c/o Nomos Ltd, 21 Napier Place, London W14 8LG ☎ 020 7603 9261

HARWOOD Alexandra *(Pf, Voc, Clt)*: 32 Duncan Road, Richmond, Surrey TW9 2JD

HAYNES Tony *(Tbn, Pf, Arr)*: 66 Myddelton Square, London EC1R 1XX ☎ 020 7251 2100

HAYWOOD Cliff *(Arr, Dms, Kbds, Gtr)*: 161 Clapham Road, London SW9 0PU ☎ 01335 344588, 0860 288460

HENDRICKS Roger *(Voc)*: 33 Templeton Avenue, Chingford, London E4 6SS ☎ 0378 035741 mob

HEWSON Richard *(Arr, Gtr)*: Walnut Tree Cottage, The Pike, Washington, West Sussex RH20 4AA ☎ 01903 892889, 01903 892889

HOROVITZ Joseph *(Pf, Md)*: 7 Dawson Place, London W2 4TD ☎ 020 7229 5333

HOWARD Kenneth: 27 Arkwright Road, Hampstead, London NW3 6BJ ☎ 020 7435 9601

HUGHES Ian *(Arr, Con, Per, Pf)*: 2 Mead Villas, Hare Street, Buntingford, Herts SG9 0EA ☎ 01763 289592, 01763 289542 fax

JACKSON Roger *(Kbds, Gtr)*: Chapel House, Bishopstone, Aylesbury, Bucks HP17 8SH ☎ 01296 747415

JARVIS Toby *(Kbds)*: 15 Ellington Street, London N7 8PP

JENKINS Karl *(Arr)*: 224 Uxbridge Road, Hampton Hill, Twickenham, Middx TW12 ☎ 020 8979 9768

JOHNSON Laurie *(Con)*: c/o Alliott Peirson, Chartered Accountants, 10 College Road, Harrow Middx HA1 1DA

JOHNSTON Adrian *(Pf, Per)*: 2 Old School Buildings, Archdale Road, London SE22 9HP ☎ 020 8299 9660

JONES Kenneth *(Org, Pf)*: Cleavers, Bishopstone, Seaford, East Sussex BN25 2UD ☎ 01323 894377

JORDAN John *(Pf)*: 3 Famet Close, Purley, Surrey CR8 2DX ☎ 020 8660 1542

KAMEI Toshio *(Vln, Gtr, Voc)*: 12 Belsize Park, London NW3 4ES ☎ 020 7435 2326, 020 7435 1067 fax

KAY Norman *(Con)*: The Summerhouse, St Donats, Llantwit Major, South Glamorgan CF61 1ZB ☎ 01446 794775 & fax

KEANE John *(Pf)*: 23 Park Avenue, London NW11 7SL ☎ 020 7482 7170

KILLER PUSSIES Tasha *(Kbds)*: c/o Bag Inc, PO Box 1797, London E1 4TX ☎ 020 7702 7842, 020 7790 0764 fax

KOUTSELINI John *(Voc, Kbds)*: 74A Beechfield Road, London N4 1PE ☎ 020 8802 9750

LAMBERT Edward *(Pf, Con)*: The Old Rectory, Smannell, Andover, Hampshire SP11 6JW ☎ 01264 336373

LAMBURN Maria *(Vla, Saxes, Pf, Clt)*: Ty Nanney, Tremadog, Porthmadog, Gwynedd LL49 9PS ☎ 01766 514798 & fax

LANGFORD Gordon *(Arr, Pf)*: 5 Poplar Tree Drive, Seaton, Devon EX12 2TW ☎ 01297 22491

LAWRENCE Alan *(Gtr)*: 118 Chertsy Court, Lower Richmond Road, Mortlake, London SW14 7BY

LEACH John *(Zit)*: 68 Lysia Street, London SW6 6NG ☎ 020 7385 0182

LEDBURY Oliver: 12 Sherbourne Street, Bristol BS5 8EH ☎ 0117 954 1583

LEE Adrian *(Md, Gtr, Man)*: 15 Ambler Road, Finsbury Park, London N4 2QT ☎ 020 7226 2822 & fax

LINDSELL Rosie *(Bsn, Cop)*: 116 Skitts Hill, Braintree, Essex CM7 1AS ☎ 01376 346520

LISK Alan *(Kbds)*: 77 Princes Avenue, London W3 8LX ☎ 020 8992 3569

LLOYD-WEBBER Andrew: c/o Escaway, 25 Lower Belgrave Street, London SW1W 0NR

LUSCOMBE Stephen *(Kbds)*: Flat 5, 19 Colville Terrace, Notting Hill, London W11 2BU ☎ 020 7243 0050

MALONEY Sheila *(Kbds)*: 49 Mansfield Road, London E17 6PH ☎ 020 8520 1338

MANSFIELD Keith *(Arr, Md)*: Rectory House, Church Lane, Warfield, Berkshire RG12 6EE ☎ 01344 882562

MARIANELLI Dario: 14A Willow Bridge Road, London N1 2LA ☎ 020 7359 9809

MATTHEWS Colin: 3 Manchuria Road, London SW11 6AF ☎ 020 7228 5591, 020 7228 2358 fax

MCNEFF Stephen *(Arr, Md)*: 131 Melbourne Grove, East Dulwich, London SE22 8RR ☎ 020 8693 8388, 0976 987896, 020 8693 8388

MERAVIGLIA Manfredo *(Gtr, Voc)*: 520B High Road, Tottenham, London N17 9SX ☎ 020 8482 0522

MIDDLETON John *(Vln)*: 35 Kingswood Avenue, London NW6 6LR ☎ 020 8969 4294

MILLS Peter *(B Gtr, Gtr, Kbds)*: Rhu Corner, Pursers Lane, Peaslake, Surrey GU5 9RG ☎ 01306 731182

MIRANDA Carlos *(Synth, Hpsd, Acc, Org)*: c/o Molecule Music, 17 Elmwood Ave, Kenton, Middx HA3 8AJ ☎ 020 8907 2455

MITCHAM David *(Md, Arr)*: 1 Lyons Green Cottages, Shillinglee Road, Plaistow, West Sussex RH14 0PH ☎ 01403 871297

MOLLISON Deborah: 25 Ashurst Road, North Finchley, London N12 9AU ☎ 020 8445 4800

MONTAGUE Stephen *(Pf)*: 2 Ryland Rd, Kentish Town, London NW5 3EA ☎ 020 7267 5416

MORGAN Bob *(Clt, T Sax, Kbds, Voc)*: 45 Addison Way, Northwood, Middlesex HA6 1SS ☎ 01923 829911

MORLEY Angela *(Con, Arr)*: 7500 McCormick Parkway, Apt 38, Scottsdale, AZ 85258, USA ☎ +1 602 596 0491

MOTION David *(Kbds)*: 28 Hormead Road, London W9 3NG

MOTTRAM Paul *(Arr, Vln, Pf)*: 32 Greens Cottage, Cottesbrook, Northants NN6 8PH ☎ 01604 505567

MYHILL Richard *(Kbds, Arr)*: 4 Albion Street, London W2 2AS ☎ 020 7262 5095, 020 7262 5096

MYLVAGANAM Max *(Dms, Per, Kbds, Gtr)*: 9 Walton Close, Harrow, Middlesex HA1 4UY ☎ 020 8863 5361

NASSAUER Sharon *(Arr, Md, Pf, Kbds)*: 38 Thornhill Square, London N1 1BE

NICOLSON Alasdair *(Con, Pf, Vln)*: 10 Christchurch Road, London SW2 3EX ☎ 020 8674 8258

NUNES Greg: 263 Eastern Avenue, Ilford, Essex IG4 5AT ☎ 020 8550 6026 & fax

NUNN Patrick *(Vln)*: 46 Albert Road, London N22 4AH ☎ 020 8881 1758

OMER Michael *(Kbds, Md)*: 12 Belsize Lane, London NW3 5AB ☎ 020 7794 6834

OSBORNE Tony *(Db, B Gtr, Arr)*: 42 Parkland Avenue, Slough, Berks SL3 7LQ ☎ 01753 541818

PARKER Jim *(Arr)*: 17 Laurel Road, Barnes, London SW13 0EE ☎ 020 8876 8571

PEGGIE Andrew *(Con, Kbds, Arr)*: 4 Colchester Avenue, London E12 5LE ☎ 020 8514 2219, 020 8478 7141 fax

PIATTI Polo *(Pf, Kbds, Md)*: 157 Capel Road, Forest Gate, London E7 0JT ☎ 020 8514 3998

POOLE Steven: 15 Lavender Gardens, London SW11 1DH

POPE Philip *(Arr, Voc, Kbds)*: Tifnams, Owlswick, Princes Risborough, Bucks HP27 9RJ ☎ 01844 345797, 01844 275404 fax

POWELL Andrew *(Arr, Con, Kbds)*: 28 Shaftesbury Road, Richmond, Surrey TW9 2TD ☎ 020 8332 7966

PRESKETT Graham *(Arr, Md, Vln, Man)*: 57 Grove Park Road, London W4 3RU ☎ 020 8995 7932, 020 8747 3917 & fax

PRICE Michael *(Arr, Pf)*: 160 Highlever Road, London W10 6PJ ☎ 020 8964 0583, 0585 759164 mob, 01223 564182

PROTTS Patrick J *(Pf, Vln, Rec)*: 128 Ruden Way, Epsom Downs, Surrey KT17 3LP ☎ 01737 352028

REES Howard *(Arr, Con)*: 19 Bourne Road, London N8 9HJ ☎ 020 8348 8894

REILLY David: 20 Yockley Close, Camberley, Surrey GU15 1QH ☎ 01276 66973

RENTSCH Veronika *(Arr)*: 162 Camden Road, London NW1 9HJ ☎ 020 7267 6258

ROCKY *(Song W)*: 2 Minet Gardens, Hayes, Middlesex UB3 3LD ☎ 020 8561 4110

RODGERS Sarah *(Bsn, Pf, Md)*: 18 Hillfielld Park, Muswell Hill, London N10 3QS ☎ 020 8444 8587

RUNSWICK Daryl *(Arr)*: 126 Jerningham Road, London SE14 5NL ☎ 020 7639 6006, 020 7639 6007

RUSH Stuart *(Arr, Pf)*: 93 Osborne Road, Hornchurch, Essex RM11 1HE ☎ 01708 620926

SADLER Gaynor *(Voc, Pf, Hrp)*: c/o Logorhythm Music Ltd, 6-10 Lexington Street, London W1R 3HS ☎ 020 7734 7443

SADLER Tony *(Gtr, Kbds, Voc)*: c/o Logorhythm Music Ltd, 6-10 Lexington Street, London W1R 3HS ☎ 020 7734 7443

SALZEDO Leonard *(Con)*: 363 Bideford Green, Leighton Buzzard, Beds LU7 7TX ☎ 01525 371126

SAUNDERS Adam *(Pf, Arr)*: 9 Cyprus Avenue, Finchley, London N3 1SS ☎ 020 8371 8256

SCOTT Matthew *(Pf, Kbds)*: 126B Farringdon Road, London EC1R 3AP ☎ 020 7837 8941

SCRIVENER Paul *(Kbds)*: 64 Colney Hatch Lane, London N10 1EA ☎ 020 8883 8834

SEKACZ Ilona *(Vln, Pf, Auto Hrp)*: Westcote Manor Farm, Edgehill, Banbury, Oxon OX15 6HS ☎ 01295 87675, 01295 87748

SHAW Francis *(Arr, Con, Pf)*: 39 Crane Grove, London N7 8LD ☎ 020 7607 8379 & fax

SIMMONS *(B Gtr, Kbds, Arr)*: 8C Blakesley Avenue, Ealing, London W5 2DW ☎ 020 8998 7318

SINCLAIR Bim *(Kbds, Arr, Db)*: 83 Smallwood Road, Tooting, London SW17 0TN ☎ 020 8767 0633

SKEAPING Roderick *(Arr, Vln, Acc)*: 19 Patshull Road, Kentish Town, London NW5 2JX ☎ 020 7485 3957, 020 7267 2957

SKEET Andrew *(Arr, Pf)*: St Mary's Flat, St Mary's Vicarage, Riverside, Twickenham, Middlesex TW1 3DT ☎ 020 8891 3204, 0411 131116 mob

SLATER Matthew *(Cop, Pf, Con)*: 29 Elmsleigh Drive, Leigh-on-Sea, Essex SS9 3DW ☎ 0467 254262, 01702 331176

SMAIL Tom *(Dms, Pf, Hrn)*: 23A Fernhead Road, London W9 3EU ☎ 020 8960 1083

SMITH Colin *(Sax, Gtr, B Gtr, Kbds)*: 21 Kersley Road, Stoke Newington, London N16 0NP ☎ 020 7254 5671

SMITH Dave *(Hrn, T Hrn, Tnd Per, Pf)*: 61A Farleigh Road, London N16 7TD ☎ 020 7241 1909

SNELL David *(Con)*: 29 Eversley Crescent, Winchmore Hill, London N21 1EL ☎ 020 8360 5881, 020 8364 1624 fax

SOTERIOU Mia *(Pf, Voc, Gtr)*: Flat 2, 208 Munster Road, London SW6 6AX ☎ 020 7385 7930

SPEARS Frank: 74 Church Avenue, Broomfield, Chelmsford, Essex CM1 7HA ☎ 01245 441147

SROKA Adrian: 32 Harton Road, Edmonton, London N9 0SG

STRACHAN Matthew *(Kbds)*: Upper Flat, 162 George Lane, South Woodford, London E18 1AY ☎ 020 8989 8600

TAYLOR George *(Voc, B Gtr)*: 10 Park House, Shore Road, London E9 7TB ☎ 020 8985 6483

THOMPSON Barbara, MBE *(Saxes, Flt)*: 48 The Ridgeway, Sutton, Surrey SM2 5JU ☎ 020 8642 3210

TILLEY Louise *(Pf, Kbds, Voc, Vln)*: 3 Brookmans Avenue, Brookmans Park AL9 7AQH ☎ 01707 665140 & fax, 0378 436643 mob

TOMALIN James *(Kbds, Gtr, Bjo, Lute)*: 3 Ferry Road, Teddington, Middlesex TW11 9NN ☎ 020 8977 6506, 0870 0554862

TORRY Clare *(Voc)*: 30 Martindale, East Sheen, London SW14 7AL ☎ 020 8878 2942

TRENCH Fiachra *(Arr, Pf)*: Easton House, Delgany, Co. Wicklow, Ireland ☎ 020 7486 6466

VAN COLLE Sue *(Pf)*: 25C Cannon Place, London NW3 1EH

WAGER Silas: 43 Baronsmere Road, London N2 9QG ☎ 020 8883 3910

WALLACE John *(Arr, Kbds, Voc, Vln)* ☎ 01268 734760, 0410 070804 mob, 01268 571325

WALTER Dick *(Arr, A Sax)*: 18 Speed House, The Barbican, London EC2Y 8AT ☎ 020 7588 0818, 01502 578550

WANG Godfrey *(Arr, Kbds, Pf, Synth)*: 7 Duke Road, London W4 2BA ☎ 020 8995 8773 & fax

WARBECK Stephen *(Pf, Acc)*: 31 Riversdale Road, London N5 2ST ☎ 020 7226 6935, 020 7503 3850 fax

WARREN John *(Arr, Cop, Flt)*: 52 St Oswalds Road, Fulford, York YO1 4PF ☎ 01904 644711

WATTS David *(Arr, Kbds, Md)*: 16 Ribblesdale Road, London N8 7EP ☎ 020 8341 2714, 0976 364770

WELLS Chris *(Per, Dms)*: 67 Oakwood Crescent, Winchmore Hill, London N21 1PA ☎ 020 8360 6046, 0973 113728

WHITTALL Paul: 10 Woolwich Road, Upper Belvedere, Kent DA17 5EW ☎ 01322 438703

WILLCOCK Ian *(Per, Pf, Con)*: 119 Brooke Road, Stoke Newington, London N16 7RJ ☎ 020 8806 4510 & fax

WILLIAMS Graham *(Arr)*: 48 Etheldene Road, London N10 3QH ☎ 020 8365 2952

WILSON Herman *(Arr, Md)*: 8 Melville Court, Goldhawk Road, London W12 9NY ☎ 020 8743 6209

WILSON Jeffery *(Sax, Clt)*: 5 Church Green, Boreham Village, Chelmsford, Essex CM3 3EH ☎ 01245 450192 fax

WISEMAN Debra *(Pf)*: 31 Kingsley Way, London N2 0EH ☎ 020 8455 4030, 020 8455 2700

WOLFSON Richard: Flat 3, 16 Rollscourt Avenue, London SE24 0EA ☎ 020 7733 9503

WYNNE John: 108 Crampton Street, London SE17 3AE ☎ 020 7701 1492

YERSHON Gary *(Pf, Flt)*: 96A York Road, Montpelier, Bristol BS6 5QQ ☎ 0117 955 1717

YOUNG Joseph *(Synth, Voc, Per, Com)*: 39 Havelock Road, Brighton, Sussex BN1 6GL ☎ 01273 507620, 0973 714589 mob

CONCERTINA
SCOTLAND

EAGLESHAM John *(Voc)*: 32 Cardonald Gardens, Glasgow G53 3PG ☎ 0141 883 2792

EYDMANN Stuart *(Vln)*: 2 St Johns Terrace, Edinburgh EH12 6NW ☎ 0131 334 5567

MORTON Robin *(Bod)*: Shillinghill, Temple, Midlothian, Scotland EH23 4SH ☎ 01875 830328

THOUMIRE Simon: 17 Redford Drive, Edinburgh EH13 0BL ☎ 0131 441 3189 & fax

NORTH WEST
BARTRAM Mike *(Man, Gtr, Bod)*: 25 Beech Avenue, Clock Face, St Helens, Merseyside WA9 4LQ ☎ 01744 817127

NORTH EAST
ANDERSON Alistair *(Nor P)*: Mount Hooley, Whittingham, Alnwick, Northumberland NE66 4RN ☎ 0166 574 631

GUMBO Harry *(Mldn, Hmca)*: 25 Hamilton Terrace, Otley, Yorks LS21 1AN ☎ 01943 465436

KERR Sandra *(Gtr, App Dulc, Auto Hrp)*: 5 Heatherleazes, Warkworth, Morpeth, Northumberland NE65 0TZ ☎ 01665 712488 & fax

SHERBURN Chris *(Gtr)*: 51 Colonels Walk, Goole, North Humberside DN14 6HJ ☎ 01405 766352

WHALEY William *(Acc, Gtr, Kbds, Voc)*: 91 Fen Road, Timberland, Lincoln LN4 3SD

MIDLANDS
BISHOP Pamela *(Gtr)*: 35 Waterloo Road, Kings Heath, Birmingham B14 7SD ☎ 0121 244 3513 eve, 0121 414 7095 day

NIXON John *(A Sax, Clt, Db, B Gtr)*: 87 Harvey Road, Buglawton, Congleton, Cheshire CW12 2DH ☎ 01260 274030

TURNER Steve *(Bjo, Man)*: 1-5 Lilly Grove, Beeston, Nottingham NG9 1QL ☎ 0115 943 0333, 0831 265272 mob, 0115 943 0444

SOUTH EAST
OLIVER Charlotte *(Gtr, Bod)*: 47 Freshfield Road, Brighton BN2 2BJ ☎ 01273 603633, 0411 345144

SMEDLEY John *(Kbds, Pf, Acc)*: 8 Bayham Road, Sevenoaks, Kent TN13 3XA ☎ 01732 460171

TOWNSEND Dave *(Acc, Vln, Kbds)*: 22 Swinbourne Road, Littlemore, Oxford OX4 4PQ ☎ 01993 705702

SOUTH WEST
LAYCOCK Timothy: 7 St Rumbolds Road, Shaftesbury, Dorset SP7 8NE ☎ 01747 855284

LONDON
CROFTS Sarah *(Mldn, Rec)*: 7 Northbrook Road, Lewisham, London SE13 5QT ☎ 020 8852 6618

DIGBY Roger: 14C Calthorpe Street, London WC1X 0JS ☎ 020 7837 5476

HARBRON Robert *(Ac Gtr, Bsn)*: 94 Roxeth Green Avenue, South Harrow, Middlesex HA2 8AQ ☎ 020 8357 3261, 0973 717786

MILNE Gerry *(Voc)*: Grove Cottage, Amyand Park Road, Oak Lane, Twickenham, Middlesex TW1 3HE ☎ 020 8892 4621

CONDUCTOR
SCOTLAND

BODDICE Nigel: 7 Orleans Ave, Jordanhill, Glasgow G14 9LA ☎ 0141 959 1825

CONWAY William *(Cel)*: 24 Granby Road, Edinburgh EH16 5NL ☎ 0131 667 4630 & fax

CURRIE John *(Com, Arr)*: The Old School House, Ballintuim, Blairgowrie, Perthshire PH10 7NJ ☎ 01250 886234

LEDGER Philip *(Pf, Org, Hpsd)*: 169 Henderland Road, Bearsden, Glasgow G61 1JD

MORGAN Allan *(Pf)*: 55 Kensington Hall Gardens, Beaumont, West Kensington, London W14 9LT ☎ 020 7610 0129

TAVENER Alan *(Md, Org)*: 172 Hyndland Road, Glasgow G12 9HZ ☎ 0141 357 0052

WILLIAMS Roger *(Hpsd, Org)*: University Music, Powis Gate, College Bounds, Old Aberdeen AB24 2UG ☎ 01224 272570

NORTH WEST
ANDERSON Ewan *(Md, Kbds, Pf, Com)*: 152 Bacup Road, Todmorden, Lancashire OL14 7HG ☎ 01706 819459

BROADBENT Derek *(Arr)*: Andante, 17 Corrance Road, Wyke, Bradford, West Yorks BD12 9LH ☎ 01274 670459

CONDUCTOR - NORTH WEST

CHATWIN David (*Bsn*): Rose Bank, Kinder Road, Hayfield, Stockport SK12 5LE ☎ 01663 744929

EZARD Donald: Allostock Grange, Middlewich Road, Allostock, Knutsford, Cheshire. WA16 9JX ☎ 01565 723366

HARDY Martin: 53 Little Moss, Scholar Green, Stoke-on-Trent, Staffs ST7 3BP ☎ 01782 783558

LOMAX Raymond (*Tym, Per, Md*): 23 The Moorings, Middlewich, Cheshire CW10 9ER ☎ 01606 836292, 07887 556916

NEWSOME Roy: 17 Belmont Drive, Seddons Farm, Bury, Lancs BL8 2HU ☎ 0161 764 2009

ROTH Alec (*Com, Jav Gam*): H13 Peabody Buildings, Wild Street, London WC2B 4BS ☎ 020 7497 3754

SNELL Howard (*Arr, Com*): Barrule Cottage, St Marks, Isle Of Man IM9 3AH ☎ 01624 825775

TROUT Jonathan: Black Rock House, 22 Nan Gells Hill, Bolehill, Wirksworth, Derbys DE4 4GN ☎ 01629 823669

TROWSKI Michael: 20 Mill Brow, Marple Bridge, Stockport, Cheshire SK6 5LL ☎ 0161 449 8148 & fax

NORTH EAST

CHAPMAN Philip: 10 Lancaster Street, Thurnsloe East, Rotherham, South Yorkshire S63 0DZ ☎ 01709 895533

DEWAR David (*Org, Hpsd, Hrn, N Hrn*): Howe Green Cottage, Old Road, Kirbymorside, York YO62 6LP ☎ 01751 432364, 0836 677230, 01439 770807

KELSEY Xenophon (*Hrn, Db*): Ashley House, Ure Bank, Ripon, North Yorkshire HG4 1JG ☎ 01765 602856

PEARCE John (*Md, Vla, Kbds*): 14 Closefield Grove, Monkseaton, Tyne & Wear NE25 8ST ☎ 0191 253 4277

RIGBY John (*Pf, Kbds*): 19 Tanfield Road, Birkby, Huddersfield, West Yorkshire HD1 5HG ☎ 01484 451803

ROBERTS Steven (*Pf, Voc, Eup*): 12 Commercial Street, Heckmondwike, West Yorkshire WF16 9JN ☎ 01924 410316

EAST

BRUNTON Phillip D (*Clt, Sax, Flt*): 66 Shott Lane, Letchworth Gdn City, Herts SG6 1SE ☎ 01462 634586

DAVIDSON Louis (*Md*): 38 Ivel Court, Radburn Way, Letchworth, Herts SG2 2NH ☎ 01462 671005

LAWRENCE Stephen (*Bq Ob*): 8 Supanee Court, French Road, Cambridge CB4 3LB ☎ 01223 564373

WOOD Christopher (*Md, Pf, Kbds*): Flat 1, 34 Clifftown Parade, Southend-on-Sea, Essex SS1 1DL ☎ 01702 338943

MIDLANDS

CASEY Neil (*Tbn, Arr, Md*): 55 Hampton Court Road, Harborne, Birmingham B17 9AG ☎ 0121 241 8179, 0976 356503

DAVIS John (*Tpt, Org*): 97 Windsor Road, Selston, Notts NG16 6JH ☎ 01773 580618

FALLOWFIELD Nicholas (*Vln*): 88 Brook Street, Stourbridge, West Midlands DY8 3UX ☎ 01384 835457

FRANCIS Gregor (*Arr, B Ldr*): 72 Davids Drive, Wingerworth, Chesterfield, Derbyshire S42 6PS ☎ 01246 231 746

HALSEY Simon: 279 High Street, Henley In Arden, Warwicks B95 5BG ☎ 01564 794873

HART David (*Md, Pf*): Hillcrest, 4 Stanton Road, Ludlow, Shropshire SY8 2LR ☎ 01584 873667

JOHNSON Stuart (*Md, Pf*): Northesk Lodge, 16 Northesk Street, Stone, Staffs ST15 8TP ☎ 01785 816053

MAYO Graham (*Pf, Org, Md*): Hollybank 5, The Orchard, Kislingbury, Northants NN7 4BG ☎ 01604 830679

SARGENT Anthony: Springfield House, 115 Greenfield Road, Harborne, Birmingham B17 0EH ☎ 0121 427 9588

SPROSTON Trevor (*Voc, Pf*): 65 High Street, Alsagers Bank, Stoke-on-Trent, Staffs ST7 8BQ ☎ 01782 720956

STOWELL David A (*Com, Eup*): 63, Witton Street, Norton, Stourbridge, West Midlands, DY8 3YS ☎ 01384 378292

VENN Paul (*Pf*): 40 Doris Road, Sparkhill, Birmingham, West Midlands B11 4NE ☎ 0121 449 6786

SOUTH EAST

AVERY John (*Md, Arr, Cop*): 4 Woodside, West Horsley, Leatherhead, Surrey KT24 6NA ☎ 01483 282220

DUMMER Stephen (*Clt, Sax, Pf*): 18 Wentworth Close, Worthing, West Sussex BN13 2LQ ☎ 01903 260592, 01903 260592

GIBSON David (*Org, Hpsd, Pf*): 2 Cuckoo Place, North Waltham, Hampshire RG25 2BJ ☎ 01256 397409

GRAY Simon (*Pf*): 83, Livingstone Road, Hove, East Sussex BN3 3WN ☎ 01273 724817, 0585 833579

HOUGHTON Nicholas (*Org, Hpsd, Pf*): 9 Cromwell Road, Burgess Hill, West Sussex RH15 8QH ☎ 01444 230779, 01444 233699 fax

SHEPHERD Adrian (*Cel*): 5 Corsica Close, Seaford, East Sussex BN25 1BL ☎ 01232 492589

WEBB William Grierson (*Bsn, Pf*): Chase Lodge, 4 Herbert Road, Alum Chine, Bournemouth, Dorset BH4 8HD ☎ 01202 757847

WILLCOCKS Jonathan (*Cel, Pf*): 3 The Square, Compton, Chichester, West Sussex PO18 9HA ☎ 023 9263 1369, 0468 420130 mob, 023 9263 1786 fax

SOUTH WEST

APPLEGATE Simon J (*Cop, Arr, Com*): Anacapri, Havelet, St Peter Port, Guernsey C.I. GY1 1BB ☎ 01481 710472 eve, 01481 728999 eve

BEDDOWS Stanley (*Com, Arr, Pf*): Pollards, Yeoford, Nr Crediton, Devon EX17 5JD ☎ 01363 84097

BESWICK John (*Md, Pf, Org, Flt*): Holly Lodge Road, Clevedon, North Somerset BS21 7JG ☎ 01275 874708, 07775 532187

DIXON-CONSTANTINE Anthony (*Md, Vla*): 9 Kingston Close, Kingskerswell, Newton Abbot, Devon TQ12 5EW ☎ 01803 875995, 0831 793242 mob

HOSE Anthony (*Pf, Hpsd*): Fairfield House, Aberdare, S Wales CF44 7PL ☎ 01685 876675 & fax

JONES Huw (*Flt, Pic, A Flt*): 88 Bryn Catwg, Cadoxton, Neath, Glam SA10 8BH ☎ 01639 630001

LOVELL-JONES Simon (*Voc, Vla, Pf*): 80 Heol Hir, Llanishen, Cardiff CF4 5AB ☎ 029 2073 5434

REED Michael (*Com, Arr, Pf*): Prince Hill House, 165 High Street, Worton, Devizes, Wiltshire SN10 5SE ☎ 01380 729 486, 020 8248 3708 fax

SAGER Sidney (*Com*): 90 Church Road, Horfield, Bristol BS7 8SE ☎ 0117 9425317

SEAMAN David (*Pf, Arr*): 7 St Benedict Crescent, Heath, Cardiff CF4 4DP

LONDON

ALWYN Kenneth (*Com, Arr*): Horelands, Broadford Bridge, Nr Billingshurst, Sussex RH14 9EA ☎ 01403 741348

APSLEY Richard (*Pf, Org*): 3 Chichester Road, Croydon, Surrey CR0 5NQ ☎ 020 8688 8675

BARLOW Alan (*Arr*): Bryn House, 126 Station Road, Ystradgynlais, Swansea SA9 1PL ☎ 01639 849497

BARR Stuart (*Pf, Voc*): 0973 379147

BATEMAN Paul (*Pf, Arr*): 134 Conway Road, Southgate, London N14 7BJ ☎ 020 8882 5375

BEDFORD Stuart (*Pf*): 76 Cromwell Avenue, London N6 5HQ ☎ 020 8348 3001

BICKET Harry: 26 St Marks Crescent, London NW1 7TU

BOWMAN Aubrey (*Pf, Com, Arr*): 7 Brownlow Road, Finchley, London N3 1NA ☎ 020 8346 1429

BRITTEN Tony (*Com, Arr, Kbds*): 1 Alleyn Crescent, West Dulwich, London SE21 8BN ☎ 020 8761 1202

BROOKER Stephen (*Md, Pf, Com, Arr*): 4 Magdalene House, Manor Fields, Putney, London SW15 3LU ☎ 020 8788 3621, 020 8788 2738 fax

BUDDEN Roy (*Md*): 33 Holly Park Gardens, Finchley, London N3 3NG ☎ 020 8346 2080

CHARITY Andrew (*Md, Pf, Org, Com*): 2C St George's Road, Mitcham, Surrey CR4 1EB ☎ 020 8640 9688

CIVIL Peter: 210 Burnt Ash Hill, London SE12 0QE ☎ 020 8857 1297

COLLIS Peter (*Md*): 14 York Close, East Leake, Loughborough, Leicestershire LE12 6HA ☎ 01509 853554

CORBETT Geoffrey (*Arr*): Queens Lodge, 53/55 Queens Avenue, Muswell Hill, London N10 ☎ 020 8340 8441

CROCKFORD Peter (*Pf*): 58 Gladstone Avenue, Wood Green, London N22 6LL ☎ 020 8888 6120

DAVIES Noel (*Pf, Hpsd, Org*): 6C Maitland Place, Lower Clapton Road, London E5 8TR ☎ 020 8985 9138

DAVIS Leonard (*Vla, Vln*): 82 Brightfield Road, London SE12 8QF ☎ 081 852 7962

DAVISON Darrell (*Cel, Com*): 14 Beaumont Road, Purley, Surrey CR8 2EG ☎ 020 8668 5883

DE LA MARTINEZ Odaline (*Com, Pf*): Room 12, Toynbee Studios, 28 Commercial Street, London E1 6LS ☎ 020 7247 2950

DODD Nicholas (*Com*): 22 Bond Gardens, Wallington, Surrey SM6 7LP ☎ 020 8395 8592

DUNK Roderick: 3 Middlebrook Road, Downley, High Wycombe, Bucks HP13 5NH ☎ 01494 445364 fax, 0860 322922 mob

ELLIS Philip (*Per*): 45 Leslie Road, East Finchley, London N2 8BJ ☎ 020 8444 7049

FAJA Angelo: 46 Mayfield Road, North Chingford, London E4 7JA ☎ 020 8529 4257, 020 8529 4257

FARIS Alexander (*Pf*): 118D Regents Park Road, London NW1 8XL ☎ 020 7586 1701

FORRELL Gene (*Pf*): 173 Riverside Drive, Apt. 6A, New York, NY 10024 - 1615, USA ☎+1 212 724 2449, +1 212 724 2530 fax

GARFORTH David (*Org*): 26 Woodbine Terrace, Harrogate HG1 5EG ☎ 01423 529423

GELLHORN, FGSM Peter (*Com, Arr, Pf*): 33 Leinster Avenue, East Sheen, London SW14 7JW ☎ 020 8876 3949

GILL Jonathan (*Md, Pf*): 3 Churston Close, Tulse Hill, London SW2 3BX ☎ 020 8674 3309, 0976 662726

GIPPS Bryan: Egerton House, Egerton, Kent TN27 9BD ☎ 01233 756354

GIPPS Ruth: Tickerage Castle, Pound Lane, Framfield, Uckfield E Sussex TN22 5RT ☎ 01825 890348

GOULDING Fraser (*Rep*): White House, Lynn Road, Walpole Highway, Wisbech, Cambs PE14 7QX ☎ 01945 880314

GRIFFITH Daryl (*Pf, Vln, Arr, Com*): 66 Harrowdene Gardens, Teddington, Middx TW11 0DJ ☎ 020 8943 9148 & fax

HARKCOM Clive (*Arr, Com*): 68 Arundel Road, Sands, High Wycombe, Bucks HP12 4NF ☎ 01494 442942

HEARD Gordon: Sinfonia, 1 The Bridle Path, Allesley Village, Coventry CV5 9PF

HOLMES James (*Pf*): "Galleons Lap", 16 Bilton Grove Avenue, Harrogate N. YORKS ☎ HG1 4HQ, 01423 566854

HUMPHRIS Ian (*Md*): 21 Brackley Road, Chiswick, London W4 2HW ☎ 020 8747 1025

INGLIS Anthony (*Md, Pf*): 11 Woodside Road, Kingston-on-Thames, Surrey KT2 5AT ☎ 020 8547 2313, 020 8974 6297 fax

INGMAN Nicholas (*Arr, Com, Pf*): 10 The Gardens, East Dulwich, London SE22 9QD ☎ 020 8693 5608 & fax

JAMES Haydn (*Md*): 50 Kenton Avenue, Sunbury, Middlesex TW16 5AR ☎ 01932 85050

JENKINS Rae (*Vln, Vla*): Address Unknown

JOPLING Orlando (*Cel*): 7 Chamberlain Street, London NW1 8XB ☎ 020 7586 3730, 0958 714136, 020 7722 3959

KEANE James (*Gtr, Per, Pf, Didj*): 15 Manse Road, Stoke Newington, London N16 7QH ☎ 020 7690 7463, 07957 433117 mob

LEWIS Vic: 4 Baxendale, Totteridge Park, London N20 0EG

MACKERRAS Sir Charles (*Arr*): 10 Hamilton Terrace, London NW8 9UG

MCLEISH Craig (*Arr, Com, Md, B Gtr*): 11 Abbots Avenue West, St Albans, Herts AL1 2JH ☎ 0589 297106

MELIA Roland: Address Unknown ☎ 020 7735 1002 & fax

MOODY Howard (*Pf, Hpsd, Org*): The Old Post Office, Markbeech, Edenbridge, Kent TN8 5NX ☎ 01342 851053 & fax

PAPADOPOULOS Marios (*Pf*): 29 Teignmouth Road, London NW2 4EB ☎ 020 8450 2714, 020 8450 0087

PHELOUNG Barrington (*Com, Cl Gtr, Per, Db*): 41 Imperial Avenue, Westcliff-on-Sea, Essex SS0 8NQ ☎ 01702 342404

PICKTHALL David (*Org, Pf*): The Briars, 63 Ingrave Road, Brentwood, Essex CM15 8AS ☎ 01277 260756

PILBERY Joseph: Allegro, 35 Laurel Avenue, Potters Bar, Herts EN6 2AB ☎ 01707 650735, 0410 480614

PROTHEROE Guy (*Arr*): 8 Alma Square, London NW8 9QD ☎ 020 7286 3944, 020 7289 9081

ROBINSON Peter (*Pf, Org, Hpsd*): 69 Fordwych Road, London NW2 3TL ☎ 020 8452 3448

ROSE Gregory (*Com, Arr*): 57 White Horse Road, London E1 0ND ☎ 020 7790 5883, 020 7265 9170 fax

SALTER Lionel (*Arr, Hpsd, Pf*): 26 Woodstock Road, London NW11 8ER ☎ 020 8458 3568

SHERWOOD Andrew (*Vln*): 2 Pelham Terrace, Lewes, Sussex BN7 2DR ☎ 01273 472548, 01426 243403 pager

SILVER Jeremy (*Pf*): 125 Jerningham Road, Telegraph Hill, London SE14 5NJ ☎ 020 7358 0047, 0973 758148

STARK Peter (*Vln*): Flat 3, 66 Oxgate Gardens, Cricklewood, London NW2 6EB ☎ 020 8208 1709 & fax, 0973 147103 mob

STENT Keith (*Md*): 13 Savona Close, Thornton Hill, London SW19 4HT ☎ 020 8947 1034

SUTHERLAND Iain (*Arr, Com*): 36 Highfield, Oxhey Lane, Carpenders Park, Herts WD1 5DZ ☎ 020 8428 2998 & fax

THOMAS Michael (*Org*): 10 Lynne Court, 20-22 Birdhurst Road, South Croydon CR2 7EA ☎ 020 8681 3477

TILBROOK Jonathan (*Pf*): 9 Ritchings Avenue, Walthamstow, London E17 6LD ☎ 020 8521 7657

TRORY Robert: 51 Tresco Road, London SE15 3PY ☎ 020 7635 7688, 020 7635 6211

VANDERNOOT Joseph (*Pf*): 20 Unwin Mansions, Queens Club Gdns, London W14 9TH ☎ 020 7385 5432

WOOLFENDEN Guy (*Com, Pf*): Malvern House, Sibford Ferris, Banbury, Oxon OX15 5RG ☎ 01295 780679, 01295 788630 fax

YOUNG Emanuel (*Pf, Com, Arr, Per*): 16 Selborne Road, Southgate, London N14 7DH ☎ 020 8886 1144

CONTRA BASSOON

NORTH WEST

LANDER Nick (*Bsn*): 12 Urban Road, Sale, Cheshire M33 7TX ☎ 0161 905 3213

NUNNS Douglas: Mannamead, West Crescent, Windermere, Cumbria LA23 1DQ ☎ 015394 45469

PARTRIDGE John (*Bsn*): 31 Duxford Close, Redditch, Worcs B97 5BY ☎ 0336 787820 pager

MIDLANDS

HARMAN Timothy: Little Paddocks, Whitton, Ludlow, Salop SY8 3DB ☎ 01584 890036

SOUTH EAST

WYVER Sheilia (*Rec*): Hilltop Gravel Hill, Chartham Hatch, Canterbury, Kent CT4 7NH ☎ 01227 730923

SOUTH WEST

HIRD Alison (*Bsn, Rec*): 7A Avalanche Road, Southwell, Portland, Dorset DT5 2DJ ☎ 01305 861481, 01305 822006 & fax

LONDON

MALLETT Timothy (*Bsn*): 49 Heather Park Drive, Wembley, Middlesex HA0 1SP ☎ 020 8902 2052, 020 8533 1372, 0378 794706 mob

WEIR Dominic (*Bsn*): Flat 1B, 63/65 Myddleton Square, London EC1R 1XX ☎ 020 7837 6919

CONTRACTOR

SOUTH WEST

OCCLESHAW Bill (*B Gtr*): Chestnut Barn, North Stoke, Bath BA1 9AT ☎ 0117 9329530

LONDON

BARNWELL Andrew (*Clt, B Clt, Saxes*): 81 Bushy Park Road, Teddington, Middx TW11 9DL ☎ 020 8943 5549, 0860 435661 mob, 020 8977 8284 fax

CAMBRIDGE Maurice: Penthouse One, Gun Place, 86 Wapping Lane, London E1 9RX ☎ 020 7702 9006 fax, 0836 355205 mob

DAKIN Arthur: The Old Post House, Hammond Street, Mappowder, Dorset DT10 2EH ☎ 01258 817802, 0468 943303 mob, 01258 817844

DAVALL Tonia: Spring Cottage, Swallowcliffe, Salisbury, Wilts SP3 5PA ☎ 01747 871767, 01767 683332 fax, 01747 871801

COPYIST

EAST

JACKMAN Diane: Frensham House, Tivetshall, St Margaret, Norwich NR15 2EB ☎ 01379 677319, 0402 399773 mob, 01379 677760

MIDLANDS

PAYNE Richard (*Arr, Hrn*): 22 Heather Court, 48 Russell Court, Moseley, Birmingham B13 8RF ☎ 0121 449 8023, 0973 440905

SOUTH EAST

RAVENSCROFT Hermione (*Pf*): 8 Priory Street, Lewes, E Sussex BN7 1HH ☎ 01273 472682

SOUTH WEST

BURKE Tony (*Wg Tba*): 25 Plymouth Road, Penarth, Cardiff, South Glamorgan CF6 2DA ☎ 029 2070 8519, 029 2046 4666

TRENAMAN Paul: The Cottage, Craig Penllyn, Cowbridge, Vale Of Glamorgan, Wales CF71 7RT ☎ 01446 774355

LONDON

APPLETON Colin (*Voc*): Spring Cottage, Swallow Cliffe, Salisbury, Wilts SP3 5PA ☎ 01747 871808, 01747 871801 fax

BARNARD Ann (*Hrn*): Holly Cottage, Nutley, East Sussex TN22 3LL ☎ 01825 712397, 01825 712103 fax

BARROW Gordon: 5 Draymans Mews, St Pancras, Chichester, West Sussex PO19 4HJ ☎ 01243 539441

BOAKS Georgina: 2 Wakefield Gdns, Upper Norwood, London SE19 2NR ☎ 020 8653 2638

BOUSTEAD Alan (*Com, Arr*): 56 Westminster Gdns., Marsham St, London SW1P 4JG ☎ 020 7828 0303

CAMBY Norma: 39 Tadorne Road, Tadworth, Surrey KT20 5TF ☎ 0173781 2922

CAMPION Beverley-Jane: Bell Farm House, Eton Wick, Windsor, Berks SL4 6LH ☎ 01753 864910

DINSLEY Brian (*A Sax, Clt, Flt*): 78 Edgecombe, South Croydon, Surrey CR2 8AB ☎ 020 8657 5141

FRASER Victor: 14 Kingswood Road, Tadworth, Surrey KT20 5EG ☎ 0173 781 2322, 01737 212275

GIBSON Tim (*Com, Arr*): 43 Peterborough Road, Leyton, London E10 6DL ☎ 020 8539 9027

GRAHAM Mark: Dakota Music Service, Suite 117, Airport House, Purley Way, Croydon CR0 0XZ ☎ 020 8288 3573/4, 020 8288 3546 fax

HODGSON Paul (*Gtr*): 16 Myddelton Park, Whetstone N20 0HX ☎ 020 8445 4045, 020 8343 8296 fax

HUYBENS Joe: 20 Victoria Road, Finsbury Park, London N4 3SQ ☎ 020 7272 4172

IHNATOWICZ Richard (*Sax, Clt, Flt*): 65 Boileau Road, Ealing, London W5 3AP ☎ 020 8991 2572

LAVENDER Peter (*Arr*): 25 Keswick Road, Bexleyheath, Kent DA7 5DU ☎ 020 8304 2302

LOEWENTHAL Martin (*Arr*): 41 Lakeside House, Eaton Drive, Kingston Hill, Kingston-upon-Thames KT2 7QZ ☎ 020 8549 2697

LOWDELL Bob: 29 Montana Road, London SW17 8SN ☎ 020 8672 8020

MEI LING Fiesta: 24 The Loning, Colindale, London NW9 6DR ☎ 020 8205 6734, 020 8205 2191 fax

MORLEY Wayne (*Tpt*): 17 Fairfield Road, London E17 6EW ☎ 020 8923 9380, 0976 959230 mob, 020 8527 8398

RAINE-YOUNG Don (*Db*): 127 Alexandra Park Road, London N22 4UN ☎ 020 8889 4809

RENNIE Michael (*Vln, Com*): 12 Newton Road, Westbourne Grove, London W2 5LS ☎ 020 7229 6070

ROBERTS Keith (*Arr, Pf*): 1 Lakeside, Oatlands Drive, Weybridge, Surrey KT13 9JB ☎ 01932 222910

SHERIDAN Olive: 49 Selvage Lane, Mill Hill, London NW7 3SS ☎ 020 8959 4572

SHILLINGFORD Ronald: 11A Croxted Road, London SE21 8SZ ☎ 020 8670 5225, 020 8244 8596 fax

STANTON Tony: 34 Oak Village, London NW5 4QN ☎ 020 7485 0390, 020 7482 5093 fax

STREATER Jillian (*Ob, Cor, Obdam*): 29 Common Road, Redhill, Surrey RH1 6HG ☎ 01737 768938

THOMAS Howard (*Arr, Com, Kbds*): 1 Averil Grove, London SW16 3ET ☎ 020 8670 2295

TOWNEND Gillian: 44 Eastwick Crescent, Rickmansworth, Herts WD3 2YJ ☎ 01923 720083, 0973 228405 mob, 01923 710587 & fax

COR ANGLAIS

SCOTLAND

BELL Morven (*Ob, Obdam, B Ob*): 39/1 Bryson Road, Edinburgh EH11 1DY ☎ 0131 313 1298

LOGAN Kirstie (*Ob, Obdam*): 32 Falkland Street, Hyndland, Glasgow G12 9QY ☎ 0141 337 1282

MIDLANDS

SAUNDERS Jane (*Ob*): 2 Avon Drive, Moseley, Birmingham B13 3PS ☎ 0121 454 7020, 0976 731331

CORDOVOX

LONDON

NEGUS Irene (*Acc, Pf*): 31 Chesterfield Crescent, Eastwood, Leigh-on-Sea, Essex SS9 5PD ☎ 01702 525316

CORNET

SCOTLAND

ALEXANDER Les (*Tpt, Rh Gtr, Voc*): 97 Land Street, Keith, Banffshire, Scotland AB55 3AP ☎ 015422 7094

HANLEY Clare (*Voc, Kbds*): Flat 1/1 9 Hampden Terrace, Mount Florida, Glasgow G42 9XQ ☎ 0141 632 3695

HOWIE Fiona (*Wh, Hmca, Gtr*): Rockville, Dunlop, By Kilmarnock, East Ayrshire, Scotland KA3 4DQ ☎ 01560 484873

MASON Phil: Shalunt, Isle Of Bute, Scotland PA20 0QL ☎ 01700 841283(t), 01700 505313 fax

THOMSON Allison (*Tpt, Flgl, Voc*): Address Unknown ☎ 01563 535183, 01563 525576

NORTH WEST

BUTLER Gregg (*Rec*): 98, Kirkham Road, Freckleton, Preston, Lancs PR4 1HT

CROSBIE Herbert (*Tpt*): 49 Lheannag Park, Anagh Coar, Douglas, Isle Of Man IM2 2DH ☎ 01624 671346

TUCKER John: 30 Mersey Crescent, Manchester M20 2YJ ☎ 0161 434 2221

WEBSTER Roger (*Tpt, Flgl*): 92 Bence Lane, Darton, Barnsley, S Yorks S75 5DA ☎ 01226 388806

WINTER Martin (*Tpt*): 7 Dingle Close, Tytherington, Macclesfield SK10 2UT ☎ 01625 501833, 01625 430807

NORTH EAST

ARCHER Robert: 2 Mount Ave, Grimethorpe, Barnsley, Yorks S72 7HG

BARRACLOUGH David: 15 Cheviot Close, Hemsworth, Pontefract WF9 4SS ☎ 01977 617522

CLASSICAL
music

The magazine the music professionals read

BROOK Colin: 38 Almscliffe Avenue, Dewsbury, West Yorks WF12 7AR ☎ 01924 451342

HARRISON John (*Tpt, Flgl, T Hrn, Hrn*): 88 Selby Crescent, Darlington, Co Durham DL3 9SD ☎ 01325 357178

HOBBINS Darryl (*Tpt*): 209 Manchester Road, Thurlstone, Sheffield S36 9QS ☎ 01226 765454

KENNEDY Michael: 37 Airstone Road, Askern, Doncaster, South Yorkshire DN6 0QA ☎ 01302 707144

KENNEDY Stewart: 104 Alfred Road, Askern, Doncaster DN6 0PZ ☎ 01302 702729

MARSHALL Richard: 52 Coniston Road, Askern, Doncaster, South Yorkshire DN6 0EH ☎ 01302 701757

MCCANN Phillip: 11 Moor Park Avenue, Beaumont Park, Huddersfield, Yorkshire HD4 7AL ☎ 0148 464 6904

PEACOCK Stephen: 217 Thornes Road, Wakefield, West Yorkshire WF2 8QR

RANDALL Shaun (*Tpt, Flgl, Clt, Flt*): 2 Old Forge Apartments, 39 Newport Road, North Cave, Hull HU15 2NU ☎ 10430 424377

EAST

FIELD Dennis (*Tbn*): 45 Sylvan Avenue, Hornchurch, Essex RM11 2PW ☎ 01708 444215

KERR Bob (*Saxes, Bjo, Eup*) ☎ 01379 384 775, 0385 304753, 01379 384875

WHITEHEAD John: 124 Gubbins Lane, Harold Wood, Romford, Essex RM3 0DP ☎ 01708 348805

MIDLANDS

BOLAN Sean: 8 Dunstall House, Stow Road, Moreton In Marsh, Glos GL56 0DR ☎ 01608 651314

HILL Mel (*Tpt*): 23 Regent Street, West End, Stoke-on-Trent ST4 5HQ ☎ 01782 845044

HYDE Raymond: 10 Cordingley Way, Donnington, Telford, Shropshire TF2 7LW ☎ 01952 612027

TAYLOR David (*Tpt*): The Coppice, Hungry Hill, Cleobury Mortimer, Nr Kidderminster, Worcs DY14 9BG ☎ 01299 270793

YATES Stephen (*Tpt, Con*): 1 Rowan Rise, Barnton, Northwitch, Cheshire CW8 4NZ ☎ 01606 797 19

SOUTH EAST

ETHERINGTON Michael (*Tpt, V Tbn, B Tpt*): 5 Hazelwood Cottages, Knowle Lane, Nr Cranleigh, Surrey GU6 8JP ☎ 01483 272798

HEAP Steve (*Dms*): PO Box 296, Aylesbury, Bucks HP19 3TL ☎ 01296 394411, 01296 392300

OGDEN Rowland (*Bb Bass, Eup, Con, Voc*): Carillion, 8 Lodge Way, Windsor, Berkshire SL4 4DS ☎ 01753 840257

SPENCER Carl (*Tpt, Pf*): Cedar Lodge, Compasses Lane, Cripps Corner, Robertsbridge, East Sussex TN32 5SE ☎ 01580 830292, 0836 258974

SOUTH WEST

CHISHOLM Stephen (*Voc, Tbn*): 24 Gidleys Meadow, Dartington, Totnes, South Devon TQ9 6JZ ☎ 01803 864 873

ELLIS Stephen (*Tpt, Flgl*): 19 Brook Close, Long Ashton, Bristol BS41 9NG ☎ 01275 393906

LEWIS Gwyn (*Tpt, Flgl*): 115 Norfolk Street, Mount Pleasant, Swansea SA2 6JB ☎ 01792 54428

LOWE Angela (*Hrn, Tpt*): 17 Park Way, Midsomer Norton, Nr Bath, Avon BA3 2HD ☎ 01761 418604

LONDON

CANDLER Michael (*Tpt*): 57 The Vale, Feltham, Middlesex TW14 0JZ ☎ 020 8751 4073

CREFFIELD Michael (*Tpt, Sax, Br Sax, Eup*): 2 Rythe Court, Protsmouth Road, Thames Ditton, Surrey KT17 0TE ☎ 020 8398 6527

LANE Steve (*B Ldr*): 32 Kenton Lane, Kenton, Harrow, Middx HA3 8TX ☎ 020 8907 5583

MCDEVITT Chas (*Tpt, Pf*): 7 Moorhouse Cottages, Westerham, Kent TN16 2ES ☎ 01959 565234, 020 7610 7188

STEER Jonathan (*Tpt, S Cnt*): 23 Blake Close, Rainham, Essex RM13 8BE ☎ 01708 552798, 0956 507499, 01708 552798

COW HORN

LONDON

LARKIN Christopher (*Hrn, Wg Tba*): 22 Athenaeum Road, Whetstone, London N20 9AE ☎ 020 8445 3016 & fax, 020 8549 1706

DARABOUKA

LONDON

ALI Cheb (*Bendir*): 13 Radcliffe Avenue, London NW10 5XU ☎ 07957 270433

BARRAK Rony (*Tabla, Per, Dms*): 32 Waddington Way, Upper Norwood, London SE19 3XJ ☎ 020 8653 3634

DHOLAK

MIDLANDS

UBHI Bawit (*Tabla, Kbds*): 40 Lighthorne Road, Solihull B9 12BD, 07771 818143

LONDON

DURVESH Aref (*Tabla, Cong, Per*): 96 Studley Grange Road, London W7 2LX ☎ 020 8579 9450

DIDJERIDU

SOUTH EAST

LORD Didge (*Per, Bong*): 37 South Holmes Road, Roffey, Horsham, West Sussex RH13 6HN ☎ 0976 368316 mob

SOUTH WEST

WALLACE Darren (*Per*): 3 Mayfield Road, Newquay, Cornwall TR7 2DQ ☎ 01637 851389

LONDON

BEAR Shining: 107B Englefield Road, London N1 3LJ ☎ 020 7354 5243

BOAKES Stephen: 27A Warleigh Road, Brighton BN1 4NT

BUCHANAN Wallis: 34 Mervyn Road, London W13 9UN ☎ 020 8579 0227

FARRENDEN Shaun: 125 Ashmore Road, London W9 3DA ☎ 020 8964 0207

IVORY Stewart (*Tbn, Sack*): 3 St Marys Close, Wavendon, Milton Keynes MK17 8LN ☎ 01908 582744

DJEMBE

LONDON

DAVIES Alicia (*Balafon, Eth Per*): 282 Loughborough Park, Brixton, London SW9 8TD ☎ 020 7738 3817, 07666 809898

MILLAR Jhalib (*Tabla, Ind Per, Jaw H, Berimb*): 65 Bayham Street, London NW1 0AA ☎ 020 7388 8205

DOBRO

NORTH WEST

RENNEY Tony (*Gtr, B Gtr, H Gtr*): 2 Derwent Close, Seaton, Workington, Cumbria CA14 1EF ☎ 01900 604045

DOUBLE BASS

SCOTLAND

ALCOCK Anthony (*Pf*): 2/2, 19 Westminster Terrace, Glasgow G3 7RU ☎ 0141 204 0529, 0411 301 253

BLACK Kenneth (*B Gtr, Gtr, Pf*): Granite Villa, Fountain Road, Golspie KW10 6TH ☎ 01408 633146

BORNET Adrian: 11A Cumin Place, Edinburgh EH9 2JX ☎ 0131 667 8659

BROWN Bob (*Voc, B Gtr*): 1 Herndon Court, Broom Road, Newton Mearns, Glasgow G77 5DW ☎ 0141 639 8318

BURNIE Angus: 20 Maisondieu Road, Elgin, Morayshire IV30 1RH ☎ 01343 546525

CAIRNEY Alan *(Vln)*: Woodside Cottage, Gartmore, Near Stirling FK8 3RR ☎ 01877 382298

CALVERT Rebecca: Reidchalmai, Rogart, Sutherland IV28 3XE ☎ 01408 641451

CAMERON Neil: (3/1) 5 Shaftesbury St, Anderston, Glasgow G3 8UN ☎ 0141 204 4868

CAMPBELL John: 68 Queensway, Annan, Dumfrieshire, Scotland DG12 5JU ☎ 0146 120 2655

CARIBE Mario *(El Db, Gtr)*: 3 West Clifton View, East Calder EH53 0HT ☎ 0131 333 1757

COOPER Lindsay *(B Gtr, Tba)*: 50 Kings Road, Portobello, Edinburgh EH15 1DX ☎ 0131 669 8097

CRAIB William *(B Gtr)*: 37 Captains Road, Edinburgh EH17 8HP

CRAWFORD Iain: 2 North Gardner Street, Flat 3/1, Partickhill, Glasgow G11 5BT ☎ 0141 339 3817

CRUICKSHANK Andrew *(Com, B Gtr)*: 21 Partickhill Road, Glasgow G11 5BP ☎ 0141 339 3308, 0589 670899 mob

CUTLER John: 4 Church Road, Giffnock, Glasgow G46 6JU ☎ 0141 638 6938

DAISLEY Patrick: 22 Roxburgh Way, Greenock PA15 4LW ☎ 01475 781653

DARKE Terry: 46 Dumgoyne Drive, Bearsden, Glasgow G61 3AW ☎ 0141 942 4930

DAVIS Sally: Flat 1/L, 77 Marlborough Avenue, Broomhill, Glasgow G11 7BT ☎ 0141 339 5935

DELANEY John: 3 Grange Road, Alloa FK10 1LT ☎ 01259 723741

DONALDSON Fiona: 7/2 West Powburn, Edinburgh EH9 3EN ☎ 0131 667 9237

DOUGAN Anna: 50 Britwell Crescent, Edinburgh EH7 6PT ☎ 0131 669 2807

DREVER Susan *(Cel)*: Easter Strathy, Ardross By Alness, Ross-Shire IV17 0YD ☎ 01349 882757

ELPHINSTONE George: 2 St Peters Place, Spital, Aberdeen AB24 3JZ ☎ 01224 633698

FERGUSON Alan *(Sp Gtr)*: 18 Woodend Drive, Glasgow G13 1QS ☎ 0141 959 4013, 01523 796448, 0141 402 1347

FORREST John: 48 Northfield Broadway, Edinburgh EH8 7PH ☎ 0131 661 3874

FREEMAN Christopher: Flat 0/1, 118 Garthland Drive, Dennistoun, Glasgow G31 2SG ☎ 0141 550 2295

GALE Frank: 19 Cameron Road, Inverness IV3 6PX ☎ 01463 221558

GALLOWAY Walter: 'Schiehallion', East Saltoun, Pencaitland, East Lothian EH34 5EB ☎ 01875 340156

HALYBURTON May *(Bq Db, Vlne)*: c/o 8 Commanders Grove, Braco, Perthshire, Scotland FK15 9PL ☎ 01786 880635

HAMILTON Armour: 7C West Bridge Street, Falkirk, Stirlingshire FK1 5RJ ☎ 01324 631275

HATRICK Thomas *(B Gtr, Gtr, Arr, Cop)*: 22 Heron Court, Clydebank, Glasgow G81 6BB ☎ 01389 890760, 01389 384016 fax, 07931 959307 mob

HILL Derek: 21 Banavie Road, Glasgow G11 5AW ☎ 0141 339 6219

INGLIS David: 6 Varna Road, Jordanhill, Glasgow G14 9NE ☎ 0141 959 2580

KANE Charles: 89 Orchard Road, Edinburgh EH4 2EX ☎ 0131 332 5779

KELLOCK Stanley: Newpark, 14 Well Street, West Kilbride, Ayrshire KA23 9EJ ☎ 01294 823211

KING Jennifer *(Pf)*: 89 Main Street, Aberdour, Fife KY3 0UQ ☎ 01383 860226

KNUSSEN Erik *(B Gtr)*: 127 High Street, Kinross KY13 7AQ ☎ 01577 865310

LEITCH Thomas: 48 Knowe Crescent, Newarthill, Motherwell ML1 5BZ ☎ 01698 833302

LOWIT Peter *(B Gtr)*: 37 Morningside Avenue, Aberdeen AB1 7NY ☎ 01224 319955

LYLE George *(B Gtr)*: 26 Belmont Street, Glasgow G12 8EY ☎ 0141 339 2293

MARGOLIS Harry *(Tbn, B Gtr)*: 14 Heathside Road, Giffnock, Glasgow G46 6HL ☎ 0141 638 0724, 0141 620 0799, 0410 579330

MARRA Michael *(Gtr, Pf, Voc)*: 18 Church Street, Newtyle, Perthshire PH12 8TY ☎ 0182 85 565

MCKAY Paul: Kiln Villa, Kilchattan Bay, Isle Of Bute, Argyllshire PA20 9NW ☎ 01700 831678

MCTIER Ian *(B Gtr)*: The Cottage, Lochgoilhead, Cairndow, Argyll PA24 8AA ☎ 01301 703225 & fax

MEADE Jenni: 5 Albany Place, St. Andrews, Fife KY16 9HH ☎ 01334 477350

NEIL Sarah *(Pf)*: Karroo House, Main Street, Reston, Berwickshire TD14 5JP ☎ 018907 61211

PELLER David *(Pf)*: T/R 32 Barrington Drive, Woodlands, Glasgow G4 9DT ☎ 0141 334 9775

PERCY Roy: 6A Abbeymount, Edinburgh, Scotland EH8 8EJ ☎ 0131 652 1131, 01426 221279

PERRY Ninian: Marrema Cottage, Binniehall Road, Slamannan, Stirlingshire FK1 3BE ☎ 01324 851155, 07005 345383 mob

RAE Michael: 90 Torrisdale Street, Glasgow G42 8PH ☎ 0141 423 8423

RAE Ronald *(Tba)*: The Nest, Portincaple, By Garelochhead G84 0EU ☎ 01436 810752

RANKIN Dorothy *(Cel)*: 36 Glasgow Road, Milngavie, Glasgow G62 6AJ ☎ 0141 956 1724

ROBB Graham *(B Gtr, Com, Pf, Arr)*: Tigh-Na-Beithe, Birnam Glen, Birnam, Dunkeld Perthshire PH8 0FN ☎ 01350 727371

ROBERTSON Lucy *(B Gtr)*: 18 Walker Street, Partick, Glasgow G11 6RE ☎ 0141 334 1000, 0378 168 751 mob

SADDLER Alan *(B Gtr)*: 49 Fairlie Street, Camelon, Falkirk FK1 4NH ☎ 01324 27132

SHIELS Brian *(B Gtr)*: 78 Brunswick Street, Edinburgh, Scotland EH7 5HU ☎ 0131 556 5214

SINTON John *(B Gtr)*: 18 Backcroft, Dunblane FK15 0BN ☎ 01786 823265, 01786 811411

SMYTH Patrick: 22 Seaforth Drive, Kinross KY13 7BD ☎ 01577 863581

STEER John *(Hpsd)*: 16 Dundonald Street, Edinburgh EH3 6RY ☎ 0131 557 3260

STEWART Alistair *(Sax)*: 40 Rankin Drive, Edinburgh EH9 3DE ☎ 0131 667 6888

STRAIN Patricia *(Cel, B Viol, Vlne)*: 40 Thornwood Terrace, Glasgow G11 7QZ ☎ 0141 334 5469

SUTHERLAND Paul: 41 Carmichael Place, Langside, Glasgow G42 9UE ☎ 0141 632 8616

THEWLIS Ron *(Pf)*: 12 Vennacher Avenue, Callander, Perthshire FK17 8JQ ☎ 01877 331759 & fax

TUNNAH James: 24 Hyvot Terrace, Edinburgh EH17 8NX ☎ 0131 664 3851

VENTERS Philip: 94 Old Dumbarton Road, Yorkhill, Glasgow G3 8PZ ☎ 0141 357 1627

WHITTAKER Leah *(B Gtr, Tbn, Gtr, B Viol)*: Room 231, Baird Hall, Sauchiehall Street, Glasgow, Scotland G2 3LN ☎ 0141 332 6415, 07771 995 893 mob, 01431 821380

WHITTAKER Ruth *(Vadag, Con, Ea Stg)*: 48 Gartymore, Helmsdale, Sutherland KW8 6HJ ☎ 014312 380

WILSON Colin *(B Gtr)*: 12 Claremont Road, Leith, Edinburgh EH6 7NE ☎ 0131 554 1377, 0468 563138

WILTSHIRE Peter *(B Gtr)*: Stanneryhaugh, By Laurencekirk, Kincardineshire, Scotland AB30 1ES ☎ 01561 340503

ZAPPULLA Fausto *(El Db, Ac Gtr)*: 77 Briarcroft Drive, Robroyston, Glasgow, Scotland G33 1RD ☎ 0141 558 3841

NORTH WEST

BAGSHAW David: 43 Marsden Road, Romiley, Cheshire SK6 4AS ☎ 0161 430 4355

BAILEY Peter: 4 Kenmore Drive, Timperley, Altrincham, Cheshire WA15 8QN ☎ 0161 980 3012

BOX Jeffrey: 49 Appleton Road, Hale, Altrincham, Ches WA15 9LP ☎ 0161 928 5616

BROADLEY Jack (*B Gtr*): 42 Dunstable Street, Levenshulme, Manchester M19 3BU ☎ 0161 224 5097

BUCKLEY Graham (*Bjo, Gtr*): 17 Woodend Lane, Hyde, Cheshire SK14 1DT ☎ 0161 368 8769

CANSDALE Roy: 11 Low Garth, Kendal, Cumbria LA9 5NZ ☎ 01539 735432

CAPP David (*B Gtr*): 92 Mile End Lane, Stockport, Cheshire SK2 6BN ☎ 0161 483 8509

COOPER Alan (*B Gtr*): 1 Beverley Road, Bolton, Lancs BL1 4DU ☎ 01204 840426

COSTELLO Stephen (*B Gtr*): The Gatehouse, Barkers Lane, Snainton, Scarborough YO13 9BG ☎ 01723 859362

DAY Brian (*B Gtr, Pf*): Fernlea, Oak Ave, Romiley, Cheshire SK6 4DN ☎ 0161 430 6940

DUFFY Robert (*B Gtr*): 63 Thornton Road, Liverpool L16 2LP ☎ 0151 722 7716

DUFTY Nigel (*B Gtr, Gtr*): 40 Hazelmere Close, Hartford, Northwich, Cheshire CW8 1QZ ☎ 01606 781908

DUPUY Nicki (*B Gtr*): 33B Clarendon Road, Manchester M16 8LB ☎ 0161 861 7391

ESCREET Michael (*Bq Db*): 11 Wellington Road, Fallowfield, Manchester M14 6FA ☎ 0161 225 8085

FLOWERS Frank: 5 Clovelly Road, Chorlton, Manchester M21 2XW ☎ 0161 881 4607

FORTUNE Douglas (*B Gtr*): 21 Keswick Drive, Frodsham, Cheshire WA6 7LT ☎ 01928 733465

FRAMPTON Ashley (*Pf, Voc*): 36 Mill Lane, Ness, South Wirral L64 4BQ ☎ 0151336 1506

GIBBON Matthew: Villas De Aljamar, M6, Casa 125, Tomares 41940, Sevilla, Spain ☎ 01630 3813

GORDON David: 2 Brompton Road, Rusholme, Manchester M14 7GA ☎ 0161 225 9381

HAMMERTON Daniel: 16 North Sudley Road, Liverpool L17 0BG ☎ 0151 728 7533

HAN Yi: Thorngate, 54 Ack Lane East, Bramhall, Stockport, Cheshire SK7 2BY ☎ 0161 439 8251

HINDE Carl: 31 Redruth Avenue, Carr Mill, St Helens, Merseyside WA11 9EY ☎ 01744 26764

HUTCHINSON Raymond: 5 Ashdown Drive, Greasby, Wirral, Merseyside M49 3QU ☎ 0151 677 0443

KENWORTHY Reg: 135 Stocks Lane, Stalybridge, Cheshire SK15 2NU ☎ 0161 303 7553

LLOYD-EVANS Owen (*B Gtr, Cel*): Brynllys, 103 Caellepa, Bangor, Gwynedd, Wales LL57 1HH ☎ 01248 352634

LYNANE David: 17, Heathcote Avenue, Heaton Norris, Stockport, Cheshire SK4 2QF ☎ 0161 432 9478

MANSON James (*Arr, Com, B Gtr*): 28, Santiago Street, Rusholme., Manchester M14 4BL ☎ 0161 225 6755

MARTIN Andrea: 39 Gorsehill Road, New Brighton, Wirral L45 9JA ☎ 0151 637 1737

MCCORMICK John (*B Gtr*): 31 Holmefield Road, Liverpool L19 3PE ☎ 0151 427 3565

MCGEOCH Roy: 16, Hodge Lane, Hartford, Northwich, Cheshire CW8 3AG ☎ 01606 77326

MILES Matthew (*B Gtr*): Address Unknown ☎ 020 7704 1351

MORGAN A (*Con*): Chevin House, 33 Avenue Road, Duffield, Derbys DE56 4DW ☎ 01332 840391, 0976 758727

MUSKETT John (*Gtr*): 20 Lowside Avenue, Bolton, Lancashire BL1 5XQ ☎ 01204 492942

NEWMAN Jake (*B Gtr*): 57 Hulmes Road, Clayton Bridge, Manchester M40 1GP ☎ 0161 681 0658

PEAK Edward (*Pf*): 70 Mill Hill Road, Irby, Wirral, Merseyside L61 4XF ☎ 0151 648 2492

PHILLIPS Ann: 9 Lindop Road, Hale, Altrincham, Cheshire WA15 9DZ ☎ 0161 980 7303

RILEY Stuart F (*Gtr, B Gtr*): 2 Hazelbank Avenue, Withington, Manchester M20 3ES ☎ 0161 445 9851

SCHIRMER Beatrice: 162 Egerton Road North, Whalley Range, Manchester M16 0DB ☎ 0161 881 9553

SHAFTOE Miriam: 9 Vincent Avenue, Flat 2, Chorlton, Manchester M21 9GR ☎ 0161 860 6097

SHIMELL A: 13 Coniston Road, High Lane, Stockport, Cheshire SK6 8AW ☎ 01663 763842

SMITH Colin (*Db*): 46 Lynnwood Road, East Didsbury, Manchester M19 1RJ

SNEAKY (*B Gtr, Cel*): 10 Trafalgar Road, Eccles, Salford M6 8SD ☎ 0161 707 8021, 01523 497435

STORER Daniel: 9 Groby Road, Chorlton, Manchester M21 8AF ☎ 0161 882 0098

STREET Carol: 6 Hadfield Road, Hadfield, Glossop, Derbyshire SK13 2AG ☎ 01457 869699

TANKARD Robin (*Tba, Sou*): Flat 2, 17 Botanic Road, Liverpool, Merseyside L7 5PX ☎ 0151 261 0857, 0151 708 9998 fax

THACKERAY Jonathan: 6, Victoria Grove, Fallowfield, Manchester M14 6BF ☎ 0161 224 3749

THOMAS Edward (*B Gtr, Gtr*): 14 Birch Road, Oxton, Birkenhead L43 5UA ☎ 0151 653 8626

THOMSON Stuart (*Pf*): 10 Everett Road, Withington, Manchester M20 3DQ ☎ 0161 445 1545, 0976 851629

TRAVERSI Francis (*B Gtr*): Glynton, Top Llan Road, Glan Conway, Conway LL28 5NP ☎ 01492 580216

VAUX Derek: Cablecroft, Cable Street, Formby, Merseyside L37 3LU ☎ 01704 831172 & fax

VICKERS Peter (*Sou, Dms*): 14 Osborne Street, Preston, Lancashire PR1 8PN ☎ 01772 822787

WALDOCK Richard (*E Gtr, B Gtr*): 3 Silverwood Avenue, 7 Stockton Road, Chorlton, Manchester M21 8BN ☎ 0161 860 5344, 0411 386978

WALKOM Charles (*B Gtr*): 2 The Riffel, Woolton Park, Woolton, Liverpool L25 6DR ☎ 0151 428 4821

WALLIS Geoff: Marsh Lane House, Nantwich, Cheshire CW5 8PH ☎ 01270 610116

WANKLYN Diana: 6 Gordon Place, Withington, Manchester M20 3LD ☎ 0161 445 8337

WEARING David (*B Gtr, Dms*): 24 Burlington Street, Ulverston, Cumbria LA12 7JA ☎ 01229 583852

WHITTAKER Eric: Flat 30, Chepstow House, Chepstow Street, Manchester M1 5JF ☎ 0161 236 9233

WILLIAMS Douglas: 137 Berwick Avenue, Heaton Mersey, Stockport, Cheshire SK4 3AT ☎ 0161 431 9953

WILLIAMS Gladys: 36 Maple Road, Brooklands, Manchester M23 9HW ☎ 0161 973 2622

WILLIAMS Leonard: 18 Sunbourne Road, Liverpool, Merseyside L17 7BL ☎ 0151 727 5675

WILLMOTT Peter (*B Gtr*): 71 Woburn Drive, Hale Barns, Altrincham, Cheshire WA15 8NE ☎ 0161 980 3381

WORSLEY Dominic: 14 Edgefold Road, Worsley, Manchester M28 7QF ☎ 0161 790 4746, 0411 360706 mob

WRIGHT Mike: Stancil House, Barn Furlong, Great Longstone, Bakewell, Derbyshire DE45 1TB ☎ 01629 640136

NORTH EAST

ALLAN Haydn (*B Gtr*): 29 Summerfield Road, Dronfield, Sheffield S18 6GZ ☎ 01246 414595

ANDERSON Graham (*B Gtr*): 119 Dryden Road, Gateshead, Tyne & Wear NE9 5TS ☎ 0191 487 8639

BARNABY Peter: 35 High Holme Road, Louth, Lincs LN11 0EX ☎ 01507 601374

BEEVER Ian: 14 Lynton Avenue, Broom, Rotherham S60 3HE ☎ 01709 363186

BRADLEY Joanne: Upper Red Brink Farm, Red Brink Lane, Hubberton, Halifax HX6 1PA ☎ 01422 839700, 01422 835943

BROWN Lancelot (*Gtr, Con, B Ldr*): 46 Hilda Park, South Pelaw, Chester Le Street, Co Durham DH2 2JP ☎ 0191 388 2986

BURGAN A: 42 The Dales, Cottingham, E Yorks HU16 5JS ☎ 01482 3845902

CARRILLO-GARCIA Roberto (*Gtr, Vadag*): 12 Swaledale Gardens, H Heaton, Newcastle-upon-Tyne NE7 7TA ☎ 0191 266 7378

CHAPMAN William (*B Gtr*): 15 Croft Terrace, Jarrow, Tyne & Wear NE32 5BN ☎ 0191 489 7980

CLARKE Richard: Address Unknown

CLOW Dionne *(Cel)*: 29 Holly Street, Wakefield, West Yorkshire WF2 9AU ☎ 01924 365734

COOPER Philip *(B Viol)*: 5 Kings Croft Gardens, Leeds LS17 6PB ☎ 0113 2685123

CROCKER Stephen *(B Gtr)*: 11 Gledhow Park Drive, Leeds, West Yorkshire LS7 4JT ☎ 0113 2624060

DICKENSON Andrew: 77 Emerson Avenue, Linthorpe, Middlesbrough, Cleveland TS5 7QJ ☎ 01642 816790

ELLIS David *(Tba, B Gtr)*: 86 Freehold Street, Spring Bank, Hull, North Humberside HU3 1RD ☎ 01482 3228672

ELSEY David *(E Gtr, B Gtr)*: 10 Holme Farm Close, Great Coates, Grimsby, Lincs DN37 9NZ ☎ 01472 882254

FERN Frank: 238 Newbold Road, Chesterfield S41 7AJ ☎ 01246 76426

FINDLEY David: 194 Burncross Road, Chapeltown, Sheffield S35 1SG ☎ 0114 2615968

FLEMING Mike *(Kbds)*: 15 New Holles Court, Worksop, Nottinghamshire S80 2LU ☎ 01909 474553

GOTT Kevin: 32A Whitecliffe Lane, Ripon, N Yorks HG4 2JL ☎ 01765 602019

HARPER William: 30 Swaledale Gardens, High Heaton, Newcastle-upon-Tyne 7 NE7 7TA ☎ 0191 266 7945

HAWKINS Annie: 85 Parkside Road, Meanwood, Leeds, W. Yorks LS6 4NA ☎ 0113 294 7151

HESLOP Thomas *(B Gtr)*: 1 Fergusons Lane, Newcastle-on-Tyne 5, Tyne & Wear NE15 7PL ☎ 0191 274 6104

HEYWOOD Derek *(B Gtr)*: 28 Holton Mount, Holton Le Clay, Grimsby DN36 5EQ ☎ 01472 82 7910

JOHNSON Blyth: Clovelly, 4 Holly Road, North Shields, Tyne & Wear NE29 9BU ☎ 0191 257 9289

JONES Graham *(B Gtr)*: 19 Carterknowle Road, Sheffield, South Yorks S7 2DW ☎ 0114 2586890

JOVANOVIC Vera: Burnham House, Park Street, Ripon, North Yorkshire HG4 2BY ☎ 01756 608272

KENNEDY Michael *(B Gtr)*: 97 Wickersley Road, Rotherham, South Yorkshire S60 3PU ☎ 01709 364448

LAING Alan: Barnham Lodge, Townend Road, Walkington, East Yorks HU17 8SY ☎ 01482 870210

LINDLEY Richard: 4 Primley Park Walk, Alwoodley, Leeds LS17 7LB ☎ 0113 2698416

MARLEY Kenneth *(B Gtr, Arr)*: 14 Victoria Street, Lindsley, Huddersfield HD3 3ED ☎ 01484 516185

MAUGHAN Karen *(B Gtr)*: Woodburn, 26 Woodland Terrace, Darlington, County Durham DL3 8NU ☎ 01325 252583

MILBURN Douglas *(B Gtr)*: 1 Derwent Gardens, Gateshead, Tyne & Wear NE9 5XQ ☎ 0191 421 5395

MILLER Paul: 15 Alaska Place, Leeds LS7 4LT ☎ 0113 2628763

MOORIN Owen *(B Gtr)*: 8 Colindale, Boston, Lincs PE21 9AZ ☎ 01205 353301

MUNRO Duncan: 3 Beechfield Road, Gosforth, Newcastle-upon-Tyne 3, Tyne & Wear NE3 4DR ☎ 0191 285 8884

NEWMAN Jack: 7 St. Christophers Road, Humberston, Grimsby, South Humberside DN36 4ED ☎ 01472 813656

NEWTON Raymond *(B Gtr, Cel, Bjo, B Ldr)*: 6 Springwell Road, Sunderland SR3 4DG ☎ 0191 528 5879

PARKER Dave: Cross Fell House, Langley Park, Durham DH7 9YF ☎ 0191 373 4599

PASSEY Francis: 2, St Leonards Court, Westgate, Pickering, N.Yorks YO18 8DN ☎ 01751 473524

RATHMELL Walter *(B Gtr)*: Bradford Tradesmens Homes, 45 Lily Croft, Heaton Road, Bradford, West Yorkshire BD8 8QY ☎ 01274 548364

RIVRON Dominic *(Cel, B Gtr)*: Spring Cottage, Mill Lane, Bellerby, Nr Leyburn, North Yorkshire DL8 5QN ☎ 01969 624292

SADLER Claire: 12 Prospect Street, Eccleshill, Bradford BD10 8AD ☎ 01274 402123

SEATON Alan *(B Gtr)*: Flat 3, 63 Highbury, West Jesmond, Newcastle-upon-Tyne NE2 3LN ☎ 0191 2815903, 0191 281 5903

SHAW Martin *(Gtr)*: 16 Ancaster Avenue, Bricknell Ave, Hull HU5 4QS ☎ 01482 3443082

SHEARN David: 14 Auckland Avenue, Loxley, Sheffield S6 6QA ☎ 0114 232 4674

SHOULDER Michael *(B Gtr, Gtr)*: Beechburn Cottage, High Grange, Crook DL15 8AZ ☎ 01388 768668

SLEE Nigel *(E Gtr)*: 16 Armley Pk Road, Leeds LS12 2PG ☎ 0113 231 0629

STABLES Nicola: 76 Netherlea Drive, Netherthong, Holmfirth, West Yorkshire HD7 2YX ☎ 01484 683182

STUART Peter *(B Gtr)*: 3 Glebe Drive, Seaham, Co. Durham SR7 0PD ☎ 0191 581 3008

THOMPSON Bernard *(Sax, Clt, Flt, Gtr)*: 11 Deansfield Close, Armshorpe, Doncaster, South Yorks DN3 3BZ ☎ 01302 835489

TILLER Richard: Address Unknown

TOFT Norman *(B Gtr)*: 14 Lockwood Avenue, South Anston, Sheffield S25 5GQ ☎ 01909 564873

WALKER Lewis *(Voc)*: 11 Rowan Tree Dell, Totley, Sheffield S17 4FL ☎ 0114 2368232

WARIN William *(B Gtr)*: 7 Nether Close, Wingernorth, Chesterfield S42 6UR ☎ 01246 233133

WITHAM Anthony *(B Gtr)*: 48330 St. Etienne, V.F., France ☎ 01033 6645 7464

YOUNG John *(Bjo, Gtr)*: 35 Beechwood Avenue, Harlow Green, Low Fell, Gateshead NE9 6PP ☎ 0191 487 7057

ZEALEY Barry *(B Gtr)*

EAST

ARNOLD Alan *(B Gtr)*: Hazeldene, Halstead Road, Eight Ash Green, Colchester CO6 3PU ☎ 01206 210348

BAKER Peter: 53 Recreation Ground, Stansted Mountfitchet, Essex CM24 8BD ☎ 01279 814865

BARKER John *(Clt)*: 46 Larkman Lane, Norwich NR5 8TY ☎ 01603 451103

BIBBY David: 'Hedgerows', Heydon Road, Aylsham, Norfolk NR11 6QT ☎ 01263 732249

BLANNIN Peter: 49 West Street, Hertford SG13 8EZ ☎ 01992 583691

BRIAN B.B. *(B Gtr, Org, Hpsd, Pf)*: Suncote, Rangell Gate, Low Fulney, Spalding, Lincs PE12 6EW ☎ 01775 768 249

CANTLON Kelly *(B Gtr)*: 47 St Pauls Road, Hemel Hempstead, Herts HP2 5DD

CHEESWRIGHT Donald *(B Gtr, Tba)*: 60 Sidegate Lane, Ipswich, Suffolk IP4 4JA ☎ 01473 724849

CROSS Kenneth: 2A Chartfield Road, Cherry Hinton, Cambridge CB1 4JY ☎ 01223 244642

DAY John *(Gtr)*: 36 Graham Mansions, Graham Road, London E8 1EY ☎ 020 8986 3827

DONALD Keith *(B Gtr)*: 433 Milwards, Harlow, Essex CM19 4SR ☎ 01279 431219

DOWLEN Olly *(Gtr, Mldn, Bjo)*: 69 Oakdale, Welwyn Garden City, Herts AL8 7QP ☎ 01707 328434

DYTHAM Nicholas *(Sou, Eup)*: 8 Frankston Avenue, Stony Stratford, Milton Keynes MK11 1DR ☎ 01908 563629 eve, 01908 055232 day

EVANS Laurence *(El Db, Gtr)*: 69 Woodhead Drive, Cambridge CB4 1FG

FITZGERALD Paul *(B Gtr, Gtrr)*: 86 Bluebell Road, Norwich NR4 7LQ ☎ 01603 259173

FOX Brian *(B Gtr)*: 24 Sotheron Road, Watford WD2 2QA ☎ 01923 467269, 0421 532220

HOLGATE David *(B Gtr)*: 18 Cow Hill, Norwich NR2 1HD ☎ 01603 611911

KACAL Nicholas *(B Gtr, Kbds, Gtr)*: c/o 189 Colchester Road, Ipswich, Suffolk IP4 4SL ☎ 0973 718 362

LEWINS Stephen *(E Gtr, Hmca, Sl Gtr)*: 2A Manor Parade, Hatfield, Herts AL10 9JS ☎ 01707 751208

MCCLEAN Sidney: 3 Posford Court, Mill Road, Colchester, Essex CO4 5LY ☎ 01206 854435

MORRIS David *(B Gtr, Gtr, Arr, Cop)*: 226 Thorpe Hall Avenue, Thorpe Bay, Essex SS1 3SE ☎ 01702 588304

PAMPLIN Jack *(B Gtr)*: 39 Grange Road, Bushey, Herts WD2 2LQ ☎ 01923 225313

PAYNE Bob: 125 Hartforde Road, Boreham Wood, Herts WD6 5JR ☎ 020 8953 3866

PEDERSEN Thomas (*B Gtr*): Flat B, 107 Havelock Road, Luton, Bedfordshire LU2 7PP ☎ 01582 483290, 0973 461396 mob

PEET Nigel: Tally-Ho Cottage, Fox Hill, St. Cross, Harleston, Norfolk IP20 0NU ☎ 01986 782520

SYKES Miranda (*E Gtr, B Gtr, Voc*): Emmanuel Cottage, Starlode Drove, W. Pinchbeck, Spalding, Lincs PE11 3TD ☎ 01775 640476

TOMS Phillip (*B Gtr, Pf, Kbds*): 19 Bale Close, Westlands, Lexden, Colchester, Essex CO3 5XP ☎ 01206 562736 & fax, 0410 356143 mob

WATERS Bryan (*B Gtr*): 195 Sandpit Lane, St Albans, Hertfordshire AL4 0BT ☎ 01727 52362

WESTON Harvey: 34 Sweet Briar, Welywn Garden City, Herts AL7 3DY ☎ 01707 323943, 01707 323943

WOODWARD Edward: 68 Larkins Close, Baldock, Herts SG7 5DG ☎ 01462 895574

WRIGHT Sally Jane: The River House, Leaside, Harpenden AL5 5AL ☎ 01582 767994, 0468 881447 mob

MIDLANDS

ATKINSON Julian: 86 Oxford Road, Moseley, Birmingham B13 9SQ ☎ 0121 449 5902

BAINES Colin (*Pf, Md*): 49 Church Road, Moseley, Birmingham B13 9ED ☎ 0121 449 2033

BAKER Peter: 44 Breach Road, Hugglescote, Leicester LE67 3SA ☎ 01530 836975

BARGH Andrew: 35, Winleigh Road, Handsworth Wood, Birmingham B20 2HN ☎ 0121 554 5461

BARNSLEY Frederick (*B Gtr*): 30 Melrose Road, Birchfield, Birmingham B20 3ES ☎ 0121 356 5664

BARROW Geoffrey (*B Gtr*): 79 Woodcote Avenue, Kenilworth, Warwickshire CV8 1BG ☎ 01926 855955

BEAN Alison (*Pf*): 184 Ratcliffe Road, Sileby, Loughborough LE12 7QB ☎ 01509 814856

BRADSHAW Steve (*Org*): 8 Reservoir Road, Cofton Hackett, Birmingham B45 8PN ☎ 0121 445 2888

BRAIME Hilary (*B Gtr*): 44 Ashfield Drvie, Moira, Swadlincote, South Derbyshire DE12 6HQ ☎ 01530 411952

CHEETHAM Carole: 15 Victoria Road, Draycott, Derbyshire DE72 3PS ☎ 01332 874234

COLE William (*Bjo, Gtr*): 238 Queens Road, Beeston, Nottingham NG9 2BG ☎ 0115 9251969

COLEMAN Bill (*B Gtr*): Cedar Cottage, Wing, Rutland LE15 8RR ☎ 01572 737280 & fax, 0802 254175 mob

COX Peter (*B Gtr, Arr, Com, Cop*): 27 Abington Park Crescent, Northampton NN3 3AD ☎ 01604 37374

DANCY Jonathan: 14 Morgan Road, Reading RG1 5HG ☎ 01734 873095

DOUST Mark: 10 Stanley Avenue, Harborne, Birmingham B32 2HB ☎ 0121 420 2684

FAHY Sally: 13 Avenue Road, Kings Heath, Birmingham B14 7TH ☎ 0121 624 2271

FALCONER Earl: Fernscan Limited, No.1. Andover Street, Digbeth, Birmingham B5 5RG ☎ 0121 633 4742

FAUTLEY Martin (*B Gtr*): 32 Main Road, Sheepy Magna, Atherstone CV9 3QR ☎ 01827 880606

FOSTER Dave (*B Gtr*): 1 Gorsty Bank, Lichfield, Staffordshire WS14 9UB ☎ 0976 434493

FOSTER Justin (*Gtr, Per*): West Gable And Shrewsbury Road, Edgmond, Shropshire TF10 8HT ☎ 01952 810671, 01952 810671

GALEY Steve (*Flt, Voc*): 10 Walmead Croft, Harborne, Birmingham B17 8TH ☎ 0121 429 3578, 0121 422 2471

GOODCHILD Mark: 3 Rear Cottage, Withy Bed Green, Alvechurch, Birmingham B48 7PN ☎ 0121 445 3876

GRAY John (*Pf, Hpsd*): 14 Beaconsfield Ave, Rugby CV22 6BY ☎ 01788 336686, 01788 336687

GRAY Paul (*B Gtr*): 31 Beech Avenue, Mapperley, Nottingham NG3 5JW ☎ 0115 9208213

GREEN Mike (*B Gtr*): 27 Holly Road, Handsworth, Birmingham B20 2BU ☎ 0121 240 4707, 07788 784684

GROSSE Paul (*B Gtr*): 71 Glengarry Way, Sinfin, Derby DE24 9NP ☎ 01332 608164

GUNAL Ugurtan (*Pf, Org, B Gtr, Voc*): 14 Falconers Rise, East Hunsbury, Northampton NN4 0RJ ☎ 01604 701228

HAMILTON Peter: The Meadows, Wallswood, Baldwins Gate, Newcastle Under Lyme, Staffordshire ST5 5LD ☎ 01782 680179

HANNAN Lawrence: 44 Mount Pleasant Road, Shrewsbury, Shropshire SY1 3BJ ☎ 01743 246770

HARPER Derek: 12 Oaklands Close, Hill Ridware, Nr Rugeley, Staffs WS15 3RJ ☎ 01543 491415

HILL Thomas Alan (*B Gtr*): 5 The Orchard Lea, Droitwich Spa, Worcs WR9 7AL ☎ 01905 795006

HUDSON Noel: 173 Sellywood Road, Bournville, Birmingham B30 1TJ ☎ 0121 472 5954

HURTLEY Don: 23 Innis Road, Canley Gardens, Coventry, West Midlands CV5 6AX

KIRKLAND Andrew: 48 Barkby Thorpe Lane, Thurmaston, Leicester LE4 8GP ☎ 0116 269 3252

KNIGHT Paul (*B Gtr, Voc*): 58, Green Lane, Coventry, West Midlands CV3 6DE ☎ 024 7641 8932

LARGE Ronald: 28 Old Barn Close, Gnosall, Stafford ST20 0DY ☎ 01785 822814

LILLEY Terry (*B Gtr, Gtr, Synth*): 6 Hazelslade Road, Rugeley Road, Hazel Slade, Cannock, Staffs WS12 5PH ☎ 0121 440 6913

LINES Trevor (*B Gtr, La Per, Crum*): 11 King Edward Gardens, Birmingham, West Midlands B20 2BE ☎ 0121 551 5048

LITVINOFF Adrian (*B Gtr*): Green Farm House, Church Lane, Whitnash, Leamington Spa, Warwickshire CV31 2HH ☎ 01926 424206

MILLAR Thomas: 163 Galton Road, Bearwood, Warley, West Midlands B67 5JT ☎ 0121 429 3250

OSBORN Barbara: 136 All Saints Road, Kings Heath, Birmingham B14 6AT ☎ 0121 444 1811

PARSONS Aneurin (*B Gtr, Gtr*): 71 Knights Court, Wellingborough, Northants NN8 4DF ☎ 01933 278 716

PEARSON Geoff (*B Gtr*): Millers Cottage, Mill Lane, Sudbury, Ashbourne Derbys DE6 5GX ☎ 01283 820010

PHILLIPS Simon: 41 Holifast Road, Wylde Green, Sutton Coldfield, West Midlands B72 1AP ☎ 0121 682 2754

ROBINS Andrew: 8 Cladswell Lane, Cookhill, Alcester, Warks B49 5JT ☎ 01527 893 029

ROWLEY Ted (*B Gtr*): 136 Blackhalve Lane, Wednesfield, West Midlands WV11 1AA ☎ 01902 732002

SPENCE John (*B Gtr*): 400 Carlton Hill, Carlton, Nottingham NG4 1JA ☎ 0115 9612153

STAUNTON Christopher: 238 Alcester Road South, Kings Heath, Birmingham B14 6DR ☎ 0121 444 8014

STEEL Brian (*B Gtr*): 7 Boleyn Close, Warwick CV34 6LP ☎ 01926 332599

TATTERSDILL John: 57 Russell Road, Birmingham B13 8RB ☎ 0121 449 0252

TEAGUE Donna: Cherry Trees, Tilstock, Whitchurch, Shrops SY13 3NR ☎ 01948 880679

THWAITES Leonard (*B Gtr*): Flat One, Hardwicke House, Abbey Road, Great Malvern, Worcs WR14 3HH ☎ 01684 575605

TOMLYN Peter (*Ac Gtr, B Gtr, Bjo*): 12 Salisbury Street, Loughborough, Leicester LE11 1HF ☎ 01509 213233

VERNON Richard (*B Gtr*): Westfield, 94 Lancaster Road, Newcastle Under Lyme, Staffs ST5 1DS ☎ 01782 620703

WALKER David: 6 The Pastures, Duffield, Belper, Derbyshire DE56 4EX ☎ 01332 840644

WALL Charles: 54 Greenhill Road, Moseley, Birmingham B13 9SS ☎ 0121 449 4423

WALLEY Brett (*B Gtr*): 313, Stone Road, Stafford ST16 1LB ☎ 01785 240387

WALTERS Julian: 83 Ravenshurst Road, Harborne, Birmingham B17 9DR ☎ 0121 427 1536

WALTERS Keith (*Voc*): 22 South Place, Ball Green, Staffs ST6 8AY ☎ 01782 865274, 01782 865274

WHEATLEY George (*B Gtr, Gtr*): 9 Bank Street, Tunstall, Stoke-on-Trent ST6 5HW ☎ 01782 826712

WORTHINGTON Howard: Shrubbery Cottage, Hinstock, Nr Market Drayton, Shropshire TF9 2SY ☎ 01952 550738

WRIGHT Brian (*El Db, Voc, Kbds, Tba*): Flat 4, 98 Putney Road, Handsworth, Birmingham B20 3PP ☎ 0121 240 1696

SOUTH EAST

ANSETT Jane (*Vlne*): 43 Victoria Crescent, Parkstone, Poole, Dorset BH12 2JQ ☎ 01202 749670

BAGOT Tony (*B Gtr*): 42 St Pauls Gate, Wokingham, Berks RG41 2YP ☎ 01189 629 092

BAILEY Anita (*Pf, Org*): 3 Woodlands Drive, Seabrook, Hythe, Kent CT21 5TG ☎ 01303 269155

BAKER Andrew (*B Gtr*): 28 St Leonards Avenue, Blandford, Dorset DT11 7NY ☎ 01258 451452

BATTEN Philip: 35 Marley Combe Road, Camelsdale, Haslemere, Surrey GU27 3SN ☎ 01428 653201, 0973 787732 mob

BELL Michael: 2 Potters Field, Ringmer, Sussex BN8 5LQ ☎ 01273 812901

BOYESEN Nicole: The Well House, Middle Road, Lytchett Matravers, Poole Dorset DT11 6HJ ☎ 01202 622381

BURGESS John: Flat 5 Normans, Norman Road, St Cross, Winchester S023 9PP ☎ 01962 844306

CLARKE Terence (*B Gtr, A Sax*): 4 New Road, Parkstone, Poole, Dorset BH12 2NQ ☎ 01202 743356

COLLINS Andrew: 26 Beaufort Road, Southbourne, Bournemouth BH6 5AL ☎ 01202 425917

COOMBES Jarrod: Flat 1, 5 Northwood Road, Whitstable, Kent CT5 2ET ☎ 01227 772243

CROWDY Andrew (*B Gtr, Gtr*): 13 Gainsborough Crescent, Henley-on-Thames, Oxon RG9 1TB ☎ 01491 571774

CUNNINGHAM Paddy: 1 Ashcroft Road, Maidenhead, Berks SL6 6JF

DALY David: 6 Field View Road, Blandford, Dorset DT11 7HJ ☎ 01258 455596, 01306 880669

DAVIES Eifion: 53 Gallys Road, Windsor, Berks SL4 5QS ☎ 01753 738778

DAVIES Sharron: 156 Weekes Drive, Cippenham, Slough SL1 2YR ☎ 01753 525432

DAWSON Philip: 58 Ridgeway Crescent, Tonbridge, Kent TN10 4NR ☎ 01732 352811, 0411 007524

DENYER Susan (*Pf*): Campile, Crescent Rise, Thakeham, West Sussex RH20 3NB ☎ 01903 742326

DOLTON Marion (*B Gtr*): Red Roofs, Lower Row, Holt, Wimborne, Dorset BH21 7DZ ☎ 01202 841188

DORMAN Rex (*B Gtr*): Flat 2, Milburn Court, Milburn Road, Bournemouth, Dorset BH9 9HJ ☎ 01202 766760

DUDDINGTON Alan: 215B Lower Blandford Road, Broadstone, Dorset BH18 8DN ☎ 01202 600774

DWYER Adrian (*B Gtr*): 1 Quayside, Queens Avenue, Christchurch, Dorset BH23 1BZ ☎ 01202 486476

EASTCOTT John: 29 Eagle Gardens, Bedford MK41 7FE ☎ 01234 215634, 0378 283144 mob

FALVEY Polly: Kinsale, 27 Bassett Green Village, Bassett, Southampton SO16 3ND ☎ 023 8076 9463

FLETCHER Clive (*B Gtr*): Upper Maisonette, 149 London Road, Dover, Kent CT17 5AS ☎ 01304 209276

FOOT Richard: 3 Lawn Road, Portswood, Southampton SO2 1EX ☎ 023 8057 2205

FRUCHT John: 21 Argyle Road, Preston Park, Brighton, Sussex BN1 4QA ☎ 01273 672499

GARSIDE Gus (*B Gtr, Voc*): 20 Hertford Road, Brighton, East Sussex BN1 7GF ☎ 01273 387487

GEEN Beverley (*Pf, Tpt*): 7 Rose Close, Hedge End, Southampton SO30 2GR ☎ 01489 784528, 0976 923533 mob

GLAZIER Frank: Address Unknown

GLEDHILL Stuart: 234 Stony Lane, Burton, Christchurch, Dorset BH23 7LB ☎ 01202 485562

GLYNN Barry (*B Gtr*): 226 Charminster Road, Bournemouth, Dorset BH8 9RW ☎ 01202 511417

GOLTON Stan (*B Gtr*): 36 Hinton Wood Avenue, Christchurch, Dorset BH23 5AH ☎ 01425 272539

GOOLD Ray: 25 Welbeck Avenue, Highfield, Southampton SO2 1ST ☎ 023 8055 6026

GRAHAM Elizabeth (*Cel, B Gtr*): 38 St Peters Grove, Canterbury, Kent CT1 2DJ ☎ 01227 459 477

GRIFFITHS Debbie: 31 Peperham Road, Haslemere, Surrey GU27 1EB ☎ 01428 643064, 0973 752510

HARPER Cliff: 34 Neva Road, Bitterne Park, Southampton SO18 4FJ ☎ Southampton 557

HARRIS Alan (*B Gtr, Tba*): 17 Victoria Road, Bournemouth, Dorset BH1 4RT ☎ 01202 554669

HOARE Alan: 60 Constable Way, College Town, Sandhurst, Hants GU47 0FE ☎ 01276 609501, 0831 354029 mob

HOLLOWAY Anthony: 6 Valley Close, St Catherines Hill, Christchurch, Dorset BH23 2RX ☎ 01202 485736

HUGHES Natasha: Linmoor Cottage, Highwood, Ringwood, Hants BH24 3LE ☎ 01425 470464, 0468 976387 mob

HURCOMBE Eddie (*B Gtr*): 4 Highdown Avenue, Worthing, West Sussex BN13 1PU ☎ 01903 690542

INKPEN Douglas (*B Gtr, Acc*): 2 Jubilee Road, Littlebourne, Canterbury, Kent CT3 1TP ☎ Littlebourne 72

JONES Brian: 84 St Johns Road, Whitstable, Kent CT5 2RL ☎ Chestfield 2903

JUB: 17 Whittall Street, Kings Sutton, Banbury, Oxon OX17 3RD ☎ 01295 810683 & fax

KAYE Jim: 48 Hyde Heath Court, Pound Hill, Crawley, West Sussex RH10 3UQ ☎ 01293 884107

KENDON Thomas (*B Gtr, Tpt*): 10 Wiston Avenue, Chichester, West Sussex PO19 2RJ ☎ 01243 533752, 01273 533752

KENIHAN David: 31 Saltern Road, Poole, Dorset BH14 8BL ☎ 01202 731190

KENNINGTON Alan: 18 Barnfield Gardens, Brighton, Sussex BN2 2HQ ☎ Btn 687546

KERSHAW 'Subbersive' Steve (*B Gtr*): 5 Cardwell Crescent, Headington, Oxford, Oxon OX3 7QE ☎ 01865 68785

KILKENNY Anthony (*B Gtr, Voc, Kbds*): 20 Orion Road, Rodwell, Weymouth, Dorset DT4 8LG ☎ 01305 786335

LOCKETT Dorian (*B Gtr, Tba*): 212 Sherwood Avenue, Streatham Hill, London SW16 5EF ☎ 020 8764 6478

MANNING Stephen: Blandford, Valley Road, Barham, Canterbury CT4 6NX ☎ 01227 831921

MASLEN Andrew (*B Tbn, Gtr, Tba*): 9 Drake Close, Horsham, West Sussex RH12 5UB ☎ 01403 274144, 01523 418693 pager

MAYBANK Christopher (*Vlne*): 20 The Butts, Otford, Kent TN14 5PR ☎ 01959 523595

MELLOR Eric (*B Gtr*): 30 Wilson Road, Bournemouth, Dorset BH1 4PH ☎ 01202 303492

MIZEN Valdon J: 1 Burlington Road, Swanage, Dorset BH19 1LR ☎ 01929 423299

NEWTON Peter (*E Gtr*): 30 Glenn Road, West End, Southampton, Hants SO3 3FT ☎ 023 8047 4588

OSMAN Adrian (*B Gtr, Pf*): 45 Nightingale Road, Freemantle, Southampton SO1 3EL ☎ 023 8078 9868

OTAKI Jasmine (*Pf*): 4 Cress Way, Faversham, Kent ME13 7NH ☎ 0195 534407

PERKINS Roger: 17 The Buttery, Christchurch, Dorset BH23 1LF ☎ 01202 473034

RACKLYETT Edward (*Org*): 53 St Michaels Avenue, Ryde, Isle Of Wight PO33 3EH ☎ 01983 567545

RICHARDSON Arthur: 13 The Borough, Canterbury, Kent CT1 2DR

RIDDLE Stephen (*T Sax, B Gtr, S Sax*): 11 Gaviots Way, Gerrards Cross, Bucks SL9 7DU ☎ 01753 884336 eve, 0426 941135

RUSSELL Simon (*El Db, Gtr, Pf*): Flat 9, 37 Sussex Square, Kemptown, Brighton BN2 5AD ☎ 01273 620176, 0411 089618

SEAMAN John (*B Gtr*): 1 Holly Dell, Holly Hill, Bassett, Southampton SO16 7EX ☎ 023 8076 6412

SEWARD Eddie (*Dms*): 'Sunny Croft', 28 Hollicondane Road, Ramsgate, Kent CT11 7PH ☎ Thanet 594061

SPACK Ronald (*B Gtr*): 27 Amberwood Gardens, Highcliffe, Christchurch, Dorset BH23 5RT ☎ 01425 277043

THOMAS Lyndon: 28 Albert Road, Ferndown, Dorset BH22 9HE ☎ 01202 872795

THOMAS Nigel (*B Gtr, Voc*): Ground Floor Flat, 9 Buckingham Road, Brighton BN1 3RA ☎ 01273 204031

TRIPP Eddie (*B Gtr*): 2 Hoburne Lane, Highcliffe, Christchurch, Dorset BH23 4HP ☎ 01425 272161

WHITWORTH Stanley: 102 Field View, Bar Hill, Cambridge CB3 8SY

WOOD Keith: 12 Lonnon Road, Colehill, Wimborne, Dorset BH21 7AX ☎ 01202 883011

WRIGHT Russell: 141 Portland Road, Bournemouth, Dorset BH9 1NG ☎ 01202 514262

YOUNG Douglas (*B Gtr*): 71 Brewer Street, Maidstone, Kent ME14 1RZ ☎ 01622 200439, 01622 755085 day

SOUTH WEST

ABELL George: 139 Fairwater Road, Cardiff CF5 3JR

ALLNATT Michael: 90 St Leonards Road, Newton Abbot, Devon TQ12 1JX ☎ 01626 364027

AMHERST Nigel: Town Mills, Staverton, Totnes, Devon TQ9 6PD ☎ Staverton 221

ASHWORTH Eric (*B Gtr*): 6 Place Nicolle, Longueville, St Saviour, Jersey, Channel Islands JE2 7RB ☎ 01534 35680

BALL Reginald (*B Gtr*): 39 Sherwood Drive, Exmouth, Devon EX8 4PX ☎ 01395 274173

BELL Jo: Treetops, Firgrove Lane, Lower Peasedown, Bath BA2 8AJ ☎ 01761 432982

BEVIR Thomas: Dumpers House, Dumpers Lane, Chew Magna BS18 8SS ☎ 01275 333928

BOWSER Ian: 19 Millers Drive, North Common, Warmley, Bristol BS30 8YN ☎ 01275 541100

BROWN Eric (*B Gtr*): 29 West Mall, Bristol BS8 4BG ☎ 0117 9738221

BULLEN Dennis (*B Gtr*): 50 The Meadows, Mallards Reach, Marshfield, Nr Cardiff, South Glamorgan CF3 8AY ☎ 01633 681494

BURNS Colin (*Voc*): Address Unknown ☎ 01934 513182

BUSHELL Hugh: 2 Queen Square, North Curry, Somerset TA3 6LT ☎ 01823 490269

CASWELL Hamilton (*Voc*): 10 Perry Road, Bristol BS1 5BG ☎ 0117 9294642

CHARLES Anthony: 70 Rue De La Pointe, St.Brelade, Jersey, C.I. JE3 8EN ☎ St.Brelade 4448

CHARLES Goudie: Springfield, 19 Penpol Road, Hayle, Cornwall TR27 4AD ☎ 01736 757351

COMPTON Ernest (*Dms*): 4 Trefelin Street, Port Talbot, Glam SA13 1DQ

CONDLIFFE Mary: 96 Brynglas Avenue, Newport, S Wales NP9 5LQ ☎ 01633 662339

COOPER Ian (*Ac Gtr, E Gtr, B Gtr*): 5 Ffrwdgrech Road, Brecon, Powys LD3 8DR ☎ 01874 610636

DALE Julian (*B Gtr*): 1A Pembroke Mansions, 1-3 Oakfield Road, Bristol, Avon BS8 2AH ☎ 0117 9737739

DYSON George (*Cel*): 28 Station Road, Pinhoe, Exeter, Devon EX1 3SA ☎ 01392 66404

EAMES Roger: Paradise Farm, Stockland, Honiton, Devon EX14 9EX ☎ 01404 881327

EDWARDS Thomas: 199 Carlisle Street, Splott, Cardiff, South Glamorgan CF2 2PE ☎ 029 2046 1205

FERNANDO Imogen: Bridge Cottage, Sherford Road, Taunton, Somerset TA1 3QY ☎ 01823 321618, 0411 342936 mob

FOWLER Samuel: Leapgate Cottage, Old Sherborne Road, Charminster, Dorchester Dorset DT2 9RH ☎ 01305 267068

FRY Peter J: Wayside House, Nill Road, Ynysybwl, Pontypridd CF37 3LS ☎ 01443 799176

FULCHER Colin (*B Gtr*): 18 Penhayes Road, Kenton, Exeter EX6 8NR ☎ Starcross 89015

FURNISH Pete (*B Gtr*): 24 Larkshead Way, Ogwell Cross, Newton Abbot TQ12 6BT ☎ 01626 56906

GARDINER Paula (*Ac Gtr, Flt*): 48 Queens Road, New Tredegar, Gwent NP2 6DY ☎ 01443 835570

GATELEY Stephen (*B Ldr*): 30 Shire Close, Hookhills, Paignton TQ4 7SW

GIBBONS Richard: 13 Earl Road, Penarth, Vale Of Glamorgan CF64 3UN ☎ 029 2070 7855

GITTINS Adam (*B Gtr*): Greenfield, 85 Kennington Avenue, Bishopston, Bristol BS7 9EX ☎ 0117 942 3799

GRAHAM Harry (*B Gtr*): 2 Southfield Close, Uphill, Weston Super Mare BS23 4XJ ☎ 01934 626571

GRAHAM-WHITE William (*B Gtr*): 407 Chepstow Road, Newport, Gwent NP9 8HL ☎ 01633 273093

GREENSMITH David (*Pf*): 4 Kymin Terrace, Penarth, South Glamorgan CF64 1AP ☎ 029 2070 9039

GREGORY Jayne: 2 Vaindre Drive, St Mellons, Cardiff CF3 0LL ☎ 029 2079 2429

GRIFFITHS David (*B Gtr, Man*): 73 Ashley Down Road, Bristol BS7 9JT ☎ 423310

GROENEVELT Benjamin (*B Gtr*): 3 Prospect Terrace, Bedminster, Bristol BS3 3BQ ☎ 0117 9631516

HASKINS Matthew (*E Gtr, B Gtr*): 8 Widcombe Crescent, Bath BA2 6AH ☎ 01225 480388

HILL Nigel: Whipton Lodge Residential H., 328 Pinnoe Road, Exeter, Devon EX4 8AS ☎ 01392 55907

HONEYMAN John: Feniton, Nr Honiton, Devon EX14 0BU ☎ 01404 850641

JENKINS John (*B Ldr, Arr*): 62 Trumlands Road, Torquay, Devon TQ1 4RB ☎ 01803 323658

KEEP Andrew (*B Gtr, Dms, Per*): 36 Southey Street, St Werburghs, Bristol BS2 9RE ☎ 0117 9855 346, 0410 103 732

KENNEDY David (*B Gtr, Tba*): 24 Torbridge Road, Horrabridge, Devon PL20 7SD ☎ 01822 854575

LANG-COLMER Claudia (*B Gtr*): 17 Bronescombe Close, Penryn, Falmouth, Cornwall TR10 8LE ☎ 01326 373300

LANGSTROTH David: 20 Princes Avenue, Roath, Cardiff CF2 3SN ☎ 029 2048 4171

LAPHAM Trevor (*B Gtr*): 7 Victoria Close, Higher Lux Street, Liskeard, Cornwall PL14 3HU ☎ 01579 346280

LAW John: Stockholm, Sigginstone, Cowbridge, S Glamorgan CF7 7LP ☎ 01446 773533

LE VAILLANT Tobye (*Cel, Voc, B Gtr*): 50 Clos Du Roncher, Rue Au Blancq, St Clement, Jersey JE2 6QZ ☎ 01534 852272

LINDSAY Michael: 100 Queens Drive, Swindon, Wiltshire SN3 1AW ☎ 01793 529796

MANN Antony (*Tbn, Tba*): 12 Causeway Terrace, Watchet, Somerset TA23 0HP ☎ 01984 634738

MARVELLY Dylan (*B Gtr, E Gtr*): 16 Pointfields Cresent, Hakin, Milford Haven, Dyfed SA73 3DA ☎ 020 8549 1706

MASON Norman: 40 Heol-Y-Deri, Rhiwbina, Cardiff CF4 6HH ☎ 029 2062 3432

MASSEY John: 73 Cromwell Road, St.Andrews, Bristol BS6 5HA ☎ 0117 9243902

MCKIM Stewart (*B Gtr*): 52 Warminster Road, Bathampton, Bath BA2 6RX ☎ 01225 318085

MILLS Martyn (*B Gtr*): Craignore, 5 Lower Knowles Road, Clevedon, N Somerset BS21 7XT ☎ 01275 341461

MORGAN Terry (*Gtr, Dms*): Tweenaways, Crowntown, Helston, Cornwall TR13 0AB ☎ 01326 562 616, 01326 565 800

MORRIS Frank: The Bungalow, Onslow Terrace, Tondu, Nr Bridgend Glam CF32 9HW

MORRIS Michael (*B Gtr, A Sax, T Sax, Bjo*): 39 Marlbrook Road, Redhill, Hereford HR2 7PY ☎ 01432 343363

MORTON Clive (*B Gtr*): 2 Weston Crescent, Horfield, Bristol BS7 8UT ☎ 0117 9756883

NEWTON Raymond: 14 Aller Vale Close, Heavitree, Exeter EX2 5NH ☎ 01392 435975

OAKES Peter (*Pf*): 17 South Walks Road, Dorchester, Dorset DT1 1ED ☎ 01305 250433

OLDER Tim (*Cel*): 22 St Francis Road, Whitchurch, Cardiff, Sth Wales CF4 1AW ☎ 029 2062 8014

OWEN Martyn (*Tba, Pf*): 19 Beatty Way, Burnham-on-Sea, Somerset TA8 2TD ☎ 01278 789027

DOUBLE BASS - SOUTH WEST

PRICE Mikeal: 6 Croft Street, Cowbridge, South Glamorgan CF7 7DH ☎ 01446 775540

REBBECK Dave *(Vln)*: 29 Thurlestone Road, Swindon, Wiltshire SN3 1EQ ☎ 01793 520420

RYAN Jeffrey: 39 Park Prospect, Graigwen, Pontypridd, Mid Glamorgan CF37 2HF ☎ Pontypridd 4055

SHERLOCK Elizabeth *(Vadag)*: El Cueto 37, Lieres, Siero 33580, Asturias, Spain ☎ + 34 985 730175, + 34 930 990 412

SMITH Peter *(Dms)*: 16 Thackeray Crescent, Melksham, Wiltshire SN12 7NH

SOWERBY Alice: 1-1 Hampton House, Cotham, Hull, Bristol BS6 6JU ☎ 0117 923 7862, 01793 771707

TAYLOR Michael: 23 Lilliesfield Avenue, Gloucester GL3 3AQ ☎ 01452 616215

TUCK Graham: 199 Bassaleg Road, Newport, S Wales NP9 3PZ ☎ 01633 666594

TURNER Ian *(E Gtr)*: Flat 1, 55 Clovelly Rd, Bideford, Devon EX39 3DF ☎ 01237 425131

VERGETTE Marcus: Coombe Farm, Highampton, Beaworthy, Devon EX21 5LJ ☎ 01837 810349

WELDRAKE Geoffrey: 18 Cowhorn Hill, Oldland Common, Bristol BS30 9QU ☎ 0117 983 9975

WHITE Roger: 92 Pembroke Road, Clifton, Bristol BS8 3EG ☎ 0117 9735408

WILLETT Marcus: Mallory, Consell Green, Toddington, Nr. Winchcombe, Cheltenham, Glos

LONDON

ALEXANDER Gill *(Gtr, Pf)*: The Tithe Barn, Mill Lane, Needham Nr Diss, Norfolk IP20 9LD ☎ 01379 852721

ALSOP Richard: 27C Gloucester Drive, London N4 2LE ☎ 020 8809 2780, 0402 280751

AMHERST Timothy: 45 Curzon Road, London N10 2RB ☎ 020 8883 4101

ANTONIA Philip *(B Gtr)*: 2 Badgers Court, 151 Forest Road, Leytonstone, London E11 1JS ☎ 020 8558 8083

ARTHY John: The Lock House, Dell Lane, Little Hallingbury, Nr Bishops Stortford Herts CM22 7SG ☎ 01279 724931

ASHMAN Micky: 9 Aberdeen Road, Harrow, Middlesex HA3 7NF ☎ 020 8427 4350

AYRE David: 68 Beaulieu Avenue, Sydenham, London SE26 6PW ☎ 020 8778 5340 & fax, 0973 721583 mob, 01306 880669 day

BABBINGTON Roy *(B Gtr, Sitar, Bag)*: 7 Sinclair Road, London W14 0NS ☎ 020 7602 3018

BAKER Dawn: 36 Grove Road East, Christchurch, Dorset BH23 2DQ ☎ 01202 486713, 01306 880 669

BAKEWELL Antonia: 37 Chimney Court, 23 Brewhouse Lane, London E1 9NU ☎ 020 7702 1685, 0498 600968 mob

BAKEWELL John: 25 Huddleston Road, London N7 0AD ☎ 020 7609 5687

BALDOCK Ken *(B Gtr, Pf, Com, Arr)*: 5 Gainsborough Road, Chiswick, London W4 1NJ ☎ 020 8994 1700 & fax, 0378 404654 mob

BALDWIN Amy: 11 Perth Road, Leyton, London E10 7PA ☎ 020 8556 1607, 01523 410541

BALDWIN David *(Gtr)*: 9 Alwyne Avenue, Shenfield, Essex CM15 8QT ☎ 01277 228381

BARLOW Thomas *(B Gtr, Voc)*: 18 Underhill Road, Dulwich, London SE22 0AH ☎ 020 8693 2849

BARTON Chris *(B Gtr, Pf)*: 39 Madeira Road, Palmers Green, London N13 5SR ☎ 020 8886 0136

BEDFORD Mark Bedders: Cc Young & Co, Chesham House, 150 Regent Street, London W1R 5FA ☎ 020 7432 0337, 020 7432 0338

BEERS Adrian: 69 Hodford Road, London NW11 8NH ☎ 020 8209 1945

BELCHER James *(B Gtr, Sou, Tbn)*: 88 Cockmannings Road, Orpington, Kent BR5 4HZ ☎ 01689 872362

BELLATALLA Roberto *(Pic, Cel)*: 68 Ashmead House, Kingsmead Estate, Homerton, London E9 5QR ☎ 020 8985 6395

BENSON Harry: 31 Buckingham Mansions, Bath Road, Bournemouth, Dorset BH1 2PG ☎ 01202 557280

BENSON Roy: 6 Heathside Gardens, Woking, Surrey GU22 7HR ☎ 01483 740256

BENSON Simon *(Com, Arr)*: Rosemead, South Hill Avenue, Harrow-on-the-Hill, Middlesex HA1 3PA ☎ 020 8423 1351

BERRY Joseph *(B Gtr, Voc)*: 137 Barnes Wallis Court, Barnhill Road, Wembley, Middx HA9 9DP ☎ 020 8621 5166, 0976 382071

BERRY Stephen *(B Gtr, Cel)*: 51 Alexandra Road, Blackburn, Lancs BB2 6DW ☎ 01254 673871

BIGGS Mihaly: 59C Cornwall Crescent, London W11 1PJ ☎ 020 7727 6436

BILHAM Colin *(Vln, Vadag)*: 11 Rosecroft, East Perry, Huntingdon, Cambridgeshire PE18 0BZ ☎ 01480 810012

BLACK Dominic *(B Gtr)*: 52 Beechhill Road, Eltham, London SE9 1HH ☎ 020 8859 1709, 01306 880669

BLANCHFLOWER Oliver *(B Gtr)*: Flat 4, 25 Uplands Road, London N8 9NN ☎ 020 8245 6071

BLENNERHASSETT James *(E Gtr, B Gtr, Cel)*: Nella Cottage, Larkhill Road, Sligo, Ireland ☎ +353 71 69686 & fax

BOADEN Victoria *(B Gtr, Pf)*: 7 Foxleas Court, Spencer Road, Bromley, Kent BR2 9RN ☎ 020 8460 5629

BOND Christine: 144 Ladywell Road, Lewisham, London SE13 7HU ☎ 020 8690 8741

BOND Rupert: 36 Crosslet Vale, London SE10 8DH ☎ 020 8691 0691

BOROS Gabor K *(Cimb)*: 357 Kenton Road, Harrow, Middlesex HA3 0XS ☎ 020 8907 7953 & fax

BORTHWICK John *(B Gtr, Arr, Com)*: 106 Westpole Avenue, Cockfosters, Herts EN4 0BB ☎ 020 8449 6110

BOSCH Leon: 8A Manor Road, Tring, Herts HP23 5DA ☎ 01442 3381891 & fax, 020 8533 1372 day

BOTWRIGHT Valerie *(Clt)*: 26 Presburg Road, New Malden, Surrey KT3 5AH ☎ 020 8942 0768

BOUCHAUX Axel: 54 Forthbridge Road, London SW11 5NY ☎ 020 7350 2712

BOUGIE *(E Gtr, B Gtr, Per)*: 46 Lambert Road, Flat 1, Brixton SW2 5BE ☎ 020 7924 9420

BRAND Graham *(B Gtr, Pf, Gtr)*: 1 Staveley Gardens, Chiswick, London W4 2SA ☎ 020 8742 8757

BRAY James *(Sou)*: 3A Oakmead Road, Balham, London SW12 9SN ☎ 020 8673 7681

BRETT Ivor *(Acc)*: 119 Pettits Lane, Romford, Essex RM1 4ER ☎ 01708 740691

BRIDGE Paul: 569 Upper Richmond Road West, Richmond, Surrey TW10 5DX ☎ 020 8878 7388

BRIDGES George *(B Gtr)*: 37 Mycenae Road, London SE3 7SF ☎ 020 8858 2344

BRIDGWOOD Jonny *(B Gtr, Gtr)*: O J Kilkenney, 6 Lansdowne Mews, London W11 3BH ☎ 020 7792 9494

BRINNEN Gerald: 75 Broadhurst, Ashtead, Surrey KT21 1QF ☎ 01372 273183

BRITTAIN Michael: Woodhouse Cottage, Marsh, Nr Aylesbury, Bucks HP17 8SP ☎ 01296 614647

BROCKLEHURST Brian *(Gtr, Per)*: 8 Claire Court, 144 Sussex Gardens, London W2 1UE ☎ 020 7262 9099

BROUGHTON David: 8 Baronsmere Rd, London N2 9QB ☎ 020 8883 5237 & fax, 07970 804815, 01306 500011 day

BROWN Alan *(B Gtr)*: 54 Lincolns Mead, Lingfield, Surrey RH7 6TA ☎ 01342 835066, 01342 836669

BROWN Clive *(B Gtr)*: 17 Greenhill Road, Colehill, Wimborne, Dorset BH21 2RF ☎ 01306 880669, 01202 883196

BROWN William *(B Gtr)*: 10 Kingswood Close, Oakhill, Surbiton, Surrey KT6 6DZ ☎ 020 8399 8782

BRUGGEMEYER Cecelia: 123 Osvorne Road, Forest Gate, London E7 0PP ☎ 020 8503 1679

BUCKOKE Peter: 35 Plimsoll Road, London N4 2EN ☎ 020 7359 1481

BURGESS Samuel *(B Gtr)*: 22 Bond Street, Stratford, London E15 1LT ☎ 020 8257 1314, 0973 861282

BURNETT Sandy *(Md, Vln)*: 90 Masbro Road, London W14 0LR ☎ 020 7603 6427

BURRELL Raymond (*Gtr*): c/o Joan Hudson & Co, 91 Taberancle Street, London EC2A 4BA ☎ 020 7253 3107

BURY Julian (*B Gtr*): 13 Stewartsby Close, Edmonton, London N18 1AN ☎ 07775 631556

BUSH Lennie (*B Gtr*): 29 The Malt House, The Drays, Long Melford, Suffolk CO10 9TP ☎ 01787 374269

BUTCHER Philip (*B Gtr, Com, Song W*): Oak House, Arthur's Folly, Parkend, Lydney, Gloucestershire GL15 4JQ ☎ 01594 563425, 01594 564544

CAMPBELL Joseph (*Clt*): c/o Joe & Co Music Ltd, 59 Dean Street, London W1V 5HH

CAMPBELL Laura (*Pf*): 89 Englefield Road, Islington, London N1 3LJ ☎ 020 7688 1394, 0976 263 065

CANONICI Corrado: 44 Tavistock Terrace, London N19 4DB ☎ 020 7281 3822 & fax

CANTRILL Simon (*Pf*): 173 Mayall Road, Brixton, London SW9

CHILTON Roy (*B Gtr, Gtr, Com*): 15 Hawkhurst Way, West Wickham, Kent BR4 9PE ☎ 020 8777 6414

CLARK Diane: 49 Warham Road, Harringay, London N4 1AR ☎ 020 8348 0930, 0850 050 522

CLARKE Frank (*B Gtr*): 40 High Street, West Wratting, Cambridge CDB1 5LU ☎ 01223 290 373

CLARKE Michael: 15 Chester Road, London E11 2JR ☎ 020 8989 1155

CLAYTON Leon (*B Gtr*): 165 Cutenhoe Road, Luton, Beds LU3 3NQ ☎ 01582 454070, 0973 297647

CLEYNDERT Andrew: 31 Oxford Avenue, London SW20 8LS ☎ 020 8540 0230

CLYNE Jeff (*B Gtr*): 10 Temple Gardens, London NW11 0LL ☎ 020 8455 2893

COLBORNE W: Address Unknown

COLE Michael (*B Gtr*): 10 Cecil Road, London N14 5RJ ☎ 020 8368 2446

COLLINS Leslie (*Voc*): 72 Purley Downs Road, Sanderstead, Surrey CR2 0RB ☎ 020 8660 5588

COLWELL Catherine: 15B Healey Street, Kentish Town, London NW1 8SR ☎ 020 7284 3649

COMAN Matthew: 4 Danby Street, Peckham, London SE15 4BU ☎ 020 7639 7716, 0973 720439 mob

COOK Francesca: 41 Carlton Avenue East, Wembley, Middx HA9 8LZ ☎ 020 8908 2572, 0411 362319

COOK Simon (*Pf, Ac Gtr, B Gtr*): 23 Lackfrod Road, Chipstead, Surrey CR5 3TB ☎ 01737 554758, 0403 460502

COOPER John: 9 Bowlers Orchard, Chalfont St Giles, Bucks HP8 4LB ☎ 01494 872553

COOPER Peter (*B Gtr*): 1 Dahlia Gardens, Micham, Surrey CR4 1LB ☎ 020 8764 0396

CORPE David (*B Gtr, Kbds*): 16 Aldwych Avenue, Ilford, Essex IG6 1DS ☎ 020 8554 8088

CORRIGAN Peter (*B Gtr*): 106 Grosvenor Drive, Hornchurch, Essex RM11 1PG ☎ 01708 440130

COX Julian (*Gtr*): 87 Elm Park Avenue, London N15 6UZ ☎ 020 8211 7109

CRABTREE Stephen: Dene Cottage, High Street, Blockley, Moreton-In-Marsh, Gloucestershire GL56 9HA

CREESE Malcolm: 31 Acacia Road, London W3 6HB ☎ 020 8896 9798, 020 8932 4836 fax, 0802 183590 mob

CROSBY Gary: P.O. Box 665, Harrow, Middlesex HA3 5BE ☎ 020 8424 2243

CROXON Thomas: 22 Hurst Road, Buckhurst Hill, Essex IG9 6AB ☎ 020 8504 2200

CULLINGTON Paul: 24 Willow Lane, Amersham, Bucks HP7 9DW ☎ 01494 721979

CUNINGHAM Juliet: 68 Swakeleys Drive, Ickenham, Uxbridge, Middx UB10 8QF ☎ 01895 238117

CURPHEY Roger (*B Gtr*): 2 Wilkes Road, Hutton, Brentwood, Essex CM13 1LH ☎ 01277 229159

DALLING Richard (*B Gtr*): 97 Oakley Street, Chelsea, London SW3 5NR ☎ 020 7351 6422

DANKWORTH Alec (*B Gtr*): 48 Caddington Road, London NW2 1RS ☎ 020 8452 9029

DAVIS Ruth: Address Unknown ☎ 020 7403 1162, 01306 880669 day

DAWES Tim (*Dms, Vln, B Gtr*): Cedar Cottage, Otmoor Lane, Beckley, Oxford OX3 9UX ☎ 01865 351847, 0973 814988 mob

DEAN Roger (*Vib, Pf*): 23 Westfield Terrace, Longford, Gloucester GL2 9BA ☎ 01452 522379

DEEGAN Matt (*Ac Gtr*): 40 Margravine Rd, Hammersmith, London W6 8HH ☎ 020 7385 6379

DENNIS Albert: 19 Temple Road, Chiswick, London W4 5NW ☎ 020 8995 6410

DENNIS Jack (*B Gtr, Vln, B Ldr*): 67 Manor Drive, Friern Barnet N20 0DT ☎ 020 8361 0052

DETTORI Gianluigi (*E Gtr*): Flat C, 50 Woodstock Road, London NW11 8QE ☎ 020 8201 8156

DEVLIN Peter: 19 St Julians Farm Road, W Norwood, London SE27 0JJ ☎ 020 8670 4740, 0410 098378 mob

DOWNS Bert: 307 Leigham Court Road, Streatham, London SW16 2RX ☎ 020 8677 9627, 01306 880669

DOWNS Geoffrey (*Tba*): 4 Rutland Road, London E11 2DY ☎ 020 8989 3633

DOYLE Julia (*Vln*): Flat 5, 50 Anson Road, London N7 0AB ☎ 020 7609 9978

DRIVER Richard (*B Gtr*): 9 Brockenhurst Road, Addiscombe, Croydon, Surrey CR0 7DR ☎ 020 8654 8207

DRUCKER Gerald (*Cntrc*): 75 College Road, Harrow Weald, Middx HA3 6EF ☎ 020 8427 4730

DUNNE Ronan (*Clt*): 341B Kentish Town Road, London NW5 2TJ ☎ 020 7482 0516, 076666 70 33 10

DUNNING Ronald: 3 Waveney Avenue, London SE15 3UF ☎ 020 7639 7287, 020 8533 1372

DURBAN Andrew: 58 Bickersteth Road, Tooting, London SW17 9SQ ☎ 020 8672 6421

DURELL Mike (*B Gtr*): Middleton Farm, Hubbards Hill, Warren Street, Lenham, Maidstone, Kent ME17 2EJ ☎ 01622 859109

EATON Lynette (*Pf*): Flat 4, 61 Montem Road, Forest Hill, London SE23 1SH ☎ 020 8690 8232, 0973 738668 mob

EDWARDS John: 55A Arlingford Road, Briston, London SW2 2SS ☎ 020 8671 0694

ELFENBEIN Asha: 53 Manor Park, London SE13 5RA ☎ 020 8244 4196

ELLIOTT Catherine: 105 Bartholomew Road, Kentish Town, London NW5 2AR ☎ 020 7267 0437

EMERY Caroline (*Pf*): 7 St Clair Drive, Worcester Park, Surrey KT4 8UG ☎ 020 8330 3188

EVANS Andrew (*B Gtr, Pf, E Pf, Synth*): 29 Argyll Mansions, Hammersmith Road, London W14 8QQ ☎ 020 7602 2707

EVANS Judith: 5 Oakthorpe Road, Oxford OX2 7BD ☎ 01865 554258

EVETTS Jack: Address Unknown

EYRES Ian: 41 Onslow Gardens, South Woodford, London E18 1ND ☎ 020 8989 7421

FALLON Jack (*Vln*): 129 Bourne Hill, Palmers Green, London N13 4BE ☎ 020 8886 5598, 020 8886 6482 fax

FAWCETT Harold: Address Unknown

FELL Simon (*B Gtr*): 24 Chauntry Road, Haverhill, Suffolk CB9 8BE ☎ 01440 707689 & fax

FENTIMEN Rhiannon (*Vln, Vla*): Meadow View, Pheasants Hill, Hambleden, Henley-on-Thames, Oxon RG9 6SN ☎ 01491 576789

FINLAYSON Tucker (*B Gtr*): 34 Hillfield Road, London NW6 1PZ ☎ 020 7794 5726

FIRTH Deborah: 172 Squirrels Heath Lane, Hornchurch, Essex RM11 2DX ☎ 01708 470 621

FOREMAN Alan (*Tba*): Address Unknown

GARSON Louis: The Squirrels, The Platt, Chenies Manor Estate, Chenies, Herts WD3 6ER ☎ 01494 764453

GEE Jon (*Bq Db, B Gtr, Voc*): Flat 2, 41 Lady Margaret Road, Kentish Town, London NW5 2NH ☎ 020 7284 3083, 0976 287795 mob

GELDSETZER Christian: 63B Paragon Place, Blackheath, London SE3 0SP

GIBBS Eric (B Gtr): Roseville, 2/42 Roseby Avenue, Clayfield, Brisbane, Queensland 4011 Australia

GIBSON Matthew: 11 Thornlaw Road, West Norwood, London SE27 0SH ☎ 020 8761 9203

GLANVILLE David: 435 Hatfield Road, St Albans, Herts AL4 0XP ☎ 01727 831529

GODWIN Michael (Tba, Sou, B Gtr): 9 Brae Court, Kingston Hill, Kingston, Surrey KT2 7QQ ☎ 020 8549 4966

GOODE Coleridge: 32 Elgin Crescent, London W11 2JR ☎ 020 7727 5897

GOODE Duncan: 53 Highworth Road, New Southgate, London N11 2SN ☎ 020 7388 0361, 0468 635135 mob

GOODE Kenneth: 9 Rowlands Avenue, Hatch End, Middx HA5 4DF ☎ 020 8428 6000

GOODWIN Peter (Kbds, Tpt): 2 Clifton Road, London N22 4XN ☎ 020 8888 2289

GORDON Jeremy: 54 Glenhouse Road, London SE9 1JQ ☎ 020 8850 3754, 01306 880669

GREEN David: 86 Pine Gardens, Ruislip, Middx HA4 9TJ ☎ 020 8868 9891

GRIFFITHS Arthur: 13 Parkside Avenue, Bromley, Kent BR1 2EJ ☎ 020 8464 3982

GRIFFITHS David: 7 Ellesmere Road, London NW10 1LJ

GULBICKI Marian: 14 Hillmore Court, Belmont Hill, London SE13 5AZ ☎ 020 8852 2320

GUY Barry (Vlne, Com): Carrickmourne, Thomastown, Co. Kilkenny, Ireland ☎ 353 0 5658708, 353 0 5658709

HALL Ian: 60 Culver Street, Newent, Glos GL18 1DA ☎ 01531 822860

HALLETT Simon: 39 Swanscombe Road, Chiswick, London W4 2HL ☎ 020 8994 7081, 020 8533 1372

HALLIGAN Anthony (Arr): R.O.S.O., PO Box 996, Code121-Seeb, Sultanate Of Oman

HAMILL Andy (B Gtr): 14A Emu Road, London SW8 3PR ☎ 020 7978 2584

HAMILTON-BOX Peter: 11 High Street, Charing, Ashford, Kent TN27 0HU ☎ 01233 714126

HARDING Caroline: 7 Kemishford, Smarts Heath Lane, Woking, Surrey GU22 0RD ☎ 01483 232001, 0976 390933 mob

HARE Lucy: 30 Ainger Road, London NW3 3AT ☎ 020 7586 8929, 01306 880669

HARLEY Malcolm (B Gtr): 3 Abbotts Ride, Off Valley Road, Billericay, Essex CM11 2DJ ☎ 01277 623384

HARLING Keith: Lavender House, 28 Hampden Hill, Beaconsfield, Bucks HP9 1BP ☎ 01494 674144, 0831 428161 mob

HARRIES Timothy (B Gtr): 72 Holly Road, Northampton NN1 4QP ☎ 01604 36782

HARROD Andrew Kear (Kbds): 5 Montdore Hse., 28 Highgate Hill, London N19 5NL ☎ 020 7263 2476

HART Richard: Flat 1, 88 Woodhill, Woolwich, London SE18 5JF ☎ 020 8316 1108

HARTGROVES Chris (B Gtr): 290 Garth Road, Morden, Surrey SM4 4NL ☎ 020 8337 2234

HARTLEY Keith: 117 Holmwood Road, Cheam, Surrey SM2 7JS ☎ 020 8393 6385

HAWKES Adam (Kbds, Arr, Md, Voc): 32 Barley Croft, Bengeo, Hertford SG14 3LN ☎ 01992 550152, 0802 861475

HAYHURST Oli (E Gtr, B Gtr): 11 Ashford Road, London NW2 6TP ☎ 020 8969 4381, 0839 482115 pager

HAYNES Sarah: 117 Swallow Street, Iver Heath, Iver, Bucks SL0 0ET ☎ 01753 654092

HAYWARD Albert: 273 Ridgemore Road, The Mallards, Leominster, Herefordshire HR6 8UJ ☎ 01568 611826

HAZLETON Ben (B Gtr): Flat 1, 60 Highgate West Hill, London N6 6BU ☎ 020 8341 9221

HEALEY Jane (Pf, Theory): 61 Morden Way, Sutton, Surrey SM3 9PQ ☎ 020 8644 3419

HEATH Lucy: 85 St Quintin Avenue, North Kensington, London W10 6PB ☎ 020 8969 8575

HEATLEY Spike: Moulin De Villery, Treverien 35190, Brittany, France ☎ +33 0299456214

HENDERSON Guy (Pf): 34 Moseley Road, Burnley, Lancs BB11 2RF ☎ 01282 839234

HENDERSON Martin (Con): 36 Treeside Road, Shirley, Southampton, Hants SO1 5FZ ☎ 023 8078 1976

HERBERT Thomas (B Gtr): 65 Benthal Road, London N16 7AR ☎ 020 8806 3959, 0956 531174

HERMAN Godfrey: 43 Rectory Lane, Byfleet, Surrey KT14 7LR ☎ 019323 51386

HETHERINGTON Peter: 65 Guibal Road, Lee, London SE12 9LY ☎ 020 8857 4204

HETHERINGTON Simon (B Gtr): 32 Selby Rd, Ealing, London W5 1LX ☎ 020 8998 1627

HIGGINS Gerry (B Gtr): Flat 4, 10/11 Palmeira Square, Hove, Sussex BN3 2JB ☎ 01273 208815

HILL John: 99 Erlanger Road, London SE14 5QT ☎ 020 7732 4011, 01306 880669 day

HODGES Peter: 57 Arragon Road, Twickenham, Middx TW1 3NG ☎ 020 8892 0899

HOLT John: 45B Hawarden Grove, Herne Hill, London SE24 9DQ ☎ 020 8671 9687, 01306 880669 day

HOOSON Edwin (Pf): 7 Lakes Road, Keston, Kent BR2 6BN ☎ 01689 858169

HORN Mark: 38 Deodar Road, London SW15 2NN ☎ 020 8871 0801

HOSFORD Liz (Pf, Flt, B Gtr): 5 Sawston Court, Linnet Way, Purfleet, Essex RM19 1NG ☎ 01708 860435, 0378 750123 mob, 01708 860435

HOSKINS John (Pf): 18 Foxley Gardens, Purley, Surrey CR8 2DQ ☎ 020 8660 7796

HOUCHIN Peter (B Gtr): Flat 2, 30 Redfield Lane, London SW5 0RQ ☎ 020 7373 4567

HOUGHAM Tony: Westbourne, The Causeway, Great Baddow, Chelmsford, Essex CM2 7JX ☎ 01245 477131, 0831 727491

HOUGHTON Lynda: 21 Desenfans Road, London SE21 7DN ☎ 020 8299 1746, 01306 880669 day

HOWLES Dominic (B Gtr): Flat 4, 21 Ellington Road, Muswell Hill, London N10 3DG ☎ 020 8883 9486

HUGHES Peter (B Gtr): 23 Press Road, Uxbridge, Middlesex UB8 1AT ☎ 01895 238792

HUNTER Sean (B Gtr): 8 Carolyn House, 95 Larkhall Rise, Clapham, London SW4 6HR ☎ 020 7720 3504, 0976 916762

HUTCHINSON George: Address Unknown ☎ 020 7373 6145

IND Peter: 207 Amyand Pk Road, Twickenham TW1 3HN ☎ 020 8891 0779

INGARFIELD Kenneth: Address Unknown

INGRAM Gerald: 11 Northwood Avenue, Purley, Surrey CR2 2ER ☎ 020 8660 3644

JAMES David: 24 Brewers Wharf, Newark-on-Trent, Notts NG24 1ET ☎ 01636 707070

JANES Anders: 143 Cannon Lane, Pinner HA5 1HU ☎ 020 8868 0453

JEFFRIES Richard (B Gtr): 48 Havelock Road, Harrow HA3 5SA ☎ 020 8933 4099

JENNINGS Ian: 16 Lawn Road, Uxbridge, Middx UB8 2TJ ☎ 01895 461 910

JOBSON John: 2 Stockens Dell, Knebworth, Herts SG3 6BG ☎ 0143 881 3550

JOHNSON Celia: Acorn Cottage, 33 New Inn Lane, Burpham, Guildford, Surrey GU4 7HN ☎ 01483 573281

JOHNSON David: Flat 12, Milton Court, Barbican Est, London EC1, 0966 513338 mob

JOHNSON Eddie (B Gtr): 106 Woodfield Road, Hadleigh, Benfleet, Essex SS7 2ET ☎ 01702 553479

JONES Andrew: 10 Ladys Close, Watford, Herts WD1 8BD ☎ 01923 800 185

JONES David: 40 Kingfisher Drive, Ham, Richmond, Surrey TW10 7UE ☎ 020 8940 8063, 01483 723644 day

KEEN Alexander (Gtr, Per): 126 Pinto Way, London SE3 9NL ☎ 020 8856 0021

KETTEL Mary: 13 Fairlight Avenue, Woodford Green, Essex IG8 9JP ☎ 020 8504 8457, 020 8502 9707 fax

KIMBER Paul (*B Gtr*): 90 Gordon Road, Peckham, London SE15 3RP ☎ 020 7277 6395, 020 7639 2582

KLEINMAN Judith: 35 Plimsoll Road, Islington, London N4 2EL ☎ 020 7359 1481

KLUTE Martin (*Org, Pf*): 173 Barnsbury Road, Islington, London N1 0EP ☎ 020 8444 4245, 0385 243583

KNIGHT Victor (*B Gtr*): The Oast, 81A Old Dover Road, Canterbury, Kent CT1 3DB ☎ 01227 765266, 020 8882 3483

KNUSSEN Kenneth: 8 Holmesley Road, Forset Hill, London SE23 1PJ ☎ 020 8291 4144, 01306 880669 day

LAING Andrew (*Tbn*): 16 Bahram Road, Polegate, East Sussex BN26 5JB ☎ 01323 486992, 07666 705542 pager

LANNIGAN Patrick: 20 Bradbourne Vale Road, Seven Oaks, Kent TN13 3QJ ☎ 01732 741890

LAURENCE Christopher: 23 Woodberry Crescent, Muswell Hill, London N10 1PJ ☎ 020 8883 7342

LAURENCE Patrick: 88 Vicars Moor Lane, London N21 1BN ☎ 020 8360 0561

LEA Michael: 19C Abercorn Road, Mill Hill, London NW7 1JH ☎ 020 8349 0075

LEARNER Art (*Gtr*): 52 Penrose Avenue, Carpenders Park, Herts WD1 5AB ☎ 020 8428 7109

LEE Richard: 12 Campdale Road, London N7 0EB ☎ 020 7263 2665

LEWIS Richard: 10 The Highlands, Hatfield Road, Potters Bar, Herts EN6 1HU ☎ 01707 660822, 01483 723644 day

LEWIS Terry (*B Gtr, Tba*): 36A Fairdene Road, Coulsdon, Surrey CR5 1RB ☎ 017375 54417

LINLEY Roger: 25 Rennets Wood Road, Eltham, London SE9 2NF ☎ 020 8850 6215

LOEWENTHAL Sara: 47 Lockey House, 243 North End Road, London, London W14 9UQ ☎ 020 7386 8410

LOFTIN John: 46 Mornington Crescent, Hadleigh, Benfleet, Essex SS7 2HP ☎ 01702 556559

LOVELLE Laurie: 127 Lee Park, Blackheath, London SE3 9HE ☎ 020 8852 2982

LOWE Trevor (*Pf*): 1 Barrett Rise, St James Park, Great Malvern, Worcs WR14 2UJ ☎ 01684 564927

MACNAMARA Mandy: 27 Avington Grove, Penge, London SE20 8RY ☎ 020 8778 9411, 020 8778 9411

MAGUIRE Caroline: 138 Severalls Avenue, Chesham, Buckinghamshire HP5 3EN ☎ 01494 771137

MAGUIRE Francis: 95, Chamber's Lane, London NW10 2RN ☎ 020 8451 4818

MAIR Stephen: 24 Richmond Road, Leytonstone, London E11 4BA ☎ 020 8556 9297

MANIKS Val (*Pf*)

MANNERS Daniel (*B Gtr, Pf, Com, Arr*): 17 Littlebury Road, London SW4 6DW ☎ 020 7622 9206

MANOLIAS Stephen (*Com, Arr*): 34 Rossall Crescent, W.Twyford, London NW10 7HD ☎ 020 8997 1350

MANSBRIDGE Michael (*Arr*): 103 Wellington Road, London E6 4EB ☎ 020 8471 7918, 0589 424993

MANSI Thomas (*E Gtr*): 60 Gordon Road, Finchley, London N3 1EP ☎ 020 8349 0559

MARJORAM Keith: Butterly Brook, Wacton, Nr Bromyard, Herefordshire HR7 4AQ ☎ 01885 488233

MARKEE Dave (*B Gtr, Gtr*): Follys End, 8A Spencer Road, South Croydon, Surrey CR2 7EH

MARRION Paul: 12 Drury Lane, Melbourn, Cambs SG8 6EP ☎ 01763 261998

MARTIN Thomas: Park View Farm, Lower Assendon, Henley-on-Thames, Oxon RG9 6AN ☎ 01306 880669 day, 020 8579 3961

MATTHEWS Peter (*Com, B Gtr, Gtr*): 164 Bond Street, Apt 1/B, Brooklyn, NY 11217/2233, USA ☎ +1 718 522 5529

MATTOS Marcio (*Cel*): 40 Sydner Road, London N16 7UG ☎ 020 7017 1254 1351, 020 7503 8417 fax

MCCARTHY Peter (*Vlne*): 120 Chewton Road, London E17 7DN ☎ 020 8223 0772

MCCORMACK Jack: 8 Nicholas Gardens, Ealing, London W5 5HY ☎ 020 8567 8074

MCGEE Billy (*B Gtr, Com, Arr*): 87 Gurney Road, Stratford, London E15 1SL ☎ 020 8555 9852

MCGEE Robin (*Pf*): 17A Highbury Terrace Mews, London N5 1UT ☎ 020 7704 2903

MCMANUS Steve (*B Gtr*): 44 Green Curve, Banstead, Surrey SM7 1NY ☎ 01737 213996

MCTIER Duncan: 106 Hounslow Road, Twickenham, Middx TW2 7HB ☎ 020 8894 5381

MEGGIDO Marc (*B Gtr*): 12A Arkwright Mansions, 206 Finchley Road, London NW3 6DE ☎ 020 7794 5197, 020 8533 1372 day

MESSEDER Andre (*B Gtr*): 75 Altyre Way, Beckenham, Kent BR3 3ED ☎ 020 8650 8273

MILES David (*B Gtr, Gtr*): 40 Regent Road, Surbiton, Surrey KT5 8NL ☎ 020 8399 2656

MILLER Kenneth: 118 Pembroke Road, London N10 2JD ☎ 020 8883 1620

MILLER Robert (*B Gtr*): 86 Fairford Gardens, Worcester Park, Surrey KT4 7BJ ☎ 020 8873 7344

MILLER Stacey: 139 Dawes Road, Uxbridge, Middlesex UB10 0RS ☎ 01895 814862

MITCHELL Duncan (*Cel*): 9 Kingston Close, Blandford Forum, Dorset DT11 7UQ ☎ 01258 451924, 01306 880669

MITCHELL Graham: 2 St Donatts Road, New Cross, London SE14 6NR ☎ 020 8691 0309 & fax, 0976 839989 mob

MOORE Paul: 12 Manor Road, Barnet, Herts EN5 2LH ☎ 020 8440 1032, 020 8533 1372 day

MOORE Peter (*B Gtr*): 30 Byron Road, Twyford, Berkshire RG10 0AE ☎ 0118 901 6501, 0589 841685 mob

MORGAN Chris: 19 Holden House, Creekside, London SE8 4SQ ☎ 020 8692 8618

MORGAN Paul (*B Gtr*): 56 Franks Avenue, New Malden, Surrey KT3 5DB ☎ 020 8949 7602

MORGAN Pete (*B Gtr*): 183 Little Bushey Lane, Bushey, Herts WD2 3RX ☎ 020 8950 3095

MORGAN Peter: 19 Lion Road, Twickenham, Middlesex TW1 4JF ☎ 020 8892 2492

MORRIS Edmund (*B Gtr*): 38 Church Road, Watford WD1 3PU ☎ 01923 224448, 0374 688961

MORTIMORE Mick (*B Gtr, Voc*): 59 Becmead Avenue, London SW16 1UJ ☎ 020 8769 8002

MOSES David (*B Gtr*): 93 Stradella Road, London SE24 9HL ☎ 020 7274 5314

MOYLAN Paul (*Com, B Gtr, Pf*): 22 Earlsmead Road, London N15 4DA ☎ 020 8801 6441, 0973 284249 mob

MUDELE Joseph (*B Gtr*): Oak Cottage, 6 Spinney Oak, Bickley, Kent BR1 2NS ☎ 020 8467 1350

MYERS Martin: 30 Park Road, Bushey, Herts WD2 3EG ☎ 020 8950 7056

NEAL Maurice: 97 Whitchurch Gardens, Edgware, Middx HA8 6PG ☎ 020 8952 2719

NEALON Michael: Flat 1, 24 Bromley Grove, Shortlands, Kent BR2 0ET

NEIGHBOUR Sarah: 36 Chesley Gardens, East Ham, London E6 3LN ☎ 020 8472 9634

NEVISON George: 11 Lea Mount Close, Dawlish, Devon EX7 9EP ☎ 01626 862892

NEWSON Gerald: Flat 23, Hungerford House, 22 Napier Place, London W14 8LY ☎ 020 7602 4778

NEWTON David (*La Per*): "Luth Cottage", The Luth, Wisborough Green, West Sussex RH14 0BL ☎ 01737 645065 day, 01737 769793 eve

NICHOLLS Benjamin (*B Gtr, Bjo, Gtr*): Flat 9, 9 Nevern Square, Earls Court, London SW5 9NW ☎ 020 7373 9854

NWANOKU Chi-Chi: 5 Talbot Road, Isleworth, Middx TW7 7HG ☎ 020 8892 4126 & fax, 0956 546 121 mob

O'TOOLE Thomas: 31 Wycherley Crescent, Barnet, Hertfordshire EN5 1AD ☎ 020 8449 6479

OLIVER Simon (*Pf*): 104 Asylum Road, London SE15 2LW ☎ 020 7358 9519

OLNEY David (*B Gtr*): 28 Denmark Road, Cottenham, Cambridge CB4 4QS ☎ 01954 250329, 0802 806979

OSBORNE Tony (*B Gtr, Arr, Com*): 42 Parkland Avenue, Slough, Berks SL3 7LQ ☎ 01753 541818

PADMORE Samuel: 17A Frederick Street, London WC1 0NF ☎ 020 7837 5713

PARIS Colin (*B Gtr*): 3 Puckeridge Cottages, Vicarage Lane, Chigwell, Essex IG7 6LU ☎ 020 8500 5254, 01306 880669

PARIS Nathaniel (*Cop*): 8 Parkside Court, Wanstead Place, London E11 2SR ☎ 020 8989 9808

PAUL Ron (*Sou, B Gtr*): Bakers Cottage, North Lane, South Harting, Petersfield, Hants. GU31 5PY ☎ 01730 259

PEARCE Gordon: Halfway House, 16A Grove Park Gardens, Chiswick, London W4 3RZ ☎ 020 8994 2653

PEIRCE Howard (*B Gtr*): 532 Charminster Road, Bournemouth, Dorset BH8 9SJ ☎ 01202 523655

PENISTON George: 18 Stanhope Avenue, Hayes, Bromley, Kent BR2 7JR ☎ 020 8462 7838

PERKINS David: 17 St Paul Street, Islington, London N1 7AH ☎ 020 7359 2117

PRECIOUS Adam: 1 Tormount Road, Plumstead, London SE18 1QD ☎ 020 8854 7557

PRENTICE Ron (*B Gtr*): The Mill, Ash Priors, Taunton, Somerset TA4 3NQ ☎ 01823 432734

PRIORI Stefano: Flat B, 90 Honeywell Road, London SW11 6EF ☎ 020 7207 7014, 020 7207 7052 fax, 0958 459282 mob

PRYCE Richard (*B Gtr*): 9 Oswin Street, London SE11 4TF ☎ 020 7735 8056

QUINLAN Joe (*B Gtr*): 22 Derwent Avenue, Ickenham, Middx UB10 8HJ ☎ 01895 674127

RAAD Henri (*B Gtr*): 10 Stayton Road, Sutton, Surrey SM1 1RB ☎ 020 8641 6959

REES-JONES John (*B Gtr*): May Cottage, 39 Slough Road, Datchet, Slough SL3 9AL ☎ 01753 581413, 0850 670789

REYNOLDS Phil (*B Gtr, Pf*): 32 Sunset Road, Denmark Hill, Camberwell, London SE5 8EA

RICHARDS John (*B Gtr, Tba*): 1 Streete Court, Westgate-on-Sea, Kent CT8 8BT ☎ 01843 832274

RICHARDSON Don (*B Gtr*): 2 New Cottages, Bendish, Hertfordshire SG4 8JD ☎ 01438 871787 & fax, 0973 112914 mob, 020 8549 1706 day

RICHARDSON Jim (*B Gtr*): 29A Alexandra Grove, North Finchley, London N12 8HE ☎ 020 8445 5684

RICHMAN Reg: 3 Mackellar House, Burgess Hill, London NW2 2DB ☎ 020 7435 2918

RICKETTS Catherine: 63 Gordon Road, Wanstead, London E11 2RA ☎ 020 8989 1452

RINGROSE Peter (*Pf, B Gtr*): Flat 8 Fircroft, 51 Copers Cope Road, Beckenham, Kent BR3 1NJ ☎ 020 8658 9601

ROBINSON Ronald: Address Unknown

RODBER John (*B Gtr*): 157 Kingston Road, Staines, Middlesex TW18 1PB ☎ 01784 452411

ROSSELL Steve (*B Gtr*): 2 Lessar Court, Clapham South, London SW4 9HN ☎ 020 8673 8530, 0802 445 853 mob, 01306 880669 day

ROWLANDS Helen: The Squirrels, The Platt, Chenies Manor Estate, Chenies, Herts WD3 6ER ☎ 01494 764453

RUNDELL Kevin: Little Mead, Tite Hill, Engelfield Green, Surrey TW20 0NH ☎ 01784 437012

SALMON Murray (*B Gtr*): 120 Hermon Hill, South Woodford, London E18 1QB ☎ 020 8989 7640

SAMUELS Ray (*Kbds*): 62 Knowlton House, Cowley Estate, Cowley Road, London SW9 6HJ ☎ 020 7735 2646

SANTOS Ricardo (*Com, Arr*): 12 Knowles Walk, Clapham Manor Estate, London SW4 6BY ☎ 020 7720 9763

SAXBY Kate: 148 Strathville Road, Earlsfield, London SW18 4RE ☎ 020 8874 9027

SCHOFIELD Angela: 17A Highbury Terrace Mews, London N5 1UT ☎ 020 7704 2903

SCOTT Bryan (*B Gtr*): Beltane, 33 Oak Hill Road, Sevenoaks, Kent TN13 1NS ☎ 01732 453260

SCOTT-TAYLOR Ian: 148 Harrowdene Gardens, Teddington, Middlesex TW11 0DN ☎ 020 8943 3792

SCULLY Mary: Flat C, 77 Newlands Park, Sydenham, London SE26 5PW ☎ 020 8778 9159, 01306 880669

SELDIS Dominic: 29 Templeway, Lydney, Glos GL15 5HU ☎ 01594 844895, 0973 414707

SENFT Enno: 109 Rosendale Road, London SE21 8EZ ☎ 020 8761 4808

SHAW Lucy: 68 Beaulieu Avenue, London SE26 6PW ☎ 020 8778 5340, 020 8366 4643

SHEERAN Ray (*B Gtr*): 9 Edgeworth House, Boundary Road, London NW8 0HR ☎ 020 7624 8149

SHENTON John (*B Gtr*): 13 Penang Street, Wapping, London E1 9RT ☎ 020 7265 1300

SHEPPARD Godfrey (*B Gtr*): 22 Hillside Road, Lancing, West Sussex BN15 0JY ☎ 01903 755623

SHERMAN Paul: 59B Crystal Palace Road, East Dulwich, London SE22 9EX ☎ 020 8693 0291, 0973 738690, 01306 880669 day

SHINGLER Steven: 55 Queens Avenue, London N21 3JH ☎ 020 8360 6313, 0966 243883

SHULMAN Manny: 106 Morton Way, London N14 7AJ ☎ 020 8886 8250

SHUTE Doug: 27 Manton Avenue, Hanwell, London W7 2DY ☎ 020 8567 1690

SILK David: Flat 1, 237 High Street, St. Mary Cray, Orpington, Kent BR5 4AX ☎ 01689 875683 & fax

SIMMONS Alan (*B Gtr*): 31 Elm Drive, North Harrow, Middlesex HA2 7BS ☎ 020 8427 5775

SIMMS Philip (*Hpsd, Con*): 82 Greenwich South Street, London SE10 8UN ☎ 020 8692 3037

SIRETT John (*Tba, Sou*): Tanglewood Cottage, 56 Monkhams Lane, Woodford Green, Essex IG8 0NR ☎ 020 8504 2465

SKEAT Leonard: The Lodge Berrys Green, Berrys Green Road, Westerham, Kent TN16 3AJ ☎ 01959 574321

SLADE Claire: 22 Boston Manor Road, Brentford, Middlesex TW8 8DR ☎ 020 8568 5333, 020 8533 1372 day

SMITH Donald (*B Gtr, Tba*): 194 Hampden Way, Southgate, London N14 7LS ☎ 020 8368 5471

SMITH Frey (*B Gtr*): Flat 2, 122 Ladbroke Grove, London W10 5NE ☎ 020 7229 3933

SMITH Kenneth: c/o Jive Aces, Saint Hill Manor, East Grinstead, West Sussex RH19 4JY ☎ 01342 300075 & fax

SMITH Ryan: 16 Hindmans Road, East Dulwich, London SE22 9NF ☎ 020 8693 3562, 0956 586 504

SOLOMON Alfred: 70 Queenswood Avenue, Wallington, Surrey SM6 8HS ☎ 020 8647 7174

SOMOGYI Arnold (*B Gtr*): 24 Albany Road, Leighton Buzzard, Bedfordshire LU7 8NS ☎ 01525 854007

SOTHCOTT Geoffrey (*B Gtr*): 111 Chanctonbury Way, London N12 7AE ☎ 020 8445 5196

SPEIRS Paul (*B Gtr*), "Elrig", Main Street, Gartmore, Stirling FK8 3RW ☎ 01877 382247

STAFFORD Guy (*Voc*): 40 Harvey Road, London N8 9PA ☎ 020 8245 9957, 0973 409201

STEPHENS Nicholas (*B Gtr*): 21E Powis Square, London W11 2AZ ☎ 020 7229 4148, 020 7460 8746 fax

STERIOPULOS Philip (*B Gtr, Gtr*): 8 Tressillian Crescent, London SE4 1QJ ☎ 020 8469 0059

STEWART Rodney (*Pf*): Leona, 17 Haw Lane, Bledlow Ridge, High Wycombe, Bucks HP14 4JJ ☎ 01494 481362

STEWART Roy (*B Gtr*): 56 Fashoda Road, Bromley, Kent BR2 9RF ☎ 020 8464 5771

STOUT Adrian (*B Gtr, Eup, Dms, Voc*) ☎ 020 8858 0253

STREET Nicola: The Old Coach House, The Paddock, Datchet, Berks SL3 9DL ☎ 01753 545926

SUTTLE David (*B Gtr*): Flat 1, 19 Humber Road, Blackheath, London SE3 7LS ☎ 020 8858 2656

SUTTON John (*B Gtr*): 46 Dennis Road, East Molesey, Surrey KT8 9ED ☎ 020 8979 9283

TARLTON Neil (*Cel*): Stable Cottage, 116A Weir Road, London SW12 0ND ☎ 020 8673 6427

TAYLOR Alan W (*B Gtr, Arr, Com*): 26 Montem Road, Forest Hill, London SE23 1SA ☎ 020 8690 5396

TAYLOR Darren: 113 Pembury Road, London N17 8LY ☎ 020 8808 1294

TAYLOR Harry (*B Gtr*): Residencial Costa Flamenca.38, 03189 Orihuela Costa, Alicante, Spain ☎ + 34 96 676 0674

THISTLEWOOD Mark: Flat 1 10 Lewisham Road, London SE13 7QR ☎ 020 8692 2286, 020 8533 1372 day

THOMPSON Danny: 43 Mount View, Rickmansworth, Herts WD3 2BB ☎ 01923 777512

THOMSON Roderick (*Cel*): 11 Queens Walk, Ealing, London W5 1TP ☎ 020 8998 3151

THORPE Simon (*B Gtr, Gtr, Vln, Dms*): 131 Glyn Road, Clapton, London E5 0JT ☎ 020 8985 3191

TYACK Clare: 12 Normandy Avenue, High Barnet, Herts EN5 2JA ☎ 020 8449 1746

UWADIAE Owen (*B Gtr*): 82 Gleneagle Road, London SW16 6AF

VARNEY J (*B Gtr*): 2 Thornhill Road, Surbiton, Surrey KT6 7TL ☎ 020 8399 8660

VAUGHAN Jonathan: 51 Palace Gardens, Buckhurst Hill, Essex IG9 5PQ ☎ 020 8506 2252

VIGAY Martin: 1 Colwick Close, Hornsey Lane, London N6 5NU ☎ 020 7272 5845

WALKER Donald: 32 Torver Road, Harrow, Middx HA1 1TH ☎ 020 8861 5108

WALKINGTON Julie (*B Gtr*): 94 Palatine Road, London N16 8ST ☎ 020 7923 4994

WALLEY Allen (*B Gtr*): 24 Bunbury Way, Epsom Downs, Surrey KT17 4JP ☎ 01372 203653, 0973 432302

WARNER Stephen (*B Gtr*): 117 High Road, North Weald, Epping, Essex CM16 6EA ☎ 01992 522155

WATERWORTH Andrew (*B Gtr*): 40 Sach Road, London E5 9LJ ☎ 020 8806 9548

WATSON Ian (*B Gtr*): 1 Pembury Court, 47 Bolingbroke Grove, London SW11 6SP ☎ 020 7978 5893

WATSON Neil: 33 Grove Park Gardens, Chiswick, London W4 3RY ☎ 020 8995 8659

WATSON Richard (*B Gtr, M Saw*): 8 Farm Lane, Shirley, Croydon CR0 8AQ ☎ 020 8777 8371, 020 8777 7975

WATTON Stacey (*Pf*): 81 Pretoria Road, Leytonstone, London E11 4BB ☎ 020 8558 4206, 0378 141 608 mob, 01306 500011

WATTS Steve: 184 Dunstans Road, East Dulwich, London SE22 0ES ☎ 020 8693 7948

WELLS Timothy (*B Gtr*): 18 Hitherfield Road, London SW16 2LN ☎ 020 8677 1540, 020 7498 6014, 0802 938 674

WESCOTT Christopher: 45 Main Street, Higham-on-The Hill, Nuneaton, Warwickshire CV13 6AH ☎ 01455 212822

WEST Christopher: 48 Royal Hill, London SE10 8RT ☎ 020 8694 9825

WEST June: Flat 4 (Top), 20 Charleville Road, West Kensington, London W14 9JH ☎ 020 7385 8382

WHITFORD David (*B Gtr*): 19 Clifton Avenue, Walthamstow, London E17 6HL ☎ 020 8527 2083, 0958 943263

WHYATT Peter (*B Gtr*): 39 Tottenham Street, London W1P 9PE ☎ 020 7436 4565

WILKINSON Mick (*B Gtr, Sou*): 3 Halifax Street, Sydenham, London SE26 6JA ☎ 020 8699 1835

WILLIAMS Stephen: 6 Colebrooke Avenue, Ealing, London W13 8JY ☎ 020 8991 5975, 01306 880669

WILLIS Dave (*B Gtr*): Temptye Farmhouse, Worth, Deal, Kent CT14 0DJ ☎ 01304 613995

WILSON Jenni: 334 Uxbridge Road, Hatch End, Middlesex HA5 4HR ☎ 020 8428 8400, 0973 103669, 01306 880669

WOOD Andrew: 20 Oakleigh Gardens, Whetstone, London N20 9AB ☎ 020 8445 9030, 0410 222057

WOOD Gareth (*Gtr, Com*): 57 Marischal Road, London SE13 5LE ☎ 020 8318 3312

WOOLF Simon (*B Gtr, Tba, Pf, Arr*): 208A Tressillian Rd, Brockley, London SE4 1XY ☎ 020 8691 7516

WORTERS Nicholas (*B Gtr*): 10 Latchmere Road, Kingston, Surrey KT2 5TW ☎ 020 8541 4782, 0956 320 774

WRIGHT Benny (*Gtr*): 3 Cowick Road, London SW17 8PE ☎ 020 8672 1891

WRIGHT Candy: 71 Scarle Road, Wembley, Middlesex HA0 4SS ☎ 020 8903 0181, 01306 880669

WRIGHT John: Prospect Cottage, High Street, Freshwater, Isle Of Wight PO40 9JX ☎ 01983 754831

YORK Peter (*B Gtr, Voc*): 6 The Knoll, Hayes, Bromley, Kent BR2 7DH ☎ 020 8462 2547

YOUNG Saffron (*B Gtr, Ob*): 17 Westbury Road, New Southgate, London N11 2DB ☎ 020 8881 7278, 0860 215211 mob

YULE Callum: 71, Ronver Road, Lee, London SE12 0NR ☎ 020 8851 5502

DULCIMER

EAST

BANKS Jon (*Hrp, Kbds*): 32 Gosselin Road, Bengeo, Herts SG14 3LQ ☎ 01992 581099

SOUTH EAST

PRESTON Andrea (*Auto Hrp*): 12 Waterford Road, Ashley, New Milton, Hants BH25 5BH ☎ 01425 618286, 0976 928412, 01425 618286

LONDON

COUZA Jim (*Ac Gtr, Bjo, Per, Spoons*): 44 Colford Road, South Mead, Bristol BS10 5JL ☎ 0117 940 7601, 0117 908 2705, 0117 908 2705

FOX Matthew (*Md, Pf, Saxes, Per*): 10B Groveway, Stockwell, London SW9 0AR ☎ 020 7587 1246, 0976 803485 mob

E FLAT BASS

EAST

BARNETT Derek: 26 Lodgeclose, Benfleet, Essex SS7 3DA ☎ 01268 753515

EARLY KEYBOARDS

SCOTLAND

KITCHEN John (*Ea Kbds, Org, Hpsd, Pf*): 34 Spottiswoode Road, Edinburgh EH9 1BL

LANGDON John (*Ea Kbds, Org, Hpsd, Pf*): 1058 Cathcart Rd, Glasgow G42 9XW ☎ 0141 649 3739

MCPHEE George (*Ea Kbds, Org, Pf, Hpsd, Con*): 17 Main Road, Castlehead, Paisley PA2 6AJ ☎ 0141 889 3528

STRACHAN Martyn (*Ea Kbds, Org, Pf, Hpsd*): 61 Stratholmond Road, Edinburgh EH4 8HP ☎ 0131 339 3217

EARLY PERCUSSION

NORTH EAST

PEEL John (*M Inst, R Wnd, Lute, Citt*): 'Southby', Bielby, Pocklington, York YO42 4JL ☎ 01759 318311

EAST

MARSHALL David (*M Inst, R Wnd, Bag, Tpt, H Gu*): Tudor Lodge, Pymoor Lane, Pymoor, Nr Ely, Cambridgeshire CB6 2EE ☎ 01353 698084

EARLY RENAISSANCE WIND

NORTH EAST

BRYAN John (*R Stg, R Wnd*): 28 Wentworth Road, York YO24 1DG ☎ 01904 652736

MERRYWEATHER James (*R Wnd, Ea Wnd, Bag, Bsn, Bq B*): 6 Ingleborough Avenue, York YO10 3SA ☎ 01904 432878, 01904 431328

RICHARDSON Ian (*R Wnd*): 1 Beech Drive, Newlay Lane, Horsforth, Leeds LS18 4LE ☎ 01943 78949

LONDON

HAMILTON Rachel (*R Inst, Bq Flt, Hrp, Flt, Voc*): 110 Sunnyhill Road, London SW16 2UL ☎ 020 8677 4235

EARLY STRINGS

SCOTLAND

BUTTERWORTH Alexandra *(Bq Vln, Vln, Pf)*: 19 Queen Street, Stirling FK8 1HL ☎ 01786 478685

CAMPBELL Patsy *(B Viol, T Viol, Tr Viol, B Re)*: The Latch, Carlops By Penicuik, Mid Lothian EH26 9NH ☎ 01968 660530

COWAN Lucy *(Bq Vln, Vln, Vla, Bq Vla, Man)*: 12A Tower Road, Tweedmouth, Berwick-upon-Tweed TD15 2BD ☎ 01289 303982

DUNN Lawrence *(Bq Vln, Vln, Vla, Bq Vla)*: 5 St Marks Lane, Portobello, Edinburgh EH15 2PX ☎ 0131 669 3394

EDWARDS Warwick *(Vadag, B Viol, Vlne)*: 22, Falkland Street, Glasgow G12 9PR ☎ 0141 334 9229

FIELD Christopher *(Ea Stg, Vln, Rec)*: 2 Maynard Road, St Andrews, Fife KY16 8RX

GODSON Daphne *(Ea Stg, Vln)*: 48/11 Learmonth Avenue, Edinburgh EH4 1HT ☎ 0131 343 1556

HALYBURTON May *(Bq Db, Db, Vlne)*: c/o 8 Commanders Grove, Braco, Perthshire, Scotland FK15 9PL ☎ 01786 880635

HASLAM Sharon *(Bq Vln, Vln)*: Flat 4, 37 Glencairn Drive, Pollokshields, Glasgow G41 4QW ☎ 0141 423 2679

JOLLY Louise *(Ea Stg, Vln, Vla)*: Glenview, Finzean, Banchory, Kincardineshire AB31 6LY ☎ 01330 850 323

LAY Robert *(Bq Cel, Cel, B Vln, B Viol, V)*: Hillview, Cochno Road, Hardgate, Clydebank, Dunbartonshire G81 6PT ☎ 01389 875996, 01426 977225 pager

MCGILL Linda *(Bq Vla, Vla)*: Address Unknown ☎ 0141 649 5669, 0141 649 5669

PELLY Mysie *(Bq Vln, Vla)*: 7 Granton Park Avenue, Edinburgh EH5 1HS ☎ 0131 552 2068

ROBINSON John *(Bq Vln, Vln, Man)*: Flat 4, 37 Glencairn Drive, Pollokshields, Glasgow G41 4QW ☎ 0141 423 2679

RYCROFT Marjorie *(Bq Cel, Cel, T Viol, B Viol,)*: 29 Airthrey Avenue, Glasgow G14 9LJ ☎ 0141 954 5020

SPAREY-GILLIES Carolyn *(Bq Vln, Vla, Bq Vla)*: Woodside, 36 Station Road, Bearsden, Glasgow G61 4AL ☎ 0141 249 0239

WEBB Liza *(Bq Vln, Vln)*: Flat 1/2, 145 Broomhill Drive, Glasgow, Scotland G11 7ND ☎ 0141 3373912

WHITTAKER Ruth *(Ea Stg, Db, Vadag, Con)*: 48 Gartymore, Helmsdale, Sutherland KW8 6HJ ☎ 014312 380

NORTH WEST

BLACK Julia *(Bq Vln, Bq Vla, Pf)*: 104 The Baulk, Biggleswade, Beds SG18 0QA ☎ 01767 318537

GERRARD Horace *(B Viol, B Gtr)*: Flat 24 Ambergate, Lee Street, Atherton, Manchester M46 0BQ ☎ 01942 887930

SHEPHERD Martin *(Lute)*: 12 Gibsons Road, Heaton Moor, Stockport, Cheshire SK4 4JX ☎ 0161 431 7704

NORTH EAST

THODEY Robin *(Lute)*: 8 Quarry Head Lane, Durham City, Durham DH1 3DY ☎ 0191 386 0217

EAST

SPRINGHAM Herbert *(B Viol, B Gtr)*: 21 Jacksons Lane, Chesterford, Saffron Walden, Essex CB10 1PU

WALL Abby *(Bq Cel)*: 14 City Road, Cambridge CB1 1DP ☎ 01223 364642

WESTLAKE Margaret *(Viol, Rec, R Inst, Crum, Shawm)*: 15 Ballygate, Beccles NR34 9NA ☎ 01502 717182

MIDLANDS

CLARKE Garry *(Bq Vln, Vln, Pf)*: Grange Cottage, Grange Road, Kinghtley, Staffs ST20 0JX ☎ 01785 284433 & fax

MCCOY Stewart *(Lute, Theorbo)*: 55 Ranelagh Grove, Wollaton, Nottingham NG8 1HR ☎ 0115 9285794

SMITH Pam *(Lute, R Wnd, Viol, Per, Citt)*: 36 Westfields, Catshill, Bromsgrove, Worcestershire B61 9HJ ☎ 01527 875033

SOUTH EAST

BROWN Caroline *(Bq Cel, Cel)*: 47 Pembroke Crescent, Hove, East Sussex BN3 5DS ☎ 01273 338400

DEATS Gareth *(Bq Cel, Cel, Pf)*: 118 West Field Road, Coversham, Reading RG4 8HJ ☎ 01189 545822

JONES Simon *(Bq Vln, Vln, Kbds)*: The Laurels, Tollerton, York YO6 2EQ ☎ 01347 838996, 01347 838887

ROBINSON Emily *(Bq Cel, Cel)*: East West Cottage, Milland, Liphook, Borden Village GU30 7JZ ☎ 01730 821408

SOUTH WEST

HAIR Christopher *(Bq Vln, Bq Vla)*: Milton Oak Cottage, Oxland Lane, Burton, Aberdaugleddau, Pembs SA73 1LG ☎ 01646 602148

MORGAN Philippa *(Bq Cel)*: 31 Middle Street, Stroud, Glos GL5 1DZ ☎ 01453 453078

RILEY Jules *(Bq Vln, Vla, Vln)*: 3 Londonderry Terrace, Maohynlleth, Powys SY20 8BG ☎ 01654 702220 & fax, 0410 209627 mob

ROBINSON Alexandra *(Bq Cel, Vla)*: 2 A Fairleigh Road, Pontcanna, Cardiff CF1 9JT ☎ 029 2023 0076

ROBINSON Dr Lucy *(Vadag, Bq Vla)*: 25 Plasturton Avenue, Pontcanna, Cardiff CF1 9HL ☎ 029 2022 8154

LONDON

ASTLE Philip *(Reb, Tab, Sack, Bq Vln, Nak)*: Little Lodge Farm, Cloot Drove, Crowland, Peterborough PE6 0JH ☎ 01733 210704

BEALBY-WRIGHT Sarah *(Bq Vln, Vln)*: 70 Parliament Hill, London NW3 2TJ ☎ 020 7435 7824

BENJAMIN Emilia *(Bq Vln, Vadag, Vln)*: 87 Lancaster Road, London N4 4PL ☎ 020 7263 2644

CAMPBELL Richard *(Vadag, Viol, Bq Cel)*: 3 Melbourne Court, Meadway, Twickenham, Middx TW2 6PH ☎ 020 8894 5905

CAUDLE Theresa *(Bq Vln, Vla, Vadam, Ea Stg, C)*: 3 Rose Cottages, Hurstbourne Tarrant, Nr Andover, Hampshire SP11 0BB ☎ 01264 736565

COOPER Marc *(Bq Vln, Vln)*: 19 South Street, Lewes, East Sussex BN7 2BT ☎ 01273 478393

CRACKNELL Alison *(Bq Vln, Vln)*: 211 Sheepcot Lane, Garston, Watford, Herts WD2 7DD ☎ 01923 449259

CRUM Alison *(Ea Stg, Vadag, Viol, Vlne, Vi)*: 87 Olive Road, London NW2 6UR ☎ 020 8452 3254

DELLER Nicola *(Vadag, Cel)*: The Keep, 18A Castle Street, Ongar, Essex CM5 9JS ☎ 01277 365702

FINUCANE Thomas *(Lute)*: 1 Lancaster Rd, Hitchin, Hertfordshire SG5 1PE ☎ 01462 440780

HARRIS Rosalind *(Bq Vln, Vln)*: 24 James Street, Epping, Essex CM16 6RR ☎ 01992 574737

HAYSTON Nicola *(Ea Stg, Bq Vln)*: 11 Heathfield South, Twickenham, Middlesex TW2 7SR ☎ 020 8287 3349

HODGSON Julia *(Vadag, Cel)*: 16 Teddington Park Road, Teddington, Middlesex TW11 8ND ☎ 020 8977 0924, 020 8404 2414

HOMBURGER Maya *(Bq Vln)*: Carrickmourne, Thomastown, Co. Kilkenny, Ireland ☎ +353 0 56 58 708, +353 0 56 58 709

HUNT William *(Vadag)*: 16 Teddington Park Road, Teddington, Middx TW11 8ND ☎ 020 8977 0924, 020 8404 2414 fax

JEANS Clare *(Bq Cel, Cel)*: 48 Norroy Road, Putney, London SW15 1PF ☎ 020 8788 7433

JEFFREY Robin *(Lute)*: 1 Church Cottages, Rotherfield, Sussex TN6 3LN ☎ 0189 285 2878

LEVY Mark *(Vadag)*: 46 Uplands Road, London N8 9NL ☎ 020 8348 4295

LINDO Sharon *(Bq Vln, Vln)*: Pipdeen, Broad Street, Uffington, Oxford SN7 7RA ☎ 01367 820541

LINELL Dorothy *(Lute, Theorbo, Gtr)*: 59 Highland Road, Northwood, Middx HA6 1JR ☎ 01923 822934, 0402 973442 mob

MICHALAK Kazimierz *(Lute, Theorbo, Citt, Bq Gtr)* ☎ 020 8469 0710

MILES Rebecca *(Bq Vln, Rec)*: 154 Choumert Road, London SE15 4AA ☎ 020 7635 8379

MILLER David *(Lute, Theorbo, Gtr)*: 10 Park Road, Chesham, Buckinghamshire HP5 2JE ☎ 01494 793506 & fax

ORSLER Helen *(Bq Vln)*: 1 Balfour Gdns, Forest Row, E Sussex RH18 5LJ ☎ 01342 822 025

PALLETT Elizabeth *(Lute, Theorbo)*: 38 Falkland Road, Harringay, London N8 0NX ☎ 020 8340 5429, 0850 685784

PARKER Joanna *(Bq Vln, Vln)*: 1 The Laurels, Kingsway Avenue, Woking, Surrey GU21 1NX ☎ 01483 721639

PINTO David *(Vadam)*: 38 Agate Road, London W6 0AH

POPE Martin *(Lute, Ea Wnd, Sack)*: 1 Boston Farm Cottages, Swyncombe Avenue, Ealing, London W5 4DT ☎ 020 8568 1445

SALAMAN Clare *(Bq Vln, Vln, H Gurd)*: 40 Wellmeadow Road, London SE13 6TB ☎ 020 8698 9143

SETH-SMITH Imogen *(Bq Cel, Cel, Vadag)*: 19C Blenheim Gardens, Willesden Green, London NW2 4NP ☎ 020 8452 6423

SKEAPING Emma *(Bq Cel, Cel, B Gtr)*: 100A Highbury Hill, London N5 1AT ☎ 020 7354 1381

SOTHCOTT John *(Reb, Vielle, Citole, Rec, Cru)*: 75 Herons Wood, Harlow, Essex CM20 1RP ☎ 01279 31588

STOTT Rachel *(Ea Stg, Vla, Bq Vla, Com, Vad)*: Basement Flat, 66 Amhurst Road, London E8 1JH ☎ 020 7704 0147

TARLING Judith *(Bq Vla, Bq Vln)*: 3 North Street, Punnetts Town, Heathfield, East Sussex TN21 9DT ☎ 01435 830839

THEO Tatty *(Bq Cel, Cel, B Vln)*: 69 Tabley Road, Islington, London N7 0NB ☎ 020 7607 0185, 07957 335694, 01603 763279

THORNDYCRAFT Rosemary *(Vadag)*: 72 Sussex Way, London N7 N7 6RR ☎ 020 7272 9009

WAYNE Henrietta *(Bq Vln)*: 3 Melbourne Court, Meadway, Twickenham TW2 6PH

WEIGAND George *(Lute, Man, Cimb)*: 72 Sussex Way, London N7 6RR ☎ 020 7272 9009

WENDLAND Peter *(Vadag, Vlne, Viol, Rec)*: Flat 9, Keswick Court, 17/19 Malyons Rd, London SE13 7XQ ☎ 020 8690 1176

WHISKIN Peter *(Bq Vla, Vadam, Bq Vln)*: 51 Queens Road, London N11 2QP ☎ 020 8889 5717

WILSON Christopher *(Lute)*: 21 Powis Square, Brighton BN1 3HG ☎ 01273 730922 & fax

WOOTTON Douglas *(Lute, Gtr, Bjo, Bq Man)*: 3 Macualay Road, London SW4 0QP ☎ 020 7622 9393

YAKELEY M *(Bq Gtr, Gtr, Vih, Lute, Cl Gt)*: 19 Linton Street, London N1 7DU ☎ 020 7354 2973

EARLY WIND

SCOTLAND

BAXTER Robert *(Ea Wnd, Tpt, N Tpt)*: 3/L, 24 Ancroft Street, Woodside, Glasgow G20 7HU ☎ 0141 332 7561

BELL Morven *(Obdam, Ob, Cor, B Ob)*: 39/1 Bryson Road, Edinburgh EH11 1DY ☎ 0131 313 1298

CAMPBELL Murray *(Cntt Zin, R Wnd, Viol, Tbn, S)*: The Latch, Carlops, Penicuik, Midlothian EH26 9NH ☎ 01968 660530

EVANS Susan *(Bq Flt, Flt, Pic)*: 6/12 Dorset Place, Edinburgh EH11 1JP ☎ 0468 322069 mob

HARROLD Shaun *(Ea Wnd, N Tpt, Pictpt, Cnt, F)*: 21 Lubnaig Gardens, Bearsden, Glasgow G61 4QX ☎ 0141 943 1157, 0468 053816 mob

HILL-AHMAD Jennifer *(Ea Wnd, Rec, Clt)*: 35 Victoria Cresc Rd, Glasgow G12 9DD ☎ 0141 339 5012

KENNY John *(Sack, Tbn, Alp Hrn, Rec, Com)*: 69 Spottiswoode Street, Edinburgh EH9 1DL ☎ 0131 447 3707

LOGAN Kirstie *(Obdam, Ob, Cor)*: 32 Falkland Street, Hyndland, Glasgow G12 9QY ☎ 0141 337 1282

MILNE John *(Sack, Tbn, A Tbn, Com)*: Flat 1, 215 Paisley Road West, Kinning Parr, Glasgow G51 1NE ☎ 0141 427 9105

MUNDAY Ray *(Ea Wnd, Tpt, Pictpt, N Tpt, C)*: 15 Cairnpark Street, Dollar, Clackmannanshire FK14 7ND ☎ 01259 742143

SHARP Paul *(Ea Wnd, Tpt, N Tpt, Cntt)*: 36A Main Road, Castlehead, Paisley, Renfrewshire, Scotland PA2 6AW ☎ 0141 889 4878, 0410 020012 mob

WILSON Lesley *(Bq Ob, Bsn)*: 226 Bankhead Road, Aberdeen, Aberdeen AB21 9HR ☎ 01224 716418, 0421 366020

NORTH EAST

SARGEANT Michael *(Ea Wnd)*: 19 Burke Street, Harrogate, North Yorkshire HG1 4NR ☎ 01423 500351

MIDLANDS

BEZNOSIUK Lisa *(Bq Flt, Flt)*: Egton Cottage, Kidd Lane, Clun Shropshire SY7 8LN ☎ 01588 640361, 020 8533 0429, 0973 831019

SOUTH EAST

RAINBIRD Noel *(Bq Bsn, Bsn, Pf)*: 45 Elmthorpe Road, Wolvercote, Oxford OX2 8PA

SARGENT Raymond *(Ea Wnd, Rec, Bag, Saxes, Voc)*: 38 Coventry Close, Corfe Mullen, Wimborne, Dorset BH21 3UP ☎ 01202 604598

SOUTH WEST

MCKENNA Sophia *(Bq Ob)*: Ty Mawr, Nant-Y-Gwreddyn, Brecon, Powys LD3 8HA ☎ 01728 648574

VAN-DER-BEEK Andrew *(Serp, Sack)*: Cantax House, Lacock, Chippenham, Wiltshire SN15 2JZ ☎ 01249 730468

LONDON

BELLAMY Alexandra *(Bq Ob, Ob)*: Flat 3, 18 Anerley Hill, Crystal Palace, London SE19 2AD ☎ 020 8659 5440

BIRCHER Katy *(Bq Flt, Flt, Rec, Pic)*: 6 Alma Road, Muswell Hill, London N10 2NG ☎ 020 8883 9435, 0410 066083 mob

CANEPA Marco *(Bq Flt, Flt)*: 5A Crebor Street, London SE22 0HF ☎ 020 8693 3086

CRAWFORD Andrew *(Ea Wnd, Bq Flt, Flt, B Gtr)*: 11 Goldsmith Close, East Acton Lane, London W3 7EZ ☎ 020 8749 2015, 020 8961 7066

DIXON Matthew *(Bq Ob, Rec)*: 47 North Hill, Highgate, London N6 4BS ☎ 020 8340 7042

DOONER Elizabeth *(Bq Flt, Flt)*: 19 Warrender Park Crescent, Edinburgh EH9 1EA ☎ 0131 229 7740

DOWNER Jane *(Bq Ob, Rec, Obdam, Obdac)*: 2 Rose & Crown, High Street, Stonesfield Witney, Oxfordshire OX8 8QJ ☎ 01993 898681

FIBBENS Alan *(Bq Flt, Rec, Flt)*: 16 Spring Grove, Loughton, Essex IG10 4QB ☎ 020 8508 0617

GREGORY James *(Ea Wnd, Flt, Pic, Bq Flt)*: Foscot Cottage, Foscot, Nr Kingham, Oxon OX7 6RH ☎ 01608 659034

IKEDA Utako *(Bq Flt, Flt)*: 9 Selborne Road, Wood Green, London N22 4TL ☎ 020 8889 9522

KERSHAW Caroline *(Bq Ob, Rec)*: Flat 4, 57 Aberdare Gardens, West Hampstead, London NW6 3AL ☎ 020 7624 2609 & fax

KING Andrew *(Bq Ob)*: 8 Claigmar Gardens, Finchley, London N3 2HR ☎ 020 8343 0186

LATHAM Catherine *(Bq Ob, Rec)*: 32 Chilswell Road, Oxford OX2 4PJ ☎ 01865 793060

MCDONALD John *(Bq Ob, Bq Flt, Rec)*: 3A Huntley Way, London SW20 0AH ☎ 020 8949 3249

MCGOWAN Keith *(Shawm, Cur, R Wnd)*: 87 Middle Lane, Crouch End, London N8 8NX ☎ 020 8340 2156 & fax, 01523 124853

MOSS Rachel *(Bq Flt, Rec)*: Flat 3, 92 Madeley Road, Ealing, London W5 2LX ☎ 020 8566 7016

PERRY Nicholas *(Ea Wnd, Cnt, Shawm)*: 20 Queen Street, St Albans, Herts AL3 4PJ ☎ 01727 866600

POPE Martin *(Ea Wnd, Sack, Lute)*: 1 Boston Farm Cottages, Swyncombe Avenue, Ealing, London W5 4DT ☎ 020 8568 1445

STOCK Hilary *(Bq Ob, Obdam, Obdac, Rec)*: 123 Dukes Avenue, Muswell Hill, London N10 2QD ☎ 020 8444 5092 & fax

WATTS Andrew *(Bq Bsn, M Inst, R Inst, Shawm)*: 81 Laugherne Road, Worcester WR2 5LY ☎ 01905 429848 & fax

WATTS Michael *(Bq Ob, Obdam, Bq Rec)*: 168 Tarring Road, Worthing, West Sussex BN11 4HG ☎ 01903 535479

WEST Jeremy *(Ea Wnd, Bag, Rec)*: 80 Vancouver Road, London SE23 2AJ ☎ 020 8473 0444, 020 8699 6926, 0958 611478

WILLIAMS Guy (*Bq Flt*): 70 Hayfield Road, Oxford OX2 6TU ☎ 01865 559771

WILLIAMS Sarah (*Ea Wnd, B Tbn, B Sack, Eup*): 47 Whymark Avenue, London N22 6DJ ☎ 020 8365 8364, 0976 298509 mob

ELECTRIC VIOLIN

SCOTLAND

FUTTER George: 80, Post Hill, Sauchie, Clacks FK10 3NU ☎ 01259 721016

HENNESSEY Andrew (*Vln, Bod, Wh, Per*): 24/2 Burgess Street, Edinburgh EH6 6RD ☎ 0131 554 4486, 0131 467 4248

PAULEY John (*Synth*): 11 Allan Street, Aberdeen, Scotland AB10 6HL ☎ 01224 594720

SOUTH EAST

STRACHAN Johanna (*Vln, Pf, Kbds, Voc*): Flat 3, 1 Denmark Terrace, Brighton, East Sussex BN1 3AN ☎ 01273 739476, 049 88 22 329

WARE Rebecca (*Vla, Vln*): St Catherines, Off Main Street, Gawcott, Bucks MK18 4HX ☎ 01280 822 270

LONDON

EVANS Kat (*Vln, Pf*): 55 Hazelville Road, Hornsey Rise, London N19 3ND ☎ 020 7281 8070

HAMBROOK Helen (*Man*): 64 Talbot Road, Old Isleworth, Middlesex TW7 7HF

HESLOP Kathryn (*Vln, Pf*): Flat C, 9 Bradiston Road, Maida Vale, London W9 3HN ☎ 020 8969 5528

HEYMAN Paul (*Kbds*): 26 Mavis Court, 4 Raven Close, Colindale, London NW9 5BJ ☎ 020 8203 3130

MEE (*Voc*) ☎ 020 7252 3417, 0956 921056

MORRIS Mo (*Vln*): 17 Forest Drive, Manor Park, London E12 5DF ☎ 020 8478 3975

ROBERTS Franklin (*Vln*): 78 Headley Grove, Tadworth, Surrey KT20 5JF ☎ 01737 361636

ELECTRIC ACCORDION

SCOTLAND

HUTTON Jimmy: 2295 Great Western Road, Glasgow G15 6UY ☎ 0141 944 3432

RICHARDSON Ian (*Pf*): 19 Kenilworth Drive, Edinburgh EH16 6DD ☎ 0131 664 1063

ROBERTSON Morag (*Voc*): 6 Montgomery Crescent, Dovecote Park, Carron, Falkirk FK2 8ND ☎ 01324 562578

NORTH WEST

HOLMES Daniel (*Pf, Kbds, Dms*): Transudanjo House, 50 Skinburness Drive, Silloth, Carlisle Cumbria CA5 4QG ☎ 016973 31623

SOUTH EAST

JENNINGS Jamie: 7 Forest Dell, Winford, Nr Sandown, Isle Of Wight PO36 0LG

SOUTH WEST

HARDING Robert: 49 Fairleigh Road, Pontcanna, Cardiff CF1 9JW ☎ 029 2021 5061

ORCHARD Harry: 36 Sheppard Road, Pennsylvania, Exeter EX4 5DD ☎ 01392 50848

SCOTT John: General Stores, Hallatrow Road, Paulton, Avon BS39 7LH ☎ Mid Norton 4131

LONDON

GRAHAM Brian (*Acc*): 1 Windermere Way, Yiewsley UB7 8LX ☎ 01895 444173, 0585 427116

LEACH Norman: 28 Castle Street, Greenhithe, Kent DA9 9AB ☎ 01322 382723

ELECTRIC CELLO

LONDON

OLIVER Max: 14 Parkhill Road, London NW3 2YN ☎ 020 7485 3555

ELECTRIC DOUBLE BASS

NORTH WEST

GOULDING Simon (*Db*): 236 Spendmore Lane, Coppull, Lancashire PR7 5DE ☎ 01257 793257

SOUTH EAST

BREE Michael (*Gtr*)

LONDON

DUNCAN Ossy (*Db, Kbds, Per*): 22 Medora Road, Romford, Essex RM7 7EP ☎ 01708 788068, 0958 939282, 01708 788068

ENGSTROM Emil (*Clt*): 3 Flinders House, Gren Bank, London E1 9QA ☎ 0961 880098

ELECTRIC PIANO

SCOTLAND

MACTAVISH D Grant (*Hmca*): 80 Udston Road, Hamilton, Lanarkshire ML3 9HX ☎ 01698 822430

NORTH EAST

GOULDING Stanley: 84 Jarvis House, Swanpool, Lincoln LN6 0EB ☎ 01522 683928

EAST

BALL Jack (*Org, Acc, Arr*): 4 The Badbers, Langdon Hills, Basildon, Essex SS16 6AU ☎ 01268 415846

MIDLANDS

BLENCOWE Ju (*Ac Gtr*): 32, Rickerscote Asenue, Stafford, Staffordshire ST17 4EZ ☎ 01785 51878

SOUTH EAST

NEWPORT John (*Org*): 62 Northumberland Avenue, Margate, Kent CT9 3LY ☎ Thanet 225058

LONDON

GOLDSTONE Simon (*Synth, Pf, Gtr*): 107A Camden Mews, London NW1 9AH ☎ 020 7267 5772, 0467 828886

ETHNIC STRINGS

LONDON

LEWIN Giles (*Eth Stgs, Vln, Eth Wnd*): 6 Bedford Street, Oxford OX4 1SU ☎ 01865 242881

EUPHONIUM

NORTH WEST

POWELL John (*T Tba, B Tpt*): 39 Water View Park, Leigh, Lancaster WN7 4JP ☎ 01942 680941, 0973 787663

WALTON Paul: 15 Muirfield Close, Wilmslow, Cheshire SK9 2QT ☎ 01625 532932, 0410 311771 mob

NORTH EAST

CHILDS Robert (*Tba*): 2 Priory Close, Swanland, Hull, North Humberside HU14 3QS ☎ 01482 3632217

EVANS Sarah ☎ 07970 692645 mob

MASON Peter (*Tba, Tpt*): 17 Milton Lane, Easington Colliery, Peterlee SR8 3DR ☎ 0191 527 3230, 0191 527 3230

ONYON Peter (*Cnt, Gtr, Sax*): 20 Beacon Road, Loughborough LE11 4BQ ☎ 01509 266254

WILLIS Simon: Pretoria, Maida Lane, Ollerton, Newark, Notts NG22 9AF ☎ 01623 823969, 0850 087736

Europe's favourite flute specialist

MIDLANDS

MALLEN Stuart (*Tba, Tbn, Md, Kbds*): 38 Links Road, Penn, Wolverhampton, West Midlands WV4 5RF ☎ 01902 344178

MEAD Steven (*Pf*): 10 Old Forge Road, Fenny Drayton, Nuneaton, Warks CV13 6BD ☎ 01827 711964 & fax

SOUTH WEST

WINTERFLOOD John: 103 Drove Road, Swindon, Wilts SN1 3AE ☎ 01793 421511

LONDON

COPLAND-CALE Mr R (*Tbn*): 6 Strathearn Road, Wimbledon, London SW19 7LH ☎ 020 8947 0547

DOWN Spencer (*Tba, Tbn*): 4 Western Court, Chandlers Way, Romford RM1 3JR ☎ 01708 734228

DURELL Sarah (*B Tbn*): 4 Parr Close, Leatherhead, Surrey KT22 7HD

HAWKES Dennis (*Tba, Tpt, Tbn, Clt*): 8 Sidcup Road, Lee Green, London SE12 8BW ☎ 020 8850 5922

FLUGEL HORN

NORTH EAST

WALTERS Mark (*Cnt, Tpt*): 'Overdale', 17 Hampole Balk Lane, Skellow, Doncaster DN6 8LF ☎ 01302 722544

EAST

DEASON Roger (*Tpt*): 39 Ranleigh Walk, Harpenden, Hertfordshire AL5 1SR ☎ 015827 61628

THOMPSON William (*Tpt*): 28 Dubbs Knoll Road, Guilden Morden, Royston, Herts SG8 0LA

SOUTH EAST

CHRISTINA (*Tpt, Kbds*): Limberlost, Riverside, Temple Gardens, Chertsey Lane, Staines, Middx TW18 3NJ ☎ 0966 453580 mob

SOUTH WEST

NORTH Chris (*Tpt, Cnt*): 39A Ranelagh Road, Mount Charles, St Austell, Cornwell PL25 4NS ☎ 01726 75984, 0973 452655 mob

LONDON

FINDLAY Thomas (*B Gtr, Club Dj*): 80A Highbury Park, London N5 2XE ☎ 020 7690 8316, 0385 987454

FLUTE

SCOTLAND

BAILIE Laura (*Pic, Bq Flt*): 6 Dalmellington Drive, Crookston, Glasgow G40 4AN ☎ 07771 550871

BREW Helen (*Pic*): 20 Station Road, Balfron, Glasgow G63 0SY ☎ 01360 440264

CARTLEDGE Lucy (*Pic*): 12 Glenorchy Terrace, Edinburgh EH9 2DQ ☎ 0131 667 1633

CHESTER Richard: Milton Of Cardross, Port Of Menteith, Stirling FK8 3JY ☎ 01877 385634, 0141 332 8311, 0141 332 3915 fax

CHISHOLM Fiona: 11 Dudley Drive, Glasgow G12 9SF ☎ 0141 357 0021

CRAIG Nicholas: Whiteside House, Dunscore, Dumfries, Scotland DG2 0UU ☎ 01387 820501

CUTHBERTSON Caroline: 81 Castle Heather Road, Inverness IV2 4EA ☎ 01463 241806

ELIOT Rosemary: 25 Kelvinside Terrace South, Glasgow G20 6DW ☎ 0141 946 0380

EVANS Anne (*Pf*): 32 Regent Street, Edinburgh EH15 2AX ☎ 0131 669 2440

EVANS Jack: 50 George Street, Edinburgh EH2 2LE ☎ 0131 226 6263

EVANS Susan (*Pic, Bq Flt*): 6/12 Dorset Place, Edinburgh EH11 1JP, 0468 322069 mob

FINLAYSON Donald (*Sax, Clt*): 11 Cairngorm Road, Glasgow G43 2XA ☎ 0141 637 8654

FRANCO Mariana (*Pic*): 304 Baker Ave, Ventura, CA 93004, USA ☎ +1 805 647 5112

FRASER Lorraine (*Pic, Voc*): 11A Thimblehall Drive, Dunfermline KY12 7UG ☎ 01383 723759

GRISI Laura (*Wh, Rec*): Acres Wild, Broadford, Isle Of Skye, Scotland IV49 9AE ☎ 01471 822505

GUERRIER Rosemary (*Pic, A Flt*): 40 Thornwood Terrace, Glasgow, Scotland G11 7QZ ☎ 0141 339 5512

GUILD Heather (*Pic*): 53 Grange Road, Edinburgh EH9 1TX ☎ 0131 667 4605

GWILT George: 39 Oxgangs Road, Edinburgh EH10 7BE ☎ 0131 445 1266

HARTLEY Elaine: 151 Alison Street, Flat3/3, Glasgow G42 8RY ☎ 0141 424 1455

HEATH Dave (*Com*): 3 Marchmont Street, Edinburgh EH9 1EJ ☎ 0131 229 8385

INGLIS Jacqueline (*Pic*): 213 Wilton Street, One-Right, North Kelvinside, Glasgow G20 6DE ☎ 0141 946 9070

KINGSLEY Paul (*Pic*): 1/1 33 Turnberry Road, Glasgow G11 5AL ☎ 0141 334 8022

KNORR Rebecca (*Tin Wh*): 13/5 Gayfield Square, Edinburgh EH1 3NX ☎ 0131 556 8550

KUYPERS Andrea (*Pic*): 2/2 69 Leslie Street, Pollokshields, Glasgow G42 2JX ☎ 0141 423 5377, 0378 281585 mob

LAURIE Jill (*Pic, Sax, Pf*): 42 Thomson Street, Dundee DD1 4LG ☎ 01382 646638

LAWSON Douglas: Dunvegan, 14 Causewayhead Road, Stirling FK9 5EN ☎ 01786 474027

LOCK Rosemary (*Pic*): Oak Royal, Aberfoyle, Stirlingshire FK8 3UX ☎ 01877 382633, 0411 649720 mob

MCCABE Michelle (*Pic*): 1 Hazel Avenue, Bearden, Glasgow ☎ 0141 563 9896, 07970 294135

MCGEOCH Colin (*Synth, Voc*): Flat 3/L, 150 Fergus Drive, North Kelvinside, Glasgow G20 6AX ☎ 0141 946 1677

MCILWHAM George (*Pic, Com, Bag, Md*): 25 Ravelston Road, Bearsden, Glasgow G61 1AW ☎ 0141 942 6779

MURRAY Jean: 11 Melville Place, Edinburgh EH3 7PR ☎ 0131 226 3392

ORMISTON George (*Vln, Gtr, Sax*): 82 Crosswood Terrace, Tarbrax, West Calder EH55 8XE ☎ 01501 785416

PINKERTON Alison (*Pic*): 29 Dyke Road, Greenrigg, Hart Hill, Lanarkshire ML7 5QT ☎ 01501 753 954

RICHARDSON Janet (*Pic*): 100 Norse Road, Scotstoun, Glasgow G14 9EQ ☎ 0141 959 7646

SHAW Joanna (*Pic*): 10 Garrioch Drive, Glasgow G20 8RS ☎ 0141 945 2880, 0860 105772 mob

SVILENOV Ret (*Kbds, Pf, Dms, Per*): c/o 5 Doonhoum Place, Alloway, Ayr, Ayrshire, Scotland KA7 4QH ☎ 01292 441 283

WALKER-THOM Lydia (*Pic, Clt, Sax, Rec*): North Craigieford Cottage, Ellon, Aberdeenshire AB41 8NL ☎ 01358 722636

WALLACE Keith (*Arr, Com*): 37 Glencairn Drive, Pollokshields, Glasgow G41 4QW ☎ 0141 423 2810

WISHART Bobby (*Clt, Saxes, Pf, Synth*): 200 Greenock Road, Largs, Ayrshire KA30 8SB ☎ 01475 686993, 01475 675917 fax

NORTH WEST

ABSON Joanne (*Pic*): 8 Kempton Close, Newton-Le-Willows, Merseyside WA12 0BD ☎ 0142 6252592

BARROW John (*Pic*): 9, Gledholt Road, Huddersfield, Yorkshire HD1 4HD ☎ 01484 533094

BHATTACHARJEE Nicholas (*Pic*): 6 Alderdale Drive, Heaton Moor, Stockport, Cheshire SK4 4AS ☎ 0161 432 8283, 0973 257927

BIRTLES Rachel (*Ctna, Wh*): 4 Tollemache Terrace, Chester CH2 3EL ☎ 01244 314688, 07970 729023

BODDINGTON Joanne (*Pic, A Flt*): 16 Corkland Road, Chorlton, Manchester M21 8UT ☎ 0161 881 0984, 0966 497159

BOOTY Jonathan (*Pic, A Flt*): 7 Stratford Avenue, West Didsbury, Manchester M20 8LZ ☎ 0161 445 9936

BOYLETT Lynda (*Pic, Voc*): 7A Lon Goed, Holywell, Flintshire CH8 7PG ☎ 01352 715537

BREWER Mary: 35 Derbyshire Road, Sale, Ches M33 3FD ☎ 0161 973 6852

BULL Sarah (*Pic, Pf*): 21 Booth Road, Hartford, Cheshire CW8 1RD ☎ 01606 74588

CHAMBERS Colin (*Pic, A Flt*): 97 Lyndhurst Avenue, Mossley Hill, Liverpool L18 8AR ☎ 0151 724 2082

CHEETHAM Marguerite: 11 Great Borne, Brownsover, Rugby, Warks CV21 1SD ☎ 01788 567092

COWDEN Susan (*Pic*): 11467 Morse Road, S W Pataskala, Ohio 43062, USA

DAVIS Richard: 138, Windlehurst Road, High Lane, Stockport, Cheshire SK6 8AF ☎ 0161 449 9620

DE LOZEY Suzanne (*Pf*): High Lorrimer, Endmoor, Kendal, Cumbria LA8 0QF ☎ 015395 60054

DOWTON Nicola (*Pic, A Flt*): Flat 6, 28 Atwood Road, Didsbury, Manchester M20 6TD ☎ 0161 434 5700, 07801 418840

DUCKWORTH Ruth (*Pf, Kbds, Gtr*): Flat 3, 9 Lancaster Avenue, Liverpool L17 3AY ☎ 0151 734 5698

EDWARDS Nicola (*Pic, Pf*): 9 Hardcastle Close, Bolton, Lancs BL2 4NR ☎ 01204 451 502

EVERETT Jenny (*Pic, Pf*): 2A Beaumont Road, Chorlton, Manchester M21 8BR ☎ 0161 882 0148, 0966 214268 mob

FENTON Judy (*Pic*): 11A Devonshire Road, Liverpool L8 3TX ☎ 0151 727 2850

FRAMPTON Pauline (*Pic*): 20 Grasmere Road, Gledholt, Huddersfield, W. Yorks. HD1 4LJ ☎ 01484 537514, 0966 477406

GALWAY George (*Clt, T Sax*): 141 Fog Lane, Didsbury, Manchester M20 0ED ☎ 0161 445 1859

GILLESPIE Russell (*Pic*): 36 Ray Avenue, Nantwich, Cheshire CW5 6HJ ☎ 01270 626937

GRAINGER Lindsay (*Pic, A Flt*): The Barn Flat, Moss Lane Farm, Moss Lane, Styal Wilmslow, Cheshire SK9 4LQ ☎ 07050 119822, 0161 437 9104

HARRIS Neil (*Pic, A Flt*): The Brook, Poplar Grove, Llanrwst, Gwynedd LL26 0ED ☎ 01492 640317

HUNTER Nichola (*Pic, A Flt*): 21 Amberwood Drive, Baguley, Manchester M23 9ND ☎ 0161 902 0505

HURST Eileen (*Pic, Bsn*): 44 Braunton Road, Liverpool L17 6AP ☎ 0151 427 3048

JELLICOE Laura (*Pic, A Flt, Con*): 9 Vincent Avenue, Chorlton, Manchester M21 9GR ☎ 0161 860 6097

JONES Collette (*Ob, Rec, Sax, Pf*): Leaholme, Grove Road, Mollington, Chester CH1 6LG ☎ 01244 851513

KANE Michael (*Bag*): 22 Beech Ave, Northerde, Manchester M23 4JE ☎ 0161 945 5331

KYNASTON Samantha (*Sax*): 46 Ford Lane, Didsbury, Manchester M20 2TJ ☎ 0161 445 5195

LORRIMAN Christine: 6, Penny Green, Cammock Lane, Settle, N. Yorks. BD24 9BH ☎ 01729 822662

LYONS Rachel: 72 Crawford Avenue, Mossley Hill, Liverpool L18 1DS ☎ 0151 475 9723, 0802 444600 mob

MACEANRUIG Heather (*Sax, Ob, Clt*): Hafod Ruffydd Uchaf, Beddgelert, Gwynedd LL55 4UU ☎ 01766 890 434

MALONE Jacqueline (*Pf*): 10 Byron Street, Chorley, Lancashire PR7 1AF ☎ 01257 262051

MARLOWE Ronald (*Pic*): 15 Turnlee Drive, Glossop, Derbyshire SK13 9XA ☎ 01457 855717

MCDONOUGH Emer (*Pic, Pf, Rec*): Flat 1, 7 Kenilworth Avenue, West Didsbury, Manchester M20 2LJ ☎ 0161 434 1842, 0411 098654 mob

MCNALLY Jane (*Clt, Sax, A Sax, Pf*): 24 Carlton Street, Prescot, Merseyside L34 6JB ☎ 0151 289 3686, 0410 481576 mob

MILLS Celia (*Pic*): 8 Hallwood Road, Handforth, Cheshire SK7 9BG ☎ 01625 522401

MILNER Jeanette (*Pic*): Beck House, Old Hutton, Near Kendal, Cumbria LA8 0NH ☎ 01539 734721

NASH Jane (*Cl Gtr, Saxes*): 19 Mayfield Road, Timperley, Altrincham, Cheshire WA15 7TB ☎ 0161 980 2894

NELSON David: 35 Old Broadway, Manchester M20 9DH ☎ 01456 450 219

O'NEILL Anna (*Kbds*): 17 Hill Lane, Blackley, Manchester M9 6PE ☎ 0161 795 9653, 0802 440424

O'NEILL Claire (*Pic*): 73 Egerton Road South, Chorlton, Manchester M21 0YH ☎ 0161 860 6193, 0411 282823

PARKER Leslie (*Pic*): 2 Almond Way, Greasby, Wirral, Merseyside L49 3QQ ☎ 0151 678 2442

PIGOTT Myra (*Pic*): 84, Vaughan Road, Wallasey, Wirral, Merseyside L45 1LP ☎ 0151 639 1027

POOLEY Hilary (*Pic*): 43 Clothorn Road, Didsbury, Manchester M20 0BP ☎ 0161 445 6896

RAINER Florica: 21 Cavendish Road, Birkdale, Southport, Merseyside PR8 4RT ☎ 01704 568155

ROSTRON Roger: 14 Bank Hall Road, Heaton Moor, Stockport, Cheshire SK4 3JR ☎ 0161 431 5517

SHELDON Hannah (*Sax, Pf, Clt*): Lane End, Leigh Road, Knutsford, Cheshire WA16 8NT ☎ 01565 653225, 0589 848852

SIMPSON Karen (*Voc, Rec*): 15 Glossop Road, Hayfield, High Peak SK22 2NF ☎ 01663 742689

SKYRME Martin (*Pic, Saxes, Clt*): 21 Preston Road, Lytham, St Annes, Lancashire FY8 5BL ☎ 01253 739118

SPIEGL F (*Pic*): 4 Windermere Terrace, Liverpool L8 3SB ☎ 0151 727 2727

STIRLING Alexandra (*Pic*): 1 Cam Street, Woolton, Liverpool L25 7RT ☎ 0151 428 1495

SUMBLER David (*Pic*): 14 Thaxted Drive, Offerton, Stockport, Cheshire SK2 5XH ☎ 0161 483 1327

UTTLEY Michelle (*Pf, Clt, Rec*): 12 Orme Avenue, Salford M6 8LT ☎ 0973 386 468 mob, 0161 789 3796

WALLER Claire (*Pf*): 20 Wakefield Road, Great Sutton, South Wirral L66 2HW ☎ 0151 348 1842, 0421 345091

WEBBER Beverly (*Rec*): Hilltop, Chester Street, St Asaph, Clwyd LL17 0RE ☎ 01745 583980

WOLOHAN Dennis (*Pic, T Sax*): 20 Broomflat Close, Standish, Nr Wigan, Lancashire WN6 0NF ☎ 01257 423309

NORTH EAST

APPLEBY Clare (*Pic, A Flt*): 545 Leeds Road, Scholes, Leeds, West Yorks LS15 4DA ☎ 0113 2646455, 0976 400743

ARMOUR Bernard (*Pic*): Address Unknown

BARKER Naomi (*Bq Flt, Rec, Pf*): 32 Thornton Crescent, Blaydon-on-Tyne, Tyne & Wear NE21 4BA ☎ 0191 414 1723

BEATTY Frances (*Pf*): Address Unknown ☎ 01347 822700

BEVERIDGE Tim (*Pic, Pf, Org*): 80 Broadmayne Avenue, High Barnes, Sunderland, Tyne & Wear SR4 8LU ☎ 0191 528 3846

BISENGALIEV Stina (*Pic*): Stockton Grange, Harewood Avenue, Harewood, Leeds LS17 9LA ☎ 01132 886 880 & fax

BORTHWICK Margaret (*Pic*): 19 Highbury, Jesmond, Newcastle-upon-Tyne, Tyne & Wear NE2 3DY ☎ 0191 281 1007

BOURNE Sue (*Pic*): 10 Sunset View, Meanwood, Leeds LS6 4LR ☎ 0113 2757167

BREAKSPEAR Julia (*Pic*): 27 Airedale Mount, Bagley Lane, Rodley, Leeds LS13 1JD ☎ 0113 2553005

BROOK John (*Pic*): 20 New Adel Gardens, Leeds LS16 6BD ☎ 0113 2675787

CAMM Howard: 48 High Street, Wolviston Village, Cleveland TS22 5JX ☎ 07970 366614, 01523 456274 pager

CARTER Nick: 3 Ure Bank Terrace, Ripon, North Yorks HG4 1JG

CLOUGH Diana (*Pf*): Beech Tree Farm, Flaxton, York YO60 7RP ☎ 01904 468797

CROFT Nicola (*Pf, Pic, Voc, Clt*): 30 Elmwood Grove, Hornbury, Wakefield, West Yorkshire WF4 5JJ ☎ 01924 274837, 07771 993721, 01709 891189

CUPMAN Beatrix (*Pic*): 1 Ridgmont Road, Bramhall, Stockport SK7 1JX ☎ 0161 439 6834

DAVIES Rebecca J (*Pic, Rec, Pf*): Flat 5, 13 Claremont Drive, Leeds LS6 4ED ☎ 0113 278 0994

DIXON Maurice (*Pic, Pf*): 7 Kinder Avenue, Dale View, North Hykeham, Lincoln LN6 8HA ☎ 01522 680930

DUNN Martin (*Pic, Wh*): Address Unknown

EKE Diane: Maristowe, Belton Road, Beltoft, Nr Doncaster DN9 1NB ☎ 01724 782924

GENNEDY *(Voc, Sax, Gtr)*: 68 Tudor Road, Intake, Doncaster DN2 6DY

HARGRAVES Linda *(Pic)*: 22 Longlands Avenue, Denholme, Bradford, Yorkshire BD13 4AP ☎ 01274 833448

HASLAM David *(Con)*: 23 William Street, Newcastle-upon-Tyne NE3 1SA ☎ 0191 284 6135

HELLIWELL Donna *(Pic, A Flt, Pf)*: 94 Heaton Road, Huddersfield HD1 4JJ ☎ 01484 540737, 01698 861673

HORSFALL George: 8 Raby Drive, East Herrington, Sunderland, Tyne & Wear SR3 3QE ☎ 0191 528 1202

HUGHES Jill *(Pic, Bq Flt)*: 17 Alexandra Terrace, Hexham, Northumberland NE46 3JH ☎ 01434 604049

LINNEMANN Henrik *(A Flt, Pic)*: 24 Carterknowle Road, Nether Edge, Sheffield S7 2DX ☎ 0114 2582906

LITTLEWOOD Andrew *(Pic, Pf, Clt)*: 8 Talbot Grove, Off Street Lane, Roundhay, Leeds LS8 1AB ☎ 0113 2697754

MASON Helen *(Rec)*: 45 Cecil Street, Lincoln LN1 3AT

MELLOR Judith *(Pic, Pf)*: 57 The Grove, Totley, Sheffield S17 4AR ☎ 0114 2361116

MILLER Sue *(Pf, Sax)*: 25 Norman Row, Kirkstall, Leeds LS5 3JL ☎ 0113 2748425

MOSELEY David *(Pic)*: 8 Brooklands, East Keswick, Leeds, West Yorks LS17 9DD ☎ 01937 572487

NEW Tim *(Saxes, Gtr)*: 55 Wellington Street, York YO10 5BB ☎ 01904 622550

ORANGE Evelyn *(Pic)*: 12 Meadow Way, Lanchester, Co Durham DH7 0QB ☎ 0191 548 4947

OWEN Stephen: 40 Kellett Road, Leeds LS12 4SG ☎ 0113 2635658

PRIOR John *(Sax, Clt)*: 46 Mount Pleasant, Louth, Lincs LN11 9DW ☎ 01507 604722

ROBINSON Peter *(Flag, Man, Gtr, Voc)*: 26 Redhills Lane, Crossgate Moor, Durham City DH1 4AW ☎ 0191 386 9723

SCALLY Michelle *(Voc)*: 69 Scott Hall Road, Chapeltown, Leeds LS7 2HH ☎ 0113 2392473, 04325 607876, 229 2541

SHUTTLEWORTH Jack *(Pic)*: Minims, 31 Moorhead Crescent, Shipley, Yorks BD18 4LQ ☎ 01274 586023

SMITH Edwina *(Bq Flt, Pf)*: 113 The Village, Strensall, York YO32 5XD ☎ 01904 490008

STEWART Brian *(Pic)*: 14 Rye Terrace, Hexham, Northumberland NE46 3DX ☎ 01434 608493

STEWART Eva *(Pic, Pf)*: 46 Warwick Street, Heaton, Newcastle-upon-Tyne, Tyne & Wear NE6 5AQ ☎ 0191 240 2037

TULLOCH Nicola *(Voc, Pic)*: Grove Lodge, Ironworks Road, Tow Law, Co. Durham DL13 4AJ ☎ 01388 731165

WADSWORTH Della: 31 Rosslyn Street, Clifton Green, York YO26 7QR ☎ 01904 644840

WARD Robert: 100 Cowrakes Road, Oakes, Huddersfield HD3 3ST ☎ 01484 655134

WARRINGTON Nicola *(Pic, A Flt)*: 298A Vicarage Road, Longwood, Huddersfield, West Yorkshire HD3 4HJ ☎ 01484 650148

WHITING Ken *(Clt, Bsn, Saxes)*: 1 Golden Lion Yard, Market Place, Thirsk, North Yorkshire YO7 1BD ☎ 01845 525032

EAST

BLAKEMAN Edward *(Pic)*: 50 Icknield Close, Wendover, Aylesbury, Bucks HP22 6HG ☎ 01296 624191

BOOKBINDER Laura *(Pic, Tnd Per)*: 22 Farriers Way, Borehamwood, Herts WD6 SQ ☎ 020 8953 3240, 04116 63885

BRAGG Keith *(Pic)*: 35 Silvesters, Harlow, Essex CM19 5NN ☎ 01279 411156, 01279 434749

BRIGHT Helen *(Pic, Pf)*: The Pureell School, Aldenham Road, Bushey, Herts WD2 3TS ☎ 0589 071095

CAROUTH Joscelin *(Pic, Pf)*: 18/20 Colneford Hill, White Colne, Essex CO6 2PJ ☎ 01787 223582

ELVIN C: 2 Central Avenue, Corringham, Essex SS17 7PJ ☎ 01375 676076, 0402 879326

GIBLEY Ruth *(Pf)*: 39 Hemmant Way, Gillingham, Beccles, Suffolk NR34 0LF ☎ 01502 712091

GLOVER Vanda *(Clt, Rec)*: 52 Leigham Court Drive, Leigh-on-Sea, Essex SS9 1PU ☎ 01702 475416

HOUTHEUSEN Howard *(Pic, Clt, Saxes)*: Buttons Close, 35 High Street, Ixworth, Bury St Edmunds IP31 2HJ ☎ 01359 230570

JEFFRIES Joanne

KING Anne *(Pic, Pf)*: 4 St Lawrence Lane, Norwich, Norfolk NR2 1ES ☎ 01603 626401

KINGSTON Jacqueline *(Pic, Pf)*: 5 Pannels Close, Glemsford, Sudbury, Suffolk CO10 7RR ☎ 0973 400757

MEADOWS Gabrielle *(Rec, Pf)*: 28 Sandringham Road, Norwich, Norfolk NR2 3RY ☎ 01603 767240

RADLEY Alison *(Pf)*: 32 Hope Street, Cambridge CB1 3NA ☎ 01223 414689

SHAW Madeleine *(A Flt, Pf)*: 40 High Street, Ashwell, Herts SG7 5NW ☎ 020 7736 6046

STUART Amanda *(Sax)*: Croeso, Church Lane, Hilton, Huntingdon Cambs PE18 9NH

WOODS Janet *(Wh, Rec, Sax)*: 11 Old Farm Road, Carlton Coleville, Lowestoft, Suffolk NR33 8RR ☎ 01502 518637, 0374 294966

MIDLANDS

ABURTO Fredy *(Pan P, Cuatro, Charango)*: 157 Evesham Road, Stratford-upon-Avon CV37 9BP ☎ 01787 294870

ASHE-ROY Hilary: 46, Granville Street, Leamington Spa, Warks CV32 5XN ☎ 01926 883433

BARLEY Helen *(Hrp)*: Tower Crest, The Compa, Kinver, Nr Stourbridge, West Midlands DY7 6HS ☎ 01384 877572, 04111 28572

BILLINGTON Anna: 110 Glen Road, Oadby, Leicester LE2 4RF ☎ 0116 271 4332

BROOKS Jenny *(Pic, A Flt)*: 32 Long Furrow, East Goscote, Leics LE7 3ZL ☎ 0116 2607314

BYAM-GROUNDS Gabrielle *(Pic, A Flt)*: Conway Cottage, Dunnington, Alcester, Warks B49 5NX ☎ 01789 778457

CAWDREY Julian: 8,Brook End Close, Henley In Arden, Warwickshire B95 5JE ☎ 0156 479 3394

CHADWICK Alison *(Pic)*: 22 Shipley Close, Heritage Mews, Branston, Burton-on-Trent, Staffs DE14 3HB ☎ 01283 569 572, 0802 433 937 mob

CHARLESWORTH Clara *(Pic)*: 50 Park Road, Earl Shilton, Leicester LE9 7EB, 0966 519103 mob

CLARK Diane *(Pic, A Flt)*: 11 Abbey Crescent, Halesowen, Birmingham B63 2HP ☎ 01384 561185

DAVIES Sonja *(Pic)*: 6 Churnet View, Oakamoor, Stoke-on-Trent ST10 3AE ☎ 01538 702882

DENNISON Alison *(Pic, A Flt)*: 15 Raeburn Drive, Toton, Nottingham NG9 6LF ☎ 0115 973 4439, 0976 515404

DRUMMOND Pippa *(Pic, Bq Flt)*: 11 Barrat Cres, Attenborough, Nottinhamshire NG9 6HH ☎ 0115 9677670

DURAN Elena: 3 Wheelers Court, Scholars Lane, Stratford-upon-Avon CV37 6HE ☎ 01789 269247

EAST Carol *(Pic, A Flt)*: 11 Manby Road, Malvern, Worcs WR14 3BD ☎ 01684 562400

FRANCIS Susan *(Pic, Wh, Bod)*: 29 Bernard Road, Oldbury, West Midlands B68 9AP ☎ 0121 421 1270, 07775 961198

FRANKLIN John *(Pic, A Flt)*: 12 Gladstone Road, Wollaston, Stourbridge, Worcs DY8 3PE ☎ 01384 838047

FREEMAN Sophia *(T Sax, Clt)*: 119 Victoria Crescent, Burton-upon-Trent, Stafford DE14 2QQ ☎ 01283 545147, 0589 676248 mob

GALLAN Anna *(Pic, Rec, Pf)*: 13 Hathaway Road, Tile Hill Village, Coventry CV4 9HW ☎ 024 7646 2275

GOODWIN Linda *(Pic, B Flt)*: 11 Granville Crest, Kidderminster, Worcs DY10 3QS ☎ 01562 751963

GOWLAND Kevin *(Pic)*: 24, Herbert Road, Bearwood, Warley, West Midlands B67 5DD ☎ 0121 429 8577

HAYWARD Ruth *(Pic, Rec)*: Terraine, Worthen, Shrewsbury SY5 9HT ☎ 01743 891294

HUMPHREYS Alison *(Pic)*: 70 Billesley Lane, Moseley, Birmingham B13 9QU ☎ 0121 449 5751

JONES Holly (*Pf*): Address Unknown ☎ 0116 2693139

LANE Andrew (*A Flt, Pic*): 69 Elmfield Crescent, Moseley, Birmingham B13 9TL ☎ 0121 449 1128

LANE Sally (*Pic, B Flt, Rec*): 90 Westbourne, Woodside, Telford, Salop TF7 5QL ☎ 01952 582220

LEAH Philip (*Pic*): 23 New England, Halesowen, West Midlands B62 9EG ☎ 0121 421 6108

LILLEY Colin (*A Flt, Pic*): 60 Norman Road, Northfield, Birmingham B31 2EP ☎ 0121 476 9210

MADDER Louise (*Pic*): 51 Brookvale Avenue, Binley, Coventry CV3 2DG

MALLETT Lisa (*Pic*): 2 Florence Place, Ombersley Road, Balsall Heath, Birmingham B12 8UX ☎ 0121 440 5586

MASON Noreen: 1 The Bridle Path, Allesley Village, Coventry, West Midlands CV5 9PF ☎ 024 7640 4696

MAYCOCK Claire (*Pic, A Sax, Clt*): 48 Coxwell Street, Faringdon, Oxon SN7 7HA ☎ 01367 241926

MCDOWALL Robert (*Pic*): 18 Birch Lane, Oldbury, Warley, Birmingham B68 0NZ ☎ 0121 421 7998, 0976 623 099

MILLS Helen (*Pic, Pf*): 47 Blenheim Road, Moseley, Birmingham B13 9TY ☎ 0121 449 2135

MORGAN Dana (*Pic*): 29 Craven Street, Melton Mowbray, Leicestershire LE13 0QT ☎ 01664 566 183

NEGUS Annette (*Pf*): 6 Blenheim Court, Sandiacre, Nottingham NG10 5PQ ☎ 0115 939 1522

NG Janine (*Sax, Clt*): 3A Higham Road, Stanwick, Northants NN9 6QE ☎ 01933 622549, 0961 300 998, 01933 622549

PARRY Russell (*Pic, Rec*): 21 St Phillips Road, Leicester LE5 5TR ☎ 0116 2737189

RAYBOULD Paul (*Pic, A Flt*): 164 Northfield Road, Kings Norton, Birmingham B30 1DX ☎ 0121 458 1229

REYNOLDS Ian (*Pic, A Flt, B Flt, Rec*): 493, Warwick Road, Solihull, West Midlands B91 1AN ☎ 0121 705 1239

ROBERTSON Caroline (*Pic*): 10 Kingsley Close, Stafford, Staffordshire ST17 9BT ☎ 01785 258557

ROPER Judeth (*Pf, Rec, A Sax*): 8 Newlands Avenue, Shepshed, Loughborough, Leicester LE12 9DW ☎ 01509 508863

RUHM Delia (*Pic*): 294 Hagley Road, Birmingham B17 8DJ ☎ 0121 429 1779

SANDERS Diana (*Voc*): 9 Crosswood Close, Loughborough, Leicestershire LE11 4BP ☎ 0115 972 2881

SCHRODER Julie (*Pic*): 42 Billesley Lane, Moseley, Birmingham B13 9QS ☎ 0121 449 2407

STEWARD Christopher (*Pic*): 14 Park Hill Road, Harborne, Birmingham B17 9SL ☎ 0121 426 4316

TEBBY Kate (*Pic, Voc, Pf*): Oakland, 184 Seabridge Lane, Newcastle, Staffs ST5 3LS ☎ 01782 613874

VANN Esther (*Cop*): Hambrook Cottage, Hereford Road, Ledbury, Herefordshire HR8 2PX ☎ 01531 670634

WALSH Fred (*Pic, A Flt*): 9 Waterloo Drive, Banbury Road, Stratford-upon-Avon, Warks CV37 7HS ☎ 01789 66407

WHATLEY David (*A Flt, Pic, Rec*): 44 Crosbie Road, Harborne, Birmingham B17 9BE ☎ 0121 427 7149

SOUTH EAST

ADAMS Sally (*Pic, Rec, A Flt*): 5 Banbury Road, Bloxham, Nr Banbury, Oxfordshire OX15 4PB ☎ 01295 720815

BASTER Cheri (*Rec, Bq Flt, Pf, Clt*): 43 Duncans Close, Fufield, Andover, Hants SP11 8EJ ☎ 01264 773124

BAXTER Diane (*Clt*): 80 Myrtledene Road, Abbey Wood, London SE2 0EU ☎ 020 8310 4857

BENTLEY Clare (*Pic*): 3 Mount Pleasant Cottages, Ide Hill, Nr Sevenoaks, Kent TN14 6JH ☎ 01732 750635

BRADDOCK John (*Pic*): Felin Gwyddil, Pontwelly, Llandysul, Dyfed SA44 4RU ☎ 01559 384506

BROWN Barbara (*Pic*): 79 Alexandra Road, Poole, Dorset BH14 9EW ☎ 01202 773294

BUSWELL John (*Pic*): 41 Midhurst Drive, Goring By Sea, Worthing, West Sussex BN12 5BD ☎ 01903 2424587

CARTLEDGE Nicholas (*Kbds*): 8 Russetts Drive, Fleet, Hants GU13 9QE ☎ 01252 628057, 0410 652168 mob

CHENEOUR Paul: 87A Queens Road, East Grinstead, West Sussex RH19 1BG ☎ 01342 300949

CLACKETT David (*Saxes, Arr*): 11 Warfield Avenue, Waterlooville, Portsmouth, Hants PO7 7JN ☎ 023 9278 3100, 023 9278 3200 fax

CLERICI Brenda (*Pic*): Nairn House, 2 Dunkeld Road, Talbot Woods, Bournemouth Dorset BH3 7EN ☎ 01202 552661

DAVIES Gareth: 16 Oakley Lane, Wimborne, Dorset BH21 1SG ☎ 01202 840219

DRYDEN Kenneth (*A Flt, B Flt, Pic, Saxes*): 7 Elmfield Way, Sanderstead, Surrey CR2 0EG

EVANS Karen (*Pic*): Church Cottage, Winterborne Stickland, Blandford, Dorset DT11 0NJ ☎ 01258 881206

GARRETT Katherine (*Tin Wh, Voice*): Coombe End Farm House, Whitchurch Hill, Pangbourne, Berks RG8 7TE ☎ 01189 984 5053

GIBSON Rachel (*Pf*): Address Unknown ☎ 01202 773421

HARRIS Alison (*Rec, Pf*): 30 Willowbed Drive, Chichester, West Sussex PO19 2JB ☎ 01243 788699

HIGGINS Janet: 33 Alexandra Road, Shirley, Southampton SO15 5DH ☎ 023 8023 7054

JOY Susan/Susi (*Pic, Com, Pf*): c/o The Vicarage, Park Avenue, Ventnor, Isle Of Wight PO38 1LD ☎ 01983 854367

JUDSON Michael David (*A Sax, Pf, Vla*): 16 Fulbert Drive, Bearsted, Maidstone, Kent ME14 4PU ☎ 01622 735880

LOCHBAUM Chloe (*Pic*): 2A Hampton Terrace, Beacon Hill Road, Hindhead, Surrey GU26 6NR ☎ 01428 605 958

LOUISE Joanna (*Pic*): Huntick Farm Cottage, Huntick Road, Lychett Matravers, Poole, Dorset BH16 6BB ☎ 01202 622753

MCCARTHY Sinead (*Pic, A Flt, Pf*): 87A Queens Road, East Grinstead, West Sussex RH19 1BG ☎ 01342 300949

MURPHY John (*Pic*): 4 Stanton Close, Damory Down, Blandford, Dorset DT11 7RT ☎ 01258 453952

NASH Julia (*Clt, Pf, Rec*): 17 Rosebery Ave, High Wycombe, Bucks HP13 7AL ☎ 01494 525703 & fax, 0831 786845 mob

NELSON Howard (*Pic*): Yew Tree Cottage, 14 Brook Street, Great Bedwyn, Marlborough, Wiltshire SN8 3LZ ☎ 01672 870929

PETHER Margaret: 82 Seagull Road, Strood, Rochester, Kent ME2 2RH ☎ 01634 722400

QUANTRILL Sally (*Pic*): 18 Carlton Square, Carlton Colville, Lowestoft, Suffolk NR33 8JL ☎ 01502 563028

SEE Janet (*Bq Flt*): 56A Kingsdown Avenue, Ealing, London W13 9PT ☎ 020 8840 0867

SHACKLETON Penelope (*Pf*): Hulgrove Farm, 93 Drayton Road, Sutton Courtenay, Abingdon, Oxon OX14 4HB ☎ 01235 531314

SMITH Denise: May Villa, 4 Downs Ave, Whitstable, Kent CT5 1RS

SMITH Dominic (*B Gtr*): Flat 1, 10 Western Place, Worthing, Sussex BN11 3LU ☎ 01903 820166

SMITH Simon (*Saxes, Flt*): 7 Montreal Road, Brighton, Sussex BN2 2UY ☎ 01273 699621

SOLDAN Robin (*Pic*): 19 Orchard Street, Chichester, West Sussex PO19 1DD ☎ 01243 531527

STILES Helen (*Pic, Gtr*): 53 Trinity Court, Grays Inn Road, Bloomsbury, London WC1X 8JX

SUTTEE Teresa (*Pf*): 7 Old Grimsbury Road, Banbury, Oxon OX16 7HG

TANNER Stephen (*A Sax, Saxes, Clt, Rec*): 32 Kimbolton Road, Copnor, Portsmouth, Hants PO3 6BY ☎ 023 9275 4628

THORNE Richard (*Pic*): 8 Musson Close, Abingdon, Oxon OX14 5RE ☎ 01235 550472

WAREHAM Donna (*Rec, Bq Flt, Clt*): 67 North Road, Portslade, Brighton, East Sussex BN41 2HD ☎ 01273 421802

WAY Janet (*Pic, A Flt*): 12 Jesse Terrace, Reading, Berks RG1 7RT ☎ 0811 950 7865 & fax

WELSH Joana (*Voc*): 140 Haviland Road East, Bournemouth BH7 6HR ☎ 01202 395363, 0976 882818

WHITE Brian (*Sax, Pic*): 4 Clifton Road, Bognor Regis, Sussex PO21 2HH ☎ 01243 821281

WILSON Fiona (*Rec*): Dells Cottage, Common Road, Dorney, Bucks SL4 6PX ☎ 01628 663255

All Flutes Plus

5 Dorset Street, London W1H 3FE
Tel: 0171 935 3339 Fax: 0171 224 2053
Email: afp@allflutesplus.co.uk http://www.allflutesplus.co.uk

WRIGHT Joanna (*Pf, Sax*): The Nurse's Cottage, Graces Lane, Chieveley, Newbury, Berkshire RG20 8XG ☎ 01635 248381, 0589 270538 mob

SOUTH WEST

ADAMS Lucy (*Pic*): 10 Langdon Road, Leckhampton, Cheltenham, Glos GL53 7NZ

ARMSTRONG Roger (*Pic*): 43 St Michaels Road, Llandaff, Cardiff CF5 2AN ☎ 029 2056 0176

BALLANTYNE Ruth (*Sax, Pf, Clt, Pic*): 70 Callington Road, Saltash, Cornwall PL12 6DY ☎ 01752 844017, 0585 065355

BAMFORD Jennifer (*Pic*): 59 Cumberland Road, Old Walcot, Swindon, Wiltshire SN3 1AB ☎ 01793 523937

BASTIN Sarah (*Pic*): Sharpitor, 15 Anne Hathaway Drive, Churchdown, Gloucestershire GL3 2PX ☎ 01452 712565, 0958 792578

BLEWETT Suzanne (*Pic*): 12 Hill View Road, Hucclecote, Gloucester GL3 3LG ☎ 01452 69414

BLOCKLEY Dale: Highbury House, Egloskerry, Launceston, Cornwall PL15 8RT ☎ 0156 685 410

BOYLE Margaret (*Voc, Tin Wh*): 4 Victoria Street, Oakworth, Keighley, Yorks BD22 7HU ☎ 01535 647848

BROWN Jacqueline (*Rec, Pf*): Brooklands, Donne Lane, Lower Odcombe, Yeovil, Somerset BA22 8TY

BUCKLAND Susan: 4 Penylan Court, Penylan Road, St Brides Major, Mid Glamorgan CF35 1SB ☎ 01656 880300

BURGE Harry (*Pic*): 14 Lansdowne Road, Crownhill, Plymouth PL6 5ED ☎ 01752 776822

BURGESS Jonathan (*Pic*): 5 Fairfield Avenue, Cardiff CF5 1BR ☎ 029 2055 3806

CAMERATA Trio: 13 Efford Road, Higher Compton, Plymouth, Devon PL3 6NE ☎ 01752 778695

COLE Susan (*Pic*): 3 Bruddel Grove, Swindon, Wiltshire SN3 1PW ☎ 01793 520379, 0802 537207

DAWTON Sally (*Pic*): 1 Southwell, Trull, Taunton, Somerset TA3 7HU ☎ 01823 337466

DOOLAN Sarah (*Clt, Rec, Sax, Pf*): Conamore, Coldridge, Crediton, Devon EX17 6AX

ELLIOTT Katie (*Pf*): 36 Heron Road, Easton, Bristol BS5 0LU ☎ 0117 9028 467

EVERINGHAM John (*Bq Flt, Pic, Rec, Clt*): 17 Collingwood Road, Redland, Bristol BS6 6PD ☎ 0117 9741781

FAIRFIELD Michael: 48 High Street, Dilton Marsh, Westbury, Wiltshire BA13 4DY ☎ 01373 823490

FOGGIN Susan (*Pf*): 3 Covingham Drive, Swindon, Wiltshire SN3 5BQ ☎ 01793 485245

GABRIEL Peter (*Pf, Voc*): Real World, Box Mill, Mill Lane, Box, Wiltshire SN14 9PL ☎ 01225 743 188, 01225 743 787 fax

GROVES Jane (*Pic, Pf*): 244 Cathedral Road, Cardiff CF1 9JG ☎ 029 2039 7714

HANDLEY Catherine (*Pic*): Cwm Cottage, Bettws, Abergavenny, Gwent NP7 7LG ☎ 01873 890135

HANNAH Jayne (*Clt, Rec*): Batstone Cottage, Budleigh Hill, Budligh Salterton, Devon EX9 7DT ☎ B/Salterton 382

HEANEY Clare: 46 Theobald Road, Canton, Cardiff CF5 1LP ☎ 029 2038 8220

HIGHTON Elizabeth: 24 Argyll Road, Exeter EX4 4RY ☎ 01392 410636

HINDLE Claire (*Pf, Clt, Sax*): Flat 13, Roundham House, Belle Vue Road, Paignton, South Devon TQ4 6ER

JONES Anthony: 1 Peppercombe Close, Urchfont, Devizes, Wilts SN10 4QS ☎ 01380 840338

KING Zoe (*Pf, A Sax, T Sax, Cel*): 11 Stmargarets Road, Swindon, Wiltshire SN3 1RU ☎ 01793 522350

LEWIS Thomas (*Pic, A Sax, Ob, Clt*): Cnwc, 19, Penrhw Road, Risca, Newport, Gwent NP1 6GA ☎ 01633 613117

MAY Elizabeth (*Pic*): 8 Wellington Street, Tongwynlais, Nr Cardiff, S Glamorgan CF4 7LP

MAY Kaja: 70 Bournville Road, Weston-Super-Mare, Avon BS23 3RR ☎ 01934 413969

MCLARIN Lyn (*Pic, A Flt*): Address Unknown ☎ 0117 9520619

MICHELL Chris (*Pic, A Flt, Eth Flts, Rec*): PO Box 875, Bath, Avon BA1 3TJ ☎ 01458 832784

MUSSON Rachel Tara (*A Sax*): 37 Warner Road, London E17 7DY ☎ 020 8509 0645

NORLAND Brigitte (*A Flt, Pic*): Yondercott House, Uffculme, Cullompton, Devon EX15 3DR ☎ 01884 840230

PACIELLO David (*Pic, A Sax, T Sax, Clt*): 36 Glasllwch Crescent, Newport, Gwent NP9 3SE ☎ 01633 256390

PALMER Albert (*Pic*): 28 Henbury Court, Station Road, Henbury, Bristol BS10 7QL

PARFITT Diane (*Pic, A Flt, A Sax*): 30 Brendon Avenue, Weston-Super-Mare BS23 0TE

PLOWMAN Lynne (*A Flt, Pic, Com*): 175 Malefant Street, Cathays, Cardiff CF2 4QG ☎ 029 2023 9198

REID Helen: Le Hocq Cottage, La Rue De La Hocq, St Clement, Jersey, Channel Islands JE2 6LF ☎ 01534 56667

ROBERTS Dafydd (*Hrp*): Bwlchgrwnog, Lon Bwlch, Cwm-Y-Glo, Caernarfon LL55 4ED

ROHAN (*Voc*): Ground Floor Flat, 32 Heathfield Place, Cardiff, Wales CF4 3JZ ☎ 029 2062 4401

ROPER Amanda (*Br Sax, T Sax, Pic*): 391 Teignmouth Road, Torquay, Devon TQ1 4RR ☎ 01803 325424

SHORLAND Jonathan (*Bag, Ob, Hrn*): 3 Aberystwyth Street, Splott, Cardiff CF2 2EW ☎ 029 2046 5639

SMITH Grace (*Pf*): 55 Eggbuckland Road, Hartley, Plymouth PL3 5JR ☎ 01752 771761

SQUIRES Maureen (*Pic*): 37 Cornwall Avenue, Swindon, Wilts SN2 1PG ☎ 01793 539353

SWAYNE Jon (*A Sax, S Sax, Bag*): 1 Gilberts Corner, Baltonsborough, Glastonbury, Somerset BA6 8RB ☎ 01458 50911

SYKES Branwen (*Pic*): Top Flat, 337 Newport Road, Roath, Cardiff CF2 1RL ☎ 029 2045 0292, 07775 786035

THOMAS Matthew (*Pic*): 107 Kennington Avenue, Bishopston, Bristol BS7 9EX ☎ 0117 9427867

THOMSETT Ian (*Sax, Clt*): 24 Ware Road, Castle View, Caerphilly, Mid Glamorgan CF38 1SX ☎ 0385 595941

TIMMS Carole (*Pic, A Flt*): 4 Sheppards Walk, Chilcompton, Somerset BA3 4FF ☎ 01761 233 982, 0973 821520

TOWNSHEND Douglas (*Pic*): Woodside Cottage, Church Lane, Glascoed, Nr Pontypool, Gwent NP4 0UA ☎ 01495 785629, 0498 672041

WATKINS Philip (*Pic, T Sax, Arr*): 53 St Gowan Avenue, Heath, Cardiff CF4 4JX ☎ 0122 611 254

WEBB Malcolm (*Pic*): 41 Priors Hill, Wroughton, Swindon, Wilts SN4 0RR ☎ 01793 813095

WHITE Nicola (*Pic, T Sax, Clt, Pf*): 85 Bowden Park Road, Crownhill, Plymouth PL6 5NQ ☎ Plymouth 708903

WHITTERIDGE Janet (*Pic*): Brookside, Top Street, Pilton, Nr. Glastonbury BA4 4DF ☎ 01749 890646

WICKHAM Hilary (*Br Sax*): High Park Cottage, Wiveliscombe, Taunton, Somerset TA4 2AB ☎ 01984 23335

WILLY Jennifer: 45 Halswell Road, Clevedon, N. Somerset BS21 6LE ☎ 01275 871763

LONDON

ADAMS Ann (*Pic, Con*): 38 Grove Road, Barnet, Herts EN4 9DE ☎ 020 8440 1050

ADAMS Fay (*Pic*): 278 Ballards Lane, London N12 0ET ☎ 020 8343 8597

ADENEY Richard: 52A Northumberland Place, London W2 5AS ☎ 020 7229 6174

ALEXANDRA Janet (*Pic*): 17A Pemberton Gdns, Islington, London N19 5RR ☎ 020 7272 1563

ALLEN Anne (*Pf*): 16 Graham Road, London N15 3NL ☎ 020 8888 8481

ALLEN Sarah (*Acc, A Flt, Pic, Tin Wh*): 23A Devonshire Close, London W1N 1LG ☎ 020 7637 0595

ANGLIM Goretti (*Wh, Uill*): 2 Kestrel Close, Hornchurch, Essex RM12 5LS ☎ 01708 551749, 0956 697448 mob

ANSON (*Pic, Pf*): 85 Bromfelde Road, London SW4 6PP ☎ 020 7627 8894, 0976 989050

BAILEY Christina (*Pf, Vln*): 4 Denison Road, Ealing, London W5 1NU ☎ 020 8998 0004

BAILEY Owian (*Pic*): 133 Riversdale Road, Highbury, London N5 2SU ☎ 020 7704 0113, 01523 113717 pager

BAIN Christopher (*Pic*): 90 Haven Lane, Ealing, London W5 2HY ☎ 020 8998 6246, 020 7354 2711

BAKER Alan (*Pic, A Flt, B Flt*): 51 Sylvan Road, Upper Norwood, London SE19 2RU ☎ 020 8771 6004, 0973 503912 mob

BAKER David (*Pic*): Cantegrilh, Le Sud, 46200 Lacave, Souillac, Lot, France

BARNARD Lianne (*Pf*): Denholme, West Street, Odiham, Hampshire RG29 1NR ☎ 01256 701782, 01306 880669 day

BECKETT Edward (*Pic, A Flt*): Carrigmor, Sheethanger Lane, Felden, Herts HP3 0BG ☎ 01442 68123

BEECHEY Keith (*R Inst, Hrp*): 36 Birchwood Avenue, London N10 3BE ☎ 020 8883 5742

BELL Kenneth (*Pic, A Flt, B Flt*): 1 Radnor Road, Harrow, Middx HA1 1RY ☎ 020 8427 6141

BELL Sebastian (*Pic, A Flt, B Flt*): Ivy Castle, Eel Pie Island, Twickenham, Middx TW1 3DY ☎ 020 8892 1308

BENNETT William (*Pic, A Flt*): 50 Lansdowne Gardens, Stockwell, London SW8 2EF ☎ 020 7498 9807

BERRY Wendy (*Pic*): 4 Oaks Close, Leatherhead, Surrey KT22 7SH ☎ 01372 374208

BEYNON Emily (*Pic, A Flt*): Churchill-Laan 177, 1078 Dx Amsterdam, The Netherlands ☎ +31 20 675 2023 & fax

BODY Caroline (*Pic*): 49 Burtons Road, Hampton Hill, Middx TW12 1DE ☎ 020 8941 4284

BOUVY Yves (*Pic, A Flt, Rec, Pf*): 324 Earlesfield Road, Wandsworth, London SW18 3EJ ☎ 020 8871 2667

BOWLER John (*Pic, A Flt*): 29 Wickham Avenue, Shirley, Croydon CR0 8TZ ☎ 020 8656 0560

BRETT Adrian (*Pic, A Flt, Rec*): 65 High Street, Hanging Heaton, Batley, West Yorks WF17 6DR ☎ 01924 452702, 01306 880669

BRETT Anna (*Pic, A Flt, B Flt, Rec*): 51 Woodville Road, South Woodford, London E18 1JT ☎ 020 8530 6548

BRICHT Nicolas (*Pic*): 12 Calais Street, London SE5 9LP ☎ 020 7737 5056, 09325 368959 pager

BROOKE Sarah: 69 Salisbury Road, Barnet, Herts EN5 4JL ☎ 020 8449 5054

BROWN Rachel (*Pic, Bq Flt, Rec*): 14 Oxford Gardens, Winchmore Hill, London N21 2AP ☎ 020 8360 0232

BUCHANAN Kate (*Pic, A Flt, A Sax, Pf*): 1 Dover House, 100 Westwood Hill, London SE26 6PD

BUNT Felicity Jane (*Pic*): 9 Spencer Gardens, East Sheen, London SW14 7AH ☎ 020 8680 3859

BURROWS Kathryn (*Pic, A Flt*): 47 Gibson Road, Ickenham, Middlesex UB10 8EW ☎ 01895 637941, 0850 362877

BUTT David: 8 St Martins Avenue, Epsom, Surrey KT18 5HS ☎ 01372 724488

CAMPBELL Margaret (*Pic, A Flt*): 90 Haven Lane, Ealing, London W5 2HY ☎ 020 8998 6246, 01306 880 669

CARR Nikki: 44 Deanhill Couirt, Upper Richmond Road West, East Sheen, London SW14 7DL ☎ 020 8878 9363

CARRE Isabelle (*A Flt, Pic, B Flt*): 13 Kingdon Road, West Hampstead, London NW6 1PJ ☎ 020 7435 5435

CARTER Jillian (*Pic*): 50 Boveney Road, Forest Hill, London SE23 3NN ☎ 020 8699 7092, 07970 956579

CHAMBERS Celia (*Pic*): Court Lodge, 27 Vine Court Road, Sevenoaks, Kent TN13 3UY ☎ 01732 460494

CHANNING Simon (*A Flt, Pic*): 30 Lancaster Avenue, West Norwood, London SE27 9DZ ☎ 020 8761 7865

CHAPMAN Robin (*Pic*): 46 Bishops Avenue, Bromley, Kent BR1 3ES ☎ 020 8464 1605

CHAPPELL Ruth: 17 Poplar Road, Leatherhead, Surrey KT22 8SF ☎ 01372 376871

CHERRY Ann (*A Flt, B Flt*): 61 Queens Drive, London N4 2BF ☎ 020 8802 5984

CLARKE Ian (*Kbds, Pic*): 274 Lynmouth Avenue, Lower Morden, Surrey SM4 4RS ☎ 020 8337 7151

CLOW Jim (*Pic, Cop*): 6 Runnymede Close, Whitton, Twickenham, Middlesex TW2 7BT ☎ 020 8894 9994

COLE Elmer (*A Flt, B Flt, Pic*): 126 Worple Road, Wimbledon, London SW19 4JF ☎ 020 8946 5622

COLLIER Andrew (*Pic, A Flt*): Coat Mael, Mael Pestivien, 22160 Callac, Bretagne France ☎ +33 2 96457758

CONSTABLE Katharine (*Pic, A Flt*): 22 Davids Road, Forest Hill, London SE23 3EX ☎ 020 8291 9045

CORE Stephanie (*Pic*): 4 Fernwood Crescent, London N20 0RN ☎ 020 8361 0406

COULCHER Jane: 102A Arran Road, Catford, London SE6 2NN ☎ 020 8698 4155

COWARD Julian (*Pic, A Flt, Rec*): 1 Almington Street, London N4 3BP ☎ 020 7272 9860

COX Anthea (*Pic, A Flt, B Flt, Rec*): Woodhouse Cottage, Marsh, Nr Aylesbury, Bucks HP17 8SP ☎ 01296 614647

COX Cecil (*Pic*): 50 Bridge Street, Sturminster Newton, Dorset DT10 1BZ ☎ 012758 473158

COX Michael (*Pic*): Lower Hayne Barton, Lower Hayne Lane, Ashill, Cullompton, Devon EX15 3NL ☎ 01884 841968

CUZNER Katherine (*Pic, A Flt, A Sax*): 52 Turnstone Close, Upper Road, London E13 0HW ☎ 020 7511 5552

DA COSTA Doris: 6 Effingham Road, Long Ditton, Surrey KT6 5JY

DANCE Denise (*Pic*): 70 Broadway, Knaphill, Woking, Surrey GU21 2RH ☎ 01483 476666

DAVIDSON Fergus (*Pic, A Flt, Wh*): Address Unknown ☎ 020 8847 1505, 01306 880669 day

DAVIES Philippa (*Pic, A Flt*): 30 Platts Lane, London NW3 7NS ☎ 020 7431 8317 & fax, 01306 880669 day

DAVIS Deborah (*Pic*): 16 Malden Hill, New Malden, Surrey KT3 4DR ☎ 020 8942 6055

DAWES Robert (*Pic*): The Rectory, 7 Braggs Lane, Wrestlingworth, Sandy, Bedfordshire SG19 2ER ☎ 01767 631596

DE BANZIE Helen (*Rec, Voc*): 32 Grasslands, Smallfield, Surrey RH6 9NU ☎ 01342 843581

DE BATS Sarah (*Pic*): Address Unknown ☎ 020 8200 0657

DESORGHER Simon (*Pan P, B Flt*): 30 Penwortham Road, Sanderstead, Surrey CR2 0QS ☎ 020 8763 9298

DI PROSPERO Allessandra (*A Sax*): 93B Kingsley Road, Hounslow, Middlesex TW3 4AH ☎ 020 8577 5087, 07957 263070

DOBING Duke (*Pic, A Flt*): 57 Grange Road, Sutton, Surrey SM2 6SY ☎ 020 8643 4425, 020 8533 1372 day, 0973 346432

DOONER Elizabeth (*Bq Flt*): 19 Warrender Park Crescent, Edinburgh EH9 1EA ☎ 0131 229 7740

DUNN Belinda: 18 Weavers Green, Sandy, Bedfordshire SG19 2TR ☎ 01767 681795, 01306 880669

EDMUND-DAVIES Paul (*A Flt, B Flt, Pic*): 6 Marlborough Crescent, Chiswick, London W4 1HF ☎ 020 8747 4855 & fax, 01306 880669

ELLIS Samantha (*Sax, Clt*): 52 Rope Street, Surrey Quays, London SE16 1TF ☎ 020 7237 6481, 0589 683529

ELLORY John (*Pic*): 6 Earleswood, Cobham, Surrey KT11 2BZ ☎ 01932 862460

EVANS David (*Pic, A Flt*): 157C St Pancras Way, London NW1 0SY ☎ 020 7209 2346

EWINS Sally Ann (*Pic*): 29 Station Road, Radlett, Herts WD7 8JY ☎ 01923 850816, 01306 880669

FILBY Anthony (*Gtr, Voc, Com*): 21 Clifford Road, New Barnet EN5 5PG ☎ 020 8441 1700

FINDON Andy (*Saxes, Clt, Eth Flts, Pan P*): 59 Brook Avenue, Edgware, Middx HA8 9UZ ☎ 020 8958 9359, 01306 880669

FISHER Jane (*A Flt, Pic*): 38 South Worple Way, Mortlake SW14 8PB ☎ 020 8876 8322

FISON Rubina (*Pic*): 72 Heol Isaf, Radyr, South Glamorgan CF4 8DZ ☎ 029 2084 3442

FITTON Judith (*Pic, A Flt*): 116 Woodwarde Road, London SE22 8UT ☎ 020 8693 8414

FITZGERALD David (*Saxes, Wi Synth*): 48 Avenue Road, Norwich, Norfolk NR2 3HN ☎ 01603 632444 & fax, 0468 573284 mob

FORBES Janet: 56 Castlebar Road, London W5 2DD ☎ 020 8997 4300

FORD Trevor (*Cntrc*): 151 Mount View Road, London N4 4JT ☎ 020 8341 6408

FRANK Evelyn (*Pic*): 40 Woodlands Ave, London N3 2NR ☎ 020 8371 0608

FRANKLYN Caroline (*Pic, A Flt, Pf*): 103A Brondesbury Road, Queens Park, London NW6 6RY ☎ 020 7372 3136

FRY Pauline (*Pf*): The Old Vicarage, Elmstone, Wingham, Canterbury CT3 1HE ☎ 01227 722 203

GAINHAM Catherine (*Pic, A Flt*): 16 Angles Road, Streatham, London SW16 2UR ☎ 020 8664 7127

GALWAY James: c/o Philip Parker, 15 Thomas More House, Barbican, London EC2Y 8BT ☎ 020 7628 3234

GELDARD Lois (*Pic, A Flt*): 20 Belfield Road, West Ewell, Surrey KT19 9SY ☎ 020 8394 2284, 020 8533 1372

GENT Alison (*Pic*): 44 Beulah Road, Tunbridge Wells, Kent TN1 2NR ☎ 01892 545955

GILLHAM Ron (*Pic*): 3 Ravenscourt Place, London W6 0UN ☎ 020 8741 2650

GLANVILLE Louise (*Pic*): Stuckenduff Cottage, Shandon, Dunbartonshire, Scotland G84 8NW ☎ 01436 821157

GOETZEE Aidan (*Pic*): 13A Highland Avenue, Acton, London W3 6ES ☎ 020 8993 6301

GOULD David (*Pic, Sax, Clt, Pf*): 47B Argyle Road, Ilford, Essex IG1 3BJ ☎ 020 8554 0172

GREALY Siobhan (*Pic*): 88 Dukes Avenue, Chiswick, London W4 2AF ☎ 020 8747 8435

GREEN Christopher (*Pic*): 208 Knightsfield, Welling Gdn City, Herts AL8 7RQ ☎ 01306 880669

GREEN Jimmie (*Sax*): 6 Pond Green, Ruislip, Middx HA4 6EW ☎ 01895 631682

GREGORY James (*Pic, Ea Wnd, Bq Flt*): Foscot Cottage, Foscot, Nr Kingham, Oxon OX7 6RH ☎ 01608 659034

GREGORY Rachel: Address Unknown ☎ 020 8974 1225

HAIGH Kerstin (*Voc*): 76 Nimrod Road, Streatham, London SW16 6TG ☎ 020 8677 5313

HALL Judith (*Pic*): Parke View, Bovey Tracey, Devon TQ13 9AD ☎ 020 8482 1896, 01306 880669

HANKIN Christine (*Pic, A Flt*): 23 Egerton Gardens, London W13 8HG ☎ 020 8998 7788, 01306 880669

HANLEY Francesca (*A Flt, B Flt, Pic*): 42 Holmesdale Road, Highgate, London N6 5TQ ☎ 020 8340 1955, 0411 395731 mob

HARDING Christopher (*Pic, Clt, Sax*): Gaya Cottage, Blacksmiths Lane, Eydon Daventry, Northants NN11 3PF ☎ 01327 262383, 0802 811126 mob

HARDY Raymond (*T Sax*): 18 Bourne Road, Bromley, Kent BR2 9NS ☎ 020 8464 3690

HARRIS Hayley (*Sax, Clt*): 70C Gengall Road, Peckham, London SE15 6NH ☎ 020 7277 9635

HARRIS Jane (*Pic, A Flt*): 29 Cadogan Road, Surbiton, Surrey KT6 4DQ ☎ 020 8339 9220, 0831 680234 mob, 020 8533 1372 day

HAVARD Judith (*Pic, A Flt*): Appin Cottage, Agates Lane, Ashtead, Surrey KT22 2ND ☎ 01372 279379, 01306 880669

HAYHURST Alison (*Pic, A Flt*): 59B Crystal Palace Road, East Dulwich, London SE22 9EX ☎ 020 8693 0291

HENDRICKSE Jan (*Didj*): 40 Wellmeadow Road, London SE13 6TB ☎ 020 8698 9143

HENSON Elena: 25 Churston Mansions, 186 Grays Inn Road, London WC1X 8ES ☎ 020 7833 8372

HETHERINGTON Mariela (*Pf*): 32 Selby Rd, Ealing, London W5 1LX ☎ 020 8998 1627

HILL Kate (*Pic*): Blenheim Cottage, Ewelme, Wallingford, Oxfordshire OX10 6QE ☎ 01491 641212, 01491 642255 fax

HIRST Michael (*Pic, A Flt*): 20 Townley Road, London SE22 8SR ☎ 020 8693 1086

HODDER-WILLIAMS Susie (*Pic*): 79 Royal Hill, Greenwich, London SE10 8SE ☎ 020 8692 3795, 0831 387180, 020 8692 6524

HODGSON Anne (*Pic*): 105 Charlton Church Lane, London SE7 7AB ☎ 020 8858 9738

HONNER Derek: Kericho, Foxhill, Hollesley, Suffolk IP12 3RA ☎ 01394 411233

HOPE Carolyn (*Pic*): 32 Hereford Road, Acton, London W3 9JW ☎ 020 8992 8426, 0956 922232

HOPKINS Anna (*Pic, Pf*): 34 Farmlands, Eastcote, Pinner, Middlesex HA5 2LW ☎ 020 8866 9451

HOWES Fiona: 6 Alma Grove, London SE1 5PY ☎ 020 7231 1034, 01306 880669

HOYLAND Alison (*Sax*): 83 Claremont Road, West Byfleet, Surrey KT14 6DZ ☎ 01932 355916

HUGHES Enid (*Pic, A Flt*): 30 Marks Avenue, Ongar, Essex CM5 9AY ☎ 01277 365694

HUNEKE Janna (*Pic, Vla*): 61 Great Dover Street, London SE1 4YF ☎ 020 7403 5402, 0973 107126

HUNT Simon (*Pic*): 40 Portland Road, London W11 4LG ☎ 020 7727 5965

HURRELL Neslihan (*Pic*): 24 Hadleigh Park Avenue, Benfleet, Essex SS7 1SA ☎ 01702 552839

HYDE-SMITH Christopher (*Pic, A Flt*): 6 Heath Drive, Sutton, Surrey SM2 5RP ☎ 020 8642 5418

JEFFERS Rachel (*Pic, A Flt*): Holmwood, 3A Chipstead Way, Woodmansterne, Surrey SM7 3JH ☎ 01737 357 097, 0976 360045, 01737 357 097

JONES Karen (*Pic*): 2 Marshall Villas, Dowlerville Road, Orpington, Kent BR6 6DZ ☎ 01689 855068

JONES Lois (*Pic*): 84 Gallants Farm Road, East Barnet, Herts EN4 8EP ☎ 020 8368 3700

JUDSON Ian (*Pic, A Flt, Rec*): Flat 2, 2 Great North Road, London N6 4LX ☎ 0956 431449 mob

KAY Diane (*Pic*): Hatchcroft House, White Notley, Witham, Essex CM8 1RG ☎ 01376 326283

KEEN Helen (*Pic, A Flt, B Flt, Eth Flts*): 68 Kilmorie Road, Forest Hill, London SE23 2ST ☎ 020 8699 8483, 0585 799551, 020 8699 5302 fax

KELBIE Catriona (*Pic*): 10 Greystone Lodge, Hanger Lane, Ealing, London W5 1EW ☎ 020 8991 0075, 0410 866751

KIDMAN Joanna (*Pic*): 6 Spring Mews, Old Schools Lane, Ewell, Epsom, Surrey KT17 1TW ☎ 020 8394 1663, 0860 387323 mob

KIPLING Timothy (*A Flt, Pic*): Flat 10, Towerside, 144 Wapping High St, London E1 9XF ☎ 020 7488 3490

KIRKUP Sarah (*Pic*): 74 Chestnut Avenue, West Wickham, Kent BR4 9EX ☎ 020 8462 2533

KOSTER Jane (*Pic*): 45 The Woodlands, Esher, Surrey KT10 8DD ☎ 020 8398 2948, 020 8533 1372

LACEY Christopher (*A Flt, B Flt, Rec, Eth Flts*): 10 Gordondale Road, Wimbledon Park, London SW19 8EN ☎ 020 8879 1075

LARSEN Rebecca (*Pic*): Flat 8 Hilldown Court, 327 Streatham High Road, London SW16 3NU ☎ 020 8679 2366, 0468 766088

LARSSON Janet (*Pic, A Flt*) ☎ 020 8533 1372 day

LEWIS Peter (*Pic, Rec*): 44 Richmond Park Road, Kingston, Surrey KT2 6AH ☎ 020 8549 7964, 0402 502899 mob

LLOYD Christopher (*Con*): 47 Greenvale Road, Eltham, London SE9 1PB ☎ 020 8850 3964

LOBECK Katharina (*Mbira*): 72 Clarendon Road, London N15 3JX ☎ 020 8809 6505 & fax

LOCKRANE Gareth (*A Flt, Pic, Pf*): 76 Fishponds Road, Tooting, London SW17 7LF ☎ 020 8888 7555

LYNDEN Patricia: 37 Dalmeny Road, New Barnet, Herts EN5 1DE ☎ 020 8449 3388

MACDONALD Janet (*Pic, A Flt, B Flt*): 'Pippins', Furze Grove, Kingswood, Surrey KT20 6ES ☎ 01737 354256

MACNUTT Penny: 24 Willow Lane, Amersham, Bucks HP7 9DW ☎ 01494 721979

MAGUIRE Conor (*Pf*)

MALLOY Matt: Bridge Street, Westport, Co Mayo, Rep Of Ireland ☎ 6674171, 667 3920

MARSH Elizabeth (*Pf, Sax*): 3 The Canvas House, 25 Queen Elizabeth Street, London SE1 2NL

MARSHALL Elizabeth (*Pic, Pf, Rec*): 18 Fraser Close, Lainden West, Essex SS15 6SU ☎ 01288 546194

MARTIN Bruce (*Pic*): 50 Read Road, Ashtead, Surrey KT21 2HS ☎ 01372 276344, 0130 688 0669

MARTIN Jaime: 89 Streathbourne Road, London SW17 8RA ☎ 020 8672 0072 & fax

MATTHEW Louise (*Pic*): 27C Hiifield Ave, London N8 7DS ☎ 01992 306979

MAYGER Graham (*Pic*): Hillside Cottage, Nash Road, G Horwood, Buckinghamshire MK17 0RA ☎ 0129 671 2643

MCCARRON Monica (*Pic, A Flt*): 18 Stamford Road, London N1 4JS ☎ 020 7923 2321 & fax, 0468 877652 mob, 020 8533 1372 day

MCCARTHY Susan (*Pic, Pf*): 13 Rue Du Repos, Paris 75020 ☎ +33 1 43702055, +33 1 43724959

MCFERRAN Darren: 69 Latimer Road, Forest Gate, London E7 0LN ☎ 020 8221 0096

MCHALE Jennifer (*Pic*): 60A Belsize Road, Basement Flat, Swiss Cottage, London NW6 4TG ☎ 020 7372 4870, 07775 842435

MCILWHAM Stewart (*Pic, A Flt*): 4 Rojack Road, Forest Hill, London SE23 2DF ☎ 020 8291 2124, 0973 705922 mob

MCLAREN Neil (*Pic*): 2 Goodwood Court, 6 Chestnut Road, West Norwood, London SE27 9LQ ☎ 020 8670 9286 & fax, 0468 893470 mob

MCLAY Bruce: Address Unknown ☎ 020 8942 0480

MCNICOL Richard (*Pic, Rec*): Overdale, 145 Park Road, Buxton, Derbys SK17 6SW ☎ 01298 79598

MELLOR Clare (*Pic*): 25 Helrose Avenue, Reading RG6 7BN ☎ 01189 669767

MELVILLE Clarissa (*Pic, A Flt*): 51 Stradella Road, Herne Hill, London SE24 9HL ☎ 020 7274 8214

MESSENT Henry: 114 Muswell Hill Road, London N10 3JD ☎ 020 8883 6399

MILAN Susan (*Pic, A Flt*): 18 St Albans Ave, Weybridge, Surrey KT13 8EN ☎ 01932 888417, 01306 880669, 01932 888427 fax

MILLER Ann (*Pic, Cop*): 1 Central Drive, St Albans, Herts AL4 0UU ☎ 01727 867507

MILLS Betty (*Pic, Pf*): Ferndene, Bracken Close, Storrington, West Sussex RH20 3HT ☎ 01903 742594

MITCHAM Sue: 1 Lyons Green Cottages, Shillinglee Road, Plaistow, West Sussex RH14 0PH ☎ 01403 871435

MOORE Joshua (*Pic, A Flt*): 32 Ditchburn Place, Cambridge CB1 2AJ ☎ 01223 303735

MORFEE Susan: 32A Clifden Road, Brentford, Middx TW8 0PF ☎ 020 8560 6621

MORRIS Patricia (*Pic, A Flt*): 81 Redston Road, London N8 7HG ☎ 020 8340 0969, 01306 880669

MORRISON Gavin (*Pic, A Flt*): 174 Vaughan Road, Harrow, Middlesex HA1 4EB ☎ 020 8864 9492

MORTON William (*Pic*): 4 Delamere Road, Ealing, London W5 3JR ☎ 020 8567 9759

MOY Kathleen (*Pic, Pf*): 120 Kingsway, West Wickham, Kent BR4 9JQ ☎ 020 8462 7075

MURPHY Sarah (*Pic, A Flt, Eth Flts*): Address Unknown ☎ 020 8656 9212

MYLES Alison (*Pic*), St Albans, Herts ☎ 01727 840187, 020 8533 1372 day

NELSEN Lisa (*Pic, A Flt*): Flat 1, 96 Station Road, Barnet, Herts EN5 1QE ☎ 020 8440 6983

NEWBOLD Sarah (*Pic, A Flt*): 25 Nursery Road, Farncombe, Godalming, Surrey GU7 3JU ☎ 01483 416620, 01306 880669

NEWMAN Nili (*Pic, A Flt, B Flt*): 8 Lambolle Road, Flat 2, Belsize Park, London NW3 4HP ☎ 020 7794 6958, 0468 838 252 mob

NEWMAN Ruth (*Pic*): 31 Southwood Lawn Road, Highgate, London N6 5SD ☎ 020 8340 3516

NIELINGER Carola (*Pic, A Flt, Vla*): 13 Tillingbourne Gardens, Finchley, London N3 3JJ ☎ 020 8346 1995 & fax

NIXON Patricia (*Pic, A Flt*): 94 Elmshurst Gardens, Tonbridge, Kent TN10 3QY ☎ 01732 770141

NOAKES Anna: 98 Marlborough Road, London N22 4NN ☎ 020 8888 9005, 01306 880669

NOLAN Francis (*Pic*): 50 Boveney Road, Forest Hill, London SE23 3NN ☎ 020 8699 7092

OGONOVSKY Margaret (*A Flt, Pic*): 27 Richmond Road, W. Wimbledon, London SW20 0PG ☎ 020 8241 8126

OLDFIELD Terry: The Old Mission Hall, High Street, Chalford, Glos GL6 8DH ☎ 01453 731933, 01453 731594 fax

OSMIALOWSKI Lisa (*Pic*): 14 Dukes Avenue, Finchley Central, London N3 2DD ☎ 020 8346 8841, 0966 530751 mob, 020 8349 0951 fax

PAICE Leonard (*Pic*): 1St Floor Flat, Friends Meeting House, 41 Park Road, Woking Surrey GU22 7DB ☎ 01483 766901

PAILTHORPE Daniel (*Pic, A Flt, Voc*): 91A Lacy Road, Putney, London SW15 INR ☎ 020 8789 1739 & fax, 0973 882185 mob

PANAYI Andrew (*Sax*): 58 Lodge Road, Feltwell, Thetford, Norfolk IP26 4DL ☎ 01842 828717, 0973 510872 mob

PARKER Annie: 29 Valley Road, Henley-on-Thames RG9 1RL ☎ 01491 576150 & fax

PARKER Eddie (*B Flt, Pf*): 15 Ambler Road, London N4 2QT ☎ 020 7226 2822

PARRY Jane (*Pic*): 3 Coniston Way, Church Crookham, Fleet, Hampshire GU13 0RS ☎ 01252 616122

PARRY Martin (*Pic*): Gate Cottage, High Street, Hinxworth, Herts SG7 5HQ ☎ 01462 743 052

PENDRY Katherine (*Pan P*): Flat 25 Park Road, Southborough, Tunbridge Wells, Kent TN4 0NU ☎ 01892 535388

PERONA-WRIGHT Nigel (*Pic, A Flt, Rec, Ea Wnd*): 9 Hillside Road, Ashtead, Surrey KT21 1RZ ☎ 01372 277703, 01372 278406 fax

PERRIDGE Joanna (*Pf, Voc*): 18 The Close, Clapham, Bedford MK41 6DP ☎ 01234 824733

PETERS Aaron (*A Sax, S Sax, Pic, T Sax*): 20 Jubilee House, Egerton Drive, London SE10 8JW ☎ 020 8692 5107

PETERS Lynn (*Pic*): 6 Robinsons Close, Ealing, London W13 0DL ☎ 020 8933 9198, 01306 500022

PICKLES Jane (*Pic, A Flt, B Flt*): 7 Cavendish Drive, Claygate, Surrey KT10 0QE ☎ 01372 464984, 01306 880669

PIRES Brenda: 93 Regal Way, Kenton, Harrow, Middlesex HA3 0SG ☎ 020 8933 2120

PLASCHKES Roshana (*A Flt, Pic*): 21 Wrentham Avenue, Queens Park, London NW10 3HS

POKE James (*Pan P, Rec, Com*): 26 Stadium Street, London SW10 0PT ☎ 020 7351 6519 & fax

POPE Anna: 55 Rokesly Avenue, Hornsey, London N8 8NH ☎ 020 8340 3789

PULLAN Harry (*Pic*): 1 Rookfield Close, Muswell Hill, London N10 3TR ☎ 020 7251 4535, 020 7490 0098

PYNE Anna (*Pic, Voc*): 6 Albert Cottages, Victoria Road, Golden Green, Tonbridge, Kent TN11 0LP ☎ 01732 852201, 01306 880669

QUINN James (*T Sax, Clt*): 199A Upper Richmond Road, Putney, London SW15 6SG ☎ 020 8789 0688

RATHBONE Rosemary (*Pic*): Tile Cottage, Water Lane, Sturry, Nr Canterbury Kent CT2 0AW ☎ 01227 711804, 020 8207 0007, 0378 628838 mob

RATTLE Ali (*Pf, Kbds, Sax*): 81 Kiln Road, Fareham, Hants PO16 7UL ☎ 01329 281294, 0850 453024

REES Carla (*A Flt, Pic, Com*): 134 Barcombe Avenue, Streatham Hill, London SW2 3BB ☎ 020 8674 3712, 0961 131565

RIVERA Stan (*B Gtr, Kbds, Sax*): 24B Colless Road, London N15 4NR ☎ 020 8808 4290, 0793 0850867

ROBB Anthony (*Pic, A Flt, Rec, Tin Wh*): 104 Top Street Way, Harpenden, Herts AL5 5TS ☎ 01582 762 470

ROBERTSON Ewan (*Pic*): 5 Meadow Close, Sevenoaks, Kent TN13 3HZ ☎ 01732 463 912

ROCHA Raul (*Per, Wi Synth, Voc*): 67 Gables Close, Camberwell, London SE5 7QE ☎ 020 7701 0435, 020 7277 6261

ROCHELLE Helen (*Pic*): 102 Inderwick Road, London N8 9JY ☎ 020 8341 7221, 0976 309851 mob

ROWSON Philip (*Pic, A Flt, Pf*): 120 Brangbourne Road, Bromley, Kent BR1 4LQ ☎ 020 8697 3241, 07970 627917

RUFFER Nancy (*A Flt, B Flt, Pic*): 66 Ferme Park Road, London N4 4ED ☎ 020 8341 6073

RUHEMANN Ileana (*Pic*): 63 Blenheim Terrace, London NW8 0EJ ☎ 020 7624 4965, 020 8533 1372 day

RUTHERFORD Samantha: 29 Ince Road, Burwood Park, Walton-on-Thames, Surrey KT12 5BJ ☎ 01932 225991

RYAN Vourneen: 5 Foster Lane, Priests Court, Cheapside, London EC2V 6HH ☎ 020 7606 1103

SANDEMAN David *(Pic)*: 73 Holmesdale Road, Teddington TW11 9LQ ☎ 020 8943 4107

SCHUELEIN Rainer *(Pic, A Flt, B Flt, Rec)*: 20 Eton Villas, London NW3 4SG ☎ 020 7722 5744 & fax

SCOTT June *(Pic)*: 13 Allenby Road, London SE23 2RQ ☎ 020 8699 4593

SEABROOK Kathryn *(Pic, A Flt)*: 24 Fletcher Lane, Leyton, London E10 6JE ☎ 020 8539 0348, 020 8533 1372 day, 0831 260924 mob

SEARCHFIELD Sheila *(Pic, A Flt, B Flt, Gtr)*: 14 Glenton Road, Lewisham, London SE13 5RS ☎ 020 8852 7886

SELVIDGE Rachel *(Pic)*: Flat C, 12 Belsize Crescent, Hampstead, London NW3 5QU ☎ 020 7794 3367

SEVILLE Clifford *(Pic, A Flt, B Flt)*: 59 Marine Drive, Bishopstone, Nr Seaford, East Sussex BN25 2RU ☎ 01323 892179

SHANKS Kathleen *(Com, Arr)*: 225 Shurland Ave, East Barnet, Herts EN4 8DG ☎ 020 8449 2342

SHARMAN Helen *(Pic, Pf)*: 42 Morley Hill, Enfield EN2 0BJ ☎ 020 8366 4447

SHARP Paul *(Pic, Pf)*: 51 Caversham Avenue, Palmers Green, London N13 4LL ☎ 020 8882 7212

SHRUBSHALL Peter *(Sax)*: 324 High Road, Tottenham, London N15 4BN ☎ 020 8885 1915

SILVERMAN Susie *(A Flt)*: 2 Brunner Close, London NW11 6NP ☎ 020 8455 7919

SIRED Carole *(A Sax)*: 13 Mentmore Terrace, London Fields, London E8 3PN ☎ 020 8533 4111

SKIPPER Sandra *(Pic, A Flt)*: 13 Kingsway, Woking, Surrey GU21 1NU ☎ 01483 725416

SLEATH Will *(Pic, A Flt, Bq Flt)*: 29A Regent Street, Rowhedge, Colchester, Essex C05 7EA ☎ 01206 729510, 020 8533 1372

SMALL Jennifer *(Pic, A Sax)*: 40 Orford Road, Walthamstow, London E17 0NJ ☎ 020 8520 2362

SMITH Kenneth *(Pic)*: 22 Thurleigh Court, Nightingale Lane, London SW12 8AP ☎ 020 8675 4220

SMITH Lenore *(A Flt, Pic, Eth Flts)*: 1 Paxton Road, Chiswick, London W4 2QT ☎ 020 8994 0863

SMITH Trudi *(Pf)*: c/o Famlies Office, 12 Reg Ra, 58 Battery, Dempsey Barracks BS PO 16 ☎ 00 49 05254 942926

SPERRY Julian: 322 Earlsfield Road, Wandsworth, London SW18 3EJ ☎ 020 8871 2667

SPIERS Jane *(Pic, A Flt)*: 33 Meynell Road, Hackney, London E9 8AP ☎ 020 8986 0163, 020 8533 1372 day, 0976 853458 mob

SPRATT Kirsten *(Pic, Pf)*: 142 Elmington Road, London SE5 7RA ☎ 020 7701 0400

STAGG Richard *(Pic, A Flt, Sh)*: 88 Kinloch Drive, London NW9 7JX ☎ 020 8200 9593

STEVENS Jane *(Pic, Pf)*: 17 Park Court, 325 Preston Road, Harrow, Middlesex HA3 0QQ ☎ 020 8904 1766, 0585 539343 mob

STEVENSON Kathleen *(Pic)*: 2A Queenswood Road, London SE23 2QS ☎ 020 8291 5235, 01306 880 669

STEVENSON Nicholas *(Sax)*: 146 Harley Street, London W1N 1AH ☎ 020 7935 9002, 0958 783594

STINTON Jennifer *(Pic, A Flt)*: 35 Priory Walk, Tonbridge, Kent TN9 2AL ☎ 01732 369041 & fax, 0467 780563

STOCKMANN Caroline *(Pic, A Flt, B Flt)*: 8 Woodside Avenue, Esher, Surrey KT10 8JQ ☎ 020 8398 9417, 01372 472524, 01372 472356

STRASBURG Nick *(Sax)*: Ground Floor Flat, 33 Mornington Terrace, London NW1 7RS ☎ 020 7372 3503

STREVENS Luke *(A Flt)*: 1A Cassidy Road, Fulham, London SW6 5QH ☎ 020 7371 7292

STREVENS Nancy *(Pic)*: Esmond Cottage, Lidwells Lane, Goudhurst, Cranbrook Kent TN17 1EJ ☎ 01580 211375

SUTHERLAND Rowland *(Pic, A Flt, B Flt)*: c/o 21 Lytton Avenue, Enfield Lock, Middx EN3 6EL ☎ 020 8361 4613, 0850 215687 mob, 01426 241935 pager

TAGGART Hilary: 35 Grove Lane, Kingston-upon-Thames, Surrey KT1 2ST ☎ 020 8549 1183

TAGGART Patrick *(Pic)*: 35 Grove Lane, Kingston-upon-Thames, Surrey KT1 2ST ☎ 020 8549 1183

TATE Gavin *(A Flt, T Sax, S Sax, A Sax)*: 220 Richmond Road, Leytonstone, London E11 4DA ☎ 020 8556 9997, 0973 751088

TAYLOR Debra: 29 Newton Road, Wimbledon, London SW19 3PJ

TAYLOR Richard *(Pic, A Flt, B Flt, Rec)*: Pipers Gate, South Drove, Broadmayne, Dorchester, Dorset DT2 8PN ☎ 01305 854025 & fax, 01306 880669

TAYLORSON Timothy *(Pf)*: 25 Manbey Grove, Stratford, London E15 1EX ☎ 020 8536 0891

TEMPLE Claire *(Pic, Sax, Pf, Clt)*: 6 Beresford Drive, Woodford Green, London IG8 0JH ☎ 020 8505 7408, 020 8505 8283

THOMAS Katey *(Pic)*: 29 Spaines, Great Bedwyn, Marlborough, Wilts SN8 3LT ☎ 01672 870908

THOMAS Kathryn *(Pic, A Flt)*: 39 Bushwood, Leytonstone, London E11 3BW ☎ 020 8518 8903, 0976 399828 mob

THOMAS Raymond: The Threshold Record Co Ltd, 53 High Street, Cobham, Surrey KT11 3DP ☎ 01932 864142/3

THOMPSON Nina *(Pic, A Flt, B Flt)*: 134 Elthorne Avenue, Hanwell, London W7 2JW ☎ 020 8579 7534, 020 8533 1372 day, 020 8840 0682

THOMSON Angie *(Gtr, Acc, Pf, Per)*: 61 Thornhill Houses, Thornhill Road, London N1 1PB

TONKINS Tracey *(Pic)*: 69 York Gardens, Walton-on-Thames, Surrey KT12 3EN ☎ 01932 220748, 07971 019445 mob

TORKE Susan *(Pic, A Flt, B Flt)*: 22 Earlsmead Road, London N15 4DA ☎ 020 8801 6441, 0973 751029 mob, 01306 880669 day

TREGGOR Judith *(Pic, Bq Flt)*: 1 Tormount Road, Plumstead, London SE18 1QD ☎ 020 8854 7557 & fax, 01306 880669 day

TRIBBLE Fay *(Pic)* ☎ 07887 511320 mob

TULLBERG Matilda *(Voc, Db, Pf)*: 24 Sansom Street, London SE5 7RE ☎ 020 7701 8598, 07970 281098, 01795 532786

TUNSTALL Sarah *(Pf)*: 21 Grenville Court, Lymer Avenue, London SE19 1LR ☎ 020 8670 0977, 0958 730 389

TURNER Nicola *(Pf)*: 41 Merewood Road, Barnehurst, Kent DA7 6PF ☎ 01322 347201

TYE Jack *(Pic, A Flt)*: 127 Fleetwood Avenue, Holland-on-Sea, Essex CO15 5RG ☎ 01255 815090

UNDERWOOD Mark *(Pic, A Flt, B Flt)*: 20 Summerhill Road, Dartford, Kent DA1 2LP ☎ 01322 287924, 020 8207 0007 day

UNDERWOOD Ruth *(Pic)*: 2 St John's Grove, London N19 5RW ☎ 020 7272 8500

VIOLA Lucia *(Clt, Voc)*: 98 Boone Street, London SE13 5SA ☎ 020 8318 5774

WAITHE Keith *(Pic)*: 20 Cantley Road, Hanwell, London W7 2BQ ☎ 020 8840 2831

WALKER Elizabeth *(Bq Flt, Flt, Rec)*: 45 Theberton Street, London N1 0QY ☎ 020 7226 8141

WALSH Kate *(Pic, A Flt, B Flt, Fl Dam)*: 99 Defoe House, Barbican, London EC2Y 8ND ☎ 020 7588 0195 & fax, 020 8533 1372 day

WALTON Simon *(Pic, A Flt)*: 27 Sprules Road, London SE4 2NL ☎ 020 7652 1305

WELCH Jennifer *(Pic)*: 34 York Road, Cheam, Sutton SM2 6HH ☎ 020 8642 8295, 01306 880669

WELSH Caroline J *(Pic, A Flt)*: 228 Wilmot Green, Bethnal Green, London E2 0BY ☎ 020 7613 3398, 07971 566808

WHEATER Tim: PO Box 69, Launceston, Cornwall PL15 7YA ☎ 01566 86308

WHITE Phillida *(Pic, A Flt)*: 7 Pembroke Avenue, Berrylands, Surbiton, Surrey KT5 8HN ☎ 020 8399 9841

WHITTAKER Elizabeth *(Pic)*: 52 Red Post Hill, London SE24 9JQ ☎ 020 7733 1328

WILKINSON Jay *(Pic, Rec)*: Laragon, Cannon Lane, Maidenhead, Berks SL6 3PH ☎ 01628 825676 & fax

WILLIAMS Averill *(Pic, A Flt)*: 78 Kenilworth Avenue, London SW19 7LR ☎ 020 8946 6857

FLUTE - LONDON

WILLIAMS Emma (*Pf*): 45A Cannon Hill, Southgate, London N14 6LH ☎ 020 8882 5333 & fax

WILLIAMS Sharon (*Pic, A Flt*): 40A Cranley Gardens, Palmers Green, London N13 4LS ☎ 020 8447 9229, 0966 486802, 020 8447 9229

WILLIS Maxine (*Pic*): 39 Church Path, Acton Green, London W4 5BL ☎ 020 8995 6303, 07957 291947

WINN Robert (*Pic, A Flt*): 14 Dukes Avenue, Finchley, London N3 2DD ☎ 020 8349 0951

WYATT Christopher (*Pic*): 2 Ashington Court, Westwood Hill, Sydenham, London SE26 6BN ☎ 020 8778 5955

WYE Trevor (*Pic*): Tamley Cottage, Hastingleigh, Ashford, Kent TN25 5HW ☎ 01233 750493

ZEE Anna (*Pic, A Sax, T Sax, Clt*): 31A Edwards Avenue, Ruislip, Middlesex HA4 6UP ☎ 020 8845 7299

ZWALF Miranda (*Pic*): 86B Brixton Hill, London SW2 1QN ☎ 020 8671 6078 & fax

FOLK FIDDLE

SCOTLAND

ALLISON Finlay (*Gtr, Man*): 16 Botanic Crescent, North Kelvinside, Glasgow G20 8QJ ☎ 0141 946 2665

BOAG David: Nicholson House, Somerfield Square, Portree, Isle Of Skye IV51 9HP ☎ 01478 613355, 01478 613399

DRIVER Fiona: Fdf Productions, Velzian Cottage, Rendall, Orkney, Scotland KW17 2EZ ☎ 01856 761695 & fax

GEDDES Amy: 16 School Road, Symington, Biggar ML12 6LT ☎ 01899 308527, 0411 019957 mob, 01555 664260 fax

HARDIE Ian (*Db, Vla*): Sutors Hill, Kingsteps, Nairn IV12 5LF ☎ 01667 454745

MARWICK Gavin: 6 School Brae, Cramond, Edinburgh EH4 6JN ☎ 0131 336 1115

MCCULLOCH Alistair (*Vln*): 65 St Phillans Avenue, Ayr, Scotland KA7 3DD ☎ 01292 287083

MCKERRON Charlie: c/o Secret Music, 5 Newton Terrace Lane, Glasgow G3 7PB ☎ 0141 564 1161, 0141 564 1221 fax

SCOLLAY Leonard: 20 Blydoit, Scalloway, Shetland ZE2 0UG ☎ 01595 880 428

SPENCER Nick: Courthill Keir, Thornhill, Dumfriesshire DG3 4DD ☎ 01848 331192

WRIGLEY Jennifer (*Pf, Kbds*): 5/F1, 13 Drummond Street, Edinburgh EH8 9TU ☎ 0131 557 6157 & fax

NORTH WEST

BACK Shaun (*Vla, Bod*): 6 Druidsville Road, Liverpool, Merseyside L18 3EW ☎ 0151 428 8119

FRANCIS Carolyn (*Vln, Per*): 16 Hinde Street, Lancaster LA1 1DX ☎ 01524 35391

LAWRENCE Jane (*Vln, Tabla, Per, Pf*): 6 Springfield Street, Lancaster, Lancs LA1 4XL ☎ 01524 389967

MANN Dave (*Man, Bjo, Gtr*): 3 Park View, Deane, Bolton BL3 4BE ☎ 01204 651119

SHOTLIFF Jennifer (*Ctna*): 75 Churchlands Lane, Standish, Wigan WN6 0XU ☎ 01257 473515

NORTH EAST

GAEL FORCE (*Mando, Kbds*): 30 Charlestown, Ackworth, Nr Pontefract, West Yorks WF7 7DU ☎ 01977 614409 & fax

JONES Belinda (*Voc, Acc, Pf, Flt*): 161 Salters Road, Gosforth, Newcastleupon Tyne ST20 0DR ☎ 0191 284 1114

KERR-ELLIOTT Nancy (*Vla*): 5 Heatherleazes, Warkworth, Morpeth, Northumberland NE65 0TZ ☎ 01665 712488

EAST

CANNELL Laura (*Rec, Cel, Wh, Voc*): 99A Unthank Road, Norwich, Norfolk NR2 2PE ☎ 01603 612693

FAIRBAIRN Hazel (*Vla, Pf*): 1 Wood End Cottages, Granchester Road, Trumpington, Cambridge CB2 2LJ ☎ 01223 845683

MIDLANDS

ANGLIM Carlene: 22 Kings Hill, Kempsey, Worcs WR5 3LJ ☎ 01905 821832

FRASER Fi (*Vln, Dul, Per, Voc*): 10 Moor Rise, Holbrook, Derbyshire DE56 0TR ☎ 01332 883472

WILSON Roger (*Gtr, Voc*): 71 Lothair Road, Leicester LE2 7QE ☎ 0116 2440528

SOUTH EAST

BERTHOUD Mahrey (*Bod, Voc*) ☎ 01273 389948

BERTHOUD Philip (*Gtr, Man, B Gtr, Bjo*): 117 Shanklin Road, Brighton BN2 3LP ☎ 01273 389948

LANGLOIS Yves (*Gtr, Voc, Dobro, Bjo*): 40 Godinton Road, Ashford, Kent TN23 1LG ☎ 01233 643059

SMITH Mike: 326 Bretch Hill, Banbury, Oxfordshire OX16 0LP ☎ 01295 255468, 0976 312667 mob

SOUTH WEST

BARTRAM Chris (*Db, Cel, Gtr, Com*): Granway House, 3 Coldharbour, Uffculme, Cullompton, Devon EX15 3EE ☎ 01884 841499

BICKFORD John (*Man, Ac Gtr, Voc*): 24 Tappers Close, Topsham, Exeter EX3 0DG ☎ 01392 877804

MOODY Helen (*Rec, Clt*) ☎ 0117 949 3222

LONDON

FAY Martin: 156 Sutton Park, Sutton, Dublin 13, Ireland ☎ Dublin 324683

KEANE Sean: 6 St Patrick's Crescent, Rathcoole, Dublin, Ireland ☎ 6674171, 6673920

LAING Barry: 2 Cornwall Avenue, Welling, Kent DA16 2PR ☎ 020 8303 6882

RANKIN Max (*H Bag*): 1 Felday Glade, Holmbury St. Mary, Dorking, Surrey RH5 6PG ☎ 01306 731491 & fax

STEVENS Paul: 50 Huntley Street, London WC1E 6DD ☎ 020 7387 7985

GLASS HARMONICA

LONDON

MALLOY Alasdair (*Per*): 84 Ferme Park Road, London N8 9SD ☎ 020 8347 6630/1, 01306 880669

GUITARS

SCOTLAND

ADAMS Christopher (*Gtr*)

ADAMSON Stuart (*Ld Gtr*): Address Unknown

AIRLIE Gerry (*Ac Gtr, Bjo, Fo Fdl*): 13 Kew Terrace, Glasgow G12 0TE ☎ 0141 339 3454

AKYEAMPONG Peter (*Gtr, Kbds, Multi*): 24 Spottiswoode Gardens, Mid Calder, West Lothian EH53 0JU ☎ 0150 688 0789

ALEXANDER Dennis (*Ac Gtr*): 16 Moray Court, Auchtertool, Kirkcaldy, Fife KY2 5XS ☎ 01592 781591 & fax, 0374 722631 mob

ALEXANDER Ronnie (*Gtr*): 25 Napiershall Street, Glasgow G20 6EZ

ANDERSEN Jens (*Gtr*): 11 Oakfield Ave, Hillhead, Glasgow G12 8JF ☎ 0141400 1366

ANDERSON Archibald (*Gtr, Voc*): 8 Bute Road, Holmhead, Cumnock, Ayrshire KA18 1BE ☎ 01290 421161

ANDERSON John (*Gtr, Voc*): 33 Wallace House, Hazlehead, Aberdeen AB1 8ET ☎ 01224 37145

ANTHONEY Douglas (*Gtr, Voc*): 35/2 Leith Street, Edinburgh EH1 3AT ☎ 0131 557 6902

ANTHONEY Gordon (*Gtr, Kbds, Voc*): 1F1 1 Kings Place, Portobello, Edinburgh EH15 1DU ☎ 0131 657 2604

ARCARI David (*Gtr, Hmca, Synth*): 192 Glasgow Road, Perth PH2 0NA

ARGONDIZZA Peter (*Gtr, Man*): 38 Hally Down Drive, Jordan Hill, Glasgow G13 1UF ☎ 0141 954 9346

108

BARCLAY John *(Gtr, B Gtr)*: 41 Spruce Road, Abronhill, Cumbernauld, Glasgow G67 3DP ☎ 01236 451604

BARRY Michael *(E Gtr, B Gtr)*: Flat 0/2, 63 Lymburn Street, Glasgow G3 8PD ☎ 0141 226 5459

BASS David *(Gtr, B Gtr)*: Dunedin, Smallholm, High Tae, Lockerbie, Dumfrieshire DG11 1JY ☎ 01576 810451

BERRY Ronnie *(Gtr, B Gtr, Db)*: 14 Nether Dallachy, Spey Bay, Fochabers, Moray IV32 7PL ☎ 01343 821451

BOLAM Frank *(Gtr, B Ldr)*: 47 Coltmuir Street, Parkhouse, Glasgow G22 6LU ☎ 0141 336 6739

BRITAIN David Leslie *(Gtr, Bjo)*: 1 Glenside Gdns, Armadale, West Lothian EH48 3RA

BROCKETT David *(Gtr, B Gtr, Kbds)*: 13 Townhead Place, Tannochside, Uddingstone, Glasgow, Scotland G71 6TG ☎ 01698 813721

BROWN Andrew *(Gtr, Kbds, B Gtr, Eth Wnd, Ea)*: 35 Old Abbey Road, North Berwick, East Lothian EH39 4BP ☎ 01620 892285

BROWN Stewart *(Gtr, Ctna, Bjo, Tin Wh, Bag)*: Straun Lodge, 27 Strathern Road, Broughty Ferry, Dundee DD5 1PP ☎ 01382 75031

BUCHANAN Cameron *(Gtr)*: 6 Dean Crescent, Riverside, Stirling FK8 1UT ☎ 01789 461605

BURCHILL Charles *(Gtr, Vln)*: 7 Belford Gardens, Edinburgh EH4 3EP ☎ 0131 332 3165

BURT George *(Gtr, Db)*: 59 Russel Street, Falkirk FK2 7HP ☎ 01324 638437

CALLIS Jo *(Gtr, Voc, Synth, Kbds)*: 3A Rochester Terrace, Edinburgh EH10 5AA ☎ 0131 229 8946

CAMPBELL Ken *(Ac Gtr, Voc, Nor P)*: Townhead Of Aber, By Gartocharn, Loch Lomond, Scotland G83 8NQ ☎ 01389 830446 & fax, 0374 824302 mob

CAMPBELL Neil *(Gtr, B Gtr)*: 1-2 Craigleadh Portree, Isle Of Skye, Scotland IV51 9DG ☎ 0147 861 3599/3436

CARLETON Iain *(Gtr, B Gtr)*: 8 Myrtle Terrace, Edinburgh EH11 1PF ☎ 0131 313 3832

CAWOOD Geoff *(Gtr, B Gtr)*: Flat 2F1, 6 Huntly Street, Edinburgh EH3 5HB ☎ 0131 557 1544

CHAURAND Anne *(Cl Gtr)*: 76 White Street, 3rd Flat Left, Glasgow G11 5DB ☎ 0141 334 5691

CHRISTIE Alan *(Gtr, B Gtr)*: 106 Droverhall Ave, Crossgates, Fife, Scotland KY4 8BW ☎ 020 8384 4962

CLARK Christopher *(Gtr)*: 30 Buckingham Terrace, Glasgow G12 8ED ☎ 01355 572667, 01355 260852

CLARK John M *(Gtr, B Gtr)*: 86 Dundonald Road, Kilmarnock KA1 1TH ☎ 01563 520793

CLARK Nigel *(Gtr, B Gtr)*: 115 Seil Drive, Simshill, Glasgow G44 5DU ☎ 0141 637 0071

CLARK Ramsay *(E Gtr, Voc, Pf, Per)*: Top Right Floor, 77 Fonthill Road, Aberdeen, Scotland AB11 6UP

COADY Alan *(Cl Gtr, Pf)*: 5 Abbey Street, Edinburgh EH7 5SJ ☎ 0131 652 0304

COLLINS Arthur *(Gtr, Voc)*: 5 Campbell Avenue, Stevenston, Ayrshire KA20 4BT ☎ 01294 466624

CONDIE James *(Gtr, St Gtr, Pd Gtr)*: 4 Upper Gilmore Terrace, Edinburgh EH3 9NN ☎ 0131 229 2907 & fax

CONNOLLY William *(Gtr, Bjo)*: Sleepy Dumpling (Music) Ltd, c/o Tickety Boo Limited, The Boathouse, Crabtree Lane, London SW6 6TY ☎ 020 7610 0122, 020 7610 0133

COUTTS Stephen *(Gtr, Vln, B Gtr, Db)*: 3 Elm Road, Killearn, Stirlingshire G63 9RY ☎ 01360 551032

CURRAN James *(Gtr, Vln, Man, A Sax, Flt)*: 21 West End Park Street, 1/1, Glasgow G3 6LH ☎ 0141 332 7702

DAVIDSON Gordon *(Gtr)*: 23/3 42 Viewpoint Place, Glasgow, Scotland G21 3AS ☎ 0141 557 1612

DAVIDSON Grant *(Gtr, Kbds, Sax)*: 130 Rosemount Place, Aberdeen, Scotland AB25 2YU ☎ 01224 642048

DAVIES Bruce *(Gtr, B Gtr, Voc)*: P.O.Box 7, Glenrothes, Fife KY6 2TA ☎ 01337 831116, 01337 831996 fax

DAVIES Gareth *(Gtr, Voc)*: 12 Rosewood Avenue, Aberdeen AB12 3DE ☎ 01224 872288, 01224 833528

DEVERS Peter *(Gtr, Dms, Bod, Pf, Man)*: 4 Craigend Crescent, Milncaue, Glasgow G62 7DU ☎ 0141 570 1889

DIMENT Neil John *(Ac Gtr, E Gtr, Voc)*: Ashbourne, 43 Mount Avenue, Kilmarnock, Ayrshire KA1 1UE ☎ 01563 535240

DONALDSON Simon *(Gtr, Voc, B Gtr)*: 16, 1/F 4, Elgin Terrace, Edinburgh EH7 5NW ☎ 0131 6661 3130, 0131 556 4081

DOUGALL Gordon *(Gtr, Kbds, B Gtr, Per, Synth)*: 2/3 21 Garturk Street, Glasgow G42 1JQ ☎ 0141 423 2704, 0141 552 3575

DOUGALL Jama *(E Gtr, Cl Gtr)*: 12 Church Street, Eyemouth, Berwickshire TD14 5DH ☎ 018907 51576

DUFFIN Graeme *(Gtr)*: The Knowe, 28 Newlands Road, Newlands, Glasgow G43 2JD ☎ 0141 649 0926, 0141 649 0926

DUNBAR Frank *(Gtr)*: 3 Stirling Drive, Hamilton, Lanarkshire ML3 9HL ☎ 01698 829605

DUNCAN Robin *(Gtr, Man, Wh, Flt)*: 1 Madill Place, Stenhousemuir, Larbert FK5 4LG ☎ 01324 556026

DUNNING Paul *(Gtr, Per, Hmca)*: 8 Garvock Terrace, Dunfermline, Fife, Scotland KY12 7UA ☎ 01383 624597

EWING Steven *(Gtr, Kbds)*: 74 Stevenson Avenue, Edinburgh, Scotland EH11 2SW ☎ 0131 539 9214

FARRELL Peter *(Gtr)*: 3 Beechgrove, Moffat, Dumfriesshire DG10 9RS ☎ 01683 220840

FATUNMBI Akin *(Gtr, Per)*: Flat 3, 36 Easter Road, Edinburgh EH7 5RG ☎ 0131 659 6313

FINDLAY Duncan *(Gtr, Bjo, Man, Bzk)*: Eastwood, 26 Drummie Road, Tillicoultry, Clackmannanshire FK13 6HT ☎ 01259 750444, 07050 165504 mob

FISCHBACHER Stephen *(Gtr)*: 11 Royston Terrace, Edinburgh, Scotland EH3 5QU ☎ 0131 552 6556

FONDA Quentin *(Gtr)*: c/o Richard Gordon Mngt., 3 Berkley Grove, London NW1 8XY ☎ 020 7483 4945

FORD John *(Gtr)*: 11 Wallace Street, Ardler, Meigle, Perthshire ☎ 01828 640545

FOX Allie *(Gtr, Dul)*: 'Marlee', 14 Hillside Terrace, Selkirk, Scottish Borders TD7 4LT ☎ 01896 752324, 0121 449 1892

FRANCIS Dave *(Gtr, Per, Man)*: 34 Prince Regent Street, Edinburgh EH5 4AT ☎ 0131 554 3092

FREW James *(Gtr, Voc, Kbds)*: 37 Galt Avenue, Irvine, Scotland G5 9TW ☎ 01294 276670

FULLARTON Andy *(Gtr, B Gtr, Kbds, Per, Song W)*: ☎ 0141 339 9093

GALLACHER George *(Gtr, Hmca)*: 14, Salisbury, Calderwood, East Kilbride, Scotland G74 3QE ☎ 0135 524 5682

GARDEN Michael *(Gtr, B Gtr, Voc)*: 39 Royal Park Terrace, Edinburgh EH8 8JA, 0131 661 0800

GAUGHAN Dick *(Gtr, Man, Bjo)*: 33 Viewcraig Gardens, Edinburgh EH8 9UN ☎ 0131 557 4898

GIBB Steve *(Cl Gtr, E Gtr, B Gtr, Bjo, Ma)*: 1 Loch Lann Court, Culloden, Inverness IV1 2UF ☎ 020 8767 4675

GILLIES Stephen *(Gtr, E Gtr, B Gtr, Bag)*: 2D Adamson Place, Cornton, Stirling FK9 5BS ☎ 01786 463673

GILMOUR John *(Gtr, B Gtr, Voc)*: 16 Kerse Park, Alloway, Ayr LA7 4UD ☎ 01292 440104, 07887 673845, 01292 440104

GIZZI Giuliano *(Gtr)*: c/o Gun, Parklene Studios, 974 Pollokshaws Road, Glasgow G41 2HA ☎ 0141 632 1111

GOLDIE John *(Gtr)*: 17 Monks Road, Airdrie ML6 9QW ☎ 01236 748711

GOWANS Lorna *(Gtr)*: 47 Penrith Drive, Kelvindale, Glasgow G12 0DQ ☎ 0141 339 2828

GRANT Isla *(Gtr, Voc, Song W)*: Cleughhead Farmhouse, Charterhall, Duns, Berwickshire, Scotland TD11 3RE ☎ 01890 840722

GRANT James *(Gtr)*: 21 Cleveden Gardens, Kelvinside, Glasgow G12 0PU ☎ 0141 423 8822

GROVES Andrew *(Gtr, Dms, Kbds, Pf, B Gtr)*: Flat 3F1, 17 Roseburn Terrace, Edinburgh, Scotland EH12 5NG ☎ 0131 313 4387

GUNN Andrew *(Gtr)*: 16A Pict Avenue, Inverness, Scotland IV3 6LX ☎ 01463 223134

HAMILTON Craig *(Gtr, Pf)*: 1 Craigleith Hill Park, Edinburgh EH4 2NR ☎ 0131 332 8090

HANRATTY Stewart *(Gtr)*: 133 Easter Road, Top Flat Left, Edinburgh EH7 5QA ☎ 0131 661 5275

110

HARLEY Keith (*Gtr*): 30 Hill Street, Tillicoultry, Clacks, Scotland FK13 6HF ☎ 01259 750576

HENDERSON David (*Gtr, Dms, Kbds*): 50 Craigmount Brae, Edinburgh EH12 8XD ☎ 0131 317 1769

HENDERSON Paul (*Gtr, Voc*): 28 Fairfield Place, Falkirk FK2 7AR ☎ 01324 634443

HENDERSON Robert (*Gtr, B Gtr*): 24 Clark Terrace, Crieff PH7 3QE ☎ 01764 653851

HENDERSON Stewart (*Gtr*): 62 The Loaning, Motherwell, Lanarkshire ML1 3HE ☎ 01689 268527

HENERY Frank (*Gtr*): 26 Duns Crescent, Coltness, Wishaw ML1 2DY ☎ Cambusnethan 38

HENRY James (*Gtr, Voc*): 228 King Street, Aberdeen AB24 5BU ☎ 01224 630152 & fax

HIGGINS John (*Ac Gtr*): ☎ 0141 357 4925

HITCHELL William (*Gtr, Voc, Kbds, Dms, Acc*)

HOGG Michael (*Gtr, Mando, Kbds, Bjo*): Mossend Farm, West Calder, West Lothian EH55 8LD ☎ 01506 871310, 07771 934984, 01506 871310

HOWARD Tony (*Gtr*): 33 St Clair Terrace, Edinburgh EH10 5PS ☎ 0131 447 5134

HULETT Alistair (*Gtr*): 2L, 64 Minard Road, Shawlands, Glasgow G41 2EQ ☎ 0141 649 0855

HUNTER Garry (*Gtr, Bjo, Man*): 62 Great Northern Road, Aberdeen, Scotland AB24 3PT ☎ 01224 481073

HUNTER Ronnie (*Gtr, Kbds, Acc, Dms*): 19 Balfair Court, Kilmarnock, Ayrshire KA3 7TD ☎ 01563 536508

HUTCHISON George (*Gtr*): 21B Mornington Avenue, Gants Hill, Ilford, Essex IG1 3QT ☎ 020 8554 8227

INGLIS Gordon Robert (*Gtr, Man, Dms*): 17 Craigs Gardens, Edinburgh EH12 8HA ☎ 0131 339 2649, 0131 335 3145

INNES Barbara (*Gtr, Man, Kbds, Voc*): 12 New Well Wynd, Linlithgow, West Lothian EH49 7EW ☎ 01506 845536

JACK Colin (*Gtr, Pf*): 35 North Balmossie Street, Broty Ferry, Dundee DD5 2PX ☎ 01382 738380

JACKSON Jill (*Gtr, Kbds, Man, Dobro, Bjo*): 44 Abbotsford Crescent, Foxbar, Paisley, Scotland PA2 0SB ☎ 01505 814774

JACKSON Stephen (*Gtr, Voc, Hmca, B Gtr, Voc*): 6 Caird Drive, Flat 2/2, Glasgow G11 5DS ☎ 0141 339 8123, 0141 227 2751

JAMIESON Piero (*Gtr, B Gtr, Kbds*): 5A Caledonian Mansions, Kelvinbridge, Glasgow G12 8HQ ☎ 0141 339 9899

JENNER Keith (*Gtr, Pf*): 14 Marshall Place, Perth PH2 8AH ☎ 01738 637902

JOHN Ewan (*Gtr, B Gtr*): 1 Hawthorn Bank Lane, Dean Village, Edinburgh EH4 3BJ ☎ 0131 225 5622

JOHNSTON Paul (*Gtr, Bjo*): Otterslea, Grunnavoe, Vidlin, Shetland ZE2 9QF ☎ 01806 7264

JONES Malcolm (*Gtr*): c/o Marilyn Ross, Agent Runrig, 1 York Street, Aberdeen AB11 5DL ☎ 01224 573100

JONES Robert (*Gtr, Cl Gtr, B Gtr, Voc, Synt*): 71 Cloan Crescent, Bishopbriggs, Glasgow G64 2HW ☎ 0141 772 6510

KEEGAN James (*Gtr*): 94 Sinclair Street, Stevenson, Ayrshire KA20 4AL ☎ 01294 601399

KELLY Peter (*Gtr, Voc, Song W*): 14 Parkway Place, Coatbridge, North Lanarkshire ML5 1JA ☎ 0123 6603396

KELSO Sandy (*Gtr*): 19 Quarry Road, Fintry, By Glasgow G63 0XD ☎ 01360 860444

KING Danny (*Gtr*): 154 Kirkland Walk, Methil, Fife KY8 2AG ☎ 01333 427757

KNOTT Steve (*Gtr*) ☎ 01505 690 000, 01505 690390 fax

LAURENSON Graeme (*Gtr, Kbds, B Gtr*): 21 Stirling Road, Larbert, Scotland FK5 4NE ☎ 01324 553337

LEAN Laurence (*Gtr, Voc*): Flat 2F2, 56 Montpelier Park, Bruntsfield, Edinburgh, Midlothian EH10 4NH ☎ 0131 229 5341

LECKERMAN Wendy (*Cl Gtr, E Gtr*): 6 Eriskay Crescent, Newton Mearns, Glasgow, Scotland G77 6XE ☎ 0141 639 8721, 070500 83139

LENNON Gerry (*Gtr, Kbds, B Gtr*): 179 Garrioch Road, Glasgow G20 8RL ☎ 0141 946 3157

LIVINGSTONE Gavin (*Gtr, Synth, Man*): 1 Mortlach Court, Buccleuch Park, Glasgow G3 6NS ☎ 0141 332 1087

LLEWELLYN Steven (*Gtr*): 11 Muirdyke Road, Coatbridge ML5 2HQ ☎ 01236 434841

MACDOUGALL Donald (*Gtr, B Gtr, Clt, Pf*): 25 Liberton Drive, Edinburgh EH16 6NL ☎ 0131 664 5211

MACGREGOR Andy (*Gtr*): 100 Hawthorn Drive, Wishaw, Lanarkshire ML2 8JN ☎ 01698 374646

MACKENZIE Clen (*Gtr, Voc*): 12 Millpark Avenue, Oban, Argyll PA34 4JN ☎ 01631 563974

MACKENZIE Kevin (*Gtr*): 22 Belmont Gardens, Edinburgh EH12 6JH ☎ 0131 668 4935

MACKINNON Micheal (*E Gtr, B Gtr, Dms, Per*): G/L 17 Cranworth Street, Hillhead, Glasgow, Scotland G12 8BZ ☎ 0141 334 7190, 0141 300 3000

MACLEAN Gordon (*Gtr, Dms, Per, B Gtr*): Torrans, Pennyghael, Isle Of Mull, Scotland PA70 6HE ☎ 01681 704295

MACLEOD Ali (*Gtr*): 2190 Dumbarton Road, Yoker, Glasgow G14 0JL ☎ 0141 954 2612

MACLEOD Iain F (*Gtr, H Bag, Bzk, Man*): 10 Cantyre Court, 102 Buccleuch Street, Glasgow G3 ☎ 0141 564 6414, 0777 1756151

MALLOCH Stephen (*Gtr*): 1/R 4 Lawrie Street, Patrick, Glasgow G11 5NL ☎ 0141 339 3249

MANLEY Alan (*Gtr, B Gtr*): 2 Granitehill Terrace, Flat 12, Persley, Aberdeen AB22 8AT ☎ 01224 696780

MARTUN Al'N (*Gtr, Dms, Kbds, Hmca*): 1 Killoch Drive, Barrhead G78 2HU ☎ 0141 881 1654

MCCORMACK James (*Gtr, Kbds*): 7 Birdsfield Court, Limetree, Hamilton, Lanarkshire, Glasgow ML3 0RN ☎ 01698 826217

MCCRONE Duncan (*Gtr, B Gtr*): East End Cottage, Gartmore, Stirlingshire FK8 3RW

MCCULLOCH Drew (*Gtr, Kbds, Voc*): 9 Dongola Road, Ayr, Ayrshire KA7 3BH ☎ 01292 261401, 0141 552 6677

MCCULLY Paul (*Gtr, Man, Hmca, Voc*) ☎ 01698 843169

MCDONALD Scott (*Ac Gtr, Voc, Hmca*): c/o Scott Ligertwood, Hong Kong Sky Dance, 9B Orkney, Braemar Heights, 7 Wai Tsui Cres, Nth Point, Hong Kong

MCDOUGALD Alastair (*Gtr, Bjo*): 41 Whitehill Gardens, Musselburgh, Midlothian EH21 6PH ☎ 0131 665 5291

MCERLAINE Alistair (*Gtr*): c/o T Whitelaw, Park Lane Studios, 974 Pollokshaws Road, Glasgow G41 2HA

MCFARLANE Peter (*Ld Gtr*): 16 Kirriemuir, Calderwood, East Kilbride, Glasgow G74 3PP ☎ 01355 901883

MCGEADY Colin (*Gtr, B Gtr, Kbds*): 8 Moncrieff Gdns, Lenzie, Glasgow G66 4NN ☎ 0141 776 3560, 07775 854700

MCGOOGAN Gerard (*Gtr*): 36 Park Road, Calderbank, Airdrie ML6 9TG ☎ 01236 608448

MCGURK Ruuairidh (*Gtr, Man, Bag, Voc, Kbds*): 7 Elmwood Manor, Bothwell, Glasgow G71 8EA ☎ 01698 854468, 0370 832562

MCIVOR Iain (*Gtr, B Gtr*): 7 Manachie Road, Forres, Moray, Scotland IV36 0JT ☎ 01309 673141

MCKIBBEN Ross (*Gtr, Voc, B Gtr, Kbds*): 01 8 High Holm Street, Port Glasgow, Renfrewshire PA14 5HQ ☎ 01475 719 085

MCKINNA Iain (*Gtr, B Gtr, Kbds*): 107 High Street, Royal Mile, Edinburgh EH1 1SG ☎ 0131 556 4882

MCLAUGHLIN Dominic (*Gtr, B Gtr, A Sax, Clt*): 7 Juniper Grove, Dunfermline, Fife KY11 5BQ ☎ 01383 620455

MCLAUGHLIN John (*Gtr*): 36 Main Street, Calderbank, Airdrie ML6 9SG ☎ 01236 754599

MCLEAN Samuel (*Gtr, B Gtr*) ☎ 0141 571 7424

MCLELLAN James (*Gtr, Kbds, Voc*): Top Flat, 19 Moorburn Road, Largs KA30 9JA ☎ 01475 687 497

MCMAHON Robert (*Gtr*): 46 Farm Road, Blantyre, South Lanarkshire G72 9DT ☎ 01698 828720

MCNEIL James (*Gtr*): 47 Campbell Avenue, Stevenston, Ayrshire KA20 4BT ☎ 01294 467546

MCPHERSON Andrew (*Ld Gtr, Rh Gtr*): 1/2 Davies Square, Duntocher, Clydebank, Glasgow G81 6DW ☎ 01389 890601

MCRAE Ryan (*Gtr, Voc*): Address Unknown ☎ 01738 560964

MCRINER Raymond (*Gtr, B Gtr*): Birch Cottage, Inverarnie, Inverness-Shire IV2 6XA ☎ 01808 521165

MCSWIGGAN Mark (*Gtr, Pf, B Gtr, Voc, Per*): 14 Trent Street, Townhead, Coatbridge ML5 2NT ☎ 01236 420004

MCVICAR Ewan *(Gtr, Auto Hrp, Bjo)*: 84 High Street, Linlithgow, West Lothian EH49 7AQ ☎ 01506 847935

MEDBOE Haftor *(Gtr)*: 133 Morningside Drive, Edinburgh, Scotland EH10 5NR ☎ 0131 4474844

MELDRUM Raymond *(Gtr)*: 93 Dundrennan Road, Langside, Glasgow G42 9SL ☎ 0141 649 1042

MIDDLETON Malcolm *(Gtr, B Gtr)*: 74 Alexander Avenue, Falkirk FK2 9DZ ☎ 01324 621825

MILL Gary *(Gtr, Kbds)*: 19 North Gyle Park, Edinburgh EH12 8LE ☎ 0131 339 2612 eve, 0131 663 1971 day

MILLER Brian *(Gtr, Voc)*: 36 Greenhill Park, Penicuik, Midlothian EH26 9EX ☎ 01968 678153

MOORE Barry *(Gtr, B Gtr)*: 23 Fairfield Place, Falkirk, Scotland FK2 7AR ☎ 01324 613484, 0410 385 321, 01324 713076

MORPH *(Gtr)*: 35 North View, Bearsden, Glasgow G61 1NX ☎ 0141 942 8673, 0141 563 6077 fax

MORRIS Brian *(Gtr, Pf, Kbds, B Gtr)*: 162 Pendeen Road, Barlanark, Glasgow, Scotland G33 4SS ☎ 0141 771 2008, 0802 280081 mob

MUNRO Donnie *(Gtr, Voc)*: Scorrybreac House, Portree, Isle Of Skye ☎ 01478 612939

MUNRO Gavin *(Gtr)*: The Cottage, Gannochy Farm, Perth, Tayside ☎ 01738 443085

MURRAY Andy *(E Gtr, Kbds)*: Beananach Cottage, Station Road, Carrbridge, Inverness, Scotland PH23 3AP ☎ 01479 841772, 01479 841696

MURRAY Kevin *(Gtr, Man, Pf, B Gtr, Per)*: East Byres Cottage, Balmerino, Fife DD6 8SB ☎ 01382 330567, 01382 330567

MURRISON Jimmy *(Gtr, B Gtr)*: Flat 5, 69 George Street, Perth, Scotland PHN 5LB ☎ 01738 442323

NELSON Stephen *(Gtr, Sax)*: 49 Fort Street, Ayr KA7 1DH ☎ 01292 280265

NOAKES Rab *(Gtr)*: Studio 1, 19 Marine Crescent, Glasgow G51 1HD ☎ 0141 429 6366, 0141 429 6377 fax

NOBLE Douglas *(Cl Gtr, E Gtr)*: 5/6 Ratcliffe Terrace, Edinburgh EH9 1SX ☎ 0131 622 4242

NORRIS Sharon *(Gtr, Man)*: 9 Turnberry Road, Hyndland, Glasgow G11 5AG ☎ 0141 334 8533, 0141 339 1119

O'CONNELL Cameron *(Gtr, Kbds)*: 8A Ramsay Court, Kincardine, Fife, Scotland FK10 4RT ☎ 01259 731852

O'HEADHRA Brian *(Gtr, Voc, Bod, Hmca)*: ☎ 01899 850258 & fax, 0802 433294

O'NEILL Shaleph *(Gtr, Kbds, Voc)*: 18 Grosvenor Crescent, Edinburgh EH12 5EL ☎ 0131 337 4886

PALMER John J *(Gtr, Voc)*: 80 Hillend Crescent, Glarkston, Glasgow, Glasgow G76 7XX

PARK James *(Rh Gtr, Org, Hmca)*: 59 Townfoot, Dreghorn, Irvine, Ayrshire KA11 4EH ☎ 01294 216007

PARK Maxwell *(Gtr, Kbds, B Gtr, Vln)*: 1 Marywood Square, 2/2, Strathbungo, Glasgow G41 2BW ☎ 0141 423 0923

PARR Jonny *(Ac Gtr, E Gtr, Kbds, Pf, Voc)*: Flat 7, 6 Loudon Terrace, Dowanhill, Glasgow G12 9AQ ☎ 0141 334 9351, 0411 888239

PATERSON Don *(Gtr)*: Flat 2F1, 12 Meadowbank Terrace, Edinburgh EH8 7AR ☎ 0131 661 3922, 07970 152844 mob

PAUL Jack *(E Gtr)*: 28 Lindsay Gardens, St Andrews, Fife KY16 8XD ☎ 01334 75888

PEARSON Graeme *(Gtr, Voc)*: 15 Rosshill Terrace, Dalmeny Station, Edinburgh EH30 9JS ☎ 0131 331 1617

PENDERS Allan *(Gtr)*: 31 Kelvin Street, Larss, Ayrshire, Scotland KA30 9BD ☎ 01475 672185

PETERS Stephen *(Gtr, B Gtr, Kbds, Vln)* ☎ 01294 465210

PHILP Gregor *(Gtr, B Gtr, Kbds, Voc)*: 29 Scott Street, Dundee DD2 2AL ☎ 01382 660243

PHIMISTER James *(Gtr)*: 69 St Clair Street, Kirkcaldy, Fife KY1 2NW ☎ 01592 266326

PLUES David *(Gtr)*: Brae Cottage, Wallacestone, Falkirk, Stirlingshire FK2 0DJ ☎ 01324 713745

POLLOCK Ronald *(Gtr)*: Phantassie, Castle Road, Wolfhill, Perthshire PH2 6DJ

POWADA Neil *(Gtr)*: The Cuillins, Bridge Of Mondynes, Fordoun, Laurencekire Kincardineshire AB30 1LD ☎ 01569 740204

PRESAVAGE Martin *(Cl Gtr, E Gtr, Pf, Kbds)*: 11 Benford Knowe, Newarthill, Motherwell, Lanarkshire ML1 5BQ ☎ 01698 734476

QUINN Paul *(Gtr, B Gtr, Dms)*: Tullochard, Scalesburn, Wick, Caithness KW1 4JH ☎ 01955 606713

RAE Ian *(Gtr, B Gtr, Kbds, Man)*: 6 Ard Connon Cottages, Old Meldrum, Aberdeenshire AB51 0EW ☎ 016512 2093

RAMAGE Andrew *(Gtr)*: 2 Gwendoline Row, Drunzie, Glenfarg PH2 9QU ☎ 01577 3435

RANKIN Joan *(Gtr, Fo Fdl)*: 8 Loch Road, Edinburgh EH4 3PW

REED Hugh *(Gtr, B Gtr)*: 23 Kingsford Avenue, Muirend, Glasgow G44 3EU ☎ 0141 429 3101

REEVES Helen *(Gtr)*

REID George *(Gtr, B Gtr, Man, Bzk)*: 261 South Gyle Road, Edinburgh EH12 9EJ ☎ 0131 538 1638

REID Steve *(E Gtr, Ac Gtr)*: 2 Victoria Crescent Road, Dowanhill, Glasgow G12 9DB ☎ 0141 339 3110

REILLY Steven *(Gtr, Kbds, Dms, Pf)*: 2 Barra Drive, Airdree, Scotland ML6 5EF ☎ 01236 755601

RENBOURN John *(Gtr)*: The Snoot, Borthwickbrae, Hawick, Scotland TD9 7LZ ☎ 01450 880335

RICE Leslie *(Gtr, B Gtr, Dms, Per, Kbds)*: G/L, 10 Dryburgh Gardens, Glasgow, Scotland G20 6BT ☎ 0141 945 1386, 0141 287 3755

RICHARD Nigel *(Gtr, Citt, Bag)*: 9 Beresford Avenue, Edinburgh EH5 3EV ☎ 0131 551 1726

RICHARDSON Stuart *(Gtr, Bjo, Man)*: 34 King Street, Lossiemouth, Moray IV31 6AB ☎ 01343 814748, 0498 613326

ROBERTSON Andrew *(Gtr)*: 19 Tannoch Drive, Milngavie, Glasgow, Scotland G62 8AY ☎ 0141 956 2908

ROBERTSON Clare *(Gtr, Auto Hrp, Bzk, Voc)*: Barrodger Cottage, Beith Road, Lochwinnoch, Renfrewshire PA12 4JX ☎ 01505 504212, 0141 558 9313, 0141 557 2430 fax

ROWAN Eric *(Gtr, Com)*: 1B Midton Road, Ayr, Scotland KA7 2SE ☎ 01292 290370

RUSSELL James *(Gtr, Wh, Mldn)*: 23 Moray Court, Auchtertool, Kirkcaldy, Fife KY2 5XS ☎ 01592 782485

SAICH John *(Gtr, B Gtr, Voc)*: 5 Crinan Cottages, Crinan, Argyle PA31 8SS ☎ 01546 830254

SCOOBY *(Gtr)*: 2 The Billy, Plean, Stirling FK7 8BS

SCOTT David *(Gtr, Kbds, Voc, B Gtr)*: 45 Clyde Street, Camelon, Falkirk FK1 4ED ☎ 01324 670887

SHADE Steven *(Gtr)*: 8 Lovedale Road, Balerno, Edinburgh EH14 7DW ☎ 0131 449 3745

SHONIWA Emmanuel *(Gtr, B Gtr)*: 79 Trinity Road, Edinburgh EH5 3JX ☎ 0131 552 3043

SINCLAIR Douglas *(Gtr, B Gtr)*: 43 Pitt Street, Newhaven, Edinburgh EH6 4BZ ☎ 0131 555 0046

SINCLAIR George *(Gtr, B Gtr)*: Dolphin House, 179 Croftfoot Road, Croftfoot, Glasgow G44 5JY ☎ 0141 569 4323

SLAVEN Mick *(Gtr, Bjo)*: 1Up/Right, 141 Deanston Drive, Shawlands, Glasgow G41 3LP ☎ 0141 423 8953

SPENCE Brian *(Gtr, B Gtr, Kbds, Voc)*: 52 Vicarage Road, Leyton, London E10 5EA ☎ 020 8558 3269

STEPHEN Graham *(Gtr, Kbds)*: 5 Dubford Crescent, Bridge Of Don, Aberdeen AB23 8FT ☎ 01224 822650, 01224 635835, 01224 647952

STEVENSON Douglas *(St Gtr, Dobro)*: 118 Langmuirhead Road, Auchinloch, Lenzie, Nr Glasgow G66 5DN ☎ 0141 775 0397

STEWART Alexander *(E Gtr, Ac Gtr)*: 6 Woodlea Park, Sauchie, Alloa, Clackmannanshire, Scotland FK10 3BG ☎ 01259 215117

STEWART Bill *(Gtr, Acc)*: 12 Strathview Terrace, Balfron, By Glasgow G63 0PS ☎ 01360 440 553

STILL Alexander *(Gtr, B Gtr, Kbds)*: 47 Birniehill Avenue, Bathgate, West Lothian EH48 2RR

SYKES Andrew *(Gtr)*: Flat J, 6 Cardigan Road, Headingley, Leeds LS6 3AG ☎ 0966 551998 mob

T.J. *(Ld Gtr)*: 19 Springvalley Gardens, Edinburgh EH10 4QF ☎ 0131 447 7092

TAJ (*E Gtr, B Gtr*): 40 Craiglockhart Terrace, Edinburgh EH14 1AJ ☎ 0131 443 7563

TAYLOR Martin (*Gtr, Man*): P.O. Box 8403, Maybole, Ayrshire KA19 7YB ☎ 01655 740217, 01655 740556 fax

TERVET Andrew (*Gtr, Cel, Pf*): 21 Lawrence Street, Flat G/R, Glasgow G11 5HF ☎ 0141 334 5311

THORNE Phillip (*Gtr*): 25 Brockwood Avenue, Penicuik, Midlothian EH26 9AL ☎ 01968 673470

TURNER Chris (*Gtr, Bzk, Man, Dms, B Gtr*): 10 Cobden Terrace, Haymarket, Edinburgh EH11 2BJ ☎ 0131 313 4442

WALES Eric (*Gtr*): 5A Tantallon Terrace, North Berwick, East Lothian EH39 4LE ☎ 01620 2337

WARDEN Neil (*Gtr*): 45/7 West Bryson Road, Edinburgh EH11 1BQ ☎ 0131 337 2042

WARE Zachary (*Gtr, Voc, B Gtr*): G/L 41 Dudley Drive, Glasgow, Scotland G12 9RR ☎ 0141 334 3436

WHITE Peter (*Gtr*): 10 Viewfield Road, Arbroath, Angus DD11 2BS ☎ 01241 879854

WHYTOCK Richard (*Gtr, Voc*)

WILLIAMSON Marie (*Gtr*): 6 Saeter, Symbister, Whalsay, Shetland ZE2 9BQ ☎ 01806 566672

WINTON Neil (*E Gtr, Cl Gtr, Ac Gtr*): 28 Forth Street, Riverside, Stirling FK8 1UF ☎ 0797 909 1279

WOODWARD Alan (*Gtr*): Flat 2L, 1011 Cathcart Road, Mount Florida, Glasgow G42 9XJ ☎ 0141 636 5948

WOOLLVEN David (*E Gtr, Ac Gtr, Dms, Kbds, Hmc*): 31 Dundas Place, Kirkliston, West Lothian EH29 9BJ ☎ 0131 333 3862

WYNESS James (*Gtr, B Gtr*): 8 Commercial Street, Edinburgh EH6 6JA ☎ 0131 553 1617

YEUDALL David (*Gtr*): 11 Struthers Place, Barassie, Troon, Scotland KA10 6UY ☎ 01292 311046, 0410 622204

YOUNG Thomas (*Gtr, Kbds*): 67 Stoopshill Crescent, Dalry, Ayrshire, Scotland KA24 4DG ☎ 01294 832890

NORTH WEST

ABBOTT Martin (*Gtr*): Stoncliffe, Long Lane, Pleasington, Blackburn BB2 6RD ☎ 01254 201181

AGGREY John (*Gtr*): Flat 5, 32 Holden Road, Waterloo, Liverpool L22 6QE ☎ 0151 476 5485, 0410 783688 mob

ALEXANDER David (*Gtr*): 3 Webster Terrace, Well Street, Cefn Mawr, Wrexham, Clwyd LL14 3AL ☎ 01978 823576

ALLEN William (*Gtr, B Gtr, Kbds*): Rose Cottage, 11 Stoneheads, Whaley Bridge, High Peak, Cheshire SK23 7BB ☎ 01663 732973

AMICK Gabriel (*E Gtr, Ac Gtr, B Gtr, Dms, Kb*): 33 Robert Street, Ramsbottom, Bury BL0 0NQ ☎ 01706 824268

ANDREWS Andy (*Gtr, Bjo, Uke*): 15 Denmark Street, Lancaster LA1 5LY ☎ 01524 37838

ARTHUR Alan (*Gtr*): 56 Mouldsworth Avenue, Withington, Manchester M20 1AW ☎ 0161 434 2450

ASHCROFT Keith John (*Gtr, B Gtr*): 85 White Lund Road, Heaton With Oxcliffe, Morecambe, Lancs LA3 3DX ☎ 01524 416714

ASHTON Stephen (*Gtr, Voc, Man*): 30 Wisbeck Road, Bolton BL2 2TA ☎ 01204 394298

ATHERTON Paul (*Gtr*): 33, Whitelow Road, Chorlton-cum-Hardy, Manchester M21 9HG ☎ 0161 881 4600

ATKINSON Gary (*Gtr*): 7 Norfolk Road, Penrith, Cumbria CA11 9AA ☎ 01768 866930

AVATAR (*Gtr, Kbds, Per, Voc*): 25 Ernest Street, Prestwich, Manchester M25 7HZ ☎ 0161 798 7519

BAILEY Lee (*Gtr*): 16 Emley Street, Levenshulme, Manchester M19 3BZ ☎ 0161 221 2535

BANN Nigel (*Gtr*): 218 Kingsway, Gatley, Cheadle, Cheshire SK8 4PB ☎ 0161 428 2627

BARLOW Stephen (*Gtr, Kbds*): 44A, Railway Street, Altrincham, Cheshire WA14 2RE ☎ 0161 928 7614, 07971 371676

BARNETT Brendan (*Gtr*): 7 Elverston Street, Northenden, Manchester M22 4NP ☎ 0161 793 2379

BARTON Peter (*Gtr, B Gtr, Dms*): Rothery House, Henthorn Road, Clitheroe, Lancashire BB7 2LD ☎ 01200 44 45 44, 01200 44 45 45

BATCHELAR Peter (*Cl Gtr, Lute*): 24, Beaumont Park Road, Beaumont Park, Huddersfield, W. Yorks. HD4 5JS ☎ 01484 326170

BEAKER Norman (*Gtr, Voc, Arr*): 14 Hawthorn Grove, Heaton Moor, Stockport, Cheshire SK4 4HZ ☎ 0161 442 7892

BEAVERS Les (*Gtr, B Gtr, Bjo*): 7 Sandown Road, Bury, Lancs BL9 8HN ☎ 0161 766 5087

BECK Michael (*Gtr, Man, St Gtr*): Flat 4, 2 York Road, Chorlton Cum Hardy, Manchester M21 9HP ☎ 0161 860 4646

BECKMANN Peter (*E Gtr, B Gtr, Kbds*): Unit 21, Townmead Business Centre, William Morris Way, London SW6 2SZ ☎ 020 7371 9667, 020 7259 9145

BELL James (*Gtr, Kbds, Dms*): Harby Brow, Mealsgate, Carlisle, Cumbria CA5 1LG ☎ 016973 20442

BELLINGHAM Felix (*Gtr, Pf, Tpt*): 38 Truro Road, Liverpool L15 9HW ☎ 0151 733 7071

BELLINGHAM Matthew (*E Gtr, Ac Gtr, B Gtr, Voc, Kb*): 117 Braemar Road, Fallowfield, Manchester M14 6PN, 0956 494539

BIRRANE James (*Gtr, Synth, Pf, Dms, Rec*): 27 Peters Court, Norwood Drive, Altrincham, Cheshire WA15 7LD ☎ 0610 980 1845

BLOMELEY Mark (*Ld Gtr, Ac Gtr*): 6 Christopher Acre, Norden, Rochdale, Lancs OL11 5FE ☎ 01706 357 861, 0410 324880

BLUGLASS Charles (*Gtr, Per*): 79 Windermere Road, Lancaster LA1 3EZ ☎ 01524 34791

BOARDMAN Dave (*Gtr, B Gtr, Kbds*): 3 Byrom Street, Salford M5 2UH ☎ 0161 848 8648, 0973 214218 mob

BOLGER Leslie (*Gtr, B Gtr*): 12 Firbank Close, Daresbury View, Runcorn, Cheshire WA7 6NR ☎ 01928 710217

BOND Peter (*Gtr*): 12 Kiln Lane, Milnrow, Rochdale, Lancs OL16 3JF ☎ 01706 521093

BOTHAM Stephen (*Gtr, Voc, B Gtr*): Great Oaks, Pollards Lane, Summerseat, Bury, Lancs BL9 5PF ☎ 01706 822301

BOWES Colin (*Gtr*): 4 Knightsbridge Close, West Park, Lytham St Annes FY8 4QW ☎ 01253 737829

BOYD Stuart (*Ac Gtr, Hmca*): Allergarth, Rowel Town, Carlisle CA6 6JU ☎ 01403 254 345

BRIDGE John (*Gtr, B Gtr*): 5 St Johns Close, Read, Burnley, Lancs BB12 7RL ☎ 01282 774393

BROGDEN Richard (*Gtr*): 22 Raglan Court, Silloth, Cumbria CA5 4BW ☎ 016973 32002

BROWN Alexander (*Gtr*): 56 Osborne Road, Cale Green, Stockport SK2 6RQ ☎ 0161 477 1966

BROWN Duncan (*Ld Gtr, Voc*): 17 Westdean Crescent, Burnage, Manchester M19 1GB ☎ 0161 443 2756

BROWN Paul (*Gtr, Bjo*): 20 St Peters Road, Fairfield, Buxton, Derbyshire SK17 7DX ☎ 01298 25074, 0860 345870

BROWNE Tim (*Gtr, B Gtr*): 5 Brownmoor Lane, Crosby, Liverpool, Merseyside L23 0TD ☎ 0151 928 2035

BROWNING Neil (*Gtr, Acc, Rec, Lute, Voc*): 8 Rhes James, Braichmelyn, Bethesda, Gwynedd LL57 3RA ☎ 01248 602608

BRYDEN Paul (*E Gtr, Cl Gtr*): 86 Victoria Avenue, Barrow-In-Furness, Cumbria LA14 5NQ ☎ 01229 835361

BUCKLEY Steven (*Gtr, B Gtr*): 80 Douglas Bank Drive, Springfield, Wigan, Lancs WN6 7HN ☎ 01942 510080

BURNS Gill (*Gtr*): 4 Mill Lane, Much Cowarne, Bromyard, Herefordshire HR7 4JH ☎ 01432 820507

CAMLIN David (*Gtr, Voc, Hmca*): Ghyll Cottage, Lamplugh Green, Workington, Cumbria CA14 4TY ☎ 01946 861080

CAMPBELL Simon (*Gtr, Voc*): The Royds, Chatburn, Clitheroe, Lancashire BB7 4LB ☎ 01200 441271

CARTLIDGE Glenn (*Gtr, T Sax*): 25 Horseshoe Avenue, Doveholes, Buxton, Derbyshire SK17 8DP ☎ 01298 815613

CATCHATOOR Hako (*Ld Gtr, Voc, Rh Gtr, B Gtr, K*): Downshire, 287 Bolton Road, Atherton, Manchester M46 9HG

CATLEY Marc (*Gtr, Voc, Man, B Gtr*): c/o Plankton Records, Sandcastle Productions, PO Box 13533, London, E7 0SG ☎ 020 8534 8500

CAUDLE Stephen (*Gtr*): The Barnes House, Naworth, Brampton, Cumbria CA8 2HE ☎ 016977 41041

CHAN Ray (*Gtr, Sitar*): 32 Langholme Close, Winstanley, Wigan, Lancashire WN3 6TT ☎ 01942 212858

CHARD Andrew (*Gtr, Pf*): 24 Darley Street, Stretford, Manchester M32 OPW ☎ 0161 282 7799

CLARK Peter (*Gtr*): 30 Kayswood Road, Marple, Stockport, Cheshire SK6 6EW ☎ 0161 221 0482

CLARKE Anthony (*Gtr*): 81 Beechfield Road, Liverpool L18 3EQ ☎ 0151 722 7241, 0976 849975, 0151 728 8258

CLYNCH Alistair (*Gtr*): 41 Woodyear Road, Bromborough, Wirral, Merseyside L62 6SY ☎ 0151 327 1645

COASE Los (*Gtr*): 48 Mereside, Stalybridge, Cheshire SK15 1JF ☎ 0161 304 9486

CONROY Sean (*Gtr*): 140 Childwall Heights, Block 2, Hartsbourne Avenue, Liverpool L25 1QJ ☎ 0151 722 0165

COOK Alec (*E Gtr, Kbds*): 5 Helmshore Road, Haslingden, Rossendale, Lancashire BB4 4BG ☎ 01706 216701

COUCH Paul (*Gtr, Pf, Dms*): 9 Gawsworth Close, Bramhall, Stockport, Cheshire SK7 2BB ☎ 0161 439 1761, 01606 861475

COWEN Athol (*E Gtr, Ac Gtr, Kbds, Bong, Hm*): 40 Gibson Street, Wrexham, Wrexham Borough County, Wales LL13 7TS

COY Adam (*Gtr, B Gtr*): 11 Tunstead Avenue, West Didsbury, Manchester M20 1JY ☎ 0161 434 9211, 0114 246 5346

CRAWFORD Neil (*Gtr, B Gtr*): 218 Minster Court, Edgehill, Liverpool L7 3QF ☎ 0151 709 3453

CUNNINGHAM Cj (*Gtr, Synth, Man*): 37 Wordsworth Avenue, Droylsden, Manchester M43 6GA ☎ 0966 263 082

CURZON Phil (*Gtr*): 4 The Mount, Todmorden, Lancs OL14 8BH ☎ 01706 819816

DAICHES Anna (*Gtr, Pf, Hmca, Bjo, Man*): 101 Todmorden Road, Burnley, Lancashire BB11 3EX ☎ 01282 454098

DAVENPORT Peter (*Gtr*): 13 St Annes Road, Horwich, Nr Bolton, Lancs BL6 7EJ

DAVIES Nigel (*Gtr, Kbds*)

DAY Paul (*Gtr, Kbds*) ☎ 0161 881 8253, 0958 623579 mob, 0161 881 8253

DEAN Mel (*Gtr, Arr*): 98, Longhurst Lane, Mellor, Stockport, Cheshire SK6 5PG ☎ 0161 427 2192

DENT Hugh (*Gtr, Hmca, Voc*): 5 Meadow Bank, Penwortham, Preston, Lancs PR1 9BL ☎ 01772 742921

DRUMM Ian (*Gtr, Kbds, Voc*): 30 Victoria Crescent, Eccles, Manchester M30 9AW ☎ 0161 707 4014

DUNFORD John (*Gtr*): 67 Lambshear Lane, Lydiate, Liverpool L31 2JX ☎ 0151 531 1752

DYSON Katherine (*Jz Gtr, Rec, Flt*): 8 Monica Avenue, Crumpsall, Manchester M8 4LJ ☎ 0161 740 4933

EVANS Deni (*Gtr, Kbds*): 1 Cilfodan Uchaf, Carmel, Caernarfon, Gwynedd, North Wales LL54 7AG ☎ 01286 881227

FAIRHURST Robert (*Gtr, Voc, B Gtr, Dms*): Greenslate Farm House, Greenslate Road, Billinge, Wigan, Greater Manchester WN5 7BG ☎ 01695 625484

FARR Paul (*Ac Gtr*): Flat 4, 84 Palatine Road, Withington, Manchester M20 3JW ☎ 0161 448 7310, 07771 863525

FARREL Conor (*Gtr, Man, Vln, Bjo*): Tanygnefedd, Gardd-Y-Foel, Holywell, Flintshire, North Wales CH8 7UA ☎ 01352 714878, 0836 382214 mob

FARROW Peter (*Gtr, Bjo, Man, Dul*): 3 The Nook, Offorton Fold, Offorton, Stockport SK2 5QA ☎ 0161 483 6140

FITZGERALD Barry (*Gtr*): 163 Grove Lane, Hale, Altrincham, Cheshire WA15 8LR ☎ 0161 980 3544

FLYNN Christopher (*Gtr, Kbds, Voc*): 157 Spruce Court, Salford, Manchester M6 5EW ☎ 0961 102 560

FODEN David (*Gtr, A Sax*): 4 Ferndale Avenue, Woodsmoor, Stockport, Cheshire SK2 7DW ☎ 0161 487 3014, 0374 111895

FORSTER John (*Gtr, Kbds, H Gtr, B Gtr*): Lonsdale Gardens, Crosby Villa, Maryport, Cumbria CA15 6TH ☎ 01900 814113, 0585 290158 mob

FRAMPTON Peter (*Gtr, Kbds*): 25 Mullion Grove, Padgate, Warrington, Cheshire WA2 0QW ☎ 01925 823 745

FREEMAN Bill (*Gtr*): 11 Stanley Villas, Greenway Road, Runcorn, Cheshire WA7 4NW ☎ 01928 566261

G Damian (*Gtr, B Gtr, Kbds, Per*) ☎ 0151 280 6797

GAGON Robert (*Gtr*): 20 Sandwell Drive, Sale, Cheshire M33 6JL ☎ 0161 969 1515, 0161 236 3745 day, 0161 236 7417

GANNON Craig (*Gtr, Kbds, Arr*): 9 Margrove Road, Salford, Manchester M6 8NW ☎ 0161 737 5978

GANNON Michael (*Gtr*): 201 Babylon Lane, Heath Charnock, Lancs PR6 9ET ☎ 01257 482534

GAYNOR Lascelles (*Gtr*): 24 Carlton Street, Prescot, Merseyside L34 6JB ☎ 0151 289 3686

GIBBONS Malcolm (*Gtr*): 2 Mornington Road, Adlington, Chorley, Lancs PR6 9NX ☎ 01257 482737

GIFFORD Derek (*Gtr, Voc, Psal*) ☎ 01695 625097

GILBERT Gillian (*Gtr, Kbds*): c/o Rebecca Boulton, X Ltd, 11 Whitworth Street West, Manchester M1 5WG ☎ 0161 237 5957

GILLIAM Nick (*Cl Gtr, Ac Gtr, B Gtr, E Gtr*) ☎ 01244 312188, 0410 479581

GILLIGAN Stephen (*Gtr, B Gtr*): 17 Acresfield Avenue, Audenshaw, Manchester M34 5SY ☎ 0161 370 3030

GLEAVE Jane (*Cl Gtr*): Chester Classical Gtr Studio, 27 William Street, Hoole, Chester CH2 3BH ☎ 01244 316973, 0585 893873 mob

GLEDHILL Peter (*Gtr*): 16 St. Georges Road, Unsworth, Bury, Lancs BL9 8JG ☎ 0161 766 6649

GLOVER Jason (*Gtr, B Gtr, Dms, Pf*): 5 Bradney Close, Blackley, Manchester M9 8WN ☎ 0161 795 1176, 0421 727 338, 0161 795 1176

GOLDSTRAW Peter (*Gtr, B Gtr, Kbds*): 2 Gatley Avenue, Fallowfield, Manchester M14 7HE ☎ 0161 226 1982

GOLDUP Treva (*Gtr, Sax*): Beechfield, 144 Barnstow Road, Barnstow, Wirral L61 1BY ☎ 0151 648 7644

GOODHEAD David (*E Gtr*): 12 Prestbury Drive, Westgate, Morecambe, Lancashire LA3 3NY ☎ 01524 422113

GORDON Stefan (*Gtr, B Gtr, Pf, Kbds*): Flat 11, 60-62 High Lane, Chorlton-Cum-Hardy, Manchester M21 9DZ ☎ 0161 860 5562

GORRIE Andrew (*Gtr, B Gtr*): 1 Parkleigh Drive, New Moston, Manchester M40 3RZ ☎ 0161 681 1477, 0836 795312

GRAY John (*Gtr, Arr, Com*): Bryn Beuno, Llanbeblig Road, Caernarfon, Gwynedd LL55 2LF ☎ 01286 675231

GREGSON Clive (*Gtr, Pf, Voc*): 3163 Parthenon Avenue, Nashville, TN 37203, USA. ☎ +1 615 298 99

GRIFFIN Lee (*Gtr, Kbds, Voc*): 2 Springfield Ave, Litherland, Liverpool L21 7PZ ☎ 0151 476 0959

GRIFFITHS Anthony (*Gtr*): 35 Ar-Y-Don, Tywyn Gwynedd, Wales LL36 0DS ☎ 01654 711768

GRIMES Stephen (*Gtr*): 141 Rock Lane, Melling, Merseyside L31 1EW ☎ 0151 531 7830 & fax

HAIGH Howard (*Gtr, Per*): 15 Salisbury Road, Marsh, Lancaster LA1 5PQ ☎ 01524 843776

HALL Gary (*Gtr*): 10, Rose Terrace, Ashton, Preston, Lancs PR2 1EB ☎ 01772 732972

HALLIWELL Francis (*Gtr, Pf, Kbds, Song W*): 6 Oakwood Avenue, Walton-Le-Dale, Preston PR5 4LL ☎ 01772 827248

HARDING Mike (*Gtr, Bjo, Man, Hrp*): Moonraker Productions Ltd, Bower Bank, Gawthrop, Dent, Cumbria LA10 5QQ ☎ 015396 25552

HARPER J (*Gtr, B Gtr, Arr*): 153 Allport Lane, Bromborough, Cheshire L62 7HW ☎ 0151 334 4379

HARTE Paul (*Gtr*): 195 Warrington Road, Goose Green, Wigan, Lancashire WN3 3PA ☎ 01942 492482

HEFFERNAN Seamus (*Gtr, Kbds*): The Garth, Commons Lane, Balderstone, Blackburn, Lancs BB2 7LL ☎ 01254 812131

HEGGIE Kenneth (*Cl Gtr, B Gtr, Man*): 14, Burford Road, Whalley Range, Manchester M16 8EL ☎ 0161 860 5217

HEHIR Michael (*Gtr*): 81 Railway Road, Stretford, Manchester M32 0QD ☎ 0161 873 8178

HEMMINGS Paul (*Gtr, St Gtr, Man*): Woodcroft, Beaconsfield Road, Liverpool L25 6EJ ☎ 0151 428 6990

HICKEY Michael (*Gtr*): 18 Bucklow Avenue, Fallowfield, Manchester M14 7AR

HICKS Anthony (*Gtr*): c/o Citroen Wells And Partners, Devonshire House, 1 Devonshire Street, London W1N 2DR

HOARTY Peter (*Gtr, B Gtr*): 32 Lockerbie Close, Cinnamon Brow, Warrington, Cheshire WA2 0LU ☎ 01925 813185

HOLDSWORTH Andrew *(Gtr)*: 28 Kenilworth Road, Penge, London SE20 7QG ☎ 020 8778 3694

HORNSBY James *(Gtr, Pd Gtr, Dobro)*: Greensight, West Green, Allowby, Cumbria CA15 6PE ☎ 01207 544240

HOWLEY Patrick *(Gtr)*: 107 Gig Lane, Woolston, Warrington, Cheshire WA1 4DN ☎ 01925 821807

HUBBARD John *(Gtr, Kbds)*: The Stables, 16 St. Annes Road, Marshside, Southport, Merseyside PR9 9TQ ☎ 01704 213068

HUGHES Laurence *(Gtr)*: 299 Liverpool Road, Birkdale, Southport PR8 3DE ☎ 01704 76257

HULSTON David *(Gtr, Dms)* ☎ 0161 653 1410

HURST Paul *(Gtr, Voc)*: 191 Menlove Ave, Allerton, Liverpool L18 3EF ☎ 0151 428 5360

INGLIS Katherine *(Gtr, Voc, Pf)*: 6A Heydean Walk, Liverpool L18 9XB ☎ 0151 494 9954

INGRAM Steve *(Gtr)*: 8 Greenbank, Ulverston, Cumbria LA12 7HA ☎ 01229 57727

ISHERWOOD Martin *(Gtr, Voc)*: 22 Newbank Towers, Salford M3 7JZ ☎ 0161 839 4366

ISHERWOOD Richard *(Gtr, Kbds)*: 150 Halliwell Road, Bolton, Lancs BL1 3QN ☎ 01204 389297

JACKSON Mark *(Gtr)*: 22 Gorsey Lane, Warrington, Cheshire WA1 3PU ☎ 01925 418540

JACKSON Wendy *(Cl Gtr)*: 8 Lloyd Street South, Fallowfield, Manchester M14 7HY ☎ 0161 226 8806

JAMES Edward *(Gtr)*

JAMES Martin *(Gtr, Pf, B Gtr, Voc)*: Address Unknown

JAMES Sue *(Gtr, Voc)*: 1 Derwent Drive, Sale, Cheshire M33 3SZ ☎ 0161 282 5668

JAMES Timothy *(Gtr, B Gtr, Pf)*: 10 Cathness Drive, Wallasey, Merseyside L45 7PW

JEFFES Frank *(Gtr)*: 15 Ormonde Road, Chester CH2 2AH ☎ 01244 380049

JOHNSON Alec *(Gtr)*: 11 Beswicks Road, Winnington, Cheshire CW8 1AP ☎ 01606 75696

JOLLY Aidan *(Gtr, B Gtr, Kbds, Per)*: 12 Lorne Street, Mossley, Ashton Under Lyne OL5 0HQ ☎ 01457 834586

JONES Christopher *(Gtr, Kbds)*: 11 Manor Drive, Great Boughton, Chester CH3 5QN ☎ 01244 316033, 0973 407296

JONES Gary *(Gtr, Voc)*: 39 Nursery Road, Prestwich, Manchester M25 3DU ☎ 0161 773 1886

JONES Michael *(Gtr)*: 15 Regent Road, Widnes, Cheshire WA8 6EP ☎ 0151 424 1562

JONES Natasha *(Gtr, Pf, Voc, Song W)*: 36 Conway Road, Hindley Green, Wigan, Lancs WN2 4PE ☎ 01942 258719

JONES Simon *(Gtr)*: 72 Gardmer Rpad, Prestwich, Manchester M23 3HU ☎ 0161 773 4436

JONES Thomas *(Gtr)*: 32 Ernest Street, Cheadle, Cheshire SK8 1PN ☎ 0161 491 4341

JUNIOR John *(Gtr, Voc)*: 12 Brunswick Terrace, Stacksteads, Bacup, Lancashire OL13 0HD ☎ 01706 875693

KANE Daz *(E Gtr, Synth)*: 73 Leyton Drive, Bury, Lancashire BL9 9TS ☎ 0161 796 3181

KAY Steve *(Gtr, Kbds, B Gtr, Voc)*: 97 Henthorn Road, Clitheroe, Lancs BB7 2NU ☎ 01200 24885

KEARNS Gerard *(Gtr, Pf)*: 1 Shadworth Close, Mossley, Ashton-Under-Lyne, Lancs OL5 9DA ☎ 01457 834566

KENNEDY David *(Gtr)*: 23 Clifton Avenue, Church Park Estate, Halewood, Liverpool L26 7ZJ

KIERNAN Michael *(Gtr)*: 20 Hayward Street, Elton, Bury, Lancs BL8 1LX ☎ 0161 705 2395

KING Dave *(Gtr)*: 4 Tan Y Bwlch, Mynydd Llandegai, Gwynedd LL57 4DX ☎ 01248 602139

KING Peter *(Gtr, Kbds)*: 21 Wycliffe Road, Urmston, Manchester M41 5AH ☎ 0161 445 4866

KIRKHAM John *(Gtr)*: 4 Grecian Street, Lower Broughton, Salford, Lancs M7 9JF ☎ 0161 792 3125

KIRKHAM Tony *(Gtr, Kbds)*: Flat D, 463 Bury New Road, Manchester M7 3NE ☎ 0385 790 751

LAUDA Pete *(Gtr, Kbds, Voc)*: 44 Anfield Road, Great Lever, Bolton BL3 3DA ☎ 01204 658397

LAWRENCE Daniel *(Gtr, Man, Bzk, Bjo, B Gtr)*: 1 Stratford Avenue, West Didsbury, Manchester M20 2LH ☎ 0161 434 2761

LAWRENCE Stewart *(Gtr, Man, Bjo)*: 3, Plover Close, Bamford, Rochdale, Lancs OL11 5PU ☎ 01706 56076

LEE Dean *(Gtr, Kbds)* ☎ 0161 330 1076

LEE George *(Gtr, Kbds, Per, Voc)*: 160D Drake Street, Rochdale, Lancs OL16 1QD ☎ 01706 640493

LEES John *(Gtr, Flt)*: Handle Group Of Companies, Pinewood Studios, Pinewood Road, Iver Heath, Buckinghamshire SL0 0NH ☎ 01753 651 001, 01753 630 555 (633)

LEWIS Stephen *(Gtr, Tpt)*: 25 Birchway Avenue, Blackpool, Lancashire FY3 8EZ ☎ 01253 397796

LEWIS Timothy *(Gtr, B Gtr, Kbds)*: 19 Greendale Road, Port Sunlight, Wirral, Merseyside L62 5DF

LINDLEY Steven *(Gtr)*: Winter Hill Cottage, Darwen, Lancs BB33 0LB ☎ 01254 774945

LITTLER Corin *(Gtr, Kbds, Club Dj)*: 665 Borough Road, Prenton, Birkenhead, Wirral L42 9QB ☎ 0151 200 6180

LOWE Jim *(Gtr)*: 5 Claremont Avenue, Chorley, Lancs PR7 2HL ☎ 01257 264570

LOWELL Timothy *(Gtr, Org, Kbds)*: 2 Long Close, Moss Side, Leyland, Lancs PR5 3WB ☎ 0411724883 mob

MACKENZIE Andrew *(Gtr, B Gtr, Bjo)*: 226 Leigh Road, Worsley, Manchester M28 4LE ☎ 0161 799 6860

MADDISON Damien *(Ac Gtr)*: 9 Warwick Road, Failsworth, Manchester M35 0QQ ☎ 0161 682 9787

MAHONY Neil *(Gtr, Dms, B Gtr)*: 31 Denham Street, Manchester M13 0FJ ☎ 0161 225 8592, 0421 734301, 0161 8776363

MANLEY Christopher *(E Gtr, Ac Gtr, Cl Gtr)*: c/o Whitehouse, Roughlee, Nelson, Lancashire BB9 6NR ☎ 01282 695128

MANNS Simon *(Gtr, B Gtr, Kbds)*: 33 Hillington Road, Sale, Cheshire M33 6GQ

MARSHALL Tyrone *(Rh Gtr, Kbds, Hmca)*: 2 Springfield Road, Leyland, Lancashire PR5 1AR ☎ 01772 431033

MASSEY Graham *(Gtr, Kbds, Vln)*: c/o 808 Statead, 101 Ducie House, 37 Ducie Street, Manchester M1 2JW

MASTERS Christopher *(Gtr, B Gtr, Jz Gtr)*: 1 Hastings Avenue, Bispham, Blackpool, Lancs FY2 0EU ☎ 01253 55421

MAYES Richard *(E Gtr, Ac Gtr, Voc)*: 34 Avonhead Road, Horwich, Bolton, Lancs BL6 5QD ☎ 01204 699677

MCCALLUM Stuart *(Jz Gtr, Pf)*: 73 Dalehead Road, Leyland, Preston, Lancs PR5 2BP ☎ 01772 431713, 01772 458310

MCCORMICK Don *(E Gtr, Voc)*: 33 Bryanston Road, Aigburth, Liverpool L17 7AL ☎ 0151 7289894

MCGROARTY Martin *(Gtr)*: 8 Osborne Road, Levenshulme, Manchester M19 2DT ☎ 0161 225 7780

MCKAY Andrew *(Gtr, Man)*: Greenlaw, 19 The Green, Dalston, Carlisle, Cumbria CA5 7QB ☎ 01228 711656

MCMAHON Roy *(Gtr, Kbds)*: Cherry Trees, School Lane, Bronongton, Nr Whitchurch Salop SY13 3HN ☎ 01948 780791

MCNALLY John *(Gtr)*: 59 Downhills Road, Blundersands, Liverpool L23 8SU ☎ 0151 924 7310

MCNEVIN-DUFF Richard *(Gtr)*: 16 Sherbourne Drive, Summit, Heywood, Lancs. OL10 4ST ☎ 01706 625477

MEAD Steve *(Gtr)*: 84 Clarendon Road, Whalley Range, Manchester M16 8LA ☎ 0161 860 6126

MEAKIN James *(Gtr)*: 83A Crudy Castell, Denbigh, Clwyd LL16 4PJ ☎ 01745 815224

MELLOR Nicholas *(Gtr)*: 216 Buxton Road, Stockport, Cheshire SK2 7AE ☎ 0161 483 9731

MIDDLETON-POLLOCK Marilyn *(Gtr, Voc, Bod, Bjo)*: 46A West Malvern Road, Malvern, Worcs WR14 4NA ☎ 01684 565105

MILLER Glynn *(Gtr, Bjo, T Sax, Hmca, Wh)*: 146 Moorside Lane, Dentopn, Manchester M34 3BW ☎ 0161 335 0396, 04325 339 325

MILTON Gregory *(Gtr)*: 13 Lucerne Street, Liverpool L17 8XT

MITCHELL Carl *(Gtr, B Gtr, Kbds)*: 57 Ivinson Road, Darwen, Lancs BB3 3AW ☎ 01254 761790, 0378 222448

MITCHELL Roy *(Gtr, Dms)*: 25 Princess Avenue, Denton, Manchester M34 3QX ☎ 0161 320 7513, 0161 336 7535, 01523 487726

MOCKLER Crispin (*Gtr, B Gtr*): 15 Malden Street, Leyland, Lancashire PR5 1TJ ☎ 01772 454985

MOONEY Claire (*Gtr, Voc*): Red Records, PO Box 44, Manchester M21 9FE ☎ 0161 248 5449

MOORE Chris (*Gtr*): The Vicarage, Winmarleigh, Preston PR3 0LA ☎ 01995 600424

MORAN Mike (*Gtr, Kbds, Pf*): 93 Barrington Road, Wavertree, Liverpool L15 3HR ☎ 0151 733 2410

MORGAN Tudur (*Ac Gtr, B Gtr, Kbds, Voc*): Bryn Teg, 17 Brig Y Nant, Llangefni Sir Fon, Cymru Wales LL77 7QD ☎ 01248 724918, 01248 750296

MORRISON James (*Gtr, Bjo, Man, Pd Gtr*): 702, Stockport Road, Longsight, Manchester M12 4GB ☎ 0161 224 0740

MUKHERJEE Rudro (*Gtr, Pf*): 200 Buxton Road, Davenport, Stockport, Cheshire SK2 7AE ☎ 0161 285 9809

MULCASTER Simon (*Gtr*): Flat 12, 29 Carmoor Road, Victoria Park, Manchester M13 0EA ☎ 0161 273 5049

MURPHY Anthony (*Gtr, Kbds, Per*) ☎ 0161 225 6948, 0385 764 638

MURPHY Gerald (*Gtr, Pf, Hmca, Voc, Song W*): 76 Snaefell Avenue, Liverpool L13 7HB ☎ 0976 918249

MURPHY Richard (*Gtr, Synth*)

MURRAY John (*Gtr*): 18 Westmorland Ave, Widnes, Cheshire WA8 6EZ ☎ 0151 424 0258

MURRAY Paul (*Gtr, Voc, Kbds*)

MUSAJI Sabir (*Gtr*): 33 Gilnow Gardens, Bolton BL1 4LG ☎ 01204 432548

NALLY Joel (*Gtr, B Gtr*): 6 Hazelbank Avenue, Withington, Manchester M20 3ES ☎ 0161 610 1303

NEEP Paul (*Gtr, B Gtr*): Tyddyn Difyr, Rhosgadfan, Caernarfon, Gwynedd LL54 7LD ☎ 01286 831094

NEILL Kevin (*Gtr, Tbn*): 69 Polefield Road, Blackley, Manchester M9 7EN ☎ 0161 740 7645

NELIS William (*Gtr, Voc, Man*): 66 Cefn A Gadair, Morfa By Bychan, Porthmadog, Gwynedd, Wales LL49 9YS ☎ 01766 51 2561, 01766 543210 day

NEWTON Peter (*Gtr*): 1 Derwent Drive, Sale, Cheshire M33 3SZ ☎ 0161 282 5668

NICHOLL Jason (*Gtr, Voc, Kbds, B Gtr*): 34 Park Avenue, Barnoldswick, Colne, Lancs BB8 5AT ☎ 01282 813354

NICHOLLS Matthew (*Gtr, Pf, Harm*): 1 Eneury Road, Wrexham, Clwyd LL11 2PH ☎ 01978 263588, 01973 290952 fax, 01978 290952

NICOL Kenneth (*Gtr, Voc*): 298 Tag Lane, Ingol, Preston, Lancs PR2 3UY ☎ 01772 721902

NORMAN Christopher (*Gtr*): Rockwood, Bradden Hills, Isle Of Man IM4 4TH

NOWELL John (*Gtr, Hmca, T Sax*): 28 Victoria Road, Tuebrook, Liverpool L13 8AW ☎ 0151 259 5957

O'HAGAN Tree (*Gtr, Bzk, Man, Bod*): 21 Douglas Street, Salford, Lancashire M7 2FE ☎ 0161 792 9503

O'NEILL Chris (*Gtr, Pf, Voc*): 68 Brookside Avenue, Eccleston, St Helens, Merseyside WA10 4RL ☎ 01744 757 661

OFFER Richard (*Gtr, Per*): 73 Fulshaw Lodge, Alderley Road, Wilmslow, Cheshire SK9 1QA ☎ 01625 522566

OUTSIDER (*Gtr*): 1 Ox Hey Close, Lostock, Bolton BL6 4BQ ☎ 01204 690108 & fax

OWEN Robert (*Gtr*): 36 Bushbys Lane, Formby, Liverpool L37 2DZ ☎ 01704 876687

PATON Kevin (*Gtr, Voc, Per*): Flat 6, 12 Devonshire Road, Liverpool L8 3TY ☎ 0151 726 1613

PATTERSON Mark (*Gtr*): 7 Craig Dinas, Stabla, Llanrug, Caernarfon Gwynedd, North Wales LL55 3PL ☎ 01286 870714

PEARSON Ken (*Gtr*): 2 Ingleton Close, Harwood, Bolton, Lancs BL2 3LJ ☎ 01204 305165

PEEL Stanley Martin (*Gtr*): 17 Rhodfa Lwyd, Colwyn Bay LL29 8BH ☎ 01492 514933

PENN Matthew (*Gtr, Voc, B Gtr, Kbds*): Flat 2, 38 College Road, Manchester M16 8FH ☎ 0161 881 9293

PERCIVAL Lynne (*Gtr, Kbds, Man, Bjo*): 20 Alderfield Road, Chorlton, Manchester M21 9JX ☎ 0161 861 8787

PETERS Michael (*Gtr, Voc*): PO Box 709, Prestatyn, Denbighshire, Wales LL19 9YR

PHILLIPS Keith (*Gtr, Pf*): 3 Cleveland Road, Stockport, Cheshire SK4 4BS ☎ 0161 442 0224

PILLING Brandon (*Gtr, Tpt, Dms*): Leeward, Windy Harbour Lane, Turton, Bolton, Lancs BL7 9AP ☎ 01204 302680

PIMBLETT Jon (*Gtr*): 5 Waters Edge, Burbo Bank Road, Blundlesand, Crosby, Liverpool, Merseyside L23 6TQ ☎ 0151 932 0993

PLEASS Martin (*Gtr, Didj, Kbds, Bjo, Hmca*): 1 Kings Close, Bebington, Wirral, Merseyside L63 8RS ☎ 0151 608 7709

POPPLEWELL Phil (*Gtr, Voc, B Gtr, Dms, Kbds*): 12 Brrokdene Road, Burnage, Manchester M19 1BQ ☎ 0161 442 3748

POTTER Gary (*Gtr*): Ivy Cottage, Old Wood Lane, Off Wood Lane, Liverpool L27 5QN ☎ 0151 489 3040

POTTS David (*Gtr*): 16 Osborne Street, Didsbury, Manchester M20 2QZ ☎ 0161 448 9080

POWELL Gary (*Gtr, Kbds, B Gtr*): 46 Hart Street, Altrincham, Cheshire WA14 1JW ☎ 0161 941 5791, 0411 004838, 0161 929 4669

POWER John (*Rh Gtr, Voc*): c/o Cast/Rock & Roll Mgmt, Studio 2, 108 Prospect Quay, Point Pleasant, London SW18 1PR ☎ 020 8516 6403

PRIESTLEY Michael (*E Gtr*): 17 Peel Park Close, Accrington, Lancashire BB5 6PL ☎ 01254 394264

PROCTOR Glen (*E Gtr, Ac Gtr, B Gtr*): 21A Hazel Road, Whitefield, Manchester M45 8EU ☎ 0161 726 1246

PROSSER Andrew (*Gtr, Kbds, Flt*): 74 Earnshaw Drive, Leyland, Lancashire PR5 1GS ☎ 01772 463834

PYATT Andrew (*Gtr*): 3 Butterbache Road, Huntington, Chester CH3 6BY ☎ 01244 345848

RAFF Gerry (*Gtr*): 418 Park Road North, Claughton, Birkenhead, Merseyside L41 0DA ☎ 0151 652 7768 & fax

RANDOM ACCESS (*Gtr, Kbds*): 7 Ormeside Court, Church Walks, Llandudno LL30 2GH ☎ 01492 870495

REID Colin (*Ac Gtr, E Gtr*): Flat 1, 23 Notting Hill, Belfast BT9 5NS ☎ 028 9038 2937

RENNEY Tony (*Gtr, B Gtr, H Gtr, Dobro*): 2 Derwent Close, Seaton, Workington, Cumbria CA14 1EF ☎ 01900 604045

REYNOLDS Garry (*Gtr, Kbds, Man*): 179 Inglewhite, Birch Green, Skelmersdale, Lancs NN8 6JQ ☎ 01695 722016

ROBERTS Brian (*E Gtr, Voc*): Flat 2, 16, Claremont Grove, West Didsbury, Manchester. M20 8GL ☎ 0161 445 2485

ROBERTS Gronw (*Gtr, B Gtr, Pf, Dms*): Garth Hudol, Rhodfar Mbr, Nefyn, Pwllheli, Gwynedd LL53 6EB ☎ 01758 720965

ROBERTS Steve (*Gtr, Voc*): 34 Exeter Road, Ellesmere Park, South Wirral L65 8AW ☎ 0151 355 9439, 01523 486611

ROBINSON Joseph (*Gtr, Kbds, Dms, B Gtr*): Flat 2, 116 Dudley Road, Manchester M16 8BR ☎ 0161 881 1892

ROGERS-HUGHES Christopher (*Gtr, Bzk, Man*): Brook Villa, Weston Rhyn, Oswestry, Shropshire SY10 7LF ☎ 01691 650498

ROSS Andy (*E Gtr, Ac Gtr*): 11 Rhodes Drive, Unsworth, Bury, Lancashire BL9 8NH ☎ 0161 796 6763

ROSS Holly (*Gtr, Voc, Kbds*): 17 Shrewsbury Drive, Bowerham, Lancaster, Lancs LA1 4BA ☎ 01524 69092

RUNDALL Nick (*Gtr*): Address Unknown ☎ 01223 240483

RYAN Michael (*Gtr*): Rocklyn, Castle Hill, Bassenthwaite Lake, Keswick, Cumbria CA12 4RG ☎ 01900 816665

SADLER Ray (*Gtr*): 6 Tarn Mount, Macclesfield, Cheshire SK11 7XX ☎ 01625 434380

SANCHOS (*Gtr, Voc, Song W*): 20 Broomfield Drive, Cheetham Hill, Manchester M8 9EE ☎ 0161 950 7323

SCOTT Timothy (*E Gtr, B Gtr, Kbds*): 40 Bakewell Road, Hazel Grove, Stockport, Cheshire SK7 6JU ☎ 01625 261 879

SEAVOR Leslie (*Gtr, Kbds, Voc*): 70 Stockbridge Lane, Huyton, Liverpool L36 3SF ☎ 0151 480 2789, 0370 933796

SETTLE Ray (*Gtr, Flt*): 31 Central Drive, Penwortham, Preston PR1 0NL ☎ 01772 744000

SHELLEY Andrew (*Gtr*): 3 Yew Tree Park Road, Cheadle Hulme, Cheshire SK8 7EP ☎ 0161 485 3609

SHIELDS Gordon (*Rh Gtr, Hmca*): 66 Charles Berrington Road, Liverpool L15 9HQ ☎ 0151 722 3634

SHOTS Duke (*Rh Gtr, Ld Gtr, B Gtr*): 16 Dystelegh Road, Disley, Stockport, Cheshire SK12 2BQ ☎ 01663 764896

SLATER James (*Ld Gtr*): 2 Slaters Yard, Station Road, Wigton, Cumbria CA7 9BA ☎ 016973 42585

SMITH Andy (*E Gtr, Ac Gtr*): 22 Tytherington Drive, Macclesfield, Cheshire SK10 2HJ ☎ 01625 433369

SMITH Bernie (*Gtr, Voc, Per, Kbds*): The Willows, 3 Jubilee Way, Lytham St. Annes, Lancs FY8 3TT ☎ 01253 726658

SMITH Neil (*Gtr, Per*): 32 Linksway Drive, Bury, Lancashire BL9 8EP ☎ 0161 796 2491

SMITH Neil (*Cl Gtr, E Gtr*): The Gallery, 177 Lee Lane, Norwich BL6 7JD ☎ 01204 468945, 0468 627398

SMITH Richard (*Gtr, Dms*): 25 Northdale Road, Wavertree, Liverpool L15 4HT

SMITH Simon (*E Gtr, Ac Gtr*): 118 Wilderspool Causeway, Warrington, Cheshire WA4 6QA ☎ 01925 497908

STANLEY Mark (*Gtr, Man*): 63 Canon Hussey Court, Islington Way, Salford, Lancs M3 5JA ☎ 0161 834 9286

STANTON John (*Gtr*): 10 Saltdene Road, Woodhouse Park, Wythenshawe, Manchester M22 1PN

STANWAY Peter (*Gtr, Dms*): 6 Sycamore Close, Birch Hill, Onchan, Isle Of Man IM3 3HW ☎ 01624 620783

STEELE Christopher (*Gtr, B Gtr*): 9 Beacon Grove, Fulwood, Preston PR2 3QU ☎ 01772 715886, 0976 580664

STEFANO (*Gtr, Voc*): 5 Oakshaw Drive, Norden, Rochdale, Lancs OL12 7AF ☎ 01706 633055

STONIER Nigel (*Gtr, B Gtr, Kbds*): 1 Etherow Close, Elworth, Sandbach, Cheshire CW11 9EY ☎ 01270 760113

STOPES Ian (*Gtr, B Gtr, Voc*): The Old Shop, Lower Street, St Asaph, Clwyd LL17 0SG ☎ 01745 582412

SUMNER Bernard (*Gtr*): c/o Rebecca Boulton, X Ltd, 11 Whitworth Street West, Manchester M1 5WG ☎ 0161 237 5957

SWAN Martin (*Gtr, Pf, Kbds, Hmca*): 14 Oaklands Ave, Cheadle Hulme, Cheshire SK8 5DE ☎ 0161 488 4824, 0370 838020 mob

TAFFORD Steven (*Gtr, Voc*): 5 Alexandra Road, Sale, Manchester M33 3EF ☎ 0161 973 8034, 0161 973 5040

TAYLOR Noel 'Tibo' (*Gtr*): 135 Smedley Road, Crumpsall, Manchester M8 0RS ☎ 0161 202 1619

THOMAS Dai (*Ac Gtr, Voc, St Gtr, Bjo, Man*): 42 Lancaster Road, Salford, Lancs M6 8AW ☎ 0161 707 4063

THOMPSON Martin (*Gtr*): 16 Avondale Road, Stretford, Manchester M32 0GB ☎ 0161 865 8146

THORPE Anthony (*Gtr, B Gtr*): 143 Marsden Road, Burnley, Lancs BB10 2QW ☎ 01282 56205

TOMLINSON Jason (*E Gtr*): Woodend, Wood Lane, Burton, South Wirral L64 5TB ☎ 0151 336 1807

TOMMIS Colin (*Gtr, Pf*): Swn Y Gwynt, Penmynydd Road, Llanfairpwll, Ynys Mon, Gwynedd LL61 5SX ☎ 01248 716542

TOWLER David (*Gtr, Bjo, Hmca, Bod*): 16 Brookdale, Todmorden, Lancs OL14 6RJ ☎ 01706 816257

TURRINGTON Brian (*Gtr, B Gtr, Kbds*): 52A Avonmore Road, West Kensington, London W14 8RS ☎ 020 7603 2169

TYRRELL Martin (*Gtr, Kbds*): 82 Ascot Court, Bury New Road, Salford, Greater Manchester M7 9DB ☎ 0161 792 3854

TYSON Liam (*Gtr, Voc*): c/o Cast/Rock & Roll Mgmt, Studio 2, 108 Prospect Quay, Point Pleasant, London SW18 1PR ☎ 020 8516 6403

VARLEY Jonathan (*Gtr, Pf, Kbds, Voc*): 15 Hollywood, Bowoon, Cheshire WA14 2LL ☎ 0161 928 1341

VEARNCOMBE Colin (*Gtr, Voc, Pf*): 6 Kyme Road, Hornchurch, Essex RM11 1AD

VERMONT Johnny (*Gtr, B Gtr, Bjo, Man*): 86 Grasmere Avenue, Workington, Cumbria CA14 3LR ☎ 01900 872891

VITALI Max (*Gtr*): 53 Spring Street, Wigan, Lancs WN1 3EX ☎ 01942 205684

WALFORD Tim (*Gtr, Dms, Eup, Tba*): 31 Roman Way, Kirkham, Preston, Lancs PR4 2YG ☎ 01772 686903

WALLACE Liam Henry (*Gtr, B Gtr, Bjo, Wh, Man*): 16 Mullion Close, Brookvale, Runcorn, Cheshire WA7 6AQ ☎ 01928 718505

WALLACE Ronald (*Gtr*): 2 Church Close, Stoneclough, Prestolee, Radcliffe, Manchester M26 1HG ☎ 01204 792700

WARD Gary (*Gtr, Voc, Per, B Gtr, Wh*): 40 Elswick Street, Darwen, Lancs BB3 3DX ☎ 01254 704006

WATERS Oliver (*Gtr, Voc, Hmca*): 17 Wimdermere Drive, Ramsbottom, Bury, Lancs BL0 9YB ☎ 023 9282 6583

WEARING Timothy (*Cl Gtr, E Gtr, B Gtr*): 24 Nursery Road, Urmston, Manchester M41 7NP ☎ 0161 747 2445

WELCH Nathan (*Gtr, B Gtr, Bjo, Synth, Db*): 6 Thornpark Drive, Lea, Preston, Lancs PR2 1RE ☎ 0468 781806

WHILE Chris (*Gtr, Voc, Dul, Per*): 130 Central Avenue, Southport, Merseyside PR8 3ED ☎ 01704 575674, 0467 275395

WHITE Paul (*Gtr, Pf*): 39 Gladstone Road, Edgehill, Liverpool L7 1QE

WHITEHEAD Paul (*Gtr*): Rose Cottage, Over Tabley, Nr Knutsford, Cheshire WA16 0PP ☎ 01565 651586

WIGLEY Hywel (*Gtr, B Gtr, Dms*): Hen Efail, Bontwewydd, Caernarfon, Gwynedd LL54 7YH ☎ 01286 830010, 029 2046 3404

WILKINSON Mark (*Gtr, B Gtr, Man, Dobro*): 8 Pennine Road, Chorley, Lancs PR6 0AW ☎ 01257 265877

WILLIAMS Daniel (*Gtr*): 2 Laurel Road, Tranmere, Merseyside L42 0JA ☎ 0151 649 0126

WILLIAMS David (*Gtr, B Gtr*): Flat 334, The Parkers Appts, 109-113 Corporation Street, Manchester M4 4DZ ☎ 0161 839 7288, 01426 156 896

WILLIAMS Iwan (*Gtr, B Gtr*): 25 Alexandra Road, Mold, Flintshire, North Wales CH7 1HJ ☎ 01352 753121 & fax

WILLINGHAM Stephen (*Gtr, Man, Bjo*): 19 Meredith Street, Manchester M14 6ST ☎ 0161 225 8499, 0976 814310 mob

WILLIS Tommy (*Gtr, H Gtr, B Gtr*): 167 Ormskirk Road, Rainford, St Helens, Merseyside WA11 8HR ☎ 01744 88 3017

WILSON Ian (*Gtr, Voc*): 34 Parrs Wood Court, Didsbury, Manchester M20 5NG ☎ 0161 44802924

WOOD James (*Gtr, Per*): 18 Greenfield Street, Lancaster LA1 3QE ☎ 01524 65298

WOOD Matthew (*Gtr, Kbds*): 25 Northwood Gardens, Greenford, Middlesex UB6 0LF ☎ 020 8795 1811

WREN Trevor (*Gtr, B Gtr, Kbds, Voc*): Canada Farm House, Long Framlington, Northumberland NE65 8EH ☎ 01665 570503

WRIGHT Steve (*Gtr, Com*): c/o Mersey TV, Campus Manor, Childwall L16 1JP

WRIGHTSON Paul (*Gtr, B Gtr, Theory*): 6 Church Road, West Kirby, Wirral, Merseyside L48 0RW ☎ 0151 625 2307

ZEITER James (*Gtr, Kbds*): c/o Rob's Records, 11 Whitworth Street West, Manchester M1 5WG ☎ 0161 237 5957

NORTH EAST

ADRENALIN JUNKIES (*Rh Gtr, B Gtr*): PO Box 513, Hull HU5 3YX ☎ 01482 449108

AEDY Arron (*Rh Gtr, Ac Gtr*): C/0 Northern Music Co, Cheapside Chambers, 43 Cheapside, Bradford, W. Yorks BD1 4HP ☎ 01274 306361, 01274 730097

ALDERDICE Martyn (*Gtr, B Gtr*): 8 Ellen Ave, Hartburn, Stockton, Cleveland TS18 3QL ☎ 01642 605962

ALIWELL Rick (*Gtr, Vln, Flgl, Pf, Voc*): 1 Hillman Close, Brale Bridge Heath, Lincoln LN4 2QR ☎ 01522 528522

ALLONBY Terry (*Gtr*): 403 Bentley Road, Doncaster, S Yorks DN5 9TJ ☎ 01302 786157

ANDERSON Greg (*Gtr, Voc, B Gtr, Hmca, A Sax*) ☎ 0191 233 2005 & fax, 01426 211387 mob

APPLETON Richard (*Gtr, Bjo, Bzk, Dul, Man*): 161 Waltham Road, Scartho, Grimsby, Lincolnshire DN33 2NG ☎ 01472 825563

ARMSTRONG Jason (*Gtr*): 34 Royal Park Avenue, Headingley, Leeds LS1 1EY ☎ 0113 274 7753

ARTHURS Richard (*Cl Gtr, Gtr, Pf*): Flat 24, 20-21 Moorland Rd, Hyde Park, Leeds LS6 1AL ☎ 0113 242 4447

ASHWORTH David (*Gtr*): Pavement Hill, The Green, Sheriff Hutton, York YO60 6SB ☎ 01347 878746

BAILEY Adam (*Gtr*): 26 Burnholme Avenue, York YO31 0NB ☎ 01904 415800

BAILEY Roy (*Gtr, Voc*): 32 Nethergreen Road, Sheffield S11 7EJ ☎ 0114 2306734

BAKER Carl (*Gtr, B Gtr, Dms, Kbds*): 10 The Glebe Way, Old Whittington, Chesterfield, Derbyshire S41 9NN ☎ 01246 471200

BALLANTYNE Steven *(Gtr)*: 26 Church Street, Longframlington, Morpeth NE65 8DL ☎ 01665 570674

BANKS Paul *(Gtr)*: 20 Trent Avenue, Huntington, York YO32 9SE ☎ 01904 768632

BARKER Ben *(Gtr)*: Hampsthwaite House, Hampsthwaite, Harrogate, North Yorkshire HG3 2HS

BARRACLOUGH Richard *(Gtr, Kbds)*: 9 Greaves Lane, High Green, Sheffield S30 4GR ☎ 0114 2844463

BARRET Debrina *(Gtr, Kbds, B Gtr, Dul)*: 138 Hotham Road North, Bricknell Avenue, Hull ☎ 01482 846812

BATT Martin *(Gtr, Voc)*: 1 Church Meadows, Bramham, Wetherby, West Yorks LS23 6TF ☎ 01937 842220, 01422 333686, 01422 334704

BAYLIS Cary *(Gtr, Pf)*: 19 Overcroft Rise, Totley, Sheffield S17 4AX

BENNETT Roy *(Gtr, Bjo)*: 1 Berkeley Close, East Herrington, Sunderland, Tyne & Wear SR3 3QA ☎ 0191 528 0112 & fax

BERSIN Michael *(Gtr, Kbds)*: West Cottage, Thorngrafton, Bardon Hill, Northumberland NE47 7AD ☎ 0143484 553

BHAJIHEAD Bavid *(Ld Gtr, Kbds)*: 19 St Johns Terrace, Leeds LS3 1DY ☎ 0113 2443581

BIRKETT James *(Gtr)*: 40C Leazes Terrace, Newcastle-upon-Tyne, Tyne & Wear NE1 4LZ

BOYES James *(Gtr, B Gtr, Kbds)*: 78 Moorgate Road, Rotherham S60 2AY ☎ 01709 375063

BRADLEY Hugh *(Ac Gtr, E Gtr, B Gtr, Flt, Wh)*: Briar Royd, Woodhead Road, Holmfirth, Huddersfield HD7 1PX

BRIGGS Martin *(Gtr)*: 16 Gledhow Park Crescent, Chapel Allerton, Leeds LS7 4JY ☎ 0113 262 1218

BRODIE Mark *(Gtr)*: 21 Edmunsbury Road, Linthorpe, Middlesbrough, Cleveland TS5 6PX ☎ 01642 827937

BROOKS Jon *(Gtr, B Gtr, Db, Brass)*: 32 College Street, Grantham, Lincolnshire NG31 6HG ☎ 01475 572895, 0802 423336 mob

BROWN Martin *(Gtr, Kbds)*: 62 Chelmsford Street, Lincoln, Lincolnshire LN5 7LL

BURNESS Jack *(Ac Gtr, Hmca, Voc)*: The Coach House, The Coppy, Beamish Park, Stanley, Co. Durham DH9 0RQ ☎ 01207 238259, 0831 425857 mob, 0191 477 0943

BYWATER James *(Rh Gtr, Hrn, Com)*: 2 Forge Cottages, Boars Head, Crowborough, East Sussex TN6 3HD ☎ 01892 654148

CAMPBELL Stephen *(Gtr, Vln, Nor P, Bjo)*: 51 Scarcroft Hill, The Mount, York YO24 1DF ☎ 01904 626862

CARTHY Martin *(Gtr)*: Hillcrest, Mount Pleasant East, Robin Hoods Bay, North Yorks YO22 4RF ☎ 01947 880622

CASH Dave *(Gtr)*: 56 Abbey Road, Bardney, Nr Lincoln, Lincs LN3 5XD ☎ 01526 398730

CHAMBERS Jeff *(Gtr, Tbn)*: 28 Hallamgate Road, Crookes, Sheffield S10 5BS ☎ 0114 268 7130 & fax

CHAPMAN Louise *(E Gtr, Vln, Pf)*: 2 Curzon Drive, Worksop, Notts S81 0LS ☎ 01909 474564, 07957 327164

CHRISTIE Jeffrey *(Gtr, Pf, Org)*: 32 High Ash Drive, Alwoodley, Leeds LS17 8RA ☎ 0113 2685528, 0385 508044 mob, 01132 665954 fax

CHRISTIE Simon *(E Gtr, Ac Gtr, Voc)*: 9 Longleat Gardens, Peeswood, Morpeth, Northumberland NE61 6TQ ☎ 01670 517821, 0410 642344

CLARKE Sean *(Gtr, Voc, Dms, Per, Kbds)*: 160 Newbiggin Road, North Seaton, Ashington NE63 0TL ☎ 01670 811028

CLAY Neville *(Gtr, B Gtr, Kbds)*: 12 Vicars Way, Longbenton, Newcastle-upon-Tyne, Tyne & Wear NE12 8UN ☎ 0191 270 2771

COATES John *(Ac Gtr)*: 8 Haywra Street, Harrogate, North Yorkshire HG1 5BJ ☎ 01423 547444, 07795 796081, 01423 547444

COCKER Jarvis Branson *(Gtr)*: Pru Harris, Rough Trade, 66 Golbourne Road, London W10 5PS ☎ 020 8960 9888

COLIN *(Gtr)*: 19 Ramsey Street, Little Horton, Bradford, West Yorkshire BD5 7NP ☎ 01274 789711

COLLUMBINE Syd *(Gtr, B Gtr)*: 89 Salutation Road, Darlington DL3 8JP ☎ 01325 243935

CONOMY Sean *(Gtr)*: 13A Mccutcheon Court, Walker, Newcastle-upon-Tyne, Tyne & Wear NE6 3LJ ☎ 07803 099601

CONWAY Shaun *(Gtr)*: Sunnybank, Station Road, Allendale Town, Hexham, Northumberland NE47 9PY ☎ 01434 683251

COOKE David *(Gtr, B Gtr, Dms, Kbds)*: ☎ 0114 255 2275

COOPER Rachel *(Gtr)*: Middle Cottage, Townhead, Eyam, Derbyshire S32 5RE ☎ 01433 63834

CORAM Jeremy *(Rh Gtr)*: 5 Parkers Mount, Kirkbymoorside, York YO62 6JB ☎ 01751 433338

CORBETT Ian *(Gtr)*: Mains Of Balfour Cottage, Birse, Aboyne, Aberdeenshire AB34 5DB ☎ 013398 86143

CORNER Chris *(Gtr)*: 2 Gypsy Lane, Marton, Middlesbrough, Cleveland TS7 8NG ☎ 01642 323116

COULDWELL Adam *(Gtr)*: The Dairy, Crain Syke Farm, North Rigton, Leeds LS17 0AD ☎ 01423 734643

CRAIG Martin *(Gtr, Voc)*: Oakdene, 3 Elm Avenue, Beechgrove, Whickham Newcastle-upon-Tyne NE16 4SR

CREE Norval *(Gtr, Vln)*: 6 Lincoln Road, Brant Broughton, Lincoln LN5 0SR ☎ 01522 788586

CROSS Simon *(Gtr, B Gtr)*: 38 Thompson Road, Sheffield S11 8RB ☎ 0114 2679649

CROWTHER Brian *(Gtr, Hmca, Kbds)*: 23 Seymour Street, Cockton Hill, Bishop Auckland, Co. Durham DL14 6JD ☎ 01388 607576

CULPIN Andrew *(Gtr)*: 18 St John Street, York YO31 7QT ☎ 01904 612441, 01523 401974

CURREY Mark *(Gtr)*: 19B Barbican Road, York YO10 5AA ☎ 01904 642 447

DAVIES Anthony *(Gtr, B Gtr, Vln, Man, Bjo)*: 9 Chapel House Buildings, Low Moor, Bradford BD12 0HR ☎ 01274 691178, 0498 5865723

DAVIES Ben *(Gtr, Voc, B Gtr)*: The Beeches, 20C Parker Lane, Mirfield, West Yorks WF14 9PA ☎ 01924 498412

DAVIES Carl *(Gtr, Kbds)*: 166A Albert Road, Sheffield, South Yorkshire S8 9RB ☎ 0114 2550138

DAWKINS Chris *(Gtr, Kbds, B Gtr, Dms)*: 16 Bolton Lane, Off Kings Road, Bradford BD2 0PG ☎ 01274 731182, 0589 115112

DAWSON Martin *(E Gtr, Ac Gtr, B Gtr, Bjo, Ma)*: 41 Castle Street, Skipton, North Yorkshire BD23 2DH

DENNETT Russell *(Ld Gtr, Kbds, Per)*: 11A Ferndale Close, Coal Aston, Nr Sheffield, S Yorks S18 6BR ☎ 01246 415715

DENSON Nicholas *(Gtr, Pf, B Gtr, Vln, Dms)*: 11 Laurel Bank Court, Headingley, Leeds, West Yorks LS6 3DX ☎ 0113 278 7360, 0973 224391 mob, 0113 225 2008

DENTON Peter *(Gtr)*: 41 Parkland View, Yeadon, Leeds LS19 7DZ ☎ 0113 2501502

DICKENS John *(Gtr, B Gtr, Voc)*: 70 Wensley Close, Ouston, Co. Durham DH2 1SE ☎ 0191 410 8649

DIXON Michael *(Gtr)*: 33 Ashton Grove, Harehills, Leeds LS8 5BR ☎ 0113 249 3779

DONKIN Martin *(Gtr)*: 4 Byron Avenue, Wallsend, North Tyneside, Tyne & Weir NE28 6NF ☎ 0191 289 3340

DONNELLY Paul *(Gtr, Bjo, Man)*: 23 Hobhill Close, Saltburn By The Sea, Cleveland TS12 1NB ☎ 01287 622189

DOUGLAS Fitzroy *(Gtr, Hmca, Kbds)*: 25 Hawley Street, Sheffield, S Yorks S1 2EA ☎ 0114 2759488

DRYDEN Dave *(Gtr, B Gtr, Bjo, Man, Voc)*: 1 Station Terrace, Station Road, Stokesley, Middlesbrough TS9 7AB ☎ 01642 712009, 0850 257867 mob

DUNN Gary *(Ld Gtr)*: 280 Fulwell Road, Fulwell, Sunderland, Tyne & Wear SR6 9AP ☎ 0191 5480367

DURBIN Robin *(Gtr, Tpt, Pf)*: 13 Wilton Grove, Headingley, Leeds LS6 4ES ☎ 0113 275 0091

DUTSON BROMLEY Darren *(Gtr)*: 12 Lynfield Mount, Shipley, Bradford, W Yorks BD18 1HG ☎ 01274 594937, 0585 497431, 01274 594937

DYE Patrick *(Gtr, Voc)*: 29 Holme Hall Crescent, Chesterfield S40 4PQ ☎ 01246 230239

ELLIOTT Max *(Gtr, Jz Gtr, Cl Gtr)*: 6 Priory Terrace, Downham Market, Norfolk PE38 9JY

EMMERSON Richard *(Gtr, Voc)*: 81 Kirton Lane, Thorne, Doncaster, S Yorks DN8 5RF ☎ 01405 817371

EMPSON Paul (*Gtr*): Evenmead, Chestnut Drive, Messingham, South Humberside DN17 3PJ ☎ 01724 867650

ERNEST Thomas (*Gtr, Pf, Kbds*): 45 Melrose Road, Sheffield, S. Yorkshire S3 9DN ☎ 0114 2499023, 01426 159 580 pager

EUESDEN Christopher (*Gtr, Kbds*): 1 Holly Terrace, York YO10 4DS ☎ 01904 628442

FERGUSON Neil (*Gtr, Kbds, Com, Cop*): 3 Lawns Close, Altofts, Normanton, West Yorks WF6 2NR ☎ 01924 890505

FISHER Ray (*Gtr*): 5 Denebank, Monkseaton, Whitley Bay, Tyne & Wear NE25 9AE ☎ 0191 252 6585

FITZMAURICE Tristan (*E Gtr, Ac Gtr*): 17 Westwood Court, Huddersfield Road, Barnsley S70 2LT ☎ 01226 245747

FRANKS Jeremy (*Gtr*): Woodhill Cottage, Calverly Lane, Chalerly, Leeds LS28 5QQ ☎ 01132 363357, 0958 253985

FROST Eleanor (*Cl Gtr, Ac Gtr*): 9 Shireoaks Row, Shireoaks, Near Worksop, Notts S81 8LP ☎ 01909 476107

GIBSON Dave (*Gtr, Voc*): 48 Otto Terrace, Sunderland SR2 7LP ☎ 0191 510 8430

GILDERDALE Miles (*Gtr, Hrn, Voc*): 22A Arthur Street, York YO10 3EL ☎ 01904 631743

GILGAN Peter (*Gtr*): Collcot, Middlewood Lane, Fylingthorpe, Whitby North Yorkshire YO22 4UB ☎ 01947 880110

GOODALL Ron (*E Gtr, B Gtr, Db, Uke*): 4 Hawthorne Avenue, Haxby, York, Yorkshire YO32 3JT ☎ 01902 769744

GOODWIN Robert (*Gtr*): The Old School House, St. John's Road, Newbold, Chesterfield, Derbyshire S41 8QN ☎ 01246 455974

GRANT Steve (*Gtr, Kbds*): Southview, 15 Ashdene Crescent, Pudsey, West Yorkshire IS28 8NS ☎ 0113 2575424, 0113 2575424

GREEHY Robert (*Gtr, B Gtr, Dms, Kbds*): 27 Peaskill Close, Rawdon, Leeds LS19 6EF ☎ 0113 2502923

GREEN James (*E Gtr*): 59 Bracken Road, Brighouse, West Yorkshire HD6 2HX ☎ 01484 718634, 0441 636781

GREENWOOD Stan (*Gtr, B Gtr, Dms*): Granville House, Granville House, Exley Head, Keighley, West Yorkshire BD21 1LT ☎ 01535 677555

GREGSON Keith (*Gtr, Flag, Man, Clt*): 8 The Elms, Sunderland SR2 7BZ

GUMBO Francois (*Gtr*): 5 Walkergate, Otley, Leeds, West Yorkshire LS21 1HB ☎ 01943 466879

GUREVITCH Harry (*Gtr, Hmca, Bjo*): 4 Malvern Ave, Ella Street, Hull HU5 EBD ☎ 01482 441188

HAIGH Kit (*Gtr*): 159 Goldspink Lane, Newcastle-upon-Tyne NE2 1NS ☎ 0191 2322538

HALL Ben (*Gtr*)

HARES Paul (*Gtr, Bjo, Man*): 6 Salt Pan Well Steps, Whitby, North Yorkshire Y022 4AB ☎ 01947 820991

HARRIS Derrick (*Gtr*): 95 Becketts Park Crescent, Headingley, Leeds LS6 3PF ☎ 0113 2741388

HARRIS Jonathan (*Gtr*): Orchard House, 8 Fyfe Grove, Baildon, Shiipley BD17 6DN ☎ 01274 852738

HARRIS Lee (*Gtr, Voc, Kbds*): 126 Salisbury Road, Maltby, Rotherham, S. Yorks S66 8JP ☎ 01709 813302

HARRISON Albert (*Gtr, Db*): 275 James Reckitt Avenue, Hull, Yorks HU8 8LQ ☎ 01482 3703229

HARROP Steven (*E Gtr, Ac Gtr, Bjo, Dobro, Ma*): 18 Haveroid Way, Crigglestone, Wakefield WF4 3PG ☎ 01924 256468, 07771 630849

HAWKINS Iain (*E Gtr, B Gtr, Dms*): Water Pump Cottage, 3A Queens Avenue, Portishead, Bristol BS20 9NH ☎ 01275 817442

HAWLEY Richard (*Gtr, B Gtr, Hmca*): 78 Empire Road, Netheredge, Sheffield S7 1GL ☎ 0114 258 4195

HEARNE Anthony (*Gtr, Bjo*): 10 The Grove, Rawmarsh, Rotherham, S. Yorks S62 6JZ ☎ 01709 525887

HERBERT Brian (*Gtr, Bjo*): 1 Princes Gate, Savile Park, Halifax, West Yorkshire HX3 0EH ☎ 01422 347186

HEYWOOD Ian (*Gtr, S Sax*): Merryweather, Ipswich Road, Brantham, Suffolk CO11 1PF ☎ 01206 393435

HIGHLEY David (*Gtr*): 30 Hanover Square, Leeds LS3 1AW ☎ 0113 245 3650

HILBERT Steven (*Gtr*): 41 Strawberry Hall Retford, Notts DN22 7EL ☎ 01777 708916

HINCHLIFFE Keith (*Gtr, Citt*): 23A Spring Hill, Sheffield S10 1ET ☎ 0114 2669896

HOGG John (*E Gtr, Ac Gtr, Pf*): 37 Cumberland Court, Cardigan Road, Headingley, Leeds LS6 3BN ☎ 0113 2752354

HOOSON Christopher (*Gtr, B Gtr, Dms*): 15 Pasture Place, Chapel Allerton, Leeds, W. Yorks LS7 4QA ☎ 0113 269 7078

HOULDSWORTH Steven (*Gtr, Voc*): 190 Thwaites Brow Road, Thwaites Brow, Keighley, West Yorkshire BD21 4SW ☎ 01535 606586, 0966 370414

HOWARD Jonathon (*Ac Gtr*): 189 Rectory Road, Bensham, Gatesmead NE8 4RQ ☎ 0191 477 0430

HOWDEN Stephen (*Gtr, B Gtr, Pf, Voc*): St Michaels, Mill Lane, Gilberdyke, Brough HU15 2UW ☎ 0143 040686

HUGHES John (*Gtr, Kbds*): c/o Martin Green Ravden, 55 Loudoun Road, St Johns Wood, London NW8 0DL ☎ 020 7625 4545

IBBOTSON Alan (*Gtr, B Gtr*): 7 Towend Lane, Deepcar, Sheffield S36 2TN ☎ 0114 288 4821

JACK Jonathan (*Gtr, Bjo, Per, Acc*): 127 Victoria Avenue, Hull, East Yorkshire HU5 3DP ☎ 01482 343159

JASNOCH John (*Gtr, Man*): 66 Robey Street, Sheffield S4 8J4 ☎ 0114 244 4550

JEFFELS Joanne (*Gtr*): 7 Cheviot Road, Monkton Village, Jarrow, Tyne & Wear NE32 5NT ☎ 0191 489 8918, 0802 726 168

JENNINGS Garry (*Gtr*): 29 Ash Road, Harrogate, North Yorkshire HG2 8EB ☎ 020 8293 0999

JOHNSON Norman (*Gtr, B Gtr, Arr, Cop*): 19 Hazel Grove, Prebend Lane Estate, Welton, Lincoln LN2 3JZ ☎ 01673 860431

JONES Dean (*Gtr, Voc*): 97 Hawley Street, Sheffield S1 2EA ☎ 0114 2758669

JONES Heather (*Gtr, Voc*): 29 Highbury Avenue, Cantley, Doncaster DN4 6AW ☎ 01302 371874

JOSEPH Martyn (*Gtr*): Shark Management, PO Box 37, Penarth, Cardiff S. Wales CF64 1EN ☎ 029 2070 0785

JUDGE Paul (*Gtr, Acc*): c/o Judgement Records, PO Box 11, York YO62 4YP ☎ 01439 788449

KAY David (*Ac Gtr*): 8 Cardigan Terrace, Heaton, Newcastle-upon-Tyne NE6 5NU ☎ 0191 265 4925

KEOGH David (*Gtr, Voc*): 37 Chandos Gardens, Gledhow, Leeds LS8 1LP ☎ 0113 2665051

KHAN Jonathan (*Gtr, Voc*): 18 Armley Ridge Road, Armley, Leeds LS12 3NP ☎ 0113 216 8406, 07970 554882

KIDDIE Alexander (*Cl Gtr*): 6 Beechroyd Terrace, Bingley, West Yorkshire BD16 1EJ ☎ 01274 565981

KIRK Richard (*Gtr, Clt*): 267 Ellesmere Road, Sheffield S4 7DP ☎ 0114 2380728

KITCHING George (*Gtr*): 2 Woodside Cottages, Dalton, Burton In Kendal, Camforth, Lancs LA6 1NL ☎ 01524 782801, 015395 63091

KUNDAN Malook (*Gtr, B Gtr, Kbds, Song W*): 163 Brookfield Road, Pollard Park, Bradford, West Yorkshire BD3 0RW ☎ 01274 783749

LAD Milan (*Gtr*): 64 Horton Grange Road, Bradford, West Yorkshire BD7 3AQ ☎ 01274 575484

LAING Jonathan (*Gtr*): 9 Southfield Green, Whickham, Newcastle-upon-Tyne NE16 4RL ☎ 0191 488 3505

LAMBERT Ronnie (*Gtr, Hmca*): 3 Titchfield, Biddick, Washington, Tyne & Wear NE38 7JS ☎ 0191 415 4665

LANE Thomas (*Gtr, Bzk, Voc*): 11 Waterloo Paddock, Leadenham, Lincs LN5 0QW ☎ 01400 72705

LANGDALE David (*Gtr*): 20 Barra Close, Donegal Road, Salthouse Road, Hull HU8 9JB ☎ 01482 792063

LANGDALE William (*Gtr*): Stone Lodge, Norton Cuckney, Mansfield, Notts NG20 9LP

LEE David (*Gtr, B Gtr*): 10 Orion Way, Grimsby, South Humberside DN34 5UA ☎ 01472 750371

LIGGINS Len (*Gtr, B Gtr, Kbds, Bal, Vln*): 1 School Lane, Wargrve, Berks RG10 8AA ☎ 01734 404672

LINAHAN Liz (*Cl Gtr, Pf, Rec, Hrp, Bzk*): 5 Hall Close, North Anston, Sheffield S25 4AX ☎ 01909 561271

LITTLEWOOD Martin (*Gtr, Voc*): 35 Bennett Street, Skipton, North Yorkshire BD23 2NJ ☎ 01756 795018

LODGE Don *(Gtr)*: 197 Queensgate, Bridlington, East Yorkshire YO16 6QU ☎ 01262 672316

LOWE Jez *(Gtr, Citt, Dul, Bjo, Hmca)*: 60 Maritime Crescent, Horden, Peterlee, Co. Durham SR8 3SX ☎ 0191 586 1938

LOWTHER Richard *(Gtr, E Gtr, Ac Gtr, Voc, Hmca)*: 81 The Boulevard, Hull HU3 2UD ☎ 01482 215816

LUCAS Egly *(Gtr)*: 6 Macaulay Drive, Lincoln LN2 4DY ☎ 01522 542062

MACKINTOSH Gregor *(Ld Gtr)*: 126 Warley Road, West End, Halifax, West Yorkshire HX1 3TG ☎ 01422 345456

MADDISON Karl *(Gtr)*: 211 Rotherham Road, Maltby, Rotherham, South Yorkshire S66 8LW

MALAKI *(Gtr, B Gtr, Kbds)*: 7 Austwick Close, Staincross, Barnsley, South Yorkshire S75 5QF ☎ 01226 386263, 0411 768668, 01226 285446

MARSDEN Robert *(Gtr, Voc, B Gtr, Pf)*: 2 Sovereign Close, Birstall, Butley, W. Yorks WF17 0RT

MAXWELL Ian *(Cl Gtr)*

MAXWELL Peter *(Gtr, Kbds)*: 83 Biddlestone Road, Heaton, Newcastle-upon-Tyne, Tyne & Wear NE6 5SN

MAYSON Jon *(Gtr, Voc)*: 11 Acacia Drive, Townville, Castleford, West Yorkshire WF10 3PF ☎ 0197 755 4097

MCALOON Martin *(Gtr, Pf)*: Kitchenware Records, St Thomas St Workshops, St Thomas Street, Newcastle-upon-Tyne NE1 4LE ☎ 0191 232 4895

MCALOON Patrick *(Gtr, Pf)*: Kitchenware Records, St Thomas St Workshops, St Thomas Street, Newcastle-upon-Tyne NE1 4LE ☎ 0191 232 4895

MCCARTHY Patrick *(Gtr)*: 2 Little Lane, Louth, Lincs LN11 9DV ☎ 01507 607541

MCCAUGHERN Dan *(Gtr, Voc)*: 30 Victoria Street, West Parade, Lincoln LN1 1HY ☎ 01522 539730

MCGREGOR Chantel *(Gtr)*: 26 Greenacre Drive, Wyke, Brandford, West Yorkshire BD12 0DH ☎ 01274 679646

MCLELLAND Jock *(Gtr, Bjo, Pf, Acc, B Gtr)*: 24 Handley Street, Sleaford, Lincolnshire NG34 8UH ☎ 01529 302742

MCMAHON Martin *(Gtr)*: 6 Bodiam Way, Grimsby, N E Lincs DN32 7ED ☎ 01472 346791

MCQUAID Stephen *(Gtr, Kbds)*: 12 Jubilee Road, Gosforth, Newcastle-upon-Tyne NE3 3UQ

MCSWEENEY Neil *(Gtr)*: 19 Kingsley Park Avenue, Millhouses, Sheffield S7 2HG ☎ 0114 267 8903, 0114 236 9809

MEREDITH Rod *(Gtr, B Gtr)*: 7 West View, Langcliffe, Settle, North Yorkshire BD24 9LZ ☎ 01729 825466

MERRETT Steve *(E Gtr, Ac Gtr, B Gtr, Voc, Pf)*: 12 Foxglove Close, Summerfields, Blaxton, Doncaster DN9 3PR

MILL Sean *(Gtr)*: 30 Mundella Terrace, Heaton, Newcastle-upon-Tyne NE4 5HX ☎ 0191 265 5041

MILLER Gary *(Gtr, Voc, Lute, Man, Bzk)*: 46 Milton Street, York YO10 3EP ☎ 01904 423 060 day

MONK Peter *(Ac Gtr, Flt, E Gtr)*: 5 Railway Street, Langley Park, Durham DH7 9YS ☎ 0191 373 3147

MOON Andrew *(Gtr, Sax)*: 17 North Farm Avenue, Grindon, Sunderland SR4 9SB ☎ 0191 534 3273, 0421 384038

MOSLEY Anna *(Gtr, Pf, Man, Hmca)*: Stonehurst, Sheffield Road, Hoyland, Barnsley S74 0DP ☎ 01226 744023

MOSLEY David *(Gtr, Voc)*: 64 Wandsworth Road, Heaton, Newcastle-upon-Tyne NE6 5AD ☎ 0191 276 4997

MUIR Kenneth *(Gtr)*: 105 The Oval, Rothwell, Leeds LS26 0EE ☎ 0113 2822566

MUKHERJEE Omith *(Gtr)*: 111 Penrhyn Road, Sheffield S11 8UP ☎ 0114 268 5024

MULDOON Wilbur *(Gtr, Voc)*: 10 Church Lane, Methley, Nr Leeds, West Yorkshire LS26 9HL ☎ 01977 557672

NEWMAN Chris *(Gtr, Man, E Gtr, B Gtr)*: 33 Bridge Lane, Ilkley, West Yorkshire LS29 9EJ ☎ 01943 602203

NIELSEN Billy *(Ld Gtr, Voc)*: Flat 1, Park Villa, 34 Valley Road, Scarborough, N Yorks YO11 2LU ☎ 01723 354536

NORMAN Stephen *(Gtr, Kbds)*: 7 Weelsby Way, Hessle, East Yorkshire HU13 0JN ☎ 01482 646110

O'DONNELL Mairead *(Gtr, Pf)* ☎ 01943 600654 & fax, 0589 173097 mob

OHERN Nicholas *(Gtr, B Gtr, Dms, Kbds, Voc)*: Black Cat Barn, Main Street, Fulford Village, York YO10 4PN ☎ 01904 673610

OWEN David *(Gtr, B Gtr)*

OXLEY Craig *(E Gtr)*: 4 Goldgarth, Grimsby, Linconshire DN32 8QS ☎ 01472 692934

PAGAN Simon *(Gtr)*: 11 Kirkfell Close, Eaglescliffe, Stockton, Cleveland TS16 0DU ☎ 01642 783110

PALLADINO Angelo *(Gtr)*: 31 Markham Crescent, Rawdon, Leeds LS19 6NG

PARKES John *(Gtr, B Gtr)*: 39 Clifton Mount, Leeds LS9 6EP ☎ 0113 2402880

PARR John *(Gtr, Pf)*: Marsh Hills Farm, Sykehouse, Nr Doncaster, S Yorks DN14 9AH

PASCALL Neil *(Gtr)*: 20 School Hill, South Crossland, Huddersfield HD4 7BY ☎ 01484 842989

PATTINSON Andrew *(Gtr, B Gtr)*: 21 Griffith Terrace, West Allotment, Newcastle -upon-Tyne NE27 0EG ☎ 0191 266 7317

PAYNE Ceri *(Gtr)*: 9 Harriot Drive, Westmoor, Newcastle-upon-Tyne NE12 0EU

PEARMAN Mark *(Gtr, B Gtr, Kbds)*: Flat 1, 12 St Johns Square, Wakefield, West Yorkshire WF1 2RA ☎ 01924 368334

PEARSON Adam *(Gtr, B Gtr, Voc, Kbds)*: 48 Cottage Road, Leeds LS4 4DD ☎ 0113 2165177

PEARSON Neil *(Gtr, B Gtr, Voc)*: 23 Brudenell Grove, Hyde Park, Leeds LS6 1HP ☎ 0113 742266

PERRY Ray *(Gtr, B Gtr, Kbds, Cong)*: Flat 1, Overton Grange, Overton, York YO30 1YN ☎ 01904 470792

PHILLIPS Norman *(Gtr)*: New Cottage, Apperley Grange, Rawdon, Leeds LS19 6LN ☎ 0113 250 7223, 0113 250 7223

PIPER Peter *(Gtr, B Gtr, Kbds, Voc, Md)*: 18 Autumn Drive, Maltby, Rotherham S66 7DZ ☎ 01709 816298

PLATT Edward *(Gtr, B Gtr)*: 47 Parkinson Close, Wakefield, West Yorkshire WF1 4NR ☎ 01924 381635

RAE Nigel *(Gtr, Man, Pf)*: 21 Drummond Avenue, Far Headingley, Leeds LS16 5JZ ☎ 0113 2758893

RAINE Graham *(Gtr, Dms, Vln, Per)* ☎ 01434 632373 & fax

RATCLIFFE Edward *(Gtr, B Gtr)*: 40 Clareville Road, Darlington DL3 8NG ☎ 01325 460108

REDFERN Jonathan *(Gtr, Eth Per, Voc)*: 13 Heaviside Place, Gilesgate, Durham City DH1 1JG ☎ 0191 383 0768

REED Christopher *(Gtr, Pf)*: 175 Dilston Road, Newcastle-upon-Tyne NE4 5AD ☎ 0191 272 3574

REED Howard T *(Gtr, B Gtr)*: The Minster Inn, 24 Marygate, York YO30 7BH ☎ 01904 624499

RICHARDS Keith *(Gtr, Hmca, Voc)*: 7 Cropstones, Bramham, Wetherby, W. Yorkshire LS23 6SG ☎ 01937 845238, 01937 845238

RICHMOND Michael *(Gtr)*: 86 Station Road, Hessle, E Yorkshire HU13 0BG ☎ 01482 641344

RIDLEY Kevin *(Gtr, Voc)*: 8 Holly Gardens, Low Fell, Gateshead, Tyne & Wear NE9 5TP ☎ 0191 487 2891

ROBERTS Sarah *(Gtr, Voc)*: 9 Gledhow Lane, Leeds LS8 1SD ☎ 0113 248 8129, 096191 2252

ROBERTSON Alan C *(E Gtr, Cl Gtr)*: 21 Shaftesbury Crescent, North Shields, Tyne & Wear NE30 3LR ☎ 0191 252 7014

ROBSON Stanley *(Gtr)*: 45 Cooper Street, Roker, Sunderland SR6 0NQ ☎ 0191 565 4372

ROTHERAY David *(Gtr)*: c/o P Cass/Beautiful South, Cavendish House, St Andews Court, St Andrews Street, Leeds LS3 1JY ☎ 0113 243 0898, 0113 234 0698

ROWINSKI David *(Gtr, B Gtr, Acc, Pf)*: 3 Aspin Way, Knaresborough, N Yorks HG5 8HL ☎ 01423 860463

RUSSELL Alistair *(Gtr, Citt, Voc)*: 6A Montagu Place, Leeds LS8 2RG ☎ Temple 328

RUSSELL Janet *(Gtr, Dul)*: 46 Bolton Road, Silsden, Nr Keighley, West Yorkshire BD20 0SY ☎ Keighley 56877

SAVAGE Neil *(Gtr, Voc)*: 30 Wansbeck, Rickleton, Washington, Tyne & Wear NE38 9EF ☎ 0191 222 1515, 0191 232 1980

SCARTH Neil *(Gtr, Voc)*: 70 High Northgate, Darlington, Co Durham DL3 0GZ ☎ 01325 250903

SCOTT Johnathan *(Gtr, B Gtr, Dms)*: 128 Willerby Road, Hull, East Yorkshire HU5 5JN ☎ 01482 564860, 0585 909461 mob

SCUTT Martin *(Gtr, Voc, Hmca)*: Armadillo Lodge, Old School Lane, Donington-on-Bain, Louth Lincs LN11 9TQ ☎ 01507 343754, 01507 343523 fax

SHEARER Gary *(Gtr, B Gtr)*: 49 Osborne Crescent, Tweedmouth, Berwick-on-Tweed, Northumberland TD15 2HU ☎ 01289 303869

SILSON Alan *(Gtr, Hmca)*: Wharfedene, Ben Rhydding Drive, Ilkley, West Yorkshire LS29 8BG

SIMONS Andrew *(Gtr)*: 37 Whites Road, Cleethorpes, N E Lincs DN35 3RL ☎ 01472 322616

SIMPSON Christopher *(Gtr)*: 16 Southwood Lane, Grassington, N Yorks BD23 5NA ☎ 01765 752024

SIMPSON Peter *(Gtr, Cl Gtr, Com, Cop)*: 9 Holmside Terrace, Craghead, Stanley, Co. Durham DH9 6ET ☎ 01207 281060

SINCLAIR Roderick *(Gtr, Pf)*: The Station House, Lintz Green, Rowlands Gill, Tyne & Wear NE39 1NN ☎ 01207 71902

SLAPPER DAVE *(E Gtr, B Gtr)*: Flat 2, 25 Cardigan Road, Leeds LS6 3AE ☎ 0113 293 9829

SMITH Martin *(Gtr)*: 193 Woodseats Road, Sheffield, S. Yorks S8 0PL ☎ 01142 819122

SMITH Peter *(Gtr)*: 20 Northcote Avenue, Holgate, York, North Yorkshire YO24 4JD ☎ 01904 782279

SMITH Steven *(E Gtr, Ac Gtr)*: 25 Evesham Road, Park End, Middlesbrough, Cleveland TS3 7EX ☎ 01642 310102

SNELL Phillip *(Gtr, B Gtr, Man, Triangle)*: 19 Manor Street, Otley, West Yorkshire LS21 1AX ☎ 01943 465772

SOLOWKA Peter *(Gtr, B Gtr)*: 35 Wensley Drive, Chapel Allerton, Leeds LS7 3QP ☎ 0113 2743404

SPENCER David *(Gtr, Voc, Kbds, B Gtr)*: 1 Clarke Court, 81 Clarke House Road, Broom Hill, Sheffield S10 2LG ☎ 0114 267 8790

STEERS Simon *(Gtr, Kbds, B Gtr, Dms, Hmca)*: 7 Senior Place, Lane End, Chapeltown, Sheffield S35 2WW ☎ 01142 869042

STEWART Doug *(Gtr)*: 42 Linden Road, Newby, Scarborough, North Yorkshire YO12 5SN

STEWART William *(Gtr, Voc)*: 133 Bedeburn Road, Jarrow, Newcastle, Tyne & Wear NE32 5AZ ☎ 0191 489 8914

STOKES Peter *(Cl Gtr, E Gtr)*: 16 Middleton Avenue, Dinnington, Nr Sheffield S31 7QQ ☎ 01909 562002

STRONG Jon *(Gtr)*: Samson Works, Clark View, Off Easy Road, Leeds LS9 8QU ☎ 0113 293 0232 & fax

STUART Hazel *(Gtr, Dms, Voc)*: 2 Barras Drive Tunsatll, Sunderland, Tyne & Wear SR5 1PP ☎ 0191 528 9514

SWIFT Jeffrey *(E Gtr, Cl Gtr)*: 94 Embleton Road, Metnley, Leeds LS26 9DA ☎ 01977 516023 & fax, 0850 101119 mob

TAYLOR Allan *(Gtr)*: 5 Rochester Wynd, Shadwell, Leeds LS17 8XU ☎ 0113 2681002

TEAGUE Nik *(Gtr)*: 51 Riding Hill, Great Lumley, Chester Le Street, County Durham DH3 4HP ☎ 0191 389 3287

THURMAN Andrew *(Gtr, Dms, Per)*: 20 Heath Lea, Well Head, Halifax HX1 2BX ☎ 01422 365047 & fax

TOMPKINS Andy *(Gtr, Dms)*: Dyke House, Back Lane, Aughton, York YO42 4PG ☎ 01757 288953

TOWNEND Jon *(Gtr, Man, Bjo)*: 58 Huntington Road, York YO31 8RE ☎ 01904 620766

VALENTINE Hilton *(Gtr, Voc)*: 69 Sandringham Gardens, North Shields, Tyne & Wear NE29 9AX

VAN SANTE Rob *(Gtr, Kbds)*: 189B Hyde Park Road, Woodhouse, Leeds LS6 1AH ☎ 0113 275 2472

VEITCH Roland *(Gtr, Voc)*: 9 Beweshill Crescent, Winlaton, Blaydon, Tyne & Wear NE21 6BW ☎ 0191 414 5570

VENEMORE Drew *(Gtr, Voc)*: 110 Goddard Avenue, Hull, East Yorkshire HU5 2BA ☎ 01482 445116

VERITY John *(Gtr, B Gtr)*: 1 Colemoreham Court, Ickwell Green, Biggleswade, Beds SG18 9EW

WADE Rebecca *(E Gtr, Ac Gtr)*: 6 Suningdlae Green, Darlington, Co Durham DL1 3SE ☎ 01325 355959

WADEY Zoe *(Gtr, Voc)*: 4 Peartree Bungalows, Blackhall Mill, Newcastle-upon-Tyne NE17 7TW ☎ 01207 561590

WALKER Christopher *(Gtr)*: 7 Eastwood Road, Hunters Bar, Sheffield S11 8QE ☎ 0114 2686850

WALKER Matthew *(Gtr)*: 38 Lane Ends Green, Hipperholme, Halifax HX3 8EZ ☎ 01422 200418, 01422 882618 day

WALKER Michael *(Gtr, Pf)*: Flat 3, 44 High Street, Scotter, Gainsborough DN21 3TL ☎ 01724 764 768, 0441 192561 mob

WALKER Patrick *(Gtr, Vln, Vla, Man)*: 8 Welbeck Road, Walkley, Sheffield S6 5AX ☎ 0114 233 0895

WALPOLE Steven *(Gtr, Pf, Kbds)*: 12 Park Drive, Greenhead, Huddersfield, West Yorkshire HD1 4EB ☎ 01484 312 353

WELLS Ruth *(Ac Gtr, Voc)*: 61 Avenue Road, Wath-upon-Dearne, Rotherham, South Yorkshire S63 7AG ☎ 01709 878361

WHELAN Andrew *(Gtr)*: 245 Batley Road, Kirkhamgate, Wakefield, W Yorks WF2 0RZ ☎ 01924 387547

WHITAKER John *(Cl Gtr)*: 17, Heather Close, Moorgate, Rotherham, S Yorkshire S60 2TQ ☎ 01709 374987

WHITE Frank *(Gtr)*: 64 Langdon Street, Sheffield S11 8BJ ☎ 0114 258 1900

WHITTLE Tony *(Gtr, Voc)*: 118 Sydney Grove, Newcastle-upon-Tyne 4, Tyne & Wear NE4 5PE ☎ 0191 272 3750

WILGAUS Frank *(Gtr, B Ldr, Voc)*: 11 Brian Avenue, Cleethorpes, Lincs DN35 7JR ☎ 01472 690047

WILSON Ben *(Gtr, Kbds, Ac Gtr)*: 2 Skottowe Crescent, Great Ayton, Middlesbrough TS9 6DS ☎ 01642 723537

WILSON David *(Gtr, B Gtr)*: 95 Malham Drive, Lakelands, Lincoln LN6 0XD ☎ 01522 889381

WILSON John *(Gtr)*: 38 Lansdowne Gardens, Jesmond, Newcastle-upon-Tyne, Tyne & Wear NE2 1HH ☎ 0191 281 0722

WINFIELD Sharon *(Gtr, Voc)*: 30 Second Ave, Heworth, York YO31 0RX ☎ 01904 425118

WITCHELL Robbie *(Gtr, Voc, B Gtr)*: 44 Louis Street, Flat 3, Springbank, Hull HU3 1LZ ☎ 01482 219935

WOODS Michael *(Gtr)*: 32 Fernwood Avenue, Garden Village, Gosforth, Newcastle-upon-Tyne NE3 5DL ☎ 0191 284 8707

WRIGHT Tony *(Gtr, Bjo)*: 3 Bog Hall, Whitby, North Yorkshire YO21 1PG ☎ 01947 601442

WROE Ian *(Gtr)*: 10 Central Avenue, Fartown, Huddersfield, West Yorkshire HD2 1BT ☎ 01484 534362

YORKE Gary *(Gtr, B Gtr)*: 12 Mount Pleasant, Holton Le Clay, Nr Grimsby, Lincs DN36 5ED ☎ 01472 827 142

EAST

ADAMS David *(E Gtr, B Gtr, Ac Gtr, Voc)*: 15 Falstone Green, Luton LU2 9JJ ☎ 01582 658641

ALCOCK Gregory *(Gtr)*: 51 Cornflower Drive, Springfield, Chelmsford, Essex CM1 6XZ ☎ 01245 468378

ANDERSON Chris *(Gtr, Kbds)*: 48 Garrison Court, Hitchin, Hertfordshire SG4 9AA ☎ 01462 441029

ARNOLD David *(Gtr, Clt, Bjo)*: 13 Glenloch Road, Belsize Park, London NW3 4DJ ☎ 020 7586 1416

ATTWOOD Stephen *(Gtr, B Gtr, Voc)*: 8 York Road, Waltham Cross, Herts EN8 7HW ☎ 01992 764086

BAILEY Paul *(Gtr)*: 24 Great North Road, Welwyn, Herts AL6 0PS ☎ 01438 715145, 0956 234617

BAKER Jo *(Gtr, Ac Gtr, B Gtr, Dms, Kbds)*: Flat 1 Whartons Court, Wymondham, Norfolk NR18 0UQ ☎ 01953 606165, 0797 899432 mob, 0432 5175604 pager

BAMFORTH Annie *(Gtr)*: 162 Alexandra Rd, Peterborough, Cambs PE1 3DL ☎ 01733 310968

BARRY J.J. *(Ld Gtr, Voc)*: 32A Broad Street, Ely, Cambs CB7 4AH ☎ 01353 669009

BEARPARK Michael *(Gtr, B Gtr)*: 1 Gardiners Lane, Ashwell, Baldock, Herts SG7 5NZ ☎ 01462 742963

BEAUMONT Jim *(Gtr, Bjo, Voc)*: 191 The Avenue, Norwich NR4 7DN ☎ 01603 501572

BERNASCONI Justin *(Gtr, Voc, Bjo, Pf, Hmca)*: 112 Chamberlayne Road, Willesden, London NW10 3JP ☎ 020 8960 7024

BETTS Kevin *(Gtr, Kbds)*: 12 The Lindens, Braintree, Essex CM7 1AY ☎ 01376 326722

BLACKMAN Daniel *(Gtr, Voc)*: 23 Maple Drive, Wicken Green Village, Fakenham, Norfolk NR21 7QA ☎ 01485 529126

BLACKWELL Llewellyn *(Gtr, Voc)*: c/o 3 Wood Road, Heybridge, Nr Maldon, Essex CM1 4PB

BLISS Vic (*Gtr, B Gtr*): 25 Morris Road, North Walsham, Norfolk NR28 0EJ ☎ 01692 406931 & fax

BOOGA (*Gtr, B Gtr*): 22 Tevorsham Road, Fulbrown, Cambridge CB1 5EB ☎ 01223 565567, 0385 352352, 01223 303503

BOOTH Rick (*Gtr, B Gtr*): 205A Hatfield Road, St Albans, Herts AL1 4SY ☎ 01727 765922

BOSMAN Andre (*Gtr, Kbds, B Gtr*): 99A Unthank Road, Norwich, Norfolk NR2 2PE ☎ 01603 612693

BOYDE Hugh (*Gtr, Vln*): 36 Bermuda Terrace, Cambridge CB4 3LD ☎ 01223 464538

BRADBEER Robert (*Ac Gtr, Rec*): 6 Harecroft Gardens, Kings Lynn, Norfolk PE30 2BY ☎ 01553 76268

BRITTON Anthony (*Gtr, Kbds*): 54 The Mead, Carpenders Park, Watford WD1 5BU ☎ 020 8421 0346, 0421 460426

BROWN Ian (*Gtr*): Topers Rant, Tannington, Suffolk IP13 7LU ☎ 01728 628686

BROWNE Denzil (*Gtr*): 142 Chells Way, Stevenage, Herts SG2 0LY ☎ 01438 355250, 01438 227393 fax

BROWNLIE John (*Ac Gtr, B Gtr, Per*): 22 Foxley Close, Norwich NR5 8DQ

BUCKLE Stuart (*Gtr*): 4 Sanderson Road, Westoning, Beds MK45 5JY ☎ 01525 714345

BURDEN David (*Gtr*): 10 Mayfield, Welwyn Garden City, Herts AL8 7EL ☎ 01707 333409

BURDEN Oliver (*Gtr, B Gtr, Dms, Voc*): 39 Francis Way, Silver End, Witham, Essex CM8 3QX ☎ 01376 583849

BURNETT Barry (*Gtr, Kbds*): 44 Harcourt Avenue, Southend-on-Sea, Essex SS2 6HU ☎ 01702 354191

BUTCHER Kevin (*Gtr, B Gtr, Kbds*): 5 Elm Close, Bentwaters Park, Rendlesham, Woodbridge, Suffolk IP12 2UP ☎ 01394 461341

CAMBRIDGE John (*Gtr*): 38 Playford Square, Vincent Road, Luton LU4 9BE ☎ 01582 599928

CAMP Richard (*Gtr, Voc*): P O Box 4039, Dunstable, Beds LU5 4YF ☎ 01582 524500, 01582 758880, 01582 758881

CAMPLING Mark (*Gtr, Pf, B Gtr*): 84 Violet Road, Norwich, Norfolk NR3 4TS ☎ 01603 406474

CARTER Peter (*Gtr, B Gtr, Sitar, Oud*): 4 Chapel Lane, Barton Bendish, Kings Lynn, Norfolk PE33 9DS ☎ 01366 347 847

CARTWRIGHT David (*Gtr, Vln, Pf, Bjo*): 6 Catharine Street, Cambridge CB1 3AA ☎ 01223 562283

CASS Dave (*Gtr, Voc*): 148 London Road, Ipswich, Suffolk IP1 2HQ ☎ 01473 214443

CHERRY John (*Gtr, Bjo, B Gtr, Voc*): 38 Drayton Road, Cherry Hinion, Cambridge CB1 4EX ☎ 01223 415 706

CLARE Dennis (*Gtr, Voc*): 11 Orchard Way, Oakington, Cambridge CB4 5BQ ☎ 01223 232637

CLARE John (*Gtr*): 234 Radlett Road, Colney Street, St Albans, Herts AL2 2EN ☎ 01923 858283

CLARKE Aaron (*Ac Gtr, E Gtr, B Gtr, Kbds, P*): 26 Rye Gardens, Clothal Common, Baldock, Herts SG7 6TB ☎ 01462 490654, 0385 575710, 01462 490270

CLARKE Jimmi (*E Gtr, B Gtr*): 38 Lorne Park Road, Lowestoft, Suffolk NR33 0RB ☎ 01502 566784

CLARKIN Paul (*Gtr*): 4 The Shires, Old Bedford Road, Luton, Beds LU2 7QA ☎ 01582 411223

COLEMAN Colin (*Gtr*): 5 Blyth Road, Norwich, Norfolk NR3 3LG ☎ 0160 348 8189

COMPTON Daniel (*Gtr, Kbds*): 346 Point Clear Road, St. Osyth, Essex CO16 8LB ☎ 01255 820126

COOMBS Mike (*Gtr, B Gtr, Bjo, Hmca*): 11 Norfolk Road, Buntingford, Herts SG9 9AN ☎ 01763 271033 & fax

CROWE John (*Gtr, Vln, Man, Voc*): 59 High Street, Wilburton, Ely, Cambs CB6 3RA ☎ 01353 740497

DAVIES David (*Gtr, Kbds*): Address Unknown ☎ 01733 310368

DAVIES Ian (*Gtr, B Gtr, Hmca, Dms*): 27 Grange Road, Wickham Bishops, Witham, Essex CM8 3LT ☎ 01621 892175

DAVIES Simon (*Cl Gtr, E Gtr, B Gtr*): 23 Dean Way, Aston Clinton, Bucks HP22 5GB ☎ 01296 632266, 01296 632266

DE ROSA Dominic (*Gtr*): 4 The Drive, Moles Farm, Ware, Hertfordshire SG12 0UG

DEAL Keith (*Gtr*): 79 Castle Road, St Albans, Herts AL1 5DQ ☎ 01727 867236

DEAN Neville (*Gtr, B Gtr*): 61 Dugard Ave, Lexden, Colchester, Essex CO3 5EL ☎ 01206 562155, 0860 943425 mob, 01206 500566

DEE Len (*Gtr, Hmca, Voc*): Alpine Rose, Moin Road, Somersham, Nr Ipswich, Suffolk IP8 4PH ☎ 01473 832510, 0370 584359 mob

DEXTER Roger (*Gtr, Kbds*): Broomwood House, Broomwood Lane, Ramsden Heath, Nr Billericay, Essex CM11 1JP ☎ 01268 711276

DICKSON Graham (*Gtr, Per*): 2 Bankside Down, Chorlywood Road, Rickmansworth, Herts WD3 4EJ ☎ 01923 779500

DIXON Peter (*Gtr*): 28 Trafford Close, Stevenage, Herts SG1 3RY ☎ 01438 724753

DOW Nicholas (*Gtr, B Gtr*): 1 Alma Close, Ipswich, Suffolk IP4 3DA ☎ 01473 219603, 0589 365202, 01473 405579

DOWDING Mark (*Gtr, Kbds*)

DUBROISE Julie (*Gtr, Voc*): Park Croft, The Park, Gt. Barton, Bury St. Edmunds, Suffolk IP31 2SU

ELLIS Lisa (*Rh Gtr, Com, Voc*): 25 Whitby Ave, Ingrave, Brentwood, Essex CM13 3NT ☎ 01277 811781

EVANS Simon (*Gtr, B Gtr*): 2 Hindles Road, Canvey Island, Essex SS8 8HT ☎ 01268 680803

FAIR Tony (*Gtr, Song W, B Gtr, Kbds*): 31 Birkbeck Meon Close, Waveney Drive, Springfield, Chelmsford CM1 7QP ☎ 01245 495981

FIFE Desmond (*Gtr, Dms*) ☎ 01733 446808, 07970 393862

FISHER Danny (*Gtr, B Gtr, Kbds*): 43B Walsworth Road, Hitchin, Herts SG4 9SU ☎ 01462 455648

FLEGG Chris (*Gtr, Voc*): 1 Barham Road, Stevenage, Herts SG2 9HX ☎ 01438 360227, 0777 5504059

FLEMING John (*Gtr*): 6 Aldeburgh Gardens, Highwoods, Colchester, Essex CO4 4XZ ☎ 01206 855190, 07801 299843

FOLEY Kenneth (*Gtr*): 75A Vicarage Road, Watford, Herts WD3 2HQ ☎ 01923 244974, 0973 941545 mob

FORD-POWELL Ken (*Cl Gtr, Pf, B Gtr, Vln, E Gtr*): 138 Woodhead Drive, Cambridge CB4 1YX ☎ 01223 425983

FOX Dianne (*Gtr, B Gtr, Voc*): 8 York Road, Waltham Cross, Herts EN8 7HW ☎ 01992 764086

FRANKLIN Brian (*Gtr, Kbds*): 13 Neagle Close, Potters Lane, Boreham Wood, Herts WD6 5PX ☎ 020 8207 3643

GAMON Mark (*Gtr*) ☎ 01799 500484, 01799 500484

GILLIES Chris (*Gtr, B Gtr*): 111 Ingles, Welwyn Garden City, Herts AL8 7HF ☎ 01707 335363

GLADWELL Robbie (*Ld Gtr, B Gtr*): 20 Layzell Croft, Great Cornard, Sudbury, Suffolk CO10 0JY ☎ 01787 378546

GLANVILLE Pascal (*Gtr, E Gtr, Ac Gtr, Chap Stk*): 498A London Road, Westcliff-on-Sea, Southend, Essex SS0 9LD ☎ 01702 390944

GLEAVE Richard (*Gtr, Db, B Gtr*): 41 Golden Riddy, Linslade, Leighton Buzzard, Beds LU7 7RH ☎ 01525 375977

GOFFEE Graham (*Gtr*): 41 Salisbury Road, Harpenden, Herts AL5 5AR ☎ 015827 64225

GOOD Graham (*Ld Gtr, Pf, Voc*): 9 Boreham Road, Great Leighs, Chelmsford, Essex CM1 5QT ☎ 01245 361956

GOODCHILD Darren (*Gtr*): 16 Rushes Court, Twyford Road, Bishops Stortford, Herts CM23 3YP ☎ 01279 654706

GORE Neil (*Gtr, Mldn, Man, Bjo, Uke*): 15 Derwent Close, Hay Wharf, Burton-on-Trent, Staffs DE14 1TS

GRACEY Nik (*Gtr, Cel, Pf, Sax, B Gtr*): 8 Park Parade, Cambridge CB5 8AL ☎ 01223 357949

GRAY Dominic (*Gtr, Voc, B Gtr, Pf*): 18 Cardy Road, Boxmoor, Hemel Hempstead, Herts HP1 1RL ☎ 01442 250160

HADDOCK Glynn (*Gtr, B Gtr, Dms, Kbds*): 7 Wick Road, Ely ☎ 01284 724131

HAMILTON John (*Gtr, Kbds*): 10 Stanley Road, Watford, Herts WD1 2QU ☎ 01923 47879

HANDS David (*Gtr, Synth, Didj, Per*): Polygraph, 12 Graham Road, Dunstable, Beds LU5 4EH ☎ 01582 606993

HARRIS Robert (*Gtr*): 7 Trent Close, St Ives, Hubtingdon, Cambridgeshire PE17 6FH ☎ 01480 495259

HARWOOD Erica (*Gtr, Clt, Dms*): 77 Northview Road, Dunstable, Beds LU5 5AH ☎ 01582 478971

HAYWARD David *(Pd Gtr)*: Four Winds, Bedmond Road, Abbots Langley, Herts WD5 0RP ☎ 01923 262076

HAYWOOD Tony *(Gtr, Voc)*: 1 Imperial Ave, Maylandsea, Essex CM3 6AQ

HEMSWORTH Ross *(Gtr)*: 4 Kingsbury Gardens, Dunstable, Beds LU5 4PX ☎ 01582 670469, 01582 605465

HEYWOOD Brian *(Gtr, B Gtr)*: 2 Borough Road, Dunstable, Beds LU5 4BZ, 01582 475655, 01582 475739

HOBSON Gregory *(Gtr)*: 107A High Street, South Benfleet, Essex SS7 1ND ☎ 01268 792329

HODGSON Lee *(Gtr, B Gtr)*: 2 The Poplars, Pitsea, Basildon, Essex SS13 2ER ☎ 01268 473535

HOOKER Steve *(Gtr, Voc)*: 149 Lonsdale Road, Southend-on-Sea, Essex SS2 4LH ☎ 01702 65403/714, 01702 292386 fax

HOULSTON Robert *(E Gtr, B Gtr, Voc)*: 12 Longacres, St Albans, Hertfordshire AL4 0DR ☎ 01727 851809

HOWARD Michael *(Gtr)*: 35 Stephenson Close, Great Yarmouth, Norfolk NR30 4NP ☎ 01493 853523 & fax

HOWMAN David *(Gtr, Kbds)*: 26 Hailes Wood, Elsenham, Bishops Stortford, Herts CM22 6DQ

HUNT Andrew *(Gtr, B Gtr, Kbds)*: 1 Roche Avenue, Rochford, Southend-on-Sea S4 1NG ☎ 01245 441724

HUTCHINSON Benjamin *(Gtr, Kbds)*: 1 Cedar Rise, Mattishall, Dereham, Norfolk NR20 3NN ☎ 01362 850836

JAKSZYK Michael *(Gtr, B Gtr, Flt, Kbds, Hmca)*: 39 Tower Hill, Chipperfield, Herts WD3 9LJ ☎ 01442 833879

JAY Justin *(Ld Gtr, B Gtr)*: 11 Tara Close, Harwich Road, Colchester, Essex CO4 3DP ☎ 01206 791438

JAY Trevor *(Gtr, Kbds, Dms)*: 349 Main Road, Dovercourt, Harwich CO12 4DN ☎ 01255 552720

JIM *(Gtr, Bjo)*: 20 Gillan Way, Houghton Regis, Dunstable, Beds LU5 5RD ☎ 01582 863882

JOHN-BAPTISTE Marcel *(Gtr, B Gtr, Pf, Dms, Per)*: 50A Marlborough Road, Watford, Herts WD1 7BB ☎ 01923 467797

JOHNSON Colin *(E Gtr, Ac Gtr)*: 28 Gun Lane, Knebworth, Herts SG3 6BH ☎ 01438 812792

JOHNSON Laurie *(Gtr)*: 58 Westward Ho!, Leiston, Suffolk IP16 4HU ☎ 01728 832010

JOHNSON Wilko *(Gtr)*: 10 Clatterfield Gardens, Westcliffe-on-Sea, Essex SS0 0AX

JONES David *(E Gtr)*: 18 Seaton Road, Welling, Kent DA16 1DU ☎ 020 8303 3989

KING Steve *(Gtr, Kbds)*: 15 Colonailhurst Ave, Braintree, Essex CM7 2SL ☎ 01376 349300, 0589 742458 mob

KNIGHT Brian *(Gtr, Hmca, Voc, Sl Gtr)*: Millstream Works, Mill Road, Leighton Buzzard, Beds LU7 7AZ ☎ 01727 859270

KNOWLES John *(Gtr)*: 4 Rothmans Avenue, Chelmsford, Essex CM2 9UE ☎ 01245 476187, 01245 471544

LAW Tony *(Sp Gtr, Synth)*: 232 North Park Avenue, Norwich, Norfolk NR4 7ED ☎ 01603 470 554

LAWRENCE David *(E Gtr, Ac Gtr, Pf)*: Flat 2, 18 Saville Street, Walton-on-Naze, Essex CO14 8PL ☎ 01255 670030

LEE Nicholas *(Cl Gtr, E Gtr)*: Silverthorn Cottage, Latchford, Standon, Herts SG11 1QX ☎ 01920 823226

LEE Tony *(Gtr)*: 8 Westcliff Ave, Cromer, Norfolk NR27 9BA ☎ 01263 514423

LERSKI Holly *(Gtr)*: 61 Colegate, Queen Ann Yard, Norwich NR3 3AG ☎ 01603 763641 & fax

LEWIS Anthony *(Gtr, B Gtr)*: Myrtle Cottage, Angel Hill, Earl Stonham, Stowmarket IP14 5DP ☎ 01449 711528, 0589 338836 mob

LILLEY Tony *(Gtr, B Gtr, Kbds)*: 9 Redwood Drive, Wing, Leighton Buzzard, Beds LU7 0TA ☎ 01296 688451

LOBEL Ivor *(Gtr, Kbds, Flt)*

LYALL David *(Gtr)*: 49 Deacons Hill Road, Elstree, Herts WD6 3HZ ☎ 020 8953 3514

MACCOLL Calum *(Gtr, B Gtr, Kbds, Voc, Dul)*: 82 Chestnut Grove, New Malden, Surrey KT3 3JS ☎ 020 8942 4887, 0976 272139 mob

MACKMAN Richard *(Gtr, B Gtr, Ac Gtr)*: 96 Alma Road, Peterborough PE1 3AW ☎ 01733 890206

MACLEAN Grahame *(Gtr, Pf, Com)*: Button Snap, 44 Streetly End, West Wickham, Cambs CB1 6RP ☎ 01223 893920, 0850 805571

MARQUIS Alan *(Gtr, B Gtr, Kbds)*: 1A Melcombe Road, South Benfleet, Essex SS7 5NB ☎ 01268 754230

MARTIN David *(Gtr, Voc, B Gtr)*: 1 Lees Close, Hertford, Herts SG13 8HN

MARTIN Keith *(Gtr, B Gtr, Kbds, Voc)*: 4 Ayrton House, 115 Olive Avenue, Leigh-on-Sea, Essex SS9 3QB

MATHEWS Ray *(Gtr)*: Lambert Cottage, Old Oxford Road, Aston Rowant, Oxon OX9 5SB ☎ 01844 351346

MCDERMOTT Stuart *(E Gtr, B Gtr, Dms, Pf)*

MCGANN Steve *(Gtr, Pf)*: 1 West Road, Saffron Walden, Essex CB11 3DS ☎ 01799 500288, 01799 523049

MCKEW Roger *(Gtr)*: 14 East Street, Manea, Cambs PE15 0JJ ☎ 01354 688162

MEAD David *(Gtr)*: 23 Keymer Way, Lexden, Colchester, Essex CO3 5XJ ☎ 01206 710051

MEDLOCK Colin *(Gtr)*: 7 Alwin Close, Sawtry, Cambs PE17 5XH

MEX Paul *(Gtr, Synth)*: Lgff, 3 Eaton Place, Brighton, East Sussex BN2 1EH ☎ 01273 572090

MILLIGAN, LLCM(TD) Max *(Gtr, Voc, B Gtr, Arr, Cop)*: The Cottage, 5 Northill Road, Cople, Bedford MK44 3TU ☎ 01234 838880

MILNER Pascha *(Pl Gtr, Gtr, B Gtr)*: 4 Tuscan Court, Pakenham Close, Chesterton, Cambridge CB4 1PN ☎ 01223 361582

MIMPRESS Stephen *(Gtr)*: 187 Raphael Drive, Shoeburyness, Essex SS3 9UR ☎ 01702 295320

MITCHELL Samuel *(E Gtr)*: 12 Rudsdale Way, Colchester, Essex CO3 4LY ☎ 01206 544937

MOFFETT Gerald *(Gtr, B Gtr)*: 79 Potter Street, Harlow, Essex CM17 9AF ☎ 01279 412769

MOLES Derick *(Gtr, Synth, Dms)*: 18 Chapel Road, Stanway, Essex CO3 5PX ☎ 01206 544857

MOLONEY Will *(Gtr)*: 1 Wadham Road, Abbots Langley, Herts WD5 0NH ☎ 01923 467620

MONKS Barry *(Gtr, B Gtr, Pf)*: 6 Mill Way, Breachwood Green, Nr Hitchin, Herts SG4 8PE ☎ 01438 833696

MOODY Doog *(Gtr, B Gtr, Kbds)*: 44 Richmond Hill, Luton, Beds LU2 7JG ☎ 01582 418818

MORAN Oliver *(Gtr)*: 4 Stoneygate Road, Luton, Beds LU4 9TG ☎ 01582 591053

MYNOTT Stephen *(Gtr, Pl Gtr)*: 162 Denmark Road, Lowestoft, Suffolk NR32 2EL ☎ 01502 568684

NEALE Rebecca *(Gtr)*: 8 Radlett Road, Watford, Herts WD2 4LP ☎ 01923 464609, 01923 211182

NELSON *(Gtr, B Gtr, Man, Dms, Bjo)*: 6 Belmont Crescent, Colchester, Essex CO4 4LX ☎ 01206 841258

NICHOLS Bernie *(Gtr, Voc)*: 4 Arran Road, Stamford, Lincs PE9 2XP ☎ 01780 55944

NICKLIN Gary *(Ld Gtr, B Gtr, Rh Gtr, Voc)*: 3 Bedford Close, Tiptree, Essex CO5 0DB ☎ 01621 815423

OXENHAM Carol *(Gtr, Voc)*: 53 Gainsborough Rise, Manton Hights, Bedford MK41 7NS ☎ 01234 309337

PAGE Bryan *(Gtr, Voc, B Gtr, Kbds)*: 26 Boydin Close, Witham, Essex CM8 1PD ☎ 01376 519870, 0410 200571, 020 7691 7552

PARKER John *(Gtr)*: 24 Martin Road, Ipswich IP2 8BJ ☎ 01473 604574

PARLE Mike *(Gtr, Bjo, Vln)*: 73 City Road, Norwich NR1 3AS ☎ 01603 618109

PATON Roger *(Ac Gtr, Gtr, Wh)*: 4 Ascot Drive, Dogsthorpe, Peterborough PE1 4EA ☎ 01733 761769, 0966 118413

PAUL Stevie *(Gtr)*: 292 Brocklesmead, Harlow, Essex CM19 4QB ☎ 01279 453407, 01279 323199

PAVITT Richard *(Gtr)* ☎ 01371 820749

PEACHEY Derek *(Gtr, Voc)*: 4 Windermere Drive, Braintree, Essex CM7 8UA ☎ 01376 327547, 01376 553016

PITCHER Steven *(Gtr)*: 36B Marshland Street, Terrington, St. Clements, Kings Lynn, Norfolk PE34 4NE ☎ 01553 829746

PITKETHLY Stephen J *(Gtr, Voc, Pf, Kbds)*: High House, Welgate, Mattishall, Dereham, Norfolk NR20 3PL ☎ 01362 850364

PITT Tony *(Gtr, Bjo)*: 52 River Avenue, Hoddesdon, Herts EN11 0JU ☎ 01992 462811

PRIOR Matt *(Gtr)*: 4 Church View, Long Marston, Nr Tring, Herts HP23 4QB ☎ 01296 661340

PURKISS Darren *(Gtr, Kbds, Synth)*: 8A Middleborough, Colchester, Essex CO1 1QT ☎ 01206 575625

RANKIN Christian *(Gtr, B Gtr)*: 43 Rooktree Way, Haynes, Bedford MK45 3PT ☎ 01234 381461

REESIE *(Gtr, Kbds, Dms)*: 10 Woolpack Close, Dunstable, Beds LU6 3BF

REID Terry *(Gtr, Voc)*: 1A Hollyoaks, Rectory Road, Bluntisham, Huntingdon, Cambs PE17 3LN ☎ 01487 841364

REIGATE Nigel *(Gtr, Man, Per)*: 4 Womersley Close, Norwich, Norfolk NR1 4QD ☎ 01603 700417

REW Kimberley *(Gtr)*: 45 Belvoir Road, Cambridge CB4 1JH ☎ 01223 213328

RHENIUS Steve *(Gtr)*: Baythorne Cottage, Baythorne End, Halstead, Essex CO9 4AB ☎ 01440 785219, 01440 785087

RIDGELEY Andrew *(Gtr)*: LP&P Management Ltd, 1/6 Clay Street, London W1H 3FS ☎ 020 7486 4889, 020 7486 4885 fax

RIDOUT Mark *(Gtr)*: 71 Great Northern Road, Donstable, Beds LU5 4BW ☎ 01582 668783

RINGE Simon *(Gtr)*: 52 Heathgate, Hertford Heath, Herts SG13 7PJ ☎ 01992 582429

ROBINSON Michael *(Gtr)*: Longrow Farmhouse, Starlode Drove, West Pinchbeck, Spalding, Lincs PE11 3TD ☎ 01775 640 279, 0860 127917

ROSSI Christopher *(Gtr, Kbds)*: 112 Culver Rise, South Woodham Ferris, Chelmsford, Essex SM3 5WG ☎ 0403 669316

RULE-MINHINETT Ray *(E Gtr, Ac Gtr, Sl Gtr)*: The Vicarage, Church Lane, Aldenham, Herts WD2 8BE

RUNDLE Anthony *(Gtr, Voc, Ctna)*: 5 Mimram Close, Bendish Lane, Whitwell, Herts SG4 8HR ☎ 01438 871424

RYALL Nick *(Gtr, Flt)*: 195 Hig Street, Chesterton, Cambridge CB4 1NL ☎ 01223 461668

SADLER Chris *(Ac Gtr, Ctna, Wh)*: 58 Campfield Road, St. Albans, Herts AL1 5HZ ☎ 01727 847354 & fax

SALLOWS Gary *(Gtr)*: 4 Onehouse Lane, Ipswich, Suffolk IP1 4NH ☎ 01473 444 900, 0411 680262, 01473 210569

SAYERS Pete *(Ld Gtr, Bjo, Dobro, St Gtr, B)*: Rosewood House, Woodditton Road, Newmarket, Suffolk CB8 9BQ ☎ 01638 661801

SCHUELLER Michael *(Gtr, E Gtr, Ac Gtr, Cl Gtr, B)*: 6 Ekin Walk, Wadloes Road, Cambridge CB5 8PH ☎ 0973 841110 mob

SCOOBY *(Gtr, Kbds)*: 58 Margaret Reeve Close, Wymomdham, Norfolk NR18 0ST

SCOT Dale *(Gtr)*: 49 Lomond Road, Grovehill West, Hemel Hempstead, Herts HP2 6PB ☎ 01442 49081

SEDGE Charles *(Gtr, B Gtr, Bjo)*: 29 Millbank, Leighton Buzzard, Bedfordshire LU7 7AS ☎ 01525 373193

SELLARS Dale *(Gtr, Voc)*: Flat 4B Dene Side, Great Yarmouth, Norfolk NR30 2HL

SHEVLIN Tony James *(Gtr)*: 78 Constable Road, Ipswich, Suffolk IP4 2UZ ☎ 01473 287132

SKULSKI Michael *(E Gtr, Ac Gtr, Dms, Mrba)*

SLADE John *(Gtr, Kbds)*: 208 Fullers Road, Harlow, Essex CM17 9AX ☎ 01279 302 178

SLATER Nick *(Gtr)*: 10 Portland Place, Whittlesey, Peterborough PE7 1SB ☎ 01733 208486, 0976 776980 mob, 01733 208128

SLAUGHTER John *(Gtr)*: 7 Burdetts Court, Potton Sandy, Beds SG19 2LW ☎ 01767 260859

SLIDE Mark *(E Gtr)*: 20 Church Lane, Walton, Felixstowe, Suffolk IP11 9DJ ☎ 01394 210343

SMARTIE *(Gtr, Kbds)*: 21A Finchley Road, Westcliffe-on-Sea, Essex SS0 8AD ☎ 01702 436426

SMITH Benjamin *(Gtr, B Gtr, Db)*: 2 Flint Cottages, Church End, Barley, Royston, Herts SG8 8JR ☎ 01763 848561

SMITH Roy *(Gtr, B Gtr, Dms, Kbds)*: 105 Edgewood Drive, Luton LU2 8ER ☎ 01582 429103

SMITH Simon *(Gtr, Voc)*: 16 Newlyn Close, Symonds Green, Stevenage, Herts SG1 2JD ☎ 01438 317942

SMITH Timothy *(E Gtr, Ac Gtr)*: 33 Tuddenham Road, Ipswich, Suffolk IP4 2SN ☎ 01473 212001

SOLLORY Lee *(E Gtr, Cl Gtr)*: Address Unknown ☎ 01923 466513

SOSNER Adam *(Gtr)*: Address Unknown ☎ 020 8420 4909

SOUTH Charlotte *(Gtr, Pf, Clt, B Gtr, Dms)*: 43 Mousehold Lane, Sprowston, Norwich, Norfolk NR7 8HL ☎ 01608 424574

SPEARMAN Michael *(E Gtr, Ac Gtr)*: 24 Lisle Road, Colchester, Essex CO2 7SB ☎ 01206 511106

ST CLAIR Terry *(Gtr, Pf)*: 63 Drayton Road, Borehamwood, Herts WD6 2DA ☎ 020 8953 4546, 0958 660094, 020 8953 4546 fax

ST JOHN Raymond *(Gtr)*: 64 Southway, Totteridge, London N20 8DB

STACEY Neil *(Gtr)*: 15 Meadowbank, Kings Langley, Herts WD4 8EP ☎ 01923 261509

STEVENS Paul *(Gtr, Ac Gtr, Ld Gtr)*: 188 Baddow Road, Chelmsford CM2 9QW ☎ 01245 284643, 01621 851851 day

STEVENSON Jeremy *(Gtr)*: 108 Invicta Road, Stone, Kent DA2 6AZ ☎ 01322 273328

STEVENSON Paul *(Gtr)*: 34 Wellington Road, Eye, Suffolk IP23 7BE ☎ 01379 870172, 0374 689976 mob

STOKES Paul *(Gtr, Voc, Kbds)*: The Chase, Gull Road, Guyhirn, Wisbech PE13 4ER ☎ 01945 450450, 0410 819120 mob

SWANNELL Nicholas *(Gtr, B Gtr, Kbds)*: 46 Sandridge Road, St Albans, Herts AL1 4AS ☎ 01727 762192

SWEETLAND Simon *(E Gtr)* ☎ 01255 429693

TAYLOR Burton *(Gtr, Flt, Kbds)*: Hilltop Farm, Pipers Lane, Caddington, Luton, Beds LU1 4DS ☎ 01727 842790, 0958 584202

TAYLOR Donald *(Gtr)*: 12 Grosvenor Close, Tiptree, Essex CO5 0JN ☎ 01621 815923

TAYLOR Jay *(Gtr, Kbds, Per)*: 59 Wickham Wharf, Ware, Herts SG12 9PT ☎ 01920 461 450

TAYLOR Terence *(Gtr, Kbds)*: 344 Kings Road, London SW3 5UR

TEE Christopher *(Gtr, B Gtr, Pf)*: 76 Valley Walk, Croxley Green, Rickmansworth, Herts WD3 3TG ☎ 01923 239990, 0956 202249

THOMAS Michael *(Gtr)*: 49 Brookfurlong, Ravensthorpe, Peterborough, Cambs PE3 7LG ☎ 01733 330597

THOMPSON David *(Gtr, B Gtr, Kbds, Voc)*: 71 Glencoe Road, Bushey, Herts WD2 3DP ☎ 020 8421 8306, 020 8950 9539

THORNE Louis *(Gtr)*: 12 Thorpe Lea Road, Peterborough, Cambs PE3 ☎ 01733 64577

TOVEY Stephen *(Gtr, Voc)*: 19 Stanfield Close, Stanway, Colchester, Essex CO3 5QX ☎ 01206 331094

TYM Robert *(Gtr)*: 12 Belvedere Road, Burnham-on-Crouch, Essex CM0 8AJ ☎ 01621 783194

UTTING William *(Gtr, Dms, Kbds)*: 6 Drury Lane, Loddon, Norwich, Norfolk NR14 6LB ☎ 01508 528865

VELLACOTT Stephen *(Gtr)*: 14 Byfield Road, Papworth Everard, Cambridge CB3 8UQ ☎ 01480 830820

VON GUNTEN Timothy *(E Gtr, B Gtr)* ☎ 0702 522667 mob

WADE Natalie *(Gtr, Dms, Voc)*: 6 Gorse Close, Scarning, Dereham, Norfolk NR19 2UT ☎ 01362 690178

WALDIE Vernon *(Gtr, Voc)*: 23 Scrub Rise, Billericay, Essex CM12 9PG ☎ 01277 654487

WALKER Shelley *(Gtr, B Gtr, Voc, Kbds, Pf)*: 54 Stirling Close, Stevenage, Herts SG2 8TQ ☎ 01438 813964

WARD John *(Gtr, B Gtr, Pf, Hmca, Voc)*: 31 Rushmere Road, Carlton Colville, Lowestoft, Suffolk NR33 8DA ☎ 01502 588137

WARREN Phil *(Gtr, Voc)*: 25 Bruce Grove, Watford, Herts WD2 5AQ ☎ 01923 223589

WATERHOUSE Michael *(Gtr)*: 10 Hartop Close, Putnoe, Bedford MK41 8HE ☎ 01234 400915

WATKINSON Michael *(Gtr, Pf, Kbds)*: 102 Bower Street, Bedford MK40 3QZ ☎ 01234 364199

WATT-ROY Garth *(Gtr, B Gtr, Pf, Voc)*: 62 Sharpenhoe Road, Streatley, Luton LU3 3PS ☎ 01582 881673

WEAVER James *(Gtr, Man)*: 2 Willow Cottages, Mersea Road, Langenhoe, Colchester Essex CO5 7LF ☎ 01206 735773

WEBB Andrew *(Gtr)*: 72 Southend Road, Wickford, Essex SS11 8DU ☎ 01268 763006

WEBB Nicholas (*Ac Gtr, Cnt, Voc*): Pear Tree Farm, Ashfield, Stowmarket, Suffolk IP14 6NA ☎ 01728 685 427, 04325 106 369

WEBB Simon (*Ac Gtr, Hmca, Voc*): Peartree Farm, Ashfield, Stowmarket, Suffolk IP14 6NA ☎ 01728 685427

WELLER Andy (*Gtr, Pf*): 7 Bloomfield Drive, Shefford, Beds SG17 5BU ☎ 01462 628948, 0370 827979

WEST Peter (*Gtr*): 1 Elm Grove, Gammons Lane, Watford WD2 6BB ☎ 01923 462380

WHEELER Martin (*E Gtr, Ac Gtr, B Gtr*): 331 Stansteadroad, Hoddesdon, Herts EN11 0QW ☎ 01992 469194

WILD Peter (*Jz Gtr*): Bramley Lodge, Ryburgh Road, North Elmham, Dereham Norfolk NR20 5ES ☎ 01362 668558

WILLIAMS A (*Gtr, E Gtr*): 34 Chiswell Green Lane, Chiswell Green, St Albans, Herts AL2 3AN ☎ 01727 863121

WILLIAMS Christopher (*Gtr, Voc*): 95 Cotlandswick, London Colney, St Albans, Hertfordshire AL2 1EQ ☎ 01727 824932

WINN Stuart (*E Gtr*): 19 Chatsworth Court, Stevenage, Hertfordshire SG2 8DY ☎ 01438 724367

WINN Tony (*Rh Gtr, Ac Gtr, Bjo, Song W*): Treetops, 21 London Road, Kelvedon, Essex CO5 9AR ☎ 01376 571296

WONG Chris (*E Gtr, B Gtr, Dms, Per, Cl Gt*): 68 Maids Causeway, Cambridge CB5 8DD ☎ 01223 355806

WOODWARD Nigel (*Gtr, Voc, Dms*): 32 The Holdings, Hatfield, Herts AL9 5HQ ☎ 01707 275502

YOUNGS Robert (*Gtr*): 26 Elizabeth Watling Close, Thetford, Norfolk IP24 1TP ☎ 01842 753259, 0802 192517 mob

MIDLANDS

ADAMS John (*E Gtr, Man, Vln*)

ADCOCK Colin (*Gtr, Sax, Clt, Flt, Pic*): 91 Parkfield Drive, Castle Bromwich, Birmingham B36 9TJ ☎ 0121 749 3752

ADGIE Glyn (*Gtr*): Flat 2, 6 Grayfield Avenue, Moseley, Birmingham B13 9AD ☎ 0121 449 9711, 0121 765 4556

ALFORD Tim (*Gtr, Voc*): 5 Wheatley Grove, Chilwell, Nottingham NG9 5AG ☎ 0115 925 8954

ALGIE Ian (*E Gtr, Cl Gtr*): 18 Sudbury Street, Derby DE1 1LU ☎ 01332 340544

ARNOLD Peter (*Gtr, Bjo*): 6 Albert Road, Kings Heath, Birmingham B14 7HE ☎ 0121 444 0070

ARROWSMITH David (*E Gtr*): 59 Queen Street, Rusden, Northants NN10 0AY ☎ 01933 412262, 0421 091930

AUSTIN Adam (*Gtr, Dms, Kbds, B Gtr*): 21 Bracebridge Street, Nuneaton, Warwickshire CV11 5PA ☎ 024 7634 9068, 07971 381273

AUSTIN Lee (*Gtr*): 244 Bancroft, Glascote, Tamworth, Staffs B77 2EY ☎ 01827 51610

BACHE John (*Gtr*): 146 Enville Road, Kinver, Stourbridge, West Midlands DY7 6BL ☎ 01384 873589

BAILEY Ross (*Gtr*): 231 Alfreton Road, Underwood, Nottingham NG16 5GX ☎ 01773 860838 & fax, 0976 815622 mob

BAKER Frederick (*Gtr, B Gtr*): 39 Edinburgh Road, Newbold, Chesterfield, Derbyshire S41 7HF ☎ 01246 273414

BATE Geoffrey (*Gtr*): 80 Mosele Road, Bilston, West Midlands WV14 6JE

BATES Phil (*Gtr, Kbds*): Doleycanney Cottage, Newchurch, Kington, Herefordshire HR5 3QT ☎ 01497 851232

BEAUMONT Rick (*Gtr, Bjo, Kbds*): The Millhouse, Croft Hill Road, Huncote, Leicestershire LE9 6GR ☎ 0116 2865502, 0116 2849934

BECKER Peter (*Gtr*): 36 Richmond Road, Nuneaton CV11 5LT ☎ 024 7634 9009

BENNETT Adrian (*Cl Gtr, E Gtr, Kbds, Theramin*): 5 Listowel Road, Kings Heath, Brimingham B14 6HH ☎ 0121 444 6019

BERESFORD Ian (*Gtr, Synth, Voc*): 18 Moorhall, Bakewell, Derbyshire DE45 1FP ☎ 01629 814121

BIRCH John (*Gtr*): 14 Church Street, Wood Lane, Stoke-on-Trent ST7 8PE ☎ 01782 723266

BIRD Bobby (*Gtr*): PO Box 2703, Moseley, Birmingham B13 9BW ☎ 0121 248 2466, 0121 248 2477 fax

BIRD Richard (*Gtr*): 21 Birchfield Avenue, Markfield, Leicestershire LE67 9UF ☎ 01530 245004, 0410 267916, 01530 245004

BLACK Matthew (*Gtr, B Gtr, Pf*): Highdown House, Harbury Lane, Bishops Tachbrook, Leamington Spa, Warks CV33 9SA ☎ 01926 423216, 0403 760524

BLAISDON Jim (*Gtr, Tpt, Voc*): 72 Hunderton Road, Hereford HR2 7AP ☎ 01432 266613

BLANK Niklas (*Gtr*): 5 Greendale Close, Atherstone, Warwickshire CV9 1PR ☎ 01827 718315

BODENHAM Harry (*Gtr*): Silverdale, 4 Castle Grove, Kenilworth, Warwickshire CV8 1NF ☎ 01926 55775

BRAILSFORD Murray (*Gtr, B Gtr, Dms*): 22 Sun Street, Derby DE22 3UL ☎ 01332 368910

BRATTON Stephen (*Gtr, B Gtr*): Common Pitts House, Shrewsbury Road, Market Drayton, Shropshire TF9 3EP ☎ 01630 652559, 0976 553146, 01630 658461 fax

BRIGHTMORE Robert (*Cl Gtr*): 9 Elizabeth Road, Hinckley, Leics LE10 0QY

BROLLY Bob (*Gtr, Dms, Voc*): 122 Keresley Road, Keresley, Coventry, West Midlands CV6 2JE ☎ 024 7633 6773

BROOKS Andy (*Gtr, Kbds, Voc*): 6 Vincent Avenue, Stratford-upon-Avon, Warwickshire CV37 6SR ☎ 01789 293979

BURFORD Ian (*Ac Gtr, B Gtr, Synth*): 35 Elizabeth Close, Wellingborough, Northants NN8 2JA ☎ 01933 227412

BURGIN Lee (*E Gtr*): 25 The Green, Handsacre, Nr Rugeley, Staffs WS15 4DP ☎ 01543 490784, 0976 516414 mob, 01827 880563

BYERS Roddy (*Gtr*): 12 Cranford Road, Chappelfields, Coventry, West Midlands CV5 8JG ☎ 01203 70943

CAMPBELL Alistair (*Gtr*): c/o Dep International, 92 Fazeley Street, Birmingham B5 5RD ☎ 0121 633 4742

CAMPBELL Robin (*Gtr*): Fernscan Limited, No.1. Andover Street, Digbeth, Birmingham B5 5RG ☎ 0121 633 4742

CARDALL Ralph (*Gtr, B Gtr, Dms*): 4 Philip Sidney Road, Sparkhill, Brimingham B11 4HY ☎ 0121 449 3732

CARLOSS Adrian (*Gtr, Voc*): 23 Crescent Road, Kidderminster, Worcs DY11 6RW ☎ 01562 861440

CARMEN (*Gtr, Voc*): 19 Tudor Road, Moseley, Birmingham B13 8HA ☎ 0121 449 9255, 0121 377 6056 fax

CARROLL David (*Gtr, Vln*): 66 Cambridge Road, Birmingham, West Midlands B13 9UD ☎ 0121 444 3472

CARTER Peter (*Rh Gtr, Dms, Bjo, Arr, Sax*): 58 The Dell, Woodston, Peterborough, Cambs PE2 9QE ☎ 01733 343552

CARTER Trevor (*Gtr, Ctna, Rec, Kbds*): 82 Uttoxeter Road, Blyth Bridge, Stoke-on-Trent ST11 9JG ☎ 01782 398657

CARTWRIGHT Danny (*Gtr*): 2 Meadow Drive, Keyworth, Nottingham NG12 5EE ☎ 0115 937 5175

CASHMORE Catherine (*Cl Gtr*): 36 Howes Lane, Finham, Coventry CV3 6PJ ☎ 024 7641 1382

CASTLE Peter (*Gtr, Voc*): 190 Burton Road, Derby DE1 1TQ ☎ 01332 346399

CEBULA Andy (*Gtr*): 19 College Street, Wellingborough, Northamptonshire NN8 3HF ☎ 01933 771524, 01933 771556

CHAMBERS Howard (*Gtr*): ☎ 0121 682 59999, 0976 579771 mob

CHENHALL Nicholas (*Gtr, Kbds*): 144 Alvechurch Road, West Heath, Birmingham B31 3PW ☎ 0121 475 4617

CHRISTIE Julian (*Gtr*): 24 North Street, Nuneaton CV10 8BL ☎ 0836 641642

CIVIL Paul (*Gtr, Kbds*): 39 Eversleigh Road, Coundon, Coventry, West Midlands CV6 2BE ☎ 024 7633 6256

CLARKE Allan (*Gtr, Voc*): 3 Roade Hill, Ashton, Northampton, Northamptonshire NN7 2JJ

CLEMO Dave (*Gtr, Man, B Gtr*): 69 Brambleside, Kettering, Northants NN16 9DP ☎ 01536 524032

CLEVERLEY Nicholas (*Gtr*): 17 Abbots Road, Kings Heath, Birmingham 14 B14 7QD ☎ 0121 444 3771

COLLETT Andrew (*Gtr*): 11 Hawthorn Croft, Oldbury, West Midlands B68 0DP ☎ 0121 422 2152

COOLING Mike (*Gtr, Kbds, B Gtr, Voc*): 32 Charles Street, Headless Cross, Redditch B97 5AA ☎ 01527 547148

COOMBS Dominic *(Gtr, B Gtr)*: 3 Loddon Close, Melton Mowbray, Leics LE13 0EZ ☎ 01664 568334

COOPER Neville *(Cl Gtr, Lute, Rec)*: 115 Stanley Road, Hinckley, Leics LE10 0HR ☎ 01455 615538

COX Andrew *(Gtr)*: Clement Keys, Nettleton House, Calthorpe Road, Edgbaston, Birmingham B15 1RL

COX Jonathan *(Ld Gtr, Ac Gtr)*: 9 Adelphi Close, Heatherton Village, Littleover, Derby DE23 7XJ ☎ 01332 516242

CRADOCK Stephen *(Gtr)*: c/o Suite 17, Jago House, 692 Warwick Road, Solihull, W. Mids B91 3DA ☎ 0121 605 8448

CREHAN Derek *(Gtr, B Gtr, Kbds)*: 28 Edgware Road, Bulwell, Nottingham NG6 9HW ☎ 0115 9750932

CRUICKSHANK Barbara *(Gtr, Pf, Acc)*: 25 Grafton Street, Coventry CV1 2HX ☎ 024 7622 0562 & fax

CURTIS Simon *(Gtr)*: 15 South Walk Close, Lichfield, Staffs WS13 7SH ☎ 01543 263285

DAGGER Robert *(Gtr, Ac Gtr, E Gtr)*: The White House, Pratts Lane, Mappleborough Green, Studley, Warks B80 7BN ☎ 01527 852632

DALE Dave *(Gtr, Man)*: 52 Hunton Road, Erdington, Birmingham B23 6AH ☎ 0121 628 9343

DANGERFIELD Christopher *(Gtr)*: 11 The Woodlands, Haden Hill, Cradley Heath, West Midlands B64 7JY ☎ 0121 501 1211

DAVENPORT Neil *(Gtr)* ☎ 0116 276 3351

DAVID Andrew *(Gtr, Per, Kbds)*: 18 Montgomery Road, Up Hatherley, Cheltenham, Gloucestshire GL5 5LB ☎ 01242 694301

DAVIES Neol *(Gtr)*: 18 Paradise House, Eden Street, Paradise, Coventry CV6 5HG ☎ 01206 664967

DAVIES Trevor *(Gtr)*: 87 Etnam Street, Leominster, Herefordshire HR6 8AE ☎ 01568 613 611

DAVIS Lester *(Gtr, B Gtr, Dms, Voc)*: Pear Tree House, 8 Albert Road, Erdington, Birmingham B23 7IT ☎ 0121 350 0342

DAVIS Stan *(Gtr, E Gtr, Jz Gtr, B Gtr)*: 7 Castle Drive, Willenhall, West Midlands WV12 4QY ☎ 01902 607457, 07970 967734 mob

DAVISON Max *(Gtr, B Gtr, E Gtr)*: 6 Henley Place, Malvern, Worcs WR14 1PG ☎ 01684 563605

DEAVALL Dean *(Gtr, Kbds, Voc, B Gtr, Dms)*: 41 Glen Ore Drive, Kings Norton, Birmingham B38 8YR ☎ 0121 451 4127

DECAMBRE Ralford *(Gtr)*: 57 Beach Road, Sparkhill, Birmingham B11 4PG ☎ 0121 773 0518

DEE Joey *(Gtr, Kbds, Dms)*: 55 Ermine Road, Rectory Farm, Northampton NN3 5ES ☎ 0958 629774

DEGVILLE Paul *(Gtr)*: 63, Brinkburn Grove, Banbury, Oxon OX16 7WX ☎ 01295 252687

DELGARDO Sandie *(Gtr, Kbds)*: The Cottage, 14 St Marys Road, Leamington Spa, Warwickshire CV31 1JW ☎ 01926 882000

DENNISON Jeffery *(Gtr, Mando, Bzk, Man)*: The Moorings, 50 Grove Road, Ansty, Nr Coventry CV7 9UE ☎ 024 7661 5582 & fax

DERRIG Sean *(Gtr)* ☎ 01604 231873

DILLETT Ross *(Gtr, B Gtr, Dms, Voc)*: 45 Sneyd Terrace, Silverdale, Newcastle Under Lyme, Staffordshire ST5 6JF ☎ 01782 621562

DINGLEY-JONES Jonathan *(Gtr, E Gtr)*: 75 Monteagle Drive, Charterfield, Kingswinford, West Midlands DY6 7RY ☎ 01384 350465

DOBSON Richard *(Gtr)* ☎ 01276 476676

DODD Julian *(Gtr, Kbds, Sax)*: 1 Benton Crescent, Bloxwich, Walsall WS3 3AH ☎ 01922 475259

DOWNING Kenneth *(Gtr)*: c/o Newman & Co, Regent House, 1 Pratt Mews, London NW1 0AD ☎ 020 7267 6899

DOWNS Stephen *(Gtr)*: 45 Bramble Ridge, Bridgnorth, Shropshire WV16 4SQ ☎ 01746 765268

DUFFY Stephen *(Gtr, Dms, Hmca, Org, B Gtr)*: PO Box 2, Bromyard, Herefordshire HR7 4UU ☎ 01432 820389

EARDLEY Ian *(Gtr)*: 204 Dimsdale Parade West, Newcastle Under Lyme, Staffordshire ST5 8EA ☎ 01782 562583, 0976 324080 mob

ELLIS Antony *(Gtr, Pf)*

ELSE Gareth *(Ld Gtr, B Gtr)*: 'Orchard House', 102 High Street, Stonebroom, Alfreton, Derby DE55 6JY ☎ 01773 873629

ESPOSITO Giovanni *(Gtr, Voc)*: 107 Cliff Rock Road, Rednal, Birmingham B45 8QF ☎ 0121 453 3093

EVANS Keith *(Ac Gtr)*: 27 Lindridge Road, Stockland Green, Birmingham B23 7HU ☎ 0121 373 4354

EVANS Stuart *(E Gtr, B Gtr, Dms)*: 2 Heather Valley, Hednesford, Staffs WS12 5TA ☎ 01543 424190, 0831 704 192

EYRES David *(Gtr)*: 4 Brougham Square, Belle Vue, Shrewsbury SY3 7PE ☎ 01743 360556

FASEY Paul *(Gtr)*: 1 Oaks Drive, Wombourne, Nr Wolverhampton, West Midlands WV5 0LA ☎ 01902 894393

FEENEY Michael *(Gtr)*: 759 Yardley Wood Road, Kings Heath, Birmingham B13 0PT ☎ 0121 443 4709

FINNEY Stephen *(Gtr, B Gtr)*: 33 Homer Street, Hanley, Stoke-on-Trent, Staffs ST1 3NZ ☎ 01782 264195

FLEAY Robert *(Gtr, Tpt, Pf, Bjo, Hmca)*: 124 Mansfield Road, Chester Green, Derby DE1 3RA ☎ 01332 603753

FOAD Paul *(Gtr)*: 1 Sefton Road, Edgbaston, Birmingham B16 8DR ☎ 0121 454 2570

FOSSEY Robert *(Ac Gtr)*: 8 Roche Close, Plains Estate, Arnold, Nottingham NG5 6RY ☎ 0115 956 9731

FOSTER Anthony *(Gtr, B Gtr, Kbds, Voc)*: 14 Cairo Street, New Basford, Nottingham NG7 7GH ☎ 07970 645441

FREETH Naomi *(Gtr, Pf, Flt, Hmca, Cel)*: 5 Kilby Court, 29-31 Brunswick Street, Leamington Spa CV31 2EB

FRISBY Mark *(Gtr, Voc, Man, Hmca)*: 42 Burton Road, Melton Mowbray, Leicestershire LE13 1DJ ☎ 0402 433448

GABBIDON Basil *(Gtr, Voc)*: 34 Clent Road, Handsworth, Birmingham B21 8DJ ☎ 0121 554 4293, 0411 254896, 0121 681 8455

GARBETT Byron *(Gtr, Kbds)*: 6 Ruchbury Close, Hawthorne Billage, Bilston WV14 0UH ☎ 01902 498825

GARNER Tyrone *(Gtr)*: 25 Wood Street, Mansfield, Notts NG18 1QB

GAUNTLETT Neil R *(Gtr, Pd Gtr, St Gtr)*: 67 Buckingham Street, Wolverton, Milton Keynes, Bucks MK12 5JB ☎ 01908 225676

GAYTTEN Robert *(Gtr)*: 28 Station Road, Great Wyrley, Walsall, West Midlands WS6 6LQ ☎ 01922 419493

GEE Barrington *(Gtr, Voc)* ☎ 0956 477548

GERRARD James *(Gtr)*: 46 Wendover Rise, Allesley Park, Coventry CV5 9JU ☎ 024 7667 4017

GILKES Max *(Cl Gtr, E Gtr, B Gtr)*: 21 High Road, Solbury, Leighton Buzzard, Beds LU7 0BT ☎ 01280 822673

GILL Chris *(Gtr)*: 67 Trejon Road, Cradley Heath, Warley, West Midlands B64 7HJ ☎ 01384 64072

GILLOTT Andrew *(Gtr, B Gtr, Kbds)*: Flat 2 12 Douglas Road, Nottingham NG7 1NW ☎ 0115 9859019, 0403 540400

GITTENS Allister *(Ac Gtr, E Gtr)*: 23 Kings Hill, Kempsey, Worcester WR5 3LJ ☎ 01905 821832

GODFREY Jonathan *(Cl Gtr)*: 18 West Malvern Road, Malvern, Worcs WR14 4NA ☎ 01684 893414

GOMM Ian *(Gtr)*: Caradoc House, Broad Street, Llanfair Caereinion, Powys SY21 0RQ ☎ 01938 810205

GOODLAD Gary *(Gtr)*: 97 Hyperion Road, Stourton, Stourbridge, West Mids DY7 6SJ ☎ 01384 375023

GORDON Carole *(Gtr, Pf, Voc)*: High Tree Cottage, Prince Hold Road, Lower Way, Thatcham, Berks RG19 3TH ☎ 016358 62822, 0860 238946, 01538 306227

GRAHAM Gary *(Gtr, Kbds, Dms, B Gtr)*: 6 Clarence Road, Handsworth, Birmingham B21 3RR ☎ 0121 240 9331

GRANA Alvaro *(Gtr, Pan Pf, Quena, Charango,)*: Address Unknown ☎ 024 7671 5594

GREENHALGH Darrell *(Gtr)*: 21 Inns Lane, South Wing Field, Derbyshire DE55 7LW ☎ 01773 520671

GRIFFITHS Alan *(Gtr)*: 31 Rose Street, Northwood, Stoke-on-Trent ST1 6PH ☎ 01782 870860

GRIFFITHS Mark *(Gtr, Db)*: 43 Falcutt Way, Northampton NN2 8NR ☎ 01604 845319

HAINES Philip *(Gtr, Bod, Dms)*: 5 Cashmore Road, Kenilworth, Warwickshire CV5 2SJ ☎ 0370 626379 mob

HALL Richard *(Gtr, Dms)*: 12 Grange Road, Hugglescote, Coalville, Leicester LE67 2BQ ☎ 01530 832557

HANCOCK Peter *(Gtr, Bjo, Uke)*: 1 Buxton Old Road, Buglawton, Congleton, Cheshire CW12 2ES ☎ 01260 270891

HAND Jonathan (*Gtr, B Gtr, Kbds, Voc*): 8A High Street, Eccleshall, Stafford ST21 6BZ ☎ 01785 851573

HARDING Brian (*Gtr, B Gtr*): 131 The Drive, Phippsville, Northampton NN1 4SW ☎ 01604 711584

HARPER Rob (*Gtr, B Gtr, Voc*): Flat 6 Greenland Court, 293 Washwood Heath Road, Birmingham B8 2XU ☎ 0121 326 0041

HARRIS Peter (*Gtr, E Gtr, Ac Gtr, B Gtr, Kb*): 14 Washington Drive, Birmingham B20 2LR ☎ 0121 515 2278, 07957 242 371

HARRISON Julian (*Gtr*): 28 Cherry Tree Avenue, Belper, Derbyshire DE56 1FR ☎ 01773 823393

HART Jason (*Gtr, B Gtr, Pf, Voc*): 10 Marshall Street, Sherwood, Nottingham NG5 4AF ☎ 0115 952 2119

HARVEY Benjamin (*Gtr*): Rose Villa, 22 The Green, Cheadle, Stoke-on-Trent, Staffordshire ST10 1PH ☎ 01538 752978

HASTINGS Simon (*Gtr, Vla*): 51 Causeway, Rowley Regis B65 8AA ☎ 0121 532 9108

HAWKESFORD Roy (*Gtr, Sax*): 1 Brook Court, Horton, Northampton NN7 2BL

HAYES Charles (*Ac Gtr, E Gtr*): 4 Stratford Drive, Wootton, Northampton NN4 6JT ☎ 01604 761335

HELM Nicholas (*Gtr, B Gtr*): 64 Marston Road, Stafford, Staffs ST16 3BL ☎ 01785 602460

HEMMINGS Karl Eric (*Gtr*) ☎ 01782 715267, 0467 640381

HEWIN Simon (*Gtr, B Gtr, Kbds, Vln, Dms*): The Hollies, Hints Road, Hopwas, Tamworth, Staffs B78 3AB ☎ 01827 64832

HILL Jason (*Gtr, Bjo, Mldn, Hrp*): 54 Price Street, Burslem, Stoke-on-Trent ST6 4EN ☎ 01782 813401

HINDS David (*Gtr, Voc, Per*): 179 The Broadway, Perry Barr, Birmingham B20 3EP

HINE Keith (*Gtr, Org*): 4 Colledge Close, Brinklow, Rugby, Warwickshire CV23 0NT ☎ 01788 832320

HINES Gavin (*Ld Gtr, Rh Gtr*): Flat 31 Chad Square, Hawthorne Road, Edgbaston, Birmingham B15 3TQ ☎ 0121 454 2690

HINES Robert (*Gtr, Man*): 37 Baker Avenue, Ashby-De-La-Zouch, Leicester LE65 2PB ☎ 01530 413010

HODGKINS Tim (*Gtr, B Gtr, Pf, Kbds*): The Croft, Whateley Green, Castle Bromwich, Birmingham B36 0AH ☎ 0121 747 4284

HOLLINSHEAD Anji (*Cl Gtr*) ☎ 01782 861370, 0374 465195

HOOPER Chris (*Gtr, Dms, Pf*): More Hall, Brockton, Much Wenlock, Shropshire TF13 6JU ☎ 01746 785604, 07970 110531, 01746 785583

HOPKINS Christopher (*Gtr, Man*): 80 Knighton Lane, Aylestone, Leicester LE2 8BE ☎ 0116 283 1927

HUGHES Robin (*Gtr, Kbds*): 27 Corbett Road, Hollywood, Worcs B47 5LP ☎ 0121 474 2183

HUGHES Timothy (*E Gtr, Cl Gtr*): 16 Spring Street, Rugby, Warwickshire CV21 3HH ☎ 01788 576674

HUNT Barry (*Gtr, Bzk, Bjo, Man, Kbds*): 156 Gillway Lane, Tamworth, Staffs B79 8PW ☎ 01827 52470 & fax, 0966 474796 mob

HUTCHINSON Mark (*Gtr, Voc*): 11 Hollowbank, Moulton Leys, Northampton NN3 7HQ ☎ 01604 643 382

HYDE Martin (*Gtr, Kbds*): 114 Drewry Lane, Derby DE22 3QU ☎ 01332 361306

HYDE Peter (*Gtr*): 7 Herbert Road, Bearwood, West Midlands B67 5DD ☎ 0121 429 4450, 0121 414 6693, 0121 414 3553

HYLAND Colin (*Gtr, Pf*): 42 Hallfields, Edwalton, Nottingham NG12 4AA ☎ 0115 974 4013

JAMES Ivor (*Gtr*): 8 Weir Bank, Stapenhill, Burton-on-Trent, Staffs DE15 9RB ☎ 01283 40220

JAMES Robert (*Gtr*): 46 Longwood Rise, Shortheath, Willenhall, West Midlands WV12 4AX ☎ 01902 635980

JAMES Spencer (*Gtr, Kbds, Voc*): 23 Nightingale Drive, Towcester, Northants NN12 7RA ☎ 01327 51969

JAMES Thomas (*Gtr, St Gtr, B Gtr*): 25 Brockhurst Avenue, Burbage, Hinckley, Leicestershire LE10 2HG ☎ 01455 618197, 0378 146459

JENKINSON Andrew (*Gtr, B Gtr*): 21 Stour Close, Oadby, Leicester LE2 4GE ☎ 0116 271 7882

JOHN Clive (*Gtr, Kbds, B Gtr, Dms, Hmca*): 57-59 Court Road, Malvern, Worcestershire WR14 3BS ☎ 0168 437 2074, 0585 639926 mob

JOHN Malcolm (*Gtr, Kbds*): 1 Mayflower Road, Daisy Farm Estate, Newthorpe, Nottingham NG16 2DA ☎ 01773 719164

JOHNSON Holly (*Gtr, Pf, Flt*): 8 St Peters Road, Harborne, Birmingham B17 0AS

JOHNSTON Gary (*Gtr, Voc*): 27 Ladymead Drive, Whitmore Park, Coventry CV6 4FJ ☎ 024 7668 0567

JONES Robert (*Gtr*): 1 Porch Farm Cottage, Weston Under Penyard, Ross-on-Wye, Herefordshire HR9 7PG ☎ 01989 767058

JOYCE Michael (*Gtr*): 12. Hall Street, Oldswinford, Stourbridge, West Midlands DY8 2JE ☎ 01384 371806

JUSTICE James (*Gtr, Kbds*): 1 Foxglove Close, Four Pools, Evesham WR11 6YU ☎ 01386 41767

KEARNS Paul (*Gtr*): 323 Jockey Road, Sutton Coldfield, West Midlands B73 5XE ☎ 0121 355 4026

KEEN Maxwell (*Gtr, B Gtr, Dms, Kbds*)

KEEN Peter (*Gtr*): 6 Little Grebe Road, Kidderminster, Worcs DY10 4AF ☎ 01562 745895

KELSEY Lisa (*Gtr*): 16 Cole Valley Road, Hall Green, Birmingham B28 0DB

KENT Andrew (*Gtr, B Gtr*): 2 Gisborne Crescent, Allestree, Derby DE22 2FL ☎ 01332 557812

KIRKHAM Natham (*E Gtr, Voc, Ac Gtr, Cl Gtr, B*): 4 Redwing Drive, Biddulph, Stoke-on-Trent, Staffs ST8 7UA ☎ 01782 523950

KIRKLEY Lisa (*Gtr*): 2 Holt Terrace, Holt Lane, Matlock, Derbyshire DE4 3LY ☎ 01629 581005

KULESZA Andrew (*Gtr, Dms, B Gtr, Kbds, Pf*) ☎ 0115 925 7567, 07970 170980

LAKE Greg (*Gtr*): 91 Park Lane, Wednesbury WS10 9PT ☎ 0121 502 4406

LAYTON Stephen (*Gtr, Bjo*): 24 Orwell Drive, West Heath, Birmingham B38 8HZ ☎ 0121 476 5398

LEE Mikey (*E Gtr, A Sax, B Gtr*): 38 Deane Road, Hillmorton, Rugby CV21 4NY ☎ 01788 576756

LEES Simon (*Gtr, Dms*): 34 Strathmore Crescent, Wombourbne, Wolverhampton, West Midlands WV5 9AS ☎ 01902 896920

LEVENTHAL Alex (*Gtr, B Gtr, Kbds, Dms*): 26 Fowgay Drive, Solihull, West Midlands B91 3PH ☎ 0121 705 7904, 07801 985076, 0121 704 0737

LEWIS Andrew (*Gtr, Pf, Kbds*) ☎ 01922 477566

LEWIS Gary (*Gtr, Kbds*): 11 Johnson Close, Darlaston, Wednesbury, West Midlands WS10 7HS

LINDAHL Mike (*Gtr, B Gtr, Voc*): 9 South Street, Long Eaton, Notts NG10 1ER ☎ 0115 9726409

LISTER Aynsley (*Gtr*): 27 Queensmead Close, Groby, Leicester LE6 0YP ☎ 0116 231 3958, 0116 287 1414

LITTLEDYKE Sion (*Gtr, B Gtr, Kbds*): 13 Harwin Road, Leicester LE5 6EF ☎ 0116 273 9396

LLOYD Vin (*Gtr, Voc*): 56 North Street, Stoke, Coventry CV2 3FW ☎ 024 7644 2468

LORAINE Josey (*Gtr*): 104 Park Road, Rugby, Warwickshire CV21 2QX ☎ 01788 540775

LORD Charlie (*Gtr, Dms, Kbds, B Gtr*): 10 Sydney Terrace, Newark, Notts NG24 4DB ☎ 01636 708756

LUKE Dave (*Gtr, Voc*): 2, Maes-Yr-Afon, Knighton, Powys, Wales LD7 1NQ ☎ 01547 560 363

LUND Richie (*Gtr, B Gtr*): 33 Mill Meadow, Tenbury Wells, Worcestershire WR15 8HX ☎ 01584 811500

MACLEOD James Andrew (*E Gtr, Ac Gtr, Voc, B Gtr*): 8 Lincoln Croft, Shenstone, Lichfield, Staffs WS14 0ND ☎ 01543 480262

MALONEY Stephen (*Gtr, Bzk, Man, H Dul*) ☎ 01827 282592

MARPLES David (*E Gtr, Ac Gtr, Cl Gtr, B Gtr*) ☎ 01564 773479

MARTIN Peter (*Gtr*): 8 Manor Farm Close, Broughton Astley, Leicester LE9 6PZ ☎ 01455 283909, 0958 421027

MASON Alan (*Gtr*): 19 Streather Road, Four Oaks, Sutton Coldfield, W. Mids B75 6RB ☎ 0121 308 3992

MATTHEWS Phil (*Gtr, B Gtr*): 8 Stanstead Road, Mickleover, Derby DE3 5PP ☎ 01332 519301

MATTS Paul (*E Gtr, Ac Gtr, B Gtr*): 23 Oxford Street, Syston, Leicester LE7 2AT ☎ 0116 2697036

MAYER Michael (*Pd Gtr, Cl Gtr*): 17, Dorsett Road Terrace, Darlaston, West Midlands WS10 8TP ☎ 0121 526 6505

MCALINDON William *(Gtr)*: 184 Deeble Road, Kettering, Northants NN15 5HW ☎ 01536 523663, 01536 523663

MCCLEAN James *(Gtr, Ac Gtr)*: 42, Binley Close, Shirley, Solihull, West Midlands B90 2RD ☎ 0121 744 9964, 0121 766 5006 day

MCCUTCHEON Ian *(Gtr, B Gtr)*: 15 Armstrong Close, South Farm, Whitnash, Leamington Spa CV31 2RA ☎ 01926 882762, 01926 88722 ext 219

MCGOUNDEN Mark *(Gtr, Voc)* ☎ 01902 601370, 0411 487272

MCLEOD Alex *(Gtr, Dms, B Gtr, Kbds)*: 33 Cox Drive, Bottesford, Notts NG13 0DJ ☎ 01949 843024

MELLOR Martyn *(E Gtr, Ac Gtr)*: 29A Poplar Avenue, Kings Heath, Birmingham B14 7AA ☎ 0121 441 4240

MEYRICK Robert *(Gtr)*: 35 Albert Road, Lenton, Nottingham NG7 2EX ☎ 0115 9783436

MILLER Ruth *(Gtr, Voc)*: c/o Rutland Records, P.O.Box 132, Leicester LE2 0QU ☎ 0116 288 4207

MILLS Vincent *(E Gtr, B Gtr)*: 18 Bach Mill Drive, Hall Green, Birmingham B28 0XN ☎ 0121 474 6378

MITCHELL Andy *(Gtr, Man, Com, Con)*: 51 Victoria Court, Leicester Road, Oadby, Leicester LE2 4AG ☎ 0116 271 0119

MORGAN Stewart *(Gtr, Dms)*

MORLEY Paul *(Gtr, B Gtr)*: 10 Stubbsfield Road, Newcastle Under Lyme, Staffordshire ST5 1NR ☎ 01782 615903

MORRISON Daniel *(Gtr, Dms)* ☎ 01604 831136

MULDOON Joseph *(Gtr, B Gtr)*: 270 Hob Moor Road, Small Heath, Birmingham B10 9HH ☎ 0121 784 4273

MURPHY Paul *(Gtr, Pf)*: 35 Northfield Road, Kings Norton, Birmingham B30 1JD ☎ 0121 433 4107, 0121 771 0090

NAGI Ram *(Gtr, Voc, Kbds, B Gtr, Dms)*: 63 Wanders Avenue, Blakenhall, Wolverhampton WV2 3HL ☎ 01902 336318, 0973 189026, 01902 620473

NEALE Simon *(Ac Gtr, E Gtr, Kbds)*: 31 Greenheath Road, Hednesford, Cannock, Staffordshire WS12 4AR ☎ 07970 796438

NELSON James *(E Gtr, Ld Gtr, Rh Gtr, B Gtr)*: 65 Taylor Road, Kings Heath, Birmingham B13 0PB ☎ 0121 441 5630

NELSON Phil *(Gtr, Synth)*: 27 St Edita's Road, Polesworth, Tamworth, Staffs B78 1LB ☎ 01827 893093

NEWMAN Bob *(Gtr, B Gtr, Vln, Voc)*: High Tree Cottage, Prince Hold Road, Lower Way, Thatcham, Berks RG19 3TH ☎ 01635 862822, 0860 238946, 01538 306227

NOLAN Robin *(Gtr)*: Hillcrest, 1 Homer Much Wemlock, Salop, Shropshire TF13 6ND ☎ 01952 728 554

NOLTE Thorsten *(Gtr, Voc, Pf)*: Flat 1 Ashbourne House, 2/4 Ascot Road, Moseley, Birmingham B13 9EL ☎ 0121 449 7281, 0121 452 2158, 0121 454 7004

O'CONNOR Iain *(Gtr)*

O'TOOLE Steve *(Gtr)*: 31A Bishop Street, Mansfield, Notts NG18 1HJ ☎ 01623 652 533, 01623 442962 fax

OSBORNE Andrew *(Gtr, Voc, Kbds, Vln)*: 2 Moray Square, Mansfield, Nottinghamshire NG19 6RS ☎ 01623 649134

OTHEN Simon *(Gtr, Pf)*: 30 Foxwell Street, Worcester WR5 2EP ☎ 01905 354072

OVERON Geoff *(Gtr, B Gtr, Voc)*: 12 Somerville Road, Leicester LE3 2ET ☎ 0116 289 1919

PARKER Christopher *(Gtr, B Gtr)*: 308 Acre Lane, Northampton NN2 8PY ☎ 01604 843536

PATRUCCI Bret *(Gtr)*: 315 Bucks Hill, Stockingford, Nuneaton CV10 9LD

PATTERSON John *(Gtr, Bjo, Mando)*: 58 The Fleet, Stoney Stanton, Leicester LE9 4DY ☎ 0116 2864330

PEAT Michael *(Gtr, Man, Mldn)*: Woodland View, Kirkham Lane, Fritchley, Derbyshire DE56 SFS ☎ 01773 853428

PEGG Bev *(Gtr, Voc, Bjo, B Gtr, Man)*: Burford House, 11 South Road, Hagley, Stourbridge, West Midlands DY9 0JT ☎ 01562 882293, 01384 560601, 0836 677234

PEGG Jon *(Gtr)*: 67 St.Thomas Road, Erdington, Birmingham B23 7RQ ☎ 0121 373 9052

PENNY Robert *(Gtr, Pf, Kbds, Vln)*: 62 New Henry Street, Oldbury, West Midlands B68 8RQ ☎ 0121 544 6751, 0966 158588

PERKINS Brian *(Cl Gtr, Lute)*: 58 Wakeley Hill, Penn, Wolverhampton WV4 5RB ☎ 01902 333237

PHILLIPS Paul *(Gtr, Voc)*: 151 Walmley Road, Sutton Coldfield, West Midlands B76 1PX ☎ 0121 351 1574

PIERZCHALLA Max *(Gtr)*: 11 East Grove, Meir, Stoke-on-Trent, Staffs ST3 5PG ☎ 01782 318671

POTTER John *(Gtr)*: 399 Yardley Road, Yardley, Birmingham B25 8NB ☎ 0121 603 8672, 07771 878842

POTTS Raymond *(Cl Gtr, E Gtr, Flt)*: 35 Jubilee Gardens, Nantwich, Cheshire CW5 7BS ☎ 01270 627067

POWELL Clive *(Gtr)*: 22 Joyberry Drive, Oldswinford, Stourbridge, West Midlands DY8 ☎ 01384 371105

PREECE Pip *(T/A PipkinMusic)* *(Gtr, Man)* ☎ 0966 545374

PRICE Ian *(Gtr, B Gtr, Voc, Kbds)*: 115 Park Farm Road, Great Barr, Birmingham B43 7QJ ☎ 0121 360 8225

PRIEST Hoodlum *(Gtr, B Gtr, Kbds)*: 38 Lee Crescent, Birmingham B15 2BJ

REED Roger *(Gtr, B Gtr, Dms)*: 1 Wentworth Gate, Harborne, Birmingham B17 9EA ☎ 0121 426 5103

REEVES Danielle *(Cl Gtr, Bjo)*: 36 Merrivale Road, Bearwood, Warley, West Midlands B66 4EJ ☎ 0121 429 5500

REHMI Jived *(Gtr, B Gtr)*: 27 Stratford Street, Sparkhill, Birmingham B11 4RH ☎ 0121 772 0787

RHEAD David *(Gtr, Voc, Mando, B Gtr)*: 3 Daintry Street, Leek, Staffs ST13 5PG ☎ 01538 385260

RICHARDS John *(Gtr, Cl Gtr, Man, Bjo, B Gtr)*: Musicians Union, Benson House, Lombard Street, Birmingham B12 0QN ☎ 0141 647 1806, 07970 424785

RICHARDS Peter *(Gtr, Kbds)*: 256 Old Oscott Cane, Great Barr, Birmingham B44 9UZ ☎ 0121 360 9478, 0705 012 8674

ROBERTS Derek *(Gtr, B Gtr)*: 1 Tennyson Street, Leicester LE2 1HS ☎ 0116 2558440

ROBINSON David *(Gtr)*: 13 Kidderminster Road, Bewdley, Worcs DY12 1AQ ☎ 01299 403161

ROBINSON Martin *(Gtr, B Gtr, Db, Bjo, Tba)*: 65 Burlidge Road, Chell, Stoke-on-Trent ST6 6SL ☎ 01782 815593

ROBINSON Roy *(Gtr)*: 95 Oxford Street, Church Gresley, Swadlincote, Derbyshire DE11 9NB ☎ 01283 217532

RODEN Stephen *(Gtr, B Gtr)*: Flat 1, 29 Sandford Road, Moseley, Birmingham B13 9DX ☎ 0121 449 0863

ROGERS David *(Gtr, Voc)*: 85, Grosvenor Road, Handsworth, Birmingham B20 3NG

ROSE Adrian *(E Gtr, Cl Gtr, Com)*: 2 Arden Close, Meriden, Nr Coventry, West Midlands CV7 7NS ☎ 01676 522670

ROSTANCE David *(Gtr)*: 9 Penn Gardens, Merefield, Wolverhampton NN4 0RX ☎ 01604 700685, 0411 607513

ROWE Timothy *(Gtr, Voc)*: 3 New Street, Chasetown, Walsall, W.Midlands WS7 8XY ☎ 01543 685550

SATTERTHWAITE Richard *(Gtr, Voc, Kbds)*: 14 Mancroft Road, Tettenhall, Wolverhampton WV6 8RS ☎ 01902 750555

SAULT Russell *(Gtr, B Gtr)*: 22 Oakland Road, Forest Town, Mansfield, Notts NG19 0EJ ☎ 01623 620423, 0589 608858

SAUNDERS John *(Gtr, B Gtr)*: 35 Carman Close, Watnall, Nottingham NG16 1JX ☎ 0115 938 5201, 0973 677745 mob

SCHOONDERWOERD Peter *(E Gtr, B Gtr)*: 31 Kintyre Drive, Stenson, Derby DE24 3JZ ☎ 01332 271104

SERGEANT *(Gtr, B Gtr, Kbds, Dms, Voc)*: 35 Clarendon Road, Edgbaston, Birmingham B16 9SD ☎ 0121 242 1947

SHANNE Marnie *(Gtr, Hmca)*: 2 Osborne Road, Penn, Wolverhampton, West Midlands WV4 4AY ☎ 01902 685 1171, 0976 294 420 mob

SHAW Mark *(Gtr)*: 85 Pelsall Lane, Rushall, Walsall, West Midlands WS4 1NE ☎ 01922 26158

SHUTTLEWORTH Alan *(Gtr)*: c/o Musicians Union, Benson House, Lombard Street, Birmingham B12 0QN

SI *(Gtr)* ☎ 01788 543568, 0976 660014 mob

SIDWELL Jason *(E Gtr, Cl Gtr, Synth)*: 9 Arundel Road, Cheylesmore, Coventry, West Midlands CV3 5JT ☎ 024 7650 1404

SIMPSON Andrew *(Gtr)*: 41 Lennox Gardens, Pennfields, Wolverhampton WV3 0RR ☎ 01902 426516, 0956 544304 mob

SKINNER Ashley *(Gtr, B Gtr)*: 50 Sandford Road, Moseley, Birmingham, West Midlands B13 9BS ☎ 0121 449 3550

SMALLWOOD Paul (Gtr): 17 St. Margarets Road, Ward End, Birmingham B8 2AB ☎ 0121 688 0937

SMITH Graham (E Gtr, Ac Gtr, Tpt): Millcroft, Kingsland, Hereford & Worcester HR6 9SW ☎ 01568 708479

SMITH Haddon (Gtr): 83 Boundary Road, Newark, Notts NG24 4AS ☎ 01636 613591, 01636 613812

SMITH John (Gtr): 3 Wood Road, Chaddesden, Derby DE21 4LU ☎ 01332 671641

SMITH John (Gtr, Db, Arr, Com, Bjo): 12 West Park Avenue, Northfield, Birmingham B31 5BQ ☎ 0121 476 9335

SMITH Mark (Gtr, Hmca, Voc, Kbds): 55 Lilac Grove, Bentley, Walsall WS2 0EY ☎ 01922 449875 & fax

SMITH Matthew (E Gtr, Tpt, El Db)

SMITH Nicholas (Gtr): 3 The Village, Abberley, Worcs WR6 6BN ☎ 01299 896962, 01299 832283

SMITH Philip (Gtr, B Gtr): 4 Riverside, Studley, Warks B80 7SD ☎ 01527 854359, 01527 854359

SMITH Philip (Gtr): Camden House, Chipping Campden, Glos, GL55 6UP ☎ 01386 840244

SMITH Richard (Gtr, Bjo): 30 Honing Drive, Southwell, Notts NG25 0LB ☎ 01656 814023

SMITH Simon (Gtr): 5 Church Lane, Leek, Staffs ST13 5ET ☎ 01538 385428

SODEN David (Gtr, Per, Kbds): 11 Ripon Street, Leicester LE2 1LW ☎ 0116 220 1620, 0116 254 4313

SPENCER Kenneth (Gtr, Pf): 14 Rivers Street, Leicester LE3 5RX ☎ 0116 233 1296

SPRAKES Patrick (Gtr, B Gtr): 39 Douglas Road, Long Eaton, Nottingham NG10 4BH ☎ 0115 9725626

SQUIRE Simon (Gtr, Kbds, Man): 148 Clarendon Park Road, Clarendon Park, Leicester LE2 3AF ☎ 0116 270 9546

STANIFORTH Philip (Gtr, B Gtr, Pf): 16 Hampton Close, Toton, Nottingham NG9 6LL ☎ 0115 9462633

STANWAY Peter (Gtr, Arr): 43 Alexandra Road, Leamington Spa, Warwickshire CV31 2DD ☎ 01926 425980

STAPP Petra (Ac Gtr, Bod): 94 Stanhope Road, Queens Park, Northampton NN2 6XJ ☎ 01604 791150

STEER David (Gtr, Kbds, B Gtr): Block 7 Flat 3, Viscount Close, Cadbury Drive, Castle Vale, Birmingham B35 ☎ 0121 624 2977

STEVENSON Andrew (Gtr): 16 Wordsworth Close, Cheadle, Staffordshire ST10 1XS ☎ 01538 754574, 0973 532061

STEVENSON Daniel (Rh Gtr, Ld Gtr, Voc)

STEWART Claude (Gtr): 9 Hallewell Road, Edgbaston, Birmingham B16 0LP ☎ 0121 454 5069

SUTHERLAND Iain (Gtr): Norbury House, Drayton Road, Wollerton, Market Drayton, Shropshire TF9 3LY ☎ 01630 685274

SWAN Terry (Ac Gtr, Bjo, Uke, Flt): 48 Fellows Road, Beeston, Nottingham NG9 1AQ ☎ 0115 922 2328

SWINDLEHURST Lynda (Gtr, Per): 106 Oxley Moor Road, Wolverhampton, West Midlands WV10 6TX ☎ 01902 785002, 0468 207287

TAYLOR Stuart (Gtr): 46 Batley Street, Meadows, Nottingham NG2 2LH ☎ 0115 914 0706

TEBBS Philip (Gtr, Voc, B Gtr, Db, Kbds): 26 Churchill Way, Burton Latimer, Northants NN15 5RU ☎ 01536 726556

TEMPEST Gregory (Gtr, B Gtr, Kbds): 5 Callan Close, Narborough, Leics LE9 5FH ☎ 0116 284 8689, 0973 937442 mob

TILDESLEY Matthew (Gtr, B Gtr, Voc): Bungalow 2, English Drove, Thorney, Peterborough PE6 0TJ ☎ 01780 450060

TIMMINS ALCM Helen (Cl Gtr, Com, Arr): PO Box 326, Shrewsbury SY3 7WG ☎ 01743 343179

TIPTON Glen (Gtr, Pf): Brook House, Wood Lane, Uttoxeter, Staffs ST14 8BD ☎ 01889 567813, 01889 562734, 01889 568535 fax

TOWNSEND Steve (Gtr, B Gtr, Kbds): 48 Albert Street, Blackgate Yard, Mansfield Woodhoose, Mansfield, Notts NG19 8BH ☎ 01623 479856, 0403 703944, 01623 636438

TUCKER Razor (Gtr, Kbds, Dms): 86 Trent Tower, 165 Duddeston Manor Road, Nechells, Birmingham B7 4JT

TWYNHAM Syd (Gtr, Voc): Lower Kingsbridge Farm, Kingsbridge, Nr Steeple Claydon, Bucks MK18 2EJ ☎ 0129673 8124

VAUGHAN Ian (Gtr, Pf, Kbds): 38 Shrewsbury Road, Market Drayton, Shropshire TF9 3DL ☎ 01630 655771

WAKELING David (Gtr, Voc): c/o Clement Keys, Nettleton House, Edgbaston, Birmingham B15 1RL

WALMSLEY John (Gtr): Opposite The George, Backwell, North Somerset BS19 3PF ☎ 01275 463128

WARDE Chris (Gtr, Bjo): 41 Southbourne Avenue, Hodge Hill, Birmingham B34 6AH ☎ 0121 783 3524

WARR Richard (Gtr, Sax, Rec, Kbds): 11A Milton Crescent, Ravenshead, Nottingham NG15 9BA ☎ 01623 707769

WATERS Bryn (Gtr, Voc): 54, Malvern Avenue, Numeaton, Warwickshire CV10 8ND ☎ 024 7638 5406

WEBB Craig (Gtr, B Gtr): 12 Sir Harry's Road, Edgbaston, Birmingham B15 2UY ☎ 0121 440 2061, 0966 157499

WEST (Ld Gtr, Rh Gtr): 4, Lancaster Road, Brierley Hill, West Midlands DY5 3QE ☎ 01384 572603

WEST Michael (Gtr, B Gtr, Kbds): 52C Alcester Road, Moseley, Birmingham B13 8BA ☎ 0121 449 2134

WESTON Lee (Gtr, Kbds): 8 Castle Crescent, Castle Bromwich, Birmingham B36 9TF ☎ 0121 748 4374

WHITEHOUSE Daniel (Gtr, Pf, Voc): 2 Marchant Road, Wolverhampton WV3 9QG ☎ 01902 688792 & fax

WHITTER James (Gtr, Pf): 81 Allen Road, Whitmore-Reans, Wolverhampton WV6 0AN ☎ 01902 227713

WHYMARK Robertjohn (Pd Gtr, Gtr, B Gtr, Hmca, Kbd): Ftc Training Wing, British Aerospace, P.O.Box 98, Dhahran 31932, Saudi Arabia ☎ 01989 851866

WIGNALL Oliver (Gtr): 151 Black Haynes Road, Seay Oak, Birmingham B29 4RE ☎ 0121 478 3186, 0976 950404 mob

WILKES Alan (Gtr, Bjo): 9 Walton Gardens, Codsall Village, Codsall, Staffs WV8 1AH ☎ 01902 843063

WILKES Douglas (Gtr, B Gtr, Synth): Leycett House, 7 Station Road, Keele, Newcastle, Staffs ST5 5AH ☎ 01782 624650, 0370 723572

WILLE Tony (Gtr, Voc): 40 Kingswood Road, Moseley, Birmingham B13 9AL ☎ 0121 449 3283

WILLIAMS Gary (Gtr, B Gtr, Kbds, Dms): 57 Strensham Road, Balsall Heath, Birmingham B12 9RD ☎ 0121 249 0810

WILLIAMS Huw (E Gtr): 11 Ash Priors Close, Coventry, West Midlands CV4 9DN ☎ 024 7646 3584

WILLMOTT Rod (Cl Gtr, Lute, Bjo, Man, Voc): 2 Pitmaston Road, St Johns, Worcester WR2 4HY ☎ 01905 427026

WILSON Bob (Gtr, Kbds, B Gtr): 17 Yew Tree Road, Edgbaston, Birmingham, West Midlands B15 2LX ☎ 0121 440 5182, 0121 440 0635

WILSON Miles (Gtr, Kbds): 9 Curzon Ave, Carlton, Nottingham NG4 1GN ☎ 0115 847 1272, 0115 866 3884

WIMPRESS Stephen (Gtr): 11 Dunster Street, Northampton NN1 3LB ☎ 01604 637719

WINCKLES Peter (Gtr): 48 Margaret Grove, Harborne, Birmingham B17 9JL ☎ 0121 426 4253

WINTER Domnic (Gtr): 46 Alcester Road, Stratford-upon-Avon, Warwickshire CV37 9DB ☎ 01789 299318

WINWOOD Stephen (Gtr, Pf): Lower Dean Manor, Northleach, Gloucestershire GL54 3NS

WOODWARD Ashley (Gtr, Pf): 1 Manor Farm Cottages, Green End Road, Fillongley, Nr Coventry, Warks CV7 8DS ☎ 01676 541150, 0958 428527 mob

WREN Colin (Gtr, Man, Hmca)

ZARA (Gtr, Timb, Cong, Tiple, Cuatr): Flat 1, 1308 Pershore Road, Birmingham B30 2XU ☎ 0121 459 6170

SOUTH EAST

ABBOTT Marguerite (Gtr, Pf): 45 Syke Cluan, Richings Park, Iver, Bucks SL0 9EP

ADELUS Bernie (Gtr, Voc): 12 Ringwood Road, Poole, Dorset BH14 0RL ☎ 01202 682577

ALBERY Robbie (Gtr): 36 Church Ponds, Castle Hedingham, Essex CO9 3BZ ☎ 07801 588036

ALLEN Mark (Gtr, Zit Hrp, App Dulc, Tiple): 54 Princes Road, Brighton, Sussex BN2 3RH ☎ 01273 603840

ALLEN Roger (Gtr): 5 Ellen Ave, Ramsgate, Kent CT11 7DD ☎ 01843 596628, 0973 400606 mob

ALLMAN Ben (Gtr): 46 The Avenue, Totland, Isle Of Wight PO39 0DN ☎ 01983 755013

ALTON Tony (Gtr, B Gtr, Voc, Arr, Bjo): 6 Bloomfield Avenue, Moordown, Bournemouth, Dorset BH9 1UA ☎ 01202 526453

ANDREWS John (Gtr, Voc): 62 Brownsea View Avenue, Lilliput, Poole, Dorset BH14 8LQ ☎ 01202 707491

ANSWER Thomas (Gtr, B Gtr): 11 Atherstone Court, Two Mile Ash, Milton Keynes, Bucks MK8 8AE ☎ 01908 560719, 07801 429730

ARMER Derek (Cl Gtr, E Gtr, B Gtr, Bjo, Re): 191 Glebe Road, Deanshanger, Milton Keynes MK19 6ND ☎ 01908 564111, 0850 012475, 01908 503811

ARMSTRONG Kevin (Gtr, B Gtr): 86 Lytton Road, Oxford OX4 3NZ ☎ 01865 718266

ARTAUD Austin (Gtr, Per, Synth, B Gtr): 37 Stonewood, Bean, Dartford, Kent DA2 8BZ ☎ 01474 709063

ASH Red (Gtr, B Gtr): 44 Lincoln Road, Parkstone, Poole, Dorset BH12 2HU ☎ 01202 749244

ASHTON Gwyn (Gtr): ☎ 01908 505249, 0956 669505, 01908 521949

ASTON Peter (Gtr, Bjo, Voc): Orchard End, Gaunts Common, Wimborne, Dorset BH21 4JR ☎ 01258 840844

ATKINSON Martin (Gtr): The Marins, Station Road, Sway, Hampshire SO41 6BA ☎ 01590 682225, 01590 683066

ATTRILL Philip (Gtr, Cnt): 3 Bowmans Drive, Battle, East Sussex TN33 0LT ☎ 01424 774672

AUSTEN Ed (Gtr, Voc): 417 Wimborne Road East, Ferndown, Wimborne, Dorset BH22 9LZ ☎ 01202 875374

BADMAN Keith (Gtr): 17 Alderbury Road, Langley, Berks SL3 8OQ ☎ 01753 545733, 0585 110185 mob

BAGGE Nigel (Gtr): Box Cottage, Station Road, Groombridge, Kent TN3 9NE ☎ 01892 864699

BAILEY Chris (Gtr, Pf): 416 Hythe Road, Willesborough, Ashford, Kent TN24 0JH ☎ 01233 632926

BAKER Lee (Gtr, Voc): 12 Golsmid Road, Hove, East Sussex BN3 1QA ☎ 01273 776885

BALCH Gareth (Cl Gtr): 64 Bradbridge Green, Singleton Hill, Ashford, Kent TN23 5WA ☎ 01233 664 327

BANKS John (E Gtr, B Gtr, Ac Gtr): 181A Kingsway, Hove, East Sussex BN3 4GL ☎ 01273 202964, 0976 849601 mob

BARBOUR Stuart (Gtr, Voc): Belmont, Plaistow Road, Ifold, West Sussex RH14 0TU ☎ 01403 753840, 01426 276872

BARNOWSKI Alan (Gtr): 20 Navarino Road, Worthing, West Sussex BN11 2NF ☎ 01903 233318

BARRETT Nicholas (Gtr, Voc): Fairfields, Ascot Road, Nuptown, Warfield, Berkshire RG42 6HS ☎ 01344 884 704

BATES Sally-Ann (Gtr): 49 Chancellors Park, Hassocks, West Sussex BN6 8EY ☎ 01273 844575, 0403 320422

BAUGI Saiid (Gtr, Voc): 79 The Grove, Bournemouth, Dorset BH9 2TX

BAYLIS Christopher (Gtr): 46 High Street, Cumnor, Oxford OX2 9QD ☎ 01865 3566

BELL Andy (Gtr): c/o Dave Newton, Suite 1 2nd Floor, George Street, Oxford OX4 1JP ☎ 01865 798 791

BENNETT Peter (Gtr, Kbds, Voc): 103 Dairymans Walk, Weybrook Park, Burpham, Guildford, Surrey GU4 7FF ☎ 01483 839093, 0402 441386

BENTLEY Richard (Gtr, Pf): 71 Walton Way, Aylesbury, Bucks HP21 7JJ ☎ 01296 431130

BIGWOOD Mark (Gtr, Voc): 42 Potters Way, Lower Parkstone, Poole, Dorset BH14 8QG ☎ 01202 747181

BILLINGHAM Edward (Cl Gtr): 53 Salisbury Road, St Leonards-on-Sea, Sussex TN37 6RX ☎ 01424 442354, 01424 442354

BISHOP Jake (Gtr): 7 Copper Beeches, Rookery Close, Preston Road, Brighton, East Sussex BN1 6DL ☎ 01273 232462, 01523 168128 pager

BLOMBERG David (Gtr): 134 Aldebury Road, Maidenhead, Berks SL6 7HE ☎ 01628 31830

BOREHAM Daniel (Gtr): 10 Elm Place, Rustington, Littlehampton BN16 3BL ☎ 01903 856015

BOWDEN Richard (Ld Gtr): 26 Sondes Place Drive, Dorking, Surrey RH4 3EG ☎ 01306 740049

BRADFORD Peter (Gtr): 32 Kingsley Crescent, High Wycombe, Buckinghamshire HP11 2UL

BRADLEY Clinton (Gtr, Voc): Red Lion Cottage, Fordingbridge Road, Aldersholt, Fordingbridge, Hants SP6 3BE ☎ 01425 657089

BRAGANZA Henry (Ld Gtr, Rh Gtr): 2 Michael Avenue, Ramsgate, Kent CT11 8AW ☎ 01843 853916, 0411 849 824

BRAILEY Peter (Gtr): 5 Somerset Road, Christchurch, Dorset BH23 2ED ☎ 01202 383137

BREWIN Simon (Gtr, B Gtr, Hmca, Voc): Nutwood House, The Street, Plaxtol, Sevenoaks, Kent TN15 0QE ☎ 01732 810682

BRITTON Christopher (Gtr): Old Oaks, Upper Clatford, Near Andover, Hants SP11 7PS ☎ 01264 337598

BROOMFIELD Tom (Cl Gtr, E Gtr, B Gtr): 28 Colville Drive, Bishops Waltham, Southampton, Hampshire SO32 1LT ☎ 01489 896653

BROWN Adrian (Gtr, Bjo, B Gtr, H Gtr, Bzk): 11 Sowell Street, St Peters, Broadstairs, Kent CT10 2AT ☎ 01843 865612, 0378 958436

BROWN Leslie (Gtr): 8 Hull Road, Bear Cross, Bournemouth, Dorset BH11 8RE ☎ 01202 575162

BUNCE Christopher (Gtr, Dms, Kbds): 310 Hughenden Road, High Wycombe, Bucks HP13 5PF ☎ 01484 437915

BURLEY Raymond (Gtr): The Willows, Aston Road, Bampton, Oxon OX18 2AL ☎ 01993 850793

BURT Peter (Gtr, Bjo): 8 Ridley Road, Rochester, Kent ME1 1UL ☎ 01634 402647

BURTON Cathy (Gtr, Pf, Kbds): Flat 8, 8 St Catherines Road, Littlehampton, West Sussex BN17 5HS ☎ 01903 734379, 01903 733061, 01903 733711

BUSHROD Andrew (Gtr, Voc): Chapel Cottage, 18 Boxhedge Road, Banbury, Oxon OX16 0BP ☎ 0800 154334, 01908 666077

CABLE Tom (Gtr): 4 Banister Court, Court Road, Southampton SO15 2JS ☎ 023 8063 9537

CAMPBELL Duncan (Gtr): 93 Chapel Street, Newhaven, East Sussex BN9 9QD ☎ 01273 512802

CARO Benjamin (Gtr, B Gtr, Kbds, Voc, Per): ☎ 0403 254053

CARTER Platts Matthew (Gtr, Kbds, Dms, Clt): 12 Runrig Mill, Chesham Bois, Amersham, Bucks HP6 6DL ☎ 01494 725063

CHAPPELL Wayne (Gtr): 2A Grove Road East, Christchurch, Dorset BH23 2DQ ☎ 01202 484784

CHI Paul (Gtr, Voc, Pf): 18 Westbourne Place, Hove, E Sussex BN3 4GN ☎ 01273 748637

CHILDISH Billy (Gtr): 11 Boundary Road, Chatham, Kent ME4 6TS ☎ 01634 814477 & fax

CHRIS (Gtr, B Gtr, Kbds): 9 Chapel Lane, Sands, High Wycombe, Bucks HP12 4BD ☎ 01494 534229

CHRISTOPHER Jeremy (Gtr): 51 Pondmoor Road, Easthamstead, Bracknell, Berkshire RG12 7JL

CLARK Piers (Gtr): Flat 2, 19 Charles Street, Brighton, East Sussex BN2 1TG ☎ 01273 691138

CLARKE Robert (Gtr, B Gtr, Pf): c/o Alleycat Complex, Katesgrove Lane, Reading, Berks RG1 2ND ☎ 0118 966 1334 & fax, 0973 563 386 mob

CLUBLEY Tom (Gtr, Kbds): 26 Stanford Avenue, Brighton BN1 6EA ☎ 01273 236512

COLLINS Gerald (Gtr, Cl Gtr, B Gtr, Kbds, Voc): 56 Grove Road, Wimborne, Dorset BH21 1BW ☎ 01202 889270

COLTART Robert (Gtr, B Gtr, Voc): 1 Foord Road, Folkestone, Kent CT20 1HH

CONDON Martin (Gtr): 7C Bank Chambers, Penn Hill Avenue, Parkstone, Poole, Dorset BH14 9NB ☎ 01202 746049

CONNELL-HINKES John (Gtr, St Gtr, Kbds): 35 Nelson Street, Oxford OX2 6BD ☎ 01865 510789

COOK Jez (Gtr): 82 St. Bernards Rd, Oxford OX2 6EJ ☎ 01865 311724

CORCORAN Chris (Gtr, Voc): 26 Curzon Road, Maidstone, Kent ME14 5BA ☎ 01622 670295

CORNWELL Brian *(Gtr)*: 54 The Layne, Elmer, Middleton-on-Sea, Bognor Regis, West Sussex PO22 6JL ☎ 01243 586346

CORNWELL Hugh *(Gtr)*: Arden, Washwell, Box, Wiltshire SN14 5DA

CORTEZ Phil *(Ld Gtr)*: 8 Britts Farm Road, Buxted, Nr Uckfield, East Sussex TN22 4LZ

CORY Phil *(Ld Gtr, Rh Gtr, Ac Gtr, Voc)* ☎ 01488 683855, 0385 790946

COSTELLO Neil *(Rh Gtr, Ld Gtr)*: 'Brightlands', 7 The Lees, Dalbury Lees, Derby DE6 5BE

COUCH Peter *(E Gtr)*: 13 Huntingbrooke, Great Holm, Milton Keynes, Bucks MK8 9DF ☎ 01908 569885

COUMBE Bill *(Gtr, B Gtr, Synth)*: 42 Ferry Road, Oxford OX3 0EU ☎ 01865 721244

COUTTS Graham *(Gtr, Hmca)*: Flat 1, 6 Waterloo Street, Hove, East Sussex BN3 1AQ ☎ 01273 723282

COX Mark *(Gtr)*: 32 Upton Way, Broadstone, Dorset BH18 9LY

CRIBB Mark *(Gtr)*

CRICK Adrian *(Gtr, Bjo, B Gtr)*: 1 Park Place, Bessels Green, Sevenoaks, Kent TN13 2QD ☎ 01732 461249

CROSSKEY James *(E Gtr, Ac Gtr, Synth)*: 25 Bailey Road, Cowley, Oxford OX4 3HU ☎ 01865 434007

CROWTHER Peter *(Gtr)*: 34 Craven Gardens, London SW19 8LU

CROZER Matthew *(Gtr)*: Woodlands, High Halstow, Rochester, Kent ME3 8SX ☎ 01634 250286, 07970 971027, 01634 255859

DAN Teddy *(Gtr, Dms)*: 10 Balfour Road, Blackbird Leys, Oxford OX4 5AQ ☎ 01865 716427, 01865 715620

DARVILL Simon *(Gtr, Dms)*: 15A Madeira Road, Ventnor, Isle Of Wight PO38 1QS ☎ 01983 868924

DAVIES Paul A *(Gtr, Per, B Gtr)*: 8 Clarendon Road, Reading, Berks RG6 7PB ☎ 0718 743313

DAVIES Philip *(Gtr)*: 125 Bower Street, Bedford, Beds MK40 3RB ☎ 01234 358558

DAVISON David *(Gtr)*: 66 The Broadway, Minster, Sheppey, Kent ME12 2RT ☎ 01795 872649

DAWSON Stephen *(Gtr, B Gtr, Dms)*: 21 Beagle Close, Abingdon, Oxfordshire OX14 2NU ☎ 01235 529596

DAY Paul *(Gtr, Hmca)*: 26 Pommander Crescent, Walnut Tree, Milton Keynes, Bucks MK7 7NH ☎ 01296 688342

DE MATOS Daniel *(Gtr)*: 113 Alpha Street, Upton, Slough SL1 1QZ ☎ 01753 537206 eve, 01628 789857 day

DE PEARLE Merlin *(Gtr, Kbds, Flt)*: 16 Avon View Road, Burton, Christchurch, Dorset BH23 7LH ☎ 01202 470957

DEAN James *(E Gtr, Ac Gtr)*: 39 The Street, Kingston, Canterbury, Kent CT4 6JQ ☎ 01227 832271

DEDMAN Nicholas *(Gtr)*: Locawood Farm, Shaftesbury Road, Gillingham, Dorset SP8 4LP ☎ 01747 822330

DEE Barrie *(Gtr)*: 19 Broomfield, Lightwater, Surrey GU18 5QN ☎ 01276 479537, 0410 123105, 01276 452975

DENGATE Paul *(Gtr)*: 29 Vale Road, St Leonards-on-Sea, Sussex TN37 6PT ☎ 01424 428924, 01424 437708

DENMAN Mark *(Gtr)*: 100A Albion Hill, Brighton, East Sussex BN2 2PA ☎ Brighton 684325

DENTON Simon *(Gtr)*: Dalema, Hadlow Park, Hadlow, Kent TN11 0HY

DICPETRIS Perkunas *(E Gtr)*: c/o 77A Wentworth Avenue, Boscombe, Bournemouth, Dorset BH5 2AH ☎ 01202 426304

DOWNS Mick *(Gtr, Kbds, B Gtr)*: 7 Irvine Close, Fareham, Hampshire PO16 7QB ☎ 01329 231937, 0780 1130249

DRAKE James *(Gtr, Kbds, B Gtr)*: 74 Applesham Avenue, Hove, East Sussex BN38 8JN ☎ 01273 880643

DRAKE Michael *(E Gtr, Cl Gtr, B Gtr, Lute)*: 19 Upper Village Road, Sunninghill, Ascot, Berks SL5 7BA ☎ 01344 23268

DUNNING Steve *(Gtr, Pf, Dms)*: 4 St. Martins House, St. Martins Street, Chichester, West Sussex PO19 1NA ☎ 01243 532172 & fax, 0410 010114 mob

DUNSTAN Dunstan *(E Gtr, B Gtr, Ld Gtr)*: 51 Broad Oak Road, Canterbury, Kent CT2 7PN ☎ 01227 455688

DURRANT Richard *(Gtr)*: 7 Britannia House, High Street, Shoreham By Sea, Susex BN43 5DX ☎ 01273 465371, 0802 582830

DZIERZANOWSKI Udo *(Ac Gtr, E Gtr, B Gtr, Per)*: 95 Albert Road, Parkstone, Poole, Dorset BH12 2BX ☎ 01202 740379, 0370 226120

EATON Chris *(Sl Gtr, Gtr)*: 3 St Mary's Road, Leatherhead, Surrey KT22 8EZ ☎ 01372 372313

ELLIS Simon *(Gtr, Voc, Kbds, B Gtr)*: 12 Grove Place, Sholing, Southampton SO19 9QY ☎ 023 8043 3112, 0589 471478 mob

ELRAIZ Jon *(Gtr, Voc, B Gtr, Dms, Kbds)*: 53 Nailsworth Cres, Merstham, Surrey RH1 3JD ☎ 01737 217599

EVANS Dan *(Ac Gtr, App Dulc)*: 61 Sillswood, Olney, Bucks MK46 5PN ☎ 01234 241976

EVANS Kenneth *(Gtr, B Gtr)*: 16 Park Way, Maidstone, Kent ME15 7DL ☎ 01622 753541

EVANS Thomas *(Rh Gtr, Voc)*: 18C Copse Mead, Woodley, Reading, Berks RG5 4RP ☎ 0118 969 4923, 020 7903 2434, 020 7837 4339

EVELEIGH Brian *(Gtr, Pf)*: 10 Camden Road, Sevenoaks, Kent TN13 3LY ☎ 01732 459530

FALLON JNR Bob *(Gtr, El Db)*: 4 Swallows Lane, Dial Post, Horsham, W Sussex RH13 8NL ☎ 01403 710657, 0589 773410

FALLOON Jason *(Gtr)*: 42 Woodlands Way, Southwater, West Sussex RH12 7HZ

FARRINGTON Matthew *(Gtr)*: 18 St Michael's Road, Maidstone, Kent ME16 8BS

FARROW Stephen *(Ld Gtr, B Gtr)*: 7 Hercules Street, Buckland, Portsmouth PO2 7EZ ☎ 023 9269 5406

FENWICK Raymond *(Gtr)*: 4 Cassons Close, Weston Hills, South Lincs PE12 6DX ☎ 01775 711885, 01775 711885

FLANAGAN Lin *(Cl Gtr, Pl Gtr, Man)* ☎ 01903 873219, 07771 684156

FLECKNEY Robin *(Gtr, B Gtr)*: 23 Carvoran Way, Wigmore, Gillingham, Kent ME8 0NT ☎ 01634 231386

FLOWER Miles *(Gtr, B Gtr, Voc, Pf)* ☎ 01295 261067

FORNACHON Peter *(Gtr, B Gtr, Kbds, Sax)*: Quince Cottage, School Lane, Pimperne, Landford Foorum, Dorset DT11 8UG ☎ 023 8084 0833

FORSYTH Eric *(Gtr, Voc)*: 15 Coppice Avenue, Ferndown, Wimborne, Dorset BH22 9PT ☎ 01202 876016

FOYLE Trevor *(Gtr, Voc)*: 26 Evelyn Road, Bournemouth, Dorset BH9 1SU ☎ 01202 527253

FRANCIS Nic *(Gtr, Voc)*: 1 Tapwood Cottages, Buckland, Surrey RH3 7BG

FRANTZ Christopher *(Ac Gtr, E Gtr)*

FREEMAN Julian *(Gtr, Kbds, Dms)*: 11 O'Connell Road, Eastleigh, Hants SO2 8QQ ☎ 023 8061 1900, 023 8032 2417

FULLER Darren *(Gtr, Dms, Kbds)*: 1 The Street, West Hougham, Nr Dover, Kent CT15 7BB

GARCIA Gerald *(Cl Gtr, Vih)*: 16 Parker Street, Oxford OX4 1TD ☎ 01865 725929, 01865 725811

GEE David *(Gtr)*: Flat 2, 18 Bulmershe Road, Reading, Berkshire RG1 5RJ ☎ 0118 926 5973, 0403 647 971

GERMAIN Roberto L. *(Gtr, Voc, B Gtr, Kbds)*: 28 Clifton Terrace, Brighton BN1 3HB ☎ 01273 324725

GILES Rob *(Gtr)*: 13 Ferris Avenue, Castle Lane West, Bournemouth, Dorset BH8 0AP ☎ 01202 549591

GILL Philip *(Gtr, B Gtr, Voc)*: 6 Keppel Road, Hastings, East Sussex TN34 2DG ☎ 01424 442405

GLOVER Michael *(Gtr, Synth)*: 8 New Odiham Road, Alton, Hants GU34 1QD ☎ 01420 88600

GOODALL Bernard *(Gtr, Vln)*: 1 Mark Close, Norway Road, Hilsea, Portsmouth PO3 5JB ☎ 023 9266 1052

GOUGH Daniel *(Gtr, Kbds)*: Flat 2, 8 Seaview Road, West Worthing, West Sussex BN11 3PD ☎ 01903 232384

GRABHAM David *(Gtr, Voc, Man, Bjo)*: Poolside Cottage, Redbrook Street, Woodchurch, Ashford, Kent TN26 3QR ☎ 01233 860789

GRAY Matthew *(Gtr)*: 55 Westmead, Windsor, Berks ☎ 01753 820330

GREEN Brett *(Gtr, B Gtr)*: 154 Halstock Crescent, Poole, Dorset BH17 9BB

GREEN Jack *(Gtr, Voc, B Gtr)*: Flat 3, 45 Melville Street, Ryde, Ryde, Isle Of Wight PO33 2AE ☎ 01985 812418

GREENWOOD John (*Gtr*): Address Unknown ☎ 01903 212450

GRINDLEY John (*Jz Gtr, Ac Gtr*): Flat Four Yardley House, Franlis Road, Broadstairs, Kent CT10 3RQ ☎ 01843 867645

GROVE Ben (*E Gtr, Cl Gtr, Bjo, Man, Voc*): Ananda, Franks Hollow Road, Bidborough, Kent TN3 0UD ☎ 01892 528815

GROVE William (*Gtr*): 116 Binfield Road, Bracknell, Berkshire RG42 2AS ☎ 01344 57991

HAINES Richard (*Gtr*): Ascott House Farm, Whichford, Shipston-on-Stour, Warks CV36 5PP ☎ 0160 884 655

HALL David (*Gtr*): 42 Cromwell Road, Whitstable, Kent CT5 1NN ☎ 01227 226290

HAMMOND Paul (*Cl Gtr, Fl Gtr*): 19 Southampton Road, Ringwood, Hants BH24 1HB ☎ 01425 476149

HANDLEY Mark (*Gtr, Hmca*): c/o Cockle Point, Marine Walk, Hayling Island, Hants PO11 9PQ ☎ 020 8749 7586

HANKIN Richard (*Gtr*): 14 Ivy Close, Gravesend, Kent DA12 5NP ☎ 01474 564979

HARBOUR Sidney (*Gtr, Voc*): Flat 4, Compton Court, 17 Penn Hill Ave, Poole, Dorset BH12 9LX ☎ 01202 741741

HARDING Michael (*Gtr, Kbds*): 3 Hartington Place, Brighton, East Sussex BN2 3LR ☎ 01273 676741

HARDING Trevor (*Gtr, B Gtr*): 142 King's Road, Newbury, Berks RG14 5RG ☎ 01635 582064, 0421 33330 mob

HARRIS Adam (*Gtr*): 28 The Paddocks, Yarnton, Kidlington, Oxford OX5 1TF ☎ 01865 841900

HARRIS Klaus (*Cl Gtr, Jz Gtr*): 11 Ewart Street, Brighton, Hants BN2 2UP ☎ 01425 489156

HARRIS Simon (*E Gtr, Hrn, Kbds*): 36 Bestwall Road, Wareham, Dorset BH20 4JA ☎ 01929 552660

HARRIS Tara (*Gtr, B Gtr*): 28 The Paddocks, Yarnton, Ridlington, Oxford OX5 1TF ☎ 01865 841900

HARRISON Rodney (*Gtr, Pf, B Gtr, Hmca*): c/o Dawes Oast House, High Street, Burwash, Etchingham, East Sussex TN19 7HA ☎ 01435 882546, 01435 882855

HARVEY Clive (*Gtr, Uke, Voc*): 4 Walnut Tree Lane, Byfleet, Surrey KT14 7AQ ☎ 01932 346796

HASTINGS Pye (*Gtr*): 15 Vernon Place, Canterbury, Kent CT1 3HG

HATTO David (*Gtr, Voc*): 123 Blackbridge Lane, Horsham, Sussex RH12 1SD ☎ 01403 218105, 01403 218105

HAWKINS Ric (*Gtr*): 26 Old Barn View, Godalming, Surrey GU7 1YR ☎ 01483 426293

HAYES Andrew (*Gtr, Kbds*): 9 Hibernia Drive, Gravesend, Kent DA12 4HT ☎ 01474 358115, 0976 625001

HEADLEY Nigel (*Gtr, Kbds*): Apartado 2382, Cerro Alagoa, 8200 Albufeira, Algarve, Portugal ☎ 0370 803008

HEMMING Paul (*Gtr, Pf*): 192 Favell Drive, Furzton, Milton Keynes, Bucks MK4 1AU ☎ 01908 505826, 0385 541390

HEPBIR Jonathan (*Gtr*): 61A Parkwood Road, Southborne, Bournemouth, Dorset BH5 2BS ☎ 01202 460472

HEWITT Donald (*Gtr*): 158 Banbury Road, Kidlington, Oxford OX5 2BY ☎ 018625 78210

HIBBERD Nick (*E Gtr, Ac Gtr*): 5 Cowden Walk, St Leonards-on-Sea, East Sussex TN30 0YR ☎ 01424 713718

HICKS David (*Gtr*): 14 Pimpernel Place, Thatcham, Berks RG18 4EY ☎ 01635 861731

HIGGINSON Jonathan (*Gtr, Voc*): Parkmeade, Colwell Lane, Freshwater, Isle Of Wight PO40 9LX ☎ 01983 75276

HIGGS Nigel (*Gtr, Bjo*): ☎ 01428 642533

HILL Richard (*Gtr*): Barn Cottage, West Orchard, Shaftesbury, Dorset SP7 0LJ ☎ 01258 472117

HILL Shane (*Gtr, B Gtr, Kbds*): 74 Prices Lane, Reigate, Surrey RH2 8AY ☎ 017372 21378

HIRST Julian (*Gtr, Voc*): Address Unknown ☎ 01424 445007, 01424 441091

HOBSON John (*Gtr*): 7 Shaw Pightle, Hook, Hampshire RG27 9SR ☎ 01256 769088

HOLLIDAY David (*Gtr, Kbds*): 47A Stourcliffe Avenue, Bournemouth, Dorset BH6 3PU ☎ 01202 436578, 01623 644307

HOOPER Nicholas (*Gtr, Con*): Muffities, The Ridings, Stonesfield, Oxford OX8 8EA ☎ 0199 389 313

HORNSBY Thomas (*Gtr*): 2 Pine Grove, Havant, Hants PO9 2RW ☎ 023 9247 6981

HOSKINS Norman (*Gtr, B Gtr, Voc*): 135 The Avenue, Greenacres, Aylesford, Kent ME20 7RF ☎ 01622 717083

HOUGH Colm (*Gtr*): 48 Parsonage Road, Cranleig, Surrey GU6 7AJ ☎ 01483 271106

HOWARD Matthew (*Gtr, B Gtr*): Hollyshaw Paddock, Camden Park, Tunbridge Wells, Kent TN2 5AD ☎ 01892 521638, 01892 540143

HUMPHREY John (*Gtr, E Gtr, Ld Gtr, Rh Gtr, G*): 19, Queendown Avenue, Rainham, Gillingham, Kent ME8 9NY ☎ 01634 377436

HUMPHRIES Jamie (*Gtr*): 18 Grecian Street, Maidstone, Kent ME14 2TS

HUNT Steve (*Gtr, Ctna, Bod*): 25 Haywards Mead, Eton Wick, Windsor, Berkshire SL4 6JN ☎ 01753 863378

HYATT Jamie (*Gtr*): 122 Wroslyn Road, Freeland, Witney, Oxfordshire OX8 8HL

HYLAND Victor (*Gtr*): 5 Pleasant Villas, Kent Street, Mereworth, Kent ME18 5QN ☎ 01622 812285

HYNES Michael (*Gtr, Man*): 4 Furzedown Cottages, Kings Somborne, Stockbridge, Hants SO20 6QJ ☎ 01794 388593

ILETT Maria (*Gtr, Kbds*): 20 Wimblestraw Road, Berinsfield, Wallingford, Oxfordshire OX10 7LZ ☎ 01865 340671

INSTONE Ayd (*Gtr, Voc*): Eldamar, Hazel Paddock, Cold Ash, Thatcham, Berks RG18 9LD ☎ 01635 865708

JACKSON Rob (*E Gtr, Ac Gtr*): 5 Sheridan Close, Stanmore, Winchester, Hants SO22 4EB ☎ 01962 815041, 0589 499844

JACKSON Tim (*Gtr*): 57 Weller Avenue, Rochester, Kent ME1 2LG ☎ 01634 406054

JENKINS Richard (*Gtr*): 36A Burleigh Road, Bournemouth, Dorset BH6 5DZ ☎ 01202 434120

JENNINGS Peter (*E Gtr, Ac Gtr*): 3 Pine Grove, Maidstone, Kent ME14 2AJ ☎ 01622 207930

JEREMIAH Kevin (*E Gtr, Pf, Kbds, Eup*): Farthings Hill, Horsham, West Sussex RH12 1TS ☎ 020 8840 8357, 0961 433655

JIM (*Gtr, B Gtr, Kbds, Dms*): ☎ 01753 645807, 0831 323053

JOHNSON Ronnie (*Gtr, Pf, Flt*): 5 Buccleuch Road, Datchet, Berks SL3 9BP ☎ 01753 594226, 0468 894771

JOHNSON Simon (*Gtr*): 49 Brookside Road, Bransgore, Christchurch, Dorset BH23 8NA ☎ 01425 673991

JOHNSTON Laurence (*Gtr, B Gtr*): 55 Silverspot Close, Rainham, Gillingham, Kent ME8 8JS ☎ 01634 371029

JONES Andrew (*E Gtr, Ac Gtr*): 19 Beethoven Rd, Basingstoke, Hants RG22 4BP ☎ 01256 329248

JONES Kenneth (*Gtr*): 16 Larcombe, Mapledown, Petersfield, Hants GU32 3LS

JONES Matthew (*E Gtr*) ☎ 01273 890664, 0374 780515 mob

JONES Philip (*Gtr, B Gtr, Bjo, Sitar*): PO Box 13, Bahrain, Arabian Gulf ☎ 973 722527, 973 222007, 973 262568

JOSHUA Paul (*Gtr, Voc*): 27 Westlands Way, Oxted, Surrey RH8 0NB ☎ 01883 712177, 0468 398 666

KAHN Jeremy (*Gtr*): 17 Fieldhead Gardens, Bourne End, Bucks SL8 5RN ☎ 01628 521549, 01628 531529

KAMM Philip (*Gtr*): 4 Lime Avenue, Alton, Hants GU34 2AE ☎ 01420 542613, 0976 153140

KANE Reuben (*Gtr*): 50B Whitmore Street, Maidstone, Kent ME16 8JU ☎ 0961 527942

KAY David (*Gtr, B Gtr*): 40 Roman Road, Hove, East Sussex BN3 4LA ☎ 01273 427513, 01273 42707

KAY Tim (*Gtr*): 21 Finbeck Way, Lower Earley, Reading, Berkshire RG6 4AH ☎ 0118 931 2427

KELLARD Colin (*Gtr, Bjo*): 15 Nathaniel Walk, Tring, Herrs HP23 5DQ ☎ 01442 82 5426

KEYS Phil (*Gtr, Voc, Hmca, Man*): 26 Mendip Road, Verwood, Dorset BH31 6UR ☎ 01202 824938

KEYWORTH Terence (*Gtr, Voc*): 38 Grange Road, Mudeford, Christchurch, Dorset BH23 4JD ☎ 01425 271509

KING Paul (*Gtr*): 10 Windsor House, Belmont Road, Whitstable, Kent CT5 1QN

KIPPER (*Gtr, Kbds*): Flat 3, Woolmer Hill House, Hatchet Drive, Haslemere, Surrey GU27 1LX ☎ 01428 652404

KIRBY Peter *(Gtr, Voc)*: 39 Emsworth Grove, Maidstone, Kent ME14 5SE ☎ 01622 679017

KNIGHT Jenny *(Gtr, B Gtr)*: 2 Chestnut Avenue, Langley, Slough, Berkshire SL3 7DE ☎ 01753 543503, 020 7359 9917

KURKJIAN Edmond *(Gtr, Pf, Dms, B Gtr, Voc)*: 5 Courtenay Gate, Kingsway, Hove, East Sussex BN3 2WJ ☎ 01273 202 140

LAIDLAW John *(Gtr)*: 5 Helena Court, Highlands Gardens, St Leonards-on-Sea, East Sussex TN38 0HT ☎ 01424 721652

LAMBERT Dave *(Gtr, B Gtr, Dms)*: 10 Norwood Rise, Minster-on-Sea, Sheppey, Kent ME12 2JE ☎ 01795 873707

LAMING Stephen *(Gtr, Tbn)*: 3 Camden Cottages, Redcot Road, Faringdon, Oxon SN7 8EA ☎ 01367 243050

LAPSLEY Clare *(E Gtr, Pf, Flt)*: 8 Denton Close, Botley, Oxford OX2 9BW ☎ 01865 864150

LAURENCE Graham *(Gtr)*: 'Spindlewood Cottage', 25 Hill Farm Road, Marlow Bottom, Bucks SL7 3LX

LAURI Stephen *(Gtr, Voc)*: 23 Weavering Close, Frindsbury, Nr Rochester, Kent ME2 4RQ ☎ 01634 714725

LAWRENCE Clive *(Gtr, Voc)*: 5 Sarsen Heights, Chatham, Kent ME5 9HW ☎ 01634 862097

LAWRENCE John *(Gtr)*: 11 Chapel Crescent, Sholing, Southampton SO19 8JU ☎ 023 8043 4568

LAZELL Matthew *(E Gtr, Kbds)*: Flat 2, Edgeware, 7 Glenfern Road, Bournemouth, Dorset BH1 2LX ☎ 01202 256592, 01426 299406 pager

LEALMAN Mike *(Gtr, Ld Gtr, Rh Gtr, B Gtr)*: 26 Huntingdon Road, Gildsworth Park, Woking, Surrey GU21 3JP ☎ 01483 721763

LEFEVRE Paul *(Gtr, Pf, Voc)*: 49 Clifton Road, Couldson, Surrey CR5 2DW ☎ 020 8660 9074

LEGGETT Jeremy *(B Gtr, Dms, Kbds)*: 35 Stratford Street, Oxford OX4 1SP ☎ 01865 240568, 0802 666828

LEONARD Christopher *(Gtr, Kbds)*: 12 Fox Dene, Barate Wood, Godalming, Surrey GU7 1YA ☎ 01483 425264

LILEY Bil *(Gtr, B Gtr, Kbds)*: 3 Buttermere Close, Cove, Farnborough, Hants GU14 0LD ☎ 01252 544645

LILL Derek *(Gtr)*: 28 Plomer Green Lane, Dowoley, High Wycombe, Bucks HP13 5TT ☎ 01494 522748

LINCOLN Peter *(Gtr, B Gtr, Pf, Voc)*: 50 Talfourd Avenue, Earley, Reading RG6 2BP ☎ 01734 666567

LIVY Martyn *(Gtr, B Gtr, Voc, Dms)*: 57 Scots Hill Lane, Purewell, Christchurch, Dorset BH23 1HG ☎ 01202 479876

LLOYD Derek *(Gtr, Voc)*: 18 Westwood Road, Loose, Maidstone, Kent ME15 6BG ☎ 01635 862407

LOCHNER David *(Gtr, Voc)*: 40 Greenacres Close, Bournemouth, Dorset BH10 7DZ ☎ 01202 572780

LOCKYER Ronald *(Gtr, B Gtr, Voc, B Ldr)*: Cedar Cottage, North Drive, Ossemsley, New Milton Hants BH25 5TJ ☎ 01590 612292

LONG Martin *(Gtr, Kbds)*: Swallows Rest, Hungerford Lane, Southend Bradfield, Reading, Berkshire RG7 6SH ☎ 01189 744261 & fax

LOVEGROVE Adrian *(Gtr)*: 10 Padwell Road, Inner Avenue, Southampton SO14 6QX ☎ 023 8033 2294

LOVELL Sonny *(Gtr)*: 13 Wicklea Road, Wick Village, Bournemouth, Dorset BH6 4LP ☎ 01202 424951

LOWE Chris *(Gtr, B Gtr)*: Twelve A, Thorney Road, Emsworth, Hants PO10 8BL ☎ 01243 374647

MADDEN Dedi *(Gtr, Voc, B Gtr)*: 16 Cornwall Road, Finsbury Park, London N4 4PH ☎ 020 8374 0267

MANLEY Barry *(Gtr, Kbds)*: 75 Pine Vale Crescent, Redhill, Bournemouth BH10 6BG ☎ 01202 530455

MARAIS John *(Gtr, B Gtr)*: 11 Perry Lane, Sherington, Newport Pagnell, Buckinghamshire MK16 9NH ☎ 01908 616392

MARFLEET Howard *(Gtr, B Gtr, Pf, Kbds)*: Pippins, Lamberhurst Road, Horsmonden, Kent TN12 8DR ☎ 01892 722045

MARSHALL Kenneth *(Gtr, Voc, B Gtr, Kbds, Hmca)*: 14 Upper St Helens Road, Hedge End, Southampton, Hants SO30 0LH ☎ 023 8040 4144, 0468 696270, 023 8040 4144

MARTIN Andrew *(Gtr)*: 6 Mavins Road, Farnham, Surrey GU9 8JT ☎ 01252 713322

MARTIN Peter *(Gtr, Kbds)*

MASSEY-COLLIER Stewart *(Gtr)* ☎ 0411 326340, 023 8048 5642

MAYO Daren *(Gtr)*: Milton Cottage, 35A Milton Lane, Durweston, Blandford, Dorset DT11 0QA ☎ 01258 452665

MCCABE Alec *(Gtr, Bjo, Pf)* ☎ 01403 700267 & fax

MCGOWAN Richard *(Ld Gtr, B Gtr)*: 51 Winchelsea Road, Rye, East Sussex TN31 7EL ☎ 01797 225693

MCINTYRE Gerald *(E Gtr, Ac Gtr, Per, Voc)*: Pearemount Cottage, 150 Dorking Road, Surrey GU4 8RJ ☎ 01483 565998, 01483 444535, 01483 568216

MEACHAM Kenneth *(E Gtr, Cl Gtr, Bod, Vln, Rec)*: 69 Maltravers Street, Arundel, West Sussex BN18 9BQ ☎ 01903 883168, 023 8076 0834

MERCY Philip *(Gtr)*: 45 High Street, Hungerford, Berks RG17 0NE ☎ 01488 682991, 0585 273684 mob

MONTGOMERY Jay (The Stash) *(Gtr, B Gtr, Pf, Eup)*: 10 Charmandean Road, Worthing, West Sussex BN14 9LB ☎ 01903 235479, 01903 782061

MOODY George *(Gtr)*: Rhinfield, Shepherds Hey Road, Calmore, Totton Hants SO40 2RD ☎ 023 8086 2591

MOORE Jonathan *(Gtr)*: 31 Edward Street, Abingdon, Oxon OX14 1DJ ☎ 01235 530346

MOORES John *(Gtr, B Gtr)*: 1 Willow Close, Flackwell Heath, High Wycombe, Bucks HP10 9LH ☎ 016285 29177

MOORWOOD David *(Gtr, Bjo)*: 31 Belmont, Wantage, Oxon OX12 9WA ☎ 012357 65648

MORLEY John *(Gtr)*: 39 Sandpiper Close, Creekmoor, Poole, Dorset BH17 7YE ☎ 01202 601038

MORRIS David *(Rh Gtr, B Gtr)*: West Barn, Northfields, Stratford Road, Deanshanger, Milton Keynes ☎ 01908 564883, 0802 222491

MURPHY Graham *(Ld Gtr, Rh Gtr, Db)*: 1 Springfield Close, Brampton Park, Ramsgate, Kent CT11 7BQ ☎ 01843 586345, 0973 897516

MURRELL David *(Gtr)*: 37, Woodland Road, Selsey, Sussex PO20 0AL ☎ 01243 602956

MYHILL John *(Gtr, Kbds, Md, Com, Arr)*: 6 Queens Road, Broadstairs, Kent CT10 1NU ☎ 01843 600059

NAISH Simon *(E Gtr, B Gtr, Per)* ☎ 01243 603156

NEAVES Keith *(Gtr, Tbn)*: Pear Tree Cottage, The Green, West Peckham, Maidstone, Kent ME18 5JW ☎ 01622 814635

NEWNHAM Arthur *(Gtr, Bjo)*: 6 Hyde Road, Shanklin, Isle Of Wight PO37 7LE ☎ 01983 864359

NEWNHAM Martin *(Gtr, Hmca)*: 6 Hyde Road, Shanklin, Isle Of Wight PO37 7LE ☎ 01983 864359

NICKOLS Timothy *(Gtr)*: 3 Forestview, Albion Place, Southampton, Hampshire SO14 2BZ ☎ 023 8063 8282

NIXON Christopher *(Gtr, Bjo, Nor P, Mldn)*: 10 Frederick Road, Deal, Kent CT14 9HB ☎ 01304 369638

NORTHEAST David *(Gtr, Kbds)*: 11 Repton Road, Earley, Reading, Berkshire RG6 2LJ ☎ 01734 663617

NOYCE Stephen *(Gtr, Voc)*: 31 Linden Drive, Liss, Hants GU33 7RJ ☎ 01730 894651

NUNN Stephen *(Gtr, Kbds)*: 26 Swan Lane, Winchester, Hampshire SO23 7AA

ORCHIN Mark *(Gtr, Man, B Gtr, Voc, Vln)*: 14 Allwood Crescent, Wivelsfield Green, East Sussex RH17 7RP ☎ 01444 84559

ORDISH Nigel *(Gtr, Pf)*: 11 Clifton Street, Brighton, Sussex BN1 3PH

OVERTON Jonathan *(Gtr, Voc)*: 30 Silver Street, Reading RG1 2ST ☎ 0118 954 9712

PAICE Sally *(Gtr, Kbds, Voc)*: 11 Manor Farm Close, Selsey, Chichester, West Sussex PO20 0LZ ☎ 01243 607231

PAILTHORPE Michael *(Gtr, Cong, Hmca, B Gtr, Dms)*: 20 Lanfranc Road, Worthing, West Sussex BN14 7ER ☎ 01903 202426

PAINE Ed *(Pd Gtr)*: Sundown, Lower Hartlip Road, Hartlip, Sittingbourne Kent ME9 7ST ☎ 01795 842731

PAINE Martin *(Gtr)*: 16 Glynswood, Chalfont, St Peter, Bucks SL9 0DP ☎ 01753 88436

PAINTER Thomas *(Gtr)*: 10 Vine Farm Close, Talbot Village, Wallisdown, Poole, Dorset BH12 5EJ ☎ 01202 530791, 07771 888949

PALMER Giles (*E Gtr, Ac Gtr*): Brookside Cottage, Dagbrook Lane, Henfield, West Sussex BN5 9SH ☎ 0173 494686, 0378 932572

PARASKEVA Kyprianos (*Gtr, B Gtr, Dms, Kbds, Bzk*): 23 Semple Gardens, Highfields, Chatham, Kent ME4 6QD, 0956 903160 mob

PARKER Andrew (*Gtr*): 6 Foxhill Court, Sussex Road, Haywards Heath, West Sussex RH16 4EB ☎ 01444 443985

PARKER Brian (*Gtr, Dms, B Gtr, Voc, Kbds*): 54 Tennyson Walk, Northfleet, Kent DA11 8LR ☎ 01474 350438

PARKER Mark (*Gtr, B Gtr, Voc*): 55 Church Lane, Highfield, Southampton SO17 1SY ☎ 023 8057 0302, 01489 891853

PARKHOUSE Richard (*Gtr, B Gtr, Voc, Dms*): Pinetree Farm, Cranborne, Dorset BH21 5RR ☎ 01725 517204, 0411 824601, 01725 517801

PARKHOUSE Timothy (*Gtr, Dms, B Gtr, Voc*): Pinetree Farm, Cranborne, Dorset BH21 5RR ☎ 01725 517204, 0411 824602

PAYNE Ian (*Gtr, Tpt*): Phoenix, Burton Road, Wool, Wareham, Dorset BH20 6EY ☎ 01929 462834

PEARCE Chris (*E Gtr, Cl Gtr, Ac Gtr, Voc, P*): 18 Creedy Gardens, West End, Southampton, Hampshire SO18 3LW ☎ 023 8034 7367, 0467 353805

PERRINS Mark (*Gtr, Pf*): 54 Fordwells Drive, The Warren, Bracknell, Berks RG12 9UL ☎ 0403 603659, 0403 603659, 01344 409998

PHIL THE RAT (*Gtr, Didj, Hmca, Voc*): 52 Pitcroft Avenue, Reading, Berks RG6 7NN ☎ 0118 9669633

PHILLIPS Charles (*Gtr, Kbds, Dms*): 53 Compton Road, Brighton, East Sussex BN1 5AL ☎ 01273 555195

PICKARD Andy (*Gtr, Man*)

PICKFORD David (*Gtr*): 137 Northmoor Way, Wareham, Dorset BH20 4EX ☎ 01924 551598

PIPER Andrew (*Gtr, Flgl, Hmca*): 17 Rhoscolyn Drive, Tattenhoe, Milton Keynes, Bucks MK4 3AE ☎ 020 8462 3229

PIPER Robin (*Gtr, Voc*): Hideaway, 2 Nevill Road, Crowborough, East Sussex TN6 2RA

PITMAN Toby (*Gtr*): 43 Mayfield Road, London N8 9LL ☎ 020 8348 3189

PLAYLE Jerry (*Gtr, B Gtr*): 37 Moorlands Road, Wing, Bedfordshire LU7 0ED ☎ 01296 682002

PLEWS Dan (*Ac Gtr, E Gtr, App Dulc, Man*): 192 Church Street, Wolverton, Milton Keynes MK12 5JS ☎ 01908 320 803, 01908 222701

PLUCK Robert (*Gtr, Bjo*): 14 Kings Drive, Gravesend, Kent DA12 5BG ☎ 01474 358741

POLLAK Crispin (*E Gtr, Pf, Hmca, Dms*): 22 Russett Gardens, Emsworth, Hants PO10 8AW ☎ 01243 379471

PORTER Kevin (*E Gtr, Ac Gtr, B Gtr*): The Black Cat, 272 Arctic Road, Cowes, Isle Of Wight PO31 7PJ ☎ 01983 280840

PREECE Ian (*Gtr, B Gtr, Synth*): 'Yonder', Derritt Lane, Bransgore, Christchurch, Dorset BH23 8AR ☎ 01425 672036

PRITCHARD William (*Gtr, B Gtr*): 15 Hedgerow Drive, Bitterne, Southampton SO18 5SF ☎ 023 8047 3940

PROSSER Gareth (*Gtr, Voc, Kbds*): 10 Spinners Walk, Marlow, Bucks SL7 2AL ☎ 01628 484 553

PUGSLEY Benjamin (*Cl Gtr, E Gtr, Ac Gtr*): 26 Folly Hill, Farnham, Surrey GU9 0BD ☎ 01252 727317

PULMAN Gay (*Gtr, Voc*): 74 Bailey Crescent, Fleetsbridge, Poole, Dorset BH15 3HB ☎ 01202 770257

PUSEY Chris (*Gtr, B Gtr, Dms, Kbds, Pf*): The Elim Christian Centre, Edmunds Road, Lane End, Nr High Wycombe, Bucks HP14 3EJ ☎ 01494 883908

PUTLAND Paul (*Gtr*): 44 Sussex Avenue, Ashford, Kent TN24 8NB ☎ 01233 627112

PUTMAN Frank (*Gtr*): 49 Lenten Street, Alton, Hampshire GU34 1HE ☎ 01420 82125

QUINNELL Leonard (*Gtr*) ☎ 01883 743914

REANEY Andrew (*E Gtr, Hmca, Kbds, Pf*): 20 Gullycroft Mead, Hedge End, Southampton SO30 4SR ☎ 01489 789646

REARDON Stephen (*Gtr*): 21 Stacey Road, Tonbridge, Kent TN10 3AP ☎ 01732 358046

REILLY Peter (*Gtr*): South Lodge, Littleworth, Partridge Green, West Sussex RH13 8JX ☎ 01403 711507

RENDLE Calvin (*E Gtr, Ac Gtr, Voc, Kbds*): Top Floor Flat, 17 Waverley Grove, Southsea, Hants PO6 1AD ☎ 023 9229 3291, 023 9286 4134

RICHARDS Bill (*Gtr*): 5 Trees Avenue, Hughenden Valley, High Wycombe, Bucks HP14 4PG ☎ 01494 562990

RICHARDSON Eric (*Rh Gtr*): Little Croft, Barnes Lane, Milford-on-Sea, Lymington Hants SO41 0RP ☎ 01590 645508

RICKARD James (*Gtr*): 39 Carlton Road, Portchester, Fareham, Hants PO16 8JJ ☎ 023 9238 6594, 023 9238 6594

RIDOUT Mark (*Gtr*): 3 New Street, Ringwood, Hampshire BH24 3AP ☎ 01425 461979, 0973 197618 mob

RILEY Robert (*Gtr*): 17A Gagglewood, Mannings Heath, Horsham, Sussex RH13 6JR ☎ 01403 268732

RIPPON Nigel (*Gtr, Dms, Per, Cel, Kbds*): 11A Lincoln Green, Chichester, West Sussex PO19 4DN ☎ 01243 788240

ROBERTS Deke (*Gtr, Kbds, B Gtr*): 13 Temple Road, Cowley OX4 2ET ☎ 01865 773273

ROBERTS Julian (*Gtr, Pf, Dms*): 88 Pankhurst Avenue, Brighton, East Sussex BN2 2YN, 0958 548942

ROCKY (*Gtr*): Flat 3, 37 Sillwood Road, Brighton, East Sussex BN1 2LE ☎ 01273 327353

RODGERS Simon (*Gtr, Vln, Kbds*): 34 Broadway Close., Witney, Oxon OX85 5GG ☎ 01993 774564

ROGERS Howard (*Gtr, Kbds, Hmca*): 248 Summerhouse Drive, Wilmington, Kent DA2 7PB ☎ 01322 521750

ROOD Mark (*E Gtr, Cl Gtr, B Gtr, Pf, Kbd*): 22 Victoria Ave, Camberley, Surrey GU15 3HX

ROSS Josephus (*Gtr, Voc, Pf*): 122B Limmer Lane, Felpham, Bognor Regis, West Sussex PO22 7LR ☎ 01243 582638, 0468 016690 mob

ROWLAND Philip (*Gtr, B Gtr*): 19 Elizabeth Close, Bracknell, Berks RG12 9SY

RUSE Michael (*Gtr*): Bridle Path, 62 High Street, Finstock, Charlbury, Oxon OX7 3DN ☎ 01993 868868

SALLIS Martin (*Gtr*)

SAVILL Martin (*Gtr, B Gtr, Voc, Kbds*): 13 Viking Road, Northfleet, Kent DA11 8ET ☎ 01474 733358, 0374 128883

SCARRATT Doug (*Gtr*): 75B Denmark Villas, Hove, East Sussex BN3 3TH ☎ 01273 728911

SCHWARTZ Curtis (*Gtr, Pf, Kbds, B Gtr, Voc*): Berry House, Ardingly, Sussex RH17 6SN ☎ 01444 892566

SCOTT Jacky (*Gtr*): 3 Corbett Close, Willen Village, Milton Keynes, Bucks MK15 9LJ ☎ 01908 605473

SCOTT Robert (*E Gtr, Ac Gtr*): 2 Rectory Place, 89 Portsmouth Road, Guildford, Surrey GU2 5DG ☎ 01483 564018

SEXTON Mark (*Gtr, B Gtr, Voc*): 2 Sea Lodge, Old Salts Farm Road, Lancing, West Sussex BN15 8JD ☎ 01903 764018

SHEPHARD Gerry (*Gtr, Voc*): 159 Botley Road, Chesham, Bucks HP5 1XR ☎ 01494 775952

SHEPHERD Jake (*Gtr*): Top Flat, 100 Abingdon Road, Oxford OX1 4PX ☎ 01865 725726

SKATES Nicholas (*Gtr*): 31 Scotts Way, Tunbridge Wells, Kent TN2 5RG ☎ 01892 539748

SKEET Christopher (*Gtr, B Gtr*): 31 Sherwood Road, Winnersh, Berks RG41 5NH ☎ 0118 978 5989

SMITH Adam (*E Gtr, Tpt, Cnt, Kbds*): 67 Bloxworth Road, Parkstone, Poole, Dorset BH12 4BN

SMITH Geoffrey (*Gtr, Voc*): The Hill, Midhurst Road, Kingsley Green, Haslemere, Surrey GU27 3LL ☎ 01483 893807

SMITH Jake (*Gtr, Voc, Bsn*): 66A Lansdown Place, Hove BN3 1FG ☎ 01273 820 251

SMITH James (*Gtr*): 77 Russell Drive, Riverslea, Christchurch, Dorset BH23 3TW ☎ 01202 488140, 0802 397885 mob

SMITH Jeffrey (*Gtr*) ☎ 01474 874273

SMITH Martin (*Ld Gtr, B Gtr*): Avondene, Ship Street, East Grinstead, West Sussex RH19 4DX

SNELL John (*Gtr, B Gtr, Pf, Kbds*) ☎ 01753 539804, 0411 789885

SPALL Stephen (*Gtr, B Gtr*): 15 Alma Road, West Malling, Kent ME19 6RP ☎ 01732 844884

SPARKE Clive *(Gtr)*: 47 Jobes Close, Balcombe, West Sussex RH17 6AF ☎ 01444 811457, 0410 160796 mob

SPENN John *(Gtr, B Gtr)*: 2 Lodbourne Green, Gillingham, Dorset SP8 4EH ☎ 01747 826004

STARTUP Benjamin *(Gtr, B Gtr, Voc)*: 40 Romsey Road, Winchester, Hants SO22 5DL ☎ 01962 849386, 0370 472337

STEPHENSON Michael *(Gtr, B Gtr)*: The Evergreens, Shootersway, Berkhamsted, Herts HP4 3TU ☎ 01442 875127

STEVENSON Gary *(Gtr)*: Home Farm House, Aynho, Nr Banbury, Oxfordshire OX17 3BG ☎ 01869 811369

STEVENSON Philip *(Gtr, B Gtr, Dms, Kbds, Pf)*: 59 Castle Street, Canterbury, Kent CT1 2PY ☎ 0403 578899, 0370 760993

STILL Simon *(Gtr)*: 140 Longland Road, Eastbourne, East Sussex BN20 8JD ☎ 01323 638696, 0370 504183 mob

STONEHILL Lou *(Gtr, B Gtr, Kbds, A Sax)*: 73 - 77 Allbrook Hill, Allbrook, Eastleigh, Hampshire SO50 4NA ☎ 023 8061 1521

STOVOLD Sid *(Gtr, B Gtr, Hmca, Dms)*: 42A Park Road, Farnborough, Hants GU14 6LG ☎ 01252 544938

STRAND Arthur *(Gtr, B Gtr, Lute)*: 7 Grove Close, St Sebastians, Nine Mile Ride, Wokingham, Berks RG11 3NA ☎ 01344 775566

STYLES Nobby *(Gtr, B Gtr, Voc)*: 17A Northgate Parade, Crawley, Sussex RH10 2DT ☎ 01293 403342

SURITA Ian *(Gtr)*: 25 Penshurst Close, Rainham, Gillingham, Kent ME8 7DT ☎ 01634 375198

SWEET Paul *(Cl Gtr, Pf, E Gtr, Sax)*: 83D Brockhurst Road, Chesham, Bucks HP5 3JE ☎ 01494 785671, 0411 140561, 01494 785671

T Nicky *(Gtr, B Gtr, Pf)*: 43 Woodbury Avenue, East Grinstead, West Sussex RH19 3NY ☎ 01342 302044

TAINIO Dean *(Ac Gtr, E Gtr, Cl Gtr, Synth,)*: 653 Loose Road, Maidstone, Kent ME15 9UT ☎ 01622 747613, 07970 559783

TAYLOR Carlton *(Gtr, Pf)*: 10 Eric Avenue, Emmer Green, Caversham, Reading RG4 8QX ☎ 01189 483663

TAYLOR David *(Gtr)*: 20 Howard Avenue, Rochester, Kent ME1 2AP ☎ 01634 843052

TAYLOR Frank *(Gtr)*: 5 Braemore Road, Hove, East Sussex BN3 4HA

TAYLOR Kevin *(Gtr, Voc)*: 24 Clandon Road, Lordswood, Chatham, Kent ME5 8YB ☎ 01634 201458

TAYLOR Richard *(E Gtr, Voc)*: 1 Upper Street, Childe Okeford, Blandford, Dorset DT11 8EF ☎ 01258 860232

TAYLOR Richard *(Gtr)*: Dawns View, Castle Road, Ventnor, Isle Of Wight PO38 1LG ☎ 0983 854486

THE DOS TRUST *(Gtr, Pf, Man)*: Ye Old Forge, Recording Studios, Bedgebury Road, Goudhurst, Kent TN17 ☎ 01580 212666, 01580 211555

THE STONE *(Gtr, Dms, Kbds, Voc)*: 12 Testwood Place, Totton, Southampton, Hants SO40 3BE ☎ 023 8048 0553

THOMAS Christopher *(Gtr)*: 31 Fontwell Close, Calmore, Totton, Hants SO40 2TN ☎ 023 8086 1366

THOMAS Evan *(Gtr)*: 5 Avocet Way, Langford Lane, Bicester, Oxon OX6 0YN ☎ Oxford 711082

THOMPSON Anthony *(E Gtr, B Gtr, Gtr)*: 45 Woodshill Lane, Ashurst Wood, West Sussex RH19 3RQ ☎ 01342 315841

THOMPSON Steve *(Gtr, Db)*: 10 Millfield Cottages, Sudeley Place, Brighton, East Sussex BN2 1HG ☎ 01273 683254

THOMSON Will *(Gtr, Pf, Rec, Wh)*: 17 Cloudesley Road, St Leonards-on-Sea, East Sussex TN37 6JW ☎ 01424 432669

THORNE Stephen *(Gtr, Dms, Voc)*: 84 Meadow Way, Verwood, Dorset BH31 6HQ ☎ 01202 825759

THRONEYCROFT-SMITH Fraser *(E Gtr, Ac Gtr, Pf)*: The Spinneys, West Street, Marlow, Buckinghamshire SL7 2BY ☎ 01628 486124

TIPPER Michael *(Ac Gtr, Man, Bjo)*: 104 Second Avenue, Farlington, Portsmouth, Hants PO6 1JU ☎ 023 9264 9379

TOWNSEND Neil *(Gtr)*: 24 Lamorna Gardens, Wester Gate, Chichester, West Sussex PO20 6RL ☎ 01243 542592

TOYE Dave *(Gtr, Man, Hmca)*: Riverway, Rapley Lane, Horsham, Surrey RH13 6QE ☎ 01403 266850, 01403 240393 fax

TREACEY Vincent *(Gtr)*: 2 Forest Close, Waltham Chase, Southampton, Hants SO32 2NB ☎ 01489 893875

TREPEKUNAS Sauliius *(Gtr, Kbds, Clt)*: 61 Elder Close, Badger Farm, Winchester SO42 4LH ☎ 01962 620980, 01962 620980

TRILBY Dave *(Gtr, Voc)*: 28 Testcombe Road, Alverstoke, Gosport, Hants PO12 2EL ☎ 023 9258 1416

TROY *(Gtr, B Gtr, Kbds)*: 1 Spring Close, Maidenhead, Berkshire SL6 7HA ☎ 01628 28626

TUCKER Matthew *(Gtr, Pf)*: The School House, Stoke Green, Stoke Poges, Bucks SL2 4HN ☎ 01753 539242

UPTON Barry *(Gtr, Kbds, Voc)*: Croakers Hatch, Manor Road, Chilworth, Hampshire SO16 7JE ☎ 023 8076 8929

VINCENT Martin *(E Gtr, Ac Gtr)*: 46 Allcroft Road, Reading, Berkshire RG1 5HH ☎ 0118 987 1117

VORTEX Eddie *(Gtr, Voc)*: Longview, Dunwood Hill, East Wekkiw, Romsey, Hampshire SO15 6FD ☎ 01794 513136

WALKER Richard *(Gtr)*: The Honeypot, Barnhill Road, Ridge, Wareham, Dorset BH20 5BG ☎ 01929 552583

WARD-WEBB Andrew *(Gtr, Bzk, Dms)*: 15 Embrook Gate, Wokingham, Berkshire RG41 1JW ☎ 01189 793969

WATKINS Greg *(Gtr, Voc, B Gtr, Kbds, Cel)*: 80 Lichfield Road, Portsmouth, Hants PO3 6DF ☎ 023 9234 8058

WATSON Christopher *(Gtr)*: 72 Marlow Road, High Wycombe, Bucks HP11 1TH ☎ 01494 526930 & fax

WATSON Nigel *(Gtr, Cong)*: The Spinney, 2 Gordons Way, Oxted, Surrey RH8 0LW ☎ 01883 716648, 01883 382689

WATSON Richard *(Gtr, Voc, Arr, Song W)*: 20 Belgrave Street, Eccles, Aylesford, Kent ME20 7HL ☎ 01622 716237

WEST Tim *(Gtr, Voc, Dul, Kbds, Hmca)*: 2 Meadway Court, Kingston Lane, Southwick, West Sussex BN42 4SL ☎ 01273 595614

WHEELER Marc *(Gtr, Voc)*: 3 Elton Road, Bodicote, Chase, Banbury, Oxfordshire 0X16 9TJ ☎ 01295 254567

WHEELER Stephen *(Gtr)*: 98 Craven Road, Newbury, Berkshire RG14 5NP ☎ 01635 48351

WHITE Peter *(Gtr, Voc)*: 7 Brooklea, Send Road, Caversham, Reading, Berkshire RG4 8EP ☎ 0118 946 1784

WHITEHORN Geoffrey *(Gtr)*: 122 Singlewell Road, Gravesend, Kent DA11 7PT ☎ 01474 355891

WILLIAMS Gary *(E Gtr, B Gtr)*: 37 Michelbourne Close, Burgess Hill, West Sussex RH15 9QX ☎ 01444 230049, 0973 414157 mob

WILLIAMS Glenn *(Ld Gtr, Rh Gtr, B Gtr, Dms, V)*: 61 Ashley Close, Halfway, Sheerness, Kent ME12 3ED ☎ 01795 663059, 0961 835577

WILLIAMS Michael *(Gtr)*: 1 Cranbourne Road, Gosport, Hants PO12 1RJ ☎ 023 9258 5388, 0860 478624

WILLIAMS Trevor *(E Gtr, Ac Gtr, Pf, Hmca, Voc)*: 4 St Denys Close, Stanford In The Vale, Faringdon, Oxon SN7 8NJ ☎ 01367 710 705

WILLIS Mark *(Gtr)*: 103 Windmill Road, Headington, Oxford OX3 7BT

WILLIS Robin *(Ac Gtr)*: Belmont House, Belmont Road, Hastings, East Sussex TN35 5NR ☎ 01424 425016

WILLMORE Barry *(Gtr, Flt)*: 10, Gleneagles Close, Harold Wood, Romford, Essex RM3 0RU ☎ 01708 345431

WILLMOUTH Tony *(Gtr)*: 17 Oak Drive, Higham, Rochester, Kent ME3 7BD ☎ 01474 823703

WILLOW Robin *(Gtr, Hrp, Voc)*: 36B Belton Road, Dollis Hill, London NW2 5PE ☎ 020 8451 2590

WILSON James *(Gtr)*: Mimosa House, Church Road, Offham, West Malling, Kent ME19 5NY ☎ 01732 842484 & fax

WILTSHIRE Neil *(Gtr)*: 31 Queens Gardens, Brighton, E Sussex BN1 4AR ☎ 01273 699214

WISEMAN Brian *(Gtr, Voc)*: 15 The Martlets, Burgess Hill, Sussex RH15 9NN ☎ 0444 233078 / 2

WORT Christopher *(Gtr)*: 2 The Acorns, Broadfield, Crawley, West Sussex RH11 9QW ☎ 01293 450025

WRIGHT Eric *(Gtr, B Gtr, Kbds)*: 21 The High Street, Rottingdean, Brighton, Sussex BN2 7HE ☎ 01273 301779

WRIGLEY Stephen *(Gtr, Per, Arr)*: 49 Viaduct Road, Brighton, Sussex BN1 4ND ☎ 01273 673687

YOUNG David *(Gtr, Voc)*: 20 Malthouse Square, Beaconsfield, Bucks HP9 2LD ☎ 01494 076800

SOUTH WEST

ALLEN Charles (*Gtr, Man*): 37 Highlanes, Gayle, Cornwall TR27 4AW ☎ 01736 757497

ALLERHAND Peter (*Gtr, Pf*): Highmere Cottage, Tyning Lane, Bath BA1 6EQ ☎ 01225 428452

ANSTEE Stuart (*Gtr*): 187 Aldergrove Road, Porth, Rhondda, Mid Glam, South Wales CF34 0LU ☎ 01443 682069

ARROW Robin (*Gtr, Voc*): Greenlands, Luppitt, Honiton, Devon EX14 0SX ☎ 01404 891720

ATKINS Stephen (*Gtr*): 2 Eastlands Yetminster, Sherborne, Dorset DT9 6NQ ☎ 01935 872011

AUGARDE Steve (*Gtr, Kbds*): 49 Queen Street, Tintinhull, Nr. Yeovil, Somerset BA22 8PG ☎ 01935 823904

AYENSU Lorraine (*Gtr*): 43 Park Crescent, Whitehall, Bristol, Bs5 7Ay BS5 7AY ☎ 0117 9518752

BARNICOAT Julian (*Cl Gtr, E Gtr, Kbds*): 10 Cuxton Meadows, Buckland Monachorum, Yelverton, Devon PL20 7NG ☎ 01822 853758

BARRETT Andrew (*Gtr*): 26B Durleigh Road, Bridgwater, Somerset TA6 7HR ☎ 425479

BARRETT Mark (*Ld Gtr, Rh Gtr, Kbds*): 5 Winstowe Terrace, Crantock, Cornwall TR8 5RS ☎ 01637 830 041

BARTLETT Paul (*Gtr*): The Flat, Archers Arcade, Lower Frog Street, Tenby SA70 8HZ ☎ 01834 843135

BATCUP Timothy (*Gtr*): 16 St. Nicholas Square, Marina, Swansea SA1 1UG ☎ 01792 641554, 01792 463980, 01792 655255

BEHENNAH David (*Gtr*): 6 Deeble Close, Plympton, Plymouth PL7 4BR ☎ 01752 338012

BENHAM Patrick (*Gtr*): Redmeads, Wagg Drove, Huish Episcopi, Langport, Somerset TA10 9ER ☎ Langport 250278

BERRYMAN Peter (*Gtr*): Blue Gates, Lodge Hill, St. Blazey Gate, Par / Cornwall PL24 2EE ☎ 01726 815609

BICK Mark (*Gtr, Kbds*): Oakdale Cottage, Furnace Lane, Newent, Glos. GL18 1DD ☎ 01531 821 840

BIRT Andrew (*Gtr*): The Bungalow, Veryan Green, Veryan, Truro, Cornwall TR2 5QF ☎ 01872 501725

BLOGGS Steve (*Gtr, B Gtr*): 84 Bromley Road, Horfield, Bristol, Avon BS7 9JD ☎ 0117 9515597

BOTTERILL Michael (*Gtr*): 12 Wollaston Road, Dorchester, Dorset DT1 1EQ ☎ 01305 266814

BOWEN David (*Gtr, B Gtr*): 124 The Marles, Exmouth, Devon EX8 4NU ☎ 01395 277264

BOWERY Al (*Gtr*): 18 Ramsay Way, Burnham-on-Sea, Somerset TA8 2TR ☎ 01278 780398

BOYD Ed (*Ac Gtr, Bzk*): ☎ 01225 310991 & fax

BRADFIELD James Dean (*Gtr*): 20 St Ivors Road, Pontillanfraith, Gwent NP2 2JH ☎ 01495 228601

BREE Patrick (*Gtr, Voc, Man, Rec*): 27 Plumbers Barton, Frome, Somerset BA11 1QQ

BRINE Nick (*Gtr, Kbds, Dms*): 3 The Padocks, Wyesham, Monmouthshire NP5 3NP ☎ 01600 716602, 0966 538 519

BROAD John (*Gtr*): Trethias Bungalow Flat, St Merryn, Padstow, Cornwall PL28 8PL

BROWN Daniel (*Gtr, B Gtr, Per, Kbds*): 5 Norland Road, Clifton, Bristol BS8 3LP ☎ 0117 973 4687

BROWNSON Lee (*E Gtr*): 17 Ashdean, Denecroft, Cinderford, Gloucestershire GL14 2LL ☎ 01594 822833

BRUNTON Richard (*Gtr, B Gtr, Kbds*): Dairy House, Lamyatt, Shepton Mallet, Somerset BA4 6NP ☎ 01749 813649

BRUSCHINI Angelo (*Gtr*): ☎ 0117 924 9489 & fax

BURNS Neil (*Gtr*): 3 Cistern Street, Totnes, Devon TQ9 5SP ☎ 01803 865784

CANNON Vinny (*E Gtr, Ac Gtr, Voc, Man*): 94 Oak Road, Horfield, Bristol, Avon BS7 8RZ ☎ 0117 949 6824

CAPRICORN (*Gtr*): 88 Blake Hill Crescent, Lilliput, Poole, Dorset BH14 8Q3 ☎ 01202 701099

CARLYON Shaun (*Gtr, Pf*): 33 Trelawney Road, St Agnes, Cornwall TR5 0TP ☎ 01872 552870

CARNABY Denis (*Gtr, Bjo*): Woodfield Lodge, Torwood Gardens Road, Torquay TQ1 1EG ☎ 01803 212196

CARR Michael (*Gtr, Voc*): Gordon House, 15 Penare Road, Penzance, Cornwall TR18 3AJ ☎ 63923

CARTER Diane (*Gtr, Voc*): 10 The Conifers, Upton Street, Gloucester GL1 4LP ☎ 01452 386126

CASWELL Richard (*E Gtr, Ac Gtr, Dobro, Kbds*): 11 St. Johns Close, Marlborough, Wiltshire SN8 1JX ☎ 01672 516518

CHANT Mike (*Gtr, Mando, Man, Didj, Per*): Glan Rhyd, Mynaclogddu, Clunderwen, Dyfed SA66 7SA ☎ 01239 831441

CHARMAN Gary (*E Gtr, Ac Gtr, B Gtr*): Baggots Cottage, 71 Crashmore Lane, Overbury, Nr. Tewkesbury, Glos GL20 7NX ☎ 01386 725676, 0468 018684

CHILDS (*Gtr, Voc*): 43 Manor View, Par, Cornwall PL24 2EL ☎ 01726 816237

CHRISTIE Andy (*Gtr*): 52 St Davids Hill, Exeter, Devon EX4 4DT ☎ 04225 570165

CLARK Bob (*Gtr*): 38 Cromwell Road, Milford Haven, Dyfed SA73 2AO ☎ 01646 690842

CLARK Paul (*Gtr, Hmca, Voc*): 37 Chafeys Avenue, Weymouth, Dorset DT4 0EJ ☎ 01305 784181

CLEWS Paul (*Gtr, Kbds*): 6A Church Street, Ilfracombe, Devon EX34 8HA

COLEMAN Jeffrey (*Gtr*): 78 Wyndham Crescent, Canton, Cardiff CF1 9EF ☎ 029 2034 5374

COLLIER Anne-Marie (*Gtr, Rec*): 3 The Spinney, Frampton Cotterll, Bristol BS36 2JS ☎ 01454 773267

CONNELL Sean (*Gtr, Kbds*): 18 Pemberton Avenue, Burry Port, Carmarthenshire, South Wales SA16 0AG ☎ 01554 834364

COOKSLEY Andrew (*Gtr, Kbds, Dms*): Holly Bank, Broadway, Ilminster, Somerset TA19 9RA ☎ 07788 507598

COTTER Joseph (*Ac Gtr, Bod, Wh*): 9A Wynford Road, Stoke Hill, Exeter EX4 7ES ☎ 01392 427994, 0441 026560

COURT John (*Gtr*): 21 Denmark Road, Bath BA2 3RE

CRADICK Martin (*Gtr, Man, Per, Dms*): ☎ 01225 331636 & fax

CRAMPTON Tim (*Gtr, B Gtr*): Fairways, Nantithet, Cury, Helston, Cornwall TR12 7RB ☎ 01326 240972

CROCKER James (*E Gtr, Ac Gtr, Man*): 2 Station Cottages, Bridestowe, Okehampton, Devon EX20 4HE ☎ 01837 861355, 01822 852274

CROWE James (*Gtr, Voc, Pf*): Tregarth, 28 Chute Lane, Gorran Haven, St Austell, Cornwall PL26 6NU ☎ 01726 843127, 01841 521200, 01841 520888

CROWTHER Dai (*Gtr, Mando, Com*): Ty Caniad, 5 Main Street, Fishguard, Pembrokeshire SA65 9HG ☎ 01348 872193

CROZIER-COLE Jerry (*E Gtr, Flt*): Garden Flat, 7 Arlington Villas, Clifton, Bristol BS8 2EF ☎ 0117 9742 559

CURNOW Duncan (*Gtr, Man, Voc*): 15 Higher Shapter Street, Topsham, Exeter EX3 0AW ☎ 01392 873003, 01837 840186

CURWEN Trevor (*Gtr*): 26 Arundel Road, Bath BA1 6EF ☎ 01225 311515

DAUM Robert (*Gtr*): Lower Farm, Thornford, Sherborne, Dorset DT9 6QQ ☎ 01935 873145

DAVIES Francis (*Gtr, B Gtr*): 36 Chertsey Road, Windlesham, Surrey GU20 6EB

DAVIES Geraint (*Gtr, Voc, Hmca*): Marin, 4 Golwg-Y-Mynydd, Craig-Cefn-Parc, Swansea SA6 5RF ☎ 01792 846668

DAVIES Robert (*Gtr*): 29 Grasmere Drive, Cwmbach, Aberdare, Rhowdda Cynon Taff CF44 0HP ☎ 01685 881545

DAVIES Robert (*Gtr, Pf*): 12 Alfred Street, Newport, Gwent NP9 7FJ ☎ 01633 665276

DAVIS Keith (*Gtr, Dobro, B Gtr, Bjo, Harm*): 6 North Street, Downend, Bristol BS16 5SY ☎ 0117 9570323

DAVIS Mike (*Rh Gtr, Dms, Per, Voc*): 16 Fordens Lane, Holcombe, Dawlish, S. Devon EX7 0LD ☎ 01626 865531

DE MELLO Agnelo (*Gtr, Kbds*): 91 Morris Street, Rodbourne, Swindon SN2 2HT ☎ 01793 511806

DEARNALEY Andrew (*Gtr*)

DEREC Andrew (*Gtr, Kbds*): Dros Yr Enfys, 28 Cowbridge Road, Brynsadler, Pontyclun Mid Glamorgan CF7 9BT ☎ 01443 226887

DEVONALD David (*Ld Gtr, B Gtr*): The Kings Arms Hotel, High Street, Kingswood, Bristol BS15 4AB ☎ 0117 967 4203

DIXON Jolyon (*Cl Gtr, B Gtr, Hmca, Kbds, Vo*): 46 Church Road, Idmiston, Nr Salisbury, Wiltshire SP4 0AT ☎ 01980 610661

DORNAN Amanda (*Gtr, B Gtr*)

DOUGLASS John (*Gtr, Kbds, Voc*) ☎ 0117 951 3163

DOWNES Paul (*Ac Gtr, Voc, Mando, Cel, Bjo*): Flat 5 Manor House, Burgmanns Hill, Lympstone, Exmouth Devon EX8 5HP ☎ 01395 266840

DUNCAN Alex (*Gtr, Kbds*): Candyland Studios, Stapleton, Farm Langtree, Torrington, N. Devon EX38 8NP ☎ 01805 601335, 01805 601620

EARL Rhoderick (*Gtr, Kbds*): 14 Hillsboro Place, Porthcawl, Mid Glamorgan CF36 3BH ☎ 01656 772935

EASTO Dave (*Gtr, B Gtr*): 56 Beauley Road, Southville, Bristol BS3 1QF ☎ 0117 9634849

EDWARDS Catrin (*Gtr, B Gtr*): 1 University Place, Splott, Cardiff CF2 2JU ☎ 029 2045 7211

EDWARDS Michael (*Gtr, B Ldr*): c/o 24 Ives Street, London SW3 2ND ☎ 020 7584 5977, 020 7838 0351

EDWARDS Richard (*Gtr*): 15 St Tudors View, Blackwood, Gwent ☎ 020 8740 6288

ELLIS Clark (*Cl Gtr, E Gtr*): 4 Panteg, Pentyrch, Cardiff CF4 8TL ☎ 029 2089 1650

ELLSWORTH Christopher (*E Gtr, Ac Gtr*): 109 Brookfield Road, Churchdown, Gloucester GL3 2PN ☎ 01452 714894, 01452 374074

ENGLISH Mary (*Gtr, Auto Hrp, App Dulc, Vln,*): 48 Faulkland Road, Oldfield Park, Bath, N.E. Somerset BA2 3LT ☎ 01225 315718, 04325 168556

EVANS Daniel (*E Gtr, Ac Gtr*): 9 Southern Terrace, Mutley, Plymouth PL4 7LS ☎ 01404 814647, 0467 893233 mob

EWINGS Thomas (*Gtr*): 3 Courtney Road, Tiverton, Devon EX16 6EE ☎ 01884 254064

EXELBY Matt (*Gtr, Pf, Vln*): Gweleath, West Trewirgie Rd, Redruth, Cornwall TR15 2TJ ☎ 01209 211561, 01209 211561

FAY Richard (*Gtr, Synth, Voc*): 2 Montague Place, Bideford, N. Devon EX39 3BX ☎ 01237 474002

FELCE David (*Gtr*): Address Unknown ☎ 0117 909 3100

FERRIS Will (*Ac Gtr, B Gtr, Pf, Mldn, Voc*): Bay Cottage, Shave Cross, Bridport, Dorset DT6 6HW ☎ 01308 868489

FRY Christopher (*Gtr*): 9 Victoria Street, Griffithstown, Pontypool, Gwent, South Wales NP4 5HH ☎ 01495 762619

GANNER David (*Gtr*): 42 Burton St, Cheltenham, Glos GL50 3NE ☎ 01242 260075

GEE Michael (*Ac Gtr, E Gtr, B Gtr*): 34 Lon-Y-Deri, Rhiwbina, Cardiff CF4 6JP ☎ 029 2061 8718

GEORGE Siswann (*Gtr, Voc, Spoons*): 26 Bassett Street, Abercynon CF45 4SP ☎ 01443 742370

GIBBS Stephen (*Gtr*): 47 Ellan Hay Road, Bradley Stoke South, Bristol BS12 0HA ☎ 0117 9311679

GODWIN Russell (*Gtr*): The Haven, Bristol Road, Congresbury, Bristol BS19 5BG ☎ 01934 835128, 0378 183668

GOODALL Peter (*Gtr, B Gtr*): Stornoway, 20 Westbourne Road, Penarth, South Glamorgan CF6 2HE ☎ 029 2070 0140

GOODWIN Gavin (*Gtr, B Gtr, Org, Dms, Voc*): 26 Melford Square, Bettws, Newport, Gwent NP9 6BL ☎ 01633 852385

GRAEBE Martin (*Gtr*): 100 Cheltenham Road, Gloucester GL2 0LX ☎ 01452 523861

GRANT Simon (*Gtr, Per, Man*): c/o Ann Hamilton, Rosedene, Lime Head, St. Breward, Bodmin, Cornwall PL30 4LU ☎ 01208 851447

GREGORIG Ian (*Gtr*): Lake View, Old Horsley Road, Nailsworth, Stroud Glos G16 0JY ☎ 0145 383 5136

GREGORY David (*Gtr*): 1 Grindel Drive, Grange Park, Swindon, Wiltshire SN5 6HD

GRIFFITHS Geraint (*Gtr, Pf, Voc*): Waun Uchaf, Ael-Y-Bryn, Tanerdy, Carmarthen, Dyfed SA31 2AH ☎ 01267 232646

GRIFFITHS Mark (*Gtr, Flt*): 94 Clos Myddlyn Beddau, Mid Glamorgan, South Wales CF38 2JT ☎ 01443 217494

GRIFFITHS Simon (*E Gtr, B Gtr*): 4 Painsway, Amesbury, Wilts SP4 7RG

GUSHER Steve (*Gtr, Kbds*): 75 Richard Street, Cathays, Cardiff CF2 4DD ☎ 029 2034 0921, 0831 630877 mob

HADDON Robert (*Gtr*): 8 Cornerswell Road, Penarth, S Glam CF6 1UZ ☎ 029 2070 9596

HAMMETT Barry (*Gtr*): 52 Ael-Y-Bryn Road, Fforestfach, Swansea SA5 8JB ☎ 01792 34484

HAMMETT Kirstie (*Gtr, B Gtr, Voc*)

HARRIS Nicholas (*Gtr*): 15 Bladud Buildings, Bath BA1 5LS ☎ 01225 484136

HARRUP Guy (*Gtr*): St Andrews, 60 Lower Oldfield Park, Bath, Avon BA2 3HP ☎ 0225 424962 / 4, 0225 331774 mob

HAWKER Lawrence (*Gtr*): Fiveways, Downe Lane Head, Odcombe, Yeovil Somerset BA22 9WU ☎ 0193 586 2283

HAYWOOD Mark (*Ac Gtr, Ld Gtr, B Gtr, Man, V*): c/o Yfawyd, Bodyddon Llanfyllin, Powys SY22 5HJ ☎ 01743 884459, 01743 272024

HEDGES William (*Gtr, B Gtr, Voc*): Coppice House, Newtown, Sixpenny Handley, Nr Salisbury, Wiltshire SP5 5PF ☎ 01725 552616

HENDERSON Kelvin (*Gtr*): 5 Bartonia Grove, Brislington, Bristol BS4 5AG ☎ 0117 977 3202, 0468 233037 mob, 0117 983 3800

HENNESSY Frank (*Gtr, Bjo, Voc*): 9 Duxford Close, Llandaff, Cardiff CF5 2PR ☎ 029 2055 2244

HILL Steve (*Rh Gtr, Voc*): The Flat, 27 Perfect View, Rivers Road, Camden, Bath BA1 5JY ☎ 01225 313357

HILLIER Simon (*Gtr*): 77 Springhill, Kingswood, Bristol BS15 1XW ☎ 0117 909 9256

HILLMAN Hank (*Gtr, Voc, Bjo, B Gtr*): 97 Tynenydd Road, Barry, Vale Of Glamorgan, S Wales CF62 8BB ☎ 01446 737938, 029 2071 2636

HODGE Al (*Gtr*): 32 St. Marys Road, Bodmin, Cornwall PL31 1NJ

HOGG Jeremy (*Gtr*): 39 Stevens Crescent, Totterdown, Bristol BS3 4UH ☎ 0117 909 2676

HOLMES Alan (*Gtr, Kbds*): 56 Eastwood Road, Broomhill, Bristol BS4 4RS ☎ 0117 971 3804

HOLTON Chico (*Gtr, Man*): Penleigh, 38 West Street, Warminster, Wiltshire BA12 8JN ☎ 01985 215291

HORTON Brian (*Gtr*): 62 Atlee Court, Lansbury Park, Caerphilly, Glam CF8 1QU ☎ 029 2086 7426

HOWARD Samantha (*Gtr, Pf, Hmca*): Corstone Farm, Broadwoodkelly, Winkleigh, Devon EX19 8EF ☎ 01837 831441

HOWARD Trevor (*Gtr, Voc, Kbds*): Japonica Cottage, Shaw, Swindon, Wilts SN5 9PJ ☎ 01793 770455

HUGHES L (*Gtr*)

HYETT Keith (*Cl Gtr, B Gtr*): 29 Barrow Close, Quedgeley, Gloucester GL2 6YP ☎ 01452 728103

IGGY (*Ld Gtr, Rh Gtr, B Gtr, Dms*): 77 Somerset Crescent, Melksham, Wiltshire SN12 7LX ☎ 01225 704661, 0421 637525 mob

INDGE Robert (*Gtr, B Gtr, Kbds*): 26 Dingle Road, Abergavenny, Monmouthshire NP7 7AR ☎ 01873 856443, 01873 857431

ISAAC Myfyr (*Gtr*): Caeheulog, Maendy, Nr Cowbridge, S Glam CF71 7TG ☎ 014463 3216

JACK Robert (*Gtr*): 2 Milland Close, Abbeymeads, Swindon, Wilts SN2 3XJ ☎ 01793 700442

JEFFERIS Philip (*Gtr, Voc*): 16 North Hill Way, Bridport, Dorset DT6 4JX

JENNER Anthony (*Sp Gtr*): Summerhill, 1 Sion Hill Place, Lansdown, Bath BA1 5SJ

JOHNSON David (*Gtr*): Ocean Breeze, 28 Fulmar Road, Rest Bay, Porthcawl, Mid Glamorgan CF36 3UL ☎ 01656 773263, 04111 47160, 01656 773263

JOHNSON Martin (*Gtr, Song W*): Glan -Yr-Afon-Uchaf, Llawr Y Glyn Caersws, Powys, Mid Wales SY17 5RJ ☎ 01686 430552

JOHNSON Mike (*Ac Gtr, Hmca, Voc*): 29 Bronawelon, Barry, South Glamorgan CF6 8PR ☎ 01446 742760

JOHNSON Robert (*Gtr, B Gtr*): 1 Little Hill, Buckland, St Mary, Chard, Somerset TA20 3SS ☎ 01460 234249

JOHNSON Simon (*Gtr, Voc, Man, Tamb*): c/o Ann Hamilton, Rosedene, Lime Head, St Breward, Bodmin, Cornwall PL30 4LU ☎ 01208 851447

JONES Mazlyn (*Gtr, Santoor*): Well Barn, Trammagenna, Camelford, Cornwall PL32 9RP ☎ 01640 213800

JONES Robert (*Gtr, B Gtr*): Flat 3, 120 High Street, Cheltenham GL50 1EQ ☎ Cheltenham 5246

JORY Sarah (*Pd Gtr*): 10 Tennyson Road, Balderton, Newark NG24 3QH ☎ 01636 701455

JULES (*Gtr, Kbds*): Higher Hallwood, Petrockstowe, Okehampton, Devon EX20 3HW ☎ 01837 810135, 0498 730978

KELLY Richard (*Gtr, B Gtr*): 26 Allt-Y-Carne, Goodwick, Pembs SA64 0AT ☎ 01348 873738, 0374 655298

KENNEDY Andrew (*Gtr*): 53 Bittern Avenue, Abbeydale, Gloucester GL4 8NG ☎ 01452 414860

KHAN Adam (*Gtr*): Hunza House, Church Road, Seven Sisters, Neath Glamorgan SA10 9DT ☎ 01639 700 473

KIMBER Rachel (*E Gtr, Ac Gtr, B Gtr, Cel, Dm*): 13 Meadow Street, Pontcanna, Cardiff CF1 9PY ☎ 029 2021 9937

KING Bob (*Gtr, Bjo, Man, B Gtr*): Hereford Cottage, Doddiscombsleigh, Exeter EX6 7PZ ☎ 01647 52621

KING Michael (*Gtr, Voc, Hmca, B Gtr, Pf*): Moordown, Northfield Road, Tetbury, Glos GL8 8HE ☎ 01666 502797, 01666 504569

KING Robert (*Gtr, Man*)

KING Roy (*Gtr*): Tanglewood, Drakewalls, Gunnislake, Cornwall PL18 9EJ ☎ 01822 833800

KNIGHT Glyn (*Gtr*): 187 College Road, Whitchurch, Cardiff, South Wales CF4 2NT ☎ 029 2061 1308

KNIGHT Barry (*Gtr, Voc*): The Village Hall Cottage, Whitchurch Canonicorum, Bridport, Dorset DT6 6RF ☎ 01297 489431

KNIGHTLEY Steve (*Gtr, Man Cel, Cuatro*): Church Cottage, Whitchurch Canonicorum, Bridport, Dorset DT6 6RQ ☎ 01297 489520, 01297 489520

LACEY Duncan (*Pd Gtr, E Gtr*): 87 Manor Road, Bradley, Barton, Newton Abbot, Devon TQ12 1SW ☎ 01626 66171

LACEY Robert (*Ac Gtr*): Windruch, Jacksons Way, Goddwick, Pembrokeshire, West Wales SA64 0EN ☎ 01348 873010

LAKEMAN Sean Nicholas (*Ac Gtr, B Gtr, Man*): 1 Bedford Place, Horrabridge, Yelverton, Devon PL20 7QD ☎ 01822 855494

LAMB Peter (*Gtr, B Gtr*): 17 Highlands, Potterne, Devizes, Wilts SN10 5NS ☎ 01380 724240

LAWRENCE Henry (*Gtr, Man, Hmca, B Gtr, Bjo*): 2 Woodmans Cottages, Brockham End, Lansdown, Bath BA1 9BZ ☎ 01225 481185

LAWRENCE James (*Gtr, B Gtr, Dms*): 112 Chester Close, New Inn, Ponty Pool, Gwent NP4 0LU ☎ 01495 753320

LAWRENCE Peter (*Gtr, Pf, Vln*): Mill Cottage, Stokeinteignhead, Newton Abbott, Devon TQ12 4QS ☎ 01626 873691

LAYCOCK Gabriel (*E Gtr, Hrn*): 7 St. Rumbolds Road, Shaftesbury, Dorset SP7 8NE

LEWIS Gary (*Gtr*): 96 Rhodfa Fadog, Parc Gwernfadog, Morriston, Swansea, S. Wales SA6 6LQ ☎ 01792 781391, 01792 781391

LEWIS Graham (*Gtr, Sl Gtr, Hmca, Pf, Bjo*): 525 Maesyrhandir, Newtown, Powys SY16 1HX ☎ 01686 623534

LEWRY David (*Gtr, Bjo, Dul, Man*): Windward, 4 Riverview, Polperro Road, Looe, Cornwall PL13 2BW ☎ 01503 264534, 0966 544213 mob

LINDRIDGE Nigel (*Ac Gtr, E Gtr*): 5 Folland Road, Glanaman, Ammanford, Dyfed SA18 2BX ☎ 01269 824996

LINNARD Carl (*Gtr*): 17 Coed Leddyn, Energlyn, Caerphilly, Mid Glamorgan CF8 ☎ 029 2086 6230

LLEWELLYN Tim (*Gtr, B Gtr, Kbds*): 20 Windsor Terrace, Totterdown, Bristol BS3 4UF ☎ 0117 9775984

LLEWELLYN Trevor (*Gtr, Kbds*): 8 Henry Street, Totterdown, Bristol BS3 4UD ☎ 0117 9721639

LORD Timothy (*Gtr*): 5 Chynowen Parc, Cubert, Newquay, Cornwall TR8 5HD ☎ 01637 830378, 07977 675492

LORING Keith (*Gtr, Pf*): St Madoc Christian Yth Camp, Llanmadoc, Gower, South Wales SA3 1DB ☎ 01792 386291

LOWE Veronica (*Gtr, Cl Gtr, Pf, Voc, Org*): 383 Innsworth Lane, Churchdown, Glos GL3 1HA ☎ 01452 856093

LUCAS David (*E Gtr, Ac Gtr, B Gtr, Db, Voc*): Orchard House, Carclew, Perran-Ar-Worthal, Nr Truro, Cornwall TR3 7PB ☎ 01872 863182, 01872 864213

LUCAS Peter (*Gtr, B Gtr, Pf*): Wisteria Cottage, Bower Chalke, Wilts SP5 5BU ☎ 01722 780744

LUTHER Paul (*E Gtr, Cl Gtr*): 295 Devizes Road, Salisbury, Wilts SP2 9LU ☎ 01722 322091

M87 (*Gtr, B Gtr*): Glen Sannox, Bryn-Y-Mor Road, Aberystwyth, Wales SY23 2HX ☎ 01970 623554

MACFADYEN Harry (*Gtr, Man, Bag*): 124 High Street, Codford, Wiltshire BA12 0NH ☎ 01985 850910

MACKERRON Nick (*Gtr*): 6 Clifton Terrace, Hayle, Cornwall TR27 4BP ☎ 01736 756787

MAGGS Hywel (*Gtr*): 39 East Grove Road, Newport, Gwent NP9 9QH ☎ 01633 273542

MANNION Peter (*Gtr, Kbds, B Gtr, Dms, Viol*): 27 Trefonen Avenue, Llandrindod Wells, Powys, Wales LD1 5YB ☎ 01597 823515

MARKS Toby Anthony (*Gtr, Kbds, Per*): Rose Cottage, Vicarage Lane, Draycott, Cheddar BS27 3SH ☎ 01934 742953, 01934 743283 fax

MARTEN Neville (*Gtr, Voc*): Flat 2, 4 Portland Place, Bath BA1 2RU ☎ 01225 462638, 01225 442244, 01225 462986

MARTIN Eddie (*Gtr, Hmca, Pf*): 33 Perry Street, Easton, Bristol BS5 0SY ☎ 01179 079358

MARTIN Elfrida (*Gtr, Voc, Man*): 12 Beauchamp Street, Riverside, Cardiff CF1 8RW ☎ 029 2023 3440

MARWOOD Keith (*E Gtr, B Gtr*): 20 Trickie Close, Tiverton, Devon EX16 6HF ☎ 0113 275 6255

MASON Peter (*Gtr*): 30 Victoria Road, Salisbury, Wilts SP1 3NG ☎ 01722 334672

MASSON Colin (*Gtr, B Gtr, Kbds, Rec, Per*): The Cottage, Greenacres Farm, Coombe Bissett, Nr Salisbury, Wiltshire SP5 4LP ☎ 01722 718639

MATTHEWS Ceri (*Gtr, Bag, Clt*): Alltfechan, Pencader, Carmarthenshire, Wales SA39 9BU ☎ 01559 384962

MAULDON Robert (*Gtr, Hmca*): 3 Fairway Close, Churston Ferrers, Brixham, Devon TQ5 0LG ☎ 01803 842866

MAYBEY Jon (*Gtr*): Ivy Cottage, Fore Street, Thorncombe, Chard, Somerset TA20 4PP

MCCULLOCH Malcolm (*Gtr, Bjo, Auto Hrp*): 29 Clanfield, Sherborne, Dorset DT9 6AZ

MEGGESON David (*Gtr, Bjo*): Egypt Cottage, Egypt Lane, Chulmleigh, North Devon EX18 7BT ☎ 01769 80206

MILLIN Stewart (*Gtr*): 88 Wootton Bassett Road, Swindon, Wiltshire SN1 5HB ☎ 01793 613785, 0589 849653

MILLS John (*Cl Gtr*): 1 Fairways, Dilton Marsh, Westbury, Wilts BA13 3RU ☎ 01373 865039

MILLS Timothy (*E Gtr*): The Forge, Lynbridge, Lynton, North Devon EX35 6BD ☎ 01598 53453

MONK John (*Gtr*): Thimble Hall, Ivy Bank Park, Entry Hill, Bath BA2 5NE ☎ 01225 310453

MONTGOMERY Doc (*Gtr, B Gtr, Dms, Kbds*): 63 Braddons Hill Rd East, Torquay, Devon TQ1 1HF ☎ 01803 201918

MOORE Simon (*Gtr*): 106 Keslake Road, Kensal Rise, London NW6 6DG ☎ 020 8969 9398

MORETON Chris (*Gtr, Bjo, Man*): 10 Castle Parade, Usk, Gwent NP5 1AA ☎ 01291 673849

MORGAN Andrew (*Gtr, Man, Bjo, Pf*): Flat 3, 2 Chaddesley Villas, Mt. Pleasant, Swansea SA1 6HA ☎ 01792 651345

MOSLEY Janet (*Cl Gtr, Kbds, Pf*): 12 The Hyde, Purton, Swindon, Wiltshire SN5 9DY ☎ 01793 772832

MOSS Martin (*Gtr*): 32 Milner Road, Horfield, Bristol, Avon BS7 9PQ ☎ 240982

MURPHY Barrie (*Gtr*): Caretakers Lodge, Bronwydd House, Porth, Rhondda, Cynon Taff CF39 9DLL ☎ 01443 680566

NELSON Michael (*Gtr, T Sax, Clt, Kbds*): The Old Vicarage, The Square, North Molton, South Molton, North Devon EX36 3HP ☎ 01598 740417

NEWMAN Caleb (*Gtr*): 43 West Lee, Cowbridge Road East, Cardiff CF1 9DR ☎ 029 2037 2215

NEWMAN Paul (*Gtr*): 43 Alstone Croft, Cheltenham, Glos GL51 8HB ☎ 01242 692205

NG Nathan (*Gtr, Kbds*): 6 Seaton Road, Bristol BS5 6BH ☎ 0117 951 8259, 0958 653891 mob

NICHOLAS Paul (*Gtr, Bjo, Man*): 21 Chapman Street, Llanelli, Dyfed SA15 3EB

NICHOLSON Pete (*Gtr, Vln*): 10 Walmesley Terrace, Walcot, Bath BA1 6DW ☎ 01225 336333

NOBLE Brian (*Gtr*): The Old Post Office, France Lane, Hawkesbury Upton, Nr Bodminton, Avon GL9 1AF ☎ 0145423 793

ORZABAL Roland (*Gtr, Kbds, Voc*): c/o Martin Greene Ravden, 55 Loudoun Road, St Johns Wood, London NW8 0DL

OSBORNE Lewis (*Gtr*): 47 Sutherland Avenue, Yate BS17 5UQ ☎ 01454 324460

PACKER Benjamin (*Gtr, Sax, Hmca*): Address Unknown ☎ 020 8422 6511

PALFREY Dafydd (*Gtr, Voc*): 10 Riverview Court, Llandaf, Cardiff, South Glamorgan CF5 2QJ ☎ 029 2055 5055

PALLETT Ian (*Gtr, B Gtr, Kbds*): Flat 1 Garden Floor, Portland House, Aberaeron, Ceredigion SA46 0AX

PALLETT Nicholas (*Gtr, B Gtr, Kbds, Voc*): 1 Grantham Road, Kingswood, Bristol BS15 1JR ☎ 0117 9353250

PARFITT (*Gtr, Pf*): 59 Stone Manor, Bisley Road, Stroud, Glos GL5 1JD ☎ 01453 758738 & fax

PARKER Jon (*Gtr, Dms*): 9 Heath Cottage, Bockhampton, Dorchester, Dorset DT2 8QL ☎ 01305 849156, 01305 251999

PARKER Keith (*Gtr, Bjo*): The Whimple, Green Lane West, Marazion, Cornwall TR17 0HH ☎ 023 8067 11438

PARTRIDGE Andrew (*Gtr, Voc*): 106 Avenue Road, Swindon, Wiltshire SN1 4DB ☎ 01793 615428

PARTRIDGE Piers (*Gtr, Dobro, Man, Didj*): The Covey, Tower House Lane, Wraxall, Bristol BS19 1JR ☎ 01275 810166 & fax

PATCHES (*Gtr, Voc*): 29 Ash Grove, Seaton, Devon EX12 2TT ☎ 01297 23184

PATTEMORE Gerald (*Gtr, Dms*): 5 Langmead Road, Crewkerne, Somerset TA18 8HQ ☎ 01460 75136

PAUL Raymond (*Gtr, Kbds, Bjo*): 131 Slad Road, Stroud, Glos GL5 1RD ☎ 01453 750125

PAVELING David (*Gtr*): Greenbanks, Gustory Road, Crantock, Nr Newquay, Cornwall TR8 7RG

PEACOCK, LWCMD Nicholas (*Cl Gtr*): 718 Newport Road, Cardiff, Wales ☎ 029 2077 7535

PENROSE Marcus (*E Gtr, B Gtr, Db*): 01872 264158, 020 8361 3521

PERRY Fraser (*Ld Gtr*): 15 Church Road, Newton Abbot, Devon TQ12 1AL ☎ 01626 333404, 0411 117589

PETT Andrew (*Gtr*): 49 Dores Road, Upper Stratton, Swindon SN2 6QU ☎ 01793 706390

PHILLIPS Ben (*Gtr, Per*): 5 Monmouth Street, Topsham, Eseter, Devon EX3 0AJ ☎ 01392 877066

PICKFORD Jonathan (*Gtr*): Windmill Cottage, St Peter, Jersey C.I. JE3 7DW ☎ 01534 83706

PIPER Max (*Gtr, Kbds, Voc*): Rockwood, 3 Westcroft Road, Holsworthy, Devon EX22 6BY ☎ 01409 253916

PLUMMER James (*Gtr*): 6 Chavenage, Kingswood, Bristol, Avon BS15 4LA ☎ 0117 9405234

PORTMAN Tom (*Gtr, Dobro, Bjo, Man*): 11 Old Wells Road, Glastonbury, Somerset BA6 8FD ☎ 01458 832 516

POWELL Owen (*Gtr*): 89 Allensbank Road, Heath, Cardiff, South Glam CF4 4PP ☎ 029 2061 7960

POWER Stephanie (*Cl Gtr, Dms, Per*): Lower Trevyr, Grosmont, Abergavenny, Gwent NP7 8HS ☎ 01267 290108

PRAZE Chris (*Gtr, Kbds, Dms*)

PROVIS Andrew (*Gtr*): 2 Shooting Park Cottages, Launceston, Cornwall PL15 9BH ☎ 01566 776129

PROVIS Geoff (*Gtr*): 18 Highfield Park Road, Launceston, Cornwall PL15 7DY ☎ 01566 775820

QUICK Jonathan (*Gtr, B Gtr, Man, Kbds*): Bridge Cottage, Templeton Bridge, Tiverton, Devon EX16 8BP ☎ 01884 860814

RAINBOW Chris (*Gtr, Voc*): 24 The Avenue, Clevedon, Avon BS21 7EA ☎ Clevedon 874751

RAWLING Michael (*Gtr*): Treverbyn House, Pendower Road, Veryan, Truro, Cornwall TR2 5QL ☎ 01872 501201, 01872 501408 day

RAWSON Paul (*Gtr, Voc*): 54 Coronation Road, Southville, Bristol BS3 1AR ☎ 0117 974 2675, 0117 904 1765, 0117 946 6575

REASON Jules (*Gtr*): Flat 1 5 Elton Road, Bishopston, Bristol BS7 8DF ☎ 0117 9423717

REILLY Lorraine (*Gtr, Pf, Kbds*): Flat 4, 62 Polsloe Road, Exeter EX1 2EA ☎ 01392 276021

RHODES David (*Gtr, Voc*): The White House, Nettleton, Nr Chippenham, Wilts SN14 7NS ☎ 01249 782359

ROBINS Tom (*Gtr*): Malahat, Penelewey, Feocok, Truro, Cornwall TR3 6 QX ☎ 01872 864055, 0839 573162

RODGE John (*Gtr, Db*): 43 Vicary Crescent, Pill, Milford Haven, Dyfed SA73 2QH ☎ 01646 698731

ROGERS Bridgitte (*Gtr*): 44 Kimberley Park Road, Falmouth, Cornwall TR11 2DB ☎ 01326 312700

ROWCLIFFE Stephen (*Rh Gtr*): 27 All Saints Road, Clifton, Bristol BS8 2JL ☎ 0117 985 0600

ROWLES Peter (*Gtr, Voc, Vln, Kbds*): 8 Edward Wilson House, Princess Elizabeth Way, Cheltenham, Glos GL51 0HB ☎ 01242 702424

RUBERRY Mark (*Gtr, Voc*) ☎ 01633 281447, 01403 170775

SABAN Justin (*Gtr, Hmca*): 43 Heywood Drive, Luton, Beds LU2 7LP

SAGE Matthew (*E Gtr*): 41 High Cross Drive, Rogerstone, Newport, Gwent NP1 9AB ☎ 01633 895870

SCOLLEN Thomas (*Gtr*): Manor Farm Lodge, Milbourne, Malmesbury, Wiltshire SN16 9JB ☎ 01666 825742

SCOTT Damien (*Gtr*): 174-175 Broadway, Treforest, Pontypridd, Mid Glamorgan CF37 1BH ☎ 01443 486475

SHANNON Hugh (*E Gtr, Ac Gtr*): Windmills, Narberth Road, Tenby, South West Wales SA70 8TJ ☎ 01834 842200

SHARP Johnny (*Ld Gtr, Sitar, Tamboor, Kbds,*): 2A Mount View Cottages, Landkey Road, Barnstaple, North Devon EX32 0HP ☎ 01271 325896

SHAW Andrew (*Gtr, Club Dj*): Melbourne, Decoy Road, Newton Abbot, Devon TQ12 1DU ☎ 01626 367076

SHAW Christopher (*Gtr, Synth, A Sax*): 4 Lock's Court, Porthcawl, Mid Glamorgan CF36 3JJ ☎ 01656 786001, 0441 443781 mob

SHIRLEY-SMITH Leo (*Gtr, Kbds*): Studio House, Elcot Lane, Marlborough, Wilts SN8 2AZ ☎ 01672 515025

SIMPSON Richard (*Gtr, B Gtr, Kbds, Dms, Voc*): 30 Fforddy Gamlas, Copper Meadow, Gowerton, Swansea SA4 3DT ☎ 01792 879433, 0402 455985 mob

SMALLMAN Mark (*Gtr, Voc*): The Stables, Downswood, Great Cheverell, Deviles, Wiltshire SN10 5TW ☎ 01380 812174, 01380 812174

SMITH David (*Gtr, Voc*): 76 Alexandra Road, Gorsenon, Swansea, S. Wales SA4 4NU ☎ 01792 891307

SMITH Robert (*Gtr, Voc*): 5 Vyvyan Road, Clifton, Bristol BS8 3AD ☎ 0117 9738265

SMY Shannon (*Gtr, Voc*): Kingshill, Cockmill Lane, East Pennard, Shepton Mallet BA4 6TR ☎ 01749 860660, 01523 400817

SOTHCOTT Graham (*Gtr, Db, B Gtr*): 16 Chantry Grove, Lawrence Weston, Bristol BS11 0QH ☎ 0117 9829591

SOUPER Hilary (*Gtr*)

SOUTHERN Graeme (*Gtr, Synth*): 5 Kirkstall Close, Toothill, Swindon SN5 8ED ☎ 01793 693356

SPEIGHT Colin (*E Gtr, Cl Gtr*): 44 Church Street, Maiden Bradley, Nr Warminster, Wilts BA12 7HW ☎ 01985 844405

SQUIRE David (*E Gtr*): 4 Oaklea Close, Kingsbridge, South Devon TQ7 1HW ☎ 01548 856517, 0410 454907

STAGLES Norman (*Gtr*): 189, Portland Road, Wyke Regis, Weymouth, Dorset DT4 9BH ☎ 01305 789748

STEER Richard (*Gtr*): 4 Princecroft, Warminster, Wiltshire BA12 8NT

STOKES Peter (*Gtr, Man, Mando*): Woodleigh, Godolphin Road, Helston, Cornwall TR13 8QN ☎ 01326 564744

STRANGE Michael (*Gtr*): 103 Bruce Street, Swindon, Wilts SN2 2EN ☎ 01793 531620

STRAUSS-SHURETY Mhairi (*Gtr, Vln, Per*): 3 Walnut Close, Cheddar, Somerset BS27 3JZ ☎ 01934 741212

STUCKEY Keith (*E Gtr*): 2 Cwmneol Place, Cwmaman, Aberdare, Mid Glam CF44 6PA ☎ 01685 870497

SULLIVAN Eric (*Gtr, B Gtr*): 63 Ackland Road, Bridgend, Mid Glamorganshire CF31 1TF ☎ 01656 68663, 0836 321 220 car

SULLIVAN Stephen (*Gtr*): 3 Lon - Y - Rhedyn, Caerphilly, South Wales CF83 1DR ☎ 029 2086 8058, 029 2086 8058

SUMMERS Al (*Cl Gtr, E Gtr, Lute*): 61 Bratton Road, Westbury, Wilts BA13 3ES ☎ 01373 864721

SUMMERS Gerry (*Gtr, B Gtr*) ☎ 0117 951 5510

TAYLOR Neil (*Gtr*): 22 Pines Road, Bitton, Bristol BS15 6JN ☎ 01225 852450

THEOBALD Danny (*Gtr, Pf*): Hazeldene, Victoria Road, Barnstaple, North Devon EX32 9HP ☎ 01271 374797

THOMAS Arthur (*Gtr, Bjo*): 469 Blandford Road, Efford, Plymouth PL3 6JE ☎ 01725 265834

THOMAS Jj (*Gtr, Kbds*): 23 Gwendraeth Town, Kidwelly, Dyfed SA17 4UB ☎ 01554 891352

THOMAS Stephen (*Gtr, B Gtr, Voc, Pf*): 9 Hawkes Ridge, Ty-Canol, Cwmbran, Gwent NP44 6JS ☎ 01633 868998

THOMPSON Colin (*Gtr*): 80 Dorchester Road, Maiden Newton, Dorchester, Dorset DT2 0BG ☎ 01300 320558

THOMPSON Keith (*Gtr, Pf, B Gtr, Hmca*): 46 Libertus Road, Cheltenham, Glos GL51 8BX ☎ 01242 581136

TILSTON Steve (*Gtr*): 17 Station Road, Oakworth, Keighley, Yorks BD22 0DU ☎ 01535 642 988

TOOGOOD Jack (*Gtr, Uke, H Gtr, B Ldr*): 70 Malvern Road, St George, Bristol 5 BS5 8JB ☎ 0117 9551227

TORRES-COLOMAR Daniel (*Gtr, Kbds, Dms*): 17A Haccombe Close, Exeter, Devon EX4 1SA ☎ 01392 217245

TOWELL Justin (*E Gtr, Ac Gtr, Kbds*): 44 Cresswell Avenue, Taunton, Somerset TA2 6LR ☎ 01823 254163

TREMAINE Jayni (*Gtr*): 16 Downend Road, Fishponds, Bristol BS16 5AP ☎ 01179 390276

TULLEY Christopher (*Gtr*)

TURLAND Terence (*Gtr, B Gtr, Flt*): Warleigh, Top Road, Downderry, Torpoint, Cornwall PL11 3LZ ☎ 0150 35 389

TURNER Jamie (*Gtr, Dms*): Manor House, North Poorton, Bridport, Dorset DT6 3TH ☎ 01308 485474 & fax, 0860 341114 mob

WALLWORK Terry (*Gtr*): 68 Polstain Road, Threemilestone, Truro, Cornwall TR3 6DH ☎ 01872 241845

WARD Martin (*Gtr, Com*): 41 Richmond Court, St Peters Street, Cardiff CF2 3AZ ☎ 029 2046 1079

WARDALE Alf (*Gtr*): 16 Thurlestone Road, Parklands, Swindon SN3 1EQ

WATKINS Paul (*Ld Gtr, Rh Gtr, B Gtr*): 20A Bishop Road, Ammanford, Carmarthenshire SA18 3HA ☎ 01269 597266, 0467 777195

WATKINS Peter (*Gtr*): Little Bowden, The Bourne, Banbury, Oxfordshire OX15 5PB ☎ 01608 737143

WATSON Barry (*Gtr, Hmca*): 362 Victoria Park Road, Leicester LE2 1XF

WATSON Michael (*Gtr, Sp Gtr, E Gtr*): Briar Cottage, 1 Back Stoke Lane, Westbury-on-Trym, Bristol BS9 3QT ☎ 0117 9620724

WATTS Greg (*Gtr*): 130 Gloucester Road, Cheltenham GL51 8NS ☎ 01242 528732

WEBBER Peter (*E Gtr, Ac Gtr, Ld Gtr, Rh Gtr*) ☎ 0117 9424418

WHEELER Daniel (*Gtr*): 94 High Street, Weston, Bath BA1 4DQ ☎ 01225 429449

WHITAKER Maxwell (*Gtr, Pf*): 34 Belvedere, Landsdown Road, Bath, Somerset BA1 5HR ☎ 01225 333970

WILDE (*Gtr, Dms, Voc*): 8 Danby Heights Close, Torquay, Devon TQ1 2HR ☎ 01803 380822

WILKINSON Bob (*Gtr, B Gtr*): 17 Bethania Road, Upper Tumble, Llanelli, Dyfed SA14 6DT ☎ 01269 841825

WILLIAMS Col (*Gtr, B Gtr*): 157 Duchy Drive, Preston, Paignton, Torbay TQ3 1EW ☎ 01803 553581

WILLIAMS James (*Gtr, Dms*): 373 Newport Road, Roath, Cardiff CF2 1RN ☎ 029 2045 0591, 029 2040 0088, 029 2025 0047

WILLIAMS Tony (*Gtr, Db*): 1 Tudor Crescent, Brynmawr, Gwent NP3 4HL ☎ 01495 311239

WILLIAMS Tony (*E Gtr, Cl Gtr, B Gtr*): 20 Quirke Street, Minehead, Somerset TA24 5TZ ☎ 01643 708701, 0370 550866 mob

WILLIAMSON Robin (*Gtr*): 32 Plasturton Ave, Cardiff CF1 7HH ☎ 029 2023 1739

WILLIS Michael (*E Gtr, Ac Gtr, Bjo*): 6 School Close, Chiseldon, Nr Swindon, Wilts SN4 0PA ☎ 01793 741359

WILSON Paul (*Gtr, Voc, Vln, Acc*): Hillfield, South Zeal, Okehampton, Devon EX20 2NY ☎ 01837 840219

WILSON Robert (*Gtr*): 158 Hulhah Road, Exmouth, Devon EX8 4RB

WIRTZ John (*Gtr*): Park Farm, Buckland Down, Frome, Somerset BA11 2RG ☎ 01373 813590, 01373 813518

WOOD Dave (*Gtr*): 190 Exwick Road, Exeter EX4 2BA ☎ 01392 434479

WOOLLS Martyn (*Cl Gtr, Gtr, Lute*): 6 Westward Place, Llangewydd Court, Bridgend, Mid Glam CF31 4XA

WOTTON Christopher (*Gtr, B Gtr, Dms, Vln*): 91 Steynton Road, Milford Haven, Pembrokeshire, West Wales SA73 1AD ☎ 01646 690567

WROTH Michael (*Gtr, B Gtr*): The Willows, Sedgemoor Road, Woolavington, Nr Bridgwater, Somerset TA7 8HN ☎ 01243 605793, 0589 733340 mob

WYGENS Jon (*Gtr, A Sax*): 37 High Street, Easton, Bristol BS56 6DW ☎ 0117 9247634

WYNN Dylan (*Gtr, Man, Cel, Ob*): Mill House, Ross Road, Abergavenny, Gwent NP7 5RF ☎ 01873 850968, 0403 361680, 01873 854850

YOUDALE Roy (*Sp Gtr, Pan P, Gtr, Flt*): 6 Highbury Road, Horfield, Bristol BS7 0BZ ☎ 0117 9511421

LONDON

ABELL Dick (*Gtr, Sax, Db, B Gtr, Man*): 14 Victoria Close, Hurst Road, Hurst Park, West Molesey Surrey KT8 9SQ ☎ 020 8224 1097

ABRAHAMS Leo (*Gtr, Pf, Voc*): 36 West Hill Road, Wandsworth, London SW18 1LN ☎ 020 8870 3239

ABRAHAMS Martin (*Gtr, B Gtr, Dms, Kbds*): 32A Courthope Road, London NW3 2LD ☎ 020 7428 9071

ADAMCZEWSKI Konrad (*Gtr*): 9 Toronto Terrace, Lewes, E Sussex BN7 2DU ☎ 01273 474268

ADAMS Brian (*Gtr*): Sayes Court Lodge, Liberty Lane, Addlestone, Surrey KT15 1LX

ADAMS Dean (*E Gtr, Ac Gtr, Voc, B Gtr, Pf*) ☎ 020 8245 0048, 0961 103737, 020 8245 0049

ADAMS Donald (*E Gtr, B Gtr, Voc*): 230 Archway Road, Highgate, London N6 5AX ☎ 020 8348 5299

ADAMS Justin (*Gtr*): 57A Randolph Avenue, London W9 1BQ ☎ 020 7289 7240

ADAMS Phil (*Gtr*): 159 Cuiken Terrace, Penicuik, Midlothian EH26 0AE

ADAMSON Ged (*Gtr, Kbds*): 54 Limes Grove, Lewisham, London SE13 6DE ☎ 020 8318 9381

ADDO Kojo (*Gtr, Kbds*): 9 Willow House, Maitland Park Villas, London NW3 2EB ☎ 020 7482 2507

ADIE Nicholas (*Gtr, Pf, Com, Arr*): 10 Westhorpe Road, London SW15 1QH ☎ 020 8788 2740

ADIVINO El (*Fl Gtr, Voc*): 46 Merceron House, Globe Road, Bethnal Green, London E2 0PA ☎ 020 8980 3243, 020 8980 5848

ADLAM Roy (*Gtr, B Gtr*): 68 Emberton Court, St John Street, London EC1V 0EP ☎ 020 7253 9473

AHWAI Robert (*Gtr, B Gtr*): 273 Park Road, Kingston-upon-Thames, Surrey KT2 5LW ☎ 020 8546 4709

AIME-AZIZA (*Gtr, B Gtr, Cong, Voc*): 12 Northgate, 445 High Road, North Finchley, London N12 0AR ☎ 020 8371 0240, 09565 84233

AITKEN Julius (*Gtr*): Flat 7, 65 Compayne Gardens, West Hampstead NW6 3DD ☎ 020 7277 1404

ALAN Gary (*Gtr, Voc, Tpt*): 5 Hillfield Lodge, Himley Road, Tooting, London SW17 9AN ☎ 020 8672 6469

ALDRED Jude (*Gtr, B Gtr, Kbds*): 10B Wyneham Road, Herne Hill, London SE24 9NT ☎ 020 7733 1172

ALDRIDGE Graham *(Gtr, Voc)*: 21 Derby Lodge, East End Road, London N3 3QG ☎ 020 8346 8991

ALEXANDER Charles *(Gtr)*: 13 Foulser Road, Tooting Bec, London SW17 8UE ☎ 020 8767 2213

ALLEN Benjamin *(E Gtr, Ac Gtr, Voc)*: 22 Tudor Way, Chase Side, Southgate, London N14 6PS ☎ 020 8886 2438, 01426 286944

ALLEYNE Ian *(Gtr, Voc)*: 47 Lodge Crescent, St Michael, Barbados, West Indies

ALLIE Yusef *(Gtr)*: 22 Florida Road, Thornton Heath, Surrey CR7 8EU ☎ 020 8679 3488

ALQUERES Gabriela *(Gtr, Voc)*: 15 Haselmere Road, London N8 9QP ☎ 020 8340 6858

AMES-HENDERSON Brian *(Gtr)*: 19 Camborne Mews, Ladbroke Grove, London W11 1QB ☎ 0958 646207

ANDERSON David *(Gtr, Kbds)*: Flat 7, 15 Cornwall Crescent, London W11 1PH ☎ 020 7727 1716

ANDERSON Emma *(Gtr)*: Flat 4, 5 Colville Houses, London W11 1JB

ANDERSON Paul *(Gtr, Dms)*: 216 Ferme Park Road, Crouch End, London N8 9BN ☎ 020 8348 0727

ANDERSON Ross *(Gtr, Kbds, Per)*: 7 Chadwick Road, London SE15 4RA ☎ 020 7732 6964

ANDERSON Ziggy *(Gtr, Pf)*: 57 Wolftencroft Close, Ingrave Street, Battersea, London SW11 2LB ☎ 020 7738 9717

ANDREW Nick *(Gtr)*: 198 Neasden Lane, Neasden, London NW10 1QA ☎ 020 8450 5993

ANDREW Philip *(Gtr, B Gtr, Voc)*: 55B Archel Road, Fulham, London W14 9QJ ☎ 020 8845 9066, 020 8748 9898

ANDREWS Christopher *(Gtr, Pf, Triangle, Tba)*: Ground Floor Flat, 12 Pinfold Road, Streatham, London SW16 2SN ☎ 020 8769 5390

ANDREWS Matthew *(Gtr, Kbds, B Gtr, Dms, Com)*: 326 Wood Vale, London SE23 3DZ

ANDREWS Stanley *(Gtr, Voc, Arr)*: 104 Blurton Road, Clapton, London E5 0NH ☎ 020 8986 0622

ANDROVIC Stipo *(Gtr, E Gtr, B Gtr)*: 76C Rochester Row, London SW1P 1JU ☎ 0956 349826 mob

ANSELL Stuart *(Gtr, Man, Bjo, Sitar)*: 26 Ferndale Road, Leytonstone, London E11 3DN ☎ 020 8539 2757

ANSTIS Stuart *(Gtr)*: c/o 115, 28-30 Wood Wharf, Horsferry Place, London SE10 9BT ☎ 020 8293 0999, 01473 828485, 020 8293 9525

ANT *(Gtr, Dms, B Gtr, Uke)*: Flat 24, Vauban Estate, Alscot Road, Bermondsey, London SE16 3QU ☎ 020 7252 1966

ANTHONY Charles *(Rh Gtr, Voc)*: 115 Damsonwood Road, Southall, Middlesex UB2 4RW ☎ 020 8843 0264

ANTOINE Anita *(Gtr, B Gtr, Voc)*: 3 Woodfrod Place, Preston Road, Wembley, Middlesex HA9 8TE ☎ 020 8723 5111

ANZALONE Maurizio *(Gtr)*: 16 Prome House, Burma Court, Green Lanes, London N16 9DU ☎ 020 7254 7020

AP GWYNEDD Peredur *(Gtr, B Gtr, Kbds)*: Flat 2B, 149 Bayham Street, Camden, London NW1 0AT ☎ 020 7267 6981

APPAPOULAY Eric *(Gtr)*: 101 Geere Road, Stratford, London E15 3PP ☎ 020 8555 3724, 0930 711 349

ARDILL Nony *(Gtr, Voc)*: 34 Parkholme Road, London E8 3AG ☎ 020 7254 0638

ARGENT Len *(Gtr)*: 27 Millbrook Gardens, Eastern Avenue, Romford, Essex RM2 5RP ☎ 01708 740107

ARKARNA *(Gtr, Kbds, B Gtr)*: 29 Beethoven St, London W10 4LJ ☎ 020 8969 0299

ARMISTEAD Brian *(Gtr, Voc)*: 39 Naylor Road, Whetstone, London N20 0HE ☎ 020 8445 1855

ARMISTEAD Paul *(E Gtr, Ac Gtr)*: 10A Lakeside Road, Palmers Green, London N13 4PR ☎ 020 8882 8426

ARMSTRONG Kevin *(Gtr)*: 13 Halstow Road, London NW10 5DB ☎ 020 8932 5888

ARROWSMITH David *(Gtr)*: Flat 10, 53 Tollington Park, London N4 3QP ☎ 020 7263 8876

ASHWORTH Dominic *(Gtr)*: 69 Humber Road, Blackheath, London SE3 7LR ☎ 020 8858 9502

ASTBURY Ian *(Gtr, Tamb)*: 6 Lansdowne Mews, London W11 3BH ☎ 020 7792 9494, 020 7792 1722 fax

ASTLEY Jon *(Gtr)*: A-Minor Record Co.Ltd, 2 Embankment, Twickenham, Middlesex TW1 3DU

ASTON Mark *(Gtr, Hmca)*: Address Unknown

ATACK Keith *(Gtr, Kbds)*: The Old School House, 16 The Lane, Tebworth, Beds. LU7 9QB ☎ 01525 875672

ATHA Graham *(Gtr, Db)*: 20 Buxton Drive, New Malden, Surrey KT3 3UZ ☎ 020 8949 3849

ATKINS Anthony *(Gtr, Dms, Voc)*: Thornton, Bounrebridge Lane, Stapleford Abbotts, Essex RM4 1LT ☎ 01708 688332

ATTWOOD John *(Gtr, Bjo)*: 32A Powis Square, London W11 2AY ☎ 020 7221 4951

AUBREY Keith *(Gtr, B Gtr, Kbds, Com)*: 15 Oxenham House, Benbow Street, London SE8 3DH ☎ 020 8691 5955

AUGUSTIN Nathaniel *(Gtr, Tbn, Voc, Tpt)*: 195 Oakington Manor Drive, Wembley, Middlesex HA9 6NA ☎ 020 8902 4700

AVERY Steve *(Gtr, Kbds, B Gtr)*

AVES Pete *(Gtr)*: 66A Upper Brockley Road, London SE4 1ST ☎ 020 8692 5001

AYIOTOU Tony *(Gtr, Voc)*: 7 Radcliff House, Bourne Estate, London EC1N 7SN ☎ 020 7242 7828, 0411 825250

BACKER Matthew *(Gtr, B Gtr, Voc)*: 11 Totteridge Lane, London N20 0EX ☎ 020 8446 3783

BACKMAN Nis *(Gtr, B Gtr, Pf)*: 20 Lytton Road, Leytonstone, London E11 1JH

BADEN-POWELL Edward *(Gtr, Kbds, B Gtr)*: D-Influence, 19 Ford Square, London E1 2HS ☎ 020 7702 7972, 020 7780 9562

BAEPPLER Thomas *(Ac Gtr, E Gtr, Gtr Synt)*: 188 Amyand Pk Road, St Margarets, Middlesex TW1 3HY ☎ 020 8891 3597

BAIKIE Peter *(Gtr, Kbds, Voc)*: Flat 2, 1 Waldenshaw Road, London SE23 3XP ☎ 020 8699 5343

BAILEY Derek *(Gtr)*: 14 Downs Road, London E5 8DS ☎ 020 8986 6904

BAILEY Gregg *(Gtr, B Gtr, Vln, Man)*: 8 Granville Rd, London N4 4EL ☎ 020 8340 2414

BAILEY Michael *(Gtr, Pf)*: 29A Belsize Square, London NW3 4HU ☎ 020 7431 2544

BAILEY Renford *(Gtr)*: 45A Downs Park Road, London E8 2HY

BAIRNSON Ian *(Gtr)*: Herons Lodge, Old Mill Lane, Bray, Berkshire SL6 2BG ☎ 01628 30950

BAISLEY Simon *(Gtr)*: 139 Crest Road, Neasden, London NW2 7NA ☎ 020 8908 2941

BAKER Andy *(Gtr, B Gtr, Kbds, Voc)*: 94 Sandmere Road, Clapham, London SW4 7QH ☎ 020 7737 4690, 01523 444578 pager

BAKER Mark *(E Gtr, Kbds, Pf, B Gtr, Dms)*: 29 Chalford Close, West Molsey, Surrey KT8 2QL ☎ 020 8873 0233

BAKER Peter *(Gtr, Kbds)*: 28 High Firs, Swanley, Kent BR8 8NS ☎ 01322 669425

BAKER Philip *(Gtr, B Gtr, Kbds)*: Flat 4, 33 Langham Road, West Green, London N15 3QX

BAKER Timothy *(Gtr)*: 327A West End Lane, West Hampstead, London NW6 1RS ☎ 020 7431 1428

BANERJEE Robin *(Gtr)*: 64A Melrose Avenue, Willesden Green, London NW2 4JT ☎ 020 8452 3697

BANNERMAN Kari *(Ac Gtr, E Gtr, Voc, Af Dms)*: 3 Blenheim Road, Stratford, London E15 1UF ☎ 020 8555 0339

BARCLAY Bill *(Gtr)*: 10 Kingsclere Court, Gloucester Road, Barnet EN5 1NB ☎ 020 8361 7609

BARFIELD Drew *(Gtr, B Gtr)*: Basement, 69 Camberwell Grove, London SE5 8JE ☎ 020 7703 9926

BARLOW David *(Gtr, Voc, Bjo)*: 18 Underhill Road, Dulwich, London SE22 0AH ☎ 020 8693 2849

BARNES Jeffrey *(Gtr, Pf)*: 72 Eltham Park Gardens, London SE9 1AR

BARNES Michael *(Gtr, Pf, B Gtr)*: 39 The Fairway, Bickley, Kent BR1 2JQ ☎ 020 8467 0338, 020 8249 0034

BARNETT Ricky *(Gtr)*: 30 Lee Church Street, Lewisham, London SE13 5SF ☎ 020 8318 2425

BARRATT Chris *(Gtr, B Gtr, Dms)*: 27 Kings Lane, Sutton, Surrey SM1 4NY ☎ 020 8395 5487

BARRE Martin *(Gtr)*: Jethro Tull Productions, P.O Box 159, Witney, Oxon OX8 6JP ☎ 01993 709901

BARREAU Andre *(Gtr, B Gtr)*: 15 Gloucester Mews, London W2 3HE ☎ 020 7724 2011

BARRETT Timothy *(Gtr, B Gtr, Pf, Uke)*: 235 Hanworth Road, Hampton, Middx TW12 3EF ☎ 020 8288 8549

BARRY J J *(Gtr)*: 49 Merrivale Mews, Yiewsley, Middlesex UB7 7LZ ☎ 01895 421605

BARTAIN Daniel *(Gtr)*: Alyamama Villag1, Villa #40, PO Box 61279, Riyadh 11565 Kingdom Of, Saudi Arabia ☎ +96 61 241 3267

BARTER Darrin *(Gtr)*: 3 Holmsdale Close, Iver, Bucks SL0 9HY ☎ 01753 655015

BARTER Ian *(Gtr)*: 10 Ponsenby Place, Pimblico, London SW1 ☎ 020 7821 1605

BARTHOLOMEW Simon *(Gtr)*: Sedley Richard Laurence, 23 Bridford Mews, Off Devonshire Street, London W1N 1CQ ☎ 020 7371 7008, 020 7371 7708

BARTON Tim *(Gtr, B Gtr, Pf)*: 23 Overhill Road, East Dulwich, London SE22 0PQ ☎ 01865 794077

BASILISCO Mario *(Fl Gtr)*: 27 Bradley Road, London SE19 3NT ☎ 020 8653 0292

BATEMAN David *(Gtr)*: 2C Wharfedale St, Earls Court, London SW10 9AL ☎ 020 7244 8809

BATES Anthony *(Gtr, B Gtr, Kbds, Dms)*: 92A Bonner Road, Bethnal Green, London E2 9JU ☎ 020 8980 4374

BATH Darrell *(Gtr, E Gtr, Ac Gtr, Dobro, Ma)*: 34A Flower Lane, Mill Hill, London NW7 2JE ☎ 020 8959 2825 & fax, 020 7722 8047

BAUTISTA Manuel *(Gtr)*: 37A Knebworth House, Springfields, Union Grove, London SW8 2RS ☎ 020 7498 3542

BAXTER Shaun *(Gtr)*: 37 Borough Road, Isleworth, Middx YW7 5DT ☎ 020 8568 6629

BEARD Ana *(Gtr, Pf)*: 10 Hawarden Road, Walthamstow, London E17 6NF

BEARDSMORE Andrew *(E Gtr, Ac Gtr, B Gtr, Kbds, V)*: 15 Michels Row, Richmond, Surrey TW9 2SU ☎ 020 8332 9554

BEASLEY Darren *(Gtr, B Gtr, Per, Synth)*: 67 Commonside East, Mitcham, Surrey CR4 2QB ☎ 020 8648 6536

BEAUCHAMP Geoffrey *(Gtr, B Gtr)*: 21A Barons Court Road, West Kensington, London W14 9DY ☎ 020 7385 9429, 0958 449130 mob, 020 7386 5253

BECK Jeff *(Gtr)*: c/o Deuce Music Ltd, 17 Hereford Mansions, Hereford Road, London W2 5BA ☎ 020 7727 5858, 020 7229 5934 fax

BECKETT John *(Gtr, Kbds)*: Flat A, 22 Hillfield Avenue, London N8 7DT ☎ 020 8347 6577

BEEBEE Chris *(Gtr)*: 110 Framfield Road, Hanwell, London W7 1NJ ☎ 020 8567 9439

BEHRENS Adam *(Gtr)* ☎ 04325 302052 pager

BELL Phil *(Gtr, B Gtr, Dms)*: Flat 3, 18 Lady Somerset Road, London NW5 1UP ☎ 020 7485 2960

BELL Richard *(Gtr, Pf, B Gtr)*: 32 Monson Road, Harlesden, London NW10 5UP ☎ 020 8965 8147

BELLSHAM Mark *(Gtr, Db, B Gtr, A Sax, T Sax)*: 39 York Gardens, Braintree, Essex CM7 6NF ☎ 01376 323160

BELMONT Martin *(E Gtr, Ac Gtr, B Gtr)*: 101A Cricklewood Broadway, London NW2 3JG ☎ 020 8450 2885

BENBOW Steve *(Ac Gtr, E Gtr)*: 55 St Marks Road, Old Hanwell W7 2PN ☎ 020 8579 6804

BENIE Noel *(Gtr, B Gtr)*: 50 Ivydale Road, London SE15 3BS ☎ 0956 431820

BENNETT Nigel *(Gtr)*: 11, Berwyn Road, Richmond, Surrey TW10 5BP ☎ 020 8876 4417

BENNETT Steve *(Gtr, Voc)*: 98 Norfolk House Road, London SW16 1JH ☎ 020 8769 3873, 020 7371 9900

BENNETT Winston *(Gtr, Voc)*: 14A Tweedale Road, Carshalton, Surrey SM5 1SU ☎ 020 8641 4240

BENTHAM John *(Gtr, Sax, Kbds)*: 45 Fawnbrake Avenue, Herne Hill, London SE24 0BE ☎ 020 7733 4922

BERDICHEVSKY Daniel *(Gtr)*: Flat 4, 855 Finchley Road, London NW11 8LX ☎ 020 8458 4843

BERG Rickard *(Gtr, Kbds)*: 73B Cromford Road, London SW18 1PA

BERNEZ *(E Gtr, Gtr, Synth)*: 169 Bellenden Road, Peckham, London SE15 4DG ☎ 020 7732 7459

BERRY Richard *(Gtr, Voc)*: 19 Novello Strret, London SW6 4JB ☎ 020 7731 1145

BERRYMAN Evan *(Gtr, Voc, Kbds, B Gtr, Tpt)*: 15 Browning Road, Leytonstone, London E11 3AR ☎ 020 8989 7405

BESPOKE MUSIC *(Gtr, Pf, Kbds, Hrn)*: 157 Hamilton Road, West Norwood, London SE27 9SE ☎ 0850 588918

BIANCOFIORE Michele *(Gtr, B Gtr, Per, Pf)*: Flat A, 10 Thorparch Road, London SW8 4RU

BIBI Robin *(Gtr, B Gtr, Voc)*: 162 Grand Avenue, Surbiton, Surrey KT5 9JA ☎ 020 8390 5593

BICKERTON Wayne *(Gtr, B Gtr)*: Flinders, 20 Watford Road, Radlett, Herts WD7 8LE ☎ 01923 85 7792

BIDDU-BIDDU *(Gtr, Cong, Md)*: 2 Falcon House, 202 Old Brompton Road, London SW5 0BU ☎ 020 7229 4798

BIDDULPH Richard *(Gtr, B Gtr, Bzk)*: 29 Denison Road, Colliers Wood, London SW19 2DJ ☎ 020 8542 2051 & fax

BIG STEVE *(Gtr, Voc, Bjo)*: 178 Royal College Street, Camden, London NW1 0SP ☎ 020 7482 6962

BIGNALL Wilton *(Gtr, B Gtr, Dms, Com, Voc)*: 77 Wedgewood House, Chinawalk Estate, Lambeth Walk, London SE22 6LN

BILBROUGH Dave *(Gtr)*: 1 Lodge Avenue, Gidea Park, Romford, Essex RM2 5AB ☎ 01708 720859

BILLETT Adrian *(Gtr, Kbds, Voc)*: 8 Golfside, Strawberry Hill, Middlesex TW2 5NR ☎ 020 8898 3540, 070 44 00 0044

BING David *(Gtr, B Gtr)*: 4 Wilderton Road, London N16 5QZ ☎ 020 8800 7166

BINNS Kerry *(Gtr, Voc, Kbds, Dms)* ☎ 01255 435175, 0966 171702

BIRKETT Christopher *(Gtr)*: Chateau Richard, St Cibard, Pimpine, France 33570 ☎ +33 557 406 292, +33 557 406 271 fax

BISHOP Jonathan *(Gtr, B Gtr, Kbds, Dms, Voc)* ☎ 020 8877 0785

BLACKHAM Robert *(Gtr, Man, B Gtr)*: 46 Auckland Road, Ilford, Essex IG1 4SE ☎ 020 8554 6482

BLACKMAN Robert *(E Gtr, Ac Gtr, B Gtr)*: 53 Storr Gardens, Hutton, Essex CM13 1HT ☎ 01277 231961

BLACKWELL John *(E Gtr, Ac Gtr)*: Flat 4, 212A Richmond Road, London E8 3QN ☎ 020 7254 2311

BLADES Thomas *(Gtr)*: The Coach House, 82 Valleyfield Road, London SW16 2JA ☎ O20 8769 2905

BLAIR Gerry *(Gtr, Kbds)*: 110A Wiverton Road, Sydenham, London SE26 5HZ ☎ 0958 381887 mob

BLAKE Adam *(Gtr, Sitar, Voc, B Gtr)*: Flat 7, 77 Linden Gdns, London W2 4EU ☎ 020 7727 1915

BLAKE Karl *(Gtr, Db, Dms)*: Bcm Swarf, London WC1N 3XX

BLAKE Richard *(E Gtr, Ac Gtr, Man, Mando, Hm)*: 84 Fairways, Waltham Abbey, Essex EN9 1SX ☎ 01992 714381

BLAKE Rod *(Gtr)*: 196C Stockwell Road, London SW9 9TB ☎ 020 7274 7994

BLEGVAD Peter *(Gtr, Voc)*: 22 Anley Road, London W14 0BY ☎ 020 7603 0410

BLOCH Nicholas *(Gtr, Man, Pf)*: 107A South View Road, London N8 7XL ☎ 020 8348 1653

BLOOMFIELD Steve *(Gtr)*: 24 Oaks Road, Stanwell Village, Staines, Middlesex TW19 7LG ☎ 01784 240119

BOBBA BLACK STAR *(Gtr)*: 6 Eleanor Close, Arnold Road, Tottenham N15 4HU ☎ 020 8808 1284, 0930 732189

BODIN Jesper *(Gtr)*: Address Unknown ☎ 020 7281 9567

BOGEN Joel *(Gtr)* ☎ 020 8446 6214

BOGIE Frank *(Ac Gtr, E Gtr, B Gtr, Kbds, B)*: 7 Buxton House, Maysoule Road, Battersea, London SW11 2BU ☎ 020 7585 0340

BOLAND Greg *(Gtr)*: 140 Castle Farm, Shankill, Co. Dublin, Ireland ☎ + 353 1 282 7090

BOLD David *(Gtr, B Gtr)*: 36 Clockhouse Road, Beckenham, Kent BR3 4JP ☎ 020 8650 0691

BOLTON Richard *(Gtr, Cel)*: 9 Wolverton Mansions, Uxbridge Road, Ealing Common, London W5 3LA ☎ 020 8992 6466

BOLTON Roger *(Gtr, Voc, Kbds, B Gtr)*: 4G Peabody Buildings, Duchy St, Waterloo, London SE1 8AW ☎ 020 7207 7564

BOLTON Steve *(Gtr, Voc)*: 40A Geoffrey Road, Brockley, London SE4 1NT ☎ 020 8692 3771 & fax, 0421 616091 mob

BONACCI Cristina *(Gtr)*: 110-112 Disraeli Road, London SW15 ☎ 020 8871 1212

BOND Alexander *(Gtr, Voc)*: 15 The Pines, Woodford Green, Essex IG8 0RW

BOND Paul *(Gtr, Voc)*: 3 Charlbury Avenue, Stanmore, Middlesex HA7 4TP ☎ 018 357 8987, 0961 305 624

BOND Philip *(Gtr, Bjo, Man, B Gtr)*: c/o Wyndhurst, 56 Burton Road, Dudley, West Midlands DY1 3DJ ☎ 01902 670 415

BOND Ronnie *(Gtr)*: c/o Ronnie Bond Music, 19 Kingly Court, London W1R 5LE ☎ 020 7439 7855

BONFIELD Neil *(E Gtr, Ac Gtr, B Gtr)*: 18 Lea Gardens, Wembley, Middlesex HA9 7SE ☎ 020 8903 9611, 0958 287 144

BONODI Lorenzo *(B Gtr)*: 84 Glocester Mews West, London W2 6DY ☎ 0958 967577

BOORER Martin *(Gtr, T Sax, Clt)*: 22 Hillfield Road, West Hampstead, London NW6 1PZ

BOOTH Judith *(Ac Gtr)*: 1 Marriott Road, Finsbury Park, London N4 3QN ☎ 020 7281 9035, 07957 272879

BORJANIC Dusan *(Cl Gtr, Fl Gtr)*: 14 Carroun Road, London SW8 1JT ☎ 020 7582 9342

BOROWSKI George *(Gtr, Pf, B Gtr)*: 102 Prestbury Road, Macclesfield, Cheshire SK10 3BN ☎ 01625 266459

BOTTOM Richard *(Gtr, B Gtr, Kbds, Voc, Per)*: Flat G, 8 Rutford Road, London SW16 2DH ☎ 020 8769 1124

BOUIC Christian *(Fl Gtr)*: 66 Leicester Road, East Finchley, London N2 9EA ☎ 020 8444 7935 & fax, 0956 988395 mob

BOULT Robin *(Gtr, Kbds, Clt)*: 15 Little Hampden Close, Wendover, Bucks HP21 6EH ☎ 01296 622942

BOUTWOOD Daniel *(Gtr, B Gtr)*: 16 Prospect Place, 212-230 Evelyn Street, Deptford, London SE8 5BZ ☎ 020 8692 8597

BOWN Andrew *(Gtr, Pf)*: 46 Madrid Road, Barnes, London SW13 9PG ☎ 020 8748 4572, 020 8741 5550

BOY Chrissy *(Gtr)*: c/o CC Young &Co, Chesham House, 150 Regent Street, London W1R 5FA ☎ 020 7432 0337

BOYLE Conor *(E Gtr, Ac Gtr, Pf)*: 14 Peters Court, 93 Kings Avenue, Clapham, London SW4 8EH ☎ 020 8678 1696

BOYLE Stewart *(Gtr)* ☎ 020 7625 4545

BRADFORD Terry *(Gtr, B Gtr)*: c/o 21 Alvechurch Highway, Lydiate Ash, Bromsgrove, Worcs B60 1NZ ☎ 0121 453 3327

BRADFORD Thomas *(Gtr, B Gtr, St Gtr)*: 58 Fords Grove, Winchmore Hill, London N21 3DP ☎ 020 8360 4647

BRADLEY Alan *(Gtr, Bjo)*: 107 Downs Road, Coulsdon, Surrey CR5 1AD ☎ 01737 554240

BRADLEY Michael *(Gtr, Kbds, Synth, B Gtr)*: Garden Flat, 42 Wray Crescent, London N4 3LP ☎ 020 7263 6871

BRADLEY Paul *(Gtr, Voc, Arab Dms)*: 78 Alkham Road, Stoke Newington, London N16 6XF ☎ 020 7249 3992

BRADLEY Robert *(Gtr, B Gtr, Kbds, Voc)*: c/o Godfrey Allan, Kinghton House, 56 Mortimer Street, London W1N 8BY ☎ 020 8974 9782, 020 7436 7400

BRADSHAW Timothy *(Gtr, Dms, Per, Pf)*: 9 Clevedon Close, London N15 3SR ☎ 07970 346846

BRADY Conor *(Gtr, B Gtr)*: 8 Leeson Park, Dublin 6, Ireland ☎ +353 1 497 2002

BRADY John *(E Gtr, Ac Gtr, B Gtr)*: Ground Floor Flat, 8 Tremlett Grove, Tufnell Park, London N19 5JX ☎ 020 7263 7893

BRAGEN Howard *(Gtr, B Gtr, Voc)*: 1 Denton Court, 14 Cranes Drive, Surbiton, Surrey KT5 8AL ☎ 020 8390 5738

BRAGG Billy *(Gtr)*: c/o Sincere Management, Flat B, 6 Bravington Road, London W9 3AH ☎ 020 8960 4438, 020 8968 8458 fax

BRAHAM Thomas *(Gtr)*: 103 Sotheby Road, Highbury, London N5 2UT ☎ 020 7359 2426

BRAMSON Susanne *(Gtr, Voc)*: 15 James Stewart House, Dyne Road, Kilburn, London NW6 7XY ☎ 020 7624 8540

BRAY Nick *(Gtr)*: 60 Harewood Gardens, Sanderstead, South Croydon, Surrey CR2 9BJ ☎ 020 8651 6626

BREEN Karl *(Gtr, Voc, B Gtr)*: 24 Dawson House, Dean Court, Dublin 8, Ireland ☎ +3531 4547941, +353 862626729

BREMNER Ewen *(Gtr, Per)*

BRIDGER Raymond *(Gtr, Kbds, Flt, Bjo)*: 53 Church Lane, Chessington, Surrey KT9 2DN ☎ 020 8397 7525

BRIDGES Timothy *(Gtr)*: 3 Creswick Road, Acton, London W3 3NH

BRIGGS William *(Gtr)*: 33 Glenluce Road, Blackheath, London SE3 7SD ☎ 020 8858 6079 & fax

BRITTAIN Max *(Gtr)*: 11 Fairlight Avenue, Windsor, Berks SL4 3AL ☎ 01753 856331, 0802 648540 mob

BRITTEN Terry *(Gtr)*: Yew Tree Cottage, Sudbrook Lane, Petersham, Surrey TW10 7AT

BRIXTON *(Gtr, Kbds)*: Flat 2, 7 Tremlett Grove, London N19 5LA ☎ 020 7263 7751 & fax

BROADBENT Jason *(Gtr)*: 6 Fairholt Close, London N16 5EL ☎ 020 8802 2524

BRODBIN Sean *(Gtr)*: 9 Ruskin Road, London N17 8ND ☎ 020 8365 0397

BROMHAM Gary *(Gtr, Voc, B Gtr, Kbds)*: Flat D, 7 Gunnersbury Avenue, Ealing, London W5 3NH ☎ 020 8723 1857

BROOKES Max *(Gtr, Voc, Kbds)*: 113 Lesley Road, London N2 3BH ☎ 020 8444 5667

BROOKS David *(Gtr)*: 82 Lambton Road, West Wimbledon, London SW20 0LP ☎ 020 8946 1933

BROOKS Kevin *(Gtr, Kbds, Per)*: 34A Yonge Park, London N4 3NT

BROUGHTON Brian *(Gtr)*: 14 Alwold Crescent, London SE12 9AF ☎ 020 8516 0129

BROWN Ciyo *(Ld Gtr, B Gtr, Voc)*: 49 Normanshire Drive, Chingford, London E4 9HE ☎ 020 8926 2135

BROWN Darren *(Gtr, B Gtr, Dms)*: 108A Stafford Road, Wallington, Surrey SM6 9AY ☎ 020 8647 8647

BROWN Dominic *(Gtr, Voc, B Gtr)*: Flat 3, 51 Bonham Road, Brixton, London SW2 5HW ☎ 020 7274 2045

BROWN Kevin *(Gtr, Voc)*: 16 Falling Lane, Yiewsley, Middlesex UB7 8AS ☎ 01895 442891

BROWN Michael *(Gtr, Dms, Kbds, B Gtr, Voc)*: 34 Sutherland Road, Edmonton, London N9 7QG ☎ 020 8805 1496

BROWN Noel *(Sl Gtr, Dobro)*: SW17 7HH ☎ 020 8682 2640

BROWN Paul *(Gtr, Pf, Tpt, Voc)*: 4 Winton Road, Farnborough, Orpington, Kent BR6 7AL ☎ 01689 852194

BROWNE Deryck *(Gtr, Voc)*: 124A Offord Rd, Islington, London N1 1PF ☎ 020 7609 7316

BROWSE Paul *(Gtr, B Gtr)*: 1 Kingsfield House, Victorian Grove, London N16 8EY

BRUCE Malcolm *(Gtr, Kbds, Com)*

BRUINSMA Cornelius *(Cl Gtr)*: 9 Sandrock Place, Shirley Hills, Croydon, Surrey CR0 5HH ☎ 020 8656 1941

BUDD Stephen *(Gtr, B Gtr)*: Flat 1, 265 Goldhurst Terrace, London NW6 3EP ☎ 020 7624 9850, 020 7586 9880

BUKIC Mirsad *(Gtr, Pf)*: 132 Roding Court, Emlyn Gardens, Shepherds Bush, London W12 9UG ☎ 020 8743 1760, 0961 306096

BULL Brian *(Gtr, Tpt, Man)*: 30 Chalkpit Lane, Dorking, Surrey RH4 1ER ☎ 01306 882334

BULL Richard Michael *(Gtr, Dms, B Gtr)*: 26 Winton Avenue, Bounds Green, London N11 2AT ☎ 020 8889 8161, 020 8889 7936 fax

BULTITUDE Timothy *(Gtr, Dms, Voc)*: 70 Marmont Road, London SE15 5TE ☎ 020 7635 0552

BURDIS Raymond *(Gtr, Pf)*: 2 &Half Gate Street, London WC2A 3HP ☎ 020 7242 6969, 020 7242 6970 fax

BURGESS Peter *(Gtr, Kbds, Voc)*: 5 Doric Place, Woodbridge, Suffolk IP12 1BT ☎ 01394 382116

BURKE Mark *(Gtr)*: 32 Millfields Road, London E5 0SB ☎ 020 8525 1445

BURLEY David *(Gtr, B Gtr, Arr, Com, Cop)*: First Floor Flat, 23 Woodside Green, London SE25 5EY ☎ 020 8656 0434

BURNS Cha *(Gtr)*: 99B Allfarthing Lane, London SW18 2AT ☎ 020 8877 0595

BURNS Hugh *(Gtr)*: 79 Brondesbury Road, London NW6 6BB ☎ 020 7624 1629

BURRELL Richard *(Gtr, Pf)*: 43 Dulverton Mansions, 166 Grays Inn Road, London WC1X 8EL ☎ 020 7278 5301

BUTLER Bernard *(Gtr)*: Gailforce Management, 30 Ives Street, London SW3 2ND

BYATT Martin *(Gtr)*: 279 Upland Road, London SE22 0DN ☎ 020 8693 8481

BYRNE Peter *(Gtr)*: 69 Athlone Road, Tulse Hill, Brixton, London SW2 2DU ☎ 020 8671 9004

CAHEN Michael *(E Gtr, Ac Gtr, B Gtr)*: 17 Rue De La Croix Moreau, 75018 Paris, France ☎ +33 192059352, +33 14205 9622

CAIRNEY Peter *(Gtr, Man)*: 4005B Colorado Ave, Nashville, TN 37209, USA

CAIRO Joel *(E Gtr, Ac Gtr, B Gtr, Voc, Kb)*: 72J Rowley Way, St Johns Wood, London NW8 0SL ☎ 020 7328 6931

CALDERWOOD Neal *(Gtr, Voc, Man, B Gtr, Pf)*: 65 Station Road, Maghera, Co Derry, Northern Ireland BT46 5EY ☎ 01648 45803

CALLAGHAN Ann *(Gtr, Voc)*: 49 Dobson House, Edmund Street, Camberwell, London SE5 7NX ☎ 020 7708 1440

CALLAGHAN Bob *(Gtr, B Gtr, Pf)*: 020 8697 7139, 0403 667483 mob

CALLAN Richard *(Gtr, Sax, Vln)*: 7 The Glade, 100 Finchley Park, Finchley, London N12 9JW ☎ 020 8445 2025

CALLARD Peter *(Gtr)*: 48 Spencer Road, Harrow, Middx HA3 7AR

CALLOW Daren *(Gtr, Voc)*: 48 Paulhan Road, Kenton, Harrow, Middlesex HA3 9AH ☎ 020 8204 3409

CALVO Robbie *(E Gtr, Ac Gtr)*: 14A Twyford Crescent, Acton, London W3 9PP ☎ 020 8896 0474

CAMPBELL Douglas *(Gtr, Pf)*: 19 Highworth Road, New Southgate, London N11 2SL ☎ 020 8368 1712

CAMPBELL Tony *(Gtr, B Gtr, Dms, Voc)*: 14 Cranbourne Road, Leyton, London E15 2DB ☎ 020 8558 8536, 020 8539 4517

CANG Matthew *(Gtr)*: 4 Bratton House, Bratton Seymour, Wincanton, Somerset BA9 8DA ☎ 01963 34319

CANNAM Anthony *(Gtr, B Gtr, Kbds, Pf)*: Basement, 472 Kings Road, Chelsea, London SW10 0LG ☎ 020 7352 8736

CAPONE Philip *(Gtr)*: 40 Woodville Road, Walthamstow, London E17 7EP ☎ 020 8521 3975

CARGILL Rory *(Gtr, Kbds, Synth)*: 29A Bennerley Road, Battersea, London SW11 6DR ☎ 020 7223 8817

CARIS Tom *(Jz Gtr)*: 5 Wallflower Street, London W12 0TE ☎ 020 8749 1378

CARLESS Timothy *(Gtr, B Gtr)*: c/o Mockin' Bird Music, PO Box 1149, Hove, Sussex BN3 1GY

CARMICHAEL Gregory *(Gtr)*: 112 St Georges Ave, Tufnell Park, London N7 0AH ☎ 020 7609 0711

CARNOCHAN Ian *(Gtr, Pf)*: 29 Gloucester Crescent, London NW1 7DL

CARPETBIGHTER Lord *(Pd Gtr)*: 19/20 Western Mews, London W9 3NZ

CARROLL Marc *(Gtr)* ☎ 020 7813 4299, 020 8968 6715

CARSON Malcolm *(Gtr, Voc)*: Top Flat, 66 Manor Avenue, Brockley, London SE4 1TE ☎ 020 8692 6819

CARTER Dean *(Gtr, Voc, Kbds)*: 23 Garrett Close, Acton, London W3 6TB ☎ 020 8896 3915

CARTER Ian *(Gtr, B Gtr, Hmca)*: 54 Normanton Park, Chingford, London E4 6HF ☎ 020 8524 7703

CARTER Johnathan *(Gtr, Per)*: c/o Knightmare Mngmt Ltd, Friars House, Suite 1, 1St Floor, 157-168 Blackfriars Rd, London SE1 8EZ ☎ 020 7928 6755

CARTER Vince *(Gtr)* ☎ 020 8310 5163

CARTWRIGHT Deirdre *(Gtr)*: 13C Glaserton Road, London N16 5QU ☎ 020 8802 4679

CARTWRIGHT Terry *(E Gtr, Bjo)*: 36 Faulconbridge Avenue, Broad Lane, Coventry, West Midlands CV5 7GA ☎ 024 7646 1177

CARUSO Tony *(Gtr, B Gtr, Dms, Kbds)*: Flat 4, 73 Station Road, Sidcup, Kent DA15 7DR ☎ 020 8309 7377

CARVELL Alan *(Gtr, Db, Voc)*: 1 Worcester Ave., Tottenham, London N17 0TU ☎ 020 8808 8118

CASEY Charlie *(Gtr, Voc, Dms)*: Flat 4, 60-62 Palace Road, London SW2 3NR ☎ 020 8483 0943

CASSWELL Michael *(Gtr)*: Angel Cottage, Manor Road, Lambourne End, Romford RM4 1NH ☎ 020 8500 0810

CASTLES Danny *(Gtr, Kbds, B Gtr)*: Address Unknown ☎ 020 8680 2463

CAVALIERE Francesco *(Cl Gtr, Ac Gtr, Oud)*: 5 Bourne Court, Ellesmere Road, London W4 3ED ☎ 020 8994 1427

CAWTHORNE Bob *(Gtr)*: 60 Harpley Square, Bancroft Road, Stepney, London E1 4ES

CB *(Gtr)*: Flat 2F, Shillington Old School, 181 Este Road, London SW11 2TB ☎ 020 7924 3684

CEAGO Tony *(Gtr, Voc)*: 20 Melrose Avenue, Wimbledon Park, London SW19 8BY ☎ 020 8946 2151, 0976 312952 mob

CHAPMAN Michael *(Gtr)*: 17 North Road Avenue, Brent Wood, Essex CM14 4XQ ☎ 01277 231522

CHAPMAN Richard *(Gtr)*: Green Leith, Rackham Road, Amberley, West Sussex BN18 9NR ☎ 01798 831302

CHARLES Cliff *(Gtr)*: Flat 1E, Shrewsbury Street, Off Delgarno Way, London W10 5DP ☎ 020 7381 5561

CHARLEY *(Gtr, Voc, Kbds)*: Flat 4, 57-59 Navarino Road, London E8 1AG ☎ 020 7923 1316

CHARLTON Ainsley *(Gtr, Voc)* ☎ 020 8299 0756

CHEADLE Matt *(Gtr)*: 97 Highview Road, Ealing, London W13 0HL ☎ 020 8998 5589

CHEVALIER Patrice *(Gtr, Voc)*: c/o Louise Harries, 9 Hawarden Road, London E17 6NS ☎ 020 8521 1642

CHIDGEY Tony *(Gtr)*: 17 Orlando Road, London SW4 0LD ☎ 020 7498 7007

CHILVERS Adam *(Gtr)*: 142 Claydon, Deacon Way, London SE17 1UF ☎ 020 7701 3035

CHODZKO-ZAJKO Maciej *(Gtr, Voc)*: 17 Claremont Road, London W13 0DE ☎ 020 8998 3855

CHOUDHRI Usman *(Gtr, Kbds, B Gtr)*: 59 Leybourne Road, Leytonstone, London E11 3BS ☎ 020 8989 1373

CHRISTIAN Rick *(Gtr, Voc)*: 18 Coopers Ave, Heybridge, Maldon, Essex CM9 4YY ☎ 01621 859561

CHRISTIE Peter *(Gtr, Uke, Tpt)*: 9 Ashdown Road, Epsom, Surrey KT17 3PL ☎ 013727 20727

CIOKAJLO Kingsley *(Gtr, Voc)*: 7A Cromwell Avenue, Highgate, London N6 5HN ☎ 020 8341 2418, 0958 947913

CLANCY Michael *(Gtr, Synth, Ld Gtr, B Gtr)*: 81 Robin Hood Way, Greenford, Middlesex UB6 7QW ☎ 020 8902 5401

CLARK James *(Gtr)*: Woolpack Inn, Benover Road, Yalding, Kent ME18 6AS

CLARK John *(Gtr)*: 5, Rosken Grove, Blackpond Lane, Farnham Royal, Slough - Berks SL2 3DZ

CLARK Neil *(E Gtr, Ac Gtr)*: 52 Argyle Street, Toronto, Ontario M6J 1N6, Canada ☎ +1 416 533 9220

CLARK Paul *(Gtr, Voc)*: 159 Erith Road, Bexleyheath, Kent DA7 6HX ☎ 01322 528831

CLARKE David *(Gtr, Pf, B Gtr, Kbds, Voc)*: 28 Breamore Road, Seven Kings, Essex IG3 9NB ☎ 020 8590 6356

CLAYTON Anthony *(Gtr)*: 122C Drakefell Road, London SE14 5SQ ☎ 020 7732 1640

CLAYTON Justin *(Gtr)*: c/o Robin Clayton Pshp, Burton House, Burton, Nr Taporley, Cheshire CW6 0ER ☎ 01829 781232

CLAYTON Lynn *(Gtr)*: 4 Tushmore Lane, Northgate, Crawley, West Sussex RH10 2JJ ☎ 0129 361 9833

CLEMPSON Clem *(Gtr)*: 31 Arminger Road, London W12 7BA ☎ 020 8749 7190

CLIFF David *(Gtr)*: 6 Conway Street, London W1P 5HG ☎ 020 7323 4302

CLIFTON David *(Gtr, Man, Sax)*: Flat A, 34-36 Gertrude Street, London SW10 0JG ☎ 020 7376 3880, 020 7460 5485

CLOAD Peter *(Gtr)*: 22 Dixon Clark Court, Canonbury Road, London N1 2UR ☎ 020 7226 9544

COATES Alan *(Gtr, Voc, Pf)*: The Gate House, 11 Pond Road, Blackheath, London SE3 0SL ☎ 020 8297 2355

COATES Simon *(Gtr, Db)*: 6 Arcadian Close, Bexley, Kent DA5 1JJ

COBURN Alexander *(Gtr, Bjo, Man)*: 148 Blandford Road, Beckenham, Kent BR3 4NQ ☎ 0973 956815

COIGLEY James *(Gtr)*: 128 Connaught Road, Teddington, Middx TW11 0QH ☎ 020 8943 3226

COLE Bj *(Pd Gtr, St Gtr, Dobro)*: 16 Harlech Road, Southgate, London N14 7BX ☎ 020 8882 6378

COLEBY Grant (*Gtr, Voc*): 22 Blackthorne Drive, Chingford, London E4 6LR ☎ 020 8529 0137, 0956 170896

COLEMAN Robert (*E Gtr*): 130A George Lane, South Woodford, London E18 6AA ☎ 020 8530 6393

COLES Andrew (*Gtr, Kbds*): 5/35 Nottingham Place, London W1M 3FE ☎ 020 7935 5234

COLLEN Philip (*Gtr, Voc*): c/o Prager & Fenton, Midway House, 27/29 Cursitor Street, London EC4A 1LT ☎ 020 7831 4200

COLLINS Edwin (*Gtr*): West Heath Studios, West Heath Yard, 174 Mill Lane, London NW6 1TB ☎ 020 7794 7758

COLLINS John (*Gtr, Kbds*): 46 Thackeray Avenue, Tottenham, London N17 9DY ☎ 020 8808 5180

COLLINS Johnny (*Gtr, Ctma, Pf*): 22 Athol Gardens, Pinner, Middlesex HA5 3XQ ☎ 020 8866 1635

COLLISSON Sacha (*Gtr, B Gtr, Kbds*): Westwood, 2 Windsor Walk, Weybridge, Surrey KT13 9AP ☎ 01932 840691, 0850 987808

COLQUHOUN David (*Gtr*): Aston Acres, Kemsley Road, Tatsfield, Kent TN16 2BH ☎ 01959 575325

COMPTON Chris (*Gtr*): 2 Canal Way, London W10 5AS ☎ 0973 159941 mob

CONNARIS Michael (*Gtr, Kbds*): c/o Mcasso Music Prod Ltd, 9 Carnaby St, London W1V 1PG ☎ 020 7734 3664

CONNOLLY Matthew (*Gtr*): Flat 2, Cable House, Lloyd Street, London WC1X 9QT ☎ 020 7833 0837

CONTOGEORGE Peter (*Jz Gtr, Kbds, Bzk, Acc, Bal*): 16 Gardeners Great Baddow, Chelmsford, Essex CM2 8YU ☎ 01245 473738

CONWAY David (*Cl Gtr, E Gtr, Kbds*): 28 Wellington Court, Glenbuck Road, Surbiton, Surrey KT6 6BL ☎ 020 8390 3413

COOKE David (*Gtr, Bjo, Uke, Pf*): 26 Lebanon Park, Twickenham, Middlesex TW1 3DH ☎ 020 8892 3393

COOPER Julian (*Gtr*): c/o Interceptor, 1St Floor, 98 White Lion Street, London N1 9PF ☎ 020 7278 8001, 020 7713 6298

COOTE Anthony (*Gtr, B Gtr, Voc*): 1 Warwick Court, Bounds Green Road, London N11 2EB ☎ 020 8881 4878

CORBETT Daniel (*Gtr, Dms, B Gtr*): 43 St Margarets Road, Hanwell, London W7 2EX ☎ 020 8579 7236

CORBOULD Graham (*Gtr*): 98 Oaklands Road, Bexleyheath, Kent DA6 7AL ☎ 020 8303 3134

CORELLO Paul (*Fl Gtr, E Gtr, Voc, B Gtr, Kb*): 11 Newtown Court, Newtown Street, London SW11 5HH ☎ 020 7498 7682

COSTELLO Elvis (*Gtr, Voc*): c/o By Eleven, 12 Tideway Yard, Mortlake, London SW14 8SN ☎ 020 8847 2481

COTTON Roger (*Gtr, Kbds*): 24 Tredegar Road, Wilmington, Dartford, Kent DA2 7AZ ☎ 01322 229884

COVERDALE John (*Gtr*): 132 College Road, College Town, Sandhurst, Berkshire GU47 0RD ☎ 01276 33781

COVINGTON Lisa (*Gtr, Kbds*): Address Unknown

COWE Matt (*Gtr, B Gtr*): 139 Langham Road, London N15 3LP ☎ 020 8889 3281, 0976 372945 mob

COX David (*Gtr, B Gtr, Voc*): Flat 4, 15 St Wilfreds Road, New Barnet, Herts EN4 9SB ☎ 020 8441 2578

COXON Graham (*Gtr*): c/o C.M.O., 35/7 Parkgate Road, London SW11 4NP

COXON John (*Gtr, Kbds, Dms*): 73 Wellington Row, London E2

CRAGG William (*Gtr, Voc*): 15A Sheen Lane, Mortlake, London SW14 8HY ☎ 020 8392 2755

CRAIG Anthony (*Gtr*): 122 Rectory Grove, Hampton, Middlesex TW12 1EF ☎ 020 8979 8318

CRAMPTON Jeff (*Gtr*): 11 The Grove, Crowborough, East Sussex TN6 1NY ☎ 01892 668097

CRANENBURGH Ernie (*Gtr, B Gtr*): 332 Southborough Lane, Bickley, Kent BR2 8AA ☎ 020 8468 7751

CRANHAM Bob (*Gtr*): Sharabeth, 43 Cockshot Road, Reigate, Surrey RH2 7HB ☎ 01737 224175

CRAWFORD Robert (*Gtr, Voc*): 40 Hebdon Road, Tooting, London SW17 7NS ☎ 020 8682 1126

CREME Lalo (*Gtr*): Lyme House, Headley Road, Tyrrells Wood, Leatherhead KT22 8QF ☎ 020 8969 0299

CREWDSON Will (*Gtr*): c/o 43 Corine Road, London N19 5EZ ☎ 020 8341 4322, 0836 778877, 020 8341 5480

CROSBIE Michael (*Gtr, Kbds*): 81 Berners Drive, London W13 0JT ☎ 020 8991 9753

CRUICKSHANK Angus (*Gtr*)

CRUZ Clinton (*Gtr*): Flat 11, 5 Stainton Road, London SE6 1AD ☎ 020 8461 2891

CUDDEFORD Paul (*Gtr*): 306B Kilburn Lane, London W9 3EF ☎ 020 8969 1591, 0410 299568

CULBERTSON Adrian (*Gtr*): 42 Lower Castain Street, Coleraine, N. Ireland BT51 5DT ☎ 01265 54213, 0831 074748, 01265 54213

CUMMINGS David (*Gtr*): 44A Mountgrove Road, London N5 2LS ☎ 020 7359 2307

CUNNINGHAM David (*Gtr, Pf, Per*): 30 Fournier Street, London E1 6QE ☎ 020 7247 1346

CURRIE Jeremy (*Gtr, Pf*): 7A Church Lane, London N2 8DX ☎ 020 8442 0602

CURTIS Adrian (*E Gtr, Voc*): 20 Gowan Avenue, Fulham, London SW6 6RF ☎ 020 7736 2001, 020 7731 7790

CURTIS Steve (*Gtr, Cong*): 152 Abbotts Drive, North Wembley, Middlesex HA0 3SJ ☎ 020 8908 2682

CUSACK Peter (*Gtr*): 79 Maury Road, London N16 7BT ☎ 020 8806 8249

CUTHBERT William (*Gtr, Dms, Pf*): Sunnyside, Forest Green, Dorking, Surrey RH5 5SQ

CYRKA Jan (*Gtr, Kbds*): c/o Andy Farrow, Northern Music Company, Cheapside Chambers, 43 Cheapside, Bradford W Yorks BD1 4HP ☎ 01274 306361, 01274 730097 fax

DA-COSTA Phil (*Gtr*): 68 Cleveland Gardens, Barnes, London SW13 0AH ☎ 020 8876 0599

DACK John (*Gtr*): 14 Lodge Drive, Palmers Green, London N13 5LB ☎ 020 8882 3422

DALEY Paul Terence (*Gtr, La Per, Dms, Kbds*): c/o Leftfield, 9 Thorpe Close, London W10 5XL ☎ 020 8960 5055, 020 8964 5954 fax

DALLAWAY Paul (*Gtr, B Gtr, Kbds*): 77 Copperfield Drive, Tottenham, London N15 4UF ☎ 020 8376 4158

DALLIN Sarah (*Gtr*): c/o Leigh Philip And Partners, 1-6 Clay Street, London W1H 3FS ☎ 020 7486 4889, 020 7486 4885 fax

DALTON Mitch (*Gtr*): Elstree Cottage, Elstree Village, High Street, Elstree Village, Herts WD6 3EZ ☎ 020 8953 3211, 01306 880669

DALTON William (*Gtr*): 82 Bishops Bridge Road, London W2 6BD ☎ 020 7243 0640, 020 7243 0470 fax

DALTREY David (*Sp Gtr, E Gtr, Ac Gtr, Lute,*): Guildhall Guitar Studio, 34 Guildhall Street, Bury St Edmunds, Suffolk IP33 1QF ☎ 01284 762076

DALY Bryan (*Gtr, Sp Gtr, Bjo*): 70 Highlands Heath, Bristol Gardens, London SW15 3TG ☎ 020 8785 2666

DALY Michael (*Gtr, Kbds, B Gtr*): 45 Dawlish Road, London N17 9HN

DALY Sarah (*Gtr, Vln, B Gtr, Pf*): 49 Gilling Court, Belsize Grove, London NW3 4XA ☎ 020 7209 4111

DANAE Pascal (*Gtr, Voc*): 19A Dickens Road, London E6 3BX ☎ 020 8472 0416

DANIELZ (*Gtr, Voc*): 8 Moriarty Close, London N7 0EF ☎ 020 7607 5716

DARBY Alan (*Gtr, Voc*): 23 Agnes R0Ad, London W3 7RF ☎ 020 8740 8428

DAVENPORT Peter (*Gtr, St Gtr, Pf, Sax, Db*): 5 Wolverton Road, Stanmore, Middx HA7 2RN

DAVENPORT Rich (*Ld Gtr, B Gtr*): 1 Wilmer Crescent, Kingston-upon-Thames, Surrey KT2 5LU ☎ 020 8546 6729, 0589 362 577

DAVEY Philip (*Gtr, Tpt, Flgl*): 20 Linkenholt Mansions, Stamford Brook Avenue, London W6 0YA ☎ 020 8748 4843

DAVID-GRAY Mark (*Gtr*): 65 Denman Road, Peckham, London SE15 5NS ☎ 020 7701 9941

DAVIDSON Les (*Gtr*): 8 Independent Place, London E8 2HE ☎ 020 7923 4818

DAVIES Dave (*Gtr, Voc*): Kinks Productions, 84 Tottenham Lane, London N8 7EE ☎ 020 8340 7873

DAVIES Huw (*Cl Gtr, E Gtr*): Flat 3D Pennybank Chambers, 11-15 Great Eastern Street, London EC2A 3EJ ☎ 020 7377 6152

DAVIES Ian (*Gtr*): 29 Forest View Road, East Grinstead, Sussex RH19 4AW ☎ 01342 24900

DAVIES Ray (*Gtr, Pf, Voc*): Kinks Properties Ltd, 84 Tottenham Lane, London N8 7EE ☎ 020 8340 7873

DAVIS Robert (*Gtr, Voc*): Brian Reza Management, 416 High Road, Harrow Weald, Middlesex HA3 6HJ ☎ 020 8954 3428

DAVIS Rod (*Gtr, Fo Fdl*): 25 Chiltern View Road, Uxbridge, Middlesex UB8 2PE ☎ 01895 846707

DAWKINS Frank (*Gtr, Arr*): 63 Faygate Crescent, Bexleyheath, Kent DA6 7NS ☎ 01322 523557

DAWSON Jim (*E Gtr, Ac Gtr, B Gtr*): 21 Grasvenor Ave, Barnet, Herts EN5 2BZ ☎ 020 8441 1794

DAWSON Phil (*Gtr, Jz Gtr, Cl Gtr, Kbds*): ☎ 020 8444 7409

DE ALMEIDA Luiz (*Gtr, B Gtr, Kbds*): 66 Lady Margaret Road, London NW5 2NP ☎ 020 7267 3845

DE BUEGER Charles (*Gtr, B Gtr, Kbds*): ☎ 020 8673 8312

DE OLIVEIRA Paulo (*Gtr, E Gtr, Cav, Voc*): 51 Oxgate Gardens, Cricklewood, London NW2 6EA ☎ 020 8452 5810

DE-BURGH Chris (*Gtr*): c/o Mismanagement UK Ltd, 754 Fulham Road, London SW6 5SH ☎ 020 7731 7074

DEACON Owen (*Gtr, Voc, Dms, B Gtr*): 13A St Albans Road, London NW10 8TU ☎ 020 8838 2966

DEADMAN Jon (*Gtr, B Gtr, Theramin*): 2 Saltoun Road, Brixton, London SW2 1EP ☎ 020 7652 0624

DEAN Ray (*Gtr, Kbds*): 40A Keston Road, London N17 6PN ☎ 020 8376 2523, 0973 733916 mob

DEANE Edmund (*E Gtr*): 1A Glyn Mansions, Hammersmith Road, London W14 8XH ☎ 020 7603 0231

DEBRETT Jon (*Gtr, B Gtr, Kbds*): 42 Woodvale, Muswell Hill, London N10 3DP ☎ 020 8365 0105

DECICCO Dominque (*Gtr, Voc, B Gtr, Hmca*): 510 Brixton Road, London SW9 8EN

DEERAL (*Gtr*) ☎ 01708 862192

DELANDRO Alando (*Gtr*) ☎ 0958 623008 mob

DELGADO Junior (*Gtr, Voc, B Gtr, Kbds, Rh Gtr*): 11 Baird Garden, London SE19 1HJ ☎ 020 7388 2228

DENCH Ian (*Gtr, Kbds*): Flat C, 539 Caledonian Road, London N7 9RH

DENIZ Frank (*Gtr, Sp Gtr, E Gtr, Bjo*): The Lodge, 12 Ammell Lane, St Margarets, Stanstead Albotts Herts SG12 8DX ☎ 01920 871167

DENNIS Garry (*Gtr, Pf*): 12 Erith Rd, Belvedere, Kent DA17 6EY ☎ 01322 400093

DENNY David (*Gtr, B Gtr, Man, Charango*): 1 Rymer Road, Croydon, Surrey CR0 6EF ☎ 020 8656 7446

DENT Jeffrey (*Gtr, B Gtr, Mldn*): 6 Riverside Walk, Isleworth, Middlesex TW7 6HW ☎ 020 8737 7307

DEPUHL Judy (*Gtr*) ☎ 00 49 201 778814

DIAMOND Jim (*Gtr, Voc*): Richman Management Ltd., Unit 229 Canalot Studios, 222 Kensal Road, London W10 5BN ☎ 020 8964 4904

DIANA Laurence (*Gtr, B Gtr, Kbds*): 139, Grove Road, Walthamston, London E17 9BU ☎ 020 8520 3241

DICK Arthur (*Gtr*): 42 Brenda Road, London SW17 7DB ☎ 020 8672 8350

DICKSON Alexander (*Gtr, Voc, B Gtr*): 2H 149 Bayham Street, Camden, London NW1 0TT ☎ 020 7485 4564

DIDIOT Stu (*E Gtr, Ac Gtr, Voc*) ☎ 020 7607 4867

DIGANCE Richard (*Gtr*): Write Good Company, PO Box 131, Romsey, Hampshire SO51 6XQ ☎ 01794 515333, 01794 514391

DINO (*Gtr, Kbds, Per*): Flat D, 3 St James Drive, Wandsworth, London SW17 7RN ☎ 020 8767 7558, 0370 607757

DISLEY Diz (*Gtr, Bjo*): 52 De Havilland Close, Yeading, Middlesex UB5 6RY ☎ 020 8845 3341

DIXON Peter (*Gtr*): 13 Kennet Close, Aylesbury, Bucks HP21 8RL ☎ 01296 432706

DODDS Gavin (*E Gtr, B Gtr, Voc*): Flat 2, 58A Marylebone Lane, London W1M 5FF ☎ 020 7224 4652

DOHERTY Malcolm (*Gtr, Voc, Pf, Dms*): 22 Half Moon Lane, London SE24 9HU ☎ 020 7733 9112

DOLAN Tony (*Gtr, B Gtr, Per, Kbds, Mando*): 81 Russell Road, Palmers Green, London N13 4RS ☎ 020 8888 5744

DOLLIMORE Kris (*Gtr*): 76 Hillfield Park Mews, Muswell Hill, London N10 3QR ☎ 020 8442 1672

DONAHUE Jerry (*Gtr*): 3411 East Chevy Chase Drive, Glendale, CA 91206, USA ☎ +1 213 464 3974, +1 213 469 9284

DONALD Martin (*Gtr*): 14 Skiddaw Close, Black Notley, Braintree, Essex CM7 8UN ☎ 01376 330116

DONE Steve (*Gtr, B Gtr, Tbn*): Flat C, 39 Museum Street, London WC1A 1LP ☎ 020 7404 0122

DONNELLY Stephen (*Gtr*): 39 Arlington Gardens, Chiswick, London W4 4EZ ☎ 020 8995 8856

DONOVAN Jason (*Ac Gtr*): c/o Chipvelvet Ltd, Alexander House, High Street, Inkberrow, Worcs WR7 4DT ☎ 01386 793445

DOOLEY Joseph (*Gtr, Hmca*): ☎ 01708 372151, 07957 342192

DORMON Bob (*Gtr, B Gtr, Voc, Kbds, Dms*): 58 Dorchester Court, Herne Hill, London SE24 9QY ☎ 020 7738 3110

DORSET Raymond (*Gtr*): 56 Robert Louis Stevenson Ave, Westbourne, Bournemouth, Dorset BH4 8EG ☎ 01202 751742

DOUGLAS Sarah (*Cl Gtr*): 131 Carr Road, Walthamstow, London E17 5EP ☎ 020 8531 7762

DOWNS Colin (*Gtr*): 50 Holly Park Road, London N11 3HD ☎ 020 8361 3192

DRAGON Ellyott (*Gtr, Voc, Hmca, Dms, B Gtr*): 30B Chaucer Road, London SE24 0NU ☎ 020 7652 3683

DRAKE Adam (*Gtr*): 24 Connaught Avenue, Loughton, Essex IG10 4DS ☎ 020 8508 1808

DRAPER David (*Gtr, Kbds, Kora*): 116 Rushmore Road, London E5 0EX ☎ 020 8986 1059

DREW Paul (*Gtr, Kbds*): 89 Hulverston Close, Sutton, Surrey SM2 6TZ ☎ 020 8770 0236, 0961 102104

DRUDY Andy (*Gtr*): 28 Leonard Avenue, Morden, Surrey SM4 6DW ☎ 020 8646 5369

DRUMMOND Terry (*Gtr, Bjo, Com, Arr*): The Tangle, 32 Pond Lane, Chalfont St Peter, Gerrards Cross Bucks SL9 9JA ☎ 01753 888639

DUFFY Billy (*Gtr*): O.J.Kilkenny, 6 Lansdowne Mews, Holland Park, London W11 3BH ☎ 020 7792 9494

DUFFY Melvin (*St Gtr, Pd Gtr, Gtr, Dobro*): 73 Barnfield Avenue, Kingston-upon-Thames, Surrey KT2 5RG ☎ 020 8546 0930, 0374 415527 mob

DUNLOP Andrew (*Gtr*): Unit F, 21 Heathmans Rd, Parsons Green, London SW6 4TJ ☎ 020 7371 7008, 020 7371 7708

DUNNE Paul (*Gtr*): 51 Manchuria Road, Battersea, London SW11 6AF ☎ 020 7228 3500

DUX Tim (*Gtr, Voc, B Gtr, Song W, Com*): 79 Longton Grove, Sydenham, London SE26 6QQ ☎ 020 8778 7147, 020 8778 1529 fax

DYER Dave (*Gtr, Tpt, Voc*): 37 Evanston Avenue, Higham Park, London E4 E4 9JS ☎ 020 8925 8313

EALES Ben (*Gtr, Flt*): 8 Carlton Road, East Sheen, London SW4 7RJ ☎ 020 8255 1602

EALOVEGA Benjamin (*E Gtr, Cl Gtr*): 17 Bisham Gardens, Highgate, London N6 6DJ ☎ 020 8340 7676, 0467 220452, 020 7323 1787

EAVES Michael (*Gtr*): 59 Valley Hill, Loughton, Essex IG10 3AL ☎ 020 8508 5539, 0973 676516 mob

EDGE The (*Gtr, Kbds*): Not Us Limited (U2), 30/32 Sir John Rogersons Quay, Dublin 2., Ireland ☎ Dublin 677 7330

EDMONDES William (*Gtr, Pf, Db*): 50 Crewdson Road, Oval, London SW9 0LJ ☎ 020 7582 1440

EDMONDS Lu (*Gtr, B Gtr, Saz, Darab*): 10 Groveway, London SW9 0AR ☎ 020 7587 0842

EDMONDSON Andy (*Gtr, Kbds, Voc*): 66A Hurstbourne Road, Forrest Hill, London SE23 2AQ ☎ 020 8699 2125

EDWARDS Carlo (*Gtr*): 65 The Chase, Wallington, Surrey SM6 8LZ ☎ 020 8680 0061

EDWARDS Dan (*Gtr*): 11 Parkview Road, New Eltham, London SE9 3QP ☎ 020 8859 0970, 0958 397892 mob

EDWARDS Jonathan *(Gtr)*: 5 Cleves Close, Loughton, Essex IG10 3NN ☎ 020 8508 6428, 04325 119781

EDWARDS Lucy *(Gtr, Acc)*: 47 Milner Road, London E15 3AD ☎ 020 7473 6176

EDWARDS Steven *(Gtr)*: 29B All Saints Road, London W11 1HE ☎ 020 7972 9665

EISLER Fil *(Gtr, B Gtr, Dms, Voc)*: 41-43 Churchway, London NW1 1LJ ☎ 020 7383 3219

ELAN *(Gtr, B Gtr, Tpt)*: 42C Edbrooke Road, Maida Vale, London W9 2DE ☎ 020 7286 9257

ELDER Jose *(Gtr, Rq Tiple)*: 24 Porten House, Porten Road, London W14 0LG ☎ 020 7371 3016

ELIOT Louis *(Gtr, Voc)*: Rise Management, First Floor, 8 Wendell Road, London W12 9RT ☎ 020 8740 8444, 020 8749 1877 fax

ELLIOTT David *(Gtr)*: 42 Parkside Avenue, Barnehurst, Kent DA7 6NJ ☎ 01322 556504

ELLIOTT George *(Gtr, Bjo, H Gtr)*: 60 Fellows Road, London NW3 3LJ ☎ 020 7722 8427

ELLIS John *(Gtr)*: 88 Woodhouse Road, Leytonstone, London E11 3NA ☎ 020 7272 6575

EMMERSON Simon *(Gtr)*: 120 Brooke Road, London N16 7RS ☎ 020 8806 5879

ETHERIDGE John *(Gtr)*: 31 Constantine Road, London NW3 2LN ☎ 020 7485 8901

EVANS David *(Gtr)*: 46 Mayfield Road, Sutton, Surrey SM2 5DT ☎ 020 8642 7883

EVANS Mark *(Gtr, Flt, B Gtr, Kbds, Dms)*: 38 Grena Road, Richmond, Surrey TW9 1XS ☎ 020 8332 6045, 0421 995291 mob

EVANS Mark *(Gtr, B Gtr, Kbds)*: 56 Trinity Gardens, London SW9 8DR ☎ 020 7738 4310

EVERARD Adam *(Ac Gtr, Kbds, B Gtr, Voc)* ☎ 020 8675 2566

EVERITT Steve *(Ld Gtr, Kbds, Dms, B Gtr)*: Keeper Cottage, Ham Lane, Shepton Mallet, Somerset BA4 4JB ☎ 01749 344971

EYRE Lee *(Gtr)*: Address Unknown ☎ 020 7263 8972

EYTLE Thomas *(Gtr)*: 67 Valley Road, Kenley, Surrey CR8 5BY ☎ 020 8660 4268

FAIRBRASS Fred *(Gtr, B Gtr)*: c/o Simon Makepeace, Martin Greene Ravden, 55 Loudoun Road, St Johns Wood, London NW8 0DL ☎ 020 7625 4545, 020 7625 5265 fax

FARMER Diane *(Gtr, Man, B Gtr)*: 22 Ashenden Road, Hackney, London E5 0DP ☎ 020 8986 6564

FARNESE Howard *(Gtr, Dms, Pf, Voc)*: 3 Kelveden House, Loughton Way, Buckhurst Hill, Essex IG9 6AJ ☎ 020 8559 0915

FARRELL Stephen *(Ac Gtr, E Gtr)*: 15 Carriglea Rise, Fir House, Dublin 24, Eire ☎ +3531 451 2650

FARRELLY Dick *(Gtr, Kbds)*: c/o 132 Braemor Road, Churchtown, Dublin 1A, Ireland ☎ Dublin 2983091

FARRUGIA Peter *(Gtr, B Gtr, Voc)*: 3 Mill Close, Carshalton, Surrey SM5 2NE ☎ 020 8669 4367, 0411 947 148, 020 8669 3730

FEARON Lenny *(Gtr, Voc)*: 3 Herbert Gardens, Kensal Rise, London NW10 3BX ☎ 020 8723 3925

FELIX-VAS Remy *(Gtr, B Gtr)*: 11 The Burroughs, Hendon, London NW4 4AR ☎ 020 8202 4609, 0402 171745

FENN Rick *(Gtr, Kbds)*: 172D West Hill, Putney, London SW15 3SL ☎ 020 8789 4155, 020 8780 9519

FENTIMEN Philip *(Gtr, Db, B Gtr)*: Meadow View, Pheasants Hill, Hambleden, Nr Henley-on-Thames, Oxon RG9 6SN ☎ 01491 576789

FENTON David *(Gtr)*: 29 Hunters Oak, Hemel Hempstead, Hertfordshire HP2 7SN ☎ 01442 216043

FENTON George *(Gtr, Tab, Synth)*: 1 Barrett Street, London W1M 6HG ☎ 020 7486 6676, 020 7486 0789 fax

FERNANDEZ Ricardo *(Gtr, Per)*: 92B College Place, London NW1 0DJ ☎ 020 7383 2911

FIELD Joseph *(Gtr)*: 4 Ardilaun Road, Highbury, London N5 2QR ☎ 020 7359 2248

FINUCANE Gavin *(Gtr, Pf)*: 97 Finborough Road, Chelsea, London SW10 9DU ☎ 020 7373 6906

FIORAMONTI Javier *(Gtr, B Gtr)*: Studio Flat, 48 Cricklewood Broadway, London NW2 3ET ☎ 020 7209 2934

FIRE Ray *(Gtr, Kbds)*: 20 Marsden Street, Camden, London NW5 3HD ☎ 020 7284 4833, 020 7485 4255

FISHER Martin *(Gtr, Voc, Kbds, Hmca, Rec)*: 81 Garth Road, Morden, Surrey SM4 4JX ☎ 020 8330 0135

FISHER-JONES Norman/Noko *(Gtr, B Gtr)*: c/o Xl Talent, Studio 7, 27A Pembridge Villas, London W11 3EP ☎ 020 7221 6200, 020 7229 7511 fax

FLANAGAN Mark *(Gtr, B Gtr, Db, Synth, Dms)*: 39 Barry Road, East Dulwich, London SE22 0HR

FLANNERY Mark *(Gtr, Voc, Kbds)*: 2A Hillside Gardens, Highgate, London N6 5ST ☎ 020 8340 7690, 020 8245 9060

FLEETHAM David *(Gtr, Voc, Clt, Kbds)*: 15 Egerton Road, Twickenham, Middlesex TW2 7SL ☎ 020 8287 5220, 0468 720 965

FLICK Vic *(Gtr)*: 2021 Ocean Ave, Apartment 225, Santa Monica, California 90405-1050, USA

FLYNN Andrew *(Gtr, Voc, Kbds)*: 178 High Holborn, London WC1V 7AA ☎ 020 7574 5280, 020 7379 5640

FOGG Rod *(Gtr, B Gtr, Db, Kbds, Arr)*: 17 A The Barons, St Margarets, Twickenham, Middx TW1 2AP ☎ 020 8892 5183

FOLEY Steven *(E Gtr, Cl Gtr, B Gtr)*: 559B Lordship Lane, Forest Hill, London SE22 ☎ 020 8693 0558

FOLLETT Emanuele *(Gtr, Voc, B Gtr)*: 22 Bartholomew Square, London EC1V 3QH ☎ 020 7251 3830

FORCIONE Antonio *(Ac Gtr, E Gtr, Man)*: 28A Devonshire Road, Chiswick, London W4 2HD ☎ 020 8995 7613, 020 8742 8963 fax

FOREMAN Kenneth *(Gtr, B Gtr, Voc, Kbds, Dms)*: 28 Hemstal Road, West Hampstead, London NW6 2AL

FORESTER Thomas *(Gtr, Pf, B Gtr)*: 34 Tufton Gardens, Hurst Park, West Molesey, Surrey KT8 1TE

FORSTER Robert *(Gtr)*: c/o 20 Cromwell Mews, London SW7 2JY ☎ 020 7225 1919

FORTIN Antonio *(E Gtr, Voc)*: 81 Clarence Avenue, New Malden, Surrey KT3 3TY ☎ 020 8942 4737

FOTHERGILL Lee *(Gtr)*: 142 Ledger Lane, Outwood, Nr. Wakefield, W. Yorkshire ☎ 01924 826664

FOWLER Lenny *(Gtr)*: 6 Lavender Avenue, Mitcham, Surrey CR4 3HH ☎ 020 8640 6324

FOWLER Robert *(Cl Gtr, Gtr, Voc)*: 17 Poplar Road, Leatherhead, Surrey KT22 8SF ☎ 01372 376871

FOX Adam *(E Gtr, Ac Gtr, B Gtr)*: 17A Milton Road, Hanwell, London W7 1LQ ☎ 020 8566 2912

FRAME Roddy *(Gtr, Voc)*: c/o 20 Cromwell Mews, London SW7 2JY ☎ 020 7225 1919

FRANCIS Mark *(Gtr, Kbds, A Sax, Flt)*: 155 Copers Cope Road, Beckenham, Kent BR3 1NZ ☎ 020 8658 5162

FRASER Don *(Gtr)*: 7 Crouch Meadow, Pools Lane, Hullbridge, Essex SS5 ☎ 01702 232989

FRASER June *(Gtr)*: 7 Crouch Meadow, Pooles Lane, Hullbridge, Essex SS5 6QF ☎ 01702 232989

FRASER Richard *(Gtr, Voc)*: 60 Hatchard Road, London N19 4NQ ☎ 020 7263 0290

FREEDMAN Bob *(Gtr, Voc)*: Flat 164 Watchfield Court, Sutton Court Road, London W4 4NE ☎ 020 8994 2063

FRIPP Robert *(Gtr)*: Discipline Global Mobile, PO Box 1533, Salisbury, Wiltshire SP5 5ER ☎ 01722 780 187, 01772 781 042 fax

FRY Michael *(Ac Gtr, Kbds, B Gtr, Hmca)*: 7 Graham House, Condover Crescent, Woolwich, London SE18 3NJ ☎ 020 8854 6739

FULCHER Seamus D *(Gtr, Man, Flt, Bjo, Cnt)*: 129C Glenthorpe Road, Hammersmith, London W6 0LJ ☎ 0956 24 13 86

FURNESS Clive *(Gtr, Voc)*: The Grange, 16 Westhall Park, Warlingham, Surrey CR6 9HS ☎ 01883 622439

G Andy *(Gtr, Per)*: Flat 2, 103 Lower Addiscombe Road, Croydon CR0 6PU ☎ 020 8654 6320, 0468 234532, 020 8656 1639

GABRIEL Andrew *(Rh Gtr, Ld Gtr, B Gtr, Kbds,)*: 9 Kimbolton Close, Lee, London SE12 0JH ☎ 020 8488 3349, 0941 100200 mob

GAFSEN Adam *(Gtr)*: Flat 5, 52 Woodland Rise, Muswell Hill, London N10 3UJ ☎ 020 8374 5896

GALLER Steve *(Gtr, Bjo, Voc, Tbn)*: 12 Eaton Way, Great Totham, Maldon, Essex CM9 8EE ☎ 01621 892656

GALLERY Roland *(Gtr)*: 1 Mayfield Avenue, London W13 9UP ☎ 020 8579 3637

GALLO Ray (*E Gtr, Gtr, Voc, Man*): 616 Green Lanes, London N8 0SD ☎ 020 8888 4666

GAMBA Giangaleazzo (*Gtr*): 1E Clissold Road, Basement Flat, London N16 9EX ☎ 020 7923 1720

GAMBLIN Paul (*Gtr*): Livonia, Portsmouth Road, Thames Ditton, Surrey KT7 0SY ☎ 020 8398 4458

GAMMONS Christian (*E Gtr, Ac Gtr, Kbds*): 37 Mount Park Crescent, Ealing Broadway, London W5 ☎ 020 8810 8334

GARBOW Geoffrey (*Gtr*): 77 Spring Road, Feltham, Middx TW13 7JA ☎ 020 8890 7843

GARCIA Nestor (*Gtr, B Gtr*): 11 Vectis Court, Borrodaile Rd, London SW18 2LE ☎ 020 8877 1456

GARCIA Victor G (*Gtr*): 144 Sabine Road, London SW11 ☎ 020 7585 1024

GAREH Daniel (*Cl Gtr, Ac Gtr, E Gtr, Pf, Fl*): 43A York Street, London W1H 1PW ☎ 020 7706 0753, 0958 202886 mob

GARRARD Stuart (*Gtr*): Furious Records, PO Box 3038, Littlehampton, West Sussex BN17 5SZ ☎ 01903 733031

GASKELL Danny (*Gtr*): 30 St Oswalds Place, Vauxhall, London SE11 5JE ☎ 020 7582 0440

GAVIN Michael (*Gtr, Bzk, Tpt, Jap Stg, Pf*): 111 Hamilton Avenue, Ilford, Essex IG6 1AB ☎ 07970 442315

GEDDON Alma (*Ld Gtr, B Gtr, Ac Gtr, Synth,*)

GENDLER Paul (*Gtr*): 53 Harwater Drive, Loughton, Essex IG10 1LP ☎ 020 8502 4984 & fax

GENEVES Jean-Jacques (*Gtr, Voc, Per*): 525 Finchley Road, West Hampstead, London NW3 7BB ☎ 020 7435 2797

GENOCKEY Sean (*Gtr*): 35 Wycliffe Road, Wimbledon, London SW19 1ES ☎ 020 8544 1604

GENOVESI Alfredo (*E Gtr, Cl Gtr*): 117 Ferndale Road, London SW4 7RL ☎ 020 7733 3423, 0336 766723 pager

GEROLEMOU Adrian (*Gtr*): 12 Kilronan, Rosebank Way, Acton, London W3 6TX ☎ 020 8896 3907

GERS Janick (*Gtr*): c/o Sanctuary Music, The Colonnades, 82 Bishops Bridge Road, London W2 6BB

GETHIN Tony (*Gtr, Pf, Kbds, B Gtr, Tpt*): 177 Forest Road, Walthamstow, London E17 6HE ☎ 020 8531 3736

GHOSHAL Neal (*Gtr*): 56 Eade Road, London N4 1DH ☎ 020 8809 5066

GIBBONS Graham (*Pd Gtr*): 27 Gryms Dyke, Prestwood, Great Missenden, Bucks HP16 0LN ☎ 01494 863438

GIBLIN Clive (*Gtr, B Gtr, Synth*): 15 Noahark Road, Dover, Kent CT17 0BX

GIBSON Elliot (*Gtr*): 55 Northumberland Avenue, Isleworth, Middlesex TW7 5JW ☎ 020 8232 8014

GILES Stephen (*Gtr*): 13 Osprey Gardens, South Croydon, Surrey CR2 8TB ☎ 020 8651 3565

GILHOOLEY Andrew (*Gtr, Voc, Man, Bzk, B Gtr*): 7C Burlington Court, Spencer Road, Chiswick, London W4 3SY

GILMOUR David (*Gtr*): c/o Gilmour Music Ltd, 43 Portland Road, London W11 4LJ ☎ 020 7221 2046

GILMOUR Mark (*Gtr, B Gtr*): 60 Westbourne Park Road, London W2 5PJ

GLADE Robert (*Gtr, Pf*): 6 Norfolk Crescent, London W2 2DN ☎ 020 7724 9370

GLAZIER Bernard (*Gtr, Voc, Per*): 21 Pelham Road, Beckenham, Kent BR3 4SQ ☎ 020 8778 7664

GLENDINING Daniel (*Gtr, Voc, Pf*): 158 High Road, Woodford Green, Essex IG8 9EF ☎ 020 8505 9288

GLENISTER Peter (*Gtr*): 20 Kings Hall Road, Beckenham, Kent BR3 1LU ☎ 020 8659 8179

GLYNNE Anthony (*Gtr, Kbds, Voc*): Honeysuckle Cottage, Wessex Way, Maidenhead, Berks SL6 3BS ☎ 01628 34186

GODRICH Nigel (*Gtr*): c/o Solar Management, 42-48 Charlbert Street, London NW8 7BU ☎ 020 7722 4175

GOGARTY Brian (*Gtr*): 93 Oaklands Road, Bexleyheath, Kent DA6 7AW

GOLDBERG Ben (*Gtr*): 43 Aborfield, Peckwater Street, London NW5 2UD ☎ 020 7813 4490

GOLDBERG Ivor (*Gtr*): 857 Finchley Road, London NW11 8LX ☎ 020 8209 1824

GOLDENBERG Simon (*Gtr, Kbds*): 32 Lydford Road, Maida Vale, London W9 3LX ☎ 020 8960 7052

GOLDING Peter (*Gtr, Hmca, Pf*): 151 Kings Road, London SW3 5TX ☎ 020 7351 3164, 020 7351 5802 fax

GOLDING Simon (*Gtr*): Address Unknown ☎ 020 8556 8412

GOLDMAN David (*Gtr, B Gtr*): 49 Bouverie Road, London N16 0AH ☎ 020 7609 7767

GOLDSMITH Anthony (*Gtr*): 20 Kingslyn Crescent, Upper Norwood, London SE19 3DG ☎ 020 8653 6977

GOLDSMITH Simon (*Gtr, Pf, B Gtr*): 59A Prince Of Wales Road, Kentish Town, London NW5 3LT ☎ 020 7482 5089

GONDWE Hawi (*E Gtr, Ac Gtr, Voc*): 201D Arlington Road, London NW1 7HD ☎ 020 7284 0529

GOOD David (*Gtr, Ctna*): 10, Whitehouse Way, Iver Heath, Bucks SL0 0HB ☎ 01753 653250

GOODES David (*Gtr*): 76 Latchmere Road, Kingston, Surrey KT2 5TW ☎ 020 8408 0830, 0589 800 479 mob

GOODMAN M J (*Gtr, Voc*): 17 Hodges Close, Bagshot, Surrey GU19 5QS ☎ 01276 472859, 0973 739325 mob

GORDON Eddie (*Gtr, Dms*): Flat 4, 15 Elsworthy Terrace, Primrose Hill, London NW3 3DR

GORDON Ian (*Gtr*): 17 Willis Close, Epsom, Surrey KT18 7SS ☎ 01372 40333

GORDON Robert (*E Gtr, Kbds, Synth, Per, Dms*): 10B Alkham Road, Stoke Newington, London N16 7AA ☎ 020 8806 4966

GORDON Stan (*Gtr, B Gtr*): 54 Warren Road, Wanstead, London E11 2NA ☎ 020 8989 3085

GORTON Geoffrey (*Gtr*): c/o Fruit, The Saga Centre, 326 Kensal Road, London W10 5BZ ☎ 020 8964 8448, 020 8964 0323

GOULD Murray (*Gtr, B Gtr, Voc, Kbds*): 5A Hanworth Park Court, Hanworth Road, Feltham, Middlesex TW13 5DG ☎ 020 8751 0899 , 0336 751308

GRAINGER Gary (*Gtr*): 86 Dibdin House, Maida Vale, London W9 1QF ☎ 020 7624 4532

GRANT Jacqueline (*Gtr, Per, Man, B Gtr, Theory*): Flat C, 122 Tresillian Road, London SE4 1XX ☎ 020 8694 1409

GRAVILLE Keith (*Gtr*): 92 Madrid Road, London SW13 9PG ☎ 020 8748 3424

GRAY Andy (*Gtr, Kbds*): 73 Broadacres, Hatfield, Herts AL10 9LE ☎ 01707 262577

GRAY Maurice (*Gtr*): 21A Waldegrave Road, London SE19 2AL ☎ 020 8771 4497

GRAY Thomas (*Gtr, Voc, Com*): Flat 3, 74 Barrow Road, London SW16 5PG ☎ 020 8677 4390

GREEDUS Paul (*Gtr, Pf, Sax*): 4 Pilgrims Lane, London NW3 1SL ☎ 020 7435 8266/8, 020 7435 1505 fax

GREEN Adam (*Gtr*): 15 Olive Blythe House, 377 Portobello Road, London W10 5XU ☎ 020 8968 0717

GREEN Colin (*Gtr, B Gtr, Arr*): 34 Sinodun Road, Didcot, Oxon OX11 8HN ☎ 01235 811850

GREEN Daniel (*Gtr, B Gtr, Dms*): 109 Cricklade Avenue, Streatham Hill, Streatham, London SW2 3HF ☎ 020 8678 1420, 0411 873386

GREEN Dominic (*Gtr, Pf, B Gtr*): 32 West End Court, Greencroft Gardens, West Hampstead, London NW6 3NU ☎ 020 7624 6529

GREEN JNR Ian (*Gtr, B Gtr, Kbds, Dms, Voc*): 27 Kimber Road, Wandsworth, London SW18 4NR ☎ 020 8265 2381

GREEN Jeff (*E Gtr*): 133 Horn Lane, Woodford Green, Essex IG8 9AF ☎ 020 8505 5104

GREEN Mick (*Gtr*): ☎ 020 8500 5413

GREEN Nicky (*Gtr, B Gtr*): Address Unknown ☎ 020 7732 1210

GREENE Tom (*Gtr, Pf*): 6 Clifton Mansions, Coldharbour Lane, Brixton, London SW9 8LL ☎ 020 7737 6243

GREENWOOD Tom (*Gtr*): 40 Culmstock Road, Battersea, London SW11 6LX ☎ 020 7228 7668, 0976 260308 mob

GRIFFITHS Derek (*Gtr*): 19 Staunton Road, Kingston-on-Thames, Surrey KT2 5TJ ☎ 020 8549 2499

GRIFFITHS Spencer (*Gtr, Pf, Tpt*): Flat B, 95 Chapel Market, Islington, London N1 9EY ☎ 020 7689 3774

GRIGUE Stephan Perez (*Gtr, Kbds*): ☎ +33 4 67 47 46 50, +33 0603533310 mob

GRINGRAS Paul (*Jz Gtr, B Gtr*): 127 Goldhurst Terrace, London NW6 3EX ☎ 020 7328 0629

GRIPPA Steve (*Gtr, Voc, Kbds*): 17 Wordsworth Road, Hampton, Middx TW12 1EW ☎ 020 8941 4246

GROCOTT Stephen (*Gtr, Bzk, Harm, Man, Hmca*): 45 Belmont Park, London SE13 5BW ☎ 020 8852 2865

GROTH Michael (*Gtr, B Gtr, Synth*): St Marys, Perivale Lane, Greenford, Middx UB6 8TL ☎ 020 8997 7256, 020 8810 4644 fax

GROVES Chris (*Gtr*): 16 Memorial Close, Heston, Middx TW5 0LN ☎ 020 8570 3767

GROVES Peter (*Gtr, Pf, Kbds*): 61 Sandbourne Avenue, Merton Park, London SW19 3EH ☎ 020 8540 9017, 0410 187883, 020 8666 4435

GUIREY Sagat (*Gtr*): 2 Warfield Road, London NW10 5LA ☎ 020 8960 5570

GURD Geoffrey (*Gtr, Kbds*): 10 Sharpeshall Street, London NW1 8YN

GUSTAVINA Mark (*Gtr, B Gtr*) ☎ 020 8372 3869, 020 8886 9426

HACKETT Stephen (*Gtr, Hmca*): 1St Floor, 89 St Margarets Road, Twickenham, Middx TW1 2LJ

HALAJKIJEVIC Gordan (*Gtr*): 10 Chalcott Lodge, 100 Adelaide Road, London NW3 3PY ☎ 020 7483 4514

HALE David (*Gtr, B Gtr, Pf, Voc*): 61 Drayton Park, London N5 1NT ☎ 020 7607 5066

HALES Ben (*Gtr, B Gtr, Voc*): 85A Springbank Road, Hither Green, London SE13 6SS ☎ 020 8265 5467

HALESTRAP Lee (*E Gtr, B Gtr, Gtr, Per*): 76 Curtis Road, West Ewell, Surrey KT19 0LQ ☎ 020 8337 1528

HALL Alan (*Gtr, Voc*): 25A Green Wrythe Lane, Carshalton, Surrey SM5 2DS ☎ 020 8647 7476

HALL Lynden David (*Gtr, Pf, Kbds, B Gtr, Dms*): 3 Knaresborough Drive, Riverside Walk, Strathville Road, Earlsfield, London SW18 4UT ☎ 020 8383 7022

HALL Richard (*Gtr, Voc*) ☎ 020 7703 8499, 0958 403782 mob

HALL Stephen (*Gtr*): 32B Fouberts Place, London W1V 1HF ☎ 020 7437 1034

HALL Stuart (*Gtr, Db, Vln, B Gtr*): Flat 1, 19 Park Road, High Barnet EN5 5RY ☎ 020 8449 9107

HAMBLETON-SMITH Sandra (*Gtr, Voc, Clars*): 31 Allenby Road, Forest Hill, London SE23 2RQ ☎ 020 8699 8342

HAMILL Drew (*Gtr*): 104 Hopefield Road, Portrush, Co. Antrim, N. Ireland BT56 8HF ☎ 01265 822982

HANCOCK Robin (*Gtr, Sax*): 38 Turneville Road, West Kensington, London W14 9PS

HAND Richard (*Gtr*): Flat 1, 61 Balcombe Street, London NW1 6HD ☎ 020 7724 3806

HANNAH Tom (*Gtr, Voc*): 133A Goldhawk Road, London W12 8EN ☎ 020 8743 9659

HARBORNE Raymond (*Gtr*): 20 Northumberland Park, Erith, Kent DA8 1HQ ☎ 01322 348354

HARCOURT Stephen (*Gtr*): 139 Pennymead, Harlow, Essex CM20 3JB ☎ 01279 431256

HARDING Elizabeth (*Cl Gtr*): 30 Fielding Way, Hutton, Brentwood, Essex CM13 1JN ☎ 01277 211581, 0956 671045

HARDY Christopher (*Gtr, Voc*): 72 Muncaster Road, London SW11 6NU ☎ 020 7223 8799

HARDY Paul (*Gtr, Voc*): 2 Manor Court, 152 Abbey Road, London NW8 7HY ☎ 020 7328 8289, 0956 291414, 020 7722 8856

HARRIS Andy (*Gtr*): 4 Crabtree Court, Clays Lane, Stratford, London E15 2UG ☎ 020 8534 5810

HARRIS Mel (*Gtr*): 38 Mount Pleasant, Biggin Hill, Westerham, Kent TN16 3TR ☎ 01959 570372, 01959 570372

HARRIS Stephen (*Gtr*): Flat A, 81 Bedford Hill, Balham, London SW12 9HD ☎ 020 8675 1552

HARRISON Malcolm (*Gtr*): 92 Roseberry Gardens, London N4 1JL ☎ 020 8348 7687

HARRISON Peter Scott (*Rh Gtr, Kbds*): 35 Talbot Gardens, Sevenkings, Ilford, Essex IG3 9TA ☎ 020 8597 9244

HARRISON Stuart (*Gtr*) ☎ 020 8858 7739

HART Daniel (*Gtr, Pf*): 134 Eversleigh Road, Battersea, London SW11 5XB ☎ 020 7223 5964

HARTLEY Bernard (*Gtr, Voc, Flt, Bjo*): 6 Warberry Road, Wood Green, London N22 4TQ ☎ 020 8881 2218

HARVEY Paul (*Gtr*): 62 Cecile Park, London N8 9AU ☎ 020 8341 3649

HARVEY Richard (*E Gtr, Cl Gtr, Md*): 12 Dene Close, Brockley, London SE4 2HB ☎ 020 7639 6824, 0378 940862 mob

HARVIE Iain (*Gtr, Ac Gtr, Pd Gtr, Dobro, O*): 4E Westpoint, 33-34 Warple Way, London W3 0RG ☎ 020 8742 0052

HASLETT Matt (*E Gtr, Ac Gtr*): 32 Canham Road, South Norwood, London SE25 6SA ☎ 020 8653 6832

HATHERLEY Charlotte (*Gtr, Pf*): 423 Hornsey Road (Flat 1), Finsbury Park, London N19 4DX ☎ 020 7263 3103

HAUGHTON Andy (*Gtr, Voc*) ☎ 020 8421 6072

HAVERON Patrick (*Gtr*): 8 Maryvale, Godalming, Surrey GU7 1SW ☎ 01483 417325

HAVES Geoff (*Gtr, Voc*): 10 Woodcote Close, Kingston, Surrey KT2 5LZ ☎ 020 8586 8134

HAWKES Mark (*Gtr, Kbds*): 236 Canbury Park Road, Kingston-upon-Thames, Surrey KT2 6LG ☎ 020 8287 5209, 07775 503067

HAWKES Peter (*Gtr*): 6 Byward Avenue, Feltham, Middlesex TW14 0EY ☎ 020 8890 4310, 07887 548198

HAWKINS Daniel (*Gtr*): 17 Maryland Walk, London N1 8QZ

HAWORTH Bryn (*Gtr, Sl Gtr, Man*): 48 Chatsworth Ave, Merton Park, London SW20 8JZ ☎ 020 8545 0026

HAWORTH Stephen (*Rh Gtr, Ld Gtr, B Gtr*): 19 Heathfield Road, Acton, London W3 8EH ☎ 020 8993 1185

HAYES Christian (*Gtr*): c/o Sanctuary Music Mngt., The Colonnades, 82 Bishops Bridge Road, London W2 6BB ☎ 020 7243 0640

HAYTO James (*Gtr*): 56 Ambler Road, Finsbury Park, London N4 2QR ☎ 020 7690 4461

HAYWARD Jonathan (*Cl Gtr, Per*): Address Unknown ☎ 020 8806 6751, 020 8806 6751

HAYWARD Justin (*Gtr*): Threshold Record Co Ltd, 53 High Street, Cobham, Surrey KT11 3DP ☎ 01932 864142/3

HEALY Kevin (*Gtr*): 9 Hill Road, Pinner, Middlesex HA5 1JY ☎ 020 8868 6547, 0958 968 224 mob

HEBDEN Kieran (*Gtr, Kbds, B Gtr*): 41 Longfield Street, London SW18 5RD ☎ 020 8871 9149

HEGGARTY Leigh (*Gtr*): 47 Floriston Avenue, Hillingdon, Middx UB10 9EB ☎ 01895 231492

HELION Perl (*Gtr*)

HELLER Jana (*Gtr, Dul, Pf, Clst*): 7C Burlington Court, Spencer Road, Chiswick, London W4 3SY ☎ 020 8995 8938

HENDERSON Forbes (*Gtr*): 6 Bolton Road, London NW8 0RJ ☎ 020 7625 4038

HENDERSON Martin (*Gtr*): Lavriston, 11 Boleyn Ave, Ewell, Surrey KT17 2QH ☎ 020 8224 7922, 020 8393 1468

HENDERSON Tamasine (*Gtr, Pf, Kbds*): 4 Lorne Terrace, Bibsworth Road, London N3 3RW ☎ 020 8343 0465, 0961 374322

HENDRY Robert (*Gtr, Voc*): 21 Durban Road, Beckenham, Kent BR3 4EY ☎ 020 8658 9956

HENNINGS Stephen (*Gtr, B Gtr*): 25 Charlton Road, Blackheath, London SE73 7EU ☎ 020 8853 2397

HEPBURN Keith (*Gtr*): 5 River Row Cottages, River Lane, Farnham, Surrey GU9 8UA ☎ 01252 710283

HERD Neil Robert (*Gtr, St Gtr, B Gtr, Man*): 54 Reardon House, Reardon Street, London E1 9QJ ☎ 020 7265 0151

HEREDIA Tito (*Fl Gtr*): 47 Hilborough Court, Livermere Road, London E8 4LQ ☎ 020 7241 3518

HEROLD Ian (*Gtr, Kbds*): 104 Caterham Drive, Coulsdon, Surrey CR5 1JG ☎ 020 8668 1089

HERON James (*Gtr, Sitar, Kbds*): 1 Glen Row, Glen Estate, Innerleithen, Peebleshire, Scotland EH44 6PX ☎ 020 7229 1229

HEWINS Mark (*E Gtr, Per, Hmca*): c/o Musart Services, Traemore Court, 81 Knollys Road, London SW16 2JW ☎ 020 8769 2012

HEWITT Dave (*Gtr*): 100 Upton Park Road, London E7 8LB ☎ 020 8279 2146

HEYAT Susan *(Gtr, B Gtr, Kbds)*: Flat 4 Hampstead Mansions, 19 Heath Street, Hampstead, London NW3 6TS ☎ 020 7794 2863, 07654 215217

HEYWARD Nick *(Gtr)*: c/o Graham Sacher Music Ltd, 36 Cranes Park, Surbiton, Surrey KT5 8AD ☎ 020 8390 1050

HICKS Clive *(Gtr, Bjo, Bzk, Uke, Man)*: Horsleydown, Wellington Parade, Walmer, Deal Kent CT14 8AD ☎ 01304 373617

HIGGINBOTTOM Craig *(Gtr)*: 7-8 Chalkfarm Road, Camden Town, London N1 8AA ☎ 020 7485 7858

HIGGINS Peter *(Gtr, Pf)*: 97 Millais Road, Leyton, London E11 4EZ ☎ 020 8558 2470

HIGHAM Darrel *(Gtr)*: 58B Malden Road, Kentish Town, London NW5 3HG ☎ 020 7209 4571

HILL Alan *(Gtr, Arr, Com)*: 44 Fairview Ave, Earley, Reading, Berks RG6 1HE ☎ 0118 962 6447

HILL David *(Gtr)*: 47 Springhill Park, Lower Penn, Wolverhampton WV4 4TS

HILL Francis *(Gtr, B Gtr, Pf)*: 21 Avenue Road, Southgate, London N14 4DA ☎ 020 8886 4677, 0421 869296, 020 8989 1145

HILLS Christopher *(Gtr)*: 61 Wilberforce Road, Finsbury Park, London N4 2SP ☎ 020 7359 2555

HILTON Geoff *(Gtr, Kbds, Dms, B Gtr)*: The Depot Studios, 29/31 Brewery Road, London N7 9QH

HOAD Paul *(Gtr, Voc, Song W)*: 32 Avondale Rise, London SE15 4AL ☎ 020 7635 8669

HOARE Brian *(Gtr)*: 12 Priory Gardens, Dartford, Kent DA1 2BE ☎ 01322 408808

HOBAN Peter *(Gtr, B Gtr)*: 34 Cowper Road, Hanwell, London W7 1EH ☎ 020 8579 3609

HOBBS Richard *(E Gtr, Cl Gtr, Dms)*: 46 Leamington Road, Harold Hill, Romford, Essex RM3 9TT ☎ 01708 378581, 01708 381312, 0958 436812

HOCIEJ John *(Gtr, B Gtr, Kbds)*: 110 Highfield Road, Woodford Green, Essex IG8 8JD ☎ 020 8505 6782, 020 8598 8984 fax

HOFNER Paul *(Gtr, Voc)*: 8 Gibson Gardens, London N16 7HB ☎ 020 7241 1798

HOGAN Gerry *(Gtr, Pd Gtr, St Gtr)*: Tree Tops, Harts Lane, Burghclere, Newbury Berks RG15 9JN ☎ 01635 27321

HOGAN Noel *(Gtr)*: c/o The Cranberries, Charlotte House, Charlotteequay, Limerick, Eire ☎ +353 61 410061

HOGG John *(Gtr, B Gtr, Dms, Pf)*: 249A Wimbledon Park Rd, Southfields, London SW16 6DL ☎ 020 8696 7202

HOLDER Noddy *(Gtr)*: c/o Newman & Co, Regent House, 1 Pratt House, London NW1 0AD ☎ 020 7267 6899, 020 7267 6746 fax

HOLLAND Bernie *(Sp Gtr, E Gtr, B Gtr)*: 1 Lynn Close, Wealdstone, Middx HA3 5LP ☎ 020 8863 3223

HOLLAND Tobe *(Gtr, Sax, B Gtr)*: 42 Edward Street, Southborough, Tunbridge Wells, Kent TN4 0HB ☎ 01892 619 764, 07771 675888 mob

HOLMES David *(E Gtr, Ac Gtr)*: 96 Salterford Road, Tooting, London SW17 9TF

HOLMSHAW Andrew *(Gtr)*: 34 Harbledown House, Mancidle Street, London SE1 4LN ☎ 020 7403 3927

HOLORAN Jamie *(Gtr)*

HOPE Harvey *(Gtr, Bjo, Man)*: The Oaks, 41 Arkwright Road, Sanderstead, Surrey CR2 0LP ☎ 020 8657 5840

HOPE Martyn *(Gtr)*: 22 Kavanaghs Road, Brentwood, Essex CM14 4NB ☎ 01277 232118

HOPE Philip *(Gtr, Kbds)*: 147 Crouch Hill, London N8 9QH ☎ 020 8341 4322, 020 8341 5480

HOPE Richard *(Gtr)*: 49G Milner Square, Islington, London N1 1TW ☎ 020 7607 1065

HOPKINS Stephen *(Gtr)*: 6A Upper Fant Road, Maidstone, Kent ☎ 01622 202674

HORNAGOLD Martin *(Gtr)*: 74 Shenfield Road, Brentwood, Essex CM15 8EW ☎ 01277 231206, 01277 202666

HORNBUCKLE Anthony *(Gtr, Kbds, Voc)*: 115 Cheam Common Road, Worcester Park, Surrey KT4 8TA

HORNBY Mark *(Gtr)*: 14 Aberdeen Gardens, Leigh-on-Sea, Essex SS9 3RH ☎ 020 7254 6246

HOUSE Peter *(Gtr, Hmca)*: 45 Acacia Road, London E17 8BN ☎ 020 8923 7355

HOWARD Martin *(Gtr, Synth, E Gtr)*: 34 Bassingham Road, Wembley, Middlesex HA0 4RL ☎ 09611 50918, 07050 349201, 07654 305596

HOWARTH David *(Gtr, Voc, Per)*: 24 Annadorn Road, Downpatrick, County Down, Northern Ireland BT30 8JU ☎ 03396 811164

HUBBARD David *(Gtr, B Gtr)*: 15 Charrington Street, London NW1 1RD ☎ 020 7387 0971

HUBBARD Neil *(Gtr)*: 59 Bassett Road, London W10 6JR ☎ 020 8969 4769

HUDSON Phillip *(Gtr)*: 54 Felixstowe Road, Kensal Green, London NW10 5SS ☎ 020 8964 1194

HUDSON Richard *(Gtr, Voc)*: 22 Friary Road, London N12 9HU ☎ 020 8445 8951

HUDSON William *(Gtr, Kbds)*: 655 Wilbraham Road, Chorlton, Manchester M21 9JT

HUGHES David *(Gtr, Pf)*: 31 Outram Road, London N22 4AB ☎ 020 8888 7401

HUGHES Paul *(Gtr)*: 6 Rangers Square, London SE10 8HR

HUMPHREY Simon *(Gtr, Kbds)*: 2 Firs Court Gardnes, Whitley Bridge, North Yorkshire DN14 0HZ ☎ 01977 662271

HUMPHREYS Peter *(Gtr)*: 32D St Julians Road, London NW6 7LB ☎ 020 7624 8019

HUNT Gerald *(Gtr, Sax, Flt, Vln, Rec)*: 12 Narford Road, London E5 8RD ☎ 020 8442 4751

HUTTON Michael *(Gtr)*: Blackburn Sachs Associates, Eastgate House, 16-19 Eastcastle Street, London W1N 7PA ☎ 020 8747 1196, 020 8995 1427

HYNDE Chrissie *(Gtr)*: c/o Gailforce Mgnt Ltd, 30 Ives Street, London SW3 2ND ☎ 020 7581 0261, 020 7584 5774 fax

IDLE Eric *(Gtr)*: Chamberlaynes, High Street, Rolvenden, Cranbrook, Kent TN17 4LW ☎ 020 7328 7246

IGNATIUS Victor *(Gtr, Voc)*: 92 Poplar Court, Gap Road, Wimbledon SW19 8JW ☎ 020 8947 7816

ILLES Robert *(Gtr, Voc, Man, B Gtr, Didj)*: Flat 4, 19 Upton Park, Slough, Berkshire SL1 2DA ☎ 01753 553109, 0468 253907

ISAACS Brad *(Gtr)*: 44 Maida Avenue, North Chingford, London E4 7JJ ☎ 020 8529 6563

ISIDORE Gus *(Ld Gtr, B Gtr, Dms, Voc)*: 59 Norfolk House Road, Streatham, London SW16 1JQ ☎ 020 8769 1975

ITAL Dave *(Gtr, Kbds, Voc, B Gtr)* ☎ 020 8314 0884, 0585 448350 mob

ITES Ras *(Gtr, Dms, Kbds)*: Address Unknown ☎ 020 8985 0284

JACKSON Mike *(Gtr, B Gtr, Hmca)*: 14 Brants Walk, Hanwell, London W7 1BU ☎ 020 8575 6982, 07957 662268

JACOB Robert *(Gtr, Pf)*: 11 Walton Terrace, Maybury, Woking, Surrey GU21 5EL ☎ 01483 776091

JAGGER Peter *(Gtr, B Gtr)*: 23 Duncan Road, Richmond, Surrey TW9 2JU ☎ 020 8940 8297 & fax

JAIMES Mark *(Gtr, B Gtr)*: c/o Voodoo, 21 Ruckholt Close, Leyton, London E10 5NX ☎ 020 8923 8368, 020 8539 8517 fax

JALLOW John *(Gtr)*: 22 Stillness Road, Forest Hill, London SE23 1NQ ☎ 020 8690 8538

JAMES Alan *(Gtr, Pf)*: 11 Howitt Road, London NW3 4LT

JAMES Chris *(Gtr, B Gtr, Kbds)*: Flat 12, Cypress Court, 83 Albemarle Road, Beckenham, Kent BR3 2NY

JAMES Stew *(Gtr, Clt)*: 28 Horton Road, London E8 1DP ☎ 020 7254 9257

JAMIESON John *(Gtr, Pf)*: 15B Charteris Road, London N4 3AA ☎ 020 7281 4637

JANAWAY Peter *(Gtr)*: 44 Sedgecombe Avenue, Kenton, Harrow, Middlesex HA3 0HN ☎ 020 8907 1917

JANI Maitreya *(E Gtr, Ac Gtr, Cl Gtr, B Gtr)*: 39A Bond Street, Ealing, London W5 5AS ☎ 020 8566 4553, 0441 097235

JANSEN Brigitte *(Gtr, Kbds)*: 49 Woodsome Road, London NW5 1SA ☎ 020 7267 1532

JARVIS Graham *(Gtr, Kbds)*: Stotfold, 39 Norfolk Farm, Pyrford, Woking GU22 8LF ☎ 01932 220304

JARVIS Paul (*Gtr, Kbds*): Flat 3, 24 Perryn Road, Acton, London W3 7NA ☎ 020 8740 9663

JASPER Lee (*Gtr, Voc*): c/o Worldspan, Axis House, 242 Bath Road, Hayes, Middlesex UB3 5AY ☎ 0966 403754

JAY Martin (*Gtr, Voc, Per*): 17 Brook Way, Chigwell, Essex IG7 6AW ☎ 020 8500 2849

JENKINS Billy (*Gtr*): 164 Algernon Road, London SE13 7AW ☎ 020 8690 8341

JENKINS Keith (*Gtr, B Gtr*): 1 Milton Road, Hampton, Middlesex TW12 2LL ☎ 020 8941 8669, 0976 737052 mob

JENKINS Nigel (*Gtr*): 8 Lord Roberts Mews, Waterford Road, London SW6 2DW ☎ 020 7371 9408

JOBSON David (*Gtr*): Ambulent, Platts Eyot, Lower Sunbury Road, Hampton-on-Thames, Middx TW12 2HF

JODELKO Rikki (*Gtr*): 48 Secker House, Minet Road, London SW9 7TP ☎ 020 7215 3673 day

JOHANNESSON Mikael (*Gtr*): Top Floor Flat, 37 Alexandra Grove, London N4 2LQ ☎ 0410 219977

JOHANSSON Glenn (*Gtr*): 4A Auriol Road, London W14 0SR ☎ 020 7603 0694, 0468 433327 mob

JOHNS Mark (*Gtr*): 2 Colwick Crescent, Highgate, London N6 5NU ☎ 020 7281 6838, 0468 117041 mob

JOHNSON Derek (*Gtr, B Gtr, Flt, Kbds*)

JOHNSON Matt (*Gtr, Kbds, Per, Voc*): C/0 Japheth Levy, 8-10 Bulstrode Street, London W1M 5FT ☎ 020 7631 3140

JOHNSON Robert (*Gtr, Pf, Kbds*): 6 Wimpole Road, Yiewsley, Middlesex UB7 7RJ ☎ 01895 420071

JOHNSON Robert (*Gtr, Voc*): 30 New High Street, Headington, Oxford OX3 7AQ ☎ 01865 64382

JOHNSTON Dawn (*Cl Gtr, Lute, Theory*): 30 Kingsway, Woking, Surrey GU21 1NT ☎ 01483 769022

JOHNSTON Terry (*Ld Gtr, B Gtr*): 27 Woodsyre, London SE26 6SS ☎ 020 8670 7666, 0831 523193 mob

JOHNSTONE Davey (*Gtr*): c/o William A Bong Ltd, 32 Galena Road, London W6 0LT ☎ 020 8741 9933

JOHNSTONE Paul (*Gtr, B Gtr, Kbds*): 12 Gresham Road, Neasden, London NW10 9BY ☎ 020 8451 0885

JOLLEY Steve (*Gtr, Voc, Per*): High Myless, Ongar Road, Stondon Massey, Near Brentwood, Essex CM15 0LD

JONES Anthony (*Gtr, Kbds*): 73 Temple Road, Croydon, Surrey CR0 1HW ☎ 020 8680 5951, 0410 549167, 020 8680 5951

JONES Carl (*Gtr, Voc, B Gtr, Kbds*): 19 Herbert Road, Kingston-on-Thames, Surrey KT1 2SP ☎ 020 8546 0744

JONES Pim (*Gtr, B Gtr*): 91 Iliffe Street, London SE17 3LL ☎ 020 7701 6422

JONES Steve (*Gtr*): c/o Anita Camarata, 10351 Santa Monica Blvd, Ste 200, Los Angeles, CA 90025 ☎ +1 310 203 1070, +1 310 203 1052 fax

JONES Trevor (*Sp Gtr*): 1 Priory Road, West Hill, Hastings, East Sussex TN34 3JL ☎ 01424 424769

JORDAN Christopher (*Gtr, B Gtr, Dms, Kbds, Hmca*): 20 Winn Road, Lee, London SE12 9RT ☎ 018/1 857 5722

JORY Simon (*Gtr, Synth*): 84 Stamford Hill, Hackney, London N16 6SX ☎ 020 8806 2773

JUPE Steve (*Gtr, Voc, B Gtr, Kbds, Per*): 33 Grafton Road, Acton, London W3 6PB ☎ 020 8993 7699

KALONJI Katumba (*Gtr, B Gtr*): Lower Flat, 49 Knighton Park Road, Sydenham, London SE26 5RN ☎ 020 8778 3539, 0956 129338

KALUBA David (*Gtr, Voc*): 94B Carlingford Road, London N15 3EH ☎ 020 8881 5704

KAMEN Chester (*Gtr*): 5 Ollgar Close, London W12 0NF ☎ 020 8740 7523

KAMLANI Kim (*Gtr, Kbds*): 53 Lancaster Road, London N4 4PL ☎ 020 7263 9772, 020 7272 4379 fax

KAPOR Nicholas (*Gtr*): 8 Lewins Road, Epsom, Surrey KT18 7TL ☎ 01372 740167

KARLSSON Fridrik (*Gtr, Ac Gtr, Cl Gtr, E Gtr, K*): 24 Simmil Road, Claygate, Esher, Surrey KT10 0RT ☎ 01372 467324, 0468 648550

KATZ Simon (*Gtr, Com*): 36 Hazel Road, London NW10 5PP ☎ 020 8960 8381

KAY Dylan (*Gtr, E Gtr*): 67 Chelsham Road, Clapham North, London SW4 6NN ☎ 020 7622 0898

KAYE Peter (*Gtr, Synth*): 229 San Vincente, Apartment D, St.David, Santa Monica, California, 90402

KEANE Gerard (*Gtr*): 556 Woodcote Avenue, Mill Hill, London NW7 2PB ☎ 020 8958 4638, 020 8959 7624

KEARNS Graham (*Gtr*): 28 Wakeman Road, London NW10 5DA ☎ 020 8960 5884

KEARNS Robert (*Gtr, B Gtr, Dms, Voc, Per*): 182 Girdlestone Walk, London N19 5DW ☎ 020 7281 4276

KEATING Kevin (*Gtr, Kbds*): 44 Weydown Close, London SW19 6JG ☎ 020 8785 3887, 07957 291726

KEILES Erwin (*Gtr, Arr, Md, Bjo*): Cedar Lodge, 83 Broadwood Avenue, Ruislip, Middx HA4 7XS ☎ 01895 625184, 01895 625343

KELBIE David (*Gtr, Man*): 112 The Avenue, London NW6 7NN ☎ 020 7794 5563

KELLIE Mick (*Gtr*): 3 Hop Pocket Close, Sissinghurst, Cranbrook, Kent TN17 21B ☎ 01580 713797, 0850 213801

KELLY Conor (*Gtr, Per, B Gtr, Tpt*): 30 Whites Square, London SW4 7JL ☎ 020 7627 8817

KELLY Dave (*Gtr, Voc*): Wisteria House, 14 Glamorgan Road, Hampton Wick, Surrey KT1 4HP ☎ 020 8977 3202

KEMP Keith (*Gtr*): 3 Watlings Close, Shirley, Croydon CR0 7XQ ☎ 020 8771 5952, 020 7617 4427, 0976 210945

KENDLER Eran (*Gtr, Synth*): 18 Garden Royal, Kersfield Road, London SW15 3HE ☎ 020 8788 0113

KENDRICK Graham (*Gtr, Pf, Voc*): PO Box 263, Croydon, Surrey CR9 5AP ☎ 020 8656 0025, 020 8656 4342

KENT Art (*Gtr*): 52 St Josephs Drive, Southall, Middlesex UB1 1RW ☎ 020 8574 4810

KEOGH Paul (*Gtr*): 24 Grove Park, Wanstead, London E11 2DL ☎ 020 8989 1589

KERR John (*Gtr, Per*): 46 Tonbridge House, Tonbridge Street, Kings Cross, London WC1H 9PE

KERSHAW Jonathan (*Gtr, Voc*): 1 Pelham Road, Beckenham, Kent BR3 4SQ ☎ 020 8778 3839

KERSHAW Martin (*Gtr, Bjo*): Flat 2, Irvine House, Dedworth Road, Windsor, Berks RG18 SL4 ☎ 01235 532136

KERSHAW Philip (*Gtr*): c/o Sound Supervision, Unit F9, Acton Business Centre, London NW10 6TD ☎ 020 8752 1694

KEVANS William (*Ac Gtr, Voc, B Gtr, Tpt, Kbds*): Flat 11, 30 Horton Road, Hackney, London E8 1DP ☎ 020 7923 7878, 07970 715046

KILMINSTER David (*Gtr, Voc, Kbds*): Address Unknown ☎ 020 8997 7625

KILMINSTER Uzumi (*E Gtr*): 53 Melrose Gardens, London W6 7RN ☎ 020 7602 9607

KINCHLEA Colin (*Gtr*): 39 Langley Road, Welling, Kent DA16 1BH ☎ 020 8310 7337

KING Dylan (*Gtr*): 8 Palace Road, East Molesey, Surrey KT8 9DL ☎ 020 8979 4814, 020 8979 4814

KING Nick (*Gtr*): 3 The Heights, Foxgrove Road, Beckenham, Kent BR3 5BY ☎ 020 8289 1571, 020 8289 1572 fax

KING Tom (*Gtr, Voc*): 17 Edwards Lane, London N16 0JJ ☎ 020 7254 4884

KINGSLAND Patrick (*Gtr*): 12 Ellison Road, Barnes, London SW13 0AD

KIORTSIS Dimitris (*Gtr, Voc*): Flat 4, 69 Carleton Road, London N7 0ET ☎ 020 7607 4718

KIRKBY J N Jason (*E Gtr, Ac Gtr, Man, B Gtr*): 103 Englefield Road, Islington, London N1 3LJ

KIRTLEY Peter (*Gtr*): 8 East Street, Southwold, Suffolk IP18 6EH ☎ 01502 723560

KLEIN Jonathan (*Gtr*): ☎ 020 7837 8004

KLENFELDT Ulf (*Gtr, Cl Gtr, B Gtr, Dms*): 33 Durban Road, West Norwood, London SE27 ☎ 020 8761 8472, 0403 475997

KLINGBERG Jon (*Gtr, Voc, Kbds, Dms, Flt*): Ringuagen 84, 118 60 Stockholm, Sweden ☎ +468 647225

KNIGHT Michael (*Gtr, Hmca*): 24 Birkbeck Road, Ealing, London W5 4ES ☎ 020 8560 6714

KNIGHTON Duncan (*Gtr, Kbds*): 105A Highbury Hill, London N5 1TA ☎ 020 7704 8833 & fax

KOHLER Robin (*Gtr, B Gtr*): 11 The Conyers, Rivermill, Harlow, Essex CM20 1NX

KORAL Robert (*Gtr*): 16 Station Road, Hounslow, Middlesex TW3 2AH ☎ 020 8572 2351

KORSAH Daniel (*Gtr, Voc, Kbds*): 18 Baldock House, Crawford Road, London SE5 9PS ☎ 020 7733 8291

KOTARAC Dragan (*Gtr, Ac Gtr, E Gtr, B Gtr, Kb*): Flat C, 13 Kingwood Road, London SW6 6SP ☎ 0956 587184 mob

KRAUSHAAR Bob (*Gtr, Kbds, Per*): 54 Upham Park Road, London W4 1PG ☎ 020 8995 0676

KRISTIAN Marty (*Gtr*): Rosecot, Nottingham Road South, Heronsgate Nr Chorley Wood, Herts WD3 5DP

LAIRD-CLOWES Nick (*Gtr, Hmca, Voc*): c/o Abacus (Mas), 8A Garlinge Road, London NW2 3TR ☎ 020 7435 0278

LAMBERT Andrew (*Gtr, Bzk, Man, Citt, Bjo*): 50 Riversdale Road, London N5 2JT ☎ 020 7226 5477

LAMBERT Stephen (*Gtr, Pf, Sitar, Hmca*): 47 Priory Pk Rd, Kilburn, London NW6 7UP ☎ 020 8930 1483, 020 7376 1150

LAMPRELL Adam (*Gtr*): 53 Highclere Street, London SE26 4EX ☎ 020 8676 8775

LANGER Clive (*Gtr, Pf*): 9 Lime Terrace, Camden, London NW1 0SN ☎ 020 7485 0439

LANGMEAD Mark (*Gtr, Bjo, B Gtr, Uke*): 105A Blackheath Road, Greenwich SE10 89D ☎ 020 8691 3757

LARSEN Peter (*Gtr, Pf, Voc*): 14B Peploe Road, London NW6 6EB ☎ 020 8968 5428

LATIMER Andrew (*Gtr*): PO Box 4876, Mountain View, California 94040, USA

LAW Simon (*Gtr, B Gtr, Voc*): St Cedds Vicarage, 185 Lodge Avenue, Becontree, Dagenham, Essex RM8 2HQ ☎ 020 8592 5900

LAWRENCE Martin (*Gtr*): 20 Beechdale Road, London SW2 2BE ☎ 020 8674 9647

LAWRENCE Stephen (*Gtr, Kbds*): 28 Engleheart Road, London SE6 2HP ☎ 020 8461 2574

LAWS Ian (*Gtr*): 113 Malham Road, Forest Hill, London SE23 1AL ☎ 020 8699 2857

LAWS Tim (*Gtr*): Bamn Management, c/o Will Stoppard, 136-144 New Kings Road, London SW6 4LZ ☎ 020 7705 7258, 020 7705 4335 fax

LAWSON Chris (*Gtr, B Gtr*)

LAYTON Paul (*Gtr, B Gtr*): 5 Station Road, Digswell, Welwyn, Herts AL6 0DF

LEA Christopher (*Gtr*): 67 Coombfield Drive, Darenth, Kent DA2 7LE ☎ 01474 703029

LEADER Michael (*Gtr, Dms*): 139 Rossmore Court, Park Road, London NW1 6XZ ☎ 020 7262 3773

LEAKE Tony (*Gtr, Sax*): Flat 3, 106 Palmerston Road, Wood Green, London N22 4RE ☎ 020 8888 1336

LEE Alvin (*Gtr*): Cawley House, 149-155 Canal Street, Nottingham NG1 7HR ☎ 0115 950 3044, 0115 950 0056

LEE Edward (*Ld Gtr, Pf*): 24 Bergholt Mews, London NW1 0BQ ☎ 020 7387 8960

LEE Hopkirk (*Gtr, B Gtr, Kbds, Dms*)

LEE Leslie (*Gtr, Flt*): 195 Applegarth House, Nelson Square Gardens, London SE1 0PZ ☎ 020 7928 4650

LEE Mannix (*Gtr, Kbds*): c/o Adelphoi Records, 71 Endell Street, Covent Garden, London WC2H 9AJ ☎ 020 7240 7250, 020 7240 7260

LEE Philip (*Gtr*): 60C Fairhazel Gardens, London NW6 3SL ☎ 020 7328 7208

LEE Ronnie (*Gtr, B Gtr, Pf, Kbds, Dms*)

LEECE Kevin (*E Gtr, Ac Gtr, Synth, B Gtr*): 18 Haycroft Gardens, London NW10 3BN ☎ 020 8965 7941

LEGENDRE Dominique (*Gtr, Com*): 69 Millbrook Road, Brixton, London SW9 7JD ☎ 020 7274 5476

LEGG Adrian (*Gtr, Com*): 17 Dombey House, London W11 4DW ☎ 020 7229 3336 & fax

LEGG Phil (*Gtr*): 330 Westbourne Park Road, London W11 1EQ ☎ 020 7792 8597

LEMMON Jonathan (*Gtr, B Gtr*): 151 Ravenscroft Road, Beckenham, Kent BR3 4TN ☎ 020 8659 3316

LEMON Judy (*Gtr, Voc, Kbds, B Gtr*): 7 Kings Court, Castlebar Park, London W5 1BY ☎ 020 8997 4963

LENG Barry (*Gtr, Kbds*): Manor Court, Manor Road, Loughton, Essex IG10 4RP ☎ 020 8502 2952

LESTER Gregory (*Gtr*): 18A Southampton Road, London NW5 4HX ☎ 020 7813 1931

LEVENTHALL Mark (*Gtr, Tpt, Pf, Com, Arr*): 12 Lomley House, Tulse Hill, London SW2 2EW ☎ 020 8674 0733, 020 8265 9580 fax

LEWIS Lee (*Gtr, Voc*): 17 Takeley Close, Waltham Abbey, Essex EN9 1QH ☎ 01992 763785, 0410 869363 mob

LEWIS Matthew (*Jz Gtr, Com, Arr*): 88 Asbuknham Grove, London SE10 8UJ ☎ 020 8691 9916

LEWIS Sid (*Gtr, B Gtr, Kbds*): 100 Portland Road, Kingston, Surrey KT1 2SW ☎ 020 8549 5900, 020 8546 3115

LEYDEN Patrick (*Gtr*): 65 Station Road, Maghera, Co Derry, Northern Ireland BT46 5EY ☎ 01648 45803

LI Simon (*Gtr*): Grd Floor Flat, 33 Rocks Lane, Barnes, London SW13 0DB ☎ 020 8288 0531, 0870 0548334 fax

LIDYARD Geoffrey (*Gtr*): 93 Byron Road, Luton, Beds LU4 0HX ☎ 01582 582228

LIESEGANG William (Billy) (*Gtr, Hmca, Kbds*): 20 Copenhagen Street, Islington, London N1 0JD ☎ 020 7278 7590 & fax, 0956 495359 mob

LIGHTMAN Richard (*E Gtr, Gtr, H Gtr, Hmca, B Gt*): 353 St Margarets Road, St Margarets, Twickenham, Middx TW1 1PW ☎ 020 8876 5034

LIMBRICK Alan (*Gtr*): 24 Elanor Grove, Barnes, London SW13 0JN ☎ 020 8876 5034

LINDES Hal (*Gtr, Voc, Kbds*): c/o Ian Amos, ICM, 76 Oxford Street, London WlN 0AX

LIPSON Stephen (*Gtr, Kbds*): 43 Agamemnon Road, London NW6 1EG ☎ 020 7794 6079, 020 7431 8189 fax

LISICKI Mark (*Gtr, Kbds*): 46 Park Ridings, London N8 0LD ☎ 020 8889 2925

LISTER Andrew (*Gtr, Synth*): 34 Nightingale House, Thomas More Street, London E1 9UA ☎ 020 7481 3619

LITHERLAND James (*Gtr, Voc*): 111 The Ridgeway, Enfield, Middlesex EN2 8NH ☎ 020 8367 3659

LLOYD Huw (*Gtr*): Steve Harnett Promotions ☎ 01206 794 337 & fax

LOFTHOUSE Chris (*Gtr, Kbds*): 20A West End Avenue, Pinner, Middx HA5 1BJ ☎ 020 8868 1380

LONGWORTH James (*Gtr*): 3 Hathorne Terrace, Calverley Grove, London N19 3LL ☎ 020 7263 2939

LOUKES Robert (*Gtr*): 215A Oxlow Lane, Dagenham, Essex RM10 7YA ☎ 020 8593 9891

LOWIS Nigel (*Gtr, Kbds*): 22 Garden Road, Bromley, Kent BR1 3LX ☎ 020 8313 3524, 020 8402 0376 fax

LUNDGREN Johan (*Gtr*)

LUSAMBO Fiston (*Ld Gtr, Rh Gtr, B Gtr*): Basement Flat, 3 Essendine Road, Maida Vale, London W9 2LS ☎ 020 7289 9368

LYDDON Rupert (*Gtr*): 6 Arlington Road, Camden Town, London NW1 7HX ☎ 020 7388 1416, 0956 845194

LYLE Graham (*Gtr, Man*): The Jimmies, Lodge Road, Sundridge Park, Bromley Kent BR1 3ND

LYNCH Tom (*Gtr, Hmca*) ☎ 020 8889 6358

LYONS Sean (*Gtr*): Bevans Cottage, 119 Snoll Hatch Road, East Peckham, Kent TN12 5DZ ☎ 01622 871184, 0394 628006

MAC Rob (*Gtr, B Gtr*): Flat 4, 252 Camden Road, London NW1 9HE ☎ 020 7916 2745, 020 7209 4990, 020 7209 5080

MACCOLL Neill (*Gtr, Voc, Man, Auto Hrp, B Gt*): 3 Topsfield Road, London N8 8SN ☎ 020 8341 7758

MACDONALD Edward (*Gtr, Voc, Tbn*): 54 Park Hill, Carshalton Beeches, Surrey SM5 3RS ☎ 020 8286 0687

MACFARLANE Malcolm (*Gtr, Ac Gtr, B Gtr, Pf*): 84 Tannsfield Road, Sydenham, London SE26 5DG ☎ 020 8676 0149

MACMAHON Niall (*Gtr, Voc*): 1A Randolph Gardens, London NW6 5EH ☎ 020 7328 8904

MAEL Ronald (*Gtr*): c/o Def Ltd, 31 Ansleigh Place, London W11 4BW ☎ 020 7221 2525

MAEL Russell (*Gtr*): c/o Def Ltd, 31 Ansleigh Place, London W11 4BW ☎ 020 7221 2525

MAHER Sean (*Gtr, Per*): 24 Bennetts Yard, North Uxbridge, Middlesex UB8 1AN ☎ 01895 52892

MALONEY Eamon (*Gtr, Pf*): 58 Drax Avenue, Wimbledon, London SW20 0EY ☎ 020 8947 1413

MANDEL Derek (*Gtr*): 8 Cecil Road, Rochester, Kent ME1 2HT ☎ 01634 406338

MANN John (*Gtr*): 90 Ladbrooke Road, Redhill, Surrey RH1 1LB ☎ 01737 219677

MANNERING Alan (*Gtr*): 135 Station Lane, Hornchurch, Essex RM12 6LJ ☎ 01708 620388

MANNING Rob (*Gtr, B Gtr, Pf, Voc*): 5 Chester Road, London N19 5DE ☎ 020 7272 9590, 07971 198737

MANZANERA Philip (*Gtr*): 3 Park Mews, 213 Kilburn Lane, London W10 4BQ ☎ 019325 64350

MANZANGI HP Safro (*Gtr, Voc, Song W, Com, Arr*): 38 Kensington Gardens Square, London W2 4BQ ☎ 0956 512432

MANZOLI Rob (*Ld Gtr, Voc, B Gtr*): c/o Simon Makepeace, Martin Greene Ravden, 55 Loudoun Road, St Johns Wood, London NW8 0DL ☎ 020 7625 4545, 020 7625 5265 fax

MARAN Mike (*Gtr, Pf*): 35 Byron Square, Trumpington, Cambridge CB2 2JL ☎ 01223 514511

MARCHANT David (*Gtr*): 15 Edward Road, Parkstone, Poole, Dorset BH14 9ES ☎ 01202 730822

MARCHE Rob (*Gtr, B Gtr, Kbds*): Flat 1, 4 Fleet Road, Hampstead, London NW3 2QS ☎ 020 7482 5699

MARI Joe (*Gtr, B Gtr, Kbds*): 31 Samuel House, Clarissa Street, London E8 4HL ☎ 020 7249 0975

MARKHAM Brendan (*Ac Gtr*): c/o 60B Hazlewell Road, Putney, London SW15 6LR ☎ 020 8785 9499, 020 8788 7660

MARLEY (*Gtr, Per, B Gtr*): 172A High Road, Tottenham, London N15 4NS ☎ 020 8493 1319

MARLOW Andrew (*Gtr, B Gtr*): ☎ 0958 637654

MARS Matt (*Gtr, Kbds*): 10 Ivor Court, Crouch Hill, London N8 9EB ☎ 020 8341 7824

MARSAC Christian (*Gtr, Sax*): 8 Gaynesford Road, London SE23 2UQ ☎ 020 8699 9733

MARSH Neil (*Gtr, Kbds, B Gtr, Hmca, Per*): Studio 39, 103 Highland Road, Bromley, Kent BR1 4AA ☎ 020 8289 3095

MARSHALL Alastair (*Gtr*): 131 Columbia Drive, Worcester WR2 4XX ☎ 0973 624853

MARSHALL Jamie (*Gtr, Voc, Man*): 15 Grove Road, Windsor, Berks SL4 1JE ☎ 01753 857072, 0976 734138 mob

MARSHALL Nicholas (*Gtr, Kbds*): 461 Fulham Palace Road, London SW6 6SU ☎ 020 7384 1291

MARSHALL Nick (*Gtr, Kbds, Dms, B Gtr, Vln*): 32 Twyford Avenue, Fortis Green, London N2 9NJ ☎ 020 8883 3729

MARSHALL Phill (*Gtr, Voc, Pf, Kbds*): 43C Bridge Road, Hampton Court, Surrey KT8 9ER ☎ 020 8941 2915

MARTIN Angela (*Gtr, B Gtr*): 2 St Thomas Road, Canning Town, London E16 1NR ☎ 020 7511 0032

MARTIN David (*Gtr, Voc*): 140 Chapter Road, London NW2 5LX ☎ 020 8459 5340, 0956 539054

MARTIN Esther (*Ac Gtr, Kbds, Voc*): c/o 1 Mount Ash Road, Sydenham, London SE26 6LZ ☎ 0956 670613, c/o 020 8289 9945

MARTIN Juan (*Gtr*): 54 Windsor Road, London N3 3SS ☎ 020 8346 4500, 020 8346 2488 fax

MARTIN Manolo (*Fl Gtr*): 37 Staines Road, Ilford, Essex IG1 2XA ☎ 020 8478 6794

MARTIN Noel (*Gtr, Voc*): 16 Derwent Road, Palmers Green, London N13 4PU ☎ 020 8886 4645

MARTIN Philip (*Gtr, Vln, Voc*): 30 Park Hill Court, Beeches Road, Tooting, London SW17 7LX ☎ 020 8767 0030

MARTYR David (*Gtr*): 7 Wirral House, Sydenham Hill Estate, London SE26 6AQ ☎ 020 8699 2917

MARVIN Hank (*Gtr*): c/o Countdown Fin. Serv. Ltd, Harley House, 94 Hart Lane, Claygate, Esher, Surrey KT10 0RB ☎ 01372 467752, 01372 462352 fax

MASIH Nabeel (*Gtr, Kbds*): 37 Skeffington Road, East Ham, London E6 2NA ☎ 020 8471 9320, 0958 739005

MASON Steven (*Gtr*): c/o Jerry Smith, Automatic, 3 Wansdown Place, London SW6 1DN ☎ 020 7386 7172, 020 7610 1250 fax

MATHISON Peter (*Gtr*): ☎ 020 8348 4137

MATTHEWS Benjamin (*Gtr, Kbds*): Toni Medcalf Mngt, Garden Flat, 83 Cambridge Gdns, London W10 6JE ☎ 020 8960 3596, 020 8960 4330

MATTHEWS Roderick (*Gtr, B Gtr*): 71 Talfourd Road, London SE15 5NN ☎ 020 7701 3619

MAUDE Tony (*Gtr, Voc, Uke*): 12 Florian Road, London SW15 2NL ☎ 020 8874 3579

MAY Brian (*Gtr, Pf*): PO Box 141, Windlesham, Surrey GU20 6YW ☎ 01344 875448

MAY Dieselle (*Gtr, B Gtr, Dms, Voc*): Ripe Management Ltd, 2 Beulah Road, London SW19 3SB ☎ 020 8255 7775, 020 8255 7776

MAY Rick (*E Gtr, Db, Kbds*): 36 Onslow Road, Richmond, Surrey TW10 6QE ☎ 020 8948 3447, 0411 395 788 mob, 020 8948 3447

MAZZARINI Stefano (*Gtr*): 55 Spruce Hills Road, London E17 4LB ☎ 020 8531 1657, 0956 401659 mob

MCARTHUR Angus (*Gtr*): Flat 2, Gloucester Villas, 10A Gloucester Drive, Finsbury Park, London N4 2LW ☎ 020 8802 3735, 0374 108075

MCCAFFREY Michael (*Gtr*): Address Unknown ☎ 020 8882 4978

MCCANN Ian (*Gtr, Bjo, Vln*): 22 Fieldend, Waldegrave Park, Twickenham, Middlesex TW1 4TF

MCCLURE Kirsten (*Gtr, Cel, Kbds*): 7 Rokeby House, Lambs Conduit Street, London WC1N 3LX ☎ 020 7242 7320, 0961 386326

MCCOOKERYBOOK Helen (*Gtr, Voc*): 12 Vale Drive, Barnet EN5 2ED

MCCORRY Martin (*Gtr*): 24 Roman Way, Islington, London N7 ☎ 020 7700 3899, 0961 802967 mob

MCCULLOUGH Henry (*Gtr, Man, St Gtr*): 20 Spruce Field Drive, Ballysally, Coleraine, Co Derry, N. Ireland BT52 2QY ☎ 028 7035 5399

MCDERMOTT Patrick (*Gtr, B Gtr*): Lackafin Broomfield, Castleblaney, Co Monaghan, Ireland ☎ +353 42 43095

MCDONALD Milton (*Gtr*): 17 Second Ave, Acton, London W3 7RX ☎ 020 8746 1070, 0831 666717

MCEWAN Steven (*Gtr*): Flat 4, 32 Clifton Road, London N8 8JA ☎ 020 8245 4426

MCGANN Mark (*Gtr, Pf, B Gtr*): ☎ 020 7435 5284, 0468 701132, 020 7794 1913

MCGILLIVRAY Bill (*Gtr, Voc, Com*): 2 Miswell Cottage, Icknield Way, Tring, Herts HP23 4JU ☎ 01442 828167

MCGOWAN John (*Gtr, B Gtr, Kbds*): Flat 1, 171 New Kings Road, London SW6 4SN ☎ 020 7731 2336, 020 7381 0059

MCGUIGAN Shane (*Gtr, Scratch*) ☎ 020 8548 1858

MCGUINNESS Tom (*Gtr, B Gtr, Man*): 74 Kensington Park Road, London W11 2PL ☎ 020 7727 2823

MCINNES Ramsay (*Gtr*): 9 Blenheim Road, London E15 1UF ☎ 0961 314614

MCINTOSH Danny (*Gtr, Per, Kbds*): 62 Riverside 1, Hester Road, London SW11 4AN ☎ 020 7223 3336

MCINTOSH Robert (*Gtr*): 6 Coldharbour, Chickerell, Weymouth, Dorset DT3 4BG ☎ 01305 782345

MCKAY John (*Gtr*): 66 Woodside Avenue, Alperton, Wembley, Middlesex HA0 1UY ☎ 020 8903 4736

MCKRIETH Breeze (*Gtr, B Gtr, Kbds*): 19D Myddelton Square, London EC1R 1YE ☎ 020 7278 2465, 0956 146590 mob

MCMASTER James (*Gtr*): Rowan Cottage, School House Live, Horsmonden, Kent TW12 8BP ☎ 01892 722953

MCMELLON Gregg (*Gtr, Clt*): 14 The Avenue, Chiswick, London W4 1HT

MCTELL Ralph (*Gtr, Pf, Hmca, Voc*): 161 Lower Richmond Road, London SW15 1HH ☎ 020 8785 6098 & fax

MEAD Jeff (*Gtr, St Gtr, B Gtr*): 26 Valmar Road, London SE5 9NG ☎ 020 7737 7100

MELROSE Robert (*Gtr, Kbds*): Top Floor Flat, 24 Dagmar Road, Camberwell, London SE5 8NZ ☎ 020 8675 4659

MERCER Kas *(Gtr, Pf)*: Basement Flat, 23 Bravington Road, London W9 3AB ☎ 020 8960 9336

MERLO Rinaldo *(Gtr, B Gtr, Pf, Rec)*: 8 Sovereign Mews, Pearson Street, Shoreditch, London E2 8ER ☎ 020 7256 0813

METCALFE Hugh *(Gtr, Vln, Dms, Voc)*: 10 Malvern House, Stamford Hill Estate, London N16 6RR ☎ 020 8806 8216

MEYNELL Anthony *(Gtr, B Gtr, Pf)*: 18 Ivor Street, Camden, London NW1 9PJ ☎ 020 7267 6785

MICHAELSON Nicholas *(Gtr)*: 18A Queens Avenue, Muswell Hill, London N10 2JN

MIHAJLOVIC Dusan *(Gtr, Kbds, Hmca)*: 25 Aden Grove, London N16 9NP ☎ 020 7254 3009

MIKE-E *(Gtr, B Gtr)*: Flat 4, 17 Gloucester Street, Pimlico, London SW1V 4DB ☎ 020 7630 0567

MILLAR Robin *(Gtr, Pf, Per, Voc)*: The Gallery, 1B Dorncliffe Road, London SW6 5LE

MILLER Adrian *(Gtr)*: 7 Tadorne Road, Tadworth, Surrey KT20 5TD ☎ 01757 812692

MILLER Andrew *(Gtr, Voc)*: 271 Royal College Street, London NW1 9LU ☎ 020 7482 0115

MILLER Dominic *(Gtr)*: Smallfield,Cody & Co., 5 Harley Place, Harley Street, London W1N 1HB ☎ 020 7631 4574, 020 7636 8391 fax

MILLER Gary *(Gtr, Kbds)*: Negus-Fancey Co.Ltd, 78 Portland Road, London W11 4QL ☎ 020 7727 2063, 020 7229 4188 fax

MILLER John *(Gtr, B Gtr, Voc)*: 19 Needham Terrace, Cricklewood, London NW2 6QL

MILLER Johnny *(Gtr, B Gtr)*: 55 Gayford Road, Shepherds Bush, London W12 9BY ☎ 020 8932 0170

MILLER Philip *(Gtr, Synth)*: 29A Colvestone Crescent, London E8 2LG

MILLER Raymond *(Gtr)*: 42A Farmer Road, Leyton, London E10 5DL ☎ 020 8539 0940

MILLER-CHEEVERS Gary *(Gtr, Dms, Kbds)*: 19 Portman Avenue, East Sheen, London SW14 8NX ☎ 020 8876 8919, 0385 997320, 020 8948 7527

MILLIGAN Ross *(Gtr, Bjo)*: Flat 1, 21 Broseley Grove, Sydenham, London SE26 5LD ☎ 020 8540 5939, 0802 795 293

MIMMO *(Gtr, Voc)*: 5 Myddelton Gardens, Winchmore Hill, London N21 2PA ☎ 020 8360 8701

MINCHIN Colin *(Gtr)*: 33 Temple Road, London W5 4SL

MITCHELL John *(Gtr, Voc, Pf)*: 6 Laytons Lane, Sunbury-on-Thames, Middlesex TW16 6LR ☎ 01932 765602

MITCHELL Vincent *(Gtr, Kbds, B Gtr)*: 93B Golders Green Road, London NW11 8EN ☎ 020 8381 4453

MOHAPI Benjamin *(Gtr)*: 97 Woodstock Way, Mitcham, Surrey CR4 1BF ☎ 020 8646 8987

MOLE Matthew *(Gtr, Kbds, B Gtr)*: 49 Gilling Court, Belsize Grove, London NW3 4XA ☎ 020 7209 4111

MOLKO Brian *(Gtr, B Gtr)*: c/o Elevator Lady Ltd, The Colonnades, 82 Bishops Bridge Road, London W2 6BB ☎ 020 7243 0640, 020 7727 2226

MOLONEY Fergus *(Gtr, Kbds, Voc)*: 153 Flora Gardens, Dalling, Hammersmith, London W6 ☎ 020 8746 3530, 0976 724716

MONA Pete *(Gtr)*: 39 Lambton Road, London N19 3QJ ☎ 020 7263 3602

MONCUR James *(Gtr)*: 14 Effingham Lodge, Surbiton Cres, Kingston-upon-Thames, Surrey KT1 2LN ☎ 020 8287 4947

MONFARIDI Hose *(Gtr)*: 8 Naseby Close, Isleworth, Middlesex TW1 4JQ ☎ 020 8560 5518

MONROSE *(Gtr, B Gtr, Kbds, Per)*: 1A Crawley Road, Enfield, Middlesex EN1 2ND ☎ 020 8360 6582, 020 8350 4372

MONROY Guillermo *(Gtr)*: 100 Manwood Road, Crofton Park, London SE4 1SE

MONTORO Rob *(E Gtr, Ac Gtr)*: 40A Shaftesbury Parade, Shaftesbury Avenue, Harrow, Middlesex HA2 0AH ☎ 020 8426 8547

MOODY John *(Gtr, Clt)*: 8 Glanfield Road, Beckenham, Kent BR3 3JU ☎ 020 8402 1963

MOODY Micky *(Gtr)*: 42 Amyand Park Road, Twickenham, Middlesex TW1 3HE

MOOK Anet *(Gtr, Pf, B Gtr)*: 120 Kentish Town Road, Flat 1, Camden, London NW1 9PY ☎ 020 7267 5325

MOORE Gary *(Gtr)*: c/o Newman & Co, Regent House, 1 Pratt Mews, London NW1 0AD ☎ 020 7267 6899, 020 7267 6746

MOORE Jamie Woods *(Gtr, Com, Arr)*: 85 Humberstone Road, London E13 9NL ☎ 020 8548 8754

MOORHOUSE Andrew *(Gtr, Kbds)*: Flat 2 Highview, 5 Holford Road, Hampstead, London NW3 1AG ☎ 020 7431 3197

MORCOMBE Richard J *(Gtr, E Gtr, Ac Gtr, Man, Bjo)*: 6 Corrib Heights, 30 Crescent Road, London N8 8DA ☎ 020 8340 3846 & fax, 0411 007023 mob

MORENO Miguel *(Fl Gtr)*: 41 Shacklewell House, Shacklewell Lane, London E8 2EQ ☎ 020 7254 0246

MORIAH Anthony *(Gtr)*: 57 Neth Erwood Road, West Kensington, London W14 0BP ☎ 020 7602 7334, 0956 607784

MORLEY Luke *(Gtr, Voc)*: Toni Medcalf Mngt, Garden Flat, 83 Cambridge Gardens, London W10 6JE ☎ 020 8960 3596, 020 8960 4330

MORRIS Peter *(Gtr, Kbds)*: 32 Berwick Street, London W1V 3RF ☎ 020 7494 1558, 020 7494 1639

MORRISON Barry *(Ld Gtr)*: 66 Chester Road, Edmonton, London N9 8JG ☎ 020 8887 0221

MORRISON Gary *(Gtr)*: 6 Holyrood Gardens, Edgware, Middlesex HA8 5LR ☎ 020 8951 3014, 0966 514 033 mob

MORRISON Ian *(Gtr)*: 63 Princes View, Dartford, Kent DA1 1RJ ☎ 01322 228336

MORRISON Van *(Gtr, Sax, Pf)*: c/o O J Kilkenny (Actnts), 6 Lansdowne Mews, London W11 3BH ☎ 020 7792 9494

MORROW Tony *(Gtr)*: ☎ 020 8847 6013, 0956 671129

MORSON Winston *(Gtr, Flt)*: 20 Grasmere Avenue, Acton, London W3 6JU ☎ 020 8993 4325

MORTIMER Timothy *(Gtr, B Gtr, Kbds)*: 32A Hanger Lane, Ealing, London W5 3HJ

MORTIMORE Bob *(Gtr, Kbds)*: The Old Cottage, Common Road, Chorleywood, Herts WD3 5LT ☎ 01923 284709

MOSES Jamie *(Gtr, Voc, Kbds)*: 32 William Road, Caterham-on-The Hill, Surrey CR3 5NN ☎ 01883 349962

MOSS Dennis *(Gtr)*: 41 Winns Terrace, Walthamstow, London E17 5EJ ☎ 020 8925 0413

MOSS Peter *(Gtr, Arr, Con, Md)*: 7 Dennis Road, Corse Mullen, Dorset BH21 3NF ☎ 01202 695 965, 041 72 83 27

MOXHAM David *(Gtr, B Gtr)*: 69 Wellington Road, Leytonstone, London E11 2AS ☎ 020 8925 1181, 0966 135884 mob

MOYSE Nigel *(E Gtr, Ac Gtr)*: 10 Denbigh Road, Ealing, London W13 8PX ☎ 020 8998 5041

MOYSE Stephen *(Gtr)*: 4 Birkbeck Road, Beckenham, Kent BR3 4SN ☎ 020 8289 5259, 0802 339 264

MUGGLETON Paul *(Gtr, Voc)*: Cedar Cottage, Princes Road, Weybridge, Surrey KT13 9BH ☎ 01409 26464

MULFORD Robert *(Gtr, Bjo)*: ☎ 020 8886 6475, 0468 960896 mob

MULHAIR Paul *(Gtr, Dms)*: 7 Junction Road, Ashford, Middlesex TW15 1NL ☎ 01784 243733

MULLARKEY Robin *(Ac Gtr, E Gtr, Pf)*: 283D Trinity Road, Wandsworth, London SW18 3SN ☎ 020 8871 0323, 0976 932936

MULLEN James *(Gtr)*: 15 North Row Flats, North Row, London W1R 1DG ☎ 020 7499 2339

MULLETT Cristobal *(Fl Gtr)*: 367A Lordship Lane, London SE22 8DD ☎ 020 8299 1356

MULLINEAUX Timothy *(Gtr, Voc, Dms, Kbds, B Gtr)*: Flat Above, 158 Franciscan Road, Tooting, London SW17 8HH ☎ 020 8767 5169

MULLINS Darrin *(Gtr)*: c/o 60B Hazlewell Road, Putney, London SW15 6LR ☎ 020 8785 9499, 020 8788 7660

MULLON Benjamin *(E Gtr, B Gtr, Kbds)*: 106 Long Elmes, Harrow, Middlesex HA3 5JY ☎ 020 8933 8929

MULVANEY Liam *(Gtr)*: 114 Petherton Road, Islington, London N5 2RT ☎ 020 7359 1764

MUNDAY David *(Gtr, Kbds, Hmca)*: 12A Denning Road, London NW3 1SU ☎ 020 7794 9660

MUNDAY Terence *(Gtr)*: 10 Burhan Uddin House, Commercial Street, London E1 6BA

MUNRO Charles *(Gtr, Pf, B Gtr, Hmca)*: 12 Lowercourt Wood, 351 Westbourne Park Rd, Nottinghill, London W11 1EU ☎ 020 7221 9773

MUNTIZ Bae *(Gtr, Kbds)*: 89A Rosendale Road, West Dulwich, London SE21 8EZ ☎ 020 7737 2130, 0956 163683 mob

MURPHY Anthony *(Gtr)*: 10 Florence House, St Anns Road, London W11 4DQ ☎ 020 7792 9044 fax

MURRAY David *(Gtr)*: c/o Iron Maiden, The Colonnades, 82 Bishopsbridge Road, London W2 6BB

MURRAY James *(Ac Gtr)*: 17 Goodhart Way, West Wickham, Kent BR4 0ER ☎ 020 8777 0248, 07775 635158

MURRAY Pete *(Gtr)*: 5 Lillie Road, Biggin Hill, Kent TN16 3QB ☎ 01959 574389

MUTIMANWA Kawele *(Gtr, B Gtr, Sax)*: 77 Churston Avenue, Plaistow, London E13 0RJ ☎ 020 8257 5431, 0956 510868

MYDDELTON Gabriel *(Gtr, Sax, Pf)*: 66 Myddelton Square, London EC1R 1XX ☎ 020 7278 1929

NADLER Stephen *(Gtr, B Gtr)*: 31 Morecambe Street, London SE17 1DX ☎ 0956 544938 mob

NAILON Alex *(Gtr)*: 29 Tamworth Street, Fulham, London SW6 1LF ☎ 0958 491717

NAKANISHI Toshio *(Gtr)*: 28 Chesterton Road, London W10 5LX ☎ 020 8969 0240

NAYLOR Patrick *(Jz Gtr)*: 224A Camden Road, London NW1 9HG ☎ 020 7482 2607

NAZAIRE Jacques *(Gtr, B Gtr, Kbds)*: 10 Gate Hill Court, 166 Notting Hill Gate, London W11 3QT ☎ 020 7229 3195

NEAL Andrew *(Gtr, Pf, Synth)*: 80 Windermere Road, Muswell Hill, London N10 2RG ☎ 020 8883 6709, 020 8245 5430

NELSON Derek *(E Gtr, Ac Gtr)*: 8A Ringcroft Street, London N7 8ND ☎ 020 7697 0255

NELSON Mark *(E Gtr, B Gtr)*: 57 Heysham Road, London N15 6HL ☎ 020 8800 1019, 020 7921 2255

NELSON Simon *(Gtr, Man, Bzk, Sitar)*: Flat 9, 9 Nevern Square, London SW5 9NW ☎ 020 8876 8926, 020 7373 9854

NELSON Stephen *(Gtr, Voc)*: 69 North Worple Way, Mortlake, London SW14 8PR ☎ 020 8878 0349

NESMON Isabelle *(Cl Gtr, E Gtr, Voc)*: 133 London Road, Ewell, Epsom KT17 2BS ☎ 020 8224 3004, 020 8224 3066 fax

NEVIN Catherine *(Gtr)*

NEWBY Monique *(Gtr)*: South Dock Marina, Lock Office, Rope Street, Plough Way, London SE16 1TW ☎ 020 7232 0303

NEWLAND Christopher *(Gtr)*: 31A Cologne Road, London SW11 2AH ☎ 020 7924 1402

NICHOLAS Andy *(Gtr, B Gtr, Voc)*: 134 Empire Avenue, Edmonton, London N18 1AG ☎ 020 8889 2270, 0378 060646 mob

NICHOLAS Grant *(Gtr, Voc, B Gtr, Kbds, Tpt)*: Flat C, 215 Camden Road, London NW1 9AA ☎ 020 7284 3001

NICHOLLS Billy *(Gtr, Pf)*: 16 Park Road, East Twickenham, Middlesex TW1 2PX ☎ 020 8891 4426

NICHOLLS John *(Gtr, Hmca, Wh, Flt)*: 12 Kilronan, Rosebank Way, Acton, London W3 6TX ☎ 01386 593589

NICHOLLS Justin *(Gtr, Kbds)*: Flat 30, 43-53 Myddelton Square, London EC1R 1YD ☎ 020 7833 1560

NICOL Simon *(Gtr)*: 16 West End, Chipping Norton, Oxon OX7 5EX ☎ 01608 641148

NIEBLA Eduardo *(Gtr)*: 24 Sangora Road, London SW11 1RL ☎ 020 7624 4701, 0956 546188 mob

NILES Richard *(Gtr)*: 34 Beaumont Road, London W4 5AP ☎ 020 8747 0946

NISBET James *(Gtr, Pf)*: Pyghtle Cottage, Denham Village, Nr Uxbridge, Middlesex UB9 5BD ☎ 01895 832063

NOLAN Sean *(Gtr)*: 41 Winsford Road, London SE6 4LS ☎ 020 8291 3950

NOLAN Tom *(Gtr, Voc)*: 4 Queens Terrace, Isleworth, Middx TW7 7DB ☎ 020 8560 3787

NORMAN Steven *(Gtr)*: c/o PO Box 8 Telepost, Paseo Vara De Rey, Galerias Cine Serra, Ibiza 07800 Baleares, Spain

NUPEN Christopher *(Gtr)*: c/o Moore Stephens, Priory House, Sydenham Road, Guildford, Surrey GU1 3RX ☎ 01483 537331 & fax

O'CONNELL Brendan *(Gtr)*: Address Unknown ☎ 020 7274 3938

O'CONNELL William *(Gtr, Vln, B Gtr, Pf, Voc)*: 83 Crofton Road, Plaistow, London E13 8QT ☎ 020 7476 8335

O'CONNOR Sinead *(Gtr, Voc, Kbds)*: c/o O.J Kilkenny & Co, 6 Landsdowne Mews, London W11 3BH ☎ 020 7792 9494

O'DWYER Eamonn *(Gtr, Kbds)*: 19 Bathurst Road, Ilford, Essex IG1 4LA ☎ 020 8518 5461

O'GRUAMA Aindrias *(E Gtr)*: 49 Chartham Court, Canterbury Gardens, London SW9 7PT ☎ 020 7274 1003

O'SHAUGHNESSY Chris *(Gtr, B Gtr)*: 19A Mansell Road, Acton, London W3 7QH ☎ 020 8743 0360

OAKENFOLD Paul *(Gtr)*: c/o Ros Earls, 140Db Management, 1 Mccrone Mews, Belsize Village, London NW3 5BG ☎ 020 7431 8271

OBERNIK-DUNMORE Sam *(Gtr, Pf)*: 29 The Colonnades, Sylvester Road, London E8 1EP ☎ 020 7249 3613

OBRIEN James *(Gtr, B Gtr, Voc)*: 40 Warwick Road, Sutton, Surrey SM1 4AP ☎ 020 8642 4596, 0956 692829

OCKENDEN Tanya *(Ld Gtr, Rh Gtr)*: 2 Spooners Road, Roffey, Horsham, West Sussex RH12 4DY

ODURO Richard *(Rh Gtr, Voc)*: 9 Marshall House, Kingston Estate, East Street, London SE17 2DZ ☎ 020 7582 6000, 0958 396417

OFFEN Christopher *(Gtr, B Gtr, Kbds)*: 29 Kedwick Road, West Wickham, Kent BR4 9AR ☎ 01322 559387, 0467 611875

OGDEN Craig *(Cl Gtr)*: 19 Myddleton Road, Wood Green, London N22 4LY ☎ 020 8889 0039 & fax

OKEY Georgette *(Gtr, Voc)*: 7 Gardner Court, Willingdon Road, London N22 6SF ☎ 020 8889 5144

OKOJIE Pedro *(Gtr, Cong, Mar)*: 32A Maberley Road, London SE19 2JA ☎ 020 7231 7084

OLDALE Luke *(Gtr, Voc)*: 5B Babbacombe Road, Bromley, Kent BR1 3LN ☎ 020 8466 6586, 0387 772368

ONEILL Daniel *(Gtr, B Gtr, Hmca, Dms)*: 75D Lewisham Way, New Cross, London SE14 6QD ☎ 020 8692 5392

ONEILL Shane *(Gtr, B Gtr)*: 62 Lincoln Road, Slade Green, Kent DA8 2DT ☎ 01322 346870

ONGLEY Marc *(Jz Gtr, Cl Gtr, Gtr)*: Flat 3, 53 Waldegrave Park, Twickenham, Middlesex TW1 4TJ ☎ 020 8607 9028

ORLANDO *(Gtr, Voc)*: 40 Denham House, White City Estate, London W12 7PE ☎ 020 8740 9020

ORMISTON Michael *(Gtr, Flt, Didj)*: 91 Devonshire Rd, Forest Hill, London SE23 3LX ☎ 020 8291 1089

ORR Carl *(Gtr)*: 17 Manchester Road, London N15 6HP ☎ 020 8800 5001

OSBORNE Keith *(Ac Gtr, E Gtr)*: 15 Hurst House, Weston Rise, London WC1X 9ED ☎ 020 7833 1571

OTTER Lee *(Gtr)*: 193 Bedonwell Road, Bexleyheath, Kent DA7 5PY

OUVRY Peter *(Gtr, Voc, B Gtr)*: Ground Floor Flat, 61 Mercers Road, London N19 4PS ☎ 020 7281 7831

OXLEY Colin *(Gtr)*: Flat 3, 3 Langdon Park Road, London N6 5PS ☎ 020 8347 6771

OXLEY Peter *(Gtr)*: 2 Larkins Lane, Old Headington, Oxford OX3 9DW ☎ 01865 741909

OYEYINKA Samuel *(Gtr)*: 47 Barforth Road, Nunhead, London SE15 3PS ☎ 020 7635 0307

PAGE Jimmy *(Gtr)*: c/o Joan Hudson & Co, 91 Tabernacle Street, London EC2A 4BA ☎ 020 7253 3107

PAGE Nicholas *(Gtr, Triangle)*: 23 Flaxman Court, Flaxman Terrace, London WC1H 9AR ☎ 020 7383 4835

PAINTER Clive *(Gtr, Dms, B Gtr)*: 315A Finchley Road, London NW3 6EN ☎ 020 7794 5895

PALMER Philip *(Gtr)*: c/o Karen Goodman, Metropolis Studios, 70 Chiswick High Road, London W4 1SY ☎ 020 8742 1111, 020 8742 2626 fax

PALMER Robert *(Gtr)*: Il Mulino, Casse Di Setto, 6935 Bosco Luganasi, Switzerland

PAPA SAM *(Gtr, Per)*: 9 Marlborough Ave, Hackney, London E8 4JP ☎ 020 7249 3335

PARFITT Rick *(Gtr)*: c/o Handle Group Of Companies, Pinewood Studios, Pinewood Road, Iver Heath, Buckinghamshire SL0 0NH ☎ 01753 651 001, 01753 630 555/633

PARKER Alan *(Gtr)*: Wistlers Wood, The Ridge, Woldingham, Surrey CR3 7AN ☎ 01883 3147

PARKER Graham *(Gtr)*: Ellisclan Ltd, c/o Beechams, 3 Bedford Row, London WC1R 4BU ☎ 020 7242 5624, 020 7405 6287 fax

PARKIN Andrew *(Gtr)*: 11 Upper Whistler Walk, Edith Grove, London SW10 0ER ☎ 020 7351 6641

PARKINSON Bill *(Gtr)*: 2 Beech Place, Epping, Essex CM16 5EJ ☎ 01992 576157

PARRICELLI John *(Gtr)*: 47 Conway Road, London N15 3BB ☎ 020 8802 5318

PARSONS David *(Gtr)*: 30 Bois Hall Road, Addlestone, Surrey KT15 2JL

PARSONS Steve *(Gtr, Voc)*: 99 The Avenue, London N10 2QG ☎ 020 8883 8625

PARTRIDGE Jo *(Gtr, Man)*: 5 Osborne House, St Marys Terrace, London W2 1SG ☎ 020 7723 4005

PASH David *(Gtr, Com, Arr)*: 470 Fulham Palace Road, London SW6 6HY

PATE Donny *(Gtr, Kbds, Dms, Vln)*: 1 Coronet Mansions, Ealing Road, Wembley, Middlesex HA0 4AZ ☎ 020 8902 8305

PATERSON Nigel *(Gtr, Kbds)*: 72 Shepherds Hill, Harold Wood, Romford, Essex RM3 0NJ ☎ 01708 342397

PATIENCE Anthony Hewitt *(Ac Gtr, E Gtr, Dms, B Gtr, Kb)*: 4-103 Anerley Road, London SE20 8AP ☎ 020 8402 1582, 0958 556840

PATTISON Graham *(Gtr)*: 35A Tankerville Road, Streatham Common, London SW16 5LL ☎ 020 8764 8372 & fax

PAUL Simon *(Gtr, Dms, Per, Clt, Vln)*: 117 Headstone Lane, North Harrow, Middx HA2 6JS ☎ 020 8421 2018

PAXMAN Michael *(Gtr, Dms)*: 13 Minorca Road, Weybridge, Surrey KT13 8DD ☎ 01932 855549

PAYNE Nicholas *(Gtr, Kbds)*: 90 Eton Rise, Eton College Road, London NW3 2DP ☎ 020 7722 2660, 020 7482 2345 day

PEARCE Matt *(Gtr, Voc)*: Attic Flat, 39 Weston Park, Crouch End, London N8 9SY ☎ 020 8340 4498

PEARSON Christopher *(Gtr, Voc)*: 272 Kingston Road, Wimbledon, London SW20 8LX ☎ 020 8543 5221

PEARSON Keith *(Gtr, Bjo, Man, Voc, Vla)*: 87 Paget Road, Trumpington, Cambs CB2 2JF

PEARSON Mark *(Gtr)*: 17 Urswick Road, London E9 6EG ☎ 020 8525 0545

PEARSON Nicholas *(Gtr, B Gtr)*: 18 The Hythe, Staines, Middx TW18 3JA ☎ 01784 457694

PENDLE *(Gtr, Hmca, Kbds)*: 14 Wilfred Finberg Court, Carleton Road, London N7 0EX ☎ 020 7609 1153, 0956 283159

PERKINS Graeme *(Gtr, Per)*: 18 St Georges Road, St Margarets, Twickenham, Middlesex TW1 1QR ☎ 020 8892 4810

PERRING Giles *(Gtr, Kbds, Per, Voc)*: 16 Warrender Road, London N19 5EQ ☎ 020 7263 9153

PERRY Kevin *(Gtr, Synth, Kbds, Voc)*: 24 Torrens Road, Stratford, London E15 4NA ☎ 020 8555 3409

PETERS Michael *(Gtr)*: 4 Stock Hill, Biggin Hill, Kent TN16 3TJ ☎ 01959 575722

PETERS Michael *(Gtr, Voc)*: PO Box 709, Prestatyn, Denbighshire, Wales LL19 9YR

PETIT Stephen *(Gtr, Voc)*: 52 Abingdon Road, London W8 6AR ☎ 020 8742 3131

PEZOZ-SANCHEZ Amado *(Gtr, Voc)*: Urb Las Farolas C/Isla De, Lobos 60, 35100 Playa Del Ingles, Gran Canaria Canary Islands ☎ +34 928 765544

PFAFF George *(Gtr, Hmca, Song W)*: 83 Parklands, Coopersale, Epping, Essex CM16 7RG ☎ 01992 572693

PHILLIPS Adam *(Gtr, Voc)*: Leonarda, Thistleworth Marine, Railshead Road, Isleworth, Middlesex TW7 7BY ☎ 020 8569 8266, 0976 389639 mob

PHILLIPS Andrew *(Gtr, Voc, B Gtr, Kbds)*: 109 Woodstock Road, London N4 3EU ☎ 020 7281 0141

PHILLIPS Anthony *(Gtr, Pf)*: 34 Englewood Road, London SW12 9NZ ☎ 020 8673 5416

PHILLIPS Freddie *(Gtr, Com, Arr)*: 178 Chessington Road, West Ewell, Surrey KT19 9XA ☎ 020 8393 6251

PHILLIPS Jonathan *(Gtr)*: 3 Endymion Road, Brixton Hill, London SW2 2BU ☎ 020 8674 1977

PHILLIPS Patrick *(Gtr)* ☎ 020 8471 3234, 01426 162798, 020 7497 0708

PICTON Simon *(Gtr)*: 140 Stanford Road, Norbury, London SW16 4QB ☎ 020 8679 4562

PIHA Sam *(Gtr)*: 10A Ridge Road, London N8 9LG ☎ 020 8348 5083

PILCHER Jonathan *(Gtr, B Gtr, Dms)*: 33 Lawn Terrace, Blackheath, London SE3 9LL ☎ 020 8852 2127

PINCH *(Gtr, B Gtr)*: Flat 106, Holly Lodge Mansions, Oakeshott, Highgate, London N6 6DT ☎ 020 8348 6605

PINCOTT Colin *(Gtr)*: 13 Mylodon Road, Lowestoft, Suffolk NR32 4BJ ☎ 01502 565 348

PINKNEY Dwight *(Gtr, B Gtr, Kbds, Voc)*: 4 Solo Way, Queensborough, Kingston 19, Jamaica WI ☎ 809 931 1324

PINNA Roberto *(Gtr)*: 104 Stroud Green, London N4 3EN ☎ 020 7281 4423

PINTO Peter J *(Gtr, Rh Gtr, Dms, B Gtr, Voc)*: 1B Grosvenor Crescent, Dartford DA1 5AP ☎ 01322 271 081

PIRAS Gianpiero *(Gtr)*: c/o One Fifteen, The Gallery, 28-30 Wood Wharf, Horseferry Place, Greenwich, London SE10 9BT ☎ 020 8293 0999, 020 8293 9525

PIRRONI Marco *(Gtr)*: Willie & Blackwell, The Barley Mow Center, 10 Barleymow Passage, London W4 4PH ☎ 020 8742 8600, 020 8742 7789

PLANER Roger *(Gtr, Pf, Voc)*: 88 Dean Street, Soho, London W1V 5AA ☎ 020 7434 0621

PLANTE John *(E Gtr, B Gtr, Db)*: 37A Vartens Road, London SW11 1RQ ☎ 020 7585 2131

PLATTS Mark *(Gtr, Voc)*: 8 Huxley Road, Welling, Kent DA16 2EN ☎ 020 8303 7436

PLAYALE Billy *(Gtr)*: 45B Arran Road, Catford, London SE6 2LT ☎ 020 8697 8286, 020 8461 0145

PLUCK Sam *(Gtr, B Gtr, Kbds)*: 6A Lordship Road, Stoke Newington, London N16 0QT ☎ 020 8211 8069

POLSON Michael *(Gtr, B Gtr, Voc)*: 64A Keslake Road, Queens Park, London NW6 6DG ☎ 020 8930 8608

POPEY Martyn *(Gtr, Db)*: 80A Hammersmith Grove, Hammersmith, London W6 7HA ☎ 020 8741 2392

PORTEOUS Colin *(Gtr, B Gtr)*: 229 Devonshire Road, Forest Hill, London SE23 3NJ ☎ 020 8291 5475, 0956 371309

POTILA Tero *(Gtr, Voc, Hmca, Kbds)*

POWELL Glyn *(E Gtr, Voc)*: 17A Kew Gardens Road, Richmond, Surrey TW9 3HG ☎ 020 8940 6858

PREISS Jonathan *(Gtr, Pf)*: 12 Exeter Road, London NW2 4SP ☎ 020 8452 2075

PRENDERGAST Danny *(Gtr)*: 8 Chestnut Close, Waddesdon, Bucks HP18 0LJ ☎ 01296 658982

PRESTON Mark *(Gtr, B Gtr)*: 85 Burford Gardens, Palmers Green, London N13 ☎ 020 8482 9589

PRICE David *(Gtr)*: 81 Wisteria Gardens, Swanley, Kent BR8 7TY ☎ 01322 660942

PRIME Kwame *(Gtr, Voc)*: 153 Tilson House, Clapham Park Estate, London SW2 4NA ☎ 020 8674 5610 & fax

PRINGLE Mark *(Gtr, Kbds)*: Flat 3, 13 Hormead Road, London W9 3NG ☎ 020 8968 8310

PROCTER Judd *(Gtr, Bjo, Uke)*: Westcroft Cottage, 134 Greencroft Gardens, London NW6 3PJ ☎ 020 7624 3429

PUDDY James *(Gtr)*: 32B Hereford Road, London W2 5AJ ☎ 020 7792 8845, 070 590 96514

PUIG Paul *(Gtr)*: 19 Poplar Road, London SE24 0BN ☎ 020 7274 6855

PULSFORD Nigel *(Gtr, Kbds)*: c/o Band Of Nigels Ltd, 96-98 Baker Street, London W1M 1LA ☎ 020 7935 5133

PUNKY J D *(Gtr, Dms, Pf)*: 9 Derwent Court, Hithe Point, Needlemands Street, London SE16 1PA ☎ 020 7262 1076, 020 7262 0152

PUSEY James *(Gtr, Sitar)*: Weavers, Church Street, Rudgwick, Sussex RH12 3DA

PYALL Nicholas *(Gtr)*: Flat 2, 6 Albert Terrace, London NW1 7SU ☎ 020 7586 1668

PYM Alexander *(Gtr)*: 14 Lessingham Avenue, Tooting Bec, London SW17 8NA ☎ 020 8767 3687, 0973 832088

PYNE Kevin *(Gtr, B Gtr, Dms, Kbds)*: 17 St Lukes Close, Swanley, Kent BR8 7XT

QUAINTRELL John *(Gtr)*: 18 Gaynesford Road, Forest Hill, London Se23 SE23 2UQ ☎ 020 8699 6286

QUINN James *(E Gtr, B Gtr)*: 27 Ranston Street, London NW1 6SY ☎ 020 7724 0993

QUINN Justin *(Gtr, Synth)*: 42 Bermuda Terrace, Cambridge CB4 3LD ☎ 01223 368281

QUNTA Tony *(Gtr, Vln, Kbds, Pf, Voc)*: 10 Ash Court, Leigham Court Road, Streatham, London SW16 3QX ☎ 020 8677 4076

RADCLIFFE Nicholas *(Gtr, B Gtr)*: 14 Kingsley Road, Palmers Green, London N13 5PL ☎ 020 8886 5979

RADEMACKER Kalle *(Cl Gtr, E Gtr, Pf, Kbds, Cel)*: Greenacres, Apt. 26, Glyn Avenue, Barnet, Hertfordshire EN4 9PJ ☎ 020 8447 1542

RAEBURN Peter *(Gtr, Voc)*: 330A Portobello Road, London W10 5RU ☎ 020 8969 1252

RAICHURA Dhiren *(Gtr, Kbds, Sax, Bzk, Santoor)*: 30 Derwent Crescent, Stanmore, Middx HA7 2NF ☎ 020 8357 9880, 0956 338842 mob, 020 8907 5811

RAINGER David *(Gtr, B Gtr)*: 8 Clarence Gate Gardens, Glenworth Street, London NW1 6AY ☎ 020 7262 3050

RALSTON Gavin *(Gtr, Kbds, Acc, Hmca)*: 21 Silverwood Road, Rathfarnham, Dublin 14 ☎ + 3531 4939402, 087 632144, 4939402

RAM Phil *(Gtr, Pf, Voc, Sax, B Gtr)*: 1st Floor, 8 Sevington Street, London W9 2QN ☎ 020 7289 9924

RAMIREZ Juan *(Gtr, Fl Gtr)*: 122B Wood Vale, London SE23 3EB ☎ 020 8693 0760, 0850 843880 mob, 020 8299 6602 fax

RAMSDEN/CASSAVETTI Nico *(Gtr)*: 1 Carlton House, 319 West End Lane, London NW6 1RN ☎ 020 7431 1885

RANDALL Dave *(Gtr, Sitar)*: 2A Redcross Way, London SE1 9HR ☎ 020 7357 6132, 0336 767121 pager

RANDALL Elliott *(Gtr, Dms, B Gtr, Synth)*: 84 Dartmouth Road, London NW2 4HA ☎ 020 8452 8121

RANDALL Vincent *(Gtr)*: 126 Sycamore Field, Harlow, Essex CM19 5RX ☎ 01279 434413

RANKU Lucas Lucky *(Gtr)*: 22 Fownes Street, London SW11 2TJ ☎ 020 7585 0364

RAVEN Clive *(Gtr, Voc)*: Flat 3, 32 Stanford Hill, Stoke Newington, London N16 6XZ ☎ 020 7502 0941

RAY Christopher *(Gtr)*: 119 Leslie Road, Leytonstone, London E11 4HF ☎ 020 8556 0676

READ Alan *(Gtr)*: 34 Lochaber Road, Lewisham, London SE13 5QU ☎ 020 8297 8224

READER Philip *(Gtr, Kbds)*: 16 Center Point, Avondale Square, Bermondsey, London SE1 5NU ☎ 020 7252 3730

RECA Coqui (Koki) *(Gtr, Voc, Tbn)*: 5 Crowfield House, 125 Highbury New Park, London N5 2DU ☎ 020 7226 5326

REES Charles *(Gtr, B Gtr)*: The Georgian House, Brooks Close, Weybridge, Surrey KT13 0LX ☎ 01932 848506

REGLI Claus *(Gtr, B Gtr, Kbds, Hmca)*: 75A Golders Green Road, Golders Green, London NW11 8EN ☎ 020 8731 9382

REID Alexander *(Gtr)*: Flat 1, 47 Effra Road, London SW2 1BZ ☎ 020 7326 4439

REID Dan *(Gtr, B Gtr, Kbds)*: 38 Cumberlands, Kenley Lane, Kenley, Surrey CR8 5DX ☎ 020 8668 5911, 020 8668 5966

REID James *(Gtr)*: c/o Alexander & Co, 7-8 Ivebury Court, 325 Latimer Road, London W10 6RA ☎ 020 8241 6210

REID Joe *(Gtr)*: 26A Anerley Hill, Crystal Palace, London SE19 2AD ☎ 020 8659 3898

REID Kenny *(Gtr, Voc, Pf)*: 22 Mckiernan Court, Shuttleworth Road, Battersea, London SW11 3DY ☎ 020 7228 2278, 0370 483372

REID William *(Gtr)*: c/o Alexander & Company, 7-8 Ivebury Court, 325 Latimer Road, London W10 6RA ☎ 020 8241 6210

RENAUD Norman *(Gtr, Kbds, Per, Com, Song W)*: 17 Corbiere House, De Beauvoir Estate, Balmes Road, London N1 5SR

RENVOIZE Paul *(Gtr, Voc)*: 18 Clifton Terrace, Finsbury Park, London N4 3JP

RENWICK Tim *(Gtr)*: Tresco, Pentewan Hill, Pentewan, St Austell, Cornwall PL26 6DD

REQUEDA Marc *(Gtr)* ☎ 020 8806 7633

REST Bernd *(Gtr, B Gtr)*: 31B Winslade Road, Brixton, London SW2 5JL ☎ 020 7733 5680

RETTIG Roger *(St Gtr, Gtr)*: 70 West 109th Street, Apartment 31, New York, USA NY 10025 ☎ +1 212 865 5556, 01523 496434 pager

REYESJUNQUERA Fernando *(Gtr, Voc)*: 19 Fairmount Road, London SW2 2BJ ☎ 020 8671 1317

REYNOLDS Bruce *(Gtr)*: 189 Portobello Road, Flat B, Notting Hill, London W11 2ED ☎ 020 7792 3779

RHYS-JONES Merlin *(Gtr, B Gtr, Kbds)*: Flat 21, 318 Hornsey Road, London N7 7HE ☎ 020 7272 2858

RIBBANS James *(Gtr)*: Unit 4, 249-251 Kensal Road, London W10 5DB ☎ 020 8964 2054

RICE Niall *(Gtr, Ld Gtr, Rh Gtr, B Gtr, K)*: 59 Leybourne Road, Leytonstone, London E11 3BS ☎ 020 8989 1373

RICHARDS John *(Gtr, Citt, H Gurd, Com)*: 40, Hurstbourne Road, Forest Hill, London SE23 2AB ☎ 020 8699 7805

RICHARDS Keith *(Gtr, Voc)*: c/o Sherry Daly, 5 Church Row, Wandsworth Plain, London SW18 1ES ☎ 020 8877 3111/3

RICHARDSON Stephen *(Chap Stk, B Gtr, Cl Gtr)*: 4 Canons Court, Cannon Grove, Fetcham, Leatherhead, Surrey KT22 9LH ☎ 01372 376852, 0976 796268

RIDEOUT Geoffrey *(Gtr)*: 2 Rose Park, Rowtown, Addlestone, Surrey KT15 1HN ☎ 01932 872381

RILEY Jonathan *(Gtr, B Gtr, Man, Kbds)*: 22 Grancille Gardens, London W5 3PA ☎ 020 8992 6240

RINALDI Lucz *(Gtr)*: 107 Biggin Hill, London SE19 3HX ☎ 020 8764 3155

ROACH Rodney *(Gtr, Voc)*: The Old Cottage, Primrose Lane, Rake, Liss, Hants GU33 7PL ☎ 01730 892468

ROBERTS Andy *(Gtr)*: The Old School House, Main Road, Little Glemham, Woodbridge, Suffolk IP13 0BA ☎ 01728 747696, 01728 747848

ROBERTS Bub *(Gtr)*: 415 Hornsey Road, London N19 4DX ☎ 020 7272 2666

ROBERTS Duncan *(Gtr, Dms, B Gtr, Kbds, Voc)*: 59 Rue De Romainville, 932660 Les Lilas, France

ROBERTS Graham *(Gtr, Bjo)*: 7 Wychwood Close, Duston, Northampton NN5 6QL ☎ 01604 587715

ROBERTS Noriko *(E Gtr, Cl Gtr)*: 37 Ridley Road, Forest Gate, London E7 0LU ☎ 020 8555 8640

ROBERTSON Charlene *(Gtr)*: 4 Vicars Road, London SE19 1HE ☎ 020 7793 0376

ROBINSON Andrew *(Gtr, Tbn, Tba)*: 26 Goldsborough House, Wandsworth Road, London SW8 2RN ☎ 020 7622 1861

ROBINSON Andrew *(Gtr)*: 4 Dibdin Road, Sutton, Surrey SM1 2JG ☎ 020 8644 6692

ROBINSON Chris *(Gtr, Kbds)* ☎ 0976 931649

ROBINSON Percy *(St Gtr, Ld Gtr, Dobro, Pd Gtr)*: Glen Dooen, New Mills, Letterkenny, Co. Donegal,. Ireland ☎ +353 7424456

ROBINSON Scott *(Gtr)*: 15 Poulcott, Wraysbury, Staines, Middlesex TW19 5DN ☎ 01784 482084

ROBSON Phil *(Gtr)*: 20 Malvern House, Stamford Hill Estate, London N16 6RR ☎ 020 8442 4381

ROCHE Eric *(Ac Gtr, E Gtr)*: 23 Waddon Close, Waddon, Surrey CR0 4JT ☎ 020 8680 0184

RODGER Leslie *(Gtr, B Gtr)*: 19 South Walk, West Wickham, Kent BR4 9JA ☎ 020 8462 7740

RODRIGUES Jake *(Ac Gtr, Acc, Db, Bjo, Voc)*: 22 Heyworth Road, Clapton, London E5 8DR ☎ 020 8986 4214

RODWELL Michael *(Gtr)*: 1, Quebec Road, Ilford, Essex IG1 4TX ☎ 020 8518 1056

ROGERS Bob *(Gtr, Voc, B Ldr)*: 11 Darwin Close, Fanborough Village, Orpington, Kent BR6 7EP ☎ 01689 58164

ROGERS Mick *(Gtr, B Gtr, Voc)*: 75 Thames Street, Weybridge, Surrey KT13 8LP ☎ 01932 859873

ROGERS Neil *(Gtr, B Gtr)*: 139 Tufnell Park Road, London N7 0PU ☎ 020 7609 2758

ROGERS Simon (*Gtr, Vln*): 46 The Grove, Ealing, London W5 5LH

ROMERO Richard (*Ac Gtr, E Gtr, B Gtr*)

ROMPESILLAS Felipe (*Fl Gtr, Per*): 1 Dauphine Court, Spencer Road, Wealdstone, Harrow, Middlesex HA3 7AS ☎ 020 8427 0136

RONNIE (*Gtr, B Gtr, Pf*): 66 Eccleston Square, London SW1V 1PJ ☎ 020 7828 3579

ROSE Edward (*Gtr, Dms*): 334 Sullivan Court, Peterborough Road, Fulham, London SW6 3BZ ☎ 020 7731 5540

ROSE Simon (*Gtr, Sax*): 8 Feltes House, Wellington Road, London NW8 9SU ☎ 020 7722 0064

ROSE Tim (*E Gtr, Ac Gtr, B Gtr*): 11 Ashford Road, Cricklewood, London NW2 6TP ☎ 020 8452 6947, 0498 665601 mob

ROSS Andy (*Gtr, Kbds, Voc, Dms*): 14 Wellfield Avenue, London N10 2EA ☎ 020 8883 2073

ROSS Filipe (*E Gtr, B Gtr, Kbds*): 11A Granville Place, High Road, North Finchley, London N1R 0AU ☎ 020 8346 5525

ROSS Malcolm (*Gtr, B Gtr, Voc*): 94 Crimsworth Road, London SW8 4RL ☎ 020 7622 6577

ROSSELSON Leon (*Gtr*): 28 Park Chase, Wembley Park, Middlesex HA9 8EH ☎ 020 8902 0655

ROSSI Francis (*Gtr*): c/o Handle Group Of Companies, Pinewood Studios, Pinewood Road, Iver Heath, Buckinghamshire SL0 0NH ☎ 01753 651 001, 01753 630 555/633

ROWLANDS Mathew (*Gtr, B Gtr, Kbds*)

ROYDEN Tony (*Gtr*): 117 Saint Johns Road, Wembley, Middlesex HA9 7JP ☎ 020 8902 1578

RUNCORN Simon (*Cl Gtr, E Gtr*): 36 Falconer Walk, London N7 7RQ ☎ 020 7686 9773

RUSDELL Vincent (*Gtr, B Gtr, Voc*): 33 St. Johns Road, Newbury Park, Ilford, Essex IG2 7BB ☎ 020 8505 9010

RUSSELL Dan (*Gtr, Kbds*): 47 Hayes Chase, West Wickham, Kent BR4 0HX ☎ 020 8777 7900

RUSSELL Ray (*Gtr, Arr*): Funnells Barn, Down Street, Nutley, Nr Uckfield, East Sussex TN22 3LG ☎ 01825 713 400, 01825 713 606

RUSSELL Steve (*Gtr, Voc, Kbds, Man, B Gtr*): 537 Fellowes Court, Weymouth Terrace, Cremer Street, London E2 8LF ☎ 07050 029840

RYAN Colin (*Gtr*): 38 Felden Street, London SW6 5AF ☎ 020 7736 1312

RYDER Keith (*Gtr*): Flat 1, 12 Carlos Street, Godalming, Surrey GU7 1BP

SAADOUN Abdelkader (*Gtr, Per, Voc, Kbds, Lute*): 22 Woodington Close, Eltham, London SE9 5BJ ☎ 020 8516 8208, 0961 402556, 020 8516 8208

SABATINI Nicodemo (*Gtr*): 43 Central Street, London EC1V 8AB ☎ 020 7490 4296, 0958 600117 mob

SABIJAN Drazen (*B Gtr*): 24 Clitterhouse Crescent, London NW2 1DD ☎ 020 8455 4074

SAGGERS Donna (*Gtr, Kbds, Voc*): 20 Burntwood Lane, Ealsfield, London SW17 0JZ ☎ 020 8947 7725, 0956 910178 mob

SAGOV Margo (*Gtr, Voc*): 10 Brookfield, Highgate West Hill, Highgate, London N6 6AS ☎ 020 8340 6189

SAID Jonathan (*Gtr, Kbds*): Flat 15 Leonard Court, Burton Street, London WC1H 9XX ☎ 020 7383 2182

SAJRAWY Michel (*E Gtr, Pf*): 14A Beaconsfield Road, Southall, Middx UB1 1DW ☎ 020 8813 8853

SALGADO Martha (*Gtr, Voc*): 11 Temple Fortune Court, Temple Fortune Lane, London NW11 7TR ☎ 020 8455 2292

SALKELD Adam (*Gtr*): 16 Blackwater Street, London SE22 8RS ☎ 020 8693 4734

SAMUELS Elaine (*Gtr, Voc, Citt, Bjo*): 79 Parkland Grove, Ashford, Middx TW15 2JF ☎ 01784 256 203

SAMUELS Neil (*Gtr, Voc, Pf, Kbds*): 132 Sutton Lane, Hounslow, Middx TW3 4JR ☎ 020 8572 3341, 0973 359 316 mob

SANFORD Don (*Gtr, Bjo, B Ldr, Pd Gtr, B Gtr*): 23 Warren Close, Horsford, Norwich NR10 3SU ☎ 01603 893844

SANFORD Gary (*Gtr*): 19 Marsden Road, London SE15 4EE ☎ 020 7639 0707

SARJEANT Derek (*Gtr, Voc, Ctna, Tpt, Cnt*): The Coach House, 4 Conyegar House, Bridport, Dorset DT6 3BA ☎ 01308 456365

SAUMAREZ Victor (*Gtr*): 22 Taeping Street, London E14 9UN ☎ 020 7515 0340, 0498 832 187, 020 7515 0340

SAUNDERS Roger (*Ld Gtr*): 66 Westrow Drive, Barking, Essex IG11 9BW ☎ 020 8591 7601

SAVALE Steve Chandra (*Gtr, Synth, Voc*): Address Unknown ☎ 020 8961 9973

SAVCIC David (*Fl Gtr*): 3 Sunbury Lane, Battersea Church Rd, London SW11 3NP ☎ 020 7350 2677 & fax

SAVILLE Vic (*Gtr*): 87 Elthorne Avenue, Hanwell, London W7 2JZ ☎ 020 8537 0715 & fax, 0370 584334

SAWHNEY Nitin (*Gtr, Kbds, Tabla*): ☎ 020 8672 0113 & fax

SCHAPPER Friedrich (*Gtr, Voc, Kbds*): 3 Ormond Road Flat B, London N19 3QG ☎ 020 7281 5572

SCHOOLING Tony (*Gtr, Kbds, Song W, Arr, Com*): 1 Carlingford Gardens, Mitcham, Surrey CR4 2AJ ☎ 020 8408 0076

SCHYFFERT Pen (*Gtr, B Gtr, Voc, Dms*): Address Unknown ☎ +46 707330500

SCOTT Andrew (*Gtr, Voc, Kbds*): c/o Abs, 2 Elgin Avenue, 2nd Floor, London W9 ☎ 020 7289 1160

SCOTT Iain (*Gtr, B Gtr*): 6 Rose Avenue, Morden, Surrey SM4 6DE ☎ 020 8648 2056

SCOTT Irene (*Gtr, Auto Hrp*): c/o 26 Cromwell Road, Beckenham, Kent BR3 4LW ☎ 020 8650 1337

SCOTT Michael (*Gtr, Kbds*): 90 Lansdowne Road, London W11 2LS

SCOTT Robert (*Gtr, Kbds*): 8 Castle Street, Ongar, Essex CM5 9JR ☎ 01277 363476 & fax

SCRIVEN Chris (*Gtr, Kbds, Bzk*): 134 Purley Oaks Road, Sanderstead, Surrey CR2 0NS ☎ 020 8657 7170

SEAL Peter (*Gtr*): 50 Raleigh Road, Richmond, Surrey TW9 2DX

SEAMAN Robert (*Gtr*): 4 Sonning Gardens, Hampton, Middx TW12 3PL ☎ 020 8783 0350

SEATLE Paul (*Ac Gtr*): 2 Leghorn Road, Harlesden, London NW10 3PH ☎ 020 8961 1505, 020 8929 1306 day

SEDDON Ambrose (*E Gtr*): 108 Sterling Gardens, New Cross, London SE14 6DZ ☎ 020 8691 5716

SEEGER Peggy (*Gtr, Bjo, Auto Hrp, Ctna, Dul*): 26 Cromwell Road, Beckenham, Kent BR3 4LW ☎ 020 8650 1337

SELLER Jimmy (*Gtr, Voc*): 42 Pine Wood, Benwell Meadow, Sunbury-on-Thames, Middlesex TW16 6SG ☎ 019327 80653

SELWYN Esmond (*Gtr*): Min-Y-Dyffryn, The Green, Gresford, Wrexham, LL12 8RG ☎ 01978 855052, 0467 390440

SENIOR Henry (*E Gtr*): 137A Railton Road, London SE24 0LT, 020 8741 5233

SERAPHICO Ricky (*Chap Stk, B Gtr, Gtr, Kbds, P*): 15 Helena Road, Walthamstow, London E17 7PY ☎ 020 8509 9660

SERCI Giorgio (*Gtr, Ac Gtr, Man*): 2B Carlton Grove, London SE15 2UE ☎ 020 7252 8424

SEYMOUR Adam (*Gtr, Voc*): 209 Wightman Road, London N8 0BA ☎ 020 8341 2323

SEYMOUR David (*Gtr, Pf, Per*): 43A Bradbeer House, Cornwall Ave, London E2 0GZ ☎ 020 8981 3509

SHAFFER Mark (*Gtr, B Gtr, Dms, Kbds*): 41 Windus Road, London N16 6UT ☎ 020 8806 4383

SHAG (*Gtr, B Gtr, Voc*): 58 Cranley Gardens, London N13 4LS ☎ 020 8886 6673

SHARMAN David (*Gtr, Voc*): 9 Cranmore Avenue, Osterley, Isleworth, Middlesex TW7 4QW ☎ 020 8577 7209 & fax

SHARP Dave (*Gtr, Voc*): c/o Dr W J Kitchingman, 33 Wensley Road, Salford M7 0GJ

SHARP Jon (*Gtr, Kbds*): 48 St Margarets Road, London NW10

SHARP Peter (*Gtr, Mando, Ea Stg*): 16 St James' Court, Grove Crescent, Kingston-upon-Thames, Surrey KT1 2DH ☎ 020 8541 4816

SHAW Andy (*Gtr, Pf*): Flat 5, Elaine Court, 123 Haverstock Hill, Blesize Park, London NW3 4RT ☎ 020 7483 2390

SHAW Jeremy (*Gtr, Pf*): 11 Quadrant Grove, London NW5 4JP ☎ 020 7482 1156

SHAW Kenny (*Gtr, Bjo*): 36A Ballina Street, Forest Hill, London SE23 1DR ☎ 020 8699 2872

SHAW Robert *(Gtr, Kbds)*: 130 Chingford Ave, Chingford, London E4 6RF

SHAW-PARKER David *(Gtr)*: 505 Keyes House, Dolphin Square, London SW1V 3NA ☎ 020 7798 8379 & fax

SHEAR Ernie *(Gtr, Bjo, Uke)*: 10 Whittington Court, Aylmer Road, Highgate, London N2 0BT ☎ 020 8340 8745

SHEEHY Michael *(Ld Gtr)*: 7 Lavidge Road, London SE9 3NE ☎ 020 8851 4401

SHEPHERD Simon *(Gtr)*: Flat 14, Royal Victoria Patriotic Bldg, Trinity Road, Wandsworth, London SW18 3SX ☎ 020 8870 7648

SHERMAN Harry *(Gtr)*: Address Unknown

SHIPTON Russ *(Gtr)*: 35 Tadmor Street, London W12 8AH ☎ 020 8743 6104

SHOBEN Timothy *(Gtr, Voc)*: 135A Brackenbury Road, Hammersmith, London W6 0BQ

SIEFF Adam *(Gtr)*: 93 St Mary's Mansions, St Mary's Terrace, London W2 1SY ☎ 020 7724 2913

SIKHARVLIDZE Tamazi *(Gtr, Pf)*: Flat F, 5 Burgonye Road, London N4 1AA ☎ 020 8374 6617

SILCOCK Graham *(Gtr, Dms)*: 40 Marchant Court, Coopers Road, London SE1 5EB ☎ 020 7231 2682

SILK Brian *(Ac Gtr, E Gtr, Kbds)*: 48 Frampton Court, Cheltenham Place, London W3 8UT ☎ 020 8992 3293

SILVER Christopher *(Gtr, B Gtr, Voc)*: 27 Gundulph Road, Bromley, Kent BR2 9LL ☎ 020 8464 9388

SIMON Roy *(Gtr, Voc)*: 91 Otterham Quay Lane, Rainham, Kent ME8 8NE ☎ 01634 372325

SIMPSON Iain *(Gtr, Kbds, B Gtr)*: 75 Colne Lodge, Colne Drive, Walton-on-Thames, Surrey KT12 3SJ ☎ 01932 246533

SIMPSON Mark *(Gtr, Kbds)*: 24A Laleham Road, Catford, London SE6 2HT ☎ 020 8697 2994

SIMPSON Steve *(Gtr, Fo Fdl, Man)*: 94 Homefield Park, Grove Road, Sutton, Surrey SM1 2DY ☎ 020 8642 6184

SKAITH Stephen *(Gtr)*: 75 Balfour Road, London N5 2HD ☎ 020 7226 2724

SKELHORN Gavin *(Gtr, B Gtr, Dms)*: 44 Priory Crescent, Beulah Hill, Upper Norwood, London SE19 3EE ☎ 020 8771 2296

SKIFFINGTON David *(Gtr, Man, Kbds)*: 60 Brick Farm Close, Off Westhall Road, Kew, Surrey TW9 4EG ☎ 020 8392 2551

SKY Dr *(Gtr, B Gtr, Sax, Kbds, Dms)*

SLADE Justin *(Gtr, Kbds, B Gtr)*: 102 Veronica Gdns, Streatham Vale, London SW16 5JS ☎ 020 8408 0303

SLEDMERE Adrian *(Gtr)*: 11 Camberwell Close, Camberwell, London SE5 8JN ☎ 020 7737 6563

SMITH Adrian *(Gtr)*: c/o Iron Maiden, The Colonnades, 82 Bishopsbrigge Road, London W2 6BB ☎ 020 7631 3929

SMITH Andrew *(Gtr, B Gtr, Kbds, Per, Voc)*: 1 Dawlish Road, Tottenham, London N17 9HR ☎ 0831 814674, 020 8808 7397

SMITH Anthony *(Gtr, Kbds)*: 83 Great Titchfield Street, London W1P 7FP ☎ 020 7580 8928, 0976 268733

SMITH Brian *(Gtr, B Gtr)*: 6 Selcroft Road, Purley, Surrey CR8 1AD ☎ 020 8668 6346, 0468 736599 mob

SMITH Charles *(Gtr, Dms)*: 7 School Road, Sunninghill, Ascot, Berks SL5 7AE ☎ 01990 22175

SMITH Colin *(Gtr)*: 36 Abady House, Page Street, London SW1P 4EW

SMITH Daniel *(Gtr, B Gtr, Kbds, Per)*: 107 Stanley Road, West Croydon, Surrey CR0 3QF ☎ 020 8684 9227

SMITH Debbie *(Gtr, B Gtr, Voc, Dms)*: Basement Flat, 38A Talfourd Road, Peckham, London SE15 5NY ☎ 020 7771 7608

SMITH Peter *(Gtr, Voc)*: 551 Watford Way, Mill Hill, London NW7 2PU ☎ 020 8959 4544

SMITH Richard *(Gtr, Dms, Voc)*: First Floor Flat, 49 Glengall Road, Wandsworth, London NW6 7EL ☎ 020 7912 1269

SMITH Robert *(Gtr)*: 97 Charlotte Street, London W1P 1LB

SMITH Robert *(E Gtr, Cl Gtr, Ac Gtr)*: 9 Editha Mansions, Edith Grove, London SW10 0NN ☎ 020 7376 7870

SMITH Roger *(Gtr)*: 2 Salisbury Road, Wood Green, London N22 6NH ☎ 020 8881 1738

SMITH Roy *(Gtr)* ☎ 020 8444 3885

SMITH Terence *(Gtr)*: 59 Burnham Crescent, Dartford, Kent DA1 5BA ☎ 01322 229934

SMITH Terry *(Gtr)*: 35 Pemberton House, High Level Drive, London SE26 6XW ☎ 020 8778 4695

SMITHSON Russell *(Gtr, Kbds)*: 77 Bell Lane, Broxbourne, Herts EN10 7EX ☎ 01992 445308

SMYTH James P (Jimmy) *(E Gtr, Ac Gtr, B Gtr, Kbds, V)*: 3 Connolly Avenue, Kinsaley Lane, Malahide, Co Dublin, Ireland ☎ +353 1 845 4747

SOBEY James *(Gtr)*: 226 Archway Road, Higate, London N6 5AX ☎ 01523 186952

SOLBERG Nils *(Gtr)*: 30 Ferndale Road, Banstead, Surrey SM7 2EX ☎ 01737 361602

SOLLY Bob *(Gtr)*: Maisonette 9, 115-121 Finchley Road, Swiss Cottage, London NW3 6HY ☎ 020 7722 5289

SOLLY Daniel *(Gtr, Voc, Kbds)*: 32B Ballina Street, Forset Hill, London SE23 1DR ☎ 020 8291 6053, 07970 646717

SPARKES Alan *(Gtr)*: 110 Oxford Road, Stone, Aylesbury, Bucks HP17 8PT ☎ 01296 748001

SPARKS Iain *(Gtr, Voc)*: 1 Cecil Court, Addiscombe Road, Surrey CR0 6SN ☎ 020 8655 0985

SPARKS Jeremy *(Gtr, Pf)*: 37 Dynevor Road, London N16 0DL ☎ 020 7254 2852

SPENCE Andy *(Gtr, B Gtr, Kbds)*: 137 Wakeman Road, London NW10 5BH ☎ 020 8932 3422, 020 8932 0921

SPENCER Charles *(Gtr)*: 102 Hazellville Road, London N19 3NA ☎ 020 7272 2003

SPENCER John *(Gtr, Voc)*: 14 Fairlawn Grove, Chiswick, London W4 W4 5EH ☎ 020 8995 1145

SPENCER Mike *(Gtr, Kbds)*: 1B Celia Road, Tufnell Park, London N19 5ET ☎ 020 7237 4630

SPOONER Marcus *(Gtr, Kbds, B Gtr, Dms)*: 3 Downbury Mews, Wandsworth, London SW18 5SN ☎ 020 8871 9092, 0956 314 364, 020 8874 7585

ST ANGE Victor *(Gtr, Song W)*: 17 Churchill Road, Willesden, London NW2 5ED ☎ 020 8451 2476

STACEY Paul *(Gtr, B Gtr, Kbds, Voc)*: 12 Elms Crescent, Clapham, London SW4 8RB ☎ 020 7498 6523, 0585 946569 mob

STACK Graham *(Gtr, Kbds)*: 27 Glenthorne Road, Kingston-upon-Thames, Surrey KT1 3DY ☎ 020 8547 3997 & fax, 0958 748213 mob

STAFFORD David *(Gtr, Pf, Com)*: 4 Shirlock Road, London NW3 2HS ☎ 020 7284 0118, 020 7485 5710 fax

STAGG Graham *(Gtr)*: 3 Hersham Close, Roehampton, London SW15 4JQ ☎ 020 8788 0864

STANLEY Ian *(Gtr)*: 38 Elm Avenue, Eastcote, Ruislip, Middlesex HA4 8PD ☎ 020 8868 9711

STANNARD Tim *(E Gtr, Fo Gtr, Voc, Flt)*: 24 Orchard Way, Addlestone, Weybridge, Surrey KT15 1NR ☎ 0411 056178

STEEL Trevor *(Ld Gtr)*: Flat D, 8 Swains Lane, London N6 6QS ☎ 020 7428 9763

STEENKAMP Erica *(Gtr)*: 8 Upton Court, Blean Grove, London SE20 8XD ☎ 020 8402 9228, 020 8249 8053

STEPHENS James *(Gtr)*: 19 Harefield Road, Uxbridge, Middlesex UB8 1PH ☎ 01895 230192

STEPHENSON Frederick *(Gtr)*: 39 Avenue Road, Southall, Middlesex UB1 3BW ☎ 020 8893 5153

STEVENS Cat *(Gtr, Kbds)*: 2 Digswell Street, London N7 8JX ☎ 020 7607 6655

STEVENSON Daniel *(Gtr, B Gtr, Kbds, Voc)* ☎ 020 7607 6467

STEVENSON James *(Gtr)*: 8A Station Parade, Kew Gardens, Surrey TW9 3PZ ☎ 020 8948 1964

STEWART David *(Gtr)*: c/o Eligible Music Ltd, 147 Crouch Hill, London N8 9QH ☎ 020 8348 2047, 020 8347 7285 fax

STEWART Robert *(Gtr)*: 38 Greenway, Hayes, Middlesex UB4 9HP ☎ 020 8845 2380

STEWART Simon *(Ld Gtr, Rh Gtr, Kbds)*: 7 Oxford Road, Wallington, Surrey SM6 8SJ ☎ 0956 167011

STEWART Tito *(Gtr, Voc, Song W)*: 14 Gaydon House, Bourne Terrace, London W2 5TG ☎ 020 7266 3473

STEWART William (*Gtr*): 21 Rusper Court, Clapham Road, Stockwell, London SW9 ☎ 020 7720 1876

STOKIC Neven (*Gtr*): 209 Carrington House, 6 Hertfrod Street, London W1Y 7TB ☎ 020 7499 0218

STONE Alexander (*Gtr, Kbds, Synth, B Gtr*)

STONE Bob (*Ac Gtr, E Gtr, Mando, Hmca, V*): 38 Edith Road, South Norwood, London SE25 5PQ ☎ 020 8665 9337

STONE David (*Gtr*): 23 Rosebank Road, Hanwell, London W7 2EW

STONE Tim (*Gtr, Voc*): 13 Clapton Common, London E5 9AA ☎ 020 8806 6037

STORRY Richard (*Gtr, Pf*): 43 Orchard Grove, Crystal Palace, London SE20 8DN ☎ 020 8679 1958

STOYSIN Branco (*Ac Gtr, E Gtr*): 59A East Dulwich Grove, London SE22 8PR ☎ 020 8693 2398

STRAEGER Anthony (*Gtr, B Gtr, Db, Dms, Kbds*): 26A Gravefield Gardens, London SW16 2ST ☎ 020 8672 2142

STRANG James (*Gtr, Pf, Kbds, Hmca*): 17 Caernarvon House, Hallfield Estate, London W2 6EG ☎ 020 7224 8969

STRUMMER Joe (*Rh Gtr, Voc*): Fisher Sassoon & Marks, Farley Court, Allsop Place, London NW1 5LG

STUART Hamish (*Gtr, B Gtr*): Top Floor, 46 Bedford Row, Holborn, London EC1R 4LR ☎ 020 7242 0675

SUGDEN John (*Gtr*): Meadow View, 9 Foundry Close, Sculthorpe, Fakenham, Norfolk NR21 9ND ☎ 01328 820210, +4141486 2666 & fax

SUMMERLAND Michael (*Gtr*): 106 Clive Road, London SE21 8BU ☎ 020 8761 9679

SUTHERLAND Mark (*Ld Gtr, E Gtr, B Gtr*): 10 Malyons Road, London SE13 7XG ☎ 020 8690 9108

SUTHERLAND Roy (*Ld Gtr, Rh Gtr, B Gtr*): 17 Lapwing Close, South Croydon, Surrey CR2 8TD ☎ 020 8651 5121 & fax

SWAN Phillip (*Gtr*): 549 Kingsbury Road, London NW9 9EN ☎ 020 8204 4276

SWINDON Graeme (*Gtr, B Gtr, Dms, Kbds, Voc*): Flat 3, 3 Manville Road, Tooting, London SW17

SWIRE Toby (*Gtr*): 30 Maplin House, Wolvercote Road, Thamesmead SE2 9TH ☎ 020 8312 1566, 0958 328733

SYLVIAN David (*Gtr, Voc*): 49 Portland Road, London W11 4LJ ☎ 020 7229 5080, 020 7229 4841

TAKOUSHIAN Missak (*Gtr, Voc, Com, Arr*): 79A Rathcoole Gardens, London N8 9NE ☎ 020 8341 2725

TALBOT Ivor (*Gtr*): Annaghmore, Newtownbutler, Co. Fermanagh, Ireland, BT92 8FA ☎ 028 6673 8144

TANNER David (*Gtr, Arr*): 164C Stafford Road, Wallington, Surrey SM6 9BS ☎ 020 8773 8319

TARNEY Alan (*Gtr*): Wilmer House, Church Road, Ham Common, Richmond Surrey TW10 5HL

TAYLOR Andy (*Gtr*): 14 Como Road, Forest Hill, London SE23 2JJ ☎ 020 8699 3334

TAYLOR Graeme (*Gtr, Man, Pf, Bjo*): 15 Eastway, Morden, Surrey SM4 4HW ☎ 020 8544 9609

TAYLOR Jon T-Bone (*Gtr*): c/o Abacabe Records, 10 Messaline Avenue, London W3 6JX ☎ 0956 304766

TAYLOR Matt (*Gtr, Voc*): 14 Thamespoint, Fairways, Teddington, Middx TW11 9PP ☎ 020 8977 3565

TAYLOR Max (*Gtr*): 66 Marlow Road, Penge, London SE20 7UZ ☎ 020 8659 5092

TAYLOR Sara (*Gtr, Pf, Kbds, Flt*): Park House YWCA, 227 Earls Court Road, London SW5 9BL ☎ 020 7373 4574, 0411 311 460 mob

TAYLOR Sebastian (*Gtr, E Gtr*): 10 London Road, Southwark, London SE1 6JZ ☎ 020 7642 1744 & fax

TAYLOR Stephen (*Gtr, Kbds, Per*): 81 Oxford Gardens, Flat 1B, London W10 5UL ☎ 020 8960 5761

TAYLOR Steve (*Gtr, Pf*): Flat 2, 39 Croydon Road, London SE27 7TJ ☎ 020 8659 1738, 0467 365490

TEMPEL Adam (Rogers) (*Gtr*): 78 Shirland Road, London W9 2EH ☎ 020 7289 9581

TEMPLE Howard (*Cl Gtr, E Gtr, B Gtr, Kbds, F*): 97A Kenilworth Road, Edgware, Middlesex HA8 8XB ☎ 020 8958 4332

TERRANO Andrea (*Gtr, Kbds, Flt*) ☎ 020 7738 6649

THE AMAZING MR SMITH (*Gtr*): Church Farm House, Loders, Bridport, Dorset DT6 3SA

THEMIS John (*Gtr, Arab Dms, Saz, Oud, Voc*): 46 The Limes Avenue, London N11 1RH ☎ 020 8368 3423

THOMAS Christopher (*Gtr*): 15 Rosemount Road, Ealing, London W13 0HJ ☎ 020 8991 2097

THOMAS Daniel (*Cl Gtr, Gtr, Man, Bjo*): 50B Grafton Terrace, London NW5 4HY ☎ 020 7267 3684

THOMAS Paul (*Gtr, Cl Gtr, E Gtr*): Flat 2, 13 Westwood Hill, London SE26 6BL ☎ 020 8776 7589

THOMPSON Arthur (*E Gtr, Gtr, Voc*): 81 Greenside Road, W Croydon, Surrey CR0 3PQ ☎ 020 8684 5017

THOMPSON Marcus (*Gtr, B Gtr, Voc*): 35 Aldriche Way, Highams Park, Chingford, London E4 9LT ☎ 020 8523 3837

THOMPSON Nicholas (*Gtr, E Gtr, Ac Gtr*): 11 Alston Road, Barnet, Herts EN5 4EU ☎ 020 8449 3617, 020 8449 0229

THOMPSON Paul (*Gtr*): 4 Tottenham Mews, London W1P 9PJ

THOMPSON Richard (*Gtr*): c/o Musicare, 16 Thorpewood Ave, London SE26 4BX ☎ 020 8699 1245

THOMSON Mark (*Gtr, B Gtr, Kbds*): 41 Crossley Street, London N7 89E ☎ 020 7697 9253 & fax

THOMSON Paul (*Gtr, B Gtr, Dms, Kbds*): 41 Methley Street, Kennington, London SE11 4AL ☎ 020 7582 2037

THORLEY Brent (*Gtr, Kbds, B Gtr*): 79 Warwick Avenue, London W9 2PP

THORNE Harry (*Gtr*): 88B Rugby Avenue, Wembley, Middlesex HA0 3DJ ☎ 020 8903 3978

TILBROOK Glenn (*Gtr, Kbds, Voc*): 45 Royal Parade Mews, Blackheath, London SE3 0TN ☎ 020 8852 4664, 01459 19649, 020 8852 4688

TIPTON Julia (*Gtr, Voc*): 10 Exeter Road, Walthamstow, London E17 7QJ ☎ 020 8520 3605

TOMPKINS Nial (*Gtr*): 1E Portnall Road, Maida Hill, London W9 3BA ☎ 020 8969 4633, 0421 311462 mob

TONG Simon (*Gtr*): 33A Devenport Street, Shepherds Bush, London W12 8NZ ☎ 01695 733310

TOOHEY Daniel (*Gtr, Didj*): 2/71 Kensington Gardens Square, Bayswater, London W2 4DG ☎ 020 7221 8881

TOURNIER Michael (*Gtr, Dms*): c/o Fluke, Rear Court Yard, Sagaland, 326 Kensal Road W10 5BZ ☎ 020 8964 4623

TOWNSHEND Pete (*Gtr, Kbds, Voc*): Eel Pie Group, 4 Friars Lane, Richmond Green, Twickenham, Middx TW9 1NL ☎ 020 8940 8171

TREEBY Ben (*Gtr*): 27A Dartmouth Road, Forest Hill, London SE23 3HN ☎ 020 8699 2658

TRETTINE Caroline (*Gtr, Voc*): 64 Lordship Park, Stoke Newington, London N16 5UA ☎ 020 8800 5143

TROUBMAN Clive (*Gtr, Com, Per, Voc*): 53 Dennison Point, Gibbins Road, Stratford, London E15 2LY ☎ 020 8519 3943

TRUONG Jack (*Gtr*): 17 Whitlock Drive, Southfields, London SW19 6SJ ☎ 020 8788 4138

TRYDE Jacob (*Gtr, Voc*): 68 Crouch End Hill, Crouch End, London N8 8AG ☎ 020 8340 3682

TSUCHIYA Masami (*E Gtr, Ac Gtr, B Gtr, Kbds*): Flat B, 106 Shirland Road, London W9 2EQ ☎ 020 7266 5186, 020 7286 2156

TUCKEY Len (*Gtr*): 21 Yew Tree Close, Hatfield Peverel, Chelmsford, Essex CM3 2SG ☎ 01245 382234

TUGWELL Paul (*Gtr*): 21 Cintra Park, Upper Norwood, London SE19 2LH ☎ 020 8289 0946

TULLY Nigel (*Gtr, T Sax, Voc*): 30 Stamford Brook Road, London W6 0XH ☎ 020 8743 3292

TURNBULL John (*Gtr*): Flat 3, 28 Wolseley Road, Crouch End, London N8 8RP ☎ 020 8348 8976

TURNER Hugh (*Gtr*): 58 Pilgrims Close, Palmers Green, London N13 4HZ ☎ 020 8886 9725, 0973 615405

TURTLE Tim E (*Gtr*): 53 Green Lane, Hanwell, London W7 2PA ☎ 020 8840 0767

TYZACK Benjamin (*Ac Gtr, E Gtr*): 34 Stanhope Gardens, London N6 5TS ☎ 020 8245 8416, 020 8341 5545

UNCLE (*Gtr, Voc, Com, Song W*): 12 Kent Avenue, West Ealing, London W13 8BH ☎ 020 8997 0414

VALE Peter (*Gtr, Pf*): Lindworth, High Street, Cookham, Berks SL6 9SJ ☎ 016285 20042

VALENTINE Leonie (*Ld Gtr, Rh Gtr, Voc*) ☎ 020 8665 6455, 0831 378094 mob

VAN EEDE Nick (*Gtr, Voc, Kbds*): c/o P.K.Hedges & Co., Keepers Cottage, Waspbourne Farm, Sheffield Pk., Uckfield, East Sussex TN22 3QT ☎ 01825 723881, 01825 724157 fax

VAN-DELLER Steve (*Gtr, Voc, B Gtr, Man*): 13 Trinity Road, Wimbledon, London SW19 8QT ☎ 020 8543 2038

VILLARS John (*Gtr, Voc*): 23 Stevenage Road, East Ham, London E6 2AU ☎ 020 8471 0015

VOSPER Al (*Gtr, B Gtr, Per*): 151 South Avenue, Southchurch, Southend-on-Sea, Essex SS2 4HX ☎ 01702 466792

VOSS James (*E Gtr, B Gtr*): 31 Vanderbilt Road, Earlsfield, London SW18 3BG ☎ 020 8871 1173

WAAKTAAR-SAVOY Pal (*Gtr, Kbds, Voc*): c/o Delancey Business, Management Ltd, 220A Blythe Road, London W14 0HH ☎ 020 7602 5424

WADDINGTON Steven (*Gtr*): 35 Melbourne Road, Bushey, Herts WD2 3LL

WAG (*Gtr, B Gtr*): 94 Roxeth Green Avenue, Harrow, Middlesex HA2 8AQ ☎ 0441 083913 mob

WALKER Len (*Gtr*): 25 The Avenue, Ickenham, Middlesex UB10 8NR ☎ 018956 33046

WALKER Nigel (*Gtr, B Gtr, Kbds*): 30 Primrose Court, 159 Hydethorpe Road, Balham, London SW12 0JQ ☎ 020 8671 9490, 07771 922737

WALKER Timothy (*Gtr*): 16A Algernon Road, London NW6 6PU ☎ 020 7624 7937

WALL Nicholas (*Gtr*): 42 Framfield Road, Hanwell, London W7 6AD ☎ 020 8840 7410

WALMSLEY Tony (*Gtr, B Gtr*): 486 Parrs Wood Road, East Didsbury, Manchester 20 M20 5QQ ☎ 0161 445 9890

WALSH Terry (*Gtr, B Gtr, Bjo*): 117 Clementine Avenue, Seaford, East Sussex BN25 2XG ☎ 01323 895082

WALTMANN Fabien ("Tobbo") (*Gtr, Kbds*): 179 Southfield Road, London W4 5LB ☎ 020 8994 1237 & fax

WALTON Peter (*Gtr, Com*): 76 Carnarvon Road, London E15 4JW ☎ 020 8519 2814, 0403 480135 mob

WARD Christopher (*Gtr, Voc, Kbds*): 9 Cadwallon Road, New Eltham, London SE9 3PX ☎ 020 8859 4780, 0441 173932

WARD John Matthew (*Gtr*): 37 Bronson Road, Raynes Park, London SW20 8DZ ☎ 020 8947 4819

WARNER Allen (*Gtr, Hmca*): 619 Copperfield, Chigwell, Essex IG7 5LD ☎ 020 8559 8355

WARNER Richard (*Gtr, Bjo, Cnt*): 25 Woodland Way, Bidborough, Tunbridge Wells, Kent TN4 0UY

WARREN David (*Gtr, Vln*): 66 Beulah Hill, Upper Norwood, London SE19 3EW ☎ 020 8653 9256

WARRINGTON Andrew (*Gtr, B Gtr*): 641 Kingston Road, Raynes Park, London SW20 8SA ☎ 020 8542 5815

WARWICK Richard (*Gtr, Voc*): c/o Factory Music, The Colannades, 82 Bishopsbridge Road, London W2 6BB ☎ 020 7243 0640

WATERLOW Rufus (*Gtr, Pf*): 81 Streathbourne Road, Wandsworth, London SW17 8RA ☎ 020 8767 1398

WATERS Stephen (*Gtr, B Gtr, Lute*): 19 Spencer Street, Hertford SG13 7AH ☎ 01992551154

WATERSON Andrew J (*Gtr*): The New Inn, 62 St Marys Road, Ealing, London W5 ☎ 0958 788824

WATSON Andy (*Gtr*): 64 Hill View Road, Chelmsford, Essex CM1 7RX ☎ 01245 258262

WATSON James (*Gtr, Kbds, B Gtr*): 1St Floor Flat, 3 Warrington Crescent, London W9 1ED ☎ 020 7289 3027

WATSON James (*Gtr*): 53 Bell Road, East Molesey, Surrey KT8 0SS ☎ 020 8941 4765, 020 8941 4765

WATT Ben (*Gtr, Voc, Kbds*): Unit 9, Acklam Workshops, 10 Acklam Road, London W10 5QZ ☎ 020 8968 7159, 020 8960 0298 fax

WAYNE Lord John Phil (*Gtr, Voc, Pf, Kbds, Per*): Longsongs Music Ltd, Recording Architecture, 21-23 Greenwich Market, London SE10 9HZ ☎ 020 8858 6883, 020 8305 0601 fax

WEBB Christopher (*E Gtr, Cl Gtr*): 6 Tatsfield Avenue, Nazeing, Essex EN9 2HH ☎ 01992 892915

WEEDON Bert (*Gtr*): Epperstone House, 45 Penn Road, Beaconsfield, Bucks HP9 2LN ☎ 01494 672697

WEEKES Alan (*Gtr*): 65 Clinger Court, Hoxton Street, London N1 5HY ☎ 020 7684 0204

WEIGHTMAN Dave (*E Gtr, B Gtr, Db*): Flat 5, 4 Henry Road, Finsbury Park, London N4 2LH ☎ 020 8211 0455

WEINBERG Dan (*Gtr, A Sax, T Sax*) ☎ 020 8888 3038, 07957 435 635

WELCH Bruce (*Gtr*): c/o Joan Hudson & Co, 91 Tabernacle Street, London EC2A 4BA ☎ 020 7253 3107

WELLER Martin (*Gtr, Voc, Song W*): 25 Quintin Ave, Merton, London SW20 8LD ☎ 020 8715 7090

WELLER Paul (*Gtr*): Solid Bond Productions, Nomis Studios, 45/53 Sinclair Road, London W14 0NS ☎ 020 7602 6351

WELLINGTON Ian (*Gtr, Voc, Pf*): 16 Brecknock Road, London N7 0DD ☎ 020 7687 1424

WERNICK Lew (*Gtr, Voc*): 83 Dartmouth Park Road, London NW5 1SL

WESSON John (*Gtr, Voc*) ☎ 020 8699 5305, 020 7384 8060 day

WESSON Sebastian (*Gtr, B Gtr, Voc, Kbds*) ☎ 020 8426 5348, 0973 941438 mob

WESTAWAY Robert (*Gtr*): 18 Rectory Lane, Long Ditton, Surrey KT6 5HS ☎ 0802 963339

WETTON John (*Gtr, B Gtr, Pf*): c/o Sedley Richard Laurence, 23 Bridford Mews, Off Devonshire Street, London W1N 1LQ ☎ 020 7255 3525

WHEATLEY Martin (*Gtr, Bjo, St Gtr, Uke*): 39 Harpenden Road, Manor Park, London E12 5HL ☎ 020 8532 2923

WHEELER Edwin (*Gtr*): Meadowcroft, Puddingcake Lane, Rolvenden, Kent TN17 4JS ☎ 01580 241236

WHITBREAD Adam (*Gtr, Voc*): 83 Hartcard Drive, Edgware, Middx HA8 8RJ

WHITE Dylan (*Gtr*): 28B Orsett Terrace, London W2 6AJ ☎ 020 7262 9803, 020 7706 1994 fax

WHITE Eddie (*Gtr, Kbds*): 244 Croxted Road, Herne Hill, London SE24 9DA ☎ 020 8671 2449

WHITE Grahame (*Gtr, Voc*): 4 Welley Road, Wraysbury, Staines, Middx TW19 5DJ ☎ 01784 482908

WHITE Paul (*Gtr, B Gtr, Kbds*): 120 Ferney Road, East Barnet, Herts EN4 8LE ☎ 020 8368 0363

WHITE Roger (*Gtr*): 3 Cumberland Gardens, Lloyd Square, London WC1X 9AF ☎ 020 7837 7522

WHITE Stephen (*Gtr, B Gtr*): 96 Hazellville Rd, Archway, London N19 3NA ☎ 020 7686 8209

WHITE Wolsey (*Gtr, Dms, B Gtr, Kbds, Voc*): 191 Laleham Road, Staines, Middlesex TW18 4NR ☎ 01784 465394

WHITTARD Peter (*Gtr*): Flat 2, 14 Elms Road, Clapham, London SW4 9EX ☎ 020 7622 1578

WHYTE Alain (*Gtr, Voc, Pf, Kbds, Hmca*): 30 Rousden Street, London NW1 0ST ☎ 020 7485 6670

WIGGY (*Gtr, B Gtr*): (Wiggy), 6 Garrod Court, Colchester, Essex CO2 0LL ☎ 020 8995 4445

WIGHT Patrick (*Gtr, Sax*): 105 Worton Road, Isleworth, Middlesex TW7 6EG ☎ 07970 351958

WIJAY-WARDENER Som (*Gtr, Voc, Dms, B Gtr, Kbds*): 18 Goddington Close, Orpington, Kent BR6 9EA ☎ 01689 830514, 0961 842623

WILKENS Ronald (*Gtr, Com, Arr*): 40 Chemin De Pont-Ceard, 1290 Versoix [Ge], Geneva, Switzerland ☎ +41 22 755 5787 & fax

WILKINSON Dianne (*Gtr*): 47B Avonwilk Road, Hounslow, Middx TW3 4DX ☎ 020 8577 1241

WILKINSON Stuart (*Pd Gtr, Gtr, Kbds*): 7B Cadogan Road, Surbiton, Surrey KT6 4DG ☎ 020 8399 8682

WILLIAMS Andrew (*Gtr*): Flat 3, 32 Lushington Road, Eastbourne, East Sussex BN21 4LL

WILLIAMS Andrew (*Gtr, Kbds*) ☎ 020 7229 3933

WILLIAMS Dean (*Gtr*): 372 Rochester Way, Eltham, London SE9 6LH ☎ 0966 212045

...S J.Owen *(Ac Gtr, Voc, Song W)*: 27 White Hart Lane, ...don N22 5SL ☎ 020 8881 8696

WILLIAMS John *(Gtr)*: The Coach House, 18A Upper Park Road, London NW3 2UP

WILLIAMSON Jackie *(Gtr, Voc)*: 33A Hoyle Road, Tooting, London SW17 0RS ☎ 020 8767 3759

WILLOUGHBY Brian *(Gtr)*: Flat 4, 47 Crown Road, St Margarets, Twickenham TW1 3EJ ☎ 020 8891 5929

WILSON David *(Gtr, B Gtr)*: Flat D, 1 Pemberton Gardens, London N19 5RR ☎ 020 7281 9185, 0956 157617

WINGATE Jason *(Gtr)*: 68 Delancey Street, London NW1 7RY ☎ 020 7482 3609

WINGATE Pauline *(Gtr, B Gtr, Voc)*: First Floor Flat, 112 Manor Avenue, London SE4 1TE

WISEFIELD Laurence *(Gtr)*: 80 The Charter Road, Woodford Green, Essex IG8 9RE ☎ 020 8504 8447

WOOD Kenneth *(Gtr)*: 76A Gascony Ave, West Hampstead, London NW6 4NE ☎ 020 7625 9110

WOOD Mark *(Gtr, Synth)*: 102 Holland Road, West Kensington, London W14 8BD ☎ 020 7603 3193, 020 7708 1608

WOOD Ron *(Gtr, Pf, Hmca, B Gtr, Dms)*: c/o Sherry Daly, 5 Church Row, Wandsworth Plain, London SW18 1ES ☎ 020 8877 3111/3

WOODCOCK Stephen *(Gtr)*: 43 Constance Road, Whitton, Twickenham, Middx TW2 7HT ☎ 020 8894 9643

WOODROW James *(E Gtr, Cl Gtr, B Gtr)*: 26 Stadium Street, London SW10 0PT ☎ 020 7351 9304

WOODWARD Keren *(Gtr)*: c/o Leigh Philip And Partners, 1-6 Clay Street, London W1H 3FS ☎ 020 7486 4889, 020 7486 4885 fax

WOOLWAY Ian *(Gtr)*: 2 Nursery Road, Chelmsford, Essex CM2 9PJ ☎ 01245 358131

WORLLEDGE Terry *(Gtr)*: Pipers, Maypole Road, Tip Tree, Colchester CO5 0EP ☎ 01621 819343

WRIGHT David *(Gtr, B Gtr, Kbds)*: 106 Carnarvon Avenue, Enfield, Middlesex EN1 3DS ☎ 020 8363 9299

WRIGHT Mervyn *(E Gtr, B Gtr, B Ldr, Md)*: Three Gables, 209 Stock Road, Billericay, Essex CM12 0SE ☎ 01277 657219

WRIGHT Peter *(Gtr, Pf)*: 50 Darlington Road, West Norwood, London SE27 0JD ☎ 020 8670 2366

WRIGHT Richard *(Gtr)*: 7 Junction Road, London W5 4XP ☎ 020 8560 3885

WYNNE Michael *(Gtr, B Gtr)*: 28 Chester Court, Lomond Grove, Camberwell, London SE5 7HS

X Neal *(Gtr)*: Flat 2, Elmar Court, 736 Fulham Road, London SW6 5SQ ☎ 020 7731 8037

XIMENES Charlson *(Gtr, B Gtr, Dms, A Sax)*: 435 Devon Mansions, Tooley Street, London SE1 2XJ ☎ 020 7403 3188

YEE Sandra *(Gtr, Dms, Kbds)*: 32 Worlingham Road, East Dulwich, London SE22 9HD

YOUNG Angus *(Gtr)*: Prager & Fenton, Midway House, 27/29 Cursitor Street, London EC4A 1LT ☎ 020 7831 4200

YOUNG Malcolm *(Gtr)*: Prager & Fenton, Midway House, 27/29 Cursitor Road, London EC4A 1LT ☎ 020 7381 4200

ZALA Nick *(Gtr, Pd Gtr)*: 18 Snowdon Cres, Hayes, Middlesex UB3 1RJ ☎ 020 8573 6838

ZARADIN John *(Gtr)*: 2 Tannery Lane, Odell, Beds MK43 7AJ ☎ 01234 720018, 07970 650322, 01234 720090

ZOLOTUHIN Adrian *(Gtr, Pf, Bal)*: 10 Shinfield Street, London W12 0HN ☎ 0976 938722

ZONGOMAN *(Pf)*: 40 Bramley Hill, South Croydon CR2 6NS ☎ 020 8680 8310

ZORAN Zok *(Gtr, Pf)*: 32 Elsynde Road, London SW18 2AN ☎ 020 8874 1390

ZWIKKER Roland *(Gtr)*: 47 Warwich Road, New Southgate, London N11 2SO ☎ 020 8368 4298

GUITTARRA BAHIANA

SOUTH EAST

PEARSON John: 1 Shipmans Way, Dover, Kent CT16 2DX ☎ 01304 826119

HAMMER DULCIMER

SOUTH EAST

SMITH Geoff *(Per, La Per, Dms)*: 108 Wilmington Way, Hollingbury, Brighton, Sussex BN1 8JF ☎ 559188

SOUTH WEST

DULCIMERS Dove: Dove Workshops, Barton Road, Butleigh, Glastonbury, Somerset BA6 8TL ☎ 01458 850682 & fax

HARMONICA

SCOTLAND

BLACK Donald: 455 Mosspark Drive, Glasgow G52 1NU ☎ 0141 427 2109, 0131 664 1214

LOVE Wendy *(Voc)*: 125 Feorlin Way, Garelochhead, Helensburgh, Dunbartonshire G84 0EB ☎ 01436 811289

MCLEOD Rory *(Voc, Gtr, Per)*: North Lodge, Livingstone Place, Galashiels TD1 1DQ ☎ 0831 209590, 0191 427 6207 eve

SCOTT Neil *(Per, Man)*: 48 Bonaly Rise, Edinburgh EH13 0QX ☎ 0131 441 3488, 0131 441 6029 fax

SPEIRS Fraser: 53 Marywood Square, Glasgow G41 2BN ☎ 0141 423 3211

NORTH WEST

ALEXANDER Jim *(Con)*: 10 Lowe Street, Macclesfield, Cheshire SK11 7NL

BUCKLEY Jack *(Tbn)*: 149 Simister Lane, Prestwich, Manchester M25 2SF ☎ 0161 643 1198

CALLAGHAN Raphael *(Gtr)*: 45 Rodney Street, Liverpool L1 9EW ☎ 0151 709 5484

CATER Seamus: 44C Clarendon Road, Whalley Range, Manchester M16 8LD ☎ 0161 860 6264, 01426 136563 pager

FAT MOUTH *(Gtr, Song W, Voc, Arr)*: Address Unknown ☎ 01625 251320

GILL Wendy *(Voc)*: The Old Shop, Lower Street, St. Asaph, Denbighshire LL17 0SG ☎ 01745 582412

WARBURTON Stuart *(T Sax)*: 12 Ashworth Street, Bury, Lancs BL8 2QZ ☎ 0161 705 2397

NORTH EAST

LANGRIDGE James *(Rec)* ☎ 01302 811874

ROBINSON Alan *(Voc)*: 68 Osgathorpe Road, Sheffield S4 7AR

Y Doctor John *(Kbds, Sax, Rec, Vln)*: 2 Coldwell Lane, Sheffield S10 5TL ☎ 0114 2301959

EAST

HARPER Charlee: 2 The Grove, Mount Street, Diss, Norfolk IP22 3QQ ☎ 01379 652396, 01379 641444

HAZLE Nicholas *(Voc, Org, E Pf)*: 20 Meadow Park, Stoke Mandeville, Aylesbury, Bucks HP22 5XH ☎ 01296 613025

LANDER Judd *(Jaw H, Bag)*: Rose Cottage, 1 Wildhill, Nr Essendon, Herts AL9 6EB ☎ 01707 656812

ROBINSON Scott *(Gtr)* ☎ 01276 476676

TATE Douglas: 12 Fallowfield, Ampthill, Beds MK45 2TP ☎ 01525 753745

MIDLANDS

COOL Ricky *(Voc, T Sax, A Sax)*: 46 Heathfield Road, Kings Heath, Birmingham, West Midlands B14 7DB ☎ 0121 443 3664

GOBIRON Dr Troy: 126, Alcester Road, Studley, Warwickshire B80 7NT ☎ 01527 857964

HUGHES Jim: 59 Bronte Farm Road, Shirley, Solihull, Warks B90 3DF ☎ 0121 744 6155

JENNINGS Stephen *(B Gtr, Pf, Gtr)*: 19 Berry Close, Rothersthorpe, Northants NN7 3JQ ☎ 01604 832726

SMITH David *(Gtr)*: 72 Oak Tree Lane, Selly Oak, Birmingham B29 6HY ☎ 0121 414 0558, 0836 643578

SOUTH EAST

ARNHOLD Gerd: Address Unknown ☎ 01865 554811, 01865 553011

GARDNER (*Voc*)

ONEILL Con (*Pf*): 21 College Road, Reading, Berks RG6 1QE ☎ 0118 926 5885

TAYLOR Christopher (*Gtr, Mldn*): 35 Stoney Road, Dunkirk, Faversham, Kent ME13 9TN ☎ Canterbury 7503

TURPIN Jem (*Voc*): 13 Eversley Road, St Leonards-on-Sea, East Sussex TN37 6QD ☎ 01424 461211

SOUTH WEST

DAWSON Julian (*Voc, Gtr, Bjo*): Shutteroaks Cottage, Hinton Lane, Crewkerne, Somerset TA18 7TR ☎ 01460 78759, 01460 78759

ELLIS Dick (*Gtr, Man*): 8 Montpelier Terrace, Mount Pleasant, Swansea SA1 6JW ☎ 01792 650592

HEWLETT Ben (*Tpt, Didj, Bod*): 6 Moorlands Road, Fishponds, Bristol BS16 3LF ☎ 0117 908 3838

MARKEY Michael (*Voc*): 7 Railway View, Briery Hill, Ebbw Vale, Gwent NP3 6UL ☎ 01495 303406

MATTHEWS James (*Uke, Flag, Per*): 5 Cleveland Row, Bathwick, Bath BA2 6QR ☎ 01225 330842

SMITH Richard: High Street House, Broadwindsor, Beaminster, Dorset DT8 3QP ☎ 01308 868602 & fax

LONDON

ADLER Larry (*Pf*): 110 Eton Hall, Eton College Road, London NW3 2DN ☎ 020 7586 5763

ARMER Eddie (*Jaw H, Man, Hrp*): Oters, Chart Lane, Brasted, Kent TN16 1LR ☎ 01959 562448

DARBY Jim: 24 Holly Park Road, London N11 3HD ☎ 020 8361 4738

DAVIS Garry: 16 Norbury Court Rd, Norbury, London SW16 4HT ☎ 020 8764 9329

DON: 44 Gaston Way, Shepperton, Middlesex TW17 8EX ☎ 01932 242924, 0956 673268 mob, 01932 253091

ECONOMIDES Anthony (*Kbds*): ☎ 020 8889 7332, 0956 945622 mob

FELTHAM Mark (*Voc*): 67 Freelands Road, Bromley, Kent BR1 3JE ☎ 020 8290 5774, 0468 046813 mob

GAMON Mitt (*Gtr, Voc*): c/o 6 Whiterock Terrace, Wadebridge, North Cornwall PL27 7EG ☎ 0120881 3100

GLASSER Adam (*Pf, Synth*): 88 Upland Road, East Dulwich, London SE22 0DE ☎ 020 8299 4906, 0958 557589 mob

GLEN Alan (*Gtr*): 72 Woods Road, Peckham, London SE15 2SW ☎ 020 7732 1127

GREY Alan (*Wh, Hrp*): 7 Hunter Road, Thornton Heath, Surrey CR7 8QJ

GRIFFITHS Matt (*Dms, Voc*): Flat 6, 471A Caledonian Road, London N7 9RN ☎ 020 7697 9872

HOPE-EVANS Peter (*Jaw H, M Bow*): 14 East Bank Road, Hampton Hill, Middlesex TW12 1RP ☎ 020 8941 6016

JONES Paul (*Voc*): Hill Crest, 66 Leopold Road, Wimbledon, London SW19 7JQ

LAMB Paul: 17 Pollard Road, Whetstone, London N20 0UE ☎ 020 8361 8546

MARS Johnny (*Voc*): 19 St. Quintin Park, Bath, Poole, Taunton, Somerset TA2 8TB ☎ 01823 412487

NEVILLE Glen (*A Sax, Didj, Voc*): 14 Skardon Place, Northill, Plymouth, Devon PL4 8HA ☎ 01752 663264

PITCH Harry (*Tpt, B Ldr, Jaw H*): Hunters Moon, Islet Road, Maidenhead, Berks SL6 8HT ☎ 01628 22895

POWER Brendan (*Man, Bod*): 41 Lealand Road, London N15 6JS ☎ 020 8880 1084, 0468 283131

REILLY, MBE Tommy: Hammonds Wood, Frensham, Farnham, Surrey GU10 3EH ☎ 01252 792422

SANKEY Lee (*Gtr*): Flat 3, 14 St Andrews Square, Surbiton, Surrey KT6 4EA ☎ 020 8399 9217

SELF Jon (*Gtr, Per, Voc*): 127 Honeywell Road, London SW11 6ED ☎ 020 7228 0225, 0374 445695 mob

STOKES John: 150 Mitcham Road, West Croydon, Surrey CR0 3JE ☎ 07801 233039

TOUSSAINT David: 25 Grove Crescent Road, Strattford, London E15 1BJ ☎ 020 8555 3785

VALHAVAS (*Kbds*): Garden Flat, 27 Rye Hill Park, Peckham, London SE15 3JN ☎ 020 7635 5392, 0958 575951

WALDEN John (*Voc, B Ldr*): 90 Shooters Hill Road, Blackheath, London Se3 SE3 8RL ☎ 020 8856 1026

WALLACE Barnaby: 12 Ham Street, Ham, Richmond, Surrey TW10 7HT ☎ 020 8948 3180, 0973 632862

WOLFIE (*Voc*): 3 Claremont Villas, Southampton Way, London SE5 7SS ☎ 020 7708 4604

YOUNG Bob: The Bell House, 9 London Road South, Merstham, Surrey RH1 3AZ ☎ 01737 645085, 01737 645086

HARMONIUM

MIDLANDS

HUGILL Andrew (*Pf, Vla*): 57 Trinity Road, Narborough, Leicester LE9 5BW ☎ 0116 286 2406 & fax

LONDON

SIMA (*Per*) ☎ 020 8251 8838, 0958 497580 mob

HARP

SCOTLAND

ANNAND Janet (*Clars, Pf*): 19/2 Rose Lane, South Queensferry, Edinburgh EH30 9XW ☎ 0131 319 1925

ASKEW Sophie (*Clars*): 2/1 Sinclair Close, Shandon Apartments, Edinburgh EH11 1US ☎ 0131 337 5560

BARNES Fiona (*Clars*): 21 Kensington Gate, Hyndland, Glasgow G12 9LQ ☎ 0141 334 0815

DE LYON Saida: 40 Regent Park Square, Strathbungo, Glasgow G41 2AG ☎ 0141 423 8665

HEWAT Corrina Dawn (*Voc, Com*): PO Box 12481, Edinburgh EH3 5YG ☎ 0131 226 4338 & fax, 0131 558 3113

HOOD Iain (*Clars*): 74 St Andrews Drive, Bearsden, Glasgow G61 4NW ☎ 0374 408458

MACMASTER Mary (*Wh, Dul*): 25 Liberton Drive, Edinburgh EH16 6NL ☎ 0131 664 5211

MARSHALSAY Karen (*Clars, Wh, Flt*): Flat 2/2, 4 Hampden Terrace, Mount Florida, Glasgow G42 9XG ☎ 0141 649 0006, 0410 496 730 mob

MCCRACKEN Meredith: 2309 Great Western Road, Old Drumcha Pel, Glasgow G15 6RT ☎ 0141 944 4472, 0850 384644

PEACOCK Judith (*Clars*): 11 Shaw Road, Milngavie, Glasgow G62 6LU ☎ 0141 956 3091 & fax

SEDDON Patsy (*Vln, Voc*): Midfield Lodge, Lasswade, Midlothian EH18 1ED ☎ 0131 660 5559, 0131 660 2337 fax

SMITH Kate (*Pf*): 16 Dargarvel Avenue, Dunbreck, Glasgow, Scotland G41 5LU ☎ 0141 427 0267

STEVENSON Savourna (*Pf*): 2 New Houses, Stobo, Peeblesshire EH45 8NX ☎ 017216 295

STEWART Wendy: Snade Mill Cottage, Dunscore, Dumfries DG2 0XA ☎ 01387 820241

THOMSON Helen (*Clars*): 3 Grandtully Drive, Kelvindale, Glasgow, Scotland G12 0DP

WEALLEANS Michelle (*Clars, Voc*): 27 Ferry Brae, North Kessock, Black Isle, By Inverness, Scotland IV1 1UH ☎ 01463 731647, 0410 571040

NORTH WEST

BELL Jean: Rosebank, 373 Clough Head Marsden, Huddersfield, Yorks HD7 6DP ☎ 01484 844167

CHRISTENSEN Anna: 128 Woodsmoor Lane, Woodsmoor, Stockport, Cheshire SK3 8TJ ☎ 0161 419 9149, 0802 456519

HUDSON Eleanor: 38 Hawthorn Road, Hale, Cheshire WA15 9RG ☎ 0161 928 9632, 0378 632350

JONES Dafydd: Bron Heulwen, Fyn Y'R Allt, Llanrwst, Gwynedd LL26 0NF ☎ 01492 641107

JONES Mair: 15 The Park, Ruthin, Clwyd LL15 1PW ☎ 01824 703844

KNOWLES Chris *(Bzk, Gtr, Vln, Wh)*: 1 Williams Buildings, Barmouth, Gwynedd LL42 1BW ☎ 01341 281199

LANTAFF Clifford: 15 Park Road, Heaton Moor, Stockport, Cheshire SK4 4PY ☎ 0161 431 9264

LEENHARDT Marie: 14 Derwent Close, Chorlton, Manchester M21 7QT ☎ 0161 434 0250

LYNN Eira: 14 Thaxted Drive, Offerton, Stockport, Chesire SK2 5XH ☎ 0161 483 1327, 0556 734909 pager

MOLIN Maxine Isabella: 150 Manchester Road, Audenshaw, Manchester M34 5PX ☎ 0161 301 4893

RHYDDERCH Llio

ROBERTS Karen: 138 Victoria Street, Glossop, Derbyshire SK13 8JF ☎ 01457 863630

SCOTT Lauren: 224 Ways Green, Winsford, Cheshire CW7 4AR ☎ 01606 553698

TUNNELL Philippa *(Pf)*: Address Unknown ☎ 0161 9453691, 0973 134152

WALKER Margaret: 59 Langham Road, Bowdon, Altrincham, Cheshire WA14 3NT ☎ 0161 928 5350

NORTH EAST

ASLIN Anita *(Pf)*: 30 Wainstones Close, Great Ayton, Middlesbrough, Cleveland TS9 6LD ☎ 01642 724255

BARRY Sean *(Kbds, Pf, Gtr)*: 142 Main Street, Seahouses, Northumberland NE68 7UA ☎ 01665 720089, 01665 575111

BENNETT Janet *(Voc, Pf, Clars)*: 13 Broxholm Road, Heaton, Newcastle-upon-Tyne, Tyne & Wear NE6 5RL ☎ 0191 2763019

DAWSON Robert *(Gtr)*: 10 Pond Side, Wootton, Ulceby, North Lincolnshire DN39 6SD ☎ 01469 588777

GILBERTSON Dorothy *(Pf)*: 6 Yarrow Drive, Harrogate, North Yorkshire HG3 2XD ☎ 01423 566813

NI'CHATHASAIGH Maire *(Pf)*: 33 Bridge Lane, Ilkley, West Yorkshire LS29 9EU ☎ 01943 602203

ROBERTS Fiona *(Pf)*: Mould Greave Farm, Marsh, Oxenhope, Keighley, W. Yorks BD22 9RT ☎ 01535 642581

STERNEFELD Frank: Silver Spoon Cottage, Emmerdale Garth, Kirkby Malzeard, North Yorkshire HG4 3SH ☎ 01765 658823

WELLS Georgina *(Pf)*: Deeming Close, Littlethorpe, Nr Ripon, North Yorks HG4 3LX ☎ 01765 677573

WRIGHT Honor: Estate Cottage, Cold Kirby, Nr Thirsk, N Yorks YO7 2HL ☎ 01845 597464

EAST

HORNE Xenia *(Voc, Pf)*: Hawthorne Farmhouse, Middleton, Suffolk IP17 3ND ☎ 01728 603445, 0797 0351181

MARSHALL Triona: 2A Fore Street, Hertford, Herts SG14 1BZ ☎ 01992 584513, 01279 842600

NICHOLLS Alison: Field House, The Haven, Fulbourn, Cambridge CB1 5BG ☎ 01223 882354 & fax

PAMPHILON Elaine *(Pf)*: The Old Rising Sun, Apthorpe Street, Fulbourn, Cambridge CB1 5EY ☎ 01223 880444

PLATTS Rohan: 3 Station Road, Willingham, Cambridge CB4 5HF ☎ 01954 260636

THORNTON Julia: 10 The Park, Redbourne, St Albans, Herts AL3 7LR ☎ 01582 792 644, 0374 237108 mob

VERITY Marigold *(Voc)*: Brambles Wood, Broxbourne Common, Broxbourne, Herts EN10 7QT ☎ 01992 463923 & fax, 020 7735 4384

MIDLANDS

ACHURCH Nick: 2 Bunyan Green Road, Selston, Nottingham NG16 6GE

BASS Rowena: 29 Northfield Avenue, Ringstead, Northants NN14 4DX ☎ 01933 460213

DOUGLAS Audrey: 13 Poplar Close, Oversley Green, Alcester, Warwickshire B49 6PL ☎ 01789 762343

HERRMANN Jill: 4 Don Close, Edgbaston, Birmingham B15 3PN ☎ 0121 455 8961

JOHNSTON Robert: 280 Moor Green Lane, Birmingham B13 8QL ☎ 0121 449 1826

WILSON Brian: 47 Burlington Road, Sherwood, Nottingham NG5 2GR ☎ 0115 9602436

SOUTH EAST

BEVIS Suzanne *(Voc, Clars)*: 9 Randall Road, Chandlers Ford, Hants SO5 1AJ ☎ 023 8025 4238

BROOME Jenny: 24 Westgate Road, Newbury, Berks RG14 6AX ☎ 01635 38379

DEERE-JONES Sarah *(Cel Hrp, Psal, Voc)*: The Cottage, California Farm, Priests Way, Swanage, Dorset BH19 2RS ☎ 01929 426091 & fax, 07970 664563 mob

FINNEMORE Audrey: 82 Western Road, Fareham, Hampshire PO16 0NT ☎ 01329 826891

HOSFORD Fiona: 69 Leylands Road, Burgess Hill, West Sussex RH15 8AF ☎ 01444 243201

MACARDLE Aileen: Flat 7, 134 Crescent Drive North, Woodingdean, Brighton, East Sussex BN2 6SF ☎ 01396 613323

OVETT Luisa-Maria *(Hrn)* ☎ 01483 360959

ROGERS Natalia *(Flt)*: 78 Alexandra Road, Parkstone, Poole, Dorset BH14 9EW ☎ 01202 730029

SALO Satu: 108 Upton Road, Slough SL1 2AW ☎ 01753 525249

SWIFT Kay Sheehan: Swans, 29 Millbank, Headcorn, Nr Ashford, Kent TN27 9RB ☎ 01622 891256

SOUTH WEST

ALDRICH-SMITH V.J.: 48 Homelands Road, Rhiwbina, Cardiff CF4 1UJ ☎ 029 2069 1195

BALDRY Elizabeth ☎ 01647 433635, 01273 204064

DARKINS Eleri *(Pf)*: 12 Pine Tree Way, Nelson, Treharris, S Wales CF46 6PA ☎ 0149525 6169

EVANS Angharad *(Pf, Cel Hrp)*: 86 Dinas Baglan Road, Port Talbot, West Glamorgan SA12 8AF ☎ 01639 884705

FISHER Peter: 54 Glenfield Road, Glenholt, Plymouth, Devon PL6 7LN ☎ 01752 776770

FRANCO Fausto: 28 Celerity Drive, Fitzhamon Quay, Altlantic Wharf, Cardiff CF1 5BJ ☎ 029 2046 4192

GRIFFITHS Ann: The Old Vicarage, Tregare, Raglan, Gwent NP5 2LH ☎ 01291 690517

HAMILTON Claire *(Pf, Kbds)*: 42 Elm Lane, Redland, Bristol BS6 6UG ☎ 0117 9731512

HARRIES Margaret *(Pf)*: 28 Mill Road, Dinas Powys, South Glamorgan CF64 2BU ☎ 029 2051 2379

ISLWYN Sali: Tyle Teg, 743 Heol Clydach, Ynystawe, Swansea SA6 5BA ☎ 01792 844228

JONES Jennifer *(Pf, Accom)*: 9 Column Street, Treorchy, Rhondda, Mid Glamorgan CF42 6SG ☎ 01443 771641

RABY Meinir: Bronwydd, 4 Tyfica Road, Pontypridd, Mid Glam CF37 2DA ☎ 01443 402178

RIBOULET Marie: 9 Cleeve Road, Knowle, Bristol BS4 2JR ☎ 0117 9723188

ROBERTS Bethan *(Pf)*: 89 Nant Celyn, Nr Pontypridd, Mid Glamorgan CF38 1AJ

ROBERTS Gwyndaf *(B Gtr)*: 25 Heol Briarmeadow, Y Ddraenen, Caerddyd CF4 9FB ☎ 029 2075 6931

SCOURFIELD Eluned *(Pf)*: Mayfield, 57 Cog Road, Sully, Penarth, Vale Of Glamorgan CF64 5TE ☎ 029 2053 1182

SWAIN Carys *(Cel, Pf)*: 15 Tan-Yr-Allt Ave, Llidiard, Penybont Arogwr CF31 1PQ ☎ 01443 228143

THOMAS Sian Morgan: Ffynnon Wen, 105 Pantmawr Road, Rhiwbina, Cardiff CF4 6XE ☎ 029 2069 3909

WYN Delyth *(Pf)*: 110 Coedriglan Drive, Culverhouse Cross, Cardiff CF5 4UJ ☎ 029 2067 0657

LONDON

ADLER Peggy: 1 Broomfield Cottages, Broomfield Road, London N13 4NN ☎ 020 8889 2436

ALLIS Julie: 406 San Antonio Road, Arcadia, CA 91007, USA ☎ +1 818 447 5046

ARNOLD Helen: Albertine, Horsham Rd, Handcross, Haywards Hth, W Sussex RH17 6DE ☎ 01444 400643

BARFORD Imogen: 30 Woodsome Road, London NW5 1RY ☎ 020 7485 1903

BEATTIE Maria: 16 Warwick Road, London E15 4LA ☎ 020 8519 5474, 020 8555 3040 fax

BELL Derek (*Kbds*): 74 Bryansburn Road, Bangor, Co.Down, N.Ireland BT20 3SB ☎ 01 667 4171, 667 3920

BENNETT Elinor: 41 Park South, Austin Road, Battersea Park Road, London SW11 ☎ 020 7498 2483

BEYNON Catherine: Merlin's Oak, Edwin Road, West Horsley, Surrey KT24 6LN ☎ 01483 283498 & fax

BLAIR Susan: Flat 1, 85 Kirkstall Road, Streatham Hill, London SW2 4HE ☎ 020 8674 0071, 0370 895002 mob

BODEN Daphne: 36 Arden Road, London N3 3AN ☎ 020 8346 5706

BOGOMAS Nina (*Voc, Kbds, Song W*): 22 Nassington Road, London NW3 2UD ☎ 020 7435 1552

BREWER Aline: 91 Wiverton Road, London SE26 5JB ☎ 020 8776 8695, 0966 152377

BROMBERG Sheila (*Pf*): 28 Monds Court, Church Road, Sundridge, Kent TN14 6DT ☎ 01959 565421

CAN Mehmet (*Sitar*): 282 Willow Road, Enfield Town, Middlesex EN1 3AR ☎ 020 8367 2244, 0468 778831 mob

CARTLEDGE Sophia: 1 Coleridge Court, Parkleys, Ham Common, Richmond, Surrey TW10 5LN ☎ 020 8546 6376, 0973 697786 mob

CLIFTON-WELKER Fiona (*Pf*): 107 Moring Road, Tooting Bec, London SW17 8DN ☎ 020 8672 2391

COLE Helen (*Cel, Pf*): 29 Ferme Park Road, Finsbury Park, London N4 4EB ☎ 020 8340 0039, 0498 525622 mob

CORDERY Jeanette: 43 Hogarth Hill, Hampstead Garden Suburb, London NW11 6AY ☎ 020 8455 0719

DALL'OLIO Gabriella: 20 Lynmouth Gardens, Perivale, Middx UB6 7HR ☎ 020 8991 6734

DAVIES Rhodri: 18 Graham Road, Chiswick, London W4 5DR ☎ 020 8994 7993, 0336 783 851 pager

DAVIS Brian (*Vla*): 3 Ardross Court, 150 Creffield Road, London W3 9PX ☎ 020 8992 5092

DUGGAN Louisa: 131 Grasmere Avenue, Wembley, Middlesex HA9 8TN ☎ 020 8904 0484, 0956 614007, 020 8863 7690

DYBALL Jeffrey: 27A Eccleston Square, London SW1V 1NZ ☎ 020 7834 6545

EAMES Tudur (*Pf*): 106A Burnt Ash Road, Lee Green, London SE12 8PU ☎ 020 8265 7079

EDWARDS Morfen: 26 Sutton Road, Muswell Hill, London N10 1HE ☎ 020 8883 7524, 01258 456353

ELLIS Osian: 90 Chandos Avenue, London N20 9DZ ☎ 020 8445 7896

EVANS Lisa: 13C Bloom Grove, West Norwood, London SE27 0HZ ☎ 020 8761 7538, 01306 880669

FINNEGAN Derbhail: Flat 5 19 The Gardens, East Dulwich, London SE22 9QE ☎ 020 8299 0489

FLETCHER Elizabeth: The Cliff, Wellington Road, Wallasey, Merseyside L45 2NL ☎ 0151 638 0468

FRAYLING-CORK Isobel: 5 Callais Street, Myatts Fields, London SE5 9LP ☎ 020 7733 6609

GOOSSENS Sidonie: Woodstock Farm, Gadbrook, Betchworth, Surrey RH3 7AH ☎ 01306 611283

GOSTICK Bethan (*Pf, Vla, Tbn, B Gtr*): 7 Woodland Way, Purley, Surrey CR8 2HT ☎ 020 8660 5810, 020 8660 5737

GRANGER Emma: 8 Christabel Close, Worton Road, Isleworth, Middlesex TW7 6EJ ☎ 020 8847 4880

GRIFFITHS Sharron: Ground Floor Flat, 133 Riversdale Road, Highbury, London N5 2SU ☎ 020 7704 0113, 0585 747066

HAYWARD Jack: 5 Sun Gardens, Burghfield Common, Reading RG7 3JB ☎ 01734 833 922

HERBERT Nuala (*Pf*): 16 Downside Crescent, Hampstead, London NW3 2AP ☎ 020 7435 9137

HIBBERT Fiona: 15 Pearman Street, London SE1 7RB ☎ 020 7633 9567, 01306 880669

HOLDEN Ruth: 48 Trewince Road, London SW20 8RD ☎ 020 8946 6864

HUGHES Carys (*Pf, Voc*): 51 Melrose Avenue, London NW2 4LH ☎ 020 8452 6421

HUGHES-CHAMBERLAIN Ann: Hindhead School Of Music, Leigh Heights, Hindhead, Surrey GU26 6BA ☎ 01428 604941

ISHERWOOD Cherry (*Pf*): 7 Kent Court, Queens Drive, Acton, London W3 0HS ☎ 020 8993 3524

JENKINS Nia: 13 Chatsworth Avenue, Bromley, Kent BR1 5DP ☎ 020 8851 9442, 0850 992336 mob

JONES Rebeca (*Pf*): 20 Kathleen Road, Battersea, London SW11 2JS ☎ 020 7924 2436

KANGA Skaila: Harewood, Lower Road, Chorley Wood, Herts WD3 5LQ ☎ 01923 284623, 020 8549 1706

KELLY Frances: 2 Charlton Mill, Charlton, Chichester, West Sussex PO18 0HY ☎ 01243 811545

KEOGH Miriam: 44 Church Crescent, London N3 1BJ ☎ 020 8349 4067, 020 8549 1706 day

KNIGHT Andrew: 39, Birkbeck Road, Mill Hill, London NW7 4BP ☎ 020 8959 7129

LEE Kevin (*Pf, Kbds, Voc*): 11 Melville Court, Croft Street, London SE8 5DR ☎ 020 7252 2376, 07775 557737

LEVANT Gayle (*Pf*): 3740 Eureka Drive, Studio City, California 91604, USA ☎ 020 7938 1628

LEWIS Bryn: 62 Hindmans Road, East Dulwich, London SE22 9NG ☎ 020 8693 8701

LISTER Jane: 32 Gilbert Road, Lambeth, London SE11 4NL ☎ 020 7582 2090

LONGHURST Victoria (*Pf*): Flat 4, 10 North Tenter Street, London E1 8DL ☎ 020 7265 1838

MACKEY Gina (*Voc*): 117 Twyford Ave, Acton, London W3 9QG ☎ 020 8993 0639

MACKINDER Julia (*Pf*): 15 Wodehouse Road, Old Hunstanton, Norfolk PE36 6JD ☎ 01485 534010

MANN Ruth: 29 Trafford Close, Hainault, Essex IG6 3DQ ☎ 020 8501 3115

MARSON John: 13 Hollycroft Avenue, Wembley, Middlesex HA9 8LG ☎ 020 8904 2928

MARTIN Alison: 32 Trinity Church Square, London SE1 4HT ☎ 020 7403 7044, 020 8549 1706

MARTIN Louise: Pooks Hill, Woodland Way, Kingswood, Surrey KT20 6NX ☎ 01737 832740

MASLIN Hilary (*Flt, Pf*): 75 Wellington Avenue, Blackfen, Sidcup, Kent DA15 9HF ☎ 020 8304 1723

MASTERS Rachel: 8 Clifton Terrace, Cliftonville, Dorking, Surrey RH4 2JG ☎ 01306 888334

MEIER Patrizia: 2 Heaton Road, Mitcham, Surrey CR4 2BU ☎ 020 8646 4407

MONGER Thomas (*Com*): 15 Vaughan House, Nelson Square Gardens, Blackfriars Road, London SE1 0PY ☎ 020 7598 20239

MOORE Angela: 2 Cranston Road, London SE23 2HB ☎ 020 8291 9535

MORLEY Sarah: 31 Beards Hill, Hampton, Middx TW12 2AQ ☎ 020 8941 4341

MORRIS Manon: Flat 2 32 Aldridge Road Villas, London W11 1BW ☎ 020 7792 2428

MORRIS-JONES Catrin: 4 Merlin Court, 10 Veals Mead, Mitcham, Surrey CR4 3SB ☎ 020 8640 2914

OWEN Thelma: 9 Dukes Avenue, Finchley, London N3 2DE ☎ 020 8346 0589

PERRETT Danielle: 144 Jerningham Road, New Cross, London SE14 5NL ☎ 020 7732 0653 & fax

POTTER Ruth: Flat 4, 44 Devonshire Street, Marylebone, London W1N 1LN ☎ 020 7637 5206, 0410 661602

PRICE Jean: 112 Grove Road, North Finchley, London N12 9EA ☎ 020 8446 1850

PRYCE Sally: 9 Oswin Street, Kennington, London SE11 4TF ☎ 020 7735 8056, 0410 380822, 020 7564 4355

RAMSDALE Emma ☎ 0973 983972 mob

RHYS Christina: 7A Well Lane, East Sheen, London SW14 7AE ☎ 020 8392 8570

ROTHSTEIN Susan: 37 Sydney Grove, Hendon, London NW4 2EJ ☎ 020 8202 4769

SEALE Charlotte: 33 Sandbrook Road, Stoke Newington, London N16 0SH ☎ 020 7254 0419

SMITH Joy: 102E Fimborough Road, London SW10 ☎ 0336 785959

SPERO Patricia: Oaks Farm, Vicarage Lane, Chigwell, Essex IG7 6LT ☎ 020 8500 6112

THOMAS Caryl: Hendre 'R Wenallt, St Athan Road, Cowbridge, Vale Of Glamorgan CF71 7LT

THOMAS Katherine: 2 Lessar Court, Lessar Avenue, London SW4 9HN ☎ 020 8673 8530

TINGAY Gillian: 33 First Avenue, London SW14 8SP ☎ 020 8392 8818

TRENTHAM Alice: 29 Greatdown Road, London W7 1JR ☎ 020 8813 2720, 0976 429332

TUNSTALL Helen: 34 Boveney Road, Forest Hill, London SE23 3NN ☎ 020 8699 8255

VAN HELLENBERG HUBAR Theresia: 31 Egerton Crescent, London SW3 2EB ☎ 020 7584 3917

VAUGHAN Karen (Pf): 94 Grimsdyke Road, Hatch End, Pinner, Middx HA5 4PW ☎ 020 8421 1817

WAKEFORD Lucy: 82 Elm Court, Acorn Walk, Rotherhithe, London SE16 1ER ☎ 020 7394 3253, 01483 451700 day

WATTS Shelia (Rec): 27 Donovan Avenue, Muswell Hill, London N10 2JU ☎ 020 8883 8961

WEBB Hugh (Pf): 58 Argyle Street, London WC1H 8ER ☎ 020 7837 4954

WEBB Julia: 4 Fairlawn Park, Sydenham, London SE26 5RU ☎ 020 8676 0962

WEBSTER Audrey: 78 Brampton Grove, Kenton, Harrow, Middx HA3 8LF ☎ 020 8907 7450

WHITE Catherine: 52 Grovewood Close, Chorleywood, Herts WD3 5PX ☎ 01923 284368

WILLEY Patricia: 28 Barkston Gardens, London SW5 0EN ☎ 020 7370 2535

WILLIAMS Rhian (Pf): 18 Annett Road, Walton-on-Thames, Surrey KT12 2JR ☎ 01932 228927

WILLIAMS Sioned (Pf): 60 Friern Mount Drive, Whetstone, London N20 9DL ☎ 020 8446 1346 & fax

WILLISON Suzanne: 2 Mallard House, Bridgeman Street, St Johns Wood, London NW8 7AN ☎ 020 7722 6796, 0973 877 510, 01494 670443

WILSON Hilary: 44A Sauncey Avenue, Harpenden, Herts AL5 4QL ☎ 01582 712243

HARPSICHORD

SCOTLAND

COATES Leon (Pf, Org): 35 Comely Bank Place, Edinburgh EH4 1ER ☎ 0131 332 4553

KITCHEN John (Org, Pf, Ea Kbds): 34 Spottiswoode Road, Edinburgh EH9 1BL

WILLIAMS Roger (Org, Con): University Music, Powis Gate, College Bounds, Old Aberdeen AB24 2UG ☎ 01224 272570

NORTH WEST

ELCOMBE Keith (Org): 34 Belfield Road, Didsbury, Manchester M20 0BH ☎ 0161 445 6661

FRANCIS David (Org, Pf): 14 Bristow Close, Westbrook, Warrington, Cheshire WA5 5EU ☎ 01925 710454

NORTH EAST

BULLIVANT Roger (Pf, Org, Con): 8 Beech Court, Beech Hill Road, Sheffield S10 2SA ☎ 0114 266 5096

CUCKSTON Alan (Pf, Arr, Con, Org): Turnham Hall, Cliffe, Selby, North Yorkshire YO8 7ED ☎ 01757 638238 & fax

FORD Anthony (Pf): 199 Victoria Avenue, Hull, N Humberside HU5 3EF ☎ 01482 343199

EAST

CAROLAN Lucy (Pf): 15 Willis Road, Cambridge CB1 2AQ ☎ 01223 560685

ENNIS Martin (Org, Pf, Clst, Harm): 100 Ramsden Square, Cambridge CB4 2BL ☎ 01223 425101

MIDLANDS

LONGDEN Pamela: 120 Main Street, Clifton Campville, Tamworth, Staffs B79 0AT

PAINTING Norman (Org, Pf, Clav): Warmington Grange, Banbury, Oxon OX17 1BT ☎ 0129 589 674

PICKERILL Mariegold (Bsn, Pf): Ulan, Lower Swell, Stow-on-The Wold, Glos GL54 1LF ☎ 01578 31192

SILK Richard (Pf, Org, Md): Gulley Green, All Stretton, Church Stretton, Salop SY6 7JT ☎ 01694 722 649

THOMSON Katherine (Pf): 58 Billesley Lane, Birmingham, West Midlands B13 9QS ☎ 0121 449 2656

SOUTH EAST

CAVE GRSM LRAM Penelope (Pf): 8 Pit Farm Road, Guildford, Surrey GU1 2JH ☎ 01483563096

COOPER Gary (Org, Pf): 32 Chilswell Road, Oxford OX1 4PJ ☎ 01865 793060, 01865 793060

GOODGER Derek (Md, Org, Pf): Tapton, 19 Langdown Lawn Close, Hythe, Southampton Hants SO45 5GW

RICHARDS Arne (Acc, Bando, Org, Pf): 31 Borrowmead Road, Headington, Oxford OX3 9QP ☎ 0186 563834

STOWE Sara (Org, Voc): 49 Pitt's Road, Oxford OX3 8BA ☎ 01865 61966, 01865 61966

SOUTH WEST

KNIGHT Stephen (Org): 6B Upper Tollington Park, Finsbury Park, London N4 4DD ☎ 020 7281 2555

SMITH Julian (Pf): 39 Ty Draw Road, Penylan, Cardiff CF2 5HB

LONDON

BLACK Adrienne (Pf, Org): 5 Uplands Road, Caversham, Reading, Berkshire RG4 7JG ☎ 0118 948 3220

BOLTON Ivor (Con): 171A Goldhurst Terrace, London NW6 3ES ☎ 020 7625 9885, 020 7625 9885

BOYLE Elizabeth (Org): 61 Ravensdale Road, Stamford Hill, London N16 6TJ ☎ 020 8800 4339, 0966 512332

BROWN Helena: 13 Borough Road, Isleworth, Middlesex TW7 5DY ☎ 020 8580 8429

CHAPMAN Jane (Voc): 41 Drayton Gardens, London W13 0LG ☎ 020 8997 7621 & fax

CLIFTON Jacqueline (Org): 1 Poets Road, London N5 2SL ☎ 020 7354 2050, 0836 370968 mob

COLE Maggie (Pf): 83 Stanlake Road, London W12 7HQ ☎ 020 8749 1853, 020 8742 9594

CUMMINGS Laurence (Org, Pf): 81 Chetwynd Road, London NW5 1DA ☎ 020 7267 2760

EDWARDS Pamela (Pf, Vln): 27 Salisbury Close, Alton, Hants GU34 2TF ☎ 01420 80082

GIBLEY Carolyn (Pf, Org): 57 Glen Albyn Road, Wimbledon, London SW19 6HB ☎ 020 8789 5902

GLEN Karen: St Marys Flat, St Marys Vicarage, Riverside, Twickenham, Middx TW1 3DT ☎ 020 8891 3204, 0956 621048 mob, 020 8355 7672 fax

GORDON David (Pf): 135 Lower Paddock Road, Oxhey, Herts WD1 4DU ☎ 01923 239038

HARPER Celia (Org, Pf): 33 Hartswood Road, London W12 9NE ☎ 020 8749 3365

HELLYER JONES Jonathan (Org): 6 Dane Drive, Cambridge CB3 9LP ☎ 01223 515688

HOLMAN Peter: 119 Maldon Road, Colchester, Essex CO3 3AX ☎ 01206 43417

JOHNSTONE James (Org): 27 Woodland Rise, London N10 3UP ☎ 020 8444 9472 fax

KING Robert (*Org, Con*): 34 St Marys Grove, London W4 3LN ☎ 020 8995 9994, 020 8995 2115

NICHOLSON Paul (*Org, Pf*): 37 Morley Hill, Enfield EN2 0BL ☎ 020 8364 6353 & fax

PINNOCK Trevor: 8 St.George's Terrace, London NW1 8XJ ☎ 020 7911 0901

REDFARN Clare (*Pf*): 84 Alexandra Gardens, Chiswick, London W4 2RZ ☎ 020 8995 6646

ROBLOU David (*Org, Pf, Con*): 109 Algernon Road, London SE13 7AP ☎ 020 8690 5652, 0973 758218 mob, 020 8244 5789 fax

ROMANO Nel (*Pf, Per*): 9 Chalcot Crescent, Primrose Hill, London NW1 8YE ☎ 020 7722 3227

ROSS Alastair (*Org*): 4 Conegra Road, High Wycombe, Bucks HP13 6DY ☎ 01494 524596

SIGSWORTH Guy (*Pf, Org, Kbds*): Address Unknown

SKUCE Peter (*Org, Kbds*): 26 Blackshaw Road, London SW17 0DE ☎ 020 8672 1338

TAN Melvyn (*Pf*): Flat 2, 5 Kensington Park Gardens, London W11 3HB ☎ 020 7792 8027

TOLL John (*Org, Pf*): Barn House, Holtwood, Hamstead Marshall, Newbury, Berks RG20 0JH ☎ 01635 253073

HIGHLAND BAGPIPES
SCOTLAND

HAY Louise (*Fo Fdl, Com*): 34 Poplar Avenue, Blairgowrie, Perthshire PH10 6SR ☎ 01250 875995

MACDONALD Iain (*Flt, Wh, Ctna*): Seann Lag, Glenuig, Lochailort, Moidart PH38 4NB ☎ 01687 470 226

MORRISON Fred (*Wh*): 141 Old Greenock Road, Bishopton, Renfrenshire PA7 5DL ☎ 01505 862275

SUTHERLAND Kenneth (*Sh P*): Top Left, 21 Cross Arthurlie Street, Barrhead, Glasgow G78 1QY ☎ 0141 880 6859 & fax

NORTH WEST

WINSTANLEY Colin: 21 Fairhaven Road, St. Annes-on-Sea, Lancs FY8 1NN ☎ 01253 726942

NORTH EAST

KELLY Jack: 30 Lewis Avenue, Sutton-on-Sea, Lincoln LN12 2JS ☎ 01507 442844

EAST

BRODERICK Tom: 9 Woodcock Close, Haverhill, Suffolk CB9 0JP ☎ 01440 703538

SOUTH EAST

PIPER 2000 (*Kbds, Gtr, Bjo*): Pibroch, 9 Corfe View Road, Corfe Mullem, Wimborne, Dorset BH21 3LY ☎ 01202 690633

SOUTH WEST

DUNBAR Patrick (*Bag*): Elms, Newcastle Emlyn, Dyfed SA38 9RA ☎ 01289 710098

LONDON

MCGRATH Helen (*Rec*): 4 Laxton Place, Regents Park, London NW1 3PT ☎ 020 7388 4935

MCLUCAS James: 28 Kent Street, London E13 8RL ☎ 020 8470 8166

SOUTH Leslie: 57 Uvedale Road, Enfield, Middlesex EN2 6HB ☎ 020 8363 5960

HORN
SCOTLAND

BAXENDALE Sue (*Hrn, Wg Tba*): 7 Garrioch Quadrant, North Kelvinside, Glasgow G20 8RT ☎ 0141 946 7520

BLACKWOOD Kenneth (*Hrn*): 118 Norse Road, Scotstoun, Glasgow, Scotland G14 9EQ ☎ 0141 954 9680

CARRICK Lindsay (*Hrn*): 26 Jordanhill Drive, Glasgow, Scotland G13 1SA ☎ 0141 959 6725

CORMACK Kevin (*Hrn*): 48 Ashwood Road, Bridge Of Don, Aberdeen AB22 8XR ☎ 01224 703571

COWLING Steven (*Hrn*): 7 Forvie Street, Bridge Of Don, Aberdeen AB22 8TP ☎ 01224 825739

DOUTHWAITE Aileen (*Hrn, Wg Tba*): Eastermound, 12 Main Road, Castlehead, Paisley, Renfrewshire PA2 6AJ ☎ 0141 887 6105, 0802 680 475 mob

DURRANT Jonathan (*Hrn, N Hrn*): 3 Victoria Circus, Glasgow G12 9LB ☎ 0141 334 4867, 07971 257 378

DUTHIE Joanna (*Hrn*): 13 Saint Ninians Terrace, Edinburgh EH10 5NL ☎ 0131 447 6959

FLOYD Charles (*Hrn, Pf, Md*): 31 Garscadden Road, Glasgow G15 G15 6UW ☎ 0141 944 1700

GIDDIS-CURRIE Joseph (*Hrn, Tba*): 40 Millar Place, Riverside, Stirling FK8 1XB ☎ 01786 473 626

GUERRIER John (*Hrn*): 40 Thornwood Terrace, Glasgow, Scotland G11 7QZ ☎ 0141 339 5512

HODGE G. (*Hrn, Pf*): 39/1 Bryson Road, Edinburgh EH11 1DY ☎ 0131 313 1298

HUTCHESON David (*Hrn*): 32 Clochbar Avenue, Milngavie, Glasgow G62 7LJ ☎ 0141570 0687, 07666 716550 pager

JOHNS Terry (*Hrn, Com*): 203 The Murrays, Edinburgh EH17 8UN ☎ 0131 664 0279

KERR Fergus (*Hrn*): Flat 2/L, 46 Herriet Street, Glasgow G41 2JY ☎ 0141 424 3550, 0802 390860

KLEIN Paul (*Hrn, Wg Tba*): 46 Ashmore Road, Merrylee, Glasgow, Scotland G43 2LS ☎ 0141 637 7311

LAMBERT Ian (*Hrn*): 31 Rockmount Avenue, Thornliebank, Renfrewshire G46 G46 7BU ☎ 0141 638 6634

LOGAN John (*Hrn, Kbds*): Flat 2/2, 127 Broomhill Drive, Glasgow, Scotland G11 7NB ☎ 0141 576 2007

MACLEAN Louise (*Hrn, Pf, Com*): 6 Miller Lane, Cromarty, Ross-Shire IV11 8XB ☎ 013817 564

MCCLENAGHAN David (*Hrn*): 6 Rosevale Road, Beardsden, Glasgow G61 ☎ 0141 942 8520

MCKENZIE Colin (*Hrn*): 43 Rannoch Street, Glasgow G44 4DD ☎ 0141 633 2301

MILDRED James (*Hrn*): 3/Left 39 Airlie Street, Hyndland, Glasgow G12 9TS ☎ 0141 357 0039

MORRISON Joan (*Hrn*): 680 Anniesland Road, Scotstounhill, Glasgow G14 0XR ☎ 0141 954 8757

POTTS Hugh (*Hrn*): 12 Dunellan Road, Milngavie, Glasgow G62 7RE ☎ 0141 956 6882 & fax

PRYCE David (*Hrn*): 1 Whitefield Terrace, Croft Road, Cambuslang G72 8PP ☎ 0141 641 7885

RIMER Richard (*Hrn*): 20 Pentland Terrace, Edinburgh EH10 6HB ☎ 0131 447 8323

SHARP John D (*Hrn*): Corrievrechan, 16 South Castle Street, St Andrews KY16 9PL ☎ 01334 479507

SMITH Ian (*Hrn, Pf, Md*): 16 Westbourne Crescent, Bearsden, Glasgow G61 4HD ☎ 0141 943 0767 & fax, 0411 457944 mob

TEMPLE Maurice (*Hrn*): Address Unknown

WAKEFORD Richard (*Hrn*): 9 Laurel Place, T/R, Thornwood, Glasgow G11 7RE ☎ 0141 339 3624

WATSON Shelagh (*Hrn*): 9 Michael Mcparland Drive, Torrance, Glasgow G64 4EE ☎ 01360 622786

WAY Aileen (*Hrn*): 29 Queen Mary Avenue, Glasgow G42 8DS ☎ 0141 423 3325

WHITE Graeme (*Hrn, N Hrn*): Davanall, Bore Road, Airdrie, Strathclyde ML6 6HX ☎ 01236 754 910

WILSON John (*Hrn*): 7 Bradan Drive, Alloway, Ayrshire KA7 4TG

NORTH WEST

AINSWORTH Jeremy (*Hrn*): 45 Verney Road, Royton, Oldham, Lancs OL2 6AZ ☎ 0161 620 4504

ATHERTON Naomi (*Hrn*): Rose Bank, Kinder Road, Hayfield, Stockport SK12 5LE ☎ 01663 744929

BALL Tim (*Hrn, Pf, Arr*): 9 Honeywood Close, Holcombe Brook, Bury, Lancs BL0 9RL ☎ 0973 796782

BARRETT Jonathan *(Hrn)*: 13 Mill Grove, Bulkeley, Malpas, Cheshire SY14 8BJ ☎ 01829 720193

BENTALL Robert *(Hrn)*: 6 Almshill Glade, Sheffield S11 9SS ☎ 0114 236 0094

BEVAN Arthur *(Hrn)*: 25 Longton Avenue, Withington, Manchester M20 3JN ☎ 0161 445 7316

BOURN Richard *(Hrn)*: c/o Halle Orchestra, The Bridgewater Hall, Manchester M2 3WS ☎ 0973 869 708

BROOK R *(Hrn)*: Ingleside, 74 Buxtonroad, Disley, Stockport SK12 2HE ☎ 01663 765322

BUSHELL Jeremy *(Hrn, Wg Tba)*: 28 Stonehaven, Bolton BL3 4UW ☎ 01204 655423

COOKE Matthew *(Hrn)*: 4 Oadby Close, Belle Vue, Manchester M12 4WJ ☎ 0161 223 7548, 07970 063421

DAVIES Peter *(Hrn)*: Address Unknown

DUFFY Liam *(Hrn, Pf)*: 23 Maldon Crescent, Swinton, Manchester M27 5PZ ☎ 0161 794 8257

EDWARDS David *(Hrn)*: c/o Haematology Dept., Glan Clwyd Hospital, Sarn Lane, Bodelwyddan, Denbighshire LL18 5UJ ☎ 0411 550643

FULLER Adrian *(Hrn)*: 14 Hermitage Road, Hale, Cheshire WA15 8BN ☎ 0161 980 4275, 0973 754763 mob

GANDEE Clive *(Hrn)*: 3 Wolseley Place, Withington, Manchester M20 3LR ☎ 0161 445 0485

GARBUTT David *(Hrn)*: 31 Amherst Road, Fallowfield, Manchester M14 6UR ☎ 0161 224 9553

GOLDBERG Rebecca *(Hrn, N Hrn)*: 96 Church Street, Old Glossop, Derbs SK13 7RN ☎ 01457 858480 & fax

GOODALL Jonathan *(Hrn)*: 42 Moss Lane, Bramhall, Stockport, Cheshire SK7 1EH ☎ 0161 439 1195

GRUNDY Neil *(Hrn)*: 2 Brammay Drive, Tottington, Bury, Lancs BL8 3HS ☎ 01204 883619

HARPER Diane *(Hrn)*: 5 Pencombe Close, Bellevue, Manchester M12 4TA ☎ 0161 231 2071

HAYWARD Russell *(Hrn, Wg Tba)*: 59 Hill Top Avenue, Cheadle Hulme, Cheadle, Cheshire SK8 7HZ ☎ 0161 485 1458

HEBBLEWHITE Bruce *(Hrn, Wg Tba)*: 11 South Drive, Upton, Wirral, Merseyside L49 6LA ☎ 0151 605 0774

HESLEWOOD Alan *(Hrn)*: 1 Tunstall Close, Upton, Liverpool L49 6PD ☎ 0151 606 0908

HOLLIDAY Claire *(Hrn, Cl Gtr)*: 44 Churchwood Road, Didsbury, Manchester M20 6TY ☎ 0161 434 9316, 0973 304477

HOWE Tom *(Hrn)*: 38 Rudchester Close, Carlisle, Cumbria CA2 7XL ☎ 01228 524299

JACKSON Timothy *(Hrn, Pf, Kbds)*: 10 Hurstway Close, Fulwood, Preston, Lancs PR2 4TU ☎ 01772 718252

JONES Ben *(Hrn)*: 93 Roundwood Road, Northenden, Manchester M22 4AD ☎ 0161 998 5741

JONES Clifford *(Hrn)*: 1B Grange Mount, Heswall, Wirral, Merseyside L60 7RB ☎ 0151 342 8742

JONES Dewi Owen *(Hrn)*: Trem Eryri, Rhosmeirch, Llangefni, Ynys Mon, Gwynedd LL77 7SJ ☎ 01248 722357

JONES Karen *(Hrn, Pf)*: Flat 2, 4 Mayfield Road, Whalley Range, Manchester M16 8FT ☎ 0161 227 9773, 0966 175653 mob

KINLOCH Catriona *(Hrn)*: 40 Box Lane, Wrexham LL12 7RB ☎ 01978 350359

KOOP Hannah *(Hrn, Pf)*: Flat 3, 18 Brighton Grove, Fallowfield, Manchester M14 5JR ☎ 0161 256 2840, 0411 604 867

MACLAREN Barbara *(Hrn)*: 28 Beech Grove, Preston, Lancashire PR2 1DX ☎ 01772 726414

MARTINSEN Annelise *(Hrn)*: 93 Roundwood Road, Northenden, Manchester M22 4AD ☎ 0161 998 5741

MEIKLEJOHN Philip *(Hrn)*: 8 Gilbert Bank, Woodley, Stockport, Cheshire SK6 1AY ☎ 0161 430 3525

MONKS Kenneth *(Hrn)*: 141 Moss Bank Road, Moss Bank, St Helens, Merseyside WA11 7DG ☎ 01744 27976

MOORE James *(Hrn)*: 25 Station Road, Mirfield, West Yorkshire WF14 8LN ☎ 01924 490362

MORGAN Veronica *(Hrn, Wg Tba)*: Merry Knowe Cottage, Slaggyford, Carlisle CA6 7NP ☎ 01434 381979

MORLEY Christopher *(Hrn, Wg Tba)*: 42 North Park Road, Bramhall, Stockport, Cheshire SK7 3JS ☎ 0161 439 5143

NICHOLSON Timothy *(Hrn)*: 154 Slade Lane, Levenshulme, Manchester M19 2EE ☎ 0161 224 3740, 0976 204713

OGONOVSKY Michael *(Hrn, Wg Tba)*: 41 Banks Avenue, Meols, Wirral, Merseyside L47 0NG ☎ 0151 632 5511

PARKIN Emma *(Hrn)*: Sunnyside, Dawbers Lane, Shaw Green, Euxton, Chorley, Lancashire PR7 6EQ ☎ 01257 452913

PETTIT-JONES Angela *(Hrn)*: 10 Lon Wynne, Colomendy Estate, Denbigh, Denbighshire LL16 5YD ☎ 01745 814648

PIGOTT David *(Hrn, Wg Tba)*: 84, Vaughan Road, Wallasey, Merseyside L45 1LP ☎ 0151 639 1027

PLUMMER Julian *(Hrn)*: 3 Beaufort Street, Heaton Park, Prestwich, Manchester M25 1EX ☎ 0161 773 2464

PROCTER Frank *(Hrn)*: Roseville, Hayeswood Lane, Halmerend, Stoke-on-Trent, Staffs ST7 8AL ☎ 01782 720967

RICHARDS Peter *(Hrn, Wg Tba, N Hrn, Pf)*: 10 Ivy Road, Poynton, Cheshire SK12 1PE ☎ 01625 874712

ROGERS Laurence *(Hrn)*: 137 Ashley Road, Hale, Altringhan WA14 2UW ☎ 0161 941 4405

SNOWDON Jeffrey *(Hrn)*: 78 Church Street, Old Glossop, Derbys SK13 9RN ☎ 01457 853137

STEEDMAN David *(Hrn)*: 62 Mill Lane, Wallasey, Merseyside L44 5UQ ☎ 0151 638 7146

STOKER Lindsey *(Hrn)*: 21 Hesketh Avenue, Didsbury, Manchester M20 2QN ☎ 0161 434 2759

STOKER Phillip *(Hrn)*: 21 Hesketh Avenue, Didsbury, Manchester M20 2QN ☎ 0161 434 2759

TAGGART Martin *(Hrn, Wg Tba)*: 53 Penkett Road, Wallasey, Merseyside L45 7QG ☎ 0151 630 3808, 0976 751349

TAYLOR Kenneth *(Hrn)*: 105 Brodie Avenue, Mossley Hill, Liverpool L18 4RF ☎ 0151 724 1459

THORNTON John *(Hrn)*: 114 Parrin Lane, Winton, Eccles, Manchester M30 8BE ☎ 0161 707 1961

TOKELEY Alan *(Hrn)*: 45 Brookfield Avenue, Poynton, Stockport, Cheshire SK12 1JE ☎ 01625 872173

WOODBURN Andrew *(Hrn)*: 114 B, Main Street, Newmilns, Ayrshire KA16 9DH

YATES Lawrence *(Hrn)*: 28 Oak St, Chapelfield, Radcliffe, Manchester M26 9JL ☎ 0161 766 9678

NORTH EAST

ASHWORTH Robert *(Hrn)*: 7 Clarence Grove, Horsforth, Leeds LS18 4LA ☎ 0113 258 1300 & fax

BLACK Bryony *(Hrn, Pf)*: 17 Hampden Street, York YO1 6EA ☎ 01904 653479

CADWALLENDER Muriel *(Hrn)*: 22 South View, Hipsburn, Lesbury, Alnwick, Northumberland NE66 3PZ ☎ 01665 830884

CLIST Donald *(Hrn)*: 16 Malmesbury Road, Chippenham, Nr Wiltshire SN15 1PW ☎ 01249 661267

DODSON Peter *(Hrn)*: 5B Mawson Lane, Ripon, North Yorkshire HG4 1PW ☎ 01765 602030

GEE Darryl *(Hrn)*: 13 Howard Road, Lindley, Huddersfield, Yorks HD3 3DW ☎ 01484 311782, 01422 366456

GOODMAN Malcolm *(Hrn, Gtr)*: The Band Of The Raf Regiment, Royal Airforce Cranwell, Sleaford, Lincs NG34 8HB ☎ 07050 622403, 0802 437919 mob

KAMPEN Paul *(Hrn)*: 74 Springfield Road, Baildon, Shipley, West Yorks BD17 5LX ☎ 01274 581051 & fax

KNOWLES Laura *(Hrn)*: 13 Clement Street, Birkby, Huddersfield, West Yorkshire HD1 5HE ☎ 01484 511343

LATIMER Colin *(Hrn)*: 127A Bawtry Road, Harworth, Doncaster, South Yorkshire DN11 8NT ☎ 01302 745765, 01302 366008, 01302 816000

LEES Andrew *(Hrn)*: 33 Harlow Terrace, Harrogate, North Yorkshire HG2 0PP ☎ 01423 561669

MACKAY Callum *(Hrn, T Hrn)*: 22 The Royd, Yarm, Middlesbrough, Cleveland TS15 9HV ☎ 01642 783080

MADIN Richard *(Hrn)*: 15 Raeburn Drive, Toton, Nottingham NG9 6LF ☎ 0115 973 4439, 0976 515403

OVERTON David *(Hrn)*: 49 Welholme Avenue, Grimsby DN32 0DZ ☎ 01472 355309

PAECHTER Sam *(Hrn, Tba)*: 12 Westover Road, Bramley, Leeds LS13 3PG ☎ 0113 2570573

PALMER Michael *(Hrn)*: 7 Northfield Avenue, Appleton Roebuck, York YO23 7EB ☎ 01904 744412

SCARFE Douglas *(Hrn)*: Westfield House, 2 Newfield Drive, Menston, Ilkley, Leeds LS29 6JQ ☎ 01943 870598

SENIOR Christopher *(Hrn)*: 2 Kingarth Avenue, Seaburn, Sunderland SR6 8DN ☎ 0191 529 5872

SHILLITO Martin *(Hrn, Flt)*: 47 Salisbury Gardens, Jesmond, Newcastle-upon-Tyne 2, Tyne & Wear NE2 1HP ☎ 0191 281 7189

SMALL Julian *(Hrn)*: Hawthorn Cottage, 12 Swan Farm Court, Deighton, York YO19 6HZ ☎ 01904 728808

THOMAS Elinor *(Hrn)*: 15 Chiltern Crescent, Sprotbrough, Doncaster, Sth Yorkshire DN5 7PE ☎ 01302 858898

TOWLER Joanne *(Hrn)*: 5 The Fairway, Pudsey, West Yorkshire LS28 7RD ☎ 0113 2578898

VAUGHAN-WEST David *(Hrn, Con, Md, Com, Arr)*: The Spinney, Scampston, Malton, North Yorkshire YO17 8NG ☎ 019442 479

WADSWORTH Janus *(Hrn)*: 31 Rosslyn Street, Clifton, York YO30 6LG ☎ 01904 644840

WILLIAMSON Michael *(Hrn, Con, Md)*: 33 Newlay Wood Rise, Horsforth, Leeds LS18 4LY ☎ 0113 2591391

WOOD James *(Hrn, Tpt)*: 20 Pannal Ash Drive, Harrogate, North Yorkshire HG2 0HU ☎ 01423 565139

EAST

DAVIES Laurence *(Hrn)*: 32 Lyndhurst Drive, Harpenden, Herts AL5 5RJ ☎ 020 8761 8939

DE JONG CLEYNDERT Christina *(Hrn, Voc, Pf)*: Spike House, London Road, Sawston, Cambridge CB2 4XE ☎ 01223 837286, 0589 768733, 01223 837286 fax

GRAY David *(Hrn)*: 64 Broom Hill Road, Ipswich, Suffolk IP1 4EH ☎ 01473 212 152

HELLEN Marian *(Hrn)*: 1 Pearse Way, Purdis Farm, Ipswich, Suffolk IP3 8TF ☎ 01473 717855

PYATT David *(Hrn)*: 6 Westwick Close, Pancake Lane, Leverstock Green, Hemel Hempstead, Herts HP2 4NH

ROBERTS Lynne *(Hrn)*: 60 Gordon Avenue, Thorpe St Andrew, Norwich, Norfolk NR7 0DP ☎ 01603 37424

SHEWAN Neil *(Hrn, Per, Pf)*: 2 The Dell, Royston, Herts SG8 9BJ ☎ 01763 244079, 0958 998137

SNOOK John *(Hrn, Pf)*: 22 Bonchurch Avenue, Leigh-on-Sea, Essex SS9 3AP ☎ 01702 76564 & fax

WALKER, MUSC, LRSM Suzannah *(Hrn)*: 20 Beechwood Drive, Thorpe St. Andrew, Norwich, Norfolk NR7 0LP ☎ 01603 700887, 0410 464696

WILKINS Julian *(Hrn, Pf, Hpsd, Org)*: Flat 1, 154 Argyle Street, Cambridge CB1 3LS ☎ 01223 410496 & fax

WILLIAMS Jonathan *(Hrn, Wg Tba)*: 38 Dacre Road, Hitchen, Herts SG5 1QJ ☎ 01462 421 468

MIDLANDS

BOTTOMLEY Lynne *(Hrn)*: 8 Bagots View, Off Parkhall Lane, Church Leigh, Nr Tean, Stoke-on-Trent ST10 4RD ☎ 01889 502530

BRIGGS Claire *(Hrn)*: 35 Lee Crescent, Edgbaston, Birmingham B15 2BJ ☎ 0121 446 5957

BULL William *(Hrn)*: Address Unknown

CARVELL John *(Hrn)*: 67 Wood Lane, Wedges Mills, Cannock, Staffs WS11 1SZ ☎ 01922 417047

CURRIE Peter *(Hrn)*: 33, Wood Lane, Harborne, Birmingham B17 9AY ☎ 0121 426 5182

DIMICELI Lilla *(Hrn, Voc)*: 29 Bullfinch Road, Basford, Nottingham NG6 0NJ ☎ 01530 813605

DISNEY Stella *(Hrn)*: Mill Farm, Farlow, Kidderminster, Worcs DY14 0LP ☎ 01746 718727, 0402 423285 mob, 01746 718540

DOWNES Frank *(Hrn)*: 1 Henderson Close, Lichfield, Staffs WS14 9YN ☎ 01543 252 895

DUDDING Paul *(Hrn)*: 61 Sutton Oak Road, Sutton Coldfield, Warks B73 6TQ ☎ 0121 353 1042

DYSON Peter *(Hrn, Wg Tba)*: 42 Beechwood Road, Bearwood, Warley, West Midlands B67 5EQ ☎ 0121 429 1764

DYSON Sally *(Hrn)*: 42 Beechwood Road, Bearwood, Warley, West Midlands B67 5EQ ☎ 0121 429 1764

FERGUSON Sian *(Hrn)*: 16, Mount Pleasant Avenue, Rookery Road, Handsworth, Birmingham B21 9QA ☎ 0121 515 1668

FINNEY Nigel *(Hrn, Pf, Kbds)*: 45 Southcrest Road, Lodge Park, Redditch, Worcs B98 7JH ☎ 01527 522378

FIRTH Nicholas *(Hrn)*: 2A Knowle Road, Stafford ST17 0DN ☎ 01785 662620

GEDDES John *(Hrn)*: 6 Stourton Close, Knowle, Solihull, West Midlands B93 9NP ☎ 01564 777273

GRAY David *(Hrn)*: 15 The Heathlands, Wombourne, Wolverhampton, West Midlands WV5 8HF ☎ 01902 896018

HALL Ralph *(Hrn, Wg Tba, Con)*: Rheindahlen Music Centre, Windsor School, c/o M Kyriakou, Bfpo 40 ☎ +49 2434 24328 & fax

HARTLEY-BENNETT Gordon *(Hrn)*: 22 Holloway, Pershore, Worcs WR10 1HW ☎ 01386 554955

HAWLEY Helen *(Hrn, Pf)*: 16 Welham Crescent, Arnold, Nottingham NG5 7LJ ☎ 0115 920 3271

HILL Timothy *(Hrn, Wg Tba)*: 100 Cooperative Street, Stafford, Staffs ST16 3BZ ☎ 01785 214769

JONES Andrew *(Hrn)*: 58 North Malvern Road, Malvern, Worcs WR14 4LX ☎ 01684 569562

JONES Martyn *(Hrn)*: 64 Allendale Road, Walmley, Sutton Coldfield, W Midlands B76 1NL ☎ 0121 313 0344

KEIGHTLEY Maryann *(Hrn)*: Flat 1, 370 Bearwood Road, Smethwick, Warley B66 4ET ☎ 0121 434 5696

KOOP Gary *(Hrn, B Gtr, Arr, Com, Cop)*: 87 Church Lane, Ravenstone, Coalville, Leics LE67 2AF ☎ 01530 811012

LOCKWOOD Edward *(Hrn, N Hrn, Wg Tba)*: 5 Friary Avenue, Lichfield, Staffordshire WS13 6QQ ☎ 01543 419719, 07050 152976

MCLOUGHLIN Rachel *(Hrn, Pf)*: 21 Gipsy Lane, Whitestone, Nuneaton, Warks CV11 4SH ☎ 024 7638 3296, 0956 303390 mob

MORRIS Peter *(Hrn)*: The Manor, Loxley, Warks CV35 9JX ☎ 01299 470084

NOCK John *(Hrn)*: 23 Yorkbrook Drive, Sheldon, Birmingham, W. Midlands B26 3HX ☎ 0121 743 7541

PARKER Robert *(Hrn)*: 129 Holme Road, West Bridgford, Nottingham NG2 5AG ☎ 0115 9822790

PAYNE Nicola *(Hrn, Pf)*: Ivy House, Whittington, Worcester WR5 2JU ☎ 01905 350055

PENNY Mark *(Hrn)*: 22 Nutfield Road, Leicester LE3 1AN ☎ 0116 2825846, 0973 712 773

PHILLIPS Mark *(Hrn)*: 37 Margaret Grove, Harborne, Birmingham B17 9JJ ☎ 0121 428 3567

REVELL Michael *(Hrn)*: 65 Cambridge Street, Stafford ST16 3PG ☎ 01785 48912

ROBERTS Steve *(Hrn)*: 65 Carless Avenue, Harborne, Birmingham B17 9BN ☎ 0121 426 3711

ROPER Allyson *(Hrn)*: 42 Imperial Rise, Coleshill, Birmingham B46 1UG ☎ 01675 466824

SAWBRIDGE Paul *(Hrn)*: Heath House, Amberley, Stroud, Glos GL5 5AE ☎ 01453 873406

STATHAM David *(Hrn)*: The Old Vicarage, Bidford-on-Avon, Warks B50 4BQ ☎ 01789 772965

THOMAS Bob *(Hrn)*: 22, Patricia Avenue, Yardley Wood, Birmingham B14 4ES ☎ 0121 474 6748

TRUMAN Paul *(Hrn, Pf)*: 31 Townley Way, Earls Barton, Northants NN6 0HR

WOODHURST Marc *(Hrn, Pf)*: Lorne House, 2 St Georges Square, Worcester WR1 1HX ☎ 01905 21360

WRIGHT Martin *(Hrn, Hnd Hrn, Pf)*: 45 Clifford Road, Bearwood, Warley, West Midlands B67 5HJ ☎ 0121 429 6344

SOUTH EAST

ATKINS Lorraine *(Hrn, Cntt)*: 13 The Green, Steventon, Abingdon, Oxon OX13 6RR ☎ 01239 820874, 01734 842826

BAYLISS Martyn (*Hrn*): 30 Dean Park Road, Bournemouth, Dorset BH1 1HY ☎ 01202 290920, 0336 728523 pager, 01202 311567

CALDICOTT Stephen (*Hrn*): Brook House, Priors Leaze Lane, Hambrook, Chichester, West Sussex PO18 8RQ ☎ 01243 572947

COX Darrell (*Hrn*): 6 Portelet Place, Hedge End, Southampton SO30 0LZ ☎ Botley 2718

COX Jonathan (*Hrn*): 6 Portelet Place, Hedge End, Southampton, Hants SO30 0LZ ☎ 014892 2718

DAVIES Ieuan (*Hrn*): 10 Southwick Road, Boscombe East, Bournemouth, Dorset BH6 5PT ☎ 01202 424922

DENYER Trevor (*Hrn*): Campile, Crescent Rise, Thakeham, West Sussex RH20 3NB ☎ 01903 742326

ETHERINGTON Alyson (*Hrn, Flt, Voc, B Gtr*) ☎ 01342 718588, 0374 658471, 01342 718588

FRANKLIN Keith (*Hrn*): 139 Rochester Road, Burham, Nr Rochester, Kent ME1 3SG ☎ 01634 669220

HARRIS Robert (*Hrn*): 3 Sitterton, Bere Regis, Wareham, Dorset BH20 7HU ☎ 01929 471115

HARRISON-PREISS Dagmara (*Hrn, N Hrn*): 38 Mill Road, Dunton Green, Sevenoaks, Kent TN13 2UZ ☎ 01735 464324, 0777 567 1581 mob, 01306 500022 day

HUBBARD Ruth (*Hrn*): 7 Orchard St, Blandford Forum, Dorset DT11 7QZ ☎ 01258 456768

KANE Mark (*Hrn, Wg Tba*): 18 Ardmore Road, Parkstone, Poole, Dorset BH14 8SA ☎ 01202 731616, 0831 767951 mob

KANE Peter (*Hrn, Wg Tba*): 18 Ardmore Road, Poole, Dorset BH14 8SA ☎ 01202 731616

NEWNHAM Alan (*Hrn*): 37 Ring Road, North Lancing, West Sussex BN15 0QF ☎ 01903 766079

NORMAN Andrew (*Hrn, Tpt, Tba, Cnt, Tbn*): Flat 3, Gordon Lodge, 8 Belvedere Street, Ryde, Isle Of Wight PO33 2JW ☎ 01983 566826

PATON Rod (*Hrn, Pf, Md*): 28 Glamis Street, Bognor Regis, West Sussex PO21 1DQ ☎ 01243 586852

PEPPER Austin (*Hrn*): 23 Cavendish Road, Aldershot, Hants GU11 1NA ☎ 01252 23823

PFAFF Malcolm (*Hrn*): West Cottage, Hethfelton, Wool, Wareham Dorset BH20 6HJ ☎ 01929 462211

PRITCHARD Kevin (*Hrn, Pf, Kbds*): 17B Willow Way, Christchurch, Dorset, England BH23 1JJ ☎ 01202 481963

REES Stephanie (*Hrn, Wg Tba*): 258A Bethnal Green Road, London E2 0AA

RUMSBY Tom (*Hrn*): Wayside, Heath Lane, Bladon, Oxford OX20 1SB ☎ 01993 811641

SILSBY Lynn (*Hrn*): 4 Alexander House, Woodley Hill, Chesham, Bucks HP5 1SL ☎ 01494 776043

SUTTON Andrew (*Hrn, Wg Tba*): 39 Penpont Water, Didcot, Oxfordshire OX11 7LR ☎ 01235 510998, 0976 278299, 01306 880669

THOMAS Richard (*Hrn*): 5 Stirling Road, Talbot Woods, Bournemouth, Dorset BH3 7JG ☎ 01202 511010

THOMPSON William (*Hrn*): Windsor Court Hotel, 34 Bodorgan Road, Bournemouth, Dorset BH2 6NJ ☎ 01202 554637

THOMSON James (*Hrn, Pf*): Tawny Orchard, Crossways Road, Grayshott, Nr Hindhead, Surrey GU26 6HD ☎ 01428 607239

WATSON Alan (*Hrn*): 11 Chichester Drive West, Saltdean, East Sussex BN2 8SH ☎ 01273 33334

SOUTH WEST

AMOS Roberta (*Hrn, Wg Tba*): 61 Coronation Road, Downend, Bristol BS16 5SN ☎ 0117 957 2168

AVERY Karyn (*Hrn*): 21 Lordsmead Rd., Mere, Warminster, Wilts BA12 6BZ ☎ Mere 860680

BECK James (*Hrn*): Coniston, Llandaff Square, St Mellons, Cardiff CF3 9UG ☎ 029 2079 2798

BROCKHURST Fiona (*Hrn*): 78 Allen Water Drive, Fordingbridge, Hampshire SP6 1RE ☎ 01425 653748

BURKE Charlotte (*Hrn*): 25 Plymouth Road, Penarth, Cardiff, South Glamorgan CF6 2DA ☎ 029 2070 8519

DAVIES David (*Hrn*): 29 Crown Rise, Llanfrechfa, Cwmbran, Gwent NP44 8UB ☎ 01633 861248

DAVIS William (*Hrn*): 7 The Avenue, Ystrad Mynach, Mid Glamorgan CF8 8AE ☎ 01443 812303

EDWARDS Daniel (*Hrn*): 10 Cumberland Street, Canton, Cardiff CF5 1LT ☎ 0589 181997

FISHER Ian (*Hrn*): 76 Birchgrove Road, Birchgrove, Cardiff, South Glamorgan CF4 1RT ☎ 029 2069 2382

FROST Emma (*Hrn*): 52 Farm Road, Weston-Super-Mare, Somerset BS22 8BD ☎ 01934 645764

GREEN Judith (*Hrn*): Hestia, Top Street, Pilton, Somerset BA4 4DF ☎ Pilton 611

GRIFFITHS Simon (*Hrn*): 21 Cefn Coed, Bridgend, Mid Glam CF31 4PH ☎ 01656 656205

HICKS Brian (*Hrn*): Tolvadden, 10 Caradon Heights, Callington Road, Liskeard Cornwall PL14 3EB ☎ 01579 42560

HORTIN Christopher (*Hrn*): Pendeen, Queens Hotel, The Promenade, Penzance, Cornwall TR18 4RG ☎ 01736 361673

JONES John (*Hrn, Wg Tba, Tba, Tbn, Tpt*): Morbys, Melbury Road, Yetminster, Sherborne, Dorset DT9 6LX ☎ 01935 873472 & fax, 0467 843751

JONES Leighton (*Hrn*): 10 Oaktree Close, Radyr, Cardiff CF4 8RW ☎ 029 2084 3716

LANGLEY Michael (*Hrn*): Severnleigh, Newlands Hill, Portishead, Bristol BS20 9AZ ☎ 0117 9847971

LLOYD David (*Hrn*): Riversdale Cottage, 17 Gabalfa Road, Llandaff North, Cardiff CF4 2JH ☎ 029 2056 6006

LOCKYER Luke (*Hrn, Com, Pf*): 37 Harle Street, Neath, Wales SA11 3DN ☎ 01639 770718, 07970 847095, 01639 770908

MACALLISTER Stephen (*Hrn*): 19 Gundry Close, Pewsham, Chippenham, Wiltshire SN15 3SP ☎ 01249 659007

MEAD Allan (*Hrn*): 39 Pine Close, South Wonston, Winchester SO21 3EB ☎ 01962 886519

MOLCHER Robert (*Hrn*): 26 Deri Road, Penylan, Cardiff CF2 5AJ ☎ 029 2048 7435

MORTON Amanda (*Hrn, Voc*): 47 Cardiff Road, Taffswell, Cardiff CF4 7RD ☎ 029 2081 0884

MUNISANY Nigel (*Hrn*): Bld. Kleyer 107, 4000, Licgc, Belgium ☎ + 32 0 41 530768

PROSSER Grenville (*Hrn*): Long Thyme Cottage, Lower Stanton Street, Quintin, Malmesbury, Wiltshire SN14 6BY ☎ 01666 837377, 0973 791035 mob

REES Alun (*Hrn*): 24 Chapel Road, Llanharn, Pontyclun, Rhondda Cynon Taff CF72 9QA ☎ 01443 229370

RUSSELL Ian (*Hrn, Pf*): 1 Saint Crispin Close, Monmouth, Gwent NP5 4UH ☎ 01600 714698

SHILLAW David (*Hrn*): 6 Picton Avenue, County Borough Of Bridgend, Mid. Glam. CF36 3AJ ☎ 01656 772174, 0802 747171

SMITH Alistair (*Hrn, Pf*): 63 High Street, Rode, Bath BA3 6PB ☎ 01373 830911

STIFF Colin (*Hrn*): Pratts Farm, Westwood, Broadclyst, Exeter EX5 3DJ ☎ 01404 822338

VENABLES Christine (*Hrn*): The Heathers, 58 Woodthorpe Drive, Bewdley, Worcs. DY12 2RH

WEST Angus (*Hrn*): 69 Pontcanna Street, Pontcanna, Cardiff CF1 9HR ☎ 029 2038 2468

WHITE Tessa (*Hrn*): Greenfields, Forthay, North Nibley, Dursley, Glos GL11 6DY ☎ 01453 542228

WILLIAMS Alun J (*Hrn, Pf*): 3 Bryn Afon Tce, Hengoed, Mid Glamorgan CF28 7LZ ☎ 01443 815682, 0976 839868

WILLIAMS Gareth (*Hrn*): 8 Belle Vue, Treforest, Pontypridd, Mid Glamorgan CF37 1TQ ☎ 01443 491388

WILLIAMS Valerie (*Hrn, Tpt*): 9 Clifford Mews, Wellington, Somerset TA21 8QJ ☎ 01823 665691

WILLIAMSON Irene (*Hrn*): 13 St Johns Crescent, Canton, Cardiff CF5 1NX ☎ 029 2022 2477

LONDON

ABBOTT Kevin (*Hrn*): 40 Vancouver Road, London SE23 2AF ☎ 020 8699 0913

ALFREDSSON Vidar *(Hrn)*: Nesbakki 21 2 Hv, 740 Neskaupstad, Iceland ☎ 477 1652

ANTCLIFF Andrew *(Hrn)*: Nightingale Old Farm, Wood Street Green, Guildford, Surrey GU3 3DU ☎ 01483 234320

ANTHONY Daniel *(Hrn)*: 343 Manhattan Building, Bow Quarter, Fairfield Road, London E3 2UQ ☎ 020 8981 4218, 0973 341731

ARNOUF Jerome *(Hrn, N Hrn)*: 36 Pandora Road, London NW6 1TT ☎ 020 7681 0021, 01306 880669

ASHTON Richard *(Hrn)*: 98 Hindmans Road, East Dulwich, London SE22 9NG ☎ 020 8693 8319, 07971 400362, 0781 693 8319

BAKER Jonathan *(Hrn, Pf)*: Address Unknown ☎ 020 8656 9753

BAKER Julian *(Hrn)*: Top Flat, 59 Hargrave Park, London N19 5JW ☎ 020 7272 6789 & fax, 0108 533 1372 day

BALLARD Janice *(Hrn)*: 194 Muswell Hill Road, Muswell Hill, London N10 3NG ☎ 020 8444 0246

BAREHAM Jonathan *(Hrn)*: 21 Felipe Road, Chafford Hundred, Essex RM16 6NE ☎ 01375482188

BATES Marcus *(Hrn)*: 14 Kilmorie Road, Forest Hill, London SE23 2ST ☎ 020 8699 6489, 01306 880669 day, 0973 212375 mob

BAYLISS Richard *(Hrn, N Hrn, Bq Hrn)*: 25 Priory Hill, Harrow, Middlesex HA0 2QF ☎ 020 8385 0152, 01306 880669, 01202 319122

BELL Stephen *(Hrn)*: Woodlands, 44 Daws Hill Lane, High Wycombe, Buckinghamshire HP11 1PU ☎ 01494 522420, 0973 751516

BENNELLICK Thomas *(Hrn, Wg Tba)*: 18 Bailie Close, Abingdon, Oxon OX4 5RF ☎ 01235 29500

BENNETT Peter *(Hrn)*: 44 New Street, Great Dunmow, Essex CM6 1BH ☎ 01371 878017, 0973 614948

BENNETT Richard *(Hrn)*: 23A Bennerley Road, London SW11 6DR ☎ 020 7223 3972, 0973 722180 mob

BENTLEY David *(Hrn, Org, N Hrn)*: 30 Imperial Close, North Harrow, Middlesex HA2 7LN ☎ 020 8866 4412

BERRY Richard *(Hrn)*: Flat 8, 9 Bernard Gardens, Wimbledon, London SW19 7BE ☎ 01483 723644, 0973 135068

BIRD Gillian *(Hrn)*: 28 Oaksford Ave, Sydenham, London SE26 6AR ☎ 020 8291 6012

BISSILL Richard *(Hrn)*: 2 Cromwell Close, St Albans, Herts AL4 9YE ☎ 01727 834329, 0777 584 7984 mob

BLACK Nigel *(Hrn)*: 91 Wiverton Road, Sydenham, London SE26 5JB ☎ 020 8776 8695

BLAKE Peter *(Hrn)*: 168 Beckenham Road, Beckenham, Kent BR3 4RJ ☎ 020 8659 5268

BOWDLER Heidi *(Hrn)*: 42 Arthurdon Road, Brockley, London SE4 1JU ☎ 020 8690 5957

BOX Philip *(Hrn, Cop)*: 27 Richmond Road, West Wimbledon, London SW20 0PG ☎ 020 8241 8126

BREWER William *(Hrn)*: 6 Neston Road, Watford, Herts WD2 4BW ☎ 01923 252324

BROWN Francis *(Hrn)*: 16 Pyotts Hill, Old Basing, Basingstoke, Hants RG24 8AR ☎ 01256 351963

BROWN Timothy *(Hrn, Wg Tba)*: 77 Fox Lane, Palmers Green, London N13 4AJ ☎ 020 8882 4899

BRYANT Jeffrey *(Hrn, Wg Tba, T Hrn)*: The Coach House, Southill Road, Chislehurst, Kent BR7 5EE ☎ 020 8468 7940

BRYCE Alison *(Hrn, N Hrn, Wg Tba)*: Flat 5, 20 Dornton Road, South Croydon, Surrey CR2 7DP ☎ 020 8688 3917, 0958 757 044 mob, 01306 500 022 day

BUCK J *(Hrn)*: 129 West End Road, Ruislip, Middlesex HA4 6JX ☎ 01895 30430

BUNYAN Rachel *(Hrn)*: 26 Orchard Gate, Greenford, Middlesex UB6 0QW ☎ 020 8900 1226

BURDEN John *(Hrn)*: 33 Old Tullygarley Road, Ballymena, Co Antrim, N. Ireland BT42 2JD ☎ 01266 45037

BUSCH Nicholas *(Hrn, Wg Tba)*: Rockells Barn, Duddenhoe End, Saffron Walden, Essex CB11 4UY ☎ 01763 838133

CAISTER Timothy *(Hrn, Wg Tba, Pf)*: 23 Holly Hill Drive, Banstead, Surrey SM7 2BD ☎ 01737 352200, 07970 680811

CANE Robin *(Hrn, Bq Hrn)*: Dunham House, 9 Brudenell Street, Aldeburgh, Suffolk IP15 5DD ☎ 01728 452688 & fax, 01306 880669 day

CARLTON Dennis *(Hrn)*: 86 The Avenue, London NW6 7NN ☎ 020 8459 8619

CARR Gordon *(Hrn)*: 6 Lichfield Avenue, Canterbury, Kent CT1 3YA ☎ 01227 453154

CASS Gregory *(Hrn)*: 37 Rue De Carouge, Ch-1205 Geneva, Switzerland ☎ 01223 206660 & fax

CASTLE Barry *(Hrn)*: 23 Garthland Drive, Arkley, Barnet, Herts EN5 3BD ☎ 020 8440 2254

CATTERICK Anthony *(Hrn)*: 59 The Crescent, Abbots Langley, Herts WD5 0DR ☎ 01923 262198

CHANCE Edward *(Hrn)*: 1 Central Drive, St.Albans, Herts AL4 0UU ☎ 01727 867507

CHIDELL Anthony *(Hrn, Wg Tba)*: 47 High Street, Robertsbridge, East Sussex TN32 5AL ☎ 01580 880336, 01306 880669 day

CLACK David *(Hrn)*: Four Seasons, Stanford Lane, Hadlow, Tonbridge, Kent TN11 0JP ☎ 01732 850938

CLACK Peter *(Hrn)*: 7 Flanders Close, Marnhull, Sturminster, Newton,Dorset DT10 1LH ☎ 01258 820149

CLARK Andrew *(Hrn, N Hrn, Pf)*: Rock Cottage, Southease, Nr Lewes, E Sussex BN7 3HX ☎ 01273 512414, 01306 880 669

CLARK Roger *(Hrn, Wg Tba, Alp Hrn)*: 55 Ulleswater Road, Southgate, London N14 7BN ☎ 020 8886 1029

CLEWS Richard *(Hrn, Wg Tba)*: 50 Dollis Avenue, Finchley, London N3 1BU ☎ 020 8543 1337, 0973 796824

CONEY John *(Hrn)*: Acred House, 29 Harrisons, Birchanger, Bishops Stortford, Herts CM23 5QT ☎ 01279 817160, 0973 508819 mob

COPUS Antony *(Hrn, N Hrn)*: Stratford, Bradfield, Reading, Berkshire RG7 6BB ☎ 01734 744 344

CROPPER David *(Hrn)*: 7 Woodfield Drive, Leverstock Green, Hemel Hempstead, Herts HP3 8LN ☎ 01442 254915

CROUCH Jason *(Hrn)*: Rousell Cottage, Mount Gardens, Sydenham, London SE26 4NG ☎ 020 8291 0325

DANSON Alan *(Hrn, Cm, Arr)*: 22 Northgates, 445 High Road, Finchley, London N12 0AR ☎ 020 8349 2346

DAVIES Chris *(Hrn)*: 22 Merton Road, Walthamstow, London E17 9DE ☎ 020 8509 1663, 01306 880669

DAVIES Vivian *(Hrn)*: 32 Medway Gardens, Sudbury, Wembley, Middx HA0 2RN ☎ 020 8904 1965

DE SOUZA Simon *(Hrn)*: 7 Ennerdale Road, Reading, Berks RG2 7HH ☎ 0118 9861349, 0468 663597

DENT Susan *(Hrn, Wg Tba, N Hrn)*: Flat A, 30 Elm Grove, London N8 9AH ☎ 020 8348 3031, 01306 880669

DIACK Jim *(Hrn)*: East Oak Cottage, Isington, Alton, Hampshire GU34 4PP ☎ 01420 23488

DIAZ Raul *(Hrn, Pf)*: 5A Vicarage Parade, West Green Road, London N15 3BL ☎ 020 8888 2110

DILLEY Richard *(Hrn)*: 64 Thirlmere Drive, St Albans, Herts AL1 5QL ☎ 01727 862921

DOUGHERTY Lisa *(Hrn, N Hrn)*: 79 Homestead Road, Becontree, Dagenham, Essex RM8 3DP ☎ 020 8595 5554, 07970 660741 mob

DUNN Marjorie *(Hrn)*: 12 Tudor Court, London E17 8ET ☎ 020 8521 4275

DUPREZ John *(Hrn, Tpt, Kbds, Com, Arr)*: Hill Farm, Bruern, Oxon OX7 6HB ☎ 01993 831737

DURKAN Jessie *(Hrn)*: 61 Mayfield Road, South Croydon, Surrey CR2 0BJ ☎ 020 8657 1058, 0961 100628

EASTOP Pip *(Hrn)*: 42 Queens Road, Leytonstone, London E11 1BB ☎ 020 8539 9352, 01306 880669 day

EDWARDS Gavin *(Hrn)*: 9 Selborne Road, Wood Green, London N22 4TL ☎ 020 8889 9522

EMOND Daniel *(Hrn)*: 38A Colville Terrace, London W11 2BU ☎ 020 7221 2881

ESSAME Jill *(Hrn, Wg Tba)*: 13 Frewell House., Bourne Estate, Clerkenwell Road, London EC1N 7UT ☎ 020 7242 5847

EVANS Lynn *(Hrn, Wg Tba)*: 50 Robin Hood Road, St Johns, Woking, Surrey GU21 1SY ☎ 01483 769043

FAULTLESS Julian *(Hrn)*: St Cross College, Oxford OX1 3LZ ☎ 020 8533 1372 day

FLETCHER Andrew *(Hrn)*: 3 Long Row, Moat Lane, Prestwood, Bucks HP16 9BS ☎ 01494 890652, 01306 880669

FLOWER Stephen *(Hrn, Pf)*: 226A Merton Road, Wimbledon, London SW19 1EQ ☎ 020 8543 4374

FLOYD Denzil (*Hrn*): 13 Halgavor Park, Bodmin, Cornwall PL31 1DL ☎ 01208 76090

FOGGIN Ellen (*Hrn*): 34 Whitestile Road, Brentford, Middx TW8 9NJ ☎ 020 8560 6728, 0973 252 053

FOLEY Dean (*Hrn*): 164 Wandle Road, Morden, Surrey SM4 6AB ☎ 020 8646 0821

GARDHAM Paul (*Hrn*): Flat 2, 15 Nightingale Road, Rickmansworth, Herts WD3 2DE ☎ 01923771633, 01306 880669

GEE Susan (*Hrn*): 26 East Hill, London SW18 2HH ☎ 020 8874 2495, 0370 917605 mob

GLADSTONE Anthony (*Hrn*): 39 Merrivale Square, Oxford OX2 6QX ☎ 01865 556094

GOLDING Tracey (*Hrn*): 2 Church Mews, Rainham, Kent ME8 8LB ☎ 01634 376235

GRAINGER Martin (*Hrn, N Hrn*): 28 Trehern Close, Knowle, Solihull, West Midlands B93 9HA ☎ 0976 709312 mob

GRAY Antony (*Hrn, Pf*): Ferndene, Bracken Close, Storrington, West Sussex RH20 3HT ☎ 01903 742594

GREEN Oliver (*Hrn*): 159 Streatham Road, Mitcham CR4 2AG ☎ 020 8648 5162, 0976 309442 mob

GUNNER Matthew (*Hrn*): 19A St Julians Farm Road, West Norwood, London SE27 0JJ ☎ 020 8670 4740, 0976 945834 mob

HALSTEAD Anthony (*Hrn, N Hrn, Pf*): 2 Clovelly Road, London N8 7RH ☎ 020 8348 0447, 0973 421626 mob

HANDY James (*Hrn*): 19 Wyndham Road, Kingston-upon-Thames, Surrey KT2 5JR ☎ 020 8546 8427

HANNA Jane (*Hrn*): 52 Boveney Road, Forest Hill, London SE23 3NN ☎ 020 8699 8895, 0976 243362

HARRIS Ronald (*Hrn, Wg Tba*): 16 Queensway, Petts Wood, Kent BR5 1EA ☎ 01689 832556

HASKINS William (*Hrn*): 20 Peckermans Wood, Sydenham Hill, Dulwich, London SE26 6RY ☎ 020 8693 1912, 0831 443319

HASSAN Jonathan (*Hrn*): 17 Cowper Road, Wimbledon, London SW19 6AA ☎ 020 8540 7178, 07050 152954

HENSEL Joanna (*Hrn, Wg Tba*): 72 Vaughan Road, Harrow, Middlesex HA1 4ED ☎ 020 8864 6146, 01306 880669, 0973 429959

HEPPELL Martin (*Hrn*): 13 Woodside Road, London SE25 5DP ☎ 020 8656 5117

HEWITT Miles (*Hrn*): 42 Tulsemere Road, London SE27 9EJ ☎ 020 8761 1620, 020 8533 1372

HILL Nicholas (*Hrn*): 1 Paxton Road, Chiswick, London W4 2QT ☎ 020 8994 0863

HIPWELL Naomi (*Hrn*): 32 Heathlands, Westfield, Hastings, E. Sussex TN35 4QZ ☎ 01424 753120, 0802 774497

HISCOCK Nigel (*Hrn, Wg Tba*): 86 Gresham Drive, Chadwell Heath, Romford, Essex RM6 4TS ☎ 020 8598 9497

HOBBS Martin (*Hrn*): 165 Breakspears Road, Brockley, London SE4 1UA ☎ 020 8691 7683

HOPKINS Shirley (*Hrn, Pis Hrn, Hnd Hrn, Alp Hr*): 50 Kings Hall Road, Beckenham, Kent BR3 1LS ☎ 020 8289 8864

HUMPHRIES John (*Hrn*): 24 Aragon Avenue, East Ewell, Epsom, Surrey KT17 2QG ☎ 020 8393 6067

HUTCHINGS Clare (*Hrn*): 174 Amherst Drive, Orpington, Kent BR5 2HL ☎ 01689 818424, 0973 452295, 01306 500022

IVORY Graham (*Hrn, N Hrn*): 45 Garibaldi Road, Redhill, Surrey RH1 6PB ☎ 01737 763708, 0976 402178 mob, 020 8533 1372

JARMAN Lynne (*Hrn*): The Shambles, Moorland Street, Axbridge, Somerset BS26 2BA ☎ 01934 733508

JENKINS Albert (*Hrn, Wg Tba*): 16 Bucklers Way, Stourvale Green, Bournemouth, Dorset BH8 0EW ☎ 01202 520184

JENKINS Huw (*Hrn*): 16 Charlotte Court, 68B Old Kent Road, London SE1 4NU ☎ 020 7703 3005, 0973 268 331, 01483 723644 day

JOHNSON Mark (*Hrn*): Denholme, West Street, Odiham, Hampshire RG29 1NR ☎ 01256 701782

JONES Alan (*Hrn, Arr*): 61 Wilberforce Road, London NW9 6AT ☎ 020 8202 4789, 020 8533 13729 day

JONES Gillian (*Hrn*): 3 Torr Road, Penge, London SE20 7PS ☎ 020 8776 8127, 01306 500022 day

KALDOR Peter (*Hrn, Tpt*): 42 Cambridge Crescent, Teddington, Middlesex TW11 8DY ☎ 020 8977 4015, 0797 0430577

KEDDIE Iain (*Hrn, Wg Tba*): 16 Fox Hill, Upper Norwood, London SE19 2UU ☎ 020 8771 2569

KENNEDY Richard (*Hrn, N Hrn, Pf*): 8 Devonshire Road, Ealing, London W5 4TP ☎ 020 8567 2857, 020 8533 1372, 01903 181903

KING Vanessa (*Hrn*): 4 Mount Pleasant View, Dalmally Road, Croydon, Surrey CR0 6LU ☎ 020 8654 3974

KORTH Nicholas (*Hrn*): Harbour St. Bride, Primrose Lane, Forest Row, East Sussex RH18 5LT ☎ 01342 825325, 0966 428725 mob

LANG Katie (*Hrn*): 13 Oldman Court, 1-20 Marvels Lane, Grove Park, London SE12 9PY ☎ 0976 402517

LANGRISH Anthony (*Hrn*): 9 Higham Hill Road, Walthamstow, London E17 6EA ☎ 020 8531 4962, 0468 570383

LARKIN Christopher (*Hrn, Wg Tba, Cow Hrn*): 22 Athenaeum Road, Whetstone, London N20 9AE ☎ 020 8445 3016 & fax, 020 8549 1706

LAURENCE David (*Hrn*): 1st Floor Flat, 163 Anerley Road, Penge, London SE20 8EF ☎ 020 8402 4339, 020 8549 1706

LAWRENCE Martin (*Hrn*): 311 Underhill Road, London SE22 9EA ☎ 020 8299 4749, 020 8533 1372 day

LAWSON Ernest (*Hrn, Vln*): 19 Gunterstone Road, London W14 9BP ☎ 020 7602 6047

LEE David (*Hrn*): 73 Pembroke Road, London E17 9BB ☎ 020 8521 0267

LEEDHAM Karen (*Hrn*): 14 Rubens Street, Catford, London SE6 4DH ☎ 020 8699 4458

LINTOTT Clare (*Hrn*): 39 Sandlands Road, Walton-on-The Hill, Tadworth, Surrey KT20 7XB ☎ 01737 814831, 01306 880669

LIPTON Jonathan (*Hrn, Wg Tba*): 14 Muschamp Road, Peckham, London SE15 4EF ☎ 020 7732 3137, 0468 823 603

LLOYD Frank (*Hrn*): 42 Hadley Road, New Barnet, Herts EN5 5QS ☎ 020 8440 8699

LLUNA Jose (*Hrn*): 15 Hawkesfield Road, Forest Hill, London SE23 2TN ☎ 020 8291 3855 & fax

LOCKE Timothy (*Hrn*): 99 The Pastures, Chells Manor Village, Stevenage, Herts SG2 7DF ☎ 01438 317647

LORD Julie (*Hrn*): 11 Girton Way, Croxley Green, Rickmansworth, Herts WD3 3QW ☎ 01923 442836

MAGEE Michael (*Hrn*): 1 Coombe Cottages, Everleigh, Marlborough, Wilts SN8 3EX ☎ 01264 850402

MARKUS Francis (*Hrn*): 13 Bardwell Road, St Albans, Herts AL1 1RQ ☎ 01727 851091, 020 8533 1372, 01727 851008

MASKELL Robert (*Hrn*): 11 Thriffwood, Silverdale, London SE26 4SH ☎ 020 8291 4092

MCGAVIN Andrew (*Hrn*): 82 Bull Lane, Rayleigh, Essex SS6 8LY ☎ 01268 742226, 020 8549 1706

MCINTOSH Robert (*Hrn, Wg Tba*): 53 Richmond Road, New Barnet, Herts EN5 1SF ☎ 020 8441 1718, 01306 880669

MCREYNOLDS Jacqueline (*Hrn*): 119 Shepherds Bush Road, London W6 7LP ☎ 020 7602 8530, 0976 254535

MEECHAM Jon (*Hrn, Wg Tba*): 241 Ivydale Road, Peckham, London SE15 3DY ☎ 020 7639 6971

MERRY Peter (*Hrn*): 107A Torriano Ave., London NW5 2RX ☎ 020 7267 7337

MITCHELL Neil (*Hrn, Wg Tba*): Address Unknown ☎ 01322 555468, 0966 155921 mob

MOLLISON Gareth (*Hrn*): 35 Ashurst Road, North Finchley, London N12 9AU ☎ 020 8445 4800

MONTGOMERY Roger (*Hrn, N Hrn, Con*): 27 Avington Grove, Penge, London SE20 8RY ☎ 020 8778 9411

MOORE Douglas (*Hrn*): Apt.39, Redwood Manor, Tanners Lane, Haslemere, Surrey GU27 2PZ ☎ 01428 658642

MORCOMBE Jonathan (*Hrn*): 5 Foster Lane, Priests Court, Cheapside, London EC2V 6HH ☎ 020 7606 1103

MORGAN Simon (*Hrn*): Kingsclere, Marlow Road, Lane End, Bucks HP14 3JP ☎ 01494 881772, 0973 377 594 mob

MOXON Andrew (*Hrn, Tba*): Studio 8B, 20-30 Wild's Rents, Tower Bridge, London SE1 4QG ☎ 020 7378 9757, 01306 880669

MURRAY Michael (*Hrn, Pf, Tba*): 54 Kings Way, Harrow, Middlesex HA1 1XU ☎ 020 8427 0886

NEWMAN Brian (*Hrn, Org*): 52 Park Avenue, Bromley, Kent BR1 4EE ☎ 020 8460 4797

NEWPORT Christopher (*Hrn*): 24 Kenrick Square, Whitepost, Bletchingley, Surrey RH1 4PU ☎ 01883 743754, 01306 880669

NORRIS Adrian (*Hrn*): 76 Victoria Road, Stroud Green, London N4 3SL ☎ 020 7272 1451, 0973 254593

NORSWORTHY Christine (*Hrn, N Hrn*): 78 Jacksons Drive, Cheshunt, Herts EN7 6HW ☎ 01992 637180, 01306 880669

NORTH Barrie (*Hrn*): 34 Chestnut Grove, Wilmington, Dartford, Kent DA2 7PG ☎ 01322 526653

O'HAODAIN Cormac (*Hrn, Hnd Hrn, Wg Tba*): 203 Murchison Road, Leyton, London E10 6LT ☎ 020 8556 9252

ORR-HUGHES Alison (*Hrn*): 41B Macdonald Road, Friern Barnet, London N11 3JB ☎ 020 8361 8252

OWEN Martin (*Hrn*): 57B Burnt Ash Road, Lee, London SE12 8RF ☎ 020 8852 0701, 0374 236990

PAINE Mark (*Hrn, N Hrn*): 54 Valnay Street, London SW17 8PT ☎ 020 8672 0472, 0374 170230 mob

PATERSON Andrew (*Hrn, Wg Tba*): 2 Pendarves Road, West Wimbledon, London SW20 8TS ☎ 020 8947 6303

PESKETT John (*Hrn, Bq Hrn, Hnd Hrn, Wg Tba*): 72 Felpham Way, Felpham, Bognor Regis, West Sussex PO22 8QU ☎ 01243 822922, 0973 511448 mob

PIGNEGUY John (*Hrn, Wg Tba, T Hrn*): 21 Brechin Place, London SW7 4QD ☎ 020 7373 8915

PRINCE William (*Hrn, N Hrn, Bq Hrn*): 18 St Albans Avenue, Weybridge, Surrey KT13 8EN ☎ 01932 888417, 01932 888427

PRITCHARD Paul (*Hrn*): 12 St Leonards Road, Thames Ditton, Surrey KT7 0RJ ☎ 020 8398 3833

RANDALL Tony (*Hrn, Con*): 39 Park Crescent, Elstree, Herts WD6 3PT ☎ 020 8953 4805

RANDELL Elizabeth (*Hrn*): 52 St Dunstans Road, London W7 2HB ☎ 020 8840 1247, 01306 880669

RATTIGAN James (*Hrn*): 34 Boveney Road, London SE23 3NN ☎ 020 8699 8255, 01459 848484/60517

RATTRAY Catherine (*Hrn, Wg Tba, N Hrn*): 21 Riffel Road, Willesden Green, London NW2 4PB ☎ 020 8452 7431, 0802 754674 mob

RAYNER Simon (*Hrn*): 44 The Grove, Ealing, London W5 5LH ☎ 020 8840 6054

REYNOLDS Clare (*Hrn, N Hrn*): 46 Lichfield Court, Sheen Road, Richmond, Surrey TW9 1AU ☎ 020 8948 1143, 07971 193 883 mob, 020 8533 1372 day

ROBERTS Emma (*Hrn*): 66 Burghill Road, Sydenham, London SE26 4HL ☎ 020 8776 7590, 0976 946802 mob

RONAYNE Pamela (*Hrn*): 98 Sandringham Road, Watford, Herts WD2 4BE ☎ 01923 254 036, 0860 941767

ROOKE John (*Hrn*): 47 Lavender Grove, London E8 3LR ☎ 020 7241 0053

RUMSEY Stephen (*Hrn*): 1 Wickham Hall Cottages, Langford Road, Wickham Bishops, Essex CM8 3JQ ☎ 01621 892229

RUTHERFORD Christian (*Hrn*): 17 Newton Road, Cambridge CB2 2AL ☎ 01223 352542, 0973 313488 mob, 01223 368534 fax

RYCROFT Frank (*Hrn, Wg Tba*): 84 Gallants Farm Road, East Barnet, Herts EN4 8EP ☎ 020 8368 3700

SATTERTHWAITE Chris (*Hrn*): Singleton Post Office, Singleton, Chichester, West Sussex PO18 0EX ☎ 01243 811 236

SEENAN Hugh (*Hrn*): 34 Field Lane, Teddington, Middx TW11 9AW ☎ 020 8977 0230

SHAW Kenneth (*Hrn*): 22 Oak Hill Crescent, Woodford Green, Essex IG8 9PW ☎ 020 8527 7787

SHEPPARD Laura (*Hrn, Wg Tba*): 19 Winns Terrace, Walthamstow, London E17 5EJ ☎ 020 8523 5184, 01426 288713

SIENKIEWICZ Henryk (*Hrn*): 3 Copeland Road, Walthamstow, London E17 9DB ☎ 020 8923 1495, 020 8533 1372 day

SMITH Gary (*Hrn*): 4 Merlin Court, 10 Veals Mead, Mitcham, Surrey CR4 3SB ☎ 020 8640 2914

SMITH Ian (*Hrn*): 20 Birchwood Drive, Lower Peover, Knutsford, Cheshire WA16 9QJ ☎ 01565 722590, 0306 880669

SMITH Mark (*Hrn, Wg Tba*): 23 Park Street, Park Street Village, St Albans, Hertsfordshire AL2 2PE ☎ 0973 262411 mob, 01306 880669

SMITH Peter (*Hrn, Wg Tba, Pf*): 25 Hampton Grove, Ewell, Epsom, Surrey KT17 1LA ☎ 020 8224 9762

SMOKTUNOWICZ Stephan (*Hrn, Hnd Hrn, Wg Tba*): 46 Lichfield Court, Sheen Road, Richmond, Surrey TW9 1AU ☎ 020 8948 1143 & fax, 0976 691 581 mob

STEGGALL Richard (*Hrn, N Hrn*): 52 Pymers Mead, West Dulwich, London SE21 8NH ☎ 020 8244 5036 & fax, 0973 658314 mob

STIRLING Stephen (*Hrn*): 150 Audley Road, Hendon, London NW4 3EG ☎ 020 8202 2050, 020 8533 1372

STOTT Ian (*Hrn*): 6 Byron Avenue, Motspur Park, Surrey KT3 6EX ☎ 020 8942 2515

STREVENS Patrick (*Hrn, Wg Tba, N Hrn*): Esmond Cottage, Lidwells Lane, Goudhurst, Cranbrook Kent TN17 1EJ ☎ 01580 211375

SUGARS Marion (*Hrn*): 11 Holley Road, London W3 7TR ☎ 020 8743 6382

TAYLOR Derek (*Hrn*): 9 The Warren, Chalfont St. Peter, Gerrards Cross, Buckinghamshire SL9 0QZ ☎ 01753 885263 & fax

THOMAS Brendan (*Hrn, N Hrn, Wg Tba*): 57 Waverley Avenue, Wembley, Middx HA9 6BQ ☎ 020 8902 2318

THOMAS Nathan (*Hrn*): Flat 10A, 82 Compagne Gardens, London NW6 3RU ☎ 020 7916 7264, 0958 451586 mob

THOMPSON Michael (*Hrn*): 26 Presburg Road, New Malden, Surrey KT3 5AH ☎ 020 8942 0768

THORNE Philip (*Hrn*): 34 Carnaton Road, Walthamstow, London E17 4DA ☎ 020 8527 8299, 0585 633935 mob

THURGOOD John (*Hrn*): 6 Lavenda Close, Hempstead, Gillingham, Kent ME7 3TB ☎ 01634 377655, 0973 285901 mob

TOPP James (*Hrn*): 69 Walwood Road, Leytonstone, London E11 1AY ☎ 020 8539 6907

TUNSTALL Anthony (*Hrn*): 12 Albert Square, Stockwell, London SW8 1BT ☎ 020 7735 5807

TYLER John (*Hrn*): 9 Tudor Road, New Barnet, Herts EN5 5NL ☎ 020 8440 2791

VIENS Antonie (*Hrn*): 7 Avenue D Anvers, Nice, France, O6000 ☎ 04 93530321

WAINWRIGHT Richard (*Hrn*): Creek Cottage, 70 Germain Street, Chesham, Bucks HP5 1LW ☎ 01494 771740, 01306 880669

WALKER Phillip (*Hrn*): 99 Webb Lane, Hall Green, Birmingham B28 0ED ☎ 0121 777 5193

WARBURTON James (*Hrn, Wg Tba*): 3 Purley Bury Avenue, Purley, Surrey CR8 1JE ☎ 020 8660 0730, 01306 880669 day

WARD John N (*Hrn*): 34 Fairholme Avenue, Gidea Park, Romford, Essex RM2 5UU ☎ 01708 471600

WARNES Ann (*Hrn*): 185 Half Moon Lane, London SE24 9JG ☎ 020 7274 3357

WARREN Graham (*Hrn, Tba*): 44 Fairholme Road, Harrow, Middx HA1 2TN ☎ 020 8863 4959

WATKINS Richard (*Hrn*): 28 Park Road, East Molesey, Surrey KT8 9LE ☎ 020 8783 1421

WHEELER David (*Hrn, Tba*): 12 Temple Road, London NW2 6PP ☎ 020 8452 5007, 0378 922310

WIDGER Andrew (*Hrn*): 15 Jackson Road, East Barnet, Herts EN4 8UT ☎ 020 8364 8241, 01306 880 669

WIDGERY K.Peter (*Hrn, Wg Tba*): 15 Western Elms Avenue, Reading, Berkshire RG30 2AL ☎ 0118 951 0812, 01306 880669 day

WILLIAMS Carsten (*Hrn*): 51 Grosvenor Road, Twickenham, Middlesex TW1 4AD, 01306 880669

WILSON W (*Hrn, Db*): 33 Sanctuary Close, Harefield, Uxbridge, Middx UB9 6LJ ☎ 01895 2183

WOODCOCK George (*Hrn, Wg Tba, Org, Pf*): 3 Rosedene Avenue, London SW16 5WZ ☎ 020 8769 0800

WOODS Philip (*Hrn, Hnd Hrn*): 139 Brookscroft Road, Walthamstow, London E17 4JP ☎ 020 8926 4552, 0973 510039

WYTHE David (*Hrn*): 39 Brandville Road, West Drayton, Middlesex UB7 9DB ☎ 01895 440693, 020 8533 1372

YEOWELL Ronald (*Hrn*): 86 Emmanuel Road, London SW12 0HR ☎ 020 8674 4564

HURDY-GURDY

NORTH EAST

BULL Peter (*Rec, Lute, Dul, Shawm*): 26 Wellhouse Avenue, Gledhow, Leeds LS8 4BY ☎ 0113 240 8250

TYLER Stephen (*Citt, M Hrp, Saz, Gtr*): 1 Charles Pitt Cottages, Cocken, Nr Great Lumley, Co Durham DH3 4EP ☎ 0191 389 2133

EAST

CHATTERLEY David (*Voc*): Ashburnham Villas, 94 High Street, Tring, Herts HP23 4AF ☎ 01442 825191

SOUTH EAST

HEAPE Emma: 1 Warren Crest, Froxfield, Petersfield, Hants GU32 1RL ☎ 01730 827265

MARTIN Philip G. (*Gtr, Voc, Bag, Citera*): 5A Tothill Street, Minster, Ramsgate, Kent CT12 4AG ☎ 01843 821859

SOUTH WEST

WALTON Jake (*Dul, Gtr, Dms*): Gentle Jane, Saint Minver, Nr Wadebridge, Cornwall PL27 6RN ☎ 01208 862417

LONDON

ATTFIELD Raymond: Treetops, Hillside Close, Winchester, Hampshire SO22 5LW ☎ 01962 863205

EATON Nigel (*Kbds, Cel*): 15 Becondale Road, Upper Norwood, London SE19 1QJ ☎ 020 8670 6128

STAPLETON Cliff (*Wood W, Per*): 31 Meynell Road, London E9 7AP ☎ 020 8986 0531

INDIAN PERCUSSION

NORTH WEST

SHANKER Bhavani (*Jaw H*): 16 Highgrove Park, Grassendale, Liverpool L19 9EQ ☎ 0151 427 4920

LONDON

MILLAR Jhalib (*Tabla, Jaw H, Berimbau, Djemb*): 65 Bayham Street, London NW1 0AA ☎ 020 7388 8205

IRISH PIPES

LONDON

BURTON Alan (*Gtr*): 111 Wood End Gardens, Northolt, Middlesex UB5 4QN ☎ 020 8423 1090

HANNIGAN Steafan (*Flt, Tin Wh, Bod, Bzk*): 190 Church Street, Wolverton, Milton Keynes MK12 5JS ☎ 01908 222942, 01908 222976, 0378 177281

JAVANESE GAMELAN

LONDON

CHANNING Andrew (*Dms, Per, Bal Gam*): 39A Hendon Way, London NW2 2LX ☎ 020 8455 1522

MEDROW Elizabeth (*Vln, Pf, Clt*): 51A Steele Road, London N17 6YJ

MENDONCA, BAMA Maria (*Cl Gtr*): 3E Theatre Street, Battersea, London SW11 5NE ☎ 020 7223 2615, 020 7223 2615

JAW'S HARP

LONDON

MILLAR Jhalib (*Tabla, Ind Per, Berimbau, Dje*): 65 Bayham Street, London NW1 0AA ☎ 020 7388 8205

KEYBOARDS

SCOTLAND

ATHERTON Mark (*Voc*): 17 Glenbrae, Bridge Of Weir, Renfrewshire PA11 3BH ☎ 01505 614568

BARNES Gregg (*Tpt, Cnt, Gtr, B Gtr*): 9 Thornwood Drive, Bridge Of Weir PA11 3JQ ☎ 01505 613789, 0411 294984 mob

BOYLE Paul: 19 Pine Grove, Calderbank, Airdrie ML6 9TR ☎ 01236 609022

BURGER Richard (*Ac Gtr*): 21 Campell Avenue, Dumbarton G82 2PQ ☎ 37 32143

CAMPBELL Edward: c/o T Whitelaw, Park Lane Studios, 974 Pollokshaws Road, Glasgow G41 2EU

CAMPBELL James: 29 Waukglen Avenue, Southpark Village, Glasgow G53 7YL ☎ 0141 621 0506

CANNON Fiona: 5 Dunottar Avenue, Shawhead, Coatbridge ML5 4LN ☎ 01236 423060, 0860 802146 mob

CONOR (*B Gtr, Voc*)

COWAN Blair: 39 Randolph Road, Broomhill, Glasgow G11 7LF ☎ 0141 334 0929

COWIE Allan: 28/7 Hoseason Gardens, Edinburgh EH12 7QS ☎ 0131 4660483

CROCKART Eric (*Gtr, Hrn*): 42 Harlaw Road, Aberdeen AB1 6YY

DEVLIN Gerald (*Gtr*): 202 Wedderlea Drive, Glasgow G52 2TA ☎ 0141 882 9880

GARDEN William (*Md, Com, Arr*): 2 Craigenbay Road, Lenzie, Kirkintilloch, Glasgow G66 5JN ☎ 0141 776 3521

GATE Colin: 2/L 51 Rose Street, Glasgow G3 6SF ☎ 0141 332 6020, 0403 475552, 0141 579 5035

GEDDES Christopher (*Gtr, Per*): Flat 1/R, 42 Ripon Drive, Glasgow G12 0DY ☎ 0141 576 2141

GILLON Stuart (*Pf*): 13 Tinto Street, Wishaw, Lanarkshire, Scotland ML2 8JD ☎ 01698 372918

GOODALL David (*Gtr, B Gtr, Sax, Dms*): 253 Kingsacre Road, Rutherglen, Glasgow G73 2EN ☎ 0141 569 3968, 07050 325442, 0141 569 9419

GREIG Michael (*Pf, Acc*): 13 Strathmore Avenue, Kirrlemuir, Tayside DD8 4DJ ☎ 01575 572725, 01382 226898

GRIGELIS Alexander (*Pf, Gtr, Dms*): Orlando Cottage, The Mount, Marston St Lawrence, Banbury, Oxon OX17 2DA ☎ 01295 711131 eve

GUILD Duncan (*Pf*): 176 Camphill Ave, Glasgow, Scotland G41 3DT ☎ 0141 632 8764

HEATLIE Robert (*Sax, Flt*): 3 Victoria Street, Edinburgh EH1 2HE

HENDERSON Andy (*Pf*): Ardoch, 24 Clark Terrace, Crieff, Perthshire PH7 3QE ☎ 01764 653851

HENDERSON Kahl: 144 Fulton Street, Anniesland, Glasgow G13 1ER ☎ 0141 954 6055

HUGHES Rodger: 11 Kilwinning Road, Irvine, Scotland KA12 8RR ☎ 01294 276496, 0468 812735

HUNTER Gillian (*Pf, Acc*): 14 Marshall Place, Perth, Tayside PH2 8AH ☎ 01738 560098

HUNTER Stephen (*Gtr*): 2/6 Glenogle Road, Edinburgh EH3 5HW ☎ 0131 556 4996

ILLINGWORTH David: Flat 0/2, 32 Dundrennan Road, Glasgow G42 9SE ☎ 0141 632 2308

JACKSON Andrew (*Rh Gtr*): 56 Foresthall Drive, Springburn, Glasgow G21 4EJ

JACKSON Ross: 16 Prestwick Place, Kirkcaldy, Fife KY2 6LG ☎ 01592 264556, 0131 667 1464

JAMES Pete (*B Gtr, Gtr*): 1475 689923

JOHNSTON Andrew: 87 Townhill Road, Dunfermline, Fife KY12 0BW ☎ 01383 739162

JONES Ean (*Voc, Org, Pf, Gtr*): 2nd Floor Right, 45 Summerfield Terrace, Aberdeen AB2 1JE ☎ 01224 641080

JONES Hilary (*Voc*): Flat 3/1, 51 Otago Street, Glasgow G12 8PQ ☎ 0141 334 3885

JUMPIN JFK ☎ 0141 959 4389

KALEID (*Synth, Ac Gtr*) ☎ 01355 261649

KENNEDY Gordon (*Gtr*): 3/2, 42 Minard Road, Shawlands, Glasgow G41 2HW ☎ 0141 636 6589

LEE Mallorca: 11 Keir Hardie Road, Stevenston, Scotland KA20 4HD ☎ 01294 465571 & fax, 0468 812735 mob

MACASKILL Paula (*Acc, Voc*): 9 Torlundy Road, Caol, Fort William, Inverness-Shire PH33 7EB ☎ 01397 700410

MACINNES Alasdair (*Dms, Acc*): 47 Monro Road, Jordanhill, Glasgow G13 1SH ☎ 0141 950 1600

MACINTYRE Robert ☎ 0141 221 7026

KEYBOARDS - SCOTLAND

MACLEAN Karen (*Acc*): 26 Woodside Terrace, Edinburgh EH15 2JB ☎ 0131 657 3426

MACLENNAN Donald (*Voc*): 5 Camus Cross, Sleat, Isle Of Skye IV43 8QS ☎ 01471 833 360 & fax

MACNEIL Michael (*Acc*): 61 Berkeley Street, Glasgow ☎ 0141 248 8664

MASTERTON James (*Pf, Org, Md*): 50 Ravelston Road, Bearsden, Glasgow G61 1AY ☎ 0141 942 4132

MCALPINE Kenneth (*Gtr*): Top Left, 185 West Princes Street, Glasgow

MCCOLL Andrew: 74 Carsaig Drive, Craigton, Glasgow G52 1AT ☎ 0141 883 5790

MCMILLAN Scott: 45 Charleston Gardens, Cove, Aberdeen AB12 3QF ☎ 01224 899539, 0839 430084 pager, 01224 572534

MCNIVEN David (*Clt, Sax, Gtr, Per*): 17 East Claremont Street, Edinburgh EH7 4HT ☎ 0131 556 0334, 0831 879697 mob, 0131 332 9210

MCPIKE Alan: 12 Falkland Road, Ayr KA8 8LW ☎ 01292 285304

MILLAR Tom: 15 Lewis Rise, Irvine, Ayrshire KA11 1HH ☎ 01294 215372

MITCHELL Samson (*Org*): Sandell, John Allan Drive, Cumnock KA18 3AG ☎ 01290 423554

MOFFAT Derek: 26D High Street, Kirkcaldy, Fife, Scotland KY1 1LU ☎ 01592 599445

MORRISON Lynn (*Vln, Voc*): Ben Dhu, Burrell Street, Comrie, Perthshire PH6 2JP ☎ 01764 670231

PERSONA: 46 Burnside Road, Gorebridge, Midlothian EH23 4ET ☎ 01875 823152

RANKIN Robin: 138 Danes Drive, Scotstoun, Glasgow G14 9BH ☎ 0141 579 0618

REEDIE Graeme (*Pf, Gtr, Dms*): Flat 1/2, 14 Fergus Drive, Glasgow G20 6AG

ROGERS Glenn: 9 Thornwood Drive, Bridge Of Weir, Renfrewshire PA11 3JQ ☎ 01505 613789

ROSS Richard (*Gtr*): Cec Management, 4 Warren Mews, London W1P 5DJ ☎ 020 7388 6500

SHAW Donald (*Acc*): c/o Secret Music, 5 Newton Terrace Lane, Glasgow G3 7PB ☎ 0141 564 1161, 0141 564 1221 fax

SLOAN Bryan: 57 Kilnford Crescent, Dundonald, By Kilmarnock KA2 9DN ☎ 01563 851261

SONGSHAN ☎ 01382 900002

STARLET Charlotte (*Pf, Voc, Per*): 2/R 1 Holmbank Avenue, Shawlands, Glasgow G41 3JQ ☎ 0141 649 9720

STIRLING Jeremy (*Pf*): 22 Westminster Terrace, Sauchiehall Street, Glasgow G3 7RU ☎ 0141 226 6825

STRACHAN Ian (*Pf, Md*): 653 Arbroath Road, Broughty Ferry, Dundee DD5 3LD ☎ 01382 732741

TURNBULL Kirk: The Arches, 2/3 Crosslea Steading, Ettrick Valley, Nr Selkirk TD7 5HT ☎ 01750 62289

VALENTINE Bert (*Con, Com, Arr, Cop*): Lymefield, 23 Main Street, East Calder, West Lothian EH53 0ES ☎ 01506 881547

WHITE Stan: Westcourt, 3 Coney Hill Road, Bridge Of Allan FK9 4EL ☎ 01786 832519

WHYTE David (*Gtr*) ☎ 0141 401 0214

WHYTE Gordon (*Pf*): 31 Dunchurch Road, Paisley PA1 3JW ☎ 0141 882 7188

WHYTE Jane (*Sax, Flt*) ☎ 0141 401 0214

WILSON John: 62 Ardrossan Road, Saltcoats, Ayrshire, Scotland KA21 5BW ☎ 01294 461610

WISHART Peter: c/o Marilyn Ross Runrig, 1 York Street, Aberdeen AB11 5DL ☎ 01224 573100

WITHERSPOON Lee (*Synth*): 69 James Lean Avenue, Dalkeith, Midlothian EH22 2AB ☎ 0131 663 5752, 0468 914898

YATES Rachael: 187 Nithsdale Road, Pollockshields, Glasgow G41 5QR

NORTH WEST

AINSWORTH Grant (*Gtr*): 'Woodlands', 25 Carrwood Road, Bramhall, Cheshire SK7 3EL

AP SION Pwyll (*E Gtr*): Berthen Gron, Clwt-Y-Bont, Caernarfon, Gwynedd LL55 3DL

BAKER Toni (*Synth, Pf, Org, Md*): 12 Milnrow Road, Smithybridge, Littleborough, Lancs OL15 0BS ☎ 01706 378141

BARKER Andrew: 224 Manchester Road, Heaton Norris, Stockport, Cheshire SK4 1NN ☎ 0161 477 2830

BEDDOW David: 24 Oakmoor Road, Baguley, Manchester M23 8NL ☎ 0161 998 0797

BELLIS Nigel (*Voc*): 67 Church Road, Rhos-on-Sea, Clwyd LL28 4YS ☎ 01492 44807

BIDMEAD John ☎ 01978 353276

BLACK Matt: 40 Belvere Avenue, Blackpool, Lancashire FY4 2LW ☎ 01253 346313

BRADLEY Philip: 35 Kingsbridge Avenue, Grappenhall Avenue, Warrrington, Cheshire WA4 2QR ☎ 01925 486232

BROGDEN Beverley: 22 Raglan Court, Silloth, Cumbria CA5 4BW ☎ 016973 32002

BROWN Leanne

BURGESS Anthony (*Synth*): 21A Station Road, Urmston, Manchester M41 9JA ☎ 0161 747 8334

BURGESS Steven: 20, Maldon Drive, Monton, Eccles, Manchester M30 9LU ☎ 0161 789 3390

CAMPEY Mark (*B Gtr, Vln*): 18 Oakdene Avenue, Darlington, Co Durham OL3 7HS ☎ 01325 269986

CARRINGTON Ian (*Gtr*): 37 Broad Oak Lane, East Didsbury, Manchester M20 5QB ☎ 0161 434 1539

CHRISTIAN Leslie (*Synth*): 75 Whitchurch Road, Withington, Manchester M20 1EZ ☎ 0961 453844

CLARKSON Anthony: 10 Margrove Close, The Pastures, Failsworth, Manchester M35 9XD ☎ 0161 681 6747

COLLING Jonathan (*Pf, Flt, Dms*): 9 Egerton Road, Hale, Altrincham, Cheshire WA15 8EE ☎ 0161 980 6237

CONNELL Andrew: 131 Lapwing Lane, Didsbury, Manchester M60 0US ☎ 0161 434 4164

COX Brian: 495 Burnley Lane, Chadderton, Oldham, Lancs OL9 0BW ☎ 0161 624 1957

DAVIS Paul (*B Gtr*): 1 Mill Lane, Northenden, Manchester M22 4HJ ☎ 0161 945 8565

DIVINE Andrew: 2 Fieldfare Close, Pheasants Wood, Thornton, Cleveleys, Blackpool FY5 2BZ ☎ 01253 865616

DIXON JNR Geoff (*Pf, Per, Gtr*): 10 Aughton Court, Beaumont Park, Lancaster LA1 2JY ☎ 01524 33672

DJ DAZE/BOMBJACK ☎ 0161 860 4679

DRELINCOURT Andrew (*Per*): 305 Hyde Road, Denton, Manchester M34 3FF ☎ 0161 336 1558

ELLIS John (*Pf, Saxes, Clt, B Gtr*): 364A Manchester Old Road, Middleton, Manchester M24 4EB ☎ 0161 654 8400

EMERSON Vic: 33/35 Rue Anna Jacquin, 92100, Boulogne Billancourt, France ☎ 010 331 4604970

ENGLAND Peter (*Tpt, Voc*): 330 Gt, Western Street, Rusholme, Manchester M14 4DS ☎ 0161 248 6616

EVANS Dewi: Hafod-Y-Bryn, Lon Ty Croes, Llanfair P G, Ynys Mon Gwynedd LL61 5JL ☎ 01248 714 411

EVANS Ray: 10 Sandringham Road, Morecambe, Lancs LA4 4NE ☎ 01524 413070, 0378 121347

FRANCIS Jeremy: 51 Southern Road, Sale, Manchester M33 6HP

GALVIN Robert (*Gtr, B Gtr*): 178 Queens Drive, Wavertree, Liverpool 15 L15 6XX ☎ 0151 722 3493

GARDNER James (*Synth, B Gtr, Per, Voc*): 3 Sylvan Valley Ave, Woodlands Park, Titirangi, Auckland 1007, New Zealand

GENTLES Malcolm (*Per*) ☎ 0410 504707

GLOVER Nigel (*Org*): 7 Roeburn Way, Penketh, Warrington, Cheshire WA5 2PF ☎ 01925 471673

GORTON Stephen (*Synth*): 2 Gateacre Walk, Brooklands, Manchester M23 9BA ☎ 0161 998 5970

HAJIPANAYI Alice (*Pf, Sax, Gtr*): Flat 7, 10 Rathen Road, Withington, Manchester M20 4GH ☎ 0161 445 1330

HALL Steven (*Org*): 11 Arnside Ave, Hazel Grove, Stockport, Manchester SK7 5AP ☎ 0161 292 6898

HARRIS Andrew (*Per*): 19 Pridmouth Road, Withington, Manchester M20 4GN ☎ 0161 448 1142, 0161 448 1142

HASLAM Mike (*Org*): 477 Warrington Road, Abram, Wigan, Lancashire WN2 5XY ☎ 01942 865766

HAYES Joseph ☎ 0161 747 2352, 0958 476705 mob, 0161 737 7195

HAYES Kenny (*Dms*): Let Management, Suit 426 Imex House, 40 Princess Street, Manchester ☎ 01923 419035, 0161 278 7711

HICKEY Andy (*Db*): 9 Smithills Drive, Bolton BL1 5RB ☎ 01204 843442, 0370 483494 mob

HILLARY David (*Voc*): Beacon Lodge, Macclesfield Road, Nether Alderley, Macclesfield Cheshire SK10 4UB ☎ 01625 583841

HORSLEY Lee (*Org*): 11 Bowler Street, Marehay, Ripley, Derby DE5 8HZ ☎ 01773 742709

HUBBARD David (*Synth*): 140 Burnage Lane, Burnage, Manchester, Lancs M19 1EF

HUNTER Mark (*B Gtr, Dms, Per, Gtr*): 10 Wetherby Grove, Burley, Leeds LS4 2JH

JACKSON Paul (*Voc, Gtr*): 67 Arthur Millwood Court, Rodney Street, Salford, Manchester M3 5HS ☎ 0161 833 9130

JAMES Tony (*Pf, Org, Synth*): 2 Larkhill Close, Timperley, Altrincham, Cheshire WA15 7AX ☎ 0161 980 5677

JENKINS Ian: 7 Harold Street, Archer Park, Middleton, Manchester M24 4AF ☎ 0161 653 3368 & fax

JONES Carys (*Pf, Voc*): Bryn Ddraenen, Padog, Betws-Y-Coed, Conway LL24 0NF ☎ 01690 770287

KAYE Marcus: 46A Ryebank Road, Firswood, Manchester M16 0FU ☎ 0161 882 0595, 0966 247 929, 0161 882 0595

KENNEDY James: 10 Temple Lane, Summit, Littleborough, Lancs OL15 9QH ☎ 01706 373035

KESTER David: 25 Parsonage Road, Heaton Moor, Stockport, Cheshire SK4 4JW ☎ 0161 442 8398, 0402 115631

KILVINGTON Paul: 12 Oak Grove, Poynton, Stockport, Cheshire SK12 1AE ☎ 01625 267343

LEES Rick (*Gtr*): 17 Garners Lane, Davenport, Stockport, Cheshire SK3 8SD

LEXICON Laurie: 3 Wardley Avenue, Whalley Range, Manchester M16 8WX ☎ 0161 860 4604

LYONS Roger (*Com, Gtr, Arr*): 56 Elnor Lane, Whaley Bridge, Cheshire SK23 7EU ☎ 01663 732078, 0966 406169

MACK Robbie: 10 Sussex Road, Cadishead, Manchester M44 5HS ☎ 0161 776 1296

MALLINSON Gareth: 3 Callington Close, Hattersley, Hyde, Cheshire SK14 3EW ☎ 0161 368 0828

MASON John (*Pf, Db*): Flat 6, 76-78 Seymour Grove, Old Trafford, Manchester M16 0LW ☎ 0161 876 5886

MCINTYRE Fritz: Smallfield Cody & Co., Accountants, 5 Harley Place, Harley Street, London W1N 1HB ☎ 020 7631 4574

MONTEVERDE Lee: 23 Hollingworth Avenue, New Moston, Manchester M40 3RB

MOORE Pete J (*Voc, Org, Gtr, Flt*): 2 Elmfield Road, Boars Head, Wigan, Lancs WN1 2RG ☎ 01942 321986

MOORHOUSE Andy (*Cel*): 9 Newton Avenue, Withington, Manchester M20 8JA ☎ 0161 434 2492

MORAN Alex (*Gtr, B Gtr*): 49 Hill Top Avenue, Cheadle Hulme, Cheadle, Cheshire SK8 7HZ

MORRIS John (*Com, Arr*): 9 Egremont Road, Whitehaven, Cumbria CA28 8NL ☎ 01946 693441

MUSGRAVE Jonathan (*Pf*) ☎ 0161 929 4183

NEARY Martin (*Per*): 49 Ashton Road, Newton Le Willows, Merseyside WA14 0AG ☎ 01925 225047, 0973 734589

NICOL Michael (*Voc*): Flat 4 Sherry Court, Aigburth, Liverpool L17 1AX ☎ 0151 734 3593

NUTTALL James (*Gtr, Tpt*): c/o Lancashire Stone Cutters, Unit 3, Ramsbottom Mill, Crow Lane, Ramsbottom, Bury BL0 9BR

OGDEN Ron (*Org, Pf*): 16 Anchorsholme Lane West, Blackpool, Lancs FY5 1LY ☎ 01253 864659

PARTINGTON Darren: 101 Ducie House, Ducie Street, Manchester M1 2JW ☎ 0161 237 9697

PEAKE Nicholas (*Synth*): 4 Oaklands Drive, Prestwich, Manchester M25 1LJ ☎ 0161 773 6825

PHUSE (*Dms, Per*): 273 Cheetham Hill Road, Dukinfield, Cheshire SK16 5JX ☎ 0161 338 2926

PIPES Tony (*Org*): 66A Canning Street, Bury, Lancs BL9 5AS

PLUME Mo (*Pf, B Gtr*): Telford's Warehouse, Tower Wharf, Chester CH1 3EZ ☎ 01244 390090, 0336 765782

POOLE Andrew: 21 Derwent Avenue, Milnrow, Rochadale, Lancashire OL16 3UD ☎ 01706 659652, 0966 144847

POPPLEWELL Andrew: 16 Austin Drive, Didsbury, Manchester M20 6EG ☎ 0161 445 8770

POWER Stephen: 20 Oak Lane, Whitefield, Manchester M45 8ET ☎ 0161 766 5455

PRICE David: 100 Bryn Moryd, Gorad, Valley, Holyhead, Gwynedd LL65 3BF ☎ 01407 740016

PRIESTMAN Henry (*Org, Gtr*): Eternal Management, 4 Rutland Avenue, Liverpool L17 2AF ☎ 0151 734 1500

PROCTER Jeremy: 25 Elms Drive, Bare, Morcambe, Lancashire LA4 6DG ☎ 01524 421158, 0778 8870602

QUESTEL-LEWIS Keith (*Dms, B Gtr, Flt, Sax*) ☎ 0161 205 5251 eve, 0161 205 0208, 0161 205 0208 fax

ROBOTHAM Paul (*Gtr*): 39 Ripon Road, Wallasey, Merseyside L45 6TP ☎ 0151 639 8904

ROSSER Scott: 201 Ruskin Road, Crewe, Cheshire CW2 7JX ☎ 01270 651093

SANDERS Daniel (*Dms*): 30 Squires Court, Salford, Manchester M5 2AD ☎ 0161 707 0014

SEAMAN Paul: 33 Liscard Grove, Wallasey, Merseyside L44 5RA ☎ 0151 630 2156

SHARP Jonathan (*Gtr*): Grassmoor, Crosby, Maryport, Cumbria CA15 6RP ☎ 01900 812856

SHARPLES Steven: 54 South Drive, Harwood, Bolton, Lancs BL2 3NL ☎ 01204 373412

SINGH Dalvinder: 45 Vincent Street, Salford, Lancs M7 2AG ☎ 0161 792 6191

STEVENS Mark (*Voc, Arr*): 1 Thornhill Close, Port Erin, Isle Of Man IM9 6NF ☎ 01624 835057

STILWELL Graham: Oakdene, Temple Avenue, Llandrwod Wells, Powys, Wales LD1 5LP ☎ 01597 823956, 04325 570052

THORPE Colin (*Gtr*): 254 Wilbraham Road, Whalley Range, Manchester M16 8GN ☎ 0161 861 9310

TIDSEY Darrin: 15 Warren Close, Bramhall, Stockport, Cheshire SK7 3LH ☎ 0161 439 2414

TUDHOPE Paul (*Gtr*): Flat 3, 24 Upper Parliament Street, Liverpool L8 1TE ☎ 0151 709 8922

UNDERHILL Gavin: 54 Benjamin Wilson Court, Sussex Street, Salford M7 1PT

VIZARD Jamie (*Pf*): 51 Gordon Road, Monton, Eccles, Manchester M30 9QB ☎ 0161 789 4219

WATERMAN Paul: The Elms, 4 Golbourne Road, Winwick, Warrington, Cheshire WA2 8SZ ☎ 01925 30975

WATKINSON Tim (*B Gtr, Rh Gtr*): 4 Gorton Fold, Horwich, Bolton, Lancs BL6 7BX ☎ 01204 699886

WHITE Gary (*Dms, Gtr, Voc*): 90 Pendle Gardens, Culcheth, Warrington WA3 4LU ☎ 01925 766940

WIGBY Amanda (*Voc*): Flat 2, 6 Hastings Ave, Chorlton, Manchester M21 9SS ☎ 0161 881 4611

WILKS Clive (*B Gtr, Dms, Gtr, Per*): 31 Victoria Road, Whalley Range, Manchester M16 8GP ☎ 0161 232 8384

WILLIAMS Andrew (*Pf, Voc*): 15 Bader Drive, Hopwood, Heywood OL10 2QS ☎ 01706 628975, 0973 642113 mob

WOOD Matthew (*Acc, Gtr, Bod, B Gtr*): 8Greenheys Road, Liverpool L8 0SX ☎ 0151 426 0130

NORTH EAST

ADDEY Douglas (*Org*): White Gable, Kirkby-on-Bain, Woodhall Spa LN10 6XL ☎ 01526 53719

ADRENALIN JUNKIES: PO Box 513, Hull HU5 3YX ☎ 01482 449108

ALSOP Steve (*Gtr*): The Gables, 86 Worksop Road, South Anston, Sheffield S25 5ET ☎ 01909 773399/56

ANTHONY Darren (*Acc, Gtr*): 17 Miles Hill Grove, Scotthall, Leeds LS7 2EW ☎ 0113 293 4264, 0410 814609, 0113 2934 264

ARTLEY John (*Gtr, Voc, Hmca*): 1A Northview Terrace, Bridlington, E Yorks YO15 2QP ☎ 01262 677381, 01262 673304

ATACK Timothy: 8 Beechwood Avenue, Pontefract, West Yorkshire WF8 4ED ☎ 01977 780728

ATKINSON Alistair *(Saxes, Clt, Flt, Arr)*: 'Rangitata', 9 Dipton Road, Beaumont Park, Whitley Bay, Tyne & Wear NE25 9UH ☎ 0191 253 3806

BAILEY Elizabeth *(Sax, Dms)*: 1 Foxfield Walk, Stairfoot, Barnsley, South Yorkshire S70 3AZ ☎ 01226 217933

BELLWOOD Derek *(Org, Arr)*: 58 Chatsworth Road, Pudsey, West Yorkshire LS28 8JX ☎ 01274 664475

BOWLES Robin *(Acc)*: 34 Armitage Road, Armitage Bridge, Huddersfield HD4 7PD ☎ 01484 664553

BROOKE Mike *(Voc, Gtr)*: 63 Raikes Lane, East Bierley, Bradford, West Yorks BD4 6RD ☎ 01274 689349

BUCKLE Jason *(Gtr, Dms, B Gtr, Voc)*: 7 Wake Road, Sheffield S7 1HF

BURNBY Stephen *(Pf, Org)*: 29 Daisy Road, Brighouse, West Yorkshire HD6 3SY ☎ 01484 713366

CARR Roger: 75 Snaithing Lane, Sheffield S10 3LF

CHESTER Scott *(Tbn)*: 221 Broadway, North Shields, Tyne & Wear NE30 3DQ ☎ 0191 2527089

COLLING Robert *(Pf, B Gtr, Sax, Acc)*: Burdon Hall Lodge, Bishopton Lane, Great Burdon, Darlington DL1 3JR ☎ 01325 284014

CONLON Sean *(Pf, Gtr, Dms)* ☎ 01276 476676

COOK John: 11 Davison Avenue, Whitley Bay, Tyne & Wear NE26 1SA ☎ 0191 252 4085

CZERWIK Jonathan *(Pf, Dms, Gtr)*: 167 Cowlersley Lane, Linthwaite, Huddersfield, West Yorkshire HD4 5UT ☎ 01484 650936

DAWSON-BUTTERWORTH Russell *(Flt, Voc, Dms, B Gtr)*: 17 Blandford Gardens, Peterborough PE1 4RU ☎ 01733 69685

DEBSKI Phil: 10 Wellington Crescent, Shipley, West Yorkshire BD18 3PH ☎ 01274 597546

DI MAGGIO Helena *(Gtr)*: 92 Hummerskwott Avenue, Darlington, Co Durham DL3 8RS ☎ 01325 464787

DOBSON John *(Org)*: 43 Pixley Dell, Delves Lane, Consett, Co Durham DH8 7DA ☎ 01207 50 6662

DOUTHWAITE Adrian: 3 Cambridge Close, Padiham, Burnley, Lancashire BB12 7DE ☎ 01282 771388

DOYLE Candida: Pru Harris, Rough Trade, 66 Golborne Road, London W10 5PS ☎ 020 8960 9888

DUNCAN Donald *(Pf)*: 99 Barnaby Crescent, Eston, Redcar & Cleveland TS6 9HL ☎ 01642 502775

EMBER Fern *(Voc)*: 29 Florence Street, Lincoln LN2 5LR ☎ 01522 526680

FISHER David *(St Gtr)*: 1 The Walk, Birdwell, Barnsley, S Yorkshire S70 5UA ☎ 01226 744455

GAD Cristo: 7 Woodroyd Terrace, West Bowling, Bradford, West Yorkshire BD5 8PQ ☎ 01274 787374

GARDNER Peter *(Org, Pf)*: 69 Cannan Avenue, Kirk Michael, Isle Of Man IM6 1HG

GORDON David *(Voc)*: 35 Hampton Road, Scarborough, N. Yorks YO12 5PU ☎ 01723 376084

GORDON Mike: The Bungalow, 58A The Esplanade, Scarborough, North Yorkshire YO11 2UZ ☎ 01723 379818 & fax

HASTINGS George *(Md, B Gtr, Flt, Com)*: 35 Chillingham Drive, Southridge, Chester Le Street, County Durham DH2 3TJ ☎ 0191 388 2953

HATCHER Annie *(Clt, Flt)*: 20 Ashfiled Terrace, Harrogate, North Yorkshire HG1 5ET ☎ 01423 531713

HIGGINS Mike *(Voc, Wood W)*: Flat 20, St Elizabeth Close, Heeley, Sheffield S14 1PG ☎ 0114 225 8676, 0114 222 1620, 0956 856060

HINDE Neil: 33 Ashworth Drive, Kimberworth Park, Rotherham S61 3AH ☎ 0114 279 5885

HONER Dean: 6A Nether Edge Road, Sheffield, South Yorks S7 1HF ☎ 01142 507 985

HOWE Liam *(Wood W)*: 6 Greenlea, Elwick, Hartlepool, Cleveland TS27 3DY ☎ 0370 500 408, 01429 268028

HUMBERSTONE Nigel *(B Gtr)* ☎ 0114 272 8726, 0114 266 8575

KEAY Grahame: 58 Broom Avenue, Broom, Rotherham, S Yorks S60 3NH

KEELEY Ralph: 43 Holeyn Road, Tynedale Rise, Throckley, Tyne & Wear NE15 9PG

KENNEDY Eliot John *(Voc, B Gtr)*: 40 Swinston Hill Road, Dinnington, Sheffield S31 7SA ☎ 01909 562272, 0850 102045 mob

KIRBY Jon: 15 Vine Street, Darlington, Co. Durham DL3 6HW ☎ 01325 283930

LACEY Jon *(Gtr)*: 28 Saffron Drive, Snaith, Goole, North Humberside DN14 9LJ ☎ 01405 861124

LIVERPOOL Martin *(Dms)* ☎ 0961 861333

LUKEMAN Jason *(Gtr, Dms)*: 111 All Alone Road, Idle, Bradford BD10 8TR ☎ 01274 619085, 0411 095903, 01274 619085

MACAULEY Lorraine: 1 Archers Lane, Algarkirk, Nr Boston, Lincolnshire PE20 2AG ☎ 01205 460 082, 0468 10734, 01205 460 082

MACAULEY Valerie: 1 Archers Lane, Algakirk, Nr Boston, Lincolnshire PE20 2AG ☎ 020 8881 4074

MALTMAN Glenn *(Pf)*: 4 Hargill Road, Howden Le Wear, Crook, Co. Durham DL15 8HL

MARRIOTT Dean: Address Unknown ☎ 0114 279 5885

MARTEZ Tony *(Gtr, B Gtr)*: 2 Springfield Grove, Brighouse, West Yorks HD6 2HZ ☎ 01484 716635, 0402 311644 mob

McKINLEY Steven *(Dms)*: 13 Teynham Road, Shirecliffe, Sheffield S5 8TU

MIDDLETON Paul: 187 West Parade, Lincoln LN1 1QT ☎ 01522 540495

MITCHELL Alan *(Dms, Tbn)*: 32 Braemer Drive, South Shields NE34 7TZ ☎ 0191 455 4515

MUNDAY John *(E Gtr)*: 12 Laurel Mount, Pudsey, West Yorkshire LS28 7QE ☎ 0113 257 4170, 0113 257 4862

MYERS Christopher *(Uke, Clt)*: 20 Northstead Manor Drive, Scarborough YO12 6AB ☎ 01723 379135

O'NEILL Michelle *(Pf, Synth, Voc)*: Flat 1, 61 Yarm Lane, Stockton, Cleveland TS18 3DX ☎ 01642 616528

PARROT *(Tpt)*: 27 Ramsey Road, Sheffield S10 1LR ☎ 01142 306912 & fax

PERRY Aerron: 23 Colenso Road, Holbeck, Leeds LS11 0DD ☎ 0113 229 2541, 0113 229 2541

PICKLES Andrew: 8 Lingmoor Close, Warmsworth, Doncaster, S Yorks DN4 9NF ☎ 01302 858497

PIGOTT Stephen *(Gtr)*: Belmont House, 42 Norfolk Road, Sheffield S2 2SY ☎ 0114 275 7145, 0831 340 529 mob, 020 8208 1717

PINKNEY Graham *(Vib, Dms, Arr)*: 85 Dolphin Court Road, Paignton, Devon TQ3 1AB ☎ 01803 523221

PISCITELLI Gino: 118 Birkby Hall Road, Birkby, Huddersfield, West Yorkshire HD2 2UZ ☎ 01484 538206

PONTON Ben *(Pf)*: 15 Devonshire Place, Newcastle-upon-Tyne NE2 2NB ☎ 0191 281 1465, 0191 281 4880

POOLE Glyn: 23 Fieldway Rise, Rodley, Leeds LS13 1EJ ☎ 0113 2558661

QUICK Tom

RAD: 49 Acaster Drive, Low Moor, Bradford BD12 0BE ☎ 01274 605557

RAFFERTY Ian *(Dms)*: 3 Mount Ave, Mount, Huddersfield, West Yorkshire HD3 3XS

REDDING Philip: 7 Wainers Close, Copmanthorpe, York YO23 3XH ☎ 01904 706760, 05890 96396

RIX Jim *(B Gtr, Dms, Gtr)*: Southcliffe, 10 Selby Road, Fulford, York YO19 4RD ☎ 01904 625088

ROBERTS Vaughan: 173 Illingworth Road, Halifax, West Yorkshire HX2 9RX ☎ 01422 244515 eve, 0422 831031 eve

ROSS Paul: 118 Penistone Road, Waterloo, Huddersfield, West Yorkshire HD5 8RN ☎ 01484 544464

SAUNDERS Alan *(Org, Pf, Vib, Arr)*: Orwell Nursing Home, Vicarage Lane, Wherstead, Ipswich IP9 2AE ☎ Ipswich 692671

SCARFE Stephen *(Clt)*: 15 South Street, Barnetby, South Humberside DN38 6JN ☎ 01652 688123

SCARGILL Gary *(Gtr, Per)*: 3 Epsom Way, Kirkheaton, Huddersfield, West Yorkshire HD5 0LE

SCOTT Christopher: 11 Waldron Street, Bishop Auckland, Co. Durham DL14 7DS ☎ 01388 663051

SCOTT Michael J (*B Gtr, Vln, Gtr*): Address Unknown ☎ 0113 2440004, 0113 242 8080

SIMPSON James: 4 Willow Gardens, Barrow-on-Humber, North Lincolnshire DN19 7SW ☎ 01469 532301, 01469 532328 fax

SMITH Keith (*Acc, Gtr*): 42 Victoria Street, Heckmondwike, West Yorkshire WF16 9HL ☎ 01924 501457

SMITH Mark: 98 Church Meadow Road, Rossington, Nr Doncaster, South Yorkshire DN11 0YD ☎ 01302 340032, 0378 041007

SUTTON Neil: 15 Blackwell Close, Sheffield S2 5PY ☎ 0973 722125 mob

SWAN Marc (*Synth*): 5 Huntingdon Gardens, Barnes, Sunderland SR3 1UE ☎ 0191 5226901, 0777 1861812

SWEET Tom: Gate House, Fenwicks Lane, York YO10 4PL ☎ 020 7923 9184, 020 7354 2525

TISBURY Geoffrey (*Gtr*): 74 Greenlands Road, Redcar, Redcar & Cleveland TS10 2DH ☎ 01642 473346

TUCKER Paul: Kitchenware Records, St Thomas Street Workshop, St Thomas Street, Newcastle-upon-Tyne, Tyne & Wear NE1 4LE ☎ 0191 232 4895, 0191 232 0262

WATERHOUSE Jay (*Dms, B Gtr, Voc*): 40 Nunroy Road, Leeds LS17 6PF ☎ 0113 2687114

WATERSON Dominic: 749 Ney Hey Road, Outlane, Huddersfield HD3 3YL ☎ 01422 370315

WATSON Alan: 14 Rookhope, Rickleton, District 13, Washington NE38 9HW ☎ 0191 417 4671

WATSON Donald (*Acc, Mldn*): 1 Hareholme Court, Esh Wood, New Brancepeth, Co Durham DH7 7HN ☎ 0191 3733429

WEBB William (*Md, Com, Arr, Song W*): 89 Copleston Road, London SE15 4AH ☎ 020 7639 1205

WELLINGTON Michael: 1 Wansbeck Court, Morpeth, Northumberland NE61 1HD ☎ 01670 514486

WHITE Dean (*Gtr, Clt*): 13 Quarry Mount Place, Woodhouse, Leeds LS6 2JE ☎ 0113 2429394

WHITE Tony (*Pf*): West Winds, 9 Menston Old Lane, Burley In Wharfedale, Ilkley, West Yorks LS29 7QA ☎ 01943 863355

WHITEHOUSE Nick (*Pf*): 15 West Park Crescent, Roundhay, Leeds LS8 2HE ☎ 0113 2930884

WILLIAMS Joe (*Gtr, B Gtr*): 130 Church Lane, Meanwood, Leeds LS6 4NR ☎ 0113 2748164

WORBY Robert (*Gtr*): 30A Spencer Place, Leeds LS7 4BR ☎ 0113 262 7302, 0113 262 2766

WYATT Robert (*Per, Voc*): 29 Queen Street, Louth, Lincolnshire LN11 9BJ ☎ 01507 607430

EAST

ALLEN Robert (*Rh Gtr, B Gtr*): 37 Hyll Close, Great Chesterford, Essex CB10 1QF ☎ 01799 531321

ATTREED David: 2 Portsmouth Road, Clacton-on-Sea, Essex CO15 1BP ☎ 01255 436079

ATTRIDGE Billy: 10 Ryelands Road, North Wootton, Kings Lynn, Norfolk PE30 3RN ☎ 01553 673942

BAKER Ward (*Gtr, Cel*): 41 Daking Avenue, Boxford, Suffolk CO10 5QA ☎ 01787 210129, 0850 941831 mob, 01206 766944

BARBER Andy (*Pf*): 66 Lattice Avenue, Ipswich, Suffolk IP4 5LL ☎ 01473 723744

BARNETT Ian (*Gtr*): 61 Tippett Court, London Road, Stevenage, Herts SG1 1XR ☎ 01438 750043

BATES Mark: 102 Cumberland Ave, South Benfleet, Essex SS7 5PA ☎ 01268 758984

BENNETT Warren (*Voc, Gtr*): 28 Gills Hill, Radlett, Herts WD7 8BZ ☎ 01923 853056

BERRIDGE Mike: The Manor House, Thelnetham, Diss, Norfolk IP22 1JZ ☎ 01379 898032

BIP Mr (*Gtr, Dms*): Occupation Road, Corby, Northants NN17 1EH ☎ 0850 200777, 01253 790157 fax

BONSON Lloyd: Tra-Lyn, Third Avenue, Stanford-Le-Hope, Essex SS17 8EW ☎ 07957 725042

BRAGG Richard: 61 Warrengate Road, North Mymms, Hertfordshire AL9 7TT ☎ 01707 643121

BRAZIER Peter F (*Pf, Voc, Gtr*): Westwood Studios, 1 The Lawns, Melbourn, Royston, Herts SG8 6BA ☎ 01763 261448

BREAR Jack: Waveney, 25 Linford Estate, Clenchwarton, Kings Lynn PE34 4BA ☎ 01553 775410

BRIGGS Hillary (*Dms, Gtr, Sax*): 25 Kingsfield Road, Oxhey, Watford, Herts WD1 4PP ☎ 01923 253920

BROWN Christopher: 27 Church Street, Gt Baddow, Chelmsford, Essex CM2 7HX, 0498 575086, 01245 322181

CARTER Bradley: 13 Bickerton Point, South Woodham Ferrers, Essex CM3 5TG, 0370 848874, 01245 322911

CASE (*Dms, Gtr*): 84 Pettis Road, St Ives, Huntingdon PE17 4NZ ☎ 01480 391613

CHECKLEY Mark (*Org, Pf*): 35 Francis Gardens, Peterborough, Cambridgeshire PE1 3XT ☎ 01733 751 403, 0468 291 768

CLEWLOW Alf: 2 Longfield Road, Tring, Herts HP23 4DQ ☎ 01442 381444, 0973 118628 mob

COADY Phillip: 25 Post Mill, Fairstead, King's Lynn, Norfolk PE30 4QY ☎ 01553 765387

COCKS Stuart (*Gtr*): 23 Paxton Road, St. Albans, Herts AL1 1PF ☎ 01727 836280, 0585 308316 mob

COOKE John (*Org, Pf*): 52 Empress Avenue, West Mersea, Essex CO5 8EX ☎ 01206 382738, 0850 487623

COOPER Jonathan: 3 Wetherby Close, Oakwood Grange, Lincs PE10 9TP ☎ 01778 394095

DAVIES David (*Gtr, Per*): 253 Halling Hill, Hanflow, Essex CM20 3JS ☎ 01279 303579

DYER Joye (*Voc*): Allegro, Clacton Road, Thorrington, Nr Colchester, Essex CO7 8JW ☎ 01206 251010

EVANS-JONES Mr M: 16 Spinney Close, Thorpe St Andrew, Norwich NR7 0PN ☎ 01603 702 589, 0860 293404, 01582 392 308 day

EWERS Anthony (*B Gtr, Dms*): 14 Cobbold Street, Ipswich, Suffolk IP4 2DN ☎ 01473 420133

FRANKLIN Mark (*Gtr*)

FRYETT Kevin (*Dms, Per, Voc, B Gtr*): 87 Ryhall Road, Stamford, Lincs PE9 1US ☎ 01780 765270, 04325 578508 pager, 01780 762919

GALLAGHER Micky: 140 Bishopsfield, Harlow, Essex CM18 6UP ☎ 01279 429828

GATHERN Graham (*Voc*): 42 Watling View, St. Albans, Herts AL1 2PA ☎ 01727 832503, 0370 754217 mob

GBLA John (*Bong*): 126 Park Lands, Rochford, Essex SS4 1SY ☎ 01702 540883

GIBBONS Ian: 33B Cambridge Road, Southend-on-Sea, Essex SS1 1ET

GLENNIE Robert: 94 Molrams Lane, Great Baddow, Essex CM2 7AL ☎ 01245 357380

GODFREY Julia: 36 Falcon Road West, Sprowston, Norwich, Norfolk NR7 8NU ☎ 01603 427364

GRAY Ronald: 12 The Readings, Harlow, Essex CM18 7BT ☎ 01279 416953

GRIFFITHS Barbara (*Acc, Voc*): 1 Station Cottages, Grunty Fen, Wilburton, Ely Cambs CB6 3PZ ☎ 01353 740101

GRIGGS Ross (*Gtr, Com*): 19 Trafalgar Square, Long Suton, Spalding, Lincs PE12 9HB ☎ 01406 364336

GROOVEBUG ☎ 01582 488157, 0468 551059

HALEY Mark: 200 Spencers Croft, Harlow, Essex CM18 6JP ☎ 01279 426631, 0966 397432 mob

HALEY Mark (*Gtr, Voc*): 12 Admiral House, Rivergate, Peterborough PE1 1ES ☎ 01733 897 065

HARDY Robert (*Gtr*): 33 Westerings, Bicknacre, Essex CM3 4ND ☎ 01245 224489, 01245 355063 fax, 0468 822282 mob

HINDS Jeremy (*Voc, Tpt*): 54 Essex Avenue, Sudbury, Suffolk CO10 6YZ ☎ 01787 377693, 01787 377693

HOLLENDER Phil: 29 Friar Walk, West Worthing, West Sussex BN13 1BL ☎ 01903 831346

HOWARD Gerald (*Org*): Wissey View, Meadow Lane, Pickenham, Nr Swaffham Norfolk PE37 8LE ☎ 01760 440323

HUDSON Colin: Upper Flat, Sea Road, Westcliff-on-Sea, Essex SS0 7HP ☎ 01268 758205, 0976 692033 mob, 01268 759440

HUSKISSON Timothy (*Clt, A Sax*): 1 Eastwood Lane South, Westcliffe-on-Sea, Essex SS0 9XH ☎ 01702 330532, 0850 291805

JARMAN Jill *(Com, Arr, Md, Pf)*: 32 Bramble Road, Leagrave, Luton, Beds LU4 9LU ☎ 01582 574429

JEFFS Philip *(Pf, Voc)*: 13 Orchard Walk, Yaxley, Peterborough, Cambs PE7 3EZ ☎ 01733 245219

JOHNS Mark *(B Gtr, Gtr, Com)*: 27 Wellesley Crescent, Potters Bar, Herts EN6 2DG ☎ 01707 850283

JONES David: Waggoners Cottage, Glenside South, West Pinchbeck, Spalding, Lincs PE11 3NU ☎ 01775 640597, 0411 269568

KELLY Russell: 56 Brompton Close, Bramingham Wood, Luton, Beds LU3 3QT ☎ 01582 594817

KIRSTEN: The Gatehouse, Hall Road, Barnardiston, Suffolk CB9 7TG ☎ 01440 786717

LEACH Rod *(Synth)*: 20A Vicarage Causeway, Hertford Heath, Herts SG13 7RT ☎ 01992 500 007

LEESON Graham: 11 King Edward Road, Goldington, Bedford MK41 9SF

MARCS D: 27 Victoria Crescent, Chelmsford, Essex CM1 1QF ☎ 01245 350355

MASQUERADE *(Pf, Synth)*: 24 Devonshire Close, Sawtry, Huntingdon, Cambs PE17 5SG ☎ 01487 831287, 01487 832739

MATT: 41 Rosebury Avenue, South Benfleet, Essex SS7 4HH ☎ 01268 754438

MCCRORIE-SHAND Andrew: Old Orchard, Oak Lane, Braziers End, Chesham, Buckinghamshire HP5 2UL ☎ 01494 758287, 01494 758984 fax

MCNEIL-WATSON Robert *(Org, Pf, Flt, Arr)*: 26 Plumtrees, Oulton Broad, Lowestoft, Suffolk NR32 3JH ☎ 01502 516488

MCNEILL David: 17 Gate Lodge Square, Noak Bridge, Basildon, Essex SS15 4AP ☎ 01268 534439

MORSLEY Austin *(Gtr)*: Yew Tree Cottage, Station Road, Hatfield Peveral, Essex CM3 2DT ☎ 01245 382194

MUNOZ Luis *(Gtr)*: 14 Kingsdale House, York Way, Welwyn, Herts AL6 9LA ☎ 01438 716177

MURPHY John *(Org)*: 6 Centurion Way, Cheshunt Fields, Colchester CO2 9RG ☎ 01206 549963

NEWBY-ROBSON Mark: 14 Station Road, Sudbury, Suffolk CO10 6SS ☎ 01787 880721

PARK Jack *(Pf)*: Flat 4, 53-57 Church Street, Bocking, Briantree, Essex CM7 5JY ☎ 01376 326501

PEARS Michael

PINDER Russ *(Pf, Synth, Voc, Md)*: 27 Stubbs Lane, Braintree, Essex CM7 3PA ☎ 01376 324684

POWNALL Gordon *(Pf, Voc, Per)*: 2 Fiddlers Hall, Tollesbury Road, Tollesbury, Maldon, Essex CM9 8RP ☎ 01621 86992, 0797 0486571, 01376 570580

PUDDICK John: 130 Aylesbeare, Shoeburyness, Essex SS3 8AG ☎ 01702 587314

REED Richard *(Dms)*: 3 Briscoe Close, Hoddesdon, Herts EN11 9DH ☎ 0370 951230

ROWE Levi: 61 Halstead Road, Frinton-on-Sea, Essex CO13 0LR ☎ 020 8501 3941, 01255 673513

SAINSBURY Ian *(Pf)*: Church Bungalow, Gayton Road, Gaywood, Kings Lynn, Norfolk PE30 4DZ ☎ 07970 893674

SILVERWOOD-BROWNE Barry *(Voc, Gtr)*: 4 Farraline Road, Watford, Herts WD1 8DQ ☎ 01923 227561

SMART Jamie: 1 Cressing Road, Whitham, Essex CM8 2NP ☎ 01621 815 524

SMITH Alexis: 28 Station Road, Whittlesford, Cambridge CB2 4NL ☎ 01223 833366, 0956 685234

SMITH Clorinda: Beach Bungalow, The Ferry, Felixstowe, Suffolk IP11 9RZ ☎ 01394 670427

SMITH Jennifer *(Pf, Voc)*: 27 Warren Crescent, East Preston, Littlehampton, West Sussex BN16 1BJ ☎ 0410 802934

STAMP Peter *(Pf)*: The Owls, 107A Elm Tree Road, Lowestoft, Suffolk NR33 9ES ☎ 01502 512894 & fax, 0802 951957

STILES George *(Flt, Voc)*: 64 Comeragh Road, West Kensington, London W14 9HT

STRELLIS Matthew ☎ 01702 309233

SUMMERS Mark ☎ 01702 295894, 01702 298880

TANSLEY Darren *(Bod)*: 25 Mill Street, Colchester, Essex CO1 2AH ☎ 01206 510023 & fax

TAYLOR Russell: 5 Vivian Close, Oxhey, Watford, Herts WD1 4DQ ☎ 01923 220486, 0410 784718

TERRY Robert *(Pf)*: 84A Gladstone Road, Watford WD1 2RB ☎ 01923 4679965

THOMAS Tommy *(Org)*: Prelude, Mill Hill, Hockering, Dereham, Norfolk NR20 3HH ☎ 01603 880581

TONGUE Sheridan *(Sax)*: Blakelands House, 38 Ickleton Road, Duxford, Cambridge CB2 4RT ☎ 01223 524 181, 0421 413362, 0966 233070 mob

TURNER James *(Gtr)*: 31 Chertsey Close, Luton LU2 9JD

TURRELL Tony *(Dms, Voc)*: 15 Bracken Way, Abberton, Colchester, Essex CO5 7PG ☎ 01206 735953

VAS (GROOVE BUG) *(Synth)*: 13 Letchworth Road, Luton, Beds LU3 2NU ☎ 0802 485724 mob

VERITY Karen *(Per, Voc)*: 1 Colemoreham Court, Ickwell Green, Biggleswade, Beds SG18 9EW ☎ 01767 627 633, 01767 627633

VINT Lee: 50 Hartley Road, Luton LU2 0HX ☎ 01582 651488, 0410 242527

WALKER Crosby *(Gtr, B Gtr, Flt)*: 30 The Hoe, Carpenders Park, Watford WD1 5AY ☎ 020 8428 7043

WARD Simon: 46 Ballingdon Street, Sudbury, Suffolk CO10 6BX ☎ 01787 373167

WHITE David *(Org, Pf)*: 27 Blackmore, Letchworth, Herts SG6 2SX ☎ 01462 481658

WILLOUGHBY Pauline: 5 Park Road, Westcliff, Southend, Essex SS0 7PE ☎ 01702 342975

WOODHOUSE Janice: 85 The Maltings, Great Dunmow, Essex CM6 1BY

WOODHOUSE R *(Voc, Dms)*: 3 Goodrich Close, Watford WD2 6BZ ☎ 01923 673915

WOOLLARD Mark: 184 Lincoln Road, Peterborough PE1 2NG ☎ 01733 345405

WORSLEY John: 40 Haylings Road, Leiston, Suffolk IP16 4DN

WRIGHT Paul *(B Gtr)*: Glebe Farmhouse, Great Witchingham, Norwich NR9 5AF ☎ 01603 871098

YOUNG Tony: 103 Beccles Road, Bungay, Suffolk NR35 1HU ☎ 01986 894854

MIDLANDS

A-ZHY: 164 Lighthorne Ave, Ladywood, Birmingham B16 8EP ☎ 0121 212 0704 & fax, 0956 231719 mob

ADE *(Synth, Pf)*: Address Unknown ☎ 01562 747248

ALCOCK Neil: 15 Lordshire Place, Packmoor, Stoke-on-Trent, Staffordshire ST7 4QD ☎ 01782 851937

ALEXANDER Matthew *(Gtr, Pf)*

ARMSTRONG Daniel: 53 St Helens Avenue, Bridgmere, Great Bridge, West Midlands DY4 7LN ☎ 0121 557 9392, 0976 989332

ARNOLD Simon: Woodham Cottage, 25 Brook Lane, Billesdon, Leics LE7 9AB ☎ 0116 259 6436

BARBER Leslie: Flat 21A Valley Lane, Lichfield, Staffordshire WS13 6SU ☎ 01543 414617

BARRETT Patrick: 6 Paradise House, Eden Street, Coventry CV6 5HG ☎ 024 7663 8707

BARRY Sean *(Pf)*: 53 Beechglade, Handsworth Wood, Birmingham B20 1LA ☎ 0121 551 4966, 0973 668845 mob

BAXTER James: 503 Burton Road, Midway, Burton-on-Trent DE11 0DQ ☎ 01283 217725

BENNETT David *(Saxes)*: 15 Fleet Crescent, Rugby, Warks CV21 4BQ ☎ 01788 573037

BHAMRAH Kulwant *(Voc)*: 18 Cubley Road, Hall Green, Birmingham B28 8EH ☎ 0121 778 3582

BIRD Stephen *(Flt)*: 7 Willow Drive, Wellesbourne, Nr Leamington Spa CV35 9SB ☎ 01789 840114

BIZZI *(Dms, B Gtr)*: 59 Havencrest Drive, Humberstone, Leicester LE5 2GL ☎ 0116 2765239, 0850 712788

BOPARAI Harjinder *(Dholak, Ind Per, Harm)*: 8 Westcott Close, Kingswinford, West Midlands DY6 8NJ ☎ 01384 287495, 0973 19510'

BOWERS Phillip: 25 Shalsecote Grove, Kings Heath, Birmingham B14 6NH ☎ 0121 444 1416

BROWN Errol: Flat 5, 88 Trafalgar Road, Moseley, Birmingham B13 8BU ☎ 0121 449 0961

BROWN Selwyn (*Pf*): c/o 42 Upper Dean Street, Digbeth, Birmingham B5 4SG

BROWN Stephen: 3 Foxcroft Close, Hammerwich, Nr Burntwood, Staffs WS7 8ST ☎ 01543 686985, 079797 66406

BROWNE Colin (*Gtr, B Gtr, Per, Voc*): The Cottage, 46 Smithfield Road, Market Drayton, Shropshire TF9 1EW ☎ 01630 654498

CAESAR Pogus (*Dms*): 7 Woodlands Road, Moseley, Birmingham B13 4EH ☎ 0121 449 6439, 0976 260178

CARRUTHERS Geoffrey: 1 Norfolk Road, Stapenhill, Burton -upon-Trent, Staffordshire DE15 9JE ☎ 01283 567262, 0498 824006

CARTLIDGE Luke (*Pf*): 51 Shirley Street, Leek, Staffs ST13 8BG ☎ 01538 383599

CHELL Peter (*Sax, Arr*): Red Lion Farm Cottage, 7 Main Road, Wetley Rocks, Stoke-on-Trent, Staffs ST9 0BH ☎ 01782 550364

CHUCKS: 1A Thornville Close, Northfields, Leicester LE4 9DT ☎ 0116 212 1869, 0958 560734 mob

CLANCY Andrew (*Voc, Dms, Per, Rec*): 43 Georges Avenue, Buebrooke, Northants NN7 3PP ☎ 01604 832754

CLIFT Roger: 20 Newton Street, Basford, Stoke -on-Trent, Staffordshire ST4 6JL ☎ 01782 631777

COOK Lisa (*Pf, Voc*): 7 Birmingham Road, Walsall, West Midlands WS1 2LT ☎ 01922 626955, 0802 755685

CORBETT Dave (*Gtr*): 37 Park Lane, Bewdley, Worcs DY12 2EU ☎ 01299 404197

CORCORAN Christopher (*Arr, Com, Clt*): 71, Central Drive, Bloxwich, Walsall WS3 2QJ ☎ 01922 478329, 01827 55334

COUSINS Gareth (*Dms, B Gtr, Gtr, Voc*): Oakleigh House, 254 Birmingham Road, Stratford-on-Avon, Warwickshire CV37 0AX ☎ 01789 415929, 01789 414916 fax

CRAWTE Michael: 101 Golden Drive, Eaglestone, Milton Keynes, Bucks MK6 5BW ☎ 01908 662551, 01908 310671

CROSS Vincent (*Voc*): 28 High Street, Weston Favell, Northampton NN3 3JW ☎ 01604 408293

DALEY Peter: 62 Latelow Road, Stechford, Birmingham B33 8JY ☎ 0121 783 5860

DOOLAN Stephen (*Voc, Per*): 21 Southfield Road, Waltham Cross, Herts EN8 7HD ☎ 01992 632187, 0336 788990

DUTTON Owen: 3 Mulberry Road, Bilton, Rugby CV22 7TD ☎ 01788 810147

DYKE Jonathan: 125 The Woodlands, Melbourne, Derby DE7 1DQ ☎ 01332 863936

EATON Christopher (*Gtr*): West Lodge, Kinver, Stourbridge, West Midlands DY7 5LT

EDWARDS David (*Per*): 17 Richmond Avenue, St Anns, Nottingham NG3 3AT ☎ 0115 958 5615, 07970 773595, 0115 9115095

EGAN Christopher (*Pf*): 157 Green Meadow Road, Selly Oak, Birmingham B29 4DS ☎ 0121 628 8143, 0973 823376

ELLUL Josephine (*Voc, Per, Dms*)

FARMER Karen (*Voc, Per, Sax*) ☎ 01536 268778

FIRMAN Andrew: 60 Hemingway Road, Meir Hay, Longton, Stoke-on-Trent, Staffs ST3 1SL ☎ 01782 315275 & fax, 0973 861437 mob

GARRETT John (*Pf, Tpt, Voc*): 2 Cross Street, Leamington Spa, Warwickshire CV32 4PX ☎ 01926 435196 ext 208, 01926 420702

GLOVER George: 59 Kensington Road, Oakhilll, Stoke-on-Trent, Staffs ST4 5BB ☎ 01782 49816

GRANDI Eugenio (*Voc*): 'Westbury', 40 Hornyold Road, Malvern, Worcs WR14 1QH ☎ 01684 572443

HAINES John (*Gtr, Voc*): Flat 7, 20 St Michaels Avenue, Northampton NN1 4JQ ☎ 01604 473201

HARDWICK Andy (*Pf*): 2 Woodlands Lane, Shirley, Solihull, West Midlands B90 2PT ☎ 0121 744 2499, 0973 134448 mob

HAWKES Andy: 12 Coleridge Walk, Headlands Estate, Daventry, Northants NN11 5AU ☎ 01327 72613

HIGGS Martin (*Pf, Synth*): 18 Drayton Leys, Hillside, Rugby CV22 5RH ☎ 01788 811937

HOLLAND Gavin (*Synth*): 8A Northfield Road, Harborne, Birmingham B17 0SS ☎ 0121 426 5001, 0370 583 380

HOULT Antony (*Per, Voc*): 144 Sileby Rd, Barrow-upon-Soar, Leics LE12 8LS ☎ 01509 416418

HOWELL Brendan: 18 Avondale Road, Whitmore Reans, Wolverhampton, West Midlands WV6 0AJ ☎ 01902 689196

HUBBALL Alan (*Org, Pf*): 93 Westridge Road, Birmingham B13 0DZ ☎ 0121 777 6638

HUNT Bill (*Arr, Com*): 139 Perryfields Road, Bromsgrove, Worcs. B61 8TH ☎ 01527 875384

HUNT Jules: 38 Christchurch Road, Abingdon, Northampton NN1 5LN ☎ 01604 37582

HUNTER Neil (*B Gtr*): 32 Evesham Road, Leicester LE3 2BD ☎ 0116 2893254

HURLEY Russell: Upper Orchard, Hoarwithy, Hereford HR2 6QR ☎ 01432 840 649, 0976 665 782

HURT Dan (*Synth*)

J.S.M.: 49 Charlecote Close, Ipsley, Redditch, Worcs B98 0TQ ☎ 01527 527838, 0973 560410

JAY Jenny: 243 Longbridge Lane, Northfield, Birmingham B31 4RE ☎ 0121 475 8687

JENNINGS Adrian (*Gtr*): 19 Gorsy Bank Road, Hockley, Tamworth, Staffordshire B77 5JD ☎ 01827 289274

JONES Gary Vaughan (*Voc*): 3 Ridge Hall Close, Caversham, Reading, Berkshire RG4 7EP ☎ 01734 475776

JONES Kenneth (*Com, Arr*): 3 The Green, Brown Edge, Stoke-on-Trent ST6 8RN ☎ 01782 504229

JONES Peter (*Pf, Clt, Dms, B Gtr*) ☎ 01623 822589

JUKES George (*Gtr, Bod*): 132 Streetsbrook Road, Shirley, Solihull B90 3PH ☎ 0121 733 2384

KNIGHT Laurence (*Synth, Pf*): 101 Kingsway, Northampton NN2 8HN ☎ 01604 844435

LAVENDER Mike (*Arr, Com, Org, Synth*): Laurel Cottage, Four Ashes Road, Dorridge, Solihull, West Midlands B93 8NE ☎ 01564 770121

LAYTON Clive (*Gtr*): 89A Newcombe Road, Earlsdon, Coventry CV5 6NH ☎ 024 7671 3685

LIM Barry (*Gtr*): 192 Lightwoods Road, Bearwood, Birmingham B67 5AZ ☎ 0121 420 3800

LOCKETT Mark (*Pf*): 101 Summerfield Crescent, Edgbaston, Birmingham B16 0EN

LOWE David: Ryland Cottage, Beacon Road, Malvern, Worcs WR14 4EH ☎ 01684 560196

LUNN Tiffany (*Dms, Per*): 25 Austin Street, Hanley, Stoke-on-Trent ST1 3HT ☎ 01782 853925

MACKIE James (*T Sax*): 44 Dallas Road, Lancaster, Lancs LA1 1TW ☎ 01524 841362

MANN Dave (*B Gtr*): 1B Wellington Street, Stapleford, Nottingham NG9 7BE

MATHARU Harry (*Tabla, Dholak, Dms*): 41 Leopold Avenue, Handsworth Wood, Birmingham B20 1EU ☎ 0121 357 5028

MCGARRY David (*Org, Com, Arr*): 8 Castleton Road, Lightwood, Stoke-on-Trent ST3 7TD ☎ 01782 326950

MISTRY Dahya (*Synth*): 15 Checketts Close, Belgrave, Leicester, Leics. LE4 5EU ☎ 0116 266 3722

MITCHELL Clifford: Shaw Cottage Farm, Upper Hulme, Leek, Staffordshire ST13 8UQ ☎ 01298 74169

MOZART Amadeus: 3 Primrose Close, Bloomfield Court, Kettring, Northants NN16 9PD ☎ 01536 522267, 01536 815621

NANTON Michael: 33 Cambridge Tower, Brindley Drive, City Centre, Birmingham B1 2NH ☎ 0121 233 2636

NAYLOR Mark (*Synth, Gtr*): 18 Bourton Crescent, Oadby, Leics LE2 4PA ☎ 0116 271 8588

NICHOLLS Geoff (*Gtr, Voc*): 94 Moat Lane, Yardley, Birmingham B26 1TJ ☎ 0121 786 2354

PANKHANIA Milesh (*Com, Per*) ☎ 0116 266 0227, 0976 693395, 0116 225 1012

PARDESI: 5 Brookside, Greatbarr, Birmingham B43 5DR, 0973 600422 mob

PARKES Roger (*Org, Pf*): 60 School Lane, Hill Ridware, Rugeley, Staffordshire WS15 3QN ☎ 01543 491624, 01543 879334 fax

PATRICK John (*Pf, Md, Arr, Com*): c/o Musicians Union, Benson House, Lombard Street, Birmingham B12 0QN
☎ 01564 784029 & fax

PATRICK Mark: 64 Weston Lane, Nuneaton, Warks CV12 9RT
☎ 024 7649 0516

PATTANI Hinal (*Pf*): 22 Ainsdale Road, Leicester LE3 0UA
☎ 0116 285 4863, 0411 443157

PEARSON Robert: 15 Malt Mill Close, Kilsby, Rugby, Warwickshire CV23 8XN ☎ 01788 822375

PORTAS Roger (*Gtr*): 2 North Street, Sutton, Ashfield, Notts NG17 4BD ☎ 01623 656349

POWELL Anthony (*Gtr, Sax*)

QUIN Andrew (*Per*): 16 Byron Close, Cheadle, Staffs ST10 1XB
☎ 01538 751019

REBELSKI Martin (*Pf*) ☎ 07970 902821

REES Elaine (*Pf, Brass, Tnd Per*): 12 Lowry Close, Bedworth, Warwickshire CV12 8DG ☎ 024 7649 0491

ROBINSON Anthony (*Tpt, Flgl, Per*): 36 Eastleigh Road, Leicester LE3 0DB ☎ 0116 2551009

ROSE David (*Pf, Gtr, Clt*): 7 Winslow Drive, Wigston, Leicester LE18 3QG ☎ 0116 2571909

RUSHTON Phillip: Oakford Cottage, Robin Hook, Whatstandwell, Matloch, Derbyshire DE4 5HF ☎ 0177385 2406

SAGOO Bally: 275 Belchers Lane, Bordesley Green, Birmingham, West Midlands B9 5RT

SAWTELL Paul (*Pf, Mldca, Synth, Md*): 20 Seymour Road, Wollescote, Stourbridge, West Midlands DY9 8TB ☎ 01384 351033

SCOTT.T.: 11 Hawthorne Terrace, Rugby, Warks

SCULLION Robert (*Ac Gtr, Dms*): Room 20, 35 Tettenhall Road, Chapel Ash, Wolverhampton WV3 9NB ☎ 01902 716478, 0961 115887

SHERRIFF Steve (*Pf, Org*): 165 Oscott School Lane, Birmingham B44 9EL ☎ 0121 366 7402, 0589 826512

SHOTTER Mark (*Per, B Gtr*): 37 Burns Street, Radford, Nottingham NG7 4DS ☎ 0115 978 7714

SIMPSON Paul (*Gtr*): 231 Caxton Street, Sunnyhill, Derby, Derbyshire DE23 7RB ☎ 01332 737850

SINGH Ajaib ☎ 0116 274 2292, 0802 456376 mob, 0116 276 1407

SMITH Noval (*St Pan*): 56 Gibson Road, Handsworth, Birmingham B20 3UD ☎ 0121 240 4271, 0956 874170 mob

SMITH Paul: 1St Floor Flat, 23 Harborough, Kingsthorpe, Northants NN2 7AX ☎ 01604 454147

SPENCER Danny (*Voc*): Walton Bank Farm, Stafford Road, Eccleshall, Staffs ST21 6JT ☎ 01785 282890 eve, 01785 282848 day, 01785 282842

STANLEY King (*Gtr, Dms*): 12 Charlotte Street, Rugby, Warwickshire CV21 3HB ☎ 0973 344960

STONE Russell (*Arr, Com*): 150 Humber Avenue, Stoke, Coventry CV1 2AR ☎ 024 7655 0629, 01926 450000 ext 2315

STUBBS Andrew (*B Gtr, Gtr*): 8A High Street, Eccleshall, Stafford ST21 6BZ ☎ 01785 851 573, 07970 665496 mob

TAMBER Manjit: 3, Talbot Road, Blakenhall, Wolverhampton, West Midlands WV2 3EW ☎ 01902 333551

TAYLOR Christopher (*Dms*): 16 Grosvenor Road, Handsworth, Birmingham B20 3NP ☎ 0121 356 9636

TAYLOR Richard: 16 Grosvenor Road, Handsworth Wood, Birmingham B20 3NP ☎ 0121 356 9636, 0973 622330, 0121 356 9636

TEW Christopher (*Gtr, Voc*) ☎ 01788 335240, 0802 960687, 01788 521782

TODD Neil: 1 Rhes-Tan-Y-Bryn, Tan-Y-Bryn-Road, Craig-Y-Don, Llandudno, Gwynedd, North Wales LL30 1UR
☎ 01492 870 813

TOMLINSON Ian: 11 Pound Close, Oldbury, Warley, West Midlands B68 8LZ ☎ 0121 552 3085

TUSTAIN William: 6 Dairy Ground, Kings Sutton, Nr Banbury, Oxon OX17 3QB ☎ 01295 811586

VIRTUE Michael: c/o Dep International, 92 Fazeley Street, Birmingham B5 5RD ☎ 0121 633 4742

WALKER John: 108 High Street, Potterspury, Northants NN12 7PQ

WEBSTER Charles (*B Gtr, Gtr*): 8 Gorsey Road, Mapperley Park, Nottingham NG3 4JL ☎ 0115 969 3426 & fax

WHEELER Aaron (*Pf, Dms, Gtr*): 18 Salop Road, Southcrest, Redditch, Worcs B97 4PS ☎ 01527 544097

WHITE Graham: 41 Clayton Drive, Thurmaston, Leicester LE4 8LQ ☎ 0116 269 7791

WILLIAMSON Mervyn: 9 Warmington Grove, Greenhow, Birmingham Road, Warwick CV34 5RZ ☎ 01926 419638

WINSHIP John: 100 Crab Lane, Tillington, Stafford ST16 1SQ
☎ 01785 211466

WOODALL John (*Org, Pf*): 86 Browns Lane, Allesley, Coventry, West Midlands CV5 9DZ ☎ 024 7640 3245

SOUTH EAST

ABBOTT Michael (*Gtr*): 18 Rock Farm Road, Whittington, Nr Lichfield, Staffordshire WS14 9LZ ☎ 01543 432699

BAKER Douglas (*Org, Pf, T Sax, Clt*): 173 Symes Road, Hamworthy, Poole, Dorset BH15 4PY ☎ 01202 682698

BALDRY Luke David: The Kilns, Snails Lynch, Farnham, Surrey GU9 8AP ☎ 01252 710244, 0378 347 963

BEETON Dominic: 22 Edington Close, Bishops Waltham, Southampton SO32 1LX ☎ 01489 891639, 01489 579990 day

BELL David: 5 Markenfield Road, Guildford, Surrey GU1 4PB
☎ 01483 830621

BELLINGHAM David (*Dms, Gtr, Per, Voc*): 3 Rumania Walk, Gravesend, Kent DA12 4HW ☎ 01474 329957

BENNETT Brian (*Md*): 32 Marshwood Avenue, Canford Heath, Poole BH16 9EP ☎ 01202 601462, 01202 686662 day

BENNETT Graham (*Pf*): 31 Manor Farm Road, Bere Regis, Wareham, Dorset BH20 7HD ☎ 01929 471538

BIRD Anthony (*Gtr*): 26A Gunters Lane, Bexhill-on-Sea, E. Sussex TN39 4EN ☎ 01424 213765

BODDY Paul (*Rh Gtr, Voc*): 42B Park Road, North Camp, Farnborough, Hants GU14 6LG ☎ 01252 517889, 07666 739219

BRACEGIRDLE Nicholas: 15 The Lagger, Chalfont St Giles, Bucks HP8 4DG ☎ 01494 872372, 01494 872372

BRACKPOOL James: 7 High Dewar Road, Rainham, Kent ME8 8DN ☎ 01634 234781, 01634 234781

BRANNIGAN Martin Sean (*Synth*): Ayling Court, 12 Ayling Lane, Aldershot GU11 3LZ ☎ 01252 659490

BRINKLOW Richard: 103 Windmill Road, Headington, Oxford OX3 7BT ☎ 01865 762209

BROWN Clive: 10 Godwit Road, Southsea, Portsmouth, Hants PO4 8YS ☎ 023 9235 9254, 023 9273 8674

BROWN Steve

BURTON Mark (*Arr*): 31 Junction Road, Reading, Berks RG1 5SA
☎ 01734 661783, 01734 661783

BUTERWORTH Christian (*Club Dj*) ☎ 01273 723233

CAMPBELL Junior (*Gtr, Arr, Com*): Greyfriars Lodge, Greyfriars Drive, South Ascot, Berks SL5 9JD

CESARZ Stan (*Pf, Gtr, B Gtr*): 27 South Western Crescent, Poole, Dorset BH14 8RW ☎ 01202 738323

CHAG Niraj ☎ 0958 665840 mob

CHURCHILL Chick: 16C Wood Street, Wallingford, Oxfordshire OX10 0AY ☎ 01491 826064, 0498 805801, 01491 826064

CLEMENTS Stuart: 4 Rutland Gardens, Sandy, Bedfordshire SG19 1JG ☎ 01767 680973

COLLINS Billie (*Br Sax, Voc*): Christmas Cottage, Little Wittenham, Abingdon, S Oxon OX14 4QU ☎ 01865 407562

COLWELL Richard (*Voc*): 14 Wellington Road, Horsham, West Sussex RH12 1DD ☎ 01403 252783

COOMBES Robert: 12 Littleworth Road, Wheatley, Oxon OX3 1NW ☎ 01865 874914

COOPER Martyn: 2 Greenways Drive, Maidenhead, Berkshire SL6 5DU ☎ 01628 626340

CORBETT David (*Pf, Org*): San Juan, 47 Fircroft Close, Tilehurst, Reading, Berks RG3 6LJ ☎ 0118 942 6559, 0956 132054, 0118 942 6559

COX Carl *(Dms, Voc, Synth)*: 15 Forest Road, Horsham, West Sussex RH12 4HJ ☎ 01403 267376

CRADDOCK Kenny *(Gtr, Voc, Clt)*: 68 St. Marys Road, Hastings, East Sussex TN34 3LW ☎ 01424 421814, 01424 421814

DAVIES Richard: 2A Alaseun Terrace, Summerville Avenue, Minster, Sheerness, Kent ME12 3LA ☎ 01795 870774

DAVIS Brett: 130 Bath Road, Thatcham, Newbury RG18 3HH ☎ 01635 847608

DAY Tony *(Arr, Com)*: 14 Matthews Close, Bedhampton, Hants PO9 3NT ☎ 023 9248 0835

DELWICHE Robin: 13 Bell Meadow, Godstone, Surrey RH9 8ED ☎ 01883 742489, 0956 919324

DENNIS Peter: 40 Lesbourne Road, Reigate, Surrey RH2 7LD

DESSOY Bernard *(Pf)*: 31 Maxwell Drive, Maidstone, Kent ME16 0QY ☎ 01622 756213

DEUTSCH Stephen: 13 Castlemain Avenue, Southbourne, Bournmouth BH6 5EH ☎ 01202 428767

DIAMOND Nicholas *(Voc, Com)*: 40 Royal Military Avenue, Cheriton, Folkestone, Kent CT20 3EF ☎ 01303 276281

DOSSETT William *(Acc, Acc)*: 159 Woodlands Road, Holtwood, Ditton, Maidstone Kent ME20 6HB ☎ 01622 718657

DYNE Malcolm *(Org)*: 33 Central Avenue, Bognor Regis, West Sussex PO21 5HT ☎ 01243 820919

ELGAR Ray *(Org, Pf, Com)*: 6 Blackfields Avenue, Bexhill, Sussex TN39 4JL ☎ 01424 843539

ELLIGATE Peter: 89B Chalky Bank Road, Rainham, Gillingham, Kent ME8 7NP ☎ 01634 387869

ELSTOB Leo: Little Braziers Farm, Bellingdon, Chesham, Bucks HP5 2UN ☎ 01494 758265, 01494 758759

ETHERINGTON Steven *(Gtr, B Gtr, Voc)*: 'Sundowners', Copthorne Bank, Copthorne, West Sussex RH10 3JQ ☎ 01342 718588, 0374 866375, 01342 718588

EVANS John Francis *(Voc)*: Flat 4 Redhill Court, Portswood Drive, Bournemouth, Dorset BH10 7DQ ☎ 01202 524643, 0802 516542, 01202 524643

FALLON Michael *(Pf)*: ☎ 01444 236716, 0410 843184, 01444 248471

FALLON Peter: Broadhill Farm House, Ockley Lane, Keymer, Hassocks, West Sussex BN6 8PA ☎ 01444 236716, 0410 843184, 01444 248471

FEARON Jeremy *(B Gtr)*: 80 Old Kiln Road, Upton, Poole, Dorset BH16 5SQ ☎ 01202 625540, 01202 631599 fax, 0836 587407 mob

FLAHANT Richard *(Gtr)*: 62 Dover Road, Walmer, Deal, Sussex CT14 7JN

FLETCHER Guy *(Voc)*: 225 Manor Way, Aldwick Bay Estate, Aldwick, W. Sussex PO21 4HS

FLOOD Mike *(Com)*: 50 Norman Road, Newhaven, East Sussex BN9 9LJ ☎ 01273 516780

GALEA Andrew: 3 Jubilee Cottages, Sutton Lane, Langley SL3 8AD ☎ 01753 542243, 0374 689 797 mob

GILLETT Jez *(Flt, Gtr)*: 41 Holliers Hill, Bexhill-on-Sea, East Sussex TN40 2DD ☎ 01424 216977, 0585 633406

GLANDFIELD Lou *(Gtr, Voc, Hrn)*: Hazelwick, Hazeldene Lane, N Chailey Lewes, East Sussex BN8 4HH ☎ 0182572 2579

GLYNN Dominic: 7 Southview Road, Warlingham, Surrey CR6 9JE ☎ 01883 622 431, 01883 626 641

HAMPSHIRE Christopher *(Synth)*: 18 Bedford Street, Brighton, East Sussex BN2 1AN ☎ 01273 698103

HAYES Martin: The Post Office, 1 Queen Street, Sandhurst, Cranbrook, Kent TN18 5HY ☎ 01580 850201, 07771 694612

HEDGER Geoffrey *(Voc)*: 70 Merry Field Drive, Horsham, Sussex RH12 2AX ☎ 01403 266408

HEIN Ricky *(Pf)*: 15 Salisbury Road, Godstone, Surrey RH9 8AA ☎ 01883 742465, 0585 322244

HENDRY David *(Dms)*: 35 Hawthorn Road, Worthing, West Sussex BN14 9LT ☎ 01903 201354

HENSEL William

HIGGINS Julian: 4 Cupernham Close, Romsey, Hants SO51 8LH ☎ 01794 512721, 0802 653931

HILLMAN George *(Tpt, Voc)*: 119 Middle Road, Shoreham By Sea, Sussex BN43 6LL ☎ Btn 464328

HOWARD Ashley: Vrouwe Anna, Brighton Marina Moorings, Brighton BN2 5UF ☎ 01273 676567, 01273 676562, 0802 783008

HOWARD Brian: 36 Westminster Close, Willingdon, Eastbourne, East Sussex BN22 0LQ ☎ 01323 500332

HOWES Ashley: The Old Cottage, Petersfield Road, Bramdean, Alresford, Hampshire TW2 5EP ☎ 01962 771354, 0860 785292

HUNTLEY Albert *(Acc)*: 5 Pear Tree Lane, Newbury, Berks RG14 2LU ☎ 01635 41092

J DJ SWEET *(Dms)*: 14 Horsa Close, Kingsmere, Eastbourne, East Sussex BN23 6TL ☎ 01323 760530, 01323 469414, 01323 469414

JACKSON Susan *(Voc)*: 57 Weller Avenue, Rochester, Kent ME1 2LG ☎ 01634 406054

JANKIEWICZ Thomas: 61 Canterbury Avenue, Slough, Berks SL2 1ED ☎ 01753 657789

JAY ☎ 01276 451109

JEFFERIS Jennifer: 15D Cheshire Drive, Townsend, Bournemouth BH8 0JU ☎ 01202 301251

JEFFERSON Michael *(Voc)*: Library House, The Street, Smarden, Ashford, Kent TN27 8NA ☎ 01233 770205

JONES Benjamin *(Pf, Per)*: 54A Kensington Place, Brighton BN1 4EJ ☎ 01273 697 334, 0161 438 0699, 01273 888 678

JONES Steve: 37 Clare Road, Maidenhead, Berks SL6 4DW ☎ 01628 25452

JONES Tinkerbell: 26 Offington Gardens, Worthing, West Sussex BN14 9AU ☎ 01903 262281

LANGLEY Stuart *(Gtr)*: ☎ 012276 506108

LARDER Jez: Barbrook Cottage, Holmesdale Road, South Nutfield, Surrey RH1 4JE ☎ 01737 822 432

LEON Robert *(Gtr)*: Trendalls Cottage, Beacons Bottom, Nr High Wycombe, Bucks HP14 3XF ☎ 01494 483121, 01494 484303

LONG Stephen *(Per)*: 25 Fulmer Drive, Gerrards Cross, Bucks SL9 7HQ ☎ 01753 888529

MACKMIN Norman: 17 Bazehill Road, Rottingdean, East Sussex BN2 7DB ☎ 01273 332033

MARC Daddy *(Didj, B Gtr)*: Flat 2, 63 The Drive, Hove, E Sussex BN3 3PF ☎ 01273 323095

MARTIN Peter *(Pf, Arr)*

MATTHEWS Antony: 31, Gloucester Ave, Cliftonville, Margate, Kent CT9 3NN ☎ 01843 226546

MAYCOCK Lee *(Pf, Voc)*: 3 Fir Avenue, New Milton, Hants BH25 6EX ☎ 01425 621682

MCGILLIVRAY Paul: 18 Lowerdown, Lydbury North, Shropshire SY7 8BB

MILLER Peter *(Gtr, Bottles, Per)*: 22 Bavant Road, Brighton, East Sussex BN1 6RD ☎ 01273 503003

MITCHELL Grant *(Com)*: 6 Meadow Way, Yaverland, Sandown, Isle Of Wight PO36 8QD ☎ 01983 406786

MONTY THE MORON *(Dms, Gtr, B Gtr, Clt)*: 55 Stafford Road, Brighton, East Sussex BN1 5PE ☎ 01273 380578

MORRELL Tom *(B Gtr, Voc)*: Stoke Brunswick School, Ashurst Wood, East Grinstead, West Sussex RH19 3PF ☎ 01342 825642, 0976 288381 mob

NAYLOR Keith *(Sax)*: 1 Deer View, Willcombe Meadow, Minehead, Somerset TA24 6LW ☎ 01643 709452

O'SULLIVAN Brian *(B Gtr)*: 4 Godmanston Close, Canford Heath, Poole, Dorset BH17 8BU ☎ 01202 600566

OAKLEY Frank *(Org, Pf)*: Cransley, 44 Fauchons Lane, Bearsted, Maidstone Kent ME14 4AH ☎ 01622 737597

OLIGARIO Phillippe *(Voc, Dms)*: 8 Claydon Court, 108 Marine Parade, Worthing, W Sussex BN11 3QG ☎ 0956 656210

OLIVER Robert *(Pf, Dms, Voc)*: 2 Rose Cottage, 56 Poole Road, Upton, Poole, Dorset BH16 5JD ☎ 01202 632469

ORFORD Martin *(Pf, Flt)*: 38 Churchill Avenue, Bishops Waltham, Southampton SO32 1SA ☎ 01489 891815 & fax

PAIN Fabian: The Bungalow, Abbotts Hill, Ospringe, Faversham, Kent ME13 0RR ☎ 01795 535734

PAYE Adrian *(Vln)*: Starvegoose House, The Mount, Flimwell, Wadhurst, East Sussex TN5 7QR ☎ 01580 879615

PEERMAN Marina: 35 Weydon Hill Road, Farnham, Surrey GU9 8NX ☎ 01252 725142

PHILLIPS Richard: 74 High Street, Newport Pagnall, Bucks MK16 8AQ ☎ 01908 216761

PINCHING Dave (*Rh Gtr*): 36 Carlton Road, Portchester, Fareham, Hants PO16 8JH ☎ 023 9278 7056

PIPER Sebastian: 38 Fawley Bottom Farm, Nr Henley-on-Thames, Oxon RG9 6JH ☎ 01491 573980

POLEYKETT Gary (*Voc*): 89, Chamberlain Avenue, Maidstone, Kent ME16 8PE ☎ 01622 727629

POLLARD Brian (*Voc, Md*): 168 Northbourne Road, Eastbourne, East Sussex BN22 8RT ☎ 01323 648294 & fax, 0836 228692 mob

POWELL Timothy: St Albans House, Lingfield Road, East Grinstead, West Sussex RH19 2EJ ☎ 01342 323819

PRICE Stuart (*B Gtr, Gtr, Dms*): 6 St Martin Close, Lower Earley, Reading, Berkshire RG6 4BS ☎ 0118 987 2372, 0802 536961, 0118 986 4749

PURVIS Robert: Flat 3, 22 Powis Square, Brighton, Sussex BN1 3HG ☎ 01273 723558

PUTTICK David (*Gtr*): Raemar, Hill House Hill, Liphook, Hants GU30 7PX ☎ 01428 723347

RADFORD Liz (*Com, Voc, Arr*): 23 Griffin Court, Station Road, Wimborne Minster, Dorset BH21 1RQ ☎ 01202 842109

REED Stephen: Apley House, Burleigh Road, Addlestone, Surrey KT15 1PN ☎ 01932 846332, 0467 610997

RICH T : 3 Park Chase, Guildford, Surrey GU1 1ES ☎ 01483 537054, 0802 568987

ROBERTS Mark: The Old Farmhouse, Upper Brailes, Banbury OX15 5AX ☎ 01608 685763, 0378 672686 mob, 01608 685739

ROBERTS Martin: 103 Forest Way, Highcliffe, Christchurch, Dorset BH23 4PU ☎ 01425 270774

ROBSON Brian (*B Gtr, Arr*): 1 Briar Close, Caversham, Reading, Berks RG4 7QH

RODWAY Stephen (*Gtr, Dms, Voc*): Chantry Mews, High St, Sevenoaks, Kent TN13 1HZ ☎ 01732 460515

ROGERS Cathy (*Ob, Pf*): 90 Clapham Common North Side, London SW4 9SG

ROLFE Alan (*Gtr, Voc*): Falt 1, 82 Central Parade, Herne Bay, Kent CT6 5JQ ☎ 01227 373914, 01227 373914

ROLFE Richard (*Gtr, Uke*): 16 Saxons Drive, Foley Park, Maidstone, Kent ME14 5HS ☎ 01622 672128

ROSS Robert: 86A Kingston Road, Portsmouth, Hants PO2 7PA ☎ 023 9261 2675, 023 9279 1706

ROWLAND David: 66 Victoria Road, Parkstone, Poole, Dorset BH12 3AE ☎ 01202 734605

RUSH Keith (*Pf, Voc, Gtr, Synth*): 22 Ediva Road, Meopham, Kent DA13 0NA ☎ 01474 812644

RUSSELL Richard (*Pf*): 222 Saltings Road, Snodland, Kent ME6 5HP ☎ 01634 241132

SAVAGE David: 18 Oakwood Road, Sturry, Canterbury, Kent CT2 0LX ☎ 01227 711480

SCHUNKER Dominic (*B Gtr*): Kent Hatch Lodge, Goodley Stockroad, Crockham Hill, Kent TN8 6TA ☎ 01732 866356

SCOTT Mark (*Song W*): 7 St Georges Court, East Grinstead, West Sussex RH19 1QP ☎ 01342 300740, 07970 791955

SILK Oliver (*Pf*): 6 Tarn Close, Southwood, Farnborough, Hampshire GU14 0RP ☎ 01252 510753

SIMMONDS Benjamin (*Pf*): 4 Howard Road, Brighton BN2 2TP ☎ 01273 685179

SMITH Andrew (*Synth*): Flat 2, 59 Lansdowne Street, Hove, East Sussex BN3 1FT ☎ 01273 206118

STEEL Brian D (*Md*): Fairbanks, Alfold Road, Cranleigh, Surrey GU6 8NB ☎ 01483 274838

STEPHENS David: Towyn, High Street, Compton, Newbury, Berks RG20 6NL ☎ 01635 578314

SWAN Charles: 4 James Street, Rochester, Kent ME1 2BY ☎ 01634 848113

SWATTON Eric (*Voc*): 11 Hassocks Court, Cuckfield Close, Bewbush, Crawley RH11 8UE ☎ 01293 530320

SWEETZER Martin: 103 Northumberland Avenue, Reading, Berkshire RG2 7PT ☎ 01734 874327

SYMES Ivan (*Gtr*): 10 Tythe Barn Solney, West Sussex RH17 5PH ☎ 01444 881534

TAIT Mike: 74 Bailey Crescent, Fleetsbridge, Poole, Dorset BH15 3HB ☎ 01202 772057

THOMPSON SOUND John: Anniversary Cottage, 12 Wish Hill, Willingdon, Eastbourne East Sussex BN20 9EX ☎ 01323 501114

THORNTON Pat (*Pf*): Barbrae Cottage, 22 Dudsbury Avenue, Ferndown, Dorset BH22 8DU ☎ 01202 871231

TORR Mike: 70 Eden Road, West End, Southampton SO18 3QX ☎ 023 8046 6227

TURNER GCLCM ASMTC Laurence J (*Pf*): Andante Cottage, 10 Leith Avenue, Portchester, Hampshire PO16 8HS ☎ 023 9232 7458

TYERMAN Marc (*Pf*): Address Unknown ☎ 01202 512237

VAN-ALLEN David: 3 Alexandra Road, Ramsgate, Kent CT11 7HY ☎ 01843 851228

WAKEMAN Adam (*Pf*): 1 The Row, High Road, Felmersham, Beds MK43 7HP ☎ 01234 782363

WALLACE David: 7 Acland Road, Charminster, Bournemouth, Dorset BH9 1JQ ☎ 01202 516073

WALLINGTON Timothy (*Gtr*) ☎ 01276 66858

WALLIS Matthew

WEBB Peter: 117 Athelstan Road, Bitterne Park, Southampton, Hants SO19 4DG ☎ 023 8033 3405, 023 8023 5128

WEST David: Yew Tree Cottage, High Street, South Newington, Near Banbury, Oxfordshire OX15 4JN ☎ 01295 720673

WHITE Peter (*Flt*): 27 Mount Pleasant Road, Hastings, East Sussex TN34 3SJ ☎ 01424 429663

WHITNEY John: 11 Drakes Avenue, Strood, Rochester, Kent ME2 3LN ☎ 01634 722992, 01634 291456 day

WILKINSON Jeremy (*Pf, Synth*): 24 Gainsborough Road, Queens Park, Bournemouth, Dorset BH7 7BD ☎ 01202 397351

WILLWARD Frank (*Pf, Arr, Com*): 18 Headley Road, Liphook, Hants GU30 7NP ☎ 01428 723586

WILSON Jesse (*B Gtr, Gtr, Dms*): 16 Station Road, East Grinstead, West Sussex RH19 1DZ ☎ 01227 459762

WRAGGY: 2 Springbok Farm, Alfold, Surrey GU6 8EX ☎ 01403 752372, 0973 102142 mob

WRAIGHT Jeff (*Synth, Voc, B Gtr, Arr*): Crofters, 10 Hampton Fields, Wick, Little Hampton, West Sussex BN17 6JB ☎ 01903 723838, 0973 679211 mob

YON Jonathan (*Voc*): 236 Willingdon Road, Eastbourne, East Sussex BN21 1XS ☎ 01323 500602

YOUNG Alan (*Acc*): 16 Cross Street, Oakfield, Ryde, Isle Of Wight PO33 1EH ☎ 01983 616240

SOUTH WEST

ACKRILL Jayne (*Voc*): 113 Wheeler Avenue, Swindon, Wilts SN2 6HL ☎ 01793 521685

ARKSUN: 50 The Street, Uley, Dursley, Glos GL11 5SY ☎ 01453 860285

BICKERSTETH John (*Gtr*): Tregarth, Bissoe, Truro, Cornwall TR3 6HY ☎ 01872 863337

BOOTH Donald (*Org*): 10 Springfield, Cerne Abbas, Dorchester, Dorset DT2 7JZ ☎ 01300 341483

BRACEWELL Steve: 39 Bryerland Road, Witcombe, Gloucester GL3 4TA ☎ 020 8361 2468

BRITTON Simon (*Dms, Pf*): 2Nd Floor Flat, 39 Green Park, Bath, Avon BA1 1HZ ☎ 01225 443003

BROWN Rick (*Gtr, Bjo, B Gtr*): 72 Foxhollows, Brack La, Bridgend, Mid Glam CF31 2NH ☎ 01656 647103

BUTT Frances (*A Sax, Clt*): 15 Beaconsfield Road, Clifton, Bristol BS8 2TS ☎ 0117 9736418

CASTLE Robert: 7 Tithe Barn Crescent, Okus, Swindon, Wiltshire SN1 4JX ☎ 01793 520 598, 01793 503 726

CHERRY Paul: 9 The Pippins, West Orchard, Warminster, Wiltshire BA12 8TH ☎ 01985 219553 & fax, 0385 793937 mob

CHOUSMER Paul: 52 Bauntons Orchard, Milborne Port, Dorset DT9 5BT ☎ 01963 250540

CLEWS Jacqueline: 6A Church Street, Ilfracombe, Devon EX34 8HB

COLLINGWOOD Timothy (*B Gtr, Gtr, Bjo*): 129 Creakavose Park, St Stephen, St Austell, Cornwall PL26 7ND ☎ 01726 824866

CROSS Edwin: 106 Warwick Avenue, Whitleigh Estate, Plymouth, Devon PL5 4BG ☎ 01752 700885

D'ABO Mike: Hillcrest House, St. Georges Avenue, Kings Stanley, Gloucester GL10 3HJ

DANIEL Charles (*Voc, Clt, Rec, Vln*): 1 Russell's Barton, The Market Place, Nunney, Frome Somerset BA11 4LX ☎ 01373 836605

DARK Ian (*Scratch*): 61 Cotswold Road, Windmill Hill, Bristol BS3 4NX ☎ 0117 953 5161

DAVID Ian (*Pf, Voc*): 6 Trelawney Gardens, Pensilva, Cornwall PL14 5PL ☎ 01579 362 847

DAVIES Andy (*Gtr*): 75 Fernlea, Risca, Gwent, South Wales NP1 6FX ☎ 01633 613342

DAVIES Gareth: Ground Floor Flat, 11 Hanbury Road, Clifton, Bristol BS8 2EW ☎ 0117 946 7363

DAVIES Paul: 20 Churchward Drive, Frome, Somerset BA11 2XL ☎ 01373 467718

DAVIS Roger (*Gtr*): 8 Grosvenor Terrace, Larkhall, Bath BA1 6SR ☎ 01225 420671

DOUGLAS-STEWART Jim (*Org, Gtr, Vib, B Gtr*): The Cedars, 14 Newlands Avenue, Exmouth, Devon EX8 4AX ☎ 01395 222482/276869, 01395 222483 fax

DOWNIE Sam: 24 Court Road, Horfield, Bristol BS7 0BT ☎ 0117 951 3954, 04325 601793

DOYLE David (*Voc*): 41 Chestnut Drive, Brixham, Devon TQ5 0DE ☎ 01803 855713

DRISCOLE Reginald (*Pf, Acc*): 47 St Catherines Crescent, Sherborne, Dorset DT9 6DE ☎ 01935 813164

ELSON Derek (*Voc*): 129 Duchy Drive, Preston, Paignton TQ3 1EU ☎ 01803 522186

EVANS Bryn (*Rh Gtr, Ld Gtr*): Address Unknown ☎ 01392 499618

EVERETT John: 8 Regents Gate, Exmouth, Devon EX8 1TR ☎ 01395 279705

FILLEUL Peter: Trellian, Rue Des Murs, St Lawrence, Jersey C.I. JE3 1EB ☎ 01534 59733

GEORGE Lloyd (*Voc, Gtr, Per, B Gtr*): 4 Graig Street, Graig, Pontypridd, Mid Glamorgan CF37 1NF ☎ 01585 322667

GERAINT Martyn (*Voc, Gtr*): Cefn Heulog, Darren Ddu Road, Glyncoch, Pontypridd CF37 3HE ☎ 01443 480620

GILBERT Simon (*Dms, Vib, Club Dj*): The Gables, Stennack, Troon, Camborne, Cornwall TR14 9JT ☎ 01209 714258

GILES Paul (*B Gtr*): 87 Fern Meadows, Brixham, Devon TQ5 9PF ☎ 01803 859043, 0468 738971

GRASSBY-LEWIS Richard (*Flt, B Clt*): 4 Sevier Street, St. Werburghs, Bristol BS2 9QS ☎ 0117 9413286

GREEN James (*Vln*) ☎ 07050 212149, 0411 277261

GRIFFIN Ian: Melody Recording Studio, 9 Mynachlog Terrace, Pontyberem, Llanelli, Dyfed SA15 5EE ☎ 01269 870870, 01639 883690

HARRIS Anthony (*Vib*): The School House, Fourlands End, Kingsand, Torpoint Devon PL10 1LR ☎ 01752 823286

HARRIS Richard: 42 Armscroft Road, Barnwood, Gloucester GL2 0SJ ☎ 01452 310707

HEARD Roger: 6 Fore Street, Hartland, Bideford, Devon EX39 6AB ☎ 01237 441616

HERN Martyn (*Pf, Voc*): 129 Ynyswen Road, Treorci, Mid Glamorgan CF42 6EB ☎ 01443 776775, 01443 778357

HINTON Jonathan: 48 Castle Street, Frome, Somerset BA11 3BW ☎ 01373 836156

HOPKINS Nigel: 65 Rhodfar Eos, Parc Gwernfadog, Morriston, Swansea, West Glamorgan SA5 6SW ☎ 01792 799531

HUNT Max: 12 Medrose Street, Delabole, Cornwall PL33 9BW ☎ 01840 211115, 01840 711115 fax

JAGO Cedric (*Voc, B Ldr*): 2 Higher Ranscombe Road, Brixham, Devon TQ5 9HF ☎ 01803 854138

JENKINS Clive (*Md*): 9 Fircroft Road, Beacon Park, Plymouth PL2 3JU ☎ 01752 709236

JOHN Philip (*Gtr*): 3 Bryn Hyfryd, Bryncethin, Bridgend, Glamorgan CF32 9UR ☎ 01656 721555

JOHN Scott: 32 Westfield Crescent, Porthcawl, Mid Glam CF36 3SG ☎ Porthcawl 5482

JONES Roy (*Hrp, Gtr, Vla, Tin Wh*): Ael-Y-Bryn, Whitchurch, Solva, Nr Haverfordwest, Pembs SA62 6UD ☎ 01437 721560

JOSEPH Michael (*B Gtr*): 1 Redbrook Close, St Martins Road, Caerphilly, Mid Glam CF8 1ED ☎ 029 2086 6233

KING Adam (*Dms*): Tanglewood, Drakewalls, Gunnislake, Cornwall PL18 9EJ ☎ 01822 833800

KRAMER Amanda (*Voc, Ac Gtr*): Paper Moon, Sunnyside, Perranporth, Cornwall TR6 0HN

LAKEMAN Samuel (*Pf*): The Firs, Crapstone, Yelverton, Devon PL20 7PJ ☎ 01822 852274

LINSEN Dave (*Org, Voc, Per*): 5 Challow Drive, Ashbury Park, Weston Super Mare, Avon BS22 9QX

LLOYD Phillip (*Pf*): 44 College Hill, Llanelli, Carms, Dyfed SA15 1EN ☎ 01554 777215

MALLETT Richard (*Synth*): 21 Keyford, Frome, Somerset DA11 1JW ☎ 01373 465 245

MARTIN John (*Pf*): 10 Cambourne Close, Highlight Park, Barry, S.Glam. CF62 8AL ☎ 01446 749159

MENTER Sam (*Sax*): Watcatch Farm, Backwell Hill, Bristol, North Somerset BS19 3EH ☎ 01275 463700, 07050 049 244, 01275 463700

MICHELLE-JO (*Org, Pf, Voc*): 7 Burford Street, Blaenavan, Gwent NP4 9PY ☎ 01495 790983, 0402 909137

MILES James: 18 Upper Oldfield Park, Bath BA2 3JZ ☎ 01225 420535, 01225 310538

MILFORD Gareth: The School House, Flaxley, Newham-on-Severn, Glos GL14 1JR ☎ 0411 529255

MINERS Roger (*Pf, Synth, Voc*): 9 Parc-An-Dowt, Grampound Road, Truro TR2 4TY ☎ 01726 882784

MONAGHAN Eugene (*Org, Com*): St Alban's Church, Cameron Street, Cardiff CF2 2NX ☎ 029 2046 3219, 029 2048 8308

MOODY Jeremy: 51 Hamilton Road, Salisbury, Wilts SP1 3TF ☎ 01722 336328

MOOR Rainy (*Gtr, Dms*)

MORTON Simon (*Tpt, Voc*): 7 Lakes Close, Brixham, South Devon TQ5 8PJ ☎ 01803 882772

MURRAY John (*Tbn*)

NASH Rob (*Pf, Synth*): 2 Oakhurst, Langley Burrell, Chippenham, Wiltshire SN15 4LG ☎ 0117 9556371

NEWTON Thomas Jerome (*Synth, Per*): 13 St James Gardens, Uplands, Swansea SA1 6DX ☎ 01792 458245, 01792 202244

OGHENO (*Per*): 6 Malvern Road, Swindon, Wiltshire SN2 1AR ☎ 01793 512456

OLIVER Timothy (*Gtr, B Gtr*) ☎ 01225 832932

PAGE Steve (*Voc*): Chanter Heights, 26 Hardy Close, Barry, S Glam CF6 3HJ

PEPLER Felix (*Synth*): 15A Kyveilog Street, Pontcanna, Cardiff, South Glamorgan CF1 9JA ☎ 029 2022 3463

PEPLER Mervyn (*Dms*): Old Stable Cottage, St Algars Farm, West Woodlands, Frome, Somerset BA11 5ER ☎ 01985 844805

PIDCOCK Andrew: 143 Oakridge, Thornhill, Cardiff CF4 9BW ☎ 029 2068 9331

POWELL David: Halezy Farm, Grampound Road, Truro, Cornwall TR2 4EJ ☎ 01726 883276

REILLY Peter (*Sax*): 53 Kingsdown Parade, Kingsdown, Bristol BS6 5UG ☎ 0117 9248494, 0117 9248494

REYNOLDS Benjamin (*Sax, Clt*): 22 The Grove, Uplands, Swansea SA2 0QT ☎ 01792 416981

RICKARDS Adrian

RIGLER Andrew (*Clt, Sax*): 40 College Avenue, Mutley, Plymouth, Devon PL4 7AN ☎ 01752 607483

ROWLANDS Ron (*Voc, Acc*): 21A Commercial Street, Kenfig Hill, Bridgend GF33 6DH ☎ 01656 745475

SHUTE Philip (*Dms*): Duckslake Cottage, Riverton, Swimbridge, North Devon EX32 0QX ☎ 01271 830012

STANLEY Ian: c/o The Wool Hall, Castle Corner, Beckington, Somerset BA3 6TA

STEVENS Nick (*Gtr*): 2E High Street, Dilton Marsh, Westbury, Wilts BA13 4DS

STUBBINGS Richard (*Com, Gtr, B Gtr, Org*): 65 Upper Cheltenham Place, Montpelier, Bristol BS6 5HS ☎ 0117 955 7204

THOMAS Barry: 29 Church House Road, Berrow, Burnham-on-Sea, Somerset TA8 2NG ☎ 01278 780625

TRAVERS Paul (*Clt*): 7 Tremena Road, St Austell, Cornwall PL25 5QG ☎ 01726 77114, 0374 786655

TUCKER Ricky (*Gtr*): 18 Southburrow Road, Ilfracombe, North Devon EX34 8JE ☎ 01271 866224

WALKER Julian (*Voc, Dms, Gtr*): East Sands, Little Cheverell, Devizes, Wiltshire SN10 4JJ ☎ 01380 812568, 01380 812568

WALTERS Geoffrey (*Org*): 6 Ruckley Gardens, Stratton, Swindon SN3 4JT ☎ 01793 822006

WATTERS Scott A (*Md, Dms, B Gtr, Tbn*): 18 Bassett Street, Redruth, Cornwall TR15 2EA ☎ 01209 214851

WELCH John: 13 Pooles Wharf, Hotwell Road, Hotwells, Bristol BS8 4RU ☎ 0117 929 3946

WEST John (*Vib*): St Johns West, Murchington, Chagford, Devon TQ13 8HJ ☎ 01647 432468

WILLIAMS Thomas: Plas-Y-Coed Inn, Plas-Y-Coed Road, Cwmfrwdoer, Pontypool ☎ 01495 762505

LONDON

2 TRUE RECORDS (*Gtr, Voc*): 42 Hughes House, Benbon Street, Deptford, London SE8 3HF ☎ 020 8691 4805, 0831 743358

ABBISS Jim (*Gtr, B Gtr*): Flat 1, 45 Essendine Road, Maida Vale, London W9 2LX ☎ 020 7289 1765

ABBOTT Nigel (*Dms, Per, Db*): Flat 3, 53 West Hill, London SW18 1PU ☎ 020 8871 4717

ABBOTT Simon (*Flt*): 48 Selwyn Avenue, Highams Park, London E4 9LR ☎ 020 8531 9524, 0956 524 086, 020 7531 9524

ABRAHAMS Paul (*Md*): Flat 2, 355 Clapham Road, London SW9 9BT ☎ 020 7207 9553

ADAMS Peter: 3 Grays Cottages, Tomkyns Lane, Upminster, Essex RM14 1TP ☎ 01708 374092

ADIMORA Omar: 72 Bryantwood Road, Islington, London N7 7BE ☎ 020 7686 0673, 0956 906629, 020 7686 0672

ALEXANDER Andrew: 33 Fairfield Court, Fairfield St, London SW18 1DZ ☎ 020 8874 1896

ALLAM Roger (*Gtr*): 62 Winston Road, London N16 9LT ☎ 020 8809 4039

ALLAN Dorothy (*Pf, Voc*): 63A Sandrock Road, London SE13 7TX ☎ 020 8691 8659, 0498 723 994 mob

ALLEN Kelly (*Voc*): 49 Regent Square, Belvedere, Kent DA17 6EP ☎ 01322 405380, 0956 591536

ALLEN Richard (*Gtr, B Gtr, Dms*): 21 Highstone Mansions, 84 Camden Road, London NW1 9DY

ALO Pete (*Gtr*): 34B Marlborough Road, London N19 4NB ☎ 020 7281 3989

AMADI Cheru (*Per*): 36B Loraine Road, Holloway, London W7 6HB ☎ 020 7686 4139, 0956 619713

AMATA Karl (*B Gtr, Dms*): 17 Frith House, Frampton Street, London NW8 8LX

ANDERSEN Toby: 60A Golborne Road, London W10 5PR ☎ 020 8969 8412

ANDERSON Roderick: 48 Roslyn Road, London N15 5ET ☎ 020 8800 9542

ANDREWS Peregrine: 79C Dorothy Road, London SW11 2JJ ☎ 020 7771 7558

ANTHONY Paul (*B Gtr*): 151 High Street, Banstead Village, Surrey SM7 2NT ☎ 01737 352870

APHRODITE: Unit 32, Cannon Wharf Business Centre, 35 Evelyn Street, London SE8 5RT ☎ 020 7231 3341, 020 7231 2744 fax

ARALEPO Anthony (*B Gtr, Dms, Voc, Per*): 8 Stoford Close, Wimbledon, London SW19 6TJ ☎ 020 8785 2720

ARCH David: Denholm House, Pinner Hill, Pinner, Middlesex HA5 3XX ☎ 020 8868 1664

ASHLEY Laurence: 169 Lennard Road, Beckenham, Kent BR3 1QN ☎ 020 8778 2540

ASKEW Roger (*Gtr*): 15 Womersley Road, London N8 9AE ☎ 020 8348 1463

AUBRY Nicolas (*Synth*): 51 Rupert Street, London W1V 7HN ☎ 020 7727 8349, 0956 511410 mob

AYLIN Peter (*Pf*): 319 Rumsey Road, East York, Ontario, M4G 1R6, Canada ☎ + 1 416 696 6041, +1 416 696 9035

AZEEZ Kehinde (*Voc*): 18 Barnard Lodge, Shaftesbury Ave, New Barnet EN5 5JP ☎ 020 8441 3630, 0956 632608 mob

BACHALI Sofiane: 25 Spencer Mews, London W6 8PB ☎ 020 7386 9730

BAGUST Christopher: Flat B, 10 Christchurch Road, Streatham Hill, London SW2 3EX ☎ 020 8671 3979

BAILEY Jess (*Arr*): 74 Burlington Lane, Chiswick, London W4 2RR ☎ 020 8995 1516

BAILEY Robert (*Arr*): 225 Southampton Way, London SE5 7EQ ☎ 020 7708 2657

BAILEY Steven: 52 Ravensbourne Park, Catford, London SE6 4RN ☎ 020 8690 9925

BAKER David: 153A Archway Road, London N6 5BL ☎ 020 8340 2084

BAKER Toby (*B Gtr, Gtr, Dms, Per*): 1 Southside, Carleton Road, London N7 0GH ☎ 020 7700 3963

BALDWIN David: 38 Radcliffe Road, Winchmore Hill, London N21 2SE ☎ 020 8364 3879

BANHAM Josephine (*Voc*): Flat 3, 20 Gloucester Drive, London N4 2LN

BANKS Anthony: Hit & Run Music, 25 Ives Street, London SW3 2ND ☎ 020 7581 0261

BANKS Christopher (*B Gtr*): 94 Roxeth Green Avenue, Harrow HA2 8AQ ☎ 020 8357 3243, 0498 863 187

BARNES Stuart: 9 Ashdown Court, 5 Idmiston Road, Worcester Park, Surrey KT4 7SE ☎ 020 8241 7956

BARNFATHER Peter (*Pf*): 59 Fourth Cross Road, Twickenham, Middx TW2 5EP ☎ 020 8898 7193

BARTON Chris (*Dms*): 47 Kings Road, Kingston-on-Thames, Surrey KT2 5JA ☎ 020 8286 2627

BATCHELLOR Heather (*Pf, Flt, Voc*): 37 Acacia Road, Mitcham CR4 1SE ☎ 020 8646 1474

BATES Django (*Com, T Hrn*): The Lost Marble Dept, 47 Ickburg Road, London E5 8AF ☎ 0973 366990

BATEY Mark (*Gtr, B Gtr*): ☎ 020 8761 1284, 0956 904 977

BEAGHEN Seamus (*Gtr*): 3 Eliot Place, London SE3 0QL

BEALE Charles (*Arr, Md, Org*): 21 Westmorland Close, St Margarets, Twickenham, Middlesex TW1 1RR ☎ 020 8892 6142

BEAMISH: 20 Aldwych Bldgs, Parker Street, London WC2B 5NT ☎ 0973 404585

BEANZ (*Gtr, B Gtr, Dms, Bzk*): 149, Elmshurst Crescent, East Finchley, London N2 0LW ☎ 020 8883 6215

BELL Michael: Flat 9, 54 Winchester Avenue, London NW6 7TU ☎ 020 7625 5078

BENBOW Richard: 168 Ladywell Road, Lewisham, London SE13 7HU ☎ 020 8690 8664

BENFORD Douglas: 63 Windmill Road, Brentford, Middlesex TW8 0QQ ☎ 020 8568 3145 & fax

BETTON Natasha: 78A Danbrook Road, Streatham, London SW16 5JX ☎ 020 8679 1451

BINDING Philip: Ambleside, 5 Clifton Close, Addlestone, Surrey KT15 2EX ☎ 01932 562066

BINNS Henry (*Cel*): 89 Canfield Gardens, London NW6 3EA ☎ 020 7624 1420 & fax, 020 7372 0495, 0976 684234 mob

BINNS Timothy: 26 Kilranock Street, London W10 4AX ☎ 020 8969 7384, 09974 622794, 020 7328 4447

BIRD David: Flat 3, 26 Sherwood Park Road, Sutton, Surrey SM1 2SQ ☎ 020 8642 5465

BIRO Daniel: 6 Maryland Walk, Popham Road, London N1 8QZ ☎ 020 7359 7825

BLACKFORD Norman ☎ 020 8806 2189

BLACKMARK (*Dms*): 2 Cromwell House, Charlotte Despard Avenue, Battersea, London SW11 5HW ☎ 020 7207 1134

BLISS (*Voc*): 46 Maudslay Road, Eltham, London SE9 1LY

BLOOD Steven (*Gtr*): 2 Islington Park Street, London N1 1PV ☎ 020 7700 4448 & fax, 0976 910215 mob

BLUE Rikki: 14 Northern Heights, Crescent Road, Crouch End, London N8 8AS ☎ 020 8347 6784

BOARDMAN Bruce *(Pf, Synth)*: 30 Holm Oak Park, Hagden Lane, Watford, Herts WD1 8XP ☎ 01923 212791

BOOKER Peter: 10 St Leonards Way, Hornchurch, Essex RM11 1FR

BOREZ William *(Pf, Gtr)*: 60 Tavistock Road, London W11 1AW ☎ 0966 296081

BOWEN Gareth: 1 Chalton Drive, Biggin Hill, Kent TN16 3TZ ☎ 01959 570020, 0410 024370

BOWYER Geoffrey *(Cel, Voc, Arr)*: 25 Mill Road, Twickenham, Middlesex TW2 5HA ☎ 020 8894 3773

BRADY William *(Club Dj)*: ☎ 020 7602 7705, 0777 1766086

BRAN Timothy *(B Gtr)*: Basement Flat, 266 Ladbroke Grove, London W10 5LP ☎ 020 8968 9392, 0860 741511

BRIDGE Bruno *(Arr, Clt)*: Bruno Bridge, 138 Essex Road, Leyton, London E10 6BS ☎ 020 7233 0542, 020 8531 8634 fax

BRIDGEMAN Duncan *(Gtr, B Gtr)*: Unit 10A, Impress House, Mansell Road, London W3 7QH ☎ 020 8932 0227, 020 8743 8427

BRIDGWATER Lindsay: 113 Strodes Crescent, Staines, Middlesex TW18 1DG ☎ 01784 455418

BRIXTON *(Gtr)*: Flat 2, 7 Tremlett Grove, London N19 5LA ☎ 020 7263 7751 & fax

BRODIE Tobi *(Scratch)*: 50A Osborne Road, Palmers Green, London N13 5PS ☎ 020 8292 2515

BRODRICK Dean *(Acc, Bsn)*: 31 A Halton Road, London N1 2EN ☎ 020 7226 2567, 0976 246 018

BROMLEY Julien *(Voc)*: Flat 6, 29 St Stephens Gardens, London W2 5NA ☎ 020 7243 1808 & fax

BROWN Matt *(Per)*: Top Flat, 93 Median Road, London E5 0PN ☎ 020 8985 5745

BUNDRICK (RABBIT) John *(Com)*: 47 Ham Hill, Stoke-Sub-Hamdon, Somerset TA14 6RW ☎ 01935 822432, 01935 822432

BURHOLT Stephen *(Gtr)*: 137 Hurst Street, Oxford OX4 1HE ☎ 01865 249168

BURLEY Philip: Heathwoods, Dorking Road, Tadworth, Surrey KT20 7TS ☎ 01737 812673

BURNBY-CROUCH Christopher: 2 Seaford Road, Seven Sisters, London N15 5DY ☎ 020 8802 0966, 07771 562251

BURNS Colin *(Gtr, Dms)*: 27 Canning Road, Walthamstow, London E17 6LT

BURROWS Matthew *(Org)*: 16 Pittsmead Avenue, Hayes, Bromley, Kent BR2 7NL ☎ 020 8462 5403

BUSHWAKA B Matthew *(Dms, Per)*: 8 Williams Road, London W13 0NS ☎ 020 8567 0321

BUTCHER Damon: 25 Cameford Court, New Park Road, London SW2 4LH ☎ 020 8671 5918

BUTLER Nigel *(Voc, Gtr)*: 70 Boxtree Road, Harrow Weald, Middlesex HA3 6TH ☎ 020 8740 6060, 020 8932 0227, 020 8743 8427

BUTTERWORTH Chris *(Dms)*

C.B.: 56 Northbrook Road, Croydon, Surrey CR0 2QL ☎ 020 8683 1354

CADDICK Helen *(Vln)*: 158 Maurice Ave, Wood Green, London N22 6PU ☎ 020 8889 3866

CAMARA Hatib: 5 Clevedon Court, West Bridge Road, Batersea SW11 3NN ☎ 020 7801 0602, 0958 237 220, 020 7720 3133

CAMERON Chris: 16 Colescroft Hill, Purley, Surrey CR8 4BB ☎ 020 8660 3982, 01378 344117 mob

CAMM Tim *(Synth)*: 7 Sheldon Close, London SE20 8LU ☎ 020 7813 1000 ext 8516

CAMPBELL Joel *(Pf, Gtr, B Gtr)*: 69 Mortimer Road, Kensal Green, London NW10 5TN ☎ 020 8960 0275 & fax

CAMPBELL-LYONS Patrick: The Cottage, 4 Bermondsey Square, London SE1 3UN

CANN Judith *(Voc, Pf, Synth)*: 82 Bushey Hall Road, Bushey, Herts WD2 2EQ ☎ 01923 221770

CANTOR Matthew: 18 Windermere Avenue, London NW6 ☎ 020 8960 0548

CARRACK Paul: c/o 1 Water Lane, Camden Town, London NW1 8NX ☎ 020 7267 1101, 020 7267 9221 fax

CASH David: 122 Sirdar Road, London N22 6RD ☎ 020 8889 1014

CASTLE Geoff *(Pf, Com, Arr)*: 19 Percy Road, London W12 9PX ☎ 020 8749 1895, 020 8932 5128 fax

CASTRO Jairo *(Gtr)*: 9 Blakewood Court, Anerley Park, London SE20 8NS ☎ 020 8249 8796, 020 8249 8797, 0956 362771

CERCIELLO Giuseppe *(Vln)* ☎ 020 8248 6255 & fax

CHADBOURN Huw *(Voc, Clt)*: Toynbee Studios, 28 Commercial Street, London E1 6LS ☎ 020 7377 9773 & fax

CHAMBERLAIN Simon: 6 Currie Hill Close, Wimbledon, London SW19 7DX

CHAMBERS Guy *(Gtr)*: Flat 14, 22 Red Lion Street, Holborn, London WC1R 4PS ☎ 020 7813 2630, 020 7813 2631 fax

CHANTLER Michael *(Voc, Per, Gtr)*: 41 Elwood Street, London N5 1EB ☎ 0336 747 756 pager

CHAPLIN Philip *(Voc)*: 1 Hythe Avenue, Bexleyheath, Kent DA7 5NZ ☎ 01322 435693

CHAPMAN Sam *(Dms)*: 9 Derwent Court, Hithe Point, Eleanor Close, London SE16 1PA ☎ 020 7394 0850, 020 7237 4862

CHARLES Desmond *(B Gtr, Dms, Gtr)*: 53 White City Road, Shepherds Bush, London W12 7EQ

CHATER ROBINSON Piers *(Com)*: 19 Lyric Road, Barnes, London SW13 9QA ☎ 020 8876 8666 day, 020 8878 8098 eve, 020 8876 7594

CHERER Oliver *(Gtr, Theramin)*: 45 Meakin Estate, Rothsay Street, London SE1 4QW ☎ 020 7357 6383

CHIAVARINI Michele *(B Gtr, Tpt)*: 115 Milson Road, West Kensington, London W14 0LA ☎ 020 7602 2349

CHRISTOPHERSON Peter: 14 Beverley Road, London W4 2LP ☎ 020 8995 1208, 020 8995 2961 fax

CICERO Guiseppe: Flat 4, 77 Church Street, London N9 8ER ☎ 020 8804 0633, 0956 530226 mob

CLARK Alan: c/o Harris & Trotter, 65 New Cavendish St, London WIM 7RD ☎ 020 7487 4393, 020 7935 1308 fax

CLARK Simon(Andy): 6 Dunsford Place, Bathwick Hill, Bath, Avon BA2 6HF ☎ 01225 337634/481290

CLARKE Alden *(Pf)*: 46 Elliotts Row, Elephant And Castle, London SE11 4SZ ☎ 020 7820 1021

CLARKE David: 83 Cork Street, Eccles, Aylesford, Kent ME20 7HQ ☎ 01622 790070

CLARKE Duncan: 13 Taunton Avenue, Raynes Park, London SW20 0BH ☎ 020 8946 3120

CLARKE Sycuano: 25 Shaftsbury Circle, South Harrow, Middlesex HA2 0AG ☎ 0370 50 3377, 020 8426 9463

CLASSEN Uschi: Flat 4, Prices Garth, 31 London Road, London SE23 3TU ☎ 020 8699 8858

CLAYDON Steven: 29 Wilton House, Dog Kennel Hill, Dulwich, London SE22 8AE ☎ 020 7733 9168

CLAYTON David: 327C Upper Richmond Road, London SW15 6SU ☎ 020 8788 6507

CLEWS Dave: 16 Lots Road, London SW10 0QF ☎ 020 7351 7289

CLIFFORD Matt *(Sax, Hrn)*: The Hollins, Hope Bagot, Ludlow, Salop SY8 3AE ☎ 01452 740 979

COBHAM Jeffrey *(Pf, Voc, Dms, B Gtr)*: 33 Boughton House, Tennis Street, London SE1 1YF ☎ 020 7403 1302

CODE D *(Pf, Gtr)*: 73 Eversley Road, Upper Norwood, London SE19 3QS ☎ 020 8771 6114, 0956 940102 mob

COHEN Chase: 30 Salehurst Close, Kenton, Harrow, Middlesex HA3 0UG ☎ 020 8204 1006

COHEN Jon *(Pf)*: 6 Gonston Close, Wimbledon, London SW19 5PU ☎ 020 8947 7466

COKER David *(Per, Gtr)*: Strage Weather Studio, 28-30 Wood Wharf, Horseferry Place, London SE10 9BT ☎ 0161 237 5957

COLA Nick *(Voc)*: c/o The Smooth Side Organisati, Stoke House, South Green, Kirtlington, Oxford OX5 3HJ ☎ 01869 351096

COLEMAN Jazz *(Pf, Flt, Vln, Voc)* ☎ 020 7323 3888, 0795 7883247

COLLCUTT Terence *(Pf)*: 8 Clerks Croft, Church Lane, Bletchingley, Surrey RH1 4LH ☎ 01883 744243

COMPTON James *(Gtr, Voc)*: 18 Palace Road, Crouch End, London N8 8QJ ☎ 020 8348 8830

CONDON Matthew *(Pf)*: 160 Swakeleys Road, Ickenham, Middlesex UB10 8AZ ☎ 01895 672354

CONGDON David *(Pf, Flt)*: 73 Halkingcroft, Langley, Slough, Berks SL3 7AZ

CONNAH Lyndon *(Voc)*: 68 Bousfield Rd, London SE14 5TR ☎ 020 7652 3117

COOK Betsy *(Voc, Arr, Sax, Flt)*: The Limes, Dairy Farm, Hillesden, Bucks MK18 4BX ☎ 01280 847062

COOK John *(Synth, Pf)*: 1 Broxted Road, Catford, London SE6 4EW ☎ 020 8699 8876

COOPER Edward: 34 Wellmeadow Road, Hither Green, London SE13 6TB ☎ 020 8695 8988

COOPER John: 10 Appledore Avenue, South Ruislip, Middlesex HA4 0UU ☎ 020 8841 6347

COOPER Michael *(Synth)*: Alkionidon 44, Appt. 1 (First Floor), Voula, 166.73, Greece ☎ Athens 8990019

COULAM Roger *(Pf, Org)*: 12 The Coppins, Fieldway, New Addington, Surrey CR0 9DE ☎ 01689 849279

COX Julian *(Per)*: 52 Windley Close, Forest Hill, London SE23 3YQ ☎ 020 8291 5935

COYTE Peter *(Voc)*: Ground Floor Flat, 10 Brondesbury Villas, London NW6 6AA ☎ 020 7372 8109, 0958 666225

COZENS Spencer *(Pf, Tpt)*: Studio 45, Limehouse Cut, 46 Morris Road, London E14 6NQ ☎ 020 7515 8137

CREW Paul *(Ob, Cor)*: 43 Haliburton Road, St Margarets, Twickenham, Middx TW1 1PD ☎ 020 8891 1162, 020 8892 7658 fax

CRICHTON Stuart *(Synth, Voc)*: Studio 7, 27A Pembridge Villas, London W11 3EP ☎ 020 7221 6200

CRICKMER Adrian *(Gtr)*: 2, Walters Mead, Ashtead, Surrey KT21 2BP ☎ 013722 75827

CROSS Alan: 45 Kilner House, Clayton Street, Kennington, London SE11 5SE ☎ 020 7582 5380

CROSS David: 16 Shaldon Mansions, 132 Charing Cross Road, London WC2H 0LA ☎ 020 7240 4068, 0976 427778, 020 7240 4068

CROSS Tim: 25 Fair Lane, Robertsbridge, Salehurst, East Sussex TN32 5AT ☎ 01580 881047

CRYSTAL Nick *(Gtr)* ☎ 0370 665 493

CULLUM Ross: Datehurst Ltd, 3 St Marys Grove, Barnes, London SW13 0JA

CURNOW Ian *(B Gtr, Tbn, Gtr, Dms)*: East Barn, Brockley Road, Whepstead, Bury St Edmunds Suffolk IP29 4SP

CURTIS Justina *(Voc)*: 3 Grasmere Road, London SW16 2DA ☎ 020 8677 1482

CUTHILL Paul *(Voc, Cel, Bsn)*: 19 Birkdale Close, Masters Drive, London SE16 3DN

DA FORCE Ricardo *(Voc)*: c/o Rupert Rohan, Entertainment Law Assoc., 9 Carnaby Street, London W1V 1PG ☎ 020 7439 6194/3089

DANIELS Alan: 26 Kitson Road, London SE5 7LF ☎ 020 7703 4182

DANIELS Simon: 60 Spring Gardens, Highbury New Park, London N5 2TD ☎ 020 7359 4211

DAVANI Dave *(Org)*: 4 Colton Road, Harrow, Middlesex HA1 1SG ☎ 020 8863 1949

DAVEY Noel *(Voc)*: Address Unknown ☎ 876 942 9654

DAVIES Mark: 52 Lyonsdown Road, New Barnet, Herts EN5 1JL ☎ 020 8441 3329

DAVIS Peter *(Per)*: 4Th Floor, 29-55 Gee Street, London EC1V 3RE ☎ 020 7251 5598

DE ARAGON Paul *(Gtr)*: Missionhouse Studios, The Cloisters, St. Frideswides, Lodorest, London E14 6LY ☎ 020 7515 1101 & fax, 0956 472624 mob

DE VRIES Marius *(Voc, Vln)*: 16 North Road, Whittlesford, Cambridge CB2 2NZ ☎ 01223 837454

DE-ANGELIS Georges: 96 Manor Road, Walthamstow, London E10 7HN ☎ 020 8556 4994

DEFSTAR: 6 Arabin Road, Brockley, London SE4 2SE ☎ 0850 722179 mob

DELANEY James: 16 Gracefield Avenue, Artane, Dublin 5, Ireland ☎ +353 18316711

DELMIRANI Ugo: Flat 2, 41 Heyford Avenue, Vauxhall, London SW8 1EA ☎ 020 7582 3364 & fax

DESCENDING ANGEL ☎ 020 8666 8949, 020 8657 0308

DEPTFORD *(Per, Gtr)*: 11 Linton Crescent, Hastings, East Sussex TN34 1TJ ☎ 020 8698 6790

DIAL Erique: 10A Muswell Hill, London N10 3TA ☎ 020 8444 2680

DJ RENEGADE (Scratch, Club Dj) ☎ 020 7780 9937

DJ SUPREME (Gtr): 29 Cubitt House, Oaklands Estate, Ponders Road, London SW4 8NG ☎ 020 8673 0369 & fax, 0468 005549 mob

DJRJ *(Pf, Dms)*: 59 Thrale Road, Streatham, London SW16 1NU ☎ 020 8677 8252

DOLAN Tom *(Voc, Clt)*: 45 Arica Road, Brockley, London SE4 2PY ☎ 020 7635 7223

DOOBAY Donald: 52 Grange Park Ave, Winchmore Hill, London N21 2LL ☎ 020 8360 6138, 0956 156733 mob, 020 8364 2776

DRIESSEN *(Gtr, B Gtr)*: 158A Graham Road, London E8 1BS ☎ 020 7254 4029

DUDMAN Peter: 13 Temple Road, South Ealing, London W5 4SL ☎ 020 8932 1531

DYNE Marcus *(B Gtr, Gtr)*: 25 Gisburn Road, London N8 7BS ☎ 020 8480 9790

DYSON Mark *(Vln, Voc)*: 34 Popes Lane, Ealing, London W5 4NU ☎ 020 8567 8341

E Mr *(Voc, Per, Gtr)*: 13 Tinniswood Close, London N5 1XS ☎ 020 7315 4257, 0467 695045 mob, 020 7315 5022

EAMES Timothy *(Per)*: 33 Ridgeview Road, Whetstone, London N20 0HH ☎ 020 8445 7077

EASTWOOD Luke *(B Gtr, Gtr, Cel, Ind Flt)*: 37 Tillotson Road, Edmonton, London N9 9AQ ☎ 020 8887 0590

EDMUNDS Tony: 5 Boscobel House, Royal Oak Road, Hackney, London E8 1BT ☎ 020 7241 4434

EDWARDS Emmanuel *(B Gtr, Sax)*: 28 Harble Down House, Manciple Street, London SE1 4LN ☎ 020 7207 3518, 0958 526606 mob

EDWARDS, GCLCM Sam *(Pf, Arr)*: 3 Lupin Drive, Springfield, Chelmsford, Essex CM1 5YJ ☎ 01245 469072, 0831 356621

EL-TOUKHY Sara *(Voc, Com, Song W)*: 82 Lothrop Street, Queens Park, London W10 4JD ☎ 020 8960 1571

ELLER Jane *(B Gtr, Gtr)*

ELLIOTT Jason *(Voc)*: c/o Prager & Fenton, Midway House, 27/29 Cursitor Street, London EC4A 1LT ☎ 020 7831 4200

ELLIS Paul: Flat 7, Christopher Lodge, Avenue Road, London N6 5DL ☎ 020 8340 7184

ELMS Gerald: 51 Devereux Road, Battersea, London SW11 6JR ☎ 020 7738 2685, 020 7252 2627 day

EMERSON Darren: 16 Dymoke Road, Hornchurch, Essex RM11 1AA ☎ 01708 728879, 01708 441754 fax, 01708 731888 fax

ERINGA David *(Gtr, Voc)*: 12 Hertford Road, Newbury, Ilford, Essex IG2 7HQ ☎ 020 8597 6125

ETTIENNE Delroy: 23 Rutland Road, Harrow, Middlesex HA1 4JN ☎ 020 8863 7987, 0973 984737 mob

EVANS Damian *(Pf, Per, Gtr, B Gtr)*: 154 Upper Brockley Road, Brockley, London SE4 1SS ☎ 020 8691 1800

EVANS Joseph *(Gtr, B Gtr)*: 79 Nimrod Road, Tooting, London SW16 6SZ ☎ 0958 486822

EVANS Melvin *(Dms)*: Flat 1, 8-12 Deptford High Street, (Admiralty Buildings), London SE8 4SF ☎ 020 8692 3220, 0956 258325

EYO George *(B Gtr)*: 8 Brayford Square, Stepney, London E1 0SG ☎ 020 7702 7814, 0958 283392

EYRE Tommy: 15737 Hesby Street, Encino, California 91436, USA ☎ +1 818 907 5532

FARRELLY Gerard *(Pf, Dms)*: 132 Braemor Road, Churchtown, Dublin 14, Ireland ☎ Dublin 01 2983091

FELIX Sasha *(Gtr)*: Silver Birches, 25 Farnham Close, London N20 9PU ☎ 020 8446 7831

FENTON Adam T *(Voc)*: 1 Upper Highway, Hunton Bridge, Kings Langley, Herts WD4 8PP ☎ 01923 261264

FERRARI *(Per, B Gtr, Club Dj)*: 43B Lancaster Road, London N4 4PJ ☎ 020 8374 3765, 0956 573239

FINCH Keith: 32 Stanhope Road, Barnet, Herts EN5 2QN ☎ 020 8447 1770

FINCH Peter: 26 Clifton Road, Hornchurch, Essex RM11 1BU ☎ 01708 721741 & fax

FINN Micky (*Per*): South Rise, Old Watlings Street, Higham, Kent ☎ 020 8694 0939, 01634 710252, 020 8694 0939

FISHER Mark: 116 Rosebery Road, Langley Vale, Epsom KT18 6AA ☎ 01372 276 589

FLOWERDEW Sean: 15 Niederwald Road, London SE26 4AD ☎ 020 8291 7650

FORD Dave (*Per*): 5 The Lye, Tadworth, Surrey KT20 5RS ☎ 01737 814371, 01737 814371

FORD Dorian (*B Gtr*): 12 Twisden Road, London NW5 1DN ☎ 020 7485 0077

FORD James T (*Bag*): 22A Alexandra Grove, London N4 2LF ☎ 020 8800 4798

FORMULA Dave: 3 Quarry Road, Louth, Lincs LN11 9HX ☎ 01507 601562

FORREST Matt (*Voc*): Flat 4, 24 Earl's Court Square, London SW5 9DN ☎ 020 7244 7043

FOSTER Nick (*Pf, Voc, Gtr, Per*): Rose & Foster Productions, 37 Skylines Village, Limeharbour, Docklands, London E14 9XT ☎ 020 7537 2147 & fax

FOWLER James: 13 Lime Crescent, Sunbury-on-Thames, Middlesex TW16 5NT ☎ 01932 761988

FOWLER Matt (*Voc, Tpt*): 24 Dawlish Drive, Pinner, Middlesex HA5 5LN ☎ 020 8248 2813

FOWNES Brandon (*Pf, Voc, Gtr*): 41 Homefield Road, Chiswick, London W4 2LW ☎ 020 8995 2767

FREDERIKSE Tom (*Vla*): 24 Countess Road, London NW5 2XJ ☎ 020 7284 0545

FREEDMAN Jerry (*Gtr*): ☎ 020 8904 9222 & fax, 0421 677841 mob

FUKUOKA Yasuko: Flat 7, Christopher Lodge, Avenue Road, London N6 5DL ☎ 020 8340 7184

FURUHOLMEN Magne (*Gtr, Voc*): c/o Delancey Business, Management Ltd, 220A Blythe Road, London W14 0HH ☎ 020 7602 5424

FYFFE Will (*Md*): Appletree Lodge, Golden Acre, Angmering-on-Sea, West Sussex BN16 1QP ☎ 01903 785782

GARABEDIAN Silva (*Voc*): 25 Muswell Road, Muswell Hill, London N10 N10 2BS ☎ 020 8883 8184

GARMAN Julian (*Sou*): 1 Silecroft Road, Bexleyheath, Kent DA7 5BL ☎ 020 8304 7658

GAUDI (*Oca, Maraz*): 22 Parkside, Dollis Hill, London NW2 6RH ☎ 020 8452 5227, 0966 523903 mob

GAVIN Alastair: 1 Winton Avenue, London N11 2AS ☎ 020 8888 5640

GAY Robert (*T Sax, Flt*): 88C Underhill Road, London SE22 0QH

GEE Danny: 58 Allerton Road, Stoke Newington, London N16 5UF ☎ 020 8800 2755

GIRDLESTONE Ian: 3 Crownstone Court, Crownstone Road, Brixton, London SW2 1LS ☎ 020 7787 0383

GIUSSANI Claudio (*Dms, Per*): 5A Margravine Gardens, London W6 8RL ☎ 020 8748 8579 & fax, 0956 497024

GLADMAN Clive (*Gtr, Voc*): 55 Hazeldell, Watton-At-Stone, Herts SG14 3SN ☎ 01322 387897

GLEADALL Peter (*Gtr*): 5 Oaktree House, Redington Gardens, London NW3 7RY ☎ 020 7435 3986

GLENNIE-SMITH Nicholas: 21 Napier Place, London W14 8LG

GORDENO Peter (*Voc*): 11 Princes Road, Weybridge, Surrey KT13 9BH ☎ 01932 843816

GOTA (*Dms, B Gtr, Gtr*): Peace Ltd, 12 Elm Grove Road, London SW13 0BT ☎ 020 8878 7935, 03747 82855 mob

GOYNS Barry (*Voc*): 24 Norfolk Place, Welling, Kent DA16 3HR ☎ 020 8854 9766

GRAHAM Bruce (*Mrba, Vib, Xyl, Glck*): 25 Milton Road, Wallington, Surrey SM6 9RP ☎ 020 8647 9967

GRAHAM Nick (*Voc*): 64 Slough Road, Iver Heath, Bucks SL0 0DY ☎ 01753 712947, 01753 712948 fax

GRAHAM Nicky (*Pf, Voc*): c/o Graham Music Publishers, 25 Heathmans Road, London SW6 4TJ ☎ 020 7371 5608, 020 7371 7629 fax

GRAㅅ Mike (*Per*): Defected Management, Ground Floor, 25 Heathmans Road, London SW6 4TJ ☎ 01883 7443813

GRAY Trevor (*Flt, Dms, Voc*): c/o Xl Talent ☎ 020 7221 6200, 020 7229 7511 fax

GREEN John (*Pf, B Gtr, Arr*): 62 Ashleigh Road, London SW14 8PX ☎ 020 8392 1216

GREEN Tom (*Pf*): 94 Shakespeare Road, London SE24 0QQ ☎ 020 7733 6564

GREENAWAY Gavin (*Vln*): 19 Burwood Road, Hersham, Surrey KT12 4AB

GREENWAY Mike (*Gtr*): 74 St James Road, Surbiton, Surrey KT6 4QN ☎ 020 8339 9791

GREGSON-WILLIAMS Rupert (*Pf*): Bagmore Cottage, Milford Road, Elstead, Godalming, Surrey GU8 6LA ☎ 0589 845711

GRESSWELL Steve (*Arr, Com*): 25 Montpelier Drive, Caversham Park Village, Reading, Berks RG4 6QA ☎ 0118 947 5520

GRIFFIN Jonathan (*Gtr, B Gtr*): ☎ 020 8655 1547

GROSS Jose (*Gtr*): 100 Adelaide Grove, London W12 0JH ☎ 020 8743 2645

GRUNDY Liam (*Gtr, Clt, Hmca*): 17 Poulett Gardens, Twickenham, Middlesex TW1 4QS ☎ 020 8744 2235

GUEST Ivor (*Pf*): 5 Wetherby Gardens, London SW5 0JN ☎ 020 7373 2120

HAGEN Peter (*Md, Pf, Hmca*): 46 South Drive, Brentwood, Essex CM14 5DL ☎ 01277 226011, 0468 748430 mob

HAGGIS (*B Gtr, Gtr, Tpt*): c/o Space Band Management, Chancery House, 319 City Road, London EC1V 1LJ ☎ 020 7713 1034

HAGUE Stephen (*Acc*): c/o Solar Management, 42-48 Charlbert Street, London NW8 7BU ☎ 020 7722 4175, 020 7722 4072 fax

HALE Keith (*Gtr*): 29 Cromwell Road, Canterbury, Kent CT1 3LB ☎ 01227 455191

HALE Simon (*Com, Arr, Md*): 31 Tregarvon Road, London SW11 5QD ☎ 020 7585 1709, 0973 620899 mob, 020 7223 8134 fax

HALLAWELL James (*Voc, Gtr*): Ground Floor Flat, 18 Elsham Road, Kensington, London W14 8HA ☎ 020 7371 2597

HAMM Ralf (*Dms, Flt*): Deschstrasse 1, 63739 Aschaffenburg, Germany ☎ +49 6021 28010, +49 172 8807988, +49 6021 28044

HAMMER Jeffrey: 24 Fernleigh Road, Winchmore Hill, London N21 3AL ☎ 020 8447 8786

HAMMILL Peter (*Gtr*): Roseneath, Sharpstone, Freshford, Bath, Avon BA3 6DA

HANDY Edmund: 9 Shirley Road, Sidcup, Kent DA15 7JW ☎ 020 8300 2715

HANVEY J Neale (*B Gtr, E Gtr*): 21 Churchill Court, Connaught Road, London N4 4NU ☎ 020 7281 2113 & fax

HARDAKER Sam (*Dms*): 42-48 Charlbert Street, London NW8 7BU ☎ 020 7722 4175, 020 7722 4042

HARDCASTLE Paul: Tudor Rose, Oakhill Road, Stapleford Abbots, Essex RM4 1JJ ☎ 020 7228 4000

HARDING Philip (*B Gtr, Gtr, Dms, Voc*): 16 Bow Brook House, Cathorne Street, London E2 0PW ☎ 020 8980 9506

HARDWICK Jamie (*Pf*): 60 Station Road, Harrow, Middx HA1 2SQ ☎ 020 8427 9626

HARDY Craig: 225 Woolwich Road, Upper Abbeywood, London SE2 0PY ☎ 020 8311 6416

HARRIS Mike

HARRIS-TAYLOR Derek (*Voc*): 6 Hermiston Avenue, London N8 8NL ☎ 020 8341 0437

HARRISON Danny (*Per*): 22 Prince Charles Way, Wallington, Surrey SM6 7BP ☎ 020 8287 1372

HART Roderick: 15/16 West Street, Rottingdean, East Sussex BN2 7HP ☎ 01273 300512, 0973 600965

HARVEY Joshua (*Gtr*): 438 St Anns Road, Haringey, London N15 3JH ☎ 020 8800 6641

HAWKEN Dominic (*Voc, Arr*): The Deluxe Corporation, 13 Charnhill Crescent, Bristol BS16 9JU ☎ 0117 9702712, 0117 9702713 fax

HAWKINS Justin (*Dms, Voc, Gtr*): 17 Maryland Walk, London N1 8QZ ☎ 020 7354 2997

HAYAT Nad: 123 Maynard Road, London E17 9JE ☎ 020 8923 7980

189

HAYLES Martin: 35 Lavender Road, Rotherhithe, London SE16 1DT ☎ 020 7232 2472

HAYNE Christopher: 76 Pepys Road, West Wimbledon, London SW20 8PF ☎ 020 8947 9806

HEMMINGS Ria (Gtr): 112 Gunnersbury Avenue, Ealing, London W5 4HB ☎ 020 8993 7441, 020 8992 9993

HENRY Brian (B Gtr, Dms, Md): 10 Yeats Court, Tynemouth Road, London N15 4AT ☎ 020 8885 1955, 0374 856981

HEWINSON Colin: 74 Beverley Road, Ruislip Manor, Middx HA4 9AS ☎ 01895 638984

HIBBERT Martin (Synth): 57 Grove Avenue, Muswell Hill, London N10 2AL ☎ 020 8444 1360, 0958 522490

HICKEY Darren: 36 Stephens Crescent, Horndon-on-The Hill, Essex SS17 8LZ ☎ 01375 677332

HICKS Colin (Gtr): 25 Beauchamp Road, London SW11 1PG ☎ 020 7228 4685, 0468 718968, 020 7766 5915

HILL Andrew (B Gtr): Big Note Ltd, Comforts Place Studio, Tandridge Lane, Lingfield, Surrey RH7 6LW ☎ 01342 893046

HILL Marcus: Flat 5, 49 Bonnington Square, Vauxhall, London SW8 1TF ☎ 020 7735 3807

HILTON Stephen (Gtr, B Gtr): 97 Windermere Road, London W5 4TB ☎ 020 7561 1583, 0956 193 834

HINDS Peter: 92 Boxtree Lane, Harrow Weald, Middx HA3 6JE ☎ 020 8421 2468, 020 8424 9191 fax

HIRSH Paul (Gtr, B Gtr): 181 Ashfield Avenue, Bushey, Herts WD2 3UQ ☎ 020 8421 8797

HOGAN Nigel: 62 Morris Avenue, Manor Park, London E12 6EP ☎ 020 8553 0625, 0956 841467 mob

HOLDAWAY Marcus (Cel): 183 Hollydale Road, Nunhead, London SE15 2TG

HOLDER Henry: 39 Bowyer House, Vermont Road, Wandsworth, London SW18 2AE ☎ 0958 328291

HOLLAND Christopher: Address Unknown ☎ 020 8858 7207

HOLLAND Jools (Gtr): Helicon Mountain Ltd, The Station, Station Terrace Mews, London SE3 7LP ☎ 020 8858 0984

HOLLINGSWORTH James: 71 Manor Road, Richmond, Surrey TW9 1YA ☎ 020 8332 9573, 020 8564 1353

HOWE Franklyn (Synth): 35 Harborough Road, Streatham, London SW16 2XP ☎ 020 8769 2944

HOWELL Robin: Flat C, 22 Fairhazel Gardens, London NW6 3SJ ☎ 020 7328 0946

HOWLETT Liam Paul (Voc): c/o Interactive Psl, 120-124 Curtain Road, London EC2A 3SA ☎ 020 7426 5130

HUGG Mike (Pf, Per): 100 Parliament Hill Mansions, Lisenden Gdns., London NW5 1NB ☎ 017 267 0092

HULBERT Simon Leigh (Per, Gtr, Voc): Jan Cottage, 48 Elmstead Lane, Chislehurst, Kent BR7 5EQ ☎ 020 8467 6046, 020 8467 4108 fax

HUNT Donald (Arr, Md): 73 Cherry Tree Walk, West Wickham, Kent BR4 9EE ☎ 020 8325 8809

HUNTE Owen (Voc): 12 Evesham Road, London N11 2RP ☎ 020 8372 3875

HUNTER Robert (Vln): 15, Lynwood Road, Ealing, London W5 1JQ ☎ 020 8997 3230

HURRELL Frazer (Voc, Gtr): 230B Tolworth Rise South, Surbiton, Surrey KT5 9NB ☎ 020 8337 5921

HUSTINGS-MOORE Tony (Gtr): Flat Q2, Clapham Junction Estate, St Johns Hill, London SW11 1UQ ☎ 020 7223 5347

IMREI Martyn (Dms, Arr): 406 Gibbet Street, Halifax, West Yorkshire HX1 4JQ ☎ 01422 364875

INGOLDSBY Denis (Gtr): The Courtyard, 42 Colwith Yard, Hammersmith, London W6 9EY

INGRAM Kurtis, 020 8699 5055

IROEGBU Ezinwa: 63 Empire Court, North End Road, Wembley Park, Middlesex HA9 0AQ ☎ 020 8902 8278

IRVING Matthew (B Gtr, Acc): 41 Albert Road, Richmond, Surrey TW10 6DJ ☎ 020 8940 6361

IRVING HOUSBY B.SC John: 31, Ingrebourne Court, 45-55 Chingford Avenue, Chingford, London E4 6RL ☎ 020 8529 6093

ISAAC Julie (Per): 123 Grafton House, Wellington Way, London E3 4UF ☎ 020 8980 3156

ISAACS Carol (Synth): 18 Eton Rise, Eton College Rd, London NW3 2DE ☎ 020 7722 4649

ISAACSON Gerald: Address Unknown ☎ 020 8421 1958

ITES Ras: 63 Dobson House, Edmund Street, Camberwell, London SE5 7NX ☎ 020 7701 6119

J. Ollie (B Gtr, Dms): 29 Beethoven Street, London W10 4LJ ☎ 020 8969 0299

J.JULES Shari ☎ 020 8555 6382, 0958 605777 mob

JACK Nicki (Voc): Address Unknown ☎ 020 7351 4526

JACKMAN Henry: 55 Sandhurst Court, Acre Lane, Brixton, London SW2 5TX ☎ 020 7274 8766

JACKMAN James (Sax): 3-9 Northwood Hall, Hornsey Lane, Highgate, London N6 5PH ☎ 020 8342 8445

JACKSON Bob (Voc): 7 Carding Close, Eastern Green, Coventry, West Midlands CV5 7BL ☎ 024 7646 6035

JAMES Brian: 46 Oldfield Road, Stoke Newington, London N16 0RS ☎ 020 7502 0372, 020 7690 7135

JAMES Luke: 40 Pickhurst Rise, West Wickham, Kent BR4 0AL ☎ 020 8777 1023

JAMESON-VINE Zeben (Gtr, Per): 46 Arundel Gardens, London W11 2LB

JANSSEN Volker: Flat 6, 160 Queenstown Road, London SW3 3QE ☎ 020 7622 9317

JAY Bee: 17-19 Lever Street, London EC1V 3QU ☎ 0956 176871 mob

JEFFRIES Peter (Com, Arr): Flat 3, 55 High Road, Bushey Heath, Herts WD2 1EE ☎ 020 8950 2012

JENKINS Dave (Voc): 43 Crookston Road, Eltham, London SE9 1YQ ☎ 020 8859 5202

JOE Smokey: 50A Osborne Road, London N13 5PS ☎ 0374 436 171

JOHANNSSON Johann: Braedraborgarstigur 7, Reykjavik, Iceland ☎ +354 5519267, +354 5617899

JOHNSON Adrian (Voc): 2 Maiden Lane, Park Street, London SE1 9HG ☎ 0956 122344

JOHNSON Griff (Pf, Md, Arr, Com): 3 Blenheim Close, Chandlersford, Eastleigh, Hants SO53 4LD ☎ 023 8025 5415, 0836 600002 mob

JOHNSON Matt (Voc): 120B Lewisham Way, London SE14 6PD ☎ 020 8305 6885

JOMOA James: 46 Summerhouse Avenue, Heston, Middlesex TW5 9DA ☎ 020 8230 2727, 0976 966206

JONES John Paul (Gtr): C-O Joan Hudson And Co, 91 Tabernacle Street, London EC2A 4BA ☎ 020 7253 3107

JONES Richard (Pf): 159 Hartfield Road, Wimbledon, London SW19 3TH ☎ 020 8540 6734, 0958 474156

JONES Stephen (Voc): 22 Derwen Drive, Rhyl, Clwyd LL18 2PB ☎ 01745 352510, 0421 403895 mob

JONES Stephen (Gtr, Didj): 80 Hadley Road, New Barnet EN5 5QR

JONES Stephen (Synth): 6B Pepys Road, Telegraph Hill, New Cross, London SE14 5SB ☎ 020 7639 1165

JOY Ashley: 5 Hamilton Court, Cumberland Place, Catford, London SE6 1LY ☎ 020 8355 9051, 020 7500 6684 mob

JULES Judge: P.O Box 13143, London N6 5BG ☎ 020 8731 7300, 020 8458 0045

K Steffan (Pf): 29 Cheverton Road, London N19 3BB ☎ 020 7272 0061

KALINSKI Dj: 8 Fairholme Mansions, London Road, Croydon, Surrey CR0 3PB ☎ 020 8665 7981

KALTENHAUSER Richard (B Gtr): 86 Chesterford Road, Manor Park, London E12 6LB ☎ 020 8514 4160

KANE Alice: 165 Hamilton Road, Golders Green, London NW11 9EB ☎ 020 8458 2614

KEEGAN Mark

KEEN Ben (Voc): 12 Hookstone Way, Woodford Green, Essex IG8 7LF ☎ 020 8506 1582, 0956 334 226

KEILES Glenn (B Gtr): 37 1st Avenue, Acton, London W3 7JP ☎ 020 8248 1661, 020 8248 7745, 0468 853011

KEWLEY Ian (Org, Hrn): Can Galan, Montferrer, 66150 Arles-Sur-Tech, France ☎ +33 468 39 17 37

KIDDY Colin: 58 The Spinney, North Cray, Sidcup, Kent DA14 5NF ☎ 020 8300 7631

KING Gordon: 8 Kingsnorth House, Silchester Road, North Kensington, London W10 6SH ☎ 020 8960 4926

KING Jamie: 2 Ryder House, High Path, South Wimbledon, Merton, London SW19 2JS

KINGSLEY Ashley

KINLEY Peter (*S Sax*): 45 George V Avenue, Pinner, Middlesex HA5 5SX ☎ 020 8863 1517

KIS (*Synth*): Flat 31, 148 Uxbridge Road, Shepherds Bush, London W12 8AA ☎ 0958 515411 mob

KLONDYKE (*Voc*): 308 Greenford Avenue, London W7 3AD ☎ 020 8933 4242, 07666 767128

KLONIS Steve (*Dms, Per*): 28 Orwell Court, Petherton Road, London N5 2QU ☎ 020 7354 3087

KNIGHT Jason (*Rh Gtr*): 215 Alexandra Park Road, London N22 7BJ ☎ 0468 430303

KNOTE Andy (*Pf, Org*): Strahlenfelserstr Z, 81243 Munchen, Germany ☎ 01044 89 811 59

KNOTT Lee (*Gtr*): 36 Elder Ave, (Ground Floor), Crouch End, London N8 8PS ☎ 020 8374 0789

KOGLIN Mike (*Dms, B Gtr*): 52C Hembaton Road, London SW9 9LJ ☎ 020 7924 0205, 020 7738 6817 & fax, 0468 361637 mob

KOI: 5 Derwent Court, Eleanor Close, Rotherhithe, London SE16 1PA ☎ 020 7237 8015

KWATEN Kwame: 13 Regina Road, London N4 3PT ☎ 020 7607 9416, 020 7607 9416

LANE Rick (*Per*): 19 Venetia Road, London W5 4JD ☎ 0585 854965 mob, 020 8840 0705

LANGAN Gary (*Tpt, Per*): 36 Kenilworth Avenue, Wimbledon, London SW19 7LW ☎ 020 8946 1047

LANGMAID Benedict: Protocol Studios, 23A Benwell Road, London N7 7BL ☎ 020 7609 5558

LARSEN Philip: 2 Turner Drive, London NW11 6TX ☎ 020 8458 2690

LASCELLES James: Address Unknown ☎ 020 7727 8181

LATHAM Clive: 2 Collingwood Road, Mitcham, Surrey CR4 3DH ☎ 020 8648 8732, 020 8287 2729 fax

LEE Adam (*Voc, Com, Arr, Gtr*): Flat 7, 86 Ruskin Street, Elwood, Victoria 3184, Australia ☎ +61 395317501

LEE Eng (*B Gtr*): 277 Hainault Road, Leytonstone, London E11 1ES ☎ 020 8539 4332

LEEYOU (*Song W*): 8 St Rapheals Way, Neasden, London NW10 0NT ☎ 020 8459 7728

LEGGATT John (*Arr*)

LENNOX Dave: 20 Heming Road, Edgware, Middx HA8 9AE ☎ 020 8952 2418

LENNY Dino: Flat 6, 124 Kings Road, Mitre House, Chelsea, London SW3 4TP ☎ 020 7584 3972

LESTER Mark (*Pf*): 196 Merton Road, Southfields, London SW18 5SW ☎ 020 8870 7830

LEWIS Byron: 4 Marston House, Overton Road, London SW9 7HA ☎ 0956 175394

LEWIS Charles (*Gtr*) ☎ 020 7241 4941

LEWIS Lindel (*B Gtr*): 52 Gooch House, Kenninghall Road, London E5 8DQ ☎ 020 8533 1879

LEWIS Ray: 51 Arabin Road, Brockley, London SE4 2SD

LEWSLEY Sebastian (*Gtr*): West Heath Studios, West Heath Yard, 174 Mill Lane, London NW6 1TB ☎ 020 7794 7758, 020 7431 2511 fax

LIDDLE Alison (*Voc*): 39 Sawyers Lawn, Ealing, London W13 0JP ☎ 020 8998 7255

LIKEN Tim: Flat 5, 8-11 Wilmington Square, London WC1X 0ES ☎ 020 7689 0815, 0370 995441 mob

LOVE Aidan (*B Gtr, Mldca*): 51 Cambria Road, Camberwell, London SE5 9AS ☎ 020 7274 5496, 020 8960 9379, 020 8960 7078

LYNCH Curt (*Dms*) ☎ 020 8352 7018, 0956 539 948

LYNCH Donald: 42 Edith Grove, London SW10 0NJ ☎ 020 7376 4585, 020 7376 4591 fax

LYNN Ian ☎ 01883 343913, 01883 346967

LYNWOOD Andy (*Pf*): 21 Winterbrook Road, Herne Hill, London SE24 9HZ ☎ 020 7733 3871, 0973 426018 mob, 020 7737 2277 fax

LYSANDROU Andy ☎ 01992 635476 & fax, 0956 247926 mob

MACKILLOP Duncan (*Gtr*): 36 Kings Road, Willesden, London NW10 2BP ☎ 020 8969 9833

MACMAHON Graham (*Gtr, Flt*): 47 Walker House, Pheonix Road, London NW1 1P ☎ 020 7837 2009, 020 7837 3009

MAGIC Mo (*Dms*), 0958 471741

MALPASS Kevin (*Per, Gtr, B Gtr, Flt*): 37 Elfort Road, Highbury, London N5 1AX ☎ 020 7226 8297

MANKO Stefan (*Per*): 17A Kingsland Road, Shoreditch, London E2 8AA ☎ 020 7613 0612

MANN Manfred (*Pf, Voc*): 488-490 Old Kent Road, London SE1 5AG

MARCUS Sultrix (*Voc*) ☎ 020 7836 4327, 0958 244707, 020 7836 4327

MARS Chris (*Voc, Gtr*): 200 Cavendish Avenue, Ealing, London W13 0JW ☎ 020 8537 1854 fax, 0836 784029 mob

MARSHALL Christopher: 26 Weiss Road, London SW15 1DH ☎ 020 8789 5868

MARSHALL Sharon (*Pf*): 9 Lindal Court, Chelmsford Road, London E18 2PJ ☎ 020 8504 1080

MARSHALL Steve (*Per*): Ridgeway Cottage, Alton Barnes, Marlborough, Wilts SN8 4LB ☎ 01672 851621

MARTIN Micheal (*Pf*): 128 Park View Road, Tottenham, London N17 9BL ☎ 020 8808 2756 & fax, 0956 401305 mob

MARTIN Victor (*Gtr, B Gtr*): 109B Brighton Road, Surbiton, Surrey KT6 5NF ☎ 020 8390 2408

MASTERSON Paul (*Pf*): Backlash Music Managment, 54 Carlton Plac E, Glasgow G5 9TW ☎ 0141 418 0053, 0141 418 0054 fax

MAX Paul (*Synth*): Flat 2, 25 Warrington Crescent, Maida Vale, London W9 1ED ☎ 020 7286 9457, 020 8459 8727

MCALEA Kevin (*Sax, Gtr*): 1 Abbots Place, London NW6 4NP ☎ 020 7624 5404

MCCAFFERY Lisa (*Voc*): 127 Honeywell Road, London SW11 6ED ☎ 020 7738 2134

MCCAULEY Shem: 1 Lancaster Court, 103 Lancaster Road, London W11 1QN ☎ 020 7221 5361

MCCUTCHEON Lee (*Dms*): 9 Dean Close, Pydford, Woking, Surrey GU22 8NX ☎ 019323 52161

MCCUTCHEON Steve (*Sax*): 9 The Alders, West Byfleet, Surrey KT14 6PH ☎ 01932 342561

MCDONALD David: c/o Fruit, Unit 104, The Saga Centre, 326 Kensal Road, London W10 5BZ ☎ 020 8964 8448

MCEVOY Michael (*Gtr, Arr, B Gtr*): 80C Olive Road, London NW2 6UL ☎ 020 8208 0031

MCGUINNESS Sara (*B Gtr*): 269 Lyham Road, London SW2 5NS ☎ 020 8678 1398

MCRACKEN Dave (*Gtr, Dms*): Ground Floor Flat, 18 Maclise Road, London W14 0PR ☎ 020 7602 2024, 0468 276494

MEEHAN Paul: 84A Kyverdale Road, London N16 6PL ☎ 020 8806 9131

MELODY: 22 Binyon House, Milton Grove, London N16 8QT ☎ 020 7503 8392

MELOY Stephen (*Gtr, Voc*): 11 Knowles Hill Crescent, Hither Green, London SE13 6DT ☎ 020 8244 6725

MELTDOWN (NICK)

MERRELL Crispin: The Oaks, Chessington Close, Epsom KT19 9EQ

MESSIANIST Mashal: 12 Stockfield Road, Streatham Hill, London SW16 2LR ☎ 020 8696 7330

MICHELMORE Guy (*Cntrc*): 35 Binden Road, London W12 9RJ ☎ 020 8740 7727, 020 8743 2523 fax

MILLER John (*Synth*): Court Music, 106 Sussex Rd, Harrow, Middx HA1 4NB ☎ 020 8861 5621

MILLER Johnny (*Per, Dms, Tpt*): Flat 5, 60 Kelross Road, London N5 2QJ ☎ 020 7226 3453

MILLER Paul (*Voc*): 43 Teddington Park, Teddington, Middlesex TW11 8DE ☎ 020 8977 6308

MINDLINKK *(Voc, Dms, B Gtr)*: 23 St Helier Court, De-Beauvoir Road, London N1 5SD ☎ 020 8493 0065 & fax, 0956 678085 mob

MINOGUE Kylie: Att: Mandy Welterveden, Ernst & Young, Becket House, 1 Lambeth Palace Road, London SE1 7EU ☎ 020 7928 2000, 020 7401 2136 fax

MINOTT Paulette *(Voc)*: 15 Wyatt Close, Vaughn Street, Off Rotherhithe Street, London SE16 1UL ☎ 020 7252 3966, 0831 196161, 020 7252 3966

MOBERLEY Gary *(Org, Arr)*: Flat 4, Grove End House, 150 Grove Terrace, London NW5 0PD ☎ 020 7267 3236

MODESTE Chris

MOJSIEJENKO Nicholas *(Md, Com, Arr)*: 25 Gabriel Street, Forest Hill, London SE23 1DW ☎ 020 8699 2838

MOON Jon *(Gtr)*: 104 Fortis Green Road, Muswell Hill, London N10 3HN ☎ 020 8444 2713, 0973 239032

MOORE David: 5 Eden Mansions, Gondar Gardens, London NW6 1HE ☎ 020 7435 9674

MOORE Timothy: 71 Parkhouse Road, Minehead, Somerset TA24 8AE ☎ 01643 706719

MORAN Paul *(Org)*: 1 Hill Court, Stanhope Road, Highate, London N6 5AP ☎ 020 8482 5839, 0374 157783

MORE Jonathon *(Dms)*: 15 Elmwood Road, Herne Hill, London SE24 9NU ☎ 020 7738 5904

MORRISON Clifton *(Voc)*: 181 Portnall Road, London W9 3BN ☎ 020 8969 6748

MOWAT Andrew: Flat 1, 20 Wightman Road, Harringay, London N4 1SQ ☎ 020 8374 3578

MOWAT William *(Pf)*: 88 Tennyson Road, London NW6 7SB ☎ 020 7328 5454

MUNNS Roger *(Clt)*: 1 Cornwall Close, Eton Wick, Berks SL4 6NB ☎ 01753 851017

MURANYI George *(Pf)*: Top Flat, 18 Carlton Hill, London NW8 0JY

MURPHY Graham *(Pf, Gtr)*: 10 Glasilawn Avenue, Glasnevin, Dublin 11, Ireland ☎ 003531 8361024

NASCIMENTO Joao *(Gtr)*: 9A Beethoven Street, London W10 4LG ☎ 020 8904 4941

NASMYTH Nicholas: 9B Almorah Road, Islington, London N1 3EN ☎ 020 7226 7383, 020 7226 7383

NEAL Tam *(Com, Arr)*: 32 Gisburn Mnsns., Tottenham Lane, London N8 7EB ☎ 020 8340 2287

NEMO *(Gtr)*: 12 Cleveland Mansions, 44 Willesden Lane, Kilburn, London NW6 7SY

NICHOLS Thomas *(Per, Dms)*: 49 Northwold Road, Stoke Newington, London N16 7DH

NICHOLSON Patrick *(Gtr, Dms)*: 206 Stockwell Road, London SW9 9TB ☎ 020 7978 9726

NOBLE Joseph: 50 Compton Road, Winchmore Hill, London N21 3NS ☎ 020 8360 3433, 0956 402241 mob

NORMAN Chuck *(Gtr, B Gtr, Voc)*: c/o Solar Management, 42-48 Charlbert Street, London NW8 7BU ☎ 020 7722 4175, 020 7722 4072 fax

NORMAN Russ V: 8 Streatham Vale, London SW16 5TE ☎ 020 8764 2590

NORRIS Richard *(B Gtr, Dms)* ☎ 020 8299 2929

NWACHUKWU Anthony: 50 Old Hospital Close, London SW12 8SS ☎ 020 8767 0375, 0956 366639 mob, 020 7336 0423

O'NEILL Justin: 76 Grange Road, Chessington, Surrey KT9 1FY ☎ 020 8715 6548

OAKLEY Lawrence: 1St Floor, 175 Tooting High Street, London SW17 0SZ ☎ 020 8682 4585

OBERMAYER Paul: 66B Mildmay Road, London N1 4NG ☎ 020 7275 8143

ODELL Ann *(Voc)*: 24 Dodds Park, Brockham, Betchworth, Surrey RH3 7LD ☎ 01737 842442

OFORI Geffrye *(Dms, B Gtr, A Sax)*: 172 Brookscroft Road, Walthamstow, London E17 4JR

OGILVIE Carlton Bubblers *(Dms)*: 48 Roundwood Road, Willesden, London NW10 9TJ ☎ 020 8451 1539

ORFORD Tim *(Gtr)*: The Thornton Flat, 180 Kingston Hill, Kingston-on-Thames, Surrey KT2 7SX

OSBORNE Stephen *(B Gtr, Tbn, Pf)*: c/o 140 Db, 1 Mccrone Mews, Belsize Vuillage, London NW3 5BG

OWEN Billy *(B Gtr, Gtr)*: 47 Gilbert Road, London SE11 4NQ ☎ 020 7820 3914

OXENDALE Peter: 20 Comyn Road, Battersea, London SW11 1QD ☎ 020 7350 2619

P.T.P. *(Per, Voc)*: 1 Pepys Court, 84-86 The Chase, Clapham Common, London SW4 0NF ☎ 020 7720 7266, 020 7720 7255 fax

PALIN Tom: 11 Charlton Kings Road, Kentish Town, London NW5 2SB ☎ 020 7209 2987

PAREIS *(Voc)*: 86A Union Road, Clapham, London SW4 6JU ☎ 020 7622 8566

PARIS Ronnie *(Gtr)*: 48 Alma Road, Wandsworth, London SW18 1AB ☎ 020 8871 9279

PARISH Joseph: Flat 2, 62 Princes Square, Bayswater, London W2 ☎ 020 7229 6621

PARK Alan: 134 Annandale Road, Greenwich, London SE10 ☎ 020 8853 1069

PARKER Ian *(Pf, Synth)*: 1A Probyn Road, Tulse Hill, London SW2 3LH ☎ 020 8671 6183, 0468 572569, 020 8671 6183

PARKES Steve *(Pf, Voc, Com, Arr)*: 9 Lichfield Way, South Croydon, Surrey CR2 8SD ☎ 020 8657 8363

PAYNE Laurence *(Md)*: 43 Farnham Road, Seven Kings, Ilford, Essex IG3 8QD ☎ 020 8599 1205

PAYNE Richard *(Pf, Org, Gtr)*: 46B Allen Road, London N16 8SA

PEARN Jon: 77 Beverley Road, Whyteleafe, Surrey CR3 0AU ☎ 020 8668 0245

PEASE Mark: 36 Ringshall Road, St Pauls Cray, Orpington, Kent BR5 2LZ ☎ 01689 833897

PEPPER Otis *(Pf, Voc)*: 100 Brampton Road, Kingsbury, London NW9 9DD ☎ 020 8238 9103, 0956 541575 mob

PERILLI Filiberto: 21 Wycherley Close, Blackheath, London SE3 7QH ☎ 020 7894 7077, 020 7617 7077

PETRIE Jamie *(Gtr, Sax)*: 9 Curwen Road, London W12 9AF ☎ 020 8740 6248, 020 8746 1113

PETTET Colin: 28 Burnt Ash Lane, Bromley, Kent BR1 4DH ☎ 020 8464 6489

PHETHEAN Guy *(B Gtr, Voc)*: 47 Prout Grove, Neasden, London NW10 1PU ☎ 020 8450 0150

PHILLIPS Josh *(Com, Pf, Org)*: 44 Hampton Court Parade, Hampton Court, Surrey KT8 9HE ☎ 020 8979 7507, 0421 414 990 mob

PHILLIPS Phil *(Voc, B Ldr)*: 1 St Crispins Way, Ottershaw, Surrey KT16 0RE ☎ 01932 873782

PLATO Graham: 27 Ambler Road, London N4 2QT ☎ 020 7359 3425

PLYTAS Nick: Garden Flat, 17A St.Charles Square, London W10 6EF ☎ 020 8960 1384 & fax

PRECIOUS *(Voc)*: 73 Kevan House, Wyndham Road, Camberwell, London SE5 0LR ☎ 020 7277 0932, 0956 913434 mob, 020 7703 6051

PRIME Matthew *(Gtr, B Gtr)* ☎ 020 8788 8238, 0585 029283

PRIZEMAN Robert *(Com, Arr)*: 8 Highwold, Chipstead, Surrey CR5 3LG ☎ 01737 556110

QUANTISE Brucie *(Gtr)* ☎ 01483 822420

QUEEN Rhythm: 39A Blenheim Crescent, London W11 2EF ☎ 0956 508 783 mob

QUENUM Phillipe *(Club Dj)*: 70 Ripplevale Grove, London N1 1HT ☎ 020 7607 2214

QUINN Peter *(Pf, Fo Fdl, Bod)*: 66A Ivydale Road, London SE15 3BS ☎ 020 7635 5908

RACE Raymond: 44 Windsor Avenue, North Cheem, Surrey SM3 9RX ☎ 020 8644 7649

RALLIE DE GALES Flora : 23 West Avenue, London NW4 9LL ☎ 020 8203 4185, 0421 528136 mob, 020 8203 4185 fax

RANDALL David: Basement, 10 Lanark Road, London W9 1DA ☎ 020 7286 9709

RANX Bubbler

RATTEE Gina *(Per)*: 22 Orchard Road, Kingston, Surrey KT1 2QW ☎ 020 8546 1866

READ Andrew *(Md)*: 50 St Johns Avenue, Brentwood, Essex CM14 5DG ☎ 01277 231030

REBBECK James: Flat 3, 20 Hornton Street, Kensington High Street, London W8 4NR ☎ 020 7937 9062, 0467 810697 mob

REEVE Don: 36 Mount Ephraim Lane, London SW16 1JD ☎ 020 8769 6425

REID Adrian: 1 Greenside Rd, Croydon, Surrey CR0 3PP ☎ 020 8684 9500

REID Errol (*Com*): 33 Ravensbourne Rd, Catford, London SE6 4UU ☎ 020 7737 3462

REID Horace (*Gtr, Per*): 35 Winterslow House, Flaxman Road, London SE5 9DQ ☎ 020 7274 1129

REID Paul ☎ 07654 266900 pager

REID Rickardo: 7 Glendown House, Amhurst Road, Hackney, London E8 2AR ☎ 020 7254 0953, 020 8244 3922

REINHARDT Max (*Synth, Gtr, Acc*): 9 Parklands Road, London SW16 6TB ☎ 020 8677 2857, 020 8677 0763

RENNOLDSON Philip: 126A Avenue Mansions, Alexandra Park Road, Muswell Hill, London N10 2AH ☎ 020 8883 4964

RHODES Sue (*Sax, Voc*): 55 Bedells Avenue, Black Notley, Braintree, Essex CM7 8LZ ☎ 01376 340485, 0370 885250

RICHARD Kelvin (*Arr*): The Dub Funk Association, PO Box 557, Harrow HA2 8QE ☎ 020 8864 4394, 020 8933 1027 fax

RICHES Peter ☎ 020 8740 0046, 020 8743 3003

RICHMAN Colin: 45 Preston Road, London SE19 3HG ☎ 020 8761 3885, 020 8670 6699

RIJEBERO James (*Gtr, Vla*): 4 Oval Road, London NW1 7EB ☎ 020 7284 2065, 0961 191941

RISTIC Boris (*Dms*): 72 Nicholl House, Woodberry Down, London N4 2TQ ☎ 020 8211 7616

RIX Geoff (*Pf, Gtr*) ☎ 020 8841 5305 & fax

ROBB Calvin: 3 Lawrence Way, Quainton Village, Neasden, London NW10 0AL ☎ 020 8830 5380

ROBBINS Ben: 178A Merton High Street, Wimbledon, London SW19 1AY ☎ 0956 570807

ROBINSON John: 76 Cotleigh Road, Westhampstead, London NW6 2NP

ROBINSON Julie (*Voc, Pf*): 22 Ashley Crescent, London SW11 5QY ☎ 020 7223 2617

ROBINSON Robbie: 11 St Saviours Road, West Croydon, Surrey CR0 2XE ☎ 020 8665 9748, 020 8665 5054

ROCSTEADY (*Dms*) ☎ 020 8926 8531, 0956 845429 mob

ROMERO Nick (*Gtr, B Gtr, Voc*): 35 Roseberry Gardens, Cranham, Upminster, Essex RM14 1NN ☎ 01708 228472

ROSCOE Alan (*Dms*): 165 Montrose Avenue, Welling, Kent DA16 2QT ☎ 020 8856 4829

ROSE David (*Pf, Org*): 108 Durlston Road, Kingston-upon-Thames, Surrey KT2 5RU ☎ 020 8549 2618

ROSE Mike (*Pf, Gtr, Voc, Per*): Rose & Foster Productions, 37 Skylines Village, Limeharbour, Docklands, London E14 9XT ☎ 020 7537 2147 & fax

ROSS Atticus: 267 Kensal Road, London W10 5DB ☎ 020 8964 2196

ROWE Matthew (*Pf*): c/o Prager & Fenton, Midway House, 27 -29 Cursitor Street, London EC4A 1LT ☎ 020 7831 4200

ROWLAND Greg (Aka Doctor X): 32 Hanover Gardens, The Oval, London SE11 5TN ☎ 020 7582 4145, 020 7735 4888 fax

ROWLANDS Tom (*Gtr*): Flat 4, 19 Moorhouse Road, London W2 5DH ☎ 020 7221 9703

RUSSELL Mark: 46 Northolme Road, London N5 2UX ☎ 020 7354 4834, 0410 098335 mob

SABIU Marco: 70 Priory Road, London NW6 3RE ☎ 020 7916 3303, 020 7916 3302

SAMPSON Andy ☎ 020 8922 6268

SANDY (*Bq Flt, Cel*): 101 Wrottesley Rd, London NW10 5TY ☎ 020 8961 8925

SARGEANT Bob (*Voc, Per, Mrba*): 185 Chevening Road, London NW6 6DT ☎ 020 8969 1287

SASHA (*Dms, Per, Gtr, Voc*): 31-33 Ansleigh Place, Off Strenleigh Place, London W11 4BW ☎ 020 7221 0044

SAUL T (*B Gtr*): 5A Farm Road, Hove, E Sussex BN3 1FB ☎ 0973 327354

SAUNDERS Malcolm (*Pf, Org*): 27 Paul's Place, Ashtead, Surrey KT21 1HN ☎ 0958 540057 mob

SAVANNAH Jonn (*Voc, Gtr, Sax*): Little Barn, Plaistow Road, Loxwood, Billingshurst, West Sussex RH14 0SX ☎ 01403 753564

SAVILLE Alex (*B Gtr*): 64 Caterham Avenue, Clayhall, Ilford, Essex IG5 0QA ☎ 020 8550 2194

SAWYER Phil (*Gtr*): 10 Eton Road, Chalk Farm, London NW3 4SS ☎ 020 7586 7706

SCHNEIDER Jonathan (*Vln*): 2 Dalkeith Grove, Stanmore, Middlesex HA7 4SG ☎ 020 8958 3372, 020 8958 3372

SCOOPER Nick (*Gtr*): 343 Chiswick High Road, London W4 4HS ☎ 0117 987 9674

SCOTT Clive: 17 Luff Close, Windsor, Berks SL4 4NP ☎ 01753 855251

SCOTT Fred (*Com*): 164 The Glade, Shirley, Surrey CR0 7UE ☎ 020 8654 0713, 020 8654 0196

SCOTT Mark: 10 Glennie Court, Lordship Lane, London SE22 8NY

SCOTT Robin (*Voc, Tpt, Gtr*): 36 Calvert Road, Greenwich, London SE10 0DF ☎ 020 8853 0898

SCOTT Vyvyon: 377A St Margarets Road, St Margarets, Twickenham, Middlesex TW1 1PP ☎ 020 8744 2488

SEBASTIAN Tania (*Pf, Gtr*): 4 Oakdene, Oaks Avenue, London SE19 1RB

SEMPLICI Valerio (*Hrn, Sax, B Gtr*): Via Carlo V, 11, 42015 Correggio (Re), Italy

SEYMOUR Patrick (*Kbds*): 61 Nightingale Road, Woodley, Reading, Berks RG3 3LU

SHAFRAN Dan J (*Tpt*): 3 Windermere Road, London N10 2RD ☎ 020 8444 7069, 0956 585 015

SHAIKH Aziz (*Gtr*): 32 Erskine Road, Walthamstow, London E17 6RZ ☎ 020 8509 1380

SHARPE John (*S Sax, Flt, Vln, Kbds*): 9 Bosgrove Road, Chingford, London E4 6QT ☎ 020 8529 8323

SHARPE William: The Lodge, Theydon Mount, Epping, Essex CM16 7PW ☎ 01992 560621

SHENTON Ann: 7A Cornwall Crescent, Ladbroke Grove, London W11 1PH ☎ 020 7460 1829, 0958 781246

SHIPSTON Roy: 2 Selwyn Court, Church Road, Richmond, Surrey TW10 6LR ☎ 020 8940 4508

SHORT-PULLMAN Darren (*Pf, Com*): 62A Wrythe Lane, Carshalton, Surrey SM5 2RP ☎ 020 8641 6210

SHORTEN Jonathan: 46 Glenluce Road, Blackheath, London SE3 7SB ☎ 020 8293 1875, 0976 692 125

SHORTER Dwayne: 11 Britannia Close, Bowlnad Road, Clapham, London SW4 7NN ☎ 020 7627 3338, 07957 701 708

SIMENON Tim (*Dms*): c/o Martin Greene Ravden, 55 Loudoun Road, St Johns Wood, London NW8 0DL ☎ 020 7625 4545

SIMMONDS Mickey (*Gtr*): 194 Hersham Rd, Walton-on-Thames, Surrey KT12 5QB ☎ 01932 245533, 01932 245533

SIMON Daniel: 14 Southborough House, Kingslake St, London SE17 2LJ

SISLEY John: 2A Eton Road, Orpington, Kent BR6 9HE ☎ 01689 606973

SKARBEK Charlie (*Gtr, Voc*): Andredsbourne, Coggins Mill Lane, Mayfield, East Sussex TN20 6UN ☎ 01435 872583

SKARBEK Sacha (*B Gtr*): 26 Belsize Square, London NW3 4HU ☎ 0191 431 7187, 0973 396312 mob

SKI: Flat C, 34 Alkham Road, London N16 7AA ☎ 020 7502 1094, 0973 387402

SMART David (*B Gtr, Dms*): 10 Cedar Close, Newbold College, St Marks Road, Binfield, Berks RG42 4AN ☎ 0956 350929 mob

SMILES Micky (*Pf, Gtr*) ☎ 020 8245 3226, 0468 374940

SMITH Andrew (*Pf*): 43 Shekespeare Road, Bexleyheath, Kent DA7 4SF ☎ 020 8303 3878

SMITH Barry (*Dms*): 8 Gisburn House, Friary Est, Friary Road, Peckham, London SE15 1SE ☎ 020 7277 6737

SMITH Carlton (*Gtr, Voc*): 60 Penwortham Road, Streatham, London SW16 6RE ☎ 0956 281084 mob, 020 8769 0089

SMITH Michael: 18 Grosvenor Gardens, London, London SW14 8BY ☎ 020 8876 0524, 020 8878 2742 fax

SMY Jamie: 128 Telford Avenue, London SW2 4XQ ☎ 020 8671 8247

SNELL David (*Gtr*): All Saints House, Woodvill Road, Leatherhead, Surrey KT22 7BP ☎ 01372 372728, 0956 446722 mob

SONOROUS STAR (*Synth, Bong, Cong*): 17A Beacon Hill, London N7 9LY ☎ 020 7700 4140, 0956 590251 mob

SOYEMI Roger: 3 Carlton House, Canterbury Terrace, Kilburn, London NW6 5DY ☎ 020 7328 1083

SPAREY Lee (*Tpt*): 35 Landor Road, London SW9 9RT ☎ 020 7274 0687, 0973 745915

SPENCE Eddy (*Arr, Com*): 3 Kendal Lane, Tockwith, York YO5 8QN ☎ 01423 358044

SPENCER Atheen (*Voc*) ☎ 07775 942 116 mob

SPONDER Timothy: 2A Curzon Road, Muswell Hill, London N10 2RA ☎ 020 8444 5395 & fax, 0370 520710 mob

SPRINGER Joyce (*Voc*): 160 Goldhurst Terr., London NW6 3HP ☎ 020 7328 1319

STACEY Luke (*Db, Voc, Per*): 4 Brittania Road, Ilford, Essex IG1 2EQ ☎ 020 8478 0276

STAINTON Christopher: 35 Herons Court, Lightwater, Surrey GU18 5YF

STANNARD Richard (*Gtr, Voc*): c/o Prager &Fenton, Midway House, 27-29 Cursitor Street, London EC4A 1LT ☎ 020 8983 5853

STATHAM Paul (*Gtr, B Gtr*): 94A East Dulwich Road, East Dulwich, London SE22 9AT ☎ 020 8299 4805

STEWART Ian: Flat 30, Quadrant House, Burrell Street, London SE1 0UW ☎ 020 7928 3779

STEWART Mark (*Sax, Clt*): 62A Warwick Gardens, London W14 8PP ☎ 020 7565 2665, 0956 826065 mob

STIRLING Jesus (*Pf, B Gtr*): 7 Halifax Ave, Kingston, Jamaica W.I.

STIRLING Marlon: 39 Princehenry Road, Charlton, London SE7 8PP ☎ 020 8473 2918, 0956 167976

STOCK Nigel: 69 College Ride, Bagshot, Surrey GU19 5EW ☎ 01276 479780

STONE Rufus (*Voc, Song W*): 390 Larkshall Road, London E4 9JB ☎ 020 8527 1335

STONEY Kevin: 1 Paramount Court, University Street, London WC1E 6JP ☎ 020 7387 6742

STRAKER Tony ☎ 020 8372 5842, 0958 781 725

STRETCH (*Voc*): 85 Orford Road, Walthamstow, London E17 9QR ☎ 020 8520 2774, 0958 688578 mob

SUAREZ Isa (*Voc, Com, Song W*): 4 Ribbon Dance Mews, London SE5 8JT ☎ 020 7701 0539

SULLIVAN Richard (*Gtr*): 60 Gleneagle Road, London SW16 6AF ☎ 020 8677 1681

SUSIMI Dele (*Gtr, Sax, Voc*): 7B Northlands Street, Camberwell, London SE5 9PL ☎ 020 8357 0663, 0961 171 739 mob, 020 8357 0663

SUTHERLAND Kevin (*Synth*): 169 Farmilo Road, Walthamstow, London E17 8JP ☎ 020 8539 3964

SVEINSSON Oskar (*Dms*): 2 Elmar Court, 736 Fulham Road, London SW6 5SQ ☎ 020 7731 8037

TAUBEN Michael (*Arr, Com*): 42 Clevedon Mansions, Lissenden Gardens, London NW5 1QP ☎ 020 7267 5875

TAYLOR Mark (*Gtr, Voc*): 33 Ouseley Road, Wraysbury, Staines, Middlesex TW19 5JB ☎ 01784 482560

TAYLOR Mark (*Gtr*): 42 Kempe Road, London NW6 6SJ ☎ 020 8969 6421

TAYLOR Paul (*B Gtr, Per*): Flat 5, 37 Sisters Avenue, Clapham Common Northside, London SW11 5SR ☎ 020 7924 4863, 0802 321438 mob, 020 7642 1233 fax

TAYLOR Phil (*Synth, Gtr, B Gtr, Voc*): 6 Newick Road, London E5 0RR ☎ 020 8985 3384

TAYLOR Tot (*Gtr, Com, Arr*): c/o Poppy, 14A Hornsey Rise, London N19 3SB ☎ 020 7281 0018

TELFORD Duncan (*Tpt*): Flat 5, 19-23 Kingslnd Road, London E2 8AA ☎ 020 7729 9248

THAKRAR Kiran (*Harm*): 30 Westmorland Road, North Harrow, Middlesex HA1 4PL ☎ 020 8427 7952

THOMAS Adrian: 6 Glendale Drive, Wimbledon, London SW19 7BG ☎ 020 8879 3788

THOMAS Alan: 39 Robert Owen House, Fulham Palace Road, London SW6 6JA ☎ 020 7386 7112

THOMAS James (*Tnd Per, Dms, Arr, Com*): 177 Sangley Road, London SE6 2DY ☎ 0956 385088

THOMPSON Jason (*Pf, Org, Voc, Gtr*): 79 Bradgate Road, Catford, London SE6 4TT ☎ 020 8314 1673, 0958 444532 mob, 020 8469 3908

THOMPSON Rod (*B Gtr*): 73 Bromfelde Road, London SW4 6PP ☎ 020 7720 0866

THORNHILL Leeroy (*Dms*)

TIMMS Arthur (*Pf*): 172 Birkbeck Road, Beckenham, Kent BR3 4SS ☎ 020 8778 4871

TIMOTHY Michael: 29 A Buxton Road, London NW2 5BL ☎ 020 8459 6086

TOBIN Penelope: 74A Woodland Gardens, Muswell Hill, London N10 N10 3UB ☎ 020 8883 0172

TODD Paul (*B Gtr, Voc*): 3 Rosehart Mews, 165A Westbourne Grove, London W11 3JN ☎ 020 7229 9776

TREZISE Henry (*Voc, Pf*): Gaybrooke House, 47 Prentis Road, Streatham, London SW16 1QB ☎ 020 8677 1715

TROY (*Voc*): 67A Alexandra Drive, Upper Norwood, London SE19 1AN ☎ 020 8670 6694, 020 8670 6694

TRUELOVE John (*Per*): Unit G, 44 St Pauls Crescent, London NW1 9TN ☎ 020 7833 4013

TRZETRZELEWSKA Barbara (*Voc*): c/o Mr D White, 59 Swains Lane, London N6 6QL ☎ 020 7813 9918, 020 7419 9714

UDHIN Reza (*Gtr, Voc, Dms*): 27 Rutland Road, Forest Gate, London E7 8PQ ☎ 020 8471 0855 & fax, 0956 520195 mob

VAUK Ingo (*B Gtr, Gtr*): 56 Buchanan Gardens, London NW10 5AE ☎ 020 8968 3115

VEE Tony (*Gtr*): 232 Foresters Drive, Wallington, Surrey SM6 9LE ☎ 020 8763 9055

VESSEY Oliver (*Pf, B Gtr*): 45 Crouch Hill, London N4 4AJ ☎ 020 7263 4933

VETTESE Peter (*Pf*): 133 London Road, Ewell, Epsom, Surrey KT17 2BS ☎ 020 8224 3004, 020 8224 3066

VINCENT Amanda (*Per*): Flat 5, 15A Cricklewood Broadway, London NW2 3JX ☎ 020 8450 1189 & fax, 0958 300679 mob

VIRGO Martin (*Com, Arr*): The Garden Flat, 17 Celia Road, Islington, London N19 5ET ☎ 020 7700 5045

VOWLES Iona ☎ 020 8571 9217

WADDINGTON Martin (*Md, Arr*): Groote Noord 17, 1141 TZ Monnickendam, The Netherlands ☎ +31 299 651450

WADE Christine (*Synth, Per*): c/o Blue Crumb Truck, PO Box 416, Cardiff CF1 8XU ☎ 020 7833 4013

WAKEMAN Rick: c/o Bajonor Ltd, Bajonor House, 2 Bridge Street, Peel, Isle Of Man ☎ 01624 844134

WALLACE Maria (*Voc*): 27 West Avenue, Walthamstow, London E17 9QN ☎ 020 8521 2306

WALLINGER Karl (*Voc*): 15-16 Brooks Mews, London W1Y 1LF ☎ 020 7493 7385

WALTERS Simon (*Md, Com*): 32 Clissold Cres, Clissold Park, London N16 9BE ☎ 020 7254 0825, 0374 166830

WARBY Frank (*B Gtr, Org, Voc*): 316 Upminster Road North, Rainham, Essex RM13 9RY ☎ 01708 553873

WARD David (*Dms*): Unit H Blackhorse Mews, Blackhorse Lane, London E17 6SL ☎ 020 8531 1118, 0958 229 888

WARE Martin: 33 Princess Road, London NW1 8JS

WARE Peter: 27 Fairfield Road, Bourneheath, Bromsgrove, Worcs B61 9JW ☎ 01527 875221

WARNOCK Colin (*Pf*): 20 Norfolk Avenue, Sanderstead, South Croydon, Surrey CR2 8BN ☎ 020 8657 0972

WATERS Miles (*Saxes, Flt, Gtr*): 10 Glade Road, Marlow, Bucks SL7 1DY ☎ 01628 72857

WATSON John (*Arr, Com, Voc*): 2 Aston View, Hemel Hempstead, Herts HP2 7NY

WATTS Dave (*Pf*): 24 Park View, Wembley, Middlesex HA9 6JX

WATTS Steve (*Org, Pf*): 3 Tamworth Place, Croydon, Surrey CR0 1RL, 0958 499875 mob

WAUGH Graham: 67A Gloucester Avenue, London NW1 ☎ 020 7372 6455, 020 7485 4255

WAYNE Jeff: Lyndhurst, Green Street, Shenley, Herts WD7 9BD ☎ 020 8207 5909

WEAVER Blue: 28 Craven Hill Mews, London W2 3DY ☎ 020 7402 3393, 0958 581778 mob

WEBB Laurant (*Gtr, Per*): 28-30 Wood Wharf, Horseferry Place, Greenwich, London SE10 9BT ☎ 020 8858 9974

WEIR Keith (*Gtr, Voc*): 128 Wellfield Road, Streatham, London SW16 2BU ☎ 020 8769 4580, 0958 647364

WEISZ Peter (*Pf, B Gtr, Voc, Gtr*): Fairway, Chesington Avenue, London N3 3DP ☎ 020 8371 8211

WELLS Richard: 64A Bovingdon Road, Fulham, London SW6 2AP ☎ 020 7731 7337 & fax

WESSON Melvyn (*Com*): 32 Cambridge Cottages, Kew, Surrey TW9 3AY

WESTERGAARD Michael: Studio 99, 99 Herbert Road, London SE18 3QH ☎ 020 8854 0860

WESTLEY Geoff (*Con, Flt*): The Cottage, Holmdale, Holmbury St Mary, Surrey RH5 6NR ☎ 01306 731212

WHEATLEY Jeremy (*Per*): 74B Streathbourne Road, London SW17 8QY ☎ 020 8682 0274, 0468 808030

WHELAN Tim (*Gtr, Flt, Voc*): 5 Didbin House, Mingard Walk, London N7 7RT ☎ 020 7358 0293

WHERRY Ian: 26 Coopers Avenue, Heybridge, Maldon, Essex CM9 7YX ☎ 01621 840930

WHITE Kevin (*Gtr*): 172A Arlington Road, Camden Town, London NW1 7HL ☎ 0956 337057 mob

WHITE Peter (*Gtr*): Address Unknown

WHITMORE Andrew: 39 Greystoke Park Terrace, Ealing, London W5 1JL ☎ 020 8998 5529

WHITTLE Sean (*B Gtr*): 15 Wells House Road, North Acton, London NW10 6ED ☎ 020 8961 0642

WICKENS (WIX) Paul: 48 Dukes Ave, London N10 2PU ☎ 020 8444 2007

WILKINS George (*Hmca*): 6 Frankfurt Road, Herne Hill, London SE24 9NY

WILKINSON Sly: Boomtown, The Gatehouse, Valetta Road, London W3 7TQ ☎ 020 8723 9548 & fax

WILLIAMS David (*Voc, Gtr, B Gtr*): 40 Adamsrill Road, London SE26 4AN ☎ 020 8244 3107

WILLIAMS David (*Voc, B Gtr, Rh Gtr*): 51 Dongola Road, London N17 6EB ☎ 020 8808 1474

WILLIAMS Hamish (*Voc*): 31 Cobham Road, South Norwood, London SE25 5NY ☎ 0956 422126

WILLIAMS Jake: Flat 15, 198 St John Street, London EC1V 4JY ☎ 020 7253 9990

WILLIAMS Jake: Flat 6, 18 Acton Street, London WC1X 9ND ☎ 020 7833 0881

WILLIAMS Paul (*Pf, Synth, Com, Md*): The Moorings, 3 High View, Cheam, Surrey SM2 7DZ ☎ 020 8642 3665, 0956 367623

WILLOX Bill (*Pf, Arr*): 20B Cloudesley Square, London N1 0HN ☎ 020 7833 8713

WILSON Paul (*Gtr, Hrn*): Native Mgnt, Unit 32, Ransomes Dock, 35-37 Parkgate Road, London SW11 4NP ☎ 020 7738 1919

WINDRICH Erik (*Gtr, Flt, Per*): 69 Eastcote Lane, South Harrow, Middlesex HA2 8DE

WINSTANLEY Liz (*Voc*): Flat 9 Delta Court, Coles Green Road, Cricklewood, London NW2 7HB ☎ 020 8450 7495

WOODMAN E (*Org, Voc*): Address Unknown ☎ 020 8881 5689

WOOLF Tim (*Gtr*): 77 Viola Avenue, Feltham, Middlesex TW14 0EN ☎ 020 8890 2952

WORRALL Bill (*B Gtr, Voc, Arr*): 55 Glentrammon Road, Green Street Green, Orpington, Kent BR6 6DF ☎ 01689 853217, 0973 197921 mob, 01689 600943 fax

WRAY Jeremy (*Gtr, Voc*): 61 Fulham Park Gdns, London SW6 4LB ☎ 020 7731 1285

WRIGHT Andrew: 52 Donnington Road, London NW10 3QU ☎ 020 8451 6754

YAAKOB Ahmad (*Voc*): 87 Fairlop Road, Leytonstone, London E11 1BE

YARDE James: 19 Rowden Road, Beckenham, Kent BR3 4NA ☎ 020 8402 3055

YEADON Gus (*Gtr, Flt, Voc*): 5 Branksome Road, Merton Park, London SW19 3AW ☎ 020 8543 6496

YORK Adrian (*Arr*): 25 Marksbury Ave, Kew, Richmond, Surrey TW9 4JE ☎ 020 8878 3102, 0370 348293 mob, 020 8255 3105 fax

YOUNG Kate (*Md*): 2A Newton Road, Cricklewood, London NW2 6PR ☎ 020 8208 2849

YOUNG Simon: Address Unknown ☎ 020 8399 9956, 0410 761697 mob, 020 8399 9946

ZAGORSKI-THOMAS Simon: 132 Camden Street, London NW1 0HY ☎ 020 7482 1237

ZEN Guidd (*Gtr, B Gtr, Voc*): 52 Bathfield Road, London SW16 5NY ☎ 020 8696 0048

ZICKUS Darius Dizzy (*Tbn, Gtr*): Flat 13, 100/102 Sutherland Avenue, Maida Vale, London W9 2QR ☎ 0956 479571 mob

ZIMMER Hans: 1 Brighton Road, Redhill, Surrey RH1 6PW

KORA

LONDON

RAVI (JP.FREEMAN) (*Gtr, Per, Song W*): 174A Alexandra Road, London N10 2ES ☎ 020 8883 3025, 0411 265011

KOTO

SOUTH EAST

HOLDING Melissa (*Pf, Acc*): 5 Butlers Court Road, Beaconsfield, Bucks HP9 1SF ☎ 01494 671584

LONDON

YANAGISAWA Rie (*Jap Stg*): 200 Russell Court, 3 Woburn Place, London WC1H 0HD ☎ 020 7278 4099

LATIN AMERICAN PERCUSSION

SCOTLAND

HUGGINS Christopher (*Cong, La Per, Af Dms*): 2 Beaumont Gate, Dowanhill, Glasgow G12 9EE ☎ 0141 357 1457

TOPPIN Jon (*Bong, Cong*): 66 Spittalfield Road, Inverkeithing, Fife KY11 1DY ☎ 01383 412703

NORTH WEST

ITESMAN Ras (*Bong, Cong, Per*): 53 Selworthy Road, Alex Estate, Moss-Side, Manchester M16 7UG ☎ 0161 226 5336

JAYASURIYA Arjuna (*La Per, Cong, Dms*): 9 Mayfield Mansions, 20 Alexandra Road South, Whalley Range, Manchester M16 8EZ ☎ 0161 226 3587

LEWIS Steve (*Cong, Per, Voc*): 56 Clarence Street, Lancaster LA2 3BB ☎ 01524 35193

SMALLEY Christine (*Cong, Per, Voc*): 284 Dickenson Road, Longsight, Manchester M13 0YL ☎ 0161 225 3086

THOMPSON Bob (*La Per*): c/o, Kitchen Corner, 3, Hightown, Crewe, Cheshire. CW1 3BP ☎ 01270 214424

NORTH EAST

BELL Sam (*La Per, Dms*): 15 Pasture Parade, Chapel Allerton, Leeds LS7 4QT ☎ 0113 2694611

CUMMINGS Andrew (*Cong, Bong, Dms, Per*): 7 Granville Terrace, Otley, West Yorkshire LS21 3EJ ☎ 01943 467719

RIVERA Paco (*Cong, Timb, Bong, Per*): 117 Western Way, Darras Hall, Newcastle NE20 9LY ☎ 01661 824094, 0498 902499

WINCKLESS Geoffrey (*La Per, Dms*): 122 Bayswater Road, Harehills, Leeds LS8 5NT ☎ 0113 248 1555

EAST

BUDD Matt (*Bong, Cong, Timb, Kbds*): 46 Coburg Place, South Woodham, Ferrers, Chelmsford, Essex CM3 5LY ☎ 01245 327062, 07971 092321

COTGROVE Mark (*La Per*): 20 Fernwood, Hadleigh, Essex SS7 2LT ☎ 01702 556228

GRACIE Leigh (*Cong, Per, Gtr*): 15 Edinburgh Close, Watton, Thetford, Norfolk IP25 6XJ ☎ 01603 618185

HYDE-SMITH Malek (*La Per, Dms*): Home Farm, Great Wilbraham, Cambridge CB1 5JW ☎ 01223 880319, 01223 881247

LATIN AMERICAN PERCUSSION - EAST

LIDGEY-HUTT Fiona (*La Per, Cong*): 55 Wildlake, Orton Malborne, Peterborough PE2 8PQ ☎ 01733 231 837

MIDLANDS

BYRNE Miki J (*Cong, Bong, Per*): 88 Gleave Road, Selly Oak, Birmingham B29 6JN ☎ 0121 471 1818

CLARE Steven (*La Per, Voc*): c/o 6 Woodland Road, Handsworth, Birmingham B21 0ER ☎ 0121 515 1558, 0121 523 5524

GILLIGAN Robert (*Cong, Dms*): 12 Bergamot Drive, Meir Park, Stoke-on-Trent, Staffs ST3 7FD ☎ 01782 399782, 0410 288182

MCGUIRE Edward (*Cong*): 14 Salcombe Avenue, Sheldon, Birmingham B26 3SQ ☎ 0121 743 3509, 0403 475277

WHEELER Andrew (*Timb, Dms, Per, B Gtr*): Mount View, Coleshill, Curdworth, Sutton Coldfield B76 9HP ☎ 01827 873094

WILTSHIRE Stuart (*Bong, Cong, Per, Gtr*): 9 Tanfield Road, Stechford, Birmingham B33 9ER ☎ 0121 608 9656

SOUTH EAST

ALBERGARIA-SAVILL Oli (*Cong, La Per*): 5 Uplands, Ashstead, Surrey KT21 2TN ☎ 01372 276715

BISHOP Roland (*La Per, Af Dms*): Top Flat, 43 St Andrews Road, Southsea, Hants PO5 1ER ☎ 023 9235 6936

RANDELL Malcolm (*La Per, Cong, Bong*): 19 Rushcombe Way, Corfe Mullen, Wimborne, Dorset BH21 3QR ☎ 01202 696032

SMITH Geoff (*La Per, Per, H Dul, Dms*): 108 Wilmington Way, Hollingbury, Brighton, Sussex BN1 8JF ☎ 559188

THOMPSON Matt (*Cong, Bong, Per*): 61 Eastgate Street, Winchester, Hampshire SO23 8DZ ☎ 01962 867612

VOLPILIERE-PIERROT Dan (*Cong, Per, Dms*): The Old Rectory, 43 Blatchington Hill, Seaford, Sussex BN25 2AL ☎ 01323 893485

LONDON

ACCIAIOLI Michael (*La Per, Dms*): Tamesis, Russell Road, Shepperton, Middlesex TW17 9HJ ☎ 01932 220280

AKPAN Sonny (*Cong, Dms, Per*): 2 Bronte House, Mayville Estate, Mathias Road, London N16 8LG ☎ 020 7503 9247

BALL Steve (*Cong, Bong, Berimbau, La Per*) ☎ 01992 767875

BARNES Neil (*Cong, Bong, Per*): c/o Leftfield, 9 Thorpe Close, London W10 5XL ☎ 020 8960 5055, 020 7737 5954 fax

BONGO BILLY (*Cong, Bong, Timb*): 18 Sarah Court, Lilliput Ave, Northolt, Middlesex UB5 5QL ☎ 020 8841 4842, 0402 379420 mob

COLLINGHAM Ray (*Cong, Per*): 56 Independent Place, London E8 2HE ☎ 020 7254 0174

CRAWFORD Paul (*Bong, Cong*): Flat 2, 49 Solon Road, Brixton, London SW4 5UU ☎ 020 7478 4607, 020 7478 4619

CRISP Joe (*La Per*): 34 Linden Avenue, London NW10 5RL ☎ 020 8960 0710

DAVIS Wendon (*Cong, Per, Voc*): c/o Mr Dale Davis, 71A Uxbridge Road, Shepherds Bush, London W12, 0378 757375 mob

DODD Tim (*Cong, La Per, Per*): Unit A1, Arena Business Centre, 71 Ashfield Road, London N4 1NY ☎ 020 8802 3999

ELLEN Sid (*Timb, Per*): 95 Grand Avenue, Surbiton, Surrey KT5 9HY

FLETCHER Chris (*La Per, Dms, Voc, B Gtr*): 106 Cleveland Gardens, London SW13 0AM ☎ 020 8878 4506, 0385 900432

FOX Steve (*La Per, Voc, Dms*): 6 Leybourne Road, Leytonstone, London E11 3BT ☎ 020 8530 7862

GADHVI Chandrashekhar (*Cong, Per*): 105 Vivian Avenue, Wembley, Middlesex HA9 6RH ☎ 020 8902 9768, 0958 504148 mob

GONZALEZ Jorge (*Timb, Cong, Bong, Tpt, Voc*): 44 Fawnbrake Avenue, Herne Hill, London SE24 0BY ☎ 020 7733 6818, 0958 792456, 020 7737 2447

HANKIN Paul (*Cong, Bong*): 57 Lingfield Avenue, Kingston, Surrey KT1 2TL ☎ 020 8549 8156

KARI-KARI Kofi (*Cong, Bong, Timb, La Per, Af*): 63 Hill Road, Muswell Hill, London N10 1JE ☎ 020 8444 5940

KHETERPAL Sudha (*Cong, Per, Tabla*): 102 Highgate Road, Kentish Town, London NW5 1PB ☎ 020 7482 2064

LURIE Robin (*La Per*): 31A Chapel Street Market, London N1 9EM ☎ 020 7837 4497

MATHUNJWA Julia (*Cong, Per*): 55 Acacia Road, Walthamstow, London E17 8BN ☎ 020 8509 2450, 0385 731256, 020 8509 2450

MATTHEWS Sean (*Cong, Dms, Per*): 73 Lewisham Way, London SE13 6QD ☎ 020 8355 4100

MILLER Dawson (*Cong*): 21E Keith Grove, London W12 9EY ☎ 020 8723 7767

MURRAY Neville (*Cong, Per, Voc, Timb, Af Dms*): 3C Clissold Road, London N16 9EX ☎ 020 7241 4711

NUZZOLI Gabriele (*La Per, Per, Dms, Cong*): Flat A, 471 Green Lanes, Palmers Green, London N13 4BS ☎ 0958 984636

ORR Hamish (*Cong, La Per*): 16 Temple House, Ward Road, London N19 5EE ☎ 020 7281 5028

PALIN Jessica (*La Per, Flt*): 62 C Highbury Hill, London N5 1AP

PATEL Bonky (*Guiro, Mar, Timb, Bong, Per*): Flat 6, 39 Harold Road, Upper Norwood, London SE19 3PL ☎ 020 8771 7679

RAVALICO Maurizio (*Cong, Bong, Per*): 39 Northfield House, Peckham Park Road, London SE15 6TL ☎ 020 7639 1078

RICHMOND Simon (*Cong, Per, Kbds*): 70 Beethoven Street, London W10 4LG ☎ 020 8968 1338

SANDIRA (*Cong, Bong, Per, Voc*): 14 Drayton Road, Willesden, London NW10 4EL ☎ 020 8961 5187

SINGH Satin El Indio (*Cong, La Per, Tabla, Ind Per*): 80 Colworth Road, Leightonstone, London E11 1HY ☎ 0468 105893

STIGNAC Bobby (*La Per, Cong, Timb, Bong, Per*): 241 Basement, Ladbroke Grove, London W10 6HF ☎ 020 8968 5002

VAN DEN BOSSCHE Karl (*La Per, Bong, Cong, Timb, Per*): 269 Lewis Trust Buildings, Vanston Place, London SW6 1AW ☎ 020 7385 6133

VERNON Mike (*La Per, Voc*): 20 Rydens Park, Walton-on-Thames, Surrey KT12 3DP ☎ 01932 221727, 0973 119705, 01932 221727

WHYTON-SMITH Steve (*La Per, Dms, Voc*): 824 Sidcup Road, New Eltham, London SE9 3NS ☎ 020 8851 1602

WIL (*Cong*): 26 Barnes House, Warltersville Road, Crouch Hill, London N19 3AN ☎ 020 7263 0133 & fax

LIBRARIAN

NORTH WEST

MCCORMICK Anthony (*Cop, Db*): 10 Troutbeck Close, Clough Wood, Runcorn, Cheshire WA7 3GJ ☎ 01928 715678

MANDOLIN

SCOTLAND

DAVEY Derek (*Bzk, Acc, Darab*): 9 Bath Street, Edinburgh, Scotland EH15 1EZ ☎ 0131 669 3924

MACKIE George (*Bjo, Bod, Tin Wh*): 90A Main Street, Lochgelly, Fife, Scotland KY5 9AA ☎ 01592 782121, 0411 299758 mob

MCMORDIE Alistair (*Bzk, Acc, Darab*): Address Unknown ☎ 0131 669 3924

MURRAY Ian (*Gtr, B Gtr*): Woodend, Libberton, Carnwath, Lanarkshire ML11 8LX ☎ 01555 840151

PAUL Rod (*Bjo, Gtr, Wh*): Ben Dhu, Burrell Street, Comrie, Crieff, Perthshire PH6 2JP ☎ 01763 670231

RICHARDSON Dave (*Citt, Ctna*): 31 Fountain Hall Road, Edinburgh EH9 2LN ☎ 0131 662 4992

ROBINSON John (*Vln, Bq Vln*): Flat 4, 37 Glencairn Drive, Pollokshields, Glasgow G41 4QW ☎ 0141 423 2679

NORTH WEST

KEARNS Bernard (*Gtr*): 10 Barcombe Close, Oldham, Lancs OL4 2PT ☎ 0161 652 6758

LEVERINGTON Les (*Bjo, Gtr, Kbds*): 5 Gorrell Close, Newchurch-In-Pendle, Burnley, Lancashire BB12 9LZ ☎ 01282 691774

MITCHELL-DAVIDSON Paul (*Com, Gtr, B Gtr, Arr*): 25 Bannerman Avenue, Prestwich, Manchester M25 1DZ ☎ 0161 798 9604 & fax, 0797 9883516

NORTH EAST

JACKSON Raymond (*Hmca, Voc*): 32 West End, Witney, Oxfordshire OX8 6NE, 0585 770751 mob

POWELLS James (*Gtr, Voc*): 55 Langdale Drive, Beaconhill Glade, Cramlington, Northumberland NE23 8EL ☎ 01670 734547

EAST

COLEMAN Nicholas (*Bjo*): 39 Catton Grove Road, Norwich, Norfolk NR3 3NJ ☎ 01603 402621

MIDLANDS

FENN Adam (*Wh*): 14 Orchard Street, Wolstanton, Newcastle Under Lyme, Staffordshire ST5 0BG ☎ 01782 623666

KANG Arjinder (*Cong, Bong, Synth, Voc*): 6 St Benedicts Close, Sandwell Valley, Sandwell, West Midlands B70 6TD ☎ 0121 525 7696

SHINER Mark (*Ac Gtr, Bod, Fo Fdl, Hmca*): 191 Selsey Road, Edgbaston, Birmingham B17 8JN ☎ 0121 420 2963

SOUTH EAST

GIBSON John (*Gtr, Dms, Bjo, Fo Fdl*): 6 Clarence Avenue, Rochester, Kent ME1 2DX ☎ 01634 400521

HARRIS Ian (*Cl Gtr, B Gtr, Uke, Mando*): 1 Tivoli Copse, Woodsidean, Brighton BN1 5NF ☎ 01273 557035

PHENIX Penny (*Gtr, Wh*): 10 Penrith Road, Basingstoke, Hamppshire RG21 8XW ☎ 01256 329702, 01256 475381

SOUTH WEST

BURNS David (*Gtr*): 1 Victoria Park Road East, Canton, Cardiff CF5 1EG ☎ 029 2023 3509

KNOCK Patrick (*Gtr*): 62 Hillview Avenue, Clevedon, Somerset BS21 6HY ☎ 01275 791075

SMITH Adrian (*Tin Wh, Gtr*): 10 Cwrt Ty Mawr, Van Road, Caerffili, Morgannwg Ganol CF8 3EQ ☎ 029 2088 9183

LONDON

ALEXANDER Phil (*Ctna, Gtr, H Gtr, Bjo*): 38 Sylvester Road, London N2 8HN ☎ 020 8346 9662

BEROWN Nico (*Rec, Hmca, Acc, Gtr*): 2 Fontenoy Terrace, Strand Road, County Wicklow, Ireland ☎ +353 286 2566

BUSH Paddy (*Mando, Didj, Synth, B Gtr*): East Wickham Farm, Wickham Street, Welling, Kent DA16 3DA ☎ 020 8854 9171

COATES Kevin (*Bq Man, Ea Stg*): 9 Chalcot Crescent, Primrose Hill, London NW1 8YE ☎ 020 7722 3227

DAVIES Jack (*Cl Gtr, E Gtr, Bjo, Voc*): 27 Sonia Gardens, Neasden, London NW10 1AG ☎ 020 8208 3654

DEL MONTE Sydney: Twenty, Kenelm Close, Harrow, Middx HA1 3TE ☎ 020 8904 8866

FLYNN Eamonn (*Gtr*): 23 Mildenhall Road, Clapton, London E5 0RY ☎ 020 8986 8195

FYFE Peter (*Gtr, Bjo*): 26 Cumberland Court, Cross Road, Croydon, Surrey CR0 6TA ☎ 020 8680 4302

GOULDING Christopher (*Gtr, Voc*)

ISAACS Jonathan (*Bak, Bjo, Bal*): Flat 2, 163 West End Lane, London NW6 2LG ☎ 020 7372 6969

JONES Derek (*Bjo, Gtr*): 62 Beechwood Road, South Croydon, Surrey CR2 0AA ☎ 020 8651 6080

KENNEY Susan (*Wh*): Flat 3 (Basement), 3 Queensdown Road, London E5 8NN ☎ 020 8533 1105

LAWRENCE Janette (*Rec*): 139 Tufnell Park Road, London N7 0PU ☎ 020 7609 2758

MOSSOP Sue: 8 Cherry Orchard Court, Spring Gardens Road, High Wycombe, Bucks HP13 7AJ ☎ 01494 446915, 0378 124696 mob

STEPHENS Alison: c/o 17 Matfield Close, Bromley, Kent BR2 9DY ☎ 020 8290 6171, 0973 111690 mob

TAYLOR Frances (*Vln*): 23 Pelham Road, London E18 1PX ☎ 020 8989 7591

THOMAS David (*Vln, Flt*): 119 Kenilworth Road, Edgware, Middlesex HA8 8XB ☎ 020 8958 4947

WILLIAMS Peter (*Gtr, Voc*): Flat I, 9 Park Hill, Carshalton Beeches, Surrey SM5 3RS ☎ 020 8715 4893

WOODHOUSE Nigel (*Gtr, Bjo*): 135 Hazelwod Drive, St Albans, Herts AL4 0UY ☎ 01727 865164

MBIRA

LONDON

DUTIRO Chartwell (*T Sax, Af Dms, Bong, Cong*): 9 Casterbridge, Abbey Road, London NW6 4DP ☎ 020 7681 0637

ROBINSON Kristyan (*Sax*): 9 Casterbridge Abbey Rd, London NW6 4DP ☎ 020 7681 0637

WEBSTER Patience (*Ctna, Per, Cong*): 69 Anstey Court, Enfield Road, Acton W3 3RD ☎ 020 8992 0461

MELODEON

SCOTLAND

NICOLSON Nancy: 22 West Preston Street, Edinburgh EH8 9PZ ☎ 0131 667 0534

NORTH WEST

HOPE Margaret (*Man, Per*): 15 New Street, Uppermill, Saddleworth, Oldham OL3 6AU ☎ 01457 876506

PETERS Brian (*Ctna, Gtr, Voc*): 72 Sheffield Road, Glossop, Derbys SK13 8QP ☎ 01457 862560

NORTH EAST

BETTISON Michael: Green Fell View, Bowes, Barnard Castle, Co. Durham DL12 9LG ☎ 01833 628343

GAMMON Vic (*Ctna, Bjo, Citt, Voc*): 12 Beechfield Road, Birkby, Huddersfield, West Yorkshire HD2 2XQ ☎ 01484 424465

GOLDSMITH Sally (*Sax, Acc, Voc*): 119 Upper Vally Road, Sheffield S8 9HD ☎ 0114 255 2369

JACK Shanty (*Uke, Bjo, Bones*): 16 Kingsway, Cleethorpes, N.E. Lincs DN35 8QU ☎ 01472 696 757

KNUTTON Keith (*Gtr*): 156 Huddersfield Road, Holmfirth, West Yorkshire HD7 1JD ☎ 01848 687261

PARKINSON Chris (*Acc, Kbds, Hmca*): 6 Blackburns Yard, Church Street, Whitby, North Yorkshire YO22 4DS ☎ 01947 601971

EAST

ALDIS Kathryn (*Dul*): 88 Lowestoft Road, Worlingham, Beccles NR34 7RD ☎ 01502 712160

GRIFFITHS Thomas (*Bsn, Voc, Wh, Kbds*): 1 Station Cottages, Grunty Fen, Wilburton, Ely Cambs CB6 3PZ ☎ 01353 740101

HOWSON Katie: 44 Old Street, Haughley, Stow Market, Suffolk IP14 3NX ☎ 01449 673695, 01449 673695

KELLY Allan (*Man, Gtr*): 38 Robin Place, Boundary Way, Watford WD2 7SN ☎ 01923 663026

MACFARLANE Alison (*Wh, Clt, Ctna*): 40 Warwick Road, St Albans, Herts AL1 4DL ☎ 01727 852111

MIDLANDS

CARE Simon: 10 Chater Street, Moulton, Northampton NN3 7UD ☎ 01604 493260, 0976 211706

CUTTING Andy (*Acc*): 21 Chapel Lane, Chaddesden, Derby DE21 4QT ☎ 01332 677046, 01332 677047

DOCTOR SUNSHINE (*Ctna, Dms, Per*): 74A King Street, Dawley, Telford, Shropshire TF4 2AQ ☎ 01952 505073

SMITH Ian (*Bag, Dms, Per*): 1 Holme Road, Matlock Bath, Derbyshire DE4 3NU ☎ 01629 57082

SPENCER Graham (*B Gtr*): 73 Lyndon Road, Olton, Solihull, West Midlands B92 7RF ☎ 0121 707 5703

SWINDLEHURST Matthew (*Tbn*): 106 Oxley Moor Road, Wolverhampton, West Midlands WV10 6TX ☎ 01902 785002, 0468 207287

TURNER Gareth: 36 Forrest Road, Far Cotton, Northampton NN4 8PA ☎ 01604 763686, 0802 453373 mob

WARREN Gareth (*Gtr, Kbds*): 5 Jeyes Close, Moulton, Northampton NN3 7GH ☎ 01604 790358

WILLETS Timothy (*Ctna, Hmca, App Dulc, Tbn*): 21 Hambrook Close, Wolverhampton WV6 0XA ☎ 01902 715235

SOUTH EAST

BURTON Julian: 7 Albert Terrace, Eastborne, East Sussex BN21 1ST ☎ 01323 641501

HOLLOWAY Keith (*B Gtr, Man, Voc*) "Coppersfield", Wildhern Andover, Hants SP11 0JE ☎ 01226 735 252

HURST Paul (*Ctna, B Gtr*): 3 Brattles Grange Cottages, Tibbs Court Lane, Brenchley, Kent TN12 7AJ ☎ 0189 272 3376

QUINN Daniel: 87 St Andrews Road, Portslade, Brighton BN41 1DD ☎ 01273 881316

STEVENS Mark (*E Gtr, Fo Fdl, Bod, Spoons*): 21 Nailsworth Crescent, Merstham, Surrey RH1 3JD ☎ 01737 217728

WHETSTONE David (*Ctna, Gtr*): 11 Alfred Terraces, Chipping Norton, Oxford OX7 5HB ☎ 01608 644388

SOUTH WEST

DAFIS Guto (*Voc, Kbds, Ac Gtr*): 12 Kyveilog Street, Pontcanna, Cardiff CF1 9JA ☎ 029 2034 1061

VAN EYKEN Tim (*Gtr, Voc, Tin Wh*): Appledore, Old Wells Road, Shepton Mallet, Somerset BA4 5XZ ☎ 01749 343730, 0370 414895 mob

LONDON

DRAPER Paul: 82 Boundary Road, Plastos, London E13 9QG ☎ 020 8548 1941

TURNER Chris (*Ctna*): 9 Glendale Avenue, London N22 5HL ☎ 020 8889 0634

MULTI INSTRUMENTAL
NORTH EAST

WOOD Andy (*B Gtr*): 92 Hartley Avenue, Woodhouse Cliff, Leeds, W. Yorks LS6 2HZ ☎ 0113 2430177

SOUTH EAST

RUGGE-PRICE James: Stainswick Manor, Bourton, Nr Shrivenham, Oxfordshire SN6 8LD ☎ 01793 784133

LONDON

LEAF Helen (*Voc, Flt, Per*): Basement Flat, 8 Crescent Road, Crouch End, London N8 8AT ☎ 020 8374 9250

MANN Terry (*Per, Saxes, Voc*): 35 Nottingham Road, Leyton, London E10 6BP ☎ 020 8556 7005, 0378 914623 mob

RYDER Anna (*Song W*): 24 Burns Avenue, Warwick CV34 6JJ ☎ 01926 400927

MUSIC DIRECTOR
SCOTLAND

BRAGG Glyn (*Arr, Com, Cop*): 1 North Dumgoyne Avenue, Milngavie, Glasgow G62 7JT ☎ 0141 956 2480

DROVER Adrian (*B Tbn, Tba, Arr, Com*): 130C Southbrae Drive, Glasgow G13 1TZ ☎ 0141 954 8983

FAHEY Brian (*Arr, Com, Con*): Tigh Geal, 13 Montgomerie Terrace, Skelmorlie, Ayrshire PA17 5DT ☎ 01475 520774, 0370 826088

GEDDES Graham (*Acc, Pf, Voc, T Sax*): 33 Corse Wynd, Kingswells, Aberdeen AB2 8TP ☎ 01224 742103

HAGGART Kevin (*Tpt, Pictpt, Kbds, Com*): Top Floor Left, 11 Summerfield Place, Aberdeen AB2 1JF ☎ 01224 642456

LAMBERT William (*A Sax, Clt, Vln*): 4 Lindsay Place, Glasgow G12 0HX ☎ 0141 339 1554

MONTEITH-MATHIE Ian (*Con, Pf, Kbds*): 8 Drumsheugh Gardens, West End, Edinburgh EH3 7QJ ☎ 0131 225 6561, 0468 094 200, 0131 226 5156

SUTHERLAND Alexander (*Tbn, Pf, Acc, Vib*): Denovan, Culsalmond, Insch, Aberdeenshire AB52 6UX ☎ 01464 84 315

THORBURN Andy (*Com, Pf, Kbds*): Tallysow Cottage, Novar, Evanton, Ross-Shire IV16 9XH ☎ 01349 830132

NORTH WEST

AKINBODE Akintayo (*B Gtr, Kbds, Per, Sax*): 18 Rutland Avenue, Withington, Manchester M20 1JD ☎ 0161 445 3017

CHADWICK Eric (*Con, Org*): 44 Broadway, Fairfield, Droylsden, Manchester M43 6FE ☎ 0161 370 3547

JUCKES Rick (*Kbds*): Ground Floor Flat, 1 Mossley Hill Drive, Liverpool L17 1AJ ☎ 0151 724 2100, 0151 724 5813

LONGDEN Lee P (*Kbds, Pf, Tbn, Arr*): PO Box 107, Manchester M14 7SL ☎ 0161 224 4530 & fax, 0802 583647 mob

MONKS Chris (*Sax, Flt, Kbds*): 6 Sugar Lane, Rainow, Macclesfield, Cheshire SK10 5UJ ☎ 01625 574420

PILKINGTON Stephen (*Pf, Org*): Glandwr Onest, Blaenffos, Boncath, Dyfed SA37 0JB ☎ 01239 841323

REYNISH Timothy (*Hrn*): Silver Birches, Bentinck Road, Altrincham, Cheshire WA14 2BP ☎ 0161 928 8364

RICHARDS Goff (*Pf, Arr, Com*): Rose Cottage, 101 Walton Road, Stockton Heath, Warrington Cheshire WA4 6NR ☎ 01925 601112

SKINNER Peter (*B Gtr*): 63 St Leonards Road, Blackpool, Lancs FY3 9RF ☎ 01253 62095/697

TRACEY Professor Ian (*Org, Pf, Hpsd*): 6 Cathedral Close, Liverpool L1 7BR ☎ 0151 708 8471

TYLDESLEY William: Saxon Lodge, Church Road, Huyton, Liverpool L36 5SJ ☎ 0151 489 2329

WINN Julian (*Pf, Synth*): 103 Gatley Road, Cheadle, Manchester SK8 1LX ☎ 0161 491 5937, 0589 977373

NORTH EAST

ELLIS John: 25 Sandcliffe Road, Wheatley Hills, Doncaster DN2 5NP ☎ 01302 21801

ROSE Basil (*Pf, Clt, Sax*): The Stone Cottage, Halldrive, Canwick, Lincoln LN4 2RG

EAST

BROWN Brian (*Con, Vln*): 11 Boswells Drive, Chelmsford, Essex CM2 6LD

BURRELL Howard (*Com, Arr*): 39 Hastings Close, Stevenage, Herts SG1 2JG ☎ 01438 221918, 01707 244441, 01707 285098 fax

CLEARY Neil (*Pf, Kbds*): 10 South Beech Avenue, Wickford, Essex SS11 8AH ☎ 01268 730300

FERRIS Kenneth (*Pf*): 58 Juniper Road, Stanway, Colchester CO3 5RY ☎ 01206 330460

LEBERMAN Martin (*Pf, Com*): ☎ 01279 505347, 0973 307504

REEVE Julian (*Kbds, Dms*): 19 Cow Lane, Rampton, Cambridge CB4 4QG ☎ 01223 410283 & fax, 0421 842337 mob

THOMAS Brian (*Com, Con, Arr, Cop*): 25B Bishop's Rd, Trumpington, Cambridge CB2 2NQ ☎ 01223 841145

MIDLANDS

ALEXANDER Mike (*Pf, Kbds, Voc, Accom*): Ivory Lodge, 3 Halloughton Road, Four Oaks, Sutton Coldfield, West Midlands B74 2QL ☎ 0121 321 1866

BAINES Colin (*Db, Pf*): 49 Church Road, Moseley, Birmingham B13 9ED ☎ 0121 449 2033

BENNETT Bob (*Tbn, Arr, Com, Pf*): Musicians' Union, Benson House, Lombard Street, Birmingham B12 0QN ☎ 0121 622 3870

DODGSON James (*Con, Com, Pf*): The Leys Cottage, 7 The Leys, Adderbury, Banbury, Oxfordshire OX17 3ES ☎ 0973 401430

EVANS John (*Pf, Arr, Com, Cop*): Casa Nos Prados, Bordeira, 8000 Faro, Algarve, Portugal ☎ + 351 (0)89 94310

HANCOCK Stephen (*Pf*): Address Unknown ☎ 01789 293833

HARDING Timothy (*Con, Pf, Kbds, Voc*): Flat 1B, 37 Grove Avenue, Moseley, Birmingham B13 9RX ☎ 0121 449 6368

HART David (*Com, Pf*): Hillcrest, 4 Stanton Road, Ludlow, Shropshire SY8 2LR ☎ 01584 873667

HIBBERT Ian (*Clt, Flt, Pic, Saxes*): 18 Diamond Avenue, Sherwood Park, Rainworth, Nottingham NG21 0FF ☎ 01623 795399

JACKSON Adrian (*Tbn*): 8 Pimpernel Drive, The Paddocks, Walsall, West Midlands, WS5 4SG ☎ 01922 647566

JOHNSON Philip (*Tbn*): 14, Apse Close, Wombourne, Wolverhampton, Staffs WV5 8BW ☎ 01902 892768

JOHNSON Stuart (*Con, Pf*): Northesk Lodge, 16 Northesk Street, Stone, Staffs ST15 8TP ☎ 01785 816053

MAYO Graham (*Pf, Org, Con*): Hollybank 5, The Orchard, Kislingbury, Northants NN7 4BG ☎ 01604 830679

PATRICK John (*Pf, Arr, Com, Kbds*): c/o Musicians' Union, Benson House, Lombard Street, Birmingham B12 0QN ☎ 01564 784029 & fax

RAE Roger (*Tbn, B Tbn, B Gtr, B Ldr*): 45 Grange Crescent, Halesowen, West Midlands B63 3ED ☎ 0121 550 6515

ROBERTS Arthur (*Pf*): 5 Maurice Road, Birmingham B14 6DL ☎ 0121 444 4946

SAWTELL Paul (*Pf, Mldca, Synth, Kbds*): 20 Seymour Road, Wollescote, Stourbridge, West Midlands DY9 8TB ☎ 01384 351033

SILK Richard (*Hpsd, Pf, Org*): Gulley Green, All Stretton, Church Stretton, Salop SY6 7JT ☎ 01694 722 649

SIMONS John (*Pf, Org, Arr*): Swaldesale, 6 Coniston Place, Trentham, Stoke-on-Trent ST4 8JL ☎ 01782 657599

STEADMAN David (*Pf*): The Lodge, Belvoir Bank, Malvern, Worcs WR14 4LY

VINCENT Paul (*Pf, Arr, Com, Cop*): Flat7, Tessier Court, 31 Manor Road, St Marychurch, Torquay TQ1 3JX ☎ 01803 316168

WELLS John (*Pf, Arr*): 3 Lockhart Drive, Four Oaks, Sutton Coldfield B75 6RR ☎ 0121 308 2878

WILLIS Robert (*Kbds, B Gtr, Com, Arr*): Cherry Trees, Stone Lane, Kinver, South Staffs DY7 6EG ☎ 01384 873184, 0978 748085

SOUTH EAST

BAYTON Dennis (*Tbn, Cop*): 11 Warbler Close, Upton, Poole, Dorset BH16 5RL ☎ 01202 624066

BENNETT Neil (*Pf, Kbds, Org*): 43A Lansdowne Street, Hove, East Sussex BN3 1FT ☎ 020 8471 3358

FRICKER Simon (*Arr, Pf, Kbds*): Flat 5, Broadlea, 24 The Broadway, Sandown, Isle Of Wight PO36 9DQ ☎ 01983 406490

HARMAN Ernest (*Ob, Md*): 53 Kenilworth Road, St Leonards-on-Sea TN38 0JL ☎ 01424 438254

JONES David (*Com, Arr*): 136 St Chads Road, Cox Green, Maidenhead, Berks SL6 3BA ☎ 01628 30694

REED Leslie (*Arr, Pf, Kbds*): Terwick Place, Rogate, Petersfield, Hants GU31 5BY ☎ 01730 821644

SOUTH WEST

DOORBAR Carolyn (*Pf, Rep*): 4 Buck Close, Gladstonbury, Somerset BA6 9PS ☎ 01458 835881

DUERDEN Fred: Little Orchard, Galmpton Farm Close, Galmpton, Nr Brixham TQ5 0NP ☎ 01803 843446

LATHAM Robert: 21 Robin Lane, Clevedon, Avon BS21 7ES ☎ 01275 873 798

PARKMAN Arthur (*Pf, Org, Com, Arr*): 126 Smyth Road, Ashton, Bristol BS3 2DP ☎ 0117 9662726

PLANK Greta: Cae Nest, Bridge Road, Bleadon, Weston Super Mare BS24 0AU ☎ 01934 626443, 01934 812010

SMITH Philip (*Pf*): 44 Larksmead Way, Ogwell, Newton Abbot, Devon TQ12 6FE ☎ 01626 331431

WARLOW Wayne (*Com, Arr, Kbds, Db*): The Haven, Ocean View, West Drive, Porthcawl, Mid Glamorgan CF36 3HT ☎ 01656 773389

WELCH Edward (*Pf, Arr*): Redhills, Stokenham, Nr Kingsbridge TQ7 2SS ☎ 01548 580347

LONDON

AITCHISON Kennedy (*Com, Arr, Con, Pf*): 8 Trinity Street, Bishops Stortford, Herts CM23 3TJ ☎ 01279 758136, 01279 832269 fax, 0836 358599 mob

ALEXANDER Jae: 9 Manville Road, Balham, London SW17 8JW ☎ 020 8767 8871

ALLEN Jude (*Pf, Kbds, Arr, Com*): 16 College Road, Kensal Rise, London NW10 5PE ☎ 020 8960 5038

AMOS Kevin (*Pf, Com, Arr*): 91 Clissold Crescent, London N16 9AS ☎ 020 7254 8596

ARNOLD David (*Tym, Dms, Pf*): David Arnold Music Ltd., Crafts Hill Farmhouse, Dry Drayton, Cambridge CB3 8DD ☎ 01954 780400, 01954 782220 fax

ATKINS Andrew (*Com, Arr, Pf, Per*): 17 Spring Gardnes, West Molesey, Surrey KT8 2JA ☎ 020 8941 2510

AXE Martyn (*Pf*): 9 Blenheim Gardens, Willesden Green, London NW2 4NL ☎ 020 8450 3818 & fax

BALCOMBE Richard (*Kbds, Arr, Cntrc*): 7 Chalks Avneue, Sawbridgeworth, Herts CM21 0BX ☎ 01279 831821, 01279 724 299

BARHAM Stuart (*Pf, Kbds*): 111 Abbeville Road, Clapham, London SW4 6EP ☎ 020 7622 8864

BARNES Derek (*Com, Arr*): 56 Further Green Road (2), Catford, London SE6 1JH ☎ 020 8698 8480

BARTER Robert (*Org, T Sax, A Sax, B Ldr*): 77 Elgar Avenue, Surbiton, Surrey KT5 9JP ☎ 020 8399 9326

BEER David (*Pf, Kbds, Arr*): 110 Kings Road, Walton-on-Thames, Surrey KT12 2RE ☎ 01932 240524

BLEZARD William (*Pf, Com*): 2 Beverley Gardens, London SW13 0LZ ☎ 020 8876 2824

BOYD David (*Pf, Clt*): 71 Madrid Road, London SW13 9PQ ☎ 020 8748 3787

BROOKER Chris (*Dms, Per, Kbds, Tpt*): 22 Chancellor Grove, West Dulwich, London SE21 8EG ☎ 020 8761 7191

BROWNE Derek (*Arr*): 94 Perry Vale, London SE23 2LQ ☎ 020 8699 9644

BURNETT Paul (*Kbds, Com, Arr*): 24C Las Vinas, Las Rolas, Denia 03700, Alicante, Spain

BURNETT Sandy (*Db, Vln*): 90 Masbro Road, London W14 0LR ☎ 020 7603 6427

CARTER David (*Kbds, Pf, Arr*): 28 Stile Hall Gardens, Chiswick, London W4 W4 3BU ☎ 020 8995 3981

CASS Ronnie (*Pf*): 27A Elworthy Road, London NW3 3BT ☎ 020 7586 4670 & fax

CHAMP Des (*Arr, Pf*): 13 Whitehouse Avenue, Boreham Wood, Herts WD6 1HA ☎ 020 8953 5126

COLEMAN John (*Arr, Com, Pf*): 24 The Loning, London NW9 6DR ☎ 020 8205 6734, 020 8205 2191 fax

COLLINSON Francis (*Pf*): Address Unknown ☎ 0189 683 240

CORRIGAN Peter (*Pf, Con, Kbds, Arr*): 103 Arica Road, Brockley, London SE4 2PS ☎ 0973 393080, 020 7732 8763

DAVIDSON Robert (*Pf, Kbds, Org, Com*): 34 Woodland Hill, Gipsy Hill, London SE19 1NY ☎ 020 8761 7924

DAVIES Nick (*Vln*): Flat 5, 6 Great Ormond Street, London WC1N 3RB ☎ 020 7209 2430, 0850 890098 mob

DIXON Michael (*Kbds, Arr, Voc*): 5 Wolsley Gardens, Chiswick, London W4 3LY ☎ 020 8747 1570

DOCTOR ALEX : 102 Goulden House, Bullen Street, Battersea, London SW11 3HH ☎ 020 7585 2651

DORRELL Mark W (*Pf, Org*): 5 Melbourne Grove, London SE22 8RG ☎ 020 8693 8247

EBBINGHOUSE Bernard (*Arr, Com, Con*): 5 Garrick Gardens, Hurst Park, East Molesey, Surrey KT8 9SL ☎ 020 8224 1047

EDGAR Kate (*Com, Arr, Clt, Arr*): 98 Church Road, London W7 3BE ☎ 020 8840 2585 & fax

EDIS Steven (*Com, Arr, Pf*): 60 Lancaster Road, Stroud Green, London N4 4PT ☎ 020 7281 8766

EDWARDS Phillip (*Com, Arr*): 25 Chalford, Wooburn Green, High Wycombe, Buckinghamshire HP10 0BS ☎ 016285 21648, 020 8993 1274 & fax

EDWARDS Rod (*Kbds*): 41 Lawrence Gardens, Mill Hill, London NW7 4JU ☎ 020 8906 1207 & fax

ENGLAND Michael: 88 Weir Road, London SW12 0NB ☎ 020 8675 0975

ETHERINGTON Mark (*Pf, Kbds, Arr*): 1 Roxley Road, Lewisham, London SE13 6HG ☎ 020 8265 7689, 0973 821387

FAULKNER Andrew (*Pf, Com*): 120 Seal Road, Sevenoaks, Kent TN14 5AX ☎ 01732 456498, 0976 731333 mob

FIRMAN David (*Arr, Synth*): 27 Sumatra Road, West Hampstead, London NW6 1PS ☎ 020 7431 0901

FOSTER Ben (*Con, Com, Pf, Hrn*): 51 Central Park East, Bow Quater, London E3 2UT ☎ 020 8983 3453

FRANCIS David (*Pf, Org, Com, Arr*): 48 Hanover Flats, Gilbert Street, London W1Y 1RE ☎ 020 7629 7047

FRANCIS George: Address Unknown

FRECHTER Colin (*Com, Pf, Kbds, Arr*): 13 The Downs, Hatfield AL10 8JW ☎ 01707 880268

FREEMAN Matthew (*Arr, Pf*): 11 Institute Road, Marlow, Bucks SL7 1BL ☎ 01628 474591 & fax, 0850 236026 mob

FRIESNER Andrew (*Com, Kbds, Pf*): 85A Kingscourt Road, Streatham, London SW16 1JA ☎ 020 8769 6747

GOLD Laurie (*Sax, Clt, Arr, Cop*): 13 Spinnaker Close, Martello Bay, Clacton-on-Sea, Essex CO15 1AY ☎ 01255 220555, 01255 430699 fax

GORDON Marilyn (*Com, Pf, Vln, Acc*): 127 Grange Road, London SE25 6TQ ☎ 020 8771 5184 & fax

HAGEN Peter (*Pf, Kbds, Hmca*): 46 South Drive, Brentwood, Essex CM14 5DL ☎ 01277 226011, 0468 748430 mob

HASLAM Michael (*Pf, Kbds*): 8 Park Avenue South, London N8 8LT ☎ 020 8341 0754, 0973 543520 mob

HAY Victoria: 64 Gore Road, Hackney, London E9 7HN ☎ 020 8533 5722

HILL Juliet (*Con, Kbds, Arr, Tpt*): 99C Bushey Hill Road, London SE5 8QQ ☎ 020 7703 9463

HILTON Roy (*Arr, Pf, Org*): 4 Gore Park Road, Eastbourne, E Sussex BN21 1TQ ☎ 01323 721601

HIND Gary (*Pf, Kbds, Arr*): 84 The Elms, Hartford, Herts SG13 7UX ☎ 0973 348287, 01992 509690 fax

HOSSACK Grant: 25 Ainger Road, London NW3 3AS ☎ 020 7722 2292

HUMPHRIS Caroline (*Pf, Arr*): 4B Yonge Park, London N4 3NT ☎ 020 7700 3706

HUTCHINSON Stuart (*Con, Com, Pf, Org*): 149 De Beauvoir Road, London N1 4DL ☎ 020 7254 7845, 0973 286944 mob, 020 7359 5183 agent

KOCH Martin (*Com, Arr, Kbds*): 62 Telfords Yard, London E1 9BQ ☎ 020 7702 3688

LEWIS Samuel (*Arr*): 55 Herzlia Heights, 4 El-Al Street, Herzlia B 46588, Israel ☎ + 972 9 9553017

LLOYD Rick (*Kbds, Gtr, B Gtr*): 21 Victoria Chambers, Luke Street, London EC2A 4EE ☎ 020 7739 2134, 0956 373172 mob

LOLE Peter (*Pf*): 110A Pendle Road, London SW16 6RY ☎ 020 8769 4560

LOWE Martin (*Kbds*): 27B Landor Road, Clapham, London SW9 9RT ☎ 020 7737 1332

MACKINTOSH Stewart (*Kbds, Arr, Cop*): 106 Boundaries Road, London SW12 8HQ ☎ 020 8672 6179, 020 8672 6179

MCMILLAN Ian (*Arr, Kbds*): Hadfields, Buckland Common, Tring, Herts HP23 6NH ☎ 01494 758595, 0973 731917 mob

MELLOR David (*Pf, Kbds*): Arbour House, Hemp Lane, Wiggington, Tring, Herts HP12 6HE ☎ 01442 823882

MOORE Peter (*Con, Arr, Pf*): 34 King Edwards Gardens, Acton, London W9 9RQ ☎ 020 8992 6287

MUNN Billy (*Pf, Org, Com, Arr*): 66 Main Road, Fairlie, Ayrshire KA29 0AB ☎ 01475 568106

MURRAY Simon J (*Pf, Arr*): Flat 4, 50 Roman Road, Bethnal Green, London E2 0LT ☎ 0973 123140

NARAYN Deane (*Com, Dms, Kbds, Pf*): 9 Wyndham Road, Kingston-upon-Thames, Surrey KT2 5JR ☎ 020 8546 8269

NEWTON Christopher (*Kbds, Hrn*): 13 Park Road, Tring, Hertfordshire HP23 6BN ☎ 01442 891768, 0468 490560 mob

ORNADEL Cyril (*Com, Arr*): 20 Oley Hagardom Street, Shikun Yisgav, Tel Aviv 69715, Israel ☎ + 972 3 6475 733

PARMLEY Andrew (*Org, Pf, Hpsd, Arr*): 125 Marsham Court, Marsham Street, London SW1P 4LB ☎ 020 7630 0159

PATRICK Nicholas (*Con, Kbds*): 51 Salisbury Road, Walthamstow, London E17 9JW ☎ 020 8521 5398

RABINOWITZ Harry (*Com*): 11 Mead Road, Cranleigh, Surrey GU6 7BG ☎ 01483 278676 & fax

RAPPS Andrew (*Pf, Kbds*): 23 Markville Gardens, Caterham, Surrey CR3 6RG ☎ 01883 343 821

RHODEN Neil: 89 Hamlet Gardens, London W6 0SX ☎ 020 8741 0983

RHODES Burt (*Com, Arr*): 19 Paragon Court, 129 Holders Hill Road, London NW4 1LH ☎ 020 8371 9896

ROBINSON Barry (*Kbds, Arr, Con*): 1 Canterbury House, Anglian Close, Watford, Herts WD1 1AL ☎ 01923 443535

ROSE Desmond (*Vln, Pf*): 1 Springfield Avenue, Telscombe Cliffs, Sussex BN9 7AP ☎ 01273 583027

RUDLAND Malcolm (*Org, Pf*): 32A Chipperfield House, Cale Street, London SW3 3SA ☎ 020 7589 9595

SAYFRITZ Mark (*Kbds, Tbn, Sax*): 156 Westbourne Grove, London W11 2RN ☎ 020 7243 2735

SCOTT Robert (*Pf*): 34 Abbey Wood Road, Abbey Wood, London SE2 9NP ☎ 020 8355 7403, 020 8311 6639

SHAPUR Fiz (*Pf, Kbds*): 23 Waterlow Road, London N19 5NJ ☎ 020 7281 1179

SHEARMAN Don (*Pf, Arr*): 4 Chaundrye Close, London SE9 5QB ☎ 020 8850 1454 & fax

SHRUBSOLE David (*Pf, Bsn, Com*): Flat 1, 166 Walm Lane, Willesden Green, London NW2 3AX ☎ 020 8452 2490, 0976 295254 mob

SILVESTER Victor (*Con*): 77 Boydell Court, St Johns Wood Park, London NW8 6NG ☎ 020 7586 1234

SKEOCH Fraser (*Com, Pf, Kbds*): Brambletye, Seymour Road, Headley Down, Hants GU35 8JX ☎ 01428 712926

SMITH Ian (*Pf, Con*): 42 Archbishops Place, Tulse Hill, London SW2 2AJ ☎ 020 8674 9353

SNELSON John (*Pf, Org*): 20 Thornby Road, London E5 9QL ☎ 020 8986 3579

SOMERS Michael (*Org*): Address Unknown

STANLEY Mike (*Kbds, Con, Arr*): 2 Maple Lodge Close, Maple Cross, Rickmansworth, Herts WD3 2SN ☎ 01923 712420, 0973 308504 mob, 01923 712421

STEELE Jan (*Saxes, Flt, Com, Clt*): 1 St Anne's Road, Caversham, Reading RG4 7PA ☎ 0118 947 7170, 020 8533 1372 day, 0403 304944 mob

STENSON Tony (*Pf, Con, Arr*): c/o 4 Suffolk Road, Enfield, Middlesex EN3 4AZ ☎ 01354 695329

STREET Kevin (*Acc, Kbds, Tpt, Arr*): 221 Kent House Road, Beckenham, Kent BR3 1JZ ☎ 020 8776 6431, 0956 537802 mob

SZIKLAFI Joseph (*Pf, Acc, Org*): 54 Grange Gardens, The Bourne, Southgate, London N14 6QN ☎ 020 8886 6055

TAYLOR Millie (*Pf*): 14 Albion Place, Old Tiverton Road, Exeter EX4 6LH ☎ 01392 211272

TESTER Alexander (*Pf, Org, Arr*): 14 Linden Crescent, Woodford Green, Essex IG8 0DG ☎ 020 8504 5035

TOMASSO Peter (*Kbds, Arr*): 12 Percy Road, Hampton, Middx TW12 2HW ☎ 020 8941 6941

WAKELEY Tom (*Pf, Org, Com, Con*): 16 Trees Avenue, Hughenden Valley, High Wycombe, Bucks HP14 4PQ ☎ 01494 563498

WARMAN Mark (*Kbds, Com, Arr, Cntrc*): 17 Carleton Road, Tufnell Park, London N7 0QZ ☎ 020 7609 5888

WARNE Derek (*Pf, Vib, La Per*): 26 Nelson Street, Norwich NR2 4DW ☎ 01603 661221

WHITE Terry (*Pf, Arr*): 5 Mays Lane, Barnet, Herts EN5 2EF ☎ 020 8441 0409

YORK Trevor (*Kbds*): 50 Derham Gardens, Upminster, Essex RM14 3HA ☎ 01708 221655

MUSICAL SAW

LONDON

CRONK Caspar (*Auto Hrp, Jug, Gtr*): 8 Langbourne Avenue, London N6 6AL ☎ 020 8340 4683, 020 7209 2378 fax

DAGG Henry (*E Gtr, B Gtr, Kbds*): 34 Millfield Rd, Faversham, Kent ME13 8BX ☎ 01795 534907

HARRISON Biff (*Bjo, Vln, Acc*): 75 Friern Road, London SE22 0AU ☎ 020 8693 9596

MOORE John (*Gtr*): 17 St Marys Terrace, London W2 1SU ☎ 020 7724 3882 & fax

NOWELL Vernon *(Bjo)*: 10 Woodbines Avenue, Kingston-upon-Thames, Surrey KT1 2AY ☎ 020 8546 0651

WATSON Richard *(Db, B Gtr)*: 8 Farm Lane, Shirley, Croydon CR0 8AQ ☎ 020 8777 8371, 020 8777 7975

NATURAL TRUMPET

SCOTLAND

HARROLD Shaun *(Pictpt, Cnt, Flgl, Ea Wnd)*: 21 Lubnaig Gardens, Bearsden, Glasgow G61 4QX ☎ 0141 943 1157, 0468 053816 mob

LONDON

MUSK David *(Pf)*: Honey Oke, Station Road, Woldingham, Surrey CR3 7DE ☎ 01883 653150, 0410 424 121

NON PLAYING MEMBER

NORTH EAST

SMITH Kenneth: 10 Graham Terrace, High Pittington, Co. Durham DH6 1AU ☎ 0191 372 0239

EAST

GWYN David: Pontins Holiday Centre, Pakefield, Lowestoft, Suffolk

MIDLANDS

ATKINS Richard: 130 Anchorway Road, Green Lane, Coventry CV3 6JG ☎ 024 7641 4228

CLUGSTON Simon: 67 School Road, Moseley, Birmingham B13 9TF ☎ 0121 449 1813

PINDER Joyce: 2 Sir Winston Churchill Place, Binley Woods, Coventry, West Midlands CV8 2BT ☎ 024 7654 3204

PRICHARD George: Flat 238, Station Road, Balsall Common, Coventry, West Midlands CV7 7EE ☎ 01676 33104

SALMON George: 62 Max Road, Coundon, Coventry, West Midlands CV6 1EQ ☎ 024 7659 4075

SEGGIE Peter: 177 Grange Mouth Road, Coventry, West Midlands CV6 3FD ☎ 024 7659 7027

SOUTH WEST

LEWIS Vera: 86 Mortimer Road, Filton, Bristol BS12 7LQ

MALE Don: 5 Canning Street, Pentre, Rhondda, Mid Glam ☎ 01443 434433

POLOWAY Harry: 14 Fields Park Avenue, Newport, Gwent NP9 5BG ☎ 01633 266078

LONDON

FAULKNER D: 49 Beverley Road, Whyteleafe, Surrey CR3 0DU ☎ 020 8660 5918

HYDE Lillian: 13 Downbank Avenue, Barnehurst, Kent DA7 6RS ☎ 01322 335360

NORTON Doreen: 5 Birchfield Grove, East Ewell, Surrey KT17 3ES

NORTHUMBRIAN PIPES

NORTH EAST

CATO Pauline *(Kbds, Pf)*: 122 Osgathorpe Road, Pitsmoor, Sheffield S4 7AS ☎ 0114 2434434

SHAW David: 2 Shafto Cottage, Craghead, Stanley, Co Durham DH9 6DW ☎ 01207 231474

TICKELL Kathryn *(Vln, Pf)*: PO Box 55, Heaton, Newcastle NE6 5YT ☎ 0191 262 1641

SOUTH EAST

BOULTON David *(Wh)*: Flat 4, 25 Hayle Road, Maidstone, Kent ME16 6PE ☎ 01622 755454

HIGGS Paul *(Uill, Sh P)*: 21 Church Street, Watlington, Oxfordshire OX9 5QR ☎ 01491 612231, 01491 612231

LONDON

WELLS Graham: 24, Gloucester Road, Teddington, Middx TW11 0NU ☎ 020 8977 2756

OBOE

SCOTLAND

ASHTON Laura *(Cor)*: 614 Dumbarton Road 1/1, Glasgow G11 6RJ ☎ 0141 339 3549

AYRE Marion *(Cor, Obdam)*: Inches Cottage, Near Glespin, By Douglas ML11 0SJ ☎ 01555 851384

BELL Morven *(Cor, Obdam, B Ob)*: 39/1 Bryson Road, Edinburgh EH11 1DY ☎ 0131 313 1298

DILLON Shaun *(Obdam, Cor, Com)*: 34 Richmond Street, Aberdeen AB25 4TR ☎ 01224 630954

FALLOWS Jacqueline *(Cor)*: 2 Golf Course Road, Bonnyrigg, Midlothian EH19 2EX ☎ 0131 663 3320

FENN Michelle *(Cor)*: 60 Old Castle Road, Cathcart, Glasgow G44 5TE ☎ 0141 637 2647

HERD Judith *(Cor, Obdam)*: 11 Bowling Green Road, Whiteinch, Glasgow G14 9NU ☎ 0141 959 6497

HILL Philip *(Obdam, Cor)*: 4 Kiltrochan Drive, Balfron, Glasgow G63 0QJ ☎ 01360 440200

JACKSON Charles *(Cor, Flt, Clt, Bsn)*: Birch Lodge, 4 Rowan Hill, Glen Darby, Kirkmichael, Blairgowrie PH10 7NA ☎ 01250 881487

JAMES Mary *(Obdam, Cor)*: 32 Moray Place, Strathbungo, Glasgow G41 2BL ☎ 0141 423 4784

JOHNSON Clare: 1 Ibert Road, Killearn, Glasgow G63 9PX ☎ 01360 550166

LAING Shiela *(Cor)*: 1A St Leonard's Road, Ayr KA7 2PR ☎ 01292 265 298

LOGAN Kirstie *(Cor, Obdam)*: 32 Falkland Street, Hyndland, Glasgow G12 9QY ☎ 0141 337 1282

LOVIE Louise: Marchpot, Inschtammack Farm, Huntley AB54 4TE ☎ 01466 794460

MACARI Amanda: 33 Brayanston Drive, Dollar, Clackmannanshire FK14 7EF ☎ 01259 743473

MAGEE Jenny *(Obdam, Cor)*: Address Unknown

MCCRACKEN Stella *(Pf, Cor)*: 6 Rosevale Road, Bearsden, Glasgow G61 ☎ 0141 942 8520

MICKLEM Henry *(Obdam, Cor)*: 1 Dryden Place, Edinburgh EH9 1RP ☎ 0131 667 5618

MILTON Simon *(Cor, Bq Ob)*: 47 Cupar Road, Newport-on-Tay, Fife DD6 8DF ☎ 01382 541090

MOUNT Rodney *(Cor)*: 18 Tentergate Gardens, Knaresborough, North Yorks HG5 9BL ☎ 01423 863718

POLLARD Rona *(Cor)*: 11 Melrose Gardens, Kelvinside, Glasgow G20 6RB ☎ 0141 946 1772

RHODES Barbara *(Obdam, Cor)*: Hillview, Cochno Road, Hardgate, Clydebank G81 6PT ☎ 01389 875996

RUNDELL Lynn *(Cor)*: 26 Castlepark Gardens, Fairlie, Ayrshire KA29 0BS ☎ 01475 568037, 0411 038 598

WEST Stephen *(Cor)*: 1 Floors Road, Eaglesham, Glasgow G76 0EP ☎ 0141 644 2100

NORTH WEST

ABBOTT Juliet *(Cor)*: 53 Penkett Road, Wallasey, Wirral L45 7QG ☎ 0151 630 3808

ALDIS Maddy: 11 Wesley Street, Eccles, Manchester M30 0QU

ARMSTRONG Warwick *(Cor)*: 9 Beech Road, Whaley Bridge, High Peak, Stockport SK23 7HP ☎ 01663 734461

AUSTEN Susan, Cumbria, 25 Longlands Road, Carlisle, Cumbria CA3 9AD, 01228 44971

BIDDER Helena *(Cor)*: 15 Manor Court, Fulwood, Preston PR2 7DU

BURROWS Denise *(Cor, Pf)*: 1 Riverbank Road, Lower Heswall, Liverpool L60 4SQ ☎ 0151 342 5190

CAMPBELL Robert: Garswood, 4 Curzon Road, Hoylake, Wirral L47 1HB ☎ 0151 632 2463

CLEGG Rachael *(Cor)*: Rocky View House, Royds Road, Rakehead, Rossendale OL13 0PF ☎ 01706 875827

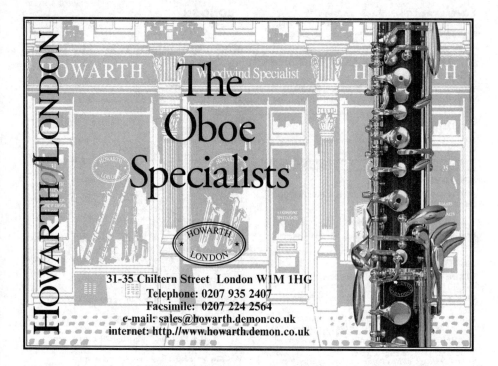

CLEMENTSON Diana: 78 Broad Lane, Nantwich, Cheshire CW5 7QL ☎ 01270 625746

COLLINS Rosie (Cor): 48 Old Road, Whaley Bridge, High Peak SK23 7HS ☎ 01663 732727

COOPER Anna (Cor, Obdam): 1 Handley Court, Riversdale Road, Liverpool L19 3QS ☎ 0151 427 6375

COWDY David (Cor): 37 Thistleton Close, Macclesfield, Cheshire SK11 8BE ☎ 01625 426328, 0850 990659 mob

DAVEY Thomas (Cor): 22 Arthog Drive, Hale, Altrincham, Cheshire WA15 0NB ☎ 0161 980 2481

DAVIES Ruth (Cor): 42 Birch Road, Oxton, Birkenhead L43 5UA ☎ 0151 653 8513

DEMPSEY Jennie: 21 Trafalgar Avenue, Wallasey, Wirral, Merseyside L44 8BP ☎ 0151 630 3374

ELTON Jas (Cor): 23 Burnside Drive, Burnage, Manchester M19 2LT ☎ 0161 224 3875

EMANUEL Jane (Pf): 25 Stanley Street, Prestwich, Manchester M25 1EG ☎ 0161 773 1178

FLETCHER Eric (Cor): 17 Longton Ave, Withington, Manchester M20 9JN ☎ 0161 445 5487

FOXWELL Heather (Cor, Bq Ob, Obdam, Obdac): 32 Fistral Avenue, Heald Green, Cheadle, Cheshire SK8 3HB ☎ 0161 499 9382

FUEST Wendy (Cor): 41 Reading Drive, Sale, Cheshire M33 5DJ ☎ 0151 336 3762

GALLOWAY Jennifer (Obdam, Cor): 4 Princes Road, Chinley, High Peak, Stockport SK23 6AB ☎ 01663 750294

GILBERT Mary (Cor): 28 Stonehaven, Bolton BL3 4UW ☎ 01204 655423

GUNSON Martin: 1 School Lane, Lytham, Lytham St Annes, Lancashire FY8 5NL ☎ 01253 739611

HOWARD Jackie (Cor): 8 The Spinney, Norley, Cheshire WA6 8LS ☎ 01928 788192, 0410 288790

ING Hazel (Cor): 24 Avon Court, Mold, Clwyd CH7 1JP ☎ 01352 755168

JONES David (Cor, Obdam): Maes Sied, Bodfari, Ne Denbigh LL16 4HU ☎ 01745 710591

LEWIS Susan (Cor): 23 Rowan Avenue, Sale, Brooklands, Cheshire M33 3NG ☎ 0161 962 7117, 0797 1749671

MCKENNA Hugh: 99 Lorraine Road, Timperley, Altrincham, Cheshire WA15 7QH ☎ 0161 980 7891, 0850 000465 mob

MCMAHON Russell (Flt, Clt, Saxes): Glyncoed, 14 Upper Garth Road, Bangor, Gwynedd LL57 2SR ☎ 01248 364928

NORRIS David (Obdam): 23 Stonehaven Close, Childwall, Liverpool L16 3GP ☎ 0151 722 2875

OLDFIELD Judith E. (Cor, Rec, Pf): Flat 4, 81 Old Lansdowne Road, West Didsbury, Manchester M20 2NZ ☎ 0161 434 9996

PARKINS Victoria (Cor): Flat 2, 108 Clyde Road, Didsbury, Manchester M20 7JN ☎ 0161 448 2178

REID Gabriel (Cor): Swindale House, Hilton, Nr Appleby, Cumbria CA16 6LU ☎ 017683 52399

RICHARDSON Sally (Cor): 16 Cheltenham Road, Chorlton-Cum-Hardy, Manchester M21 9QN ☎ 0161 718 5627

RINGROSE Emma (Cor): 9 Wilton Street, Whitefield, Manchester M45 7FT ☎ 0161796 8015, 0797 0854525 mob

SIMPSON Richard (Cor): Roquebrun, Reservoir Road, Whaley Bridge, Stockport, Cheshire SK12 7BW ☎ 01663 734979, 0831 696 847

SMALL Jonathan (Cor): Millfield, Vyner Road North, Bidston Hill, Birkenhead, Merseyside L43 7PZ ☎ 0151 652 2763

SMITH Wendy (Cor, Rec): 18 Queens Road, Onchan, Isle Of Man IM3 4AG ☎ 01624 622580

SWAIN Christine: 58 Newgate Road, Sale, Cheshire M33 4NQ ☎ 0161 905 3385, 0410 199 358

SWIFT Alexandra (Cor): Chartwell, 2 Nutgrove Hall Drive, St Helens, Merseyside WA9 5PY ☎ 01744 811730, 0589 548293

TAYLOR Valerie: 150 Oldfield Road, Altrincham, Cheshire WA14 4BJ ☎ 0161 928 2117

TWIST Linda (Cor, Obdam): Maes Sied, Aberwheeler, Bodfari, Near Denbigh, Clwyd LL16 4HU ☎ 01745 710591

WOOD K: 20 Western Drive, Liverpool L19 0LX ☎ 0151 427 1854

WOODROW Gillian: Roselle, Buxton Road, Chinley, High Peak, Derbyshire SK23 6DR ☎ 01633750368

NORTH EAST

ANELAY Angela (Cor, Pf): 98B Tadcaster Road, Dringhouses, York, N Yorks YO24 1LT ☎ 01904 707481

BRETT Susan (Bsn, A Sax, B Sax, Flt): 11 Westwood Avenue, Linthorpe, Middlesbrough, Cleveland TS5 5PY ☎ 01642 823360

BURNAGE Susan (Pf, Gtr, Voc): 5 Farcroft Grove, Wincobank, Sheffield S4 8BP

COLE Andrew: Orchard House, 97 Fitzwilliam Street, Swinton, S Yorks S64 8RL ☎ 01709 584087

CULL Philip (Cor, Arr): 23 Spring Street, Stockton-on-Tees, Cleveland TS18 3NR ☎ 01642 602629

ENGLISH Jane (Cor): Woodlands, Littlethorpe, Ripon, North Yorkshire HG4 3LR ☎ 01765 602537

GLOSSOP Zoe (Cor): 1 Wilkinson Street, Worsborough Common, Barnsley, South Yorkshire S70 4HZ ☎ 01226 295365, 0860 291070

GODFREY Claire: 8 Talbot Grove, Off Street Lane, Roundhay, Leeds LS8 1AB ☎ 0113 2697754

HAMILTON Ian (Cor): 9 Beauchief Rise, Sheffield S8 0EL ☎ 0114 2368544

HAYWARD John (Cor): 4 Broad Gates, Silkstone, Barnsley, South Yorkshire S75 4HD ☎ 01226 792086

HEWITT Richard: Flat 1 Middleton Lodge, Stray Road, Harrogate HG2 8AR ☎ 01423 560913

KEECH Diana (Cor): 18 Clumer Street, Princes Avenue, Hull, North Humberside HU5 4JX ☎ 01482 346106

KELLETT Colin (Cor): 31 Bridge Park, Gosforth, Newcastle-upon-Tyne NE3 2DX ☎ 0191 285 3672 & fax

LOWE Catherine (Cor, Obdam): 12 Grove Lane, Headingley, Leeds LS6 2AP ☎ 0113 225 6934

MCINTYRE Douglas (Cor): 7 Onslow Gardens, Low Fell, Gateshead, Tyne & Wear NE9 6HL ☎ 0191 487 5268

MELLOR John: Address Unknown

PALMER Carole (Cor, Pf): 3 Glenfield, Off Sunnybank Road, Greetland, Nr Halifax W. Yorks HX4 8JW ☎ 01422 372246, 0585 089441 mob

ROUSSEAU Judith (Obdam, Cor): 6 Maplewood, Hilda Park, Chester Le Street, Co Durham DH2 2LB ☎ 0191 388 2498

SCOTT Paul (Cor): 1 Springfield Close, Eckington, Sheffield S21 4GS ☎ 01246 431562, 0973 634372

SMITH James (Pf, Org, Voc): Greenacres, 6 Main Street, Scothern, Lincoln LN2 2UF ☎ 01673 862507, 01426 154660

STEPHENSON James (Cor): 45 Whirlow Court Road, Whirlow, Sheffield, South Yorkshire S11 9NS ☎ 0113 2365 029

STRETTON Jane (Cor): 22 Morrison Street, Castleford, West Yorkshire WF10 4BE ☎ 01977 731266

STRINGER John: 3 St Peters Grove, York YO30 6AQ ☎ 01904 671132

VYNER Edward (Cor): 154 Burtonstone Lane, York YO30 6DF ☎ 01904 624083

WINFIELD Roger: Whamlands, Nine Banks, Whitfield, Nr Hexham Northumberland NE47 8HJ ☎ 01434 345239

WRIGHT Philippa (Cor): Milnthorpe House, Station Road, Alne, York YO61 1TP ☎ 01347 838591

EAST

BAKER Marilyn (Pf, Voc): 39 The Cherry Orchard, Hadlow, Tonbridge, Kent TN11 0HU

BURDEN Rachel (Vln): 10 Mayfield, Welwyn Garden City, Herts AL8 7EL ☎ 01707 333409

CARLSON Neil (Cor, Obdam): 65 Westgarth Gardens, Bury St Edmunds, Suffolk IP33 3LG ☎ 01284 704667

FORBES Cherry (Cor, Bq Ob, Pf): 149 Angel Street, Hadleigh, Suffolk IP7 5BY ☎ 01473 822337

GERRARD Gillian (Pf): 7 Fairways, Braiswick, Essex CO4 5TX ☎ 01206 852516

CLASSICAL
music
The magazine the music professionals read

TRY A SAMPLE SUBSCRIPTION
12 issues for £23
(**35% OFF** the cover price)

£2.95
Every fortnight

MONEY BACK GUARANTEE
If the magazine fails to live up to your expectations, simply drop us a line and we will refund you for any unpublished issues.

Please send your cheque (payable to *Rhinegold Publishing Ltd*)
to: **Rhinegold Publishing Ltd (CM Subs), FREEPOST, Gravesend, Kent DA12 3BR**

Fax: 01474 325557
Email: subscriptions@rhinegold.co.uk
Website: www.rhinegold.co.uk

CREDIT CARD HOTLINE: 01474 334500   (office hours)

MILES Gillian *(Cor)*: 20 Church Lane, Toppesfield, Nr Halstead, Essex CO9 4DS ☎ 01787 238045

OLIVER Victoria *(Cor)*: 10 Barrymore Walk, Raileigh, Essex SS6 8YF ☎ 01268 773788, 0402 366926

TYRRELL Rebecca *(Cor)*: 13 The Fields, Tacolneston, Norwich, Norflk NR16 1DG ☎ 01953 789615, 01483 504629, 01953 789615

WEALE Judith *(Sax, Cor)*: 47 Beverly Road, Ipswich, Suffolk IP4 4BU ☎ 01473 271740

MIDLANDS

ARDEN-TAYLOR Paul *(Cor, Obdam, Rec, Ea Wnd)*: 11 Romsley Hill Grange, Farley Lane, Romsley, Nr Halesowen, West Midlands B62 0LN ☎ 01562 710801

BENTLEY Alaster *(Cor, Obdam)*: 16 Marshall Avenue, Shipston-on-Stour, Warwicks CV36 4HN ☎ 01608 664207, 0973 335146 mob

COWSILL David *(Cor)*: Ulan Lower Swell, Stow-on-The Wold, Glos GL54 1LF ☎ 01451 31192

EVANS Anna *(Cor, Obdam)*: 17 Islip Road, Oxford OX2 7SN ☎ 01865 559068

GILCHRIST Margaret: Sunnyside, Mill Lane, Station Road, Mickleover, Derbys. DE3 5FQ ☎ 01332 512774

GREEN Helen *(Rec)*: 12 Badsey Fields Lane, Badsey, Evesham, Worcs WR11 5EX ☎ 01386 833335

GRIPTON Sue *(Cor)*: 46, High Park Avenue, Wollaston, Stourbridge, West Midlands DY8 3NE ☎ 01384 393419

HARVEY-BROWN Stacey *(Cor, Bsn)*: Yew Tree, Uttoxeter Road, Lower Tean, Staffs ST10 4LN ☎ 01538 723896

HODGES Alan *(Cor)*: 177, Doxey, Stafford ST16 1EQ ☎ 01785 251785

KELLY Jonathan: 35 Barclay Road, Bearwood, Warley, West Midlands B67 5JY ☎ 0121 429 9018

MCKAY Elspeth *(Flt, Pic, T Sax)*: 3 Repton Close, Stafford ST17 4TG ☎ 01785 256017, 07979 496604

MOGRIDGE Jessica *(Cor, Obdam)*: April Cottage, Little Harrowden, Wellingborough, Northamptonshire NN9 5BB ☎ 0589 164997

MOORE Patricia *(Cor, Obdam)*: The White House, Stock Green, Redditch, Worcs B96 6TB ☎ 01386 792542

O'CONNOR Karen *(Cor)*: 449 Reddings Lane, Tyseley, Birmingham B11 3DF ☎ 0121 778 1336 & fax

OLLESON Hillary *(Cor, Obdam)*: 538 Derby Road, Adams Hill, Nottingham NG7 2GY ☎ 0115 9786495

PHILLIPS Jennifer *(Cor)*: 37 Margaret Grove, Harborne, Birmingham B17 9JJ ☎ 0121 428 3567

REAKES Richard *(Cor)*: 24 Wheatmoor Rise, Sutton Coldfield, West Midlans B75 6AW ☎ 0121 378 1278

REYNOLDS Alison *(Cor)*: 4 The Minster, Penn Fields, Wolverhampton WV3 7BH ☎ 01902 344081

ROBINSON Julie *(Cor)*: 3 Barnstaple Close, Allesley Green, Coventry, Warks CV5 7PJ ☎ 024 7640 5283

ROWSON Malcolm *(Cor)*: 37 Stratford Road, Warwick, Warwickshire CV34 6AS ☎ 01926 491785

RUNDLE Timothy *(Voc, Pf, B Gtr)*: 20 Oberon Close, Rugby, Warks CV22 6LZ ☎ 01788 811338

SWAN Nicola *(Cor, Pf)*: 307 Meeley Road, Selly Oak, Birmingham B29 6EL ☎ 0121 415 5964

THEOBALD Ruth: Grange Cottage, Grange Road, Knightley, Staffs ST20 0JX ☎ 01785 284433 & fax

THOMAS David *(Cor, Bsn)*: 14 Valley Road, Wistaston, Crew, Cheshire CW2 8JX ☎ 01270 650507

THOMAS Sylvia *(Cor, A Sax)*: 14 Valley Road, Wistaston, Crewe, Cheshire CW2 8JX ☎ 01270 650507

WALDEN Peter *(Obdam)*: 2 The Drive, Colletts Green, Powick, Worcs. WR2 4SA ☎ 01905 830592

WEIGALL Richard *(Obdam)*: 5, Grove Avenue, Moseley, Birmingham, West Midlands B13 9RU ☎ 0121 449 0945

WHATLEY Alison *(Cor, Obdam)*: 44 Crosbie Road, Harborn, Birmingham B17 9BE ☎ 0121 427 7149

WOOLF John: 35 School Road, Moseley, Birmingham B13 9TF ☎ 0121 449 9608

WOOLFENDEN Jane: Malvern House, Sibford Ferris, Banbury, Oxon OX15 5RG ☎ 01295 780679

YAXLEY Nigel John *(Cor)*: Garden House, Dam Road, Tickhill, Doncaster, South Yorkshire DN11 9QX ☎ 01302 750755

SOUTH EAST

BRAZIER Philip *(Cor, Obdam)*: St Georges, 10 Lakewood Road, Chandlers Ford, Hampshire SO5 1ES ☎ 023 8025 2720

BRIDGE Geoffrey *(Cor, Obdam, Con)*: 27 Pinewood Road, Ferndown, Dorset BH22 9RP ☎ 01202 877014

BRITTON Vanessa *(Obdam, Cor, Bq Ob)*: 80 Windmill Road, Mortimer, Berkshire RG7 3RJ ☎ 0118 933 3409 & fax

CARTER Gillian *(Cor)*: 164 Church Street, Sturminster Marshall, Wimborne, Dorset BH21 4BU ☎ 01258 857049

CROWTHER Ian *(Cor)*: 10 Longport, Canterbury, Kent CT1 1PE ☎ 01227 763965

ELIAS Ruth: 64 Collington Avenue, Bexhill, East Sussex TN39 3RA ☎ 01424 211176

HARPER Sylvia *(Cor)*: 16 St Georges Road, Farnham, Surrey GU9 8NB ☎ 01252 727240

HUNT James *(Cor)*: 69 Lonnen Road, Wimborne, Dorset BH21 7AU ☎ 01202 884940

IONIDES Sarah *(Cor)*: 8 South View Terrace, Henfield., Sussex BN5 9ES ☎ 01273 494312

JAMES Mark *(Cor, Con)*: 20 Hampton Place, Brighton, East Sussex BN1 3DD ☎ 01273 208680

KAY Edward: 54 Upton Way, Poole, Dorset BH18 9LZ ☎ 01202 602336

KING Carolyn *(Cor, Obdam)*: 5 Edward Street, Abingdon, Oxon OX14 1DJ ☎ 01235 522774

KNIGHTS Andrew *(Obdam, Cor)*: 28 Pemberton Road, Lyndhurst, Hants SO43 7AN ☎ 023 8028 2376

LEADBETTER Susan *(Cor, Obdam)*: Flat 2, 3 Clarenden Road, Bournemouth BH4 8AJ ☎ 01202 765 890

LEPAGE Katharine *(Cor)*: Wayfaring House, 8 Smithers Lane, East Peakham, Tombridge, Kent TN12 5HT ☎ 01622 871576, 0966 195991

PAGE Caroline *(Cor)*: Woodcote, 18 Prout Bridge, Beaminster, Dorset DT8 3AY ☎ 01308 862047

PORTER Rachel *(Obdam, Cor)*: 39 Green Road, Reading, Berks RG6 2BS ☎ 01734 261600

PYE Helen Mavis *(Cor, Obdam)*: 14 Southridge Rise, Crowborough, East Sussex TN6 1LG ☎ 01892 654593

RENDLE Peter: 12 Harbour Hill Crescent, Poole, Dorset BH15 3QA ☎ 01202 679812

ROACH Adrian: 56 Mill Rise, Westdene, Brighton, East Sussex BN1 5GH ☎ 01273 881570

ROLLES Annie *(Cor)*: 2 Frensham Heights Rd, Rowledge, Farnham, Surrey GU10 4DX ☎ 01252 793904

SARTIN Paul *(Voc, Vln, Wh, Pf)*: 23 Jeune Street, Oxford OX4 1BN ☎ 01865 203365

SPICER Charles *(Cor, Ea Wnd)*: 3 The Square, Spencers Wood, Reading, Berks RG7 1BS ☎ 0118 988 4337

WILLITS Lucinda *(Cor, Pf)*: 11 Exleigh Close, Bitterne, Southampton, Hants SO18 5FB ☎ 023 8039 6066

SOUTH WEST

ADAMS Elin: Murmur-Y-Mor, 6 Somerset View, Aberogwr CF32 0PP ☎ 01656 880337, 04325 235792 pager

ADAMS Graeme *(Cor)*: 10 Langdon Road, Leckhampton, Cheltenham, Glos GL53 7NZ

BALDWIN Janet *(Cor, Obdam)*: 146 Reservoir Road, Gloucester GL4 6SA ☎ 01452 303981

BLEWETT Lorna *(Pf, Cor)*: The Old Chapel, Front Street, Chedzoy, Bridg Water Somerset TA7 8RE ☎ 01278 424757

BYRT Linda *(Cor, Obdam)*: 8 Belmont Road, Tiverton, Devon EX16 6AR ☎ 01884 258312, 0966 431769

CLARKE Louise *(Cor, Flt, Sax)*: Beech House, 45 Draycott Road, Chiseldon, Wilts SN4 0LJ ☎ 01793 741076

CODD Jean Marsden *(Cor, Obdam)*: 40 Highfields, Llandaff, Cardiff CF5 2QB ☎ 029 2056 2962, 07970 173952 mob

COWLEY David (*Cor*): 13 St Johns Crescent, Canton, Cardiff CF5 1NX ☎ 029 2022 2477

CRAIG Celia (*Cor, Bq Ob, Vln*): 34 Bridge Street, Chepstow, Monmouthshire NP6 5EY ☎ 01291 620746, 0976 547031

DEWIS (*Pf*): Opus.I, Wrafton, Nr Braunton, N Devon EX33 2DN

DYER Graham (*Cor*): 68 Maes-Y-Sarn, Pentyrch, Nr Cardiff CF4 8QR ☎ 029 2089 1593

FISHER Fay (*Cor, Obdam*): 144 Barnwood Road, Gloucester GL4 7JT ☎ Glos 612395

FULLARD Simon (*Cor, Obdam, Pf, Org*): Flat 15, Cedar Drive, Dursley, Glos GL11 4EB ☎ 01453 549486, 0498 647729

JACOBY Elizabeth (*Cor, Bsn, C Bsn, Obdam*): Burton House, West Bexington, Dorchester, Dorset DT2 9DD ☎ 01308 898289

JOHNSTON Murray: 64 Heol Isaf, Radyr, Cardiff, South Glamorgan CF4 8DZ

KING Andrew: 4 Cave Cottages, Badminton Road, Downend, Bristol BS16 6DB ☎ 0117 983 4591

KITT Derek (*Pf, Org*): 1, Liskeard Road, Saltash, Cornwall PL12 4HE ☎ 01752 853781

MILLER Stephanie (*Cor*): 6 Langstone Cotttages, Langstone, Nr Newport, Gwent, South Wales NP6 2LY ☎ 01633 411107, 07970 034091

PROBERT David (*Cor*): 24 Windsor Crescent, Radyr, Cardiff CF4 8AE

REES Peter (*Obdam, Cor, Bq Ob*): 65 Cranwells Park, Bath, Avon BA1 2YE ☎ 01225 422242

SENTER Catherine (*Obdam, Cor*): 18 St Michaels Road, Llandaff, Cardiff CF5 2AP ☎ 029 2055 5908

SISWICK Julie (*Cor, Flt, Clt*): 11 Shetland Close, Ramleaze, Shaw, Swindon SN5 9RZ ☎ 01793 876697

TANNER Catherine (*Cor*): Flat 1, 12 Richmaond Road, Roath, Cardiff CF2 3AS ☎ 029 2031 9522, 07669 103528 pager

TAYLOR Gillian (*Cor, Obdam*): 94 Plassey Street, Penarth CF64 1EN ☎ 029 2070 9335, 01306 880669

WILSON Ronald (*Cor*): Mudgley Elms, Mudgley, Nr. Wedmore, Somerset BS28 4TH ☎ 01934 712863

LONDON

ALLEN Judith (*Cor*): Flat 1, 10 Lewisham Road, London SE13 7QR ☎ 020 8692 2286, 0402 382010 mob

ALTY Alison (*Cor, Obdam*): 70 Cheriton Square, London SW17 8AE ☎ 020 8675 2638, 01306 880669

ANDERSON John (*Cor*): 51 Waveney Avenue, London SE15 3UQ ☎ 020 7635 9862 & fax

ARGIROS Marios: 12 Park Avenue, London NW11 7SJ ☎ 01663 751269, 01306 500022

BAIGENT Mark (*Cor, Obdam, Obdac, Bq Ob*): 44, Perryfields Road, Southgate, Crawley, W. Sussex RH11 8AB ☎ 01293 533179, 08509 14024

BAILEY Helen: Flat 3, 11 Mays Hill Road, Bromley, Kent BR2 0HN ☎ 020 8464 6793

BARNETT John (*Cor, Rec*): 6 Eton Place, Eton College Road, London NW3 2BT ☎ 020 7722 2025

BENDA Nicholas (*Bq Ob, Cor*): The Cloisters, 145 Commercial Street, London E1 6EB ☎ 020 7375 2002

BESSELL John (*Cor*): 608 Mierscourt Road, Rainham, Kent ME8 8RQ ☎ 01634 365496

BLACK Ian (*Cor, Obdam*): 15, Newton Manor Close, Off High Street, Swanage, Dorset BH19 1JS ☎ 01929 423954

BLACK Neil (*Obdam, Cor*): 29 Northway, London NW11 6PB ☎ 020 8458 7961

BOHLING Sue (*Cor*): 95 Marlow Road, London SE20 7XW ☎ 020 8325 1031, 0973 335514 mob, 020 8549 1706

BOLTE Barbara (*Cor*): 42 Frater Avenue, Toronto, ON, M4C 2H6, Canada ☎ +1 416 467 6147

BOYES Deborah (*Cor*): 11 King Street, Chesham, Buckinghamshire HP5 1LZ ☎ 01494 791239, 020 8533 1372 day

BRAWN Victoria (*Cor*): Flat 4, 39 Central Hill, Upper Norwood, London SE19 1BW ☎ 020 8655 7152, 0850 695 116, 020 8533 1372 day

BRITTON Michael (*Cor*): 42 The Mall, Southgate, London N14 N14 6LN ☎ 020 8882 5108

BROADBENT Rachel (*Cor*): 39A Palmerston Crescent, Palmers Green, London N13 4UE ☎ 020 8886 3413, 0976 943508

BROWN James (*Cor*): 44 Baskerville, Malmesbury, Wiltshire SN16 9BS ☎ 01666 825242

BROWNE Geoffrey (*Cor, Obdam, B Ob*): 76 Poplar Grove, New Malden, Surrey KT3 3DN ☎ 020 8942 2443, 020 8549 1706

BURROW Joan (*Cor, Obdam*): The Sycamores, Double Street, Spalding, Lincs PE11 2AA ☎ 01775 760994

CAIRD George: 15 Chad Road, Edgbaston, Birmingham B15 3ER ☎ 0121 455 0195, 0121 454 1663, 0121 455 0912

CALDICOTT Louise (*Cor, Obdam*): 154 Clarence Road, Wimbledon, London SW19 8QD ☎ 020 8540 8145

CANTER Robin (*Obdam, Cor, Bq Ob, Obdac*): 22 Tavistock Terrace, Upper Holloway, London N19 4DB ☎ 020 7272 0888

CARR Simon (*Cor, Saxes, Clt*): 73A Rances Lane, Wokingham, Berks RG40 2LQ ☎ 0118 979 3360, 0850 559479 mob

CAUTHERY Andrew (*Cor*): Mardon, Farnham Lane, Haslemere, Surrey GU27 1EX ☎ 01428 651453

CHAMBERS Carolyn (*Cor, Obdam*): 26 Barnfield Rise, Andover, Hants SP10 2UQ ☎ 01264 364292

CLARKE Helen (*Cor*): Woodlands, Easebourne Lane, Midhurst, W Sussex GU29 9AY ☎ 01730 812621

CLEMENT-EVANS Huw (*Cor*): 97 Hindes Road, Harrow, Middlesex HA1 1RX ☎ 020 8861 4052, 0976 313261 mob

CLEMMOW Katie (*Cor, Obdam*): 270 Friern Road, London SE22 0BB ☎ 020 8693 4905, 01306 880669

COATES Tamara (*Cor, Obdam*): 83 Corringham Road, London NW11 7DL ☎ 020 8458 4897

CONTRACTOR Ruth (*Cor*): 50 Osprey Heights, 7 Bramlands Close, London SW11 2NP ☎ 020 7642 8350, 0802 987739 mob, 020 7642 8350

COWIE Christopher: 19 Grange Hill, South Norwood, London SE25 6SX ☎ 020 8771 3770, 01306 880669

CRAEN Peter (*Cor*): 147 Haling Park Road, South Croydon, Surrey CR2 6NN ☎ 020 8688 4605

CRAEN Tom (*Cor, A Sax, Clt*): 2A Ventnor Avenue, Stanmore, Middx HA7 2HU ☎ 020 8907 1171

CREW Paul (*Kbds, Cor*): 43 Haliburton Road, St Margarets, Twickenham, Middx TW1 1PD ☎ 020 8891 1162, 020 8892 7658 fax

CROSSMAN John (*Cor*): 86 Park Grove Road, Leytonstone, London E11 4PU ☎ 020 8558 2672

CROWTHER Jill (*Cor, Obdam*): 3 Eskdale Ave, Chesham, Bucks HP5 3AX ☎ 01494 776769

DARBYSHIRE Alun (*Cor*): 55 Palmerston Road, Wimbledon, London SW19 1PG ☎ 01306 880669 day, 0378 985291 mob

DAVIES Maxine (*Cor*): 22 Merton Road, Walthamstow, London E17 9DE ☎ 020 8509 1663

DE BRUINE Frank: Snelliusstraat 92, 2517 Rk Den Haag, Holland ☎ +31 70 3635429, +31 70 3622436 fax

DICKINSON Stella (*Cor, Obdam*): 130 St James Lane, Muswell Hill, London N10 3RH ☎ 020 8883 0657, 01306 880669 day

DODS Deirdre (*Obdam, Cor*): 11 York House, Abbey Mill Lane, St. Albans, Hertfordshire AL3 4HG ☎ 01727 839697

DRAPER Matthew (*Cor*): Flat 5, 9 Crouch Hall Road, London N8 8HT ☎ 020 8347 8749, 0973 821450, 020 8372 9395

EARLE Richard: 27 Grange Road, Lewes, East Sussex BN7 1TS ☎ 01273 475200

EASTAWAY James (*Bq Ob, Rec*): 93A Breakspears Road, Brockley, London SE4 1TX ☎ 020 8246 90823

EATON Tim (*Cor*): 73 Holden Close, Goodmayes, Dagenham RM8 2QT ☎ 020 8597 0361

EDWARDS Susan (*Cor, Obdam*): Frogmore, Church Lane, Thorpe, Ashbourne, Derbyshire DE6 2AW ☎ 01335 350 378

ELIOT Margaret (*Cor*): 6A Hillbury Road, London SW17 8JT ☎ 020 8673 2260

EVANS Jane (*Cor, Obdam, B Ob*): "Stretton", Manor Close, East Horsley, Surrey ☎ KT24 6SB, 01483 281839, 0973 75 0973 mob

FEILD Eugene *(Obdam, Cor)*: 9 Pandora Road, West Hampstead, London NW6 1TS ☏ 020 7435 4778, 0973 197299 mob

FEILDING Emma *(Cor, Obdam)*: Flat 4, 1 Marjorie Grove, London SW11 5SH ☏ 020 7350 0185

FERRAN Marcia *(Cor, Obdam)*: 166A Northview Road, London N8 7NB ☏ 020 8348 8879, 01306 880669

FORBES Stephen *(Cor, Obdam)*: 9 Nicholas Gardens, Pyrford, Surrey GU22 8SD ☏ 01932 353062, 0370 920017 mob

FOSTER Lucy *(Cor)*: 9 Uffington Road, West Norwood, London SE27 0RW ☏ 020 8761 8201

FRANCIS Sarah *(Obdam, Cor)*: 10 Avenue Road, London N6 5DW ☏ 020 8340 5461, 020 8347 5907 fax

FRANKEL Laurence *(Obdam, Cor, Pf)*: 39 Norton Road, Uxbridge, Middx UB8 2PT ☏ 01895 254 708

FREEDMAN Sara *(Cor, Rec)*: 105 Priory Park Road, London NW6 7UY ☏ 020 7372 7311

FREER Anthony *(Cor)*: 122 Merland Rise, Tadworth, Surrey KT20 5JA ☏ 01737 358239

FRIEND Marion *(Cor)*: 90 Blagdon Road, New Malden, Surrey KT3 4AE ☏ 020 8949 3103

FROST Susan *(Cor, Pf, Sax, Clt)*: 16A Darell Road, Kew, Richmond, Surrey TW9 4LQ ☏ 020 8878 3845

FYFE Elizabeth *(Cor)*: Tanyard House, Chilton Foliat, Nr Hungerford, Berks RG17 0TG ☏ 01488 683830

GARNER Alan *(Cor)*: 19 Miswell Lane, Tring, Hertfordshire HP23 4DD ☏ 01442 826 901, 0976 646 467 mob

GASKELL Helen *(Cor)*: Hcr, Cow Lane, Tring, Hertfordshire HP23 5NS

GEER Christine *(Cor)*: Longwood Barn, Carters Hill, Underriver, Nr Sevenoaks Kent TN15 0SN ☏ 01732 761812

GILES Pamela *(Cor)*: 45 Great Arthur House, Golden Lane Estate, London EC1Y 0RE ☏ 020 7253 3950

GIRDWOOD Julia: 30 Lancaster Avenue, West Norwood, London SE27 9DZ ☏ 020 8761 7865

GLOVER Anne *(Cor)*: 23 The Green, Fetcham, Leatherhead, Surrey KT22 9XE ☏ 01372 457721

GOODEY Paul *(Cor, Pf)*: Garden Flat, 53 Regina Road, London N4 3PT ☏ 020 7272 2862

GOOSSENS Joan *(Cor, Pf)*: 191 Sandy Lane, Cheam, Surrey SM2 7EU ☏ 020 8642 3316

GOSBY Jennifer *(Cor)*: Hale Cottage, 221 Hale Street, East Peckham, Tonbridge, Kent TN12 5HY ☏ 0162 287 1626

GOY Joy *(Cor)*: 52 Bishopsgate Walk, Spitalfield Lane, Chichester, West Sussex PO19 4FQ ☏ 01243 783700

GRAEME Peter *(Obdam)*: Grenovic, 4 French Mill Lane, Shaftesbury, Dorset SP7 8EU ' 01747 854420

GREENE Ann *(Obdam, Cor)*: 20 Barrington Road, London N8 8QS ☏ 020 8348 0740

GRINT [WHARTON] Sara *(Cor)*: 6 Tower Road, Orpington, Kent BR6 0SQ ☏ 01689 837113, 0973 385970

HAMER Philip *(Pf)*: Basement Flat, 13 Berkley Place, Wimbledon Village, London SW19 4NN ☏ 020 8946 3259

HARDWICK Ian *(Cor)*: Kingsclere, 70 Dovercourt Road, Dulwich, London SE22 8UW ☏ 020 8693 5356

HARRIS Kathryn *(Cor, Pf)*: 10 The Firs, 44-46 Lawrie Park Gardens, Sydenham, London SE26 6XN ☏ 0976 430847, 01306 880669

HARRIS Lindy: Ashlea, Oakwood Drive, East Horsley, Surrey KT24 6QF ☏ 01483 283346

HENNESSY Gail: 118 Chewton Road, Walthamstow, London E17 7DN ☏ 020 8521 5983, 020 8926 2797 fax

HIGGINS Thomas: 37 Victoria Avenue, Surbiton, Surrey KT6 5DL ☏ 020 8390 1020

HINCHLIFFE Robert *(Cor)*: 4 The Jays, Nightingale Wood, Uckfield, East Sussex TN22 5YG ☏ 01825 767149

HOLLAND Nicky *(Rec, Pf, Cor)*: 35 St Stephens Avenue, Shepherds Bush, London W12 8JB ☏ 020 8749 5089

HOOKER Christopher *(Cor)*: 21 Kings Road, Barnet, Herts EN5 4EF ☏ 020 8449 6178

HOSKINS Clare *(Cor)*: 40 Midland Terrace, London NW2 6QH ☏ 020 8450 4857

HOUGHTON Joseph: 4 Greengate Hutton, Preston, Lancs PR4 5FH ☏ 01772 613564, 0973 392082 mob

HOWELLS Mark: 18 Gloucester Road, North Harrow, Middlesex HA1 4PW ☏ 020 8427 6936 & fax, 01306 880669 day, 0973 176632 mob

HULSE Gareth: 270 Friern Road, London SE22 0BB ☏ 020 8693 4905

HUNT Gordon *(Cor, Obdam)*: Goodmans Farm, Tumblefield Road, Stansted, Sevenoaks Kent TN15 7PR ☏ 01732 822618

IFEKA Althea *(Obdam, Cor, Rec, Voc)*: 64B East Street, Barking IG11 8EQ ☏ 020 8591 4285, 020 8507 9085

INGLETON Rachel *(Cor)*: 15 Kinver Road, London SE26 4NT ☏ 020 8244 3180

JAMES Natalie *(Cor)*: 35 Brentham Way, Ealing, London W5 1BE ☏ 020 8997 6820

JANEY *(Obdam, Cor, Vln)*: 21 Broomhill Court, Snakes Lane West, Woodford Green, Essex IG8 0BQ ☏ 020 8505 3363, 0410 229132, 020 8505 3363

JEANS Michael *(Cor)*: 17 Plympton Avenue, London NW6 7TL ☏ 020 7328 0768

JORDAN Heather *(Cor)*: 91 Brands Hill Avenue, High Wycombe, Bucks HP13 5PX ☏ 01494 527826

KAMEN Michael *(Kbds)*: 11 Stanley Crescent, London W11 2NA

KEEBLE Kim *(Cor, Obdam)*: Gaya Cottage, Blacksmiths Lane, Eydon, Daventry, Northants NN11 3PF ☏ 01327 262383, 020 8533 1372

KEEL Mary *(Cor)*: Address Unknown

KELLY Dominic *(Pf)*: 169 Farley Road, Selsdon, South Croydon, Surrey CR2 7NN ☏ 020 8251 9978, 0589 352692, 020 8251 9977

KIRK Julian Robert *(Cor)*: 28 Luscombe Court, Park Hill Road, Shortlands, Bromley, Kent BR2 0XQ ☏ 020 8460 6242

KIRK Tanya *(Cor, Pf)*: 28 Luscombe Court, Park Hill Road, Shortlands, Bromley, Kent BR2 0XQ ☏ 020 8460 6242

KNIGHT Janice *(Cor, Obdam, B Ob)*: 29 Northway, London NW11 6PB ☏ 020 8458 7961

LAURENCE Lesley *(Cor)*: 163 Anerley Road, London SE20 8EF ☏ 020 8402 4339

LAWLEY John *(Cor, Ob)*: 9 Dukes Avenue, Finchley N3 2DE ☏ 020 8346 0589

LEWIS Juliet *(Cor, Pf)*: 120A Brondesbury Park, London NW2 5JR ☏ 020 8830 0193, 020 8533 1372 day

LIGHT Sarah *(Cor)*: 21B Ommaney Road, New Cross, London SE14 5NS ☏ 020 7732 6696, 0976 953044 mob

LINLEY Elizabeth *(Cor)*: 58 Vernham Road, London SE18 3HB ☏ 020 8855 3696, 0860 887477

LIVELY Josephine *(Cor, Obdam)*: 22 Methuen Park, Muswell Hill, London N10 2JS ☏ 020 8442 0589, 0976 411735 mob, 01306 880669 day

LLOYD Rebecca *(Cor)*: 19 Winnsterrace, Walthamstow, London E17 5EJ ☏ 020 8523 5184, 0966 214267

LORD Roger *(Cor, Obdam)*: The Old Meeting House, St. James Street, Shaftesbury, Dorset SP7 8HF ☏ 01747 854999

MACDONALD Anne *(Cor, Obdam)*: 17A Broad Street, Teddington, Middlesex TW11 8QZ ☏ 020 8943 2478, 01306 880669 day

MACKAY Sandra *(Cor, Obdam)*: 14 Limesford Road, Nunhead, London SE15 3BX ☏ 020 7639 1087, 0850 045864 mob

MANNING Laura *(Cor, Pf, T Sax, Clt)*: 26 Manchester Grove, Isle Of Dogs, London E14 3BG ☏ 020 7515 4619, 0956 225766 mob

MANNING Penelope *(Cor)*: 11 Northcotts, Hatfield, Herts AL9 5ES ☏ 01707 269418

MARSDEN Ellen *(Cor)*: 56 Courtenay Road, Walthamstow, London E17 6LZ ☏ 020 8521 0844, 020 8521 0844

MARSHALL Jane *(Cor)*: Llwyn Idris, Brynsiencyn, Llanfairphllgwyngyll LL61 6BQ ☏ 01248 430903, 01248 430833 fax, 01306 880669

MARSHALL Keith *(Cor)*: 41 Shirley Drive, Hounslow, Middx TW3 2HD ☏ 020 8894 2068

MARSHALL Sheila *(Cor)*: 5 Pine Grove, Maidstone, Kent ME14 2AJ ☏ 01622 673853, 07971 861322

MARWOOD Caroline *(Obdam, Cor, Rec)*: 19 Burghill Road, Sydenham, London SE26 4HJ ☏ 020 8244 3172, 01306 880669

MAXWELL Melinda: 42 Norbiton Avenue, Kingson-on-Thames, Surrey KT1 3QR ☎ 020 8549 9178, 020 8549 1706 day, 020 8974 5660 fax

MCCOLL Anthony (*Cor*): 39 Nightingale Road, East Molesey, Surrey KT8 2PQ ☎ 020 8979 8307

MCKEAN Helen (*Cor, Bq Ob*): 2A Montreal Road, Ilford, Essex IG1 4SH ☎ 020 8518 6384

MCMILLAN Clare (*Cor, Pf*): 102 Speed House, Barbican, London EC2Y 8AU ☎ 020 7920 9670, 01523 111320

MCQUEEN Helen (*Cor, Obdam*): 6 Fishersdene, Claygate, Esher, Surrey KT10 0HT ☎ 01372 464948

MILLER Tess (*Cor, Obdam, Rec*): 12 Eleanor Grove, London SW13 0JN ☎ 020 8392 2408

MONTAGU Moyra (*Obdam, Cor*): Brook Farm, Parbrook, Glastonbury BA6 8PB ☎ 01458 850993, 01458 851066

MOORE Kieron (*Cor*): 35 St Stephens Avenue, Shepherds Bush, London W12 8JB ☎ 020 8749 5089

MORGAN Dick (*Cor*): 8 Grand View, Burlington Road, Swanage, Dorset BH19 1LS ☎ 01929 425047, 01306 880669

MOSBY Paul (*Cor, Obdam, Eth Obs*): 4 Creighton Avenue, London N10 1NU ☎ 020 8444 9830

NAGY Stephen (*Cor*): 14 Menelik Road, London NW2 3RP ☎ 020 7435 5681

NICKLIN Celia: Wensum Lodge, 19 Park Hill, Carshalton, Surrey SM5 3SA ☎ 020 8647 1119, 020 8395 2589 fax

NYE Stephen (*Cor, Obdam*): 46 Coley Avenue, Reading, Berks RG1 6LN ☎ 0118 9581885

O'NEAL Christopher (*Cor*): 14 Marius Road, Balham, London SW17 7QQ ☎ 020 8772 0710, 020 8772 0711 fax

OTAKI Bryony (*Cor, Obdam*): Malt House, 28 St Margarets Street, Rochester, Kent ME1 1TU ☎ 01634 811601

PALMER Hilary (*Cor, Sax*): 178A Chase Side, Enfield, Middlesex EN2 0QX ☎ 020 8366 4846, 07970 717196

PEACH Geraldine: 12 Hampton Court, Alexandra Park Road, London N22 7UH ☎ 0467 761154

PENDRILL Christine (*Cor*): 55 Southbrook Road, Lee, London SE12 8LJ ☎ 020 8318 3238

PFAFF Graham (*Obdam, Cor*): The Barn, Layston Park, Royston, Herts SG8 9DS ☎ 01763 242847

PHILPOT Claire (*Cor*): 7 Durham Road, East Finchley, London N2 9DP ☎ 020 8883 7395, 01306 880669

PILBERY Mary (*Cor, Obdam*): Allegro, 35 Laurel Avenue, Potters Bar, Herts EN6 2AB ☎ 01707 650735

POLMEAR Jeremy (*Cor, Obdam, A Sax*): 9 Beversbrook Road, London N19 4QG ☎ 020 7263 4027, 020 8533 1372

POOLE Quentin (*Cntrc, Con, Arr*): Hadfields, Buckland Common, Tring, Herts HP23 6NH ☎ 01494 758595

PORCAS Jennifer (*Cor, Obdam*): The Old Meeting House, St. James Street, Shaftesbury, Dorset SP7 8HF ☎ 01747 854999

POWELL David (*Cor*): 19 Gibbon Road, Kingston-upon-Thames, Surrey KT2 6AD ☎ 020 8287 4575

POWELL Helen (*Cor*): 25 Rotherwood Close, Wimbledon, London SW20 8RX ☎ 020 8543 2929, 0973 817713, 01306 880669

PRESLY David (*Cor*): 178 Gloucester Terrace, Bayswater, London W2 6HP ☎ 020 7262 2661

PROCTOR Judy (*Cor*): 20A New Quebec Street, London W1H 7DE ☎ 020 7258 0764 & fax, 020 8533 1372 day

RADCLIFFE Mark (*Bq Ob*): Flat 4, 57 Aberdare Gardens, London NW6 3AL ☎ 020 7624 2609

RAGGE Melanie (*Cor*): Michaelhouse, Mill Lane, Wootton, Woodstock Oxon OX20 1DJ ☎ 01993 813620, 020 8660 2522

RAWSTRON Helen (*Obdam, Cor*): Rose Cottage, 1 Barracks Lane, Spencers Wood, Reading, Berkshire RG7 1BB ☎ 0118 988 2511

ROBSON Anthony (*Rec, Bq Ob*): 35 Yeading Avenue, Rayners Lane, Harrow, Middx HA2 9RL ☎ 020 8866 5364

ROWLANDS Adrian (*Cor*): 88 Adelaide Road, Ealing, London W13 9EB ☎ 020 8579 6478

SALTER Graham (*Cor, Obdam, B Ob*): Bearsden, 25 Hampstead Lane, London N6 4RT ☎ 020 8348 8498, 01306 880 669, 0976 830309 mob

SANDERS Joseph (*Cor*): 61 Abbbotshall Road, Catford, London SE6 1SQ ☎ 020 8697 6277, 020 8698 6352 fax

SAUNDERS Eve (*Cor, Obdam*): 46 Whitworth Road, London SE18 3QB ☎ 020 8854 0381, 0956 653316 mob

SCHILSKY Erika (*Cor, Pf*): 104 Blackborne Road, Dagenham, Essex RM10 8SP ☎ 020 8593 8439

SCOTT Ruth (*Cor*): 26 Clarendon Court, Sidmouth Road, London NW2 5HB ☎ 020 8459 4700, 020 8533 1372 day

SCOTT Sarnia (*Cor*): 65 Monmouth Road, Hayes, Middlesex UB3 4JJ ☎ 020 8561 1213

SHEPHARD Jo (*Cor, Obdam*): 8 Milestone Road, Knebworth, Herts SG3 6DA ☎ 01438 814052

SKINNER Katrina (*Cor*): 38 Cloisters Road, Letchworth, Hertfordshire SG6 3JS ☎ 01462 673040

SMART David (*Flt, A Sax*): Flat 16 Marlborough House, Osnaburgh Street, London NW1 ☎ 0468 08169

SMEETON Roger (*Cor, Sax*): 16 Ormonde Road, Godalming, Surrey GU7 2EU ☎ 014868 4816

SMITH Catherine (*Cor, Obdam*): 30 Cleveland Gardens, London SW13 0AG ☎ 020 8878 3017

SMITH Imogen (*Cor*): 34 Lytton Road, New Barnet EN5 5BY ☎ 020 8449 5670

SMITH Richard (*Cor, Obdam, B Ob, Heck*): 7 Wathen Road, Dorking, Surrey RH4 1JU ☎ 01306 882008, 01306 880669 day

SMITH Susan (*Cor*): 7 Wathen Road, Dorking, Surrey RH4 1JU ☎ 01306 882008, 01306 880669 day

SPIERS Max (*Cor, Obdam, Pf*): Flat B 81 Camberwell Church St, London SE5 8RB ☎ 0956 343090 mob, 020 7740 6576

SPRECKELSEN Katharina: Ground Floor Flat, 8 Acland Road, London NW2 5AU ☎ 020 8451 9401

ST JOHN Kate (*Cor, Sax*): 40 Arkwright Road, London NW3 6BH ☎ 020 7794 9549

STORER Hilary (*Cor, Obdam*): 19 Gibbon Road, Kingston-upon-Thames, Surrey KT2 6AD ☎ 020 8287 4575

STROUD Cathy (*Cor, Obdam*): 24 Windsor Park, Dereham, Norfolk NR19 2SU ☎ 01362 853319, 0589 315052 mob

SUTCLIFFE Jock (*Cel*): 94 Woodfield Lane, Ashtead, Surrey KT21 2DP ☎ 01372 275781

SYKES Belinda (*Rec, Bq Ob*): 31A Vestry Road, London SE5 8PG ☎ 020 7708 3529

TALBOT Joby (*Sax, Pf, Com*): 49 Westmeston Avenue, Rottingdean Heights, Saltdean, East Sussex BN2 8AL ☎ 01273 300652, 020 7701 2521

TAYLOR Holly (*Pf*): Flat 2 Somerset House, The Farmlands, Northolt, Middlesex UB5 5EP ☎ 020 8930 1654

TAYLOR Lara (*Cor, Pf*): 21 Bluebell Close, Bedford MK42 0RN ☎ 01234 359221, 0468 977310

TENNICK Angela (*Cor*): 16 Gander Hill, Haywards Heath, West Sussex RH16 1QX ☎ 01444 453197

THEODORE David (*Cor*): 30 Selborne Road, London N14 7DH ☎ 020 8886 4950

THOMAS David (*Cor*): 12 Forburg Road, Stoke Newington, London N16 6HS ☎ 020 8806 2643, 01306 880669

TINDALE Margaret: 25 Monivea Road, Beckenham, Kent BR3 1HJ ☎ 020 8658 5398

TODD Hazel (*Cor, Obdam*): 9 Ward Close, Wokingham, Berkshire RG40 1XE ☎ 0118 978 5866

TRINER Imogen (*Rec, Cor*): ☎ 01306 880669 day, 0589 498462 mob

WALPOLE Victoria (*Cor, Obdam*): 4 Prior Grove, Chesham, Bucks HP5 3AZ ☎ 01494 786162, 01306 880669

WALTERS Hayley: 8 Towers Mews, Ashenden Road, London E5 0ES ☎ 020 8533 7390, 0976 853367

WARD Leila (*Rec*): 100 Roydene Road, Plumstead, London SE18 1QA ☎ 020 8521 8705, 0973 255073 mob

WAREHAM Geoffrey (*Cor*): 16 Eastbury Court, Eastbury Road, Watford, Herts WD1 4JX

WATTS Timothy (*Cor*): 5 Uplands Road, Caversham, Reading RG4 7JG ☎ 0118 948 3220

WEST Julian (*Cor*): 9 Morval Road, London SW2 1DG ☎ 020 7207 3236, 04325 152429 pager

WHITE John (*Cor, Obdam*): 49 Langley Drive, London E11 2LN ☎ 020 8989 2685

WHITE Penny *(Cor)*: Ground Floor Flat, 68 Compton Road, Brighton, E Sussex BN1 5AN ☎ 01273 562882

WHITTOW Marion *(Cor, Obdam)*: 47 South Hill Park, London NW3 2SS ☎ 020 7435 6694

WICKENS Derek *(Cor)*: Oudergemse Weg 86, Tervuren 3080, Belgium ☎ +32 2 767 7184 & fax

WIGGINS Peter *(Cor, Obdam)*: 20 Barrington Road, London N8 8QS ☎ 020 8348 0740

WILSON David *(Cor)*: 26 Adamsrill Road, London SE26 4AN ☎ 0958 651878

WINFIELD Michael *(Cor, Obdam)*: Spring Barn, Southwater Street, Southwater, West Sussex RH13 7BN ☎ 01403 734235

WOLFE John *(Cor)*: 15 Hillview Gardens, North Harrow, Middlesex HA2 6HJ ☎ 020 8863 3849

WOOD Lorraine: 49 Grove Road, London N12 9DS ☎ 020 8446 0812

WOOD Victoria *(Cor, Obdam)*: Goodmans Farm, Tumblefield Road, Stansted, Sevenoaks Kent TN15 7PR ☎ 01732 822618

WOODS Nicki *(Obdam, Cor)*: 12 Orlando Road, Clapham, London SW4 0LF ☎ 020 7498 7514, 0961 410755

ONDES MARTENOT

SOUTH WEST

LAMB Robert: 13 West Mall, Clifton, Bristol BS8 4BQ ☎ 0117 973 1529

LONDON

EVANS Dr Francois *(Con)* ☎ 020 8533 1723, 0956 891960

MILLAR Cynthia *(Kbds)*: Address Unknown

ONE MAN BAND

NORTH WEST

MOSER Peter *(Acc, Tpt, Kbds, Voc)*: The Hothouse, 13-17 Devonshire Road, Morecambe LA3 1QS ☎ 01524 831997

ORGAN

SCOTLAND

ARMSTRONG Norman *(Pf)*: 10 Boswall Green, Edinburgh EH5 2AZ ☎ 0131 552 4820

BERTRAM Simon *(Pf)*: 9 The Old Maltings, Lower High Street, Thame, Oxfordshire OX9 3AF ☎ 01844 260847

BRETT Simon *(Ctna, Wh, Pf, Gtr)*: Newlands, 17 Buttermere Avenue, Whitkham, Newcastle-upon-Tyne NE16 4EX ☎ 0191 420 8423, 0468 933968

BYRAM-WIGFIELD Timothy *(Pf)*: 4B Rosebery Crescent, Edinburgh EH12 5JP ☎ 0131 313 5670

CAPLAN Stuart: 42/2 Silverknowes Crescent, Edinburgh EH4 5JB ☎ 0131 312 7535

DUFF Robert *(Kbds, Pf)*: 6 Sorn Road, Auchinleck, Ayrshire KA18 2HL ☎ 01290 421247

FINDLAY Ian *(Pf, Arr, B Ldr)*: 202 Silvertonhill Ave, Hamilton, Lanarkshire ML3 7PF ☎ 01689 282751

GILL Michael: 36 Savaar Drive, Kilmarnock, Ayrshire ☎ 01563 32449

GORMLEY John *(Pf, Hpsd)*: 3 Hilary Drive, Garrowhill, Glasgow G69 6NP ☎ 0141 773 0946

KITCHEN John *(Hpsd, Pf, Ea Kbds)*: 34 Spottiswoode Road, Edinburgh EH9 1BL

LANGDON John *(Hpsd, Pf, Ea Kbds)*: 1058 Cathcart Rd, Glasgow G42 9XW ☎ 0141 649 3739

MCINTYRE Tom: 13 Hill Street, Larkhall, Lanarkshire ML9 2HA ☎ 882799

MCPHEE George *(Pf, Hpsd, Con, Ea Kbds)*: 17 Main Road, Castlehead, Paisley PA2 6AJ ☎ 0141 889 3528

NIEMINSKI Simon *(Pf, Hpsd)*: 15/11 Easter Dalry Road, Edinburgh EH11 2TP ☎ 0131 337 4854, 07957 364 367

ROGERS Ian *(Hpsd, Pf, Kbds)*: 62 Redford Avenue, Colinton, Edinburgh EH13 0BU ☎ 0131 441 1070

SHEARER Andrew: 240 Prestwick Road, Ayr, Scotland KA8 8NW ☎ 01292 268232

SMITH John *(Pf, Kbds)*: 22 Seres Road, Clarkston, Glasgow G76 7QT ☎ 0141 638 5215

SPARK Rod *(Pf, Voc)*: 4 Duddingston House Courtyard, Milton Road West, Edinburgh EH15 1JG ☎ 0131 661 4558

STRACHAN Martyn *(Pf, Hpsd, Ea Kbds)*: 61 Stratholmond Road, Edinburgh EH4 8HP ☎ 0131 339 3217

NORTH WEST

BAILEY Kenneth *(Pf)*: 32 Laurel Grove, Southport PR8 6BE

BARLOW Eric *(Pf)*: 23 Beech Avenue, Stockport, Cheshire SK3 8HA ☎ 0161 480 6467

BARLOW Ken: 10 Hunt Fold Drive, Greenmount, Bury BL8 4QG ☎ 01204 884245

BEAUMONT Andrew *(Pf, Dms)*: 38 Mornington Crescent, Felpham, Bognor Regis, West Sussex PO22 8HS ☎ 01243 865126

BEESLEY John *(Pf, Kbds)*: 8 Hawksworth Drive, Formby, Liverpool L37 7EZ ☎ 01704 876544, 0976 889113 mob, 01704 831993 fax

BORTHWICK Morgan: 14, Patrick Avenue, Rhyl, Clwyd, North Wales LL18 4TU ☎ 01745 353264

BOWDLER John: 2 Lingmoor Close, Hawkley Hall, Wigan WN3 5SB ☎ 01942 321259

BRADLEY Billy *(Pf)*: 55 Sunny Road, Southport PR9 7LX ☎ 01704 226119

BROWN Charles ☎ 01772 316395, 0973 179356 mob

CHRISTISON Alfred *(Kbds, Voc)*: 110 Norbreck Road, Thornton Cleveleys, Lancs FY5 1RP ☎ 01253 353205

CREBER Ursula: 229 Broadoak Road, Ashton-Under-Lyne, Lancs OL6 8RR ☎ 0161 330 2977

DOOLEY Evelyn *(Pf)*: 6 Lowfield Grove, Stockport, Cheshire SK2 6RR ☎ 0161 285 9279

ECCLES Graham *(Pf)*: The Coach House, Llannerch Park, St Asaph LL17 0BD ☎ 01745 730 559, 01745 730 559

ELLIS Graham *(Pf, Hpsd, Con)*: 19 Wentworth Close, Noctorum, Wirral L43 9HX ☎ 0151 653 5541, 0378 876 448

ENSTON Christopher: Hillgrove, Corwen Road, Treuddyn, Mold CH7 4LD

FIELD Wilf: 43 Woodlands Drive, Hoole, Chester CH2 3QQ ☎ 01244 325372

FROST Ronald *(Pf, Hpsd)*: 510 Holcombe Road, Greenmount, Bury, Lancs BL8 4EJ ☎ 01204 883338

GRAY Ian *(Kbds)*: 84A Liverpool Road, Penworth, Preston, Lancs PR1 0HT ☎ 01772 748942

GREENHALGH George *(Pf)*: 1 Victoria Street, Southport PR9 0DU ☎ 01704 47732

GREGORY Robert: 2 Lancaster Drive, Chester CH3 5JW ☎ 01244 344160 & fax

GRESCH David *(Vib)*: 58 Hereford Street, Werneth, Oldham, Lancs OL9 7RE ☎ 0161 652 1872

HAIGH Harry *(Kbds, Tbn, Dms)*: 285 Greenacres Road, Oldham, Lancs OL4 2DP ☎ 0161 633 3004

HOLMES Michael *(Kbds)*: 26 Stocks Gardens, Stalybridge, Cheshire SK15 2RD ☎ 0161 338 2371

HORNSBY Thomas *(Pf)*: No.1 Seafield Cottages, Ffyynnongroew, Holywell, Clwyd CH8 9SW ☎ 01745 560988

HOULDER David *(Pf)*: 17 Cathedral Close, Liverpool L1 7BR ☎ 0151 709 3171

J Stephen *(Kbds, B Gtr)*: 72 Harrington Road, Workington, Cumbria CA14 2UE ☎ 01900 601108, 07771 957210

JONES Trevor: 111A Cambridge Road, Southport PR9 9SB ☎ 01704 211563

KELSALL Phil: 9 Maltkiln Grove, Little Eccleston, Nr Preston, Lancs PR3 0YG

KENYON Brian: 280A Bolton Road West, Ramsbottom, Bury, Lancs BL0 9PX ☎ 01706 82 3726

LOVE Martin *(Kbds, Pf)*: 27 Ballaughton, Manor Hill, Braddan, Isle Of Man IM2 2NZ ☎ 01624 26816

MITCHELL Charles *(Pf, Md)*: 30 Montrose Drive, Southport, Merseyside PR9 7JA ☎ 01704 220551

MORGAN Kevin (*Pf*): 8 May Street, Bolton, Lancashire BL2 1AQ ☎ 01204 385147

PARKER Alan: 17 Alcester Close, Walshaw Park, Bury, Lancs BL8 1QE ☎ 0161 764 8207

POWELL Graham (*Pf*): 137 Larkfield Lane, Southport, Merseyside PR9 8NR

REECE Gary (*Kbds*): 11 Mitchell Street, Leigh, Lancs WN7 4UH ☎ 01942 748593, 0421 913007 mob

ROBERTS Dave (*Pf*): 32 Ashbourne Street, Norden, Rochdale, Lancs OL11 5SW ☎ 01706 631394

ROBERTSON Bernard (*Hpsd, Clst, Pf*): 44, Conifer Gardens (2), Streatham, London SW16 2TY ☎ 0161 969 1096, 020 8533 1372 day

ROBINSON Christopher: 23 Slinger Road, Cleveleys, Blackpool, Lancs FY5 1BN ☎ 01253 855293

ROBSON Clarice (*Pf*): 1 Norbreck Court, Norbreck Road, Thornton Cleveleys, Lancs FY5 1RW ☎ 01253 54005

RODWAY John: 94 Blackcarr Road, Baguley, Manchester M23 8PN ☎ 0161 998 3494

SMITTON Charles (*Md*): Address Unknown

SPARKS Michael (*Kbds*): 4 Orchard Avenue, Bolton-Le-Sands, Carnforth, Lancs LA5 8HP ☎ 01524 735109

SPEIGHT Kevin (*Pf*): 23 Royles Court, Woodland Avenue, Thornton Cleveleys, Lancs FY5 4ET

STUART Peter (*Kbds, Pf*): Welwyn, Preston Road, Inskip, Preston, Lancs PR4 0TP ☎ 01772 690789, 0836 278995, 01772 690789

SUNDERLAND Marc (*Kbds, Gtr, Clt, Dms*): 6 Whinney Heys Road, Blackpool, Lancs FY3 8NP ☎ 01253 395308, 0410 233942, 01253 399494

SZAKALY Thomas (*Synth, Clt, Pf*): 3 Roach Place, Wardleworth, Rochdale, Lancs OL16 2DD ☎ 01706 44410

TRACEY Professor Ian (*Pf, Hpsd, Md*): 6 Cathedral Close, Liverpool L1 7BR ☎ 0151 708 8471

WALLBANK Raymond: 42 Woodlands Road, Ansdell, Lytham St Annes, Lancashire FY8 4BX ☎ 01253 736462

WARNER Hilary (*Pf, Kbds*): Castell, Tynlon, Ynys Mon, Gwynedd LL65 3LQ ☎ 01407 720098

WELLS Ian: Flat 27 Kingsway Court, 3 Burroughs Gardens, Liverpool L3 6EH ☎ 0151 207 1725

WOOD Trevor (*Kbds*): 3, Pennine Avenue, Chadderton, Oldham, Lancs OL9 8PH ☎ 0161 633 2881

YOUNG Cedric (*Pf*): 26 Mansfield Road, Flixton, Manchester M41 6HE ☎ 0161 747 2868

NORTH EAST

BAKER Michael (*Hpsd, Pf*): 633 Newbold Road, Chesterfield S41 8AA ☎ 01246 73437

BATTY Douglas (*Pf*): 4 Corona Drive, Lancaster Drive, Lambwath Road, Hull Yorks HU8 0HH ☎ 01482 3782889

BEAUMONT Howard (*Pf, Kbds*): 52 West Bank, Scarborough, North Yorkshire TO12 4DX ☎ 01723 354990

BELLWOOD Derek (*Arr, Kbds*): 58 Chatsworth Road, Pudsey, West Yorkshire LS28 8JX ☎ 01274 664475

BISHOP Sharon (*Brass, T Hrn*): Fairways, Glebe Terrace, Easington, Peterlee, Co Durham SR8 3DH ☎ 0191 527 0037

BORTOFT Tim (*Pf, Arr*): 5 Stoney Haggs Rise, Seamer Road, Scarborough, North Yorkshire YO12 4LN ☎ 01723 378439

CARNEY Barbara (*Acc, Pf, Arr, Cop*): 8 Rock Terrace, Glasshoughton, Castleford, West Yorkshire WF10 4RB ☎ 01977 559387

CARTER Michael (*Pf, Tpt, T Sax, A Sax*): 22 High Street, Killamarsh, Sheffield S21 1BN ☎ 0114 247 2746

COOK Colin (*Kbds*): Corner Cottage, Hawerby Park, Hawerby Nr Grimsby DN36 5PX ☎ 01472 840004

COOLING Leslie (*Pf*): 13 Kendal Grove, Ardsley, Barnsley, Yorks S71 5DW ☎ 01226 288230

CROSS Douglas: 286 Heneage Road, Grimsby DN32 9NW ☎ 01472 57864

DOWNING William (*Pf*): c/o Mrs J Daddy, 27 Gloucseter Street, Gipsyville, Hull HU4 6PB

EASTON David (*Pf*): 14 Castleton Crescent, Skegness PE25 2TJ ☎ 01754 763044

FELLOWES Douglas (*Acc, Pf*): 3 North Close, Kirkfield Way, Royston, Barnsley Yorks S71 4NS ☎ 01226 723297

FINDLAY Gordon (*Pf*): 73 Sherwood Drive, Anlaby Common, Hull HU4 7RG ☎ 01482 3506804

FLYNN John (*Pf*): 29 Brompton Road, Linthorpe, Middlesbrough, Cleveland TS5 6JU ☎ 01642 823608

FRECKLETON Cleve (*Pf, B Gtr*): 91 Whinmoor Crescent, Wellington Hill, Leeds, W Yorks LS14 1EQ ☎ 0113 2738513, 0411 539204

GAUNT Peter (*Pf, Md*): 17 Victoria Road, Upper Moor, Pudsey, W Yorks LS28 7SW ☎ 0113 2565630

GREENWOOD Gordon (*B Ldr*): 10 Meadow Road, Bridlington YO16 4TD ☎ 01262 671555

HANSON Leonard (*Pf, Synth, E Pf*): 9 St Michaels Close, Skidby, Hull HU16 5TY ☎ 01482 3875418

HANSON Reginald (*Pf*): 28 Lyndale Avenue, Southend, Essex S32 4BZ ☎ 01702 464103

HASTIE John (*Pf*) ☎ 01904 644528, 01904 651330

HETHERINGTON George (*Pf*): Deighton House, 14 St Johns Road, Nevilles Cross, Durham City DH1 4NU ☎ 0191 386 1206

HOBBS Jason (*Pf*): 4-6 Tyne Road, Stanley, Co. Durham DH9 6PT ☎ 01207 233126

HORSEY Alan (*Hpsd, Pf, Kbds*): 42 Lane Ends Green, Hipperholme, Halifax HX3 8EZ

HOWCROFT Jason (*E Pf*): 138 Station Road, Billingham, Cleveand TS23 1PD ☎ 01642 649684

HUDSON Bert (*Pf*): 19 Anson Road, Bilton Grange, Hull HU9 4SN ☎ 01482 375092

LEACH Kevin (*Kbds*) ☎ 01723 892662

LISHMAN Dave (*Pf*): Beech House, 27 St. Marys Grove, Tudhoe Village, Spennymoor, Co. Durham DL16 6LR ☎ 01388 815439

LOXAM Arnold (*Pf*): Sorrento, 7 Moorside Walk, Drighlington, Bradford, Yorks BD11 1HL ☎ 0113 2852768

MACKFALL Richard (*Pf, Synth, Flt*): Hendwick Hall, Scoreby, Gate Helmsley, York YO41 1NP ☎ 01759 371900

MASON Norman: 26 Kensington Avenue, Normanby, Cleveland TS6 0BS

MOORE Kathleen: 14 Lothian Road, Middlesbrough, Co Cleveland TS4 2HR ☎ 01642 244050

MURDEN Norman (*Pf*): 93 Gillshill Road, Hull HU8 0JL ☎ 01482 3799364

NIFTON Muriel (*Pf*): 3 Estcourt Street, Newbridge Road, Hull HU9 2LR ☎ 01482 3224492

PROUDLOCK Thomas: 82 Durham Road, Blackhill, Consett, Co Durham DH8 5TH ☎ 01207 502193

PULMAN Ray (*Pf, Synth*): 59 Main Road, Washingborough, Lincoln LN4 1AU ☎ 01522 790349

RANDLES Philip: 239 Westminster Crescent, Intake, Doncaster DN2 6PJ ☎ 01302 320145

REAY Bryan (*Pf*): 37 Henley Gardens, Wallsend, Newcastle, Tyne & Wear NE28 0DL ☎ 0191 289 1454

RENSHAW Robin (*Synth, Voc, Pf, B Ldr*): 27 Kingsway, Nettleham, Lincoln LN2 2QA ☎ 01522 752458

SARJANTSON Douglas (*Pf, Acc*): 52 Louth Road, Holton Le Clay, Grimsby, Lincs DN36 5DZ ☎ 01472 823132

SEAWARD E (*Pf, B Ldr*): 47 Kirklands Rd, Hull, North Humberside HU5 5AX ☎ 01482 3571086

SHEPHERD Malcolm: 65 Princess Road, Seaham, Co Durham SR7 7QT ☎ 0191 581 5143

SHREEVE John (*Pf*): 173 Welholme Road, Grimsby DN32 9LR ☎ 01472 355512

SMALLER Frank (*Kbds*): 105 Northlands Road, Winterton, North Lincs DN15 9UL ☎ 01724 733005, 0802 738555

WEATHERALL Alan: 1 Trinity Road, Cleethorpes, Lincs DN35 8UH ☎ 01472 602720

WOOD Colin (*Pf*): 68 Redland Drive, Kirkella, Hull HU10 7UY ☎ 01482 3655622

WOODHEAD I (*Pf*): 194 Lee Street, Hull HU8 8NP ☎ 01482 374495

WORTH Chris (*Kbds*): 38 Shaw Drive, Scartho, Grimsby, South Humberside DN33 2JB ☎ 01472 752328

EAST

BRAND John (*Pf*): 317 Norwood Road, March, Cambs PE15 8TN ☎ 01354 58136

BRENNAN Hugh: Address Unknown ☎ 01603 45065

BROWN Dot (*Pf, E Pf*): Old Tearie Farmhouse, Darnaway By Forres, Forres, Morayshire IV36 0ST

CLIBBENS Sylvia: 21 Sish Lane, Stevenage, Herts SG1 3LS ☎ 01438 354641, 01438 354699

EASTICK William (*Pf*): 7 Hemnant Way, Gillingham, Beccles, Suffolk NR34 0LF ☎ 01502 717308

FRANKS Ronald (*Pf*): 39 Chard Drive, Luton, Beds LU3 4EQ ☎ 01582 580736, 01582 821838

HADDOCK Lawrence (*T Sax*): Rosery, Green Lane, Kessingland, Suffolk NR33 7RP ☎ 01502 740172

HUGHES Christopher (*Pf, Hpsd*): Little Corner, Cross Oak Road, Berkhamsted, Hertfordshire HP4 3NA ☎ 01442 863263

HYDE Hugh (*Pf*): 61 Magdalen House, Stoney Stratford, Bucks MK11 1PN ☎ 01908 263273

JACOBS Jean (*Pf*): 8 Frog End, Great Wilbraham, Cambridge CB1 5JB ☎ 01223 881049

JEWELL Ronald (*Pf*): 853 The White House, Regents Park, London NW1 3UP ☎ 020 7383 5090

KNIGHTLEY David: 2 River Close, Mepal, Ely, Cambs CB6 2AN ☎ 01353 777 049

LUCAS Andrew: 31 Abbey Mill Lane, St Albans, Herts AL3 4HA ☎ 01727 851810

LYNN Warren (*Pf, Gtr*): 10 Nunns Way, Grays, Essex RM17 5SS ☎ 01375 405421

MARSHALL Bridget (*Pf*): 9 The Crest, Ware, Herts SG12 0RR ☎ 01920 60454

PARNELL Andrew (*Pf, Hpsd*): 16 Glenferrie Road, St Albans, Herts AL1 4JU ☎ 01727 867818 & fax

READ Bernard (*Pf, Kbds*): 4 Weston Grove, Fulbourn, Cambridge CB1 5DY ☎ 01223 880486

ROGERS Ronald (*Kbds*): 49 Armond Road, Witham, Essex CM8 2HB ☎ 01376 513352

ROWE Michael (*Pf, Synth, Kbds, B Gtr*): 147 Crouch Hill, London N8 9QH ☎ 020 8341 4322, 0836 778877, 020 8341 5480

SHIPP Julie: 1 Harvard Court, Highwoods, Colchester, Essex C04 4SQ ☎ 01206 752 465

WATTS Richard (*Pf*): 151, Heath Road, Leighton Buzzard, Beds LU7 8AD ☎ 01525 379949

WILLIAMS David (*Kbds, Voc, Eup, Brass*) ☎ 01953 603842, 0410 248509 mob

WRIGHT Derek (*Pf*): 2 Magdalen Square, Gorleston, Gt Yarmouth NR31 7BY ☎ 01493 661646

MIDLANDS

AIKMAN Arthur (*Pf*): 6 Tregorrick Road, Exhall, Nr Coventry CV7 9FF ☎ 024 7631 3956

ALLEN Ronald (*Pf*): 23 Comsey Road, Birmingham B43 7RG ☎ 0121 360 8553

ANDERTON Terry (*Pf*): 35 Moreton Street, Chadsmoor, Cannock, Staffs WS11 2HL ☎ 01435 77197

BADDELEY Wayne: 3 Manifold Close, Silverdale, Newcastle, Staffs ST5 6RY ☎ 01782 612624

BAILEY David (*Pf, Gtr*): 22 Ashurst Road, Walmley, Sutton Coldfield B76 1JE ☎ 0121 351 3186

BENTLEY Reg (*Pf*): 11 Brittain Road, Cheddleton, Leek, Staffs ST13 7EH ☎ 01538 360597

BOONHAM John (*Pf*): 5 Romsley Close, High Heath, Pelsall, Walsall, West Midlands WS4 1AF ☎ 01922 684297

BOULTON Phil: 8 Allgreave Close, Middlewich, Cheshire CW10 0NL ☎ 01606 835307

BROOKES Trevor (*Pf*): Spring Cottage, Spout Lane, Light Oaks, Stoke-on-Trent, Staffs ST2 7LR ☎ 01782 535444

BULLEY Denise (*Pf, Hrn*): 80 Woolmer Road, The Meadows, Nottingham NG2 2FB ☎ 0115 952 8603

BULLOCK Ron (*Pf*): 301 Heath End Road, Nuneaton, Warwickshire CV10 7HQ ☎ 024 7634 6896

CLARKE Bob: 80 Catesby Road, Radford, Coventry, West Midlands CV6 3EW ☎ 024 7659 6854

CRAIG Paul: 12 South Close, Brauwstow, Daventry, Northants NN11 7JE

DAWSON Dawn: 7 Costa Row, Long Bennington, Nr Newark, Notts NG23 5DY

DIPPLE John (*Pf*): 3 Aylesmore Close, Olton, Solihull, West Midlands B92 7DA ☎ 0121 707 8892

DYSON Norman (*Hpsd*): 32 Bromsgrove Road, Romsley, Halesowen, West Midlands B62 0ET ☎ 01562 710014

EDWARDS Ryan: 82A Alfreton Road, Newton, Alferton, Derbys DE55 5TQ ☎ 01773 873588

ELLIS Sharon (*Voc, Cel*): 11 St Peters Avenue, Witherley, Atherstone, Warks CV9 3LN

FISHER Roger (*Pf, E Pf, B Gtr, Clt*): 64 Whitley Court Road, Quinton, Birmingham B32 1EY ☎ 0121 422 8590

HARGREAVES Bob: 11 Beech Road, Oadby, Leicester LE2 5QL ☎ 0116 271 4024

HAYWARD William (*Pf, Kbds, Md, Arr*): Kenneth Lodge, Dogpole, Shrewsbury SY1 1ET ☎ 01743 246256

HUDSON John (*Kbds*): 35 Park Road, Kenilworth, Warwickshire CV8 2GF ☎ 01926 851579

I Jay (*Pf, Tbn*): Karnak, 193 Pretoria Road, Ibstock, Leicester LE67 6LQ ☎ 01530 262528

INGLEY David: 55 Belle Vue, Wordsley, Stourbridge, West Midlands DY8 5DB ☎ 01384 274500

LAND Ian: 63 Eccleshall Road, Walton, Stone, Staffs ST15 0HJ ☎ 01785 812849

LINAKER Sonia (*Kbds, Pf*): 10 Livingstone Street, Worcester WR5 2ES ☎ 01905 360115, 0467 813127

LLOYD Mark (*Kbds*): 8 Elm Road, Middlewich, Cheshire CW10 0AX ☎ 01606 832057

LUCAS Adrian (*Pf*): 13 College Green, Worcester WR1 2LH, 01905 611139 fax

MATTHEWS Charles (*Pf*): 10 Nursery Close, Mickleton, Chipping Campden, Gloucestershire GL55 6TX ☎ 01386 438078

MEDLOCK Johnny (*Kbds, Pf*): 140 Station Street East, Coventry, West Midlands CV6 5FN ☎ 024 7668 6587

PEACE Dave (*Kbds, Pf*): 25 The Spinney, Bradwell Village, Milton Keynes, Bucks MK13 9BX ☎ 01908 321238

PIPER Ray (*Sax*): Kimberley, Bury Bank, Nr Stone, Staffs ST15 0QA ☎ 01785 813483

PUGH Philip: 3 Weston Mill Lane, Via Billing, Northampton NN3 3HJ ☎ 01604 36610

ROGERS Tony (*Pf*): 33 Woodend Raod, Walsall, W Midlands WS5 3BE ☎ 01922 621 223, 0385 223696

SCOTT Norman: 1 Little Marsh Grove, Penkridge, Stafford ST19 5SF ☎ 0178571 4854

SHARPE Donald (*Kbds, Pf*): 24 Fonton Hall Drive, Fulwood, Sutton In Ashfield, Nottinghamshire NG17 1LD ☎ 01623 555969, 0973 720438 mob, 01623 555979 fax

TAYLOR David (*Kbds, Db, Pf*): 4 Western Avenue, Sedgley, Dudley, West Midlands DY3 3PD ☎ 01902 671047

THOMPSON Kevin J: 14 Buttermere Court, Congleton, Cheshire CW12 4JD ☎ 01260 277460

TOLLEY Alison (*Kbds*): 12 Badminton Close, Dudley, West Midlands DY1 2UH ☎ 01384 234264

WALKER Michael: 20 Whitehill Road, Desbrough, Northants NN14 2JZ ☎ 01536 760634

WATT Daniel (*Voc*): 79 Winchester Road, Delapre, Northampton NN4 9AZ ☎ 01604 761504, 0973 423665

WHITTAKER Anthony: 83 St Helens Road, Leamington Spa, Warwickshire CV31 3QG ☎ 01926 421107

WILLIS Brian (*Kbds*): 24 Erica Drive, Whirnash, Leamington Spa, Warks CV31 2RS ☎ 01926 428405

SOUTH EAST

ABDEY Eric: 142 Crescent Road, Ramsgate, Kent CT11 9RE ☎ 01843 585872

ALLEN Dave (*Acc, Com*): 24 Cricketers Close, Hawkinge, Folkestone, Kent CT18 7NH

ORGAN - SOUTH EAST

ARNOLD John (Pf): 28 Saxon Road, Faversham, Kent ME13 8QB ☎ Faversham 53244

BAILEY Leonard: 9 Bouverie Avenue, Harnham, Salisbury, Wilts SP2 8DT ☎ 01722 337289

BERGIN Johnny: 5 Saxonhurst Close, Bournemouth, Dorset BH10 6LL ☎ 01202 533408

BISHOP Chiz (Pf, Arr): Harmony, 137 Anns Hill Road, Gosport, Hants PO12 3RE ☎ 023 9235 0226

BOYD William: Pheasants Walk, Poplar Lane, Bransgore, Christchurch Dorset BH23 8JE ☎ 01425 673026

CAUSON Hitch (Pf, Kbds, Acc): Rose Cottage, The Hurst, Winchfield, Hants RG27 8DF ☎ 01252 845093

COOKE Michael (Pf): 39 Douglas Avenue, Whitstable, Kent CT5 1RT ☎ 01227 272427

COURT Jean: 3 Johns Green, Sandwich, Kent CT13 0DE ☎ Sandwich 612112

CROSBY Les (Pf): Crosby Court, 50 Kings Avenue, Poole, Dorset BH14 9QJ ☎ 01202 744626

DALLEY John (Pf): 13, Sancroft Road, Old Town, Eastbourne, E Sussex BN20 8HA ☎ 01323 34348

DOWIE Christopher (Pf, Hpsd): 23 Venator Place, Wimborne Minster, Dorset BH21 1DO ☎ 01202 882083

EVANS Michael (Pf): 1 Bennett Close, Castle Grove, Newbury, Berkshire RG13 1PU ☎ 01635 40952

FLETCHER-CAMPBELL Christopher (Vla, Pf, Vln, Per): Bloxham School, Banbury, Oxon OX15 4PE ☎ 01295 720443

FRASER-HILL Gregory: 14 Dales Close, Windmill Hill, Hailsham, East Sussex BN27 4TJ ☎ 01323 833220

GLOVER Bernard (Acc): 79 The Dale, Widley, Hants PO7 5DD ☎ 023 9237 5620

GOULD Sydney: 27 Fort Road, Margate, Kent CT9 1HF

HALL Martin (Pf, Vla): 36 Bealing Close, Bassett, Southampton SO16 3AX ☎ 023 8067 2845

HARRIS Michael (Pf): 15 Ladywood Place, Eliburn, Livingston, West Lothian EH54 6TA ☎ 01506 410477 & fax, 0421 076063 mob

HAZELL Gary (Kbds): 27 Henbury Rise, Corfe Mullen, Wimbourne, Dorset BH21 3TE ☎ 01202 604324

HEATH Antony (Pf, Gtr): 15 Quex View Road, Birchington, Kent CT7 0DZ ☎ 01843 841018

HEIGHWAY John (Pf, Voc): 14 The Cloisters, Windsor Castle, Berkshire SL4 1NJ ☎ Windsor 862327

HUGHES Phil (Pf, Flt, Pic): 14 John Tapping Close, Walmer, Deal, Kent CT14 7QY ☎ Deal 362181

JENKINSON John (Voc): 3 Riverlea Road, Christchurch, Dorset BH23 1JQ ☎ 01202 486624

JOHNSON Tina (Acc, Pf): 12, Baldslow Road, Hastings, Sussex TN34 2EZ ☎ Hastings 427785

JONES Ron (Acc, Kbds): 2 St Johns Glebe, Rownhams, Southampton, Hants SO16 8AX ☎ 023 8073 3701

JUDD Roger (Pf, Hpsd): 23 The Cloisters, Windsor Castle, Berkshire SL4 1NJ ☎ 01753 863493

JUPP BA (HONS) MUSIC Bridget (Pf): 30 Milbury Crescent, Bitterne, Southampton, Hampshire SO18 5EH ☎ 023 8021 1312, 023 8090 6174

KING Mike (Pf, Kbds, Saxes, Clt): Flat 3 Aspen House, West Terrace, Folkestone, Kent CT10 1TH

LAMB Charles (Gtr): 52 High Oaks Close, Locksheath, Hants SO3 6XS ☎ 01489 582148

LAYZELL Jim (Pf, Acc, Synth, Kbds): 71 Rectory Avenue, Corfe Mullen, Wimborne, Dorset BH21 3EZ ☎ 01202 692334

LEADER Philip: 121 Acorn Avenue, Cowfold, Nr Horsham, West Sussex RH13 8RT ☎ 01403 864343

MANNION Christopher (Pf): 47 Peppercombe Road, Old Town, Eastbourne, Sussex BN20 8JN ☎ 01323 645197

MARTIN Terry (Pf): 69 Pound Road, Old Netley, Burlesdon SO3 8FF ☎ 023 8040 2668

MARTINE Ray (Pf): 18 Monument Road, Chalgrove, Oxford OX44 7RH ☎ 01865 890487

MCBRIDE Prince (Pf, Acc): Netherleigh Hall, 22 Fairmount Road, Bexhill, East Sussex TN40 2HN ☎ 01424 734902, 01424 223068 day

PRICE Austin (Pf): 44 Bader Road, Canford Heath, Poole BH17 7PP ☎ 01202 673654

PULLEN Doreen (T Sax, Clt): 34 Charnock Close, The Orchards, Hordle, Lymington, Hants SO41 0GU ☎ 01425 620048, 0378 787342 mob

SHANKS Norman (Clt): 92 Millmead Road, Margate, Kent CT9 3QR ☎ Thamet 26068

SMITH David (Pf, Voc): 15 Roxburgh Drive, Foxhall, Manor Park, Didcot, Oxon OX11 7HF ☎ 01235 814835

STACEY Robert (Pf): Melotone House, 80 High Street, Wooton Bridge, Ryde Isle Of Wight PO33 4PR ☎ 01983 883896

STICKLER Richard (Kbds, Synth): The Timbers, Hook Park Road, Nr Warsash, Southampton SO31 9HE ☎ 01489 575049

STINTON Philip (Kbds, Pf, Tpt): 19 Kitbridge Road, Carisbrooke, Newport, Isle Of Wight PO30 5RF ☎ 01983 527322

THORNE David (Pf, Hpsd): Flat 2, Cathedral House, St Thomas' Street, Old Portsmouth, Hants PO1 2EZ ☎ 023 9281 6017

TOMLIN Ted (Tpt, Vln, Dms, Voc): 89 Capel Street, Capel, Nr Folkestone, Kent CT18 7HF ☎ Folkestone 2422

TREDRAY Margaret (Pf): 79 Ashampstead Road, Southcote, Reading, Berkshire RG3 3LB ☎ 01734 598793

WESTON Glenn (E Pf, Synth): 28 Lyons Drive, Weydown Park, Guildford, Surrey GU2 6YP ☎ 01483 234321

WOOD Brian (Flt, E Pf, Synth): 10 Brooklands Close, Fordwich, Canterbury, Kent CT2 0BT ☎ 01227 710720

WOODBURY David (Pf, Kbds, B Ldr): 51 New Road, Bournemouth, Dorset BH10 7DP ☎ 01202 576633

WOOLDRIDGE Michael (Pf): 23 Burlington Gardens, Portslade, Brighton, East Sussex BN41 2DS ☎ 01273 424746

WRIGHT Paul (Pf, Hpsd): Copse Cottage, Steventon, Hants RG25 3BH ☎ 01256 397445

YARWOOD Geoffrey (Pf): 50 Cyril Road, Bournemouth, Dorset BH8 8QD ☎ 01202 302162

SOUTH WEST

BACON Philip (Pf): 23 Llwyndern Drive, West Cross, Swansea DE6 6FX ☎ 01792 67754

BARRY Brendan (Kbds): 3 Craig-Yr-Haul Drive, Castleton, Gwent CF3 8SA ☎ 01633 680206

BEALE Mike (Pf): 83, Sandgate, Stratton St Margaret, Swindon SN3 4HH ☎ 01793 826465

BOORMAN Peter (Db, Com): 4 Catherine Street, St Davids, Haverfordwest, Dyfed SA62 6RJ ☎ 01437 720178

BORTHWICK Dickie: 9 Clarence Road, Littlesea Estate, Weymouth, Dorset DT4 9EE ☎ 01305 785222

COCKRAM Raymond (Flt, Pic): 1 Culm Haven, Uffculmie, Cullompton, Devon EX15 3EL ☎ 01884 840542

COURT Robert: 40 St Augustine Road, Heath, Cardiff CF4 4BE ☎ 029 2061 9436

DAVIES Eric (Pf): 11 Richmond Drive, Fairview, Hirwaun, Aberdare, Mid Glam CF44 9UH ☎ 01685 813781

EVANS Donald (Voc, B Ldr): 4 Clock House, Nether Stowey, Bridgwater, Avon TA5 1LJ ☎ 01278 732123

EYLES Timothy (Pf): 46 Ashford Road, Swindon SN1 3NS ☎ 01793 486581

GARSIDE Alison (Pf, Kbds): Alson House, Somerton, Castle Street, Keinton Mandeville, Somerset TA11 6DX ☎ 01458 223043

GIBBONS Kenneth: 102 Abbots Road, Hanham, Bristol BS15 3NR ☎ 0117 9673248

GILMORE-JAMES Terence (Pf, Con, Arr): Ty Cerbyd, Station Road, Ponthir, Newport, Gwent NP6 1GQ ☎ 01633 421299

GRIFFITHS Michael (Acc, Ob): 21 Cefn Coed, Bridgend, Mid Glamorgan CF31 4PH

GRIST Raymond (Acc, Pf, B Ldr): 47 Eden Vale Road, Westbury, Wiltshire BA13 3NY ☎ Westbury 823207

HALL William (Pf): 80 Gwendoline Street, Treherbert, Rhondda, Glam CF42 5BP

JENKINS Robert (Kbds, Pf): 66 Cecil Road, Gowerton, Swansea, W Glamorgan SA4 3DE ☎ 01792 872663

JOLLIFFE Carl (Pf, Acc): 9 Deer Park, Saltash, Cornwall PL12 6HE ☎ 01752 843809

JONES Douglas (*Pf*): Westhaven, 9 West Road, Nottage, Porthcawl CF36 3SN ☎ 0165671 4186

JONES Gregory (*Acc*): Suncourt, Wheal Venture Road, Carbs Bay, St Ives, Cornwall TR26 2PQ

JONES Kerry (*Pf*): 31 Graigwen Road, Cymmer, Porth, Rhondda Mid Glam CF39 9HA ☎ Porth 684525

JOYCE Thelma (*Pf, Voc*): 1 Andrews Way, Hatt, Saltash, Cornwall PL12 6PE ☎ 01752 856892

KENNEDY Adrian: 194 Old Laira Road, Mutley, Plymouth, Devon PL3 6AE ☎ 01752 669883

LEWIS Gareth (*Pf*): 377 Birchgrove Road, Birchgrove, Swansea, Glam SA7 9NN ☎ 01792 814321

LINDSAY Nigel (*Pf*): 59 St Marychurch Road, Torquay TQ1 3HG ☎ 01803 33568

LLOYD Thomas (*Dms*): 13 Edward Street, Porth, Rhondda, Glam CF39 9SR ☎ 01443 683349

PEARCE Montague (*Pf*): 28 Westborne Heights, Redruth, Cornwall TR15 2TQ ☎ 01209 212343

RANDALL Mark (*Pf, Hpsd*): 50 Linden Road, Westbury Park, Bristol BS6 7RP ☎ 0117 9243674

RAYMOND Timothy (*Pf*): Seaview Cottage, The Parade, Sandsend, Whitby, North Yorks YO21 3SZ ☎ 01377 267 312

RICHARDS Jean (*Pf, Acc*): Gorswen, Devons Road, Babbacombe TQ1 3PR ☎ 01803 312958

RIGLER Sue: Morlais, 68 Newton Road, Bishopsteignton, Teignmouth, Devon TQ14 9PP ☎ 01626 778367

ROBERTS John (*Pf*): 21 Bryn Siriol, Penpedairheol, Hengoed, Mid Glamorgan CF82 7TA

ROSE Barry (*Pf, Voc*): Level Crossing, Milking Lane, Draycott, Somerset BS27 3TL ☎ 01727 851810

SCALLY Dennis (*Kbds*): 7 Hill Head Park, Brixham, Devon, Warwickshire TQ5 0HG ☎ 018045 55864

SHEPHERD Neil (*Voc, Kbds, Pf*): 26 Vicarage Gate, St Erth, Hayle TR27 6JB ☎ 01734 752435, 07970 325046, 01736 752435

TUNBRIDGE Clive (*Pf*): 36 Quarry Dale, Rumney, Cardiff CF3 8BR ☎ 029 2079 2345

WARD Mark (*Pf, Vib*): East Farm, Buckland Ripers, Weymouth DT3 4BP ☎ 01305 812281

WATKINS Graham (*Pf*): 6 Vaynor Street, Porth, Rhondda, Glam CF39 0DA ☎ 01443 684368

WEEDON Penelope (*Pf*): 10 Richmond Road, Uplands, Swansea SA2 0RB ☎ 01792 473840

WILCE Malcolm: 51 Baynham Road, Mitcheldean, Glos GL17 0JR

WILLMOT S (*Pf, Saxes, Clt*): 4 Whipton Barton Road, Exeter EX1 3LP ☎ 01392 68426

LONDON

BALDWIN Gary (*Kbds*): 75 Lincoln Road, Forest Gate, London E7 8QN ☎ 020 8471 0907

BELL David: 8 Clave Street, Wapping, London E1 9XQ ☎ 020 7488 3650

BENTLEY Ed (*Pf, B Gtr, E Gtr, Ac Gtr*): 51A Vicars Road, London NW5 4NN ☎ 020 7813 1430 & fax

BEST Hubert: 84 Clare Court, Judd Street, London WC1H 9QW ☎ 0956 339894

BIRCH John: Fielding House, The Close, Salisury, Wilts SP1 2EB ☎ 01722 412 458

BIRD Denise (*Pf*): 62 South Eden Park Road, Beckenham, Kent BR3 3BG ☎ 020 8777 8478

BOWERS-BROADBENT Christopher (*Com*): 94 Colney Hatch Lane, Muswell Hill, London N10 1EA ☎ 020 8883 1933

COULSON Richard (*Hpsd*): Hartleigh, 86 West Grove, Walton-on-Thames, Surrey KT12 5PD ☎ 01932 229171

CURROR Ian (*Pf, Hpsd*): 22 West Road, Royal Hospital, Chelsea, London SW3 4SR ☎ 020 7730 7395

DAGG Stephen (*Hpsd*): 49 Manor Avenue, Brockley, London SE4 1TD ☎ 020 8694 8597, 020 7928 3844

DARLINGTON Jay (*Pf*): Varunastra Productions Ltd, Gelfand Rennart Feldman Brown, 82 Brook Street, London W1Y 2NL ☎ 020 7629 7169, 020 7491 7454

DAVEY Colin (*Pf, B Gtr, Db*): 168 Dagnam Park Drive, Harold Hill, Essex RM3 9RT ☎ 01708 379 001

DOCHERTY Anthony: 22 Albert Road, Rayleigh, Essex SS6 8HN ☎ 01268 771537

EATON Derek (*Pf*): 14 Danemere Street, Putney, London SW15 1LT ☎ 020 8788 6786

FIRMAN Roger: Flat 11, Middle Walk, Commercial Way, Woking Surrey GU21 1XT

GAMAL El (*Acc*): 18 Dolphin Road, Kensington Fields, Northolt, Middx UB5 6UQ ☎ 020 8841 2656

GUTTERIDGE Simon: 41 Vanderbilt Road, Earlsfield, London SW18 3BG ☎ 020 8870 4082

HAMMOND Mark (*Pf*): 39B Carlton Avenue, Kenton, Harrow, Middx HA3 8AX ☎ 020 8909 2687

HARPER Norman (*Pf, Con*): 50 Elmwood Road, Herne Hill, London SE24 9NR ☎ 020 7274 1712, 020 7274 1712

HARVERSON Alan (*Hpsd*): 34 Park Farm Close, London N2 0PU ☎ 020 8883 2553

HENNIN Michael: 74 Churchbury Lane, Enfield, Middlesex EN1 3TY ☎ 020 8363 4209

HICKS Malcolm (*Kbds, Pf, Con*): 7 Taylor Close, Hampton Hill, Middlesex TW12 1LE ☎ 020 8979 8666

JAWAL Papa (*Synth, Per, Af Dms, Hmca*): Flat 9, 259 Camden Road, Islington, London N7 0HW ☎ 0956 111786 mob

KENJI: Top Floor Flat, 68 Chesterton Road, London W10 6EP ☎ 020 8968 8283

KING Stephen (*Pf*): 82 Lodge Avenue, Gidea Park, Romford, Essex RM2 5AL ☎ 01708 749038

LANG Josephine: 3 Barham House, Molyneux Street, London W1H 5HW ☎ 020 7262 9133

LE GRICE Jane (*Pf*): 212 Osward, Courtwood Lane, Croydon, Surrey CR0 9HG ☎ 020 8651 4841

LE-TOUZEL Jane (*Pf, Arr, Com*): 86 Portland Road, London W11 4LQ ☎ 020 7727 9215

LIGHT John (*Pf, Hpsd, Com, Arr*): 35 Park Road, South Wanstead, London E12 5HG ☎ 020 8923 8800

MARSHALL Wayne (*Pf*): 18 Fielding Road, London W14 0LL ☎ 020 7603 5944

MORIS Ed (*Gtr, Clt, Synth*): 11 Cambridge Road North, Chiswick, London W4 4AA ☎ 020 8994 8799, 0956 449867

MORRIS Bension: 3 St Margarets Road, Edgeware, Middx HA8 9UP ☎ 020 8958 4018

MYNARD Maureen (*Kbds, Pf*): Rye Lodge, 1 Rye Walk, Ingatestone, Essex CM4 9AL ☎ 01277 353892

O'DONNELL James A (*Hpsd, Pf*): 94 Denbigh Street, Pimlico, London SW1V 2EX ☎ 020 7834 7982

PENNEY Ken (*Pf*): 7 Westpole Avenue, Cockfosters, Barnet, Herts EN4 0AX ☎ 020 8449 0925

POPPLEWELL Richard: 23 Stanmore Gardens, Richmond, Surrey TW9 2HN ☎ 020 8332 7301

PRICE Alan (*Pf, Voc*): c/o Newman & Co., Regent House, 1 Pratt Mews, London NW1 0AD ☎ 020 7267 6899, 020 7267 6746

RICE Derek (*Pf, Kbds*): 6 Dunspring Lane, Barkingside, Ilford, Essex IG5 0TZ ☎ 020 8550 7675

RIDGEWAY-WOOD John (*Pf, Hpsd*): The Watch House, Wood Close, London E2 6ET ☎ 020 7739 8163, 020 7729 8701

STONEHAM Henry (*Pf, Arr, B Ldr*): 50 Newberries Avenue, Radlett, Herts WD7 7EP ☎ 01923 7722

SUMMERS Douglas: 59 Kingsway, Petts Wood, Kent BR5 1PN ☎ 016898 15938

TROLL Phil (*Voc*): 9 Bignold Road, Forest Gate, London E7 0EX ☎ 020 8221 2337

VERNON Tony (*Pf*): 35 Jarrow Road, Chadwell Heath, Essex RM6 5RH ☎ 020 8597 1334

WELLS Jeremy (*Pf*): 56 Grange Road, London SE1 3BM ☎ 020 7642 5642

WINTER Murray (*Pf*): 184 Lyndhurst Road, London N22 5AU ☎ 020 8889 2082

WRIGHT Richard (*Kbds*): 16 Lexham Mews, London W8 6JW ☎ 020 7937 0993, 020 7937 8976 fax

ORIENTAL DRUMS

LONDON

MIDDLE EAST MUSIC ORG (*Dms*) ☎ 020 8746 1627

OUD

LONDON

ALSAADY Ahmed (*Arab Dms*): Flat C, 392 York Way, London N7 9LW ☎ 020 7607 7215, 0958 747917

CLOUSTON Keith (*Arr, Com, Gtr, Ir Bzk*): 15 Wimbolt Street, London E2 7BX ☎ 020 7729 7234

PAN PIPES

NORTH EAST

STAFFORD Brian (*Wh, Flt*): 21 Bright Street, Skipton, North Yorkshire BD23 1QQ ☎ 01756 798285 & fax

LONDON

LINEHAM Charlie (*Eth Flts*): 53 Ingram House, Daling Way, Bow, London E3 5NL ☎ 020 8983 1512

PARAGUYAN HARP

EAST

PENNY Nick (*Gtr*): 51 Gordon Road, Oundle, Peterborough PE8 4LD ☎ 01832 272783

PERCUSSION

SCOTLAND

ADAM David (*Dms*): 129 Old Greenock Road, Bishopton PA7 5BB ☎ 0141 571 4294

AITCHISON Jacqueline (*Per, Pf*): 4 Dunnichen Gardens, Bishopbriggs, Glasgow G64 1AD ☎ 0141 772 2823

ALLAN James (*Dms, Kbds, Per, Gtr, B Gtr*): 529 Sauchiehall Street 2/1, Charing Cross, Glasgow G3 7PQ ☎ 0141 221 7708

ALLEN Jay (*Per, Tym, Flex*): 40 Braeside Avenue, Milngavie G62 6LJ ☎ 0141 956 2618, 0802 607700

ANDERSON Peter (*Dms*): 9 Calder Place, Falkirk FK1 2QZ

ARNOTT William (*Dms, La Per, Per*): Flat 2/L, 13 Temple Gardens, Anniesland, Glasgow G13 1JJ ☎ 0141 954 4187, 07977 106011

BALDI Giulio (*Dms*): 74 Bawhirley Road, Greenock, Inverclyde PA15 2LT ☎ 01475 721414, 01475 724274

BAMFORD Richard (*Dms, Cong, Per, Vib*): 11 Wellington Place, Edinburgh EH6 7EQ ☎ 0131 554 5341, 0973 385870

BANCROFT Thomas (*Dms, Com, Arr*): Birkhedges Cottage, Spittalrig, Nr Haddington, East Lothian EH41 3SU ☎ 01620 826613 day

BARCLAY Graeme (*Per, Dms, Tym*): Address Unknown ☎ 0141 357 3290

BAYNE Iain (*Dms, Per*): c/o Marilyn Ross, Agent 'Runrig', 1 York Street, Aberdeen AB11 5DL ☎ 01224 573100

BERTHON Darell (*Dms, Per*): 273 Clepington Road, Dundee DD3 7UE

BIRCH Lachie (*Dms, Per*): 14 Dumgoyne Drive, Bearsden, Glasgow G61 3AD ☎ 0141 942 8239, 0411 034690 mob

BLACKLOCK Ian (*Dms*): 16 Newmains Road, Edinburgh EH29 9AL ☎ 0131 335 3049

BLAKELY John (*Dms*): Address Unknown

BOYLE Tommy (*Dms, Per, Tym, Tnd Per*): Burnside, 7 Neukfoot Lane, Uplawnmoor, East Renfrewshire G78 4DH ☎ 01505 850410, 01523 424261 pager, 0797 1521807 mob

BROCKETT Ainslie (*Dms, Tpt, Per*): 80 Randolph Drive, Stamperland, Glasgow G76 8AP ☎ 0141 637 0844

BROWN,B.ENG Stuart (*Dms*): 21 Bradfield Avenue, Glasgow G12 0UW ☎ 0141 339 1688

BUNTING Allan (*Dms*): 56 Mainwaring Drive, Summersfield, Wimslow, Cheshire SK9 2QD ☎ 01625 531182

BURNS Duncan (*Dms*): 1 Beech Court, Doune, Perthshire FK16 6HT ☎ 01786 841507

BURNS Keith W (*Dms, Per*): 54/4 Queen Charlotte Street, Leith, Edinburgh EH6 7EX ☎ 0131 553 7885

BYRON Graham (*Dms*): 100 Stewart Drive, Irvine, Ayrshire, Scotland KA12 0RT ☎ 01294 276993

CAMPBELL David (*Dms, Per*): 8 Whitslade Street, Provanhall, Glasgow G34 9PY ☎ 0141 771 5439

CARGILL Suzy (*Per, Tym, Bod, Gtr*): 21 Beechgrove Terrace, Perth PH1 1HZ ☎ 01738 623098

CHRISTIE Brian (*Dms*): 15 Barnton Gardens, Edinburgh EH4 6AF ☎ 0131 336 2790

CHRISTIE Graham (*Dms, Gtr*): 30 Huntly Avenue, Giffnock, Glasgow G46 6LW ☎ 0141 638 4807

CLARKE Tina (*Per, Voc*): Flat 3/2, 7 Stewartville Street, Partick, Glasgow G11 5PE ☎ 0141 357 2160

CLEMENTS Mat (*Per*): 21/10 Leith Street, Edinburgh EH1 34T ☎ 0131 557 4911

CLYDE Thomas (*Dms*): Address Unknown ☎ 0141 649 3644

COLBURN Richard (*Dms, Kbds*): Church Hall, 24 Novar Drive, Hyndland, Glasgow G12 9PU ☎ 0141 339 1804

CONNOR Mary (*Dms*): Address Unknown ☎ 0141 556 4443

COOKE Alistair (*Dms, Per*): T/L 185 Garrioch Road, Glasgow G20 8RL ☎ 0141 579 6342

CORBETT Heather (*Per, Tym, Cimb, Pf*): 33 Faskally Avenue, Bishopbriggs, Glasgow G64 3PJ ☎ 0141 772 3152, 07050 168772 mob, 0141 772 3152 fax

COULTER Ian (*Per, Tym*): 18 Wellshot Drive, Cambuslang, Glasgow G72 8BT ☎ 0141 641 8762, 0378 785603 mob

CUNNINGHAM Thomas (*Per, Dms, Gtr*): 30 Ralston Road, Bearsden, Glasgow G61 3BA ☎ 0141 931 5902

DALE Alan (*Dms*): 41 Livingstone Court, New Farm Loch, Kilmarnock, Scotland KA3 7QT ☎ 01563 537473, 0402 208554

DIBBS Martin (*Dms, Per, Tym*): Ground Floor Right, 3 Morgan Street, Stobswell, Dundee DD4 6QE ☎ 01382 453431

DOIG Alexander (*Dms*): 30 Crichton Drive, Grangemouth, Stirlingshire FK3 9DF ☎ 01324 482825

DON Stuart (*Dms*): 9 Old Aisle Road, Kirkintilloch, Glasgow G66 3HH ☎ 0141 777 6838

DOW Pamela (*Per*): Barrochan, 53 St Andrews Drive, Glasgow G41 5JQ ☎ 0141 429 1233, 0141 420 3602

DRUMMOND James (*Dms, La Per, Voc*): 3 William Street, Coatbridge, Lanarkshire ML5 4EZ ☎ 01236 420683

DUGGAN Daniel (*Per, Gtr, Pf*): 6 St. Ellas Place, Eyemouth, Scotland TD14 5HP ☎ 018907 51204

DUPIN Valerie (*Dms, Per*): 34 Cecil Street, Hill Head, Glasgow G12 8RJ ☎ 0141 339 8144

EOGHAIN James (*Dms, La Per*): 2F3 18 Bruntsfield Place, Edinburgh, Scotland EH10 6HN ☎ 0131 229 3988

FIERSTONE Ray (*Dms*): 3 Queen Margaret Road, Glasgow G20 6DP ☎ 0141 946 3184, 01360 551023

FINDLAY Alan (*Per*): 171 Abbotsford Court, Glenrothes, Fife KY6 2LT

FINDLAY Colin (*Dms, Per*): 2 Camp Cottages, Motherwell ML1 2RY ☎ 01698 266294

FLAHERTY Daniel (*Per*): 8 Crawford Lane, Partick, Glasgow G11 6TL ☎ 0141 579 1308

FULLBROOK Richard (*Per*): 26 Acharn, Perth, Perthshire PH1 2SR ☎ 01738 620082

FULTON Arty (*Dms, Per*): Edinbane, 52 Manse Road, Nairn IV12 4RS ☎ 01667 451231

GOODMAN Ronnie (*Dms, Per, La Per, Con, Com*): Flat 1/R, 472 Paisley Road West, Glasgow G51 1PX ☎ 0141 427 7161 & fax

GORGON James (*Dms*): 6 Shields Avenue, St Andrews, Fife KY16 8BJ ☎ 01334 76847

GORMAN Shane (*Dms, Gtr*): 1/5 Maritime Court, Chapel Lane, Edinburgh EH6 6ST ☎ 0131 467 1264

GOW David (*Dms*): 4 Glenochil Road, Falkirk, Scotland FK1 5LT ☎ 01324 625044

GROSSART James (*Dms, Per, Arr*): 13 Dudley Avenue, Edinburgh EH6 4PL ☎ 0131 554 3145

HALLIDAY Neil (*Dms*): c/o Richard Gordon, 18 Wheeler, PO Box 3645, London N7 8TX

HARDING Wendy (*Per, Pf*): 11 Mallard Close, Kempshott, Basingstoke RG22 5JP ☎ 01256 329009

HARLEY Sandy (*Dms*): 31 Moss Road, Tillicoultry, Clackmannanshire FK13 6NS ☎ 01259 750176

HAROLD Mae (*Per, Dms, Tym*): Address Unknown

HASTINGS Andrew (*Dms*) ☎ 0131 556 6304

HEPBURN Harold (*Dms*): 43 Laurel Avenue, Dalneigh, Inverness IV3 5RP ☎ 01463 221963

HIRST Nigel (*Dms, Kbds, Gtr*): 49 Otago Street, Kelvinbridge, Glasgow G12 8PQ ☎ 0141 334 5796

HOOD Derek (*Dms, Voc*): 3 Victoria Road, Alexandra Park, London N22 4XA ☎ 020 8881 0767

HUGHES Richard (*Dms*): 3 Creagan Park, Tobermory, Isle Of Mull PA75 6PT

HUNTER Craig (*Dms*): 21 Constitution Place, Edinburgh EH6 7DJ ☎ 0131 553 5533, 0131 554 7551

HUNTER Jennifer (*Dms, Voc*): 4 Kirkstone Close, Newlands Muir, East Kilbride, Glasgow G75 8SU ☎ 0141 644 4971

HUTCHISON George (*Dms*): 31 Mayburn Loan, Loanhead, Mid Lothian EH20 9EN ☎ 0131 440 0652

HYND Richard (*Dms*): 974 Pollokshaw Road, Glasgow G41 2HA ☎ 0141 636 1389

I'ANSON Chris (*Per, Dms*): 18 Merrygreen Place, Stewarton, Kilmarnock, Scotland KA3 5EJ ☎ 01560 485490, 0771 995363

JACK Don (*Dms, Kbds, Gtr*): Redding House, Redding, Falkirk FK2 9TR ☎ 01324 716827

JAMIESON Michael (*Dms, Per*): 35 Buchan Drive, Perth PH1 1NQ ☎ 01738 631615, 0467 881550, 01738 561204

JOHNSTON Alan (*Dms*): 17 Brook Street, Broughty Ferry, Dundee DD5 1DN ☎ 01382 77098

JOHNSTONE Michael (*Dms, B Gtr, Gtr*): 18/3 Westfield Road, Edinburgh EH11 2QR ☎ 0131 337 3935

KERR Robert (*Dms, Per, Pf*): 1 School Road, Kilbirnie, Ayrshire KA25 7AU ☎ 01505 68 3119, 0141 339 4497

KETTLE William (*Dms*): 95 Mcculloch Street, Pollokshields, Glasgow G41 1NT ☎ 0141 429 3481

KINLOCH Robert (*Dms*): 4 Ruthven Avenue, Giffnock, Glasgow G46 6PQ ☎ 0141 638 3585

KOWALSKI Brian (*Dms*): 45 Rose Street, Thurso, Caithness KW14 7HW ☎ 01847 896526

KYLE Bill (*Dms*): 8 Mortonhall Road, Edinburgh EH9 2HW ☎ 0131 667 1687

LEIGH Lauri (*Dms, Per, Gtr, Kbds, Brass*): 40/18 Queenmary Street, Bridgeton, Glasgow G40 3DN ☎ 0141 556 6481, 0141 353 4672, 0141 353 4705

LIRONI Steve (*Dms, Gtr, Kbds*): 1 Hatherley Gardens, London N8 9JH ☎ 020 8341 4196

LIVINGSTONE Nigel (*Dms*): 2 The Stables, Bleachers Way, Huntingtowerfield, Perth PH1 3HY ☎ 01738 583856

LYONS Carol (*Per, Pf*): Address Unknown ☎ 0141 332 4334

LYONS David (*Per, Pf*): 32 Moray Place, Glasgow G41 2BL ☎ 0141 423 4784

MACDONALD Calum (*Per, Voc*): c/o Marilyn Ross Runrig, 1 York Street, Aberdeen AB11 5DL ☎ 01224 573100

MACKIE Kevin (*Dms, Cong*): 2 Garriochmill Way, North Kelvinside, Glasgow G20 6LL ☎ 0141 357 4238, 0410 573421 mob

MACKINTOSH James (*Dms, Per*): 87 Spottiswoode Street, Marchmont, Edinburgh EH9 1BZ ☎ 0131 447 5377

MARSHALL Robert (*Per, Dms, Tym, Vib*): 3 Millichen Road, Glasgow G23 5HQ ☎ 0141 942 5309

MARTIN Craig (*Dms, Per*): Flat 8 James Watt Street, Glasgow G2 8NF ☎ 0141 221 3526

MATHIESON Ken (*Dms, Zit, Arr, B Ldr*): 20 Kylepark Crescent, Uddingston G71 7DQ ☎ 01698 814475

MCALLISTER Andrew (*Per, Pf, Synth, Tin Wh, Vln*): 39 Bowes Rigg, Stewarton, Kilmarnock, Ayrshire KA3 5EN ☎ 01560 483191

MCCABE Raymond (*Dms, Bod*): c/o 2 Stonylee Road, North Carbrain, Cumbernavld G67 2LT ☎ 01236 611766/615716

MCCORRY John (*Dms, Per*): 56 Strathfillan Road, East Kilbride, Glasgow G74 1DA

MCFARLANE Ross (*Dms, Per*) ☎ 01236 872683

MCGEACHIE James (*Dms, Tym*): 2 Cheviot Gardens, Bearsden, Glasgow G61 4QS ☎ 0141 942 8182

MCGLYNN Kevin (*Dms*): 4A Wilson Road, Lochgilphead, Argyll PA31 8TR ☎ 01546 602867

MCLEAN William (*Dms*): 129 Glenalmond Street, Sandyhills, Glasgow G32 7TF ☎ 0141 778 4880

MCLEVY Frank (*Dms*): 9 Robson Street, Dundee DD4 7JQ ☎ 01382 862189

MCMURDO Thomas (*Per*): 12, Leslie Road, Kilmarnock, Ayrshire, Scotland KA3 7RR ☎ 01563 535638

MCRAE Colin (*Dms, Per*): Binniehill House, Binniehill Road, Slamannan, Falkirk FK1 3BE ☎ 01324 851 926

MERRITT George (*Dms*): 6 Merryton Tower, Motherwell ML1 2LU ☎ 68329

MIDGLEY Robb (*Dms, Tnd Per, Tym, Cong, La P*): 33C Brisbane Road, Largs, Ayrshire KA30 8LS ☎ 01475 673 739

MILLAR Gus (*Dms*): 6-8 South Street, Kingskettle, Fife KY15 7PL ☎ 01337 830360

MILLER Andrew F (*Dms*): 118 Bruce Gardens, Dalneigh, Inverness IV3 5BE ☎ 01463 222249

MILNE Stuart (*Dms, Voc*): The Cottage, Pitbladdo Farm, By Cupar, Fife KY15 4QD ☎ 01334 656862

MORBEY Jeremy (*Dms*): 30 Hamilton Drive, Hillhead, Glasgow G12 8DR ☎ 0141 339 9381

MORROW Alastair (*Dms*): Brentham Park House, Brentham Crescent, Stirling FK8 2BA ☎ 01786 471317

MORROW Chris (*Dms*): 2/1, 932 Dumbarton Road, Whiteinch, Glasgow G14 9UQ ☎ 0141 339 4781

MOUSDALE (*Dms*): 10 Carnoustie Crescent, Bishopbriggs, Glasgow G64 1BD ☎ 0141 772 6117

MOYES Darren (*Dms, Per*): 56 Donaldfield Road, c/o Reilly, Bridge Of Weir, Renfrewshire PA11 3JF ☎ 01505 613643

MUNRO Stuart (*Dms*): 22 Blackchapel Close, Edinburgh EH15 3SJ ☎ 0131 669 0418

MURRAY Ian (*Dms, Per*): Bridgehouse Cottage, Mauchline Road, Hurlford, Kilmarnock KA1 5JX ☎ 01563 884348

NELSON William (*Dms*): 46 Harrowden Road, Inverness IV3 5QN ☎ 01463 236482

O'BRIEN Gavin (*Dms*): 12 Blacket Place, Edinburgh, Scotland EH9 1RL ☎ 0131 667 4275

OSUJI Justin (*Dms, Gtr*): Flat 3/1, 1221 Argyle Street, Glasgow G3 8TQ

PATERSON Marc (*Dms, B Gtr, Gtr, Voc, Kbds*) ☎ 0141 777 6945, 0421 845982

PEFFER David (*Dms*): 11 Fulmar Court, Bishopbriggs, Glasgow G64 1XA ☎ 0141 772 2066

PURSE Robert (*Per, Tym, La Per, Dms*): Flat 12 The Old School, Lintwhite Crescent, Bridge Of Weir PA11 3LJ ☎ 01505 690309, 0973 719145 mob, 01505 615864 fax

QUINN Paul (*Dms, Per*): 52 Mavisbank Gardens, Bellshill, Lanarkshire ML4 3ES ☎ 01698 333294

RAE 25/3 Mount Lodge Place, Edinburgh, Scotland EH15 2AD ☎ 0131 657 5087

RAMSAY John (*Dms*): 94 Tryst Road, Stenhousemuir, Falkirk FK5 4QJ ☎ 01324 553682

RAMSAY John (*Dms*): 39 Craigmount Hill, Edinburgh EH4 8DH ☎ 0131 339 5547

RAMSAY Robert (*Dms*): 30 Victoria Street, Alloa, Clackmannanshire FK10 2DZ ☎ 01259 724409

RANKIN Alasdair (*Per, Tym, Dms*): 27 Thorndene, Elderslie PA5 9DB ☎ 01505 3231 928

REDMAN Ben (*Dms, Tym, Per, La Per*): 56 Pilmuir Street, Dunfermline, Fife KY12 0QG ☎ 01383 624788

REID Ian J (*Dms*): 231 Dalkeith Road, Edinburgh EH16 5JR ☎ 0131 667 6459

REILLY James (*Dms*): 68 Main Street, Calderbank, Airdrie ML6 9SG ☎ 01236 608679

RENNIE Robert (*Dms, Spoons, Per*): 8 Queens Road, Aberdeen, Scotland AB15 4ZT ☎ 646988

ROBERTS Gordon (*Dms*): 35 Murrayfield, Bishopbriggs, Glasow G64 3DS ☎ 0141 772 5839

ROSE Elspeth (*Per*): 60 Clober Road, Milngavie, Glasgow G62 7SR ☎ 0141 956 3259

SANDERSON Nat (*Dms*): 263 Ayr Road, Newton Mearns, Renfrewshire G77 6AW ☎ 0141 639 3539

SAVAGE Paul (*Dms*): 12 Chantinghall Road, Hamilton, Lanarkshire ML3 8NP

SCOTT David (*Dms*): The Caravan, Kellas Smithy, Kellas, By Broughty Ferry, Dundee DD5 3PD ☎ 01382 350670

SCOTT Iain (*Per, Dms*): 369 Arbroath Road, Dindee, Scotland DD4 7SQ ☎ 01382 462419

SINCLAIR Dave (*Dms, Per*): 177A Commercial Street, Kirkcaldy, Fife, Scotland KY1 2NS ☎ 01592 205172

SMITH Murray (*Dms*): Calle Central 29, Xanadu, Monte Alto, Fase 2, Benalmadena 29630, Malaga, Spain ☎ +34 5 244 4910 & fax

SNEDDON Montgomery (*Dms*): 28 Lindsay Avenue, Kilbirnie, Ayrshire, Scotland KA25 7HR ☎ 01505 683492

SNEDDON Robert (*Dms*): 32 Larchfield Crescent, Wishaw, Lanarks ML2 8TY ☎ Cambusnethen 38

STARK Alan (*Per*): 47 Rowallan Gardens, Broomhill, Glasgow G11 7LH ☎ 0141 339 6752

STEPHEN Jack (*Dms*): 30 Craig Gardens, Cults, Aberdeen AB15 9TN ☎ 01224 868829

STEPHENSON Ronnie (*Dms*): 15 Leighton's Square, Alyth, Blairgowrie, Perthshire, Scotland PH11 8AQ ☎ 01828 633393

STEWART David (*Dms*): 15 Hillpark Green, Edinburgh EH4 7TB ☎ 0131 312 6221

SUTHERLAND James (*Per, Cong, Bod, Citt*): 5B Union Street, Edinburgh EH1 3LT ☎ 0131 556 9463

SUTHERLAND Jane (*Dms*): c/o Glasgow Sculpture Studios, 24 Craigmont Street, Glasgow G20 8BT ☎ 0141 945 4200

SWANSON David (*Dms*): 3 Marine Lodge, 21 Westgate, North Berwick, East Lothian EH39 4AE ☎ 01620 892751, 09731 83411

SWEENEY Thomas (*Dms*): 48 Glencroft Road, Glasgow G44 5RB ☎ 0141 637 4486

SWEET Darrell (*Dms*): 27 Munro Street, Kirkcaldy, Fife, Scotland KY1 1PY ☎ 01592 641778

TAYLOR James (*Dms, Per, Bod*): P.O Box 8403, Maybole, Ayrshire, Scotland KA19 7YB ☎ 01655 740536

THOM Billy (*Dms*): 7 Springbank Crescent, Dunblane FK15 9AP ☎ 01786 822227

TILSTON Alan (*Dms*): 6 Park Drive, Thorntonhall, Glasgow G74 5AS ☎ 0141 644 4171

TOAL Robert (*Dms, Pf, Gtr*): 34 Tay Street, Coatbridge, Lanarkshire, Scotland ML5 2NB ☎ 01236 440251

TRAVIS Michael (*Dms, Per*): Pirnie Cottage, Avonbridge Road, Slamannan, By Falkirk FK1 3DJ ☎ 01324 851015

URQUHART Derek (*Dms, Gtr*): 28 Castleheather Road, Inverness IV2 4EA ☎ 01463 239924

VERTH John (*Dms*): 10 Dryden Terrace, Edinburgh EH7 4NB ☎ 0131 556 1531

VIPOND Douglas (*Dms, Per*): 31 Broomhill Drive, Glasgow, Scotland G11 7AB ☎ 020 7388 5300

WALKER Gordon (*Dms*): 2 Hazel Dene, Bishopbriggs, Nr Glasgow G64 1TZ ☎ 0141 762 0532

WATSON John (*Dms*): 23 Corse Wynd., Kingswells, Aberdeen AB15 8TP ☎ 01224 745260

WELSH Matthew (*Dms, Voc*): 28 Craigside Court, Westfield, Cumbernauld G68 9EE ☎ Cumbernauld 363

WHITELAW Ian (*Per, Voc, Kbds, Gtr, Dms*): 15 Holyrood Crescent, Kelvinbridge, Glasgow G20 6HJ ☎ 0141 339 4945 & fax

WILKINS Brian (*Dms, Per*): 1 Mary Street, Dunoon, Argyll, Scotland PA23 7ED ☎ 01369 705953

WILKINSON Roy (*Dms*): 3A Parkhead Lane, Airdrie ML6 6NB ☎ Airdrie 69081

WILSON Alexander (*Dms*): 30 Harvey Bank Grove, Cumnock, Ayrshire KA18 1EN ☎ 01290 421955

WOOD Fergus (*Dms*): Ledard Farm, Kinlochard, By Aberfoyle FK8 3TL ☎ 018777 219

WYLIE Colin (*Dms, Per, Pf*): 3 Kings Crescent, Eldersleigh, Renfrewshire PA5 9AD ☎ 01505 343790

YATSURA Urusgi (*Dms*): 170 Menzies Road, Balornock, Glasgow G21 3NF ☎ 0141 558 6376

YOUNG Sally (*Per, Kbds*): 23 Seath Avenue, Langbank, Scotland PA14 6PD ☎ 01475 540 507, 01475 540507

NORTH WEST

ADAMS Mark (*Dms, Per*): 68 Rosefield Avenue, Higher Bebbington, Wirral L63 5JU ☎ 0151 644 8253, 0374 900929

ALI Linton (*Dms*): 1 Frin Close, Liverpool, Merseyside L27 6PT ☎ 0151 498 4510

ALLABY Matthew (*Dms, Per, Kbds*) ☎ 0161 232 9716

ANDREWS Darren (*Dms*): 80 Falcondale Road, Winwick, Warrington WA2 8ND ☎ 01925 639911, 0585 642736 mob

ANTROBUS Anthony (*Dms*): 3 Fox Lane, Waverton, Chester CH3 7PQ

APPLEBY Colin (*Dms, Per, Gtr*): 8 Watson Road, South Shore, Blackpool FY4 1EG ☎ 01253 342116, 01253 402403, 0410 703627

APPLETON Alan (*Dms*): 5 Mill Lane Crescent, Southport PR9 7PF ☎ 01704 27188

BAKER R (*Dms*): 25 Copperfield Road, Cheadle Hulme, Cheshire SK8 7PN ☎ 0161 439 5757

BARLOW Paul (*Dms*): 26 Lynton Drive, Bebington, Liverpool L63 3EH

BARLOW Philip (*Dms*): South Lodge, The Village, Singleton, Blackpool FY6 8LL

BARRINGTON Jonny (*Dms, Per, Kbds*): 38C High Lane, Chorlton-Cum-Hardy, Manchester M21 9DZ ☎ 0161 881 4380

BEECHAM Ian (*Dms, Voc*): 15 Boundary Rd, West Kirby, Wirral L48 1LE ☎ 0385 538446, 0151 625 2001

BEECROFT Joe (*Dms*): 14 Pinedale Close, Whitby, South Wirral, Cheshire L66 2UJ ☎ 0151 339 5923

BEESLEY Max (*Dms, La Per*): 105 Milford Drive, Levenshulme, Manchester M19 2RY ☎ 0161 432 4081

BELL Andrew (*Dms, Per*): 7 Lilac Avenue, Bury, Lancs BL9 9LP ☎ 0161 797 6401

BENGRY Peter (*Per, Dms*): Flat 2, 3 Bairstow Street, Preston, Lancashire PR1 3TN ☎ 01772 203793

BERNARDIN Jim (*Dms, Mrba, La Per, Pf, Tnd Pe*): 19 Bury Road, Edgworth, Bolton BL7 0AY ☎ 01204 853718

BIRD Diane (*Per*): 16 Fairways, Fulwood, Preston, Lancs PR2 8FX ☎ 01772 715298

BIRKBY Peter (*Per, Arr, Com*): 40 Park Avenue, South Kirkby, Pontefract, W Yorks WF9 3PG ☎ 01977 648645

BLACK Douglas (*Dms, Per, Tym, Pf*): Flat 4, 23 Clyde Road, West Didsbury, Manchester M29 2ND ☎ 0161 434 9620

BLACKSTOCK Kenneth (*Dms, Per, Tym*): 62 Farnworth Road, Penketh, Warrington, Cheshire WA5 2TS ☎ 01925 727885

BOLD Andrew (*Dms, Per*): 19 Mayfield Road, Timperley, Altrincham, Cheshire WA15 7TB ☎ 0161 980 2894

BOND Geoffrey (*Dms*): 2 Mill Avenue, Gt Sankey, Warrington, Cheshire WA5 3HL ☎ 01925 722938

BOOTH John (*Dms, Per*): 55 Poll Hill Road, Heswall, Merseyside L60 7SW ☎ 0151 342 1944

BOWYER Keith (*Dms, Per*): 40 Alderley Road, Therwal, Warrington, Cheshire WA4 2JA ☎ 01925 601953

BRADBURY Peter (*Dms, Per*): 24 Needham Drive, Cranage, Cheshire CW4 8FB ☎ 01477 535662

BRADLEY Jan (*Per*): 29 Warwick Rd, Chorlton, Manchester M21 0AX ☎ 0161 881 0059

BRADY Leslie (*Per*): 4 Castle Shaw Road, Offerton, Stockport, Cheshire SK2 5ND ☎ 0161 483 5189

BRENNAN Pol (*Dms, Synth, Flt*): Powerswood, Thomastown, Co. Kilkenny, Ireland ☎ +353 562 4928 & fax

BRIANT Samuel (*Dms*): 38 Clifton Street, Failsworth, Manchester M35 9EE ☎ 0161 682 2146

BRIDGE James (*Per*): Shackleton Farm, Shawforth, Rochdale, Lancs OL12 8XD ☎ 01706 853166

BRIGGS Zoey (*Dms, Per, Voc*): 64 Plattlane, Rusholme, Manchester M14 5NE ☎ 01942 701302

BRODIE Emma (*Per, Tym, Dms*): Flat 31, 88 Brantingham Road, Whalley Range, Manchester M16 8LZ ☎ 0161 862 9341, 01383 850318

BROWN Christopher (*Dms, Per, Gtr, Kbds*): 7 Woodrouffe Terrace, Carlisle, Cumbria CA1 2EH

BROWN Leo (*Dms, Per*): 23 Carpenters Lane, West Kirby, Wirral L48 7EX ☎ 0151 625 5011, 0151 625 0241

BUCK Arthur (*Dms*): 125 Nicolas Road, Chorlton, Manchester M21 9LS ☎ 0161 881 7089

BURNSIDE Raymond (*Dms*): 67 Belmont Park Road, Leyton, London E10 6AX

BUTTERWORTH Stephen (*Dms*): 42 Mansfield Avenue, Denton, Manchester M34 3WR ☎ 0161 336 0130

BYRNE Daniel (*Dms, Per*): 23 Atherley Grove, Chadderton, Oldham, Lancs OL9 8DD ☎ 0161 684 7286

CAPSTICK Peter (*Dms*): 68 Carr Road, Nelson, Lancs BB9 7SR ☎ 01282 698 465

CARLISLE Liz (*Per, Voc*): 27 (3) Sandon Street, Liverpool L8 7NS ☎ 0151 709 7562

CARNEY Andrew (*Dms*): 76 Northen Grove, West Didsbury, Manchester M20 2NW ☎ 0161 434 2216

CARVER Alison (*Per, Arr, Pf*): 'Marlpool', 41B Barracks Lane, Macclesfield, Cheshire SK10 1QJ ☎ 0161 434 8847

CAVANAGH Chris (*Dms, Per*): 123A Halton Road, Runcorn, Cheshire WA7 5QX ☎ 01928 569180, 0374 603978

CHARLES Richard (*Per, Dms*): 5 Holly Fold, Whitefield, Manchester M45 8SR ☎ 0161 796 7679

CHEETHAM Maurice (*Dms, Per, Tym, Arr, Com*): 35 Kiln Lane, Dentons Green, St Helens, Merseyside WA10 6AD ☎ 01744 630347, 0850 234043 mob

COULTHARD Paul (*Dms*): 64 Coulport Close, Knotty Ash, Liverpool L14 2EL ☎ 0151 259 6579

COWIE Reginald (*Dms*): 6 Mona Terrace, Douglas, Isle Of Man ☎ 01624 675462

CRAIG Scott (*Dms, Per*): Address Unknown ☎ 0161 438 0699

CROMPTON Don (*Dms, Tym, Per*): 57 Worsley Road, Farnworth, Bolton, Lancs BL4 9LR ☎ 01204 74310

CRUIKS Christopher (*Per*): 35 Longford Road, Chorlton, Manchester M21 1WP ☎ 0161 718 6466

CULLEN Linda (*Per, H Dul, Wh, Voc*): 15 Park Cottages, Greenfield, Oldham OL3 7LP ☎ 01457 871600, 0410 379225 mob

CUNLIFFE George (*Dms*): 34 Yarlside Road, Barrow In Furness, Cumbria LA13 0ER

DANDO Terry (*Dms, Per*): 7 Llandudno Road, Rhos-on-Sea, Clywd LL28 4TR ☎ 01492 547528

DANIEL Geraint (*Per, Tym*): 177 Turncroft Lane, Stockport, Cheshire SK1 4AX ☎ 0161 476 5926

DANIELS Thomas (*Dms*): 40 Sandy Lane, Preesall, Poulton-Le-Fylde, Fleetwood, Lancs FY6 0EH ☎ 01253 810981

DARBY Gerald (*Dms, Per*): Newman & Company, Regent House, 1 Pratt Mews, London NW1 0AD ☎ 020 7267 6899, 020 7267 6746

DARWIN Peter (*Per*): 19/21, George Street, St Helens, Merseyside WA10 1DA ☎ 01744 57812

DAVIES Peter (*Dms*): Tan-Y-Bryn, Aber, Llanfairfechan, Gwynedd LL33 0LN ☎ 01248 680837

DOLMAN David (*Dms*): 83 Lawton Road, Waterloo, Liverpool L22 9QL ☎ 0151 928 1974, 0151 727 7455

DRUM (*Dms, Per, Kbds, Bsn*) ☎ 01758 750586, 01758 750596 fax

EDDOWES Peter (*Dms*): 5 Warwick Avenue, Lancaster LA1 4HB ☎ 01524 66062

ELLIOTT Bobby (*Dms*): c/o Messrs Citroen Wells, Devonshire House, 1 Devonshire Street, London W1N 2DR

ELLIOTT Steven (*Dms*): 35 Southouver, Daisy Hill, Westoughton, Bolton BL5 6HS

FEILD Gordon (*Dms*): 4 Linden Drive, Mickle Trafford, Nr Chester, Chester CH2 4QT ☎ 01244 300883

FELL Milo (*Dms, La Per, Per*): Flat 3, 19 Lincoln Grove, Longsight, Manchester M13 0DX ☎ 0161 274 4388

FINCH Greg (*Dms, Per, Kbds, Gtr*): 29 Stephendale Avenue, Bamber Bridge, Preston, Lancs PR5 6ZP ☎ 01772 36002

FISH George (*Dms*): Haulgh Cottage, 89 Radcliffe Road, Bolton, Lancs BL2 1NU

FLETCHER Alistair (*Dms, B Gtr*): ☎ 01422 885345, 0161 969 7907

FLINN Peter (*Per, Org*): Fron Hyfryd, Marian-Glas, Anglesey, Gwynedd LL73 8PE ☎ 0585 400951 mob

FORD Eric (*Dms*): ☎ 01704 546854

FRANKS Timothy (*Dms*): 9 Albert Road, Wilmslow, Cheshire SK9 5HT ☎ 01625 522142

FRY Alan (*Dms*): Netherleigh, 42 Biggar Bank, Barrow In Furness, Cumbria LA14 3YF ☎ 01229 471657

GARDNER Trevor (*Dms*): 94 Childwall Road, Liverpool L15 6UX ☎ 0151 737 2453, 0402 905302

GAUGHRAN Philip (*Dms*): 202, Butterstile Lane, Prestwich, Manchester M25 9UN ☎ 0161 773 1982

GILBERT Steven (*Dms*): 198 Manchester Road, Broadheath, Altrincham, Cheshire WA14 5LD ☎ 0161 928 5934

GODLEY Kevin (*Dms*): c/o O J Kilkenny & Co, Chartered Accountants, 6 Lansdowne Mews, London W11 3BH ☎ 020 7792 9494

GOODFELLOW John (*Dms*): 265 Blakelow Road, Macclesfield, Cheshire SK11 7EH ☎ 01625 614199

GOODWIN James (*Dms, Per, Tym, La Per*): Flat 10 Mayfield Mansions, 20 Alexandra Road South, Whalley Range, Manchester M16 8EE ☎ 0161 226 4665

GRANGE Herbert (*Dms*): 48 Boothfields, Knutsford, Cheshire WA16 8JU ☎ 01565 632651

GREENWOOD David (*Dms*): 81 Ryles Park, Macclesfield, Cheshire SK11 8AL ☎ 01625 423418

GREGORY Stephen (*Dms, Per*): 47 Norden Road, Rochdale, Lancs OL11 5PN ☎ 01706 713482

GRIFFITHS Philip (*Dms*): 119 Norfolk Road, Borras Park, Wrexham LL12 7SD ☎ 01978 354450

GURLEY Norman (*Dms*): 45 Toxteth Street, Hr Openshaw, Manchester M11 1EP

HAIGH Phillip (*Dms, Per*): 17 Whitelodge Avenue, Huyton, Liverpool L36 2PT ☎ 0151 481 0246

HALL Ron (*Per*): 45 Cable Road, Hoylake, Wirral L47 2AZ ☎ 0151 632 2152

HAMPSON Leslie (*Per, Gtr, Voc*): 88 Cambridge Road, Ely, Cambridge CB7 4HU ☎ 01606 834385

HANSON-USHER Moira (*Per, Tym*): 5 Nursery End, Nanpantan Road, Loughborough, Leics. LE11 3RB ☎ 01509 262525, 01509 211541 fax

HARPER Michael (*Per, Tym*): 8 Stoodley Grange, Lee Bottom Road, Todmorden, Lancashire OL14 6JR ☎ 01706 810 576, 0802 698647

HARRIES Michael (*Dms*): 45 Poplar Grove, Sale, Cheshire M33 3AX ☎ 0161 962 4373

HARRISON Richard (*Dms*): Flat 13, 130 Old Birley Street, Hulme, Manchester M15 5GL ☎ 01925 753465

HARRISON Stephen (*Dms, Gtr, B Gtr*): 26 Lodore Drive, Carlisle CA2 7SG ☎ 01228 23451

HARRISON,BA,HONS Anthony (*Dms, Per*): 13 Davenport Road, Hazel Grove, Stockport, Cheshire SK7 4EZ ☎ 0161 456 5924, 0467 633267 mob

HASSELL David (*Dms, Per*): 22 Park Road, Timperley, Altrincham, Cheshire WA14 5AU ☎ 0161 962 1339

HASTINGS Sophie (*Per, Tym, Dms, La Per*): Flat A, 245 Barlowmoore Road, Manchester M21 7QL ☎ 0161 881 9192, 0956 170257 mob, 020 8857 1043

HAYLER Richard (*Dms*): 88 Beech Gardens, Rainford, St Helens WA11 8DW ☎ 01744 885479

HEALD Mike (*Dms*): 11 Chorley Road, Westhoughton, Nr Bolton, Lancs BL5 3PD ☎ 01942 813138

HEGAN Patrick (*Dms, Per, Flt, Kbds, Voc*): 33 Melborne Street, Manchester M7 1YA ☎ 0161 962 6128

HENSHAW Elliott (*Dms*): 20 Moor Lane, Wilmslow, Cheshire SK9 6AP ☎ 01625 524620

HEXT David (*Per, Tym, Dms*): 12 Lime Avenue, Urmston, Manchester M41 5DE ☎ 0161 747 8632

HEYWOOD David (*Dms, Per, Kbds*): St Pauls Vicarage, Hollin Lane, Rawtenstall, Rossendale, Lancashire BB4 8HT ☎ 01706 228634, 0468 410116

HICKSON Andrew (*Dms, La Per*): 818 Burnage Lane, Burnage, Manchester M19 1RS ☎ 0161 442 3255

HOGGARTH Craig (*Dms, Xyl, Cl Gtr, Pf*) ☎ 01900 604122

HOLDEN Timothy (*Dms, Per*): 1 Thornbush Close, Lowton, Warrington, Cheshire WA3 2JU ☎ 01942 716322, 09662 58064

HOLLINS Clayton (*Dms, Per, Sax*): Eskdale, 1 Westbury Drive, Buckley, Flintshire CH7 3BA ☎ 01244 548633

HOLMES Christopher (*Dms, Voc*): 64 Rakewood Drive, Moorside, Oldham, Lancs OL4 2NP ☎ 0161 633 8472

HOLMES Joan (*Dms, B Gtr, Tamb, T Sax*): Transudanjo House, 50 Skinburness Drive, Silloth, Carlisle Cumbria CA5 4QG ☎ 016973 31623

HOWELL-JONES Richard (*Dms, Per, Voc*): Flat 11, 18, Wardle Road, Sale, Cheshire M33 3DB ☎ 0161 976 1118

ILLINGWORTH Patrick (*Dms*): 65 Imogen Court, Regents Park Flats, Asgard Drive, Salford M5 4TQ ☎ 0161 834 3465, 0976 714001

INGHAM Kenneth (*Per*): 33 Ballacrosha, Ballaugh, Isle Of Man IM7 5AG ☎ 01624 897897

JACKSON Kenneth (*Dms*): Newbrick House, Hill Street, Pentre Broughton, Wrexham Clwyd LL11 6DA ☎ 01978 751433

JACKSON Susan (*Dms, Pf, Vln*): 27 Rippingham Road, Withington, Manchester M20 3FX ☎ 0161 445 0963

JAGO Chris (*Dms, Gtr*): 139 North Hill Street, Liverpool, Merseyside L8 8AE ☎ 0151 709 4375, 0151 280 5472

JENNINGS John (*Dms*): 21 Peel Moat Road, Heaton Moor, Stockport, Cheshire SK4 4PL ☎ 0161 442 3224, 0410 536515

JOHN Karl (*Per*): Flat 2, 29 Falkner Street, Liverpool L8 7PU

JOHNS Graham (*Per, Tym, Mar*): 17 Burnham Road, Calderstones, Liverpool L18 6JU ☎ 0151 724 1072, 0151 729 0592 fax

JOHNSON Philip (*Dms*): 157 Bradford Road, Farnworth, Bolton, Greater Manchester BL4 0HY ☎ 01204 35497

JONES Robert (*Dms*): Balmoral Drive, High Lane, Stockport, Cheshire SK6 8BN ☎ 01663 763304

JOYCE Michael (*Dms, Per*): 11 Springfield Road, Altrincham, Cheshire WA14 1HE

KENYON Richard (*Dms*): 8 Birch Grove, Knutsford, Cheshire WA16 8AX ☎ 01565 653612

KINGSLOW Andrew (*Per, Pf*): 54 Mill Lane, Blackley, Manchester M9 6PE ☎ 0161 740 6325, 0468 060875

LACEY Rick (*Dms, Per*) ☎ 01706 825877

LAHERTY Leo (*Dms*): 55 Hillsborough Drive, Unsworth, Bury, Lancs BL9 8LF ☎ 0161 796 1955

LARN Colin (*Dms*): 19 Hillside Drive, Christchurch BH23 2RS

LAWSON Stephen (*Dms, Kbds, Per*): 9 Young Street, Radcliffe, Manchester M26 4QG ☎ 0161 723 1751, 07771 722 467

LEA Robert (*Per, Tym, Bod*): Marlpool, 41B Barracks Lane, Macclesfield, Cheshire SK10 1QJ ☎ 01625 428318

LEE Ric (*Dms, Tym*): Bank Top Cottage, Meadow Lane, Millers Dale, Derbyshire SK17 8SN

LEG Peg (*Per, Bod*): 11 Alma Street, Walsden, Todmorden, Lancs OL14 6QJ ☎ 01706 817302

LEIGH Jeffrey (*Dms*): 42 Micawber Road, Poynton, Cheshire SK12 1UP ☎ 01625 878814

LEYLAND Ken (*Dms*): 94 Blackcarr Road, Baguley, Manchester M23 8PN ☎ 0161 998 3494

LITTLEWOOD Stanley (*Dms*): 16 Portugal Street, Haulgh, Bolton, Lancs BL2 1AP ☎ 01204 25039

LLEWELLYN Rhys (*Dms, Gtr*): Dane Bank Farm, Knutsford Road, Holmes Chapel, Cheshire CW4 7DE ☎ 01477 5432217

LLOYD Philip (*Dms, Per*): 23 Knutsford View, Hale Barns, Altrincham, Cheshire WA15 8SU ☎ 0161 980 1984, 07970 937132

LOMAS Adrian (*Dms, Gtr, B Gtr*): 46 Woodfield Road, Cheadle Hulme, Cheshire SK8 7JS ☎ 0161 486 1455

LOWE Christopher (*Per*): 45 Garth Avenue, Surby, Isle Of Man IM9 6QZ ☎ 01624 832127

LYNCH Ged (*Dms, Cong*): 33 Water Street, Rachub, Bangor, North Wales LL57 3EU ☎ 01248 602951

MAC Tony (*Dms, Per*): 19 Molyneux Road, Waterloo, Liverpool L22 4QY ☎ 020 8284 1595

MACE Dawn (*Per*): 2 The Cedars, Saughall Massie, Wirral, Merseyside L46 5NU ☎ 0151 677 9323

MACK Arty (*Dms, Voc*): 40 Briar Road, Thorton, Cleveleys, Lancashire FY5 4NA ☎ 01253 823044

MACKENZIE Wally (*Dms, Md*): 99 Stockport Road, Mossley, Ashton Under Lyne, Lancs OL5 0RB ☎ 01457 834177

MANSELL Carl (*Dms, Kbds, Xyl*): 80 Toxteth Street, Higher Openshaw, Manchester M11 1HA ☎ 0161 301 1422

MARK Robert (*Dms*): 5 Frances Street, Crewe, Cheshire CW2 6HF

MARKLAND Brian (*Dms*): 36 Deerhurst Road, Thornton-Cleveleys, Lancashire FY5 3HG ☎ 01253 821514

MARSDEN Julian (*Dms*): 435 Queens Drive, Stoneycroft, Liverpool L13 0AQ ☎ 0151 228 1157, 0151 707 2622

MARTIN Roy (*Dms*): 238 London Road, Northwich, Cheshire CW9 8AQ ☎ 01606 43037

MAXI (*Dms, Per*): 124 Ringlon Park Road, Swinton, Manchester M27 0HD ☎ 0161 281 1299

MCCARROLL Anthony (*Dms*): 32 Lonsdale Road, Levenshulme, Manchester M19 3FL ☎ 0161 225 8460

MCDOWELL Gary (*Per*): 1 Pine Hill, Highton Wood Hill, Tromode, Isle Of Man IM2 5NJ ☎ 01624 673948

MCGREEVY Michael (*Dms*): 10 Devon Close, Walton Le Dale, Preston, Lancashire PR5 4QQ ☎ 01772 321759

MELBOURNE John (*Per*): 12 Bramley Close, Wilmslow, Cheshire SK9 6EP ☎ 01625 531240

MEYER Richard (*Per*): 3 Malthouse Close, Trefonen, Oswestry, Shropshire SY10 9BT ☎ 01691 671 592

MILNER John (*Dms, Pf, Com, Arr*): 33 Rose Bank Street, Leek, Staffordshire ST13 6AG ☎ 01538 382197

MINNS Howard (*Dms*): 69 Radley Drive, Old Road, Aintree, Liverpool L10 2LG ☎ 0151 474 3540

MITCHELL Bruce (*Dms*): 77 Central Road, Manchester M20 4YD ☎ 0161 445 6876

MOORE Simon (*Dms, B Gtr, Kbds*): 35 Agecroft Road West, Prestwich, Manchester M25 9RE ☎ 0161 773 6915, 0161 280 9514

MOORHOUSE H (*Per*): 20 Tromode Park, Douglas, Isle Of Man ☎ 01624 676776

MORGAN Greg (*Dms, B Gtr, Kbds*): 7 Wellington Street, Milnrow, Rochdale OL16 3DP ☎ 01706 352140

MORRIS Stephen (*Dms*): c/o Rebecca Boulton, X Ltd, 11 Whitworth Street West, Manchester M1 5WG ☎ 0161 237 5957

MORRISON Chas (*Dms, Gtr, Pf*): 125 Market Street, Edenfield, Bury, Lancs BL0 0JJ ☎ 01706 824835

MULLIN Tim (*Dms*): 9 Elliott Street, Farnworth, Bolton, Lancashire BL4 9QG ☎ 01204 795424

MURPHY Tracy (*Dms, Kbds, Voc*)

NAMIAH (*Per, Kbds, Voc*): 79 South Radford Street, Rivrdale Village, Kersal, Salford, Manchester M7 3GY ☎ 0161 792 3925, 0161 232 1132, 0161 232 7132 fax

NORRIS Bert (*Dms*): 24 St Heliers Drive, Salford M7 4PP ☎ 0161 740 9330

O'BRIEN James (*Dms*): 9 Egerton Road, Prescot, Liverpool L34 3LS ☎ 0151 426 9903

O'CARROLL Thomas (*Dms, Per, Pf, Kbds*): 11 Belgrave Road, Wrexham, Clwyd LL13 7ES ☎ 01978 290931

O'HARE S (*Per*): 21 Highview Road, Douglas, Isle Of Man IM2 5BQ ☎ 01624 627803

O'SHAUGHNESSY Terry (*Dms, Gtr*): 122 Inskip, Birch Green, Skelmersdale, Lancashire WN8 6JU ☎ 01695 556804, 01695 556804

OATES Ronald (*Dms, Vib*): 7 Ingleton Road, Edgeley, Stockport, Cheshire SK3 9NN ☎ 0161 480 4538

ONEILL Keith (*Dms, Tpt*): c/o Cast/Rock & Roll Mgmt, Studio 2, 108 Prospect Quay, Point Pleasant, London SW18 1PR ☎ 020 8516 6403

PARMIGIANI Riccardo (*Per*): 19 Caistor Close, Manchester M16 8NW ☎ 0161 861 8043

PARROTT Nigel (*Per*): 24 Westbourne Road, Urmston, Manchester M41 0XP ☎ 0161 747 3713

PARTRIDGE Michael (*Dms, Pf, Tbn*): 34 Newcombe Road, Holcombe Brook, Lancs BL0 9UT ☎ 01204 882459

PATRICK Paul (*Per, Tym, Dms*): 212 Wythenshawe Road, Northenden, Manchester M23 0PH ☎ 0161 998 4461

PEGG Kenneth (*Dms*): 61 Pendyffryn Road, Rhyl, Clwyd L18 4DE ☎ 01745 334 614

POORE Jak (*Per, Dms, Pf, Vln, Gtr*): 40 Kings Road, Prestwitch, Manchester M25 0LE ☎ 0161 773 5034

POWER Roy (*Dms*): 256 Yew Tree Lane, Dukinfield, Cheshire SK16 5DN ☎ 0161 338 4637

POWNCEBY John (*Dms, Per, Hmca*): 3 Brookfield Avenue, Great Crosby, Liverpool L23 3DN ☎ 0151 924 5078

PRICE Jonathan (*Dms*): 26 Marland Fold, Marland, Rochdale, Lancs OL11 4RF ☎ 01706 59130

PRITCHARD Melvyn (*Per*): The Handle Group, Pinewood Studios, Pinewood Road, Iver Heath, Buckinghamshire SL0 0NH ☎ 01753 651 001, 01753 630 555/633

PSYCHO C (*Dms*): 4 Park Side Road, Fallowfield Manchester, Manchester M14 7JG ☎ 0161 226 9730

PUZZAR Stanley (*Dms*): Island Hotel, 4 Empress Drive, Douglas, Isle Of Man IM2 4LQ ☎ 01624 676549, 01624 625846

REYNOLDS Gerry (*Per*): 12A Birchill Crescent, Onchan, Isle Of Man IM3 3HX ☎ 01624 671113

ROBERT Paul (*Dms*): PO Box 6351, Laguna Niguel, California, 92607, USA

ROBERTS Matthew (*Dms, Per, Kbds*): 40-42 Slater Street, Liverpool L1 4BX ☎ 0151 709 6905, 0151 707 1341

ROBERTS Stephen (*Dms*): Damson Cottage, Wornish Nook, Somerford Booth, Congleton, Cheshire CW12 2JP ☎ 01260 224565

ROBINSON Gary (*Dms*): 9 Grantham Road, Birkdale, Southport, Merseyside PR8 4LS ☎ 01704 560451

ROBINSON Ian (*Dms, Tnd Per, Tym, Eup*): 7 Byron Close, Blacon, Chester CH1 5XF ☎ 01244 378810

ROMANO Vincent (*Dms*): Silverstones, 6 Victoria Road, Penrith, Cumbria CA11 8HR ☎ 01768 865590

ROSCOE John (*Dms*): 239 Motram Road, Stalybridge, Cheshire SK15 2RF ☎ 0161 338 8323

ROTHWELL John (*Dms, Db*): 184 Rufford Road, Crossens, Southport, Merseyside PR9 8HU ☎ 01704 220874

ROTHWELL Phil (*Dms*): 197, Dunkirk Lane, Leyland, Preston, Lancs PR5 3SN ☎ 01772 465322

RYAN Paul (*Dms*): 25 Robarts Road, Anfield, Liverpool L4 0TY ☎ 0151 260 6342

RYAN-CARTER Adam (*Dms, Per, Kbds*): 1 South Meade, Chorltonville, Manchester M21 8EB ☎ 0161 860 6642

SCAIFE James (*Dms*): 2 Sunningdale Drive, Thornton, Thornton-Cleveleys, Lancs FY5 5AQ ☎ 01253 866456

SCHALOM Guy (*Dms, Per, Pf*): 73 Altrincham Road, Gatley, Cheadle, Cheshire SK8 4EG ☎ 0161 291 0954, 0161 428 5945

SCHOFIELD Paul (*Dms*): 50 Ney Street, Waterloo, Ashton-Under-Lyne, Lancashire OL7 9NL ☎ 0585 954184

SEAR Gordon (*Dms, Tpt*): 11 Cliffe Lane, Barrow In Furness LA14 4HU ☎ 01229 824898

SHORTT David (*Dms*): 65 Whitehurst Road, Heaton Mersey, Stockport, Cheshire SK4 3NY ☎ 0161 431 9001

SLATER John (*Per*): 1, French Barn Lane, Higher Blackley, Manchester M9 2PB ☎ 0161 795 3444

SLATER Rueben (*Dms*): 3 Slaters Yard, Station Road, Wigton, Cumbria CA7 9BA ☎ 016973 44678, 0585 467 252

SMITH Caroline (*Per, Tym, Pf*): 6 Plymouth Grove West, Lonesight, Manchester M13 0AG ☎ 0161 273 7598

SMITH Kirk (*Dms*): 26 Lyon Street, Barrow-In-Furness, Cumbria LA14 1NU ☎ 01229 432980

SMITH Neil (*Dms, Gtr*): 30 Dyne Avenue, Rusholme, Manchester M14 5SY ☎ 0161 248 0725

SMITH Richard (*Dms*): 44 East Downs Road, Cheadle Hulme, Cheadle, Cheshire SK8 5ES ☎ 0161 485 4415

SPILLETT Adrian (*Per*): 26 Hall Road, Rusholme, Manchester M14 5HL ☎ 0161 248 0402, 07970 899481

SPROXTON Andrew (*Per, Gtr*): 13 Florence Street, Barrow, Cumbria LA14 2DB ☎ 01229 826783

STAPLES Peter (*Dms*): 17 The Quadrant, Forbes Road, Offerton, Stockport Cheshire SK1 4HJ ☎ 0161 480 6991

STAVORDALE John (*Dms, Vib*): 40 Canberra Rd, Bramhall, Stockport, Cheshire SK7 1LG ☎ 0161 439 5315

STEVEN Gary (*Dms, Pf, Kbds*): 182 Hereford Way, Middleton, Manchester M24 2NJ ☎ 0161 345 9636, 0411 483 654

STEWART Daniel (*Dms, B Gtr, Gtr*): 33 Windsor Road, Tuebrook, Liverpool L13 8BA ☎ 0151 259 1083

STUART Paul (*Dms, Per, Voc*): 45 Needham Road, Liverpool L7 0EE ☎ 0151 283 4200 & fax

SUTTON Mike (*Dms, Theory*): 70 Becconsall Lane, Hesketh Bank, Preston, Lancs PR4 6RR ☎ 01772 815929, 0468 064479

SVEINSSON Agust (*Dms*): Lyndhurst, Moss Lane, Garstang, Lancashire PR3 1PD ☎ 01995 600162, 0370 567096 mob

TAFARI Levi (*Per*): 16 Dombey Street, Liverpool L8 5TL ☎ 0151 709 5585

TAYLOR Roy (*Dms*): 13 Windsor Road, Ashton In Makerfield, Nr Wigan, Lancs WN4 9EP ☎ 01942 510845

THOMAS Bryan (*Dms, Per*): Tan-Y-Bryn, Gogarth Road, Llandudno, Gwynedd LL30 2AP ☎ 01492 879455

THOMPSON Rupert (*Dms*): 36 Gower Road, Hyde, Cheshire SK14 5AD

TIDSWELL Irven (*Dms, B Ldr*): 31 Poulton Old Road, Blackpool, Lancashire FY3 7LB ☎ 01253 391104

TOLLEY Anthony (*Dms*): 12 Airdale Avenue, Marton, Blackpool, Lancashire FY3 9LH ☎ 01253 760446

TOOLE Gordon (*Dms, Tym*): 22 Emerald Avenue, Blackburn, Lancs BB1 9RP ☎ 01254 262696

TREACEY Andrew (*Dms, Per*): 55 Ribblesdale Road, Streatham, London SW16 6SF ☎ 020 8696 0218, 0973 334152

TURNER Andrew (*Dms, Gtr*)

TURNER Paul (*Per, Tym*): 105 Wigshaw Lane, Culcheth, Warrington WA3 4AD ☎ 01925 767098

TURNER Robert (*Dms, Per*): 10, Faulkner Drive, Timperley, Altrincham, Cheshire WA15 7PT ☎ 0161 980 7614

TYAS David (*Dms, Per*): 12 Croft Court, Stony Lane, Honley, Huddersfield, W.Yorks HD7 2HB ☎ 01484 665234

VERNON Howard (*Per, Dms*): 22 Fold Crescent, Carrbrook, Stalybridge, Cheshire SK15 3ND ☎ 01457 837579

VICKERS Diane (*Per, Dms*): 11 Bank Road, Skerton, Lancaster LA1 2DG ☎ 01524 64616 & fax

VINE David (*Dms, Voc, Rh Gtr*): 8 Seaton Road, Wallasey, Wirral L45 5HJ ☎ 0151 639 8306

VOGLER Andrea (*Per, Tym*): 17 Beech Hurst Close, Whalley Range, Manchester M16 8EP ☎ 0161 881 1377, 0976 850858

WALKER B.A.HONS. Michael (*Dms, Per, Kbds*): 31 Clive Road, Daisy Hill, Westhoughton, Bolton BL5 2HR ☎ 01942 819431, 0370 807 890

WALSH Bo (*Dms*): 55 Surrey Road, Blackley, Manchester M9 8AU ☎ 01611288 2028

WALSH David (*Dms*): 38 Kirkstone Drive, Norbreck, Cleveleys, Lancs FY5 1QH ☎ 01253 866636

WALTON Vincent (*Dms*): Hurstlea, 6 Pikes Lane, Glossop, Derbyshire SK13 8EA ☎ 01457 866775

WARD Chris (*Dms*): 7 Warwick Street, Haslingden, Rossendale, Lancs BB4 5LR ☎ 01706 225931

WARD Daniel (*Dms, Per*): 75 Cromwell Avenue, Whalley Range, Manchester M16 0BG ☎ 0161 861 7107

WARD John (*Per, Tym*): 5 Cairndale Drive, Leyland, Preston PR5 2BX

WAUGH Roland (*Dms*): 161 Pendlebury Towers, Stockport SK5 7RW ☎ 0161 480 5386

WELLS David Daniel (*Dms*): 169 Foxdenton Lane, Middleton, Manchester M24 1QN ☎ 0161 652 6560

WESTWOOD Tim (*Dms, Kbds, Voc*): Farndale, Cliburn, Cumbria CA10 3AL ☎ 01931 714683

WHETTAM Andrew (*Per, Tym, Mrba*): 9 Ivy Road, Poynton, Cheshire SK12 1PE ☎ 01625 8588878

WHITEHEAD Kevin (*Dms, Per*): 11 Fitton Street, Shaw, Oldham, Lancs OL2 7HN ☎ 01706 844859

WHITWAM Barry *(Dms)*: 26 South Park Road, Gatley, Cheadle, Cheshire SK8 4AN ☎ 0161 428 6460

WHITWORTH John *(Dms)*: 9 Campbell Road, Swinton, Manchester M27 5QG ☎ 0161 794 3194

WHYMENT Martin *(Dms)*: 20 Bowness Ave, Rochdale OL12 7DN ☎ 01706 356448

WILKINSON Clive *(Dms)*: 57 Worsley Road, Farmworth, Bolton, Lancs BL4 9LR

WILKINSON Jane *(Dms)*: 14 Westminster Avenue, Whalley Range, Manchester M16 0AN ☎ 0161 882 0094, 07970 346037

WILLIAMS Jonathan *(Per, Kbds, Gtr)*: 3 Buccleach Court, Barrow In Furness, Cumbria LA14 1TD ☎ 01229 833406, 01229 470015

WILSON Abiola *(Dms, Cong, Per)*: 12 Hartington Street, Moss Side, Manchester M14 4RW ☎ 0161 226 4119

WOOD Stephen *(Dms)*: 8 Cotswold Drive, Royton, Oldham, Lancs OL2 5HD ☎ 0161 624 3305

WORDSWORTH Malcolm *(Dms)*: 14 Newlands Road, Morecambe, Lancs LA4 5SQ ☎ 01524 423371

WREN Isobel *(Per, Sax, Pf, Vln)*: 38 Parkhill Avenue, Crumpsall, Manchester M8 4RA ☎ 0161 795 3637

WRIGHT Christopher *(Dms, Gtr, Hmca, Voc, Kbds)*: 15 Lancatser Terrace, Acrefair, Wrexham, Clwyd LL14 3HP ☎ 01978 822664

YOUNG Paul *(Per, Voc)*: 63 Hale Road, Hale, Altrincham, Cheshire WA15 9SH ☎ 0161 941 2778

YOUNG Richard *(Dms, La Per, Tnd Per)*: 16 Brookfield Way, Earby, Barnoldswick BB18 6YQ ☎ 01282 844109

NORTH EAST

ADAIR John *(Dms)*: 101 Newlyn Drive, Parkside Dale, Cramlington, Northumberland NE23 9RW ☎ 01670 731542, 0589 713628 mob, 01670 731322

ADAMS Lee *(Per, Tnd Per, Dms)*: 12 Northwold Road, Scarborough, N Yorks YO11 3HG ☎ 01723 584829

ALLEN Simon *(Dms, Per, Kbds, B Gtr)*: 5 Claremont Avenue, Leeds LS3 1AT ☎ 0113 234 0650

ARNOLD Mark *(Dms, Tym, Tnd Per)*: 5 Oak Park Rise, Barnsley, South Yorks S70 4PB ☎ 01226 299495, 07970 880191

ARTHUR Bruce *(Dms)*: 7 Chester Street, Sandyford, Newcastle-upon-Tyne, Tyne & Wear NE2 1AT

ARTHUR Frank *(Dms)*: 25 Northfield Road, Crookes, Sheffield S10 1QP ☎ 0114 266 0408

ASHBY Charles *(Dms, Per, La Per)*: 125 Avondale Road, Shipley, W. Yorks BD18 4QZ

ATKINSON Neil *(Dms, Rh Gtr, Voc)*: 12 Wensley Road, Chapel Allerton, Leeds, West Yorkshire LS7 2LX ☎ 0113 2683996

AYRES Frank *(Dms, Tym, Xyl, Vib, Glck)*: 19 Hillcrest Drive, Milescroft, Beverley, North Humberside HU17 7JL ☎ 01482 3865455

BAILEY David *(Per, Clt)*: 124 Huddersfield Rd, Barnsley, S Yorks S75 1HA ☎ 01226 283628

BAILEY Gerald *(Dms)*: 57 Hollythorpe Road, Sheffield S2 9NF ☎ 0114 255 0565

BANKS Nicholas *(Dms)*: Pru Harris, Rough Trade, 66 Golborne Road, London W10 5PS ☎ 020 8960 9888

BARNEY Steven *(Dms, Per)*: 158 West Parade, Lincoln LN1 1LF ☎ 01522 543157, 0589 122937 mob

BARRETT Nicholas *(Dms, Tym, Vib, Xyl)*: 14 Bunting Close, Norton, Sheffield S8 8JE ☎ 0114 2749845

BARROTT Nicholas *(Per, Tym, Dms)*: 13 Fountayne Street, York YO31 8HN ☎ 01904 627437

BEANE Norman *(Dms)*: 54 Shaw Drive, Scartho, Grimsby, South Humberside DN33 2JB ☎ 01472 873873

BECKETT Simon *(Per)*: Flat 3, 51 Kenwood Park Road, Nether Edge, Sheffield, South Humberside S7 1NE ☎ 0114 250 8070

BEERE Trevor *(Dms)*: 28 Grosvenor Road, Scarborough YO11 2NA

BELL Andrew *(Dms)*: 3 Redhills Terrace, Redhills Lane, Durham City DH1 4AX ☎ 0191 384 6083

BELL Phillip *(Dms)*: 2 Swinhoe Gardens, Woodlands Park, Newcastle-upon-Tyne, Tyne & Wear NE13 6AF ☎ 0307 370209 mob

BIGGIN Peter *(Dms, B Gtr, Kbds)*: 4 Sawnmoor Road, Thurcroft, Rotherham, South Yorkshire S66 9EA ☎ 01709 549207 & fax

BIGGS Brett *(Dms)*: 34 Gawber Road, Barnsley, South Yorkshire S75 2AF ☎ 01226 280202, 04325 366586 pager, 07977 311898 mob

BLACK Barry *(Dms, Tym, Per)*: 20 Elmsleigh Gardens, Cleadon Village, Nr Sunderland, Tyne & Wear SR6 7PR ☎ 0191 536 4748 & fax, 0973 636801 mob

BLANCHARD Richard *(Dms, La Per, Pf, Gtr, Voc)*: 7 Fern Terrace, Stanningley, Leeds, West Yorkshire LS28 6JA ☎ 0113 254868, 0410 614622

BOTTOMLEY Ronald *(Dms)*: 18 Second Avenue, Horbury, Wakefield WF4 6HB ☎ 01924 270760

BRANT Helen *(Per, Pf, Clt)*: 67 Middlesex Street, Barnsley, South Yorkshire S70 4JS ☎ 01226 284005

BRIDGEWATER Paul *(Dms, Bod, Vln)*: 43 West Banks, Sleaford, Lincs NG34 7QB ☎ 01529 304466

BRIGGS Geoffrey *(Dms)*: 63, Rievaulx Way, Guisborough, Cleveland TS14 7AY ☎ 01287 633084

BRINDLEY Francesca *(Per)*: 56 Crambeck Village, Welburn, York YO60 7EZ ☎ 01653 618889

BROADY Andi *(Per)*: Oblivion Studios, 74-76 Dovecot Street, Stockton-on-Tees TS18 1HA ☎ 01642 606969, 01642 608007

BRODERICK Ansell *(Per, Dms, Gtr, Kbds)*: 19 Francis Street, Leeds LS7 4BY

BROOKS William *(Dms)*: 19 Baron Avenue, New Waltham, Grimsby, Lincs DN36 4NF ☎ 01472 815715

BROWN John *(Dms)*: 54 Atkinson Road, Fulwell, Sunderland SR6 9AT ☎ 0191 5483908

BRUMBY James *(Dms)*: 216 Silver Lonnen, Denton Burn, Newcastle-upon-Tyne, Tyne & Wear NE5 2HH ☎ 0191 2748136

BUTLER Matthew *(Per)*: 3 Station Road, Thorpe-on-The-Hill, Lincoln LN6 9BS ☎ 01522 681420, 01522 681420 fax

CANNELLI Tony *(Dms)*: 261 Western Road, Crookes, Sheffield S10 1LE ☎ 0114 2684678

CANTOR Rafi *(Dms)*: 67 Ling Lane, Scarcroft, Leeds LS14 3HY ☎ 0113 2893143

CARR Sam *(Dms)*: 17 Rockley View, Tankersley, Barnsley, Sth Yorks S75 3AN ☎ 01226 744801

CASWELL David *(Dms, Gtr)*: 7 Lingthwaite, Dodworth, Barnsley, South Yorks S75 3TJ ☎ 01226 202165

CHAPMAN Jon *(Dms)*: 115 Park Lane, Darlington, Co. Durham DL1 5AQ ☎ 01325 281277

CHEETHAM Roy *(Dms)*: 1 Broadlands Avenue, Owlthorpe, Sheffield S20 6RL ☎ 0114 2475287

CHIPCHASE Gary *(Dms)*: 17, Baslow Crescent, Dodworth, Barnsley, Yorkshire S75 3SG

CLAISHER Mik *(Dms)*: 6 Tavistock Road, Sheffield, South Yorkshire S7 1GG ☎ 0114 258 3580

CLARK John *(Dms, Per)*: The Rookery, West Ashby, Horncastle, Lincs LN9 5PT ☎ 01507 527867, 0966 464922 mob, 01507 343011

CLAYTON Stephen *(Per)*: 6 Woodleigh, Savile Road, Hebden Bridge, West Yorkshire HX7 6NB ☎ 01422 843008

CLOSE Geoff *(Per, Clt, S Sax)*: 32 Meadow Bank Avenue, Sheffield S7 1PB ☎ 0114 2587509

COCKS Adam *(Per, Pf)*: 2B Kensington Terrace, Hyde Park, Leeds LS6 1BE

COOK Andrew *(Dms, Per)*: 173A Howard Road, Walkley, Sheffield S6 3RU ☎ 0114 281 6742

COOPER David *(Dms)*: 11 Whitfield Road, Fulwood, Sheffield S10 4GJ ☎ 0114 230 6396 & fax

COTTERILL Ian *(Dms, Pf, Kbds)*: 26 Ferndale Road, Leytonstone, London E11 3DN ☎ 020 8539 2757, 0802 413495 mob

CUSACK Graham *(Dms, Per, Voc)*: Flat 4, 49-51 Daventry Street, London NW1 6DT ☎ 020 7723 1914

DANIEL Keith *(Dms)*: 9 Petrie Crescent, Rodley, Leeds LS13 1NT ☎ 0113 299588

DAVIES Martin *(Dms, Per)*: 4 Hollins Mill Lane, Sowerby Bridge, West Yorkshire HX6 2QG ☎ 01422 316439

DEACON Peter *(Dms, Voc)*: 21A Brookfield Road, Headingley, Leeds LS6 4EJ ☎ 0113 2740138

DEAN Michael *(Dms)*: 1 Little Moor, Scarlet Heights, Queensbury, Bradford, W Yorks BD13 1DB

DEARMAN Gerald *(Dms)*: The Jaize, Market Rasen Road, Dunnholme, Lincoln LN2 3QZ ☎ 01673 62488

DENNIS Kelvin *(Dms, Tpt)*: 4 Morville Court, Beckfield Walk, Ingleby Barwick, Stockton-on-Tees TS17 0XY ☎ 01642 769168

DENTON John *(Dms)*: 13 West View, Wrekenton, Gateshead, Tyne & Wear NE9 7UY ☎ 0191 487 4439

DICK Malcolm *(Dms, Per)*: 17 Swanton Close, Meadow Rise, Kenton, Newcastle-upon-Tyne NE5 4SL

DICK Norman *(Dms)*: 38 Bromley Walk, Redhouse Farm, Gosforth, Newcastle-upon-Tyne NE3 2BH ☎ 0191 285 6633, 0973 791941

DIXON Brian *(Dms)*: 29 Hillside Court, Transmere, Birkenhead, Merseyside L41 9EE ☎ 0151 652 1754

DOUGHTY Mark *(Dms, Pf)*: 9 Drifield Road, Beverley, East Yorkshire HU17 7LP ☎ 01482 869646

DRANSFIELD Mark *(Per, Tym)*: Address Unknown ☎ 01274 876696, 0850 847188

EATON Wilfred *(Dms)*: 40 Newbold Back Lane, Brockwell, Chesterfield S40 4HQ ☎ 01246 38100

EDGAR Jack *(Dms, Per, Tpt, Voc)*: 1 Holly Lane, Stainton, Middlesbrough, Cleveland TS8 9AQ ☎ 01642 592005

ELLIOT Colin *(Per, B Gtr, Voc, Kbds)*: 13B Wharncliffe Road, Broomhall, Sheffield S10 2DH ☎ 0114 2700763

ELSEY Eric *(Dms)*: 24 Ayresome Terrace, Leeds LS8 1BH ☎ 0113 2666075

FAIRCLOUGH Peter *(Dms, Per)*: 150 Knowle Lane, Sheffield S11 9SJ ☎ 0114 2364845

FEENEY Andrew *(Dms)*: 27 Sydney Street, Chesterfield S40 1DA ☎ 01246 206673

FERRY Simon *(Dms)*: 43 Main Street, Crawcrook, Gateshead, Tyne & Wear NE40 4TY

FLETCHER Stephen *(Dms, Flt, Pf, Kbds)*: 9 Manor Road, Hurworth Place, Nr Darlington, Co Durham DL2 2HH ☎ 01325 720251, 07971 549447

FORBES Ian *(Dms, Per)*: 27 Montague Street, Lemington, Newcastle-upon-Tyne 5, Tyne & Wear NE15 8RY ☎ 0191 264 8347

FORSTER Peter *(Dms, Per, Tym, Md)*: 12 Harrogate Terrace, Murton, Seaham, Co. Durham SR7 9PQ ☎ 0191 526 8081 & fax, 0589 522032 mob

FRANCIS Paul *(Dms, Per, Pf)*: 16 Chesterton Court, Horbury, Leeds WF4 5QU ☎ 01924 367468, 0973 698041 mob

FRANEY Kevin *(Dms)*: 10 Westerdale, Parkside, Spennymoor, Co Durham DL16 6SD ☎ 01388 815203

FRANKISH Paul *(Per, Kbds, Pf, Dms, Tpt)*: 37 Belgrave Drive, Anlaby High Road, Hull, North Humberside HU4 6DR ☎ 01482 352911

GALE Roy *(Dms)*: 33 Lifford Road, Wheatley, Doncaster DN2 4BY ☎ 01302 365090

GAMMON Aaron *(Per, Dms)*: 51 Bexley Terrace, Leeds, West Yorkshire LS8 5NX

GIBBINSON Walter *(Dms)*: 27 Wakefield Avenue, South Shields, Tyne & Wear NE34 7QN ☎ 0191 4541107

GOODILL Tim *(Dms, Per, Com, Arr)*: 37 Denton Ave, Roundhay, Leeds LS8 1LE ☎ 0973 141735, 0113 269 4337

GOURLAY Ian *(Dms)*: 6 Cortland Road, Bridgehill, Consett, Co Durham DH8 8QD ☎ 01207 591541

GRANT Simon *(Dms)*: The Bungalow, Shooters Lodge, Main Street, Nocton, Lincoln LN4 2BH ☎ 01526 323209, 0589 648483 mob

GREENWOOD Alexander *(Dms, Vib, Voc)*: 54 Granville Terrace, Binchester, Bishop Auckland, Co Durham DL14 8AT ☎ 01388 663 242

GREGORY Rob *(Dms, Voc, Per, Zit, Ob)*: 203 Morninglow Road, Firth Park, Sheffield S5 6SG ☎ 0114 2498206

GRIMES Alan *(Dms, Voc)*: 34 Tyne Road, Stanley, Co Durham DH9 6PY ☎ 01207 234869

GUNSON Laurence *(Per, Tym)*: Holly Cottage, Front St, Naburn, York, N Yorks YO19 4RR ☎ 01904 653920

HAGGER Dale *(Dms)*: 10 Borughton Gardens, Brant Road, Lincoln LN5 8SW ☎ 01522 533327

HALFYARD Paul *(Dms)*: 8 Meadow Close, Reepham, Lincs LN3 4ED ☎ 01522 751214

HALL John *(Dms)*: 37 Moor Lane, N Hykeham, Lincoln LN3 9AE ☎ 01522 692827

HARRIS Irving *(Dms)*: 36 Limesway, Gawber, Barnsley S75 2NR ☎ 01226 241837

HARRISON David *(Dms)*: 427 Newtondale, Sutton Park Estate, Hull, N Humberside HU7 4BW ☎ 01482 835413

HARRISON Kenneth *(Dms)*: 34 Stornaway Square, Spring Cottage, Hull HU8 9LJ ☎ 01482 3793694

HARRISON Kerry *(Dms, Kbds)*: 21 St. Ann's Mount, Leeds LS4 2PH ☎ 0113 274 0712 & fax

HARRISON Norman *(Dms)*: 56 Bendict Road, Hull HU4 7DP ☎ 01482 3643919

HEMPSALL Mr R R *(Dms)*: 2 Brookbank Close, Hall Farm Estate, Sunderland, Tyne & Wear SR3 2UE ☎ 0191 5289877

HENDERSON Albert *(Dms)*: 1 Hamsterley Drive, Crook, Co Durham DL15 9PT ☎ 01388 762227

HESSION Stephen *(Dms)*: 41 Hanover Square, Leeds LS3 1BQ ☎ 0113 2431569

HODGSON G. *(Per)*: 24 Willow Park Drive, Shelf, Halifax, West Yorkshire HX3 7TZ ☎ 01274 670359

HOLMES Stephen *(Dms)*: 12 Sackup Lane, Dzrton, Barnsley S75 5AN ☎ 01226 385675

HOME Matthew *(Dms)*: 18 Consort Terrace, Leeds LS3 1ET ☎ 0113 243 3454

HOWARD Robert *(Dms, Per)*: 9 Golcar Brow Road, Meltham, Huddersfield, West Yorks HD7 3LD ☎ 01484 852788

HUDSON Keith *(Per)*: 70 Cobwell Road, Retford, Notts DN22 7DD ☎ 01777 708075

HUDSON Paul *(Dms, Per)*: 62 Church Road, Low Fell, Gateshead, Tyne & Wear NE9 5RJ ☎ 0191 482 0132

HUMBERSTONE Clive *(Dms, Per, Kbds)*: ☎ 0114 266 8575 & fax

INGHAM Alan *(Dms)*: 82 Eastbourne Avenue, Gateshead, Tyne & Wear NE8 4NH ☎ 0191 422 4422

JACKSON John *(Dms)*: 44 Grange Avenue, Grange Park, Bedlington, Northumberland NE22 7EW ☎ 01670 824531

JAMES Debbie *(Per, Tym)*: 9 Beechwood Row, Leeds LS4 2LY ☎ 0113 2749094

JESSOP Stephen *(Dms)* ☎ 0191 237 5593

JOHNSON David *(Dms)*: 7 Grampian Close, Huntington, York YO32 9RT ☎ 01904 768937

JONES Jed *(Dms, B Gtr, Voc)*: Piuslaan 95, 5643 Pt, Edindhoven, De Netherlands ☎ 01904 654922

KAINE Martyn *(Dms)*: 129 Debeauvoir Road, Islington, London N1 4DL ☎ 020 7254 3717

KAPLAN Stuart *(Dms)*: 8 Dale View, Steeton, Nr Keighley, West Yorkshire BD20 6PN ☎ 01535 657571

KEANE Michael *(Dms)*: 3 Lynmouth Close, Stainton Manor, Middlesbrough, Cleveland TS8 9NH ☎ 01642 286908, 01642 286909

KENNEDY John *(Dms, Voc)*: 77 Southfields, Stanley, Co Durham DH9 7PF ☎ 01207 23 6661

KENNEDY Terry *(Dms)*: 22 Scholey Road, Wickersley, Rotherham S66 0HU ☎ 01709 544684

KIRKLAND David *(Dms, Per)*: 9 Grange Lane, Burghwallis, Doncaster DN6 9JR ☎ 01302 723792

KOHUT Steven *(Dms, Per)*: 2 Church Lane, Dinnington, Sheffield S31 7LY ☎ 01909 565615

LAIDLAW Raymond *(Dms)*: 67 Hotspur Street, Tynemouth, Tyne & Wear NE30 4EL ☎ 0191 297 1806, 0410 596749 mob, 0191 251 331 fax

LAMMING George *(Dms)*: 14 Southfield Avenue, Grimsby, Lincs DN33 2PA ☎ 01472 825852

LANGDALE Barry *(Dms)*: 31 West Chilton Terrace, Chilton, Ferryhill, Co. Durham DL17 0HH ☎ 01388 720424

LAWRENCE David *(Per, Tym)*: 18 Barlby Grove, Linley Heights, Hackenthorpe, Sheffield S12 4NB ☎ 0114 2470300

LEACH Alan *(Dms, Pf)*: 18 Malton Avenue, Heworth, York YO31 7TT

LEE John (*Dms, Per, La Per, Tym, Tnd Pe*): 41, Spoon Hill Road, Sheffield, Yorks S6 5PA ☎ 0114 2348849

LEEMING Sydney (*Dms*): Address Unknown

LEWIS Jak R (*Dms, Gtr, Voc*): 80 Cherrybank Road, Norton Woodseats, Sheffield S8 8RD

LONGSTER George (*Dms, Org*): 9 Vicarage Close, Hunmanby, Filey, N Yorkshire YO14 0NW ☎ 017238 90645

LOWTHER Graeme Eric (Brush) (*Dms*): 7 Stockwith Road, Walkeringham, Doncaster, South Yorks DN10 4JE ☎ 01427 891452

MARKHAM Alan (*Dms*): Address Unknown

MATHARU Inder (*Per, Ind Per, Tabla, Tamp*): 85 Gledhow Park Avenue, Leeds LS7 4JL ☎ 0113 293 8938

MATTHEWS Peter (*Per*): 14 St Stephens Drive, Aston, Sheffield, South Yorkshire S31 0EP ☎ 0114 2873034

MCARTHUR Roy (*Dms*): 150 Chesters Avenue, Longbenton, Newcastle-upon-Tyne 12 NE12 8QE ☎ 0191 266 3603

MCGOVERN Bernard (*Per, Dms, Glck, Xyl*): 1 Quarry Moor Park, Harrogate Road, Ripon, North Yorkshire HG4 3AQ ☎ 01765 690258

MCGOWAN Craig (*Dms, Kbds*): 39 East-Park Road, Leeds LS9 9JD

MCGRATH Paul (*Dms*): Ramblers, Holford, Bridgwater, Somerset TA5 1RY

MCNAMARA Rodney (*Dms*): 74 Greenwood Mount, Meanwood, Leeds LS6 4LG ☎ 01832 741108

MEKKAOUI Abdellatif (*Dms, Per, Voc*): 37 Aldrich Road, Cleethorpes, South Humberside DN35 0DP ☎ 01472 696530

MORRELL Dane (*Dms, Cong*): 1 The Shopping Centre, Garden Village, Hull HU8 8QE ☎ 26193 20279

MURRAY Donald (*Dms*): 69 Lambath Road, Hull, Yorks HU8 0EZ ☎ 01482 375628

MYERS Geoff (*Dms*): 7 Park View Terrace, Primrose Lane, Halton, Leeds LS15 7QT ☎ 0113 2643785

NAYLOR Leslie (*Dms*): 334 Ings Road, Hull HU8 0NA ☎ 01482 3702250

NELSON Robert (*Dms, Per*): Croft House, Cornriggs, Cowshill, Upper Weardale, Co Durham DL13 1AF ☎ 01388 537215

NETTLETON David (*Per*): 14 Carlyle Street, Mexborough, South Yorkshire S64 9DE ☎ 01709 581770

O'CONNOR Tony (*Dms*): 107 West Garth, Cayton, Nr Scarborough, Yorks YO11 3SG ☎ 01723 582641

O'NEILL Kevin (*Dms*): Flat 1, 61 Yarm Lane, Stockton, Cleveland County TS18 3DX ☎ 01642 616528

ORTON Ross (*Dms*): Middle Flat, 3 Priory Place, Netheredge, Sheffield S7 1LS ☎ 0114 250 9395

PATRICK Maxwell (*Dms, Kbds, Gtr*): 107 Castleton Road, Hope Nr Sheffield S30 2RD ☎ 01433 621315

PATTERSON Shirley (*Per, Voc*): 14 St Andrews Avenue, Scunthorpe, South Humberside DN17 2RQ ☎ 01724 866487

PAYNE Ray (*Per, Tym, Tbn*): 89 Edge Junction, Thornhill, Dewsbury, West Yorkshire WF13 ☎ 01924 469360

PEASE Nigel (*Per, Dms*): 74 Queens Drive, Barnsley, S Yorks S75 2QE ☎ 01226 205770

PERRY John (*Dms*): 57 Poplar Road, Cleethorpes, Lincs DN35 8BH ☎ 01472 699463

PIKE Jonathan (*Dms, Pf, Gtr, B Gtr*): 7 Broomhill Avenue, Moortown, Leeds, West Yorkshire LS17 6JS ☎ 0113 689558

PILSBURY Brian (*Dms, La Per*): Flat 3, 43 Garfield Road, Scarborough, North Yorks YO12 7LJ ☎ 01723 375007

PINNELL Steve (*Dms, Per*): Valderrama, 17 Castlereagh, Wynard Park, Billingham, Co. Cleveland TS22 5QF ☎ 01740 644556

PLATTS Mark (*Dms, Per, Kbds*): Address Unknown ☎ 0113 244 0004, 0113 242 8080

PRENDERGAST Christopher (*Dms, Gtr, Kbds*): The Limes, Church Hill, Easingwood, York, North Yorkshire YO6 3JU ☎ 01347 821672, 01904 623680

PRIESTLEY James (*Dms, Gtr*): 31 Toyne Street, Sheffield S10 1HH

PRINGLE Gev (*Dms*): 28 Cotswold Gardens, High Heaton, Newcastle-upon-Tyne, Tyne & Wear NE7 7AE ☎ 0191 281 9301

RAMSKILL Keith (*Dms, Per*): 33 Farrar Street, Barnsley, South Yorks S70 6BT ☎ 01226 289075

RAWLING Dene (*Dms, Gtr, Kbds*): 251 Granville Road, Sheffield S2 2RP ☎ 0114 273 7711 & fax

RICHARD Barrie (*Dms*): 39 Linga Lane, Bassingham, Lincolnshire LN5 9LD ☎ 01522 788355

ROBERTS Tom (*Dms*): 4 Lancaster Park Road, Harrogate, North Yorkshire HG2 5SW ☎ 01423 884517

ROBERTSON Iain (*Dms, Pf, Cnt*): 63 Northcote Street, South Shields, Tyne & Wear NE33 4DJ ☎ 0191 423 1693

ROBERTSON Mark A (*Dms*): 57 Front Street, East Boldon, Tyne & Wear NE36 0SD ☎ 0191 519 4742

ROBINSON James (*Dms*): 17 St Johns Grove, Wakefield, W Yorks WF1 3SA ☎ 01924 362375, 0403 188167

ROBSON Frederick (*Dms, Voc*): 54 Pendrill Street, Beverley Road, Hull HU3 1UU ☎ 01482 3212910

SALES Dominic (*Per*): 17 Chesterton Drive, Honley, Huddersfield, West Yorkshire HD7 2EW ☎ 01484 663733, 0976 954807

SANDBACH Stanley (*Per*): 15 Silverwood Avenue, Filey, North Yorks YO14 0DN ☎ 01723 513433

SANDERSON Douglas (*Dms, Voc*): 27 Dornoch Crescent, High Ridge Estate, Windy Nook, Gateshead, Tyne & Wear NE10 9BA ☎ 0191 469 4281

SCRIVEN Tony (*Dms*): Central Hotel, 35-47 New Briggate, Leeds LS2 8JD ☎ 0113 2941 456, 0113 2941 551

SELLERS Cyril (*Dms*): 114 Boothferry Road, Hessle HU13 9AX ☎ 01482 3640182

SHEPARD John (*Dms, Per*): 18 Newton Garth, Leeds LS7 4JZ ☎ 0113 262 9685, 0113 262 9685

SHEPHERDSON Paul (*Dms*): 73 The Wolds, Castle Park, Cottingham, Hull HU16 5LQ ☎ 01482 3849140

SKILBECK Ben (*Dms, Pf, Kbds, Gtr*): 2 Rosehill, Kellfield, Low Fell, Gateshead, Tyne &Wear NE8 5XU ☎ 0191 420 1300, 0161 257 6165

SMITH Carl (*Dms, Per*)

SMITH Keith (*Dms, Per*): 14 Mitford Drive, Chase Park, Sherburn, Durham DH6 1QS ☎ 0191 372 0749, 0191 372 2173

SMITH Paul (*Dms, Per*): 28 Rudston Avenue, Wolviston Court Estate, Billingham, Cleveland TS22 5BN ☎ 01642 559685

SMITH Paul (*Dms, Per*): Netherwood, 50, Thorn Lane, Roundhay, Leeds LS8 1NF ☎ 0113 2689300

SOMERVILE Colin (*Dms, Gtr, B Gtr*): 3 Simonburn, Oxclose, Washington, Tyne & Wear NE38 0NJ ☎ 0191 417 8940

SOULSBY Peter (*Dms*): 16 Cheldon Close, Whitley Bay, Tyne & Wear NE25 9XS ☎ 0191 251 5167, 0191 259 6707

SPENCER Peter (*Dms, Gtr*): 8 Southway, Tranmere Park, Guiseley, Leeds LS20 8HX ☎ 01943 872889, 0370 994561 mob, 01943 870047 fax

SPENCER Thomas (*Dms*): 15 Cranbourne Street, Off Wellington Lane, Hull HU3 1PP ☎ 01482 214610, 01262 400919 mob

STEAD David (*Dms*): c/o P Cass/Beautiful South, Cavendish House, St Andrews Court, St Andrews Street, Leeds LS3 1JY ☎ 0113 243 0898, 0113 234 0698

STEPHENSON Robert (*Dms, Tym, La Per*): 64 Barras Avenue West, Blyth, Northumberland NE24 3LR ☎ 01670 366297, 0374 466253 mob

STORES Jeff (*Dms*): Lowland Cottage, Newcastle Road, Sunderland SR5 1RP ☎ 0191 536 9766

STUTT Keith (*Per*): Melody Cottage, South Glebe, Lockington YO25 9ST ☎ 01430 810272

SWITALSKI Stephen (*Dms*): 14 Oxford Road, St. John'S, Wakefield, W. Yorkshire WF1 3LB ☎ 01924 386388, 0802 196213 mob, 01924 290333

SYKES Christopher (*Per*): 1B Foster Avenue, Crossland Moor, Huddersfield HD4 5LN ☎ 01484 654038

TAYLOR John (*Dms*): 222 Hawthorns Way, Shelley, Huddersfield HD8 8PZ ☎ 01484 606034

THEAKER Norman (*Dms*): Address Unknown

THOMAS Neil (*Dms, Per*): 5 Parracombe Close, Ingleby Barwick, Stockton-on-Tees, Cleveland TS17 0NY ☎ 01642 751066

THOMPSON Jeffrey (*Dms*): 4 Richmond Hill House, Stradbroke Road, Sheffield S13 8LR ☎ 265 1531

TILBROOK Adrian (*Dms*): 9 Dunbar Drive, Eaglescliffe, Stockton-on-Tees, Cleveland TS16 9EG ☎ 01325 480807

TILSED John (*Dms*): 76 Jubilee Road, Wheatley, Doncaster DN1 2UD ☎ 01302 325134

TOKO (*Dms, Kbds*): 23 Grosvenor Square, Sheffield S2 4NS ☎ 0114 221 4981, 07771 594062, 0114 221 4981

TUCKLEY D (*Dms*): Queens Court, 5 Queens Terrace, Scarborough, North Yorkshire Y012 7HR ☎ 01723 368665

TULLOCH David (*Dms, Tym, Per*): Grove Lodge, Iron Works Road, Tow Law, Co. Durham DL13 4AJ ☎ 01388 731165

TURBULL W (*Dms*): Bryan Lodge, Station Road, Upper Poppleton, York YO26 6PX ☎ 01904 795263

TURNBULL Gordon (*Dms*): 10 Highmoor, Kirkhill, Morpeth, Northumberland NE61 2AL

VICKERS Timothy (*Dms*): 15 Greenwood Mount, Meanwood, Leeds LS6 4LG ☎ 0113 2754417

VINCENT-SMITH Robin (*Per*): 265 School Road, Crookes, Sheffield S10 1GQ ☎ 0114 266 8672

WADE Ashley (*Dms*): 6 Sunningdale Green, Darlington, Co Durham DL1 3SB ☎ 01325 355959

WAKE Martin (*Per, Pf, Gtr, Org*): Lilford House, 18 Main Street, Witton Park, Bishop Auckland, County Durham DL14 0DX ☎ 01388 606411, 07288 674409

WALKER James (*Dms*): 32 Fairisle, Ouston, Chester Le Street, Co Durham DH2 1JT ☎ 0191 410 2817

WARD Jonathan (*Dms, Per, Af Dms, Pf*): 12 Harrison Street, Heworth, York YO31 1DG ☎ 01904 421511

WATTON Gary (*Dms, Tnd Per*): 40 Park Hill, Bradley, Huddersfield, West Yorks HD2 1QG ☎ 01484 559608, 0973 336532 mob

WELFORD Steven (*Dms*): Victoria House, Wrelton, Nr Pickering, Yorks YO18 8PG ☎ 01751 72169

WHIELDON Lee (*Dms, Per*): 65 The Garth, Coulby Newham, Middlesbrough TS8 0UG ☎ 01642 597813

WHITAKER Hugh (*Dms, Voc, Gtr, Kbds*): c/o Bayou Gumbo, 25 Hamilton Terrace, Otley, W. Yorkshire LS21 1AN ☎ 01943 465436, 01943 851157

WHITE Alan (*Dms*): 10 Durham Road, Ferryhill, Co. Durham DL17 8LD ☎ 01740 651909

WHITE David (*Dms, Kbds, Org, Pf*): 35 Wigfield Drive, Ward Green, Barnsley, South Yorkshire S70 5JE ☎ 01226 204256

WILKINSON David (*Dms*): c/o 7 Witton Drive, The Grange Estate, Spennymoor, Co.Durham DL16 6LU ☎ 0850 245747

WILKS Joe (*Dms*): 27 Stonebridgegate, Ripon, North Yorkshire HG4 1LH ☎ 01765 601179

WILSON Anthony (*Per, Gtr*): 55 Windsor Crescent, Ovingham, Northumberland NE42 6AS ☎ 01661 830035

WILSON Michael (*Dms*): 2 Waydale Close, Kirkby Moorside, York YO6 6ET ☎ 01751 432368

WOODWARD Daniel (*Dms, Per, Kbds*): 16 Rombalds Place, Armley, Leeds, West Yorkshire LS12 2BD ☎ 0113 263 4690

WOODWARD Malcolm (*Dms, Per*): 28 Armley Ridge Road, Leeds LS12 3NP ☎ 0113 2790989

WOOTTON Barry (*Dms*): 7 Clifton Court, Fieldside Thorne, Doncaster, S Yorks DN8 4BH ☎ 01405 812070

WRIGHT J (*Dms*): 191 Woodhall Way, Beverley, North Humberside HU17 7JU ☎ 01482 3867109

YATES Alan (*Dms*): Leaside, Frosterley, Bishop Auckland, Co. Durham DL13 2RH

YEATS Alexander (*Dms, Per*): 21 Kensington Terrace, Headingley, Leeds LS6 1BE ☎ 0113 2742936

EAST

AIRZEE Robert (*Dms*): 6 Cotman Road, Prettygate, Colchester, Essex CO3 4QJ ☎ 01206 540325

ALLEN Freddie (*Dms*): 29 Carvers Croft, Woolmer Green, Knebworth, Herts SG3 6LX ☎ 01438 816438

ALMOND David (*Dms*): 16 Coombe Road, Bushey, Herts WD2 3SP ☎ 020 8386 1065

ARNOLD Leslie (*Dms*): 43 Windermere Crescent, Limbury, Luton, Beds LU3 2PR ☎ 01582 582207

BADHAM Tony (*Dms*): 51 Halleys Ridge, Hertford, Herts SG14 2TH ☎ 0199 258 2379

BALCON Terence (*Dms*): 15 Three Mile Lane, Costessey, Norwich NR5 0RR ☎ 01603 742968

BALDWIN Graham (*Dms, Per*): 9 Cedars Way, Newport Pagnell, Bucks MK16 0DR ☎ 01908 616298

BANNIGAN Jerome (*Dms*): 37 Cockle Way, Shenhey Radlett, Herts WD7 9JT ☎ 01923 854294

BARLOW Peter (*Dms*): 30 Boxted Road, Hemel Hempstead, Herts HP1 2QH ☎ 01442 251148

BARNES Harry (*Dms, Dms*): Address Unknown

BATTING Roger (*Dms, Per*): 15 West Close, Alconbury Weston, Huntingdon, Cambs PE17 5JT ☎ 01480 891369, 0410 547131

BAXTER Alan (*Dms*): 4 Rothmans Avenue, Chelmsford, Essex CM2 9UE ☎ 01245 476187, 01245 471544

BEAMENT Stephen (*Per, Dms, Kbds, Pf*): 52 Hookfield, Harlow, Essex CM18 6QQ ☎ 01279 304606

BENBROOK Matthew (*Dms, Gtr, Kbds*): 11 Wincoat Drive, South Benfleet, Essex SS7 5AH ☎ 01268 756340

BENNETT Roland (*Dms*): 242 Shephall Way, Stevenage, Herts SG2 9RE ☎ 01438 740163

BLAIN J (*Dms*): 26 Warwick Road, Luton LU4 8BH

BOUCHER Alex (*Dms, La Per*): 1 Queen's Close, Stansted, Essex CM24 8EJ ☎ 01279 815126, 01279 816662

BOWDEN Colin (*Dms*): Brook House, Cherry Tree Lane, Debenham, Suffolk IP14 6QT ☎ 01728 860286

BRADY Colin (*Dms*): 46B St Benedicts Street, Norwich NR2 4AQ ☎ 01603 665929

BRIGHT Martin (*Per*): 18 Church Street, Whittlesey, Cambs PE7 1DB ☎ 01733 204616

BROUGHTON Tim (*Dms, Per*): 27 North Street, Maldon, Essex CM9 5HH ☎ 01621 841 756

BUCK Dennis (*Dms*): 69 Middletons Lane, Hellesdon, Norwich NR6 5NS ☎ 01603 429983

BUCK Stephen (*Dms*): 4 Wood Road, Heybridge, Maldon, Essex CM9 7AS

BUCKINGHAM Bryan (*Dms*): 29, Beverley Gardens, Jersey Farm, St. Albans, Herts AL4 9BJ ☎ 01727 837555

BUDGE William (*Dms*): 28 Taywood Close, Stevenage, Hertfordshire SG2 9QP ☎ 01438 312718

BUNKER Clive (*Dms*): 24 Mardle Road, Linslade, Leighton Buzzard, Beds LU7 7UT ☎ 01525 373731

BURNETT Barbara (*Dms, B Gtr, Gtr*): 44 Harcourt Avenue, Southend-on-Sea, Essex SS2 6HU ☎ 01702 354191

BUTTERS John (*Dms, Per*): Bamburgh House, Mill Road, Battisford, Nr Stowmarket IP14 2LJ ☎ 01449 774706

CECIL Marc (*Dms, La Per*): 118 Rectory Road, Hadleigh, SS7 2NQ ☎ 01702 557975, 07957 288076

CLARKE Alan (*Dms*): 32 Cranleigh Road, Leigh-on-Sea, Essex SS9 1SY ☎ 01702 715835

CLAYTON Eddy (*Dms, La Per, Md*): 3 Goodwood Avenue, Watford, Herts WD2 5LA ☎ 01923 236616, 0831 353384

CODLING Paul (*Dms*): 3 Highview Avenue, Great Clacton, Clacton-on-Sea, Essex CO15 4DY ☎ 01255 436470

COOPER Thomas (*Dms*): 45 Belvoir Road, Cambridge CB4 1JH

CORBYN Michael (*Dms*): Benvenuto, Coltishall Road, Tunstead, Norfolk NR12 8QZ

CULHAM Graeme (*Dms*): 12 Linton Road, Shoeburyness, Essex SS3 9HY ☎ 01702 299389

DARKING Paul (*Dms*): 4 Vinery Road, Cambridge CB1 3DP ☎ 0122 357 3125

DE SILVA Kenneth (*Dms, Db, B Gtr, Voc*): 25 Coombe Drive, Dunstable, Beds LU6 2AE ☎ 01582 668611

DE-OLIVEIRA Bosco (*Per*): 58 Rosemary Avenue, London N3 2QN

DENHAM James (*Dms*): 12 Pig Lane, St Ives, Cambs PE17 4QE ☎ 07887 704342, 01480 462101

DI PALMA Phillip (*Dms, Per*): 69 York Street, Norwich, Norfolk NR2 2AW ☎ 01603 632189

DONALDSON Andrew *(Per)*: 36 Adams Well, Edinburgh EH13 0FF ☎ 0131 441 6033

DOWDING Andrew *(Dms, Per)*: 80 Conies Road, Halstead, Essex CO9 1BD ☎ 01787 472603

DRAPEAU Mark *(Dms, Per)*: 36 Hunters Way, Welwyn Garden City, Herts AL7 4NP ☎ 01707 333539, 01707 325111

DRAY Richard *(Dms)*: 121 Downhall Park Way, Rayleigh, Essex SS6 9QZ ☎ 01268 781700

DREW James *(Dms, Per, Pf)*: 8 Summerlands Road, Marshalswick, St. Albans, Herts AL4 9XB ☎ 01727 830162, 01426 149075 pager

DUTTON Mark *(Dms)*: 36 The Walk, Eight Ash Green, Colchester, Essex CO6 3QG ☎ 01206 544438, 01206 544448

EDGSON Roger *(Dms)*: 129 Handside Lane, Welwyn Gdn City, Herts AL8 6TA

ELGOOD Jack *(Dms, Gtr, Voc)*: 42 Swanstand, Jackmans Estate, Letchworth, Herts SG6 2QN ☎ 01462 676709

EVANS Christophe *(Dms, Pf, Tnd Per)*: Homewood Farm Lane, Loudwater, Rickmansworth, Herts WD3 9JX ☎ 01923 774436

FORDE Jermain *(Dms, Pf, B Gtr, Per)*: 35 The Court Way, Carpenders Park, Watford, Herts WD1 5DP ☎ 020 8386 8900, 0958 742974

FORSEY David *(Dms)*: 19 Adams Close, Ampthill, Beds MK45 2UB

FRANCIS Paul *(Dms)*: Orchard Bungalow, London Road, Great Horkesley, Colchester Essex CO4 4DA ☎ 01206 271634

GIBSON Mark *(Dms, Per, Tnd Per)*: 16 Station Road, Rayleigh, Essex SS6 7HL ☎ 01268 770633, 0831 205539

GIBSON Pearl *(Per)*: 378 Spring Road, Ipswich IP4 5NE ☎ 01473 441813

GILLINGS Gerry *(Dms)*: 10 Stradbroke Road, Ipswich IP4 4LS ☎ 01473 274036

GOODMAN Toby *(Dms, La Per, Pf)*: 117 Sandpit Lane, St Albans, Herts AL4 0BP ☎ 01727 760932, 01727 765183

HAILEY Raymond Kenneth *(Dms)*: 1 Prested Hall, Farm Cotts, London Road, Feering Essex CO5 9EQ ☎ 01376 571467

HALSEY John *(Dms, Gtr, Voc)*: Pump House, Half Moon Lane, Redgrave, Suffolk IP22 1RX ☎ 01379 890488

HAMPER Stephen *(Dms)*: 66 North Western Avenue, Garston, Watford WD2 6AE ☎ 01923 680754

HARDING Stan *(Dms, Voc)*: 9 Lilford Road, Billericay, Essex CM11 1BS ☎ 01277 655850

HARDY Neil *(Dms)*: 1 Market Hill, Halstead, Essex CO9 2AR ☎ 01787 477222

HARRIS Kevin *(Dms)*: 510 Main Road, Dovercourt, Harwich, Essex CO12 4HH ☎ 01255 508703

HERCULES Carlos *(Dms)*: 73 Ketton Cloe, Luton, Beds LU2 0RQ ☎ 01582 658385, 0958 387734

HEWITT Andy *(Dms)*: 7 Arden Close, St Johns, Colchester, Essex CO4 4JP ☎ 01206 502328

HOCKRIDGE David *(Dms)*: The White Cottage, 22 Thorpe Avenue, Peterborough, Cambs PE3 6LA ☎ 01733 554635

HOGGER John *(Dms)*: 2 Wellington Gardens, Spring Road, Ipswich, Suffolk IP4 5LX ☎ 01473 728146 & fax

HOLLINGWORTH Jane *(Dms, Per)*: 36 Fison Road, Cambridge CB5 8TL ☎ 01223 292977

HOWELL Richard *(Dms)*: 75 Oliver Street, Ampthill, Beds MK45 2SA ☎ 01525 404192

HUBBARD Richard *(Per, Dms, Kbds)*: Ennerdale Cottage, 16 Straight Road, Lexden, Colchester, Essex CO3 5BT ☎ 01206 564216

HUMBLES Paul *(Dms)*: 32 Dammersey Close, Markyate, Herts AL3 8JS ☎ 01582 842370

HUNT Richard *(Dms)*: Higham Park Farmhouse, Higham Park Road, Rushden, Northants NN10 0SL ☎ 01933 55143

HYNES Steven *(Dms)*: 76 Winstanley Road, Saffron Walden, Essex CB11 3EX ☎ 01799 501025

JACKSON Robert *(Dms)*: 7 The Chase, Pinchbeck, Spalding, Lincs PE11 3RS ☎ 01775 768863

JARVIS Margaret *(Dms, Per)*: 2 Hoo Wood Cottage, Hoo Nr Woodbridge, Suffolk IP13 7QR ☎ 01473 690699, 01473 737167

JOHNSON Stephen *(Dms)*: 3 Lammas Way, Ampthill, Beds MK45 2TR ☎ 01525 404110

JONES Barry *(Dms, Per, Voc, Gtr, Man)*: Shimpling Place, Burston Road, Shimpling, Norfolk IP21 4UB ☎ 01379 740 461

KERRIDGE Rowland *(Dms, Per)*: 353 Luton Road, Harpenden, Herts AL5 3LZ ☎ 0158 27 61040

LANGSTON Chas *(Dms, Per, B Gtr, Rh Gtr, Voc)*: 99 Francis Way, Silver End, Witham, Essex CM8 3QU ☎ 01376 583459

LARCOMBE David *(Per)*: 30 Ainsworth Street, Cambridge CB1 2PD ☎ 01223 565719

LELLIOTT Raymond *(Dms)*: 65 Brookes Road, Flitwick, Beds MK45 1BY ☎ 01525 716229

LEZ *(Dms, Gtr, A Sax)*: 24 Oak Road, Bedford MK42 0HJ ☎ 01234 341202

LONG Richard *(Dms)*: 98 Harwich Road, Little Clacton, Clacton-on-Sea, Essex CO16 9NJ ☎ 01255 861903

LONG William *(Dms)*: 8 Newlands Park, Bedmond Road, Bedmond, Herts WD5 0RR ☎ 01923 268175

LOUISE Janel *(Dms, Per)*: 12 Richard Hicks Drive, Oakley Manor, Scarning, Dereham NR19 2TN ☎ 01362 694817

LOVE Kate *(Per, Flt, Cnt, Pf)*: 457 Main Road, Dovercourt, Essex CO12 4HB ☎ 01255 507365

LUSK Susan *(Dms, Kbds)*: 36 Pembury Road, Westcliffe-on-Sea, Essex SS0 8DS ☎ 01702 335258

MACLAUGHLAN Glenn *(Dms)*: 1 Polehanger Lane, Hemel Hempstead, Herts HP1 3PT ☎ 01442 216723 & fax

MAITLAND Chris *(Dms, Voc)*: 3 Long Stanton Road, Oakington, Cambs CB4 5AB ☎ 01223 234161, 0421 497112

MAJOR Lee *(Dms)*: 16 Bartles Hollow, Ketton, Stamford, Lincs PE9 3SF ☎ 01780 721046

MARCHANT Chris *(Dms)*: 161 London Road, Stanford Rivers, Nr Ongar, Essex CM5 9QB ☎ 01708 688 392

MASQUERADE *(Dms, Per)*: 24 Devonshire Close, Sawtry, Huntingdon PE17 5SG ☎ 01487 831287, 0585 579686, 01480 411089

MATHEWS Merlin *(Dms, Per)*: 39 Mawson Road, Cambridge CB3 9JD ☎ 07970 644515, 01223 368579

MAYNE David Charles *(Dms)*: 3 Long Court, Mardyke Park, Purfleet, Essex RM19 1GA ☎ 01708 862216, 0860 383373

MCKENZIE Matthew *(Dms, Gtr, Pf, Sax)*: Orchard Barn, The Street, Thorpe Abbotts, Diss, Norfolk IP21 4JB ☎ 01379 668030

MERCEL Dave The Fly *(Dms)*: 120 Langdale Road, Dunstable, Beds LU6 3BT ☎ 01582 608222

MILWAY Ben *(Dms)*: Northfidge, The Avenue, Ampthill, Bedfordshire MK45 2NR ☎ 01325 840850

MORGAN Charles *(Dms)*: c/o 49 Cedar Road, Berkhamsted, Herts HP4 2LB ☎ 01442 877 260, 0973 407383

MOULDING Kenneth *(Dms)*: 6 Kirkdale Court, Pakefield, Lowestoft, Suffolk NR33 0JX ☎ 01502 564899

NASH Clive *(Dms)*: 26 The Risdens, Harlow, Essex CM18 7NH ☎ 020 8597 2337, 0831 164939 mob

NEAL Alexander *(Per, Tym, Pf, Tpt)*: 77 King Harold Road, Colchester, Essex CO3 4SF ☎ 01206 571861

NEATE Robert *(Dms)*: 25 High Street, Stanstead Abbotts, Herts SG12 8AS ☎ 01920 877366

NICKLIN Edward *(Dms)*: 9 Brett Avenue, Gorleston-on-Sea, Norfolk NR31 6HE ☎ 01493 668878

NOBES Roger *(Per, Dms, Vib, Pf, Md)*: 41 Manton Road, Hitchin, Herts SG4 9NP ☎ 01462 436816

OLDHAM Ronald *(Dms)*: 46 Belswains Lane, Hemel Hempstead, Hertfordshire HP3 9PW ☎ 01442 253180

PARKER Paul *(Per)*: 4 Dukes Court, Kings Road, Flitwick, Beds MK45 1UP ☎ 01525 713690

PAWLEY Raymond *(Per, Dms)*: ☎ 01206 851668, 0585 293352 mob

PERKINS Mark *(Dms, Voc)*: Parklands Flat 4, 30 Fonnereau Road, Ipswich, Suffolk IP1 3JP ☎ 01473 213921

PETTERS John *(Dms)*: Rose Cottage, Hannath Road, Tyddgote, Wisbech, Cambs PE13 5NA ☎ 01945 420673

PHELPS John *(Dms)*: The Old Rectory, North Creake, Fakenham, Norfolk NR21 9JJ

PILGRAM Brian *(Dms)*: 6 Church Lane, Bradwell, Gt Yarmouth, Norfolk NR31 8QW ☎ 01493 664784

PORTER Joseph *(Dms, Voc)*: Blyth Power, PO Box 255, Harrogate HG1 5ZL ☎ 0831 222098

POSTON Alan *(Dms)*: 19 Church Road, Harold Park, Romford, Essex RM3 0JX ☎ 01708 342095

RANSON Misty *(Dms)*: 41 Stanley Avenue, St Albans, Hertfordshire AL2 3AA ☎ 01727 868644

REYLAND Trevor *(Dms, Per)*: 5 Boleyn Way, Boreham, Chelmsford, Essex CM3 3JJ ☎ 01245 469720

RICE Ian *(Dms, Voc)*: 16 Francis Close, Station Road, Tiptree, Colchester CO5 0BT ☎ 01621 817320

RICHARDSON Clive *(Dms, Per, Gtr, Kbds)*: 15 Victoria Street, Fleixstowe, Suffolk IP11 7EW ☎ 01394 283825, 0410 237865

RICHARDSON Gavin *(Dms, Per, Voc, Gtr)*: 123 Durban Road West, Watford, Hertfordshire WD1 7DT ☎ 01923 467637

RISDON Damian *(Dms)*: Red Lodge, Golf Lane, Aldeburgh, Suffolk IP15 5PY ☎ 01728 452385

ROBERTS Penny *(Per, Pf)*: One West Lodge, Park Road, Tring, Hertfordshire HP23 6BU ☎ 01442 891678

ROBINSON Stephen *(Dms)*: 15 Burlington Gardens, Hadleigh, Essex SS7 2JJ ☎ 01702 559946

ROBINSON Tom D *(Dms, Voc, Gtr)*: 1 Hales Aimshouses, Lower Somerton, Hartest, Suffolk IP29 4NF ☎ 01284 789600

ROGERS Martin *(Dms)*: 170 Rushton Grove, Church Langley, Harlow, Essex CM17 9PT ☎ 01279 629105

ROGERS Paul *(Dms)*: 71 Coronation Avenue, Whittlesey, Peterborough, Cambs PE7 1XD ☎ 01733 755318, 020 7918 9510

ROLLINS Keith *(Dms, Per, Voc)*: 27 Warren Crescent, East Preston, Littlehampton, West Sussex BN16 1BJ

RUSHMORE Michael *(Dms, B Gtr, Gtr)*: Address Unknown ☎ 01473 270989

RUTTLEY Edward *(Dms, Per, Gtr, B Gtr)*: Chris-Wyn, The Raceground, Spalding, Lincs PE11 3AP ☎ 01775 711078

SAN REMO Steevi *(Dms, Per)*: 32 Havenside, Little Wakering, Essex SS3 0JT ☎ 01702 218783

SAVAGE Nigel *(Dms, Bod, Per)*: 3 Linton Road, Balsham, Cambridge CB1 6HA ☎ 01223 893085

SCOTT Anthony *(Dms)*: 34 Lee Close, Cottenham, Cambridge CB4 4AG ☎ 01954 250661

SEYMOUR Matthew *(Dms)*: 24 Holcombe Crescent, Ipswich, Suffolk IP2 9QL ☎ 01473 414045

SHURLOCK John *(Dms, Voc)*: 29 King Harold Road, Colchester, Essex CO3 4SB ☎ 01206 540339

SINDEN Toby *(Dms)*: 6 Carrington Avenue, Boreham, Herts WD6 2HA ☎ 020 8953 1625

SIVIER William *(Per, Tym, Dms)*: 27 Thistle Green, Swavesey, Cambridge CB4 5RJ ☎ 01954 231113, 0370 970355 mob, 01954 201529

SOMERVILLE Robert *(Dms)* ☎ 01702 353656

SOUTH Brian *(Dms, Gtr, Voc)*: 70 Broome Grove, Wivenhoe, Colchester, Essex CO7 9QT ☎ 01206 824816

SOUTHERDEN BA, HONS John *(Dms, B Gtr, E Gtr, Kbds)*: Elcon, 497 Beehive Lane, Galleywood, Chelmsford, Essex CM2 8RL ☎ 01245 250570, 01226 388183

SOUTHGATE James *(Dms, Gtr, Kbds)*: 127 Butt Road, Colchester, Essex CO3 3DP ☎ 01206 764261

SPARKES Anne *(Per, Rec)*: 74 Cavendish Road, Cambridge CB1 3AF ☎ 01223 512300

STANTON Stan *(Dms)*: Mapleton, Berrister Place, Raunds, Wellingborough, Northamptonshire NN9 6JN ☎ 01933 626577

STAPLETON Ian *(Dms, Gtr, Voc, Kbds)*: 6 Mill Road, Stilton, Peterborough PE7 3XY ☎ 01733 243917

STEPHENSON Steve *(Dms)*: 61 Edinburgh Road, Newmarket, Suffolk CB8 0QD ☎ 01638 602371

SUGDEN Benjamin *(Per, Com)*: The Cottage, 167 Abbots Road, Abbots Langley, Herts WD5 0BN ☎ 01923 264386

SUGDEN Mark *(Dms, Tpt)*: Sears Barn, Pednor Road, Chesham, Bucks HP5 2SS ☎ 01494 782228

SWEETLAND David *(Dms)*: 54 Chilburn Road, Clacton-on-Sea, Essex CO15 4NX ☎ 01255 429693

TABERNER John *(Dms)*: 39 Silk Mill Rd, Oxhey, Watford, Herts WD1 4JW ☎ 01923 232246

TAFARO Michael *(Dms, Kbds, Pf, Per)*: 39 Cambridge Road, St Albans, Herts AL1 5LD ☎ 01727 835887, 01727 813228

THOMPSON Chris *(Dms, Gtr)*: 73 Miswell Lane, Tring, Herts HP23 4DR ☎ 01442 891325

THORBORN Ian *(Dms)*: 16 White Lodge Close, Kempston, Bedford MK42 7ED ☎ 01234 302919

TRACEY Clark *(Dms)*: 8 Oliver Road, Bennetts End, Hemel Hempstead, Hertfordshire HP3 3PY ☎ 01442 243835, 0421 324491 mob

TURNER Colin *(Dms, Per)*: Harwin, 43 Peartree Lane, Danbury, Essex CM3 4LS ☎ 01245 223778

TURNER Ian *(Dms, Pf, Kbds, Gtr)*: 9 Ramsey Road, Ely, Cambridge CB7 4RL ☎ 01353 668739

TYLER Barry *(Dms, Per, W Bd, Spoons)*: 9/11 Market Hill, Saffron Walden, Essex CB10 1HQ ☎ 01799 522766

VINCENT Terry *(Dms)*: 22 Windridge Close, St Albans, Hertfordshire AL3 4JP ☎ 01727 862727

VIRLEY Keith *(Dms)*: 18 Wicklow Road, Ipswich IP1 5NQ ☎ 01473 745905

WAITE Bill *(Dms)*: 56 Woodhouse Lane, East Ardsley, Wakefield, W Yorkshire WF3 2LE ☎ 01924 870340

WALKDEN Michael *(Dms, Flt)*: 59 Pearse Way, Warren Heath, Ipswich IP3 8TF ☎ 01473 710132

WALSH Richard *(Dms)*: 63 Broadacres, Hatfield, Herts AL10 9LE ☎ 017072 68036

WATERS Michael *(Dms)*: Dalmeny House, 2 The Boulevard, Sheringham, Norfolk NR26 8LH ☎ 01263 822932

WELLS Frederick *(Dms)*: 27 Nappsbury Road, Luton, Bedfordshire LU4 9AL ☎ 01582 591824

WEST Ronald *(Dms)*: 50 Warwick Road, Ipswich, Suffolk IP4 2QE ☎ 01473 211714

WHITTAKER David *(Dms, Per, Tbn, Sack, Rec)*

WICKER Simon *(Dms)*: 13 Davys Close, Wheathampstead, Herts AL4 8TL ☎ 01582 832709

WILSON Terence *(Dms)*: 27 Sacombe Road, Hemel Hempstead, Herts HP1 3RQ ☎ 0410 485 308

WOODLEY Mark *(Per)*: 42 Highfield Street, Stoney Stanton, Leics LE9 4DF ☎ 01455 274412, 0836 768182

WORTLEY Barry *(Dms)*: 105 Netherwood Green, Norwich NR1 2JG ☎ 01603449444, 0402 278267 mob

WRIGHT John *(Dms)*: 60 Mill Road, Whittlesey, Peterborough, Cambs PE7 1SN ☎ 01733 208530

YORK Timothy *(Dms)*: 17 Ganels Close, Billericay, Essex CM11 2TQ ☎ 01277 624892

MIDLANDS

ADAMS Ken *(Dms)*: 71 Ostlers Lane, Cheddleton, Nr Leek, Staffs ST13 7HS ☎ 01538 360734

ALCOCK Douglas *(Dms, Voc)*: 20, Harvard Avenue, Honeybourne, Evesham, Worcs WR11 5XU ☎ 01386 832483

ALDERSEA Jon *(Dms, Per, Kbds)*: 90 Stone Road, Trent Vale, Stoke-on-Trent, Staffordshire ST4 6SP ☎ 01782 658797, 01782 659050, 01782 658797

ALDRIDGE Mark *(Dms)* ☎ 0121 446 5461, 0958 377315 mob

ALEXANDER Evan *(Per)*: 31 St Barnabas Street, Wellingborough, Northants NN8 4LW ☎ 01933 273265

ALLATSON Lee *(Dms, Per)*: 64 Scraptoft Lane, Leicester LE5 1HU ☎ 0116 2768 734, 0976 161626 mob

ALLCOCK Garry *(Dms, B Ldr)*: 617 Bristol Road South, Birmingham B31 2JS ☎ 0121 475 7524

ARCHER Mitchell *(Dms, Per)*: 170 Eachelhurst Road, Walmley, Sutton Coldfield, West Midlands B76 1EL ☎ 0121 351 2280, 0831 858277 mob

ASTLEY Carl *(Dms)*: 66 Hillstone Road, Shard End, Birmingham B34 7PY ☎ 0121 747 9408

AUBERTIN Terry *(Dms, Per)*: 34 Grant Road, Stoke Heath, Coventry CV3 1GQ ☎ 024 7644 5646

AYRES A *(Per, Tym)*: 3 Barnstaple Close, Allesley Green, Coventry, Warks CV5 7PJ ☎ 024 7640 5283

BACHELARD Daniel *(Dms, Per, Clt, Gtr)*: 5 Sandy Lane, Bramcote, Nottingham NG9 3QT ☎ 0115 925 6995, 0951 4752, 0951 5166

BAILEY Simon *(Dms, Gtr)*: 46 Ashbourne Road, Wolverhampton WV1 2RX ☎ 01902 452157

BARBER Richard *(Dms)*: 6 Davett Close, Leicester LE5 6RB ☎ 0116 274 2857

BARKER Spike *(Dms, B Gtr)*: Flat 4, 31 Wakegreen Raod, Moseley, Birmingham B13 9HL, 0976 639544 mob

BARLOW Russell *(Dms)*: 23 Bertelin Road, Stafford ST16 3JJ ☎ 01785 601253

BARRON Christine Angela *(Dms, Per, Com, Song W, Theory)*: 27 Madeira Croft, Coventry CV5 8NX ☎ 024 7667 9827 & fax, 0831 498194

BARWELL Steven *(Dms, Per)*: 58 Fernleigh Avenue, Mapperley, Nottingham NG3 6FL ☎ 0115 993 1650 & fax

BATEMAN Edward *(Dms)*: 16 Field Avenue, Milton, Stoke-on-Trent ST2 7AS ☎ 01782 543303

BENNETT Derek *(Dms)*: 2 Brockmoor Close, Chawn Park, Pedmore, Stourbridge, Worcs DY9 0YL ☎ 01384 370340

BENNETT George *(Dms)*: 12 Sherborne Gardens, Codsall, Staffs WV8 1BN ☎ 01902 844096

BIRD Tim *(Dms)*: 41 Pennine Way, Duston, Northampton NN5 6AT ☎ 01604 587560

BOFFEY Graham *(Dms)*: 14 Cedar Street, Mansfield, Nottinghamshire NG18 2RZ

BOOL Helen P *(Per, Tym)*: 82 Beaconsfield Street, West Bromwich, West Midlands B71 1QJ ☎ 0121 525 5316, 0973 353983 mob

BOWDEN Graham *(Dms)*: 73 Mere Road, Wigston, Leicester LE18 3RN ☎ 0116 2811653

BOWDLER Bill *(Dms)*: 36 Grasmere Avenue, Green Lane, Coventry, West Midlands CV3 6AY ☎ 024 7641 0262

BROWN Bill *(Dms)*: 327 Hipswell Highway, Wyken, Coventry, West Midlands CV2 5FQ ☎ 024 7645 1994

BROWN David *(Dms)*: 749 Burton Road, Midway, Swadlincote, Derbys DE11 0DN ☎ 01283 224225

BROWN Delroy *(Dms, Per, Voc)*: 1 The Hollies, Off Montague Road, Smethwick, Warley B66 4PE ☎ 0121 565 4855

BROWN James *(Dms)*: Fernscan Limited, No.1.Andover Street, Digbeth, Birmingham B5 5RG ☎ 0121 633 4742

BROWN Kevin *(Dms)*: 46 Summerhill Avenue, Kidderminster, Worcs DY11 6BY ☎ 01562 747965

BROWNE Graham *(Dms)*: 27 Shaftesbury Road, Earlsdon, Coventry CV5 6FL ☎ 024 7671 5728, 024 7667 8078

BRUTON Roger *(Dms)*: 53 Paganel Drive, Dudley, West Midlands DY1 4AZ ☎ 01384 252857

BUCKLEY Alan *(Dms)*: 125 Sandwell Street, Highgate, Walsall, West Midlands WS1 3EG ☎ 01922 30779

BULLOCK Neil *(Dms)*: 15 Graham Road, Halesowen, West Midlands B62 8LJ ☎ 0121 559 7373

BULLOCK Richard *(Dms)*: 3 Whitfield Way, Kingsthorpe, Northampton NN2 8LG ☎ 01604 820144

BURNHAM Don *(Dms)*: 11 Arbury Avenue, Foleshill, Coventry CV6 6FD ☎ 024 7668 0845

BUTTERLY Kevin *(Dms, Per)*: 77 Church Road, Hartshill, Nr Nuneaton, Warwickshire CV10 0LU ☎ 024 7639 5366

CADMAN Steve *(Dms)*: 37 Sandy Lane, Newcastle Under Lyme, Staffs ST5 0LX ☎ 01782 610515

CALDICOTT Anthony *(Dms)*: 46 The Croftway, Birmingham, West Midlands B20 1EG ☎ 0121 358 1730

CAPALDI Phil *(Dms, Voc)*: 39 Alexandra Road, Hampton, Evesham, Worcs WR11 6QQ ☎ 01386 48307

CARROLL Johnny *(Dms, Rec)*: 22 Cotesheath Street, Joiners Square, Hanley, Stoke-on-Trent ST1 3JD ☎ 01782 262763, 0410 347146 mob

CARTER Gareth *(Dms)*: 70 Dunblane Drive, New Cubbington, Leamington Spa CV32 7TL ☎ 01926 315244

CATER Peter *(Dms)*: 22 Holte Drive, Four Oaks, Sutton Coldfield, W. Midlands B75 6PR ☎ 0121 308 2259

CEREDIG Huw *(Per, Tym, Pf)*: 20 Ombersley Road, Droitwich, Worcs WR9 8JE ☎ 01905 779736

CHARLERY Roger *(Per, Voc)*: 8A Garlinge Road, London NW2 3TR

CHARLTON Andrew *(Dms)*: c/o 3 Millfield Road, Metheringham, Lincs LN4 3HZ ☎ 01526 320273 & fax

CHARLTON Trevor *(Dms, Per)*: 206 Dower Road, Four Oaks, Sutton Coldfield, West Midlands B75 6SZ ☎ 0121 308 2876

CHEETHAM Neville *(Dms)*: 15 Victoria Road, Draycott, Derbyshire DE72 3PS ☎ 01332 874234

CHESLIN Wal *(Dms)*: 229 Tennyson Road, Coventry, West Midlands CV2 5JE ☎ 024 7645 3398

CHESTER John *(Dms)*: 71 Grayswood Avenue, Chapelfields, Coventry CV5 8HL ☎ 024 7667 5584

CHILLY *(Dms, Voc)*: 18 High Street, Astwood Bank, Redditch, Worcs B96 6DB ☎ 01527 893918

CLARKE Glen *(Dms, Voc)*: Rose Cottage, Prestidge Row, The Green Morton, Pinkney Northampton NN11 3NJ ☎ 01295 760412

CLARKSON Ransford *(Dms)* ☎ 0956 553498

COCHRANE Diom *(Dms, Bjo, H Gurd, Gtr)*: Glemusk, Newbury Park, Ledbury, Herefordshire HR8 1AT ☎ 01531 635492

COCKAYNE David *(Dms)*: 1 Quantock Rise, Shepshed, Nr Loughborough, Leics LE12 9JR ☎ 01509 600574, 0370 522945 mob

COOLEY Jase *(Dms, Voc, Per)*: 21 Garrick Court, Garrick Road, Lichfield, Staffs WS13 7DR ☎ 01543 253035

CORMELL Alastair *(Dms)*: 14 Oakleigh Road, Oldswinford, Stourbridge, West Midlands DY8 2JX ☎ 01384 393067, 01384 74469, 01384 74995

COTTERILL Peter *(Per, Dms)*: 180 Sandbach Road, Lawton Heath End, Church Lawton, Stoke-on-Trent ST7 3RB ☎ 01270 877708

COTTON Margaret *(Per, Tym, Pf, Xyl)*: 57 Elmfield Crescent, Moseley, Birmingham B13 9TL ☎ 0121 449 3196

COTTRELL Neil *(Dms)*: 144 Bridle Lane, Sutton Coldfield, West Midlands B74 3HQ

COTTRELL Ronald *(Dms)*: 21 School Road, Hockley Heath, Solihull, West Midlands B94 6QH ☎ 01564 782742

COX Geoffrey *(Dms)*: The Willows, 1 Acacia Drive, Lower Pilsey, Chesterfield Derbyshire S45 8DY ☎ 01246 855998, 0831 690821

CRANER Robert *(Dms, Per, Pf, Kbds, Voc)*: 35 Lake Street, Lower Gornal, Dudley, West Midlands DY3 2AT ☎ 01902 661169

CUMMINGS George *(Dms, Vib)*: 5 Berkley Crescent, Birmingham B13 9YD ☎ 0121 777 7183

CURRIE David *(Dms, Per)*: 4 Tennyson Drive, Attenborough, Nottingham NG9 6BD ☎ 0115 925 0464, 0860 656620

D'SA Malcolm *(Dms)*: 10 Mervyn Road, Leicester LE5 4NH ☎ 0116 273 9344

DANDRIDGE Alfred *(Dms)*: 52 Bridget Street, Rugby CV21 2BH ☎ 01788 73845

DANGERFIELD Nicholas *(Dms)*: 11 The Woodlands, Haden Hill, Cradley Heath, West Midlands B64 7JY ☎ 0121 501 1211

DAVENPORT Jeff *(Dms, Per, Tpt)*: Walnut Cottage, Spendlove Farm, Ashleyhay, Wirksworth, Derbyshire DE4 4AH ☎ 01629 822875

DAVIES Gary *(Dms, Per)*: Address Unknown ☎ 0121 705 0914

DAVIS Matthew *(Dms, Xyl, Glck, Tym, Per)*: 8 Sunbury Close, New Park, Trentham, Stoke-on-Trent ST4 8XT ☎ 01782 642154, 0976 767503 mob

DENVER Seamus *(Dms, Per)*: 53 Addison Road, Kings Heath, Birmingham B14 7EN ☎ 0121 441 3575

DOCHERTY Stephen *(Dms, Gtr)*: 37 Mill Lane, The Butts, Walsall, West Midlands WS4 2BH ☎ 01922 613913

DUNKLEY Michael *(Dms, Org)*: 10 Sorrel Road, Heselrig Manor, Hamilton, Leicester LE5 1TE ☎ 0116 2461636

DUTFIELD Gerald *(Dms)*: Greenacres, Shoulton Lane, Hallow, Nr Worcester WR2 6PU ☎ 01905 640753

DUTTON Roy *(Dms)*: 52 Farlow Road, Northfield, Birmingham B31 3AE ☎ 0121 458 4487

DYSON Lewis *(Per)*: 11 Temeside, Ludlow, Shropshire SY8 1PD ☎ 01584 874700

ELKINGTON John *(Dms)*: 6, Parry Road, Wyken, Coventry, West Midlands CV2 3LZ ☎ 024 7668 4933

ELY James *(Dms, Per)*: 40 School Road, Irchester, Northants NN29 7AW ☎ 01933 386228, 0976 700378

ETHERINGTON Anthony *(Dms)*: 73 Broad Lane, Coventry CV5 7AH ☎ 024 7671 5812

FARNELL Thomas *(Dms)*: 94 Leasow Drive, Edgbaston, Birmingham B15 2SW ☎ 0121 472 5664

FARRER Rob *(Per, Tym)*: The Grange, 50 Main Street, Hoby, Leics LE14 3DT ☎ 01664 434232

FERRIDAY Keith *(Dms)*: 19 Harvey Road, Buglawton, Congleton, Cheshire CW12 2BZ ☎ 01260 276371

FISHER John *(Dms, Vib, B Ldr)*: 14 Clayton Drive, Castle Bromwich, Birmingham B36 0AN ☎ 0121 747 2601

FISHLEY Anthony *(Dms)*: 28 Square Close, Woodgate Valley, Birmingham B32 3TH, 0958 926681

FLETCHER Guy *(Dms, Vln, Man, Gtr, B Gtr)*: 7 Prince Of Wales Row, Moulton, Northampton NN3 1UN ☎ 01604 647682

FOX The *(Dms, B Gtr, Gtr, Kbds, Sax)*: Three Spores House, Unit 5 Wiltell Works, Upper St John Street, Lichfield WS14 9ET ☎ 01543 303200, 09730 703355

FREEMAN Alan *(Dms)*: 26 Honeysuckle Close, Alford Road, Sutton-on-Sea, Lincolnshire LN12 2ST

FREEMAN Gerry *(Dms)*: 13 Walmley Ash Road, Sutton Coldfield, West Midlands B76 1HY ☎ 0121 351 1513

FUZZ *(Dms)*

GARRETT Malcolm *(Dms, Per)*: 14, Nevin Grove, Great Barr, Birmingham B42 1PE ☎ 0121 331 4318

GIBSON John *(Dms, Per)*: 35 Sylvan Avenue, Northfield, Birmingham B31 2PG ☎ 0121 477 4067

GOODBAND John *(Dms)*: 4 Reeve Drive, Kenilworth, Warwickshire CV8 2GA ☎ 01926 853039

GRAYSTONE Stephen *(Dms)*: 21 Walmer Meadow, Aldridge, Walsall, West Midlands WS9 8QQ

GREENHOUSE Philip *(Dms, B Gtr, Gtr)*: 2 Rose Cottages, Bleathwood, Ludlow, Shropshire SY8 4LG ☎ 01584 711076, 0973 850305

GREENWAY John *(Dms)*: 4 Seamore Close, Hampton Magna, Warwicks CV35 8SU ☎ 01926 494519

GRIFFITHS Benjamin *(Dms, Per)*: 42 Eric Lock Road West, Bayston Hill, Shrewsbury, Shropshire SY3 0QA ☎ 01743 872164

GRIFFITHS Gordon *(Dms)*: Brockhall, Main Road, Meriden, Coventry, West Midland CV7 7NG ☎ 01676 22690

HACKNEY Alan *(Dms)*: 7-30 Victoria Centre, Nottingham NG1 3PE ☎ 01709 530195

HALL Peter *(Per, Tym)*: 200 Hockley Road, Hockley, Tamworth, West Midlands B77 5EY ☎ 01827 289260

HARVEY David *(Dms)*: 57 Wysall Road, Northampton NN3 8TP ☎ 01604 415811, 0780 1455163

HARVEY Martin H *(Dms)*: 69 Sandringham Avenue, Willenhall, West Midlands WV12 5TG ☎ 01922 403403

HAWLEY Russell *(Per)*: 26 Webster Avenue, Weston Coyney, Stoke-on-Trent, Staffs ST3 5SX ☎ 01782 318978

HAYWOOD Beverley *(Per, Dms, La Per, Vib)*: 22 Green Lane, Pelsall, Walsall, West Midlands WS3 4PA ☎ 01922 692199

HEARD Jonathan *(Dms)*: 12 Fylingdale, Brampton Park, Northampton NN2 8UR ☎ 01604 243864, 0585 738003

HEATON Phil *(Per, Vln, Citt, Flt)*: 86 Derby Road, Draycott, Derby DE72 3NX ☎ 01332 874186

HEMMINGSLEY Carl *(Dms)*: 24 Rutland Crescent, Bilson, West Midlands WV14 6LR ☎ 01902 653112

HENNESSEY Bill *(Dms)*: 16 Sorrell Avenue, Upper Tean, Staffs ST10 4LY ☎ 01538 723696

HEPBURN Donavan *(Dms)*: 108 Edmund Road, Saltley, Birmingham B8 1HE ☎ 0121 328 6158, 0956 809930

HERBERT Andrew *(Per, Tym, Dms)*: 19 Gilldown Place, Pakenham Village, Edgbaston, Birmmingham B15 2LR ☎ 0121 440 7278, 0976 755025

HILL Gary Oliver *(Dms)*: 15A Alexandra Road, Halesowen, West Midlands B63 4DJ ☎ 0121 550 1918

HISLAM Nicholas *(Dms, Per, S Sax, A Sax, T Sax)*: 97 Knighton Church Rd, Leicester LE2 3JN ☎ 0116 2704124

HOLDER Simon *(Per, Gtr)*: 7 Falcon Close, Kiddminster, Worcs DY10 1NN ☎ 01562 865097

HOLLAND-HANBURY Nigel *(Dms)*: The Flat, New Delhi, 46 The Tything, Worcester WR1 1JT ☎ 0777 5580196

HOLMES Dave *(Dms)*: 25 Moseley Road, Bilston, Wolverhampton, West Midlands WV14 6JB ☎ 01902 601679

HORNBY Len *(Dms, Tbn)*: 249 Beake Avenue, Coventry, West Midlands CV6 3BA ☎ 024 7659 5681

HOSE Paul *(Dms, Gtr)*: 10 Rugby Close, Southglade Park, Nottingham NG5 9RL ☎ 0115 903 4352, 0115 903 8054 fax

HOWE Bobby *(Dms, Tym)*: 9 Park Court, Allesley, Coventry, West Midlands CV5 9GS ☎ 024 7640 2439

HOWLES David *(Dms, Per, Tym)*: 14 Birmingham Road, Kidderminster, Worcs DY10 2BX ☎ 01562 751917, 0860 479371

HURREN Jim *(Per, Tym)*: 40 Muscott Street, St James, Northampton NN5 5EY ☎ 01604 581993

ILIFFE Nick *(Dms)*: 53 Purvis Road, Rushden, Northamptonshire NN10 9QA ☎ 01933 312531

INGHAM Marcus *(Dms, Kbds)*: 0121 608 0230, 0956 427232 mob

JACKSON Leonard *(Dms)*: 64 Edinburgh Road, Oldbury, Warley B68 0SR ☎ 0121 422 5296

JACKSON Trevor *(Dms, Per)*: 7 Sandy Close, Wellingborough, Northants NN8 3AY ☎ 01933 226057 & fax

JAMO *(Dms, Per, B Gtr, Kbds)*: Flat 14, 24 Rann Close, Ladywood, Birmingham B16 8RG

JEAVONS Colin *(Per)*: 41 Links Road, Penn, Wolverhampton WV4 5RF ☎ 01902 335431

JEFFERSON Geoff *(Dms, Kbds, Gtr)*: 59, West House Grove, Kings Heath, Birmingham, B14 6PS ☎ 0121 443 2815

JENKINSON James *(Dms, Per)*: 21 Stour Close, Oadby, Leicester LE2 4GE ☎ 0116 271 7882, 0958 672034 mob

JENNINGS Lee *(Dms, Tym)*: 65 The Meadway, Headless Cross, Redditch, Worcs B97 5EA

JERVIS Andy *(Dms, Glck)*: 9 Portland Drive, Stockingford, Bucks Hill, Nuneaton CV10 9HZ ☎ 024 7634 7464

JOHN Ronnie *(Dms, Per, Voc)*: 64 Hatherton Street, Butts, Walsall WS4 2LQ, 0958 273602 mob

JONES Arthur *(Dms)*: 14 Grice Road, Hartshill, Stoke-on-Trent, Staffs ST4 7PJ ☎ 01782 623084

JONES James *(Per)*: 8 Livingstone Road, Kings Heath, Birmingham B14 6DJ ☎ 0121 443 2876

JONES Nigel *(Dms, Gtr)*: 56 Bedford Street, Crewe, Cheshire CW2 6JD, 01270 532512 day

KELLIE Michael *(Dms, Gtr, Pf)*: 22 Holly Road, Edgbaston, Birmingham B16 9NL ☎ 0121 452 1150

KETCH Gordon *(Dms, B Ldr, Voc)*: 7 Winsford Close, Newhall, Sutton Coldfield, West Midlands B76 8EU ☎ 0121 329 3318

KEYTE Jason *(Dms)*: 14 Mortimers Close, Hollywood, Birmingham B14 4PW ☎ 0121 430 4178

KIDMAN Kenneth *(Dms)*: 16 Queen Street, Waingroves, Ripley, Derbyshire DE5 9TJ ☎ 01773 746026

KIRK John *(Dms)*: Flat 2 53 Durham Road, East Finchley, London N2 9DR ☎ 020 8883 2922

LITTLE Jamie *(Dms)*: Luckman Cottage, Warren Grove, Washwood Heath, Birmingham B8 2XL ☎ 0121 328 8277

MAKHENE Josh Sello *(Dms)*: 73E Rosebery Square East, Rosebery Avenue, London ECIR 4PU ☎ 020 7278 6047

MANSER Paul *(Dms, Kbds, Voc)*: 5 Coleridge Walk, Daventry, Northants NN11 5AU ☎ 01327 878328

MARK *(Dms, Per)*: 73 Canon Street, Leicester LE4 6NH ☎ 0116 266 3349, 0976 848955 mob

MARSDEN Paul *(Per)*: 38 Red Lion Street, Alvechurch, Worcs B48 7LF ☎ 0121 445 6131, 0121 447 7390 fax

MASSEY Steven *(Dms)*: 359 Dawlish Drive, Ubberley Estate, Bucknall, Stoke-on-Trent ST2 0RH ☎ 01782 325063

MATTU Amit *(Dms, Per)*: 3 Postbridge Road, Stivichall, Coventry CV3 5AG ☎ 024 7669 0376

MAYNARD Fergie *(Dms)*: Bcm Palace, London WC1N 3XX

MCCARTHY Paul *(Dms, Per)*: 15 Telegraph Street, Stafford, Staffs ST17 4AT ☎ 01785 48069

MCFARLANE Philip (*Dms*): 247 Old Church Road, Little Heath, Coventry CV6 7DZ ☎ 024 7666 8312

MCGUIRE Gerard (*Dms*): 14 Salcombe Avenue, Sheldon, Birmingham B26 3SQ ☎ 0121 743 3509

MELLOR David (*Dms*): Roselea, Lower Road, Barnacle, Nr Coventry CV7 9LD ☎ 024 7661 9592

MERRY Ronald (*Dms*): 6 Station Road, Stoke Golding, Nr Nuneaton CV13 6EZ ☎ 01455 212567

MERV (*Dms, Synth, Kbds*): 59, George Road, Erdington, Birmingham B23 7QE ☎ 0121 373 5392, 0831 744589, 0121 686 4851

MEZULIS Peter (*Dms, Per*): 8 St Johns Close, Lutterworth, Leics LE17 4QN ☎ 01455 554757

MIDDLETON Brian (*Dms*): The Lord Lyon Inn, Stockcross, Newbury, Berks RG20 8LL ☎ 01488 608366

MILLER Hugh (*Per*): 9 The Villas, Stoke-on-Trent ST4 5AH ☎ 01782 847770

MILLEST Simon (*Dms, Per*): 1 Blackfield Cottages, 6Th Avenue, Greytree, Ross-on-Wye, Herefordshire HR9 7BB ☎ 01989 768350, 0831 707233

MILLWARD Geoffrey (*Per, Dms*): 39 Millfield Crescent, Milton, Stoke-on-Trent ST2 7DF ☎ 01782 535491

MILLWARD Nick (*Dms, Voc*): 3 Glebe Road, Alvechurch, Birmingham B48 7PS ☎ 0121 445 1368

MILNER Peter (*Dms*): 15 Underbank Lane, Moulton Leys, Northampton NN3 7HH ☎ 01604 495186

MONOMANIA (*Dms, Voc, Gtr, Pf, Per*): 10 The Promenade, Victoria Park, Nottingham NG3 1HB ☎ 0115 958 2701

MOOD Darren (*Per*): 7 Joanhurst Crescent, Shelton, Stoke-on-Trent, Staffs ST1 4LA ☎ 01782 286956, 0961 990413

MOORS Joel (*Per*): 9 Langdale Court, Congleton, Cheshire CW12 4JP ☎ 01260 271919

MORGAN Mark (*Dms*): 11 Stanford Avenue, Great Barr, Birmingham B42 1JP ☎ 0121 357 1538

MOULSHER John (*Dms*): 145 Lentons Lane, Coventry, West Midlands CV2 1NZ

MOUNTFORD John (*Dms*): 3 Betley Hall Gardens, Betley, Crewe, Cheshire CW3 9BB ☎ 01270 820630

MOZZER (*Dms*): 88 Park Road, Silverdale, Newcastle-upon-Tyne, Staffs ST5 6LP ☎ 01782 624636

MURFIN Muff (*Dms, Gtr*): The Old Smithy, Post Office Lane, Kempsey, Worcester WR5 3NX ☎ 01905 820659

MURFIN Paul (*Dms, Per*): 409 Ford Green Road, Norton, Stoke-on-Trent ST6 8LX ☎ 01782 534013

MUTCH Geoff (*Per, Vln*): 34, Foster Street, Kinver, Stourbridge, West Midlands DY7 6EB

NEALE Douglas (*Dms*): 38 Laburnham Crescent, Northampton NN3 2LF ☎ 01604 714308

NELSON Phillipp (*Dms*): 13 Lamport Close, Meadows Estate, Wigston, Leicester LE18 3WH ☎ 0116 2119914

NESBITT Stephen (*Dms*): 38, Pendragon Road, Perry Barr, Birmingham B42 1RN

NEWBURY Paul (*Dms, Pf, Gtr*)

NEWELL Catherine (*Per*): 16 Mount Pleasant Avenue, Rookery Road, Handsworth, Birmingham B21 9QA ☎ 0121 515 1668

NICHOLLS John (*Dms*): 55 Moat Avenue, Green Lane, Coventry CV3 6BT ☎ 024 7641 9767

NICHOLS Alex (*Dms, Gtr*): Ashbourne, Pinewood Road, Ashley Heath, Market Drayton, Shropshire TF9 4PP ☎ 01630 673383, 07979 553654

OAKLEY Monty (*Dms, B Gtr, Gtr*): 4 St Judes Avenue, Mapperley, Nottingham NG3 5FG ☎ 0115 952 5297

ORTON Art (*Dms*): 105 Vale View, Stockingford, Nuneaton CV10 8AP ☎ 024 7632 9709

PALMER Ian (*Dms, Per*): Wentworth House, Little Aston Park Road, Little Aston, Sutton Coldfield, Staffs B74 3BZ ☎ 0121 580 9355

PALMER Steve (*Dms*): 74 Stockwell Road, Handsworth, Birmingham B21 9RJ ☎ 0121 507 1528

PARKER Matthew (*Dms, Gtr, B Gtr*): 4 Kingland Drive, Old Milverton, Leamington Spa, Warwickshire CV32 6BL ☎ 01926 425311

PARKIN Michael (*Dms*): 14 Malvern Road, Headless Cross, Redditch B97 5DH ☎ 01527 403008

PARRATT Tom (*Dms*): ☎ 0115 9582305, 01523 167438

PARVEZ Mohammed (*Dms*): 308 Elizabeth House, 2 Waterloo Way, Leicester LE2 0QE ☎ 0116 2510434

PATTERSON Grant (*Dms*): 96 Church Road, Northfield, Birmingham B31 2LE ☎ 0121 624 4824, 0802 709552

PAYNE Robin (*Dms, Per*): 30 Church Street, Shipston-on-Stour, Warwickshire CV36 4AP ☎ 01608 661588

PERRINS Simon (*Dms*): 59 Wheelers Lane, Kings Heath, Birmingham B13 0SE ☎ 0802 379413

PETERS Rob (*Dms, Per, Gtr, Cel, Kbds*): 2 Leighton Road, Mosley, Birmingham B30 2LG ☎ 0121 449 0129

PICK Cliff (*Per, Tym*): Lytham Cottage, Dunnington, Nr Alcester, Warks B49 5NX ☎ 01789 778681

PITFIELD Alan (*Dms*): 12 Southgreen Close, Berry Hill, Mansfield, Notts NG18 4PX ☎ 01623 25000

PRICE David (*Dms*): 107 St Pauls Road, Smethwick, Warley, West Midlands B66 1EY ☎ 0121 601 0615

PROCTOR Wayne (*Dms, Gtr*): Englefield Maida Lane, Ollerton, Nr Newark, Notts NG22 9AF ☎ 01623 824768, 0797 1521122

RANDALL Gary (*Dms*): Flat 4, The Maisonettes, Oval Road, Erdington, Birmingham B24 8PW ☎ 0121 373 8026

REBELLO Simone (*Per*): 79 Station Road, Biddulph, Stoke-on-Trent ST8 6BT ☎ 01782 518734

REYNOLDS Ashley (*Dms*): ☎ 0115 953 3585, 0966 194973 mob

RICHARDS Albert (*Dms*): Address Unknown ☎ 0116 2362795

RICHARDS Cyrus (*Dms, Kbds, B Gtr, Voc*): 1 Portsea Close, Cheyles More, Coventry CV3 5JQ ☎ 024 7650 6270

RICHARDS Tony (*Dms*): 68 Woodside Road, Ketley, Telford, Shropshire TF1 4HE ☎ 01952 401688

RICHARDSON Ian (*Dms*): 3 Thrapston Road, Finedon, Northants NN9 5DG ☎ 01933 680581

RICHARDSON Jamie (*Dms*): 9 Fir Tree Close, Forest Town, Mansfield, Notts NG21 9ES ☎ 01623 487925

RICHARDSON Robert (*Dms*): 110 Lear Drive, Wistaston, Crewe, Cheshire CW2 8DS ☎ 01270 663731, 0585 858773 mob

RIDDLE Antony (*Dms, Per*): 83 Cross Lane, Mountsorrel, Leicester LE12 7BX ☎ 0116 230 3102

ROBERTS Bunny (*Dms*): 16 Friswell Drive, Off Spring Road, Foleshill, Coventry CV6 7NG ☎ 024 7666 7344

ROBINSON Richard (*Dms*): 20 Scotch Firs, Fownhope, Herefordshire HR1 4NW ☎ 01432 860664

RODWELL Brian (*Dms, Per*): 22 Moat Rd, Loughborough, Leics LE11 3PN ☎ 01509 232779

ROSE Richard (*Dms*): 1A Vancouver Avenue, Radcliffe-on-Trent, Notts NG12 2ES ☎ 0115 933 4448

ROTHE Walter (*Dms*): 11 Bristle Hill, Buckingham, Bucks MK18 1EZ ☎ 01280 814604

ROWE Andrew (*Dms*): Lind Home, Woodhouse Lane, Amington, Tamworth, Staffs B79 3AH ☎ 01827 68808, 0976 701902 mob, 01827 880563

RUSSELL Ian (*Dms, Per*): c/o 86 Hanbury Road, Dorridge, Solihull, West Midlands B93 8DL ☎ 01564 773848

RUSSELL Paul (*Dms*): 105 Kimberley Road, Nuthall, Notts NG16 1DD ☎ 0115 9383517

SALLIS Richard (*Dms, Tym*): 37 Tyninghame Avenue, Tettenhall, Wolverhampton WV6 9PP ☎ 01902 832855

SANTRY Gary (*Dms*): Croft Cottage, Bausley, Crew Green, Shrewsbury SY5 9BN ☎ 01743 884621

SAVAGE Alan (*Dms*): 135 Park Lane, New Duston, Northampton NN5 6QW ☎ 01604 581086

SAY Michael (*Dms*): School House Cottage, Over Lane, Hazelwood, Derby DE6 4AG ☎ 01332 840037

SHEEHAN Ashley (*Dms, Tpt*): 33 Chepstow Way, Bloxwich, Walsall, Staffs, West Midlands WS3 2NB ☎ 01922 403585

SHEINMAN Charles (*Dms, Kbds*): 33 Kingsley Road, Northampton NN2 7BN ☎ 01604 722261

SHENTON Keith (*Dms*): 25 Greenside Avenue, Baddeley Green, Stoke-on-Trent ST9 9PQ ☎ 01782 541254

SHIRLEY Robert *(Dms, B Ldr)*: 47 Shirburn Road, Leek, Staffs ST13 6LD ☎ 01538 384033

SIGGERS Ron *(Dms)*: 195 Sullivan Road, Coventry, West Midlands CV6 7JU ☎ 024 7668 9425

SIMMONS Robert *(Dms, Voc, Gtr)*: 6 Rowan Crescent, Coseley, Bilston, West Midlands WV14 9QA ☎ 01902 77755

SIMPSON David *(Dms, Rh Gtr)*: 12 Aston Chase, Aston Lodge Park, Little Stoke, Stone, Staffs ST15 8SE ☎ 01785 819001

SIMPSON Denis *(Dms)*: 25 Birch Avenue, Barrow-on-Soar, Loughborough, Leics LE12 8SJ ☎ 01509 620819

SIMPSON Michael *(Dms, Per)*: 2 Birch Close, Charlton Kings, Cheltenham, Glos GL53 8PJ ☎ 01242 521961

SMALLWOOD Mark *(Dms, Per)*: 20 Castello Drive, Castle Bromwich, Birmingham B36 9TB ☎ 0121 681 5352

SMITH Alan *(Dms)*: 48 Etruria Gardens, City Road, Derby DE1 3RL ☎ 01332 294842

SMITH Andrew *(Dms, Gtr)*: 'Woodlands', Ramshorn Road, Oakamoor, Stoke-on-Trent, Staffs ST10 3BZ ☎ 01538 702463

SMITH Graham *(Dms)*: 50 Hither Green Lane, Bordesley, Redditch B98 9BW ☎ 01527 66692

SMITH Jeremy *(Per)*: 'Heronbrook', Chesterfield Road, Two Dales, Matlock, Derbyshire DE4 2EZ ☎ 01629 733964, 0467 386139

SMITH Nicholas *(Dms, Per)*: Sibson Mill, Sibson, Wellsborough Road, Leicester CV13 6LR ☎ 01827 880506, 0976 826687 mob

SMITH Robert *(Per)*: 17 Christleton Avenue, Crewe, Cheshire CW2 8TD ☎ 01270 258664

SOCCI Stephen *(Dms, Per, Tym)*: The Willows End, 177A Nethercote Gardens, Shirley, Solihull, West Midlands B90 1BJ ☎ 0121 474 2259, 0973 461725, 0121 474 2259 fax

SPARE Martin *(Dms, Per)*: 45 Lynton Street, Derby DE22 3RW ☎ 01332 293493

SPEDDING Paul *(Dms)*: 34 Old Tannery Court, Bewdley, Worcs DY12 2DS ☎ 01299 401234, 0411 622947

SPENCE Rowen *(Dms, Per)*: 67 Woodend, Handsworthwood, Birmingham B20 1EW ☎ 0121 358 5507, 0410 444 716

SPENCELEY Ivan *(Dms)*: 69 Elvaston Road, North Wingfield, Chesterfield, Derbyshire S42 5HH ☎ 01246 85 1526

SPENCER Stuart *(Dms)*: 6 Everitt Drive, Knowle, Warks B93 9EP ☎ 01564 776561

SQUIRES Adam *(Dms)*: Flat 1, 48 Town Street, Duffield, Derby DE22 ☎ 01332 552199

STEVENS Laurie *(Dms)*: 124 Daventry Road, Cheylesmore, Coventry, West Midlands CV3 5DG ☎ 024 7650 1842

STEVENS Mark *(Dms, Per, Tpt)*: 34 Thorpeeville, Moulton, Northants NN3 7TR ☎ 01604 642887, 0589 091109

STICKMAN *(Dms, Cong, Berimbau)*: 104 Egypt Road, New Basford, Nottingham NG7 7GN ☎ 0115 8410545

STONE Brian *(Dms, Per)*: 9 Church Street, Ellesmere, Shropshire SY12 0HD ☎ 01691 623821

STREET Steve *(Dms)*: 47 Lickey Rock, Nr Bromsgrove, Worcester B60 1HF ☎ 0121 445 5878, 0121 445 5878

T. Lynton. *(Dms, Per, Voc, Gtr, Pf)*: 22 Alperton Drive, Pedmore, Stourbridge, Worcestershire DY9 9EW ☎ 01299 826893

TAMS Cedric *(Dms)*: 5 Sandwell Walk, Caldmore, Walsall WS1 3ER ☎ 01922 724237

TAYLOR Carl *(Dms, B Gtr)*: 24 Charlecote Rd, Whitmore Park, Coventry CV6 2HZ ☎ 024 7633 6044

TAYLOR Charles *(Dms)*: 37 Charles Street, Warwick CV34 5LQ ☎ 01926 493239

TAYLOR Mark *(Dms, Per)*: 80 Warwick Street, Leicester LE3 5SD ☎ 0116 299 6269

TAYLOR-HOLMES B *(Dms)*: 76 Albert Park Road, Malvern, Worcester WR14 1RR ☎ 01684 891282

THORPE Bill *(Dms)*: 29 Orchard Drive, Eastern Green, Coventry, West Midlands CV5 7FP ☎ 024 7646 5478

TOPLIS Raymond *(Dms)*: 1 Oundle Dve, Ilkeston, Derby DE7 5DX ☎ 0115 932 6618

TRING Lisa *(Dms, Pf, B Gtr)*: 40 Avondale Road, Carlton, Nottingham NG4 1AF ☎ 0115 961 8715, 07930 403248

TUSTIN Michael *(Dms)*: 18 Leyland Road, Attleborough, Nuneaton CV11 4RP ☎ 024 7634 4439

TYACK David *(Dms, B Gtr, Gtr, Kbds)*

VALENTINE Art *(Dms, B Ldr, Voc)*: Belvedere, 17 Lancing Avenue, Leicester LE3 6HF ☎ 0116 2857730

WALKER Billy *(Dms, Per)*: 1 Kingsfield Close, Rainworth, Mansfield, Notts NG21 0FD ☎ 01623 407586

WALLIS George *(Dms)*: Millford House, Pemberley Court, 560 Kenilworth Road, Balsall Common, Coventry CV7 7RZ ☎ 01676 535975

WARD Donald *(Dms, Tbn, Tym, Tnd Per)*: 17 Saville Road, Skegby, Sutton In Ashfield NG17 3DF ☎ 01623 514555

WARD Nicholas *(Dms)*: 24 Buckingham Road, Castle Bromwich, Birmingham B36 0JP ☎ 0121 770 3423

WARD Tim *(Dms)*: 10 Over Mill Drive, Selly Park, Birmingham B29 7JL ☎ 0121 471 2033

WATERFALL Alan *(Dms, Gtr, Voc)*: 6 Glen Road, Whatstandwell, Matlock, Derbyshire DE4 5EH ☎ 01773 857289

WATERMAN Kevin, *(Per, Dms)*: 304A Hamstead Road, Great Barr, Birmingham B43 5EN ☎ 0121 358 0485, 0973 860 826 mob

WATTS Barry *(Dms)*: 35 Bratch Common Road, Wombourn, South Staffs WV5 8DD ☎ 01902 898273

WEBSTER George *(Dms)*: 17 Beverley Drive, Kirkby In Ashfield, Notts NG17 7FF ☎ 01623 753996

WESTRUP Raymond *(Dms)*: 85 Kings Road South, Oakham, Leics LE15 6PB ☎ 01572 756865

WILD Martin *(Dms)*: 10 The Crescent, Moulton, Northants NN3 7UW ☎ 01604 499408

WILKES David *(Dms)*: 9 Walton Gardens, Codsall Village, Codsall, Staffs WV8 1AH ☎ 01902 843063

WILLETS Janice *(Per)*: 21 Hambrook Close, Wolverhampton WV6 0XA ☎ 01902 715225

WILLEY Norman *(Dms)*: 55 Postern Road, Tatenhill, Burton-on-Trent DE13 9SJ ☎ 01283 517182

WILLIAMS David *(Dms)*: 65 Catterick Drive, Mickleover, Derby DE3 5TY ☎ 01332 516564, 07775 795281, 01332 516564

WILLIAMS David *(Dms)*: 46 Coppice Road, Arnold, Nottingham NG5 7HU ☎ 0115 9764407

WILLIAMS James *(Dms)*: 92 Larkhall Lane, Harpole, Northants NN7 4DF ☎ 01604 830439

WILLIAMS Vaughan *(Dms)*: 42 Kingsthorpe Grove, Northampton NN2 6NT ☎ 01604 715388

WISE Richard *(Dms)*: 93 Evelyn Road, Sparkhill, Birmingham B11 3JH ☎ 0121 771 1731

WITHAM Ray *(Dms)*: 8 Sedgemere Grove, Balsall Common, Coventry, West Midlands CV7 7GP ☎ 01676 33569

WOOD Des *(Dms)*: 26 Park Road, Coventry CV1 2LD

WOODING James *(Dms)*: 28 Winchester Road, Northampton NN4 9AY ☎ 01604 761806

WRIGHT Douglas *(Dms, Tym, Xyl, La Per)*: 94 Leicester Road, Sutton-In-The-Elms, Broughton Astley, Leicester LE9 6QF ☎ 01455 282624

WRIGHT Drew *(Dms)*: 20 Mackinley Avenue, Stapleford, Nottingham NG9 8HU ☎ 0115 917 0812

YATES Dean *(Dms)*: 19 Tresillian Road, Exhall, Coventry CV7 9FN ☎ 024 7631 1840

YORK Graham *(Dms, Per)*: 233 High Street, Honiton, Devon EX14 8AH ☎ 01404 41727

YORK Keith *(Dms, Per)*: 64B Alcester Road South, Kings Heath, Birmingham B14 7PT ☎ 0411 433082 mob

SOUTH EAST

ADAMSON Frederick *(Dms)*: 12 King Street, Walmer, Deal, Kent CT14 7JL ☎ 01304 364883

AITKEN Paul *(Dms, Per, Gtr)*: Stoneleigh, 3A The Leys, Chipping Norton, Oxon OX7 5HQ ☎ 01608 641592 day, 01608 641969

ALKEMA Jan *(Dms, Gtr, Pf)*: 52B Sheen Park, Richmond, Surrey TW9 1 UW ☎ 020 8255 7614

ALLARDYCE Michele *(Per, Glck, Kbds)*: 7 Lansdowne Square, Hove, Sussex BN3 1HE ☎ 01273 208042

ALLEN Christopher (*Dms*): Ardenlea, Cinder Path, Hook Heath, Woking, Surrey GU22 0ER ☎ Woking 63231

ANDERSON Stig (*Dms*): 194 South Farm Road, Worthing, West Sussex BN14 7TP ☎ 01903 234179

ANSELL Geoffrey (*Dms, Per*): 3 Yardley Street, Brighton, E Sussex BN1 4NU

ANTHONY Michael (*Dms*): 309 Wilson Avenue, Rochester, Kent ME1 2SS ☎ 01634 407139

ARBER Ronald (*Dms*): 34 Langdale Close, Rainham, Gillingham, Kent ME8 7AQ ☎ 01634 387365

ARNOLD Thomas (*Dms, Per, Org, Acc*): Bevernbridge Farm Cottage, South Chailey, East Sussex BN8 4QH ☎ 01273 400378

ASHENASHAE (*Dms, Bong, Timb, Didj*) ☎ 01403 251752

ASHFORD Darren (*Dms, Cong*): 9 Willow Road, Chinnor, Oxon OX9 4RA ☎ 01844 51735

AUGARDE Anthony (*Dms*): 18 Carlton Road, Oxford OX2 7SA ☎ 01865 56952

AUSTIN Robert (*Dms*): Aylstone, Birtley Road, Bramley, Surrey GU5 0JA ☎ 01483 892420

BAKER James (*Per, Tpt*): 1 Hadlow Road, Tonbridge, Kent TN9 1LE ☎ 01732 351502

BAKER Vittoria (*Per, Gtr, Kbds, Wood W*): 32 Friars Wharf, St Ebbes, Oxford OX1 1RU

BAKER Wilfred (*Dms*): 12 Baldslow Road, Hastings TN34 2EE ☎ 01424 427785

BALL Ray (*Dms*): 8 Hilda Road, Poole, Dorset BH12 2HW ☎ 01202 731393

BANKS Tristan (*Dms, Per*): 181A Kingsway, Hove, London BN3 4GL ☎ 020 8552 1038

BARCOTT Donn (*Dms*): 39 John Street, Rochester, Kent ME1 1YJ ☎ 01634 405037

BARNARD Ian (*Dms*)

BARNETT Guy (*Dms*): 44 Lowndes Grove, Shenley Church End, Milton Keynes MK5 6EG ☎ 01908 504317

BATES Bill (*Per*): 3 Cedar Close, Meopham, Gravesend, Kent DA13 0ED ☎ 01474 813015

BATSON Gareth (*Dms, Per, Voc*): 67 Lakes Lane, Beaconsfield, Bucks HP9 2JZ ☎ 01494 674347

BEAVIS Paul (*Dms*): 1 The Close, Avon Castle, Ringwood, Hants BH24 2BJ ☎ 01425 480436

BECKET Joe (*Per*): 107 Greenham Wood, Northlake, Bracknell, Berks RG12 7WH ☎ 01344 50448

BECKETT David (*Dms, Per, Pf, Gtr*): 1 Ormuz Cottages, New Chapel Road, Lingfield, Surrey RH7 6BD ☎ 01342 835005

BEIRNE John (*Dms*): 10 Old Road, Romsey, Hants SO51 7WH ☎ 01794 830405

BENHAM Trevor (*Dms*): 60 Stratford Street, Iffley Road, Oxford OX4 1SW ☎ 01865 247310

BENJAFIELD Richard (*Per, Tym, Mrba*): 11 Sheldon Court, Lower Edgeborough Road, Guildford, Surrey GU1 2DU ☎ 01483 533892, 0973 429237

BENNETT George (*Dms*): Blackboy Lodge (3), Main Road, Fishbourne, Chichester, W. Sussex PO18 8AN ☎ 0973 373477 mob

BENNETT Martyn (*Dms*): 4 Height Approach, Upton, Poole, Dorset BH16 5QZ ☎ 01202 623710

BERKLEY Gerald (*Per*): Merrydown Cottage, Bury Hollow, Bury, West Sussex RH20 1PA ☎ 01798 831869

BEVAN Cyril (*Dms*): 8 Vicarage Road, Staines, Middlesex TW18 4YF ☎ 01784 455499

BLACK David (*Dms*): 11 Solent Heights, Horse Sands Close, Southsea PO4 9UQ ☎ 07801 355065

BLACK Martin (*Dms, Pf*): 2 Downview Avenue, Ferring, Worthing BN12 6QN ☎ 01903 44057

BLAKE George (*Dms*): 31 Curlieu Road, Oakdale, Poole, Dorset BH15 3RJ ☎ 01202 672314

BONETT Kevin (*Dms*): 46 Olive Road, Coxford, Southampton, Hants SO16 5FS ☎ 023 8077 7184

BOOROFF Stephane (*Dms, Per*): 37 Burtons Road, Hampton Hill, Middlesex TW12 1DE ☎ 020 8941 1167, 0860 585479

BORENIUS Louis (*Dms, Vib, Pf*): 80 Barnett Road, Brighton, Sussex BN1 7GH ☎ 01273 506073, 0976 617884 mob

BOUZIDA Nasser (*Dms, Org*): Flat 13, 3 Porchester Road, Newbury, Berkshire RG14 7QJ ☎ 01635 552760

BOWDEN Alex (*Dms, Ld Gtr*): Field End House, Glebe Lane, Abinger Common, Nr Dorking, Surrey RH5 6JQ ☎ 01306 731337, 01306 731359

BOWN Julian (*Dms, Per*): 71 Shaggy Calf Lane, Slough, Bucks SL2 5HN ☎ 01753 24227

BRACE George (*Dms*): 6 Bossington Road, Adisham, Nr Canterbury, Kent CT3 3LL ☎ 01304 840377

BROWN Bill (*Dms, Cong, Tym*): 47 Fairfax Road, Woking, Surrey GU22 9HN ☎ 01483 765712/ 835098, 0976 719493 mob

BRUFORD Alexander (*Dms*): High Broom, Moon Hall Road, Ewhurst, Surrey GU6 7NP ☎ 020 8427 7327

BUCKLEY George (*Dms, B Ldr*): 9A New Road, Bournemouth, Dorset BH10 7DN ☎ 01202 571156

BUNNETT Keith (*Dms*): 1 Harcourt Grange, 3 Belle Vue Crescent, Southbourne, Bournemouth B11 3BW ☎ 01202 432417

BURGESS Timothy (*Dms, Per, Voc*): Hawthorns, The Downs, Off Mill Lane, Bluebell Hill, Chatham, Kent ME5 9RA ☎ 01634 867033, 01634 231308

BURT Micky (*Dms*): 45A Eversfield Place, St Leonards-on-Sea, East Sussex TN37 6DB ☎ 01424 430681

BURVILLE Eric (*Dms*): 23 Downs Walk, North Peacehaven, East Sussex BN10 8AQ ☎ 01273 585659

BYRNE Alan (*Dms*): 37 Broomfield Drive, Alderholt, Nr Fordingbridge, Hants SP6 1PT

CADDY Joe (*Dms, Per*): Heatherbank House, Hungerford Lane, Southend Bradfield, Reading, Berkshire RG7 6JJ ☎ 0118 9744126, 01426 180 872

CAESAR Julian (*Dms, Voc*): 37 Gower Road, Redbridge, Southampton SO16 9BQ ☎ 0802 435544

CALCUTT Sid (*Dms, Md*): 1 Wellington Court, Crossways Road, East Cowes, Isle Of Wight PO32 6HZ ☎ 01983 295490

CALLENDER Jon (*Dms*): 128 Park Avenue, Purbrook, Portsmouth, Hampshire PO7 5DP ☎ 023 9237 7915, 023 9221 4126

CARD J G (*Dms*): 25 Hartley Court Gardens, Cranbrook, Kent TN17 3QY ☎ 01580 713365

CARPENTER Doug (*Dms*): 30 Gorsewood Road, St Johns, Woking, Surrey GU21 1UZ ☎ 01483 474419

CARRINGTON Christopher (*Dms*): 104 Marlowe Road, Worthing, West Sussex BN14 8EZ ☎ Worthing 33052

CARTER Charles (*Dms*): 30 Normay Rise, Wash Common, Newbury, Berkshire RG14 6RY ☎ 01635 550628

CHALKER Michael (*Dms, Tym, Per*): 9 Duval Drive, Rochester, Kent ME1 2SY ☎ 01634 842503

CHAPMAN John (*Dms*): Wootton Edge, Bashley Common Road, New Milton, Hants BH25 5SQ ☎ 01425 613452

CHAPPELL Jonathan (*Dms, Per*): 4 Walker Close, Eastbourne, East Sussex BN23 6AQ ☎ 01323 642081

CHARLES Kevin (*Dms*): 103 Crescent Drive South, Wooding Dean, Brighton BN2 6SB ☎ 01273 307251

CHILD Glen (*Dms, Pf*): 44 The Pastures, High Wycombe, Bucks HP13 5LY ☎ 01494 443445, 0780 3340140

CHIMES Polly (*Per*): Hunters Rest, Weedon Hill, Hyde Heath, Amersham Bucks HP6 5RN ☎ 01494 786701

CHOCQUEEL-MANGAN Matthew (*Dms, Pf*) ☎ 01227 830050

CHRISTMAS Anthony (*Dms*): Mayfield, Long Lane, Bursledon, Southampton SO3 8DA ☎ 023 8040 3108

CLARK Bernard (*Dms, Per*): 54 Great Lane, Bierton, Nr Aylesbury, Bucks HP22 5BX ☎ 01296 20953

CLEALL Robert (*Dms*): 102 The Tideway, Rochester, Kent ME12 2NN ☎ 01634 848771

CLINE-BAILEY William (*Dms, Per*): 53 Langdale Close, Rainham, Kent ME8 7AE ☎ 01634 394501, 01523 485454

COLBERT Laurence (*Dms, Tabla, Gtr*): 39 James Street, Cowley, Oxford OX4 1ET ☎ 01865 437937

COLBURT Peter (*Per, Dms, Tym*): Address Unknown ☎ Shoreham 4345

COLE John (*Dms*): 28 Victoria Road, Alton, Hants GU34 2DQ ☎ 01420 88219

COLLISON Dennis (*Dms, B Ldr*): The Firs, 9 Oakwood Close, Burgess Hill, Sussex RH15 0HY ☎ Burgess Hill 55

COOK John (*Dms*): 84 Parkside, Shoreham-By-Sea, Sussex BN43 6HA ☎ 0179 17 3710

COOK Lee (*Dms*): ☎ 023 9261 7053, 023 9259 4580

COOPER Albert (*Dms*): 70 Glen Road, Woolston, Southampton SO2 9EH ☎ 023 8044 4559

COTTEE Andrew (*Per, Dms, Pf, Arr*): 48 Anglesey Avenue, Maidstone, Kent ME15 9SU ☎ 01622 744978, 020 8673 0049, 07970 154408

COUZENS Jon (*Dms*): 5 Linda Grove, Cowplain, Waterlooville, Hants PO8 8UX ☎ 023 9225 1039, 023 9266 4911

COVENEY Maurice (*Dms*): 151 Saxton Street, Gillingham, Kent ME7 5EH ☎ 01634 850718

CRAMB Ian (*Dms, Pf, T Sax, Clt*): 13 Priestley Road, Wallisdown, Bournemouth BH10 4AW

CRANHAM Peter (*Dms*): Sharabeth, 43 Cockshot Road, Reigate, Surrey RH2 7HB ☎ 01737 224175

CROLEY Paul (*Dms, Per, Kbds*): Flat 2, 43 Lower Market Street, Hove, East Sussex BN3 1AT ☎ 01273 749394

CROUCH Philip (*Dms, Per, Gtr*): 87 Shaftesbury Avenue, Chandlers Ford, Eastleigh, Hampshire SO53 3BQ ☎ 023 8026 8628

CUBBERLEY Gary (*Dms, Per*): 12 Gladstone Road, Horsham, West Sussex RH12 2NN ☎ 01403 264890, 0956 834560 mob

CULLUM Jonathan (*Dms*): 15 Blenheim Road, Reading RG1 5NG ☎ 0118 926 7756

CUNNINGHAM Blair (*Dms*): 28 Cuckoo Drive, Heathfield, East Sussex TN21 8AR ☎ 01435 864555, 01435 864555

DARCE Adrian (*Dms, Per, Gtr*): 7 Blenheim Road, Shirburn, Oxon OX9 5DN ☎ 01491 614085, 0468 098718

DAVEY Terence (*Dms*): 85 Radnor Park Rd, Folkestone, Kent CT19 5BU ☎ 01303 241533

DAVIDGE Ronald (*Dms*): Brentor, Spring Road, Lymington, Hants SO41 3SP ☎ 01590 74720

DAVIS Byron (*Dms*): Field House, 9 Kiln Lane, Woodside Windsor Forest, Winkfield Berks SL4 2DU ☎ 01344 883985

DAVIS Ronald (*Dms*): 179 Northdown Road, Cliftonville, Kent CT9 2PA ☎ 01843 224287

DAY Ann (*Dms*): 4 Victoria Street, Whitstable, Kent CT5 1JA ☎ 01227 772143

DE JONGE John (*Per, Dms*): Flat 3, 26 Bedford Place, Brighton, Sussex BN1 2PT ☎ 01273 323959

DEAN Dixie (*Dms*): c/o Mrs Malcomson, 1 Cranbourne Road, Gosport, Hants PO12 1RJ ☎ 01730 268307

DEBNAM Alex (*Dms, Bod*): 71 Millais Road, Southampton, Hampshire SO19 2FX ☎ 023 8044 0835/492157

DEWEY Derek (*Per*): Ivordere, Catteshall Lane, Godalming, Surrey GU7 1LW ☎ 01483 563201

DICKINSON David (*Dms*): 7 Tower Place, West End, Southampton, Hampshire SO30 3DL ☎ 023 8047 4651, 0973 316293

DIFFORD Simon (*Dms*): 9 Copse Road, Overton, Hants RG25 3JL ☎ 01256 770498

DINNAGE Paul (*Dms*): 26 Hinters Hill, High Wycombe, Bucks H13 7EW ☎ 01494 522010

DISTIN Terry (*Dms, Vib*): The Sands Hotel, Culver Road Sea Front, Sandown, Isle Of Wight PO36 8AT ☎ 01983 402305

DODGSON Philip (*Dms*): 202 Sidbury Cur Road, Tidworth, Hants SP9 7EX ☎ 01980 842326

DOFFMAN Mark (*Per*): 2 Norreys Avenue, Oxford OX1 4SS ☎ 01865 245537

DOLAN Jeremy (*Per*): Culross Manor, Wimlands Lane, Faygate, West Sussex RH12 4SP ☎ 01293 851656, 01293 851273

DUDGEON Gus (*Per*): Mole Cottage, Church Street, Cobham, Surrey KT11 3EG ☎ 019326 2055

DURHAM Christopher (*Dms, Per*): 51 Montefiore Road, Hove, E Sussex BN3 6EP ☎ 01273 770947

DURHAM Peter (*Dms*): 103 High Street, Shanklin, Isle Of Wight PO37 6NS ☎ 01983 863617

EDDOLLS John (*Dms*): Address Unknown

EDWARDS Luke (*Dms*): 15B Madeira Road, Ventnor, Isle Of Wight PO38 1QS

ELLIS Nick (*Dms*): 114, Wheaton Road, Bournemouth, Dorset BH7 6LL ☎ 01202 420635

ELLMER John (*Dms, Clt, Saxes, Vib*): 9 Warren Road, Willmington, Dartford, Kent DA1 IPS ☎ 01322 292778

ELROY Wally (*Dms*): 10 Pengelly Avenue, Bournemouth, Dorset BH10 6DR ☎ 01202 574934

EMBER Alvern (*Dms, Gtr*): Saxonhurst, 76 Portsmouth Rd, Woolston, Southampton SO19 9AN ☎ 023 8044 3931 & fax

ENGLISH John (*Dms*): 50 Wharfdale Road, Poole, Dorset BH12 2ED ☎ 01202 738119

EVANS Claudette (*Dms, Gtr, Voc*): 61 R.L. Stevenson Avenue, Bournemouth, Dorset BH4 8ED ☎ 01202 768084

EVANS Richard (*Dms*): 14 Markenfield Road, Guildford, Surrey GU1 4PB

EVEREST Gary (*Dms*): 110 Springfield Road, Edenbridge, Kent TN8 5HH ☎ 01732 863576

FALKNER Adam (*Dms*): 16 Reigate Road, Letherhead, Surrey KT22 8RA ☎ 01372 373012, 01523 105303

FALLOWELL Peter (*Dms, Per, Gtr, Kbds, Arr*): 48A Arthur Roadavenue, Wokingham, Berks RG41 2SY

FANTINI Anthony (*Dms, Bong*): 9A Wildown Road, Bournemouth, Dorset BH6 4DP ☎ 01202 432201

FARMER Gareth (*Dms*): 6 Elm Close, Wheatley, Oxford 0X33 1UW ☎ 01865 872284

FAULKNER Janet (*Per*): 16 Heather View Road, Parkstone, Poole, Dorset BH12 4AQ ☎ 01202 743251

FEAST Les (*Dms*): 4 Linden Road, Westgate, Kent CT8 8BY ☎ 01843 836400

FERRONE Stephen (*Dms, Per*): Att; Nancy Miller, Cavaricci & White Ltd, 416 Nova Albion Way, San Rafael, CA 94903 USA ☎ +1 415 472 1125

FIRSHT Samuel (*Dms*): 133 New Church Road, Hove, East Sussex BN3 4BE ☎ 01273 419927

FOLEY Graham (*Dms, Per, Pf*): 11 Sylvan Lane, Hamble, Hampshire SO31 4QG ☎ 023 8045 6455

FRANCIS Edward (*Dms, B Ldr, Dms*): 2 Tamworth Road, Boscombe, Bournemouth, Dorset BH7 6JG ☎ 01202 301313

FRANCIS Terence (*Dms*): 32 College Street, Salisbury, Wilts SP1 3AL ☎ 01722 339212

FRANKLIN Mark (*Dms, Per, Voc*): 33 Thorney Leys, Witney, Oxon OX8 7AX ☎ 01993 774429, 07899 723802

FRANKLIN Martin (*Per, Kbds*): 12 Keswick Court, Stoke Road, Slough, Berks SL2 5AN ☎ 01753 554567, 01753 554567

FRENCH David (*Dms, Kbds*): 15 Pavenham Road, Carlton, Bedford MK43 7LS ☎ 01234 720258

FRYATT Glenn (*Dms, Mbira, Timb*): 200 Powerscourt Road, North End, Portsmouth PO2 7JP ☎ 023 9266 7778, 0336 745885 pager

GEARING David (*Dms, B Ldr*): 3A Cranbury Close, Otterbourne, Winchester, Hants SO21 2EH ☎ 01962 714403

GENOCKEY Liam (*Dms, Per, Gtr*): 22 Collier Road, Hastings, East Sussex TN34 3JR ☎ 01424 431154

GEORGE (*Dms, Cel*): 52 Pitcroft Avenue, Reading RG6 1NN ☎ 0118 966 9633

GEORGE Dave (*Dms, Per*): 1 New Road, Wool, Nr.Wareham, Dorset BH20 6DX ☎ 01929 463939

GIBSON Michael (*Dms*): 20 Southampton Hill, Titchfield, Fareham, Hampshire PO14 4AJ ☎ 01329 510362

GIBSON Stephen (*Per*): 57 Abelwood Road, Long Hanborough, Oxon OX8 8DD ☎ 01993 882132, 0976 919262 mob

GILL William (*Dms*): 8 Mountbatten Court, Bircmett Road, Aldershot, Hants GU11 1LY ☎ 01252 344168

GLANVILLE Spencer (*Dms*): 172B Locksway Road, Portsmouth, Hants PO4 8LE ☎ 023 9283 8632

GLENN Harry (*Dms, Db, Voc*): Downs Cottage, Thorley Road, Yarmouth, Isle Of Wight PO41 0SH ☎ 01983 760507

GLOCKLER Nigel (*Dms, Per*): 13 Princes Square, Hove, Sussex BN3 4GE

GODDARD James (*Dms, Voc, Pf, B Gtr, Gtr*): 15 The Binghams, Maidenhead, Berkshire SL6 2ES ☎ 01628 76055

GOOD Paul (*Dms, Gtr*): 10 Whitehouse Way, Iver Heath, Bucks SL0 0HB ☎ 01753 653250

GOODWIN Simon (*Dms*): 18 Herbert Road, Brighton, Sussex BN1 6PB ☎ 01273 565529

GORELICK Simon (*Dms, Voc*): Platyhelminthes Towers, 128 Markham Road, Bournemouth BH9 1JE ☎ 01202 519796

GOULD Philip (*Dms, Per*): East Cottage, Trigon, Wareham, Dorset BH20 7PD ☎ 01929 553997

GRAHAM John (*Dms, Per, B Gtr, Kbds, Gtr*): 38 Woodland Road, Selsey, West Sussex PO20 0AL ☎ 01243 603156, 0402 646772 mob, 01243 607664

GREEN Mark (*Dms, Per, Cong, Pf*): 3 Wharf Cottages, Stonebridge Wharf, Shalford, Surrey GU4 8EH ☎ 01483 452486

GREENE David (*Dms, Pf*): 18 Spring Gardens Road, High Wycombe, Bucks HP13 7AG

GREENHILL Simon (*Dms, Per, Voc*): 15A Seamoor Road, Bournemouth, Dorset BH4 9AA ☎ 01202 767369

GRIFFIN Jeffrey (*Dms*): 38 Jewell Road, Bournemouth, Dorset BH8 0JQ ☎ 01202 399329

GROOM Don (*Dms*): 32 Burstead Close, Hollingdean, Brighton BN1 7HT ☎ 559085

GRUNDY Dan (*Dms*): The Red House, 106 The Street, Capel, Dorking, Surrey RH5 5JY ☎ 01306 711121

HALES Steve (*Dms, B Gtr, Kbds*): 24 Waverley Road, Freemantle, Southampton, Hants SO15 1JG ☎ 023 8032 1257

HALL Chris (*Dms*): 103 Bull Lane, Eccles, Aylesford, Kent ME20 7HT ☎ 01634 241262

HALL John (*Dms*): 28 Liddel Way, Badgers Copse, Chandlers Ford, Hants SO5 3QG ☎ 023 8025 5690

HALL Laurence (*Dms, Kbds, Voc*): 4 Cedars Court, The Cedars, Burpham, Guildford, Surrey GU1 1YZ ☎ 01483 574997

HALLAM Timothy (*Dms*): 11 Dracaena Gardens, Shanklin, Isle Of Wight PO37 7JQ ☎ 01983 863898

HAMMOND John (*Dms*): 53 Knowsley Road, Cosham, Portsmouth, Hants PO6 2PD ☎ 023 9232 4901

HAMMOND Richard (*Dms*): 14 Carlyle Close, Newport Pagnell MK16 8PZ ☎ 01908 616683, 0402 557807

HANDFORD Greg (*Dms, Pf, Gtr*): Treetops, Deanwood Road, Jordans, Bucks HP9 2UU ☎ 01494 675988

HANNAN Patrick (*Dms, Voc*): 68 Reading Road South, Fleet, Hants GU13 9SD ☎ 01252 616394, 0973 213353, 01256 701106 fax

HARRIS Ian (*Dms, Gtr, B Gtr, Kbds, Vln*): 13 Westgate Terrace, Whitstable, Kent CT5 1LB

HARRIS Steve (*Per, Vln, Md, Arr, Cop*): 6 Selwyn Drive, Yateley, Hampshire GU46 6QF ☎ 01252 661360

HART Ronald (*Dms*): 29 Arundel Drive West, Saltdean, Brighton, East Sussex BN2 8SJ ☎ 01273 305342

HARTLEY Martyn (*Dms*): 55 Nelson Road, Gillingham, Kent ME7 4LR ☎ 01634 301 863, 0467 680 931

HAWKES Derek (*Dms*): 163 Queenborough Road, Sheerness, Kent ME12 3EN ☎ 01795 663004

HAWORTH Gary (*Dms, Per*): 10 St Marys Road, Hartley Wintney, Hook, Hampshire RG27 8EZ ☎ 01252 842406

HAYMAN Steve (*Dms*): 21 Woodgate Meadow, Plumpton Green, Lewes, East Sussex BN7 3BD ☎ 01273 890139 & fax

HEDGECOCK John Bernard (*Dms, Kbds*): 42 East Lockinge, Wantage, Oxon OX12 8QD

HEDLEY Adam (*Dms, Per, Voc*): 101 Dudden Close, Townhill Way, West End, Southampton, Hampshire SO18 3QB ☎ 023 8047 3852

HEELEY Brian (*Dms, Per*): 128A Spring Road, Bournemouth, Dorset BH1 4PU ☎ 01202 304629

HETHERINGTON Ronald (*Dms*): 70 Arnett Avenue, Wokingham RG11 4EE ☎ 01734 730360

HEYMERDINGER Tim (*Dms*): 2 Northcroft, Shenley Lodge, Milton Keynes, Bucks MK5 7BE ☎ 01908 671688

HIGGINS David (*Dms*): 89A Westbourne Street, Hove, East Sussex BN2 3PF ☎ 01273 727361

HIGGINSON Daniel (*Dms, Voc, Gtr, Pf*): Parkmeade, Colwell Lane, Freshwater, Isle Of Wight PO40 9LX ☎ 01983 755276, 07666 723441 pager

HOBBS Paul (*Dms, Per*): 50 Ambridge Grove, Peartree Bridge, Milton Keynes, Bucks MK6 3PQ ☎ 01908 692547

HOLLICK Kenneth (*Dms, La Per*): 47 Pilsdon Drive, Canford Heath, Poole, Dorset BH17 8EJ ☎ 01202 602342

HORWOOD Jack (*Dms, Vib*): 40A Canford Bottom, Colehill, Wimborne, Dorset BH21 2HD ☎ 01202 881201

HOWCROFT Craig (*Dms, Voc, Kbds*): 10 Burnt House Lane, Bransgore, Christchurch, Dorset G05 ☎ 01425 674181

HUGGETT Roy (*Dms*): 37 Jubilee Road, Waterlooville, Hants PO7 7RE ☎ 017014 250403

HUNT Royston (*Dms, Per, Tym*): 15 Gatland Lane, Maidstone, Kent ME16 8PJ ☎ 01622 728309, 01622 726214

IAAZANE Ali (*Per, Darab, Com*): 34 St Mary's Terrace, Hastings, East Sussex TN34 3LR ☎ 01424 429 858

IVE Peter (*Dms*): 27 Blythe Road, Maidstone, Kent ME15 7TR ☎ 01622 763753

JACKSON Bert (*Dms*): 4 Thornley Road, Bournemouth, Dorset BH10 6DZ ☎ 01202 579218

JAMES Andrew (*Dms, Per*): 109 Palmerston Road, Chatham, Kent ME4 6NB ☎ 01634 329458

JAMIESON Lindsay (*Dms, Pf, Flt, Voc*): c/o Mr & Mrs J B Jamieson, 44 Rounton Road, Church Cookham, Fleet, Hants GU13 0JH

JARRETT Frank (*Dms, Voc*): 'The Pad', 3 The Park, Naish Farm, New Milton, Hants BH25 7RN ☎ 01425 271553

JAY Steve (*Dms*): 10 Richmond Close, Calmore, Totton, Hants SO4 2TH ☎ 023 8086 1977

JENKINS Andrew (*Dms, Per*): 584 Grange Road, Gillingham, Kent ME7 2UH ☎ 01634 570133

JOHNSON William (*Dms*): 65 Cryalls Lane, Sittingbourne, Kent ME10 1NZ ☎ 01795 421242

JONES Peter (*Dms*): 25 Evenlode Way, Sandhurst, Berkshire GU47 9RG ☎ 01344 771797, 0839 035342

JORDAN Mark (*Dms*): 14A The Granville, Victoria Parade, Ramsgate, Kent CT11 8DF ☎ 01843 852439

KELLNER Steven (*Dms, Per*): 113 Church Road, Hove, East Sussex BN3 2AF ☎ 01273 720005

KENNELL David (*Per, Dms, Tym*): 4 Hillside Road, Verwood, Dorset BH31 7HE ☎ 01202 820736

KENT Avril (*Per*): 24 Moy Avenue, Eastbourne, East Sussex BN22 8UF ☎ 01323 20744

KEYS Jonathan (*Dms, Voc*): 19 Captains Close, Sutton Vallence, Nr Maidstone, Kent ME17 3BA ☎ 01622 844088, 0411 166817

KING Gareth (*Dms, Pf, B Gtr*): 4 Hayes Lane, Wimborne, Dorset BH21 2JE ☎ 01202 882827, 0961 164707

KING Gary (*Dms*): 70 Tower Road West, St Leonards-on-Sea, East Sussex TN38 0RL

KING Jeff (*Dms, Voc*): 01635 846464, 0958 353532, 01635 846464

KIRBY Steve (*Dms, Voc, Flt*): The Cottage, Gravel Hill Lodge, Benham Chase, Stokecross, Newbury, Berkshire RG20 8LQ

KNIGHT Alex (*Dms, Pf*): Roughwood, Butchers Lane, Three Oaks, East Sussex TN35 4NG ☎ 01424 751080

KNIGHT Barry (*Dms*): 33 Castle Road, Allington, Nr Maidstone, Kent ME16 0PP ☎ 01622 753830

KNIGHT Gavin (*Dms, Per*): The Cottage, 1A Bursledon Road, Hedge End, Southampton, Hants SO30 0BP ☎ 01489 795659

LAMBERT Matthew (*Dms, B Gtr, Gtr, Voc*): Flat 5 Belvedere Court, 12 Trinity Crescent, Folkestone, Kent CT20 2ET ☎ 01303 259446, 01303 259446

LASLETT Phillip (*Dms*): Rosedale, Marshborough, Sandwich, Kent CT13 0PF ☎ Ash 812231

LAY Peter (*Dms*): 92 Mid Street, South Nutfield, Surrey RH1 4JH ☎ 01737 822726, 01737 822726

LIGHT Tim (*Dms, Gtr*): 9 Fairway Close, Copthorne, Crawley, West Sussex RH10 3PX ☎ 01342 716431

LIGHTFOOT Leslie (*Dms*): 51 Ferndale Road, New Milton, Hants BH25 5EX ☎ 01590 61540

LITTLE Phil (*Dms, Per*): 34A Pevensey Road, St Leonards-on-Sea, East Sussex TN38 0LF ☎ 01424 717326

LONERGAN Dick (*Dms, B Gtr*): 116 London Road, Camberley, Surrey GU15 3TJ ☎ 01276 24410

LONGMORE Ken (*Dms, Vib, Xyl, B Ldr*): 26 St Catherines Road, Bournemouth, Dorset BH6 4AB ☎ 01202 426507

LOVELOCK Andrew (*Dms*): 15 Windlesham Gardens, Shoreham By Sea, West Sussex BN43 5AD ☎ 01273 463389

LOWREY Robin (*Dms*): Brae Foot, 16 Upper Bourne Lane, Boundstone, Farnham, Surrey GU10 4RQ ☎ 01252 793821

MAGUIRE Damian (*Dms, Vln, Gtr, Kbds, Voc*): 1 St. Clements Gardens, Boscombe, Bournemouth, Dorset BH1 4ED ☎ 01202 399114

MAIN-ELLEN Mark (*Dms, Gtr, Voc*): 102 The Broadway, Sheerness, Isle Of Sheppey, Kent ME12 1TS ☎ 01795 667027

MANKTELOW John (*Dms*): 16 Chamberlain Avenue, Maidstone, Kent ME16 8NR ☎ 01622 205657

MANNING Leo (*Dms, Gtr*): 30 Raleigh Crescent, Goring By Sea, West Sussex BN12 6EE ☎ 01903 240725

MARDEN David (*Dms*): 16 Stroud Close, Colehill, Wimborne, Dorset BH21 2NX ☎ 01202 883366

MARSH Tex (*Dms*): 79 West Front Road, Pagham Beach, Pagham, Nr Bognor Regis, West Sussex PO21 4TB ☎ 01243 263657

MARSHALL Gary (*Dms, Per*): 57 Station Road, Cropredy, Oxfordshire OX17 1PT ☎ 01295 758644, 0589 226886, 01295 262166

MARSHALL Jim (*Dms*): Address Unknown ☎ 01908 582364

MAYNARD Leslie (*Dms*): 6 Malan Close, South Canford Heath, Poole, Dorset BH17 7PU ☎ 01202 675564

MCCARTHY Haydn (*Dms*): 21 Cox Close, Muscliffe Park, Bournemouth, Dorset BH9 3LT ☎ 01202 524475

MCDADE Steven (*Dms, Per*): 10 Norfolk Rd, Shirley, Southampton, Hants SO15 5AS ☎ 023 8033 7570

MCMURRAY Donald (*Dms*): 16 Brunswick Square, Hove, Sussex BN3 1EH ☎ 01273 721765

MCNAMEE-HEALY Cameron (*Dms*): 20 Bernstein Road, Brighton Hill, Basingstoke, Hampshire RG22 2ND ☎ 01256 463368, 0589 690680

MELLERS Neil (*Dms, Per*): 1 Raleigh Road, Rose Green, Bognor Regis, West Sussex PO21 2NA ☎ 01243 264723

MILLS Andrew (*Dms, Hmca, Voc*): 11 Abbotstone Avenue, Havant, Hants PO9 2HL ☎ 023 9248 1978

MILLS Des (*Dms*): Newbarn House, 2 Braemar Way, Bersted, Bognor Regis, West Sussex PO21 5DP ☎ 01243 823626

MILLS Frederick (*Dms*): 74 Nutwood Avenue, Betchworth, Surrey RH3 7LT ☎ 01737 843287

MOGER Anthony (*Dms, Pic*): The Duck House, 175 Mill Road, Burgess Hill, West Sussex RH15 8DA ☎ 01444 244673

MORGAN Brett (*Dms*): 4 Furzeland Way, Sayers Common, Albourne, West Sussex BN6 9JB ☎ 01273 835764

MORRIS David (*Dms, Gtr, Pf*): Flat 5, 11 Gordon Avenue, Bognor Regis, West Sussex PO22 9LG ☎ 01243 842186, 01243 739170, 01243 788707

MORRIS Tim (*Dms, Kbds, B Gtr, Voc*): Address Unknown ☎ 01428 608821

MORTIMORE Malcolm (*Dms*): Lovelace House, 109 High Street, Lewes, East Sussex BN7 1XY ☎ 01273 486 309

MURRAY Holly (*Dms*): Top Flat, 12 Goldsmus Road, Hove, East Sussex BN3 1QA ☎ 01273 776885

MUXLOW John (*Dms*): 44A Denmark Villas, Hove, Brighton, Sussex BN3 3TE ☎ 01273 206134

NEAL David (*Per*): 14 Mayville Road, St Peters, Broadstairs, Kent CT10 3ET ☎ 01843 602114

NEAVES Michael (*Dms*): 1 Swindon Road, Horsham, West Sussex RH12 2HE ☎ 01403 257953

NEAVES Richard (*Dms*): 3 Gaywood Walk, Worthing, West Sussex BN13 2SE ☎ 01903 263016

NORTH Neil (*Dms, Gtr*): Granby, Barns Farm Lane, Storrington, West Sussex RH20 4AH ☎ 01903 744155 & fax

O'BRIEN Mike (*Dms, Voc*): Colt Studios, Farley Hall, Farley Hill, Reading, Berkshire RG7 1UL ☎ 0118 973 5306

O'HALLORAN Mark (*Dms, Kbds*)

OTTAWAY Scot (*Dms, Kbds*): 152 Anton Way, Aylesbury, Bucks HP21 9HS ☎ 01296 433106, 0958 397053

PALMER Timothy (*Per, Tym*): 12 Oxford Street, Wolverton, Buckinghamshire MK12 5HP ☎ 01908 320115

PANETTA Carlo (*Dms*): 24 Acacia Close, Croft Street, Surrey Quays, London SE8 5EQ

PARRY Ronald (*Dms*): 16 Varndean Holt, Brighton, East Sussex BN1 6QX ☎ 01273 501544

PARTIS Lee (*Dms*): 41 Queens Park Terrace, Brighton BN2 2YA ☎ 01273 620977

PATTERSON Steven (*Dms, Pf, Gtr*): The Griggs, Ashford Road, New Romney, Kent TN28 8HP ☎ 01797 364647, 0958 702476

PAVLOU Louis (*Dms, Gtr, B Gtr, Voc*): 18A York Road, Rochester, Kent ME1 3DP ☎ 01634 828742

PENGELLY Allan (*Dms*): 77 Bishops Road, Itchen, Southampton SO19 2FD ☎ 023 8044 0007, 0141 089 7366

PETERS Charles (*Dms*): 69 Langney Road, Eastbourne BN21 3QD ☎ 01323 26821

PETTENGELL James (*Dms*): 12 Woodside Close, Ferndown, Dorset BH22 9LG ☎ 01202 894514

PHILPOTT Barry (*Dms, Pf, Org, Voc*): Heymar Stables, Whitstable Road, Herne Bay, Kent CT6 8BL ☎ Herne Bay 67641

PILBEAM David (*Dms, Kbds*)

POTTER Malcolm (*Dms*): 4 Murrin Road, Maidenhead, Berkshire SL6 5EQ ☎ Maidenhead 3608

POWELL Nigel (*Dms, Gtr, Kbds, B Gtr, Voc*): 20 B Ock Street, Abingdon, Oxon OX14 5BZ ☎ 01235 536350 & fax

POWER Patrick (*Per, B Gtr*): Flat 2, 5 Montpelier Cres, Brighton, E Sussex BN1 3JF ☎ 01273 726793, 01273 419347

PRAGER Samuel (*Dms*): 136 Corhampton Road, Bournemouth, Dorset BH6 5PD ☎ 01202 482973

PRICE Tony (*Dms*): 154, Ham Road, East Worthing, Sussex BN11 2QS ☎ Worthing 211296

PRIEST Daniel (*Per, Tym, Dms, La Per*): 17 Granville Road, Bournemouth, Dorset BH5 2AQ ☎ 01202 431655, 0973 744560 mob

PRIESTLEY Chris (*Dms*): Ground Floor Flat, 48 Wilbury Road, Hove, East Sussex BN3 3PA ☎ 01273 721175

PULLEN K (*Dms*): 18 Sandymead Road, Bournemouth, Dorset BH8 9JY ☎ 01202 301347

RAE Christian (*Dms, Per, Pf*): The Shambles, Westhorpe Road, Marlow, Bucks SL7 1LD ☎ 01628 485363, 01628 891003

RASHEED Aadil (*Dms, Per, Cong, Bong, Kbds*): Wellington Cottage, 21 Wyles Street, Gillingham, Kent ME7 1ND ☎ 01634 854865

REA Mark (*Per*): 44A Richmond Street, Brighton, Sussex BN2 2PD ☎ 01273 689226

REDDINGTON Laurence (*Dms*): 56 Hockmore Tower, Pound Way, Cowley, Oxford OX4 3YG ☎ 01865 716482

RENDELL Ernest (*Dms, Voc*): 54 The Broadway, Northbourne, Bournemouth, Dorset BH10 7EZ ☎ 01202 770134

REVITT Neil (*Dms, Per, B Gtr, Rh Gtr*): 54 West Street, Olney, Bucks MK46 5HR ☎ 01234 713154

REYNOLDS Peter (*Dms*): 27 Streete Court, Westgate-on-Sea, Kent CT8 8BT ☎ 01843 834451

RICHARDS Jack (*Per*): Belmont, Castle Road, Ventnor, Isle Of Wight PO38 1LG ☎ 01983 855845

RICHARDS Victor (*Dms, Vib*): 6 Fort Gate, Newhaven, Sussex BN9 9DR ☎ Btn 516097

ROSE Dawn (*Dms*): 6 Newcroft Cottages, Selsfield Road, Little London, Ardingly, West Sussex RH16 6TJ ☎ 01444 892552, 01444 892552

ROSE Mac (*Dms*): 51 Mudeford Lane, Christchurch, Dorset BH23 3HN ☎ 01202 475569

RYAN Petea (*Dms, Gtr*) ☎ 01273 680850

SALAD Mark (*Dms*): 14 Mount Pleasant, Aylesbury, Bucks HP19 3AQ ☎ 01296 87343

SANDELL Ian (*Per*): 46 Ringmer Road, Worthing, West Sussex BN13 1IDT ☎ 01903 531077, 0797 0352763, 01903 538552

SANDWELL George (*Dms*): 111 Grosvenor Place, Margate, Kent CT9 1UX ☎ Thanet 221429

SAUNDERS Gerald (*Dms, Per*): 12 Lincoln Avenue, Bournemouth, Dorset BH1 4QS ☎ 01202 302414

SCHUNKER Adam (*Dms*): Chellows Park, Chellows Lane, Crowhurst, Surrey RH7 6LU ☎ 01342 835434

SCOTT Kevin (*Dms, Voc*): 9 Derwent Close, Addlestone, Surrey KT15 2JQ ☎ 01932 886538

SCRIVEN Graham (*Dms, Voc*): 1 Wealdstone Place, Springfield, Milton Keynes MK6 3JF ☎ 01908 674855

SELLARS Robin (*Dms*): St Francis De La Sales, Ruxbury Road, Chertsey, Surrey KT16 9NH ☎ 01932 571946

SENFF Mitchel (*Dms*)

SHARLAND Alan (*Dms, Gtr, Kbds*): 54 Staplehurst, Woodenhill, Bracknell, Derbyshire RG12 8DB ☎ 01344 428679

SHEFFORD Justin (*Dms, Per, Vln, Pf*): 8 Victoria Road, Golden Green, Tonbridge, Kent TN11 0LP ☎ 01732 851265

SIMMS Dave (*Dms*): 46 Howe Drive, Beaconfield, Bucks HP9 2BD ☎ 01494 674312

SINGLETON Leo (*Dms*): Broad Lane Cottage, Newtown, Newbury, Berks RG20 9AX ☎ 01635 48837

SININERD Owen (*Dms*): Top Flat, 159 Ditching Rise, Brighton, East Sussex BN1 4QR ☎ 01273 570147, 01273 622940

SLADE Christopher (*Dms, Per*): Downgate Lodge, Silverden Lane, Sandhurst, Kent TN18 5NU ☎ 020 7831 4200

SMITH Christopher (*Dms, Voc*): 70 Sydenham St, Whitstable, Kent CT5 1HL ☎ 01227 276484, 020 7292 6314

SMITH Geoff (*Per, La Per, H Dul, Dms*): 108 Wilmington Way, Hollingbury, Brighton, Sussex BN1 8JF ☎ 559188

SMITH Jason (*Dms, Per*): 3 Rye Road, Hastings, East Sussex TN35 5DA ☎ 0973 782818

SMITH Martin (*Dms, Eup, Per*): 10 Sussex Court, Ashenground Road, Haywards Heath, West Sussex RH16 4PA ☎ 01444 456884, 01737 778711 day

SMITH Mcgregor (*Dms*): 17 Cleveland Court, Chine Crescent Road, Bournemouth BH2 5LG ☎ 01202 765147

SMITH Trevor (*Dms*): 13 St Paul's Crescent, Shanklin, I.O.W. PO37 7AW ☎ 01983 866116, 07775 866826

SNOODEN Matthew (*Dms, Per, Kbds, Man, Hrp*): 70 Poulters Lane, Worthing, West Sussex BN14 7SZ ☎ 01903 261488, 01273 462440

SOLOMON Philip (*Dms*): 20A Newmarket Road, Brighton, East Sussex BN2 3QF ☎ 01273 608916

SPICER Hal (*Dms*): 324 Meggeson Avenue, Townhill Park, Southampton SO18 2HF ☎ 023 8055 1998

SPONG Les (*Dms*): 60 Upper Road, Kennington, Oxford OX1 5LJ ☎ 01865 735452

SPURLING William (*Dms, Per, Pf*): 24 Dodds Park, Brockham, Betchworth, Surrey RH3 7LD ☎ 01737 842442, 01737 842442

STURGIS Mike (*Dms*): 50 Summers Road, Farncombe, Surrey GU7 3BD ☎ 01483 418998, 01483 456788

SULLIVAN Terence (*Dms, Per, Gtr, Kbds*): The Old Bells, Silver Street, Lymington, Hants SO42 0FN ☎ 01425 620553

SUMMERS Anthony (*Per, Tym, Arr, Pf*): Moorings, Bishops Down Park Road, Tunbridge Wells, Kent TN4 8XR ☎ 01892 538223

SWEENEY Victor (*Dms*): 5 Wymers Close, Burnham, Bucks SL1 8JR

TAGFORD James (*Dms*): 59 Broadmead Road, Folkestone, Kent CT19 5AW ☎ Folkestone 2580

THEW Graeme (*Per, Tym, Dms*): 31 Kent Road, Gravesend, Kent DA11 0SZ ☎ 01474 325823

THOMAS David (*Dms, Per, Cel, Kbds*): 46 Lower Market Street, Hove, East Sussex BN3 1AT ☎ 01273 738985, 01892 782848

THOMAS Owen (*Dms, Gtr, Kbds, Pf*): Woodfield Farm, Milton O Stour, Gillingham, Dorset SP8 5PX ☎ 01747 824729, 01747 824986

THOROLD Rupert (*Dms*): Frogpool Cottage, 93 High Street, Chobham GU24 8LY ☎ 01276 857385

THORPE Raymond (*Dms*): Top Flat, 25 Alexanda Road, Margate, Kent CT9 5SP ☎ Thanet 223021

THOW Harry (*Dms, Voc*): 56 King John Avenue, Bournemouth, Dorset BH11 9RU ☎ 01202 577853

TIBBS Graham (*Dms, Per*): 34 Norman Road, Tunbridge Wells, Kent TN1 2RT ☎ 01892 522519

TODD David (*Dms*): 15 Hambledon Close, Lower Earley, Reading, Berks RG6 3TD ☎ 0118 962 5888

TOLFREE Lawrence (*Dms*): 4 The Caravans, Railway Tavern, 56 Station Road, North Elmham, Dereham, Norfolk NR20 5HH ☎ 01362 668764

TOWNSEND Daniel (*Per, Dms*): 32 Bayswater Drive, Rainham, Gillingham, Kent ME8 8TF ☎ 01634 363258

TOZER Lois (*Dms, Flt*): Flat 5 Belvedere Court, 12 Tirnity Crescent, Folkestone, Kent CT20 2ET ☎ 01303 259446, 01303 259 446

TRIGWELL Dave (*Dms*): Nen Thorn West, Hammerwood Road, Ashurst Wood, W Sussex RH19 3RU ☎ 01342 825156

TRIM Andrew (*Dms*): 25 Reap Lane, Sweethill Estate, Southwell Portland, Dorset DT5 2DW ☎ 01305 823287

TUNNICLIFFE Angela (*Per, Dms*): 14 Townsend Road, Chesham, Bucks HP5 2AA ☎ 01494 294527, 0958 578587

TURNER Peter (*Dms*): 216 High Street, Herne Bay, Kent CT6 5AX ☎ 01227 371210

VAN HOOKE Peter (*Dms, Per*): Kemprow Farm, High Cross, Oakridge Lane, Aldenham, Herts WD2 8BR

VAN RYNE Alistair (*Dms, Per*): The White House, West Street, Sompting, West Sussex BN15 0AP ☎ 01903 236253

VAUGHAN Stephen (*Dms, Per*): 36 Victoria Road, Blandford Forum, Dorset DT11 7JR ☎ 01258 456460

VINALL Jaimie (*Dms*): 11 St. Michaels Terrace, Lewes, East Sussex BN7 2HX ☎ 01273 478893, 0976 854396 mob

VINCENT Raymond (*Dms, Per*): The Crooked House, Shillingstone, Nr Blandford, Dorset DT11 0SF ☎ 01258 860007

VITTY Keith (*Dms*): 10 Bray Court, Windsor Road, Bray, Maidenhead, Berks SL6 2DR ☎ 01628 620397 & fax

WADSWORTH Paul (*Dms, Gtr, Pf*): 10 Hollingdean Road, Brighton BN2 4AA ☎ 01273 623337

WALDMANN Alexander (*Dms*): 4 Apsley Road, Oxford OX2 7QY ☎ 01865 553822

WALLER Garry (*Dms*): 25 Hemmingway Road, Aylesbury, Bucks HP19 3SD ☎ 0184421 3410

WALSH Patrick (*Dms*): 30 Milton Road, Sutton Courtenay, Abingdon, Oxon OX14 4BS ☎ 01235 847129

WARD Arthur (*Dms*): 9A East Cams Close, Down End, Fareham, Hants PO16 8RP ☎ 01329 510994

WARD Gavin (*Dms*): 7 Ashdown Court, Vernon Road, Uckfield, East Sussex TN22 5DX ☎ 01825 768995

WARNER Ernest (*Dms*): Church View, Temple Lane, East Meon, Nr Petersfield, Hants GU32 1NT ☎ 01730 823227

WATSON Robin (*Dms, Per*): 125 Partridge Gardens, Wecock Farm, Cowplain PO8 9XH ☎ 023 9271 8959

WATTS Ray (*Dms*): 17 Portman Crescent, Bournemouth, Dorset BH5 2ER ☎ 01202 429159

WATTS-PLUMPKIN Nigel (*Dms, Voc*): Stepping Stone, Post Office Road, Inkpen, Hungerford, Berks RG17 9PY ☎ 01488 668475, 0488 668475

WELLER Tim (*Dms, Per*): 51 Henslowe Road, East Dulwich, London SE22 0AR ☎ 020 8693 9893, 0973 695 068 mob, 020 8480 0682 fax

WELLINGS Clive (*Dms*): 76 Hamilton Road, Reading, Berkshire RG1 5RD

WELLS Bobby (*Dms, Voc*): 9, Tuxford Mews, Watermead, Reading, Berkshire RG30 2NW ☎ 0118, 950 7005

WHATMORE Stuart (*Per, Tym*): 12 Kinver Close, Romsey, Hampshire SO51 7JU ☎ 01794 501133, 07970 686112

WHITE Andy (*Dms, Per*): 101 Peabody Road, Farnborough, Hampshire GU14 6EB ☎ 01252 548779

WHITE David (*Per*): 82 St Richards Road, Deal, Kent CT14 9JU ☎ Deal 633100

WHITE Roy (*Dms*): 18 Coniston Road, Redbridge, Southampton, Hants SO16 9BT ☎ 023 8086 4008

WHITTINGHAM Marc Andrew (*Per*): 20 Westwood Gardens, Chandlers Ford, Eastleigh, Hampshire SO53 1FN ☎ 023 8026 6871

WICKSON Simon (*Dms*): 47 Pinsley Road, Long Hanborough, Witney, Oxford OX8 8JQ ☎ 01993 881770

WILDISH Valentino (*Dms*): 18 St Michael's Road, Maidstone, Kent ME16 8BS

WILLIAMS Paul (*Per*): 86A Irving Road, Southbourne, Bournemouth, Dorset BH6 5BL ☎ 01202 430569 & fax, 01426 282805 pager

WOLLEN James (*Dms*): 32 Sylvan Way, Grange Estate, Church Crookham, Hants GU13 0QP ☎ 01252 628621

WRIGHT Anthony (*Dms*): 47 Havelock Road, Dartford, Kent DA1 3HY ☎ 01322 280427

WRIGHT Chris (*Dms*): 4 The Chestnuts, Lower Shiplake, Henley-on-Thames RG9 3JZ ☎ 01734 402372

YOUNG Ian (*Dms, Per*): 89 Cherry Way, Alton, Hants GU34 2AT ☎ 01420 542129

SOUTH WEST

ABENDSTERN John (*Per*): 2 Ovington Terrace, Victoria Park, Cardiff CF5 1GF ☎ 029 2023 1813

ALDERTON Glenn (*Dms*): 1 The Patchway, Wiltshire SN10 3SW ☎ 01380 726389, 0410 878172 mob

ALDRIDGE Kenneth (*Dms*): 65 Mackie Road, Filton, Bristol BS12 7LZ ☎ 0117 9691729

ALLISON John (*Per, Dms*): 55 Pocketts Wharf, Maritime Quater, Swansea, W/Glamorgan SA1 3XL ☎ 01792 655682

ANSTICE-BROWN Sam (*Dms, Tbn, Arr, Cop*): 2 Church Street, Kingsbury Episcopi, Martock, Somerset TA12 6AU ☎ 01935 812177

APLIN Albert (*Dms, Voc*): Trelyn, Deepway Gardens, Exminster, Nr Exeter EX6 8BE ☎ 01392 832620

ARTHURS Debbie (*Per, Voc, T Sax*): 17 Rothermere Close, Up Hatherly, Cheltenham GL51 5UU ☎ 01242 575831

BAILEY Thomas (*Dms, Sax, Voc*): 125 St Georges Road, Hotwell 5, Bristol BS1 5UW ☎ 0117 9298540

BAKER Bernard (*Per, Tym, Xyl*): 10 Abbotsridge Drive, Ogwell, Newton Abbot, Devon TQ12 6YS ☎ 01626 52054

BANKS Wilfred (*Dms*): Address Unknown

BEACROFT Geoffrey (*Dms*): Rowan House, Longmead Close, Norton St Philip, Bath BA3 6NS ☎ 01373 834181, 01225 445885 day

BEALING Leonard (*Dms, B Ldr*): 47 St Michaels Road, Melksham, Wiltshire SN12 6HN ☎ 01225 702688

BEAVER Philip (*Dms, Per*): Hill Farm, Cad Road, Ilton, Ilminster, Somerset TA19 9HF ☎ 01460 53995

BENNETT John (*Dms*): Montrose, 48 Byron Road, Newport, Gwent NP9 ☎ 01633 264790

BLACK Lindsay (*Dms*): 36 Langer Way, Clydach, Swansea SA6 5JX ☎ 01792 845833

BOOBYER Keith (*Dms*): Grove Lodge, Staplegrove Road, Taunton, Somerset TA2 6AN ☎ 01823 274670

BRADLEY Graham (*Per, Dms, Tym*): 3 Alexandra Street, Cathays, Cardiff CF2 4NT ☎ 029 2022 0894, 07050 124134, 07971 959474

BRASHER Hugh (*Dms, Per, Pf, Gtr*)

BRIAN Robert (*Dms, Per, Kbds, Voc*): 29 Paul Street, Corsham, Wiltshire SN13 9DG ☎ 01249 715473

BROKENSHIRE Robert (*Dms, Per, Tym*): Benacre, Troubridge Road, Helston, Cornwall TR13 8DQ ☎ 01326 561486

BROOK John (*Dms, Per*): 23 Greenbank Terrace, Falmouth, Cornwall TR11 2SW ☎ 01326 313977

BROWN Daniel (*Dms*): 46 Water Lane, Tiverton, Devon EX16 6RB ☎ 01884 252059

BROWNE Jack (*Dms, B Ldr*): 16 Coulsdon Road, Sidmouth, Devon EX10 9JJ ☎ Sidmouth 77770

BURNS Richard (*Dms*): 33 Jupes Close, Exminster, Devon EX6 8BD ☎ 01392 824909

BUTLIN Matthew (*Per, Dms*): 3 Abelia Close, Paignton, South Devon TQ3 3TQ ☎ 01803 852964

CAMPBELL Hilary (*Per*): 31 Mount Could Road, Plymouth PL4 7PT ☎ 01752 788182 & fax, 01752 223893

CARVER Jack (*Dms*): 97 Bromley Road, Horfield, Bristol BS7 9JE ☎ 0117 952 5273

CAVANAGH Damien (*Dms, St Pan, Gtr, B Gtr*): 564A Kingston Road, Raynes Park, London SW20 8DR ☎ 020 8543 2441, 020 7836 5411 ext 3701

CHUBB Graham (*Dms*): 3 Wyndham Farm Cottages, Allington, Nr Salisbury SP4 0DB ☎ 01980 610400

CLAPPERTON Julien (*Dms, Per*): 144 Sylvia Avenue, Bristol BS3 5BZ ☎ 0117 9716 147

CLIFT Roger (*Tnd Per*): 5 Bloomfield Close, Newport, Gwent NP9 9ET ☎ 01633 282268

COLWYN Lord Ian (*Dms, Tpt*): 29 Oakley Gardens, London SW3 5QH ☎ 020 7351 9224

COOK Kevin (*Dms, Per*): 48 Chedworth, Yate, Bristol BS17 4RY ☎ 01454 325132

COOKSON Andrew (*Per, Dms, Tym*): 24 Durham Street, Grangetown, Cardiff CF1 7PB ☎ 029 2066 5548

COOPER Douglas (*Dms*): 2 Gloucester Street, Weymouth, Dorset DT4 7AP ☎ 01305 775706

COOPER Freddie (*Dms, Per*): 8 Wesley Court, Wootton Bassett, Swindon, Wilts SN4 8JZ ☎ 01793 848306

COPLEY James (*Dms*): 3 Ashley Road, Bathford, Bath BA1 7TT ☎ 01225 859001

COX Peter (*Dms, Voc*): 8 Higher Holcombe Drive, Teignmouth, South Devon TQ14 8RF ☎ 01626 773736

CROSSEN Steven (*Dms, Per*): Fourways, Teign Valley Road, Christow, Devon EX6 7QA ☎ Christow 52468

CUTLER John (*Dms*): 4 Rowland Close, Hampton Dene, Hereford HR1 1XF

DAVIES Donald (*Dms, Voc*): Park View, Upton Manor Road, Brixham, Devon TQ5 9QZ ☎ 01803 857745

DAVIES Martin (*Dms, Kbds*): Fourways, Walpole, Bridgwater, Somerset TA6 4TF ☎ 01278 685110, 0589 656496 mob

DAVIS Andrew (*Dms, Per, Voc*): Flat 1 Elton Road, Clevedon, Avon BS21 7RF ☎ 01275 342239, 0378 475299

DAVISON Brian (*Dms*): 1 Sloo Cottage, Horns Cross, Bideford, North Devon EX39 5EA ☎ 01237 451588

DAY Neil (*Dms, Per, Efl Bass*): 33 Heol Ty Gwyn, Llanbradach, Nr Caerphilly, Mid Glam CF8 3PA ☎ 029 2088 6521

DEAMER Clive (*Dms, Voc*): 49 First Avenue, Oldfield Park, Bath, Avon BA2 3NW ☎ 01225 420652

DEAN Derek (*Dms*): 4 The Quarry, Cam, Dursley, Gloucester GL11 6HS ☎ Dursley 47410

DIGGLE Julian (*Dms, La Per, Sax*): Westleigh, 5 Summers Street, Lostwithiel, Cornwall PL22 0DH

DIKE Ronald (*Dms*): 59 Byron Road, Cheltenham, Glos GL51 7EY ☎ 01242 510558

DOWNS John (*Dms*): 375 Bakers Ground, Parkway North, Stoke Gifford, Bristol BS12 6GG ☎ 01454 772702

DR MAN (*Dms, Voc*)

DRAPER Edward (*Dms*): 16 Halsdon Avenue, Exmouth, Devon EX8 3DL ☎ 01395 277428

DRAY Alan (*Dms*): Paddock's Lodge, 23 Wood Lane, Chippenham, Wilts SN15 3DW ☎ 01249 650093

EDDY John (*Dms, B Ldr*): 58 Queens Road, Park Estate, Warmley, Bristol BS15 5EJ ☎ 0117 9675900

ELIAS Manny (*Dms, Per*): 10 Chilton Road, Bath BA1 6DR ☎ Bath 315986

ETHERINGTON Mark (*Dms, Tbn, Gtr*): 6A High Street, Cullompton, Devon EX15 1AA ☎ 01884 32902

EVANS Adrian (*Dms, Per*): 20 Spartan Close, Langstone, Newport, S. Wales NP6 2BH ☎ 01633 413728, 0860 707587 mob

EVANS Geraint (*Dms*): 47 Sherwood Street, Llwynypia, Rhondda, Cynon Taff, Mid Glam CF40 8TF ☎ 01443 433104

EVANS Gregory (*Dms*): 15 Anderson Place, Newport, Gwent NP9 6QR ☎ 01633 854679

FAIRCHILD Percival (*Dms, Per*): St Kilda, Mont Du Ouaisne, St Brelade, Jersey, C.I. JE3 8AW ☎ 01534 45224

FENNELL Tony (*Dms*): The White House, Redwick Road, Redwick, Bristol BS12 3LU ☎ 01454 632004

FERRIS Jim (*Dms*): 31 Hereford Close, Exmouth, Devon EX8 5QT ☎ 01395 275839

FEZ (*Dms, Per*): Airfield Studios, St Merryn, Padstow, Cornwall PL28 8PU ☎ 01841 521290, 0370 613909, 01841 520888

FIELD Scott (*Dms*): c/o Pat Sage, Corner House, St Florence, Temby, Pembrokeshire SA70 8QE ☎ 01834 871812

FISHER Stuart (*Dms, Per*): Brook Hall, North Bradley, Trowbridge, Wiltshire BA14 9PT ☎ 01225 775020

FITZGIBBON Martin *(Dms)*: Nibley House, Blakeney, Glos GL15 4AR ☎ 01594 510260

FLYNN Chris *(Per)*: 22 Folly Lane, Stroud, Gloucestershire GL5 1SD ☎ 01453 762759

FOWLER Charles *(Dms)*: Leapgate, Old Sherbourne Road, Dorchester, Dorset DT2 9RH ☎ 01305 267068 & fax

FOWLER Harry *(Dms)*: 62 Nutfield Grove, Filton, Bristol BS12 7LJ ☎ 0117 9831059

FOWLES Anthony *(Dms, Tym)*: 100 Queensholm Drive, Downend, Bristol BS16 6LQ ☎ 0117 9563580

FRANCIS Rory *(Dms, Per)*: 2 West Farm Cottages, Toller Whelme, Beaminster, Dorset DT8 3NU ☎ 01308 862843

GAIL-LOUISE *(Dms)*: Pondlands, Francis Well, Carmarthen, Dyfed SA31 2AD ☎ 01267 237550

GAYWOOD David *(Per)*: 22 Well Street, Exeter, Devon EX4 6QR ☎ 01392 35381

GIBBON John *(Dms, Per)*: 56 Old Barn Way, Abergavenny, Gwent NP7 6EA ☎ 01873 3282

GIDDINGS John *(Per, Tym)*: 23 Woodland Grove, Westbury-on-Trym, Bristol BS9 2BD ☎ 0117 9681315

GIRLING Chris *(Per)*: 41 Lansdowne Road, Canton, Cardiff CF5 1PQ ☎ 029 2034 5609

GIRLING Philip *(Per)*: 32 Vaughan Avenue, Llandaff, Cardiff CF5 2HS ☎ 029 2056 8202

GORE Simon *(Dms)*: 133 British Road, Bedminster, Bristol BS3 3BY ☎ 0117 963 4496

GREENWOOD Chico *(Dms)*: Marine Lodge, Capstone Crescent, Ilfracombe, N. Devon EX34 9BT ☎ 01271 866768

GREER Andrew *(Dms)*: Kittys Cottage, 10 Home Farm Way, Ilminster, Somerset TA19 9BX ☎ 01460 54584

GREGORY Ian *(Per)*: 26 Tismeads Crescent, Old Town, Swindon, Wilts SN1 4DR ☎ 01793 643448

GRIFFITHS Andrew *(Dms, Per)*: 50 Churchward Avenue, Swindon, Wiltshire SN2 1NH ☎ 01793 826671

GRIFFITHS David *(Per, Tym)*: 25 Axminster Road, Penylan, Cardiff, South Glam CF5 2AR ☎ 029 2021 5791, 07970 913468

GRIFFITHS Huw *(Dms, Per)*: 5 Dumfries Street, Treherbert, Rhondda, Mid-Glamorgan, South Wales CF42 5PL ☎ 01443 773398

GRIFFITHS Matthew *(Per, Dms, Tym, Pf)*: 47 Home Park Road, Saltash, Cornwall PL12 6BH ☎ 01752 844670

GRUNDELL Richard *(Dms)*: 118 Coburg Road, Dorchester, Dorset DT1 2HR ☎ 01305 261272

GRUNDY John *(Per, Pf)*: 3 Duchy Drive, Preston, Paignton, Devon TQ3 1HB

GWYNEDD Osian *(Dms, Pf, Kbds, Sax, Gtr)* ☎ 029 2033 3948

HALL Alfred *(Per)*: 24 Clos Paumelle, Bagatelle Road, St Saviour, Jersey, C.I. JE2 7TW ☎ 01534 26247

HALL John *(Per)*: c/o 132 Station Road, Kingswood, Bristol BS15 4XU ☎ 0117 956 8359, 01633 870984

HAMILTON Ross *(Per, Dms, Pf)*: 'Moonraker', Commons Close, Mullion, Cornwall TR12 7HY ☎ 01326 240375, 07775 698958 mob, 01326 240778 fax

HAMLIN Gareth *(Per, Dms)*: 209 Penrhiwceiber Road, Mountain Ash, Rhandda-Cyon-Taff CF5 3UN ☎ 01443 475093, 0766 875638

HARBERD Cyril *(Dms)*: 4 Queen Square, Westbury, Wiltshire BA13 2LR ☎ Westbury 823392

HARDING Matthew *(Dms, Pf)*: 5 Emerald Street, Roath, Cardiff CF2 1QA ☎ 029 2046 0548

HARFIELD Ross *(Dms, Per)*: 86 Saxonleas, Winterslow, Salisbury, Wilts SP5 1RW ☎ 01980 862775, 0411 506389

HARRIS Colin *(Dms)*: 20 Summerway, Whipton, Exeter EX4 8DA ☎ 01392 467562

HARRIS Mark *(Dms, Per)*: 43 Coed Arhyd, Castlemead, St Fagans, Cardiff CF5 4TZ ☎ 029 2059 7041, 0976 884437

HARRIS Stephen *(Tnd Per, Pf, Clt)*: 93 High Street, Treorchy, Rhondda, Cynon Taff CF42 6PD ☎ 01443 436731

HARRISON Richard *(Dms)*: 4 Conway Drive, Broadmayne, Dorchester, Dorset DT2 8AF ☎ 01305 852470

HAWKER Stephen *(Dms)*: 2 Orchard Rd, Coalpit Heath, Bristol BS17 2PB ☎ 01454 778171

HAZELHURST-HOWLES Damon *(Dms)*: Two Way, Oakhill, Nr Bath, Somerset BA3 5AS

HELM Jonathan *(Per)*: 8 Ty Cerrig, Pentwyn, Cardiff CF2 7DN ☎ 029 2073 3437, 0802 482962 mob

HELMORE Mark *(Dms)*: 20 Fowey Road, Worle, Weston-Super-Mare, Avon BS22 0ST ☎ 01934 518750

HELSON Robert *(Dms, Pf)*: Basement Flat, 34 Cornwallis Crescent, Clifton, Bristol BS8 4PH ☎ 0117 9736665

HEMPELL John *(Dms)*: 35 Coffeelake Meadow, Lostwithiel, Cornwall PL22 0LT ☎ 01208 872856

HENDERSON W *(Dms, B Ldr)*: 8 Plas Derwen View, Monmouth Road, Abergavenny, Gwent NP7 9SX ☎ 01873 2442

HENNESSEY Brian *(Dms, Pf)*: Hedgerows Mount Lane, Roadwater, Somerset TA23 0QY ☎ 01984 641273, 029 2065 6160

HEYWARD Mark *(Per, Dms)*: 25 Wilton Way, Abbotskerswell, Newton Abbott, S Devon TQ12 5PG ☎ 01626 332071

HICKS Robert *(Dms)*: 18A High Street, Tonyrefail, Rhondda CF39 8PG ☎ 01443 673558

HILEY Paul *(Per)*: 1 St Olaves Mews, Bartholomew Street East, Exeter EX4 3BN ☎ 01392 498695

HORGAN Alun *(Dms, Per)*: 49 Margaret Street, Tynewydd, Rhondda, Gynon Taff, South Wales CF42 5LT ☎ 01443 774291, 0777 1780593

HOWARD Terence *(Dms)*: 16 Field Close, South Cerney, Glos GL7 5XQ ☎ 01285 860421

HOWELL Geoffrey *(Dms)*: 14 Millbridge Gardens, Minehead, Somerset TA24 5XA ☎ 01643 706559

HUGHES Chris *(Dms, Kbds)*: Amusments Ltd, The Woolhole, Castle Corner, Beckington, Somerset BA3 6TA ☎ 01373 830731

HUGHES Lionel *(Per)*: 143 Delffordd, Rhos, Pontardawe SA8 3EN ☎ 01792 863048

HUMM Brena *(Per)*: 49 Lower Way, Chickerell, Weymouth, Dorset DT3 4AR ☎ 01305 782671

JAMES E *(Dms)*: Pontlands, Francis Well, Carmarthen, Dyfed SA31 2AD ☎ 01267 237550

JONES Derek *(Dms)*: 17 Duffryn Close, Coychurch, Bridgend, Mid Glam CF35 5TA ☎ 01656 862168

JONES Derek *(Dms, Voc)*: Farrowdene, 2 Clos Des Mielles, St Brelade, Jersey JE3 8FE ☎ 01534 42133

JONES Dewi *(Dms)*: 47 Pontardulais Road, Penllergaer, Swansea SA4 1AY ☎ 01792 893436

JONES Glyn *(Dms, Voc)*: Glenview, Innerbrook Road, Torquay TQ2 6AG ☎ 01803 605066

JONES Melvyn *(Dms)*: Jalna, 1 Dan-Y-Coed, Caerphilly CF83 1HU ☎ 01222 8699

JONES Norman *(Dms, Vib, Voc)*: Waikiki, 9 Abbey Close, Mont A L'Abbe, St Helier Jersey JE2 3FG ☎ 01534 63348

JONES Philip *(Dms)*: 67 Armscroft Road, Barnwood, Gloucester GL2 0SJ ☎ 01452 539025

JONES Steven *(Dms, Voc)*: 66 Station Road, Burry Port, Carmarthenshire, South Wales SA16 0LW ☎ 01554 832421

JOSEPH John *(Dms)*: 21 St Nicholas Road, Wild Mill, Bridgend CF31 1RT ☎ 01656 656685

JOSH Rogan *(Dms, Per, Gtr, B Gtr, Pf)*: c/o Ann Hamilton, Rosedene, Lime Head, St Breward, Bodmin, Cornwall PL30 4LU ☎ 01208 851447

KASSELL Don *(Dms)*: Magnolia House, Kennel Lane, Cattistock, Nr Dorchester, Dorset DT2 0JJ ☎ 01300 321010

KEEL John *(Dms, Per)*: 63 Cheyney Walk, Westbury, Wilts BA13 3UH ☎ 01373 823389

KENDALL Allan *(Dms, B Gtr)*: 4 Greig Drive, Goodleigh Rise, Barnstaple, Devon EX32 8AG ☎ 01271 346369

KING Rex *(Dms)*: The Glebe House, Sheviock, Torpoint, Cornwall PL11 3EH ☎ 01503 230393

LAWSON Fraser *(Dms)*: 27 Heol-Y-Delyn, Lisvane, Cardiff, S Glam CF4 5SQ ☎ 029 2075 5020

LEVY Laurence *(Dms, B Ldr)*: Avalon, The Avenue, Combe Down, Bath, Avon BA2 5EF ☎ Bath 837550

LEWIS Peter *(Dms)*: 222 St Teilo Street, Pontardulais, W.Glamorgan SA4 1LQ ☎ 01792 883695

LOCKE Martyn (*Dms, Per, Bsn, Arr, Md*): 13 Alexander Road, Rhyddings, Neath, West Glamorgan SA10 8DY ☎ 01639 632612, 0802 494368

MADDOCKS Gordon (*Dms, Per, Sax, Clt, Bones*)

MADIGAN Brian (*Dms, Flt, Voc, Kbds, Gtr*): 12 Bladus Buildings, Bath BA1 5LS ☎ 01225 463088

MANUEL Robert (*Dms, Voc, Ld Gtr, Rh Gtr, B G*): 7 Belmont Road, St Austell, Cornwall PL25 4UP ☎ 01726 66109

MAPSTONE Craig (*Per, Pf, Gtr, Brass, B Gtr*): 34 St Christophers Drive, Caerphilly CF83 1DD ☎ 029 2088 4758

MARCEL Dean (*Per, Kbds*): 14 Lamborough Crescent, Clarbeston Road, Pembrokeshire SA63 4UZ ☎ 01437 731734, 0421 381381

MARSHALL Andrew (*Dms, Per*): 31 Jubilee Street, Newquay, Cornwall TR7 1LA ☎ 01637 851227

MARTIN Gary (*Dms, B Ldr*): The Post Office, Melin Court, Nr Neath, W.Glamorgan SA11 4AT ☎ 01639 710204

MATHIESON Iain (*Dms*): 15 Bryn Road, Wesham, Weymouth, Dorset DT4 0NP ☎ 01305 785528

MATTHEWS James (*Dms, Per*): Isfryn, Cnwch Coch, Aberystwyth, Dyfed SY23 4LQ ☎ 01974 3319

MCINTOSH Paul (*Dms*): 3 Longfield, Quedgley, Glos GL2 3NQ ☎ 01452 557859

MCKENZIE Owen (*Dms*) ☎ 01792 522139

MENNIM Robert (*Dms*): Heronfield, East Lyng, Taunton, Somerset TA3 5AU ☎ 01823 698732

MERRETT Peter (*Dms, B Ldr*): 45 Jubilee Road, Weston-Super-Mare BS23 3AW ☎ 01934 620655 & fax

MICHAEL Philip (*Dms*): 3A Orchard Close, Barnstaple, Nth Devon EX31 2DF ☎ 01271 45218

MILLARD Percy (*Dms*): 14 Gordon Road, Taunton, Somerset TA1 3AU

MILLER Dusty (*Dms, Tym, Tnd Per*): 5 Margaret Park, Hartley Vale, Plymouth, Devon PL3 5RR ☎ 01752 774337

MILLS Robert (*Dms*): 14 Farmhouse Close, Nailsea, Bristol BS48 2HY ☎ 01275 856744

MITCHELL John (*Per, Tym, Dms*): Watergate, Lower Treluswell, Penryn, Cornwall TR10 9AT ☎ 0468 975908 mob

MORGAN Kenneth (*Dms*): Address Unknown ☎ 0117 937672

MORLEY Jeffrey (*Dms*): 11 Mansel Street, Port Talbot, West Glamorgan SA13 1BL ☎ 016339 884129

MORRIS Hal (*Dms*): 110 Cooks Close, Bradley Stoke, Bristol BS12 0BB ☎ 01454 613763

MORTIMORE Darren (*Dms*): 24 Buller Road, Newton Abbot, Devon TQ12 1AB ☎ 01626 331829

NASH Ian (*Dms*): Sunningdale Bungalow, Carno Street, Rhymney, Gwent NP2 5EE ☎ 01685 840071, 0585 637341 mob

NEWMAN Anna (*Per, Tym*): Lilac Cottage, 55 Doulting, Nr Shepton Mallet, Somerset BA4 4QF ☎ 01749 880219

NEWTON James (*Dms*): Strete House Cottage, Whimple, Exeter EX5 2PL ☎ Whimple 822161

NICHOLAS Lee (*Dms*): 3 Gelli-Unig Terrace, Pontywaun, Crosskeys, Gwent NP1 7GF ☎ 01495 270917

NIXON Andy (*Dms, Per*)

NUGENT Clarence (*Dms*): 460 Gladstone Road, Barry, South Glam CF63 1NL ☎ 01446 746337

OAKLEY David (*Dms*)

OHARA John (*Dms, Per, Pf*): 259 Wick Road, Brislington, Bristol BS4 4HR

ORRELL Tony (*Dms, Per*): 23 Selworthy Road, Knowle, Bristol BS4 2LF ☎ 0117 977 1952

OSBORNE Jeremy (*Dms*): 11 The Twynings, Kingswood, Bristol BS15 1XS ☎ 612620

PAINE Michael (*Dms, Voc*): 282 Tavy House, Duke Street, Devonport, Plymouth Devon PL1 4HL ☎ 01752 568269

PATTERSON Allan (*Dms*): 41 The Chase, Brackla, Bridgend, Mid Glam CF31 2JS ☎ 01656 767475, 0973 482256

PEARSON Jack (*Dms*): 34 Summerlands Court, Liverton, Newton Abbot, South Devon TQ12 6HB ☎ 01626 821036

PHILLIPS Eric (*Per, Kbds*): 34 Llantrisant Road, Llandaff, Cardiff CF5 2PX ☎ 029 2055 4105

PHILLIPS Gary (*Dms, Per*): 5 Heol-Yr-Yspol, St. Brides Major, Vale Of Glamorgan CF32 0TB ☎ 01656 880096

PHILLIPS William (*Dms*): 40 Ilston Way, West Cross, Swansea, Glam. SA3 5LG ☎ 01792 403170

PIERCE Christine (*Dms*): Maple House, 30 Severn Avenue, Weston Super Mare, Avon BS23 4DQ ☎ 01934 624130

POOLE Ian (*Dms*): 46 Rhydhelig Avenue, Heath, Cardiff CF4 4DE ☎ 029 2052 0917

POOLEY Norman (*Tnd Per*): 1 Ash Grove, Llanellen, Abergavenny, Gwent NP7 8TE

POPE Christopher (*Dms*): 43, Northover Road, Westbury O Trym, Bristol, Avon BS9 3LN ☎ 0117 9506744

POTTER John (*Dms, Per*): Lindos, Strete, Dartmouth, Devon TQ6 0RS ☎ 01803 770098, 0831 879476, 01803 770363

POWELL James (*Dms, Per*): Hook Farm, Stoke Trister, Wincanton, Somerset BA9 9PL

POWER David (*Dms, Per*): Old Well House, Rough Street, Corsham, Wiltshire SN13 9TR ☎ 01225 810607

PRIOR Clifton (*Per, Dms*): 6 Warwick House, Castle Court, Westgate Street, Cardiff CF1 1DH ☎ 029 224461

PRIOR Keith (*Dms, Per*): 30 St Thomas Street, Penryn, Falmouth, Cornwall TR10 8JN ☎ 01326 373015

PULLEN Ashley (*Per*): 32 Waite Meads Close, Purton, Swindon, Wilts SN5 9ET ☎ 01793 770104

PUXTY Tony (*Dms*): 9 Gertrude Street, Abercynon, Mountain Ash, Mid Glam CF45 4RL ☎ 01443 740738

PYKE Douglas (*Dms*): 23 Priors Road, Cheltenham GL52 5AB

QUAMMIE Quinton (*Dms*): Address Unknown ☎ 029 2045 6518, 0976 167085 mob

REAY Jason (*Dms, Per*): 70A Rock Lane, Stoke Gifford, Bristol BS34 8PG ☎ 0117 9694197, 0385 987708

REECE Damon (*Dms*): 26 York Gardens, Clifton Village, Bristol BS8 4LN ☎ 0151 727 0367

REES Jonathan (*Dms*): 62 Belgrave Road, Gorsenon, Swansea, S. Wales SA4 6RF ☎ 01792 894441

RIDOUT Gillian (*Per*): 22 Y Cileant, Penyrheol, Caerphilly, Mid Glamorgan CF8 2NB ☎ 029 2086 6917

RIPPON David (*Dms*): 5 Rustic Close, Tycoch, Swansea SA2 9LZ ☎ 01792 290238

ROBINSON Howard (*Dms*): 37 Victoria Road, Barry, South Glamorgan CF62 6PG ☎ 01446 743107

ROBINSON James (*Per, Dms, Pf*): 51 Treyew Road, Truro, Cornwall TR1 2BY ☎ Truro 76201

ROBINSON Tim (*Dms*): 32 Albert Park Place, Montpelier, Bristol BS6 5ND ☎ 0117 954 1342

ROCHE Patrick (*Dms*): 97 Maple Avenue, Chepstow, Gwent NP6 5RT

RODGERS Mark (*Dms*): 46 Dovers Park, Bathford, Bath BA1 7UD ☎ 01225 589009

ROPER David (*Dms*): 29 Bmton Ferry Road, Neath, W. Glamorgan, S. Wales SA11 1AF ☎ 01639 641395

ROSS Stuart (*Dms, Per, B Gtr*): 151 Castle Road, Salisbury, Wiltshire SP1 3RR ☎ 01722 321997

ROTH Stephen (*Dms*): 63 Halsteads Road, Barton, Torquay, Devon TQ2 8HB ☎ 01803 311117

RUTLAND Jennifer (*Per, Pf, Tym*): 72 Cornerswell Road, Penarth, South Glam CF6 1WA ☎ 029 2070 5092

SALMON Derek (*Dms, Per*): 16 Aller, Monkton Ave, Western Super Mare SA24 9DB ☎ 07803 239712

SANDERS Jim (*Dms*): 13 Howard Road, Thornbury, Bristol BS35 1JN ☎ 01454 885304

SARGEANT Derek (*Dms, Per*): Littlefield Cottage, Salterton Road, Exmouth, Devon EX8 5BW ☎ Exmouth 263988

SARTIN Maurice (*Per*): Downside, Sheeplands Lane, Sherborne, Dorset DT9 4BU ☎ 01935 814611

SAUL Peter (*Dms, Kbds, Ac Gtr*): Broadgate, Bodmin Street, Holsworthy, Devon EX22 6BH ☎ 01409 254111, 0802 732593 mob

'SCEPTICS BAND' (*Dms, Gtr*): 36 Heol Barri, Caerphilly, South Wales CF83 2LY ☎ 029 2086 4195

SCHILLACE Michele (*Dms, Per*): Louisiana, Wapping Road, Bathurst Terrace, Bristol BS1 ☎ 0117 9265978

SCOTT Jim (*Per, Dms*): 56 Newcastle Street, Swindon, Wilts SN1 2LG ☎ 01793 533051

SCOTT Jim (*Dms, Per*): 56 Newcastle Street, Swindon, Wilts SN1 2LG ☎ 01793 533051

SCOTT Julian (*Dms, Gtr*): 5 Leigh Road, Westbury, Wiltshire BA13 3QN ☎ 01373 822674

SHANNON Christopher (*Per*): 69 Goodrington Road, Paignton, Devon TQ4 7HZ ☎ 01803 844014

SHOOFIELD Tim (*Dms, Cimb*): 30 Bridle Close, Hookhills, Paignton, South Devon TQ4 7ST

SIMON Theo (*Dms, Voc*): Kingshill, Cockmill Lane, East Pennard, Shepton Mallett BA4 6TR ☎ 01749 860660, 01523 400817

SMIT (*Glck, Triangle, B Gtr, Gtr, D*): 13 Castle Street, Exeter, Devon EX4 3PT ☎ 01392 496706, 0410 328874 mob, 01326 378720

SMITH Adam (*Dms, Pf*): Ground Floor Flat, 21 Ravenswood Road, Redland, Bristol BS6 6BN ☎ 0117 983 6059, 07970 713790

SPARKES Christopher (*Dms*): 2 Samares Manor Cottages, La Blinerie Lane, St Clements, Jersey C.I. JE2 6QT ☎ 01534 32058

STANFIELD Mark (*Dms*): 18 Ash Grove, Clevedon BS21 7JS ☎ 01275 875096

STIGINGS Thomas (*Per*): 17 Cadewell Lane, Shiphay, Torquay TQ2 7AG ☎ 01803 63219

STOCKWELL Michael (*Dms, Per*): 66 Glan Rhyd, Coed Eva, Cwmbran, Gwent NP44 6TY ☎ 01633 480464

SUMMERS Gillian (*Dms, Per*): 61 Bratton Road, Westbury, Wiltshire BA13 3ES ☎ 01373 864721

TAYLOR Albert (*Per*): 5 Highfield Crescent, Paignton, Devon TQ3 3TP ☎ 01803 557029

THOMAS Edgar (*Dms*): 119 Durham Road, Newport, Gwent NP9 7HU ☎ 01633 251688

THOMPSON Wally (*Per, Vib*): Flat 4, Greve D'Azette Court, St Clements, Jersey JE2 6RT ☎ 01534 23180

THORPE Peter (*Per*): Rosevine, Swyre Road, Puncknowle, Dorchester, Dorset DT2 9BP ☎ 01308 897739

TOCKNELL Alan (*Dms, B Gtr, Gtr*): 5 Northfield, Folly Lane, Stroud, Gloucestershire GL5 1SS ☎ 01453 750472, 01426 632482 pager

TOFT Don (*Dms*): 2 Trevarric Road, St Austell, Cornwall PL25 5JN ☎ 01726 67664

TOMLINSON Roy (*Dms*): 10 Conway Street, St Helier, Jersey C I JE2 3NT ☎ 01534 871570

TRACEY Scott (*Dms, Per, Gtr, B Gtr, Voc*): 86 St. Lukes Crescent, Totterdown, Bristol BS3 4SA ☎ 0117 9771607

TREVETT Jack (*Dms, Voc*): 130 West Bay Road, Bridport, Dorset DT6 4AZ ☎ 01308 423099

TWEEN Andrew (*Dms, Per, Tnd Per, Pf*): 2 Chester Court, Victoria Avenue, Redfield, Bristol BS5 9NE ☎ 0973 915479

TYRRELL Andrew (*Per*): 29 Castle Hill, Banwell, Weston-Super-Mare BS24 6NX ☎ 01934 822857

UGALDE Bryan (*Dms, Tnd Per*): 2 Blakes Park, Addington, Liskeard, Cornwall PL14 3EY ☎ 01579 340176, 0410 500 642, 01579 348787

VAN HEAR Simon (*Per, B Gtr*): 15 St Johns Road, Lower Weston, Bath, Somerset BA1 3BW ☎ 01225 428402

WARREN Simon (*Dms*): 132 Pen-Y-Caeau Court, Pantside, Newbridge, Gwent NP1 5LZ ☎ 01495 247916

WASS Barry (*Dms*): 22 Wells Avenue, Feniton, Honiton, Devon EX14 0DL ☎ 01404 850495

WATSON Edward (*Dms*): Windrush, Belmont Avenue, Hucclecote, Glos GL3 3SF ☎ 01452 616865

WEBBER Martin (*Dms*): 80 Manor Road, Manselton, Swansea SA5 9PN ☎ 01792 462670

WELLS Roger (*Dms*): 32 Hudds Hill Road, St George, Bristol BS5 7QG ☎ 0117 955 5616

WEST Maureen (*Dms*): St Johns West, Murchington, Chagford, Devon TQ13 8HJ ☎ 01647 432468

WESTWELL Paul (*Dms, Per*): 10 Turberville Place, Canton, Cardiff CF1 9NX ☎ 029 2064 1774

WESTWOOD Kenneth (*Dms*): Mellow Cottage, Hewletts Drove Rivers Corner, Sturminster Newton, Dorset DT10 2AE ☎ 01258 72379

WHEELER Arthur (*Dms*): Tarmline, 6 Elmhurst Road, Hutton, Nr Weston Super Mare BS24 9RJ ☎ 813044

WHITE Sid (*Dms*): 8 Clare Road, Kingswood, Bristol BS15 1PJ

WHITE Will (*Dms*): Dry Arch House, 17 Dry Arch, Farleigh Wick, Bradford-on-Avon, Wilts BA15 2PX ☎ 01225 859 898, 0410 468854

WIGENS Paul (*Dms, Com*): 13 Nottingham Street, Bristol BS3 4SS ☎ 0117 977 1044

WILDE William (*Dms*): 66 The Hollies, Ty-Llwyd Park, Quakers Yard, Treharris, Mid Glam CF46 5LB

WILLES Dennis (*Dms*): Crown Hill House, 100 Easton Street, Portland, Dorset DT5 1BT ☎ 01305 860734

WOOD Douglas (*Dms*): 11 Badger Vale Court, Podsmead, Gloucester GL2 5FQ ☎ 01452 301655

WRAIGHT Andrew (*Dms, Gtr, Kbds*): 26 North Street, Old Town, Swindon SN1 3JX ☎ 01793 535220, 0966 244428

WRIGHT Jack (*Dms*): 29 Old Rectory Mews, Bridge Hill, St Columb Major, Cornwall TR9 6BZ ☎ 01637 881318

WRIXTON Robert (*Dms, Sax*): Sweet Briar, West Road, Bridport, Dorset DT6 6AE ☎ 01308 456403

YOUNG Shane (*Dms, Gtr*): 20 Goldsborough Close, Gloucester GL4 7ST ☎ 01452 383008

LONDON

ABBOTT Paul (*Dms, Cong, Af Dms*) ☎ 01273 248538

ABRAHAM Daren (*Dms*): 2B Ashley Road, Islington, Hornsey, London N19 3AE ☎ 020 7686 1695, 0961 312 627

ACCIAIOLI Michael (*Dms, La Per*): Tamesis, Russell Road, Shepperton, Middlesex TW17 9HJ ☎ 01932 220280

ADAMS David (*Dms, Per, Pf, Kbds*): 24 Mylne Close, Cheshunt, Herts EN8 0PS ☎ 01992 633130

ADAMS Dawne (*Dms, Per*): 3 Chestnut Road, Raynes Park, London SW20 8ED ☎ 020 8395 0656

ADAMS Ian (*Dms, Per*): 77 Lionel Road, Brentford TW8 9QZ ☎ 020 8568 0594

ADAMS Terry (*Dms, Per*): 10 Dukes Court, Brighton Road, Addlestone, Surrey KT15 1PQ

ADLER Arnold (*Per*): 25 Purcells Avenue, Edgware, Middlesex HA8 8DP ☎ 020 8958 7227

AGARD Michael (*Dms, Per, Kbds, Vln, Gtr*): 41C Knox Road, Forest Gate, London E7 9HD ☎ 020 8519 8908

AGGISS Adam (*Dms, Per*): Heathcote, Station Road, Woldingham, Surrey CR3 7DB ☎ 01883 653106

AKINGBOLA Sola (*Per, Dms*): 21 Brenley House, Tennis Street, London SE1 1YG ☎ 020 7378 6488

AKINSHOLA Taiwo (*Dms, Kbds, Voc*): 27 Tillotson Road, Edmonton, London N9 9AQ ☎ 020 8884 1067

ALBRIGHTON Che (*Dms, Per*): 73 Arkham Road, Stoke Newington, London N16 6XE ☎ 020 8806 3460

ALDEN Timothy (*Tnd Per, Xyl, Per, Org*): Top Floor Flat, 52 Linden Gardens, Chiswick, London W4 2EH ☎ 020 8742 8407

ALDRIDGE Luke (*Dms, Per, Tym*): 60 Roxborough Road, Harrow, Middlesex HA1 1PA ☎ 020 8933 2381, 0961 160103

ALEXANDER Steve (*Dms, Per*): 9 Rectory Gardens, Crouch End, London N8 7PJ ☎ 020 8348 3599

ALEXANDER Tommas (*Dms*): Flat A, 2-4 Cecile Park, Crouch End, London N8 9AX ☎ 020 8374 048 & fax

ALLARDYCE Patricia (*Per, Tym*): 211B Upper Richmond Road, Putney, London SW15 6SQ ☎ 020 8780 1541, 01306 880669

ALLEN Eric (*Per*): 34 Dingle Lane, Solihull, W. Mids B91 3NG ☎ 0121 705 1597

ALLEN Jeffrey (*Dms, Per*): 59 Mountview Road, London N4 4SS ☎ 020 8341 5948

ALLEN John (*Dms*): 2 Hazelgreen Close, London N21 3SL ☎ 020 8360 9634

ALLEN Martin (*Per*): 51 Lansdowne Gardens, London SW8 2EL ☎ 020 7720 5015 & fax, 0973 661737 mob

ALLEN Richard (*Dms*): c/o Prager & Fenton, Midway House, 27/29 Cursitor Street, London EC4A 1LT ☎ 020 7831 4200

ALLEN Simon (*Per*): 40 Wellmeadow Road, London SE13 6TB ☎ 020 8695 1189

MUSIC EDUCATION YEARBOOK

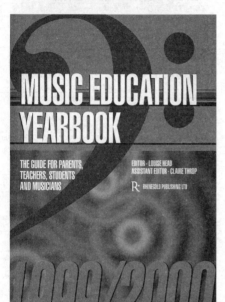

The Guide for Parents, Teachers, Students and Musicians

Provides contact information, course details, scholarship policy and entry requirements for all independent schools, conservatoires, colleges and universities nationwide.
Plus world music, local authorities, music and book publishers, information technology, youth orchestras and choirs, teacher resources, summer schools and more.

Published each May
700 pages

HOW TO ORDER

Please send a cheque for **£18.00** (inc. p&p) payable to *Rhinegold Publishing Ltd* to: **MEYB Sales, Rhinegold Publishing, FREEPOST, London WC2H 8BR**.

TELEPHONE:	**0171 333 1721** (or 020 7333 1721 after 22 Apr 2000)
FAX:	**0171 333 1769** (or 020 7333 1769 after 22 Apr 2000)
EMAIL:	**sales@rhinegold.co.uk**
WEBSITE:	**www.rhinegold.co.uk**

ALLEYNE Cheryl (*Dms, Voc*): 9 Croxford Gardens, Woodgreen, London N22 5QU ☎ 020 8889 9534

ALLIS Mark (*Dms, Tnd Per, La Per, Tpt*): 36A St James Road, Sutton, Surrey SM1 2TN ☎ 020 8642 0509

ALLISON Darren (*Dms, Per, Gtr*): 18A Avondale Avenue, Woodside Park, Finchley, London N12 8EJ ☎ 020 8446 0999

ALLUM Robert (*Dms, Per, Voc*): 31 Meadow Way, Chigwell, Essex IG7 6LR ☎ 020 8500 6224, 020 8500 6224

ALMAN Robert (*Dms, Per*): 42 The Drive, South Woodford, London E18 2BL ☎ 020 8530 3372

ALTMAN Darren (*Dms, Per, Pf*): 62 Spring Gardens, Highbury, London N5 2DT ☎ 020 7704 9012, 0378 577 464

ANDERSON Murray (*Dms, Per*): 69 Landsdowne Lane, Charlton, London SE7 8TN

ANTONIO Trevor (*Per*): 37A Albacore Crescent, London SE13 7HW ☎ 020 8488 1458

APPLETON Nigel (*Dms, B Gtr*): Flat 3, 16 Ribblesdale Road, Hornsey, London N8 ☎ 020 8341 0215, 0956 369899 mob

ARGUELLES Steve (*Dms, Per*): 79B Helix Road, London SW2 2JR

ARTHURTON Ian (*Dms, Per, Kbds*): 44 Carr Road, Northolt, Middlesex UB5 4RA ☎ 020 8422 7121, 0410 487283

ASHER James (*Dms, Kbds*): 34 Starfield Road, London W12 9SW ☎ 020 8746 1153, 020 8740 6711 fax

ASHER Peter (*Per, Gtr*): 6 Phillimore Gardens, London W8 7QD ☎ 020 7937 8384, 020 7376 0180 fax

ATKINS Matthew (*Dms, Per*) ☎ 020 8372 7552, 07801 893 484

ATKINSON Jonathan (*Dms, Per*): Flat 1, 31 Blenheim Park Road, S Croydon CR2 6BG ☎ 020 8686 8815, 0705 0162722 mob

AUSTIN Dennis (*Dms, Per*): 81 West Street, Bexleyheath, Kent DA7 4BP ☎ 020 8301 0142

AVERY Nick (*Dms, Gtr*): 95 Dupowt Road, Raynes Park, Wimbledon, London SW20 8EH ☎ 020 8543 4610 & fax

AVORY Michael (*Per*): Kinks Properties Ltd, 84 Tottenham Lane, London N8 7EE ☎ 020 8340 7873

AWIN Tony (*Dms, Per, Gtr, Kbds*) ☎ 020 7585 0539

AYERS Anthony (*Dms*): 24, Colonels Walk, Enfield, Middx EN2 8HN ☎ 020 8367 4368

BAAH Philip (*Dms*): 143 Albert Rd, South Norwood, London SE25 4JS ☎ 020 8656 2933

BACON Simon (*Dms, Per*): 3 Drayton Road, Leytonstone, London E11 4AR ☎ 020 8558 2869, 07971 523 887

BADEJO Peter (*Dms, Per*): 51 Radcliff House, Bourne Estate, Clerkenwell Road, London EC1N 7TY ☎ 020 7482 4292

BAILEY Richard (*Dms, Per, Cong*): c/o Sugarcane Music, The Flat, 177 South Ealing Road, London W5 4RH ☎ 020 8847 2695

BAIRD Paul (*Dms*) ☎ 01322 271615

BAIRD Fabian (*Per, Dms, Tym*): 121 St James Drive, Upper Tooting, London SW17 7RD ☎ 020 8672 0423, 0402 162452

BAKER Christopher (*Dms, La Per, Kbds*): Top Flat 43 Filey Avenue, Stoke Newington, London N16 6JL ☎ 020 8806 6151, 07899 667148

BAKER Julian (*Dms, Kbds, Scratch, Vib*) ☎ 020 8241 4730

BAKER Michael (*Per, Tym*): 1 Hadlow Road, Tonbridge, Kent TN9 1LE ☎ 01732 351502

BAKER Stan (*Dms, Voc*): 3 Kingsley Close, Dagenham, Essex RM10 7BQ ☎ 020 8220 4635, 020 8592 9307

BALL Malcolm (*Per, Dms, Tym, Kbds, Arr*): 79 Chalgrove Crescent, Clay Hall, Ilford, Essex IG5 0LX ☎ 020 8551 3879

BALL Robin (*Dms*): 373A Camden Road, London N7 0SH ☎ 020 7700 5586 & fax

BANKS Stephen (*Dms, Per, Vln*): 36 Beechwood Road, London N8 7NG ☎ 020 8348 9266, 07957 855458

BAPTISTE Austin (*Dms*): 29 Court House Gardens, London N3 1PU ☎ 020 8346 3984

BARBER Anthony (*Per, Voc*): 28 Birchwood Avenue, Beckenham, Kent BR3 3PZ ☎ 020 8650 9315

BARCHILD Teresa (*Dms, Per*): 13 Daubeney Tower, Pepys Estate, Bowditch, Deptford, London SE8 3QN ☎ 020 8691 9543

BARCLAY Andrew (*Per, Tym*): 2 Marshall Villas, Dowlerville Road, Orpington, Kent BR6 6DZ ☎ 01689 855068

BARKER Martyn (*Dms, Per*): 141 Florence Road, Wimbledon, London SW19 8TL ☎ 020 8542 5760

BARKER Nicholas (*Dms*): c/o One Fifteen, The Gallery, 28-30 Wood Wharf, Horseferry Place, Greenwich, London SE10 9BT ☎ 020 8293 0999, 020 8293 9525

BARKER Richard (*Dms, Per*): 155 Kingsman Street, St Mary's Estate, Woolwich, London SE18 5PS ☎ 020 8316 4362

BARON Chris (*Dms, Per*): 23 The Green, Fetcham, Leatherhead, Surrey KT22 9XE ☎ 01372 457721, 0973 308 737 mob

BARON Peter (*Per*): 2 Grove Road, London NW2 5TB ☎ 020 8459 2784

BARRADAS Miguel (*Dms, Per*): 254 Muswell Hill, Broadway, London N10 3SH ☎ 020 8883 5271

BARRETT John (*Dms, Acc, Gtr*): 130 Somervell Road, South Harrow, Middlesex HA2 8TS ☎ 020 8422 4985

BARRETT Stan (*Per*): 4 Moorland Gate, Christchurch Road, Ringwood, Hants BH24 3BD ☎ 01425 474080

BARRY Dave (*Dms, Per*): 10 Trevelyan Road, London SW17 9LN ☎ 020 8672 7158

BARRY Tim (*Per*): 21 Barham Close, Weybridge, Surrey KT13 9PR ☎ 01932 847097, 01306 880669, 0973 731916 mob

BARTI Kim (*Dms, Per*): Unit 70, Freshwharf Estate, Highbridge Road, Barking, Essex IG11 7BP ☎ 020 8591 1475 & fax, 0956 360324 mob

BARTLETT Bryan (*Dms, Per*): c/o 49 Plough Lane, Wallington, Surrey SM6 8JN ☎ 0976 406379

BARTLETT Keith (*Per, Tym*): Lynwood House, 25 Station Road, Wimborne Minster, Dorset BH21 1RQ ☎ 01202 848665

BASS Cyril (*Dms, Per, Tym, Glck, Vib*): 11 Walden Way, Emerson Park, Hornchurch, Essex RM11 2LB ☎ 01708 443949

BATES Joseph (*Dms, Per, B Gtr*): 65 Station Road, Maghera, Co Derry, Northern Ireland BT46 5EY ☎ 01648 45803

BATES Neil (*Dms, Per*): Address Unknown ☎ 0973 284321 mob

BATES Nigel (*Per*): 1C Glossop Road, Sanderstead, South Croydon, Surrey CR2 0PW ☎ 020 8651 3037, 01306 880669

BATISTA Jorge (*Per*): Flat 5, 73/75 Bell Street, London NW1 6SX ☎ 0956 530920, 020 7706 4824

BAYLIS Tasha (*Dms, Per*): Flat 23, 139-141 Haverstock Hill, London NW3 4RX ☎ 020 7722 0637, 0956 850963

BEALE Colin (*Dms*): 9 Riverview Road, Ewell, Epsom, Surrey KT19 0LF ☎ 020 8335 3144

BEAMENT Peter (*Per*): 54 Kingsfield Road, Oxhey, Herts WD1 4PS ☎ 01923 223457

BEARD Richard (*Per*): 22 Osbaldeston Road, London N16 7DP

BEARD Tony (*Dms*): Ground Floor, 103 West 78th Street, New York, NY 10024, USA ☎ +1 212 787

BEASLEY Richard (*Dms*): 138A Gordon Road, West Ealing, London W13 8PJ ☎ 020 8998 4292, 0976 242725

BEATTIE Austin (*Per, Tym*): 37 Atlanthus Close, Lee Green, London SE12 8RE ☎ 020 8297 1422

BEAUMONT (*Dms*) ☎ 01784 435768, 0860 188303

BEDWELL Justin (*Dms, Voc*): 68 Adela Avenue, New Malden, Surrey KT3 6LD ☎ 020 8942 2786, 0956 841065

BEECHING Tom (*Dms, Per, Tpt, Flgl*): 146 Lincoln Avenue, Twickenham, Middlesex TW2 6NP ☎ 020 8893 8829

BEEDLE Martin (*Dms*): 8 Grange Mill, Coggeshall, Essex CO6 1RA ☎ 01376 561 585

BEESLEY JNR Max Gig (*Per, Vib, Kbds, Dms*): 105 Milford Drive, Levenshulme, Manchester M19 2RY ☎ 0860 708655

BEESTON Julian (*Dms*): Flat 39, Victoria Court, Kingsbridge Avenue, London W3 ☎ 020 8896 0834 & fax

BELL Chris (*Dms, Per*): 2 Bolingbroke Road, London W14 0AL ☎ 020 7603 1629

BENNETT Brian (*Per*): c/o Joan Hudson & Co, 91 Tabernacle Street, London EC2A 4BA ☎ 020 7253 3107

BENNETT Guy (*Per*): 38 Berkeley Avenue, Bexleyheath, Kent DA7 4HA ☎ 020 8303 2861

BENNETT Rex (*Dms, La Per*): 1 Ellery Close, Cranleigh, Surrey GU6 8DF ☎ 01483 276393

BENSON Sebastian (*Dms, Per, Pf, Kbds*): 89 Lionel Road, Brentford, Middlesex TW8 9QZ ☎ 020 8560 7327

BERNSTEIN Howard (*Dms, Kbds*): 8 Lonsdale Avenue, Giffnock, Glasgow G46 6HG ☎ 0141 638 5156

BEST Matthew (*Dms*): Flat 2, 19 Irving Street, London WC2H 7AU ☎ 020 7930 8303

BIANCO Anthony (*Dms*): 56 Alexander Park Road, London N10 2AD ☎ 020 8444 4628

BIGDEN Alf (*Per, La Per*): c/o 97A Connaught Ave, Frinton-on-Sea, Essex CO13 9PS ☎ 0976 262881

BIGHAM Edward (*Per, Pf*): 32 Bloem Fontein Road, London W12 7BX ☎ 020 8743 8179

BILBO (*Dms, Per*): 22A Hawthorn Road, Willesden, London NW10 2ND

BINKS Les (*Dms, Per*): 103 Grosvenor Road, Hanwell, London W7 1HR ☎ 020 8840 3306 & fax

BIRCH Buster (*Dms, Per*): 54A Chatsworth Road, Hackney, London E5 0LP ☎ 020 8525 5785

BIRCHALL Hamish (*Dms*): 9 Crestview, 47 Dartmouth Park Hill, London NW5 1JB ☎ 0973 519245

BISHOP Ronald (*Dms, Db, B Gtr*): Address Unknown ☎ 020 8658 6714

BIXLEY Susan (*Per, Tym*): 15 Oakfield Road, Ashted, Surrey KT21 2RE ☎ 01372 276949, 0498 627485

BLACKBURN Anthony (*Dms*): Kandy, 41 Marischal Road, Lewisham, London SE13 5LE ☎ 020 8297 9555

BLADES Glenroy (*Dms, Kbds*) ☎ 020 8694 8330, 07970 394620

BLADES James (*Per, Tym*): 191 Sandy Lane, Cheam, Surrey SM2 7EU ☎ 020 8642 3316

BLAIR Roger (*Per, Tym*): 9 Downsview Court, Palm Grove, Guildford, Surrey GU1 1JS ☎ 01483 560991

BLANCHARD John (*Per*): 25 Whitegate Gardens, Harrow Weald, Middlesex HA3 6BW ☎ 020 8954 2284

BLANDEN Noel (*Dms, Per*): 12 Wellington Road, Westgate-on-Sea, Kent CT8 8DT ☎ 01843 833028

BLEASBY Keith (*Per*): 303 Westborough Road, Westcliff-on-Sea, Essex SS0 9PT

BLOCK Brandon (*Per, Sax*): 14 Stanford Close, Ruislip, Middlesex HA4 7RP ☎ 01895 473941, 0468 740350

BODGER Phil (*Dms, Per, Gtr*): 14 Sudley Street, Brighton BN2 1HE ☎ 01273 671148

BOITA Peter (*Dms, Per, La Per, Synth*): 7 The Claydons, Claydon Drive, Surrey CRO 4QX ☎ 020 8667 9708, 020 8686 4984 fax

BONHAM Jason (*Dms*): c/o Joan Hudson, 91 Tabernacle Street, London EC2A 4BA ☎ 020 7253 3107

BOORER Steven (*Dms, Gtr, Kbds*): Greystones, Lingfield Road, East Grinstead, Sussex RH19 2EJ ☎ 01342 315738

BOSE Jonathan (*Per*): 17 Sea View Road, Leigh-on-Sea, Essex SS9 1AT ☎ 01702 715204

BOULD Miles (*Per, Dms*): 96 Greyhound Road, London N17 6XN ☎ 020 8808 5377, 0976 919004 mob

BOURKE Stan (*Per*): 31 Kingswood Road, Garston, Herts WD2 6EF ☎ 01923 675578

BOURKE Tony (*Dms, Cong*): 31 Kingswood Road, Garston, Herts WD2 6EF ☎ 01923 675578, 0802 501902

BOWDEN James (*Dms, Bod, Gtr, Wh*): 19 Lansdowne Road, Walthamstow, London E17 8QT ☎ 020 8520 8323, 04325 372 346 pager

BOWDEN Ronald (*Dms*): 23 Ingram Way, Greenford, Middx UB6 8QG ☎ 020 8578 6196

BOWERS-BROADBENT Henry (*Dms, Com, Arr, Pf*) ☎ 020 8444 2357, 020 8883 1933

BOYCE Gerry (*Per*): Gardens Cottage, 48 New Road, Penn, High Wycombe, Buckinghamshire HP10 8DL ☎ 01494 817548

BRADLEY Michael (*Dms, Tnd Per*): 305 Ivydale Road, London SE15 3DZ ☎ 020 7635 7234, 0973 861375 mob

BRADSHAW Nicholas (*Per*): Flat 3, 84 Eltham Road, Lea Green SE12 8UE ☎ 020 8852 8540

BRANNICK Chris (*Per, Tym*): 123 Osborne Road, Forest Gate, London E7 0PP ☎ 020 8471 4810, 0850 614745 mob

BRATT Andrew (*Dms, La Per, Per*): 217 Manchester Road, Isle Of Dogs, London E14 ☎ 020 7515 0518, 0411 131869

BRAY Pete (*Dms*): Apartado 130, 8100 Loule, Algarve, Portugal ☎ +351 89 415906

BRENNAN Paul (*Dms, Per*): 10B Effra Road, Rathmines, Dublin 6, Ireland ☎ +353 1 496 0774, 087 2765530, 01 496 0774

BRESLAW Joshua (*Dms, Per*): 43 Fairwall Hse, Glebe Estate, Peckham Road, London SE5 9QW ☎ 020 7771 6682, 07957 327 638

BRETT-HOGAN James (*Dms, Per*): 45 Eaton Road, Ilford, Essex IG1 2UD ☎ 020 8514 1704

BREWER Barry (*Dms*): Three Pirates, 40 High Knocke, Dymchurch, Kent TN29 0QD ☎ 01303 874615, 0385 934048 mob

BREWER James (*Dms, Per*): 47B Parkhurst Road, London N7 0LT ☎ 020 7609 7232, 0802 156362

BRIDGEMAN Noel (*Dms, Cong, Bong, Timb*): 145 Foxfield Grove, Raheny, Dublin 5, Eire ☎ 831 1559

BRIDGES John (*Dms*) ☎ 01268 416662

BRINGLOE Paul (*Dms, Per*): 6 Austins Court, 1-23 Peckham Rye, London SE15 3NR ☎ 020 7639 5409, 0403 513976

BROAD Graham (*Per*): Tall Trees Cottage, Winkfield Road, Ascot, Berks SL5 7EX ☎ 01344 28106

BROCKLEHURST Neil (*Dms, Per*): 19 Nutberry Avenue, Grays, Essex RM16 2TL ☎ 01375 401112, 0410 427075

BROOK Derek (*Per, Tym, Glck*): Flat A, 15 Oxford Park, Ilfracombe, North Devon EX34 9JS ☎ 01271 865241

BROOKER Jonathan (*Dms*): 67 Spa Hill, Upper Norwood, London SE19 3TW ☎ 020 8653 2130, 0403 845972, 020 8241 9743

BROWN Alan (*Per, Dms, La Per*): 2 Langdon House, 60 Leather Lane, London EC1N 7TN ☎ 020 7916 8846, 0973 778257 mob

BROWN Geoff (*Dms, Per*): 15 Opendale Road, Burnham, Slough SL1 7LY ☎ 01628 680821

BROWN Paul (*Dms*): 22A Osborne Road, Palmers Green, London N13 5PS ☎ 020 8350 4968

BROWN Rodney (*Dms*): 1 Harman Avenue, Lympne, Nr Hythe, Kent CT21 4LA ☎ 01303 260887

BROWN Stephen (*Dms*): 67 Castlewood Road, London N16 6DJ ☎ 020 8809 4807, 0976 606 068

BROWN Trevor (*Per, Dms*): 3 Overton Road, Abbey Wood, London SE2 9SH ☎ 020 8310 1483

BRUCE Deborah (*Dms, Song W, Per, Voc, B Gtr*): 13 Queensgate Place, Off Kings Gate Road, Kilburn, London NW6 4JS ☎ 020 7372 0616

BRUFORD William (*Per*): Bill Bruford Productions Ltd., High Broom, Pitch Hill, Ewhurst, Surrey GU6 7NP ☎ 01483 276841

BRYAN Russ (*Dms*): Rusper, 29 Istead Rise, Gravesend, Kent DA13 9JE ☎ 01474 832743

BRYANT David (*Dms*): 104 Longley Road, Tooting, London SW17 9LH ☎ 020 8767 2688

BRYANT Richie (*Dms*): 176 Meadowcroft, Swindon, Wiltshire SN2 6LE ☎ 01793 822067

BRYANT Terl (*Dms, Per*): 225 Burntwood Lane, Earlsfield, London SW17 0AL ☎ 020 8879 0054

BRZEZICKI Mark (*Dms*): 1 Sycamore Way, Teddington, Middx TW11 9QQ ☎ 020 8943 5102

BUDD Paul (*Dms*): Teesdale, North Road, Havering-Atte-Bower, Romford, Essex RM4 1PR ☎ 01708 725669

BURGESS William (*Per*): 9A George Lane, South Woodford, London E18 1LN ☎ 020 8532 9263

BURGESS Richard (*Dms, Per, Com*): PO Box 646, Mayo, MD 21106, USA ☎ +1 410 956 9116

BURROWS Bryn (*Per*): Flat 7 Adam Court, 61 Thicket Road, Sutton, Surrey SM1 4PX

BUSHELL Adam (*Dms*): 39 St Johns Hill, Battersea, London SW11 1TT ☎ 020 7223 0192

BUTTERFIELD Stu (*Dms*): 5 Dukes Avenue, London N10 2PS ☎ 020 8883 2953

BYE Tim (*Dms*): 9 Dorien Road, Rayners Park, London SW20 8EL ☎ 020 8543 1244, 04325 557085

BYNG Frank (*Dms, Per*) ☎ 020 7235 2752, 020 8671 0337

BYRNE Lloyd (*Per, Dms*): 46 Loreto Avenue, Rathfarnham, Dublin 14, Ireland ☎ +3531 4963404

CADORE Cosimo (*Dms*): 22 Parkside, London NW2 6RH ☎ 020 8452 5227, 0956 154186 mob

CALDAS John *(Dms)*: 39 Cedar Court, Colney Hatch Lane, London N10 1EG ☎ 020 8883 2885

CALLAGHAN Robert *(Per, Kbds, Didj)*: 35A Tankerville Road, Streatham Common, London SW16 5LL ☎ 020 8764 8372

CALLOW Haydn *(Dms)*: 35 Union Road, Northolt, Northolt, Middlesex UB5 6UB ☎ 0589 031 699

CAMPBELL Kevin *(Dms, Per)*: Address Unknown ☎ 01280 821 545, 0973 845 829

CANG Gil *(Dms, Kbds)*: 40A Inverness Street, London NW1 7HB ☎ 020 7284 0441

CAPALDI Jim *(Dms, Gtr, Pf)*: P.O. Box 272, London N20 0BY ☎ 020 8368 0340

CARLING Martin *(Dms)*: 21 Effra Mansions, Crownstone Road, London SW2 1LU ☎ 020 7733 5178, 0468 080 374

CARMICHAEL Jim *(Dms)*: Flat 1, 88-90 Beaconsfield Road, Brighton, East Sussex BN1 6DD ☎ 01273 330541, 0973 176088 mob

CARNEY Leonard *(Dms)*: 43 Rosemount Road, London W3 9LU ☎ 020 8248 9344

CARPENA Francesco *(Dms, Kbds)*: 8 Etherstone Road, London SW16 2RA ☎ 020 8769 7122

CARR Helen *(Dms, Clt, Pf)*: 49 Avenue Gardens, London W3 8HB ☎ 020 8896 0560

CARR Tony *(Dms, La Per)*: 36 Rossall Crescent, London NW10 7HD ☎ 020 8997 6937

CARRINGTON Simon *(Per)*: 36A Bouverie Road, London N16 0AJ ☎ 020 8800 1158

CARROLL Walter *(Dms, Voc)*: 38 Azalia Drive, Swanley, Kent DR8 8HZ ☎ 01322 664950

CARTER Paul *(Per, Kbds)*: 66 Finsbury Park Road, London N4 2JX ☎ 020 7704 1068, 020 7729 6218 fax

CASH Nicholas *(Per, Dms)*: 74 Love Day Road, London W13 9JX ☎ 020 8567 1296

CASSERLEY Lawrence *(Per)*: Chiltern Cottage, Haw Lane, Bledlow Ridge, Bucks HP14 4JG ☎ 01494 481 381

CASSIDY Eugene *(Dms)*: 1A Vine Gardens, Ilford, Essex IG1 2QH ☎ 020 8478 1338

CATER Pete *(Dms)*: 59 Boreham Holt, Allum Lane, Elstree, Herts WD6 3QQ ☎ 020 8953 3830, 0831 419958

CATILO Napoleon *(Dms, Gtr, B Gtr, Kbds)*

CATTERMOLE Nicholas *(Per, Sax, Bag, Flt)*: Flat 71 Juniper House, Pomeroy Street, London SE14 5BY ☎ 020 7207 3371

CATTINI Clem *(Dms)*: 15 Blenheim Close, Winchmore Hill, London N21 2HQ ☎ 020 8360 8880

CAVE John *(Per, Xyl)*: 24 Redlands Lane, Broadwindsor, Nr.Beaminster, Dorset DT8 3ST ☎ 01308 867652

CHANA Shan *(Dms, Per, T Sax)*: 8 Juniper Court, 71 Mulgrave Road, Sutton, Surrey SM2 6LR ☎ 020 8643 5282

CHAPMAN Darren *(Per)* ☎ 020 8768 1638

CHAPMAN Gerald *(Dms)*: 43B Talbot Road, Highgate, London N6 4QS ☎ 020 8348 1301

CHAPMAN Thomas *(Per, Voc)*: 2 Jordan Road, Perivale, Middx UB6 7BT ☎ 020 8997 8914

CHAR Lou *(Per, Bong)*: 35 Morden Road, Mitcham, London CR4 4DE

CHARLTON George *(Per)*: Avedis, Doles Lane, Off Barkham Road, Wokingham, Berkshire RG41 4EA ☎ 01189 781593

CHARMAN Nigel *(Per)*: 155 New House Park, St Albans, Herts AL1 1UT ☎ 01727 857 680, 01306 880669

CHASTANET Maxine *(Dms, Gtr)* ☎ 020 8896 1195

CHEEL Ronald *(Dms)*: 76 Waddington Way, Upper Norwood, London SE19 3UA ☎ 020 8653 7290

CHESCOE Laurie *(Dms)*: 175 Kent House Road, Beckenham, Kent BR3 1JZ ☎ 020 8778 2396

CHIPPENDALE Brian *(Dms)*: 22 Kingsmere Park, Kingsbury, London NW9 8PL ☎ 020 8205 3977

CHOPPING Ian *(Per, Tnd Per, Tym)*: Bramley Hedge, Oaks Lane, Postwick, Norwich, Norfolk NR13 5HD ☎ 01603 435623, 0850 122349

CHOWRIMOOTOO Michele *(Dms)* ☎ 020 7251 8458

CHRIPPES Peter *(Per, Tym)*: Freshfields, Mere Road, Hindon, Wilts SP3 6DW ☎ 01747 820773

CHURCH Daniel *(Dms)*: 24C Grand Parade, London N4 1LG ☎ 020 8802 8288

CLAPSON Martin *(Dms, Tpt)*: 5 Kingsway, South Green, Billericay, Essex CM11 2QF ☎ 01277 624302

CLARK Al *(Dms, Per)*: 172 Lakedale Road, Plumstead, London SE18 1PU ☎ 020 8317 1216

CLARK Benedict *(Dms, Tabla, Per)*: 19 Oxford Road, London SW15 2LG ☎ 020 8785 7111

CLARK David *(Dms, Kbds, Gtr, Voc)*: 13 Lilleishall Rd, Clapham Common, London SW4 0LN ☎ 020 7672 9920

CLARK Francis *(Dms, Gtr)*: 16 Milman House, Milman Street, London SW10 0BU ☎ 020 7351 5293

CLARK Kevin *(Dms)*: Flat 3, 115 Green Lane, New Eltham, London SE9 3XA ☎ 020 8850 3216, 0956 805971, 0181 294 0171

CLARKE Lisa *(Dms, Per, A Sax, B Gtr)*: 114 Canonbie Road, London SE23 3AG ☎ 020 8699 2514

CLARVIS Paul *(Per)*: 100 Village Road, Enfield, Middlesex EN1 2EX ☎ 020 8360 4975

CLAYDON Mark *(Dms, Per)*: 112 Winchcombe Road, Carshalton, Surrey SM5 1RN ☎ 020 8395 0173, 0839 761880 mob

CLIFFORD Winston *(Dms)*: 26 Oronsay Walk, Marquess Estate, Essex Road, London N1 2QT ☎ 020 7359 3015, 0956 892171

COBBETT G *(Dms)*: Address Unknown

COCCIA Dominic *(Dms)*: 22 Shandon Road, Clapham, London SW4 9HR ☎ 020 8673 3503

COLDRICK Mark *(Per, Dms, Pf)*: 46 St Fillans Road, London SE6 1DG ☎ 020 8697 2574, 0973 640904 mob

COLE George *(Dms)*: 6 Morley Street, Cooper Close, London SE1 7QU ☎ 020 7401 2586

COLEMAN Peter *(Dms)*: 91B London Road, Tonbridge, Kent TN10 3AJ ☎ 01732 359219

COLES Richard *(Dms, Per)*: 380A Kingston Road, Raynes Park, London SW20 8LN ☎ 020 8287 3247

COLLINS Philip *(Per, Pf, Gtr)*: c/o Hit & Run Music Ltd, 30 Ives Street, London SW3 2ND ☎ 020 7581 0261, 020 7584 5774 fax

COLLIS Bill *(Dms, Per)*: 36 Whellock Road, Chiswick, London W4 1DZ ☎ 020 8994 5729

CONSOLI Pascal *(Dms)*: 117 Hale Lane, London NW7 3SB ☎ 020 8906 8482

CONWAY Gerry *(Dms)*: 37 Earlswood Road, Redhill, Surrey RH1 6HD

COOK Barry *(Dms)*: 41 Redstone Park, Redhill, Surrey RH1 4AI ☎ 01737 763374

COOK Bobby *(Per)*: 13 Truesdale Road, Birchtrees, Beckton, London E6 4PT ☎ 020 7476 4472, 0976 879676

COOK Don *(Dms, La Per)*: 93 Wood Lane, Isleworth, Middx TW7 5EG ☎ 020 8568 2341, 07970 376510 mob

COOMBS George *(Dms)*: 32 Vermont Road, Sutton, Surrey SM1 3EQ ☎ 020 8644 9063

COOPER Geoffrey *(Dms, Voc)*: 15 Lilac Road, Hoddesdon, Hertfordshire EN11 0PG ☎ 01992 461089

COOPER Jason *(Dms, Per, Voc)*: Address Unknown ☎ 020 8360 9126, 020 8364 1450

COOPER Jim *(Dms, Cong, Per)*: 20 Annandale Road, London SE10 0DA ☎ 020 8853 1540

COOPER Joseph *(Per)*: 48 Rothschild Road, Chiswick, London W4 5HT ☎ 020 8994 0919, 0421 410200

COPELAND Stuart *(Dms, Gtr)*: Kent Foundation Labs Ltd, 9729-33 Culver Boulevard, Culver City, California, 90232, USA ☎ +1 310 838 8895, +1 310 838 8898

CORRADI Max *(Dms, Per)*: Ground Floor, 32 Cricketfield Road, London E5 8NS ☎ 020 8533 0944

COTON Gary *(Dms)*: 19 Bishops Court, 6 Radcliffe Rd, Croydon, Surrey CR0 5QH ☎ 020 8686 9058

COULCHER Peter *(Dms)*: 22 Bushey Road, Croydon, Surrey CR0 8EU ☎ 020 8777 8535

COULTER Alan *(Per)*: 85 Jamestown Road, London NW1 7DB ☎ 020 7267 8596

COWAN Norman *(Dms)*: Trevanion Cottage, 135 Totteridge Lane, London N20 8NS ☎ 020 8445 9330

COWELL Simon (*Per, Gtr, Kbds*): c/o Vanya Seager, Arista, Cavendish House, 423 New Kings Road, London SW6 4RN ☎ 020 7973 8040, 020 7371 9324 fax

COX Allan (*Dms*): 14 Astra Court, King Georges Avenue, Watford, Herts WD1 7TA ☎ 01923 212198, 0976 230878 mob

COX Caspar (*Dms, Voc, Per*): 4 Cicada Road, Wandsworth, London SW18 2NW ☎ 020 8870 8342, 0467 303593 mob

COX Geoffrey (*Dms*): 8 Meadowcroft, Chalfont St. Peter, Gerrards Cross, Bucks SL9 9DH ☎ 01753 883626, 0467 352723 mob

COX John (*Dms*): 20 Springvale Terrace, London W14 0AE ☎ 020 7603 8758

COX Terence (*Dms, Per*): Binisafua 11, Sant Lluis Menorca, Baleares, Spain ☎ 188725, 150890

COXON Geoffrey (*Dms, Per*): 97 Percy Road, Hampton, Middlesex TW12 JS ☎ 020 8979 5716

CRABBE Philip (*Per*): 41 Codrington Hill, London SE23 1LR ☎ 020 8314 5633

CRAIGIE Peter (*Dms, Per*): 54 Crosier Way, Rulslip, Middlesex HA4 6HF ☎ 01895 630154

CREASEY Barry (*Dms*): 21 Beaumont Park, Danbury, Chelmsford CM3 4DE ☎ 01245 227959

CREESE Stephen (*Dms*): 19A Uplands Road, Crouch End, London N8 9NN ☎ 020 8374 0393, 0930 730288

CROCKFORD Barny (*Dms, Flt, Gtr, B Gtr*): 154 Corbyn Street, London N4 3BD ☎ 020 7263 4199

CROME Bert (*Dms*): 21 Vian Avenue, Enfield Highway, Enfield, Middlesex EN3 6LQ ☎ 01992 761389

CROSS Malcolm (*Dms, Per, Voc, Kbds*): 287A Kentish Town Road, London NW2 2JS ☎ 0956 593379 mob

CROWE Nicholas (*Dms, Kbds, Voc*): 26 Rutland Court, Denmark Hill, London SE5 8EB ☎ 020 7274 9320, 0961 310179

CUMBER Peter (*Dms*): 41 Summer Road, East Molesey, Surrey KT8 9LX ☎ 020 8339 0216

CUMMINGS Daniel (*Per, Cong*): 8 Broomleaf Road, Farnham, Surrey GU9 8DG ☎ 020 7498 2591, 020 8994 1930 fax

CUPIDO Josefina (*Dms, Per, Voc*): 155 Maryland Road, Wood Green, London N22 5AS ☎ 020 8889 0216

CURRIE Colin (*Per*): 88A Belsize Road, London NW6 4TG ☎ 020 7372 5925, 0973 889893, 020 7372 5925

CUTHBERT Peter (*Dms, Per*): 77 Blegborough Road, London SW16 6DL ☎ 020 8677 2108

CUTLER Chris (*Per*): 79 Beulah Road, Thornton Heath, Surrey CR7 8JG ☎ 020 8771 1063, 020 8771 3138 fax

CUTTING Michael (*Dms, Gtr, Voc*): 113 Riverside Close, Clapton, London E5 9SU ☎ 020 8806 0376

DAGLEY Christopher (*Dms*): 439A Alexandra Avenue, Rayners Lane, Harrow HA2 9SE ☎ 020 8429 3191

DALMEDA Jarren (*Dms, Rapper*): 91 Clifford Gardens, Kensal Rise, London NW10 5JG ☎ 020 8968 7241

DANE Philip (*Dms*): 152 Vaughan Road, Harrow, Middx HA1 4EB ☎ 020 8423 6376

DANIEL Bryan (*Dms*): 55 Chalgrove Road, Tottenham, London N17 0JD ☎ 020 8801 1696

DARE Graham (*Dms, Per, Tym, La Per*): 89 Grayswood Drive, Mytcham, Camberley, Surrey GU16 6AS ☎ 01252 514301, 0958 326565

DAVI.T. (*Dms*): 37 Holland Road, Kensal Green, London NW10 5AH ☎ 020 8968 6003

DAVID Martyn (*Dms, Per*): 1 Roughtallys, Epping Road, North Weald, Essex CM16 6BH ☎ 01992 524143

DAVIES Simon (*Dms, Gtr*): ☎ 020 8444 8226

DAVIS Paul (*Dms*): 62 Leyfield, Worcester Park, Surrey KT4 7LR ☎ 020 8241 0412

DAWSON Andrew (*Dms*): 4 Ribble Close, Woodford Green, Essex IG8 7LY ☎ 020 8505 8425

DAY Richard (*Dms, Arr, Pf*): 246 Limes Avenue, Chigwell, Essex IG7 5LZ ☎ 020 8501 4629

DE MARTINO Julian (*Dms, Per, Rh Gtr, Voc*): 115 Beechwood Gardens, Gants Hill, Ilford, Essex IG5 0AQ ☎ 020 8220 0362, 0468 475629 mob

DE-BOER Jean-Victor (*Dms*): 4 Hurlstone Road, London SE25 6JD ☎ 020 8771 3898

DE-SOUZA Barry (*Dms*): The Cottage, Old Park Ride, Waltham Cross, Herts EN7 5HX ☎ 01992 622672

DEAN Johnny (*Dms, Per*): 28 Essenden Road, Sanderstead, Surrey CR2 0BU ☎ 020 8657 5268

DEEDAR (*Dms*): 102 Osbourne Road, Forest Gate, London E7 0PL ☎ 020 8552 1042

DEGENHARDT Hugo (*Dms*): c/o 73A Chetwynd Road, London NW5 ☎ 020 7681 0425

DELANEY Eric (*Per*): 2 Vandome Close, Custom House, London E16 3SA ☎ 020 7474 6834, 0402 114095 mob

DEMARINIS Anja (*Dms*): 18 Wellington House, Western Avenue, London W5 1EX ☎ 020 8810 6238

DENSHAM Barry (*Dms, B Ldr*): Herons Wood, Slines Oak Road, Woldingham, Surrey CR3 7HL ☎ 0188 365 2038

DESAI Sagar (*Dms, Tabla, Kbds*): 83 Bush Grove, Stanmore, Middlesex HA7 2DY ☎ 020 8952 0777 & fax, 0956 597821 mob

DEWAR Andrew (*Per, Dms*): 43 Rosebury Gardens, London N8 ☎ 020 8340 6394

DIAL Angie (*Per*): 70 Boxtree Road, Harrow Weald, Middlesex HA3 6TH ☎ 020 8954 4867, 020 8743 8427

DIAMOND Ross (*Dms, Gtr*): 87 Bayston Road, London N16 7NB ☎ 020 7249 9098

DILLEY Tony (*Dms*): 56 Pickhurst Park, Bromley, Kent BR2 0TW ☎ 020 8466 7542

DILLON John (*Dms*): 25 Whittington Road, London N22 4YS ☎ 020 8888 7925, 0402 127986

DIPALMO Reg (*Dms*): 44 Corney Road, Chiswick, London W4 2RA ☎ 020 8995 2740

DITCHAM Martin (*Per, Dms, La Per*): 10 Glyn Mansions, Hammersmith Road, London W14 8XH ☎ 020 7603 5469, 020 8932 4184

DOCHERTY James (*Dms, B Ldr*): 22 Albert Road, Rayleigh, Essex SS6 8HN ☎ 01268 771537

DODDS Roy (*Dms, Per*): 4 Caverswall Street, Shepherds Bush, London W12 0HG ☎ 020 8743 8107

DOE Terry (*Dms, Per*): 106 St Georges Drive, Carpenters Park, Watford WD1 5HD ☎ 020 8428 5683, 0976 707995 mob

DONALDSON John (*Per*): 17 Wychwood Close, Craigwell, Bognor Regis, Sussex PO21 4DW ☎ 01243 262154

DONKIN Geoffrey (*Dms*): Flat 3, 150 Blythe Road, Brook Green, London W14 0HD ☎ 020 7603 0198, 0374 850121

DONKOR Elvis (*Per*): 11 Sillitoe House, Colville Estate, London N1 5NH

DORAN Michael (*Per, Tym*): 47 Rosendale Road, West Dulwich, London SE21 8DY ☎ 020 8766 6164

DOUBLE George (*Dms, Per, Voc*): 49 Graham Mansions, Graham Road, Hackney, London E8 1EU ☎ 020 8525 7994

DOUGLAS Leslie (*Dms, Voc, Md*): 32 Manor Road, Wallington, Surrey SM6 0AA ☎ 020 8647 4783

DOURIET Leonel (*Per, Cong, Timb, Bong*): 42 Cecil Road, London N10 2BU ☎ 020 8883 9637

DOWDALL Graham (*Dms, Per*): 68 Fernlea Road, Balham, London SW12 9RW ☎ 020 8675 0614

DOYLE Peter (*Dms*): 8 Hampden Court, Hampden Road, Muswell Hill, London N10 2HN ☎ 020 8444 4460

DR RUBBERFUNK (*Dms, Per, Gtr, Kbds, Tbn*) ☎ 020 8549 8147, 0468 791488, 020 7371 9490

DREES Michele (*Dms, La Per, Gtr, Voc*): 10 Bloomfield Court, Bloomfield Road, Highgate, London N6 4ES ☎ 020 8348 6736, 0956 230484

DREW Martin (*Dms*): 38 College Road, Wembley, Middx HA9 8RJ ☎ 020 8908 0558

DRUMHEAD (*Dms, Per, Kbds, B Gtr, Gtr*): 42 Boileau Road, Ealing, London W5 3AH ☎ 020 8997 2782

DRUMMOND Jackie (*Dms, Per*): 43 Riverdale Road, Plumstead, London SE18 1PA ☎ 020 8854 4193

DUGMORE Geoffrey (*Dms, Per, Arr, Voc*): 43 St Albans Avenue, Bedford Park, London W4 5JS ☎ 020 8994 4422

DUHALDE Fernando *(Per, Hmca)*: 10B Victoria Road, London N4 3SQ ☎ 020 8342 9304

DUNN Geoffrey *(Dms, Per)*: 171 Martin Way, Morden, Surrey SM4 4AR ☎ 020 8542 5489, 020 8947 6200

DURNFORD Alexander *(Dms, Ac Gtr, B Gtr, Kbds)*: 31A Limes Road, West Croydon, Surrey CR0 2HF ☎ 020 8684 3641

DYANI-AKURU Thomas *(Per, Dms, Kbds)*: Flat 1, 84 Camberwell Road, London SE5 0EG ☎ 020 7277 1536

DYER Julie *(Per, Tym, Pf)*: Ground Floor Flat, 29 Agnew Road, Forest Hill, London SE23 1QH ☎ 020 8699 2091, 0973 889746

EARLEY Kevin *(Per, La Per)*: 315A Upper Elmers End Road, Beckenham, Kent BR3 3QP ☎ 020 8402 7107, 0860 809973

EASTWOOD Cj *(Dms)*: 51 Francis Avenue, Ilford, Essex IG1 1TS ☎ 020 8553 0682

EBSWORTH Andrew *(Dms, Per)*: 110 Strathdon Drive, London SW17 0PP ☎ 020 8946 9932, 020 8871 4270 day

ECCLES Noel *(Per)*: c/o Edge Manning & Co, Solicitors, 31 Lower Lesson Street, Dublin 2, Ireland

EDGE Graham *(Per)*: Threshold Records Co Ltd, 53 High Street, Cobham, Surrey KT11 3DP ☎ 01932 864142/3

EDGOOSE Simon *(Dms, Per)*: 11 Melbourne Court, Sydney Road, Muswell Hill, London N10 2NN ☎ 020 8444 1837

EDWARDS Jon *(Dms)*: 16 Crouch Hill, London N4 4AU ☎ 020 8281 7303

EDWARDS Karlos *(Per)*: 1 Princes Close, Kingsbury, London NW9 9QT ☎ 020 8204 8574

EDWARDS Lyn *(Dms, Per)*: 54 Wolseley Gardens, Chiswick, London W4 3LS ☎ 020 8995 4325

EKLAND Bob *(Dms, Voc)*: 74 Seaford Road, South Tottenham, London N15 5DT ☎ 020 8802 4803

EL SAFY Farok *(Per, Tabla)*: 1 Hamilton Villas, Ongar Road, London SW6 1RJ ☎ 020 7610 2930

ELLIOTT Alexander *(Per)*: 2 Kirkstall House, Abbots Manor, London SW1V 4JW ☎ 020 7828 3209

ELLIOTT Stuart *(Dms)*: 5A Springdale Road, London N16 9NS ☎ 020 7923 7189

ELLIS Robert *(Dms, Pf, Per)*: 43 Wingfield Road, Sherborne, Dorset DT9 3HJ ☎ 01935 817268

EMERY Terry *(Per)*: Wood End, Bakers Wood, Denham, Middlesex UB9 4LG ☎ 01895 832942

EMNEY Brian *(Dms)*: 14 Gordon Avenue, Sanderstead, Surrey CR2 0QN ☎ 020 8668 9366

ENGDAHL Caroline *(Dms)*

ENYA.(N.RYAN) *(Per, Arr)*: Treesdale, Church Road, Killiney, Dublin, Eire ☎ Dublin 312580

ESMOND Dick *(Dms, B Ldr)*: 4 Adelaide Road, West Ealing W13 W13 9EB ☎ 020 8567 5574

ESSEX David *(Dms, Pf, Gtr)*: Lamplight Music, 109 Eastbourne Mews, London W2 6LQ ☎ 020 7402 5169

EVANS Guy *(Dms, Per)*: 29 Primrose Hill Court, King Henry's Rd, London NW3 3QS ☎ 020 7722 6124

EYERS Robert *(Dms)*: 96A Algernon Road, Lewisham, London SE13 7AW ☎ 020 8690 2995, 01523 191142 pager

FAIRBAIRN Keith *(Per, Tym, Dms, La Per)*: 11 Crayton Road, Ampthill, Beds MK45 2LE ☎ 01525 840465, 01370 397126 mob

FAIRBANK Julian *(Per, Dms)*: 36 Argyle Road, North Harrow, Middx HA2 7AJ ☎ 020 8863 4208

FAIRBANKS Brian *(Dms)*: 23 Rosewood Court, Orchard Road, Bromley, Kent BR1 2TT ☎ 020 8464 2214

FALL David *(Dms)*: 107 Lewis Trust Estate, Vanston Place, Fulham SW6 1BU ☎ 020 7381 3196, +446 11 82 06 96

FAR.I *(Per)*: 1 Donnington House, Union Road, London SW8 2RU ☎ 020 7720 9286

FARMER Peter *(Dms)*: 410 Clarke Street, Northcote, Victoria 3070, Australia ☎ +61 3 9489 8724

FEARN Dennis *(Dms, Vib, Voc)*: 9 Waylands, Swanley, Kent BR8 8TA ☎ 01322 664259

FENNER Clive *(Dms)*: 27 Cambridge Road, Wanstead, London E11 2PL ☎ 020 8989 9345

FENTON Julian *(Dms)*: 226A Stockwell Road, London SW9 9SU ☎ 020 7737 6059, 07775 778886

FERNANDES Tony *(Per)*: 23 Rushbrooke Close, High Wycombe, Bucks HP13 7QN

FERRAO Hans *(Dms)*: Ground Floor Flat, 62 Madeira Road, Streatham, London SW16 2DE ☎ 020 8769 7636

FERRERA Stephen *(Dms, Per)*: 60 East 42nd Street, Suite 3112, New York, New York 10165 /3197 ☎ +1 212 687 3939

FINCH Stephen *(Dms)*: 71 Marlborough Road, Romford, Essex RM7 8AD ☎ 01708 757623 & fax

FINCHAM Alistair *(Dms)*: 172 The Fairway, Ruislip, Middlesex HA4 OSH ☎ 020 8845 4200

FINLAY Rick *(Dms, Per, Cop)*: 25A Rosslyn Avenue, East Barnet, Herts EN4 8DH ☎ 020 8361 0265, 020 8368 6293 fax, 0831 376175 mob

FIORILO Oliver *(Dms)* ☎ 020 7379 0038, 020 7497 8909

FISHER Damian *(Dms)*: 56 Arundel Road, Marston Moretaine, Beds MK43 0JU ☎ 01234 766791, 0973 635798

FISHER Harold *(Per)*: Harewood, Lower Road, Chorley Wood, Herts WD3 5LQ ☎ 01923 284623, 081 549 1706 day

FISHWICK Mathew *(Dms)*: 221 Ashmore Road, London W9 3DB ☎ 020 8969 4381, 07970 680817

FLEEMAN Jim *(Dms, Per)*: 95 Belgrave Road, London SW1V 2BQ ☎ 020 7565 2857, 0976 156125 mob

FLETCHER Alastair *(Dms)* ☎ 020 7243 0640, 020 7243 0470

FLETCHER Mark *(Dms)*: 121 Heath Way, Erith, Kent DA8 3LZ ☎ 01322 405795, 0976 285309

FLISZAR Dicki *(Dms, Gtr)*: 14 Mollison Drive, Wallington, Surrey SM6 9BY ☎ 020 8647 0390

FLY T G *(Dms, Wh)*: 4 Upwey House, Whitmore Road, London N1 5PT ☎ 020 7613 2955, 01782 685 590

FORDJOUR Robert *(Dms)*: Flat 3, 131 St James Road, West Croydon, Surrey CR0 2UW ☎ 020 8251 9037, 04325 335777 pager

FORDREE John *(Dms)*: 276 Eastern Avenue, Redbridge, Ilford, Essex IG4 5AA ☎ 020 8554 5576, 020 8518 6584

FOSTER Neil *(Per, Tym, Dms)*: 51 Endsleigh Gardens, Ilford, Essex IG1 3EQ ☎ 020 8554 0314, 0973 932195

FOWLER Paul *(Dms, Per, Gtr, Voc)*

FOX Marc *(Per, Voc, Arr)*: 79 Frithville Gardens, London W12 7JQ ☎ 020 8746 0742, 0421 491017, 020 7973 0332

FRANCE Martin *(Dms, Per)*: 11 Winchester Cottages, Copperfield Street, London SE1 0EP ☎ 020 7357 7347

FRANCE Nic *(Dms, Per)*: 5 Meldreth Road, Shepreth, Royston, Hertfordshire SG8 6PS ☎ 01763 262683, 0976 792203 mob

FRANCIS Karl *(Per)*: Address Unknown

FRANCIS Kenneth *(Dms, Voc)*: 116 Wakehurst Drive, Southgate, Crawley, Sussex RH10 6BZ ☎ 01293 34052

FRANCOLINI David *(Dms, Gtr)* ☎ 020 7243 0640 mob

FRASER Mathew *(Dms, Voc)*: 12 Inverton Road, Nunhead, London SE15 3DD ☎ 020 7252 8742

FREAKY FROG *(Dms, Kbds, Com)*: 28 Scrudditts Square, Radlett, Herts WD7 8JS ☎ 01923 469627

FRY Peter *(Per, Tym)*: 24 Maclean Road, Forest Hill, London SE23 1PD ☎ 020 8699 4992, 01306 880669

FRY Tristan *(Per, Tym, Pf)*: 141 Willifield Way, London NW11 6XY ☎ 0956 435197

FULLBROOK Charles *(Per, Tym)*: 2 Warner Road, London N8 7HD ☎ 020 8340 7869

FULLER John *(Dms, Vib)*: 21 Fieldway, Broad Oak, Brede, East Sussex TN31 6DL ☎ 01424 883168

FURBER Paul *(Dms, Per)*: 106 Drakefield Road, Tooting Bec, London SW17 8RR

G-RAY *(Per, Arr)*: 5 Englefield Close, Croydon, Surrey CR0 2TU

GABRIEL Pascal *(Per, Synth)*: Studio 4, 1 Cahill Street, London EC1Y 8PH

GAIN Stuart *(Per, Dms)*: Long Wall, Crayburne, Betsham, Kent DA13 9PB ☎ 01474 833997, 0374 161996 mob

GALE Christopher *(Dms, Per)*: 9 Beckford Drive, Crofton, Orpington, Kent BR5 1SH ☎ 01689 877034

GALE Derek *(Dms)*: 6 Somerford Estate, Somerford Grove, London N16 7TL ☎ 020 7249 7832

GALLAIS Lydie *(Dms)*: 5 Etherley Road, London N15 3AL ☎ 020 8809 4263

GAMMONS Rod (*Dms, Per, Kbds, Gtr, Voc*): 33 Bournehall Ave, Bushey, Herts WD2 3AU ☎ 020 7950 1485, 020 8950 1294 fax

GANEVA Daniella (*Mrba, Vib, Per*) ☎ 0976 804606, 020 8292 0255

GANGADEEN (*Dms*): 101 Antill Road, Bow, London E3 5BW ☎ 020 8983 0943

GANLEY Allan (*Dms, Arr, Com*): 5 Asher Drive, Ascot, Berks SL5 8LJ ☎ 01344 882396

GARNER Tim (*Dms*): 7 Warwick Place, Ealing, London W5 5PS ☎ 020 8579 8027, 0402 890654 mob

GARVEY Nigel (*Per, Tym*): 23 Chapel Street, Wellesbourne, Warwick CV35 9QU ☎ 01789 840920

GEOFF ("Pinball") (*Dms, Per*): 13 Gibson Gardens, Stoke Newington, London N16 7HB ☎ 020 7254 0138, 020 7254 6700

GERRAND Fergus (*Per, Dms, Kbds*): 3 Old School Terrace, Jubilee Road, Cheam, Surrey SM3 8DL ☎ 020 8642 5066, 0958 443880

GIBBONS Beth (*Per, Voc*): c/o Fruit, 326 Kensal Road, London W10 5BZ ☎ 020 8964 8448

GIFFORD Robert (*Dms*): 2 Crownfield, Old Nazeing Road, Broxbourne, Herts EN10 6QX ☎ 01992 469257

GILBERT Simon (*Dms*): c/o Interceptor Enterprises, First Floor, 98 White Lion Street, London N1 9PF ☎ 020 7278 8001, 020 7713 6298 fax

GILCHRIST Stephen (*Dms, Vla*): 1 Fountain Cotteages, The Marld, Ashtead, Surrey KT21 1RG ☎ 01372 273853, 0958 475373 mob

GILLIAM Clare (*Per, W Bd*): 70A Mansfield Road, c/o The Launderette, London NW3 2HU ☎ 020 7267 1374 & fax

GIOVANNINI Davide (*Dms, Af Dms, Per, Voc*): Flat 1, 84 Camberwell Road, London SE5 0EG ☎ 020 7701 4275

GISCOMBE Norman (*Per*): 122 Roedean Avenue, Enfield, Middlesex EN3 5QN ☎ 020 8805 0288

GLEADHILL Andrew (*Per, Dms, Kbds, Tpt*): 11 Beech Road, Horfield, Bristol BS7 8RP ☎ 0117 909 6564

GLEDHILL Rachel (*Per, Tym*): 11 Tyttenhanger Green, St Albans, Herts AL4 0RN ☎ 01727 812887

GLENDINING Thomas (*Dms, Per*): 158 High Road, Woodford Green, Essex IG8 9EF ☎ 020 8505 9255

GLENTWORTH Mark (*Per*): 10 Coney Acre, Croxted Rd, London SE21 8LL ☎ 020 8761 3597

GLYNN Gareth (*Dms*): 55 Claverdale Road, London SW2 2DJ ☎ 020 8674 2507

GODDARD Robin (*Dms, Tnd Per*): 182 Lower Morden Road, Morden, Surrey SM4 4SS ☎ 020 8330 0550

GODFREY Simon (*Dms, Gtr, Voc*): 21 North Worple Way, London SW14 8QA ☎ 020 8287 1097

GOLDRING David (*Per, Kbds*): c/o M.G.R Accountants, 55 Loudon Road, London NW8 0DL ☎ 020 7625 4545

GOLDSMITH Timothy (*Dms, Per*): 343A Upper Richmond Road West, East Sheen, London SW14 8EA ☎ 020 8878 8962

GOLDSPINK Brian (*Dms, Pf, B Gtr*): 30 Brooklands Road, Romford, Essex RN17 7EG ☎ 01708 788570

GONELLA David (*Dms, Tym*): 10 Leopold Road, Chatham, Kent ME4 5SX ☎ 01634 827674, 0802 671373

GOODWIN Daniel (*Dms, Per*): 13A Trevelyan Road, London SW17 9LS ☎ 020 8767 0390

GOODWIN Sarah-Jane (*Dms, Kbds*): 2 Clifton Road, Wood Green, London N22 4XN ☎ 020 8888 2289, 020 8881 2303

GOODYER Tim (*Dms*): 11 Kings Street, Chesham, Bucks HP5 1LE ☎ 01494 791239

GORDON Cameron (*Dms, Per, Con, Md*): 37 Devonshire Road, Palmers Green, London N13 4QU ☎ 020 8447 8692, 0802 849411 mob

GORDON Lisa (*Dms, Per, Gtr*): 18 Milson Road, West Kensington, London W14 0LJ ☎ 020 7610 5313, 01523 141291

GORDON Tom (*Dms, Tym, Per, Pf*): 55A Fernthorpe Road, Streatham, London SW16 6DP ☎ 020 8769 8218

GORHAM Carl (*Dms*): 1 Royal Place, Greenwich, London SE10 8QF ☎ 020 8692 1590

GRACE Paul (*Dms, Per*): 34 Shelley Avenue, Hornchurch, Essex RM12 4BT ☎ 01708 478597, 020 8594 0666, 020 8591 2355

GRAHAM John (*Dms*): 10 Garston Grove, Finchampstead, Wokingham, Berks RG11 4YF ☎ 01734 731930

GRAHAME Alan (*Per, Vib, La Per*): Orchard Cottage, Stoke Row Rd, Peppard Common, Henley-on-Thames, Oxon RG9 5JD ☎ 01491 628333, 0831 443763 mob

GRANGE Pierson (*Dms, Per, Voc*): 3 Walter Court, Lynton Terrace, Lynton Road, Acton, London W3 9DX ☎ 020 8993 5768

GRANT Michael (*Per, Tym*): 44 Eden Way, Beckenham, Kent BR3 3DJ ☎ 020 8650 2585

GRANT Tim (*Dms, Per*): 81A Falkland Road, London NW5 ☎ 020 7284 0851

GRANTLEY Steve (*Dms, Per*): 17 Bourton Close, Hayes, Middlesex UB3 3PU ☎ 020 8573 9516

GRAY Andy (*Dms*): 75 Bramblewood Close, Carshalton, Surrey SM5 1PQ ☎ 020 8647 0369

GREEN Benedict (*Dms, Gtr*): Flat 2, 9 Yonge Park, London N4 3NU ☎ 020 7609 9512, 020 7323 8303

GREEN Ian (*Dms, Per, La Per*): 223 Hayes Lane, Kenley, Surrey CR8 5HN ☎ 020 8668 5690

GREEN Steve (*Dms, Per*): 88A Swabey Road, London SW18 3QZ ☎ 020 8265 3348, 0956 481 736 mob

GREENHAM Peter (*Per*): 122 Goldhurst Terrace, London NW6 3HR

GREEVE Micky (*Per, Xyl, Tym*): 41 The High, Streatham High Road, London SW16 1EY ☎ 020 8769 2702

GREGORY Michael (*Dms, Per*): 89 Winchester Road, St. Margarets, Twickenham, Middlesex TW1 1LA ☎ 020 8892 1956

GRIFFIN Roger (*Per, Pf*): 28 Cromwell Avenue, Thame, Oxon OX9 3TD ☎ 01844 261098

GRIGG Michael (*Dms*): 105 Lowen Road, Rainham, Essex RM13 8QD ☎ 01708 525709

GUARD Barrie (*Per, Kbds, Md*): 116 Ember Lane, Esher, Surrey KT10 8EL ☎ 020 8398 1274

GUARD Sebastian (*Dms, Per*): Flat 6, 39 Auckland Road, Upper Norwood, London SE19 2DR ☎ 020 8653 2673, 0966 394931

GUAZZOTTI Giovanni (*Dms*): 16A Camden Road, London NW1 9DP

GUEGAN Neil (*Dms, Per, Gtr*): 270 Coldharbour Lane, Flat 6, London SW9 5OH ☎ 020 7642 0947

GUITARD Jean-Luc (*Dms, Gtr, Kbds*): Flat 27, Holm Court, Le May Avenue, London SE12 0BD ☎ 020 8740 6863, 020 7408 1174

GUPTA Raj (*Dms, Kbds*): Top Flat, 1 Bentinck Street, London W1M 5RN ☎ 020 7935 3918

GUY Martin (*Dms*): 153 Dunmow Road, Bishop's Stortford, Hertfordshire CM23 5HQ ☎ 01279 654841

H David (*Dms, Kbds, Per, Arr*): 3 Ringwood Close, Eastbourne, E Sussex BN22 8UH ☎ 07050 257566, 01323 439176, 0403 845333

HADAWAY Jose Carlos (*Dms, Pf*): 63 Rendlesham Road, Clapton, London E5 8PJ ☎ 020 8533 9461

HAGUE Ian (*Dms*): 42 Clapham Common, West Side, London SW4 9AR ☎ 020 7228 1202

HAKIN Alan (*Per, Xyl*): Quaverley, 2 Polesden View, Great Bookham, Surrey KT23 4LN ☎ 01372 459707

HALE Daniel (*Dms*): 18 College Road, Harrow Weald, Middlesex HA3 6EB ☎ 020 8863 8495, 07970 379322, 01403 823313

HALFORD Chris (*Dms*): 16 Acacia Grove, New Malden, Surrey KT3 3BJ ☎ 020 8949 1434, 0976 329017 mob

HAMBROOK Stefan (*Dms, Gtr*): Top Flat, 30 Topsfield Parade, Crouch End, London N8 8PT ☎ 020 8374 5958, 0973 440825

HAMMOND Gary (*Dms, Per*): 60 Lugard Road, London SE15 2SZ ☎ 020 7277 8193, 0421 502659 mob

HAMMOND Scott (*Dms*): 13 Stewartsby Close, Edmonton, London N18 1AN, 0976 418690 mob

HANCOCK Garrad (*Dms*): 9 Cubitt Terrace, Clapham, London SW4 9AU ☎ 020 7622 5655

HANSON Simon (*Dms*): 11 Lucerne Mews, London W8 4ED ☎ 020 7727 2631, 0589 439 609 mob

HARDMAN Christopher (*Per, Kbds, Gtr*) ☎ 0966 185073 mob

HARMAN Bernard (*Per*): 29 Meridian Court, Bagshot Road, Ascot, Berks SL5 9JW ☎ 01344 291538

HARPER Michael (*Per*): 25 Pasadena Park, East Hill Road, Otford, Kent TN15 6YD ☎ 07666 727471 pager, 0956 493448 mob

HARPER Phillip (*Per, Dms*): 27 Approach Close, Spencer Grove, London N16 8UQ ☎ 020 7503 6048

HARRIES Alun (*Dms, Per, Voc*): 122 Hounslow Road, Whitton, Twickenham, Middlesex TW2 7HB ☎ 020 8755 1272, 0374 169881 mob

HARRIS Antony (*Dms, Per, Gtr, B Gtr*): 14 Oxford Road, Finsbury Park, London N4 3HA ☎ 020 7272 8541, 0973 114252

HARRIS Steven (*Dms*): Flat 9, 4 Tavistock Road, Croydon, London CR0 2AT ☎ 020 8667 0256

HARRIS Thomas (*Dms*): 11 Richmond Road, Leytonstone, London E11 4BY ☎ 04325 174837 pager

HARRISON Gavin (*Dms*): 101 Herkomer Road, Bushey, Herts WD2 3LS ☎ 020 8950 6691, 0468 608437

HARRISON Oliver (*Dms, Gtr, Kbds*): Vale Cottage, Vale Of Health, Hampstead, London NW3 1AX ☎ 020 7287 1155

HARRISON Roger (*Per, Dms, La Per*): One West Lodge, Park Road, Tring, Hertfordshire HP23 6BU ☎ 01442 891678 & fax

HARROD John (*Per, Tym*): Address Unknown

HARRY Levy (*Per, Dms, Voc*): The Basement, 4 Dagmar Road, London SE5 8NZ ☎ 020 7277 0344

HART George (*Dms, Per, Pf, Sax, B Gtr*): 11 Queens Road, Leytonstone, London E11 1BA ☎ 020 8558 4000, 0958 469482 mob, 020 8558 4032

HARWARD Richard (*Per, La Per*): 11 Runnymede Court, Fontley Way, Roehampton, London SW15 4NT ☎ 020 8785 0308

HATHWAY Kevin (*Per*): 25 Park Avenue North, London N8 7RU ☎ 020 8347 9697 & fax

HATTEE David (*Dms, Per*): 39 Armoury Road, London SE8 4LA ☎ 020 8692 3518, 0973 638302 mob

HAWKES Jodie (*Dms*): The Herons, Laleham Reach, Chertsey, Surrey KT16 8RP ☎ 01932 562212

HAWKINS Robert (*Dms*): 4 Eagle Lane, Snaresbrook, London E11 1PF ☎ 020 8989 2144

HEARN Martin (*Dms, La Per*): Stix School Of Rhythm, Kings Arms Yard, Church Street, Ampthill, Bedford MK45 2PJ ☎ 01525 840157, 0378 261811

HEATH Elizabeth (*Dms, Per*): 13 Hales Prior, Calshot Street, London N1 9JW ☎ 020 7713 7006, 04988 48809

HENDERSON Andrew (*Dms*): 5 Kilmarsh Road, London W6 0PL

HENDERSON Peter (*Per, Tym*): 24 Mondscourt Cottages, Church Road, Sunridge, Sevenoaks, Kent TN14 6DT ☎ 01959 565271

HENDERSON Richard (*Dms, Pf*): Lavriston, 11 Boleyn Ave, Ewell, Surrey KT17 2QH ☎ 020 8224 7922, 020 8393 1468

HENDERSON Stephen (*Per, Tym, Tnd Per, La Per, Bq*): c/o M.A.S. Master S Yard, 180A South Street, Dorking, Surrey RH4 2ES ☎ 020 8810 6848, 01306 500022

HENRIT Robert (*Dms*): 3 Esther Close, Winchmore Hill, London N21 N21 1AW ☎ 020 8360 8437

HENRY Errol (*Dms, Kbds, B Gtr, Gtr*): 60 Wilson Drive, Wembley, Middx HA9 9TX ☎ 020 8908 4599, 020 7488 2900 fax

HENTY Timothy (*Per, Tym, Dms*): ☎ 020 8467 5205

HERON Paul (*Dms*): 6 Eleanor Close, Arnold Road, Tottenham N15 4HU ☎ 020 8808 1284, 0468 831181

HEWITT Mark (*Dms*): Hutton Hall Lodge, Hutton Village, Hutton, Brentwood, Essex CM13 1RX

HEWITT Steven (*Dms*): c/o Lisa Ferguson, The Colonnades, 82 Bishops Bridge Road, London W2 6BB ☎ 020 7243 0640

HEYMAN Preston (*Per, Dms*): Flat 1, 3 Abbey Gardens, London NW8 9AS ☎ 020 7328 4577

HIGGINBOTTOM Christopher (*Dms*): 7 Ashley Grove, Staples Road, Loughton, Essex IG10 1HS ☎ 020 8508 9612

HIGGINS Richard (*Dms*): Summerfields, 13A Limes Avenue, Horley, Surrey RH6 9DH ☎ 01293 774578

HILL William (*Dms, Per*): 3 Coppice Close, Great Dunmow, Essex CM6 2SL ☎ 01371 876 856

HILTON Stuart (*Dms, Voc*): 36 Danby Street, Peckham, London SE15 4BU ☎ 020 7277 8981

HIROTA Joji (*Per, Com, Shak*): 242 Worton Road, Isleworth, Middx TW7 6EF ☎ 020 8568 0240

HISCOCK Stephen (*Dms, Per*): Basement Flat, 21 Thorngate Road, London W9 2DN ☎ 020 7289 3162

HISEMAN Jon (*Dms, Per, Com*): 48 The Ridgway, Sutton, Surrey SM2 5JU ☎ 020 8642 3210

HOARE Simon (*Per, Kbds, Gtr, Dms*): 19A Cliff Villas, Garden Flat, London NW1 9AT ☎ 020 7267 7191

HODGE Iain (*Per, Pf*): 55 Tudor Way, Hillingdon, Middx UB10 9AA ☎ 01895 230687

HODSON Joseph (*Per*): 10 Winston Court, Headstone Lane, Harrow, Middx HA3 6PF ☎ 020 8428 2501

HOE Ivan (*Dms, Per*): 12 The Grove, Finchley, London N3 1QL ☎ 0976 920430

HOGAN Neil (*Dms*): 216 Stock Road, Billericay, Essex CM12 0SH ☎ 01277 622237, 0802 896418 mob

HOLDSWORTH Cyril (*Per, Tnd Per*): 29 Mayfield Avenue, London N12 9JG ☎ 020 8445 7994

HOLLAND James (*Per, Tym*): Wood Cottage, The Grange, Amersham Road, Beaconsfield, Bucks HP9 2UG ☎ 01494 677436

HOLLAND Steve (*Dms, Voc*): 96 Eskdale Avenue, Northolt, Middx UB5 5DL ☎ 020 8841 3233

HOLROYDE Geoff (*Dms, Per, Pf*): 1st Floor Flat, 36 Sinclair Road, London W14 0NS ☎ 020 7603 2156

HOLT Roger (*Dms*): Beachway, 19 Ulwell Road, Swanage, Dorset BH19 1LF ☎ 0929 423077

HOOD J.F.T. (*Dms, Kbds*): 37 Buspace Studios, Conlan Street, London W10 5AP ☎ 020 8969 1600

HOOPER Jon (*Dms, Per*): 55 Dairsie Road, Eltham, London SE9 9XN ☎ 020 8859 1474

HOOPER Tom (*Per*): 67 Grasmere Avenue, Wembley, Middx HA9 6TF ☎ 020 8904 8103

HOPKINS Graham (*Dms, Pf, Gtr, B Gtr*): c/o 44 Loughbollard, Clane, Co Kildare, Ireland

HOPKINS Philip (*Dms, Per, Hmca*): 5 Claygate Road, Dorking, Surrey RH4 2PR ☎ 01306 742680

HOWARD Daniel (*Dms*): 52A Peckham High Street, Peckham, London SE15 5DP ☎ 020 7732 2980

HOWARD Michael (*Dms, Per, Bod*): 57 Cantwell Road, London SE18 3LL ☎ 020 8244 0169

HOWE Dylan (*Dms, Per*): 143 Gloucester Avenue, London NW1 8LA ☎ 020 7722 7518, 0850 181 269 mob

HOWELL Peter (*Dms*): Walsh Manor, Walshes Road, Crowborough, East Sussex

HOWELLS Jonathan (*Dms, Tpt, Gtr, Wh*): 1 Kennedy Close, Orpington, Kent BR5 1HP ☎ 01689 81116, 041100 6960

HOWES Robert (*Per, Tym*): Fir Tree Farm, 110 Sluice Road, Denver, Norfolk PE38 0DZ ☎ 0136 638 5293, 0136 638 4330 fax

HOWLAND Peter (*Dms, Tnd Per*): 33 Claygate Road, Dorking, Surrey RH4 2PR ☎ 01306 887530

HUDSON Reg (*Dms*): Meadowbank, 6 Middlings Rise, Sevenoaks, Kent TN13 2NS ☎ 01732 457147

HUGALL Christopher (*Per*): 86 Wolfington Road, West Norwood, London SE27 0RQ ☎ 020 8670 6979, 020 7738 3994

HUGGETT Andrew (*Dms*): 7 Macfarlane Road, London W12 7JY ☎ 020 8743 1049, 0956 210486 mob

HUGGETT Mark (*Dms, Voc, Per*): 49 Haslemere Road, Thornton Heath, Surrey CR7 7BF ☎ 020 8689 5335

HUGHES Martin (*Dms*): 128 Sandhurst Road, London SE6 1XD ☎ 020 8698 9547

HULLEY David (*Per, Tym, Vib, Dms*): 21 Stratton Road, Merton Park, London SW19 3JG ☎ 020 8540 5583

HUMPHREY John (*Dms, Per*): 22 Hawley Road, Wilmington, Dartford, Kent DA1 1NR ☎ 01322 276409

HUNT Christopher (*Dms*): 111 Wedgewood House, Lambeth Walk, London SE11 6LW ☎ 020 7582 5491

HUNT David (*Per*): 7 Foxleas Court, 4 Spencer Road, Bromley, Kent BR1 3WB ☎ 020 8460 5629, 0468 312270, 020 8289 0887

HUNTINGTON Peter (*Dms, Pf*): 5 Wellington Terrace, Harrow, Middlesex HA3 3EP ☎ 020 8423 1078

HURST Robin (*Dms, B Ldr*): 174 Harrow View, Harrow, Middlesex HA1 4TL ☎ 020 8427 9444

HUSBAND Gary (*Dms, Pf, Kbds, Ac Gtr*): 50B Randolph Avenue, London W9 1BE ☎ 020 7286 0821

HUTCHINSON Ben (*Dms, La Per, Per*): 1A Chaseville Parade, Winchmore Hill, London N21 1PG ☎ 020 8373 0438, 0468 107434 mob

HYDE Gary (*Dms, Per*): 13, Downbank Avenue, Barnehurst, Kent DA7 6RS ☎ 01322 335360

HYDER Ken (*Dms, Per*): 69 Ravenslea Road, Balham, London SW12 8SL ☎ 020 8673 1873

IBRAHIM Sherif Zaki (*Dms*): 1 Stafford Close, London NW6 5TW

IBRAHIM Tansay (*Dms, Per*): 266 Lower Addiscombe Road, Croydon, Surrey CR0 7AE ☎ 020 8656 9958

IF Owen (*Dms*): 119 Railton Road, Brixton, London SE24 0LT ☎ 020 7737 1605

INGRAM Douglas (*Per*): 9A Marden House, Pembury Estate, Bodney Road, London E8 1AZ ☎ 020 8533 1136

INNES David (*Per*): 7 Fife Hill Park, Aberdeen AB2 0NS ☎ 01224 723483

INSTRALL Graham (*Per, Dms*): 60 Mayfield Crescent, London N9 7NJ ☎ 0976 804606, 020 8292 0255

IZAAK Ras (*Per*): 94 St Pauls Tower, Beaumont Road, Leyton E10 5BW

J.M. Nick (*Dms, Per*): 9A Pemberton Road, London N4 1AX ☎ 020 8348 4638

JACKSON Alan (*Dms*): 184 Ardgowan Rd, Catford, London SE6 1XA ☎ 020 8698 6911

JACKSON David (*Per, Tym*): 25 Rothschild Road, Chiswick, London W4 5HT ☎ 020 8742 7430, 0973 188373

JACKSON Stephen (*Dms*): 56A Broad Street, Teddington, Middlesex TW11 8QY ☎ 020 8255 1913, 0850 360774 mob

JAMES Brad (*Dms*): 28 Horton Road, London E8 1DP ☎ 020 7254 9257

JAMES David (*Dms, Per*): 62 Park Road, New Barnet, Hertfordshire EN4 9QF ☎ 020 8440 2382

JAMES Gary (*Dms, Per*): Toni Medcalf Mgmt, Garden Flat, 83 Cambridge Gdns, London W10 6JE ☎ 020 8960 3596, 020 8960 4330

JARDIM Luis (*Per*): 62 Eastwalk, East Barnet EN4 8JU ☎ 020 8368 0761/7

JAYES Simon (*Dms, Per*) ☎ 020 8645 9585, 0802 499727

JEFFREY Richard (*Dms, Kbds*): 72 Grosvenor Terrace, London SE5 0NW ☎ 020 7722 4175, 020 7722 4072

JENKINS Bob.Jnr (*Dms*): 40 Montague Avenue, Sanderstead, Surrey CR2 9NH ☎ 020 8657 5294

JENKINS Terry (*Per*): 23 The Drive, Havefield Place, Ickenham, Middx UB10 8AF ☎ 01895 255244

JENNER Clive (*Dms, Per, Pf, Voc, Ob*): 12 Felix Road, West Ealing, London W13 0NT ☎ 020 8567 5471

JENNINGS Neale (*Dms*): 12 Cranmer Road, Hampton Hill, Middlesex TW12 1DW ☎ 020 8979 2488, 01426 368552

JERVIER Paul (*Dms*): 108 Perry Rise, London SE23 2QP ☎ 020 8291 5421

JOHN David (*Dms, Per*): 73A Tufnell Park Road, London N7 0PS ☎ 020 7607 6421

JOHN Martyn (*Dms*): 90 Birdbrook Road, Kidbrooke, London SE3 9QP

JOHNSON Brian (*Per*): 1 Guernsey House, Eastfield Road, Enfield, Middx EN3 5UZ ☎ 020 8805 5819

JOHNSON David (*Dms, Pf, Vln, Com, Voc*): 10 Burntwood Close, Wandsworth, London SW18 3JU ☎ 020 8870 3450 & fax

JOHNSON John (*Dms*): 41B Kinsgate Road, London NW6 4TD ☎ 020 7625 6905

JOHNSON Lawrence (*Per, Pf*): 151 Windmill Road, Edmonton, London N18 1LL ☎ 020 8372 8366

JOHNSON Len (*Per, Tym, Xyl, Vib*): Flat 1 Park Lodge, 17 Victoria Park Road, Exeter, Devon EX2 4NT ☎ 01392 422178

JOHNSTON James (*Dms, Per*): 19 Petworth Road, London N12 9HE ☎ 020 8445 9504

JOHNSTONE Tam (*Dms, B Gtr, Gtr, Kbds, Voc*): 13D Turle Road, London N4 3LZ ☎ 020 7561 0645

JONES Andrew (*Per, Dms, Gtr, Kbds*): 47B Devonshire Drive, Greenwich, London SE10 8JZ ☎ 020 8692 7152

JONES Bryon (*Dms, Kbds, Voc*): 83 Kendal Avenue, Edmonton, London N18 1NE ☎ 020 8803 9110, 020 7404 0306

JONES Derek (*Dms, Per, Tym, Vib*): 178 Hall Lane, Upminster, Essex RM14 1AT ☎ 01708 227177

JONES Djina (*Per, Voc*): 101 Loughborough Road, London SW9 7TD ☎ 020 7274 8744

JONES Douglas (*Dms*): 14 Brants Walk, Hanwell, London W7 1BU ☎ 020 8575 6982, 0403 815826

JONES Lindsay (*Dms, Kbds, Gtr, B Gtr*): Top Flat, 1371 London Road, Norbury, London SW16 4BE ☎ 0973 251703

JONES Robin (*Per, La Per*): 64 East Walk, East Barnet, Herts EN4 8JU ☎ 020 8368 3323

JOYCE Noel (*Per*): Well Cottage, 106 West Street, Ewell Village, Surrey KT17 1XR ☎ 020 8393 0482, 0378 670185

KARAN Chris (*Per, La Per*): 110 Stag Lane, Edgware, Middx HA8 5LL ☎ 020 8204 2341

KARNO Gilbey (*Dms*): Max-Rimmele-Str 72, 86316 Friedberg, Germany ☎ 0821 60 20 11, +49 821 60 20 12 fax

KASAI Tatsuya (*Dms*): 126 Fairbridge Road, Upper Holloway, London N19 3HU ☎ 020 7263 8410, 0961 394521

KATCHE Manu (*Per, Dms*): 17 Callow Street, Apt C, London SW3 6BJ

KEEFE Brent (*Dms*): 16 Auckland Road, Upper Norwood, London SE19 2DL ☎ 020 8653 6215

KEEN James (*Dms*): 134A Midhurst Road, London W13 9TP ☎ 020 8579 5710

KEENE Melvyn (*Dms*): 22 Freeland Park, Holders Hill Road, Hendon, London NW4 1LP ☎ 020 8346 7591

KELLY Edmund (*Per*): 63 Banner House, Banner Street, London EC1Y 8SX

KELLY Sam (*Dms*): 2 Hillborough Court, 32 Roxborough Park, Harrow, Middlesex HA1 3AZ ☎ 020 8864 2019 & fax, 0468 457071 mob

KEMBER Sara (*Dms, Pf, Kbds*): 237C High Road, Harrow Weald, Middlesex HA3 5EE ☎ 020 8427 0776, 0966 154162

KENDELL Robert (*Per, Tym*): 33 Stretton Road, Addiscombe CR0 6EQ ☎ 020 8654 9712, 0973 796330

KENDLE Jackie (*Per, Tym*): 40 Gordon Road, Carlshalton Beeches, Surrey SM5 3RE ☎ 020 8395 9252, 0976 288675 mob, 020 8401 6179

KENNEDY Brian (*Dms*): 60B Hazlewell Road, Putney, London SW15 6LR ☎ 020 8785 949, 020 8788 7660

KENT Paul (*Dms, Per*): 25 Rodney Road, Ongar, Essex CM5 9HN ☎ 01277 364437

KEOGH Stephen (*Dms, Per*): 44 Church Crescent, London N3 1BJ ☎ 020 8349 4067 & fax

KERR Roger (*Dms*): 214 Brighton Road, Purley, Surrey CR2 4HB ☎ 020 8668 6580

KETTEL Gary (*Per*): 98 Marlborough Road, London N22 8NN ☎ 020 8888 9005, 01306 880669

KEVIN Bobby (*Dms*) ☎ 01737 210641

KILBORN Orlando (*Dms*): 6 Rue Galilee, 83610 Collobrieres, France ☎ +33 4 94 48 07 09

KILEY A.D. (*Dms, Per*): 209 Ravenslea Road, Balham, London SW12 8DA ☎ 020 8675 9049

KIMBER Christopher (*Per*): 2 Peaks Hill, Purley, Surrey CR8 3JE ☎ 020 8660 4254

KIMBERLEY James (*Dms, Voc, Per*): 3 Currie House, Abbott Road, Poplar, London E14 0LT ☎ 020 7987 3020

KINCAID Jan (*Dms, Per, Pf*): Sedley Richard Laurence, 23 Bridford Mews, Off Devonshire Street, London W1N 1LQ ☎ 020 8840 6892

KING Mark (*Dms, Db*): c/o Mgr Management, 55 Louden Road, St Johns Wood, London NW8 0DL ☎ 020 7792 4313, 020 7792 3323

KING Patrick (*Per, Dms*): 57 Mountfield Road, London N3 NW4 2DR

KING Reginald (*Dms, Voc*): 9 The Ridgeway, Chingford, London E4 6QN ☎ 020 8529 3587

KING Sylvester (*Dms*): Flat 1, 77 Sunnyside Road, London N19 3SL ☎ 020 7281 3171, 01426 210569

KINSEY Tony (*Per, Com, Arr*): 5 The Pennards, French Street, Sunbury-on-Thames, Middx TW16 5JZ ☎ 01932 783160

KIRBY Gerald (*Per*): 16 Wymondley Road, Hitchin, Herts SG4 9PH ☎ 01462 459156

KIRK Lewis (*Dms, Gtr*): 79 Fitzjohns Avenue, Hampstead, London NW3 6PA ☎ 0410 810 557

KIRKE Simon (*Per*): 30 W. 10th Street, New York City, NY 10011, USA

KITCHEN Elizabeth (*Dms, Per, Kbds*): 1 Warwick Road, London N11 2SA ☎ 020 8361 3245

KITTS Michael (*Dms, Tym*): 72 Haig Court, Chelmsford, Essex CM2 0BJ ☎ 01245 284560

KNIGHT Bob (*Dms*): 163 Flat D, Hemingford Road, Islington, London N1 1BZ ☎ 020 7609 2977, 0976 249950

KNOWLES Greg (*Per, Dms, La Per, Cimb*): 40 Basingfield Road, Thames Ditton, Surrey KT7 0PD ☎ 020 8398 2706

KODISH Paul (*Dms, Per*): 6 Garrick Park, Hendon, London NW4 1JN ☎ 020 8203 5789

KRUK Michael (*Dms, Per*): 22 Friars Court, Harcourt Road, Wallington, Surrey SM6 8AX ☎ 020 8773 1386, 0378 150017 mob

LAFFY Stephen (*Dms, Per*): 16 Euston Avenue, Watford WD1 8LY ☎ 01923 232468

LAMBERT Allan (*Dms, Per, Kbds, Pf, Gtr*): c/o Harris And Trotter, 65 New Cavendish Street, London W1M 7RD ☎ 0151 226 1303

LANE James (*Dms*): 18 Ravenswood Road, London SW12 9PJ ☎ 020 8673 0135

LARDNER Jeffrey (*Dms, Per*): 59 Pettits Lane, Romford, Essex RM1 4HA ☎ 01708 750741

LAURENCE Stuart (*Per, Dms*): 1106 High Road, Whetstone, London N20 0QX ☎ 020 8446 1272

LAW Simon (*Dms, Per, Kbds, Voc*): 132 Drakefell Road, London SE14 5SQ ☎ 020 7639 4344

LAWLESS Jim (*Per, La Per*): 1 The Strand, Ferring, West Sussex BN12 5QX ☎ 01903 240609

LAWN George (*Per, Tym*): The Poplars, The Street, Bridgham, Norwich, Norfolk NR16 2AB ☎ 01953 717493

LAWRENCE Quinny (*Dms*): 71 Calmont Road, Bromley, Kent BR1 4BY ☎ 020 8464 4052

LAWRENCE Winston (*Dms, Per*): 23 Branksome Avenue, London N18 1HB ☎ 020 8482 7567, 0973 302088 mob

LAWS Chris (*Dms, Per*): 42 Station Road, West Byfleet, Surrey KT14 6DR ☎ 01923 51794

LAWSON Don (*Per*): 14 Rushdene Avenue, East Barnet, Herts EN4 8EW ☎ 020 8368 8450

LAYTON-BENNETT Marc (*Dms, Per*): 30 Topsfield Parade, (First Floor Flat), Crouch End, London N8 8PT ☎ 020 8374 6625

LE MESSURIER James (*Dms, Per*): 30 Woodgate Drive, Streatham Vale, London SW16 5YQ ☎ 020 8679 9458

LEA Simon (*Dms*): 38A Abbeville Road, Clapham, London SW4 9NG ☎ 020 8673 3596, 0976 247448 mob

LEBAIGUE James (*Dms*): 37 Pemberton Terrace, London N19 5RX

LEBLANC Keith (*Dms*): Ground Floor Flat, 79 Digby Crescent, London N4 2HS ☎ 020 8809 6300

LEE Chris (*Per*): 47 Chiltern View Road, Uxbridge, Middlesex UB8 2PF ☎ 01895 52637

LEE Crissy (*Dms*): 112 Gunnersbury Avenue, Ealing, London W5 4NB ☎ 020 8993 7441, 0374 198340 mob, 020 8992 9993

LEE Hamilton (*Dms, Per*): 12 Ruston Mews, London W11 1RB ☎ 020 7229 4629

LEE Jon (*Dms*): 68 St Julian Road, Newport, Gwent NP9 7RX ☎ 01633 255881, 07979 498635

LEE Jonathan (*Dms, Vln, Kbds, B Gtr*): 33 Glenthorne Road, London N11 3HU ☎ 020 8361 1828

LEES Stephen (*Dms, Per*): 2 The Gatehouse, Smarts Heath Road, Woking, Surrey GU22 0RF ☎ 01483 235133

LEPPARD Greg (*Dms, Per*): 68 Thorpedale Road, London N4 3BW ☎ 020 7281 2696, 0958 456203 mob

LETLEY Matthew (*Dms*): 112 Barnfield Wood Road, Beckenham, Kent BR3 6SX ☎ 020 8650 1929

LEVIN Tony (*Dms, Per*): Asterton Hall Farm, Asterton, Lydbury North, Shropshire SY7 8BH ☎ 01588 650408

LEWINSON Peter (*Dms*): 11 Thornton Avenue, Streatham, London SW2 4HL ☎ 020 8678 6857, 0956 552279

LEWIS Dal (*Dms, Per, Kbds, Gtr, B Gtr*): 50 Jail Lane, Biggin Hill, Kent TN16 3SA

LIMBRICK Simon (*Per, Com*): 3 Arbuthnot Road, London SE14 5LS ☎ 020 7732 4590, 0370 236855 mob

LINDUP Michael (*Per, Pf*): 80 Beverley Way, London SW20 0AQ

LINES-WELCHMAN Helena (*Dms*): ☎ 020 8423 5420, 0378 860248 mob

LINGWOOD John (*Dms*): Yew Tree Cottage, The Green, Warmington, Nr Banbury, Oxon OX17 1BU ☎ 01295 690351

LINSCOTT Jody (*Per*): 132 Lansdown Lodge, Lansdown Road, London N17 9XX

LINTER Derek (*Per, La Per, Voc*): Address Unknown ☎ 020 8777 7054

LITTLE Carlo (*Dms*): Chatswood, 60 Barn Hill, Wembley Park, Middlesex HA9 9LQ ☎ 020 8385 1192, 07788 957951

LLOYD Mark (*Dms*): 87 Elm Park Avenue, Tottenham, London N15 6UZ ☎ 020 8211 7109

LOCKE David (*Per*): 1 Coleshill Road, Teddington, Middlesex TW11 0LL ☎ 020 8977 9531

LOCKETT Peter (*Per, Dms*): 26F Upper Park Road, Belsize Park, London NW3 2UT ☎ 020 7586 8971, 0976 426773 mob

LOFTS Geoff (*Per*): 18 Amberley Crescent, Boston, Lincs PE21 7QQ ☎ 01205 368145

LONEY Cyril (*Dms*): 13 David Coffer Court, Upper Park Road, Belvedere, Kent DA17 6JB ☎ 013224 37830

LONG Craig (*Dms*): 134 Upperton Road East, Plaistow, London E13 9LR ☎ 020 8472 7414, 0958 534858

LONG Stephen (*Per, Tym*): 31 West End Court, Greencroft Gardens, London NW6 3NU ☎ 020 7624 0756

LONGHURST Cliff (*Dms, Per*): Chantecler, Altwood Bailey, Maidenhead, Berks SL6 4PQ ☎ 01628 23433

LONGMORE Scott (*Dms*): 13 Chatsworth Road, Chiswick, London W4 3HY ☎ 020 8995 1257

LONGWORTH Deborah (*Dms*): 123 Garfton House, Wellington Way, London E3 4UF ☎ 020 8983 3764

LOWE David (*Dms*): 88 Foxborough Gardens, London SE4 1HY ☎ 020 8314 5938

LUCAS Daniel (*Dms, Gtr*): Flat 2, 11 - 13 Orlando Road, Clapham Common SW4 0LE ☎ 020 7622 1990, 0956 104 141, 020 7622 1990

LYNN Alan (*Dms*): 4-7 The Vineyard, Off Sanctuary Street, London SE1 1QL ☎ 020 7403 0007

LYTTON Tony (*Dms*): Flat 29, Gainsborough Lodge, South Farm Road, W Worthing, Sussex BN14 7AX ☎ 01903 31897

MACCORMACK Geoff (*Per, Kbds*): 32 Lydford Rd, London W9 3LX ☎ 020 7289 7968

MACDONALD James (*Dms*): 3 Harvil Rd, Ickenham, Middx ☎ 01895 253981

MACDONALD Peter (*Dms, Per, Voc*): 12 Anley Rd, London W14 0BY ☎ 020 7602 1135

MACDONNELL Tony (*Dms, Per*): 53 Cedarville Gardens, Streatham, London SW16 3DA ☎ 020 8764 4856

MACFARLANE Hugh (*Per*): Urb Calpe Park, Bloque 9, No 8, 03710 Calpe (Alicante), Spain

MACINTOSH Adrian (*Dms, Per*): 51 Drew Gardens, Greenford, Middlesex UB6 7QF ☎ 020 8902 2786

MACK Charlie (*Dms, Per*): 143 Melbourne Court, Gibbson Street, Newcastle NE1 2AT ☎ 0191 232 4621

MACLURE Andrew (*Dms*): c/o Jeff Werner, 40 Werneth Hall Road, Clayhall, Ilford, Essex IG5 0DA

MACMANUS Liam (*Dms, Voc*): 24 River Way, Twickenham, Middx TW2 5JP ☎ 020 8241 3363

MAGEE William (*Dms*): 283 Beckenham Road, Beckenham, Kent BR3 4RL ☎ 020 8659 8898

MALABAR Clive (*Per, Pf*): 42 Morley Hill, Enfield EN2 0BJ ☎ 020 8366 4447

MALLOY Alasdair (*Per, Gl Hmca*): 84 Ferme Park Road, London N8 9SD ☎ 020 8347 6630/1, 01306 880669

MALONEY Anthony (*Per, Tym*): 69 Kingsmead Road, London SW2 3HZ ☎ 020 8674 8983

MANOILOVICH Vancho (*Dms, La Per, Per*): 35 Willis House, Grantham Road, London E12 5QZ ☎ 020 8514 8813

MANTERO Francesco (*Dms, Voc*): Via Regino 40, 22012 Cernobbio, Como, Italy 22012 ☎ 020 7736 6805, +39 315 12502, +39 338 5035 766

MANTINI Leonardo (*Dms, Per*): Flat 8, 293 St Anns Road, London N15 3DR ☎ 020 8442 8514

MARCANGELO Richard (*Dms, Per*): 50 Clementina Road, Leyton, London E10 7LS ☎ 020 8556 6643

MARCHANT Brian (*Dms*): 4 Kindersley Close, East Grinstead, W.Sussex RH19 3NJ ☎ 01342 327454

MARCHE Winston'Wyn' (*Dms, Per, B Gtr*): 22 Baxter Road, Edmonton, London N18 2EY ☎ 020 8884 2190

MARKHAM Brian (*Per, Dms*): 25 Orme Road, Kingston-on-Thames, Surrey KT1 3SD ☎ 020 8942 6970, 0589 966007 mob

MARKIN Ian (*Dms*): 128 Bader Way, Rainham, Essex RM13 7HU ☎ 01708 523057

MARRIOTT Ian (*Dms*): 47 Hendfield Court, Beddington Gardens, Wallington, Surrey SM6 0JQ ☎ 020 8773 4032, 0411 625273 mob

MARSHALL Frank (*Per*): Cherry Trees, 13 High View Ave North, Brighton, Sussex BN1 8WR ☎ 01273 501143

MARSHALL Gordon (*Dms, Kbds*): 12 Sandringham Avenue, London SW2 8JY ☎ 020 8543 1906 & fax

MARSHALL John (*Dms*): 43 Combemartin Road, London SW18 5PP ☎ 020 8788 0933 fax

MARTIN Andrew (*Dms, Per, Tym*): 58 Grange Avenue, London N12 8DL ☎ 020 8446 6657

MARTIN Denny (*Dms*): 5 Holmewood Close, Cheam, Surrey SM2 7JL ☎ 020 8393 3524

MARTIN Peter (*Dms, Per*): Falsterbo Gatan 28B, 24136 Malmo, Sweden

MARTIN Philip (*Dms, Voc*): 8 Oakmeade, Hatch End, Pinner, Middlesex HA5 4DA ☎ 020 8428 3392

MARTIN Terry (*Dms*): 223 Watford Way, Hendon, London NW4 4SL ☎ 020 8203 9619

MARYON-DAVIS Alan (*Per, Voc*): 4 Sibella Road, London SW4 6HX ☎ 020 7720 5659

MASON Darren (*Dms*): 81 Almond Avenue, South Ealing, London W5 4YB ☎ 020 8908 3643

MASON Derek (*Per*): 147 Tudor Drive, Kingston-upon-Thames, Surrey KT2 5NT ☎ 020 8546 2713

MASON Nick (*Per*): c/o Emka, 43 Portland Road, London W11 ☎ 020 7221 2046

MATTACKS David (*Dms*): Poyningshurst, Coos Lane, Slaugham, West Sussex RH17 6AD ☎ 01444 400336, 01444 401453 fax

MATTHEWS Glyn (*Dms, Per*): 40 Glasslyn Road, Crouch End, London N8 8RH ☎ 020 8341 2976

MAUREL Alain (*Dms, Per*): 36 Priory Grove, London SW8 2PH ☎ 020 7720 7744, 020 7627 2585

MAY David (*Dms*): 2 Harby-Browe, Grafton Close, Worcester Park, Surrey KT4 7JY ☎ 020 8873 3031

MAY Joanne (*Per, Tym*): 145 Perry Rise, Forest Hill, London SE23 2QU ☎ 020 8699 5216, 0973 721260 mob

MAY Peter (*Per*): 11 Frederica Road, North Chingford, London E4 7AL

MAYERAS Beatrice (*Tamb, Voc*): 259 Kennington Lane, London SE11 5QU ☎ 020 7582 6012, 020 7733 9112

MAYES Paul (*Dms*)

MAYGER Spencer (*Dms*): 73 Pages Lane, Uxbridge, Middlesex UB8 1XT ☎ 0956 309449 mob

MAYNE Caroline (*Dms, Kbds*): ☎ 020 8752 5787, 0976 686850 mob

MCBRAIN Nicko (*Per*): Iron Maiden Holdings, The Colonnades, 82 Bishopsbridge Road, London W2 6BB

MCCREA Ronald (*Per, Tym, Xyl, Glck, Vib*): Yew Tree Cottage, Post Office Road, Knodishall, Saxmundham, Suffolk IP17 1UG ☎ 01728 830881

MCDERMOTT Eric (*Dms, Vib*): 12 Avenue Close, The Green, West Drayton, Middlesex UB7 7PP ☎ 01895 445026

MCDERMOTT Tom (*Dms, Per, Kbds, B Gtr*): 63 Cleggan Park, Ballyfermot Upr, Eire, Dublin 10 ☎ 626 2256

MCDONOUGH Matthew (*Dms, Per*): 87 Beresford Road, Hornsey, London N8 0AG ☎ 020 8292 0480, 020 8348 8578

MCELROY Maurice (*Dms, La Per*): Garden Flat, 72 Hillfield Road, London NW6 1QA ☎ 020 7431 0470

MCFARLANE Philip (*Dms, Per*): 14 Alexandra Walk, Victoria Cresent, Upper Norwood, London SE19 1AL ☎ 0956 370878 mob

MCGLASSON Andy (*Dms, Per*): 9 Hilda Vale Close, Farnborough, Orpington, Kent BR6 7AH ☎ 0168 9854912, 0831 875520

MCGREGOR Nigel (*Per*): First Floor Flat, 5 Windsor Road, Willesden Green, London NW2 5DT ☎ 0976 303091

MCKENZIE Adrian (*Dms, Voc, Song W, Kbds*): ☎ 0958 422619 mob

MCKENZIE Derrick (*Dms, Kbds, B Gtr*): ☎ 020 7483 0444

MCKENZIE Ian (*Dms, Kbds, Gtr, Per, B Gtr*): 112B Tressillian Road, Brockley, London SE4 1XX ☎ 020 8469 3759

MCLAREN Andrew (*Dms*): 52 Wordsworth Road, Hampton, Middlesex TW12 1ER ☎ 020 8979 7447

MCLAREN Julian (*Dms, Per*): 8 April Close, Orpington, Kent BR6 6NA ☎ 01689 855723, 0956 291509 mob

MCLEAN Godfrey (*Dms, Gtr*): 139 Blythe Road, London W14 0HL ☎ 020 7602 1051

MCULLOCH Alan (*Dms, Per*): 30 Georgiana Street, London NW1 0EA ☎ 020 7813 7868

MCVEY Anthony (*Dms, Per, Tym, La Per*): 103 Wallwood Road, London E11 1AP ☎ 020 8556 9116, 0468 760327 mob, 132691

MEEKUMS Gary (*Dms*): 131 Church Road, Bexleyheath, Kent DA7 4DN ☎ 020 8304 7039

MELIUS Perry (*Dms, Per*): 3 Alton House, Bromley High Street, Bow, London E3 3BB ☎ 020 8980 6773

MELROSE Thomas (*Dms, Kbds*): 208 Poplar Grove, Friern Barnet, London N12 3NX ☎ 020 8361 3396

MENDOZA-MORENO Alonso (*Per, La Per*): 65 Hyde Thorpe Road, Balham, London SW12 0JE ☎ 020 8673 3076

MERRITT Albert (*Per*): Bournehurst, Hamm Court, Weybridge, Surrey KT13 8YA ☎ 01932 845174

MERRY Simon (*Dms*): Flat 3, 10 Robinson Road, Colliers Wood, London SW17 9DW ☎ 020 8542 4601, 0585 858441

METZ Dominique (*Dms*): 23 Mayfield Gardens, Hanwell, Middlesex W7 3RB ☎ 020 8575 8079, 0777 565 42 62

MIDDLE EAST MUSIC ORG (*Dms, Or Dms*) ☎ 020 8746 1627

MILLER Colin (*Dms*): 32 Reddown Road, Coulsdon, Surrey CR5 1AX ☎ 017375 55863

MILLER Ian (*Dms, Per*): 23 Dewar Place Lane, Edinburgh EH3 8EF ☎ 0131 228 1686

MILLER John (*Dms, Pf*): Flat I, 4 Windstock Close, London SE16 1FL ☎ 020 7231 1457

MILLETT Robert (*Per, Tym, Dms*): 117 Inwood Road, Hounslow, Middx. TW3 1XH ☎ 020 8577 6309 & fax, 0973 175099 mob

MILLINGTON Ginger (*Dms, Kbds, Voc*): Flat 10, The Mulberry, Aspen Vale, Whyteleafe, Surrey CR3 0XB ☎ 0973 198604 mob

MILLS Derek (*Dms*): 31 Hatch Gardens, Tadworth, Surrey KT20 5LE ☎ 01737 356727

MILLS Paul (*Dms, Gtr*): 9A Suttons Lane, Hornchurch, Essex RM12 6RD ☎ 01708 473519, 020 7820 6672

MISSINGHAM Andrew (*Dms*): 15 Sherringham Avenue, London N17 9RS ☎ 020 8885 1541

MITCHELL John (*Per, Arr, Cop, Pf*): 15 The Island, Thames Ditton, Surrey KT7 0SH ☎ 020 8339 0850

MONDESIR Mark (*Dms*): 79 St Stephens Road, Ranwell West Estate, London E3 5JN ☎ 020 8981 3104

MONK Howard (*Dms, Per*): 55A The Broadway, Crouch End, London N8 8DT ☎ 020 8374 6278

MONSON Darren (*Dms*): 30 Woodhouse Road, Leytonstone, London E111 ☎ 020 8221 0266

MONTAGU Jeremy (*Per, Tym, Con*): 171 Iffley Road, Oxford OX4 1EL ☎ 01865 726037

MONTI Steven (*Dms*): 70 Woodland Rise, Muswell Rise, London N10 3UJ ☎ 020 8444 5713

MORENA Mick (*Dms*): 58A Walterton Road, Maida Vale, London W9 3PJ ☎ 020 7289 3136, 020 7265 0284

MORGAN Barry *(Dms, Per)*: Firs Cottage, The Street, Bramber, Steyning, West Sussex BN44 3WE ☎ 01903 816661

MORGAN John *(Dms, Per, B Gtr, Rh Gtr)*: 2 Glenburne Road, Tooting, London SW17 7PS ☎ 020 8682 1395

MORGAN Jonathan(Joff) *(Per, Dms, Tym)*: Mayfield House, 8 Lake Walk, Adderbury, Oxfordshire OX17 3PF ☎ 01295 812970, 0973 840739

MORLAND Mig *(Dms)*: Address Unknown ☎ 020 7607 0369

MORRICE Binky *(Per)*: 744 Fulham Road, London SW6 5SF ☎ 020 7736 5466

MORRIS David *(Dms)*: 48 Bridge Road, Uxbridge, Middlesex UB8 2QP ☎ 01895 847508

MORRIS Geoffrey *(Dms)*: 7, Ringwood Avenue, Rushmore Hill, Pratts Bottom, Kent BR6 7SY ☎ 01689 857343

MORRIS Pee Wee *(Dms)*: 76 Idlecombe Road, Tooting, London SW17 9TB ☎ 020 8682 2974

MORRISON Will *(Dms, Per, Voc)*: Basement Flat, 138 Waller Road, London SE14 5LU ☎ 020 7639 0970

MORRISS Peter *(Dms, Per)*: 24 Monkhams Lane, Woodford Green, Essex IG8 0NS ☎ 020 8505 1550

MORTON Ian *(Dms, Voc)*: 66 Hubent Road, London E6 3EY ☎ 020 8471 7577

MORTON Simon *(Dms)*: 25 Sefton Court, Great West Road, Hounslow, Middlesex TW3 4BG ☎ 020 8570 3311

MOYO Thomas *(Per)*: 41 Whitbread Close, Hampden Road, Tottenham, London N17 0YB ☎ 020 8801 1874, 020 8801 6346, 020 8801 1874/6346

MULLEN Larry *(Dms)*: Not Us Limited (U2), 30/32 Sir John Rogersons Quay, Dublin 2, Ireland ☎ Dublin 677 7330

MUNDEN Dave *(Per)*: Fairmile, Silwood Close, Ascot, Berks SL5 7DX ☎ 01344 24044

MURCOTT Dominic *(Dms, Mrba, Per)*: 51B Elsinore Road, London SE23 2SH ☎ 020 8291 9315, 01523 122500 pager

MURPHY Arran *(Dms)*

MURPHY Malcolm *(Dms, Voc)*: 27 Mossfield, Cobham, Surrey KT11 1DF ☎ 01932 867994

MURRAY Simon *(Dms, Kbds)*: 21 Wycn Elm Road, Hornchurch, Essex RM11 3AA ☎ 01708 478540, 0468 690007 mob, 020 7470 8868

MURRELL Trevor *(Dms, Per)*: 19 Dalkeith Road, Ilford, Essex IG1 1JD ☎ 020 8514 5305

MUSTO Chris *(Dms, Per)*: 25 Hollycroft Avenue, Wembley, Middx HA9 8LG ☎ 020 8904 4003

NALL Christopher *(Per, Timb)*: The Bramlings, 111 Kings Road, Biggin Hill,Westerham, Kent TN16 3NQ ☎ 01959 571950

NASH Stephen *(Dms)*: 64 Clonmore Street, Southfields, London SW18 5EY ☎ 020 8874 5311

NATKANSKI Michael *(Dms, Pf)*: 36A Selsdon Road, West Norwood, London SE27 0PG ☎ 020 8761 6890

NAWAZ Haq *(Dms, Kbds)*: 19 All Saint Road, London W11 1HE ☎ 020 7792 8167

NELSON Alex *(Dms)*: 61 Elmbourne Drive, Upper Belvedere, Kent DA17 6JE ☎ 01322 433273

NEWBY Richard *(Dms, Per)*: 40 Mill Road, Twickenham, Middlesex TW2 5HA ☎ 020 8255 9194

NEWMARK Andrew *(Dms)*: Didling Manor, Didling, Midhurst, West Sussex GU29 0LQ ☎ 01730 812638

NEWTON Rodney *(Per, Com, Tym, Arr, Con)*: 378A Oakleigh Road North, Whetstone, London N20 0SP ☎ 020 8361 2208

NGWABA Ike *(Dms, Voc)*: Flat 7, Seymour Buildings, Seymour Place, London W1H 5TQ ☎ 020 7724 5102, 0467 498876 mob

NICE Stephen *(Dms)*: 9 Fishers Close, Puckeridge, Herts SG11 1TD ☎ 01920 822474

NICHOL Tom *(Per)*: Dundrumin Lodge, 20 Bayhams Field, Sharpthorne, W Sussex RH19 4PZ ☎ 01342 810256

NICHOLLS Geoffrey *(Dms, Per)*: 32 Baker Road, London NW10 8UA ☎ 020 8965 2579

NOLAN Sheila *(Per, Com, Org)*: 22 Westland Close, Stanwell Village, Middlesex TW19 7NA ☎ 01784 247524, 0850 524802

NORTH (NORVILL) Roy *(Dms)*: 120 Crescent Drive South, Woodingdean, Brighton, Sussex BN2 6SA ☎ 01273 303910

NORTHCOTT Raymond *(Per)*: 8 Lower Tail, Carpenders Park, Watford, Herts WD1 5DD ☎ 020 8428 6166

NUNN Roger *(Dms)*: 2 Cork House, 77 Leesons Hill, Orpington, Kent BR5 2LF ☎ 01689 839383

NUTTY Kevin *(Per, Tym)*: 75 Holland Road, London W14 8HL ☎ 020 7602 5196

NWANI Emmanuel *(Dms, Kbds)*: 83 Cleveley Crescent, Hanger Lane, Ealing, London W5 1DZ ☎ 020 8922 7968, 0956 223140

O'CALLAGHAN Cion *(Dms, Per)*: c/o 12 Granville Close, Killiney, Co Dublin, Ireland ☎ +353 1 2857025

O'CONNOR Thomas *(Per)*: c/o Mrs S Cornall, 5 Warwick Crescent, Hayes, Middx UB4 8RE ☎ +61 2 9692 0220 & fax

O'DONNELL Thomas *(Dms)*: 2 The Mount, Susan Wood, Chislehurst BR7 5NG ☎ 020 8467 0754

O'NEILL Brendan *(Dms)*: 53 Wanstead Park Avenue, Wanstead, London E12 5EL ☎ 020 8989 9151

O'RIORDAN Gerald *(Dms, Per)*: 59 Camborne Avenue, Ealing, London W13 9QZ ☎ 020 8566 3794

O'SHEA Roy *(Dms)*: Flat 2, 266 Upper Street, London N1 2UQ ☎ 020 7359 0513

O'TOOLE Gary *(Dms)*: 302 Essex Road, Islington, London N1 3AU ☎ 020 7359 4565

ODEGBAMI Denise *(Dms, Voc)*: 437B Kingsbury Road, Kingsbury, London NW9 9DT ☎ 020 8204 2281, 0956 598950, 020 8357 8837

ODELL Roger *(Dms)*: Oak House, Church Road, Great Yeldham, Essex CO9 4PR ☎ 01787 237653

OHM David *(Per)*: 85 Kemble House, Loughborough Estate, Barrington Road, London SW9 7EF ☎ 020 7274 5117

OLATUNSI June *(Dms, Voc)*: 12 Burgess House, Bethwin Road, Camberwell, London SE5 0X2 ☎ 01426 151128, 020 7708 5965

OLIVER Matthew *(Dms)*: Flat 8, Willow Court, 148 Woodcote Road, Wallington, Surrey SM6 0PF ☎ 020 8669 3514

ORMROD Nicholas *(Per)*: 65 Granleigh Road, London E11 4RG ☎ 020 8926 7825, 020 8926 7824 fax

ORR Bobby *(Per)*: 'Radici', One Pin Lane, Farnham Common, Bucks SL2 3RD ☎ 01753 645592

OSBORN Michael *(Per, Tym, Per)*: 70 Thames Court, Greenview Avenue, Shirley, Croydon CR0 7QU ☎ 020 8654 4571

OVERHEAD Philip *(Per, Dms, Gtr, Voc, Kbds)*: Flat C, 29 Marlborough Road, London N19 4NA ☎ 020 7686 0273

OWEN Glyn *(Dms)*: 11A Walm Lane, Willesden Green, London NW2 5SJ ☎ 020 8830 4374

PAINE James *(Dms, Per)*: 77 Lionel Road, Brentford, Middx TW8 9QZ ☎ 020 8568 0594

PALMER Carl *(Per)*: 6 South Close, Hadley Green, Barnet, Herts EN5 5TP ☎ 020 8449 2649

PANAYIOTOU Marios *(Dms)*: 974 High Road, Whetstone, London N20 0QG ☎ 020 8343 9082

PANDA George *(Dms, Per)*: 3 Richet, Longfield, Colindale, London NW9 5ST ☎ 020 8201 3855, 01523 782440

PANDIT Dinesh *(Per)*: 34 Longfield Avenue, Mill Hill, London NW7 2EG ☎ 020 8203 1838

PAPAGEORGIOU Nicolaos *(Per, Dms)*: Flat 8, 4 Tetherdown, London N10 1NB ☎ 020 8374 7662, 0411 649 122

PAPWORTH Barrie *(Per)*: Spadgers Cottage, Well Penn, Cliffe, Rochester ME3 7SD ☎ Rochester 22001

PARISH Len *(Dms)*: 24 Middle Green, Doddinghurst, Essex CM15 0QT ☎ 01277 82281

PARK John *(Dms, Per, Voc)*: 7 Beavers Crescent, Hounslow, Middlesex TW4 6ET ☎ 020 8577 3564, 0958 220536 mob

PARKER Michael *(Dms)*: 162A Park Road, Crouch End, London N8 8JT ☎ 020 8341 3049

PARKER-SHARP Clive *(Dms, Per)*: 12 Tylers Close, Godstone, Surrey RH9 8AN ☎ 01883 742257 & fax

PARKINSON Tony *(Per, Tnd Per)*: 132 Main Road, Quadring, Lincs PE11 4PW ☎ 01775 821215

PARNELL Jack *(Per)*: The Old Royal, Victoria Street, Southwold, East Suffolk IP18 6JF ☎ 01502 724 378

PARNELL Marc *(Dms, Per, Kbds)*: 27 Harold Road, London E11 4QX ☎ 020 8558 2866

PARNELL William *(Dms, Kbds)*: 29 Dyne Road, Kilburn, London NW6 7XG ☎ 020 7328 5760

PATTINSON Iian *(Dms, Per)*: 27B Ballards Lane, London N12 0ET ☎ 07970 830217

PATTMAN David *(Dms, Per)*: 75 Castlemead, Camberwell Road, London SE5 0EB ☎ 020 7703 4810

PAY Richard *(Dms, Tym, Per)*: 76 St Georges Road West, Bromley, Kent BR1 2NP ☎ 020 8467 3755, 0498 798 740

PAYNE Howard *(Dms, Gtr)*: 31 Merrivale, Oakwood, London N14 4TE ☎ 020 8482 1114

PEARCE Dave *(Dms)*: 26 Dunblane Road, London SE9 6RS ☎ 020 8856 5030

PEARCE Ian *(Dms, Per, Kbds)*: ☎ 020 8287 4567

PEARSON Simon *(Dms, Per)*: Flat 3, 102 Cazenove Road, Stoke Newington, London N16 6AD ☎ 020 8806 7059, 0836 725198 mob

PECK Anne *(Per, Voc)*: 48B Berriman Road, London N7 7PS ☎ 020 7609 5649

PERRY Peter *(Per)*: 5 Catherall Road, Quadrant Estate, London N5 2LE ☎ 020 7226 8088

PERSSON Hans *(Dms, Gtr, B Gtr, Arr)*: 119 Harvist Road, London NW6 6HA ☎ 020 8968 0171

PERT Morris *(Per, Kbds, Com)*: The Chalet, 189 Blachrick, Rhiconich By Lairg, Lairg, Sutherland IV27 4RU ☎ 01971 521 314

PHILLIPS Barry *(Dms, Per)*: Heather Cottage, Brighton Road, Burgh Heath, Tadworth, Surrey KT20 6BN ☎ 01737 355821

PHILLIPS Simon *(Dms)*: 3377 Coy Drive, Sherman Oaks, CA 01423, USA ☎ +1 818 986 1904, +1 818 986 3019

PHUTURE Phil *(Dms)*: 30A Fairland Road, Stratford, London E15 4AF ☎ 020 8534 9991

PICKERING Michael *(Dms, Per)*: St Thomas's Villas, 259 Lordship Lane, East Dulwich, London SE22 8JF ☎ 020 8299 6957, 020 8693 9910

PINTO Simon J *(Dms, Gtr, Rh Gtr, B Gtr, Voc)*: 17 Northumberland Way, Barnehurst, Kent DA8 3NT ☎ 01322 345630

PIPER John *(Dms, Per)*: 20 Beaumont Road, London SW19 6RG ☎ 020 8785 4069, 0956 546027 mob

PLA Roberto *(Dms, Cong, Bong, Timb)*: 97 Clements Road, East Ham, London E6 2DP ☎ 020 8472 8712, 020 8471 5603

PLUMB Stephen *(Dms, Per, Tym)*: 2 Northcote Road, Sidcup, Kent DA14 6PW ☎ 020 8302 7433

PLUMMER Craig *(Dms)*: 7A Chalfont Road, London SE25 4AA ☎ 020 8653 9749, 0802 187334 mob

POCOCK Louis *(Dms)*: 75 Masterman Road, East Ham, London E6 3NW ☎ 020 8470 9662

POLLITT Jack *(Dms, Gtr, B Gtr, Pf)*: 26 Lidfield Road, London N16 9LX ☎ 020 7241 5727, 0956 599580

POOK Andrew *(Dms, Per)*: 46 Reeve Road, Wood Hatch, Reigate, Surrey RH2 7PH ☎ 01737 246265

POOLE Julian *(Per, Tym, Dms)*: 10 Hillside Gardens, Cline Road, London N11 2NH ☎ 020 8368 1612, 0973 205458 mob

POPPLE Terence *(Dms, Per)*: 17 Great College Street, Brighton, E Sussex BN2 1HJ ☎ 01273 694511

POWDRILL Joy *(Per, Tym)*: 118 Woodsmoor Lane, Stockport SK3 8TJ ☎ 020 7727 5314, 0850 001829 mob

POWELL Dave *(Dms)*: The White House, Flanchford Road, Reigate, Surrey RH2 8QR ☎ 01737 242781

PRENTICE Geoffrey *(Per, Tym)*: 11 Browning Road, Enfield, Middx EN2 0EN ☎ 020 8363 0728

PREVOST Eddie *(Per)*: 2 Shetlocks Cottages, Matching Tye, Nr Harlow, Essex CM17 0QR ☎ 01279 731517

PRICE Cliff *(Per, Kbds)*: 124 Dorney Tower, Fellows Road, London NW3 3PL ☎ 020 7916 7551

PRICE Derek *(Per)*: 50 Woodlands, North Harrow, Middx HA2 6EW ☎ 020 8866 5147

PRICE Mark *(Dms)*: 57 Hillfield Avenue, London N8 7DS ☎ 020 8348 9799

PRIEST Mathew *(Dms, Voc)*: 271 Royal College Street, London NW1 9LU ☎ 020 7482 0115

PRIMROSE Neil *(Dms)*: Unit F, 21 Heathmans Rd, Parsons Green, London SW6 4TJ ☎ 020 7371 7008 & fax

PROCTOR Martin *(Per, Tym, Voc)*: 9 Greenfield Way, Crowthorne, Berkshire RG45 6TL ☎ 01344 762656

PROFETIC *(Dms, Voc)*: 186 Perry Rise, Forest Hill, London SE23 2QT ☎ 020 8291 3690

PULLEN Michael *(Per)*: 16 Chelston Road, Ruislip Manor, Middx HA4 9SB ☎ 01895 633078

PURCELL Alan *(Dms)*: 82 Edenfield Gardens, Worcester Park, Surrey KT4 7DY ☎ 020 8224 9748

QUIGLEY Stephen *(Per, Tym)*: Flat 2, 17 Marmora Road, Honor Oak, London SE22 0RX ☎ 020 8299 3306

RACHER Matthew *(Dms)*: 20 Lytton Road, Leytonstone, London E11 1JH ☎ 07957 440 346

RAMAZANOGLU Emre *(Dms, Cong)*: 38 Russia Lane, Bethnal Green, London E2 9LW ☎ 020 8981 9339, 0961 428252

RAMZY Hossam *(Dms, Per)*: PO Box 265, East Grinstead, West Sussex RH19 3GN ☎ 01342 315162, 01342 323549

RANDLE Alan *(Dms, La Per, Tym, Kbds, Glck)*: 68 St Domingo House, Leda Road, Woolwich, London SE18 5QP ☎ 020 8855 3239

RANKEN Andrew *(Dms, Voc)*: 20 Sydner Road, London N16 7UG ☎ 020 7249 9780

RAT SCABIES *(Per, Dms, Kbds, Gtr)*: 27 Brook Road South, Brentford, Midx TW8 0NN ☎ 020 8332 0032, 020 8400 9536

RAVENHILL Colin *(Dms, Gtr)*: 29 Southdown Avenue, Boston Manor, London W7 2AG ☎ 020 8840 4900

RAWBONE Nick *(Dms)*: Leslie Lodge, 48 Oxhey Road, Oxhey, Herts WD1 4QQ ☎ 01923 334657 & fax, 0976 268208 mob

RAWLINS Peter *(Dms)*: 9B Sunningvale Avenue, Biggin Hill, Kent TN16 3BU ☎ 01959 75259

REES Calum *(Dms)*: 74 Stratton Road, Sunbury-on-Thames, Middlesex TW16 6PQ ☎ 01932 784151

REES Paul *(Dms, Per, Song W, Gtr)*: 36 Mcintosh Road, Romford RM1 4JJ ☎ 01708 705599

REES Vaughan *(Dms, Pf, Gtr)*: 27 Crescent Road, Caterham, Surrey CR3 6LE ☎ 01883 340187

REEVES Barry *(Dms)*: 3 Lawrie Court, Kenton Lane, Harrow Weald, Middlesex HA3 6AP ☎ 020 8954 0370

REEVES Bernard *(Dms)*: 14 Woodmere, London SE9 5NT ☎ 020 8850 1173

REFIK Samir *(Dms, Bendir, Voc)*: 39 Woodgrang Road, Flat E, Forestgate, London E7 8BA ☎ 020 8534 1079, 0797 9774453

REGIS Preston *(Dms, Per, Bong, Voc, Rapper)*: 17 Ohio Road, Plaistow, London E13 8EL ☎ 020 7473 4880

REYNOLDS John *(Dms)*: 29 Hacton Lane, Hornchurch, Essex RM12 6PH ☎ 01708 508149

REYNOLDS John *(Dms)*: Flat 18D, Durham Terrace, London W2 5PB ☎ 020 7229 0001

RICH Jeffrey *(Dms, Per)*: The Handle Group Of Companies, Pinewood Studios, Pinewood Road, Iver Heath, Buckinghamshire SL0 0NH ☎ 01753 651 001, 01753 630 555/633

RICH Matthew *(Per, Tym)*: Flat B, 39 Felday Road, London SE3 7HQ ☎ 020 8314 0825, 0976 669845 mob, 01306 880669

RICHARDSON John *(Dms)*: 35 The Drive, Potters Bar, Herts EN6 2AR ☎ 01707 657 357

RICOTTI Frank *(Per, Com)*: Thimble Farm, Green Lane, Prestwood, Buckinghamshire HP16 0QE ☎ 01494 866101, 020 8549 1706

RIFF Alex *(Dms, Kbds, Tpt, B Gtr)*: 57C Woolacombe Road, Blackheath, London SE3 8QJ ☎ 020 8488 2018, 0958 563550

RIGBY Ian *(Dms)*: 206 Alexandra Road, London N10 3DH ☎ 020 8444 5260, 01234 343039

RILEY Adam *(Dms, Timb)*: 20 Bradshaw Close, London SW19 8NL ☎ 020 8879 3188

RILEY Michael *(Dms, Per)*: 20 Orchard Road, Sidcup, Kent DA14 6RD ☎ 020 8300 3905, 0589 361703, 020 8316 7066

RILEY Peter *(Dms)*: 15 Tyler Way, Brentwood, Essex CM14 4WE ☎ 01277 230608, 0468 040717 mob

RIMSHOTT Professor *(Dms, Per)*: 3 Myatt House, Templar Street, London SE5 9JD ☎ 020 7737 1042

RITCHIE Fiona *(Per, Tym)*: 15 Hawkesfield Road, Forest Hill, London SE23 2TN ☎ 020 8291 3855, 01306 880669

RITCHIE Stuart *(Dms)*: 10 Linden House, Linden Grove, Nunhead, London SE13 3QB ☎ 020 7639 6250

ROBERTS Alan *(Per)*: 44 Bruce Walk, Windsor, Berks SL4 4NB ☎ 01753 857761

ROBERTS David *(Dms)*: 259 Kennington Lane, London SE11 5QU ☎ 020 7582 6012

ROBERTS Dylan *(Dms, Per)*: 89 High Street, Wimbledon Village, London SW19 5EG ☎ 020 8946 8885

ROBERTS Eryl *(Dms, Per, Tym, Xyl, Cong)*: 35 Plympton Road, Kilburn, London NW6 7EH ☎ 020 7372 0748, 0958 747422

ROBERTS Gareth *(Dms, Per)*: 45A Queen Mary Road, Upper Norwood, London SE19 3NN ☎ 020 8670 2950, 0468 076842

ROBERTS Mark *(Dms, Per)*: 50 Ealing Park Mansions, South Ealing Road, Ealing, London W5 4QH ☎ 020 8579 3025

ROBERTS Sheaw *(Dms, Kbds)*: 89 Sawdbrook Road, Stoke Newington, London N16 0SL

ROBERTS Stephen *(Dms, Per)*: 2 Beartty Street, Camden, London NW1 7LN ☎ 020 7209 4717, 0961 818109

ROBERTSON Andrew *(Dms)*: 30 Woodhouse Road, Leytonstone, London E11 3NE ☎ 020 8221 0266, 0973 856762

ROBINSON Jonathan *(Dms, Per, Pf)*: 1 Mortimer Road, East Ham, London E6 3PQ ☎ 020 8552 4974

ROBINSON Michelle *(Per, Voc)*: 96 Musard Road, Hammersmith, London W6 8NP ☎ 020 7610 3786

ROBINSON Neil *(Dms, Per)*: Address Unknown ☎ 01702 52 7165, 0374 640 214

ROBINSON Paul Kevin *(Dms)*: 1 Hunters Lodge, Hatherden, Andover, Hants SP11 0HG ☎ 01264 735430, 0468 323060

ROBINSON Wayne *(Dms)*: 56 Westdown Road, Catford, London SE6 4RL ☎ 020 8690 2176

ROMAN Adam *(Dms, Per)*: Flat 2, 440 Upper Richmond West, Richmond, Surrey TW10 5DY ☎ 0966 175269

ROMO Bengt *(Dms)*: Focus Business Management Ltd, The Colonnades, 82 Bishops Bridge Road, London W2 6BB ☎ 020 7243 0640, 020 7243 0470

ROSS Iain *(Dms, B Gtr, Gtr)*: 38 Thornhill Square, London N1 1BE

ROSS Paul *(Dms)*: 45 The Glade, Glayhall, Ilford, Essex IG5 ONQ ☎ 020 8550 5061

ROULEAU Franck *(Dms, Kbds)*: 38 Quererford Road, Holloway, London N7 9SG ☎ 020 7607 5914, 0956 354 202

ROUNCE Brett *(Dms, Bong)*: Station House, High Road, Chigwell, Essex IG7 6NT ☎ 020 8559 8403

ROUX Clive *(Per)*: 298 Kings Road, Kingston-upon-Thames, Surrey KT2 5JL ☎ 020 8549 6923

ROWLAND Jason *(Dms, Kbds)*: 88 Chiswick Village, London W4 3BZ ☎ 020 8742 1528

ROWLAND Neil *(Dms, Per, Tym, Tnd Per)*: 14 Duncan Close, New Barnet, Herts EN5 5JJ ☎ 020 8447 0414, 0467 418019 mob

ROWNTREE David *(Dms)*: c/o C.M.O, Ransomes Dock, 35/37 Parkgate Road, London SW11 4ND

ROY Jimmy *(Per)*: 11 Curtis House, Ladderswood Way, London N11 1SB ☎ 020 8361 9541

ROYTUNDA Fat Al *(Dms)*: 33 Oldsfield Road, Sutton, Surrey SM1 2NB ☎ 020 8641 2816

RUFFY Glen *(Dms, B Gtr)*: 15B Benson Road, Forest Hill, London SE23 3RL ☎ 020 8291 4771

RUMBLES Kenny *(Dms, Per, Spoons, Vib)*: The Basement Flat, 12G Westbourne Terrace Road, Little Venice, London W2 6NG ☎ 020 7266 5663

RUOCCO Joanne *(Dms, Per, Pf)*: 376B Hanworth Road, Hounslow, Middlesex TW3 3SN ☎ 020 8577 0019

RUSHTON Stephen *(Dms, Per, Voc)*: 7 Feltham Hill Road, Feltham, Middlesex TW13 7NA ☎ 020 8587 0296

RUSSELL Peter *(Dms, Gtr, Voc)*: Highpoint, Walkers Lane, Church Brampton, Northamptonshire N6 8DZ ☎ 01604 842053

RYAN Pat *(Per, La Per)*: 63 Stanwell Lea, Middleton Cheney, Nr Banbury, Oxon OX17 2RF ☎ 01295 710482

SABO Chuck *(Dms)*: c/o 16B High Road, Willesden, London NW10 2QG ☎ 020 8451 3121

SAIT Ronald *(Dms)*: 298 Rayleigh Road, Thundersley, Essex SS7 3XB

SALKIN David *(Dms, Gtr, B Gtr)*: 10 Pentire Road, Walthamstow, London E17 4BZ ☎ 020 8523 1299, 0956 801949

SALMINS Ralph *(Dms, Per, Tym)*: 5 The Limes, Welwyn Garden City, Hertfordshire AL7 4BD ☎ 01707 334423, 01707 320431 fax

SALVONI Lou *(Dms)*: 75 Uplands Road, Crouch End, London N8 9NH ☎ 020 8340 9749

SAM SAM THE BONGO MAN *(Per, Pf, Dms, Voc)*: Flat 1, 12 Nevern Place, London SW5 9PR ☎ 020 7259 2343

SAMPSON Timothy *(Dms)*: 210 Brockley Grove, Crofton Park, London SE4 1HG ☎ 020 8690 2926, 0958 614304 mob

SAN JUAN Stefan *(Dms, Per)*: 185A Haverstock Hill, London NW3 4HQ ☎ 020 7431 4652

SANDERS Mark *(Dms)*: 81 Osbaldeston Road, London N16 6NP ☎ 020 8806 6182, 020 8674 4983

SANDERSON Nick *(Dms, Voc)*: 41F Bassett Road, London W10 6LB ☎ 020 8968 3247

SANDS Ian *(Dms, Per)*: 102 Whittion Dene, Hounslow, Middx TW3 2JU ☎ 020 8230 6685, 0973 742301

SANGER Stephen *(Dms)*: 14 Hazelwood Court, Neasden Lane North, London NW10 0AF ☎ 020 8208 3224

SAPPLETON David *(Dms, Per)*: 411 Norwood Road, West Norwood, London SE27 9BU ☎ 020 8655 7261

SAUNDERS Mark *(Dms, Gtr, Kbds)*: 980 Peace Street, St Pelham, New York, 10803, USA ☎ +1 914 738 4844, +1 914 738 9177 fax

SAUNDERS Stephen *(Dms)*: 4 Willow Terrace, High Street, Eynsford, Kent DA4 0AH ☎ 01322 864602

SAVAGE Alan *(Dms)*: Flat 4, 110 Burnt Ash Road, London SE12 8PU ☎ 020 8852 3979

SAWTELL Stephen *(Dms)*: 151 Shardeloes Road, New Cross, London SE14 6RT ☎ 020 8691 2223

SAXBY Timothy *(Dms, Per)*: 10 Collindale Avenue, Sidcup, Kent DA15 9DW ☎ 020 8302 5594

SAYER Eddy *(Dms, Per)*: 26 Church Lane, London N2 8DT ☎ 020 8883 2852

SCANTLEBURY Anthony *(Dms, B Gtr)*: 149B Ferndale Road, London SW4 7RR ☎ 020 7207 1465

SCARFF Richard *(Dms, Per, Kbds)*: 44 Northcote Road, Gravesend, Kent DA11 7BS ☎ 01474 358133, 0402 985219 mob

SCHELLING Laura *(Dms)*: 79 Blaker Court, Fairlawn, London SE7 7ES ☎ 020 8319 4629

SCHULTZBERG Robert *(Dms)*: 1 Raeburn Street, London SW2 5QT ☎ 020 7274 3697

SCHWIER Peter *(Per, Clt, Voc)*: 3 The Barn, Lynch Farm, West Milton, Nr Bridport, Dorset DT6 3SN ☎ 01308 485280

SCOTT Malcolm *(Dms, Per, Pf)*: 59 Westwood Park, London SE23 3QG ☎ 020 8291 3076, 0956 224425

SCOTT Matthew *(Dms, Kbds)*: Gff 2 Aristotle Road, Clapham, London SW4 7UZ ☎ 020 7498 5355

SCOTT Simon *(Dms)*: 4 Cleve House, 7-9 Cleve Road, London NW6 3RN ☎ 020 7624 5571

SCOTT Stanley *(Dms)*: 70 Ellison Road, Sidcup, Kent DA15 8BL

SCOTT-BARRETT Dominic *(Dms, Per, Voc)*: 14 Lansdowne Gardnes, London SW8 2EG ☎ 020 7627 0412, 020 7730 5564 fax

SEALY Norman *(Dms, B Gtr, Pf)*: ☎ 0956 324454 mob

SEAR Andrew *(Dms)*: 14 Hill Road, Theydon Bois, Essex CM16 7LY ☎ 01992 812102

SEDGE James *(Dms)*: 61 Roslyn Road, Tottenham, London N15 5JB ☎ 020 8800 7515

SEEWI Assaf *(Dms, Per, Cong, La Per)*: 44E New Cross Road, London SE14 5BD ☎ 020 7652 2905 & fax, 0336 713254 pager

SEGAL Jack *(Per, Voc)*: Flat 26, Navarina Mansions, Dalston Lane, Hackney London E8 1LB ☎ 020 7254 6607

SENIOR Matthew *(Dms, Per)*: 26 St Julians Farm Road, West Norwood, London SE27 0RS ☎ 020 8761 1333, 0468 511979 mob

SERAME David *(Dms, Tamb, Voc)*: 14 Rainhill Way, Bow, London E3 3JD ☎ 020 8981 5016

SERIAU Francis *(Dms, Per)*: 28 Oakley Avenue, Ealing, London W5 3SD ☎ 020 8992 5876

SEYMOUR Terry *(Per)*: 27 Wimbotsham Road, Downham Market, Norfolk PE38 9PE ☎ 01366 384372, 0850 817859 mob

SHANNON Les *(Per, Voc)*: 21 Rossington Avenue, Boreham Wood, Herts WD6 4JX ☎ 020 8953 4219

SHARPE Trevor *(Dms, Per)*: 88 Loveridge Road, London NW6 2DT ☎ 020 7625 5861 & fax

SHAW Nicola *(Dms)*: 11 Redding House, Harlinger Street, Woolwich, London SE18 5SR ☎ 0402 508462

SHEARER Matt *(Dms, Sax)*: 6 Woodside Road, Woodford Green, Essex IG8 0TR ☎ 020 8504 3611, 020 8491 6202

SHERIDAN Patricia *(Dms)*: 5 Branton Road, Horns Cross, Greenhithe, Kent DA9 9JU ☎ 01322 383481

SHERMAN Cyril *(Per)*: Southernlea, Wykeham Rise, Totteridge, London N20 8AJ ☎ 020 8446 5923

SHERMAN Ted *(Dms, Per, Sax)*: 17 Cumberland Road, Acton, London W3 6EX ☎ 020 8993 3464

SHIINO Kyoichi *(Dms, Per)*: 69 Charlbert Court, Mackennal Street, St Johns Wood, London NW8 7DB ☎ 020 7733 8108, 020 7460 1398

SHIPWAY Nigel *(Per)*: 3 Palmerstone Road, Earley, Reading RG6 1HL ☎ 0118 966 6633, 0976 695861 mob, 0118 926 9883 fax

SHUTTLEWORTH David *(Dms, Per)*: JPR Management, 4E Westpoint, 33 - 34 Warple Way, London W3 0RG ☎ 020 8742 0052, 020 8742 0051 fax

SIBBETT Barry *(Dms)*: Charwyn, The Broadway, Crockenhill, Kent BR8 8JH ☎ 01322 664551

SIDELNYK Steven *(Dms)*: c/o Native Management, Unit 32, Ransomes Dock, 35-37 Park Gate Road, London SW11 4NP ☎ 020 7738 1919, 07775 652 880

SIELOFF Reginald *(Dms)*: 25 Kingdon House, Galbraith Street, London E14 3LP ☎ 020 7987 1190

SILVESTER Corrina *(Dms, Per)* ☎ 04325 239107 pager

SIMMONS Daniel *(Dms)*: Flat 4, 18 Hollycroft Avenue, London NW3 7QL ☎ 020 7794 9543

SIMMS Nicholas *(Dms)*: 21 Alconbury Road, London E5 8RG ☎ 020 8806 8378

SIMON Paul *(Dms, Voc)*: 19 Eastbourne Road, Brentford, Middlesex TW8 9PG ☎ 020 8568 6957

SIMPSON Lilian *(Per, Tym)*: 54 Kingsfield Road, Oxhey, Herts WD1 4PS ☎ 01923 223457

SIMPSON Michael *(Per)*: 70 Alexandra Drive, Upper Norwood, London SE19 1AN ☎ 020 8670 3184, 0498 603 180 mob

SINCLAIR Cameron Roy *(Per, Tym, Com)*: 7 Saunders House, Canada Street, Surrey Quays, London SE16 1SJ ☎ 020 7394 8464 & fax, 0374 969139 mob, 020 8533 1372 day

SINGER Ray *(Per)*: 32 Well Walk, London NW3 1BX ☎ 020 7794 8880

SKELTON Matt *(Dms, Per)*: 11 Malpas Road, New Cross, London SE4 1BP ☎ 020 8694 0404, 0378 425625

SKELTON Paul *(Dms)*: 26 Somerford Way, Rotherhithe, London SE16 1QW ☎ 020 7231 3906

SKINNER Michael *(Per, Voc)*: 138 Springbank Road, London SE13 6SU ☎ 020 8698 7885, 020 8461 5910 fax

SKINNER Tom *(Dms)*: 66 Dartmouth Park Road, London NW5 1SN ☎ 020 7267 4791, 020 7485 3742

SLOAN John *(Dms)*: 32 Murray Road, Wimbledon, London SW19 4PE ☎ 020 8946 3201

SLOWLEY Paul *(Dms)*: 183 Firs Lane, Winchmore Hill, London N21 3HY ☎ 020 8360 5853, 0378 504034

SMALL Andrew *(Per, Dms, Kbds, B Gtr, Gtr)* ☎ 0468 368436 mob

SMITH Alex *(Dms)*: Room 2, 21 Churchfield Road, Acton, London W3 6BD ☎ 020 8992 3494

SMITH Christopher *(Dms)*: 76 Danbury Crescent, South Ockenden, Essex RM15 5XF ☎ 01708 670 459

SMITH Colin *(Per)*: Orchard Lodge, Spratts Alley, Ottershaw, Surrey KT16 0HX

SMITH Denis *(Dms)*: 11 Cromwell Avenue, London W6 9LA ☎ 020 8748 1708

SMITH Derrick *(Dms)*: 138 Rochester Drive, Bexley, Kent DA5 1QF ☎ 01322 524236

SMITH Eric *(Dms)*: 4 The Chase, Bexleyheath, Kent DA7 5AT ☎ 01322 556151

SMITH James *(Dms)*: 11 Hotham Road, Putney, London SW15 1QL ☎ 020 8785 0306

SMITH Michael *(Dms, Per)*: 8 Shrublands Drive, Lightwater, Surrey GU18 5QS ☎ 01276 473670

SMITH Philip *(Per, Voc)*: 8 Cromwell Road, Kingston-upon-Thames, Surrey KT2 6RE ☎ 020 8241 4434

SNOW John *(Dms, Per, Tabla)*: 22 Longlands Park Crescent, Sidcup, Kent DA15 7NE ☎ 020 8300 9165

SOAN Ashley *(Dms)*: Flat 2, 35 Blackheath Park, London SE3 9RW ☎ 020 8463 0150

SODEN Paul *(Dms)*: Address Unknown ☎ 01372 276774

SPARROW Edwin *(Dms, Tym, Tnd Per, La Per)*: 132 Stonefall Avenue, Harrogate, North Yorks HG2 7NT ☎ 01423 888693

SPEAKMAN Thomas *(Dms, Per, Tym)*: 73 Ruddlesway, Windsor, Berks SL4 5SG ☎ 01753 866622

SPENCER Martin *(Dms)*: Address Unknown ☎ 020 8455 5319

SPEVOCK Edmund *(Dms)*: 31 Barnsbury Close, New Malden, Surrey KT3 5BP ☎ 020 8942 8429

SPIKE Andrew *(Dms, Per, Kbds)*: 23B Courtney Road, London N7 7BQ ☎ 020 7700 5383

SPINETTI Henry *(Dms, Per)*: 72 Whoberley Avenue, Coventry CV5 8EQ ☎ 024 7671 2531 & fax

SPOONER Richard *(Dms, Per)*: 369A Cranbrook Road, Ilford, Essex IG1 4UQ ☎ 0370 778283

SPOONS Sam *(Spoons, Dms, Uke, Vln, Voc)*: 1 St Johns Hill Grove, Battersea, London SW11 2RF ☎ 020 7228 6339

SRIH Harbans *(Dms, Per)*: 32 Lochaber Road, London SE13 5QU ☎ 020 8852 2110

STACEY Jeremy *(Dms, Kbds, Voc)*: 12 Elms Crescent, Clapham, London SW4 8RB ☎ 020 7498 7359

STAMS Erik *(Dms, Per, Gtr)* ☎ 020 7229 0043

STANCLIFFE Fred *(Per, Tym, Xyl, Glck, Vib)*: 72 Raglan Court, Empire Way, Wembley Park, Middx HA9 0RF ☎ 020 8902 4178

STARDUST Dave *(Dms, Per, Gtr)*: 67 Doveney Close, St Pauls Cray, Orpington, Kent BR5 3WE ☎ 01689 878367

STEAD David *(Dms)*: 23 Tewkesbury Close, London N15 6SJ ☎ 020 8802 5589

STEEDMAN Heather *(Per, Tym)*: 2 Thirlmere Gardens, Wembley, Middx HA9 8RE ☎ 020 8904 9049

STEPHENSON Shawn *(Dms)*: 1 Newnes Path, Huntingfield Road, London SW15 5JA ☎ 020 8878 1724

STEVENS Rob *(Dms)*: 1 Chase Court Gradens, Enfield, Middlesex EN2 8DH ☎ 020 8366 3082

STEWART Ewan *(Dms, La Per, Cong)*: 2B Lorn Road, Brixton, London SW9 0AD ☎ 020 7274 9716

STEWART Godfrey *(Per, Com)*: 122 Wargrave Avenue, London N15 6UA ☎ 020 8800 6770

STOKES Glenn *(Dms)*: 5A Ellesmere Court, Seymour Villas, Anerley, London SE20 8TY ☎ 020 8659 0151

STONE Horace *(Dms)*: 46 The Meadows, Ingrave, Brentwood, Essex CM13 3RN ☎ 01277 810785

STRIPF Markus *(Dms)*: 148 Muswell Hill, Broadway, London N10 3SA ☎ 020 8444 1410

SULLIVAN Lee *(Dms, Per)*: 2A The High Street, New Malden, Surrey KT3 4HE ☎ 020 8949 6109

SUPPLE Danton *(Per)*: 17 All Saints Road, Ladbroke Grove, London W11 1HA ☎ 020 7229 0531

SUTTON John *(Dms)*: Old Thatch Cottage, 85 Coggleshall Road, Marks Tey, Essex CO6 1LS ☎ 01206 211918

SUTTON Philip *(Dms)*: 18 Alford Court, Shepherdess Walk, London N1 7JW ☎ 020 7253 4229, 020 7609 7409

TABRETT Malcolm *(Dms)*: c/o 32 Nurser Rise, Dunmow, Essex CM61XW ☎ 01371 872515

TAILOR Sanja G. *(Per, Voc, Kbds)*: 121 Preston Road, Wembley, Middx HA9 8NN

TATSUHARA Ichiro *(Dms, Per)*: 71 Reighton Road, Clapton, London ☎ 020 8806 0326

TAYLOR Alan *(Per, Tym)*: 284 Hither Green Lane, London SE13 6TS ☎ 020 8461 3167

TAYLOR Caroline (*Dms, Per*): 131 Glyn Road, London E5 0JT ☎ 020 8985 3191

TAYLOR Crispin (*Dms, Per, B Gtr, Kbds, Gtr*): Flat C, 9A Yerbury Road, London N19 4RN ☎ 020 7272 6489

TAYLOR Eddie (*Dms*): 39 Calvert Road, Barnet, Herts EN5 4HH ☎ 020 8449 2851

TAYLOR Leo (*Dms, Per*): Address Unknown ☎ 020 8342 9179

TAYLOR Mark (*Dms*): 90 Briery Way, High Street Green, Hemel Hempstead, Herts HP2 7AN ☎ 01442 250624

TAYLOR Mark (*Per, Tnd Per*): 92 Theydon Street, Walthamstow, London E17 8EL ☎ 020 8518 7906, 0956 808319

TAYLOR Norman (*Per, Tym*): 18 Brunswick Street, Walthamstow, London E17 9NB ☎ 020 8521 7792

TAYLOR Philip (*Dms, Per*): c/o Caroline Cox, 62 Humbolt Road, London W6 8QT

TAYLOR Roger (*Per*): PO Box 159, Godalming, Surrey GU8 6YJ ☎ 01428 682426

TAYLOR Steve (*Dms, Per, Kbds*): 59 Churchbury Road, Enfield, Middlesex EN1 3HP ☎ 020 8292 2160, 020 8373 7304 fax

TAYLOR Woodie (*Dms*): 10 Woburn Court, Wellesley Road, Croydon, Surrey CR0 2AE ☎ 020 8686 6458

TELEMACQUE Ron (*Dms, Per*): 12 Foxley Close, Mountford Estate, London E8 2JN ☎ 020 7249 6951

TELFER Edward (*Dms, Pf, Kbds, Voc, Rapper*): 10 Whitelock House, Gascoyne Estate, Cassland Road, London E9 5BL ☎ 020 8533 0673

TEMPEST Troy (*Per*): Gorwallt Fach, Oefn Coch, Llanrhaeadr Y.M, Oswestry SY10 0BT ☎ 01691 780452

TEMPLE David (*Dms*): 4D Cannon Meadow, Tewin, Welwyn, Herts AL6 0JT ☎ 01438 717720

TERIAN Christopher (*Per, Tym, Pf*): 84 Astonville Street, London SW18 5AJ ☎ 020 8874 0294

TERREY David W (*Dms*): 45 Salop Road, London E17 7HS ☎ 020 8521 2806 & fax

THACKER Clive (*Dms*): 23A The Green, Ealing, London W5 5DA ☎ 020 8579 1355

THACKER David (*Per, Voc*): 3 Pelham Road, Bexley Heath, Kent DA7 4LT ☎ 020 8306 9001

THAIR Richard (*Per, Dms, Pf, Voc*): Flat 4, 68 Comeragh Road, London W14 9HR ☎ 020 7381 4127

THARP Ian (*Dms*): 8 Selwyn Road, New Malden, Surrey KT3 5AT ☎ 0976 392898

THOMAS Ian (*Dms*): 243 The Vale, Golders Green, London NW11 8TN ☎ 020 8458 4535

THOMAS Peter (*Per*): 2842 Hollyridge Drive, Los Angeles, California 90068, USA ☎ +1 323 962 1836, +1 323 962 1874

THOMAS Richard (*Dms, Per, Gtr, Sax, Kbds*): 1st Floor, 66 Ashmore Road, Maida Vale, London W9 3DG ☎ 020 8968 4829

THOMPSON Adele (*Per*): 10 Frankham House, Frankham Street, London SE8 4RL ☎ 020 8692 8576

THOMPSON Michael (*Dms, B Gtr, Per*): 020 8968 0359, 0956 803519 mob

THOMPSON Paul (*Dms*): 46 Edge Hill, Darras Hall, Ponteland, Northumberland NE20 9RR ☎ 01661 871013

THORNBER Kraig (*Dms, Per*): Address Unknown ☎ 020 7237 7279

TIBBLE Howard (*Per*): 41 Elm Park Road, Finchley, London N3 1EG ☎ 020 8349 1622

TICKLE David (*Dms*): 5 Lavender Road, Rotherhithe Street, London SE16 1DZ ☎ 020 7232 1986, 0956 850452 mob

TILLEY Edward (*Dms, Per, Gtr, Kbds, Voc*): 39 Abingdon Mansions, Pater Street, London W8 6AB ☎ 020 7937 7805

TOFF Alex (*Dms*): 24B Eaton Park Road, Palmers Green, London N13 4EL ☎ 020 8882 8724, 0973 553678

TOMKINS Trevor (*Per*): 14 Bellamy Street, London SW12 8BU ☎ 020 8675 1455

TOMS Elliot (*Dms, Per*): 33 Ashley Drive, Tylers Green, Penn, Bucks HP10 8BQ ☎ 01494 812742, 0831 450982 mob

TONKS John (*Dms*): 10 Bankhurst Road, London SE6 4XN ☎ 020 8690 5001

TONTOH Frank (*Dms, Per*): 37 Fairfields Crescent, London NW9 0PR ☎ 020 8905 0699

TOSH David (*Per, Timb*): 83 Belgrave Road, London E11 3QP ☎ 020 8989 6768

TOSH Stuart (*Per, Voc*): 12 Dixon Drive, Weybridge, Surrey KT13 0XJ ☎ 01932 827008

TOWNSEND Rob (*Per*): 13 Sidney Road, St Margarets, Twickenham, Middlesex TW1 1JP

TROWER Terence (*Per, Com, Arr*): 6 Abbey Mews, Laleham Park, Laleham, Nr Staines, Middlesex TW18 1SH ☎ 01784 465424

TROY Dameon (*Dms, Kbds*): 0956 139029

TUNMER Ollie (*Dms, Per, La Per*): We12 Kingston University, Kingston Hill, Kingston-upon-Thames, Surrey KT2 7LB ☎ 0403 140810

TURNER Andrew (*Tnd Per, Dms, Tym, Per*): 35 Lewisham Park, Lewisham, London SE13 6QZ ☎ 020 8244 4240, 0850 695 776 mob

TURNER James (*Per, Dms*): 14 Hollingbourne Gardens, Ealing, London W13 8EN ☎ 020 8998 9335

TURNER John (*Dms*): 27, Cartmel Road, Bexley Heath, Kent DA7 5EA ☎ 013224 35172

TURNER Roger (*Dms, Per*): 34 Lancaster Road, London W11 1QR ☎ 020 7221 3188

TWYFORD Benjamin (*Dms*): 10 Siddens Road, Forest Hill, London SE23 2JQ ☎ 020 8699 0958

TWYMAN Nick (*Dms, Per, Kbds, Com, Arr*): 15 Harley Court, High Road, London N20 0QD ☎ 0976 272682

UGHI Federico (*Dms*): 2 Edward Road, Walthamstow, London E17 6LU ☎ 020 8503 6920, 0958 510664, 020 8503 6920

URWIN Paul (*Dms, Com, Arr*): 27 Crookston Road, Eltham, London SE9 1YH ☎ 020 8859 2801

VALAT Jean-Marc (*Dms, Gtr*): Address Unknown

VAN GELDER Nick (*Dms, Per, Gtr, B Gtr*): 6 Tremlett Grove, London N19 5JX ☎ 020 7281 4066

VEAR Anthony (*Per, Dms*): Ralph Tubbs, Wenlock Basin, Wharf Road, London N1 7RX ☎ 020 7336 0003

VERRELL Ronald (*Dms*): 57 Angel Road, Thames Ditton, Surrey KT7 0AZ ☎ 020 8398 1109

VINCENT-BROWN Matthew (*Dms, Voc, Pf*): 83 Camelot House, Camden Park Road, London NW1 9AS ☎ 020 7267 7445

VINTNER Steven (*Dms, Per*): 34 Whitestile Road, Old Brentford, Middlesex TW8 9NJ ☎ 020 8560 6728, 0831 769950

VOM Stephen (*Dms*): c/o Deiss, Euler Str 21, 40477 Dusseldorf, Germany ☎ +49 211 488630 & fax

VORA Anup (*Per, Cong, Bong, Tabla, Af Dm*): 95 Byron Avenue, Cranford, Middlesex TW4 6LU ☎ 020 8707 3669, 0956 326146

VOYAGER (*Dms, Kbds, Gtr, B Gtr*): c/o Jackie Khan, Unitone, The Dairy, 43-45 Tunstall Road, London SW9 8BZ

WACKETT Robert (*Dms*): 104 Mahon Close, Enfield, Middx EN1 4DJ ☎ 020 8363 9160

WAGLAND James (*Dms*): 65 Newlands Road, Tunbridge Wells, Kent TN4 9AR ☎ 01892 21677

WAGSTAFF Anthony (*Per, Tym*): 7 Grantham Gdns, Chadwell Heath, Romford, Essex RM6 6HH ☎ 020 8597 6770, 0956 292175 mob

WALKER Graham (*Dms*): 2 St Paul's Road East, Dorking, Surrey RH4 2HR ☎ 01306 881015

WALKER Mark (*Dms*): 165 Green Lane Road, London SE9 3SZ ☎ 020 8850 3314

WALL Jorgen (*Dms, B Gtr, Gtr, Kbds, Voc*): Hogalidsg 25, 117 30 Stockholm, Sweden ☎ +46 8 847608, +46 708674900

WALLER Paul (*Dms, B Gtr, Kbds*): 020 7423 9993, 020 7423 9996

WALLMAN Anthony (*Dms, Per*): 27 Hornbean Road, Theydon Bois, Epping, Essex CM16 7JU ☎ 01992 812084

WALTERS David (*Dms*): c/o Knightmare Mgmt Ltd, Friars House, Suite 118, 1st Floor, 157-168 Blackfriars Road, London SE1 8EZ ☎ 020 7928 6755

WALTERS Patrice (*Dms*): 2 Dartmouth Road, Brondesbury, London NW2 4EU ☎ 020 8248 4709

WARBURTON Julian (*Per*): 39 Finland Road, London SE4 2JE ☎ 020 7639 9503

WARD Ashley (*Dms, Per, Ac Gtr, Hrn, Pf*): 32 Laurel Avenue, Potters Bar, Herts EN6 2AB ☎ 01707 659742, 0958 447294 mob

WARD Graham *(Dms)*: 4622 Columbus Avenue, Sherman Oaks, CA 91403, USA ☎ +1 818 789 9953, +1 818 481 8992, +1 818 789 9954

WARNER Leon *(Dms, Clt, Saxes, Bsn)*: 11 York Way, Welwyn, Herts AL6 9LB ☎ 01483 716081, 0385 758067

WASHINGTON Steve *(Dms)*: 70 Lillingstone House, Hornsey Road, London N7 7LZ ☎ 020 7700 4022

WATTERS Robin *(Dms)*: 33 Camplin St, London SE14 5QX ☎ 020 7639 2954

WATTS Charlie *(Per)*: c/o Sherry Daly, 5 Church Row, Wandsworth Plain, London SW18 1ES ☎ 020 8877 3111/3

WEBB David *(Dms, Gtr, Pf)*: Flat 10 Westbury Court, Nightingale Lane, London SW4 9AA ☎ 020 8673 2767

WEBB John *(Dms, Kbds)*: 86 Staines Road, Wraysbury, Berks TW19 5AA ☎ 01784 2311

WEBB Richard *(Dms)*: 59 Eden Park Avenue, Beckenham, Kent BR3 3HT ☎ 020 8658 5710

WEBBERLEY Stephen *(Per)*: 6 Northway Court, Litchfield Way, London NW11 6NX ☎ 020 8458 7859

WEBSTER Dave *(Dms, La Per, Cong, Tym)*: 42 Alberta Road, Bush Hill Park, Enfield, Middx EN1 1JB ☎ 020 8366 8188, 0374 605543

WELLARD Gordon *(Dms)*: 107A Victoria Park Road, Hackney, London E9 7JJ ☎ 020 8533 0851

WELLER Charles *(Per)*: 59 Shetland Road, Haverhill, Suffolk CB9 0LR ☎ 01440 704416

WELLS Colin *(Dms, Per)*: 47 St James's Avenue, Beckenham, Kent BR3 4HF ☎ 020 8650 1069

WELSFORD Andrew *(Dms)*: 71 Templeton Avenue, Chingford, London E4 6SS ☎ 020 8257 2065

WELSH Mark *(Dms, Kbds, Pf, Voc)* ☎ 0956 639665

WESTON Ray *(Dms, Per)*: Flat B, 4 Craven Hill, London W2 3DS ☎ 020 7262 5265

WHITAKER Simon *(Dms, Per, Voc)*: 20 Almhouse Lane, Chessington, Surrey KT9 2ND ☎ 020 8391 1052

WHITE Carl *(Dms)*: 2 Scowcroft House, Craig Gardens, South Woodford, London E18 2JX ☎ 020 8989 3862

WHITE Gregory *(Dms, Per)*: Brookside House, The Street, Chilcompton BA3 4HB ☎ 01702 75584, 020 8566 1691

WHITE Kate *(Per)*: 12 Nassington Road, London NW3 2UD ☎ 020 7433 1263

WHITE Steven *(Dms)*: 49 Riefield Road, London SE9 2QE ☎ 020 8850 2047

WHITE Yvonne *(Tamb, Cong, Mar, Voc)*: 21 Andrew Court, Church Rise, Forest Hill, London SE23 2UR ☎ 020 8531 5562, 020 8523 4159 fax

WHITEFORD David *(Dms, B Ldr)*: 133B Grange Road, Ramsgate, Kent CT11 9PT ☎ 01843 590986, 0585 839587 mob

WHITEWOOD Ian *(Dms, Voc)*: 4 Trelawn Road, Brixton, London SW2 1DJ ☎ 020 7771 3024, 0956 503142

WHITTEN Chris *(Dms)*: 120 Narbonne Avenue, Clapham Common, London SW4 4LG ☎ 020 8675 0176, 020 8673 6542 fax

WHYTE Jim *(Dms, Pf)*: 74 Mealey Road, Manor Park, London E12 6AR ☎ 020 8478 5125

WICKENS Lee *(Dms)*: 21 Onslow Gardens, Wallington, Surrey SM6 9QL ☎ 020 8395 8541

WICKINS David *(Dms)*: 69A Albion Drive, London E8 4LT ☎ 020 7254 5433

WILDCAT Will *(Dms, Per)*: 17-19 Lever Street, Off Goswell Road, London EC1 ☎ 020 7251 5950

WILKIN Mark *(Dms)*: The Garden Flat, 7 Bennett Park, Blackheath, London SE3 9RA ☎ 020 8355 8916

WILKINSON Kevin *(Dms)*: Heddons Cottage, Finches Lane, Baydon Nr Marlborough, Wilts SN8 2JL ☎ 01672 541015

WILKINSON Neal *(Dms)*: 18 Barclay Road, London SW6 1EH ☎ 020 7731 5053

WILLCOX Gary *(Dms, Per)*: 2 Elliott Road, Chiswick, London W4 ☎ 020 8742 8863

WILLIAMS Leonard *(Dms, Per)*: 2 Buryfield, Lydiard Millicent, Swindon, Wilts SN5 9NF ☎ 01793 770715

WILLIAMS Simon *(Dms)*: 29 Brook Drive, Harrow, Middlesex HA1 4RT ☎ 020 8863 0204, 0966 188358

WILLIAMS Stephen *(Dms, La Per, Gtr)*: 23 Westfield Road, Surbiton, Surrey KT6 4EL ☎ 020 8399 6662

WILLIAMS Steve *(Dms, Per)*: Flat 2, 49 Wimbledon Park Road, Southfields, London SW18 5SJ ☎ 020 8877 0108

WILLIAMSON Stephen *(Dms)*: 38 Caldervale Road, Clapham, London SW4 9LZ ☎ 020 7627 2390

WILLMOTT Sean *(Per, Kbds)*: 67 Duke Road, Chiswick, London W4 2BN ☎ 020 8742 7522

WILSHERE Brian *(Dms, Per, Com)*: 20 Clifton Road, Wallington, Surrey SM6 8AN ☎ 020 8773 4570, 0585 634127

WILSON Derek *(Dms)*: Via Chiusi 52, 00139 Rome, Italy ☎ +39 6 8121189, +39 7366331

WILSON Matt *(Dms, Per)*: 9A Woodland Road, New Southgate, London N11 1PN ☎ 020 8368 3886

WILSON Willie *(Dms)*: 50A The Avenue, Brondesbury Park, London NW6 7NP ☎ 020 8459 0481

WIMPRESS Daniel *(Dms, Per, Kbds, Gtr, Tpt)*: 5 Corrance Road, London SW2 5RD ☎ 020 7738 3860, 07970 027621

WINSTON Giselle *(Per)*: 99 Melrose Avenue, London NW2 4LX ☎ 020 8452 0053

WINTER-HART Paul *(Dms)*: Varunastra Productions Ltd, Gelfand Rennert Feldman Brown, 82 Brook Street, London W1Y 2NL

WITHERS David *(Dms, Per)*: 76 Victoria Road, New Barnet, Herts EN4 9PE

WITHERS John *(Dms)*: 120 Queenswood Gardens, Wanstead, London E11 3SG ☎ 020 8530 7621

WOLF Robert *(Dms, Kbds, Gtr, Pf, Voc)*: 7A Coverton Road, Tooting Broadway, London SW17 0QW ☎ 020 8767 2365

WOODGATE Daniel Woods *(Dms)*: Cc Young & Co, Chesham House, 150 Regent Street, London W1R 5FA ☎ 020 7432 0337, 020 7432 0338

WOODWARD Justin *(Per, Dms)*: 1A Argyle Road, West Ealing, London W13 0LN ☎ 020 8810 5053, 0973 637933

WOOLWAY Colin *(Dms)*: 16 Old Palace Lane, Richmond, Surrey TW9 1PG ☎ 020 8948 3960, 020 8948 3960

WORTH Bobby *(Dms)*: 6 Penrith Close, Beckenham, Kent BR5 5UF ☎ 020 8663 0713

WRIGHT Stewart *(Dms, Pf, Gtr, Rec, Voc)*

WRIGHT Tim *(Per, Dms, Vln)*: Ground Floor Flat, 18 St Germans Road, Forest Hill, London SE23 1RJ ☎ 020 8690 4429, 0589 410597 mob

WYLES Christopher *(Dms, Per)*: 143 Camberwell Road, London SE5 0HB ☎ 020 7703 9104

WYNDHAM Stephen *(Dms)*

YEO Oscar *(Dms, Voc)*: 226 A-Alpha Windsor Road, Bray, Berks SL6 2DT ☎ 01628 71298

YOUSSEF My *(Dms, Per, B Gtr, Gtr, Kbds)*: 168C Portnall Road, London W9 3BQ ☎ 020 8960 1468

ZACK Johnny *(Dms)*: 25 Fleetwood Close, Tadworth, Surrey KT20 5QG ☎ 0958 778682 mob

ZARATE Morgan *(Dms, Per)*: Flat 3, 65 Carleton Rd, London N7 0ET ☎ 020 7609 1961, 020 7281 2793

ZIESENISS Claus *(Dms, Per)*: Dampfmuehlenweg 8, D-47799 Krefeld, Germany ☎ +49 177 6928972

PIANOFORTE

SCOTLAND

ALEXANDER Peter: 3 Randolph Terrace, Stirling FK7 9AA ☎ 01786 462280

ALSTON Andrew *(Kbds, Acc)*: 41 Cloyston Street, North Kelvinside, Glasgow G20 ☎ 0141 945 3375

ANDERSON Robert (Bert) O *(Kbds)*: 31 Glebe Court, Portlethen, Aberdeen AB12 4XR ☎ 01224 780260

ARMSTRONG Craig *(Synth)*: 19 Verona Avenue, Glasgow G14 9DZ

BAILLIE Allan: 46 Bellevue Road, Prestwick KA9 1NJ ☎ 01292 475373

BANEL Mark: 29 Bruntsfield Place, Edinburgh EH10 4HJ ☎ 0131 229 4061

BARNES Mary *(Voc, Vln, Vla)*: 57 Courthill Ave, Cathcart, Glasgow G44 5AA ☏ 0141 637 6911

BARNETT Michael *(Com, Ob, B Gtr, R Wnd)*: 270 North Woodside Road, North Kelvinside, Glasgow G20 6LX ☏ 0141 337 6867, 07887 796063 mob

BEARD *(Acc, Gtr)*: 8 Cleuch Road, Causewayhead, Stirling FK9 5EX ☏ 01786 472128, 0421 508 334

BELL John: 416 Great Western Road, Glasgow G4 9HZ ☏ 0141 334 0688, 0141 445 4295

BLACK Ian *(Clt)*: 135 Waverley Crescent, Livingston, West Lothian EH54 8JR ☏ 01506 412109

BLAIR Walter *(Org)*: Earlish, 2 John Street Lane, Helensburgh G84 9NA ☏ 01436 674662

BREINGAN Stan: 8 Ailsa Street, Prestwick, Ayrshire KA9 1RH ☏ 01292 678148

BROOKS Hilary M *(Md, Kbds)*: 43 Athole Gardens, Glasgow G12 9BQ

BRUCE Sheila: 13, Drumdevan Road, Inverness, Scotland IV2 4BZ ☏ 01463 711979

CAIRNS Alexander *(Org, Voc)*: 26 Mauchline Road, Catrine, Ayrshire KA5 6SW ☏ 01290 51 415

CALDER Stephen *(Org, Acc)*: 51 Merchant Street, Peterhead, Aberdeenshire AB42 1DU ☏ 01779 474500

CALDER Thomas: 81 Victoria Park Drive North, Glasgow G14 9PJ ☏ 0141 569 7542

CARRICK Andrew *(Kbds, Gtr, B Gtr)*: Top Left Flat, 55 Gardner Street, Partickhill, Glasgow G11 5DA ☏ 0141 341 0304

CHALMERS Bill *(Kbds, B Ldr)*: 2 Pedwarden Road, Gannochy, Perth, Scotland PH2 7JW ☏ 01738 625831

CHRISTIE Ian *(Org, Acc, Kbds, Md)*: 4 Hayworth Avenue, Laurieston, Falkirk, Stirlingshire FK2 9NH ☏ 01324 624604

CLARK Derek *(Con, Org, Hpsd)*: Dalmally, 96 East King Street, Helensburgh, Dunbartonshire G84 7DT ☏ 01436 672332

COCHRANE Lynda *(Com)*: 11 Rosslyn Terrace, Glasgow G12 9NA ☏ 0141 334 5607

CONAGHAN Stuart *(Kbds, Gtr, B Gtr)*: 35 Polnoon Avenue, Knightswood, Glasgow, Scotland G13 3HG ☏ 0141 959 3399

CORBETT Heather *(Per, Tym, Cimb)*: 33 Faskally Avenue, Bishopbriggs, Glasgow G64 3PJ ☏ 0141 772 3152, 07050 168772 mob, 0141 772 3152 fax

CORDINER A *(Kbds)*: 3 Kingsborough Gardens, Hyndland, Glasgow G12 9QA ☏ 0141 357 4853

COSKER James *(Kbds)*: 2 Ardlui Road, Ayr KA8 8LU ☏ 01292 260344, 0589 149945 mob

COWAN Anne F *(Voc)*: 6 Gloucester Avenue, Burnside, Rutherglen, Glasgow G73 5AT ☏ 0141 647 4515

COWIE Anna: Address Unknown

CRAWFORD John *(Org, Synth)*: 61 Springfield Park Road, Burnside, Glasgow G73 3RG ☏ 0141 647 4934

CREE Gordon *(Kbds, Voc)*: 86 East Main Street, Darvel, Ayrshire, Scotland KA17 0HT ☏ 01560 322505

CULL Roger: 7 Oxford Terrace, Edinburgh EH4 2EL ☏ 0131 332 5466

CULLEY Gerry *(Tbn)*: 9 Dunearn Street, Broughty Ferry, Dundee DD5 3NP ☏ 01382 776477

CUNNISON Belinda *(Ob)*: 7/1 South Sloan Street, Edinburgh EH6 8SS ☏ 0131 467 4237

CURRALL James *(Vln)*: 9 Greenhill Place, Edinburgh EH10 4BR ☏ 0131 447 2584

CUTHBERTSON Allan *(Kbds)*: 572 Crow Road, Glasgow G13 1NP ☏ 0141 959 3667

DEVLIN-THORP Jeremy *(Kbds, Accom)*: 23 Brighton Place, Edinburgh EH15 1LL ☏ 0131 468 0762, 0131 468 0218 fax

DON Nigel *(Com, Arr)*: 12 Kelso Place, Dundee DD2 1SL ☏ 01382 667251

DONALD George: 12 Kincarrathie Crescent, Perth PH2 7HH ☏ 01738 622425

DUGUID Irvin *(Kbds)*: 53 Braeside Street (6/R), N. Kelvinside, Glasgow G20 6QT ☏ 0802 615031

DUNCAN Robert *(Org, Kbds)*: 46 Beechwood Road, Arbroath, Angus DD11 4HU ☏ 01241 879604

EVANS Russ *(Org, Sax)*: 38 Kirk Brae, Edinburgh EH16 6HH ☏ 0131 664 5831 & fax

FLEETWOOD Joe *(Voc, Kbds, Gtr, Ac Gtr)*: 21 Hospitalfield Gradens, Arbroath, Angus DD11 2LQ ☏ 01241 872933

FLUSH Paul Kendal *(Kbds)*: Pastoriestraat 33, 3150 Wakkerzeel, Belgium ☏ 0032 16 602664

FOTHERINGHAM Elizabeth *(Voc)*: 106 Chamberlain Road, Jordanhill, Glasgow G13 1RX ☏ 0141 954 4042

FRASER Jock *(Kbds, Org, Acc, B Ldr)*: 26 Ness Bank, Inverness, Invernesshire IV2 4SF

GOLJANEK Ewa *(Kbds, Flt, Gtr)*: 306B Great Western Road, Aberdeen AB10 6PL ☏ 01224 575754, 07801 499393

GORMAN James: 2 Caird Avenue, Greenock PA16 7TD ☏ 01475 723704

GOWRIE James *(Kbds)*: 16 Ardmillan Street, Carntyne, Glasgow G33 3BY ☏ 0141 770 5700

GROSSART Steven *(Synth, Kbds)*: 153 Craigmount Brae, Edinburgh EH12 8XW ☏ 0131 339 6242

HARKNESS Eleanor: 38 Inglewood Road, Alloa, Clackmannanshire, Scotland FK10 JJ ☏ 01259 720514

HARRISON Paul *(Kbds)*: 2F2, 5 Spittal Street, Edinburgh EH3 9DY ☏ 0131 228 8140

HERRIOT Alan *(Arr, Com)*: 25 Milton Bridge, Penicuik, Midlothian EH26 0RD ☏ 71 78224

HILLMAN Mary *(Org, Acc)*: 3 Yarrow Park, St Leonards, East Kilbride G74 2HP ☏ East Kilbride 3

HOGG Rosemarie *(Kbds)*: 1 Forsyth Place, Cromarty, Ross-Shire, Scotland IV11 8XW ☏ 01381 600349

HOUSTON John: 35 Hathaway Lane, Glasgow G20 8NG ☏ 0141 945 0718

HUNTER Michael *(Dms, Gtr, B Gtr)*: 44 Station Road, Bearsden, Glasgow, Scotland G61 4AL ☏ 0141 943 1065, 0141 943 2226

IRVINE Joseph *(Acc)*: 13 Caird Drive, Glasgow G11 5DZ ☏ 0141 334 3494

JARVIE Marshall *(Kbds, Acc)*: 21 Rosefield Gardens, Uddingston, Lanarkshire G71 7AW ☏ 01698 814310

JARVIS Bill: 18 Castle Road, Dollar, Clackmannanshire FK14 7BE ☏ 01259 742584

JOHNSTON Alan: 13 Third Avenue, Glasgow G44 4TH ☏ 0141 570 1058

JOHNSTON Fiona *(Kbds)*: Otterslea, Grunnavoe, Vidlin, Shetland ZE2 9QF ☏ 01806 577264

JOHNSTONE Iain *(Tba, T Hrn, Tpt, Acc)*: 60 Craighouse Avenue, Edinburgh EH10 5LL ☏ 0131 446 9196

JOHNSTONE Muriel A: Muse Cottage, Allanton, Duns, Berwickshire TD11 3JZ ☏ 0189 081 8884

KENMUIR Callum *(Vla, Cnt)*: 39 Rhu Road Higher, Helensburgh, Argyll & Bute G84 8QH ☏ 01436 673203

KITCHEN Alan *(Acc, Hrn, Org)*: 58 Novar Drive, Hyndland, Glasgow G12 9TZ ☏ 0141 357 1382

LAMB Giles *(Kbds, Voc)*: 24 Cecil Street, Glasgow G12 8RH

LEITCH Hazel *(Vln)*: Thornlea, 3 St Leonards Road, Ayr KA7 2PR ☏ 01292 266406

LIDDELL Clair *(Com)*: 52/4 Fraser Homes, Spylaw Bank Road, Edinburgh, Scotland EH13 0JE ☏ 01983 521 007

LIPMAN David *(Acc)*: Address Unknown

LITHGOW Beverley: 18 Grampian Mobile Homes, Elrick, Westhill AB32 6TJ ☏ 01224 744065

MABBOTT Gordon *(Org, Bsn)*: 5 Crummock Park House, 26 Head Street, Beith, Ayrshire KA15 3EU ☏ 01505 506040

MACCLEAVER Grace *(B Ldr)*: 17 Waulkmill, Fossoway, Kinrossshire KY13 7UJ ☏ 01577 840284

MACKAY Thomas: 56 Overtoun Drive, Rutherglen, Glasgow G73 2QE ☏ 0141 647 5488

MACKENZIE Hamish: 5 Hagart Road, Houston, Johnstone PA6 7JH ☏ 01505 613735

MACPHERSON Ian *(Org, Arr, Com, Song W)*: 26 Queens Avenue, Edinburgh EH4 2DF ☏ 0131 332 3128

MARSHALL Andy *(Kbds)*: 24B Magdala Crescent, Coates, Edinburgh EH12 ☏ 0131 313 2606

MCCANN Patrick *(Md)*: Address Unknown ☏ 0131 334 3634

MCCAULEY Sean (*Acc, Wh*): 61 Peel Street, Glasgow G11 5LY ☎ 0141 357 6384 & fax, 0370 595382 mob

MCCULLOCH George (*Acc, Md*): Address Unknown

MCDONALD Bernard (*Kbds*): 14 Boghead Road, Dunbarton G82 2HP ☎ 01389 765336

MCDONALD David (*Kbds*): 76 Beechlends Drive, Clarkston, Glasgow G76 7UX ☎ 0141 639 1259

MCEWAN James (*Org, Kbds*): 3/1, 1046 Dumbarton Road, Whiteinch, Glasgow G14 9UL ☎ 0141 950 6762

MCGHIE Bruce (*Kbds*): 13 Robertson Street, Greenock PA16 8NL ☎ 01475 21505

MCGIRR Alastair: Aulnoye, 44 Cattlemarket, Clackmannan, Clacks FK10 4EH ☎ 01259 214 888

MCGUINNESS David (*Org*): 19 Havelock Street, Glasgow G11 5JF ☎ 0141 339 0605 & fax

MCINTOSH Donald (*Org*): Flat 15, Novar Court, 12 Novar Drive, Hyndland, Glasgow G12 9PU ☎ 0141 334 9316

MCNAMEE Hugh: 1557 Gt Western Road, Glasgow G13 1HN ☎ 0141 959 9937

MILLIGAN David (*Com*): PO Box 12481, Edinburgh EH3 5YG ☎ 0131 226 4338 & fax

MILLIGAN John (*Kbds*): 15 Church Square, Galashiels TD1 3JJ

MILNE Ian (*Kbds, Arr*): Earlsmohr, 85 High Street, Invervrie, Aberdeenshire AB51 3QJ ☎ 01467 620606

MITCHELL David (*Gtr, Sax, Voc*): 99 St Leonards Street, Flat 2Fa, Edinburgh EH8 9QY ☎ 0131 662 4273

MITCHELL James K (*Org*): Ravenscraig, Stenness, Stromness, Orkney KW16 3EY ☎ 01856 851494

MITCHELL Neil (*Gtr*): 1 Park Gate, Glasgow G3 6DL ☎ 0141 353 1515

MORRISON Ronald (*Org*): 9 Craigie Park, Aberdeen AB25 2SE ☎ 01224 642936

MUIR James (*Org*): Meadowside Farm, Coupar Angus, Blairgowrie, Perthshire PH13 9ER

MUOTUNE Jim (*Per, B Gtr*): Flat 2/L 13 Thornwood Gdns, Glasgow G11 7PJ ☎ 0141 572 1480, 0411 685 884, 0141 572 1478

MURDOCH Cameron (*Org, Hpsd*): Flat 1, 10 Dorset Square, Glasgow G3 7LL ☎ 0141 221 8837

NEWTON David: Foxlea, Oakley Lane, Oakley, Hants RG23 7JT ☎ 01256 782236

NICOL Andrew (*Accom*): Flat 3/1, 1403 Dumbarto Road, Glasgow G14 9XS ☎ 0141 954 1780, 0589 275288

NOLAN Mike (*Kbds, Org, Gtr, Voc*): 2 The Steading, Ashfield, Dunblane FK15 0JT ☎ 01786 825918

O'KEEFE Peggy: 9 Ashton Road, Glasgow G12 8SP ☎ 0141 334 5232

O'LEARY Thomas (*Acc*): 27 Mull Terrace, Bourtreehill, Irvine, Ayrshire KA11 1HR ☎ 01294 212542

PATERSON Foss (*Kbds*): St Ronans, 101 Lothian Street, Bonnyrigg, Midlothian EH19 3AG ☎ 0131 663 9323, 08701 142 185, 0131 663 9323

PATRICK David (*Kbds*): Torvaig, Tak'Ma'Doon Road, Kilfyth G65 0RS ☎ 01236 824825

PEACHEY Lynda (*Gtr, Voc, Per, Song W*): 17 Richmond Terrace, Edinburgh, Scotland EH11 2BY ☎ 0131 346 0249, 0131 477 2371 fax

PENMAN Alan (*Kbds, Gtr*): Flat 2/2, 12 Tollcross Road, Parkhead, Glasgow G31 4XD ☎ 0141 554 9242

PETTIGREW Robert (*Flt*): 9 Argyle Place, Edinburgh EH9 1JL ☎ 0131 667 6861

PRENTICE Brian (*Kbds*): 14 Park Place, Lanark ML11 9HH ☎ 01555 662071, 0831 560720

RASTOPTCHINA Anna: 86 Deanston Drive, Shawlands, Glasgow G41 3LH ☎ 0141 6497666

REVEL Cluness (*Gtr*): 57 King Harald Street, Lerwick, Shetland Isles ZE1 0ER ☎ 01595 692170

REW Angela (*Gtr, Dul*): 11 Bramdon Street, Edinburgh EH3 5DY ☎ 0131 556 0334

RICHMOND Edward: Address Unknown ☎ 01563 22867

ROBB Marion (*Voc*): 78 Millhouse Crescent, Kelvindale, Glasgow G20 0UD ☎ 0141 946 7155

ROBERTSON James (*Org*): 5A Parkburn Road, Kilsyth, Glasgow G65 9DH ☎ 01236 822226

ROXBURGH John: Address Unknown ☎ 0141 632 7149

RUTHERFORD Maureen (*Org, Voc*): 108 Cedar Grove, Perth, Scotland PH1 1RJ ☎ 01382 641854

SAWERS Ingrid: 9 Springvalley Terrace, Edinburgh EH10 4QB ☎ 0131 447 1264

SCOTT Cedric (*Org*): 21 Duncombe Street, Glasgow G20 0LZ

SEIVEWRIGHT Robert: The Old Joinery, Lintfieldbank, Coalburn, Lanarkshire ML11 0NJ ☎ 01555 820369

SHAND Peter (*Hpsd, Md, Arr*): 94 Queensborough Gardens, Glasgow G12 9RX ☎ 0141 339 0829 & fax, 0585 537 556 mob

SHAW Alexander (*Org*): 54 Pilrig Street, Edinburgh EH6 5AS ☎ 0131 554 5391

SHEPHERD Esma: 15 Balgownie Crescent, Bridge Of Don, Aberdeen AB23 8EJ ☎ 01224 703487

SINCLAIR Mark (*Kbds*): 94 Dalry Road, Ardrossan, Ayrshire, Scotland KA22 7JZ ☎ 01294 601614

SMITH George: Address Unknown

SMITH Nat: Pavilion, Stewarton, Ayrshire KA3 3ES ☎ 01560 484315

SMITH Penelope: 17 Douglas Muir Drive, Milngavie, Glasgow G62 7RS ☎ 0141 956 4685 & fax

SPENCER Dominic: 15 Windsor Square, Penicuik EH26 8ES ☎ 01968 679299

STEWART Jill: 148 Capelrig Road, Newton Mearns, Renfrewshire G77 6LA ☎ 0141 639 4963

STIVEN Lena: c/o Thomson, 3 Cameron Court, Cloch Road, Gourock PA19 1AP ☎ 01475 632562

TAYLOR David (*Kbds, Org*): 80 Earlspark Avenue, Glasgow G43 2HD ☎ 0141 637 3473

TAYLOR Margaret: 55 Drum Brae South, Edinburgh EH12 8SX ☎ 0131 339 1664

TAYLOR Sandy: Dumfin Sawmill, Glenfruin, By Helensborough G84 9EE ☎ 0138 985 0656

TENNANT William (*Acc*): Address Unknown

TINGEY Giles (*B Gtr*): 3/1, 97 Sanda Street, Glasgow G20 8PT ☎ 0141 945 2958, 0141 945 4587

TURNER John (*Gtr*): 'Lyndene', 21 Kings Road, Beith KA15 2BQ ☎ 01505 504981, 0468 178033, 01505 503778

WANDS Edna (*Voc*): Braidlee, Jenny Moores Road, St Boswells, Roxburghshire TD6 0AN ☎ 0183 52 2442

WATT David (*Vln, Gtr, B Gtr*): 1 Melville Terrace, Glenfarg, Perthshire PH2 9NN ☎ 01577 830 345

WHYTE Douglas (*Kbds*): 101 Bank Street, Irvine KA12 0PT ☎ 01294 275259, 0860 300128 mob

WILKES Judith (*Voc*): 16 Tay Terrace, Newport-on-Tay, Fife DD6 8DG ☎ 01382 542352

WILKINSON Ruth (*Hrn*): Flat 2/1, 13 Wilton Drive, North Kelvinside, Glasgow G20 6RW ☎ 0141 946 8014

NORTH WEST

ADDERLEY Diane (*Flt, Gtr*): 6 Greengate Lane, Prestwich, Manchester M25 3HW ☎ 0161 798 6044

ALCOCK George: Induna, 18 School Road, Onchan, Isle Of Man IM3 4LA ☎ 01624 675395

ALLARDYCE Darren (*Kbds, B Gtr, Dms, Per*): 20 Sussex Street, Salford, Lancs M7 9QE ☎ 0161 834 1684

ALLEN Keith (*Kbds, Md*): 1 Tyndall Avenue, Moston, Manchester M10 9PH ☎ 0161 682 6172

ALMOND Martin (*Kbds, Org*): 7 Kings Drive, Hoddlesden, Darwen, Lancs BB3 3RB ☎ 01254 705219, 01254 873680

ALSTON Pauline (*Hpsd, Clst, Accom*): 12 Wilson Road, Wallasey, Merseyside L44 8BU ☎ 0151 639 2732

ANDRUSIER Tamar: 48 Kingshill Road, Manchester M21 9FY ☎ 0161 881 1520

ASSHETON Robert (*Kbds, Ac Gtr*): Cotewood Bungalow, 5 Brown Heath Road, Christleton, Chester CH3 7PN ☎ 01244 336669

BAKER Andrew (*Gtr, Org*): 135 Moss Road, Birkdale, Southport, Merseyside PR8 4JA ☎ 01704 560905

BAKER Charles *(Kbds)*: 40 Long Close, Leyland, Preston PR5 3WB ☎ 01772 466486

BARNWELL Edward *(Kbds)*: Flat 1, 72 Clyde Road, West Didsbury, Manchester M20

BARRACLOUGH Winston *(Org, Arr, Com, Cop)*: 4 Brickfield Lane, Littleton, Chester CH3 7DH ☎ 01244 332354

BARRAND Roderick *(Accom)*: 4 Stow Gardens, Malvern Grove, Withington, Manchester M20 1HL ☎ 0161 434 2796

BARRATT Philip *(Kbds)*: St James Vicarage, 120 Shaw Road, Thornham, Rochdale, Lancs OL16 4SQ ☎ 01706 645256, 07775 646733

BISSELL Christine *(Acc, Clt)*: 15 Denmark Street, Lancaster LA1 5LY ☎ 01524 37838

BLEASDALE John *(Gtr, Synth)*: 40 Boucton Avenue, West Kirby, Wirral, Merseyside L48 5WZ ☎ 0151 625 7756

BOLTON Norman *(Tpt)*: 190 New Lane, Oswaldtwistle, Lancs BB5 3QW ☎ 01254 388667

BOOKER Jack *(Org)*: 38 Whitegate Drive, Blackpool, Lancs FY5 9AL ☎ 01253 391286

BRACEWELL Alan: 420 Ripponden Road, Oldham, Lancs OL4 2LJ ☎ 0161 624 3235

BRAMWELL Jonathan *(Tpt, Gtr)*: 45 Egerton Road, Davenport, Stockport, Cheshire SK3 8TQ ☎ 0161 483 0555

BRITTON John *(A Sax, Clt)*: Address Unknown

BROADGATE Noel *(Kbds)*: 46 Cherry Tree Way, Helmshore, Rossendale, Lancs BB4 4JZ ☎ 01706 227133

BROMILOW LRAM ATCL ALCM W *(Org)*: 102 Birchley Road, Billinge, Nr Wigan, Lancs WN5 7QN ☎ 01744 892448

BROWN Peter *(Kbds, Cel)*: High Dale Park House, Satterthwaite, Ulverston, Cumbria LA12 8LJ ☎ 01229 860226

BRYN-PARRI Annette: Cynefin, Deiniolen, Gwynedd LL55 3LU

BUCKLE Ian: 30A Spring Street, Oldham, Lancs OL4 2BD ☎ 0161 620 8072

BURROWS Stephen *(Kbds, B Gtr, Voc)*: 14 Parkhill Avenue, Crumpsall, Manchester M8 4RA ☎ 0161 795 8030

CAINE James: 40 Banks Howe, Onchan, Isle Of Man IM3 2ER ☎ 01624 676975

CALVERT Bryan: 144 Framingham Road, Sale, Cheshire M33 3RG ☎ 0161 973 1530

CAMPBELL THORNTON Peter: 18 Uppingham Road, Wallasey, Wirral L44 2BT ☎ 0151 638 5019, 0151 630 1554

CASEY Richard *(Kbds)*: Flat 4 21 Cocklane Road, Charlton, Manchester M21 8UP ☎ 0161 861 8473, 0374 691011

CHADWICK Graham *(Kbds, Org, Tbn)*: 11A Winifred Street, Passmonds, Rochdale, Lancs OL12 7ND ☎ 01706 341927

CHAMBERS Rebecca *(Kbds, Voc)*: 18 New Hey Road, Cheadle, Cheshire SK8 2AQ ☎ 0161 428 1604

CONNELL Patrick *(Kbds)*

COSGROVE Declan *(Kbds, Gtr)*: 65 War Office Road, Bamford, Rochdale OL11 5HX ☎ 01706 58625

CRANVILLE.A.L.C.M. Patricia *(Voc)*: 14A Pendyffryn Road, Rhyl, Denbighshire LL18 4RU

CROWE Eyre *(Org)*: 7 Melrose Avenue, Sale, Cheshire M33 3AZ ☎ 0161 973 4539

CROWLEY Vincent *(Md)*: Address Unknown

CULBERT Tom: 10 Shropshire Drive, Wilpshire, Blackburn, Lancs BB1 9NF ☎ 01254 249606

DAVIES Ann: Y Glain, Glan Tryweryn, Frongoch, Y Bala, Gwynedd LL23 7NT ☎ 01678 520327

DAVIES Harvey: 5, Lon-Y-Waen, Tyddyn Isaf, Menai Bridge, Anglesey, N.Wales LL59 5QH ☎ 01248 715 844

DAVIES Helen: 7 Menai Ville, Menai Bridge, Gwynedd, North Wales LL59 5ES ☎ 01248 713336

DEARDEN Guy: Howarth Pastures Barn, Pot House Lane, Syke, Rochdale, Lancs OL12 9PP ☎ 01706 350465

DEARNLEY Dorothy *(Voc, Kbds, Org)*: 11 North Drive, Heswall, Wirral, Merseyside L60 0BB ☎ 0151 342 4490

DEATH Stewart: 7 Knutsford Avenue, Old Trafford, Manchester M16 7SA ☎ 0161 226 1432

DOREY Simon *(Gtr)*: 12 Hambleton Close, Bury, Nr Manchester BL8 2JP ☎ 0161 764 9647

DORFMAN Selwin *(Voc)*: 18 Hollow Oak Lane, Delamere Park, Cuddington, Cheshire CW8 2XN ☎ 01606 888323

DRAKE Eric *(Org)*: 42 Meadow Crescent, Carleton, Blackpool FY6 7QX ☎ 01253 883889

DUARI Meena Louise *(Vln)*: 92 Blackburn Road, Padiham, Burnley, Lancs BB12 8JZ ☎ 01282 863342

DUNN Jonathan: 4 Cromwell Avenue, Penwortham, Preston PR1 9AU ☎ 01772 494473, 0777 1618303

DURBIN Rose *(Kbds)*: 43 Grange Road, Chorlton, Manchester M21 1NZ ☎ 0161 861 9363

EATON James *(Kbds)* ☎ 01254 383101

ELIS Hefin *(Gtr, B Gtr)*: Bryn Gellyg, 22 Lon Ddewi, Caernarfon, Gwynedd LL55 1BH ☎ 01286 676458

EVANS Richard *(Cel)*: 22 Murray Road, Ealing, London W5 4XS ☎ 020 8847 2852

FAINT Peter *(Kbds)*: 126 Vancouver Quay, Salford Quays, Manchester M5 2TX ☎ 0161 888 2306

FISHER Howard: Newhaven, Holywell Road, Flint, Clwyd CH6 5RR ☎ 01352 735822

FLETCHER Paul *(Voc)*: 7 Goyt Road, Stockport, Cheshire SK1 2EZ ☎ 0161 429 8318

FLYNN B: 10 Ivy Lane, Moreton, Wirral, Merseyside L46 8SJ ☎ 0151 678 9908

FRY Bridget *(Hpsd, Vln)*: 480 Aigburth Road, Liverpool L19 3QE ☎ 0151 427 2344

FYLES Kenneth *(Kbds, Cnt)*

GADIAN Wendy: 84 Barcombe Avenue, Streatham Hill, London SW2 3AZ

GALBRAITH Colin: 189 Garstang Road, Fulwood, Preston PR2 8JQ ☎ 01772 717762, 01995 600661

GAMBLE Mary: 22 Midhurst Street, Deeplish, Rochdale, Lancs OL11 1PL ☎ 01706 32364

GARNER Paul *(Kbds)*: 19 Charlton Close, Palacfields, Runcorn, Cheshire WA7 2UN ☎ 01928 790796, 01928 578040

GILLIES Marion: 66 Duke Street, Southport PR8 1JE ☎ 01704 532118

GLYN Gareth *(Org, Tym, Per, Vln)*: Frogwy Fawr, Llangwyllog, Llangefni, Gwynedd LL77 7PX ☎ 01248 750418

GOGGINS Mark *(Kbds, Md)*: 15 Abinngton Road, Sale, Cheshire M33 3DL ☎ 0161 973 5874

GOODHAND Francis *(Per, Org)*: Flat 2 11 Dovedale Road, Mossley Hill, Liverpool L18 1DN ☎ 0151 280 9345

GOODWIN Neville: 6 Southway, Droylsden, Manchester M43 6EH ☎ 0161 370 3477

GOUGH John: 1 Makepeace Close, Vicars Cross, Chester, Cheshire CH3 5LU ☎ 01244 45627, 01244 345627

GREEN David *(Kbds)*: 28 Burnell Court, Hopwood, Heywood, Lancs OL10 2NW ☎ 01706 360547

GREENALD David *(Kbds, Gtr, Kbds, Voc)*: 21 Kingsley Road, Boughton Heath, Chester CH3 5RR ☎ 0151 427 6030

GRINDELL John *(Clt)*: 12 Rhodfa Ganol, Nant Parc, Johnstown, Wrecsam Clwyd LL14 1PW ☎ 01978 842752

GUPPY Eileen *(Org, Kbds)*: 36 Old Lancaster Road, Catterall, Garstang, Lancs PR3 0HN ☎ 01995 601884

HADLEY Colin *(Org, Kbds)*: 13 Mount Road, Fleetwood, Lancashire FY7 6EZ ☎ 01253 770394

HAGUE Chistopher *(Org, Kbds)*: 3 Kirkway, Kirkholt, Rochdale, Lancashire OL11 2JD ☎ 01706 638774

HALL Peter: 32 Sharrard Road, Intake, Sheffield S12 2FG ☎ 0114 2657731

HANCOCK Michael: 34 Holme Head Way, Carlisle, Cumbria CA2 6AJ ☎ 01228 527106

HARRISON Brian *(Org, Sax)*: 125 Lawsons Road, Thornton Cleveleys, Blackpool, Lancs FY5 4PL ☎ 01253 853041

HARRISON Gerard *(Kbds, Flt, Sax)*: 134 Monfa Road, Bootle, Merseyside L20 6LP ☎ 0151 922 0636

HARWOOD Roland *(Kbds)*: 6 Bentinck Road, Altrincham, Cheshire WA14 2BP ☎ 0161 928 3596

HAYWARD Robert: 1C Lyndhurst Road, Wallasey, Merseyside L45 6XA ☎ 0151 630 7158

HEWINS Edwin (*Org*): 'Hillcrest', Wern Road, Rhosesmor, Mold, Flintshire CH7 6PY ☎ 01352 780334

HOGGER Alan (*Org*): Address Unknown ☎ 0151 727 2593, 0151 283 3557

HOLMES Alison (*Flt, Rec, Gtr*): 'Greenbank', Sherrington Lane, Brown Knowl, Broxton, Cheshire CH3 9JU ☎ 01829 782 711

HOOSON Vivienne (*Org*): Meadow House, Meadow Gardens, Craig Y Don, Llandudno, Gwynedd LL30 1UW ☎ 01492 879861

HORTH Michael (*Kbds*): 58 Florist Street, Shaw Heath, Stockport SK3 8DX ☎ 0161 429 9277

HORTON Christine (*Vln*): 125 Wallasey Road, Wallasey, Merseyside L44 2AB ☎ 0151 639 5340

HOUGHTON Neville (*Md, Arr*): 20 Tedder Avenue, Burnley, Lancs BB12 6DL ☎ 01282 424958

HOWARTH Alan (*Kbds, Org*): Bankfield, Boggard Lane, Charles Worth, Glossop SK13 5HL ☎ 01457 854257

HUTCHINS Adam (*Kbds, Voc, Tbn*): 126 Bangor St, South Reddish, Stockport, Cheshire SK5 7QA ☎ 0113 289 9813, 07957 288550

INGHAM Barry (*Org, Gtr*): 68 Fielding Lane, Oswaldtwistle, Accrington, Lancashire BB5 3BH ☎ 01254 381767

JACKSON Paul (*Kbds, Voc*): 26 Waterside Drive, The Moorings, Market Drayton, Shropshire TF9 1HU ☎ 01630 657 910, 0370 941455 mob

JEFFERY Matthew (*Kbds, Gtr, Bjo*): 8 Collingwood Road, Levenshulme, Manchester M19 2AW ☎ 0161 224 9659, 0410 794786 mob

JOHNSON Edward (*Arr*): 1 Florence Street, Barrow In Furness LA14 2DB ☎ 01229 822501

JOINER Robin (*Kbds, Saxes*): 8 Dartford Road, Urmston, Manchester M41 9DE ☎ 0161 835 3392

JONES David (*Kbds*): 100 Barton Road, Stretford, Manchester M32 9AE ☎ 0161 283 3061

JONES Ilid Anne (*Org, Md*): 'Dolellog', Dinas, Llanwnda, Caernarfon, Gwynedd, N.Wales LL54 7YN ☎ 01286 830381, 01286 830381

JONES Lawrence: 84 Imogen Court, Regents Park, Regent Road, Salford, Lancs M5 4TQ ☎ 0161 832 5409, 0831 192 515

JONES Peter: 24 Annesley Road, Wallasey, Merseyside L44 9DA ☎ 0151 638 0391

JONES Rhys (*Org, Md*): 26 Plas Uchaf Avenue, Prestatyn, Clwyd LL19 9NR ☎ 01745 888114

JONES Rona: 6 Donnington Way, Saltney, Chester, Cheshire CH4 8BR ☎ 01244 675423

JONES Tim (*Kbds, Flt*): 1 Laburnham Way, Llay, Wrexham, Clwyd LL12 0NJ ☎ 01978 853230

KEIR Andrew (*Kbds*): 4B Linden Road, Didsbury, Manchester M20 2QJ ☎ 0161 434 1029

KERSHAW David: 11 Thornyholme Drive, Knutsford, Cheshire WA16 8BT ☎ Knutsford 52694

KIERNAN Alf (*Org*): 23 Farrar Lane, Adel, Leeds LS16 6AD ☎ 0113 2671950

LANGFIELD Valerie: 82 Queens Road, Cheadle Hulme, Cheadle, Cheshire SK8 5HH ☎ 0161 486 6605

LAWRENCE Jeff (*E Pf, Kbds*): 63 Stanley Road, Morecambe, Lancashire LA3 1UR ☎ 01524 417731

LAWSON Peter (*Org, Db*): The Old Co-Op, Church Street South, Old Glossop, Derbyshire SK13 7RU ☎ 01457 862555

LAWTON Jack (*Org*): 23 Kenilworth Road, Ainsdale, Southport, Merseyside PR8 3PE ☎ 01704 574003 & fax

LEE J: 125 Norbreck Road, Blackpool, Lancs FY5 1QF

LEESE Jonathan (*Kbds*): 50 The Crescent, Radcliffe, Manchester M26 3LQ ☎ 0161 723 5562

LESTER Paul: 57 Worsley Road, Bolton, Lancs BL4 9LR ☎ 01204 74310

LEVER Timothy (*Gtr, Sax*): c/o Freedom Management, Suite 4, 19 Brunswick Terrace, Brighton BN3 1HL ☎ 01273 748599

LINGWOOD Peter (*Org, Kbds, Arr, Com*): 23 Crowshaw Drive, Lower Healey, Rochdale, Lancs OL12 0SR ☎ 01706 861468, 0850 496331

LLOYD Martyn (*Kbds, Md, Com, Arr*): 43 Knowle Avenue, Ainsdale, Southport, Merseyside PR8 2PB ☎ 01704 575064

LOAT Alan: 7 Lavender Close, Fulwood, Preston PR2 9RA ☎ 01772 791424

LOVELESS Alex (*Com, Voc*): 12 Parkhead Road, Ulverston, Cumbria LA12 9NX ☎ 01229 585433

LUNN Michael (*Bjo, Gtr*): Heaton House, Leck, Nr Kirkby Lonsdale, Lancashire LA6 2HZ

LUNTS Michael (*Arr, Com*): 23 Queen Street, Glossop, Derbys. SK13 8EL ☎ 01457 865891

LYNE David (*Kbds*): 3 Russia Street, Accrington, Lancs BB5 1SH ☎ 01254 384253

MARTIN Peter ☎ 0161 881 9764

MASSEY Derek: 133 Ashton Road, Newton Hyde, Cheshire SK14 4BH ☎ 0161 368 4694

MATTHEWS Julie (*Gtr, Voc*): 130 Central Avenue, Southport PR8 3ED ☎ 01704 575674

MEREDITH David (*Org*): 2 Mount Park, Conwy, Gwynedd LL32 8RN ☎ 01492 596448

MILES John: 7 Well Row, Broadbottom, Hyde, Cheshire SK14 6AR ☎ 01457 763701

MILLAR Phil (*Kbds, Ac Gtr*): 53 Park Crescent, Wilmslow, Cheshire SK9 4BR ☎ 01625 537696

MILNE David (*Org*): 297 Park Road, Blackpool, Lancs FY1 6RW ☎ 01253 762465

MILNER Michael (*Kbds*): 73 Main Road, Seaton, Workington, Cumbria CA14 1HX ☎ 01900 61268

MOORE Stephen (*Org*): 25 Westbrook Drive, Maqcclesfield, Cheshire SK10 3AQ ☎ 0162 543 1583

MORRIS Harvey (*Org*): Redvers Cottage, 2 Ormond Avenue, North Shore, Blackpool, Lancs FY1 2LW ☎ 01253 593572

MUNRO Anna Marie (*Voc, Clt*): Chez Pierre, 15 Mostyn Avenue, Craig-Y-Don, Llandudno LL30 1YS ☎ 01492 878604

NASH Patrick (*Arr, Com*): 6 Greenway Road, Cheadle, Cheshire SK8 3NR ☎ 0161 437 2000

NEWTON Gloria: 25 Oxford Street, Morecambe, Lancs LA4 5JG ☎ 01524 411424

NICHOLAS Dave (*Org*): 59 Rosedale Road, Tranmere, Birkenhead, Cheshire L42 5PQ ☎ 0151 645 5846

NIXON Doris (*Org*): 11 Stanley Avenue, Prestwich, Manchester M25 7AR ☎ 0161 773 1475

O'DONNELL Gary (*Voc, Song W*): Flat 2, 44 Sheil Road, Liverpool L6 3AE ☎ 0151 261 1442

OVENS Joan: 69 Coral Avenue, Huyton, Lancashire L36 2PY ☎ 0151 489 3285

OWEN Eirian: 13 Fronwnion, Dolgellau, Gwynedd LL40 1SL ☎ 01341 423076

OWEN Mair (*Hrp*): Bryn Goleu, Llansannan, Dinbych LL16 5LF ☎ 01745 870632

PARKER Stephen (*Sax, Gtr, Dms, Per*): 15 Newbank Tower, Bridgewater Street, Salford M3 7JZ ☎ 0161 834 3514

PARKER Vincent: 16 Victoria Square, Whitefield, Manchester M25 6AL ☎ 0161 766 8458

PEACOCK Eddie (*Org, Md*): 48 Belvedere Road, Thornton Cleveleys, Blackpool, Lancs FY5 5DG ☎ 01253 860949

PENDLETON Brian (*Md, Arr*): 264 Bramhall Lane, Davenport, Stockport, Cheshire SK3 8TR ☎ 0161 483 9832

PFEUTI Paul: Crooklands House, Crooklands, Milnthorpe, Cumbria LA7 7NW ☎ 015395 67635

PORTEOUS ALCM Guy: 40 Astley Road, Harwood, Bolton BL2 4BR ☎ 01204 304755

POWELL Roy: Agathe Grondahls Gate 20, 0478 Oslo, Norway ☎ +47 2215 0661, +47 950 65442

PRIEST Steven (*Kbds, B Gtr*): 19 Malvern Close, Shaw, Oldham, Manchester OL2 7RE ☎ 01706 846785, 01706 881397

PURVES Melanie (*Kbds, Tpt*): 25 Addison Close, Chorlton-on-Medlock, Manchester M13

RAMSBOTTOM Steve (*Org, Kbds*): 40 Milton Drive, Poynton, Cheshire SK12 1EY ☎ 01625 875430, 0802 490967

READ Adrian: 44 Springfield Lane, Royton, Oldham, Lancs OL2 6XN ☎ 0161 624 6929

REYNOLDS Michael: Farleton House, Farleton, Lancaster LA2 9LF ☎ 01524 594025

ROCHFORD John (*Acc, Per*): 5 Cherry Tree Avenue, Poynton, Stockport, Cheshire SK12 1QQ ☎ 01625 876819

RICHARD D (*Kbds, Org, Voc*): 150 Parsonage Road, Withington, Manchester M20 4WY ☎ 0161 445 3355

ROONEY Joe: 47 Bryniau Road, West Shore, Llandudno, Gwynedd LL30 2EZ ☎ 01492 860288

ROTHERHAM John: 24 Kettleshulme Way, Poynton, Stockport, Cheshire SK12 1TB ☎ 01625 877408

SASSOON Julie (*E Vln, Vln, Kbds, Flt*): 6 Lidgate Grove, Didsbury, Manchester M20 6TS ☎ 0161 445 2856

SCOTT Donald (*Voc*): 19 Greystone Road, Carlisle, Cumbria CA1 2DG

SHAW Janeen: 2 Oswald Road, Llandudno, Gwynedd LL31 9EP ☎ 01492 573 349

SIMPSON Janet (*Clst, Per*): Roquebrun, Reservoir Road, Whaley Bridge, Stockport, Cheshire SK12 7BW ☎ 01663 734979, 0831 696 842

SLY Marcus ☎ 01706 819197

STALKER William (*Org*): Withens, Cold Coats, Clapham, Lancaster, Lancs. LA2 8HZ ☎ 01468 41073

STARKEY Jonathan (*Kbds*): 11-13 Victoria Road, Ellesmere Port, South Wirral, Cheshire L65 8BU ☎ 0151 356 0019

STEELE Matthew (*Kbds, Dms, Tpt*): 16 Belfield Road, Didsbury, Manchester M20 6BH ☎ 0161 434 2424, 0161 445 3423

STIRLING Penelope (*Vln*): 159 Henrietta Street, Ashton Under Lyne, Lancashire OL6 8PH ☎ 0161 344 2177

TATE Ian: 122 Kingsleigh Road, Heaton Mersey, Stockport, Cheshire SK4 3PG ☎ 0161 443 2917

TEMPERLEY Michael (*Voc*): 10 Healey Street, Rochdale OL16 1UU ☎ 01706 653428, 0585 293970, 01706 650519

TESTA Fernando (*Sax, Gtr*): 10 Torbay Road, Chorlton, Manchester M21 2XD ☎ 0161 881 6964

THOMSON Barbara E (*Vla, Vln*): Summer House, Station Road, Kirk Michael, Isle Of Man IM6 1EZ ☎ 01624 878380

TRUFIT Norman (*Org*): 16 Kirkstone Drive, Norbeck, Blackpool, Lancashire FY5 1QJ ☎ 01253 855301

TURNER Chris (*Voc, Kbds, Sax*): 23 Grosvenor Avenue, Rhyl, Denbigshire, North Wales LL18 4HA ☎ 01745 353090

WALKER Helen (*Kbds, Org, Arr, Com*): 31 Clive Road, Daisy Hill, Westhoughton, Bolton BL5 2HR ☎ 01942 819431, 0370 807890

WALL Chris (*Voc, Org*): 54 Vaughan Road, New Brighton, Merseyside L45 1LP ☎ 0151 630 3278

WALTERS David (*Clst, Kbds*): 21 Woolacombe Road, Childwall, Liverpool L16 9JG ☎ 0151 722 2324

WATT Anthony (*Kbds, Per*): 18 Lansbury House, 76 Whalley Road, Whalley Range, Manchester M16 8AH ☎ 0161 226 5456

WESTWOOD Rowly (*Org, Kbds, Md*): 15 Liverpool Road, Blackpool, Lancs FY1 4HH ☎ 01253 302114

WETHERALL Richard (*Kbds, Acc*): Flat 6, 627 Wilbraham Road, Chorlton, Manchester M21 9JT ☎ 0161 882 0047

WHITTAKER Anthony (*Org, Hpsd, Com, Arr*): 13 Eastford Road, Warrington, Cheshire WA4 6EX ☎ 01925 575609, 0410 115089

WILCOCK Christopher (*Kbds, Vln*): Flat 2, 11 Alexandra Drive, Aigburth, Liverpool L17 8TA ☎ 0151 283 3458

WILLIAMS Gillian (*Vln, Org*): Arlwyn, 99 Lon Ceredigion, Pwllheli, Gwynedd LL53 5RA ☎ 01758 612466

WILLIE Anne (*Voc*): Longrigg Cottage, Eskdale Green, Holmrook, Cumbria CA19 1TW ☎ 019467 23149

WILSON John: Meadow Way, Church Road, Mellor, Via Stockport Ches SK6 5PR ☎ 0161 449 9583

WOOD Lesley (*Flt, Clt, Sax*): 5 Lowfields Close, Eastham, Wirral, Merseyside L62 9BL ☎ 0151 327 3853, 0151 328 0843

WOODS John (*Rep*): 42, Northwich Road, Weaverham, Cheshire CW8 3BD ☎ 01606 851422

WRIGHT Henry: 77 Balmoral Drive, Churchtown, Southport PR9 8QH

WRIGHT Vernon (*Acc*): 143 Cae Gwilym Lane, Cefn Mawr, Wrexham, Clwyd LL14 3PG ☎ 01978 820662

WYSE Josephine: 27 Hereford Drive, Prestwich, Manchester M25 0AG ☎ 0161 773 5525

YOUNG GNSM ARCM Jennifer: 26 Brook House Close, Harwood, Bolton BL2 3QS ☎ 01204 525861

ZEHM Norbert (*Kbds, Com*): 21 Cavendish Road, Southport, Merseyside PR8 4RT ☎ 01704 568155

NORTH EAST

ADAMSON Richard (*Acc, Mldn*): 14 Westmacott Street, Ridsdale, Hexham, Northumberland NE48 2TJ ☎ 01434 270072

ALLSOPP Peter (*Org, Hpsd, Kbds*): 8A Rothbury Terrace, Newcastle NE6 5XH ☎ 0191 276 1683

ALP Christine (*Flt, Pic*): 25 St Clements Road, Harrogate, North Yorkshire HG2 8LU

BAILEY Gavin (*Voc*): 130 Colwyn Road, Hartlepool, Cleveland TS26 9BL ☎ 01429 231590

BAKER Kathleen (*Flt, Gtr*): 184 Scartho Road, Grimsby, Lincs DN33 2BP ☎ 01472 874963

BARON Mark (*Gtr, Voc, Org*): 25 Pinfold Close, Swinton, Mexborough, S. Yorks S64 8JE ☎ 01709 584304

BARRY Tina (*Gtr, Voc*): 22 Hawkesworth Avenue, Guiscley, Leeds LS20 8EJ ☎ 01943 870847

BECK Paul (*Voc, B Gtr*): 3 Osborne Road, Chester Le Street, Co Durham DH3 3DS ☎ 0191 388 6210

BEDFORD Andrew (*Vln, Vla*): 4 Highfield Drive, Bradford BD9 6HN ☎ 01274 495935

BELL Goeffrey (*Kbds*): 16 Leafield Road, Darlington, Co Durham DL1 5DE ☎ 01325 466630

BELL Katie (*Sax, Tnd Per*): 25 Wedderburn Drive, Harrogate, North Yorkshire HG2 7QF ☎ 01423 885127

BENNETT Patrick (*Org, Hpsd, Com, Md*): Farmley Cottage, 52 High Street, Nettleham, Lincoln LN2 2PL ☎ 01522 752997, 07775 933220

BINNS Catherine (*Voc*): 'Montana', 222 Savile Park Road, Halifax, West Yorkshire HX1 2XS ☎ 01422 343876, 07970 370665

BINNS Christopher (*Arr, Com*): Montana, 222 Saville Park Road, Halifax, West Yorks HX1 2XS ☎ 01422 343876

BLACKMORE Julian (*Kbds, Gtr*): c/o 243 Whitchapel Road, Scheles, Cleetheaton BD19 6HN

BOTTOMLEY David (*Kbds, Voc*): Old Hall, Boghall, Whitby, N. Yorkshire YO21 1PG ☎ 01947 603825

BOWN Eileen: 3D Ailesbury Street, Sunderland, Tyne & Wear SR4 6EW ☎ 0191 514 3658

BRACKENBURY Ian (*Org*): 63 Paxton Road, Tapton, Chesterfield, Derbyshire S41 0TL ☎ 01246 272385

BRATKOWSKI Cheryl (*Per, Vla*): 42 St Helens Road, Harrogate, North Yorkshire HG2 8LD ☎ 01423 883374, 0421 334586 mob

BRIGHTMAN Robert (*Org*): 43, The Oval, North Anston, Sheffield S25 4BX ☎ 01909 563074

BROADBENT Don (*Org*): 34 Candler Avenue, West Ayton, Scarborough, North Yorkshire YO13 9JN ☎ 01723 864510

BROCKLESBY Harold: 3 Whitgift Close, Laceby, Grimsby DN37 7DQ ☎ 01472 343392

BULLARD Martin (*Org, Synth, B Gtr, Dms*): Enrick House, Balnain, Drumnadrochit, Inverness IV63 6TL

BURTENSHAW Leslie (*Db, Con*): 41 Main Street, Kilnwick, Driffield, East Yorkshire YO25 9JD ☎ 01377 270385

BUTLER Gerald (*Md*): 7 Rockhampton Close, West Norwood, London SE27 0NG ☎ 020 8769 5190

CALVERT Gillian (*Kbds*): 17 Roxburgh Place, Heaton, Newcastle-upon-Tyne NE6 5HU ☎ 0191 265 4095

CARTMELL Tom (*Kbds*): 23 Eglingham Village, Alnwick, Northumberland NE66 2TX ☎ 01665 578406

CASS Dave (*Synth, Org, B Gtr*): Flat 7 Marton House, East Marton, Nr Skipton, North Yorkshire BD23 2LP ☎ 01282 843009 & fax, 0410 636918, 439098

CHESTER Richard (*Gtr*): 63 Spring Street, Barnsley, South Yorkshire S70 1PE ☎ 01226 295145

CLEAVER Michael: 201 Stainbeck Road, Leeds LS7 2LR ☎ 0113 2694329

COCKERILL Craig (*Org, Vla, Acc*): 20 Laurel Bank, Haughshore Road, Halifax, West Yorkshire HX1 3LE ☎ 01422 343760, 0976 691726 mob

CONSTANCE Peter (*Db, Per, Gtr, Flt*): Hill Top Farm, Law Lane, Clint, Harrogate HG3 3HN ☎ 01423 770483

CORRICK Gordon (*Kbds, Org*): 131 Compass Road, Beverley High Road, Hull, Yorkshire HU6 7AW ☎ 01482 805804

CRESSWELL Bryan (*Md*): 35 Bridge Park, Gosforth, Newcastle-on-Tyne, Tyne & Wear NE3 2DX ☎ 0191 285 2645

CROFT Philip (*Acc*): 2 Endowood Road, Sheffield S7 2LZ ☎ 0114 2363758

CROMARTY Bob (*Org*): 138 Valley Drive, Harrogate, North Yorks HG2 0JS ☎ 01423 888136

CROSSLAND Jill: 56A Ranelagh Road, Ealing, London W5 5RP ☎ 020 8579 4394

DALBY Peter: 5 Greencliffe Drive, York YO30 6NA ☎ 01904 655996

DALTON Nigel (*Synth*): 25 Badgers Wood, Park Lane, Cottingham, North Humberside HU16 5ST ☎ 01482 849020

DANIELLE Michael: 5 Bowburn Close, Gateshead NE10 8UG ☎ 0191 455 4459

DAUBNEY Kenneth (*Org, A Sax, Clt, Md*): 121 Vally Prospect, Newark, Notts NG24 4QW ☎ 01636 702577

DAVISON John (*Org*): 8 Skipton Close, Ferryhill, Co Durham DL17 8ST ☎ 01740 652874

DAY Stuart (*Vln*): 185 Scalby Road, Scarborough, North Yorkshire YO12 6TB ☎ 01723 371765, 0378 058032

DENHAM Jean: Av. J. Santos Rein 35, Edf. Trinidad Est.3, 29640 Los Boliches, Fuengirola, (Malaga) Spain

DON Graham (*Kbds, Org*): 30 Longridge Drive, Whitley Lodge, Whitley Bay, Tyne & Wear NE26 3EN ☎ 0191 251 8060, 07970 868551

DOWSE John (*Org*): 6 St Michaels Close, Billinghay, Lincoln LN4 4EZ ☎ 01526 860356

DRESSLER Andrew (*Kbds*): 9 Mowson Crescent, Worrall, Sheffield S30 3AG ☎ 0114 2862209

DU-FRESNE Graeme: 25 Queens Road, High Wycombe, Buckinghamshire HP13 6AQ ☎ 01494 461117

DYER Andrew (*Db*): Appletree House, 5 Church Street, Castleton, Whitby, N Yorks YO21 2EQ ☎ 01287 660656

ELLIOTT Ron (*Acc*): 34 Evelyn Road, Sheffield S10 5FF ☎ 0114 2663615

ENNIS Colin (*Synth*): 38 Lawe Road, South Shields, Tyne & Wear NE33 2EU ☎ 0191 454 6657

ETHERINGTON Matthew (*Synth, A Sax*): 16 Anderson Ave, Leeds LS8 5EG ☎ 0113 248 6339

FOX Denis (*Synth, Dms*): 90 Lindisfarne Road, Newton Hall, Durham DH1 5YQ ☎ 0191 386 1922

GAMBLE Danny: 685 Whitehall Road, New Farnley, Leeds LS12 6HB ☎ 0113 2632827

GARDEN Stuart (*Synth*): 24 Cambrian Terrace, Holbeck, Leeds LS11 8JB

GEPFF (*Kbds, Con, Voc, Ob*): Green Shutters, 299 Twentywell Lane, Bradway, Sheffield S17 4QG ☎ 0114 235 2575

GILROY Michael (*Kbds*): 35 Calverley Moor Ave, Pudsey, West Yorkshire LS28 8EL ☎ 01274 666438

GLOVER Stephen (*Kbds*): 23 St. Pauls Parade, Doncaster, S Yorks DN5 8LD ☎ 01302 784865

GOLDMAN Daniel (*Kbds, B Gtr*): 27 Primley Park Avenue, Leeds LS17 7HX ☎ 0113 295 6926, 0956 668016

GREAVES Jack (*Org*): Wayside, Leeds Road, Collingham, Nr Wetherby Yorks LS22 5AA ☎ 01937 573579

GREGORY John Brandon (*Kbds*): 17 Hunter Hill Road, Hunters Bar, Sheffield S11 8UD ☎ 0114 2663372

HALL Bob (*Gtr, Man*): 5 Prospect Place, Totley Rise, Sheffield S17 4HZ ☎ 0114 2363309

HALSEY Denys (*Org, Arr, Md*): 4 The Close, Romanby, Northallerton, North Yorkshire DL7 8BJ ☎ 01609 770442

HARPER William (*Org*): 3 Ashleigh Grove, Benton, Newcastle 2, Tyne & Wear NE12 8EY ☎ 0191 266 1201

HARRISON Francis (*Org, B Ldr*): 5 White House Close, Main Street, Willerby, Hull HU10 6BQ ☎ 01482 3650525

HENESY Charles (*Acc, Org, Arr*): 51 Moorfield, Hebden Bridge, West Yorkshire HX7 8SG ☎ 01422 842598

HILTON Andrew (*Org, Voc, Clt*): 30 Barlings Avenue, Scunthorpe, North Lincolnshire DN16 2AY ☎ 01724 856007, 0421 055775 mob

HIND Matthew (*Kbds, Sax, Clt, Flt*): 85 Jacobs Well Lane, Wakefield, West Yorkshire WF1 3PB ☎ 01924 379902

HOGG Robert: 11 Captain Cooks Crescent, Marton, Middlesbrough, Cleveland TS7 8NN ☎ 01642 315934

HOLDSWORTH Andrew (*Kbds, B Gtr*): 37 Birkdale Road, Dewsbury, West Yorks WF13 4HG ☎ 0973 348813

HOPSON Yvonne (*Kbds, Org*): 45 Medina Way, Barugh Green, Barnsley, South Yorks S75 1NF ☎ 01226 384131, 01226 353370, 01226 384131

HUNTER Eanswyth (*Kbds, Ob, Cor, Org*): The Gatehouse, Castle Howard, York YO60 7BT ☎ 01653 648498

HUTCHINSON William (*Org, Arr*): 18 Northcote Avenue, Newcastle-upon-Tyne 5 NE5 5AN ☎ 0191 267 5644

HUTTON Alex: 57 Springfield Road, Millhouses, Sheffield S7 2GE ☎ 0114 236 0905

IZATT Raymond (*B Ldr*): 54 Montague Road, Bishopthorpe, York YO23 2SS ☎ 01904 705871

JACKSON Michael (*Kbds, Voc, Vib, A Sax*): 23 Norman Place, Roundhay, Leeds LS8 2AW ☎ 0831 178066

JACKSON Peter (*Kbds, Org*): Hollydown House, 18 Trevor Street, Aberdare, Mid Glam CF44 7NL ☎ 01685 883843

JAMES Alexander (*Dms*): 31A Hanover Square, Leeds LS3 1AW ☎ 01132 343175

JONES Derry (*Org, Synth, Acc, Voc*): 44 Tewitwell Road, Harrogate, N Yorks HE2 8JJ ☎ 01423 502370 & fax

JORDAN Phil: 27 Beckhill Gate, Potternewton, Leeds LS7 2RZ ☎ 0113 237 1889

JOULES Brian: 11 Pagehall Close, Grantham Avenue, Scarthoe, Grimsby DN33 2HF ☎ 01472 877130

JOWSEY J (*Org*): 3 Northfield Way, Scalby, Scarborough, Yorks YO13 0PW ☎ 01723 368690

KAY Ken (*Org*): 178 Amersall Road, Scawthorpe, Doncaster, Yorks DN5 9PW

KENDALL Florence: Address Unknown

KIERNAN Howard (*Org*): 23 Farrar Lane, Adel, Leeds LS16 6AD ☎ 0113 2671950

LAIDLER Tom (*Org*): 24, Westfield Approach, North Greetwell, Lincoln LN2 2RQ ☎ 01522 750527

LAUGHLIN Richard (*Kbds, B Gtr*): 109 Pateley Close, Newton Aycliffe, Co. Durham DL5 7NG ☎ 01325 313069

LEE Patrick (*Kbds, Db, Brass*): 64 Station Road, Burley In Wharfedale, Ilkley LS29 7NG ☎ 01943 862599

LENTON Suzanne (*Voc, Kbds*): 9 Pennithorne Road, Baildon, W Yorks BD17 5PB ☎ 0113 252 4778, 0860 450769 mob

LEVITT Anne: Scite House, 377 Halifax Road, Liversedge, W Yorks WF15 8DU ☎ 01274 873228

MACSHERRY Fiona: 6 Gledhow Park View, Leeds LS7 4JS

MAKINSON Alan (*Org*): 27 Helston Green, Middleton, Leeds LS10 4NY ☎ 0113 2712872

MANNERS Kim (*Kbds, Voc*): 28 Weelsby Avenue, Grimsby, Ne Lincs DN32 0AQ ☎ 01472 234566

MAYALL Arthur (*Org*): 39 Gray Street, Lincoln LN1 3HH

MCCAMMON Cyril: c/o B A Mccammon, 27 High Street, Clayton West, W Yorks HD8 9PD ☎ 01484 860907

MOORE Ray (*Org, Com, Arr, B Ldr*): Edf Lisasol 2D, Torreblanca, 29640 Fuengirola, Malaga, Spain

MORRELL Kenneth (*Org, Arr, Com*): 10 Holly Close, High Ford Park, Hexham, Northumberland NE46 2RF ☎ 01434 608272

MORRIS Edna (*Org*): 68 Marsden Court, Farsley, Pudsey, West Yorks LS28 5SH ☎ 0113 257 7637

MULLINS Andrew (*Gtr*): Westfield Villa, Belgrave Mount, Wakefield, Yorkshire WF1 3SB ☎ 01924 361550

MUNOZ David (*Kbds*): 41 Regent Park Terrace, Leeds LS6 2AX ☎ 0113 275 3242

MURRAY David: 5 Osborne Gardens, Whitley Bay, Tyne & Wear NE26 3PG

NANKIVELL Hugh *(Kbds, Gtr, Vla, Per)*: 30 Imperial Road, Marsh, Huddersfield HD3 3AF ☎ 01484 535039

NAYLOR Gordon *(Clst)*: 9 Breckenbeds Road, Lowfell, Gateshead-on-Tyne, Tyne & Wear NE9 6HB ☎ 0191 442 1205

NELSON Andrew *(Cel, Rec, Kbds)*: Woodbine House, Newton-Le-Willows, Bedale, N. Yorkshire DL8 1TG ☎ 01677 450227

NEWTON Race *(E Pf, Synth)*: Dogtree Bank Farm, Grosmont, Whitby YO22 5PJ ☎ 01947 895306

NOBLE John *(Org, Com)*: 7 Balmoral Road, Dunscroft, Doncaster DN7 4LJ ☎ 01302 841268

PARROCK Tristan *(Kbds)*: 14 Allott Street, Hoyland Common, Barnsley, S. Yorkshire S74 0NF ☎ 01226 746560

PATTERSON David *(Vln, Vla, Com)*: 40 Cheswick Crescent, Keadby, Scunthorpe, North Lincs DN17 3DQ ☎ 01724 783546

PATTISON John *(Kbds, Per, Com, Arr)*: 3 St Marys Walk, Scarborough, N Yorkshire YO11 1RN

PEACOCK Bob *(Arr, Kbds)*: 52 Reeth Road, Linthorpe, Middlesbrough, Cleveland TS5 5JX ☎ 01642 815943

PEARCE-DAVIES Eileen: 52 Victoria Street, Clayton West, Huddersfield, West Yorkshire HD8 9NW ☎ 01484 608557

PELL Robert *(Com)*: 291 Wakefield Road, Denby Dale, Huddersfield, West Yorkshire HD8 8RX ☎ 01484 863023

PICKARD Martin *(Con)*: 12 Wilton Grove, Leeds, West Yorkshire LS6 4ES ☎ 0113 2782091

PIPER Sheila *(Voc)*: Apperley House, Hillside Road East, Rothbury, Morpeth, Northl'D NE65 7PT ☎ 01669 620483, 01669 620565

PORTMAN Eugene: Sempre Fidelis, Wire Mill Lane, Newchapel, Lingfield Surrey RH7 6HJ

PULMAN Mark *(Kbds, Bsn, Accom, Md)*: 223 Windsor Road, Carlton-In-Lindrick, Worksop, Notts S81 7DH ☎ 01909 732565

PURVIS Harold *(Kbds, Md)*: Geeswood House, Whittis Road, Haydonbridge, Northumberland NE47 6AQ

QUARMBY Jonathan *(Flt)*: 6 Crimicar Lane, Fulwood, Sheffield S10 4FB ☎ 0114 2754959, 0114 275 4915

QUERNS John: 5 Dorset Close, Harrogate HG1 2LR ☎ 01423 525486

RICHARDSON Gerry *(Org)*: 9 Queens Road, Jesmond, Newcastle-upon-Tyne, Tyne & Wear NE2 2PQ ☎ 0191 2811263 eve, 0191 200 4760 day

RICHARDSON Roger *(R Wnd)*: Todd Hall, Todd Lane North, Lostock Hall, Preston, Lancs PR5 5US ☎ 01772 620003

ROBERTS George: 3 Elder Grove, Haxby, York YO3 8GE ☎ 01904 769042

ROBINSON Douglas *(Org)*: 27 Pearson Road, Cleethorpes, Lincs DN35 0DR ☎ 01472 692766

ROUSSOU Eugenia: 3 Murrayfeilds, West Allotment, Newcastle-upon-Tyne NE27 0RD ☎ 0191 270 1670

ROWE John *(Org, Kbds)*: 22 Francis Street, Stanley Crook, Co Durham DL15 9SB ☎ 01388 762930

RUDD Norman *(Org)*: Address Unknown

SACKER Judi: 130 Broomspring Lane, Sheffield S10 2FD ☎ 0114 2738678

SEATON Ronald *(Org)*: 32 Kenilworth Way, Redcar, Cleveland TS10 2LS ☎ 01642 471860

SEELEY Paul *(Md)*: 137 Wilmer Road, Heaton, Bradford, Yorks BD9 4AG ☎ 01274 544847

SEYMOUR Peter *(Org, Md)*: 11 Bootham Terrace, York YO30 7DH ☎ 01904 652799, 01904 432431, 01904 338349 fax

SHAW Louis *(Org)*: 17 Burnside Avenue, Sheffield S8 9FR ☎ 0114 255 2608

SHERIFF Jami: 13 Wilton Grove, Meanwood, Leeds LS6 4ES ☎ 0113 2750091

SIBBALD John: 18 Hepscott Drive, Beaumont Park, Whitley Bay, Tyne & Wear NE25 9XJ

SIDDOL Simon ☎ 0113 225 9071

SILD Stephen *(Clt)*: 22 Beachfield Drive, Hartlepool, Cleveland TS25 5AS ☎ 01429 221087

SIMPSON Kathleen: 48 Cookridge Avenue, Leeds LS16 7LZ ☎ 0113 2679781

SLADEN Matthew *(Kbds, B Gtr, Dms, Per)*: 45 West Park Drive West, Roundhay, Leeds LS8 2ED ☎ 0113 217 1232, 07977 404728

SMITH D: 12 Park Avenue, Scarborough, Yorks YO12 4AG ☎ 01723 366165

SMITH Fraser *(Kbds, Voc, B Gtr)* ☎ 0467 765921 mob

SOLOMON Leo: 1 Maple Grove, New Waltham, Grimsby, South Humberside DN36 4PU ☎ 01472 82 4463

SPENCER Grant *(Flt)*: 16 Robert Street, Harrogate, North Yorkshire HG1 1HP ☎ 01423 565222

SPOORS Barry *(Org, Kbds, Theory)*: 81 Sunny Blunts, Peterlee, Co Durham SR8 1LP ☎ 0191 586 4115

STAFFORD Graeme *(Vln)*: Sandylaw, Houghton Road North, Hetton-Le-Hole, Tyne & Wear DH5 9QE ☎ 0191 526 4654

STENHOUSE Linda *(Kbds, Sax, Cel)*: 21 London Street, New Whittington, Chesterfield S43 2AQ ☎ 01246 450034

STEVENSON Cath *(Kbds, Rec, Fo Gtr)*: 66 Stocks Way, Shepley, Huddersfield HD8 8DN ☎ 01484 604126

STORRY John *(Kbds)*: 99 Swinshead Road, Wyberton Fen, Boston, Lincs PE21 7JG ☎ 01205 54644

STRAUGHAN Richard *(Tba)*: 28 Lyndhurst Grove, Low Fell, Gateshead, Tyne & Wear NE9 6AU ☎ 0191 487 3806

STURDY L *(Org)*: 61 Scalby Road, Scarborough, N Yorks YO12 5QL ☎ 01723 372725

TABOIS Peter: 95 Welholme Avenue, Grimsby DN32 0BP ☎ 01472 78787

TATTON Joseph: 13 Wilton Grove, Headingley, Meanwood, Leeds LS6 4ES ☎ 0113 275 0091

TAWS Johnny *(Org, B Ldr, Acc, Vib)*: 63 Beech Road, Tynemouth, North Shields, Tyne & Wear NE30 2TW ☎ 0191 258 0788

TAYLOR Heather *(Org, Acc, Voc)*: Wrens Nest, 33 Ardsley Road, Worsborough Dale, Barnsley S70 4RJ ☎ 01226 200881

TELFORD Stephen *(Org)*: 4 West View, Gilesgate, Durham DH1 1HZ ☎ 0191 386 5380

THIRLWAY Sebastian: 264 Tamworth Road, Newcastle-upon-Tyne NE4 ☎ 0191 213 0482 & fax

THOMPSON Christie *(Kbds)*: Whin Hill Farm, Askwith, North Yorkshire LS21 2JJ ☎ 01943 850010

TIMMS David *(Org, Saxes, Arr)*: 79 Shaw Lane, Barnsley S70 6HY ☎ 01226 284320

TROTTER Michael *(Md)*: 21 Clifton Avenue, Eaglescliffe, Stockton-on-Tees TS16 9BA ☎ 01642 648071

VAUSE David *(Sax, Flt, B Gtr, Gtr)*: 22 Beaumont Park Road, Beaumont Park, Huddersfield, West Yorkshire HD4 5JS ☎ 01484 420334

WADE Anne: 76 Thorpe Lane, Almondbury, Huddersfield HD5 8UF ☎ 01484 547691

WADSWORTH Cyril: 6 High Street, Carcroft, Doncaster, S Yorks DN6 8DP ☎ 01302 723634

WARBURTON Val: Halcyon Cottage, 28 Hawksley Avenue, Chesterfield S40 4TW ☎ 01246 273533

WHITE Joel *(Kbds, Gtr)*: 67 Batemoor Road, Batemoor, Sheffield S8 8ED ☎ 0114 237 8422, 0114 258 1900

WHITHAM Barry *(Kbds, Hrn, Synth)*: 2 Abbey Drive West, Grimsby, South Humberside DN32 0HH ☎ 01472 358916

WHITFIELD Steve *(Kbds, Vib)*: 6 Grosvenor Place, North Shields, Tyne & Wear NE29 0NH ☎ 0191 258 2635

WHITTINGTON Paul *(Kbds, Clt, T Sax)*: 49 Sandholme Drive, Burley In Wharfedale, Ilkley, West Yorkshire LS29 7RG ☎ 01943 864323, 0468 626387

WILLIAMS Kenneth *(Org)*: 105 Dovedale Road, Herringthorpe, Rotherham S65 3AW ☎ 01709 377950

WILTSHIRE Christopher *(Md)*: 27 Hallam Grange Rise, Fulwood, Sheffield S10 4BE ☎ 0114 2302401 & fax

WOODS Huntley *(Org)*: 2 Myenza Apartments, Priest Popple, Hexham, Northumberland NE48 1PS ☎ 01434 601 089

WOODWARD Julia *(Cel)*

WOOLLISCROFT Adrian *(Per)*: 17 Denholme Grove, Kings Heath, Birmingham B14 5BP

WRIGHT Kenneth: 11 Tweed Street, Saltburn-By-The-Sea, Cleveland TS12 1JR

YEADON Fred (*Org*): 61 Main Street, Flookburgh, Grange Over Sands, Cumbria LA11 7LB

EAST

ALLEN Ronald (*Org, Kbds*): c/o Mrs V. M. Doran, 12 Bishops Path, Burnham-on-Sea, Somerset TA8 1RF ☎ 01278 794252

ANDREAS Louie (*Synth, Gtr, Bzk*): 9 Mirbecks Close, Worlingham, Beccles, Suffolk NR34 7RS ☎ 01502 710751

ANSELL Peter (*Kbds*): 79 Attimore Road, Welwyn Garden City, Herts AL8 6LG ☎ 01707 325817

ANTONIOU Michael (*Kbds*): 194 Hagden Lane, Watford, Herts WD1 8ND ☎ 01923 251813

ARGENT Rodney (*Org, Voc, Hmca*): The Red House, Silsoe, Beds MK45 4DX

BADHAM Margaret: 51 Halleys Ridge, Hertford, Herts SG14 2TH ☎ 0199 258 2379

BECK Simon (*Kbds, Voc*): 3 Medhurst Close, Dunchurch, Rugby CV22 6QQ ☎ 0802 402408 mob

BIRCH Catherine (*Gtr, Voc*): 93 Green Lane, Vicars Cross, Chester CM3 5LB ☎ 01244 316566

BOLTZ Michael (*Kbds, Org, Gtr*): 78 Rectory Grove, Leigh-on-Sea, Essex SS9 2HJ ☎ 01702 480534

BONNEY Helen (*Org*): 1 Shepherds Hall, 3 Market Lane, Linton, Cambs CB1 6HU ☎ 01223 893752, 01223 890930 & fax

BOWMAN Ronald (*Acc, A Sax, S Sax*): 4 Anglers Way, Cambridge CB4 1TZ ☎ 01223 426691

BRACKLEY Jane: 7 Conway Close, Felixstowe, Suffolk IP11 9LP ☎ 01394 285008

BROWN Simon (*Kbds*) ☎ 01603 454495

BRYANT Barry: 1 Oak Villas, East Ruston, Stalham, Norwich NR12 9JG ☎ 01692 650093

BURROWS Helen (*Vln, Org, Voc, Flt*): 17 Squires Lane, Martlesham Heath, Ipswich, Suffolk IP5 3UG ☎ 01473 625196

CANN Antoinette: 7 Gurlings Close, Haverhill, Suffolk CB9 0EG ☎ 01440 761436, 01440 708107 fax

CANN Claire: 7 Gurlings Close, Haverhill, Suffolk CB9 0EG ☎ 01440 761436, 01440 708107 fax

CAPOCCI Michael (*E Pf, Vib*): 207 Mile Cross Lane, Norwich, Norfolk NR6 6RA ☎ 01603 413443

CARTER Don: The Old Barn, Church Farm, Aislaby, Whitby North Yorkshire YO21 1SW

CASSIDY James (*Clt, T Sax*): 37 Buckingham Road, Borehamwood, Hertfordshire, England WD6 2RA ☎ 020 8953 6207

CHIVERS David (*Kbds, Clt, Acc*): 34 Nelson Street, Brightlingsea, Essex CO7 0DZ ☎ 01206 305107

CLEARY Joseph: 164 Highfield Road, Ipswich, Suffolk IP1 6DJ ☎ 01473 745231

CLEVELAND Ivan (*E Pf, Org, Synth*): 56 Park Road, Lowestoft, Suffolk NR32 1SP ☎ 01502 564139

COCHRANE Guy: 5 Gibbs Close, Little Merton, Norwich NR9 3NU ☎ 01603 811026, 01426 246320

COLE Michael (*Sax*): 93 Leggatts Wood Avenue, Watford, Herts WD2 5RL ☎ 01923 251117, 03783 37874

COOKE Jeremy (*Org*): 23 Orchard Close, Watford, Hertfordshire WD1 3UD ☎ 01923 35478

COOMBES Douglas (*Kbds, Per, Rec, Con*): Brook House, 24, Royston Street, Potton, Sandy / Beds SG19 2LP ☎ 01767 260985

COX Mitchell: 18 Willian Road, Hitchin, Herts SG4 0LR ☎ 01462 450 519

DAGUL Guy (*Vla*): Britwell Lodge, Castle Square, Benson, Oxfordshire OX10 6SD ☎ 01491 39721

DAY Steven (*Kbds*): 2 Uplands Road, Clacton-on-Sea, Essex CO15 1BB ☎ 01255 426988, 0585 631568

DONEGAN John: 27 Nascot Wood Road, Watford, Herts WD1 3SE ☎ 01923 246 369, 020 8492 0504

DYER Jonathan (*Kbds, Gtr, Tpt*): 180 Rainsfrod Road, Chelmsford, Essex CM1 2PD ☎ 01245 261088, 0370 601467

ELTHAM Robert: Searchlight, School Road, Kelvedon Hatch, Brentwood, Essex CM15 0DH ☎ 01277 72452

FABECK Walter: 57C Derby Road, Watford, Herts WD1 2LZ ☎ 01923 38120

FLECKNEY Clive: 79 Wigram Way, Stevenage, Herts SG2 9UX ☎ 01438 315986

GARDNER Alan (*Kbds, Md, Com*): 4 Alexandra Road, Hitchin, Herts SG5 1RB ☎ 01462 433788

GERRELLI Kenneth (*Acc*): 30 Cobb Green, Woodside Estate, Watford, Herts WD2 7HZ ☎ 01923 674414

GOODRUM Dennis: 43 The Avenue, Hertford, Herts SG14 3DS ☎ 01992 587341

GRAVER Michael (*Kbds*): 24 Richmond Drive, Watford, Herts WD1 3BG ☎ 01923 238556

GRAY Nigel (*Gtr*): 136 Winford Drive, Broxbourne, Herts EN10 6PW ☎ 01992 471321, 01992 426521

GREENLAW Verina (*Accom*): Redcourt, 52 Burges Road, Thorpe Bay, Essex SS1 3AX ☎ 01702 587187

HALL Ambrose Edison (*Db*): Cherry Tree House, Hacheston, Nr Woodbridge, Suffolk IP13 0DR ☎ 01728 746371

HAND Raymond (*E Pf*): Rose Wood Cottage, 6 Church Street, Wheathamstead, Hertfordshire AL4 8AW ☎ 01582 834265

HARRIS Douglas: 4 Hanson Way, Pershore, Worcs WR10 1QW ☎ 01386 561690

HARRISON Frank: 49 City Road, Cambridge CB1 1DP ☎ 01223 356144, 0402 092119

HARVEY Simon (*Kbds, Org, Vla*): 26 Shearers Way, Boreham, Chelmsford CM3 3AE ☎ 01245 451151

HEAVISIDE Colin (*Org, Kbds, Tpt*): 12 Totham Hill Green, Great Totham, Essex CM9 8DX ☎ 01621 893067

HEAWOOD Marian (*Kbds*): 16 Carrington Avenue, Flackwell Heath, Buckinghamshire HP10 9AL ☎ 01628 851 293

HOLMES Graham (*Clt*): Hillview Cottage, Curlew Green, Kelsale, Saxmundham, Suffolk IP17 2RA ☎ 01728 602110

HONEY Paul: 26 Fieldhead Gardens, Bourne End, Bucks SL8 5RN ☎ 01628 526469

HUGHES Trevor (*Org, Con*): 50 Whitehorn Lane, Letchworth, Herts SG6 2DJ ☎ 01462 675496

HUME Donald (*Vib, Org*): The Coach House, Upper Zig Zag Road, Ventnor, Isle Of Wight PO38 1BY ☎ 01983 852606

HURD William (*Kbds*): 242 Plumber Avenue, Hockley SS5 5NZ ☎ 01702 201165

JARVIS Christopher (*Acc*): 2 Hoo Wood Cottages, Hoo, Nr Woodbridge, Suffolk IP13 7QR ☎ 01473 737767, 01394 670699

JONES John (*Org*): 33 Alexander Road, Aylesbury, Bucks HP20 2NR ☎ 01296 434731

JONES Stephen (*Hpsd, Org*): 6 Barnfield Road, Marshalswick, St Albans, Herts AL4 9UP ☎ 01727 864007

KAVANAVICH Kerrie: 10 Felmongers, Harlow, Essex CM20 3DH ☎ 01279 432049

KEMP R K Roger (*Kbds, Gtr, B Gtr*): 116 Bloomfield Street, Ipswich, Suffolk IP4 5JJ ☎ 01473 726074

LANCASTER Kevin: 34 Richardson Way, Whittlesey, Peterborough PE7 1RS ☎ 01733 202320, 0976 776976 mob, 01733 208128

LANE-SIMS Michael (*Kbds, Gtr, Hmca*): 30 Cordell Road, Long Melford, Sudbury, Suffolk CO10 9EH ☎ 0976 221975, 01787 370547

LAWRENCE Jean: Dutch Cottage, 192 Thorpe Hall Ave, Thorpe Bay, Southend-on-Sea, Essex SS1 3SF ☎ 01702 585359

LITTON Martin: 7 Bridge Street, Hay-on-Wye, Herefordshire HR3 5DE ☎ 01497 821088

LUCY LIVE! (*Voc, T Sax*): 484 Hitchin Road, Round Green, Luton, Beds LU2 7ST ☎ 01582 612 969, 0956 454 868, 020 7613 0865

MAKOWER Will (*Kbds, Voc, Vln*): 1B St. Margarets Square, Cambridge CB1 4AP ☎ 01223 565564

MALKINSON Chris (*Kbds*): 7 Allandale, St Albans, Herts AL3 4NG ☎ 0973 174318, 01582 842916

MANN Harprith (*Kbds, Synth, Per*): 18 Eastbourne Avenue, Stevenage, Herts SG1 2EX ☎ 01438 362657

MARRIOTT Beryl (*Kbds, Acc*): Gate Lodge, Burcott, Wing, Leighton Buzzard, Beds LU7 0LZ ☎ 01296 688286

MARRIOTT Denis (*E Pf, Org, Arr*): 3 Park Lane, Southwold, Suffolk IP18 6HL ☎ 01502 723449

MAUL John (*Synth, Com, Arr*): 118 Valley Green, Woodhall Farm, Hemel Hempstead, Herts HP2 7RQ ☎ 01442 56182

MEAD Philip: 31 Lingholme Close, Cambridge CB4 3HW ☎ 01223 357431

MERA Nick (*Vla, Cop*): Dakota Music Service, Suit 117, Airport House, Croydon CR0 0XZ ☎ 020 8288 3573, 020 8288 3574, 020 8288 3546

MEREDITH Bill (*Kbds*): 7 Furness Close, Bedford MK41 8RN ☎ 01234 407814, 0468 588484, 01234 407815 fax

MITCHELL Ray (*Gtr*): 1 Nonsuch Meadow, Meadow Lane, Sudbury, Suffolk CO10 6FJ ☎ 01787 370570

MORTIMER Anthony (*Org, Rh Gtr, Clt*): 9 Honeywood Road, Colchester, Essex CO3 3AS ☎ 01206 560342

MURPHY Michael: 32 Carlton Road, Wickford, Essex SS11 7NB ☎ 01268 762345

NEWPORT Mark (*Kbds*): 114 Dorrington Close, Biscot Road, Luton, Beds LU3 1XR ☎ 01582 724121, 0973 382708

PEARSON Roy (*Tpt, Com*): 55 Summerfield Road, Luton, Beds LU1 1UH ☎ 01582 455425

PRINGLE Ben (*Kbds, Gtr*): 21 Amwell Road, Cambridge CB4 2UM ☎ 01223 327002

PYNE Anne (*Sax*): 14 Fishponds Road, Hitchin, Herts SG5 1NR ☎ 01462 431206

REASON Richard (*Com*): Maltings Farm House, Cardington, Beds MK44 3SO ☎ 01234 838048

RECKNELL James (*Org*): 3 Park Gate Cottages, West Stow, Nr Bury St Edmunds IP28 6ET ☎ 01284 728861

REYNOLDS Samuel (*Org*): 69 Woodbridge Road East, Ipswich, Suffolk IP4 5QL ☎ 01473 726295

ROBERTS Brian (*Org, Synth, Kbds*): 24 Medow Bank, Oxhey, Herts WD1 4NP ☎ 01923 230411

ROBINSON Philip (*Synth*): 51 Aldykes, Hatfield, Herts AL10 8ED ☎ 01707 883651

ROSE Diane (*Voc*): Neptune House, 43 King Street, Aldeburgh, Suffolk IP15 5BY ☎ 01728 452275

ROSEBERY David (*Org, Voc*): The Yews, 21 Hillside, New Barnet, Herts EN5 1LT ☎ 020 8449 0021

ROUND-TURNER Charlie (*Kbds, Voc, Song W, Arr*): The Square House, Church Road, Carlton, Nr Newmarket, Suffolk CB8 9JZ ☎ 0589 790 870

RYALL Samuel (*Kbds, Org*): 44 Bouchers Mead, Chelmsford, Essex CM1 6PJ ☎ 01245 451515, 01245 355625

RYAN Joy (*Gtr, Rec, Wh, Clt*): 4 Nursery Gardens, Welwyn Garden City, Herts AL7 1SF ☎ 01707 339 648

SAUNDERS Cloe (*Kbds*): 5 Ringstead Road, Paston, Peterborough PE4 7PN ☎ 01733 572566

SAUNDERS James (*Kbds, Per*): 71 Queensway, Great Cornard, Sudbury, Suffolk CO10 0HQ ☎ 01787 311174

SCOTT Harry

SCOTT Ian: 127 Melbourne Road, Bushey, Watford, Herts WD2 3ND ☎ 020 8950 3193

SILLS Raymond: 3 Cranleigh Gardens, Luton, Bedfordshire LU3 1LS ☎ 01582 25012

SISSON Richard: The Mill, Breachwood Green, Nr Hitchin, Herts SG4 8PH ☎ 01438 833452

SMITH Michael (*Gtr, Kbds*): 9 Falkland Road, Kentish Town, London NW5 2PS ☎ 020 7485 3085, 020 7482 0332

SMITH Ray: Oudegracht 121, 1811Cc Alkmaar, Holland ☎ 0172 117151, 0172 112883

SNELSON Catherine (*Gtr, Voc*): Address Unknown ☎ 01954 200138

STEEL Philip (*Dms, Sax, W Bd*): 6 Moss Drive, Haslingfield, Cambs CB3 7JB ☎ 01223 871482

STERLING Andrew (*Com*): The Old Meeting Room, Main Road, Chelmondiston, Ipswich IP9 1DX ☎ 01473 780856

STEWARD Harold: 19 Monks Horton Way, St Albans, Herts AL1 4HA ☎ 01727 59768

STIRLING-BUICK Njal (*Hpsd, Accom, Con, Org*): 38 St. James Rd, Harpenden, Herts AL5 4PB ☎ 01582 760672

THOMPSON Amy: 56 Outwell Road, Emneth, West Norfolk PE14 0DU ☎ 01945 588685

TOBIN Candida (*Cl Gtr, Theory*): The Old Malthouse, Knight Street, Sawbridgeworth, Herts CM21 9AX ☎ 01279 726625

TOLL Peter (*Synth, H Gurd*): Limbrey Toll Productions, Studio Seven, Muspole Workshops, Muspole Street, Norwich NR3 1DJ ☎ 01603 766314

TOMPKINS Andrea (*Voc*): 16 Richard Street, Dunstable, Beds LU5 4BH ☎ 01582 665724

TRICKER Alf (*Org*): Address Unknown ☎ 01462 732466

TURNER Stephen (*Kbds*): 15 Wynchlands Crescent, St Albans, Herts AL4 0XW ☎ 01727 833649

VICKERS Adam (*Gtr, Dms, Voc, Song W*): 55 North Street, Stilton, Peterborough PE7 3RP ☎ 01733 240609

VIRLEY Nigel (*Kbds, Arr, Com, Bsn*): The Flat, Woodlands Holbrook, Ipswich, Suffolk IP9 2PT ☎ 01473 328188

WALKER Benjamine (*Voc*): 8 Exeter Close, Bourne, Lincs PE10 9NP ☎ 01778 423200

WESTON Veryan: Helsbury, 25 Meadway, Welwyn Garden City, Herts AL7 4NQ ☎ 01707 331643

WHITESIDE Simon (*Com*): 67 Geary Road, London NW10 ☎ 020 8208 1346

WILLIAMS Roger (*Kbds, Org, Gtr, Tpt*): 7 St. Andrews Close, Slip End, Luton, Beds LU1 4DE ☎ 01582 410230

WILLIAMS Russell (*A Sax, Clt, Org*): 66 Angle Ways, Stevenage, Hertfordshire SG2 9AR ☎ 01438 220536 & fax, 0976 674991 mob

WOOLLARD Peter (*E Pf, B Ldr*): 110 Windmill Park, Clacton-on-Sea, Essex CO15 3RZ ☎ 01255 420002

MIDLANDS

ACHESON Keith (*Org, Voc*): 1 Lowercroft Way, Sutton Coldfield, West Midlands B74 4XF ☎ 0121 353 3727

ALEXANDER Mike (*Kbds, Voc, Md, Accom*): Ivory Lodge, 3 Halloughton Road, Four Oaks, Sutton Coldfield, West Midlands B74 2QL ☎ 0121 321 1866

ALLEN Richard (*Kbds, Voc*): 67 St.Thomas Road, Erdington, Birmingham B24 7RQ ☎ 0121 373 9052

AMANN Timothy: 26, Spring Road, Edgbaston, Birmingham B15 2HA ☎ 0121 440 6186

ANDREWS John: 40 Ryland Road, Birmingham B15 2BN ☎ 0121 440 3895

ARCHER Richard (*Org*): 11 Frampton Ave, Leicester LE3 0SG ☎ 0116 2857193

ATKINSON Robert: 1 Mollington Road, Whitnash, Leamington Spa CV31 2JR ☎ 01926 421655

AUSTEN Wendy (*Ob, Voc, Song W*): Cedarwood, Naunton Beauchamp, Worcs WR10 2LL ☎ 0973 644904

BAILEY Terence (*Kbds, Synth*): Staverton, 7 Torrance Close, Branston, Burton-on-Trent, Staffs DE14 3GX ☎ 01283 548765, 0370 662190

BAKER James (*Gtr*): 130 Wilmott Drive, Milehouse, Newcastle-Under-Lyme ST5 9AP ☎ 01782 769279

BARNES Brian (*Org*): 163 Duncan Road, Aylestone, Leicester LE2 8EH ☎ 0116 2831942

BARRETT Trevor (*Org*): 26 Grindcobbe Grove, Rugeley, Staffs WS15 2NJ ☎ 01889 584664, 0374 601794 mob

BERRY Alan (*Org, Clt*): 375 City Road, Edgbaston, Birmingham, West Midlands B17 8LD ☎ 0121 4297623, 0966 287802

BETTS Andrew: 45 Wadhurst Road, Birmingham B17 8JF ☎ 0121 429 4182

BETTS John: 12 Crossleys, Fleckney, Leicestershire LE8 0BY ☎ 0116 2402727

BILL Keith: The Dower House, Nr Stowrbridge, Bobbington, West Midlands DY7 5DE ☎ 01384 221480

BLAKE Wayne (*Kbds, B Gtr, Rh Gtr, Dms*) ☎ 0973 401009

BLOUNT Matthew (*T Hrn, Tpt, Flt*): 13 St James Green, Cotes Heath, Eccleshall, Stafford ST21 6RU ☎ 01782 791351

BLUNN Nick (*Md, Com, Arr*): Cedarwood, Naunton Beauchamp, Worcs WR10 2LL ☎ 0973 719691

BROOKSHAW David (*Org, Hpsd*): 48 York Place, Worcester WR1 3DS ☎ 01905 28900

BROTHERTON John (*Org*): 384 Bromford Road, Hodge Hill, Birmingham B36 8JH ☎ 0121 783 6702

BROWN Sam *(Org)*: 33 Bache Street, West Bromwich, West Midlands B70 7EW ☎ 0121 553 1430

BROWNE Janine *(Kbds)*: The Coach House, Arley Mews, Leamington Spa, Warwickshire CV32 5ND ☎ 01926 423183

BUCKBERRY Ivan *(Org)*: 14, Welham Crescent, Arnold, Nottingham NG5 7LJ ☎ 0115 9264364

BUCKEE Robert *(Gtr, Club Dj)*: 37 Church Street, Finedon, Northampton NN9 5NA ☎ 01938 681808, 07801 476815

BUCKNALL Christopher *(Kbds)*: 36 Ebers Road, Mapperley Park, Nottingham NG3 5DZ ☎ 01159 624494

BURCHELL Anthony *(E Pf, Org, B Ldr, Acc)*: 100 St Gerrards Road, Solihull, West Midlands B91 1UD ☎ 0121 705 5062

BURNS Elaine *(Vln)*: 80 Hampton Lane, Solihull, West Midlands B91 2RS ☎ 0121 704 4450

BURTON Tommy *(A Sax, T Sax, Br Sax)*: Brooklands, Horsebrook, Brewood, Staffordshire ST19 9LP ☎ 01902 850734

CALDECOTT Brian: 116, Station Road, Wythall, Birmingham B47 6AB ☎ 01564 826659

CAMPBELL Colin *(Org, B Ldr, Arr, Cop)*: 16 Clarry Drive, Four Oaks, Sutton Coldfield, West Midlands B74 2RA ☎ 0121 308 6518

CARTER Roy *(B Gtr, Gtr)*: 15 Majuba Road, Edgabaston, Birmingham B16 0PD ☎ 0121 246 8431, 0403 669748, 0121 2423752

CARTWRIGHT Kenneth *(Arr, Com, Cop)*: 2 Cedar Road, Wednesbury, Staffs WS10 0BD ☎ 0121 556 2433

CAVE Brett *(Per, Clt)*: 49 Seaforth Drive, Hinkley, Leics LE10 0XJ ☎ 01455 448 163, 0411 070725 mob

CHAPMAN Margaret: 10 Bulls Head Lane, Stoke Green, Coventry, West Midlands CV3 1FR ☎ 024 7644 1143

CHISNALL Leslie *(Org)*: 16 Southward Road, Haydock, St Helens WA11 0RD ☎ 01942 729031

CLARKE Jonathan *(Org, Bsn)*: 24 Landor Road, Knowle, Solihull, West Midlands B93 9HZ ☎ 01564 776912

CLARKE Oliver *(Hrp)*: Foxhills, Stourbridge Road, Wombourne, South Staffordshire WV5 0JN ☎ 01902 897853, 0374 666480 mob

CLARKE Richie *(Kbds)*: 76 Tweed Tower, Birchford Road, Penny Barr, Birmingham B20 5JN ☎ 0121 356 5813, 0121 698 1000

CLEAVER Ron: 34 Boswell Road, Shakespeare Gardens, Rugby, Warwics CV22 6JD ☎ 01788 812445

CLEMAS James *(Kbds)*: 33 Reynard Way, Holly Lodge Drive, Kingsthorpe, Northampton NN2 8QS ☎ 01604 845808

COATES Ian *(Org)*: 26 Morfa Gardens, Coundon, Coventry CV6 1PX ☎ 024 7659 2954

COLEMAN John *(Kbds, Org, Per)*: 90 Kingshurst Road, Northfield, Birmingham B31 5LN ☎ 0121 478 0661

COLLIS Christopher: 95 Tessall Lane, Northfield, Birmingham B31 2SA ☎ 0121 476 4610

COLLISSON Stephen: 53 Russell Road, Hall Green, Birmingham B28 8SF ☎ 0121 777 6643, 0881 841470, 0121 777 6643

CONSTANTINOU Stace *(Cel, Db)*: 107 Ardington Road, Northampton NN1 5LS ☎ 01604 471948

CONWAY Christopher *(Synth, E Gtr, Ac Gtr, Man)*: 53 Cromer Street, Leicester LE2 1PG ☎ 0116 2739263

CORBET Alan *(Kbds)*: 14 Broad Street, Warwick, Warwickshire CV34 4LT ☎ 01926 403970, 0468 461270 mob

COTTERELL Archie *(Org)*: Silkeborg, 16 Queens Road, Calf Heath, Wolverhampton, Staffs WV10 7DT ☎ 01902 790727

COX: 818 Bristol Road, Selly Oak, Birmingham B29 6NA ☎ 0121 414 1288

DAGLEY David: 47 Hanbury Road, Dorridge, Solihull, West Midlands B93 8DW ☎ 01564 230020, 0958 447765 mob

DAINES Nicholas *(Kbds)*: Flat A, Sutherland View, Stone Road, Tittensor, Staffordshire ST12 9HR ☎ 01782 657487, 01782 715715 day

DAVIS Michael *(Kbds, Org)*: 14 Grange Road, Erdington, Birmingham B24 0DE ☎ 0121 682 2630

DEAN Alan *(Hpsd, Kbds)*: 4 Carrwood, Knutsford, Cheshire WA16 8NG ☎ 01565 52838

DENT Graham *(Kbds)*: 49 St.Nicholas Avenue, Kenilworth, Warks CV8 1JW ☎ 01926 52507

DRAPER D *(E Pf)*: 30 Orchard Way, Bilton, Rugby, Warwickshire CV22 7PS ☎ 01788 811183

DUGGINS Paul *(Acc)*: 36 Park Hill Road, Harborne, Birmingham B17 9SL ☎ 0121 426 2672, 0121 233 0064

DUNSTAN James *(Gtr, Sax)*: 10 Bull Street, Harborne, Birmingham B17 3HH ☎ 0121 428 1469

EGGLESTON James *(Org, Hrn)*: The Post House, 18 Main Street, Keyworth, Nottingham ☎ 0115 937 2021

ELDEN Michael *(Flt)*: St.Barnabas Rectory, Church Road, Worcester WR3 8NX ☎ 01905 23785

EVANS John *(Md, Arr, Com, Cop)*: Casa Nos Prados, Bordeira, 8000 Faro, Algarve, Portugal ☎ +351 (0)89 94310

EVENETT Roy *(Gtr, Db)*: 26 Arundel Road, Wordsley, Stourbridge, West Midlands DY8 5EQ ☎ 01384 294978

EVERITT Ralph: 1, Newfield Road, Radford, Coventry, West Midlands CV1 4DZ ☎ 024 7622 3880

FAIRHURST Richard *(Kbds)*: 27 Hollies Way, Bushby, Leicestershire LE7 9RL ☎ 0116 2416127

FEENEY Eric *(Acc, Com, Cop)*: 9 Thetford Road, Great Barr, Birmingham B42 2JA ☎ 0121 357 2419

FISHER Roy: Four Ways, Earl Sterndale, Buxton, Derbyshire SK17 0EP ☎ 0129 883 279

FISHLOCK Clive *(Kbds, Voc)*: 7, Theobald Road, Canton, Cardiff CF5 1LP ☎ 029 2022 2942

FLEISCHER Marion *(Bsn, Kbds, Gtr)*: Brook Cottage, 6 Chapel Crescent, Hadnall, Shrewsbury, Shrops SY4 4EQ ☎ 01939 210966

FORD Andrew *(Kbds)*: 2 Arrow Barns, Eardisland, Nr Leominster, Herefordshire HR6 9BN ☎ 01544 388263

FOWLER Karen *(Clt)*: Windmill Cottage, Hillside, Ditton Priors, Bridgnorth, Shropshire WV16 6TP ☎ 01746 712281

FOWLER Michael *(Synth, Arr, Com, Cop)*: 154 Boldmere Road, Sutton Coldfield, West Midlands B73 5UD ☎ 0121 354 8707, 0589 437755 mob

FOX Sylvia *(Theory, Kbds)*: 9 Kingshill Drive, Kings Norton, Birmingham B38 8SA ☎ 0121 459 4531

FRANKLIN Harry: 117 Chatsworth Drive, Hucknall, Nottingham NG15 7NU

FREEMAN Kenneth *(E Pf)*: Brokenhill, Abberley, Worcester WR6 6AR ☎ 01299 896279

FREYA Jo-Anne: 95 Laurie Avenue, Forest Fields, Nottingham NG7 6PH

FULLER Gareth *(Kbds, Tpt, Vln)*: 68 Beaumont Drive, Cherry Lodge, Northampton NN3 8PS ☎ 01604 450420

FURNISH Alfred *(Org, Clt)*: 19 The Lealand, East Farndon, Market Harborough, Leics LE16 9SQ ☎ 01858 62034

GAYE Althea *(Arr, Com, Cop)*: 231 Castle Lane, Solihull, Warks B92 8SW ☎ 0121 743 5835

GEE Stephen *(Gtr, B Gtr, Ctna, Wh)*: 16 Caledon Road, Sherwood, Nottingham NG5 2NG ☎ 0115 960 8056, 0115 9109153

GILL David *(Org, Synth)*: 16 Sycamore Green, Cannock, Staffs WS11 2PN ☎ 01543 877593

GODSALL Jill: 17 Rectory Gardens, Solihull, Warks B91 3RL ☎ 0121 705 0968

GRAY Catherine *(Kbds)*: 2 Fighting Close, Kineton, Warwick CV35 0LS ☎ 01926 640735

GREENHAM Maurice *(Org, Tbn)*: 1 Linley Road, Hartshill, Stoke-on-Trent, Staffs ST4 6AX ☎ 01782 613429

GRUMMETT Barry: 163 Loughborough Road, Hathern, Loughborough, Leics LE12 5HZ ☎ 01509 843431, 0468 334159

HALL Joan: 202, Woodside Avenue South, Green Lane, Coventry, West Midlands CV3 6BG ☎ 024 7641 9973

HALL John *(Kbds, Sax)*: 9 Squires View, Stoke-on-Trent ST4 2HN ☎ 01782 412658

HANCOCK Stephen *(Md)*: Address Unknown ☎ 01789 293833

HARPER Virginia *(Clt)*: 12 Oaklands Close, Hill Ridware, Nr. Rugeley, Staffs WS15 3RJ

HARRIS Sue *(Ob, Dul, Rec, Mldn)*: 4 Caefelyn, Norton, Presteigne, Powys LD8 2UB ☎ 01544 267632

HAWKINS Ronald *(Kbds, Acc, B Ldr)*: 20 Gwendoline Way, Shire Oak, Walsall, West Midlands WS9 9RG ☎ 01543 821587

HEELEY Roger (*E Pf*): 126 Brooklands Road, Birmingham B28 8JZ ☎ 0121 777 8096

HELLIER Ruth (*Vln*): 7 Mossfield Road, Kings Heath, Birmingham B14 7JE ☎ 0121 444 8326

HEMMING John (*Gtr, Dms*): 15 Chantry Road, Birmingham B13 8DL ☎ 0121 442 4491 & fax, 0958 398383 mob

HESTER Kate (*Cel*): 32 Wallace Road, Selly Park, Birmingham B29 7ND ☎ 0121 429 8009

HILL Kathrine: 43 St. Andrews Rd, Malvern, Worcs WR14 3PT

HILL Matthew (*Kbds, Tpt*): 12 Loxton Court, Mickleover, Derby DE3 5PH ☎ 0468 931720 mob

HIPKISS Barry (*Org, Arr, Com, Cop*): Oak Lea Birch Grove, Cooks Cross, Alveley, Bridgnorth Salop WV15 6LS ☎ 01746 780861

HOLMES John (*Kbds*): Keepers Cottage, Cheltenham Road, Broadway, Worcester WR12 7LX ☎ 01386 853941

HOOPER Tony (*Kbds, Org, Com*): 2 St Austell Road, Park Hall, Walsall, West Midlands WS5 3EF ☎ 01922 35109

HORA Johanna (*Com*): The Wingfield Arms, Montford Bridge, Shrewsbury, Shropshire SY4 1EB

HORTON Ronald: 8 Thorncliffe Road, Great Barr, Birmingham B44 9DB ☎ 0121 360 9794

HOWARD Christopher (*Org, Hpsd*): 5 Bostock Close, Elemesthorpe, Leicester LE9 7SR ☎ 01455 851661

HOWARD Jimmy (*Kbds*): 18 Davenport Terrace, Hinckley, Leicestershire LE10 1EZ ☎ 01455 890332, 01455 611569 fax

HUDSON Robert: 11A Worcester Road, Woodthorpe, Nottingham NG5 4HW ☎ 0115 956 7952

HUGHES Adrian (*Org, Kbds*): 20 Peveril Road, Duston, Northampton NN5 6JW ☎ 01604 585946

HUGHES Glenn (*Kbds*): 2 Kings Walk, Leicester Forest East, Leicester LE3 3JP ☎ 0116 224 9290

HUGHES Jonathan (*Kbds, A Sax*): 19 Frederick Road, Sutton Coldfield, West Midlands B73 5QW ☎ 0121 354 7192

HUNTER Larraine (*Clt*): 'Penryn' Tower Road, Ashley Heath, Nr Market Drayton, Shropshire TF9 4PU ☎ 01630 672556

HURST Derek (*B Gtr*): 38 Hollington Road, Tean, Stoke-on-Trent, Staffs ST10 4JY ☎ 01538 722413

IBBETT Jane (*Clt*): 14 Clarendon Street, Earlsdon, Coventry CV5 6EX ☎ 024 7671 6148

ILIFFE Steven: 41 Lady Bay Road, West Bridgford, Nottingham NG2 5DT ☎ 0115 9861870

JAMES E (*Synth, Tba, Gtr*): 7 Deppers Bridge, Leamington Spa, Warwickshire CV33 0SX ☎ 01926 613280

JOHN Daniel: 49 Francis Road, Acocks Green, Birmingham B27 6LT ☎ 0121 605 4330

JOHNSON Raymond (*Org*): 19, Rainsbrook Drive, Crowhill, Nuneaton, Warwickshire CV11 6UE ☎ 024 7637 5885

JONES George (*Org*): 5 Winterton Road, Hemsby, Great Yarmouth NR29 4HH ☎ 01493 732146

JONES Ian (*Clt*): 4 Thornhill Road, Wallbridge Park, Leek, Staffs ST13 8HN ☎ 01538 384344

JONES Michael: The Studio, 7 Mount Lane, Stourbridge, West Midlands DY8 1HZ ☎ 01384 393706

JONES Stuart (*Kbds*): 12 Tysoe Drive, Sutton Coldfield, West Midlands B76 2UJ ☎ 0121 378 1641

JONES Tryphena (*Wood W, Voc*): 15 Old Fallings Lane, Fallings Park, Wolverhampton, West Midlands WV10 8BH ☎ 01902 737584

KEAY Peter (*Kbds*): 64 Salstar Close, Aston, Birmingham B6 4PP ☎ 0370 211 887, 0121 333 6128

KENRICK Hilgrove (*Kbds, Voc, T Sax, Clt*): 37 Richmond Hill Road, Edgbaston, Birmingham B15 3RR ☎ 0121 454 4720, 0121 455 0184 fax

KENT Sayan: 110 Woodside Ave South, Coventry CV3 6BE ☎ 024 7641 8912

KERSHAW David (*Clav, Harm, Vla, Rec*): Baird House, Croft Bank, West Malvern, Worcs WR14 4DF ☎ 01684 561379

KIMBERLEY Carol: 4 Arundel Drive, Mansfield, Notts NG19 6AP ☎ 01623 653269

KING Colin: 2 Westhill Road, Kings Norton, Birmingham B38 8RX ☎ 0121 458 3545

KING Zara (*Gtr, Dms, B Gtr, Hmca*): 46 Bathley Street, The Meadows, Nottingham NG2 2LH

LAIRD Jonathan (*Kbds, Voc*): 145 Park Hill Road, Marborne, Birmingham B17 9HE ☎ 0121 428 1476, 0370 500093

LAMBERT Michael: 21 Edwal Road, Weston Coyney, Stoke-on-Trent, Staffs ST3 5HH ☎ 01782 319997

LANE David (*Synth*): 321 Highters Heath Lane, Hollywood, Birmingham B14 4TA ☎ 0121 604 2740, 0410 079934 mob

LEADBETTER Richard (*Kbds, Dms*): 79 Broomfield Road, Kidderminster, Worcs DY11 5PH ☎ 01562 744102

LEE Eddie (*E Pf*): 2. The Orchard, Marston Green, Birmingham B37 7DH

LEEK Andrew (*Gtr, Hmca*): 14 The Hayes, Willenhall, West Midlands WV12 4RA ☎ 01902 602438

LEIGH Tony: 2 Houses Hill, Kirkheaton, Huddersfield, West Yorkshire HD5 0PA ☎ 01484 514255

LEWIS-JONES Christopher (*Acc*): 2 Hedley Villas, Sherwood Rise, Nottingham NG7 7BN ☎ 0115 979 0085

LISMORE Jenifer (*Org, Ob, Clt, Rec*): 25B Church Street North, Old Whittington, Chesterfield, Derbyshire S41 9QN ☎ 01246 455178

LOCK Terence: 10 Welland Road, Barrow-on-Soar, Leics LE12 8NA ☎ 01509 412877

LOCOCK Victoria: Norwood Cottage, Hall Grounds, Rolleston-on-Dove, Burton-on-Trent, Staffs DE13 9BS ☎ 01283 813816

LOUGHRAN Anne (*Ctna, Gtr, Vla, Wh*): Old School House, Llanfairwaterdine, Knighton, Powys, LD7 1TU ☎ 01547 520339

LOVELOCK Michael (*Voc, Gtr, B Gtr, Cel*): 106 Pipers Hill Road, Kettering, Northants NN15 7NW ☎ 01536 510015, 07771 567702

MANSFIELD Stephen (*Kbds, Synth, Org*): Corbyn, 32 The Rise, Newhall, Swadlincote, Derbyshire DE11 0RU ☎ 01283 214117, 0374 499065

MARCH Harold (*Org*): 231 Kettering Road, Kingsley, Northampton NN2 7DU ☎ 01604 713103

MARCH Sylvia: 1 Olden Road, Rectory Farm, Northampton NN3 5DD ☎ 01604 786148

MATTS Harry: 74 Lugtrout Lane, Solihull, Warwickshire B91 2SN ☎ 0121 704 9967

MAYO Graham (*Org, Con, Md*): Hollybank 5, The Orchard, Kislingbury, Northants NN7 4BG ☎ 01604 830679

MITCHELL Steven (*Kbds, Org*): 5 Rushton Grove, Cobridge, Stoke-on-Trent, Staffs ST6 2HR ☎ 01782 265022

MONKS Bob (*E Pf, Acc*): 10 Shakespeare Street, Stoke, Coventry, West Midlands CV4 2JZ ☎ 024 7644 7889

MOORE John (*Kbds*): Sanderlings, 92-94 Main Street, Ratby, Leicester LE6 0LL ☎ 0116 2394737

MORGAN Beverly: 15 Clover Lane, Wall Heath, West Midlands DY6 0DT ☎ 01384 271741

MORLEY Jeanette (*Rec*): 24 Grendon Close, Tile Hill, Coventry CV4 9GG ☎ 024 7646 7742

MORRELL Rebecca (*Voc, Clt, Rec*) ☎ 01782 751575

MORTIMORE Cyril (*Org*): 21 Charles Field Road, Rugby CV22 5PQ ☎ 01788 816824

MORTON John (*Org, Synth, Clt*): 118 Egypt Road, Basford, Nottingham NG7 7GN ☎ 0115 970 4410, 0850 486527

MULLINGS Victor: Address Unknown ☎ 0385 704359

MURPHY Michael (*Synth, Acc*): 139 Lordswood Road, Harborne, Birmingham B17 9BL ☎ 0121 427 4276

MURTAGH Andrew (*Kbds*): 99 Pendragon Road, Perry Barr, Birmingham B42 1RJ ☎ 0121 551 4398

NEMBHARD Carl (*Per, B Gtr, Rh Gtr*): 30 Algernon Road, Edgbaston, Birmingham B16 0HX ☎ 0121 454 7485

NEWPORT Neil (*Kbds*): 7 Poplar Close, Banbury, Oxon OX16 9EU ☎ 01295 254073

NIBLETT Ben (*Gtr, Voc*): Flat B, 100 Oxford Road, Moseley, Birmingham B13 9SQ ☎ 0121 449 8677, 0836 697368

NOCK John (*Org*): 72 Max Road, Quinton, Birmingham B32 1LB ☎ 0121 422 7318

NOEL Lincoln (*Vln, Org*): 32 Oakleigh Drive, Duston, Northampton NN5 6RP ☎ 01604 756266

NUTMAN Jonathan: 2 Bell Ave, Aston-on-Trent, Derby DE72 2BE ☎ 01332 792659

O'NEIL Bruce: 23A Woodland Ave, West Hagley, Stourbridge, W Midlands DY8 2XQ ☎ 01562 885179, 0973 803068

OLD David (Org, Org): 1 Kinros Close, Highlands, Northampton NN3 1BP ☎ 01604 645014

OWENS Stephen (Kbds, Per): 202 Lindsworth Road, Kings Norton, Birmingham B30 3SB ☎ 0121 451 1450, 0966 136389

PACE Julie (Voc, Accom): 31 May Avenue, May Bank, Newcastle, Staffs ST5 0NH ☎ 01782 614086

PARKINSON Benjamin (Synth, Arr): 10, Millbrook Road, Kings Heath, Birmingham B14 6SE ☎ 0121 444 1375

PATRICK John (Md, Arr, Com, Kbds): c/o Musicians Union, Benson House, Lombard Street, Birmingham B12 0QN ☎ 01564 784029 & fax

PEARS Michael (Kbds): 35 Cubbington Road, Lillington, Leamington Spa CV32 7AA ☎ 01926 888381

PEMBERTON Mark (Kbds, Org): 65 Marton Drive, Wellington, Telford, Shropshire TF1 3HR ☎ 01952 419057, 0378 342075

PENDLEBURY Keith: Tyddyn Corn1, Botwnnog, Pwllheli, Gwynedd OL53 8HA ☎ 0175 873 0360

PREECE Dane: 23 Oakwood Road, Smethwick, Warley, West Midlands B67 6BX ☎ 0121 565 4043

PRYER D (Org): 151 Manor Lane, Halesowen, West Midlands B62 8QN ☎ 0121 550 1122

READMAN Peter (Tpt, Con, Com, Arr): 55 Hampton Court Road, Harborne, Birmingham B17 9AG ☎ 0121 241 8179

REEVES John (Org): 24 Lavender Avenue, Coundon, Coventry, West Midlands CV6 1DB ☎ 024 7659 4861

REID Raina: 8 Dunstall House, Stow Road, Moreton In Marsh, Glos GL56 0DR ☎ 01608 651314

RICH Harold (Arr, Com, Cop): 17 Tysoe Close, Hockley Heath, Solihull, West Midlands B94 6QG ☎ 01564 783872

RICHARDS Delph (Kbds, Md, Accom): 4 Holbrook Close, Walton, Chesterfield, Derbys S40 3JP ☎ 01246 234124

RICHES Neil: 22 Larkhill, Rushden, Northants NN10 9BG ☎ 01933 55865

RILEY Ian (Synth, Flgl, Tpt, B Gtr): 2 Robins Close, Hartwell, Northampton NN7 2HZ

ROBERTS Arthur (Md): 5 Maurice Road, Birmingham B14 6DL ☎ 0121 444 4946

ROBERTS Shirley: 3 Preston Street, Shrewsbury, Shropshire SY2 5PG ☎ 01743 353433

ROBERTS Stephanie (Hrp): 6 Preston Street, Shrewsbury, Shropshire SY2 5NY ☎ 01743 248966/53

ROBINSON Tim (Man, Gtr, Bjo): 6 Marldon Road, Kings Heath, Birmingham B14 6BJ ☎ 0121 444 6184

RODEN Vic (Org): 115 Hermitage Road, Wyken, Coventry, West Midlands CV2 5GD ☎ 024 7644 3931

ROWLEY Jacqueline (Kbds, Flt, Rec): 30 St Edmunds Avenue, Porthill Newcastle, Staffs ST5 0AB ☎ 01782 614989

RUDDICK Joanna (Kbds, Vln): 10 Westgrove Avenue, Monkspath, Solihull, West Midlands B90 4XN ☎ 0121 733 7264, 0421 019527

SANCHEZ Michael (Voc, Gtr): PO Box 143, Kidderminster, Worcs DY10 1YU

SAVILLE Tommy (Org): 76 Bowbridge Gardens, Bottesford, Notts NG13 0AZ ☎ 01949 42736

SAWTELL Paul (Mldca, Synth, Md, Kbds): 20 Seymour Road, Wollescote, Stourbridge, West Midlands DY9 8TB ☎ 01384 351033

SCOTT John (Org): 17 Barn Close, Mansfield, Notts NG18 3JX ☎ 01623 284445

SEAR Natalie (Vln, Clt): ☎ 01604 416200, 0403 163822

SHARPE Neil (Vla, Voc): 54 Aspley Park Drive, Aspley, Notingham NG8 3EG ☎ 0115 9292784

SHEPHERD John (Synth, Gtr): Pedington Forge, Enchmarsh, Church Stretton, Shropshire SY6 7JX ☎ 01694 771386

SHUTT Karen: 14 Craig Walk, Alsager, Stoke-on-Trent, Staffs ST7 2RJ ☎ 01270 874157

SIMONS John (Org, Arr, Md): Swaldesale, 6 Coniston Place, Trentham, Stoke-on-Trent ST4 8JL ☎ 01782 657599

SIMPSON Graham (Org): 20 The Avenue, Harpfields, Stoke-on-Trent ST4 6BJ ☎ 01782 614374

SMITH Barbara: 15 Newington Close, Coundon, Coventry, West Midlands CV6 1PQ ☎ 024 7659 2405

SMITH Daniel (Vln, Voc, Ob, Gtr): 21 Banners Gate Road, Sutton Coldfield, Brimingham, West Midlands B73 6TY ☎ 0121 354 8392, 09733 24771

SMITH Gerry (Acc): 50 Parkhill, Moseley, Birmingham B13 8DT ☎ 0121 449 5335

SMITH Peter (Kbds, Org): Willenhall Cemetery Lodge, Bentley Lane, Willenhall, West Midlands WV12 4AE ☎ 01902 606645

SMITH Roy (Org): 21 May Avenue, Tunstall, Stoke-on-Trent, Staffs ST6 6EN ☎ 01782 838221

SMITHYMAN Ernest (Clt, Sax, Voc): 313 Littleworth Road, Hednesford, Staffs WS12 5HY ☎ 01543 871874

SPARE Walter: 1 Warwick Close, Thornton, Nr Leicester LE67 1BZ

SPEDDING Frank (Hpsd, Com): 17 Digby Avenue, Mapperley, Nottingham NG3 6DS

SPENCER Gill (Vln): 190 Main Road, Meriden, Coventry, Warks CV7 7NG ☎ 01676 22592

STANIFORTH Thomas (Org): 4 Freeboard Road, Braunstone, Leicester LE3 2UN ☎ 0116 2895518

STOTT Katharine: The Cottage, Friday St, Pebworth, Stratford-upon-Avon, Warks CV37 8XW ☎ 01789 720394

SWINFORD Nigel (Org): 29 Grange Park Road, Bromley Cross, Bolton, Lancs BL7 9YA ☎ 01204 56598

TAYLOR George (Voc, Vib, Arr, Com): 39 Buckleys Green, Alvechurch, Birmingham B48 7NG ☎ 0121 445 3153

TAYLOR Harold: 37 East Road, Brosgrove, Worcs B60 2NW ☎ 01527 874402

TAYLOR Kaye: 10 Jessan Road, Walsall, West Midlands WS1 3AS ☎ 0121 922 634103

TAYTON Simon (Org, Com, Arr, Accom): 45 Hill Top, Arley, Coventry CV7 8FZ ☎ 01676 542510 & fax, 01523 127985 pager

TERRY Louise (Accom): Mithil Stonedown, 102 County Drive, Fazeley, Tamworth, Staffs B78 3XF ☎ 01827 311703

THOMAS Dave (Kbds, B Gtr): 78 Swadlincote Road, Woodville, Burton-on-Trent DE11 8DB ☎ 01283 217910

THOMPSON Chris (Kbds, Saxes, Clt): 21 Alport Croft, Bordesley, Birmingham, West Midlands B9 4PJ ☎ 0121 753 1726

TITE Martyn (Kbds): 116 Bedford Street, Derby DE22 3PE ☎ 01332 347465

TOBIN Des: 6 Bakers Lane, Sutton Mews, Chaplefields, Coventry, West Midlands CV5 8PR

TODD Barry (Kbds): 120 Lillington Road, Leamington Spa, Warks CV32 6LW ☎ 01926 424652

TODD Peter (Per): 41 Lea Road, Abington, Northampton NN1 4PE ☎ 01604 601775

TOPPING Sylvia: Grey Roof, Marsh Lane, Cheswardine, Market Drayton, Shropshire TF9 2SF ☎ 01630 86 354

TROMANS Stephen (Kbds, Com, Arr): 19 Newlands Drive, Halesowen, West Midlands B62 9DX ☎ 0121 422 2546

TUFFIN Dave (Kbds, Voc): 27 Rose Hill, London Road, Worcester WR5 1EY ☎ 01905 352875

UNDERWOOD Sue: 16 Kinlet Close, Winyates East, Redditch, Worcs B98 0PN ☎ 01527 503489

VENN Paul (Con): 40 Doris Road, Sparkhill, Birmingham, West Midlands B11 4NE ☎ 0121 449 6786

VENUS Bryn (Kbds): 26 Silhill Hall Road, Solihull, West Midlands B91 1JU ☎ 0121 705 1342

VERE Penny (Hpsd): Rock Cottage, 74 North Malvern Road, Malvern, Worcs WR14 4LX ☎ 01684 575300

VIGARS Irene (Kbds): 6 Crick Road, Hillmorton, Rugby CV21 4DX ☎ 01788 576907

VINCENT Paul (Md, Arr, Com, Cop): Flat7, Tessier Court, 31 Manor Road, St Marychurch, Torquay TQ1 3JX ☎ 01803 316168

WAIN Peter (Kbds, Org): ☎ 0121 420 3097

WAITE Brian: 127A Sutton Park Road, Kidderminster, Worcs DY11 6JG ☎ 01562 755308

WALKER David: 2 Maxwell Street, Breaston, Derbyshire DE72 3AH ☎ 013317 4593

WAUGH Duncan (*Dms, Tbn*): 35 Allendale Road, Walmley, Sutton Coldfield, West Midlands B76 8NL ☎ 0121 313 1922

WAYNE Philip (*Org*): 24 Orwell Road, Walsall WS1 2PJ ☎ 01922 626832

WELLS John (*Md, Arr*): 3 Lockhart Drive, Four Oaks, Sutton Coldfield B75 6RR ☎ 0121 308 2878

WELLS Muriel: 15 London Road, Great Glen, Leicester LE8 9GF ☎ 0116 2593733

WESTACOTT Bronwen: 13 Bernard Street, Carrington, Nottingham NG5 2AE ☎ 0115 985 6217

WESTON Clifford: 26 Ribblesdale Avenue, Hinckley, Leicestershire LE10 1SY ☎ 01455 239128

WHEATLEY Richard (*Gtr, Dms, Tbn*): 21 Nab Hill Avenue, Leek, Stafford ST13 8EF ☎ 01538 387211

WHITE P (*Org*): 40 Windmill Road, Nuneaton CV10 0HL ☎ 024 7639 2676

WILSON Malcolm: 312 Alcester Road South, Kings Heath, Birmingham B14 6EN ☎ 0121 444 2043

WOODHEAD John (*Kbds, Org, Gtr, B Gtr*): Finbrook, Dalehouse Lane, Kenilworth, Warwickshire CV8 2JZ ☎ 024 7641 8150

WYATT Roger (*Tbn*): 55 School Road, Evesham, Worcester WR11 6PT ☎ 01386 446916

SOUTH EAST

AED James (*Gtr, B Gtr*): 56 Minster Road, Godalming, Surrey GU7 1SR ☎ 01483 423645

AINSWORTH Edmund: Brigadoon, 14 Nevill Road, Hove, East Sussex BN3 7BQ ☎ Brighton 728303

AKEHURST Anthony (*Org, Synth*): Homelands, Winchelsea Rd, Guestling, Hastings TN35 4LW ☎ 01424 813215

ALLEN Clive (*Voc, Org*): Lower Flat, 14 Gladstone Terrace, Brighton, Sussex BN2 3LB ☎ Brighton 692037

ARNOLD Peter: 58 Western Road, Tunbridge Wells, Kent TN1 2JQ ☎ 01892 542568

ASPINALL Norman (*Org*): 9 Marlborough Court, Coley Avenue, Reading, Berkshire RG1 6PP ☎ 01734 595989

ATAR (*Sax, B Gtr, E Gtr*): 'Stonewalls', Hempton, Deddington, Banbury, Oxfordshire OX15 0QS ☎ 01869 338 439

ATKINS Malcolm (*Kbds*): 41 Bullingdon Road, Oxford OX4 1QJ ☎ 01865 721564

BAKI Nadia (*Voc, Clt, Gtr*): 32 Pegasus Way, East Grinstead, West Sussex RH19 3NW ☎ 01342 312839, 0132 325870, 01342 327169

BALL Patricia: 16 Old Church Lane, Duddingston, Edinburgh EH15 3PX

BANAGAN Colin (*Kbds*): 7 Greenhayes, 46 Springfield Road, St Leonards-on-Sea, East Sussex TN38 0TZ ☎ 01424 441 778

BARKER Alan: 78 Station Road, Portslade, Brighton, Sussex BN41 1DF ☎ Brighton 417515

BARNETT Roy: 20 Cheddington Road, Bournemouth, Dorset BH9 3NB ☎ 01202 240115

BATE Lawrence (*Arr, Com, Cop*): 21 West Street, Ryde, Isle Of Wight PO33 2QQ ☎ 01983 567994

BAXTER Timothy (*Kbds, B Gtr*): The Elms, Sarre, Nr Birchington, Kent CT7 0LE

BENNETT Fiona (*Tpt*): Chapel Farm, New Road, Greenham, Newbury, Berks RG19 8RZ ☎ 01635 42814, 01635 35585

BENNUN Colin (*Didj, B Gtr, Accom*): 30 Silver Road, Oxford, Oxon OX4 3AP ☎ 01865 240820, 01865 251004

BEVAN Sydney (*Org*): 13 Woodlands Park, Main Road, Yapton, Nr Arundel, West Sussex BN18 0EZ ☎ 01243 551146

BIBBY Robin (*Synth, Tpt, Gtr, B Gtr*): 67 Muir Road, Ramsgate, Kent CT11 8AU ☎ 01843 582264, 01843 588505

BINDING Judith: Ashway, 33 Grand Avenue, Camberley, Surrey GU15 3QJ ☎ 01276 27342 & fax

BLANCHARD Lee: 13 High Firs Gardens, Halterworth, Romsey, Hants SO51 5QA ☎ 01794 516799, 0976 510872 mob

BLISSETT Andrew (*Synth, Voc*): Yogi Barn, 2 Manor Farm Barns, Toot Baldon, Oxon OX44 9NG ☎ 01865 343865

BOLINGBROKE Paula (*Flt*): 114 Churchwood Drive, Tangmere, Chichester PO20 6GB ☎ 01934 876187

BORZYMOWSKA Izabela (*Kbds*): Hawes Farm Cottage, Lower Assendon, Henley-on-Thames, Oxon RG9 6AN ☎ 01491 577554

BOTTRILL Andrew: 29 Temple Road, Temple Cowley, Oxford OX4 2ET ☎ 01865 712763

BOWERS Edward (*Hmca, Gtr*): 68 Church Road, Long Hanborough, Nr Witney, Oxon OX8 8JF ☎ 01993 881012

BRANSON Peter (*Flt*): The Lodge, Seymour Court, Marlow, Bucks SL7 3DB ☎ 01628 482 718

BRAWN Geoffrey (*Con*): Flat 2, 35 Adelade Crescent, Hove, East Sussex BN3 2JJ ☎ 01273 749073

BRENT Michael: 55 The Fairways, Wentworth Drive, Christchurch, Dorset BH23 1RB ☎ 01202 488516

BRENTON Rebecca (*Clt, Sax, Rec*): Greenview, 6 New Road, Milford, Godalming, Surrey GU8 5BE

BRIANT Alan (*Acc*): 10 Redhouse Mews, Station Road, Liphook, Hants GU30 7DN ☎ 01428 722368 & fax

BROWN Donovan (*Org, Hpsd, Con*): Sandy Lane Cottage, Sandy Lane, Watersfield, Pulborough RH20 1NF ☎ 01798 831057

BUCKERIDGE Corin (*Vla, Org*): 140B Kennington Lane, London SE11 4UZ

BULSON Philip (*Vib*): Playford Rise, Arnewood Bridge Road, Sway, Lymington, Hampshire SO41 6DA ☎ 01590 682240

BURDEN Elizabeth: The Pastures, Vicarage Lane, Swanmore, Southampton, Hants SO32 2QT ☎ 01489 892695

BURRAS William (*Kbds*): Sandstones, Burnhams Road, Little Bookham, Surrey KT23 3AU ☎ 01372 458432

BURROWS Jonathan (*Org, Arr, Cop*): 9 Honeywood Close, Canterbury, Kent CT1 1XF ☎ Canterbury 6041

BUSBY Paul (*E Pf, Tbn*): 46 Ballard Drive, Ringmer, Lewes, East Sussex BN8 5NU ☎ Ringmer 813188

BUTTON Jean (*Gtr*): 1 Schofields Way, Bloxham, Banbury, Oxon OX15 4NS ☎ 01295 721920

CAMPBELL Colin: 6 Westbury Close, Fleet, Hants GU13 9HR ☎ Fleet 29554

CAMPBELL Douglas (*B Ldr*): 8 Gorse Road, Corfe Mullen, Wimborne, Dorset BH21 3SJ ☎ 01202 699143

CAMPBELL John (*Kbds*): 12 Blackthorn Close, Tilehurst, Reading, Berks RG31 6ZY ☎ 01734 415755

CAPOCCI Nicholas (*Kbds*): 9 Cedric Road, Westgate, Kent CT8 8NZ ☎ 01843 834367

CARTER Margot (*Rec, Vla*): 138 Old Church Road, St. Leonards-on-Sea, East Sussex TN38 9HD ☎ 01424 852920

CHAMBERLAIN Joe (*Acc, Org*): 43 Whitfield Avenue, St Peters, Broadstairs, Kent CT10 3HX ☎ Thanet 64479

CHRISTIE Steven (*Org, B Gtr, Dms, Gtr*): 023 8089 7361, 023 8086 3375

CLARIDGE Mike: 17 Links Drive, Christchurch, Dorset BH23 2RE ☎ 01202 478359

CLARKE Jane (*Gtr, Voc*): 4 Nursery Road, Tunbridge Wells, Kent TN4 9BZ ☎ 01892 547106

CLARKE John: Silver Birches, Jays Lane, Roundhurst, Haslemere, Surrey GU27 3BL ☎ 01428 4672

COLCHESTER Sheila (*Gtr*) ☎ 0956 284172

COLLINS Ronald: 7 Cowleas Close, Awbridge, Nr Romsey, Hants SO5 0HQ ☎ 01794 40007

COOK BERENDINA Jill (*Vln, Rec*): Greystones, Pyrford Road, West Byfleet, Weybridge, Surrey KT14 6QY ☎ 019323 42187

COOKE Peter (*Kbds*): 102 The Primary, High Street, Isle Of Wight PO30 1NL ☎ 01983 521488

COOMBS William: 8 Flower Crescent, Ottershaw, Chertsey KT16 0NS ☎ 0193287 2597

COOPER-SHERRING Mary: 9 Western Avenue, Ensbury Park, Bournemouth, Dorset BH10 5BN ☎ 01202 534499

CORDLE Matthew (*Vln*): 256 Rodway Road, Tilehurst, Reading RG30 6EG ☎ 0118 962 5577, 01491 681000

CORNFORD Malcolm (*Kbds*): 15 Pulborough Avenue, Hampden Park, Eastbourne, Sussex BN22 9QX ☎ 01323 503439, 0410 203 555 mob

COTTRELL Geoffrey (*Rec, Synth, Com*): 66 Pitts Road, Headington, Oxford OX3 8AE ☎ 01865 779351

COWLARD Barbara: 9 Newcombe Road, Southbourne, Bournemouth, Dorset BH6 5LX ☎ 01202 434730

COWNDEN Richard (*Voc*): 14 Wolverlands, Yeovil, Somerset BA22 7LQ ☎ 0101 33 6524675

CRAYFORD Marshall (*Tpt*): 44 Green Lane, Broadstairs, Kent CT10 2RR ☎ Thanet 61319

CUNNINGHAM John (*Gtr*): 106 Station Road, Aylesford, Kent ME20 7JW ☎ 01622 790392

D'INVERNO Raymon (*Flt*): 26 Thornbury Avenue, Shirley, Southampton SO1 5BR ☎ 01703 20928

DANIELS Alan (*Org*): 33 Bramley Avenue, Canterbury, Kent CT1 3XW ☎ 01227 766377

DAWNEY Michael (*Org, Com, Arr*): 5 Queens Road, Parkstone, Poole, Dorset BH14 9HF ☎ 01202 741596

DEFFERD Trevor (*Kbds, Clt, Md, Con*): 48 Victoria Mews, Park Lane, Newbury, Berks RG14 1EN ☎ 01635 34582

DELANY William: Address Unknown

DENNY Louise (*Acc*): Arun House, 58 Sedlescombe Road South, St. Leonards-on-Sea, Sussex TN38 0TJ ☎ 01424 714222

DILLON-WELCH Jonathan (*Kbds*): Chatsworth, Madeira Road, Littlestone, New Romney, Kent TN28 8QX ☎ 01797 361132, 070500 97085

DIXON Peter (*Vib*): 6 Gunwin Court, Aldwick, Bognor Regis, West Sussex PO21 4BW ☎ 01243 262058

DOD Derek (*Synth*): 36 Brougham Road, Southsea, Hants PO5 4PA ☎ 023 9282 9819

DORMER Craig (*Org, Db*): Tregony, Love Lane, Iver, Bucks SL0 9QT ☎ 01753 654049, 0498 527292, 020 7724 4900

DOWLEY Miles (*Gtr, Voc*): Ground Floor Flat, 12 Truscott Avenue, Bournemouth, Dorset BH9 1DQ ☎ 01202 547992

DOYLE Philip: 52 Old Farm Gardens, Blandford, Dorset DT11 7UU ☎ 01258 455266

DUKE Henry: 82 Amberley Drive, Hove, Sussex BN3 8JP ☎ Brighton 770817

DUTTON Richard (*Org, Synth*): 57 Great Clarendon Street, Oxford OX2 6AX ☎ 01865 552024, 01865 730815

DYKE-SMITH Mr T J (*Kbds*): 28 Lindford Chase, Lindford, Bordon, Surrey GU35 0TB ☎ 01420 478063, 0976 165120 mob

EDNEY Phillip (*Gtr, Tbn*): 54 Bryne Road, Balham, London SW12 9JB

EDWARDS Mark (*Kbds*): 1 Balsdean Farm Cottages, Balsdean, Rottingdean, Brighton, East Sussex BN2 7LA ☎ 01273 308 865

ELLIOTT John (*Tpt*): 44 Springfield Road, Guildford, Surrey GU1 4DP ☎ 01483 538988

ELLIOTT Kevin (*Kbds, Org, Tpt, Dms*): 42 Cliffe Road, Strood, Rochester, Kent ME2 3DR ☎ 01634 710344

EMERSON David (*Kbds, Gtr, Voc*): Flat 16, 56 Westover Road, Bournemouth BH1 2BS ☎ 01202 290451

EMERY Helen (*Ob*): Flat 1, 3 Wykeham Rd, Worthing, West Sussex BN11 4JG ☎ 01903 238792

ENGLISH Michael: The Old Post Office, Bedchester, Shaftesbury, Dorset SP7 0JU ☎ 01747 811212

FARIA Robert: 240 Gloucester Road, Brighton, East Sussex BN1 4AQ ☎ 01273 694669, 0956 367937, 01273 694669

FIELD Beatrice (*Voc*): 36 The Phelps, Kidlington, Oxon OX5 1SU ☎ 01865 371805

FIELDER Robert: Alberta House, Kings Park Drive, Bournemouth BH7 7AG ☎ 01202 396282

FISHER Andy (*Tpt*): 11 Hornbeam Gardens, West End, Southampton ☎ 023 8036 1951

FLINT James (*Gtr*): 25 Merdon Ave, Chandlers Ford, Eastleigh, Hampshire SO53 1EH ☎ 023 8025 4445, 0410 416660

FLORIDES Chris (*Kbds, B Gtr*): 72 Highlands Road, Horsham, West Sussex RH13 5NB ☎ 01403 240967

FORD Peter (*Org, Synth*): 96 Puddletown Crescent, Poole, Dorset BH17 8AN ☎ 01202 773007

FRANCIS Paul (*Org, Kbds*): 24 Balmoral Close, Lordswood, Southampton, Hants SO16 8ER ☎ 07010 707020, 07050 605922 mob

FRANKLIN Nikki (*Voc*): Ridleys, Balcombe Road, Crawley, West Sussex RH10 3NY ☎ 01293 425737, 01293 889016

GABRIEL Ella: 29A Berwick Road, Marlow, Bucks SL7 3AR ☎ 020 8861 1169, 01628 475348, 0958 339263

GEE Allegra (*Pf*): Flat 3, 24 Browning Avenue, Bournemouth BH5 1NN ☎ 01202 392783

GLAVEY Radina: The House on-The Park, Riverside, Marlow, Buckinghamshire SL7 2AB ☎ 01628 473853, 01628 890280

GODWIN Charles: 66 Glenfield Avenue, Bitterne, Southampton SO2 4EU ☎ 023 8055 6089

GODWIN Saskia (*Clt*): Winkton Lodge Cottage, Winkton, Christchurch, Dorset BH23 7AR ☎ 01202 484185, 01202 4741920

GOULD Peter: 29 Harland Crescent, Shirley, Southampton SO15 7QB ☎ 023 8070 1641

GREENSHIELDS Lynne (*Kbds, Voc, Org*): 24 Sandringham Close, Bournemouth, Dorset BH9 3QP ☎ 01202 533832

GRIFFITHS Arthur (*Org*): 15 Tangmere Place, Gibson Road, Canforth Heath, Poole BH17 7QY ☎ 01202 679727

GUNTRIP Raymond

HALL Garth: Yew Tree Cottage, 21 Church Road, Steep, Petersfield, Hants GU32 2DW ☎ 01730 231765

HALL Phinehas (*Cel, Gtr, Dms, Voc*): Glenbervie School Road, Rowledge, Farnham, Surrey GU10 4BW ☎ 01252 793527

HALLIDAY James: 123 Hollingbury Road, Brighton, Sussex BN1 7JN ☎ 01273 354613

HARDIN Eddie (*Org, Synth*): 20 Sovereign Court, Chobham Road, Sunningdale, Berks SL5 0HH ☎ 01344 291041, 01344 25061

HARDING Sam: 14 Waldren Close, Pitwynes, Poole, Dorset BH15 1XS ☎ 01202 666139

HARDYMAN Don (*Arr, Kbds*): 67 Richmond Park Avenue, Bournemouth, Dorset BH8 9DN ☎ 01202 394938

HARGREAVES Sean: 2 Pewley Way, Guilford, Surrey GU1 3PY ☎ 01483 572439

HARMON Keith: 52 Helen Avenue, Feltham, Middlesex TW14 9LB ☎ 020 8751 0417

HARRIS Keith (*Gtr*): Hillside Cottage, Farm Lane, Crawley, Near Witney, Oxon OX8 5TL ☎ 01993 773664

HASLETT John (*Vib*): 13 Broughton Close, Ensbury Park, Bournemouth BH10 6JB ☎ 01202 528 664

HAWKES Brian: The Old Orchard, Ellesborough Road, Butlers Cross, Aylesbury, Buckinghamshire HP17 0XH ☎ 01844 343222

HAYDOCK Neil (*Kbds, Gtr*): 3 Hedge End, Barnham, Bognor Regis, West Sussex PO22 0JP ☎ 01243 555125

HAYMAN Keith (*Gtr*): 40 Kaye Don Way, Weybridge, Surrey KT13 0UX ☎ 01932 856139, 0836 555056 mob

HAYNES Francis (*Org, Md*): The Cottage, 70 Padnell Road, Cowplain, Hants PO8 8EB ☎ 023 9226 2034

HAYWARD Peter (*Synth, Acc, Rec*): 21 Granville Park, London SE13 7DY

HEARTON Alan (*Kbds*): 5 Teviot Close, Guildford, Surrey GU2 6GS ☎ 01483 852542, 0467 386196, 01483 85542

HEWS Richard (*Org, Con*): 43 Parkfield Road, Worthing, Sussex BN13 1EP ☎ Worthing 65066

HEYWOOD Sandra (*Kbds, Vln*): 102 Church Way, Wheatley, Oxford OX33 1LU ☎ 01865 874307

HIGHAM Michael: North Cottage, Starveall Farm, Well Barn Estate, Moulsford, Oxfordshire OX10 9JR ☎ 01491 652 750, 0966 235365 mob

HILL Stephen (*Kbds, H Dul*): 52 Alexandra Road, Reading, Berks RG1 5PP ☎ 0118 926 1999

HOCKING Chris (*Kbds*): 16 Malvern Place, Bartestree, Herefordshire HR1 4AU ☎ 01432 851202, 01432 850952

HOCKNEY John (*Vib*): 31 Crestway, Luton, Chatham, Kent ME5 0BB ☎ 01634 846835

HOFFMEISTER James (*Kbds*): 11 Woodstock Road, Gosport, Hampshire PO12 1RS ☎ 023 9234 7638

HOLT Richard (*Kbds, B Gtr*): 76 Alexandra Road, Parkstone, Poole, Dorset BH14 9EW ☎ 01202 749778

HOPPER Jennifer (*Vla, Vln, Clt, Rec*): 50 Loosen Drive, Maidenhead, Berkshire SL6 3UT ☎ 01628 823259, 01628 829504

HUGHES Catherine (*Vln, Sax, Kbds, Gtr*): 51 Park Crescent Terrace, Brighton BN2 3HE ☎ 01273 680073

INSLEY Daniel (*Kbds, Dms, Com*): 59 Elaine Ave, Strood, Rochester, Kent ME2 2YW ☎ 01634 295495

JAMES Stanley: Samares, The Lees, Boughton Aluph, Ashford Kent TN25 4HX ☎ 01233 624749

JONES Dave (*E Pf, Org, Synth, Harm*): 59 Hackington Road, Tyler Hill, Canterbury, Kent CT2 9NE ☎ 01227 462463

JONES Mark (*Kbds, Dms*): 44 Burcote Drive, Anchorage Park, Portsmouth, Hants PO3 5UD ☎ 023 9266 4754

JUBY Luke (*Kbds, Sax, Flt*): Merlin's, St. Leonards Hill, Windsor, Berks SL4 4AT ☎ 01753 859382

KALETH James: 251 Dyke Road, Hove, Sussex BN3 6PA ☎ 01273 556613

KELLY Peter (*Vln*): 40 A Preston Close, Ryde, Isle Of Wight PO33 1DJ ☎ 01983 565864

KING Bryan (*Kbds*): 8 Maplehurst Close, St Leonards-on-Sea, East Sussex TN37 7NB

KING George (*Org*): 5 Wood Lane Close, Sonning Common, Reading, Berks RG4 9SP

KING Glenda (*Kbds, A Sax*): 5 Yew Tree Close, Newton Longville, Nr Milton Keynes MK17 0DG ☎ 01908 643 806, 0802 979806

KING Paul (*Clt*): 1 Claire Court, 67 Howard Road, Shirley, Southampton, Hampshire SO15 5BG ☎ 023 8034 6769, 0468 387811

KING Terry (*Kbds*): 26 Coronation Avenue, Bournemouth, Dorset BH9 1TN ☎ 01202 537856

KIRKMAN Dorothy (*Kbds, Org*): Woodacre, Chobham Road, Horsell, Woking, Surrey GU21 4AL ☎ 01483 715885

KIRTLEY Al (*Kbds*): Chestnut Tree Cottage, Brick Hill, Valley End, Chobham, Surrey GU24 8TL ☎ 01276 856603

LAPHAM Peter: Flat 1, 60 York Road, Tunbridge Wells, Kent TN1 1JY ☎ 01892 525957

LASKY Simon (*Com*): Dell Cottage, Church Road, Penn, Bucks HP10 8NX ☎ 01494 812236, 0966 404022

LAURENCE Grahame (*Org, Kbds, Md*): 1803 Wimborne Road, Bear Cross, Bournemouth, Dorset BH11 9AY ☎ 01202 574144

LAWRENCE Anthony: 189 Loddon Bridge Road, Woodley, Reading, Berks RG5 4BP ☎ Reading 690625

LAWRENCE Ralph: 17 Raymond Road, Shirley, Southampton SO1 5AG ☎ 023 8022 1493

LAXTON Elaine (*Vln, Gtr*): 26B Rosebery Avenue, Hampden Park, Eastbourne, East Sussex BN22 9QB ☎ 01323 509554

LEPORT Jeannette (*Vln, Gtr, Rec*): 25 Leigh Grove, Banbury, Oxon OX16 9LN ☎ 01295 255448

LEVER Dennis (*Org*): 45 Starmead Drive, Wokingham, Berkshire RG40 2JA ☎ 01734 783489

LEWIS Alan (*Ob, Sax, B Gtr, Dms*): Stoney, Park Lane, Lane End, High Wycombe, Bucks HP14 3LB ☎ 01494 881651

LEWIS Sharon (*Gtr, Acc, Voc*): No 6 Flat 3 Alfred Road, Brighton BN1 3RG ☎ 01273 323980

LITTLE Matt (*Kbds, B Gtr, Gtr, Flt*): 19 Kingfisher Close, Rowlands Castle, Hants PO9 6HG ☎ 023 9241 3748

LLOYD Geoffrey (*Voc*): 86, Melfort Road, Thornton Heath, Surrey CR4 7RN

LOMAS Trevor (*Kbds*): 104 Middlemead Road, Bookham, Surrey KT23 3DD ☎ 01372 457274

LONG Naomi (*Sax, Voc, Gtr*): 22 Halfpenny Close, Barming, Maidstone, Ket ME16 9AJ ☎ 01622 725877, 01426 300637

LONGLEY Chick (*Org, B Ldr*): Ridge Cottage, Corfe Lodge Road, Broadstone, Dorset BH18 9NF ☎ 01202 692555

MACKEY Justin (*Kbds, Voc, Com*): 18 Lynden Close, E Grafton, Marlborough, Wilts SN8 3US

MANN John: 13 Hawthorn Close, Saltdean, Brighton, Sussex BN2 8HX ☎ 01273 337833

MARTIN Brian (*Kbds, Org*): 44 Lake Hill, Sandown, Isle Of Wight PO36 9HF ☎ 01983 407156

MARTIN Gil (*Org, Arr, Md*): Oaklands Cottage, Babs Oak Hill, Sturry, Canterbury, Kent CT2 0JR ☎ 7710535

MARTIN Marcus: 29 Hillside Avenue, Worthing, Sussex BN14 9QR ☎ 01903 200232

MARX Steve (*Acc, E Gtr, Ac Gtr*): 'The Shambles', 8 Tubb Close, Bicester, Oxon OX6 8BN ☎ 01869 253448, 0976 178350, 01869 253448

MASTERSON Cliff (*Kbds, Voc, Com*): 92 Astra Drive, Gravesend, Kent DA12 4QE ☎ 01474 362547

MATHEWS Stanley (*Org*): 4 St Nicholas Street, Old Portsmouth, Hants PO1 2NZ ☎ 023 9282 6794

MCCARTHY Desmond (*Sax, Clt*): Address Unknown ☎ 023 9273 1900

MEARNS Stella (*Per, Voc*): 2 Knights Way, Alton, Hampshire GU34 1PJ ☎ 01420 86031

MELLORS Katie (*Flt, Voc*): 48Ambleside, Botley, Southampton, Hants SO30 2NT ☎ 01489 782868

MILES Raymond (*Org, Kbds*): Skipper's Cuddy, 32 Downs Walk, Peacehaven, East Sussex BN10 7ST ☎ 01273 586886

MILLER Judith: 19 Lucasters Road, Haywards Heath, W. Sussex RH16 1JN ☎ 01444 450372

MITCHELL Arthur: 55 Balfour Road, Brighton, East Sussex BN1 6ND ☎ 01273 507954

MOORE Gary: 38 Holly Hill, Bassett, Southampton, Hants SO16 7EW ☎ 023 8076 0501 & fax, 0585 949433 mob

MORRIS John (*Org, Synth, B Ldr*): 67 Jewell Road, Bournemouth, Dorset BH8 0JL ☎ 01202 392540

MORRISH Stephen (*Kbds, Cnt, Hrn, Voc*): Bunga Raya, 36 Forest Road, Bordon, Hants GU35 0BP ☎ 01420 474191

MR D (*Kbds, Tpt, Gtr, Rec*): 24 Alfred Road, Birchington, Kent CT7 9NJ ☎ 01843 843056 & fax

MUDGE Bill (*Kbds*): 14 Middle Road, Lymington, Hampshire SO41 9HF ☎ 01590 677162, 0468 081481 mob

NEAL Leo (*Md, B Ldr*): 159 Belle Vue Road, Bournemouth, Dorset BH6 3EN

NEAL Patrick (*E Pf, Org, Kbds*): 7 Rebbeck Road, Bournemouth, Dorset BH7 6LW ☎ 01202 432811

NEWBERRY Cecil (*Org*): 24 Carlton Road, Eastbourne BN22 7EN ☎ 01323 25016

NEWMAN Chris: 22 Vernon Road, Copnor, Portsmouth, Hampshire PO3 5DS ☎ 023 9269 3988

NEWTON Malcolm (*Kbds*): 18 Albany Terrace, New Street, Ringwood, Hants BH24 3AD ☎ 01425 472416

NOON Graham (*Kbds*): 24 Eversfield, Southwater, West Sussex RH13 7GF ☎ 01403 730098

NORMAN Harry (*Org, E Pf, Synth*): 16 Fairdene, Southwick, Brighton, Sussex BN42 4QN ☎ 01273 884379

O'NEILL Patrick: Somerhill, 6 Cambourne Avenue, Westgate, Kent CT8 8NA ☎ Thanet 32388

OBRIEN Sarah (*Gtr*): 12 St Wilfrids Road, Burgess Hill, West Sussex RH15 8BD ☎ 01444 232097, 0958 805540

OLIVER Michael: 64 Eskdale Avenue, Ramsgate, Kent CT11 0PB ☎ Thanet 581199

ORMISTON Susan (*Clt*): 15 Withy Close, Romsey, Hampshire SO51 7SA ☎ 01794 517599

PAGETT Thomas: 112 Kinson Road, Bournemouth, Dorset BH10 4DJ

PAINTER Greg: 'Longways', 1B Cuckoo Bushes Lane, Chandlersford, Eastleigh, Hants SO5 1JW ☎ 023 8025 3406

PALMER Philip (*Org, Kbds*): 27 Brierley Road, Northbourne, Bournemouth, Dorset BH10 6EB ☎ 01202 573743

PAPWORTH Peter (*Org*): Flat 1 Nairn Court, Talbot Woods, Bournemouth, Dorset BH3 7BE ☎ 01202 546392

PEACE Hazel (*Acc*): Address Unknown

PEARCE Butch: 29 Park Gardens, Christchurch, Dorset BH23 3PQ ☎ 01202 482947

PENTECOST Rickard (*Kbds*): 22 Croft Road, Old Town, Hastings, East Sussex TN34 3HJ ☎ 01424 714606

PHAROAH Kenneth (*Org*): 90 Dean Road, Bitterne, Southampton SO2 5AU ☎ 023 8046 2130

PICKETT Martin (*B Gtr*): 19 Northampton Road, Oxford OX1 4TG ☎ 01865 726462

PIGA Daniele (*Kbds*): 124 Oxford Road, Harston, Oxford OX3 0RE ☎ 01865 622890

POSKITT Kjarton (*Kbds, Gtr, Multi*): 30 Wentworth Road, York YO2 1DG ☎ 01904 652884

PRESTON Colin (*Kbds, B Gtr, Flt, Gtr*): 4 St Giles Street, New Bradwell, Milton Keynes MK13 0BE ☎ 01908 311639

PRICE Dennis (*Org*): 32 Gurney Road, Shirley, Southampton SO1 5GG ☎ 023 8077 2016

REDMOND Patrick (*B Ldr*): 10 Montpelier Terrace, Brighton, East Sussex BN1 3DF ☎ 01273 326680

REES-WILLIAMS David (*Org, Ob*): 18 Clyde Street, Canterbury, Kent ☎ 01227 456552

REEVES Darren (*Tpt, Voc*): Mille Failte, Bones Lane, Burton, Petersfield, Hants GU31 5SE ☎ 01730 264284, 0498 755924, 01730 262159

REEVES Robert: 79 Sandy Lane, Fairoak, Eastleigh, Hants SO5 7GA ☎ 023 8069 2649

ROBERTS Anthony (*Org, Arr, Voc*): 10 Connell Road, Poole, Dorset BH15 3AT ☎ 01202 380519

ROBERTS Henry (*Vib*): Old Danworth Cottage, Danworth Lane, Hurstpierpoint, Sussex BN6 9LN ☎ 01273 833110

ROBINSON Peter (*Kbds, T Sax*): 84 Balcombe Road, Horley, Surrey RH6 9AY ☎ 01293 776322, 0161 707 0512

ROCKHILL Katherine (*Kbds, Vln*): 3 Celtic Drive, Andover, Hampshire SP10 2UA ☎ 01264 351453, 0498 692037 mob

ROSS Angela (*Theory*): Peppercorn Cottage, 13 Manor Road, South Hinksey, Oxford OX1 5AS ☎ 01865 327909, 01865 327909

ROUSE Helen (*Vln*): 19 Eston Court, Bradville, Milton Keynes, Bucks MK13 7DF ☎ 01908 318386, 020 7210 3107 day

RUSSELL Peter: 1, Magnolia Close, Wick, Bournemouth, Dorset BH6 4LQ ☎ 01202 420322

SATTERLY Christopher: 2 Leicester Road, Shirley, Southampton SO1 2NY ☎ 023 8077 1848

SAUNDERS Nicolas: 3 Cleveland Road, Chichester, West Sussex PO19 2HF ☎ 01243 539543

SCOTT Jonathan (*Gtr, Voc*): 10 Durlston Drive, Bognor Regis, West Sussex PO22 9EH ☎ 01243 820291

SCUTT Cyril: 12 Parkwood Close, Tunbridge Wells, Kent TN2 3SX ☎ 01892 537000

SEABROOK Terence: 11 Bernard Road, Brighton, East Sussex BN2 3ER ☎ Brighton 673914

SEARLE-BARNES Paul: High Corrie, Letton Close, Blandford, Dorset DT11 7SS ☎ 01258 451782

SEED Christopher (*Sax, Rec*): 3 Brewers Lane, Twyford, Winchester, Hants SO21 1RQ ☎ 01962 715134

SHADE Terence (*Kbds, B Ldr*): 90 Glenferness Avenue, Talbot Woods, Bournemouth BH3 7EY ☎ 01202 532413

SHINN Donald (*Org*): 84 Newlands Avenue, Shirley, Southampton, Hants SO15 5ES ☎ 023 8077 2813

SIDWICK Keith (*Kbds*): Broadlands, 6 Valette Road, Bournemouth, Dorset BH9 3JB ☎ 01202 513852

SIMMONDS Maurice (*Org*): 5 Oak Grove, Bognor Regis, Sussex PO22 9JL ☎ 01243 820727

SKENE-KEATING Paul (*Voc, Com, Arr*): Popps Farm, Gun Hill, Nr Horam, East Sussex TN21 0LA ☎ 01825 872744

SKINNARD Andrew (*Vln*): 5 Manor Terrace, Fern Road, Farncombe, Godalming, Surrey GU7 3EP ☎ 01483 427152

SLOMAN Carol (*Vln, Flt, Gtr*): 19 Cornwall Gardens, Brighton BN1 6RH ☎ 01273 552000

SMITH Stephen (*Kbds, Voc, Md, Org*): 167 Ringwood Road, St Leonards, Ringwood, Hants BH24 2NP ☎ 01425 473432

SMITH Trevor (*Org, Kbds*): 45 North Way, Seaford, East Sussex BN25 3HP ☎ 01323 896004

SPANNER Leslie (*Org*): 27 Newcombe Road, Southampton SO15 2FT ☎ 023 8033 3673

SPARKS Ned (*Org, Acc*): 2 Audley Court, Tennyson Road, Freshwater, Isle Of Wight PO40 9DR ☎ 01983 754515

STEPONITIS Bernie (*Org, Db, St Pan*): 6 Second Avenue, Hove, East Sussex BN3 2LH ☎ 01273 208543

STOKES Anthony: Flat 17, Hannagh Grange, Northcote Road, Bournemouth BH1 4SJ ☎ 01202 512298

STRINGER John (*Org*): 18 Speen Hill Close, Newbury, Berks RG13 1QR ☎ Newbury 45211

SUMMERFIELD John (*Db, Kbds*): 5 Scott Avenue, Rainham, Gillingham, Kent ME8 8BL ☎ 01634 379438

SUSSEX Kate: 19 Latimer Road, St Helens, Isle Of Wight PO33 1TR ☎ 01983 874962

SYLVESTER Jayne H: Corner Close, Whitmead Lane, Tilford, Farnham, Surrey GU10 2BP ☎ 01252 783166, 01252 781633

TAYLOR Denis (*E Pf, Voc*): 14 Vicarage Way, Burton, Christchurch, Dorset BH23 7NE ☎ 01202 482323

TAYLOR Frank: Address Unknown

THOMPSON Jack: Flat 13, 301 Wimborne Road, Poole, Dorset BH15 3DH ☎ 01202 670012

THORNE Christopher (*Kbds, Hrn*): 74 Hevers Avenue, Horley, Surrey RH6 8DA ☎ 01293 771 896

TIMBERLAKE Charles (*E Pf*): 24A The Square, Titchfield, Hants PO14 4AF ☎ 01329 845265

TIMBLER John: 74, Cowper Street, Hove, Sussex BN3 5BN ☎ Brighton 774375

TOOK Ernest (*Org, Kbds*): 7, Warren Court, 81, Underdown Road, Southwick, Sussex BN4 4HN ☎ Brighton 593903

TOP CAT (*B Gtr*): 119 Corhampton Road, Boscombe East, Bournemouth BH6 5NZ ☎ 01202 427704

TWISELTON Simon (*Com*): 22 Durweston, Blandford, Dorset DT11 0QE ☎ 01258 455525

URRY Michael (*B Ldr, Db*): 15 Eastport Lane, Lewes, Sussex BN7 1TL ☎ Lewes 2931

VANDERHEYDEN Timo (*B Gtr, Kbds, Gtr, Per*): PO Box 21, East Grinstead RH18 5YH

WAGSTAFF Nicholas (*Kbds*)

WALCH Peter (*Org, Synth*): 2, Sandringham Close, Bournemouth, Dorset BH9 3QP ☎ 01202 534255

WALLACE Graeme (*Org, Gtr, Voc*): 17A Girton Close, Titchfield Common, Fareham, Hants PO14 4QZ ☎ 01489 602456

WARDELL Tony (*Org*): 8 Partridge Walk, Poole, Dorset BH14 8HL ☎ 01202 707187

WARDEN Percy (*B Ldr, Acc*): 20 Saltdean Drive, Saltdean, Sussex BN2 8SB ☎ 01273 333334

WEBBER David (*Kbds*): 10 The Birches Close, North Baddesley, Southampton, Hampshire SO52 9HL ☎ 023 8073 3983

WEST Colin (*E Pf*): 29 Colehill Crescent, Bournemouth BH9 3QG ☎ 01202 527 199

WHEELER Frank (*Tbn*): Capers, Forelands Farm Lane, Bembridge, Isle Of Wight PO35 5TJ ☎ 01983 873432

WHENNELL Richard (*Arr, Voc*): 25 Manor Road, Windsor, Berkshire SL4 5LP ☎ 01753 866924

WHITE Bernard (*Org*): 2 Salcombe Avenue, Copnor, Portsmouth, Hants PO3 6LD ☎ 023 9235 2591

WHITE Gregory: 1 Haleswood, Cobham, Surrey KT11 2NF ☎ 01932 865143

WHITE Ian (*Kbds*): 102 Heathfield Crescent, Mileoak, Brighton, East Sussex BN41 2YR ☎ 01273 414994

WHITE Mark (*Kbds, Gtr, Com*): Kinghton, 7 Marley Combe Road, Haslemere, Surrey GU27 3SN ☎ 01428 644 626

WHITE Raymond (*Org*): 217 Devonshire Avenue, Southsea, Hants PO4 9EE ☎ 023 9273 1714

WHITNEY Terence: Highcroft, Goring Road, Steyning, Sussex BN44 3GP ☎ Steyning 812555

WHITTAMORE Monica (*Voc*): 63 Chantry Road, Kemptson, Bedford MK42 7QU ☎ 01234 853496

WHITTELL Adrian (*Org, Clt*): 6 Conrad Close, Parkwood, Rainham, Kent ME8 9SD ☎ 01634 387367

WRIGHT Lawrie (*Kbds, Gtr, Db, B Gtr*): 21 Radstock Road, Reading RG1 3PS ☎ 01734 612127

SOUTH WEST

ADAMS Ronald (*Org, Arr, B Ldr*): 7 Oxford Road, Worthing, West Sussex BN11 1XG ☎ 01903 529892

ADELE Maia (*Synth, Cel, Gtr, Vla*): ☎ 0411 569807, 01437 769660

AHLERS Claude (*Dms*): 87 Redland Road, Bristol BS6 6RD ☎ 0117 924 5511

ALLEN George (*Org, Kbds*): 7 Wesley Lane, Southwick, Trowbridge, Wiltshire BA14 9NU ☎ 01225 858028, 01225 852228

ALLPASS Andrew (*Kbds, Synth, Org*): 4 Pembery Road, Bedminster, Bristol, Avon BS3 3JR ☎ 0117 9664589

ALSOP Graham: 35 Elburton Road, Sea Mills, Bristol BS9 2PZ
☎ 0117 9682814

ALVEY Michael (*Kbds, B Gtr, Tbn*): 6 Peters Crescent, Marldon, Paignton, South Devon TQ3 1PQ ☎ 01803 525178

ANDERSON Jack (*Clt*): 12 Moseley Grove, Uphill, Weston Super Mare BS23 4SF ☎ 01934 620483

ANDREWS Edna (*Org*): Applecroft, Meavy Bourne, Yelverton, Devon PL20 6AR

ARMSTRONG Rosalie: 43 St Michaels Road, Llandaff, Cardiff CF5 2AN ☎ 029 2056 0176

ASH Jacqueline (*Org, Kbds*): 3 Hillcrest Road, Hayle, Cornwall TR27 4NR ☎ 01736 753514

BACON Desmond: Newport Hill Cottage, North Curry, Somerset TA3 6DJ ☎ 01823 490058

BADDER Martin (*Kbds*): Old Orchard, Notton, Lacock, Chippenham, Wiltshire SN15 2NF ☎ 01249 730295

BAGGOTT John (*Kbds*): 13 Walnut Crescent, Kingswood, Bristol BS15 4HX ☎ 0117 961 2329

BAKER Richard (*Db, Org*): 107 Upper Bristol Road, Weston-Super-Mare, North Somerset BS22 8ON ☎ 01934 413727

BALL Dawn: 89 Leighton Avenue, Park South, Swindon, Wilts SN3 2JG ☎ 01793 644051

BAMFORD Gary (*B Gtr*): 12 Meadowsweet Close, Haydon Wick, Swindon, Wilts SN2 3QX ☎ 01793 703682, 01793 772622

BARKER Clifford (*Kbds, Org*): 33 Yeomead, Nailsea, Bristol BS19 1JA ☎ 01275 790419, 0468 436365 mob, 01275 855634

BARNARD Henry: Porthmeor, Third Avenue, Colesdown Hill, Billacombe Nr Plymouth PL9 8AN ☎ 01752 41475

BARON Michael (*Org, Con*): 2 School House, Pillowell, Nr Lydney, Gloucester GL15 4QT ☎ 01594 562526

BEAHAM-POWELL Nigel (*Kbds*): 7 The Paragon, Clifton, Bristol BS8 4LA ☎ 0117 9731619

BENET Pamela (*Voc*): 17 Colley End Park, Paignton, Devon TQ3 3BY ☎ 01803 525576

BISHOP David (*Org*): 27 Stowey Road, Yatton, Bristol BS49 4HX ☎ Yatton 832661

BLACKWOOD Peter: Virginia House, 44 Bristol Road, Keynsham, Avon BS18 2BE ☎ 0117 9862578

BLANCHARD Christine (*Com*): 4 Skirrid Road, Abergavenny, Monmouthshire NP7 5UA ☎ 01873 857609

BLOMFIELD Jim (*Kbds*): 63 Park Street, Totterdown, Bristol BS4 3BJ ☎ 0117 977 8557

BOYCE Edward (*Org, Md*): Chewton, Cardiff Road, Creigiau, Cardiff CF4 8NL ☎ 029 2089 0103

BRAIN Reg (*Org*): Address Unknown

BRAINE Anthony (*Synth*): 4 Langham Road, Knowle, Bristol BS4 2LJ ☎ 0117 977 9917 & fax, 0385 756082

BREESE Emma: 64 All Saints Road, Cheltenham, Glos. GL52 2HA

BROOKES Ritchie (*Org, Kbds*): 33 Fleckers Drive, Hatherley, Cheltenham, Glos GL51 5BB ☎ 01242 234792

BROOKS Robert (*Org, Voc*): Flat 16, Elmsdale Court, Byron Road, St Helier, Jersey, Channel Islands JE2 4LQ ☎ 01534 317000

BROOMHALL John (*Kbds*): Tenth View, Watledge Bank, Watledge, Glos. GL6 0AY ☎ 01453 836647

BROWN Anne (*Vln*): 21 Windsor Road, Porthcawl, Mid Glamorgan CF36 3LR ☎ 01656 782632

BROWN Paul (*Org*): 11, Kents Road, Wellswood, Torquay, South Devon TQ1 2NN ☎ 01803 211140

BUCKLEY Geoffrey: The Old Cottage, Treadam, Llantilio Crossenny, Nr Abergavenny NP7 8TA ☎ 01600 85354

BURNHAM Catherine (*Flt*): Mosel, Trecarne, Tremar Liskeard, Cornwall PL14 5EF ☎ 01579 344612

BUTCHER Joseph (*Vla, Cong, La Per*): 25 St Julian Street, Baneswell, Newport, Gwent, S. Wales NP9 4GP ☎ 01633 252370

CHAMBERLAIN Cyril (*Org*): 4 Pentre Banadi, Killay, Swansea SA2 7DD ☎ 01792 204412

CHEER John (*Org, Vln*): 77 Minny Street, Cathays, Cardiff CF2 4ET ☎ 029 2034 2276

CHEW Caroline: Helwell, 57 Doniford Road, Watchet, Somerset TA23 0TE ☎ 01984 684988

CLASS Sarah (*Kbds, Clt, Voc*): 16 Abbotsford Road, Cotham, Bristol BS6 6HB

CLUTTERBUCK Paul: 9 St Annes Close, Pittville, Cheltenham, Glos GL52 2QJ

COLLETT David: 80 Fouracre Crescent, Downend, Bristol BS16 6PU

COOK Leonard: 372 Portway, Shirehampton, Bristol BS11 9UD

CORNFIELD Philip (*Db*): 25 Lichfield Gardens, Richmond, Surrey TW9 1AP

COSGRAVE Mike (*Kbds, Gtr, B Gtr*): 33 Wyndham Avenue, Exeter EX1 2PQ ☎ 020 8672 8293

COTTIS Nicholas: The Studio, Badworthy Cottage, Didworthy, South Brent Devon TQ10 9EG ☎ 01364 72937

COTTLE David (*Org, Tpt*): 45 Southward Lane, Newton, Mumbles, Swansea SA3 4QD ☎ 01792 368 171

COTTRELL Sue (*Clt, A Sax*): 151 Mallards Reach, Marshfield, Cardiff, Cf3 8Nl CF3 8NL ☎ 01633 681322

CRIPPS Rod (*Org*): 26 Turkdean Road, Cheltenham, Glos GL51 6AL ☎ 01242 228548

CYNAN Geraint (*Synth*): 41 Church Road, Whitchurch, Cardiff CF4 2DY ☎ 029 2062 5803, 0585 542552

DAVIES Austin (*Arr*): Rossmore, 90 Colcot Road, Barry, Glamorgan CF6 8BS ☎ 01446 733551

DAVIES Bryan: 3 Morris Terrace, Ferndale, Rhondda, Mid Glamorgan CF43 4ST ☎ 01443 730891

DAVIES Henry (*Db, Sou, Arr, B Ldr*): 33 Stanbury Avenue, Fishponds, Bristol BS16 5AL ☎ 0117 9646500

DAVIES John: 5 Englefield, Wooton Bassett, Swindon, Wiltshire SN4 8BZ ☎ 01793 852749

DAVIES Susan: 82 Liskeard Road, Saltash, Cornwall PL12 4HG ☎ 0175 55 3646

DAWSON Mark (*Org, Arr*): The Brambles, Rue Du Hocq, St. Clement, Jersey, C.I. JE2 6LF ☎ 07979 724059

DENHAM Michael: 1 The Spinney, Broadmayne, Dorchester, Dorset DT2 8UH ☎ 01305 852626

DENNY Debra

DORNEY Kevin (*Kbds, Gtr*): 289 Milton Road, Weston Super Mare, Somerset, Avon BS22 8JB ☎ 01934 620991

DRAISEY James (*Kbds, Saxes, Clt, Flt*): ☎ 01633 895042, 0378 896056

DU VALLE Cecil (*Synth, Arr, Com*): Stara Masha, East Taphouse, Liskeard, Cornwall PL14 4NJ ☎ 01579 20636

EASTMAN Cyril (*Acc*): Hillside, Higher Warberry Road, Torquay TQ1 1SF ☎ 01803 27388

EDMUNDS Chris (*Acc, Mldn, H Gurd*): Carina, Tower Hill Road, Crewkerne, Somerset TA18 8BJ ☎ 01460 73052

EVANS Euros (*Cel*): Ty Uchaf, Upper Farmhouse, Rhoose, Vale Of Glamorgan CF62 3EP ☎ 01446 710335, 01446 710795 fax

EYLES Frederick: 129 Wells Road, Bath BA2 3AN ☎ Bath 20196

FILLMORE Miriam (*Clt*): Middlewick, 10 Brookhall, Rue Des Pres, St Helier, Jersey, C.I. JE2 7QF ☎ 01534 23848

FINCH Matthew (*Org*): 33 Trinity Road, Combe Down, Bath ☎ 01225 840264

FITKIN Graham (*Kbds, Com*): 4 Lisbon Terrace, St Buryan, West Cornwall TR19 6DX ☎ 01736 810927

FORBES Jerry (*Kbds, Gtr*): Hingstone House, Kit Hill, Callington, Cornwall PL17 8HW ☎ 01579 370350 & fax

FRYER Ruth: 76 Lakeside Drive, Cardiff, South Wales CF2 6DG ☎ 029 2076 2891

FURNEAUX Joanna (*Rec*): 10 Landseer, North Cheriton, Templecombe, Somerset BA8 0AS ☎ 01963 34541 & fax

GALLIMORE Joseph (*Kbds*): 5 Brent Road, Horfield, Bristol BS7 ☎ 0117 9857717

GARD John-Paul (*Org*): 64 Church Road, Soundwell, Bristol BS16 4RQ ☎ 01523 111033

GARLAND Miranda (*Voc*): Ground Floor Flat, 197 Cheltenham Road, Cotham, Bristol BS6 5QX

GAY Elsie (*Vln*): 7 High Park, Knowle, Bristol 4 BS14 9AH ☎ 0117 9774593

GIBBIN Hilary: Hunts Hill House, Hunts Hill, Blunsdon, Wiltshire SN2 4BN ☎ 01793 706265

MUSIC TEACHER will...

* Guide you on the interpretation of set works for GCSE and the ULEAC Anthology
* Familiarise you with the latest computer hardware and music software for schools
* Keep you up to date on the relevant courses and seminars
* Provide reviews of the sheet music and books published during the year

Monthly £2.95

ANNUAL SUBSCRIPTION PRICES:

United Kingdom £34; airmail Europe £41; airmail outside Europe £47 (N & S America, Africa, Middle East and Hong Kong); £50 (Australia, New Zealand, Japan and Far East); surface mail worldwide £37

To subscribe please send your cheque (in pounds Sterling made payable to Rhinegold Publishing Ltd) to: Rhinegold Publishing Ltd (MT SUBS), Freepost, Gravesend, Kent DA12 2BR

CREDIT CARD SUBSCRIPTIONS
Tel: 01474 334500 (office hours); Fax: 01474 325557

Music Teacher

First published in 1909

The magazine for everyone concerned with music education

FREE Music Teacher GUIDES

Music Teacher subscribers are also sent up to six FREE supplementary guides published during the course of the year on subjects such as Notes for the Associated Board Piano and Violin Exams and Summer Schools

Modern Music

probably the south west's biggest stockists of group gear

all top names and major agencies under one roof

hire • tuition • repairs • demo tapes • part exchanges

including Cornwall's specialist drum department

01872 271701

Kenwyn Street • Truro

GIBBONS John *(Org, Ob, Con)*: 149 Woodhouse Avenue, Perivale, Greenford, Middlesex UB6 8LQ ☎ 020 8991 5063

GILLICK Stanley *(Cop, Com)*: 3 Danes Way, Pinhoe, Exeter, Devon EX4 9ES ☎ 01392 66466

GODDARD Jeremy *(Voc, E Pf, Dms)*: Redland Green Farm, Redland Green, Bristol BS6 7HF ☎ 0117 942 0256, 0117 942 0256

GODDARD Paul *(Voc, Sax, Gtr)*: Redland Green Farm, Redland Green, Bristol BS6 7HF ☎ 0117 9420256

GOLDSMITH Richard *(Song W, Com, Arr)*: Highfields, Bownham Park, Rodborough Common, Stroud, Gloucester GL5 5BY ☎ 01453 873641, 01453 872150

GOOCH Jonathan *(Gtr)*: Blue Haze, Seatown, Nr Bridport, Dorset DT6 6JT ☎ 01297 489259, 01305 251428

GOSS Luke *(Acc, Gtr, Hrn, Didj)*: 5 Arran Street, Roath, Cardiff, South Wales CF2 3HR ☎ 029 2047 2115

GREENHALGH Mark *(Kbds, Flt, Gtr)*: 3 Bury Mead, Codford, Warminster BA12 ONU ☎ 01985 851 014

GREENLEE Martin *(Kbds, Gtr, Dms)*: 100 Barton Road, Barnstaple, Devon EX32 8NG ☎ 01271 344402

GREENWAY Charles *(Kbds, Vln)*: 41 Long Acre Drive, Nottage, Porthcawl, Mid Glamorgan CF36 3SB ☎ 01656 786581, 0468 296613 mob

GRIFFITHS Gareth *(Org, Db, Clt, Vln)*: Upper Flat, 47 Pontcanna Street, Cardiff CF1 9HR ☎ 029 2064 4618

GRIFFITHS Jonathan: 7 Tylchawen Crescent, Tonyrefail, Porth, Mid Glamorgan CF39 8AL ☎ 01443 676752

GROVE Peter *(Per)*: 21 Heronswood, Salisbury, Wiltshire SP2 8DH ☎ 01722 325771 & fax

GULLIFORD Jonathan *(Org, Voc, Vln)*: 81 The Hollies, Quakers Yard, Treharris, Mid Glamorgan CF46 5PP ☎ 01443 410699

GUY John: 8 Hillside Crescent, Goodwick, Dyfed SA64 0JU ☎ 01348 874520

HAMILTON Rachel *(E Pf, Flt)*: 2 Ivy Lane, Fishponds, Bristol, Avon BS6 3QL ☎ 0117 958 4368

HARROD Sheila *(Voc)*: 8 Mellow Ground, Haydon Wick, Swindon, Wilts SN2 3QJ ☎ 01793 725863

HART Chris *(Acc)*: 38 High Street, Marshfield, Chippenham, Wilts SN14 8LP ☎ 01225 891453

HARVEY Frank *(Org, Clt)*: 26 Waite Meads Close, Purton, Nr Swindon, Wilts SN5 9ET ☎ 01793 770139

HARWOOD Juliet *(Voc)*: 618 Dorchester Road, Weymouth DT3 5LH ☎ 01305 814940

HAWKES Philip *(Kbds, Tpt)*: 101 Browning Road, Milehouse, Plymouth, Devon PL2 3AW ☎ 01752 563804

HAWKINS Mary *(Voc, Flt, Ac Gtr, B Gtr)*: Stoneleigh, Thornhill Road, Sth Marston, Swindon SN3 4RY ☎ 01793 825070

HILL Vaughan *(Voc, Kbds, Song W)*: 9 Queen Victoria Road, Westbury Park, Bristol BS6 7PD ☎ 0117 9741135

HODGSON Janet *(Ob)*: 112 Headlands Grove, Upper Stratton, Swindon, Wiltshire SN2 6HP ☎ 01793 531399

HOOPER David *(Org)*: 13 Washington Close, Preston, Paignton, Devon TQ3 2QJ ☎ 01803 664382

HOROBIN Liz *(Flt)*: 42 Somerset Rd, Frome, Somerset BA11 1HE ☎ 01373 466405

HUGO Peter *(Kbds)*: 115 Thrupp Lane, Thrupp, Stroud, Glos GL5 2DQ ☎ 01453 882134

HURDEN Sammy *(Voc)*: Yew Tree Cottage, Wytherstone, Nr Powerstock, Dorset DT6 3TQ ☎ 01308 485407

HURLEY Alan *(E Pf)*: 9 Teviot Road, Keynsham, Bristol BS31 1QS ☎ 0117 9092402

HUTCHINGS Gillian *(Kbds)*: 1 The Glebe, All Cannings, Devies, Wilts SN10 3NW ☎ 01380 860530

INCLEDON Rosalind *(Kbds, Tbn, Tpt, Clt)*: 13 Ernesettle Crescent, Hight Saint Budeaux, Plymouth, Devon PL5 2ET ☎ 01752 361434

IRONS Howard *(Gtr)*: Holcombe Farm, Oakhill Road, Dawlish, Devon EX7 0LJ ☎ 01686 862243

JAMES Sian *(Hrp)*

JOEL Dr *(Kbds, Ind Per)*: 62 Wingfield Grove, Trowbridge BA14 9EN ☎ 01225 760612 & fax

JONES David *(Con)*: 40 Abertaw Road, Newport, Gwent NP9 9QP ☎ 01633 278153, 0585 292402 mob

JONES Dyfan *(Com, Kbds, Gtr)*: 14 Clifton Street, Aberdar, Morgannwg Ganol, Mid Glamorgan S.Wales CF44 7PB ☎ 01685 873440

JONES Konrad *(Org, Arr)*: 14 Windsor Street, Caerphilly, Mid Glamorgan CF8 1FW ☎ 029 2088 6553

JUBINSKY Julian *(Acc)*: 67 Henley Drive, Highworth, Swindon, Wilts SN6 7JU ☎ 01793 764121, 01793 764121

KAY Julian *(Flt)*: 14 The Beeches, Trowbridge, Wilts BA14 7HG ☎ 01225 768 885

KELLY David *(Kbds, Cel)*: Marston Inn, Marston Magna, Yeovil, Somerset BA22 8BX ☎ 01935 850365

KNIGHT Alfred: Trengilly, Longbrook, Chillington, Knightsbridge, South Devon TQ7 2LX ☎ 01548 580127

LAMB Bert *(Gtr, Bjo)*: 44 White Street, Easterton, Devizes, Wiltshire SN10 4PA ☎ 01380 813555

LANDRY Les *(Org)*: 28 Maple Avenue, Torpoint, Cornwall PL11 2NE ☎ 01752 812896

LANFEAR Paul *(Com)*: 120 Charlton Road, Kingswood, Bristol BS15 1HF ☎ 0117 960 2937

LAUGHARNE David *(Kbds, Synth)*: 60 Purcell Road, Penarth, South Glamorgan CF64 3QN ☎ 029 2070 7470

LYON David *(Kbds, Com, Arr)*: 1 St. Rumbolds Road, Shaftesbury, Dorset SP7 8NE ☎ 01747 55903

MACAULAY Mary *(Vln, Acc, Voc)*: ☎ 01803 875985, 0976 427762

MAGGS John *(Org, Kbds)*: 54 Murch Road, Dinas Powys, Vale Of Glamorgan CF64 4RD ☎ 029 2051 5443

MAINTENANT Fred *(Tpt)*: Springdown House, Springhill, Kingsdown, Bristol BS2 8HX ☎ 0117 924 0944, 0117 924 0944

MANLEY Joyce: 38 Ennerdale Avenue, Longlevens, Gloucester GL2 0EF ☎ 01452 532780

MARAMIS Dimitris: 2A Colum Road, Cathys, Cardiff, Wales CF1 3EG ☎ 07889 943863, 029 2034 4906

MARSHALL Julian *(Kbds, Vln)*: 19 Corn Park, South Brent, Torquay TQ10 9DG ☎ 01364 73572

MARTIN Peter *(Synth)*: 8 Balaclava Rd, Cardiff, South Wales CF2 5BB ☎ 029 2048 5011

MASSOCCHI Jeanette *(Voc)*: The Old Cottage, Treadam, Llantilio Crossenny, Nr Abergavenny,Gwent NP7 8TA ☎ 01600 85354

MAY Kenneth *(Org)*: 11 St Gabriels Avenue, Peverell, Plymouth PL3 4JQ ☎ 01752 266091

MAYES Joanna *(Voc)*: Claremont House, Claremont Avenue, Kingskerswell, Newton Abbot, Devon TQ12 5HA ☎ 01803 874 034

MAYO Sandra *(Flt, Voc)*: Kington Cottage, 4 Sutton Road, Kington Langley, Nr Chippenham, Wiltshire SN15 55NE ☎ 01249 758122

MCCARTHY Heather: 37 Hungerford Road, Lower Weston, Bath BA1 3BU ☎ 01225 444703

MILVERTON Craig *(Kbds)*: 85 Portland Street, Newtown, Exeter, Devon EX1 2EG ☎ 01392 210034

MOBBS Kenneth *(Hpsd, Org)*: 16 All Saints Road, Bristol, Avon BS8 2JJ ☎ 0117 9733613

MORETON Russell *(Clt)*: 38 Seager Drive, Windsor Quay, Cardiff CF1 7QA ☎ 029 2066 4211

MORGAN Basil *(Org)*: 65 Lower Redland Road, Bristol, Avon BS6 6SR ☎ 0117 9733316

MORRIS Margaret *(Kbds)*: 39 Marlbrook Road, Hereford HR2 7PY ☎ 01432 343363

MURRAY Andrew *(Kbds, Per)*: 6 Southfield Road, Heathfield, Bideford, N Devon EX39 4BY ☎ 012372 76827

NAIR Dhevdhas *(Santoor)*: April Cottage, 31A Lower Street, Chagford, Newton Abbot, Devon TQ13 8AZ ☎ 01647 432457, 020 7359 0840

NEGUS Anthony *(Clt)*: 56 Westbourne Road, Penarth, South Glam CF64 3HB

NEWTON Edmund: 9 Willis Court, Marine Drive, Burnham-on-Sea, Somerset TA8 1NL

NICOLL John *(E Pf, B Gtr, Com, Arr)*: 67A Westover Road, Westbury-on-Trym, Bristol BS9 3LP ☎ 0117 950 1188

OSBORNE Kelly *(Rec)*: 3 Third Ave, Trecenydd, Caerphilly, Mid Glamorgan, S. Wales CF83 2SH ☎ 029 2086 0941, 01523 783899 pager

OWEN Albert *(E Pf, Synth, Com, Flt)*: Melindwr, Ponterwyd, Aberystwyth, Dyfed SY23 3JY ☎ 01970 85603

PAGE Andy *(Org)*: 1 Plum Tree Road, Locking Castle, Weston-Super-Mare, Somerset B22 ☎ 01934 620668, 01426 687760 pager, 0831 760930 mob

PALMER Kristian J *(Md, Arr, Org, Rec)*: 3 North Bank, Otterburn Villas, Jesmond, Newcastle-upon-Tyne NE2 3AR ☎ 01495 758764, 0191 21 21 462, 0378 257 647 mob

PARKIN Christopher *(Gtr, Voc)*: 3 Stowey Road, Yatton, North Somerset BS49 4HS ☎ 01934 838 919

PARSONS Richard *(Kbds)*: 28 Market Street, Yeovil, Somerset BA20 1HZ ☎ 01935 413131, 0378 292391

PATTERSON Nick: Coach House, Ridgway, Colyton, Devon EX13 6RP ☎ 01297 553385

PAYNE Brian *(Kbds)*: The Ridge, Porth Parade, Porth, Newquay, Cornwall TR7 3JZ ☎ 01637 879183

PEARCE Roger: 6 The Ryelands, Randwick, Stroud GL6 6HG

PECK Michael: Browns Park, Marham Church, Bude, Cornwall EX23 0NZ ☎ 01288 361565

PEEL Ken *(Kbds, Gtr)*: Flat 3, 14 Park Place, Clifton, Bristol BS8 1JP ☎ 0117 909 4908, 0973 173765 mob

PENHORWOOD Carole *(Synth)*: 36 Donald Road, Uplands, Bristol BS13 7BU

PENROSE Richard *(Arr, Trans)*: 78 St Peters Way, Porthleven, Nr. Heston, Cornwall TR13 9BB ☎ 01326 573943

PLANK Kathleen: 20 Ruskin Avenue, Mount Pleasant, Rogerstone, Newport Gwent NP1 0AA ☎ 01633 893860

POLLOCK Michael *(Hpsd, Cel)*: 30 Penylan Terrace, Cyncoed, Cardiff CF3 7EU ☎ 029 2048 5968

POMEROY Dennis *(Acc)*: 17 Priors Wood Road, Taunton, Somerset TA2 7PS ☎ 01823 274178

PRESDEE John *(Db, Rec)*: 66 Wildbrook, Port Talbot SA13 2UN ☎ 01639 883920

PRICE David *(Kbds)*: 77 Tudor Street, Abergavenny, Gwent NP7 5DH ☎ 01873 858165

PRICE-EVANS Raymond *(E Pf, Kbds)*: Phoenix House, 2 Cwm Fedw, Machen, Newport, Gwent NP1 8QD ☎ 01633 440878

PROLE Thomas: Grey Tiles, Ashley, Box Corsham, Wiltshire SN13 8AJ ☎ Box 742309

PURKISS Marc *(Kbds)*: Top Flat, 161 Coronation Road, Bedminster, Bristol BS3

PYSANCZYN Andre *(Synth, Gtr, E Gtr, B Gtr)*: 129 Goddard Avenue, Swindon, Wilts SN1 4HX ☎ 01793 497142

QUINN Paul *(Kbds)*: Little Manor, West Hewise, Weston Supermare, Avon BS24 6RR ☎ 01934 876877

RAWLINGS Graham *(Acc)*: 6 Hills Close, Keynsham, Nr Bristol BS18 1SW ☎ Bristol 862114

REA Colin *(Flt)*: 17 Fore Street, Totnes, Devon TQ9 5DA ☎ 01803 865940

REES F *(Org)*: Hillend Farm, Llangennith, Swansea SA3 1HN ☎ 01792 827204

RICHARDS Eryl *(Cel)*: 14 Waunlon, Newton, Porthcawl, South Wales CF36 5RT ☎ 01656 771421

RICHARDS Sharon *(Vln)*: West View, Broughton View, Wick, South Glamorgan, Wales CF71 7QH ☎ 01656 890248

RIDDELL Don *(Org)* ☎ 01803 666343

RILEY Lewis *(B Gtr, Tabla, Gtr)*: 16 Riverside, Swallowfields, Totnes, Devon TQ9 5JB ☎ 866242

RIX Egon: 28 Bickington Lodge Estate, Bickington, Barnstaple, North Devon EX31 2LH ☎ 01271 78341

RODEN David *(Kbds)*: 43 Hamilton Road, Southville, Bristol BS3 1LL ☎ 0117 953 3812

RODEN Margaret *(Org)*: 56 Greville Road, Southville, Bristol BS3 1LE ☎ 0117 9636779

ROE Janet *(Flt, Sax, Clt, Gtr)*: 6 Donnington Grove, The Lawn, Swindon SN3 1HD ☎ 01793 485082

ROSSER Pete *(Acc, Gtr)*: Bridge Halt, Paganhill Lane, Stroud, Glos. GL5 4JU ☎ 01453 763565

ROSSI Denis *(Org)*: 21 Grange Drive, Buckeridge Towers, Teignmouth, Devon TQ14 8QB ☎ 01626 778919

ROWE Adam *(Kbds)*: Flat 6, 4 Lansdown Place, Lansdown Road, Cheltenham, Glos GL50 2HU ☎ 01242 233254, 0976 389658 mob

SADKA Ivan: 74 South Road, Sully, Nr Penarth, Glam CF64 5SL ☎ 029 2053 0225

SALMON Peggy *(Voc)*: Hinnies, Leg O Mutton Corner, Yelverton, Devon PL20 6DJ ☎ 01822 853310

SCHOLES Philippa *(Sax)*: 'Glenshira', 14 Roundway Gardens, Devizes, Wiltshire SN10 2EF ☎ 01380 723 729, 0585 511193

SCOTT Philip: Woods Corner, Cliddesden, Nr Basingstoke, Hants RG25 2JF ☎ Basingstoke 466

SHORLAND Alec *(Org)*: 18 Blake Cresc, Stratton, Swindon, Wilts SN3 4LR ☎ 01793 826013

SIDGWICK Arthur *(Kbds, Gtr)*: Minim House Music, Minim House, 39 Cornmill Crescent, Alphington Exeter EX2 8TL ☎ 01392 56834

SMITH Philip *(Md)*: 44 Larksmead Way, Ogwell, Newton Abbot, Devon TQ12 6FE ☎ 01626 331431

SNELL Ivor *(Org)*: 118 Bromley Heath Road, Downend, Bristol BS16 6JJ ☎ 574236

SOBY Dave *(Kbds)*: Eastdown, Farmhouse, The Broomford Estate, Jacobstowe, Okehampton, Devon EX20 3RH ☎ 01837 851666

SPENCER Jeff *(Gtr, Vla, Sax, Flt)*: Garden Flat, 23 Great Norwood Street, Cheltenham, Glos GL50 2AW ☎ 01242 527179

STARK Dennis *(Org, Kbds, Voc)*: 4 Grovenor Road, Weymouth, Dorset DT4 7QL ☎ 01305 774792

STEELE Alexander *(Kbds)*: 301 Old Bathe Road, Cheltenham GL53 9AJ ☎ 01242 524607, 01242 543290, 01242 543273

STEIN Jonathan *(Acc, Gtr)*: 28 Stafford Road, St Werburghs, Bristol BS2 9UN ☎ 0117 9095894

SUMMERS Sarah *(Per, Clt)*: 6 Melbourne Close, Lawn, Swindon, Wiltshire SN3 1JB ☎ 01793 523034

SUMNER Alison *(Voc, Sax, Flt)*: Copelands, 8 South Hayes Copse, Landkey, Barnstaple, Devon EX32 0UZ ☎ 01271 79663

SURGENOR Ingrid *(Hpsd, Cel)*: 8 Hillary Close, Llanishen, Cardiff CF4 5AU ☎ 029 2075 6161

TALMAGE Stuart M *(Kbds, Gtr)*: 105 Hemerdon Heights, Plympton, Plymouth, Devon PL7 2HA ☎ 01752 344362, 0836 298892

TAYLOR Barnaby *(Gtr, B Gtr)*: 1 Harley Place, Bristol BS8 8JT ☎ 0117 973 7806

TAYLOR Jonathan *(Kbds)*: Top Flat, 2 Richmond Road, Montpelier, Bristol BS6 5EW ☎ 0117 9413576

TELFER John *(Hpsd, Rec)*: 49, Belvoir Road, St Andrews, Bristol BS6 5DQ ☎ 0117 9243505

THIGHPAULSANDRA *(Org, Synth, Theramin)* ☎ 029 2039 0943 & fax

THOMAS Margaret *(Org, Acc)*: 38 Tresawls Avenue, Truro, Cornwall TR1 3LA ☎ 01872 277173

THOMPSON Lawrence *(Org, Voc)*: 55 Park Place, Risca, Gwent NP1 6BN ☎ Npt 612380

TONGS Paul *(Voc)*: 18 Buller Road, St Thomas, Exeter WA2 7JE ☎ 01392 412701

WALTER John *(Kbds, Gtr)*: 1 Magdalene Close, Totnes, Devon TQ9 5TQ ☎ 01288 356676

WATERS Ben: 100 Church Street, Upwey, Weymouth, Dorset DT3 5QE ☎ 01305 812775

WETHERELL Eric *(Org)*: 24 The Crescent, Henleaze, Bristol BS9 4RW ☎ 0117 9628652

WHISH Thomas: 20 Cranford Close, Worle, Weston Super Mare, Somerset BF22 8QZ ☎ 01934 511045

WHITE Gillian *(Org)*: Ty Gwyn, Nantyderry, Abergavenny, Gwent NP7 9DW ☎ 01873 880842

WICKHAM Hazel: 39 Kings Drive, Bishopston, Bristol BS7 8JW ☎ 0117 946587

WIGHTMAN David *(Gtr, B Gtr, Dms, Voc)*: 55 Underhill Road, Stanford Bishop, Matson, Gloucester GL4 6HD ☎ 01452 534386, 07970 42795

WILES Benjamin *(Kbds, Voc)*: 2 Wyck Beck Road, Brentry, Bristol BS10 7JE ☎ 0117 9509509, 0117 9509507

WILLIAMS Jane *(Vln, Gtr, Voc, Rec)*: 30 Pentrebach Road, Glyntaf, Pontypridd CF37 4BW

WILLIAMS Joseph (*Org, Vln*): 13 St Margarets. Road, Whitchurch, Cardiff CF4 7AA ☏ 029 2062 6238

WILLIAMS Marion: 16 Windsor Road, Barry, South Glamorgan CF6 8AW ☏ 01446 733552

WILSON Jen: 8 Chaddesley Terrace, Mount Pleasant, Swansea, West Glamorgan SA1 6HB ☏ 01792 466083

WILSON-DICKSON Dr.Andrew (*Hpsd*): 25 Plasturton Avenue, Pontconna, Cardiff CF1 9HL ☏ 029 2022 8154

WITTS Michael (*Org*): Mirenda, 294 F, Bradley Lane, Holt, Trowbridge / Wiltshire BA14 6QE ☏ Nth Trwbrdge 78

WOODMAN Colin: 14 Farm Drive, Cyncoed, Cardiff CF2 6HQ ☏ 029 2075 2903

WOODWARD Tim (*Kbds, Org*): 2 Crownhill Park, Torquay, Devon TQ2 5LN ☏ 018031 211430

WRIGHT Henry (*Voc, Kbds, Tpt*): Address Unknown ☏ 01823 672493

YOUNG Valerie (*Vln*): 33 Hathaway Road, Upper Stratton, Swindon, Wilts SN2 6TX ☏ 01793 826857

LONDON

A.O (*Voc, Per*): 38 Oak Way, London W3 7LD ☏ 020 8932 0483

AACHT Kweku (*Kbds, Clt, Voc*): 15 Linford House, Whiston Road, London E2 8SD ☏ 0956 177973

ABBEY Francis (*Kbds, Tbn, T Hrn*): 10 Southcroft Road, Tooting, London SW17 9TR ☏ 020 8672 9578

ADAMS Cliff: 15 Margaretta Terrace, London SW3 5NU ☏ 020 7352 0574

ADELMAN Mark: 53 Stonard Road, London N13 4DJ ☏ 020 8886 9712, 0973 757484 mob

AKED Tansy (*Kbds, Con, Vln, Ob*): Garden Flat, 8A Bristol Gardens, London W9 2JG ☏ 020 7266 4490, 0850 257399 mob

ALDERKING Seann (*Kbds*): 13 Cavendish Drive, London E11 1DN ☏ 020 8926 8003, 020 8926 6519

ALDWINCKLE Robert (*Hpsd, Org*): 4 Gloucester Cottages, Croft Road, Hastings, East Sussex TN35 3HN ☏ 01424 715435

ALEXANDER Phil (*Kbds*): 7B Northbrook Road, London SE13 5QT ☏ 020 8463 0425, 0956 978701

ALEXANDER-MAX Susan (*Clav*): Flat One, 38 Fairhazel Gardens, London NW6 3SJ ☏ 020 7328 9347, 020 7328 4689

ALLDER Robert (*Org*): 26 Edward Road, Chadwell Heath, Romford, Essex RM6 6UH ☏ 020 8599 5198

ALLDIS Dominic (*Voc, Com*): 122 Dawes Road, Fulham, London SW6 7EG ☏ 020 7381 2963

ALLEN Geraldine (*Voc, Gtr, Kbds*): 26C Lower Marsh, London SE1 7RJ ☏ 020 7261 0682

ALLEY John (*Org, Hpsd, Synth, Con*): 97 The Lindens, Loughton, Essex IG10 3HT ☏ 020 8508 7575, 0956 373786

ALOM Samsul: 2 Landseer House, Frampton Street, London NW8 8LH ☏ 020 7723 5940, 0956 942499 mob, 020 7491 8586 day

ALPERT Stephen (*Org*): 117 West Street, East Grinstead, West Sussex RH19 4EN

AMAZING HARRY (*Gtr*): 14 Station Road, Bexleyheath, Kent DA7 4AR ☏ 020 8301 3228

AMBACHE Diana: 9 Beversbrook Road, London N19 4QG ☏ 020 7263 4027 & fax

AMBLER Mark (*Kbds*): 297 Eversleigh Road, London SW11 5XS ☏ 020 7228 5495

AMOS Richard (*Kbds, Voc*): 11A Ashness Road, London SW11 6RX ☏ 020 7738 9581

ANDERSON Christopher (*Kbds, Flt, Gtr, Voc*): Flat 3, 30 Vicarage Road, Hampton Wick, Kingston-on-Thames KT1 4ED ☏ 020 8977 3190

ANDERSON D. Sutton (*Org, Con*): 28 Cavendish Avenue, London N3 3QN ☏ 020 8349 2317

ANDREWS Dave (*Kbds*): Ground Floor Flat, 3 Clifton Road, Crouch End, London N8 8HY ☏ 020 8348 9790

ANDREWS Stuart (*Kbds*): 42 Raleigh Drive, Tolworth, Surbiton, Surrey KT5 9PR ☏ 020 8330 3396

ANGELL Frances (*Kbds*): 2 Saint Donatts Road, London SE14 6NR ☏ 020 8691 0309, 0468 053 690 mob

ANGILLEY Neil (*Kbds, Tpt*): 3 Shandon Court, Endwell Road, Brockley, London SE4 2NE ☏ 0956 135922

ANSELL Stephen: 58 Duncan Road, Ramsgate, Kent CT11 9QH ☏ 01843 594649

ANSTISS Hayley (*Voc*): 11 Gordon Road, Yiewsley, Middlesex UB7 8AH

APPLEBY Kim (*Per*): c/o Prager & Fenton, Midway House, 27/29 Cursitor Street, London EC4A 1LT ☏ 020 7831 4200

APPLETON David: 81 Chatsworth Road, London E5 0LH ☏ 020 8986 9197

ARAM Vicki (*Voc*): 43 Baronsmere Road, London N2 9QG ☏ 020 8883 3910

ARISS Nathan (*Gtr*): 51 Girton Road, Sydenham, London SE26 5DH ☏ 020 8778 3491

ARMATAGE Justine (*Vln, Kbds*): 107 Gibson Gardens, Stoke Newington, London N16 7HH ☏ 020 7923 1024

ARMATRADING Joan (*Gtr*): BMG International, Bedford House, 69-79 Fulham High Street, London SW6 3JW ☏ 020 7973 0980

ARMOUR Janie (*Acc*): Lower Flat, 225 Tufnell Park Road, Islington, London N19 5EP ☏ 020 7607 6852

ARNOLD George: 63 Fairlie House, 21 Pantle Walk, Uxbridge, Middlesex UB8 1LY ☏ 01895 252327, 020 7729 4700

ASHANTI Makeeba (*Gtr*)

ASHCOMBE John (*Org, Per, Vib*): 11 Bourne Hill, Palmers Green, London N13 N13 4LJ ☏ 020 8886 8385

ASHER John (*Kbds, Hrn*): 74 Chaplin Road, London NW2 5PR ☏ 020 8451 1776

ASHFORD Simon: 23 Knights Templar Way, High Wycombe, Bucks HP11 1PX ☏ 01494 534972

ASHWORTH John: 54 Worcester Road, Sutton, Surrey SM2 6QB ☏ 020 8643 0166

ASPLAND Robin (*Kbds*): 64 Peel Road, South Woodford, London E18 2LG ☏ 020 8505 4401

ATKINSON Cliff (*Synth, Org*): 16 Hillbury Road, Tooting Common, London SW17 8JT ☏ 020 8675 0825

ATKINSON Georgina: 145 Petherton Road, London N5 2RS ☏ 020 7359 7206, 020 7359 6150

ATKINSON Richard (*Kbds, Com, Arr, Con*): c/o 32 Princes Avenue, Desborough, Northants NN14 2RQ ☏ 01536 760713

AUSTIN Dean (*Kbds, Voc*): Keira, 14 Heathwood Gardens, London SE7 8ES ☏ 020 8855 5578, 0378 400520

AUSTIN Victor (*Tbn*): Ground Floor, 44 Dartmouth Park Hill, London NW5 1HN ☏ 020 7272 6636

AXTELL Daniel: 54 Horncastle Road, Lee, London SE12 9LA ☏ 020 8516 5698, 0374 643224 mob, 020 8857 5069

BABB Angus (*Gtr*): 153 Hazel Grove, Sydenham, London SE26 4JJ ☏ 020 8676 0723

BAGA Ena (*Org*): 313 Latymer Court, Hammersmith Road, London W6 7LD ☏ 020 8748 2460

BAKER Helen (*Kbds*): 12 Exeter Road, London NW2 4SP ☏ 0973 383760

BAKER Stephen (*Com*): 90 Dartmouth Park Hill, Highgate, London N19 5HU ☏ 020 7281 1001, 0956 360439 mob, 020 7281 1223

BALCON Kenneth (*Org*): Mirage, Homefield Way, Tye Green, Essex CM7 8HX ☏ 01376 26188

BALLEN Reuben (*Org, Acc*): 2 Red Oaks Close, Ferndown, Dorset BH22 9TY ☏ 01202 897035

BARCA-AMES Lily (*Vln*): 40 Lowndes Street, London SW1X 9HX ☏ 020 7235 7519

BARCLAY Kenneth: 5 St Michaels Rd, London SW9 0SL ☏ 020 7737 4590

BARKER Angela (*Voc, Org, Md*): 53 Hatchlands Road, Redhill, Surrey RH1 6AP ☏ 01737 762603

BARLOW Dominic (*Arr, Com*): The Coach House, 112A Woodhill, London SE18 5JL ☏ 020 8854 5714

BARNES David: 21 Lower Camden, Chislehurst, Kent BR7 5HY

BARNES Jill: 27 Marble Hill Close, Twickenham, Middx TW1 3AY ☏ 020 8892 6328

BARNETT Will (*Kbds*): 263 Hampstead Road, Camden Town, London NW1 3EA ☏ 020 7681 0619, 020 7438 4057, 020 7240 8739

The magazine for
everyone concerned
with music education

Music

Teacher

First published in 1909

MUSIC TEACHER will...

* Help you focus your teaching methods

* Guide you on the interpretation of set works for GCSE and the ULEAC Anthology

* Familiarise you with the latest computer hardware and music software for schools

* Advise you on how to engender in your pupils a positive attitude towards instrumental practice

* Inform you about the history and development of the major conservatoires and music colleges

* Keep you up to date on the relevant courses and seminars

* Provide reviews of the sheet music and books published during the year

FREE Music Teacher GUIDES

Music Teacher subscribers are also sent up to six FREE supplementary guides published during the course of the year on subjects such as Notes for the Associated Board Piano and Violin Exams and Summer Schools

Monthly £2.95

ANNUAL SUBSCRIPTION PRICES: United Kingdom £34; airmail Europe £41; airmail outside Europe £47 (N & S America, Africa, Middle East and Hong Kong); £50 (Australia, New Zealand, Japan and Far East); surface mail worldwide £37

To subscribe please send your cheque (in pounds Sterling made payable to Rhinegold Publishing Ltd) to: Rhinegold Publishing Ltd (MT SUBS), PO Box 47, Gravesend, Kent DA12 2BR

CREDIT CARD SUBSCRIPTIONS
Tel: 01474 334500 (office hours); Fax: 01474 325557

FOR A FREE SAMPLE COPY telephone 0171 333 1720

BARRATT David (*Gtr*): 42 Gyllyngdune Gardens, Seven Kings, Ilford, Essex IG3 9HJ ☎ 020 8472 1623

BARRY Jim: 262 Lampton Road, Hounslow, Middx TW3 4EX ☎ 020 8572 3800

BATTEN Peter: 10 Avenue Road, Belmont, Surrey SM2 6JD ☎ 020 8643 0455

BEACH Howard: 42 Ash Hill Road, Ash, Aldershot, Hants GU12 6AB ☎ 01252 26909

BEADLE Richard (*Kbds, Tpt, Gtr*): 78B Chobham Road, Stratford, London E15 1LZ ☎ 020 8534 3002, 07971 108563

BEAMENT Ted: 32 Home Close, Harlow, Essex CM20 3PB ☎ 01279 436570

BEAN Richard (*Sax, Clt*)

BEARD Paul (*Kbds*): 27 Kings Road, Willesden Green, London NW10 2BP ☎ 020 8451 9921, 07775 578717 mob

BECK Gordon: Justlee, 1 Gravel End, Coveney, Ely, Cambs CB6 2DN ☎ 01353 778 574

BEEBEE David (*B Gtr*): 11B Luxor Street, London SE5 9QN ☎ 020 7733 4229

BEER Matthew (*Voc*): The Vicarage, 58 Hill Rise, Cuffley, Hertfordshire EN6 4RG ☎ 01707 874 126

BEESON Roger: 117, Darwin Road, Ealing, London W5 4BB ☎ 020 8568 1344

BEKOVA Ms: 76 Honeybrook Road, Clapham South, London SW12 0DN

BENJAMIN George (*Com*): c/o Harold Holt, 31 Sinclair Road, London W14 0NS

BENNETT Dina: 41 Thirlmere Road, London N10 2DL ☎ 020 8444 4426

BENSON Alan: 10 Waldeck Road, Ealing, London W13 8LY ☎ 020 8998 9734

BENSON Clifford: 76 Quarry Hill Road, Tonbridge, Kent TN9 2PE ☎ 01732 364204

BERESFORD Steve (*B Gtr*): Ground Flr Flt (East), 62 Oxford Gardens, London W10 5UN ☎ 020 8960 3130, 020 8960 5183

BERKOVITCH Valerie (*Org*): 2 Mazenod Avenue, West Hampstead, London NW6 4LR ☎ 020 7625 7938, 0797 121 5486

BERRY Alan (*Kbds*): 12 Allbrook House, Danebury Avenue, Aton Estate, London SW15 4HB ☎ 020 8788 4458

BERRY Alison (*Kbds, Synth, Vln*): Flat B, 2 Finlay Street, Fulham, London SW6 6HD ☎ 020 7736 7242, 01426 277779 pager

BETTERIDGE Stephen: 6 Folly Avenue, St Albans, Herts AL3 5QD ☎ 01727 811443

BETTS Michaela (*Ob, Dms*): 16 Rabbits Road, Manor Park, London E12 5HZ ☎ 020 8514 6791

BILLING Jane (*Gtr, Voc*): 51 Copthorne Road, Felbridge, East Grinstead, West Sussex RH19 2PB ☎ 01342 324417

BIRD Adam (*Tpt*): 15 Waldegrave Road, Bromley, Kent BR1 2JP ☎ 020 8249 5829, 0777 188 0777, 020 8249 5829

BIRD Philip (*Gtr*): c/o Peters Fraser & Dunlop, 503 The Chambers, Chelsea Harbour, London SW10 0XF

BIRD Robert (*E Pf, Voc*): Malanda, Oldfield Road, Bromley, Kent BR1 2LE ☎ 020 8467 8998

BISHOP Adrian (*Voc*): 28 Lewgars Avenue, Kingsbury, London NW9 8AS ☎ 020 8933 7147

BLACKWELL Martin (*Org, Synth*): 2 Morton Gardens, Wallington, Surrey SM6 8EX ☎ 020 8647 9841

BLAIR Christine (*Com*): 5 Wealdwood Gardens, Hatch End, Middx HA5 4DQ ☎ 020 8428 8303

BLAKE Howard (*Com, Con*): Studio Flat 6, 18 Kensington Court Place, London W8 5BJ ☎ 020 7937 1966

BLOOM Bernie (*Vib*) ☎ 020 8840 6786 & fax

BOLAM Ken (*Per*): 28 Sylvan Road, Snaresbrook, Wanstead, London E11 1QN ☎ 020 8989 8005

BOOTH Barry: 126 Mallinson Road, London SW11 1BJ ☎ 020 7223 0049

BOROWIECKI Teddy (*Acc, Kbds, Gtr*): 47 Gowrie Road, London SW11 5NN

BOWATER Ronnie (*Kbds, Org*): 71 Heron Hill, Upper Belvedere, Kent DA17 5HJ ☎ 01322 430880

BOWEN Jules (*Kbds*): 136 Wordsworth Road, Hampton, Middlesex TW12 1ET ☎ 020 8979 1656

BRADLEY Laurence (*Vln, Org*): 32 Fairlawns, Upper Shoreham Road, Shoreham-By-Sea, West Sussex BN43 6BW

BRADSHAW Susan: 55 Compton Road, London N1 2PB ☎ 020 7226 8675

BRAND Neil (*Kbds, Md*): 56 Mayall Road, London SE24 0PJ ☎ 020 7737 6705

BRATHWAITE Vibert (*Kbds*): 3 Park Road, Ilford, Essex IG1 1SB ☎ 020 8553 1591

BREEN Abs ☎ 01276 476676

BRERETON Charles (*Org, Kbds*): 166 All Souls Avenue, Willesden, London NW10 3AB ☎ 020 8459 5422

BRERETON Frank (*E Pf, Kbds*): 93 Springfield Road, New Southgate, London N11 1RL ☎ 020 8368 7908, 07970 981 385

BRIDGES Ronald (*Org*): Toll Bar Cottage, 12 Chelmsford Road, Shenfield, Essex CM15 8RQ ☎ 01277 221276

BRISCOE Anthony (*B Gtr, Gtr*): 30 Claverdale Road, Upper Tulse Hill, London SW2 2DP ☎ 020 7703 4324, 0961 408 281

BRODERICK Deborah (*Synth, Kbds*): 28 Cressy House, Queens Ride, London SW13 0HZ ☎ 020 8788 9841

BRODERICK Golda (*Vln, Gtr, Acc*): 2 Whittlesea Path, Harrow Weald, Middlesex HA3 6LP ☎ 020 8428 8057

BROOKER Gary: Wintershall, Dunsfold, Surrey GU8 4PB ☎ 01608 677100

BROOKS David (*Voc, Gtr*): 28 Sinclair Road, West Kensington, London W14 0NH ☎ 020 7603 8907

BROUGHTON Stephen (*Org, Synth*): 14 Queens Road, Barnet, Hertfordshire EN5 4DG ☎ 020 8449 5382

BROWN David-Joseph (*Kbds, Com, Arr*): Flat C, 9 Bradiston Road, Maida Vale, London W9 3HN ☎ 020 8969 5528

BROWN James (*Kbds*): 45B Bassett Street, London NW5 4PG ☎ 020 7485 3959

BROWN Kenny (*Arr*): 37B Balham Park Road, Balham, London SW12 8DX ☎ 020 8673 3951

BROWN Leon (*Kbds*): 79 Bradgate Road, Catford, London SE6 4TT ☎ 020 8690 8085, 0956 519227, 01523 436997

BROWN Tanya: Flat 4 Pascall House, Draco Street, London SE17 3HP ☎ 020 7701 7716

BROWN Trevor (*E Pf, Synth, Arr, Com*): 168 Harefield Road, Uxbridge, Middx UB8 1PP ☎ 01895 254100, 01895 272707 fax

BROWNRIDGE Angela: 118 Audley Road, London NW4 3HG ☎ 020 8202 0274

BUDD Iris (*Kbds*): 'Teesdale', North Road, Havering-Atte-Bower, Essex RM4 1PR ☎ 01708 725669

BUGDEN James (*Kbds, Org*): 5 Temple Fortune Hill, Hampstead Garden Suburb, London NW11 7XL ☎ 020 8455 8173, 0956 143509

BUNKELL David (*Org, Tbn*): 62 Kewferry Road, Northwood, Middlesex HA6 2PG ☎ 01923 828837/827921

BURBIDGE Victor: Penny Black Cottage, 20 High Street, Epping, Essex CM16 4AB ☎ 01992 576 047

BURCH John (*Kbds, Com, Arr*): 55 Millstrood Road, Whitstable, Kent CT5 1QF ☎ 01227 274898

BURDETT Lesley (*Kbds*): 4 Bournside Crescent, Southgate, London N14 6SP ☎ 020 8447 8092, 0468 437 180 mob

BURFORD Geoffrey: 184A Gloucester Terrace, London W2 6HT ☎ 020 7262 6443

BURLEY Elizabeth: Flat 5, 42 Elmbourne Road, Tooting Bec, London SW17 8JJ ☎ 020 8767 5353

BURMAN David (*Kbds, Tpt, A Sax*): 12 Woodberry Way, London N12 0HG ☎ 020 8445 3462

BURNETT Richard: Finchcocks, Goudhurst, Kent TN17 1HH ☎ 01580 211702

BURR James: 37 Layhams Road, West Wickham, Kent BR4 9HD ☎ 020 8462 5321

BURRELL Paul (*Synth*): 37 South Road, Bishops Stortford, Herts CM23 3JQ ☎ 01279 659155

BURTON Susan (*Acc*): 233A Queens Road, London SE15 2NG ☎ 020 7252 9376 & fax

BUSH Martin (*Sax*): 16 Elm Park Road, London N3 1EB ☎ 020 8371 0202

BUSIAKIEWICZ Richard: 20 Woburn Court, Wellesley Road, Croydon, Surrey CR0 2AE ☎ 020 8680 7055

BUTLER John: 105 Ritherdon Road, London SW17 8QH ☎ 020 8673 5467

BUTTERS Nick (*Org, Hpsd*): 6 Station Road, Hampton, Middx TW12 2BX ☎ 020 8979 0454

CALNAN Anthony: 72 Amblecote Road, London SE12 9TW ☎ 020 8851 4823

CALVERT Stuart: 1 Norlington Road, London E11 4BE ☎ 020 8928 0612

CAMERON Hilary (*Voc, Kbds, Com, Flt*): 83B Harlescott Road, London SE15 3DA ☎ 020 7358 1524

CAMPBELL Adam (*Arr*): 6 Ladbroke Gardens, London W11 2PT ☎ 020 7727 2137

CAMPBELL Francis (*Kbds, B Gtr, Gtr*): c/o 45 Addison Way, Hampstead Garden Suburs, London NW11 6AR ☎ 020 8458 9700

CARDWELL Richard (*Kbds*): 41 Homefield Road, London W4 2LW ☎ 020 8995 4305, 0802 745107 mob

CAREY Timothy: 20 Butlers Close, Broomfield, Chelmsford, Essex CM1 7BE ☎ 01245 443771

CARR Carlina: 29A Greencroft Gardens, London NW6 3LN ☎ 020 7624 2977

CARR Jennifer (*Kbds, Voc*): 33 Glenthorne Road, London N11 3HU ☎ 020 8361 1828

CARR Michael (*Org, Vib*): 39 Clitterhouse Crescent, London NW2 1DB ☎ 020 8458 1020 & fax

CARROLL Richard (*Gtr, B Gtr, Voc, Hmca*): 9 Runcorn House, Kingsbridge Circus, Harold Hill, Essex RM3 8LX ☎ 01708 458378, 0966 188683

CARTER Jack: 61 Barth Road, Plumstead, London SE18 1SF ☎ 020 8854 0845

CARTER Robert (*St Pan*): 10 Compton Road, Winchester, Hampshire SO23 9SL ☎ 01962 860790

CARTER Simon (*B Gtr, Dms*): 76 Latchmere Road, Kingston-on-Thames, Surrey KT2 5TW ☎ 020 8541 5545

CASEY Neil: 242 Amhurst Road, Hackney, London E8 2AG ☎ 020 7254 8447

CASSON Sue (*Com, Voc*): 1 The Coachyard, Chiddingstone Castle, Hillhoath Road, Chiddingstone, Kent TN8 7AD ☎ 01892 870973

CATER John: 11 Westover Road, London SW18 2RE ☎ 020 8870 4875

CAVELL Jonathan (*Synth*): 66 Strcahan Road, Bow, London E3 5DB ☎ 020 8983 4699

CEPEDA Jose (*Synth, B Gtr*): 20A Peckham Hill Street, London SE15 6BN ☎ 020 7732 3987, 0956 914755

CHAN Jeanne (*Voc*): 6 Penn Gardens, Chislehurst, Kent BR7 5RY ☎ 020 8467 7024

CHANCE Michael (*Org*): 6 Railway Street, Brighton, Sussex BN1 3PF

CHAPMAN Audrey: 14 Tankerville Road, London SW16 5LL ☎ 020 8764 4793

CHAPMAN Ben (*B Gtr*): 1B Hampton Road, Twickenham TW2 5QE ☎ 020 8894 2543, 0973 794350

CHAPMAN Greg (*Kbds, Acc*): 44 Adelaide Avenue, Brockley, London SE4 1YR ☎ 020 8469 0609

CHAPMAN Toby (*Dms*): 422 Footscray Road, New Eltham, London SE9 3TU ☎ 020 8850 8373

CHAPPLE Richard (*Acc, Gtr*): 64 Marlings Park Avenue, Chislehurst, Kent BR7 6RD ☎ 01689 813606, 07050 187669

CHASE Elizabeth (*Kbds*): ☎ 020 7723 9955

CHEEKS Judy (*Gtr*): 87 Hurlingham Court, Ranelagh Gardens, London SW6 3UR ☎ 020 7731 1688 & fax

CHERRIE Mark (*St Pan, Gtr, B Gtr, Cel*): 17 Manor Close, Kingsbury, London NW9 9HD ☎ 020 8238 9376

CHESHIRE Wylliam (*Kbds, Synth, Dms*): Address Unknown ☎ 020 7403 5338 & fax

CHESTER Craig (*Kbds*): 20A Royal Avenue, London SW3 4QF

CHICK Eddie: 9 Copse Road, Cooden, Bexhill-on-Sea, East Sussex TN39 3UA ☎ 01424 3615

CHILVERS Paul (*Org*): 324 High Road, London N15 4BN ☎ 020 8885 1915

CHINA John (*Org*): 49 Warwick Gardens, Harringay, London N4 1JD ☎ 020 8802 8032

CHOROSZEWSKI Zbigniew (*Acc*): 76 Bromfelde Road, London SW4 6PR ☎ 020 7622 3037

CHOWN Julian (*Org, Synth, Voc*): 93B Kingsley Road, Hounslow, Middlesex TW3 4AU ☎ 020 8577 5087, 01523 731337 pager

CHURCHILL Peter (*Arr, Com*): Flat 4, 30 Onslow Gardens, Muswell Hill, London N10 3JU ☎ 020 8444 9171

CHURNEY Russell (*Kbds, Gtr*): 71 Wells House Road, London NW10 6ED ☎ 020 8961 6662

CLARKE Miranda (*Cel*): 12 Hilly Fields Crescent, London SE4 1QA ☎ 020 8692 2546

CLARKE Norman (*Org, Kbds*): 46 Elliotts Row, London SE11 4SZ ☎ 020 7582 0862 & fax, 0836 210185 mob

CLARKE Terry (*Kbds*): 57 Glebe Gardens, New Malden, Surrey KT3 5RU ☎ 020 8942 5255

CLAYTON Kenny (*Md*): 24 Morgan Hse, Ullington Gdns, London SW1 2LF ☎ 020 7834 8855, 020 7834 8855

CLIPSHAM Caroline: 10 Ranmore Road, Cheam, Surrey SM2 7LT ☎ 020 8393 4608, 07887 778567 mob, 020 7928 9030

CLOUGHTON Roy (*Org*): 7 Riverside Walk, Colchester, Essex CO1 1RD ☎ 01206 765 057 & fax

CLOUTS Philip (*Bong, Gtr, Voc*): 108A Tollington Park, London N4 3RB ☎ 020 7281 0997

COATES Richard (*Org*): 13 Wolseley Road, Chiswick, London W4 5EG ☎ 020 8994 2027, 020 8994 2027

COCKLE Alexander (*Kbds*): Ellwyn, Allet, Truro, Cornwall TR4 9DP ☎ 01872 77983

COHEN Jonathan (*Org*): 33 Devonshire Road, London W4 2EX ☎ 020 8995 5613

COHEN Kenneth: 110B Priory Road, London NW6 3NS ☎ 020 7267 4240

COHEN Leon (*Arr*): 24 Ingram Road, London N2 9QA ☎ 020 8883 5744

COLAM Simon (*Kbds*): Flat A, 54 Chatsworth Road, London E5 0LP ☎ 020 8525 5785, 0973 359 432

COLE Stephen (*Vln*): 24 Nettleden Avenue, Wembley, Middx HA9 6DP

COLEMAN David (*Con*): 31 Roedean Crescent, London SW15 5JX ☎ 020 8392 9989

COLEMAN Matthew (*Ob, Dms*): 1 Newry Road, St. Margarets, Twickenham, Middlesex TW1 1PJ ☎ 020 8892 1168, 0956 521691 mob, 020 8891 1050

COLEMAN Stephen (*Kbds, Con*): Flat 1, 84 Compayne Gardens, London NW6 3RU ☎ 020 7722 9360

COLES Richard (*Sax*): Number 37, Grafton Underwood, Nr.Kettering, Northamptonshire NN14 3AA ☎ 01536 330341 & fax, 01585 967960

COLLINSON Alex: 6 St. Georges Terrace, Peckham Hill Street, Peckham, London SE15 6DA ☎ 020 8568 7867

CONNELL Myles (*Gtr*): Flat 4, 69 Cornwall Gardens, London SW7 4BA ☎ 020 7937 9037

CONNERY Sam: 49 Yorkshire Close, London N16 8EU ☎ 020 7249 3798, 020 7281 4597

CONSTABLE John: 13 Denbigh Terrace, London W11 2QJ ☎ 020 7229 4603

COOK Martin (*Com, Arr*): 50 Chesham Road, Kingston, Surrey KT1 3AQ

COOPER Henry (*Org*): 15 Lawrence Hill Road, Dartford, Kent DA1 3AG ☎ 01322 225126

COOPER Julie (*Kbds, Com, Arr*): 15 Kelmscott Road, London SW11 6QX ☎ 020 7801 0942

COOPER Sally (*Kbds, Clt*): 20 Somers Road, London E17 6RX ☎ 020 8520 7556

COPAS Belinda: Flat 2, 77 Roxborough Road, Harrow, Middlesex HA1 1NT ☎ 020 8933 6448, 0378 898778 mob

COPPARD Tessa: 10E Vanbrugh Park Road West, Balckheath, London SE3 7QD ☎ 020 8858 0126

COPPERTHWAITE James *(Kbds, Clt, B Gtr)*: 13 Brett Road, London E8 1JP ☎ 020 8533 2313

CORBETT Peter: Rosemary, 21 Shell Road, London SE13 7TW ☎ 020 8244 7837

CORLEY Stephen *(Kbds)*: 87 Elm Park Avenue, Tottenham, London N15 6UZ ☎ 020 8211 7109

COSMAS Genie *(Voc)*: 77A Hindmans Road, East Dulwich, London SE22 9NQ

COSTELLO Ben *(Org, Flt)*: 28 Geneva Road, Kingston-upon-Thames, Surrey KT1 2TW ☎ 020 8255 1474, 0589 659324

COURTENAY Bunny: 116 Oakfield Road, Benfleet, Essex SS7 5NN ☎ 01268 752510

COWLEY Christopher: 13 The Cedars, Milland Road, Hailsham, East Sussex BN27 1TG ☎ 01323 846304

COWLEY Neil *(Kbds, Vln, Vla)*: 35A Errol Gardens, Hayes, Middlesex UB4 9EP ☎ 020 8845 4493

COX Derek: 4 Johns Court, Mulgrave Road, Sutton, Surrey SM2 6LT ☎ 020 8642 6807

CRACKNELL Gillian: 50 Compayne Gardens, London NW6 3RY ☎ 020 7328 5056

CRAYFORD Helen *(Rep, Hpsd)*: 2A Surrey Road, North Harrow, Middx HA1 4NH ☎ 020 8863 4659 & fax

CRESSWICK Ernest: 2 Rowfant Mans, Rowfant Road, London SW17 7AS

CRITCHINSON John *(E Pf)*: Flat 12 Carisbrook, Colney Hatch Lane, Muswell Hill, London N10 1EJ ☎ 020 8883 6037

CROOKE Sidney *(Hpsd, Clst)*: Address Unknown

CROPPER Sarah *(Sax)*: 208 Langthorne Road, London E11 4HS ☎ 020 8926 6150, 07957 310259

CROSSMAN Fredrik *(Md, Hrn)*: The Garden House, 2 Rockmead Rd, Fairlight Cove, East Sussex TN35 4DJ ☎ 01424 814166

CROZIER Hugh *(Voc)*: 149 Cheam Road, Sutton, Surrey SM1 2BP ☎ 020 8643 4134

CUNNINGHAM Olli *(Kbds, Clt, Sax)*: 17 Noyna Road, London SW17 7PQ ☎ 020 8767 1441, 0973 600748 mob

CURRAN Sara *(Kbds, Voc, Gtr)*: 7 Copse Hill, Purley, Surrey CR8 4LL ☎ 020 8660 3418

CUTMORE Jcf *(Kbds, Gtr, Per)*: 202 Samuel Lewis Buildings, Liverpool Road, Islington, London N1 1LJ ☎ 020 7607 4723

DALBY John: 63 Gunnersbury Lane, London W3 8HG ☎ 020 8992 1269

DALLY Nikhil *(Jav Gam)*: 22A South Avenue, Egham, Surrey TW20 8HG ☎ 01784 453347

DALTON Mary: 27 Liphook Crescent, Forest Hill, London SE23 3BN ☎ 020 8699 4227

DANDY Alan *(E Pf, Org)*: 30 Park Road, East Molesley, Surrey KT8 9LE ☎ 020 8979 6657

DARVAS Kevin: 37 Layfield Road, Hendon, London NW4 3UH ☎ 020 8202 3373

DAVID Frank *(Voc, Gtr, B Gtr, Per)*: 4 Lynmouth Road, Fortis Green, London N2 9LS ☎ 020 8482 9951

DAVIDSON-KELLY Kirsteen: 7 Milton House Mansions, Shacklewell Lane, Dalston, London E8 2EH

DAVIES Ben *(Gtr, B Gtr)*: 88 Ashburnham Grove, Greenwich SE10 8UJ ☎ 020 8691 9916

DAVIES Jennifer *(Cel)*: 1St Floor Flat, 33 Dynham Road, London NW6 2NS ☎ 020 7624 7316

DAVIES Peter *(Voc)*: 41 Homefield Road, Chiswick, London W4 2LW ☎ 020 8400 5695

DAVIES William *(Org, Con, Arr, Hpsd)*: 10 Fayre Meadow, Robertsbridge, East Sussex TN32 5AU ☎ 01580 880380

DAVIS Jeremy *(Vln, Cel)*: 1 Kerbela Street, Shorditch, London E2 6DP ☎ 020 7739 2737

DAVIS Paul *(Tbn)*: 66 Huggetts Lane, Willingdon, Eastbourne, East Sussex BN22 0LU ☎ 01323 507289, 0378 396498 mob

DAVISON Roger: 49 Orford Road, Walthamstow, London E17 9NJ ☎ 020 8520 4518

DAWES Hubert: 6 Winterdyne Mews, Weyhill Road, Andover, Hants SP10 3AG ☎ 01264 324467

DAWSON Nick *(Clt)*: 31 Jubilee Avenue, Romford, Essex RM7 9LS ☎ 01708 723801

DAY Steve *(B Gtr, Voc, Per)*: 142 Priory Park Road, London NW6 7UU ☎ 020 7372 6906

DE JONG Ronald *(Kbds)*: 38 Western Gardens, Ealing, London W5 3RU ☎ 020 8992 0341

DE RANCE Hero *(Com)*: 3 Woburn Court, Bernard Street, London WC1N 1LA ☎ 020 7837 1553

DE'WALE Edward: Flat 3, 1 Roslyn Close, Mitcham, Surrey CR4 3BB ☎ 020 8241 6178

DEE Brian *(Org)*: 130 Sheering Mill Lane, Sawbridgeworth, Herts CM21 9ND ☎ 01279 723320

DEL BIANCO Gianluca *(Acc)*: 193 Park South, Austin Road, Battersea, London SW11 5JN ☎ 020 7207 9726

DENNIE Courtney *(Gtr, Dms, Voc)*: 7 Newby Street, South Lambeth, London SW8 3BQ ☎ 020 7622 5891, 0956 576744, 020 7627 5532

DENNIS Philip *(Kbds, Md, Org)*: 43 Hitchin Road, Arlesey, Beds SG15 6RR ☎ 01462 834953, 0976 239026

DEWARRENNE David: 3 A, Grasmere Road, Bromley, Kent BR1 4BA ☎ 020 8460 2671

DIAZ Joanne *(Kbds, Com)*: 3C Goddington House, Off Court Road, Orpington, Kent BR6 9AT ☎ 016898 36993, 0411 329052 mob

DIBDIN Daniel *(Kbds)*: 19 Blackstone Road, London NW2 6DA ☎ 020 8452 2931, 0836 552650 mob

DICKIE Neville: The Ivories, 31 Banstead Road, Carlshalton Beeches, Surrey SM5 3NS ☎ 020 8643 2239 & fax

DIGNAM Kate *(Vln)*: 27 The Dell, Orchard Avenue, London N3 3NL ☎ 020 8371 0032

DJ OBERON *(Synth)* ☎ 020 8881 1036, 020 8888 4014

DJUDUROVIC Dragan *(Acc, Per)*: 22 Bartle Road, London W11 1RF ☎ 020 7221 7692

DOBINSON John *(Sax, Gtr)*: 96 Toms Lane, Kings Langley, Herts WD4 8NL

DOBS *(Kbds, Gtr, Voc)*: 295A Ladbrook Grove, London W10 6HE ☎ 020 8968 1526, 0973 295113 mob

DOCKRELL-TYLER Elizabeth *(Vln)*: 3 Trevor Close, East Barnet, Herts EN4 8AR ☎ 020 8449 8589, 0589 314318

DODGE Andrew *(Md)*: 18 Waldeck Road, Strand-on-The Green, London W4 3NP ☎ 020 8995 1977

DONALDSON John *(Synth)*: 27 Abernethy Road, London SE13 5QJ ☎ 020 8318 0653

DONOVAN John *(Kbds, Org)*: 19 Barnehurst Road, Bexley Heath, Kent DA7 6EY ☎ 01322 553850, 0966 265950 mob

DOURADO Timothy *(Kbds, Voc, Gtr)*: 72 Winterton House, Deancross Street, London E1 2QR ☎ 020 7791 3297, 0956 833 903 mob

DOVE John *(Gtr, Bjo, Acc)*: Flat 4, 38 Redcliffe Road, London SW10 9HJ ☎ 020 7352 7875

DOWNES Geoffrey *(Org, Synth)*: Address Unknown ☎ 01633 4506003, 01633 450666

DRINKWATER Neil *(Kbds, Arr, Md)*: 6 Stradbroke Grove, Buckhurst Hill, Essex IG9 5PD ☎ 020 8505 9572

DUDMAN Colin: 24A St Marks Rise, London E8 2NL ☎ 020 7249 8819

DUFFY Martin *(Org)*: c/o Scream Heights Management, 1 Cowcross Street, London EC1M 6DR ☎ 020 7490 8841

DUNN Christopher *(Org, Ob, Sax, Hmca)*: 138 Chestnut Avenue South, Walthamstow, London E17 9EL ☎ 020 8223 0121

DUNNE Patrick *(Gtr)*: 44 Middleton Road, London E8 4BS ☎ 020 7249 5705

DUNSTALL Clive *(Kbds, Synth, Tpt, Arr)*: 40 Cordingley Road, Ruislip, Middlesex HA4 7HQ ☎ 01895 622208

DUNSTALL Ernie *(Arr)*: 3-Dunorlan Cottages, Halls Hole Road, Tunbridge Wells, Kent TN2 4RE ☎ 01892 522094, 0370 228028

DURRENT Peter *(Com, Md)*: Blacksmith Cottage, Bures Road, Little Cornard, Sudbury Suffolk CO10 0NR ☎ 01787 373483

DUSSEK Michael *(Kbds)*: 2 Morecambe Gardens, Stanmore, Middlesex HA7 4SP ☎ 020 8206 0706

EALES Geoff *(Kbds, Arr, Md, Com)*: 47 Howard Close, New Southgate, London N11 1EH ☎ 020 8368 9010, 01378 261180

EARLEY Judith: 23A Hanover Road, London N15 4DL ☎ 020 8885 5063

EBBAGE David *(Md)*: 75 Claremont Road, Tunbridge Wells, Kent TN1 1TE ☎ 01892 27970

EBBEN Guy *(Gtr, Sax)*: 94 Sandmere Road, Brixton, London SW4 7QH ☎ 020 7737 4690, 0410 329583

ECCLESTONE Daniel *(Gtr)*: Address Unknown ☎ 020 8800 1589

EDINGTON John: 4Bushwood Road, Kew, Richmond TW9 3BQ ☎ 020 8940 6403, 020 8332 1877

EDMONDS Gavin *(Kbds, Tpt)*: 445A Uxbridge Road, Southall, London UB1 3ET ☎ 0976 744878

EDWARDS Andrew: 5 Highgrove Court, 69 Park Road, Beckenham, Kent BR3 1QG ☎ 020 8658 2667, 01524 414780

EDWARDS Carlton *(Com, Md)*: 1St Floor Flat, 168 Park Road, London N8 8JT ☎ 020 8374 1060

EDWARDS Catherine: 66 Drakefell Road, London SE14 5SJ ☎ 020 7732 9399

EGAN Raymond *(Org, Arr, Con)*: 39 Hawthorn Road, Edmonton, London N18 N18 1EY ☎ 020 8807 7066

EL-YAFI Nizar: Flat 2, Essel House, 29 Foley Street, London W1P 7LB ☎ 020 7255 1710

ELDRIDGE Paul *(Kbds)*: 15B Theatre Street, Battersea, London SW11 5NE ☎ 020 7350 1437

ELLSBURY Brian: 30 City View, Overhill Road, London SE22 0PZ ☎ 020 8693 2215, 0956 482146 mob

ELMS Roderick *(Org, Hpsd)*: 23 Bethell Avenue, Ilford, Essex IG1 4UX ☎ 020 8518 6342, 020 8533 1372

ELWIN David: 14 Princes Road, Wimbledon, London SW19 8RB ☎ 020 8540 8426

ENGLISHBY Paul *(Kbds)*: 17 Mount Pleasant Road, Hither Green, London SE13 6RD ☎ 020 8690 7740

ENYA *(E.Bhraonain)* *(Synth)*: 6 Danieli Drive, Artane, Dublin 5, Ireland ☎ Dublin 312580

ERIEMO Beverley: 5 Hume Court, Hawes Street, Islington, London N1 2EQ

ETTRIDGE Pete: Address Unknown ☎ 020 7928 6401

EVANS Andrew *(Clt)*: 190 Thessaly Road, London SW8 4ED ☎ 020 7627 4796, 0378 921 520

EVANS Ceri *(Kbds, B Gtr)*: 59 Greenend Road, Chiswick, London W4 1AH ☎ 020 8747 8307 & fax

EVERETT S: 40 Grafton Road, Worcester Park, Surrey KT4 7QP ☎ 020 8330 1255

FAGG James: 77 Berwick Road, Welling, Kent DA16 1RL ☎ 020 8301 3787

FAGGIONI Valerio *(Kbds, Voc)*: 52 Pathfield Road, London SW16 5NY ☎ 020 8696 0048

FAHEY Siobhan: c/o Punclose Ltd, 2nd Floor, 2-4 Lambton Place, London W11 2SH ☎ 020 7792 5981, 020 7792 5092

FAIRHOLME Fred *(Com)*: 16 Mayplace Close, Barnehurst, Kent DA7 6DT ☎ 01322 529209

FARNON David *(Org)*: Les Villets Farm, La Rue Des Villets, Le Gouffre, Forest, Guernsey C.I. GY8 0HP

FAWCETT Caleb *(Kbds, Per, T Sax, Gtr)*: 82 Minford Gardens, Shepherds Bush, London W14 0AP ☎ 020 7371 1317

FEARON Phillip *(Gtr)*: 1 Perth Avenue, Kingsbury, London NW5 7JP ☎ 020 8200 5638

FEDERICI Paul *(Voc)*: 43 Churnfield, Six Acres Estate, Biggerstaff Street, London N4 3PL ☎ 020 7263 2415, 609 5443

FENN Naomi *(Gtr)*: 34 Amherst Road, Sevenoaks, Kent TN13 3LS ☎ 01732 456089

FENN-SMITH Jeremy *(Flt, S Sax, T Sax, Pic)*: 159 Queens Road, London SW19 8NS ☎ 020 8540 5939

FENTON Bernie *(Arr, Com)*: 17 Poplar Avenue, Luton, Bedfordshire LU3 2BP ☎ 01582 504785

FERNER Alan *(Synth, Kbds)*: 66 Beechwood Gardens, Ilford, Essex IG5 0AG ☎ 020 8550 0717

FERRY Bryan *(Voc)*: Dene Jesmond Ent Ltd, c/o Harris & Rotter, 65 New Cavendish St, London W1M 7RD

FIELDING Mark: 28 Firs Lane, Winchmore Hill, London N21 3ES ☎ 020 8245 8106

FIELDS Wallace: 45, Highcliffe Gardens, Redbridge, Ilford, Essex IG4 5HP ☎ 020 8550 2352

FIENNES Magnus *(Kbds, Dms, Per, Hrn)*: Address Unknown ☎ 020 8964 1223, 020 8964 9914

FILIPE Nuno: 9A Beethoven Street, London W10 4LG ☎ 020 8960 1406

FILSELL Jeremy *(Org, Voc)*: 13 Beaumont Place, Isleworth, Middlesex TW7 7LB ☎ 020 8891 1712 & fax

FINLOW Nicolas *(Kbds, Org)*: 33B Ashbourne Grove, London SE22 8RN ☎ 020 8693 5085

FISHER Jeremy *(Md, Ob)*: 59 Fearnley House, Vestry Road, London SE5 8SR ☎ 020 7703 0136, 01426 159222 pager

FLINDERS John: Flat 3, 51 Byne Road, Sydenham, London SE26 5JG ☎ 020 8659 4458

FLYNN Declan *(Gtr)*: Top Floor Flat, 80A Tyrwhitt Road, Brockley, London SE4 1QB ☎ 020 8691 0748

FORD Gillian *(Hrn)*: 65A Lower Road, Sutton, Surrey SM1 4QR ☎ 020 8643 0725 & fax, 07970 723301 mob

FOSTER Nigel: Flat 1, 42 The Crescent, Wimbledon Park, London SW19 8AN ☎ 020 8879 0323, 0973 292992 mob

FOSTER Stan *(Arr, Con, Com)*: 18 Egremont Road, Hardwick, Cambridgeshire CB3 7XR ☎ 01954 211043

FOWKE Jon *(Kbds, Arr, Com)*: Warwick Cottage, 53 Mandeville Road, Enfield, Middx EN3 6SL ☎ 0973 307845

FOX Nigel: 33 Meadway, Staines, Middlesex TW18 2PW ☎ 01784 460642

FOXLEY Ray: 27 Mount Park Crescent, Ealing, London W5 2RN ☎ 020 8998 3043

FOXLEY Simon *(Arr)*: 105 Forburg Road, London N16 6HR ☎ 020 8806 6631

FRANK Mary *(Vln)*: 148 Purves Road, London NW10 5TG ☎ 020 8960 3046

FRANKEL David *(Vla)*: 6 Woodrow Court, Haybourne Road, London N17 0SX ☎ 020 8801 6088

FRANKLIN Maxine: 62 Redcliffe Gardens, London SW10 9HD ☎ 020 7370 3630

FRANKLIN Stephen *(Synth, Com)*: 16 Highdown Road, Roehampton, London SW15 5BU ☎ 020 8788 7130

FRASER Jo-Anne *(Vla, Gtr, Lute)*: 164 Sterling Gardens, Sanford Street, London SE14 6EZ ☎ 020 8691 7627

FRENCH Stephen *(Synth)*: 2 Nutbrook Street, London SE15 4LE ☎ 020 7732 2178

FRIEDMAN Aron *(Kbds, Voc, Dms)*: 34C Webbs Road, Battersea, London SW11 6SF ☎ 071 738 9627/92

FRIESEGREENE Timothy: 30 Cranfield Road, London SE4 1UG

FROST Christopher *(Kbds)*: 126 Lexington, Bow Quarter, Fairfield Road, London E3 2UE ☎ 020 8981 8284 & fax, 0468 437963 mob

FUJISAWA Reiko: 57 Maidstone Road, New Southgate, London N11 2JS ☎ 020 8368 2527, 020 8361 8665

GABRIELLE Anne *(Hpsd)*: 74 Vivian Avenue, Hendon NW4 3XG ☎ 020 8202 4935

GAMLEY John: 1 Talbot Road, London N6 4QS ☎ 020 8348 1482

GAMMON Philip *(Acc)*: 19 Downs Avenue, Pinner, Middx HA5 5AQ ☎ 020 8866 3260

GARRICK Michael *(B Ldr, Com, Md)*: 12 Castle Street, Berkhampstead, Herts HP4 2BQ ☎ 01442 864989, 01442 384493 fax

GATTI Luca *(Dms, Gtr)*: 32 Monson Road, London NW10 5UP ☎ 020 8553 0768

GEE Jonathan *(Voc)*: 21 William Street, Leyton, London E10 6BD ☎ 020 8556 7883

GIBBS Margaret: 1 Cleve Road, London NW6 3RG ☎ 020 7624 8583

GILLESPIE Anna *(Flt, Per)*: 20 Ropery Street, Mile End, London E3 4QF ☎ 020 8983 1555, 0956 326194

GLANVILLE Shaun *(Vln)*: 114 Highbury Park, London N5 2XE ☎ 020 7359 8334

GLASMAN Joseph *(Kbds)*: 41 Thirlmere Road, London N10 2DL ☎ 020 8444 4426

GLAVIN Helen *(Kbds, Voc)*: 137 Tildesley Road, Putney, London SW15 3AU ☎ 020 8785 7612, 020 8785 7612

GLEDHILL Norman (*Arr*): 1 Cumberland Drive, Hinchley Wood, Esher, Surrey KT10 0BG ☎ 020 8398 3494

GLIGOROFF Thomas: Flat 2, 9 Myddelton Square, London EC1R 1YE ☎ 020 7837 3073

GODZISZ Wojtek (*Gtr, B Gtr*): 74 Askew Road, London W12 9BJ ☎ 020 8749 2883

GOLDSTEIN Martin (*Md, Hpsd*): 104 St Leonards Road, Windsor, Berks SL4 3DD ☎ 01753 840653

GOLDWATER Stephen: 131 Wentworth Road, London NW11 0RJ ☎ 020 8455 6365

GORDON David (*Hpsd*): 135 Lower Paddock Road, Oxhey, Herts WD1 4DU ☎ 01923 239038

GORMAN Michael (*Kbds, Gtr*): 55 Ribblesdale Road, London SW16 6SS ☎ 0973 114724 mob

GOSLING Susie (*Kbds, Flt, A Sax*): 25 Royal Victor Place, Old Ford Road, Bow, London E3 5SS ☎ 020 8980 6950, 0976 740655

GOUGH Christine: 10 Hans Crescent, London SW1X 0LJ ☎ 020 7584 5470

GOULD John (*Md, Com*): 26B West Hill Road, Brighton, East Sussex BN1 3RT ☎ 01273 726397

GOUT Alan (*Tbn, Con, Arr*): 2 Beaufort Lodge, 168 Kew Road, Richmond, Surrey TW9 2AS ☎ 020 8948 3074 & fax

GRAHAM Laurence (*Kbds, Gtr, Dms*): 38 East Road, Chadwell Heath, Romford, Essex RM6 6XP ☎ 0956 262987 mob, 020 8597 5868

GRAY (*Voc*): 12 Chambers Road, Holloway, London N7 0LZ ☎ 020 7607 0794

GRAY Stephen (*Com, Arr*): 28 The Roman Way, Glastonbury, Somerset BA6 8AB ☎ 01458 834226 & fax

GRAYSON Angela: 7 Sopwith Avenue, Chessington, Surrey KT9 1QE ☎ 020 8391 4205

GREENBERG Talya (*Gtr*): Donna, 7 Willenhall Avenue, New Barnet, Herts EN5 1JN ☎ 020 8368 3312, 0956 278904

GREGORY Christian: 8 Arlington Close, East Twickenham, Middlesex TW1 2BE ☎ 020 8744 0958

GREGORY Roy: 53 Woodcock Dell Ave, Kenton, Harrow, Middx HA3 0NU ☎ 020 8904 1006

GREGORY Sam Paul: 32 Whitehills Road, Loughton, Essex IG10 1TS ☎ 020 8502 2500

GREIG Stanley (*Dms*): 17A Priory Terrace, London NW6 4HL ☎ 020 7328 6602

GRIFFITHS Leslie (*Gtr*): 85A Coleraine Road, London SE3 7PF ☎ 020 8858 3975

GRIFFITHS Paul (*Org, Hpsd*): 76 Gipsy Hill, Upper Norwood, London SE19 1PD

GROWER Alexis: Magrath & Co., 53-54 Maddox Street, London W1R 9PA ☎ 020 7495 3003

GULVIN Michael (*Tpt*): 291 Corbets Tey Road, Upminster, Essex RM14 2BT ☎ 01708 228637

GUTKIND Diana (*Kbds, Synth, Voc*): 344 Alexandra Park Road, London N22 4BD ☎ 020 8889 2760

GUTMAN Stephen: 155A Stoke Newington High St., London N16 0NY ☎ 020 7254 7763

HAGEN Peter (*Md, Kbds, Hmca*): 46 South Drive, Brentwood, Essex CM14 5DL ☎ 01277 226011, 0468 748430 mob

HALL Cliff (*Org*): Thrums, Old Farm Road, Off The Avenue, Hampton, Middx TW12 3QT ☎ 020 8941 5584

HALL Kyra: The Gramarye, Waynflete Avenue, Croydon, Surrey CR0 4BS ☎ 020 8404 7083

HAMER Mick: 46 Wilton Avenue, London W4 2HY ☎ 020 8994 8091

HAMILTON Roy (*Voc*): 591 Copperfield, Limes Farm Estate, Chigwell, Essex IG7 5LE

HAMILTON Steve (*Kbds*): 1 Newman Court, 37-39 Station Rd, Finchley, London N3 2SJ ☎ 020 8371 0248 & fax, 0973 654816

HANEY Janet Elizabeth: 79 Queenswood Road, Forest Hill, London SE23 2QR ☎ 020 8291 1728

HARDING Eric: 91 Cadbury Way, Yalding Road, London SE16 3XA ☎ 020 7237 6155

HARDWICK James: 120 Tachbrook Street, London SW1V 2ND ☎ 020 7834 3522

HARDY Paul (*Org, Gtr, Acc*): 86 Highlands Heath, Bristol Gardedns, Putney SW15 3TY ☎ 020 8788 9115

HARMSWORTH Atalanta (*Kbds, Synth*): The Little Grange, 188 Murray Road, Ealing, London W5 4DA ☎ 020 8560 3214, 0973 134880

HARPER David (*Org, Kbds*): 1 Mallard Way, Yateley, Hampshire GU46 6PG ☎ 01252 878922, 01252 878784 fax

HARPER Frederick (*Org, Voc, Arr*): 281 Long Elmes, Harrow, Middlesex HA3 6LE ☎ 020 8421 1415

HARPHAM James (*Rec, Com*): Tog Hill, Calstone, Calne, Wiltshire SN11 8PZ ☎ 01249 812300

HARRIS Max (*Arr, Com*): Checkmate, Chequers Lane, Walton-on-The Hill, Surrey KT20 7RB ☎ 01737 812744

HARRIS Richard: 75 St Georges Drive, London SW1V 4DB ☎ 020 7630 9246

HARRIS Tris (*S Sax*): 24 Lowther Hill, Forest Hill, London SE23 1PY ☎ 020 8690 4087, 0956 385401 mob

HARRISON Christopher (*Kbds, Gtr, Md*): 26 Wellington Gardens, London SE7 7PH ☎ 020 8858 7377

HARRISON Karl (*Voc, Song W, Arr*): 16 Wixom House, Romero Square, London SE3 ☎ 020 8473 9918, 0956 515561 mob

HARRISON Tom: 85 The Slade, Daventry, Northants NN11 4HP ☎ 01327 310609

HARROD David: 15 Eltringham Street, London SW18 1TD ☎ 020 8877 3603

HARVEY Aston: 1 Kingfisher Close, Kenton Lane, Harrow Weald, Middx HA3 6DA ☎ 020 8954 9855

HARVEY Graham (*Gtr*): 9 Heron Drive, Stanstead Abbotts, Ware, Herts SG12 8TU ☎ 01920 877638

HARVEY Patrick (*Cel, Org, Hpsd, Com*): Aynescombe Cottage, Aynescombe Path, Thames Bank, London SW14 7QR ☎ 020 8876 4356

HARVEY-PIPER Penelope: 23 Belvedere Grove, London SW19 7RQ ☎ 020 8946 1064

HASLAM Dominic (*Kbds*): 31 Inner Park Road, Wimbledon, London SW19 6DF ☎ 020 8789 4904, 07887 526 729

HATCH Tony (*Arr, Md*): 3 Warwick Way, London SW1V 1QU ☎ 020 7976 6021, 020 7976 6431 fax

HATT Chris (*Kbds*): 268 Ongar Road, Brentwood, Essex CM15 9EA ☎ 01277 213823

HATTON Janet (*Voc*): 1 Roseneath Avenue, Winchmore Hill, London N21 3NE ☎ 020 8360 5674

HATTON Neil (*Synth, Org*): 1 Roseneath Avenue, Winchmore Hill, London N21 3NE ☎ 020 8360 5674

HAWES Pat (*Kbds, Voc*): 12 Fane Way, Maidenhead, Berks SL6 2TL ☎ 01628 35481

HAWKINS Ian (*Org*): 341 Durnsford Road, Wimbledon Park, London SW19 8EF

HAWKSHAW Alan (*Org, Hpsd, Clst, E Pf*): Second Floor, 143 Charing Cross Road, London WC2H 0EE ☎ 020 7434 9678, 020 7434 1470 fax

HAYES Lesley: 14A Agamemnon Road, London NW6 1DY ☎ 020 7794 0763

HAYWOOD John (*Com*): 57C Westhill Road, Putney, London SW18 1LE ☎ 020 8875 9865

HEAD Raymond: The Firs, 10 Worcester Road, Chipping Norton, Oxfordshire OX7 5XX ☎ 01608 642025

HEADEY Stuart (*Org, Ac Gtr, B Gtr*): 531 Commonside East, Mitcham, Surrey CR4 1HH ☎ 020 8764 9514

HEATH Bobby (*Kbds*): 22A High Street, Hampton Hill, Middx TW12 1PD

HEATH Kate: 6 Westbourne Road, London N7 8AU ☎ 020 7700 4497

HEATH Sally: Timbers, Woburn Hill, Weybridge, Surrey KT15 2QG ☎ 01932 845881

HECKEL Stefan (*Kbds, Acc*): 187 Tufnell Park Road, London N7 0PU ☎ 020 7609 4927 & fax

HENDERSON Allie (*Cel*): 11 Leigh Gardens, London NW10 5HN ☎ 020 8969 3135 & fax

HENDERSON Graham (*Kbds, Acc, Gtr, Mando*): 4 Caverswall Street, London W12 0HG ☎ 020 8743 8107

HENDRY Linn: 4 Chelmsford Square, London NW10 3AR ☎ 020 8459 1475

HENESY Paul: 15 Aldwych Buildings, Parker Street, London WC2B 5NT ☎ 020 7831 3506

HENNESSEY Mike: Tobel Strasse 2, 78591, Durchhausen, Germany ☎ +49 7464/3061, +49 7464/3195

HERRIDGE David (*Org, Kbds, Voc*): 13 Lubbock Court, Lubbock Road, Chislehurst, Kent BR7 5JW ☎ 020 8295 1030

HERRIOTT Richard M J (*Kbds, Synth, Com*): 1 Kerry View, Horsforth, Leeds LS18 4DQ ☎ 0113 259 1580

HERSCHMANN Heinz (*Md, Arr, Con*): 32 Ellerdale Road, London NW3 6BB ☎ 020 7435 5255

HERSH Benjamin (*Vln, Voc*): 71 Leverton Street, London NW5 2NX ☎ 020 7424 0490

HERSHMAN Nick (*Voc, Gtr*): 102 Abbey House, Garden Road, London NW8 9BY ☎ 020 7289 7739

HEWIE Christopher (*Dms, Gtr, B Gtr, Voc*): 19 Ferrybridge House, China Walk Estate, Lambeth Road, London SE11 6NB ☎ 020 7735 8032, 020 7924 0162 fax

HEWSON David (*Synth, Flt*): Crosshand House, 38 Chislehurst Road, Bickley, Kent BR1 2NW ☎ 020 8295 0838, 020 8295 0839

HILL Barbara (*Hpsd*): 1 Frognal Gardens, London NW3 6UY ☎ 020 7435 9210

HILL Steve (*Kbds, Md, Arr*): 36 Warwick Road, Thames Ditton, Surrey KT7 0PS ☎ 020 8398 4132

HILL Thomas (*Kbds, Gtr*): 27 Wallwood Road, London E11 1OQ ☎ 020 8556 7916

HILSUM Leonard (*Acc*): 34A Park Mansions, Vivian Avenue, London NW4 3UU ☎ 020 8202 9128

HIPKIN Murray (*Hpsd, Cel, Md*): 26 Gorse Road, Cookham, Maidenhead, Berkshire SL6 9LL ☎ 01628 810491

HIRSCH Jake (*Kbds*): 2 Southwood Lawn Road, London N6 5SF

HITCHMAN Nigel: 126 Lexington Building, Bow Quarter, Fairfield Road, London E3 2UE ☎ 020 8981 8284 & fax, 0802 749210 mob

HODGE Basil (*Kbds*): 35D Mansfield Road, Ilford, Essex IG2 3BB ☎ 020 8800 6435

HOETEE Yanuwn (*Gtr*): 129A Sumatra Road, West Hampstead, London NW6 1PL ☎ 020 7431 6623

HOGAN Terry (*Org, Gtr, B Gtr*): 44 Seafield Road, New Southgate, London N11 1AS

HOLDER Michael (*Kbds*): 18 Alma House, Napoleon Road, Clapton, London E5 8TF ☎ 020 8986 1407

HOLLAND Nicola (*Voc*): c/o 15 Andrews House, Barbican, London EC2Y 8AX

HOLLAND Vincent: 29 Rythe Road, Claygate, Surrey KT10 9DG ☎ 01372 465067

HOLLER Felix (*Kbds*): 6 Lyttleton Road, London N8 0QB ☎ 020 8881 2612

HOLLINGWORTH Andrew (*Flt, Kbds, Synth*): 63 Co Whitbread Road, Crofton Park, London SE4 2BD ☎ 020 8692 6019

HOLLOWAY Laurie: Elgin, Fishery Road, Bray, Berkshire SL6 1UP ☎ 01628 37715, 01628 776232 fax

HOLLOWAY Robert: 241 Ashford Road, Laleham, Staines TW18 1RR ☎ 01784 253589

HOLLOWAY Yvonne (*Voc, Vln, St Pan, Rec*): 10 Cliffstone Court, Shorncliffe Road, Folkestone, Kent CT20 2ND ☎ 01303 259892

HOLMES Richard (*Md, Arr, Synth*): 18 Baylis Crescent, Burgess Hill, West Sussex RH15 8UP ☎ 01444 257427, 0802 250510

HOLMES Shaun: 24B Black Boy Lane, South Tottenham, London N15 ☎ 020 8809 5422 & fax

HONEYBORNE Jack: 32 Cranmer Avenue, London W13 9SH ☎ 020 8579 0540

HOOKWAY Tony (*Org, Synth, B Gtr, Voc*): 24 The Avenue, Loughton, Essex IG10 4PT ☎ 020 8508 1855, 020 8502 3097

HORLER John: 60 Lamberhurst Road, London SE27 0SE ☎ 020 8670 5086

HORNE Stephen (*Kbds, Flt*): Ground Floor Flat, 111 Chapter Road, Willesden Green, London NW2 5LH ☎ 020 8459 7785

HOWARD Leslie (*Org, Con*): 128 Norbury Crescent, London SW16 4JZ ☎ 020 8764 8364

HOWELL Allan (*Kbds, Voc*): 82 Drummond Drive, Stanmore, Middlesex HA7 3PE ☎ 020 8954 3686

HOWES Chris (*E Pf*): 40 Stafford Road, Sidcup, Kent DA14 6PU ☎ 020 8300 6590

HUGHES Eric (*Org, Arr, Com*): 65 Mount Pleasant, Ruislip, Middlesex HA4 9HQ ☎ 020 8841 2880

HURST Jonny (*Voc, Synth*): 75 Chambord Street, Shoreditch, London E2 7NJ

HUTCHINSON Matthew (*Synth*) ☎ 020 8800 8480

HUTTON Adrian (*Gtr, B Gtr*): Lower Lodge, Donnington, Ledbury, Herefordshire HR8 2HX ☎ 01531 890 616, 0973 736132 mob

HYATT Michael (*Hpsd*): 8 Brickwall Close, Burnham-on-Crouch, Essex CM0 8HB ☎ 01621 786643

HYLAND Wyn (*Kbds*): 174 Vaughan Road, Harrow HA1 4EB ☎ 020 8864 9492

HYMAS Tony: The Field Cottage, Bagendon, Cirencester, Gloucestershire GL7 7DU ☎ 01285 831728

ILES Nikki (*Acc*): Flat 4, 30 Onslow Gardens, Muswell Hill, London N10 3JU ☎ 020 8444 9171

ILLER Martin (*Gtr, Bjo*): 1A Etheldene Ave., Muswell Hill, London N10 3QG ☎ 020 8442 1690

INGLE Anthony (*Com, Md, B Gtr, Acc*): 9 Beechfield Road, London SE6 4NG ☎ 020 8314 0402

INGLEBY Mark (*Kbds, A Sax*): 50 Ivy Road, Brockley, London SE4 1YS ☎ 020 8694 8250

INGRAM Alexander (*Hrn*): 8 Richmond Ave, London SW20 8LA ☎ 020 8540 6791

INNES Don (*Kbds*): 23 Halford Road, Ickenham, Middlesex UB10 8PY ☎ 01895 2 32271

INNES Neil (*Org, Gtr*): Brices Farm, Stoney Lane, Debenham, Nr. Stowmarket, Suffolk IP14 6PU ☎ 01728 860302

IRELAND Helen (*Md*): 57 Whitehorse Road, Stepney, London E1 0ND ☎ 020 7790 5883

ISHMAEL Clement (*Org, Voc, Tpt*): 62 Aldbourne Road, London W12 0LN

JACKSON Art (*Org, Voc*): Address Unknown

JACKSON Catherine (*Flt*): 66 Bawdsey Avenue, Newbury Park, Ilford, Essex IG2 7TJ ☎ 020 8590 8890

JACKSON Daniel (*Rep*): 32 Harvard Court, Honeybourne Road, London NW6 1HL ☎ 020 7435 6069, 0973 106938

JACOBSEN Peter (*B Gtr*): c/o Mrs D Jacobsen, 4 Highfield Drive, Westcliff-on-Sea, Essex SS0 0TB ☎ 01702 339192

JAEGER Lincoln (*Voc, S Sax*): 217A Bramley Road, Oakwood, London N14 4XB ☎ 020 8367 2621

JAMIESON Gaby (*Gtr*): 1 Waldron Mews, Old Church Street, London SW3 5BT ☎ 020 7351 4741, 07771 784027, 020 7351 1959

JAMIESON James (*Sax, Gtr, Voc, Clt*): Flat 1, 7 Salisbury Road, Hove, E. Sussex BN3 3AB

JARRATT Jeff: Forestdene, Hadley Green West, Barnet, Herts EN5 4PP ☎ 020 8449 0830

JAY Irving (*Arr, Com*): 11 Belmont Avenue, Palmers Green, London N13 4HD ☎ 020 8882 1150

JAYES Catherine (*Md*): 13 Upland Mews, London SE22 9EE ☎ 020 8693 3804

JEROME: 21A Hythe Road, Thornton Heath CR4 8QQ ☎ 020 8771 8953

JESSOP Francesca: 229 Russell Court, Woburn Place, London WC1H 0ND ☎ 020 7837 4179

JOHN Elton (*Voc*): Elton John Mngt, 7 King Street Cloisters, Clifton Walk, London W6 0GY ☎ 020 8748 4800, 020 8563 1359

JOHNSON Alistair (*Kbds*): Flat 54, Globe Wharf, Rotherhithe Street, London SE16 1XS, 0468 125 242 mob

JOHNSTON David (*Kbds*): 36 Oakfield Road, Ashtead, Surrey KT21 2RD ☎ 01372 275293

JONES Clare (*Hpsd*): 7 Regency Court, Surbiton, Surrey KT5 8QB

JONES David: Heathwood, Fakenham Road, Taverham, Norwich, Norfolk NR8 6HR ☎ 01603 867 219

JONES Ian (*Kbds*): 78A Dynham Road, London NW6 2NR ☎ 020 7625 4474 & fax

JOSEPH Julian (*Clt, Dms*): 85 Cicada Road, Wandsworth, London SW18 2PA ☎ 020 8874 8647, 020 8877 9783 fax

JOSEPHS Mildred (*Ob*): Flat 3, 125 Castlenau, London SW13 9EL ☎ 020 8748 9758

JOZEFOWICZ-BUKOWSKA Suzanne (*Kbds, Voc, Md, Sax*): Address Unknown ☎ 020 8892 2709, 0973 723052 mob

KAHN Harry (*B Ldr, Arr*): 1 Miriam Court, Aylmer Road, London N2 0BY ☎ 020 8347 5559

KANAVA Nicola-Jane: 13 Canada Avenue, Edmonton, London N18 1AS ☎ 020 8350 4741, 0370 406752, 020 8245 1596

KAUFMAN Paul (*Kbds*): 20 Dudley Road, Ilford, Essex IG1 ES ☎ 020 8478 8237

KAY David: 388 Green Lane, New Eltham, London SE9 3TQ ☎ 020 8333 1907

KAY Peter (*Org, Md, Com*): 34 Woodland Rise, Muswell Hill, London N10 3UG ☎ 020 8883 8452, 020 8444 2628 fax

KEATING Terence (*St Gtr*): 24 Lothair Road South, London N4 1EL ☎ 020 8342 8605

KEEN Gabriel (*A Sax, Dms, Gtr, Vln*): 130 Shoreditth High Street, London E1 6JE ☎ 020 7613 4439

KELLY Julian (*Hpsd, Org, Arr, Md*): 12 Lateward Road, Brentford, Middlesex TW8 0PJ ☎ 020 8568 0884, 0973 835285

KELLY Sharon: 35 Chalcot Road, Primrose Hill, London NW1 8LP ☎ 020 7722 7806

KEMP Michael: 9 St Matthews Parade, Kingsley Park, Northampton NN2 7HS ☎ 01604 722 335

KENNARD George (*E Pf, Kbds, Arr, Com*): 48 Welling Way, Welling, Kent DA16 2RT ☎ 020 8856 9614

KENWARD Elaine (*Vla, Clt*): 79 Westwood Drive, Little Chalfont, Bucks HP6 6RR

KERPNER Robert (*Synth, Gtr, Md*): 5 Ravensbourne House, Arlington Road, E. Twickenham TW1 2AX ☎ 020 8892 5873

KEYS Robert (*Con*): Red Lion Court, Stalbridge, Sturminster Newton, Dorset DT10 2LR ☎ 01963 362999

KHANU Arnold: 52 Watcombe Road, South Norwood, London SE25 4UZ ☎ 020 8654 6251

KIBBLE Christopher (*Kbds*): 96 Brayards Road, Peckham, London SE15 2BU ☎ 020 7732 6998

KIEVE Daniel (*Voc*): 63 Roebuck Lane, Buckhurst Hill, Essex IG9 5QX ☎ 020 8504 1905, 04325 612844

KILPATRICK Charles: 133A Roundwood Road, Willesden, London NW10 9UL ☎ 020 8459 6911

KIMSEY Chris (*Gtr*): c/o Rspg, 21 Bedford Square, London WC1B 3HH ☎ 0162082 6150

KING Denis: 55 Parliament Hill, London NW3 2TB ☎ 020 7794 5110

KING Philip: 19 St Albyns Mead, Rottingdean, Brighton BN2 7HY ☎ 01273 242822

KING Roy (*E Pf, Synth*): 9 Harrow Gardens, Orpington, Kent BR6 9WD ☎ 01689 877070

KNIGHT Bruce (*Kbds*): 17 Crucible Close, Chadwell Heath, Romfrod, Essex RM6 4PZ ☎ 020 8597 2533

KNIGHT Frances: 40 Mandeville Road, Canterbury, Kent CT2 7HD ☎ 01227 785257

KNIGHT Judyth (*Com*): 10 Nicoll Court, Nicoll Road, London NW10 9AD ☎ 020 8965 1310

KNIGHT Paul (*Md*): Elhanan, 7 Christchurch Square, London E9 7HU ☎ 020 8533 7605

KNIGHT Reg: 9 Plane Tree Court, Brook Green, London W6 7BE ☎ 020 7603 2668

KNOWLES Cadine (*Voc*): 20 Eustace Road, Fulham, London SW6 1JD ☎ 020 7386 0031, 0956 998470

KOFFAN Laszlo: 39 Fallodon House, Tavistock Crescent, London W11 1AX ☎ 020 7727 6765

KOLLER Hans: 19 Manchester Road, London N15 6HP ☎ 020 8802 3526

KUERMAYR Gunther: 14 Albion Yard, 331 - 335 Whitechapel Road, London E1 1BW ☎ 020 7247 9299 & fax

KUNIYOSHI Akemi: 91 Goldhurst Terrace, London NW6 3HA ☎ 020 7625 4316

KUTCHMY Irita (*Wood W, Voc, Com*): 54 Washington Road, Worcester Park, Surrey KT4 8JH ☎ 020 8337 4396

LACEY Simon (*Kbds*): 2 Dumont Road, London N16 0NS ☎ 020 7241 5228

LADE Stephen: 130 Croxted Road, West Dulwich, London SE21 8NR ☎ 020 8670 2342

LAMBERT Richard (*E Pf, Kbds*): 13 Waddington Way, Upper Norwood, London SE19 3XH ☎ 020 8653 4372

LAMBERT Sandra (*Kbds, Synth*): 59 Pettits Lane, Romford, Essex RM1 4HA ☎ 01708 750741

LANE Simon Douglas: Little Cottage, 12 Church Street, Hampton, Middlesex TW12 2EG ☎ 020 8979 2480

LANGE Stephanie (*Kbds*): 81 Goldsmith Lane, Roe Green Village, Kingsbury, London NW9 9AR ☎ 020 8204 5017

LANKESTER Charlie (*Synth, Gtr, Voc, Song W*): 4 Midmoor Road, London SW12 0EN ☎ 020 8673 2597

LANZON Phil (*Org, Synth*): c/o Uriah Heep Prod. Ltd, 18 Savill Court, Savill Row, Woodford Green, Essex IG8 0UH ☎ 020 8852 7499

LATARCHE Vanessa: 8 Rivermount, Lower Hampton Road, Sunbury-on-Thames TW16 5PH ☎ 020 8847 5363 & fax

LAUPER Cyndi (*Org, Voc*): 34 Brook Lane North, Brentford, Middlesex TW8 0QW ☎ 020 8232 8661

LAURENCE Zack (*Com, Arr, E Pf, Synth*): 1 Glanleam Road, Stanmore, Middx HA7 4NW ☎ 020 8954 2025 & fax

LAW John: 28 Blythwood Road, London N4 4EU ☎ 020 7561 1506

LAWRENCE Betty (*Com, Md*): 75B Lancaster Road, London W11 1QG ☎ 020 7229 0360

LAZARO David (*Synth, Kbds, Gtr, Voc*): 61A Upper Brockley Road, London SE4 1SY ☎ 020 8694 6560

LE FOE Ben (*Kbds, Gtr*): 37 Ashley Gardens, Ambrosden Avenue, London SW1P 1QE ☎ 020 7834 5378

LE SAGE Bill (*Vib, Com, Arr*): 21 Park Road, London W7 1EN ☎ 020 8567 2394

LEACH Jeff (*Kbds, Org*): Flat A, Elm Place, Bruce Grove, London N17 6UU ☎ 020 8801 7457, 0802 235196

LEANEY Tony (*Voc, Arr, Com, Kbds*): Lantern Cottage, Cobham Way, East Horsley, Surrey KT24 5BH ☎ 01483 283034

LEDIGO Hugh (*Com, Arr*): 28 Worlds End Lane, Green St. Green, Orpington, Kent BR6 6AQ ☎ 01689 856170

LEDINGHAM Iain (*Hpsd, Org*): Ranmoor, Croft Road, Chalfont St Peter, Bucks SL9 9AF ☎ 01753 884628

LEE Christopher (*Kbds*): Ground Floor Flat, 49 Limes Grove, London SE13 6DD ☎ 020 8265 3368

LEE David (*Md, Com, Arr*): 1 Astor Close, Kingston-on-Thames, Surrey KT2 7LT ☎ 020 8549 2105, 020 8286 6505 fax

LEEMAN Kevin: 9 Essendine Road, London W9 2LS ☎ 020 7289 1522

LEESE Eric (*Synth*): 147 Preston Hill, Kenton, Middlesex HA3 9XA ☎ 020 8204 1666

LEGGE Anthony (*Org*): 48 Birch Grove, London W3 9SS

LEIGH Stephen (*Kbds*): 48 Grosvenor Road, Dagenham, Essex RM8 1NL

LELONG Chad: Flat 7, 56 Pembridge Villas, London W11 3EG ☎ 020 7727 6109

LEMON Brian (*Arr*): 8 Bloomsbury Close, Western Gardens, London W5 3SE ☎ 020 8992 1826

LENNOX Ann (*Flt, Voc*): 19 Mngnt.(La Lennoxa Ltd), Unit 32, Ransomes Dock, 35-37 Parkgate Road, London SW11 4NP ☎ 020 7738 1919

LEONARD Adrian (*Kbds, Gtr*): 36 Fanshaws Lane, Brickenden, Herts SG13 8PF

LEONARD Conrad: 40 Alwyne Road, Wimbledon, London SW19 7AE ☎ 020 8946 0876

LESTER Harold (*Acc, Hpsd, Rep*): 57 St Leonards Road, London SW14 7NQ ☎ 020 8878 0021

LEWIS Arthur: Address Unknown

LION Margaret: 5 Sussex Way, Holloway, London N7 6RT ☎ 020 7263 2365

LISTER Martin (*Kbds, Gtr, Voc*): 57 Exeter Road, Hanworth, Middlesex TW13 5NY ☎ 020 8894 7584

LLEWHELLIN David: 2 Basing Way, Valley Park, Chandlers Ford, Hants SO53 3PG ☎ 023 8026 2235

LLOYD William *(B Gtr, Synth)*: Flat 2, 95 Addiscombe Road, Croydon, Surrey CR0 0JH ☎ 020 8655 2954, 0797 0900862

LOCANTRO Tony: 1 Blackstone Road, London NW2 6DA ☎ 020 8452 6805

LOCKEY Saskia: Studio 12, 13 Castletown Road, West Kensington, London W14 9RH ☎ 020 7385 5540, 07970 867906

LOCKHART Robert: 33 Findon Road, London W12 9PP ☎ 020 8749 5147

LODDER Stephen *(E Pf, Synth)*: Flat C, 53 Clapton Common, London E5 9AA ☎ 020 8806 9576, 0850 364209 mob

LOFTIN Fred: 34 New Road, Shoreham-By-Sea, West Sussex BN43 6RA ☎ 01273 454094

LONG Wendy *(Kbds)*: Ground Floor Flat, 8 Tremlett Grove, London N19 5JX ☎ 020 7263 7893

LOSI Marco *(Voc, Gtr)*: 24 Dollis Ave, Finchley, London N3 1TX ☎ 020 8346 8626

LOUIS Leslie *(Org, Acc, Accom)*: 40 St Johns Road, St Johns, Woking, Surrey GU21 1SA ☎ 01483 723249

LOWE Chris *(Kbds)*: 15 Fullers Road, South Woodford, London E18 2QB ☎ 020 8504 7189, 020 8527 2311x255

LOWE-WATSON Andrew *(Com, Md)*: Flat 2, 155 Hemingford Road, London N1 1BZ ☎ 020 7609 8639

LUBBOCK Jeremy *(Arr)*: c/o 89 Elizabeth Street, London SW1W 9PG ☎ 020 7730 3816

LUND David: 100 Frognal, Hampstead, London NW3 6XU ☎ 020 7435 5958

LYON Jason: 11 Heralds Place, Kennington, London SE11 4NP ☎ 020 7582 7626

LYSANDER Ebonard *(Kbds, Synth, Gtr, B Gtr)*: Flat 6, Yates Court, 228 Willesden Lane, London NW2 5RH ☎ 020 8451 4120

MACDONALD Robert *(Con)*: 3 Paultons St, London SW3 5DP ☎ 020 7731 0711

MACKAY David *(Db, Arr)*: Toftrees, Church Road, Woldingham, Surrey CR3 7JX ☎ 01883 652201

MACKICHAN Blair *(Dms, Gtr)*: 2 Cambridge Gardens, 1St Floor Flat, London W10 5BU

MACKIE David *(Con)*: 187A Worple Road, Raynes Park, London SW20 8RE ☎ 020 8946 7892

MACLEAN Neil *(Kbds)*: 30 Brondesbury Villas, London NW6 6AA ☎ 020 7624 0054

MACMANUS Kieran *(Flt, Wh, Bod, Gtr)*: 24 River Way, Twickenham, Middx TW2 5JP ☎ 020 8241 3363, 020 8894 3590

MADDOCK Malcolm *(Synth, Com)*: Godbolts Cottage, 187 Coggeshall Road, Marks Tey, Colchester, Essex CO6 1HS ☎ 01206 210 196

MADGWICK Richard *(E Pf)*: 36A Orchard Rise, Shirley, Croydon, Surrey CR0 7QY ☎ 020 8776 1966

MAGUIRE Paul *(Md)*: 233 Waldegrave Road, Strawberry Hill, Twickenham, Middlesex TW1 4TA ☎ 020 8892 3006

MAINE Vicki *(Kbds, Voc)*: 'Crestway', 93 Wemborough Road, Stanmore, Middlesex HA7 2ED ☎ 020 8907 0062

MAJUMDAR Anna: Minden, Blenheim Road, Pilgrims Hatch, Brentwood, Essex CM15 9LP ☎ 01277 229013

MALCOLM Austin *(Org)*: 139 Pasteur Gardens, Edmonton, London N18 N18 1AH ☎ 020 8807 5078

MALLALIEU Jonathan *(Vla, Arab Dms)*: 42 Gledstanes Rd, London W14 9HU ☎ 020 7385 7883

MALLANDAINE Jean *(Hpsd, Org, Clst)*: 24 Elmtree Green, Great Missenden, Buckinghamshire HP16 9AF ☎ 01494 862925, 01494 890676 fax

MARCUS Bryan: 46 Cromer Road, New Barnet, Herts EN5 5HT ☎ 020 8449 4831, 020 7283 0691

MARCUS Derek: Harmony, Hawkshead Road, Little Heath, Potters Bar, Herts EN6 1LU ☎ 01707 653667

MARKWICK Steve *(B Gtr)*: 62 Sydner Road, London N16 7UG ☎ 020 7254 1328

MARQUEZ Marina *(Flt, Org, Cuatro)*: 12 Knowles Walk, Clapham Manor Estate, London SW4 6BY ☎ 020 7720 9763

MARSDEN Robin *(Clt, T Sax, Acc, Rec)*: 100 Seymour Road, London N8 0BG ☎ 020 8348 9471

MARSH John *(Org)*: 40 Hillcrest Road, London E17 4AP ☎ 020 8527 3809

MARSHALL Frankie *(Synth, Gtr, Voc)*: 1 Selwyn Court, Lee Terrace, Blackheath, London SE3 9SZ ☎ 020 8318 2951

MARSHALL Peter *(Synth, Brass, Flgl)*: 34 Tredegar Square, London E3 5AE ☎ 020 8981 0071

MARTIN Roger *(Org)*: 2A Killieser Avenue, Streatham Hill, London SW2 4NT ☎ 020 8674 8661

MASON Janette *(Kbds, Flt, Cntrc)*: 155 Maryland Road, London N22 5AS ☎ 0956 374677

MASON Margaret *(Org, Vib)*: 897 Harrow Road, Wembley, Middx HA0 2RH ☎ 020 8904 2467

MASSEY Andrew: 41 Mill Road, Wimbledon, London SW19 2NE ☎ 020 8543 7632, 01426 171256

MATHEWS Lester: Elm Cottage, 11 Oakhill Place, London SW15 2QN ☎ 020 8871 0751

MAXIM John: 7 Exford Gdns, Lee, London SE12 9HE ☎ 020 8857 4206

MAY Jack *(Org)*: Flat 4, Room 5, Laurel Dene, 117 Hampton Road, Hampton Hill, Middlesex

MAY Simon: Helstonleigh, 17 South Hill, Guildford, Surrey GU1 3SY

MAYALL Gaz *(Kbds, Mldca, Voc, Per)*: 615A Harrow Road, London W10 4RA ☎ 020 8960 4258

MAYS Sally: Stella Maris, Anglesea Road, Kingston-upon-Thames, Surrey KT1 2EW ☎ 020 8546 8677

MCARTHUR Neil *(Com, Arr, Md, Gtr)*: 1St Floor Flat, 24 Albion Rd, Stoke Newington, London N16 9PH ☎ 020 7249 9349, 020 7607 5573 fax

MCAULEY Brendan *(Flt, Bjo, Voc)*: 10 Harewood Road, Wimbledon, London SW19 2HD ☎ 020 8543 5334

MCCARTHY Ken: Glorian, Grove Lane, Chalfont St Peter, Bucks SL9 9JU ☎ 01753 884689

MCCONNEL James *(Flt, Org, Acc)*: Billingford Hall, Billingford, Nr. East Dereham, Norfolk NR20 4RF ☎ 01362 668097

MCFARLANE Frank *(Org, Md)*: 30 The Gardens, 125 Clapton Common, London E5 9AD ☎ 020 8802 6098

MCFARLANE Zara *(Voc)*: 101 Sheppy Road, Dagenham, Essex RM9 4LB ☎ 020 8262 9540

MCGEE Bobby: Address Unknown

MCGOWAN Tommy: 26 Aldridge Avenue, Stanmore, Middlesex HA7 1DD ☎ 020 8204 6093

MCINTOSH Thomas: The Old School, 5 Bridge Street, Hadleigh, Suffolk IP7 6BY ☎ 01473 822596

MCINTYRE Paul *(Kbds, Saxes)*: 3 Turasmore Park, London Terry, Ireland BT48 0FF ☎ 01504 265883

MCKEE Eric: 22 Gelsthorpe Road, Collier Row, Romford, Essex RM5 2NA ☎ 01708 23975

MCKENZIE Mike *(Voc)*: 4 Petrie Close, 33 Exeter Road, London NW2 4SJ ☎ 020 8450 6785

MCLEAN Benet *(Kbds, Gtr, B Gtr, Voc)*: 48 Southill Avenue, Harrow, Middlesex HA2 0NQ ☎ 020 8422 7668

MCLEOD Callum: 81 St Stephens Road, London W13 8JA ☎ 020 8998 3608, 020 8998 3698

MCMANUS Christopher *(Org, Hpsd)*: 16 Ravenscraig Road, Arnos Grove, London N11 1AD ☎ 020 8361 1628

MCNICOLL Robert *(Gtr)*: 4 Denzil Road, London NW10 2UP ☎ 020 8451 9558, 020 7766 5206/7, 020 7766 5208

MCPHERSON Kevin *(Kbds, Voc)*: 82 Hawkwood Crescent, Chingford, London E4 7PJ ☎ 020 8524 9402, 0958 494622 mob

MEAD Philip: 189 Whittington Road, London N22 8YP ☎ 020 8889 5454

MEADE Leonard *(Org)*: 9 Greenwood Drive, Highams Park, London E4 9HL ☎ 020 8531 5562, 020 8523 4159 fax

MEALING John *(Org, Synth, E Pf, Arr)*: Willow Loft, Hurley-on-Thames, Nr Maidenhead, Berks SL6 5NB ☎ 0162 882 4283

MELLECK Lydia *(Md)*: 10 Burgess Park Mansions, Fortune Green Road, London NW6 1DP ☎ 020 7794 8845

MELLING Steve: 14 Portland Avenue, Gravesend, Kent DA12 5HE ☎ 01474 357444

MELVILLE Charles: Ivydene, The Common, Damerham, Fordingbridge, Hampshire SP6 3HR ☎ 01725 518584

MELVIN Rieke (*Rec*): 31 Westhorpe Road, Putney, London SW15 1QH ☎ 020 8785 2713

MELVIN Rod (*Voc*): 20 St Barnabas Road, Walthamstow, London E17 8JY ☎ 020 8520 4361

MENDOZA Rod (*Org, Md*): 27 Bournemouth Road, London SW19 3AR ☎ 020 8540 5819

MERRY Maurice: 565 Harlestone Road, Northampton NN5 6NX ☎ 01604 756021

MERRY Michael: 166A Jamaica Road, London SE16 4RT ☎ 020 7237 4902

METLISS Jeremy (*Kbds, Cel, Gtr, B Gtr*) ☎ 020 8958 7776

MIDDLETON Kathleen: 69 Carlton Terrace, Cambridge Road, Edmonton, London N18 N18 1LD ☎ 020 8807 1914

MIDDLETON Max: Wassicks Farm, Haughley, Stowmarket, Suffolk IP14 3NP ☎ 01449 673218

MIEKAUTSCH Dieter: 15 Plymouth House, Devonshire Drive, London SE10 8JZ ☎ 020 8265 5089

MILES Terry (*Kbds*): 2 Ashfield Yard, Off I21-123 Ashfield Street, Whitechapel, London E1 3DY ☎ 020 7790 9215

MILES Tom (*Kbds, Md*): 155 Brook Drive, London SE11 4TG ☎ 020 7582 4551

MILLAR Duncan (*Synth*): 16A Almeida Street, London N1 1TA ☎ 020 7354 3967

MILLER Brian (*E Pf, Kbds, Arr, Com*): 55 Goldsmith Road, Friern Barnet, London N11 3JG ☎ 020 8368 7071

MILLER Jimmy (*Kbds*): 56 Willow Crescent West, New Denham, Uxbridge, Middlesex UB9 4AU ☎ 01895 233042

MILLER Robert (*Synth*): 9 Cresford Road, London SW6 2AH ☎ 020 7736 4892

MILLER Steven: Top Flat, 24 Rita Road, Vauxhall, London SW8 1JU ☎ 020 7735 1503

MILLNS Paul (*Voc, Com*): 102 Disraeli Road, Putney, London SW15 2DX ☎ 020 8788 5687

MILLS Dan (*Kbds, Voc*): 4 Laurel Gardens, Chingford E4 7PS ☎ 0958 523515

MILLS Gavin (*Flt*): 36 Dalkeith Grove, Stanmore, Middlesex HA7 4SF ☎ 020 8958 3889, 0468 471 678, 020 8958 1989

MILLS Simon: 26 Lynton Road, Queens Park, London NW6 3BL ☎ 020 7328 8384

MILNES Paul: The Garden Flat, 102 Jerningham Road, London SE14 5NW ☎ 020 7207 0009

MITCHELL Christopher (*Db*): 4 St.Clair Close, Reigate, Surrey RH2 0QB ☎ 017372 43791

MITCHELL Clayton: 13 Darfield Road, Crofton Park, London SE4 1ET ☎ 0956 514489 mob

MITCHELL Hugh: 21A Loftus Road, Shepherds Bush, London W12 7EH ☎ 020 8749 6373

MOORE Dudley (*Vln, Org*): c/o A Morgan Maree & Assoc., 4727 Wilshire Boulevard, Suite 600 Los Angeles, California 90010 USA ☎ +1 213 939 8700

MOORE Steve (*Kbds*): 356 Bastable Avenue, Barking, Essex IG11 0LL

MORAN David (*Clt, Sax, Kbds*): 50 Castelnau Gardens, London SW13 8DU

MORAN Mike (*Org, Synth, Arr*): Ballinger Lodge, Ballinger Common, Great Missenden, Bucks HP16 9LQ ☎ 01494 8661613, 01494 890694 fax

MORDISH Louis (*Org, Con, Arr, Md*): 55 West Hill, Wembley Park, Middx HA9 9RP ☎ 020 8904 6017

MORGAN Chris (*Kbds, Voc, Gtr*): 90 Onslow Gardens, South Kensington, London SW7 3BS ☎ 020 7373 8010

MORGAN Steven: 5 Southborough House, Kinglake Street, London SE17 2LJ ☎ 020 7708 0608

MORGAN Thomas (*Voc, Per*): 13 Montague Ave, London SE4 1YP ☎ 020 8691 4914

MORGENSTERN Julian (*Dms*): 34 Thislewaite Road, London E5 0QQ ☎ 020 8533 1372, 020 8533 1367 fax

MORIARTY James: 129 Dulwich Road, London SE24 0NG ☎ 020 7733 8748

MORLEY Joseph (*Kbds, Arr, Com, Cop*): 45 Nightingale Lane, Hornsey, London N8 7RA ☎ 020 8341 4271 & fax

MORRIS Darren (*Impro, Com*): 1St Floor, 259 Well Street, Hackney, London E9 6RG ☎ 020 8525 5715, 01426 340083 pager

MORRIS Victor (*Hpsd*): 45 Madrid Road, London SW13 9PQ ☎ 020 8748 4544

MORROW Geoffrey (*Voc*): 6A The Avenue, Finchley, London N3 2LB ☎ 020 8346 8613, 020 8346 8614

MORWOOD Michael (*Org, Accom, Con*): 1 Michelangelo Court, 1 Stubbs Drive, London SE16 3EB ☎ 020 7237 3566

MOSLEY Kathryn: 14 Doughty Street, London WC1N 2PL ☎ 020 7430 1668

MOSONYI Pierre (*Con*): 6A Fairbourne Road, London N17 6TP ☎ 020 8801 6150

MOXOM Nigel (*Synth, Org, Voc*): 31 Forest Way, Orpington, Kent BR5 2AG ☎ 01689 821919

MOXON-BROWNE Kicki (*Bsn*): 37 Mowbray Road, London NW6 7QS ☎ 020 8451 1851

MUENDE Paul: 253 Tavistock Crescent, London W11 1AE ☎ 020 7792 4302

MUIR Peter (*Com, Acc, Bones, Org*): 5 Queens Avenue, Whetstone, London N20 0HZ ☎ 020 8959 6603

MURRAY Peter (*Kbds*): 60 Winchester Close, Thorley Park, Bishops Stortford, Herts CM23 4JQ ☎ 01279 757920

MURRAY Peter (*Org*): 37 Galba Court, Augustus Close, Brentford, Middlesex TW8 8QT ☎ 020 8560 6180

MYERS Thalia: 26 Caterham Road, London SE13 5AR ☎ 020 8318 2031

NAIFF Lynton: 17 Parkfields, London SW15 6NH ☎ 020 8788 3729

NALLY David (*Kbds*): 66 Grovesner Park Road, Walthamstow, London E17 ☎ 020 8521 4376, 0370 780217 mob

NATHOO Irfan (*Kbds, B Gtr*): 1 Bonser Road, Strawberry Hill, Twickenham TW1 4RQ ☎ 020 8744 0986

NAYLOR Ben (*B Gtr, Synth*): Top Flat, 147 Wightman Road, Hornsey, London N8 0BB ☎ 020 8245 4821

NDLAZILWANA Dasree (*Voc*): 16 Charles Barry Close, Off Cubitt Terrace, Clapham Common, London SW4 6AQ ☎ 020 7771 9328

NEAL Simon (*Org, Hpsd*): 10 Hamilton Road, London NW10 1NY ☎ 020 8452 1556, 020 8452 3467 fax

NEIGER Rachel (*Org, Flt, Vln*): Flat 10, 15 Clanricorde Gardens, London W2 4JJ ☎ 020 7229 2461, 0973 213795

NEWMAN Andy (Thunderclap) (*Voc, Sax*): 5 Rectory Gardens, Clapham, London SW4 0EE ☎ 020 7622 3122

NICHOLAS Nick (*Com*): 1 Bamborough Gardens, London W12 8QN ☎ 020 8743 1802

NICHOLLS Simon: 49 Grove Road, London N12 9DS ☎ 020 8446 0812

NICHOLS Keith (*Tbn*): 33 Rosemary Drive, Redbridge, Ilford, Essex IG4 5JD ☎ 020 8924 8405

NICHOLSON 'A Jay' (*Kbds, Voc*): 34 Frome House, Rye Hill Estate, Peckham Rye East, London SE15 3JF ☎ 020 7277 6044, 020 7732 6553

NIEVE Steve (*Synth, Org, Clt*): 3 Rue Dulac 75015, Paris, France ☎ +33 142 199205

NIGHTINGALE Trevor (*Synth*): 5 Meadow Close, Halstead, Essex CO9 1NA ☎ 01787 476108

NOBLE Austin (*Kbds*): 44 Mallard Point, Rainhill Way, Bow, London E3 3JE ☎ 020 8981 8402

NOBLE Liam (*Kbds*): 131 Glyn Road, London E5 0JT ☎ 020 8510 9417

NORDEN Elizabeth (*Kbds, Com*): 65 Camden Road, London NW1 9EU ☎ 020 7284 3635, 07957 483351

NORMAN Frank (*Acc, B Ldr*): 13 Beulah Road, Sutton, Surrey SM1 2QG ☎ 020 8642 3046

NORONHA Maria (*Kbds*): 83 Stondon Park, Forest Hill, London SE23 1LD ☎ 020 8699 4107

NORRIS Marian (*Org*): 116 Alderney Street, London SW1V 4HA ☎ 020 7828 9600

NORTON Jamie: c/o Orchard House, Bournemouth Road, Blandford St Mary, Dorset DT11 9LP ☎ 0976 239025 mob

NOTES Freddie (*Bong, Voc*): 15 Michelson House, Black Prince Road, London SE11 6HX ☎ 020 7587 0802

NUNN Richard (*Clst, Acc, Hpsd*): Crix House, Braintree Road, Cressing, Essex CM7 8JB ☎ 01376 325528

NYE Steven: 22 Scarlet Ct, Saint Charles, MO 63304-6775, USA ☎ +1 417 779 5183

NYMAN Michael (*Synth*): 47 St Quintin Avenue, London W10 6NZ

O'BRIEN David (*Kbds, Voc, Ind Flt*): 5A Temple Road, Ealing, London W5 4SL ☎ 020 8579 4031

O'KANE Cormac (*Kbds, Gtr*): 58 Florence Road, New Cross, London SE14 6QL ☎ 020 8691 1571

O'MALLEY Tony (*E Pf, Voc*): 7 Darcy House, London Fields, London E8 3RY ☎ 020 7275 7649, 020 7275 7649

O'REGAN Matthew (*Kbds, Com, Arr, B Ldr*): 73 Dominion Drive, Collier Row, Romford, Essex RM5 2QS ☎ 01708 741596, 0589 308852 mob

O'TOOLE Mary: 31 Wycherley Crescent, Barnet, Herts EN5 1AP ☎ 020 8449 6479

OAKMAN Steven Mark (*Dms, Kbds*): 18 Heath Park Road, Romford RM2 5UB ☎ 01708 441501

OCKENDON Hugh (*E Pf, Org, Synth*): 44 Sevenoaks Way, Orpington, Kent BR5 3AF ☎ 020 8325 3999

OCONNOR Chris: 20D Highbury New Park, London N5 2DB ☎ 020 7359 1756

ODEI Benjamin (*Kbds, Dms*): 96 Wyatt Park Road, Streatham Hill, London SW2 3TP ☎ 0976 956103

OFFER Andrew (*Voc, Kbds, Accom, Com*): 59 Dartmouth Court, Dartmouth Grove, London SE10 8AT ☎ 020 8691 6413

OHARA Leigh (*Tym, Per*): 2 Oxley House, The Forest, London E11 1PJ ☎ 020 8989 9670, 01426 270328

OLINS Charles (*Voc*): 59 Cambridge Street, London SW1V 4PS ☎ 020 7821 8045

OLIVER Anthony (*Org, Vln*): 51 Melville Place, Essex Road, Islington N1 8ND ☎ 0410 538952

ONERVAS Samuel: Flat 3 Park Mansions, 28 St Pauls Avenue, London NW2 5TD ☎ 020 8451 3479, 07979 854740

ORR Jason (*Kbds*): 85A Carter Street, Kennington, London SE17 3GN ☎ 020 7701 7965, 0956 339 865

OSBORNE James (*Gtr, Arr, Cop, Com*): 79 Orchard Grove, Chalfont St Peter, Bucks SL9 9ET ☎ 01753 890737

OTIS Geraint (*Voc, Acc*): 28 Balham Park Road, London SW12 8DU ☎ 020 8673 0617

PACEY Martin (*Org*): H23 Du Cane Court, Balham High Road, London SW17 7JS ☎ 020 8675 9041

PACKWOOD Mark (*Eup*): 89A Wells House Rd, London NW10 6ED ☎ 020 8961 7448

PAGEL Jonathan (*Sax*): 32B Glengarry Road, London SE22 8QD ☎ 020 8299 2593

PALMER Greg (*Kbds, Ob*): 27A Eade Road, London N4 1DJ

PALMER Neil: Mon Reve, Cudham Lane North, Cudham, Nr.Sevenoaks Kent TN14 7RB ☎ 01689 862692, 01689 860494

PAMPHILON Nicholas (*Kbds, Vln, Bong, Sax*): 64 Wyclif Court, Wyclif Street, London EC1V 0EL ☎ 020 7490 5780, 0839 471777 pager

PAOLA Anna (*Voc, Acc*): Studio Flat, 72 Gt Titchfield Street, London W1P 7AF ☎ 020 7323 4277

PARK Simon (*Org, Synth*): Creek End, Burcot, Abingdon, Oxfordshire OX14 3DJ ☎ 01865 407606/407885, 0836 549167 mob, 01865 407885 fax

PARKER Johnny: 6 Kestrel House, Pickard Street, London EC1V 8EN ☎ 020 7689 0172

PARKER Mick (*Acc, Kbds, Org, Md*): 168 Tamworth Lane, Mitcham, Surrey CR4 1DE ☎ 020 8648 8108

PARKER Tom (*Arr*): 42 Kensington Mansions, Trebovir Road, London SW5 9TQ ☎ 020 7370 6610

PARKER Veronica (*Clt, Voc, Kbds, Arr*): 48 Sherringham Avenue, London N17 9RN ☎ 020 8808 8947

PARREN Chris (*Org*): 20 Thorneyhedge Road, Chiswick, London W4 5SD ☎ 020 8995 2012

PARTRIDGE Jennifer: Vine Cottage, 116 Deanway, Chalfont St Giles, Bucks HP8 4LQ ☎ 01494 874852

PATON Adrian (*E Pf*): 27 Kenmare Gardens, London N13 5DR ☎ 020 8807 1460

PATTERSON Drew (*Org, E Pf*): 22 Glen-Albyn Road, Argylle Estate, Off Inner Park Road, London SW19 6HD ☎ 020 8788 7080

PEACH Joss (*Kbds, Per*): 6A Samos Road, Anerley, London SE20 7TV ☎ 020 8402 5395

PEARCE Bobby: c/o 112 Gunnersbury Ave, London W5 4HB ☎ 01708 688 002

PEARCE John (*E Pf*): 16 Cardinal Close, Worcester Park, Surrey KT4 7EH ☎ 020 8330 3636

PEARN Matt (*Kbds, Gtr, Tpt*): 45 Holmdene Avenue, North Harrow, Middlesex HA2 6HP ☎ 020 8723 4312

PEARSON Guy (*Kbds, Gtr*): 13 Avenue Road, Hampton, Middlesex TW12 2BH ☎ 020 8979 5079

PEARSON Johnny (*Com, Arr, Con*): Saxons, Bishops Walk, Addington Hills, Nr Croydon Surrey CR0 5BA ☎ 020 8656 7626

PEARSON Leslie (*Clt, Org, Hpsd*): Tree Tops, St Cathrines, Hook Heath, Woking, Surrey GU22 0HW ☎ 01483 727577

PELA Suzy (*Kbds, Voc, Flt*): 80 Windermere Avenue, London N3 3RA ☎ 020 8349 1830

PENDLEBURY Karl (*Kbds*): 184 Cottimore Lane, Walton-on-Thames, Surrey KT12 2BJ ☎ 01932 703 569, 0956 208131 mob

PERES DA COSTA Neal (*Hpsd*): 53 Tresco Road, London SE15 3PY ☎ 020 7358 1170

PERKINS David (*Kbds, Arr, Cop*): Church House, Chertsey Road, Shepperton, Middx TW17 9LF ☎ 01932 222932

PERRIN Glyn (*Cel*): 4 Rochester House, Rushcroft Road, London SW2 1JR ☎ 020 7326 1096 & fax

PERRIN Roland (*Kbds, Acc*): 47A Waldram Park Road, London SE23 2PW ☎ 020 8341 6156

PESKETT Phillip: 92 Pathfield Road, Streatham, London SW16 5NY ☎ 020 8769 7480, 0976 266852

PETERS Colin: 48 Friary Road, Friern Barnet, London N12 N12 9PB ☎ 020 8445 2434

PETTIT David (*Org*): 40 Greenford Avenue, Hanwell, London W7 3QP ☎ 020 8579 0420

PHAROAH Franke (*Voc*): 62 Offord Road, London N1 1EB ☎ 020 7609 2956

PHILIPS David (*Voc, Gtr*): 16 Basildene Road, Hounslow, Middlesex TW4 7LE ☎ 020 8577 9469

PHILLIPS Kenneth (*Arr, Md*): 62 Andorra Court, 151 Widmore Road, Bromley, Kent BR1 3AE ☎ 020 8464 5701

PHILLIPS Marilyn: 48 Oban Road, City Beach, Perth, Western Australia 6015 ☎ +61 9 385 7873 & fax

PIATTI Polo (*Kbds, Com, Md*): 157 Capel Road, Forest Gate, London E7 0JT ☎ 020 8514 3998

PIPKIN Dominic (*Kbds, Dms*): 196 Alexandra Mansions, Middle Lane, Crouch End, London N8 7LA

PISTOL Julia (*Hpsd*): 20 Dickerage Road, Kingston-upon-Thames, Surrey KT1 3SS ☎ 020 8942 7070

PITE Ronald (*Org*): 10 Astoria Mansion, Streatham High Road, London SW16 1PS ☎ 020 8769 6308

PLEDGE Andrew (*Org, Hpsd, Cel*): 130 The Crossways, Heston, Middx TW5 0JR ☎ 020 8570 1462

PLOWRIGHT Dennis (*Org*): 166 Ribblesdale Road, Streatham, London SW16 6SR ☎ 020 8677 7003

POLLOCK Angie (*Kbds, Voc*): 29A Warwick Ave, London W9 2PS

PONTZEN Peter (*Kbds, Md, Com*): 1 Blenheim Terrace, Chipping Norton, Oxon OX7 5HF ☎ 01608 642718, 01608 645217 fax

POPE Nicholas: 10 Annesley Road, Blackheath, London SE3 0JX ☎ 020 8319 4620

POPE Victoria (*Voc*): 128 Rushmore Road, London E5 0EY ☎ 020 8986 8023

POPPY Andrew (*Kbds, Gtr, B Gtr, Flt*): 22C Breakspears Road, Brockley, London SE4 1UW ☎ 020 8691 8646

PORILO Gregory (*Org*): 27 Brenda Road, Upper Tooting, London SW17 7DD ☎ 020 8672 8095 & fax, 0956 386679 mob

PORTMAN Rachel (*Vla, Org*): 14 Ladbroke Gardens, London W11 2PT

POSTILL Isabelle: 69A Albion Drive, London E8 4LT ☎ 020 7254 5433

POTTER Sarah (*Voc*) ☎ 020 7737 4564

POWELL Harriet (*Acc, Flt*): 22 Bergholt Mews, Elm Village, London NW1 0BQ ☎ 020 7387 3343

POWELL Samantha (*Kbds, Voc*): 3 Knaresborough Drive, Riverside Walk, London SW18 4UT ☎ 020 8333 7022

POWER Suzannah (*Flt*): 110 Wakehurst Road, Battersea, London SW11 6BT ☎ 020 7228 6039

PRESLAND Carole: 167 Venner Road, Sydenham, London SE26 5HX ☎ 020 8776 9982 & fax

PRESTON Gary: Flat 3, 59 Mayfield Road, Sanderstead, Surrey CR2 0BJ ☎ 020 8651 3548

PRICE John (*Kbds, Arr*): 23A Beaufort Road, Kingston-upon-Thames, Surrey KT1 2TH ☎ 020 8549 2730

PRIEST John (*Kbds*): 1 Lowry Lodge, Harrow Road, Wembley, Middlesex HA1 2EA ☎ 020 8795 3154

PRIESTLEY Brian (*Arr*): 120A Farningham Road, Caterham, Surrey CR3 6LJ ☎ 01883 347746

PRIGGE Sonke (*Kbds, Gtr, Voc*): 3 Stonechat Square, London E6 5LQ ☎ 020 7474 9174

PRITCHETT Robert: 53 Cathcart Road, London SW10 9DH ☎ 020 7352 4247

PRUESS Craig (*Tpt, Synth*): 121 Lincoln Park, Amersham, Buckinghamshire HP7 9HF ☎ 01494 725550, 01923 822462

PRUSLIN Stephen (*Hpsd, Clst, Org*): 8 George House, Victoria Place, Richmond, Surrey TW9 1RU ☎ 020 8948 7404 & fax

PUCKETTE Muriel Waters: 213 Park Crescent, Erith, Kent DA8 3EF ☎ 01322 330789

PUDE Charles (*Arr*): 112 Ingleside Crescent, Lancing, Sussex BN15 8ER ☎ 01903 754645

PUGH Brian (*Arr, Cop*): 6 Raith Avenue, Southgate, London N14 7DU ☎ 020 8882 0015

PURCELL Simon (*Arr*): 15 Essex Street, Forest Gate, London E7 0HL ☎ 020 8257 0708

QUINLAN Kevin (*Kbds, B Gtr, Voc*): 6 Kingsley Road, Wimbledon, London SW19 8HF ☎ 020 8542 0554, 0410 090418

RAHMAN Zoe (*Kbds*): Flat D, 11 Durham Terrace, Bayswater, London W2 5PB ☎ 020 7229 5196

RALLS Stephen (*Hpsd*): 74 Follis Avenue, Toronto, Ontario, Canada M6G IS6

RAMM Nicholas (*Kbds, Per*): 40A Mottingham Road, London SE9 4QR ☎ 020 8857 7480

RAMSDEN Janet (*Accom*): 67 St James Road, Sutton, Surrey SM1 2TG ☎ 020 8661 9405

RANDALL Robert (*Arr, Kbds, Vla*): Flat 2 Camrose Court, Harewood Road, South Croydon CR2 7AL ☎ 020 8681 3135

RATHBONE Joyce: 31 Chepstow Place, London W2 4TT ☎ 020 7229 0219

RAWSON Denis (*Md*): 33 Hanover Court, Keith Grove, London W12 9EP ☎ 020 8743 9018

RAYNER Harry (*Acc*): 39 The Woodlands, London SE13 6TZ ☎ 020 8698 1871

RAZZELL Luke: 30 Ingram Road, London N2 9QA ☎ 020 8365 4996, 04325 265287

READDY William (*Org, Kbds, Synth*): 3A Heath Court, Park Road, Uxbridge, Middlesex UB8 1NU ☎ 01895 255346, 0589 328630 mob

READER James (*Saxes, Clst*): 28 Malden Fields, Bushey, Herts WD2 2QA ☎ 01923 233185, 0973 509696

REBELLO Jason (*Com*): 9 Kingscliffe Gardens, Southfields, London SW19 6NR ☎ 020 8789 3238 & fax

REEKIE Alan (*Kbds, Gtr*): 157 Hamilton Road, London SE27 9SE ☎ 020 8670 9964

REEVES Paul (*Org, Kbds*): 267 Kings Road, Kingston-upon-Thames, Surrey, 0589 456 994

REGIS Kaw (*Gtr, B Gtr, Dms, Flt*): 16 Irby House, Tulse Hill, London SW2 2HJ ☎ 020 8671 9312, 0374 491666 mob

REICH Max: 3 Park Mansions, 28 St Pauls Avenue, London NW2 5TD ☎ 020 8451 3479, 07979 854750

REITH Angela (*Gtr*): 47 Mayton Street, London N7 6QP ☎ 020 7609 8153

REYNOLDS Peter (*Org*): 59 Beverley Way, London SW20 0AW ☎ 020 8942 3461

REYNOLDS Robert (*Gtr*): Address Unknown ☎ 020 7435 0121

RICH Laura-Jane (*Arr, Com, Rec, Voc*): 39 Wanstead Park Road, Ilford, Essex IG1 3TG ☎ 020 8491 6247

RICHARDS Roger: 22 Wyatts Road, Chorley Wood, Herts WD3 5TE ☎ 01923 282516

RICHARDS Tim (*Kbds, Com*): Flat 3, 129 Honor Oak Park, London SE23 3LD ☎ 020 8291 5221

RICHMOND Marcus (*Gtr*)

RILEY Howard: Flat 2, 53 Tweedy Road, Bromley, Kent BR1 3NH ☎ 020 8290 5917

RINGHAM Benjamin (*Voc, Gtr*): 12 Wellfield Ave, Muswell Hill, London N10 2EA ☎ 020 8883 1567, 0958 648553 mob

RIXEN Nicholas (*Kbds*): 16 Stodmarsh House, Cowley Road, London SW9 6HH ☎ 020 7820 0593

ROACHFORD Andrew (*Db, Dms, Voc*): Unit 30, Abbey Business Centre, Ingate Place, London SW11 3NS ☎ 020 7720 0444, 020 7720 0404

ROBERTS Terence (*Synth*): 7 Ilfracombe Gardens, Chadwell Heath, Romford RM6 4RL ☎ 020 8599 0425, 020 7832 3111 day

ROBERTSON Duncan (*Rep*): 38 Reidhaven Road, Plumstead, London SE18 1BU ☎ 020 8316 0172, 0958 572164

ROBERTSON Eric (*Org, Hpsd, Arr*): 34 Westmount Park Road, Weston, Ontario M9P 1R6, Canada ☎ 020 7416 24531

ROBERTSON-BARKER Helen (*Rep*): Sussex Arms Cottages, 17 Rutland Road, Twickenham TW2 5ER ☎ 020 8755 3105

ROBINS Robyn (*Kbds*): 48 The Limes, Enniskillen Drumlyon, Co. Fermanagh, Northern Ireland BT74 5NB ☎ 01365 328897, 01365 329437

ROBINSON Andrew: 26 Hillsborough Court, Mortimer Crescent, Kilburn, London NW6 5NR ☎ 020 7624 5870

ROBINSON Eric (*Per*): 246 Ashmore Road, London W9 3DD ☎ 020 8964 2384

ROBINSON Philip (*Kbds, Flt*): Flat 5, 1 Sterndale Road, London W14 0HT ☎ 020 7371 4919, 0956 834 112

ROBINSON Stephen (*Kbds, Arr*): 9 Parkview Court, Broomhill Road, London SW18 4JG ☎ 020 8870 5184

ROCHE Henry: 36 Melbury Gardens, London SW20 0DJ ☎ 020 8946 2913

ROSE Stephen (*Hpsd, Flt, Org*): 6 Craven Avenue, Ealing, London W5 2SX ☎ 020 8579 3108

ROSE Steve (*Db*): 77 Grosvenor Road, Muswell Hill, London N10 2DU ☎ 020 8442 1985

ROSLYN Stuart: 20C Camden Hill Road, Upper Norwood, London SE19 1NR

ROSS Matt (*Org*): 16 Emlyn Road, Stamford Brook, London W12 9TE ☎ 020 8743 1966

ROTHMAN Jonathan (*Kbds*): 15 Malpas Drive, Pinner, Middx HA5 1DG ☎ 020 8868 1498

ROUND Michael (*Per, Arr*): 52 Stuart Road, Wimbledon Park, London SW19 8DH ☎ 020 8947 6364

ROWAN Jamie (*Voc*): Ground Floor, 70 Minet Avenue, London NW10 8AP ☎ 020 8961 4823

ROWE Elizabeth: The Vicarage Flat, St Stephens Road, London E3 5JL ☎ 020 8981 1405, 0385 501573

ROWLANDS Maxim (*Per, Arr, Cop*): 20 Thorn Close, Bromley, Kent BR2 8DH ☎ 020 8468 7794

ROWLANDS Steven (*Synth, Per*): 840A Green Lanes, London N21 2RT ☎ 020 8350 9710

ROWLEY David: 44 George Peabody Court, 2 Burne Street, London NW1 5DR ☎ 020 7723 8008

RUBIN Ronald (*Db*): Flat 3, 12 Frognal Gardens, London NW3 6UX ☎ 020 7435 5548

RUSSELL Jennifer (*Voc*): Foxton Mill, Osmotherley, North Yorkshire DL6 3PZ ☎ 01609 883377

RUSSELL Lloyd: Upper Maisonette, 150 Tollington Park, London N4 3AD ☎ 020 7281 4130

RUSSOM Paul (*Kbds, Gtr, B Gtr*): 70 Woodland Rise, London N10 3UJ

RUTHERFORD Jonathan (*Com, Arr, Md*): Woodlands, Sandly Lane, Iken, Woodbridge, Suffolk IP12 2EU ☎ 01728 688484 & fax

RYALL Imogen (*Per*): 15 West Street, Rottingdean, East Sussex BN2 7HP ☎ 01273 300512

RYDER Katherine: 29 Ladas Road, West Norwood, London SE27 0UP ☎ 020 8670 5761 & fax

RYDER Mark (*Gtr*): 2 Oakley Street, London SW3 5NN ☎ 020 7352 5751

SABERTON Peter (*Kbds, Synth*): 3 Lynette Avenue, London SW4 9HE ☎ 020 8675 1672

SAGGESE Matteo (*Kbds*): 36 Burns Road, Harlesden, London NW10 4DY ☎ 020 8961 0315, 0467 307812

SALTER Timothy (*Org, Hpsd, Com, Con*): 26 Caterham Road, London SE13 5AR ☎ 020 8318 2031 & fax

SANDER Peter (*Arr, Com*): 73 The Avenue, London NW6 7NS ☎ 020 8459 1781

SANDERS Geoffrey (*Kbds*): 64 Buxton Lane, Caterham, Surrey CR3 5HF ☎ 01883 342663

SARGENT Kevin (*Dms, Per*): 1 Heathcote Road, Epsom, Surrey KT18 5DX ☎ 01737 272 8364

SAUNDERS Antony: Box Cottage, Brister End, Yetminster, Sherborne, Dorset DT9 6NH ☎ 01935 873199

SAUNDERS Brian (*Kbds, A Sax*): Avalon, 31 Medora Road, Romford, Essex RM7 7EP ☎ 01708 733284, 0467 701284, 01708 733284

SAUNDERS Camilla (*Tbn, Acc, Veena*): 146 Widdenham Road, London N7 9SQ ☎ 020 7607 4104

SAVAGE Marcus (*Kbds, Md*): 66 High Road, Salcombe Park, Loughton, Essex IG10 4QU ☎ 020 8508 4898 & fax, 0850 905923 mob

SCANDRETT Lindsay (*Voc, B Gtr*): 31B Melrose Avenue, Cricklewood, London NW2 4LH ☎ 020 8450 3493, 020 8452 6708

SCARLETT Niara ☎ 020 7278 5021, 0966 149741 mob

SCHOGGER Daniel (*Kbds*): Oak Hampden, Hendon Wood Lane, London NW7 4HS ☎ 020 8959 1251

SCHURMANN Margaret: 25 Homecroft Road, London N22 5EL ☎ 020 8888 7977

SCOTT Derek (*Org, Cel, Arr*): Blythe House, 14A High Street, Wangford, Suffolk NR34 8RA ☎ 01502 578711

SCOTT Glenvin (*Kbds, Voc, Dms, B Gtr*): 31B Dundonald Road, London NW10 3HP ☎ 020 8968 9496, 01747 871564

SEEZER Maurice (*Kbds, Acc, Gtr*): 54 Millmount Avenue, Drumcondra, Dublin 9, Ireland ☎ Dublin 371569

SEGAL Emily: 54 Montpelier Road, London SE15 2HE ☎ 020 7639 4968

SELL Colin: 20 Kersley Road, London N16 0NP ☎ 020 7249 6612

SELWYN Peter: 54 Montpelier Road, London SE15 2HE ☎ 020 7639 4968

SHAHADAH Owen (*Gtr, B Gtr, Dms, Per*): 17 Hatton House, Hindmarsh Close, London E1 8JJ ☎ 020 7488 1533

SHANKLAND Nicholas (*Kbds, Voc*) ☎ 020 7837 2587

SHARP Tim (*Acc*): 4 Deans Road, London W7 3QB ☎ 020 8579 8642

SHAW Claire (*Kbds*) ☎ 020 8543 0835, 07971 224821

SHAW Richard: 45A Cannon Hill, Southgate, London N14 6LH ☎ 020 8882 5333 & fax

SHAW Susan: 143 Harrow View, Harrow, Middx HA1 4SX

SHEARMUR Edward (*Kbds, Org*): c/o Ms V Bennett, Abacus (M.A.S.), 76C Hillfield Road, London NW6 1QA ☎ 020 7435 0278, 020 7435 0582

SHELLEY Howard (*Con*): 38 Cholmeley Park, Highgate, London N6 5ER ☎ 020 8341 2811

SHELTON Michael (*Org*): The Debt, South Hill Avenue, Harrow-on-the-Hill, Middlesex HA1 3PA

SHERBOURNE Janet (*Voc*): 1 St Annes Road, Caversham, Reading RG4 7PA ☎ 0118 947 7170

SHERIFF Naadia (*Flt*): 31 Sanders Lane, Mill Hill East, London NW7 1BX ☎ 020 8531 1505

SHOSTAK Cathy (*Flt, Kbds, Pic, Ac Gtr*): 34 Ventnor Drive, London N20 8BP ☎ 020 8445 3112 & fax, 0585 157380 mob

SILKOFF David: 29 Trafford Close, Wickets Way, Hainault, Ilford, Essex IG6 3DQ ☎ 020 8501 3115

SILVA Victy (*Com, Voc*): 143 Camberwell Road, London SE5 0HB ☎ 020 7703 5185

SILVER Jason (*Kbds*): 16 Oakmead Gardens, Edgware, Middx HA8 9RW ☎ 020 8959 5824

SILVER Leonard (*Vln*): 22 Ingleby Way, Wallington, Surrey SM6 9LR ☎ 020 8647 3788

SIMMONS Ian (*Kbds, Synth, Org*): New Kingswood, Lower Boyndon Road, Maidenhead, Berks SL6 4DD ☎ 01628 624878

SIMMONS Richard (*E Pf, Synth*): 31 Henville Road, Bromley, Kent BR1 3HX ☎ 020 8464 5378

SIMPSON Sally: 3A Khartoum Road, Tooting, London SW17 0GA ☎ 020 8767 9956, 0958 390487

SKEETE Mark: 39 Sedgewick Road, Leyton, London E10 6QP ☎ 020 8558 3031

SLADE Julian: 86 Beaufort Street, (Grnd Flr/Basemnt), London SW3 6BU ☎ 020 7376 4480

SLAPPER Clifford: First Floor Flat, 30 Store Street, London WC1E 7BS ☎ 020 7323 0792, 0956 360 164 mob

SMART David: 112 Gunnerbury Avenue, Ealing, London W5 4HB

SMITH Alan (*Synth*): 16A Bartram Road, Crofton Park, London SE4 2DQ ☎ 020 8699 1473

SMITH Andrew (*Cel*): 52 Mulgrave Road, Willesden, London NW10 1BT ☎ 020 8450 0507

SMITH Caroline: 12 Sherwood Court, Seymour Place, London W1H 5TH ☎ 020 7262 9159, 0956 188833

SMITH Chris (*Gtr*): 15 Yeatman Road, London N6 4DS ☎ 020 8348 2012

SMITH David (*Kbds, Md, Rec*): Flat 3, 78 Shooter S Hill Road, Blackheath, London SE3 7BQ ☎ 020 8319 0299

SMITH Geoffrey (*Kbds*): 14 St Albans Road, Woodford Green, Essex IG8 9EQ ☎ 020 8491 6551

SMITH John G (*Md, Com*): 35 Lower Maidstone Road, New Southgate, London N11 2RU ☎ 020 8361 6545

SMITH Mark (*Org*): 239 Shakespeare Avenue, Hayes, Middlesex UB4 9AG ☎ 020 8841 9198

SMITH Ned Lloyd (*Kbds, B Gtr, Dms, Per*): 114 Carlton House, Canterbury Terrace, Queens Park, London NW6 5DU ☎ 020 7328 2866

SMITH Neville (*Org*): Hawthorns, Batts Lane, Pulborough, West Sussex RH20 2ED ☎ 01798 872606

SMITH Pamela (*Rep*): 75 Dunvegan Road, Eltham, London SE9 1RZ ☎ 020 8850 6848

SMITH Sandra (*Hpsd, Org*): 21A Rutland Park, London NW2 4RE ☎ 020 8451 2810

SMITH Timothy: 32 Park Grove, Bexleyheath, Kent DA7 6AA ☎ 01322 559228

SMITH Tracie (*Gtr, Kbds*): 56 Leggatt Road, Stratford, London E15 2RQ ☎ 020 8257 3159

SONNENBLIK Norbert (*Acc*): 14 Vaughan Avenue, London W6 0XS ☎ 020 8748 7549

SORRELL Jonathan: 344 Manwel Dimech Street, Sliema, Malta

SOUTH William (*Kbds, B Gtr, Gtr, Voc*): 71A Adelaide Avenue, London SE4 1JY ☎ 020 8314 0601

SOUTHGATE John (*Virg, Kbds*): 12 Nassington Road, London NW3 2UD ☎ 020 7433 1263

SPELLAR Judith (*Vln, Vla, Gtr, Clt*): 115 London Lane, Bromley, Kent BR1 4HF ☎ 020 8464 0197

SPURR Richard (*Kbds, Org*): 54 Beresford Gardens, Enfield, Middx EN1 1NW ☎ 020 8363 7131

SQUIRES Chris: Flat 1, 37 Tierney Road, London SW2 4QL ☎ 020 8674 3163

STANLEY Matthew: 35 Wendover Road, Staines, Middlesex TW18 3DE ☎ 01784 740861

STANNARD Roy (*B Ldr*): 28 Autumn Drive, Belmont, Sutton, Surrey SM2 5BA ☎ 020 8661 2114

STAPLETON John (*Voc*): 3A Hinstock Road, Plumstead Common, London SE18 2TQ ☎ 020 8855 7813

STARR Maxine ☎ 01895 462812, 0956 325895

STEFANO (*A Sax, T Sax, Kbds, Dms*): 16A Ainsworth Way, Boundary Road, St. John's Wood, London NW8 0SR ☎ 020 7624 7278

STEVENS Edmund (*Org, Kbds*): 2F Devonshire Road, London W4 2DT ☎ 020 8995 5849, 020 8747 8937

STEVENS Norman (*E Pf, Org, Arr, Cop*): 2 Willingdon Way, Lower Willingdon, Eastbourne, East Sussex BN22 0NJ ☎ 01323 505238

STEWART Jo: Willow Glen Cottage, Mays Green, Cobham Surrey KT11 1NJ ☎ 01932 863935

STEWART Roy (*Org*): 13 Hawkswood, Covingham Park, Swindon, Wilts SN3 5AH ☎ 01793 528444

STOCK Michael (*Synth, B Gtr, Gtr, Voc*): c/o Mary Fox, Hundred House, 100 Union Street, London SE1 0NL ☎ 020 7928 4444

STOKES Russell (*Flt*): 36 North Way, Kingsbury, London NW9 0RG ☎ 020 8204 3023

STONE Colin: 50 Lowlands Road, Harrow, Middx HA1 3AN ☎ 020 8423 3915, 020 8933 0249

STOREY Michael (*Kbds, Hmca, Per*): Flat 2, 19 Fawley Road, London NW6 1SJ ☎ 020 7794 9853

STREVETT Keith (*Kbds, Com*): 29 Weston Park, Crouch End, London N8 9SY ☎ 020 8348 8301

STUCKEY Robert (*Kbds, Org, Com, Arr*): 9 Keystone Crescent, London N1 9DS ☎ 020 7278 7246

STUDDEN Allan (*Arr, Com*): Rainbow Cottage, Wheelers Hill, Little Waltham, Chelmsford, Essex CM3 3LY ☎ 01245 360311

STURMEY Andrew (*E Pf, Kbds, Org, Arr*): 4 Elmhurst Villas, Cheltenham Road, London SE15 3AE ☎ 020 7639 1916

STURROCK Kathron: 81 Lacy Road, London SW15 1NR ☎ 020 8780 3266, 0973 543525, 020 8780 0600 fax

SUMMERS Neville: 68 East Hill, South Darenth, Nr Dartford, Kent DA4 9AW ☎ 01322 863280

SUTHERLAND Shelagh (*Vln, Voc*): 34 Harborough Road, London SW16 2XW ☎ 020 8769 7115

SUTTON Derek (*Org*): 8 Sandhurst Way, Sanderstead, Surrey CR2 0AH ☎ 020 8657 6594

SUTTON Timothy (*A Sax*): 79 Telegraph Place, London E14 9XA ☎ 020 7531 6533, 0976 754741

SWAN Clive (*Md*): 28 Tooveys Mill Close, Kings Langley, Herts WD4 8AG ☎ 01923 269036, 01923 266339 fax

SWAN Kelly (*Kbds, Voc*): 7A Angel Road, Thames Ditton, Surrey KT7 0AU ☎ 020 8398 5451, 0421 432234 mob, 020 8398 9022

SWAN Richard (*Voc, Gtr, B Gtr*): 29 Foxborough Gardens, Brockley, London SE4 1HU ☎ 020 8690 9764, 0973 629165 mob

SWITHINBANK Chris (*Pan P*): 15 Priory Road, Chiswick, London W4 5JB ☎ 020 8994 9844, 0958 359348

SYMCOX Benedicte (*Ob, Rec*): 127 Barnett Wood Lane, Ashtead, Surrey KT21 2LR ☎ 01372 818 603

SYMES Julian

TABERNER Jonathan: 18 Garden Place, Hawthorn Close, Horsham, West Sussex RH12 2BD ☎ 01403 257320

TAGE Paul (*Dms*): P O Box 1, Chipping Ongar, Essex CM5 9HZ ☎ 01277 362916, 01277 365046

TAGGART Robert (*Kbds*): 35 Grove Lane, Kingston-upon-Thames, Surrey KT1 2ST ☎ 020 8549 1183

TAMPLIN Peter: Windyknowe, The Avenue, Kingston Nr Lewes, East Sussex BN7 3LL

TATE Rita: 4 Avonmore Mansions, Avonmore Road, London W14 8RN ☎ 020 7603 6728

TAVERNER Derek (*Org*): 40 Belgrave Court, Wellesley Road, W4 4LG ☎ 020 8994 2523

TAYLOR Brian: 22 Genesis Close, Stanwell, Staines, Middlesex TW19 7BE ☎ 020 8898 7314

TAYLOR Christopher (*Accom*): 566 Forest Road, Walthamstow, London E17 3ED ☎ 020 7485 3375

TAYLOR John: Glebe Cottage, Kingsford Street, Mersham, Ashford Kent TN25 6PE

TAYLOR Johnny (*Org*): 56 Grosvenor Road, Wanstead, London E11 2ES ☎ 020 8989 0832

TAYLOR Winifred: High Trees, Oak Lane, Minster-on-Sea, Sheerness Kent ME12 3QW ☎ 01795 873073

TEAPE Ronnie (*Kbds, Voc*): 14 Crewys Road, Childs Hill, London NW2 2AA ☎ 020 8458 4325

TEERS Stephen (*Per, Tbn*): 50 Highview Road, West Ealing, London W13 0JN

TELFER Michael (*B Gtr, Kbds*): 20 Crandale House, Pembury Estate, Pembury Road, Hackney, London E5 8LN ☎ 020 8525 1836

TEPER Daniel (*Acc*): Don Bosco, Nine Elms Pier, 87 Kirtling Street, London SW8 5BP ☎ 020 7498 1598

TERMER Denny (*E Pf, Org*): 89 Halstead Road, London N21 3DR ☎ 020 8360 5347

THARME Brian (*Kbds*): 37 Park Road, High Barnet, Herts EN5 5SE ☎ 020 8440 0226, 0956 561424, 020 8440 0226

THISTLETON Nick (*Kbds, Voc*): 143 Bishops Mansions, Stevenage Road, London SW6 6DX ☎ 020 7736 4727

THOMAS Annemarie (*Kbds, Voc, Tpt*): 9B Osborne Road, Palmers Green, London N13 5PT ☎ 020 8886 2029, 0860 117056 mob

THOMAS Christopher (*Voc, Gtr*): 2 Mortimer Road, London W13 8NG

THOMAS Darren (*Flt*): 35 Clifford Court, Heathfield Road, Wandsworth, London SW18 3JE ☎ 020 8870 6844

THOMAS Hywel: 51 Chelsea Gardens, Chelsea Bridge Road, London SW1W 8RG ☎ 020 7730 7785

THOMAS John (*Com, Arr*): 22A Chesterton Road, London W10 5LX ☎ 020 8964 5410

THOMAS-BOSOVSKAYA Olga: 13F Hyde Park Mansions, Cabbell Street, London NW1 5BD ☎ 020 7724 4572

THOMPSON Alan (*Cel, Md*): 37 Kentish Road, Upper Belvedere, Kent DA17 5BW ☎ 01322 441515

THOMPSON Bunny (*Arr*): 7 Pembroke Avenue, Berrylands, Surbiton, Surrey KT5 8HN ☎ 020 8399 9841, 0836 685488

THOMPSON Joe (*Acc, Synth*): 45 Lambs Conduit Street, London WC1N 3NG ☎ 020 7831 6856

THOMSON Kelvin (*Kbds*): 70 Potters Lane, Barnet EN5 5BQ ☎ 440 5545/441 3513, 0850 283393

THOMSON Paul (*Clt, Org, Voc*): 30 Tortoiseshell Way, Berkhamsted, Herts HP4 1TB ☎ 01442 879807, 020 7439 2375 fax

THROUP Andrew G (*Clt, Sax*): Flat 3, Honor Oak Mansions, Underhill Road, Dulwich, London SE22 0QP ☎ 020 7924 3960

TILBURY John: 3 West Cross, High Street, Tenterden, Kent TN30 6JR

TILT Marcus (*Kbds, Acc*): 24 Eaton Close, Stanmore, Middlesex HA7 3BT ☎ 020 8954 1515

TIPPETT Keith (*Com*): The Cottage, Tortworth, Wotton Under Edge, Gloucestershire GL12 8HG ☎ 01454 260757

TODD Joan (*Voc*): 15 Romborough Way, Lewisham, London SE13 6NS ☎ 020 8473 4861

TODD William (*Tbn, Db, Voc*): 21 Walden Road, Chislehurst, Kent BR7 5DH ☎ 020 8690 0815

TOMALIN Nicholas: 74 Meanley Road, Manor Park, London E12 6AR ☎ 020 8478 5125, 0973 861 673

TOMES Susan: 180 South Park Road, London SW19 8TA ☎ 020 8540 5522

TOMS Frank: 33 Ashley Drive, Tylers Green, Penn, High Wycombe, Bucks HP10 8BQ ☎ 01494 812742

TONG Daniel: Flat 4, Hillside, 41 St Mary's Road, Long Ditton, Surrey KT6 5HB ☎ 020 8398 8231, 01223 514539

TOWNLEY Simon: 12A Watford Road, Sudbury Town, Wembley, Middlesex HA0 3EP ☎ 020 8908 5895

TOWNSEND Ian: 33B Chipstead Valley Road, Cousldon, Surrey CR5 2RB ☎ 020 8668 5191 fax, 01523 115378

TRACEY Stan: 12 Cotlandswick, London Colney, Herts AL2 1EE ☎ 0172 782 3286

TRAVIS Sarah (*Synth*): 38 Palmerston Crescent, Palmers Green, London N13 4UA ☎ 020 8882 8963, 0421 373727

TREIGER Norman (*E Pf, Voc*): 42 Holders Hill Avenue, Hendon, London NW4 1ET ☎ 020 8203 0718

TREW Jennifer: 22 Pembroke Road, Walthamstow, London E17 9PB ☎ 020 8420 2045, 0976 795 855

TREWEEK James (*Kbds*): 43B Ennersdale Road, London SE13 6JE ☎ 020 8333 6523, 01438 351926 mob

TRIBBLE James (*Vln, Vla, Vielle, Viol*): 1061 Garratt Lane, Tooting, London SW17 0LN ☎ 020 8672 3027

TROON Vivian (*Clst, Hpsd, Arr, Com*): 90 Becmead Avenue, Kenton, Middlesex HA3 8HB ☎ 020 8907 8428

TURK Warwick (Rick) (*Gtr*): The Lodge, Theydon Mount, Epping, Essex CM16 7QA ☎ 01992 560621, 01992 560621

TURNER Cecil: Address Unknown

TURNER Martin (*Kbds, Org, B Gtr*): 130 Theobalds Park Road, Crews Hill, Enfield, Middlesex EN2 9BN ☎ 020 8363 8787, 0336 772086, 020 8363 8787

TURRELL Paul (*Kbds, Gtr, B Gtr, Dms*): 2A High Street, New Malden, Surrey KT3 4HE ☎ 020 8949 6109, 020 8540 5646

TURVEY June: 243A Kilburn Lane, London W10 4BQ ☎ 020 8969 7717

TWINER D: 22 Lee Park, London SE3 9HQ ☎ 020 8852 5439

TWITCHEN George: 43 Loudwater Close, Sunbury-on-Thames TW16 6DD ☎ 01932 781828

USHER Donald (*Org*): 41 Lesney Park Road, Erith, Kent DA8 3DQ ☎ 01322 35290

VAN KAMPEN Claire: 164A Acre Lane, London SW2 5UL ☎ 020 7274 6688

VASYLENKO Tamara (*Kbds*): 3 Grantham Road, London SW9 9PD ☎ 020 7787 4407

VAUSE Louis (*Kbds, Acc*): Basement Flat, 6 Cliff Villas, London NW1 9AL ☎ 020 7485 4690

VERMA Shan (*Tabla, Kbds*) ☎ 020 8723 7559

VEULENS Marietta: 108 Railton Road, Herne Hill, London SE24 0JY ☎ 020 7326 1859

VICARY Andrea (*Vln*): 212 Sherwood Avenue, London SW16 5EF ☎ 020 8764 6478

VINE Tim (*Kbds, B Gtr, Tpt, Vln*): 75A Churchfield Road, Acton, London W3 6AX ☎ 0410 537861, 0956 982823

VINES Josephine (*Arr*): Flat 4, 245 Cavendish Road, Balham, London SW12 0BP ☎ 020 8675 6720

VINTEN Jonathan (*Kbds*): 32 Farleigh Road, Warlingham, Surrey CR6 9EA ☎ 01883 625160, 0410 098720 mob

VINTER Andrew (*Kbds, Arr*): 6 Charlton Close, Ickenham, Uxbridge, Middx UB10 8BW ☎ 01895 859824 & fax, 020 8549 1706

VORZANGER Edward (*Acc*): Address Unknown ☎ 020 7834 1386

WADE Anthony (*Voc, Ac Gtr*): 102 Rochester Street, Chatham, Kent ME4 6RR ☎ 01634 842470

WADE T: 17A Devon Road, South Darenth, Nr.Dartford, Kent DA4 9AA ☎ 01322 863543

WADE Vic (*Kbds, Org*): 51A Victoria Road, Laindon, Basildon, Essex SS15 6AW ☎ 01268 411267

WALES Jonathan (*Kbds, Cel*): 33 Alleyn Road, West Dulwich, London SE21 8AD ☎ 0831 342 891

WALKER James (*Hrp*): The Brooklands, 57 Shottery, Stratford-upon-Avon CV37 9HD ☎ 01789 204315

WALKER Joe (*Kbds, Cntrc*): 39 Mountfield Road, Ealing, London W5 2NQ ☎ 020 8998 5814

WALKER Nina: 12 Ainsdale Road, Ealing, London W5 1JX ☎ 020 8998 0419

WALKER Sarah (*Flt*): 38 Strode Street, Egham, Surrey TW20 9BX ☎ 01784 438521

WALLACE Andrew (*Kbds*): 55 Ribblesdale Road, Streatham, London SW16 6SF ☎ 020 8696 0218

WALLACE David: 99 Sutton Court, Sutton Court Road, Chiswick, London W4 3JF ☎ 020 8400 2951

WALLACE Simon (*Synth, B Gtr*): 91 Albert Palace Mansions, Lurline Gardens, London SW11 4DH ☎ 020 7622 6992

WALSH Brendan (*Kbds*): 190 St Barnabas Road, Woodford Green, Essex IG8 7DU

WALTERS Art (*Org*): Flat 3, Melisa Court, Avenue Road, London N6 5DH ☎ 020 8340 0904

WALTON Robert (*Arr, Com, Md*): 41 Pitman Court, Lower Swainswick, Bath, Avon BA1 8BD ☎ 01225 337750

WARD George: 52 Daneswood Avenue, Catford SE6 2RQ ☎ 020 8698 6770

WARREN Debbie: 4 Bailey Road, Westcott, Nr Dorking, Surrey RH4 3QS

WARREN Paula (*Kbds*): 116 Oxley Close, Rolls Road, London SE1 5HP ☎ 020 7231 3667

WASTELL William (*Arr, Org*): 1 Mulberry Court, Strawberry Hill Road, Twickenham TW1 4QA ☎ 020 8892 2246

WATKIS Trevor: 28 Mansford Street, Bethnal Green, London E2 7AJ ☎ 020 7613 2697

WATSON James (*Kbds*): 13 Stewartsby Close, London N18 1AN ☎ 020 8803 4683, 0973 117895

WATSON Neil (*Kbds*): 24 College Road, Walthamstow, London E17 9DF ☎ 020 8509 2463, 0468 955461 mob

WATSON Pete (*Dms, Per*): 338 Devon Mansions, Tooley Street, London SE1 2XQ ☎ 020 7207 0685

WEBB Julia (*Flt, Voc*): 13 Palace Mews, Fulham, London SW6 7TQ ☎ 0370 987 700, 020 7381 8092

WEBB Reginald (*Org, Gtr, Voc*): 1 Candlefield Cottages, Birch Street, Brich, Nr Colchester C02 0NL ☎ 01206 330062 & fax

WEBB Roger: 13 Palace Mews, Fulham, London SW6 7TQ ☎ 071 381 8092

WEBLEY Warren (*Kbds*): Ground Floor Flat, 6 Godolphin Road, London W12 8JE ☎ 020 8746 2577

WEBSTER Neil: 124 Queen Anne Ave, Bromley, Kent BR2 0SD ☎ 020 8520 9548

WEBSTER Paul: 63 South Edwardes Square, Kensington, London W8 6HL ☎ 020 7602 6402

WEEDON Paul (*Tbn*): Waterfields, Shepherds Hill, Merstham, Surrey RH1 3AD ☎ 01737 644469, 01523 454 203

WEINBERG Barry (*Synth, Kbds, Voc*): 28 Blenheim Gardens, Wembley, Middlesex HA9 7NP ☎ 020 8904 7025, 0956 372323 mob

WELDON Nick: 24 Ryland Road, London NW5 3EA ☎ 020 7284 0226

WEST Andrew: 51 Brondesbury Villas, London NW6 6AJ ☎ 020 7328 3385

WESTBROOK Mike (*Com*): Brent House, Holbeton, Nr Plymouth, Devon PL8 1LX ☎ 01752 830589

WESTROP Stephen (*Org, Hpsd*): 18 Wilmer Crescent, Kingston-on-Thames, Surrey KT2 5LU ☎ 020 8541 5810

WESTWOOD Jeremy: 71 Gloucester Street, Pimlico, London SW1V 4EA ☎ 020 7821 7076

WHALLEY Clare (*Vln*): 2 Rutland Grove, Hammersmith, London W6 9DH ☎ 020 7723 2825

WHEELEY Ken: 41 Merryfields Avenue, Hockley, Essex SS5 5AN ☎ 01702 202211

WHELAN Andrew (*Kbds*): 88A Weston Park, Crouch End, London N8 9PP ☎ 020 8348 6507, 020 8292 3944 fax

WHITE Daniel (*Kbds*): 59 Swains Lane, London N6 6QL ☎ 020 7813 9918, 020 7419 9714

WHITE Harry: Address Unknown

WHITE John (*Com, Synth, Tba, Tbn*): 21 Chippendale Street, London E5 0BB

WHITE Meredith (*Kbds*): Flat 2, 13 Minster Road, London NW2 3SE ☎ 020 8452 3834, 0976 286989

WHITEHOUSE Nicolas (*Flt, Pic, Kbds*): 120 Murchison Avenue, Bexley, Kent DA5 3LL ☎ 01322 524964

WHITTAKER Peter (*Org*): 17 Helena Road, London, . NW10 1HY ☎ 020 8450 9412

WILKINS Wayne (*Kbds, Org, Vln*): 8 Green Court Ave, Shirley Park, Croydon, Surrey CR0 7LD ☎ 020 8662 0880, 0966 154394 mob

WILKINSON Jeremy: 39 Bridgman Road, Chiswick, London W4 5BA ☎ 020 8742 7648

WILLETT Elisha: Stocks, Claygate Road, Laddingford, Kent ME18 6BJ ☎ 01892 730670, 0402 593716 mob

WILLIAMS Clare (*Hpsd, Org*): 4 Solway House, 20 Auckland Hill, West Norwood, London SE27 9PH ☎ 020 8761 2328, 0966 411128

WILLIAMS Gareth (*Gtr*): 14 Cecil House, 99/100 Marylebone High Street, London W1M 3DD ☎ 020 7224 2681

WILLIAMS Ian *(Kbds, Gtr)*: 39 Dunlace Road, London E5 0NF ☎ 020 8533 6482

WILLIAMS Kate: 17 Helena Road, London NW10 1HY ☎ 020 8450 9412

WILLIAMS Peter *(E Pf, Org, Acc, Arr)*: 33 Meadow Road, Earley, Reading, Berks RG6 7EX ☎ 0118 9264845

WILLIAMS Shiu-Ju *(Org)*: Flat 1, 20 Dornton Road, South Croydon, Surrey CR2 7DP ☎ 020 8688 2546

WILLIAMS Susan *(Vln, Rec)*: 69 A Caulfield Road, East Ham, London E6 2EL ☎ 020 8472 8982

WILLIAMSON Clive: 9 Onslow Gardens, Wallington, Surrey SM6 9QL ☎ 020 8647 3781, 0831 890972 mob

WILLIAMSON Nick: 10A Maryland Road, London N22 5AJ ☎ 020 8881 6078, 0976 423777 mob

WILLIS Christopher *(Vln)*: 122 Canterbury Road, Harrow, Middlesex HA1 4PR ☎ 020 8863 8722

WILLOUGHBY Frank *(Acc, Vib, Org, Arr)*: 7 Sandown Court, Station Road, Redhill, Surrey RH1 1BA ☎ 01737 763863

WILLS Warren: Address Unknown ☎ 020 8802 4779

WILSON Alan *(Org, Hpsd, Com)*: 66 Crombie Road, Sidcup, Kent DA15 8AU ☎ 020 8300 9606, 020 8300 2243 fax

WILSON Alex *(B Gtr)*: 158 Godley Road, Earlfield, London SW18 3HE ☎ 020 8871 0618, 0370 744 639

WILSON Peter *(Com, Kbds)*: 74 Coleraine Road, Blackheath, London SE3 7PE ☎ 020 8858 0720

WILSON Robert: 76 Agdon Street, London EC1V 0BP ☎ 020 7253 1197

WINGFIELD Peter *(Kbds, Voc)*: 47 Combemartin Road, London SW18 5PP ☎ 020 8788 9147

WOLFF Stephen *(Cel)*: 3 Park House, Camberwell Green, London SE5 7PP ☎ 020 7708 2028

WOOD Colin *(Kbds)*: 6 Pentney Road, London SW19 4JE ☎ 020 8946 2300

WOOLCOCK Rebecca *(Cel)*: 214A Kilburn High Road, London NW6 4JH ☎ 020 7372 0755, 07970 686660

WOOLWICH Jeremy *(Com)*: 2 Beaconsfield Road, Ealing, London W5 5JE ☎ 020 8567 0229, 0836 795069, 020 8567 0231

WRIGHT Dee *(Voc)*: 1 Malcolm Way, Snaresbrook, London E11 1PW ☎ 020 8989 8163

WRIGHT Sid *(Arr, Vib)*: Calle Js Elcano 4, Las Palomas 4, Fuengirola, Malaga

WYKE Andrew *(Voc)*: 3 Duntshill Road, London SW18 4QN ☎ 020 8877 342, 0403 570963, 01923 286097

WYKES David: 16 Park Hall Road, London N2 9PU ☎ 020 8444 7789

YEOH Nikki *(Kbds)*: 1 Rodney House, Donegal Street, London N1 9QF ☎ 020 7837 7524

YOULE Joanne *(Voc)*: 30 Palewell Park, London SW14 8JG ☎ 020 8878 9076

YOUNG Alistair *(Org, Hpsd, Clst)*: 18 Churchfield Avenue, North Finchley, London N12 0NT ☎ 020 8446 5394, 020 8549 1706

YOUNG James: 57 Woodgrange Gardens, Bush Hill Park, Enfield, Middx EN1 1ER ☎ 020 8366 0220

YOUNG Richard *(Voc, Arr, Md)*: 10 Minshull Place, Park Road, Beckenham, Kent BR3 1QF ☎ 020 8650 2737

ZAKSS Leah *(Clt, Per)*: Garden Flat, 55 Highbury Hill, London N5 1SU ☎ 0961 368 738, 020 7359 6532 eve

QUENA

NORTH WEST

GREEN Rosie *(Pan P, Per, Acc, Kbds)*: 71 Bouverie Street, Chester CH1 4HF ☎ 01244 372629

RAPPER

SCOTLAND

MC VOYAGER : 9 Fells Rigg, Carmondean, Livingston, W. Lothian EH54 5AE ☎ 01506 490210

LONDON

AGYEI Steve *(Voc, Kbds, Dms, B Gtr)*: 3 Dale Avenue, Hassocks, West Sussex BN6 8LW ☎ 01273 843888

BAYSEE Duke: 13 Salway House, Thornhill Road, Leyton E10 5LZ ☎ 020 8556 4126, 0831 151994

BENNETT Kevin *(Voc)*: 47 Loughborough Park, London SW9 8TP ☎ 020 7733 5225, 020 7738 4804, 020 8274 9870 fax

CHINEY.T *(Voc)*: 99 Edinburgh House, Lanark Road, London W9 1QS ☎ 0961 598 598

CODJOE Samuel *(Voc, Song W)*: 52 Birdport Road, Thornton Heath CR7 7QG ☎ 020 8240 8650

HALM Nana: 63 Dover Flats, Old Kent Road, London SE1 5NL ☎ 020 7231 9383, 07050 611548

HANDSOME Mikey: 78 Ashburton Avenue, Ilford, Essex IG3 9ER ☎ 020 8594 0631

IMUERE Stephen: 36 Mermaid Tower, Bringer Grove, London SE8 5ST ☎ 0151 469 0573, 0956 980 830

INTENZ-LEONARDO *(Club Dj)*: 105 Highbury Station Road, London N1 1SY ☎ 020 7609 1712

LORD Michael ☎ 020 8881 9952

MC Mc *(Song W)*: 128 Empress Avenue, Manor Park, London E12 5EU ☎ 020 7607 4940

ROBINSON Lee: Flat 7 Belvoir Lodge, 101 Overhill Road, Dulwich, London SE22 0PR ☎ 020 8693 0570, 07970 728456

TENDAI *(Kbds, Dms, Song W)*: 50 Tantallon Road, Balham, London SW12 8DG ☎ 020 8673 3876, 0958 274716, 020 8673 3876

THOMAS Marcus: The Bank Flat, 130A George Lane, London E18 1AZ ☎ 020 8530 6393

RECORDERS

SCOTLAND

HILL-AHMAD Jennifer *(Rec, Clt, Ea Wnd)*: 35 Victoria Cresc Rd, Glasgow G12 9DD ☎ 0141 339 5012

WISHART I *(Rec, Kbds, Voc)*: 9 Essex Park, Edinburgh EH4 6LH ☎ 0131 339 2951, 0378 402 564

NORTH WEST

MCCARTHY Jamie *(Rec, Vln, Voc, Tnd Per, Sax)*: 139 Dale Street, Liverpool, Liverpool L2 2JH ☎ 0151 236 9163

TURNER John *(Rec, Flt)*: 40 Parsonage Road, Heaton Moor, Stockport, Cheshire SK4 4JR ☎ 0161 432 4682

NORTH EAST

PASHLEY Claire *(Rec, Clt, Flt, Pf, Kbds)*: 14 Folds Crescent, Sheffield, South Yorkshire S8 0EQ ☎ 0114 235 1508

STRONG Rae *(Rec, Vln, Pf)*: Headingley House, 158 Swinston Hill Road, Dinnington, Sheffield S31 7SB ☎ 01909 562511

EAST

HODGES Maurice *(Rec)*: 35 Thoday Street, Cambridge CB1 3AS ☎ 01223 572236

MALLETT John *(Rec, Vln, Shawm, Vla, Sax)*: 39 High Street, Earith, Huntingdon, Cambs PE19 3PP ☎ 01487 841563, 0860 443493, 01487 841563

STOBART Henry *(Rec, Bag, Shawm, Charango, Tb)*: Darwin College, Cambridge CB3 9EU

MIDLANDS

BAINES Emily *(Rec)*: 49 Church Road, Moseley, Birmingham B13 9ED ☎ 0121 449 2033

BAKER Paul *(Rec, R Wnd, H Gurd, Bag, Vln)*: 21, Oakfield Avenue, Kingswinford, West Midlands DY6 8HJ ☎ 01384 295210

DALE Alison *(Rec, Pf)*: 14 Newhayes Road, Tunstall, Stoke-on-Trent, Staffordshire ST6 5UF

DAVIS Alan *(Rec, Clt, Sax)*: 180 Shenley Fields Road, Birmingham B29 5BP ☎ 0121 475 7180

ROBBINS Zoe *(Rec, Org, Clt, Sax, Flt)*: 15 Knowle Hill Road, Netherton, Dudley, W Midlands DY2 0HW ☎ 01384 232957

SMYTH Carol *(Rec, Gtr)*: 38 Kings Road, Erdington, Birmingham B23 7JS ☎ 0121 386 2492

WASTIE Heather *(Rec, Wcap, Voc, Pf)*: 25 Hailstone Close, Rowley Regis, Warley B65 8LJ ☎ 01384 252632 & fax, 0850 529637 mob

298

SOUTH EAST

LOUGHREY Michelle *(Rec)*: 13 King Edward Rise, Ascot, Berks SL5 8JZ ☎ 01344 883454, 07970 730220

MENDES Galina *(Rec, Pf, Vln)*: 22 The Gallops, Lewes, East Sussex BN7 1LR ☎ 01273 474982

SCHEPORAT Gudi *(Rec)*: 51 Sillwood Street, Brighton BN1 2PS ☎ 01273 720495

SOUTH WEST

BURGESS Paul *(Rec, R Wnd, Vln, Kbds)*: 23 Haywards Road, Charlton Kings, Cheltenham, Glos GL52 6RQ ☎ 01242 518676

CRUMP Nick *(Rec, Bag, Cimb)*: 12 Breach Lane, Shaftesbury, Dorset SP7 8LE ☎ 01747 853176

PETERS Carolyne *(Rec, Flt, Pf, Sax, Bsn)*: 80 Monthermer Road, Cardiff CF2 4QY ☎ 029 2037 3402

PLATER Roger *(Rec, Clt, Pf)*: 26 Bassett Street, Abercynon CF45 4SP ☎ 01443 742370

WHEELOCK Emma *(Rec, Vln)*: Treowen, Wonastow, Nr Monmouth, Monmouthshire NP5 4DL ☎ 01600 740412

LONDON

BARLOW Jeremy *(Rec, P Tab, Hpsd, Regal, Com)*: 20 Leverton Street, London NW5 2PJ ☎ 020 7267 7176

BECKETT Rachel *(Rec, Flt, Bq Flt)*: 28 Barnes Avenue, Chesham, Bucks HP5 1AP ☎ 01494 778117, 01494 771728

CLEMENTS Antony *(Rec, Vln, Pf)*: 24 Tweedmouth Road, Plaistow, London E13 9HT ☎ 020 8470 2674

GREENWAY Rhiannon *(Rec)*: 5 Well Court, 740 London Road, North Cheam, Surrey SM3 9BX ☎ 020 8641 2754

JACKMAN Andrew *(Rec, Com, Con, Arr)*: Frensham House, Station Road, Tivetshall St Margaret, Norwich Norfolk NR15 2EB ☎ 01379 677 319

JONES Suzie *(Rec, Flt, Pf)*: 62 Beechwood Road, South Croydon, Surrey CR2 0AA ☎ 020 8651 2911, 020 8651 6080

KEELER Emily *(Rec)*: 1 Brookfield Park, London NW5 1ES ☎ 020 7485 7451

KLEIN Susan *(Rec)*: 60A Oakhurst Grove, East Dulwich, London SE22 9AQ ☎ 020 8299 3096

MANYUMBU Emily *(Rec, Pf, Vla, Flt, Crum)*: 194 Hampton Road, Chingford, London E4 8NT ☎ 020 8524 4279

MCCREERY Jean *(Rec)*: 25B Albany Road, Stroud Green, London N4 4RR ☎ 020 8347 8345, 070500 49683 mob

PAGE Elizabeth *(Rec, Viol)*: Address Unknown ☎ 020 8255 3148

PRING Debra *(Rec, Crum)*: The Atic, 101 King Charles Road, Surbiton, Surrey KT5 8PG ☎ 020 8395 1729, 0385 256767

SHAW Marian *(Rec)*: 102 Woodhill, Woolwich, London SE18 5JL ☎ 020 8855 2573

SOLOMON Ashley *(Rec, Bq Flt, Flt)*: 90 Long Lane, London N3 2HX ☎ 020 8349 4265, 020 8346 2896

THOMSON Ellen *(Rec, Ea Stg, Vln, Fo Fdl)*: Top Flat, 5 Colebrooke Avenue, Ealing, London W13 8JE ☎ 020 8991 1293

THORBY Pamela *(Rec, Ea Wnd, Eth Wnd)*: 51 Thornhill House, Fourth Floor, Thornhill Road, London N1 1PB ☎ 020 7607 9541, 01223 312400 agent

REPETITEUR

SOUTH WEST

GREENWOOD Andrew: 5 Archer Road, Penarth, South Glamorgan CF64 3HW ☎ 029 2070 8887

SANTOOR

LONDON

DEOORA Kiranpal Singh *(Tabla, Dilruba)*: 16 Meadow Road, Southall, Middlesex UB1 2JE ☎ 020 8574 3445 & fax

SARANGI

MIDLANDS

SANDHU Surinder: 17 Dimmock Street, Wolverhampton, West Midlands WV4 6HG ☎ 01902 404320, 0973 925828

SAXOPHONES

SCOTLAND

BAKER Ronnie *(A Sax, Clt)*: 27, Winifred Street, Kirkcaldy, Fife KY2 5SR ☎ 01592 205735

BALLINTYNE Duncan *(A Sax, Clt)*: 24 London Road, Kilmarnock KA3 7AQ ☎ 01563 525357

BANKS Solomon *(T Sax, Clt, Flt)*: 25 Bellwood Street, Glasgow G41 3EX ☎ 0141 632 4834

BARELLA Timothy *(T Sax, Clt, B Clt, Flt)*: Maybank, 185 East Clyde Street, Helensburgh, Scotland G84 7AG ☎ 01436 72865

BEAUVOISIN Allon *(Br Sax, S Sax, A Sax, B Clt,)*: 38 Clarinda Court, Harestanes, Kirkintilloch, Glasgow G66 2SD ☎ 0141 775 3398

BENTLEY Harry *(A Sax, Clt)*: 6 Fauldshead Road, Renfrew PA4 0RY ☎ 0141 562 5350

BRAWLEY Michael *(A Sax, S Sax, Pf, Com)*: 190 Wellhall Road, Hamilton, Scotland ML3 9XP ☎ 01698 283972

BROCKETT Arthur *(Sax, Pf, Acc, Hmca, Gtr)*: 33 Berwick Drive, Glasgow G52 3EP ☎ 0141 892 0221

BROWLIE Douglas *(Br Sax, A Sax, S Sax)*: Apt.3E, 22 Springbank Gardens, Dunblane, Perthshire FK15 9JX ☎ 01786 823626, 01786 464745

BROWN Lorna *(So Sax, A Sax, Br Sax, Flt)*: 21 Bradfield Avenue, Kelvindale, Glasgow G12 0QH ☎ 0141 339 1688, 07801 115849

BRUCE Keith *(Sax, Clt)*: Forthview, Forth Street, Cambus, Clackmannanshire FK10 2NU ☎ 01259 723418

BRUCE Robert *(A Sax, Vln, Voc)*: 247, Charleston Drive, Dundee, Scotland DD2 4HL ☎ 01382 644797

BURNETT Frank *(T Sax, Acc, Clt)*: 132 Braehead Way, Bridge Of Don, Aberdeen AB22 8SD ☎ 01224 709631

CAMPBELL Robert *(A Sax, T Sax, Flt, Clt, S Sax)*: 45 Viewmount Drive, Glasgow G20 0LP ☎ 0141 579 6569, 0141 556 3301, 0141 554 4558

CHALMERS Thomas *(S Sax, A Sax, T Sax, Flt, Clt)*: 5 Beauly Drive, Craigshill, Livingston, West Lothian EH54 5LG ☎ 01506 433928

CLARKE Ralph *(A Sax, Br Sax, Clt)*: 117 Newton Street, Greenock PA16 8SH ☎ 01475 795428

CORBETT Alan *(A Sax, T Sax, Clt, Voc)*: 62 Tryst Road, Stenhousemuir, Falkirk FK5 4QH ☎ 01324 554388

CROMBIE Douglas *(A Sax, T Sax, Clt)*: Tomari, Mansegate, Dunscore, Dumfries DG2 0TD

DAVIDSON Jack *(A Sax)*: 18 Raith Drive, Kirkcaldy, Fife KY2 5NW ☎ 01592 267014

DEANS Michael *(T Sax, Flt, Clt)*: 28 Ancroft Street, Glasgow G20 7HU ☎ 0141 332 2932

DEANS Robert *(T Sax, Clt, Flt)*: 10A Aurs Road, Barrhead, Glasgow G78 2PW ☎ 0141 881 7381

DOUGHTY Ian *(A Sax, Clt)*: 2 Namayo Avenue, Laurieston, Falkirk FK2 9LX ☎ 01324 624801

DUFF Jack *(Sax, Pf, Clt)*: Dalwin Lodge Guest House, 75 Mayfield Road, Edinburgh EH9 3AA ☎ 0131 667 2294

ELLIOTT Bill *(Br Sax, A Sax, Clt)*: 42 Nevis Avenue, Little Earnock, Hamilton ML3 8UA ☎ Hamilton 459545

ESSON Gordon *(T Sax, Clt)*: 69 Jeanfield Road, Perth PH1 1PB ☎ 01738 620985

EVANS Iestyn *(Sax, Gtr, Pf)*: 38 Kirk Brae, Edinburgh EH16 6HH ☎ 0131 664 5831

FAGAN John *(Saxes)*: 17 Lynnburn Avenue, Bellshill, Lanarks ML4 3EL

FARRELLY Jay *(A Sax, Clt)*: 30 Arnhall Place, Glasgow G52 1PT ☎ 0141 883 3308

FERRI Manny *(T Sax, A Sax, Clt, Flt)*: 89 Weirwood Ave, Garrowhill, Baillieston G69 6LW ☎ 0141 771 1466

FIFIELD Fraser *(Sax, Bag, Wh)*: Flat 1/L, 91 Sanda Street, North Kelvinside, Glasgow G20 8PT ☎ 0141 946 4834

FORBES Stewart *(Saxes, Clt, B Clt, Flt, Pic)*: 2 Moorfield Avenue, Kilmarnock KA1 1TS ☎ 01563 544386

FORD Billy *(T Sax, Clt, Dms)*: 5 Angus Terrace, Oban, Argyll PA34 4EG ☎ 01631 562419

HAW Dave (*T Sax, Clt, Flt*): Braefield, Ruthven Street, Auchterarder PH3 1BX ☎ 01764 662988

HUNTER Colin (*Sax, Clt, Flt*): 82 Duthie Terrace, Aberdeen AB10 7PR ☎ 01224 312353

INNES William (*Sax, Clt*): 148 Gardner Drive, Aberdeen AB12 5SA ☎ 01224 874430

JOHNSTON Robert (*Sax, Clt*): 20 Craigs Avenue, Edinburgh EH12 8HS ☎ 0131 334 4802

KELLY Robert (*Sax, Br Sax, A Sax, Clt, B Cl*): 77 Castlehill Road, Bearsden, Glasgow G61 4DY ☎ 0141 942 5395

KERSHAW Martin (*A Sax, S Sax, Clt, Flt*): Baird House, Croft Bank, West Malvern, Worcs WR14 4DF ☎ 01684 561379

KETTLEY Stephen (*T Sax, S Sax, Flt, Per*): 2Nd Flat, 12 Caledonian Road, Edinburgh EH11 2DG ☎ 0131 346 4088

KING Leonard (*Sax, Gtr, Voc*): Leanach Quarry, Culloden Moor, Inverness IV1 2FS ☎ 01463 792914

LEWIS William (*T Sax, Clt, Vln*): 23 Craigpark Drive, Glasgow G31 2NW ☎ 0141 554 3255

LINDSAY Patrick (*Br Sax*): 11 Old Bothwell Road, Bothwell, Lanarkshire G71 8AW ☎ 01698 852540

LIVINGSTONE James (*T Sax, Vln*): 32 Barnwell Terrace, Glasgow G51 4TP ☎ 0141 445 1604

MACDONALD George (*T Sax, Kbds*): 3F3 28 Broughton Road, Edinburgh EH7 4ED ☎ 0131 557 3755

MACDONALD Raymond (*Sax, Pf, Gtr*): 17 Polwarth Street, Hyndland, Glasgow G12 9UD ☎ 0141 334 3669

MCARTHUR Gail (*T Sax, S Sax, A Sax, Flt, Clt*): 95 Mull, St Leonards, East Kilbride, Glasgow G74 2DU ☎ 01355 244405

MCCORMACK Daniel (*A Sax, Clt*): 11 Ibris Place, Northberwick15, East Lothian EH39 4BD ☎ 01620 3433

MCCUSKER Thomas (*T Sax*): 55 Crescent Road, Glasgow G13 3RY ☎ 0141 959 2680

MCGINNIS John (*Saxes, Vln*): 70 Dowrie Crescent, Glasgow G53 5NF ☎ 0141 883 5402

MCKELVIE Raymond (*Saxes, Flt, Clt*): 5 Caldwell Avenue, Glasgow G13 3AN ☎ 0141 954 7582

MCLELLAND George (*A Sax, Clt*): 77 Fenwick Road, Giffnock, Glasgow G46 6JA ☎ 0141 633 1032

MCMASTER Bill (*A Sax, Clt*): 87 Garrowhill Drive, Baillieston, Glasgow G69 6NL ☎ 0141 771 1744

MCNAUGHTON D (*Sax*): 43 Ashley Drive, Edinburgh EH11 1RP ☎ 0131 337 5458

MILLAR Ian (*T Sax, Pf*): 34 Dalkeith Road, Edinburgh EH16 5BS ☎ 0131 667 2491, 0131 667 1525 fax

MORRICE James (*Sax, Flt*): Garden Cottage, Jordanstone, Alyth, Perthshire PH11 8LY ☎ 01828 633137

MOY Norman (*Saxes, Flt, Clt*): 236 Rosemount Place, Aberdeen AB2 4XT ☎ 01224 462187

O'NEIL Frank (*T Sax, Flt, Br Sax*): Kalinka, Auchtubh, Balquhidder, Lochearnhead, Perthshire FK19 8NZ ☎ 01877 384215

O'SHANNON Terri (*S Sax, A Sax, T Sax, Br Sax,*): 24C Plantation Road, Stornoway, Isle Of Lewis HS1 2JS

PROCTOR William (*A Sax, Clt*): 56 Emerson Road, Bishopbriggs, Glasgow G64 1QH ☎ 0141 772 3454

REILLY Stanley (*Saxes, Flt, Pic, Clt*): 101 Torphin Crescent, Greenfield, Glasgow G32 6NN ☎ 0141 774 8784

ROBERTS David (*T Sax, A Sax, S Sax*): Coryban, Old Chapel Walk, Inverurie, Aberdeenshire AB51 4TY ☎ 01467 621786

ROBERTSON Douglas (*Sax, Hmca*): 111 Prospecthill Circus, House 198, Toryglen, Glasgow, Scotland G42 0LT ☎ 0141 643 2253, 07788 923707

SANDERSON Derek (*Saxes, Clt, Org*): Ellenbank, Hillside, Portlethen, Aberdeen AB12 4RB ☎ 01224 780641

SCHROEDER Franziska (*A Sax, T Sax*): 1/2A Albany Street, Edinburgh EH1 3QB ☎ 0131 556 0393, 07971 780233

SCRIMGEOUR David (*A Sax, T Sax, Kbds, Voc*): 90 Tay Street, Tayport, Fife DD6 9DB ☎ 01382 552039

SKILLEN Derrick (*Sax, Flt, Clt*): 2/5, 44 Waterside Street, Glasgow G5 0NP ☎ 0141 429 0543

SMITH George (*Sax, Clt*): 67A Busby Road, Clarkston G76 7BW ☎ 0141 644 3011

SMITH Thomas (*Sax*): 17 Peatville Terrace, Edinburgh EH14 2EB ☎ 0131 443 3864

SMITH Tommy (*T Sax, S Sax*): PO Box 3743, Lanark ML11 9WD ☎ 0410 585231, 0141 423 5747

SNYDER Michael (*A Sax*): Barrodger Cottage, Beith Road, Lochwinnoch, Renfrewshire PA12 4JX ☎ 01505 504212

STEWART Michael (*A Sax, T Sax, S Sax, Clt*): 74 Rowan Court, Port Glasgow, Renfrewshire PA14 5NA ☎ 01475 743 742

STRACHAN D (*T Sax, Clt, Vln, Voc*): 2 Bruce Road, Downfield, Dundee, Angus DD3 8LL ☎ 01382 825659

SWAN Leon (*Sax, Clt, Flt*): 18 Heathside Road, Giffnock, Glasgow G46 6HL ☎ 0141 638 5506

THOMPSON Frank (*T Sax, A Sax, Br Sax, Clt, Fl*): 40 Almond Avenue, Renfrew PA4 0UT ☎ 0141 885 0029

TOWNDROW Paul (*A Sax, S Sax, Pf, Clt, Dms*): 3 Arran Drive, Glenmavis, Airdrie ML6 0PT ☎ 01236 761608, 0402 324599 mob

TURNER Tommy (*Sax, Clt, Flt*): 27 Elgin Street, Dunfermline, Fife KY12 7SA ☎ 01383 722151

WILSON David (*T Sax, Clt*): 434 St Georges Road, Flat 23B, Glasgow G3 6JP ☎ 0141 332 4512

WILSON Graeme (*T Sax, S Sax*): 155 Moffat Street, Flat 2/1, Glasgow G5 0ND ☎ 0141 429 1134

WOOD John (*Sax*): 2 Orchard Brae West, Edinburgh EH4 2EW ☎ 0131 332 7105

NORTH WEST

ADAMS Derek (*Saxes, Clt*): 5 Allonby Close, Oxton, Birkenhead, Wirral L43 9JE ☎ 0151 653 2163

BAGWELL Victor (*Saxes, Clt, Flt*): 6 Ardee Road, Broadgate, Preston, Lancs PR1 8EN ☎ 01772 252 309

BAK Nik (*Sax*): 79 Buxton Road, New Mills, High Peak, Derby SK22 3JT ☎ 01663 743693

BANKS Gareth (*Sax, Voc, Bod, Wh, Gtr*): 18 Brichfield Way, Lydiate, Liverpool L13 4DS

BASEY William (*Saxes, Clt*): 8 St Albans Road, Tan Y Fron, Wrexham, Clwyd LL11 5SY ☎ 01978 751487

BEECH Roy (*Sax, Clt, Flt*): 120 Norcliffe Road, Bispham, Blackpool, Lancs FY2 9EW ☎ 01253 53067

BIRTWISTLE Stephen (*T Sax, S Sax, A Sax, Clt*): 507 Lytham Road, Blackpool, Lancs FY4 1RE ☎ 01253 348094

BONNEY Gordon (*Sax, Clt*): 13 Harrington Avenue, Blackpool, Lancs FY4 1QE ☎ 01253 41810

BOWDEN Eric (*T Sax, Clt*): 52 Cliffe Road, Glossop, Derbys SK13 8NY ☎ Glossop 62746

BRACE Thomas (*T Sax, Clt, A Sax*): 100 St David's Road, Leyland PR5 2XY ☎ 01772 422775

BROOKS Stanley (*A Sax*): 3 Rochdale Road, Edenfield, Ramsbottom, Bury, Lancs BL9 0JT

BROWN Derek (*Sax*): 6 Alston Road, Blackpool, Lancashire FY2 0TD ☎ 01253 56332

BROWN Norman (*Saxes, Clt, Flt*): 6 Walton Road, Altrincham, Cheshire WA14 4NE ☎ 0161 941 1305

BUCKLAND Robert (*Sax, Clt*): 27 Birkdale Close, Tytherington, Macclesfield SK10 2UA ☎ 01625 425840, 0976 728699 mob

BUILT FOR COMFORT (*Sax*): 6 Victoria Street, Knutsford, Cheshire WA16 6HY ☎ 01565 650112

CADMAN Julia (*Br Sax, T Sax, A Sax*): 31 Hale Gate Road, Halebank, Widnes, Chashire WA8 8LR ☎ 0151 425 3758 eve, 0161 834 6066 day

COLQUHOUN Andy (*Sax, T Sax, A Sax, Clt, Flt*): 5 Woodfield Road, Thornton, Thornton-Cleveleys, Blackpool Lancs FY5 4EQ ☎ 01253 824534

COX (SENIOR) Gary (*Saxes, Wood W*): 22 Torkington Road, Gatley, Cheadle, Cheshire SK8 4PR ☎ 0161 428 5749

CROWTHER Brian (*Saxes, Clt, Flt*): 51 Stanley Road, Whitefield, Manchester M45 8QW ☎ 0161 280 5307

DALE Brian (*Sax, Flt, Clt, Acc, Pf*): 21 Eustace Street, Warrington, Cheshire WA2 7JU ☎ 01925 573719

DARBY Ruth *(S Sax, A Sax, T Sax, Clt, Pf)*: Flat 6, 7 Cresswell Grove, West Didsbury, Manchester M20 2NH ☎ 0161 448 9816, 0585 367899 mob

DAVIDSON Doug *(T Sax, Flt, A Sax)*: Maryland, Snugborough, Union Mills, Isle Of Man IM4 4LT ☎ 01624 851460

DAVIS Tony *(T Sax, A Sax)*: Balne Beck House, 18 Silcoates Street, Wakefield, West Yorkshire WF2 0DU ☎ 01924 290659

DEAN Robert *(T Sax)*: 5 Cloverley Drive, Timperley, Cheshire WA15 7PY ☎ 0161 980 2149

DENNISON Elizabeth *(Sax, Flt, Clt)*: 12 Curzon Road, Heald Green, Cheadle, Cheshire SK8 3LN ☎ 0161 436 1806, 0973 661 242

DIAZ Arturo *(Sax, Voc, Gtr, Per)*: 3/5 Pedder Street, Morecambe, Lancs LA4 5DY ☎ 410927 / 736726

DOWNING Lorna *(T Sax, A Sax, Clt, Voc)*: 30 Lyndhurst, Ashurst, Skelmersdale, Lancashire WN8 6UH ☎ 01695 722875

DUCKERS Kenneth *(Sax, Db)*: 19 Shaftesbury Avenue, Penketh, Warrington WA5 2PD ☎ 01925 726840

DYSON John *(A Sax, T Sax, Flt, Rec)*: 8 Monica Avenue, Crumpsall, Manchester M8 4LJ ☎ 0161 740 4933

EISENTRAUT Jochen *(Sax, Pf, Gtr)*: Yr Hafan, St Davids Road, Caernarfon, Gwynedd LL55 1EL

ELLISON Charles *(T Sax, Clt, Flt)*: 2 Duxbury Close, Maghull, Liverpool L31 9PD ☎ 0151 526 4739

ELLISON John *(Sax, Clt, B Gtr)*: 587 Blackpool Road, Ashton, Preston PR2 1LH ☎ 01772 729833

FAWKES Alan *(Saxes)*: Stoneycroft Hall, Foxholes Road, Horwich, Lancs BL6 6AL ☎ 01204 697447

FLEETWOOD Roger *(Saxes, Clt, Flt)*: 4 Woodlands Road, Ashton-Under-Lyne, Lancs OL6 9DU ☎ 0161 330 5127

FRANCE Timothy *(A Sax, T Sax, Flt, Clt)*: 46 Priory Street, Bowdon, Altrincham, Cheshire WA14 3BQ ☎ 0161 929 1563

FREKE Nicholas *(A Sax, T Sax)*: 46 Kingsway, Pendlebury, Swinton, Manchester M27 4JW ☎ 0411 284 834

FROST Norman *(Sax, Clt, Flt, Voc, B Gtr)*: 30 Poll Hill Road, Heswall, Wirral L60 7SN ☎ 0151 342 6975

GAROFALO Enrico *(Sax)*: 19A Bent Lane, Prestwich, Manchester M25 7DL ☎ 0161 773 8459, 0966 513347 mob

GILL Ronald *(Br Sax, A Sax)*: 13 Banks Howe, Onchan, Isle Of Man IM3 2EN ☎ 01624 622530

GLASGOW Bill *(A Sax, Clt, Flt, T Sax, Rec)*: 11 Lees Hall Crescent, Fallowfield, Manchester M14 6XZ ☎ 0161 225 3400

GREEN Martyn *(Sax, Kbds)*: 118 Shelley Street, Leigh, Lancs WN75EX ☎ 01942 676317

HALE Michael *(Saxes, Flt, Clt)*: 6 Lauderdale Avenue, Cleveleys, Blackpool, Lancs FY5 3JP ☎ 01253 867033

HALL Mike *(T Sax, S Sax)*: 70 Barkers Lane, Sale, Cheshire M33 6SD ☎ 0161 973 7052

HALLAM John *(Sax, Clt, Flt)*: 2 Curzon Green, Offerton, Stockport, Cheshire SK2 5DJ ☎ 0161 483 5460

HALLIWELL Rick *(Saxes, Clt, Flt)*: 3 Waddington Close, Lowton, Warrington WA3 2DR ☎ 01942 606648

HARGREAVES Gary *(T Sax, A Sax, Clt, Flt)*: 21 Newhey Road, Milnrow, Rochdale, Lancs OL16 3NP ☎ 01706 341858

HARGREAVES Philip *(T Sax, Flt, S Sax)*: 8 Beverley Road, Wavertree, Merseyside L15 9HF ☎ 0151 733 2288

HARRISON Bill *(Sax, Clt, Flt)*: 371 Devonshire Road, Blackpool, Lancs FY2 0RE ☎ 01253 54213

HELLIWELL John *(Saxes, Clt, Flt)*: Stack House, Giggleswick BD24 0DN ☎ 01729 823386, 01729 825178 fax

HIGGINS Suzanne *(Saxes, Flt, Clt)*: 344A Palatine Road, Nortenden, Manchester M22 4HD ☎ 0161 945 2317, 0976 712047

HIGGINSON Colin *(Sax, Clt, Flt)*: 40 Kensington Avenue, Old Colwyn, Colwyn Bay, Clwyd LL29 9ST ☎ 01492 515006

HOPE Mike *(T Sax, A Sax, Clt, Flt)*: Forest Rise, 14 Bonville Chase, Dunham Park, Altrincham, Cheshire WA14 4QA ☎ 0161 928 2570

HORNBY Edward *(Sax, Gtr)*: 157 Spruce Court, Belvedere Road, Salford M6 5EW ☎ 07771 721622

HOWISON Julian *(A Sax, S Sax, Flt, La Per)*: Bransingham, 24A Birch Grove, Rusholme, Manchester M14 5JU ☎ 0161 224 3003, 07957 256267

HUNNISETT Bruce *(T Sax, S Sax, Flt, Gtr)*: 74 Rossett Avenue, Timperley, Cheshire WA15 6EX ☎ 0161 969 2153

JOBSON John *(Saxes, Hmca)*: 6 Sandringham Park Drive, New Longton, Preston, Lancs PR4 4ZS ☎ 01772 616740

JOHNSTON Philip *(T Sax, Gtr)*: 41 Barnfield, Much Hoole, Preston PR4 4GE

JONES Michael *(A Sax, T Sax, Flt)* ☎ 01244 372232, 01523 795458

KELLY Henry *(A Sax, T Sax)*: 1A Bonis Crescent, Great Moor, Stockport, Cheshire SK2 7HH ☎ 0161 483 9097

KINGDON George *(A Sax, T Sax, B Gtr, Flt, Clt)*: 4 Wallacre Road, Wallasey, Merseyside L44 2DY ☎ 0151 639 7076

LATHAM Warren *(Sax, Dms)*: 11 Lower Fold Avenue, Royton, Lancashire OL2 6UG ☎ 01706 882477

LENNI *(Sax)*: 14H Kingsleigh Road, Heaton Mersey, Stockport, Cheshire SK4 3QG ☎ 0161 442 1650

LINDSAY Geoffrey *(A Sax, T Sax, Br Sax, Clt, Fl)*: 43 Meadowcroft Avenue, Hambleton, Blackpool, Lancs FY6 9AD ☎ 01253 700868

LING Paul *(A Sax, Br Sax, Clt)*: 17 Gambrel Bank Road, Ashton-Under-Lyne, Lancashire OL6 8TW ☎ 0161 330 7670

LLOYD Kenneth *(Saxes, Clt, Flt, Tpt)*: 12 Clumber Road, Poynton, Stockport, Cheshire SK12 1NS ☎ 01625 875459

LOFTHOUSE Francis *(Sax, Clt)*: 30 Maycroft Avenue, Carleton, Blackpool, Lancs FY6 7NE ☎ 01253 883352

MACKENZIE William *(Sax, Clt, Vln)*: 15 Powys Road, Llandudno, Caerns LL30 1HZ

MANSHIP Michael *(Saxes, Wood W)*: 12 Honeywood Close, Holcombe Brook, Bury, Lancs BL0 9RL ☎ 01204 883628

MARSDEN Roger *(A Sax, S Sax, Flt, Kbds, Clt)*: 4 Westage Lane, Great Budworth, Cheshire CW9 6HJ ☎ 01606 892160, Fax 01606 892394

MARTINELLI Gary *(Sax, Kbds)*: 41 Reeves Road, Chorlton, Manchester M21 8BU ☎ 0161 881 6789

MCCAUSLAND John *(Br Sax, A Sax, Flt, Clt, S Sa)*: 5 Station Road, Ainsdale, Southport, Merseyside PR8 3HR ☎ 01704 574722

MELVILLE Thomas *(Saxes, Clt)*: Address Unknown

MOLE *(A Sax, Per, Gtr, B Gtr, Chara)*: 71 Bouverie Street, Chester CH1 4HF ☎ 01244 372629

MULHEARN Richard *(Sax, Clt, Flt, Kbds, Com)*: 98 Brookdale Road, Liverpool L15 3JF ☎ 0151 733 3361

NEWBOLD Ronald *(Saxes, Clt)*: 21 Levens Drive, Morecambe, Lancs LA3 1JN ☎ 01524 850893

NICHOL Gordon *(A Sax, T Sax, Br Sax, Clt, Ar)*: Woodlands, Birkby Moor, Maryport, Cumberland CA15 6RN ☎ 01900 812324

NOBLE Louis *(T Sax, A Sax)*: 6 Westminster Close, Wrexham, Clwyd LL12 7AY ☎ 01978 312443

NXUMALO Trevor *(A Sax)*: 96 Summervale House, Vale Drive, Oldham OL9 6JB ☎ 0161 626 2371

PARK Graeme *(Sax, Clt)*: PO Box 7, Woolton, Liverpool L26 6LZ

PERRY Terence *(A Sax, Clt, Voc, Flt)*: 97 Raeburn Avenue, Eastham, Wirral, Merseyside L62 8BD ☎ 0151 327 1673

PILLINGER Helen *(Sax, Voc, Pf)*: Flat B, 44 Clarenden Road, Whalley Range, Manchester M16 8LD ☎ 0161 860 4845

POLLITT Samuel *(Sax, Clt)*: 690 Bury Road, Bolton, Lancashire BL2 6JD ☎ 01204 382677

PURNELL Joel *(Sax)*: 28 Edinburgh Road, Little Lever, Bolton, Lancs BL3 1TG ☎ 01204 792295

PURVES Simon *(A Sax, S Sax)*: 24 South Balley Drive, Colne, Lancashire BB8 8BG ☎ 01282 865 946, 01523 795 736

RADCLIFFE Arthur *(T Sax)*: 3 Cronk Drine, Union Mills, Isle Of Man IM4 4NG ☎ 01624 851737

REUBEN Graham *(Sax, Clt)*: 26, Burndale Drive, Unsworth, Bury, Lancs BL9 8EN ☎ 0161 766 8738

RILEY Alan *(Br Sax, Clt, Flt, V Tbn)*: 57 Ashfield Road, Bispham, Blackpool, Lancashire FY2 0EN ☎ 01253 353764

ROADHOUSE John *(Saxes, B Sax, Clt, B Clt, Flt)*: 262 Brantingham Road, Manchester M21 0QZ ☎ 0161 881 4689

ROBINSON Martin *(Sax, Flt, Pf)*: Flat 1 Broadlands, 1 Alexandra Drive, Liverpool L17 8TA ☎ 0151 728 7531

SALISBURY Harold *(Saxes, Clt, Flt, Md)*: 4 Grosvenor Place, Preston, Lancs PR2 1ED ☎ 01772 726397

SCOTT Andrew *(Saxes, Com)*: 224 Ways Green, Winsford, Cheshire CW7 4AR ☎ 01606 553698

SHAW Stephen *(Saxes, Clt, Flt)*: The Hollies, 65 Wood Lane, Timperley, Altrincham, Cheshire WA15 7PR ☎ 0161 980 5973

SHAW HULME Neil *(Sax, Clt, Flt, Voc)*: Old Stones, Unwin Pool, Pott Shrigley, Cheshire SK10 5SE ☎ 01625 575311, 0831 886756 mob

SHERMAN Pete *(Sax, Flt, Clt)*: 8 Abbots Nook, Chester, Cheshire CH2 2BB ☎ 01244 374474

SPARKES John *(Sax, Clt)*: 70 Newhouse Road, Marton, Blackpool, Lancashire FY4 4JJ ☎ 01253 66764

STEVENSON Leslie *(Sax, Flt, Clt)*: 3 Andrews Walk, Barnston, Wirral L60 2SF ☎ 0151 342 8278

SUTTON Tony *(Saxes, Clt)*: 6 Bro Lleweni, Bodfari, Denbigh, Denbighshire, Clwyd LL16 4BQ ☎ 01745 710595

THOMSON Jimmy *(Sax, Clt, Flt)*: 34 Rowlands Lane, Thornton Cleveleys, Lancashire FY5 2QU ☎ 01253 869414

VICKERS Roy *(Saxes, Flt)*: 11A Arnold Close, Preston, Lancs PR2 6DX ☎ 01772 798536

WARD Charles *(Sax, T Sax, A Sax, S Sax, Clt)*: The Cottage, Small Lane South, Halsall, Nr Ormskirk L39 7JX ☎ 01704 840880

WARD Christopher *(T Sax, Gtr, Per)*: 37 Sandown Crescent, Gorton, Manchester M18 7WG ☎ 0161 231 3375

WESLEY Amos *(Sax, Clt, Pf, Org)*: Address Unknown

WILKS Ralph *(Sax, Clt)*: 21 Norris Road, Blacon, Chester CH1 5DY ☎ 01244 376441

WILLESCROFT Simon *(Sax)*: 53 Old Road, Mottram, Hyde, Cheshire SK14 6LW ☎ 01457 762224, 0410 264514 mob

WILLIAMS Christopher *(A Sax, Cel, Clt)*: Wright Robinson Hall, Altrincham Street, Manchester M1 7JA ☎ 0161 236 6627

WILLIAMS Kevin *(T Sax, A Sax, Clt)*: 19 Stanley Avenue, Wallasey Village, Merseyside L45 8JN ☎ 0151 638 4588

WILSON Andrew *(A Sax, So Sax, T Sax, Clt, Pf)*: 3 Corran Close, Winton, Eccles, Manchester M30 8LP ☎ 0161 789 2092

WIMPENNY Richard *(Sax, Clt, Flt)*: 10 Bettridge Place, Wellesbourne, Warwickshire CV35 9LY ☎ 01789 840693

WINCH Reginald *(Sax, Clt, Flt)*: 73-75 Church Street, Dukinfield, Cheshire SK16 4LU ☎ 0161 330 2478

WOODHOUSE John *(Sax, Clt, Flt)*: 27 Mayfield Drive, Bare, Morecambe, Lancashire LA4 6ES ☎ 01524 416798

WOOLLATT Horace *(Sax)*: 15 The Ridgeway, Nelson, Lancs BB9 0DS

NORTH EAST

ALKER Martin *(Saxes, Pf, Voc, Synth, Flt)*: 3 Fairview Gardens, Richmond, North Yorkshire DL10 4NP

ALLENBY Dave *(Saxes, Clt, Pf)*: 28 Langholm Crescent, Darlington, County Durham DL3 7SU ☎ 01325 465439

ALLERTON Fred *(A Sax, Ob, Clt, T Sax)*: 20, Harnham Avenue, West Chirton, North Shields, Newcastle Tyne & Wear NE29 7LA ☎ 0191 257 3043

ARCHER Martin *(S Sax)*: 5 Oakholme Mews, Sheffield S10 3FX ☎ 0114 2667180

ARMSTRONG Niall *(A Sax, Br Sax, Clt)*: Three Coins, Forstersteads, Allendale, Wexham Northumberland NE47 9AS ☎ 01434 683 559

ARMSTRONG Sarah *(Sax)*: 294 Bolehill Road, Walkley, Sheffield S6 5DF ☎ 0114 2321340

BARBER Ron *(A Sax, Clt, Arr)*: 108 Church View, Church Fields, Sherburn-In-Elmet, Leeds LS25 6HZ ☎ 01977 682615

BATESON Kenneth *(Saxes, Clt)*: 14 The Paddock, High Mill Lane, Addingham, Ilkley, W. Yorkshire LS29 0RE

BECK Michael *(T Sax, A Sax)*: Moorlands, 78 Kingfield Road, Brincliffe, Sheffiled S11 9AU ☎ 0114 2584999

BEIGHTON Steven *(Sax, Flt, B Gtr, Kbds)*: 123 Argyle Road, Meersbrook, Sheffield, South Yorkshire S8 9HJ ☎ 0114 2585390

BENNETT Andrew *(A Sax, T Sax, Clt, Flt)*: 1 Oakdene Avenue, Darlington, Co. Durham DL3 7HR ☎ 01325 485559

BLACK David *(Saxes, Kbds, Flt, Arr)*: Ferndale, Peareth Hall Road, Washington, Tyne & Wear NE37 1NR ☎ 0191 4165883

BONE Steven *(T Sax, Br Sax, A Sax, Voc)*: 4 Hamilton Drive, Ashbrooke, Darlington, County Durham DL1 3TS ☎ 01325 461808

BOWN Edward *(Saxes, Clt, Flt, Pic, Db)*: 11 Wrenbeck Close, Otley, Leeds LS21 2BU ☎ 01943 464322

BOYD Martin *(A Sax, T Sax, Br Sax, Clt, Fl)*: 3 Grove Terrace Lane, The Groves, York YO31 8PL ☎ 01904 635759

BRETT John *(A Sax, Br Sax, Flt)*: 11 Westwood Avenue, Linthorpe, Middlesbrough, Cleveland TS5 5PY ☎ 01642 823360

BREWER Asha *(T Sax, Voc, S Sax, Pf)*: c/o 56 Cleasby Road, Menston, Ikley, West Yorkshire LS29 6HN ☎ 01943 870496

BRIDGE Derek *(A Sax, T Sax, B Sax, Clt, Flt)*: 30 Lingfield Road, Yarm, Cleveland TS15 9RB ☎ 01642 785760

BRINKWORTH Thomas *(T Sax, Dms)*: 9 Charles Street West, Lincoln LN1 1QP ☎ 01522 24059

BROOKER Frank *(T Sax, A Sax, Clt, Flt)*: 32 Hayton Wood View, Aberford, Leeds LS25 3AN ☎ 0113 2813384

BULL Naomi *(Sax, Clt)*: 14 Pnynton Wood Crescent, Bradway, Sheffield S17 4NB ☎ 0114 2351737

CALLAGHAN Robert *(A Sax, T Sax, S Sax, Clt, Acc)*: 102 Teesdale Avenue, Billingham, Cleveland TS23 1NH ☎ 01642 656761

CALVER Harold *(Sax, Clt, Flt)*: 33 Stokesly Grove, High Heaton, Newcastle, Tyne 7 NE7 7AU ☎ 0191 266 5973

CARTER Peter *(T Sax, A Sax, Clt, Flt)*: 14 Danby Close, Rickleton, Washington, Tyne &Wear NE38 9JB ☎ 0191 417 7716

CASE Matthew *(Sax, Kbds, Eup)*: Millrace. Mill Lane, Darlington, Co. Durham DL1 2XQ ☎ 01325 353742

CHRISTAN Lawrence *(T Sax, A Sax, Br Sax, Clt, Ar)*: 3 College View, Delves Lane, Consett, Co Durham DH8 7DP ☎ 01207 502366

CLARK Roderick *(Sax, Clt)*: 15 Fifth Avenue, Heaton, Newcastle-on-Tyne NE6 5YL ☎ 0191 265 3277

COATES Stanley *(Sax, Clt)*: 11 Dundrennan, District 7, Washington, Tyne & Wear NE38 7TX ☎ 0191 417 4731

COLLINS Charlie *(Sax, Flt, Clt, Per)*: 13 Headland Drive, Sheffield S10 5FX ☎ 0114 2662260

COOPER Raymond *(Saxes, B Gtr, Bjo, Vln, Flt)*: Sandburn, Malton Road, Hopgrove, York YO3 29TW ☎ 01904 468208

DALES Raymond *(A Sax, T Sax, Flt, Clt)*: 16 Dunedin Avenue, Hartburn, Stockton-on-Tees, Cleveland TS18 5JF ☎ 01642 645415

DAVIS Thomas *(T Sax, Clt)*: 34 Front Street, Fence House, Houghton Le Spring DH4 6DS ☎ 0191 385 3635

DENTON Glyn *(A Sax)*: 3 Bridge House Court, Tinkers Hill, Carlton In Lindrick, Worksop, Notts S81 9EQ ☎ 01909 733777

DEVERE Andrea *(Sax)*: 'Grangefield', 20 Cade Hill Road, Stocksfield, Northumberland NE43 7PT ☎ 01661 8452556, 07970 616031

DONNELLY Donal *(Sax, Flt, Clt, Pf)*: 20 Watergate, Methley, Leeds, W Yorkshire LS26 9BY ☎ 01977 517735

EDGE Stuart *(Saxes, Flt, Clt)*: Flat 1, 52 Victoria Road, Headingley, Leeds LS6 1AS ☎ 0113 2787531, 0589 444 230

GILLON Sharon *(Saxes, Kbds, Per)*: Rose Cottage, Moorend Lane, Silkstone Common, Barnsley S75 4RA ☎ 01226 792276, 01226 792276

GILPIN William *(Saxes, Clt, Md)*: 41 Muncastergate, York YO31 9JX ☎ 01904 412815

GREAVES Gordon *(Saxes, Clt, Flt)*: 171 Stonelow Road, Dronfield, Sheffield S18 6EQ ☎ 01246 413666, 0114 274 5193

GREY Stanley *(Saxes, Clt, Flt)*: 38 Hallams Close, Filey, N Yorks YO14 0AG ☎ 01723 515791

HARDY David *(Saxes, Clt, B Clt, Flt, Pic)*: 120 Barnsley Road, Sandal, Wakefield, Yorks WF1 5NX ☎ 01924 251661, 0378 390850

HARROD Vic *(T Sax, Clt, A Sax, Br Sax, Fl)*: 136 Wolsey Way, Nettleham Park, Lincoln LN2 4TW ☎ 01522 829859

HERITAGE Tom *(Saxes, B Clt, Clt, Flt, Pic)*: 12 Blackbrook Avenue, Lodge Moor, Sheffield S10 4LT ☎ 0114 230 5547, 0802 751155

HIRST Willie *(Sax, Clt, Flt, Rec)*: Belmont House, Bell Lane, Ackworth, Pontefract WF7 7JH ☎ 01977 611107

HODGSON Ron (*Sax, T Sax*): 27, Tintagel, Great Lumley, Chester Le Street, Co Durham DH3 4NF ☎ 0191 3886432

HOLMES Alexandra (*A Sax, T Sax, Voc*): Flat 6 Raynville Road, Armley, Leeds LS12 2TF ☎ 0113 2899501

HOOLEY George (*S Sax, A Sax, T Sax, Clt*): Alassio, 184 Nethermoor Road, Wingerworth, Chesterfield S42 6LH ☎ 01246 863290, 0468 194447 mob

HUGHES Jack (*A Sax, T Sax, Clt, Flt*): "Honeywell", Elmscroft, Main Road, Wrangle, Boston, Lincolnshire PE22 9AG ☎ 01205 817879

HULL Arthur (*Saxes, Clt*): 6 Westfield Avenue, Boston, Lincs PE21 8AW ☎ 01205 62054

HUTCHINSON Matthew (*A Sax, Clt, Flt*): 25 Dene Lane, Fulwell, Sunderland SR6 8EH ☎ 0191 5485500

INGHAM Richard (*Saxes, Clt*): Greenroyd House, 31 Agbrigg Road, Sandal Magna, Wakefield WF1 5AB ☎ 01924 257826 /25

JAFRATE Keith (*Sax, Per, Voc*): 23 Cowcliffe Hill Road, Birkby, Huddersfield, West Yorkshire HD2 2NY ☎ 01484 547022

JAMES Terence (*T Sax, A Sax, Clt*): 295 Cromwell Road, Grimsby DN31 2BH ☎ 01472 358752

JENKINS Ian (*Saxes, Flt, Clt*): 24 Almshouse Lane, New Millerdam, Wakefield WF2 7ST ☎ 01924 255614

JESSUP William (*Saxes, Org, Vln*): 98 Hessle Avenue, Boston, Lincs PE21 8DE ☎ 01205 363446

JOHNSON Stuart (*S Sax, T Sax, Synth, Clt, B C*): Cameleon Management, PO Box 102, Middlesborough, Cleveland TS5 5YS ☎ 01642 829177

JONES Paul (*Saxes, Pf, Clt, Flt*): 38A Abbeville Road, Clapham, London SW4 9NG ☎ 020 8673 3596, 0973 694090 mob

JOWETT Benn (*A Sax, Clt*): White Cross Cottage, 36 Main Street, Bishopthorpe, Yorkshire YO23 2RW ☎ 01904 705107

KAVANAGH Richard (*Saxes*): 9 Coldwell Lane, Sandygate, Sheffield S10 5TJ ☎ 0114 2630660

KNIGHT Gordon (*Sax*): 146, Beckfield Lane, York YO26 5QT

LANGFIELD Denis (*Saxes, B Ldr, Clt*): 22 Alton Way, Mapplewell, Nr Barnsley S75 6EY ☎ 01226 385257

LINSLEY Gary (*A Sax, T Sax*): 18 Southlands, High Heaton, Newcastle-upon-Tyne, Tyne & Wear NE7 7YJ ☎ 0191 281 1000

LOVELL Andy (*Saxes, Clt, B Clt, Flt, Pic*): 12 Olliver Lane, Skeeby, Richmond, North Yorkshire DL10 5DP ☎ 01748 823159, 0839 494705

LYONS Peter (*T Sax*): 16 Hobart Street, Sheffield S11 8DB ☎ 0114 2584935

MACDONALD Stuart (*T Sax, Flt, Clt*): 32 Fearnley Court, Wooldale, Homefirth, Huddersfield HD7 1UD ☎ 01484 684638, 0860394304

MACHON Paul (*Sax, Flt, Clt*): 66 Kirkgate, Hanging Heaton, Batley, West Yorkshire WF17 6DJ ☎ 01924 458592

MARSHALL Jeffrey (*Saxes, Clt, Flt, Ob, Bsn*): Address Unknown ☎ 01935 840623

MAXWELL Erik (*T Sax, Clt*): Flat 20, 17 Clarges Street, London W1Y 7PG

MCGARRY Pat (*Saxes, Flt, Clt, Arr*): 10 Douglas Avenue, Soothill, Batley, West Yorkshire WF17 6HG ☎ 01924 475961, 0973 817707 mob

MEARS Andy (*Saxes, Clt*): 16 Upland Crescent, Roundhay, Leeds, West Yorks LS8 2TB ☎ 0113 2482352, 020 8868 8856

MILLS Frederick (*Sax, Clt*): 11 Windmill Rise, York YO26 4TU ☎ 01904 792249

MILLS Julia (*Sax, Pf*): Greenroyd House, 31 Agbrigg Road, Sandal Magna, Wakefield,W.Yorks WF1 5AB ☎ 01924 257826

MINNS Peter (*A Sax, T Sax, S Sax, Clt, Flt*): 1 Woodgate Road, Spring Bank West, Hull HU5 5AH ☎ 01482 354562

MORAN Tom (*Saxes, Clt, Flt, Org, Kbds*): 6 Osprey Way, South Shields, Tyne & Wear NE34 0HA ☎ 0191 455 1316

MORRIS Keith (*A Sax, B Gtr, Kbds*): 5 Bentinck Road, Newcastle/Tyne, Tyne & Wear NE4 6UT ☎ 0191 273 5326

MOULD Sidney (*T Sax, Clt, Flt*): 5 Hawkeshead Road, Redcar, Cleveland TS10 1JY ☎ 01642 477676

MOWAT Arthur (*Sax, Clt, Flt, Org, B Ldr*): 49, Ingleside Road, North Shields, Northumberland NE29 9PB ☎ 0191 257 5284

NUGENT Gerald (*T Sax, Clt*): 62 Serlby Lane, Harthill, Sheffield S26 7YE ☎ 01909 771142

NUTTALL George (*A Sax, Clt*): 21 Priors Close, New Waltham, Grimsby DN36 4QZ ☎ 01472 812750

ORMISTON David (*Saxes, Clt, Flt*): 26 Stonehaugh Way, Ponteland, Newcastle-upon-Tyne NE20 9LX ☎ 01661 820 755

OWEN Lyndon (*T Sax, S Sax, B Clt*): 33 Rushworth Place, Rushworth, Sowerby Bridge, West Yorkshire HX6 4RB ☎ 01422 825265

PETERS Jane (*Saxes, Flt, Pic, Clt*): 300 Redmires Road, Redmires, Sheffield S10 4LD ☎ 0958 420667

POLLARD Eric (*T Sax, Clt*): 121 Bamburgh Avenue, South Shields, Tyne & Wear NE34 7SZ ☎ 0191 456 0582

PRIESTLEY Mark (*T Sax, S Sax, Gtr*): 14 Moor Grange Rise, Leeds LS16 5BP ☎ 0113 2287087

PRINCE Simon (*T Sax*): Flat 126 St Thomas Court, Manchester Road, Huddersfield, West Yorkshire HD1 3HU ☎ 01484 519151

PRYCE Granville (*Sax, Per*): 16 Woodend Court, Parkside Estate, West Bowling, Bradford, West Yorkshire BD5 8QL

RAINE Bridget (*Saxes, Vln*) ☎ 01434 632373 & fax

RAYNES Harry (*T Sax*): Address Unknown

READ Tony (*T Sax, Clt*): 9 Grimsby Rd, Waltham, Grimsby DN37 0PS ☎ 01472 230616

ROBINSON Dennis (*A Sax, Clt*): Ridgemont, 46 Park Road North, Chester Le Street, Co Durham DH3 3SD ☎ 0191 388 4552

ROBINSON George (*Saxes, Clt, Flt, Pic, Pf*): 64 Wantage Road, Carrville, Co Durham DH1 1LR ☎ 0191 386 6892

ROBINSON Keith (*Sax, Ac Gtr, Kbds*): 41 Humford Way, Bayard Woods, Bedlington, Northumberland NE22 5ET

ROBSON Kim (*A Sax, Clt, Flt, Bsn*): 23 The Sycamores, Burnopfield, Newcastle-upon-Tyne NE16 6PH ☎ 01207 71596

ROCHESTER Percy (*Sax, Clt, Vln*): 73 Bolbec Road, Fenham, Newcastle-upon-Tyne 4, Tyne & Wear NE4 9EQ ☎ 0191 274 1081

ROSS Steven (*T Sax, A Sax, Clt, Flt, Org*): 116 Station Road, Billingham, Stockton-on-Tees TS23 1PD ☎ 01642 551449

SABEY Richard (*A Sax, Clt, Pf, Rec, Gtr*): 21 Ilkley Road, Otley, West Yorkshire LS21 3PN ☎ 01943 466256, 01943 466256

SALFIELD Stephen (*T Sax, S Sax, A Sax*): 15 Tapton House Road, Sheffield S10 5BY ☎ 0114 2684632

SCHOFIELD Michael (*Saxes, Clt, Flt*): 185 New Road, Middlestown, Wakefield WF4 4NY ☎ 01924 270297

SCOTT Richard (*Saxes, Pf*): 13 Claremont Grove, Leeds LS3 1AX ☎ 0113 2452269

SHAKESPEARE Colin (*A Sax, Clt, B Ldr*): Flat 3, Holly Lodge, 15 Carr Lane, Willerby, Hull HU10 6JP ☎ 01482 651893

SINGLETON Stephen (*Sax*): 13, Endcliffe Vale Road, Sheffield S10 3EN ☎ 0114 2685757

SMITH Bill (*A Sax, T Sax, Clt, Flt*): 8 Greenwood Square, Grindon, Sunderland, Tyne & Wear SR4 8JT ☎ 0191 5342342

SNEDDON William (*Saxes, Clt, Ob, Flt*): 17 Monks Meadows, Kitty Frisk, Hexham, Northumberland NE46 1LF ☎ 01434 600729

SNELL Syd (*Saxes, Clt*): 55 Almond Avenue, Swanpool, Lincoln LN6 0HB ☎ 01522 683654

STEELE John (*A Sax, S Sax, Pf*): North Sheen, South Street, West Rainton, Tyne & Wear DH4 6PA ☎ 0191 584 1616

STRINGER Jack (*Sax, Clt*): 15 Holmesdale Close, Dronfield, Sheffield S18 6EZ ☎ 01246 417353

STUDDERT-KENNEDY Nick (*A Sax, Br Sax*): 20 Maude Street, Darlington DL3 7PW ☎ 01325 266442

SWOPE Brad (*Sax, A Sax, T Sax, Clt, Flt*): 15 Troutbeck, York YO24 2RE ☎ 01904 705156, 0498 703862

TATE Gordon (*Sax, Clt*): 21 Abingdon Street, High Barnes, Sunderland SR4 7RU ☎ 0191 514 7963

TAYLOR James (*A Sax*): 15 Westhill Road, Grimsby, South Humberside DN34 4SG ☎ 01472 343392

TAYLOR Jonathan (*T Sax, Flt*): 8 Lucas Place, Leeds LS6 2JB ☎ 0113 2455439

THOMPSON Gerald (*Saxes, Clt*): 17 Corporation Street, Barnsley, Yorks S70 4PQ ☎ 01226 285187

TOOMEY Mark (*A Sax, S Sax, T Sax, Clt, Flt*): 15 Springwell Close, Deans Park, Wolviston, Billingham, Cleveland TS23 3FB ☎ 01642 565851

VALLANCE Dave (*T Sax, B Gtr*): 11 Tollergate, Scarborough YO11 1RR ☎ 01723 369814

VERNER Austin (*B Sax, A Sax, T Sax, Clt, Flt*): 1B Danes Terrace, Lincoln LN2 1LP ☎ 01522 33347

WALKER Kenneth (*Saxes, Clt*): 25 Almond Crescent, Swanpool, Lincoln LN6 0HN ☎ 01522 684462

WALKER Sam (*T Sax, A Sax, Clt, Flt, Pf*): Woodwinds, Merrylands Road, Bookham, Surrey KT23 3HP ☎ 01372 452375, 0113 231 0629

WALLACE Richard (*A Sax, Clt*): 30 Winds, Lonnen Estate, Meadowdale, Murton, Seaham, Co. Durham SR7 9TG ☎ 0191 526 5727

WARD Michael (*A Sax, Flt*): 105 Ranby Road, Sheffield S11 7AN ☎ 0114 266 6458

WEBSTER Andrew (*A Sax, T Sax, Flt, Pic, Pf*): 23 Templegate, Leeds LS15 0PQ ☎ 0113 264 3729

WELLINGTON Julian (*Sax, Clt*): 26 Ashton Terrace, Harehills, Leeds LS8 5BU ☎ 0113 2489234

WHITTLE Brian (*Sax, Clt, Flt*): 47 Deneway, Lockhaugh, Rowlands Gill, Tyne & Wear NE39 1BB ☎ 01207 542688

WILKINSON Kenneth (*Sax, Clt, Flt, Pic*): 69 Lane End, Pudsey, Leeds LS28 9AQ ☎ 0113 255 5946

WOODTHORPE Arthur (*Sax, Clt*): 10A Wensley Road, Harrogate, North Yorks HG2 8AQ ☎ 01423 564361, 0850 693104 mob, 01423 531847 fax

WOOLGAR Richard (*T Sax, A Sax, Clt, Flt*): Surgery House, Wragby, Lincoln LN3 5QU ☎ 01673 857164

YOUNG J (*T Sax, Clt*): Address Unknown

EAST

APPLETON Norman (*Saxes, Flt*): 61 Friarage Road, Aylesbury HP20 2SD ☎ 01296 431040

ARDIN Antony (*Sax, Flt, Wi Synth*): 84 Fairmead Avenue, Westcliff-on-Sea SS0 9SA ☎ 01702 432733, 0956 662935

AYERS Evie (*T Sax, Clt*): 170 Woodland Drive, Watford, Herts WD1 3DB ☎ 01923 222910

AYRES Roger (*T Sax, A Sax*): 9 Mortimer Hill, Tring, Herts HP23 5JT ☎ 0144 282 3265

B. Roy (*A Sax, T Sax, Clt, Hmca*): 227 Monks Walk, Buntingford, Herts SG9 9DY ☎ 01763 272756

BANYARD Ray (*A Sax, S Sax, Clt*): 42 St Georges Road, Felixstowe IP11 9PN ☎ 01394 271667

BARBER Doug (*A Sax, Clt, Flt, S Sax*): 43 Bromeswell Road, Ipswich, Suffolk IP4 3AT ☎ 01473 253846

BARBER Peter (*A Sax, Clt, T Sax*): 7 Pulford Road, Leighton Buzzard, Beds LU7 7AB ☎ 01525 371296

BARNES Dee (*Sax, Clt, Kbds*): 16 Church Lane, Norton Village, Letchworth, Herts SG16 1AJ ☎ 01462 676883

BARNES John (*Saxes, Efl Clt, Clt, B Clt, V*): 16 Worton Road, Isleworth, Middx TW7 6HN ☎ 0181 560 7593

BATESON Gordon (*Sax, Pf*): Odd Spring, Off Stocks Road, Aldbury, Tring, Herts. HP23 5RU ☎ 01442 85 209

BAYNE John (*Saxes, Clt, Db, B Clt*): 58 Argyll Avenue, Luton, Beds LU3 1EQ ☎ 01582 36255

BENTON Brian (*T Sax, S Sax, Flt*): 22C Grange Street, Clifton, Beds SG17 5EW ☎ 01462 814100

BODDY Suzi (*Sax, Flt, Clt, Pf*): 9A Church Lane, Cheddington, Leighton Buzzard, Beds LU7 0RU ☎ 01296 668919, 0402 510339 mob

BRAY Colin (*Saxes, Clt, Pf, Vib*): 2 Deacons Close, Elstree, Herts WD6 3HX ☎ 020 8953 6417

BROWN Graeme (*T Sax, Clt, Voc, Ld Gtr, Tpt*): 49 Lorne Road, Lowestoft, Suffolk NR33 0RG ☎ 01502 565862

BRUSH Andy (*Sax, Wi Synth*): 10 New Town Road, Colchester, Essex CO1 2DH ☎ 01206 511719, 0370 935163 mob

BRYAR Quentin (*Sax, Clt*): 7 Harrow View Road, Ealing, London W5 1NA ☎ 020 8248 6829

BUDGEN Adrian (*Br Sax, Clt, T Sax, A Sax, S*): 222 High Road, Trimley, St. Martin, Ipswich IP10 0RG ☎ 01394 278006

CAMERON Bruce (*Sax, Gtr*): 31 Orchard Way, Haddenham, Cambs CB6 3UT ☎ 01353 741966 fax, 01353 740358 eve

CATCHPOLE Nathaniel (*A Sax, T Sax, Pf, Wi Synth, F*): 297 Frinton Road, Holland-on-Sea, Clacton-on-Sea, Essex CO15 5SP ☎ 01255 812420

CHAPMAN John (*Saxes, Clt, B Clt, Flt*): 16 Woodfield Gardens, Leigh-on-Sea, Essex SS9 1EW ☎ 01702 715681

CONNOR Charles (*Sax, Clt, Pf*): 94 Lakeside, Isleham Marina, Isleham, Ely, Cambs CB7 5SL ☎ 01638 780111

CULMER Tony (*A Sax, Clt*): 11 Ashby Drive, Upper Caldecote, Biggleswade SG18 9DJ ☎ 01767 315534

DELLER Neil (*Sax, Clt, Pf*): 5 Marlborough Close, Bishops Stortford, Herts CM23 3NT ☎ 01279 659318

DEVONSHIRE Paul (*Sax, Clt, Flt*): The Grange, Western Road, Tring, Herts HP23 4BN ☎ 0144282 2688

DIMMOCK Clive (*S Sax, A Sax, Clt, Flt*): 25 Woodberry Road, Wickford SS11 8XQ ☎ 01268 560234

DOBBS Elizabeth (*Sax*): 73 Jaywick Lane, Clacton, Essex CO16 8BG

DOGGETT Philip (*Br Sax, Clt, A Sax, Flt, A Fl*): Dudswell Rise, Dudswell, Berkhamsted, Herts HP4 3SZ ☎ 01442 873443, 01442 870402 fax

DONNISON Glyn (*T Sax*): 26 Portland Road, Newmarket, Suffolk CB8 0NP ☎ 01638 602025

DOWNS Katherine (*Sax*): 15 Cambridge Road, St Albans, Herts AL1 5LH ☎ 01727 838417

DRAYCOTT Ian (*T Sax, Flt, Pic, Pf, Clt*): 21 Cowgate, Norwich, Norfolk NR3 1SZ ☎ 01603 660631

ETHERINGTON Leigh (*Sax*): 71 Great Northern Road, Dunstable, Beds LU5 4BW ☎ 01582 668783

FARRINGTON John (*T Sax, A Sax, Clt*): 21 Duke Street, Old Fletton, Peterborough PE2 8EB ☎ 01733 343413

FAWCUS Paul (*A Sax, T Sax, Flt, Clt, S Sax*): The Flat Little Sutton, Little Sutton Lane, Langley, Berks SL3 8AN ☎ 01753 595308

FISCHER Mark (*T Sax*): 22 Anstee Road, Luton, Beds LU4 9HH ☎ 01582 504483

GOSS Charles (*A Sax, Clt*): 13 Cowper Road, Markyate, St Albans, Hertfordshire AL3 8PP ☎ 01582 841727

HAGON Andrew (*T Sax, Br Sax, B Gtr*): 2 Mayflower Road, Park Street, St. Albans, Herts AL2 2QR ☎ 01727 768381

HARRISON Ian (*T Sax, Pf, Kbds*): 39 Silverdale Road, Bushey WD2 2LY ☎ 01923 237978

HINGSTON Michael (*A Sax, T Sax*): 25 Oakfield Close, Potters Bar, Herts EN6 2BE ☎ 01707 663685

HOLT John (*T Sax, A Sax, Flt, Clt*): 41 Priory Way, Hitchin, Herts SG4 9BH ☎ 01462 436626

HOPGOOD Adrian (*Sax, A Sax, Clt, Flt*): 71 Princethorpe Road, Ipswich, Suffolk IP3 8NU ☎ 01473 727778

HORTON Hannah (*A Sax, Bsn, Clt*): 6 Springhill, Widdington, Saffron Walden, Essex CB11 3AA ☎ 01799 540694, 0410 972073

HUNT Roy (*T Sax, Br Sax, Clt, Pic*): 194 High Street, Clapham, Bedfordshire MK41 6BS ☎ 01234 359208

INGHAM David (*T Sax, A Sax, S Sax, Clt*): 15 Princes Road, Lowestoft, Suffolk NR32 2NJ ☎ 01502 585433

JACOBS Laurie (*T Sax, A Sax, S Sax, Clt, Flt*): 38 Church Street, Werrington, Peterborough, Cambs PE4 6OE ☎ 01733 312525

JOLLY Paul (*S Sax, A Sax, Br Sax, Clt, Fl*): 53 Talbot Road, Luton, Beds LU1 7RN ☎ 0850 207346

JONES D (*Saxes, Flt, Bsn*): 24 The Avenue, Bletsoe, Beds MK44 1QF ☎ 01234 781824

KEEFER Cyril (*Sax, Clt, B Ldr, Voc*): 23 Bridewell Close, Mildenhall IP28 7RB ☎ 01638 712349

KIDMAN Henry (*A Sax, Clt*): 54 Queen Ediths Way, Cambridge CB1 4PW ☎ 01223 248713

KIRKBY Derek (*Sax, Clt, Flt, Wood W*): 2 Swan Close, Ivinghoe Aston, Leighton Buzzard, Beds LU7 9DN ☎ 01525 222422

LAMB Brian (*T Sax*): 5 Chapel Street, Billericay, Essex CM12 9LT ☎ 01277 643 960

LANDYMORE Julian (*Saxes, Clt, Flt, Com, Cop*): 19 Lawrance Lea, Harston, Cambridge CB2 5QR ☎ 01223 871232

LIGHT Patrick (*Saxes, Clt, Flt, Bsn*): 10 Century Road, Ware, Herts SG12 9DY ☎ 01920 464825

LINGLEY Joanne (*Sax*): 73 Bridgewater Road, Ipswich, Suffolk ☎ 01473 685187

MARTIN Jeremy (*Sax, Flt, Clt, Pf, Con*): 36 Sea King Crescent, Colchester CO4 4RJ ☎ 01206 852243

MCCONNACH Bruce (*T Sax, S Sax*): 174 High Road, Bushey Heath, Watford, Herts WD2 1NP ☎ 020 8950 5121

MCKAY George (*A Sax, Flt, Br Sax, T Sax*): Seaview, Salisbury Road, Cromer, Norfolk NR27 0BW ☎ 01263 511866 & fax

MCKENNA Joe (*T Sax, Clt*): 3A Cardiff Road, Norwich NR2 3HR ☎ 01603 621875

MILLEN Penny (*Sax, Voc*): 55 Catchacer, West Street, Dunstable, Beds LU6 1QD ☎ 01582 475791

MITCHELL Fiona (*A Sax, Pf, T Sax, Clt*): 70 Bury Street, Norwich, Norfolk NR2 2DN ☎ 01603 666458

MOFFAT Neil (*T Sax, A Sax, Clt*): 21 Valley Road, St Albans, Hertfordshire AL3 6NB ☎ 01727 859782

MORYS Melbourn (*T Sax, B Gtr*): 20 Fabins Close, Coggeshall, Colchester, Essex CO6 1QB ☎ 01376 561942

MOULTON Sally (*A Sax, T Sax, Clt, Flt, Pf*): 9 Nelson Close, Ashbocking, Ipswich, Suffolk IP6 9NL ☎ 01473 785289, 0410 554516 mob

MURRAY John (*A Sax, Clt, S Sax, T Sax, Flt*): 5 Saltdean Close, Luton, Beds LU2 8QN ☎ 01582 658472

NUNN Jonathan (*Sax, A Sax, T Sax, Br Sax, B*): House 22 Room 43, Castle Irwell, Off Cromwell Road, Salford M6 6DB ☎ 0161 279 5611

NYE Andrew (*A Sax, Clt*): 1 Ballards Row, College Road, Aston Clinton, Bucks HP22 5EY ☎ 01296 632 220

OLIVERE Robert (*Sax, Clt*): 55 Fir Lane, Lowestoft, Suffolk NR32 2RB

PHILLIPS Jim (*Br Sax, A Sax*): 8 Mildred Avenue, Boreham Wood, Herts WD6 1ET ☎ 020 8953 5633

POLLEY Deryck (*Saxes, Clt*): The Ibstock, Wymondham Road, Wreningham, Norfolk NR16 1AT ☎ 01508 488248

PRICE Gareth (*Sax, Kbds*): Dykewood, Chorleywood Road, Rickmansworth, Herts WD3 4ES ☎ 01923 771115, 0973 832585, 01923 896501

PULLIN David (*S Sax, Clt, A Sax, T Sax, Flt*): 2 Greenhills Road, Norwich NR3 3ET ☎ 01603 632308

PYNE Christopher (*Sax, Flt, Clt, Voc*): 14 Fishponds Road, Hitchin, Herts SG5 1NR ☎ 01462 431206

RADFORD Tony (*Saxes, Bjo*): Wellun Cottage, High Street, Coddenham, Ipswich IP6 9PN ☎ 01449 760629

RIPPER John (*Saxes, Clt, Flt*): 129 Southgate Road, Potters Bar, Herts EN6 5ES ☎ 01707 642787

ROBINSON Spike (*T Sax*): 120 Long Brandocks, Writtle, Essex CM1 3JR ☎ 01245 420475

RODGERS David (*T Sax, S Sax*): 1 Hedley Rise, Luton, Beds LU2 9UB ☎ 01582 452475, 0142 044967

ROGERS Frederick (*T Sax, A Sax, Clt*): 17 The Nordalls, Kessingland, Lowestoft NR33 7UE ☎ 01502 741082

ROWE Charles (*Sax, B Clt, E Flt, Clt, Flt*): 8 Hamels Mansion, Knights Hill, Buntingford, Herts SG9 9NA ☎ 01920 821774

ROWLAND Trevor (*Sax, Gtr*): 203 Dereham Road, Norwich, Norfolk NR2 3TE ☎ 01603 627049

SAPSED Leonard (*Saxes, Kbds, Dms*): Gazebo Barn, Grundisburgh Road, Woodbridge, Suffolk IP13 6HX ☎ 01394 383820

SCOTCHER Terry (*T Sax*): 166 Green End Road, Chesterton, Cambridge CB4 1RN ☎ 01223 423171

SCOTT Geoff (*T Sax, A Sax, Clt*): 48 Hornbeam Spring, Knebworth, Hertfordshire SG3 6BE ☎ 01438 226930

SEBASTIAN Frank (*Saxes, Clt, Flt*): 26 West Street, Harwich, Essex CO12 3DB ☎ 01255 507227

SHAKESPEARE Phil (*T Sax*): The Bards, Chorleywood Road, Rickmansworth, Herts WD3 4EU ☎ 01923 773536

SHARP Karen (*T Sax*): Flat 13, 21 Constitution Hill, Ipswich, Suffolk IP1 3RG ☎ 01473 221019, 0410 439167

SIMMS Andrew (*Sax, Clt*): Underhill, Beck Road, Saffron Walden, Essex CB11 4EH ☎ 01799 521897, 01904 416948

SIMONS Martin (*T Sax, S Sax, Hmca, Clt, Flt*): 7 Home Farm Way, Westoning, Bedfordshire MK45 5LL ☎ 01525 715898, 03746 55384 mob

SINGHJI Oriol (*S Sax, T Sax, Pf, Dms*): 124 Duxford Road, Whittlesford, Cambridge CB2 4NH ☎ 01223 832461, 0370 387 600

SLATER Rodney (*B Sax, Clt, T Sax*): Frog Cottage, 13 High Street, Arlesey, Beds SG15 6RA ☎ 01462 834753

STACE Julian (*T Sax, Clt*): 2 Heather Cottages, St. Annes Road, London Colney, Herts AL2 1NY ☎ 01727 826429, 0860 215 038 mob

STEEL Terry (*Saxes, Clt, Flt, B Clt, A Flt*): 45 Belgrave Road, Eastwood, Leigh-on-Sea, Essex SS9 5ET ☎ 01702 511547

THOMPSON Katie (*Sax, Clt*): 28 Lodge Hall, Harlow, Essex CM18 7SX ☎ 01279 428379

TOPPLE Roy (*T Sax, Clt, Tpt*): 59 Grimston Lane, Trimley St Martin, Felixstowe, Suffolk IP11 0SA ☎ 01394 275384

TURNER Ben (*A Sax, Clt, Flt, Br Sax*): 7 Dugdale Hill Lane, Potters Bar, Hertfordshire EN6 2DP ☎ 01707 656331

TURNER Jason (*T Sax, S Sax*): 25 London House, Canons Corner, Edgware, Middlesex HA8 8AX ☎ 020 8958 9830

WADE Dick (*A Sax, Br Sax, Clt*): 35 Cherry Hill, St Albans, Herts AL2 3AT ☎ 01727 851392

WALKER Nicholas (*Saxes, Flt, Pf, Com, Arr*): 5 Smallford Lane, Smallford, St Albans, Herts AL4 0SA ☎ 01727 822967

WALLER Norman (*A Sax, Clt, S Sax*): 5 Lawrence Road, Eaton Ford, St Neots, Cambs PE19 3RP ☎ 01480 219684

WARREN Deborah (*Sax, Clt, Vla*): 141 Cavendish Street, Ipswich, Suffolk IP3 8BG ☎ 01473 250956

WHITE Robert (*Sax, Clt, Flt, Pf, Ob*): 84 Cozens-Hardy Road, Sprowston, Norwich, Norfolk NR7 8QG ☎ 01603 419972, 0585 542424

WILLIAMS Fredric (*T Sax, Gtr, Voc*): 7 Tudor Close, Bromham, Bedford MK43 8LB ☎ 01234 824117

YOUNGMAN Simon (*A Sax*): 65 Armes Street, Norwich NR2 4JY ☎ 01603 617917

MIDLANDS

AAGRE Froy (*T Sax, S Sax*): Flat 4 43 York Road, Edgbaston, Birmingham B16 9HY ☎ 0121 454 4379

AJAO Steve (*Saxes, Gtr, Voc*): Flat 4, 7 Queenswood Road, Moseley, Birmingham B13 9AU ☎ 0121 449 4993

ALDRIDGE Chris (*Saxes, Flt, Clt, Synth*): 28 Wolverhampton Road, Pelsall, Walsall, West Midlands WS3 4AB ☎ 01922 692087, 0378 526108

ASHBY Jack (*T Sax*): 11 Long Lane, Brownshill Green, Coventry CV5 9EP ☎ 024 7633 3527

ASHLEY Ceri (*Sax, Clt*): 3 Kingsland Cottages, Longden, Coleham, Shrewsbury, Shropshire SY3 7DY ☎ 01743 243139

ASHTON Peter (*T Sax, B Sax, B Clt, Flt*): 26 Copthorne Road, Pennfields, Wolverhampton WV3 0AB ☎ 01902 341828

ASTILL Norman (*Sax, Clt*): 202 Scraptoft Lane, Leicester LE5 1HX ☎ 01572 723620

ATTRIDE Don (*Saxes, Clt, Flt, Pic*): 104 Leicester Road, Narborough, Leicester LE9 5BE ☎ 0116 2865924

B Stevie (*Sax, Per*): 11 Hinckley Road, Nuneaton CV11 6LG ☎ 024 7634 8152

BAILEY David (*T Sax*): 35 Chillaton Road, Whitmore Park, Coventry CV6 4ET ☎ 024 7666 1079

BEWICK John (*Saxes*): 'Highways', Wolverton Road, Norton Lyndsey, Nr. Warwick CV35 8JL ☎ 01926 498856

BILL Douglas (*A Sax, T Sax, Clt, Flt*): 63 Park Street, Madeley, Telford, Shropshire TF7 5JV ☎ 01952 418248

BILLINGHAM Tony (*A Sax, T Sax, Clt, Flt*): Lapal House, Lapal Lane South, Halesowen, Worcs B62 0ES ☎ 0121 550 1272, 0121 503 0326

BIRTLES Gary (*A Sax, Synth, Voc*): 13 Lytton Road, Leicester LE2 1WH ☎ 0116 270 1517

BISHOP John (*A Sax, Clt*): 11 Bransford Rise, Catherine De Barnes, Solihull, Warks B91 2TP ☎ 0121 705 5836

SAXOPHONES - MIDLANDS

BRAITHWAITE James (*A Sax, T Sax, Pf*): 72 Alcester Road, Studley, Warwickshire B80 7NP ☎ 01527 853818

BROAD Les (*Sax, Clt, Flt, Org, Acc*): 52 Ashdene Close, Sutton Coldfield, West Midlands B73 6HL ☎ 0121 354 8696

BROOKS Anna (*Saxes, Pf, Vln*): 21 Alport Croft, Bordesley, Birmingham, West Midlands B9 4PJ ☎ 0121 753 1726

BULLERS Adrian (*Saxes, Clt, Flt, B Clt, Pic*): 10, St.Mary's Close, Marston Mortaine, Bedfordshire MK43 0QZ ☎ 01234 765368

BURGESS Nancy (*Br Sax, A Sax, Cel, Flt, Wh*) ☎ 0121 456 2526, 01523 787287 pager

BURNEY Mike (*T Sax, A Sax, Clt, Flt*): 132 Oldrenshaw Road, Sheldon, Birmingham B26 3ND ☎ 0121 743 2032

BUTCHER Bill (*A Sax, Pf*): Whiteoaks, Oak Lane, Allesley, Coventry CV5 9BX ☎ 01676 22933

CAFFELLE Sandie (*B Sax, Flt, T Sax, A Sax*): The Boundary, Lugwarding, Hereford HR1 4AS ☎ 01432 850358, 0989 762206

CALDWELL Robert (*A Sax, T Sax, Clt*): 3 Vicarage Hill, Badby, Daventry NN11 3AP ☎ 01327 704694

CHAPMAN Mark (*A Sax, T Sax*): 14 Bellhouse Lane, Staveley, Chesterfield S43 3UA ☎ 01246 476749

CHARD David (*A Sax*): 72 Talbot Road, Northampton NN1 4JB ☎ 01604 21118

CLARK Peter (*Sax*): 1 Turnberry, Amington, Tamworth, Staffs B77 4NR ☎ 01827 61830

CLATWORTHY Gina (*A Sax, T Sax, Pf, Clt, Flt*): 3 Aboyne Close, Edgbaston, Birmingham B5 7PQ ☎ 0121 440 7627

CLIFFORD John (*T Sax, Clt*): 81 School Road, Hall Green, Birmingham B28 8JQ

CLYNES Kenneth (*Saxes, Clt*): 1 Collingbrook Avenue, Crewe CW2 6PN ☎ 01270 68553

COATES Bruce (*T Sax, S Sax*): The Octagon, 16 Beeches Farm Drive, Northfield, Birmingham B31 4SD ☎ 0121 477 5554

CODLING Andrew (*A Sax, T Sax*): 30A Birchwood Avenue, Dordon, Tamworth, Staffs B78 1QU ☎ 01827 892652

COOKE Alfred (*Saxes, Clt*): 4 North Road, Ruddington, Nottingham NG11 6AD ☎ 0115 9213154

CRABB Colin (*A Sax, T Sax, S Sax, Clt, B C*): 41 West Drive, Pershore Road, Edgbaston, Birmingham B5 7RR ☎ 0121 472 3845

DAMPIER Allan (*Saxes, Clt, B Clt, Flt, Pic*): 113 Higgins Lane, Quinton, Birmingham B32 1LH ☎ 0121 422 6429

DANNREUTHER Charlie (*T Sax, Flt*): 12 Manor Road, Lillington, Leamington Spa, Warks CV32 7RJ ☎ 024 7657 2511

DARLISON Ron (*A Sax, Clt*): The Cottage Astley Court, Breach Oak Lane, Corley, Coventry CV7 8AU ☎ 01676 540550

DAVALL Cynthia (*T Sax, A Sax*): 69 Moor Street, Earsldon, Coventry CV5 6EU ☎ 024 7667 0379

DAVIES Chris (*Br Sax, T Sax*): 72 Birchwood Crescent, Mosley, Birmingham, West Midlands B12 8BW ☎ 07971 840166

DAVIES Michael (*Sax, Pf, Gtr*): Address Unknown ☎ 0121 624 3901

DAVIS Alvin (*Sax, Tpt, Flt, Kbds, Voc*): Flat 2, 56 Crompton Road, Handsworth, Birmingham B20 3QG ☎ 0831 120059 mob

DEMPSEY James (*A Sax*): 34 St Georges, Castle Douglas, Kirkcutbrightshire D67 1LN ☎ 01556 502484

DEVEREUX John (*A Sax, Clt, Flt*): 42 Clarence Street, Kidderminster, Worcs DY10 1RS ☎ 01562 752520

DOLTON Aaron (*Sax, Gtr, Pf, Per*): c/o Arne Jensen, Fundervestervang 32, 8600, Silkeborg, Denmark ☎ +45 86851336

DOVEY Norman (*A Sax, T Sax, Clt, Flt, B Ldr*): 10 Pear Tree Road, Great Barr, Birmingham B43 6HY ☎ 0121 357 3622

DR PESKY (*Sax, Flt*): 14 Duncan Avenue, Huncote, Leicester LE9 6AP ☎ 0116 286 7871

DROUET Ben (*Sax, Pf, Clt, Voc, Rec*): Barn Lea, Holcot Road, Brixworth, Northants NN6 9BS ☎ 01604 880940

DRYER-BEERS Thomas (*Sax, Clt, Flt, Bno, Wh*): 187 Jackmans Place, Letchworth, Herts SG6 1RG ☎ 01462 673531

DUNMORE John (*A Sax, Clt, T Sax*): 8 Moulton Road, Holcot, Northampton NN6 9SH ☎ 01604 781241

EDWARDS Owen (*Saxes, Flt, Pic, Clt, Bsn*): 1 The Walk, Kilburn, Derby, Derbyshire DE5 0PP ☎ 01332 881627

EMENY Trevor (*A Sax, T Sax, Br Sax, Clt, Fl*): 41 Fir Tree Road, Fernhill Heath, Worcester WR3 8RE ☎ 01905 455815

ENTWISTLE Eric (*A Sax, Clt, B Ldr*): 195 Damson Lane, Solihull, West Midlands B92 9LD ☎ 0121 705 1612

ESPLEY Frank (*Saxes, Clt, Bjo*): 16 Fenton Road, Bucknall, Stoke-on-Trent ST2 9JE ☎ 01782 267101

ETHERINGTON Joanna (*T Sax, Clt, Flt, B Gtr, Voc*): 98 Saffron Road, South Wigston, Leicester LE18 4UN ☎ 0116 2776909, 0467 350171

EVANS Keith (*T Sax*): 11, Witley Avenue, Halesowen, West Midlands B63 4DN

FAWCETT Andrew (*A Sax, S Sax, T Sax*): The Poplars, Croft Lane, Little Shrewley, Warwick CV35 7HL ☎ 01926 484029

FEWKES John (*A Sax, Pf*): The Meadows, 44 Main Street, Houghton-on-The Hill, Leicester LE7 9GD ☎ 0116 243 3912

FORMAN John (*A Sax*): 56 Villiers Street, Nuneaton, Warks CV11 5PJ ☎ 024 7638 3659

GARWOOD Alan Robert (*T Sax*): 84 Olton Road, Shirley, Solihull B90 3NN ☎ 0121 744 9248

GIDMAN Brian (*Saxes, Clt, Flt*): 11 Langford Road, Newcastle Under Lyme, Staffs ST5 3JZ ☎ 01782 617998

GILLIGAN Craig (*A Sax, T Sax, S Sax*): 131 Falcon Road, Meir Park, Stoke-on-Trent ST3 7FU ☎ 01782 399163, 0421 528713

GLIDEWELL Richard (*A Sax, T Sax, Clt, Flt, B Sax*): 5 The Willows, Hollywood, Birmingham B47 5EE ☎ 0156482 6262

GOUGH Geoff (*A Sax, Clt, Flt, B Ldr*): 2 South Street, Sheepwash, Beaworthy, Devon EX21 5NA ☎ 0140 923 421

GRAHAM John (*Sax, Clt, Flt*): 2 High Heath Close, Bourneville, Birmingham B30 1HU ☎ 0121 459 1727

GRAY Bill (*A Sax, Clt, Flt*): 87 London Road, Coventry, West Midlands CV1 2JQ ☎ 024 7622 2859

GRAY Dave (*Saxes, Clt*): 615 Sutton Road, Aldridge, West Midlands WS9 0QH ☎ 01922 53656

GRAY Mike (*S Sax, T Sax, A Sax*): 28 Barneswallis Drive, Leegomery, Telford, Shropshire TF1 4XT ☎ 01952 255205

GREGORY Alfred (*A Sax, Clt, B Ldr, Db*): Abbeyfield, 39 Silverbirch Road, Birmingham B24 0AE ☎ 0121 350 4166

GUMBLEY Chris (*Saxes, Clt, Pf, Synth*): 53 Peel Terrace, Stafford ST16 3HE ☎ 01785 259144

HAMILTON Andy (*T Sax*): 37 Rodney Close, Ladywood, Birmingham B16 8DP ☎ 0121 454 6964

HAND Richard (*Sax*): 233 Seabridge Lane, Newcastle Under Lyme, Staffordshire ST5 3LS ☎ 01782 613635

HARRIS Jamie (*T Sax, S Sax, Pf*): 89 Highway Road, Evington, Leicester LE5 5RF ☎ 0116 2730960

HARVEY Barry (*Sax, Clt*): 7 Martin Ave, Leicester Forest East, Leicester LE3 3JH ☎ 0116 2392595

HATTON L (*T Sax, Br Sax, Flt, Clt*): 133 Dovedale Road, Wolverhampton, Staffs WV4 6RE ☎ 01902 884576

HAYDEN Graham (*A Sax, Br Sax, Vla*): 20 Dunvegan Close, Coombe Park, Coventry, West Midlands CV3 2PA ☎ 024 7645 5039

HISLAM Nicholas (*Sax, Dms, Per, A Sax, T Sax*): 97 Knighton Church Rd, Leicester LE2 3JN ☎ 0116 2704124

HOGG Norman (*A Sax, T Sax, Br Sax, Clt, Fl*): 65 Warren Road, Great Barr, Birmingham B44 8QH ☎ 0121 350 3751

HOLLINGSWORTH Catherine (*A Sax, Clt, T Sax*): 153 Mansfield Road, Selston, Notts NG16 6BD ☎ 01773 810374

HOLLIS Paul (*Saxes, Flt, Clt*): 56 Thorney Wood Road, Long Eaton, Nottingham NG10 2DY ☎ 0115 9725678

HOLLOWELL Allan (*T Sax*): 447 Birchfield Road East, Northampton NN3 2TE ☎ 01604 416014

HORTON Tildi (*T Sax, A Sax*): Flat 1 Pollybrooks Yard, 216 High Street, Lye, Stourbridge, West Midlands DY9 8JX ☎ 01384 898271

HUGHES Brian (*A Sax, T Sax*): 39 Ridgway, Barton Seagrave, Kettering NN15 5AQ ☎ 01536 513973

HULME Clifford (*Saxes, Clt*): 22 Marsh Avenue, Wolstanton, Newcastle Under Lyme, Staffs ST5 8BB ☎ 01782 627777

HUNT James (*S Sax, Br Sax, T Sax, Clt, Fl*): 3 Teme Street, Tenbury Wells, Worcestershire WR15 8BB ☎ 01584 810613, 01523 112412

HURST Jim (*T Sax*): 11 Church Hill Close, Solihull, Birmingham, West Midlands B91 3JB ☎ 0121 705 0954

INGLEHEART Claire (*Sax, Flt, Vln*): 164 Querneby Road, Mapperly, Nottingham NG3 5HS ☎ 0115 9523331

JACKSON Bob (*T Sax, Clt*): 40 Blenheim Road, Moseley, Birmingham B13 9TY ☎ 0121 449 5859

JAGER Alan (*T Sax, Clt, S Sax*): 60 Arden Vale Road, Knowle, Solihull, West Midlands B93 9NW ☎ 01564 777888

JOHNSON Leonard (*T Sax, A Sax*): Pen-Y-Bryn, Weston Road, White Gritt, Nr Minsterley, Shropshire SY5 0JJ ☎ 01588 650356

JOHNSTONE John (*T Sax, Clt*): 107 Dennis Avenue, Beeston, Notts NG9 2RD ☎ 0115 9224652

JONES Arthur (*Br Sax, A Sax, Clt*): 13 Welland Close, Dalebrook, Winshill, Burton-on-Trent DE15 0AG

JONES Bob (*A Sax, T Sax, Clt, Voc*): 33 Ashlawn Crescent, Solihull, West Midlands B91 1PR ☎ 0121 705 8970

KETTLEWELL E (*T Sax, Voc, Flt, Gtr*): 56 Leabrooks Road, Somercotes, Derbyshire DE55 1HB ☎ 01773 603276

KINCH Soweto (*Sax, Pf, Rapper*): 28 Grapton Road, Handworth, Birmingham B21 ☎ 0121 241 3661, 07930 311353

KOPINSKI Jan (*T Sax, S Sax, A Sax*): 22 Nelson Road, Daybrook, Nottingham NG5 6JE ☎ 0115 9265484

LEWIS Dutch (*Saxes, Wood W*): 14 Cherry Orchard, Pershore, Worcs WR10 1EL ☎ 01386 553557

LILLEYMAN Trevor (*A Sax, Clt*): 20 Denmead Avenue, Wigston, Leicestershire LE18 1DL

LLEWELLYN William (*A Sax, T Sax, Clt, Flt, Voc*): 15 Barnfields Lane, Kingsley, Stoke-on-Trent, Staffordshire ST10 2DG ☎ 01538 753807

LLOYD Joanna (*Sax, Clt, Kbds*): ☎ 01827 285780, 0976 719205 mob

LOWE William (*Sax, A Sax, S Sax, Clt*): 23 Hollyfield Road South, Sutton Coldfield, West Midlands B76 8NY ☎ 0121 378 4195 day, 0121 355 1376 eve

LYONS James (*Sax, Clt*): 44 Coronation Avenue, Alvaston, Derby DE2 0LR

MARSHALL John (*Saxes, Clt, Flt*): 139 Bramcote Lane, Wollaton, Nottingham NG8 2QH ☎ 0115 9284141

MARTIN Benjamin (*Sax, Flt*): 31 Gorsey Bank, Wirksworth, Derbyshire DE4 4AD ☎ 01629 826495

MATHER Don (*T Sax, A Sax, B Ldr*): 68 Dillotford Avenue, Styvechale, Coventry, West Midlands CV3 5DT ☎ 024 7641 2366

MATTHEWS Graham (*Saxes, Clt, B Clt, Flt*): 116 Millfield Road, Bromsgrove, Worcs B61 7BU ☎ 01527 872969

MCLEAN Andy (*Sax, Kbds, Clt*): 288A Newbury Lane, Oldbury, Warley, West Midlands B69 1JG ☎ 0121 552 8502

MEREDITH Martin (*A Sax, Kbds*): Flat 5, 153 Russell Road, Moseley, Birmingham B13 8RR ☎ 0121 449 9868

MEREDITH Simon (*A Sax, Br Sax, T Sax, Clt, Fl*): 20 Radway Close, Church Hill North, Redditch B98 8RZ ☎ 01527 65348 & fax

MONKS Gil (*Saxes, Flt, Clt, B Gtr*): 221 G Swallow Fields, Crateford Lane, Gailey, Stafford ST19 5PZ ☎ 01902 791559

NEALE Allison (*A Sax, S Sax, Flt*): 19 Rugby Road, Kilsby, Nr Rugby Warwickshire CV23 8XX ☎ 01788 822345

NICE Colin (*Sax, Clt, B Gtr*): 13 Henderson Close, Lichfield, Staffs WS14 9YN ☎ 01543 254448

NICHOLLS Andy (*T Sax*): The Coach House, 27 Knighton Road, Leicester LE2 3HL ☎ 0116 270 8294

NORTHALL George (*T Sax, S Sax, Clt*): 21 Hereford Close, Aldridge, Walsall, West Midlands WS9 8HX ☎ 01922 456910, 0121 623 2575, 0121 623 2772

O'LOUGHLIN William (*Saxes, Clt, St Pan, B Ldr, Fl*): 133 Boyne Road, Sheldon, Birmingham B26 2QG ☎ 0121 628 9931

OHAGEI Noel (*Sax, Per, Voc*): 138 Kildy Avenue, Ladywood, Birmingham B16 8EW ☎ 0121 684 9214

ORTON Kenneth (*Saxes, Flt, Clt, Ob*): 46 Coventry Road, Bedworth, Nuneaton, Warwickshire CV12 8NN ☎ 024 7631 5967

OVERTON Mark (*Saxes*): 64, Wandsworth Road, Kingstanding, Birmingham B44 9LV ☎ 0121 360 2035

PARKINSON Peter (*A Sax, T Sax, Flt, Wi Synth*): Brotton Hatch, Brockton, Nr Much Wenlock, Shropshire TF13 6SR ☎ 01746 785272

PARRY Diane (*Br Sax, A Sax, S Sax, T Sax,*): 25 Wentworth Park Avenue, Harborne, Birmingham B17 9QU ☎ 0121 427 4224, 0956 444 787

PATERSON Joseph (*T Sax, A Sax, Clt, B Clt, Flt*): 21 Melton Drive, Edgbaston, Birmingham B15 2NB ☎ 0121 440 1806

PHILLIPS Norman (*A Sax, T Sax, S Sax, Clt*): 293 Barnes Hill, Birmingham B29 5TX ☎ 0121 475 6177

PICKERING Michelle (*Sax, Clt, Pf, Flt*): 7 Orchard Close, Southwell, Nottingham NG25 0DY ☎ 01636 816671 & fax, 0966 246760 mob

POOLE Stan (*A Sax, T Sax, Clt, Flt*): 31 Malvern Drive, Aldridge WS9 8LL ☎ 01922 54820, 01922 52596

RAE Robert (*A Sax, T Sax, Br Sax, Clt, Ar*): 30 Valentine Road, Kings Heath, Birmingham B14 7AJ ☎ 0121 441 5077

RAYBOULD Stephen (*A Sax, B Sax*): 5 Carlyle Road, Edgbaston, Birmingham B16 9BH ☎ 0121 454 8429

RENFORD James (*A Sax, T Sax, S Sax, Flt*): Flat 21, King Edward Gardens, Hamstead Road, Handsworth, Birmingham B20 2BE ☎ 0121 554 8545

RILEY Herbert (*A Sax, Br Sax*): 57 Gilbert Avenue, Rugby, Warwicks CV22 7BZ ☎ 01788 812440

ROBB Damon (*Saxes, Clt*): 122 Richmond Street, Penkhull, Stoke-on-Trent ST4 7DU ☎ 01782 844132, 0468 894350

ROBB Pete (*T Sax, A Sax, Saxes, Flt*): 33 Tilling Drive, Stone, Staffordshire ST15 0AA ☎ 01785 813033

ROBINSON Mark (*A Sax, Org, Pf*): 28 Dexter Way, Birchmoor, Tamworth, Staffordshire B78 1AZ ☎ 01827 331971

RUSSELL-SMITH Colin (*A Sax, T Sax, Br Sax, Clt*): 29 Hillary Close, Ashby Fields, Daventry, Northamptonshire NN11 5SN ☎ 01327 703906

SANDERSON John (*T Sax, Flt, S Sax*): 6 Shaws Hill, Whatstandwell, Derbys DE4 5EP ☎ 01773 85606

SCRAGGY (*Sax, Clt*): 16 Westfield Road, Smethwick, Warley, West Midlands B67 6AW ☎ 0121 558 2516

SHELLEY John (*Sax, Clt*): 46 Woodland Avenue, Overstone, Northampton NN6 0AJ ☎ 01604 494856

SHILLINGFORD Andrew (*Saxes*): 41, Sutton Park Rise, Kidderminster, Worcs DY11 7NQ ☎ 01562 861219

SHINGLER Luke (*T Sax*): Flat 4, 124 Selwyn Road, Edgbaston, Birmingham B16 0HN

SHUTLER Stella (*A Sax, T Sax, Br Sax, Flt, B*): 14 Cranwell Court, Meadow Rise, Bulwell, Nottingham NG6 8WQ ☎ 0115 975 3105, 0402 977546 mob

SLATER Leon (*Saxes, Flt*): 3 Birch Grove, Meir Heath, Stoke-on-Trent ST3 7JN ☎ 01782 394325

SMITH Ian (*Saxes, Flt, Pic, Clt*): 194 Hay Green Lane, Bourneville, Birmingham B30 1RH ☎ 0121 458 7789, 0966 143835

SMITHYMAN Ernest (*Sax, Clt, Pf, Voc*): 313 Littleworth Road, Hednesford, Staffs WS12 5HY ☎ 01543 871874

SOLOMON Nick (*Sax, Flt, Gtr, Cel*): Harpfields, Burford, Tenbury Wells, Worcestershire WR15 8HP ☎ 01584 810099

SPENCER Alan (*A Sax, Br Sax, Clt, Flt*): 17 Third Avenue, Priory Road, Gedling, Notts NG4 3LL ☎ 0115 9611734

SPIERS Stuart (*Saxes, Clt*): Maple Lodge, 24 London Road, Shrewsbury, Shropshire SY2 6NU ☎ 0174 363 016

STAFFORD Richard (*Saxes, Flt, Clt*): 77 Emerson Road, Poets Corner, Coventry CV2 5HU ☎ 024 7644 1243

STOKES David (*A Sax, T Sax, B Sax, Clt, Flt*): 8 Shireland Close, Friary Road, Handsworth Wood, Birmingham B20 1AN ☎ 0121 554 8056

STYLES Gerry (*A Sax, Clt*): 164 Albany Road, Earlsdon, Coventry CV5 6NG ☎ 024 7671 5022

TAYLOR Andy (*A Sax, Clt, Flt*): 18 Wilton Road, Kettering, Northamptonshire NN15 5JX ☎ 01536 511188

TAYLOR Frederick (*A Sax*): Little Oaks, 1 Donkey Lane, Ashford Carbonell, Ludlow Salop SY8 4DA ☎ 01584 831522

TAYLOR Mat (*Sax, E Gtr, Flt, Gtr, Kbds*): Flat 2, Withymoor Court, Oaks Crescent, Wolverhampton WV3 9SA ☎ 01902 569492

TAYLOR Roy (*Saxes, Clt*): 4 Mayer Avenue, Newcastle, Staffs ST5 9EE ☎ 01782 852376

TAYTON Steve (*Sax, Flt, Clt, Pf, Com*): 45 Hill Top, Arley, Nr Coventry CV7 8FZ ☎ 01676 542510 & fax

TEMPEST Roger (*A Sax, Pf, Clt, Flt*): 12 Birch Lane, Oldbury, Birmingham B68 0NZ ☎ 0121 422 9695 & fax

THEODOULOU Nathan (*Sax, Gtr, Kbds, B Gtr, Flt*): 72 Hanson Avenue, Shipston-on-Stour, Warwickshire CV36 4HS ☎ 01608 663252, 0973 692898 mob

THOMPSON Harry (*Sax*): 21 Farriers Way, East Goscote, Leicester LE7 3ZE ☎ 0116260 6502

THORPE Mel (*Saxes, Flt, Clt*): 20 Barrow Road, Burton-on-The Wolds, Loughborough, Leicestershire LE12 5TB ☎ 01509 880946

TONKS Valerie (*Sax, Flt, Clt*): 4, Cheswick Way, Cheswick Green, Shirley, Solihull B90 4EX ☎ 015646 3911

TRAVERS Brian (*T Sax, Clt*): c/o Dep International, 92 Fazeley Street, Birmingham B5 5RD ☎ 0121 633 4742

TROTT Malcolm (*T Sax, Clt*): 16 Crossley Close, Barrow-on-Soar, Leicestershire LE12 8QL ☎ 01509 412984

TUCKLEY John (*T Sax, Flt*): 15 Lytham Road, Rugby CV22 7PA ☎ 01788 814146

VARGA Paul (*Saxes*): 18, Isleworth Drive, Mackworth Estate, Derby DE22 4JR ☎ 097 322 1222

VISSER Andy (*S Sax, T Sax, Clt*): 21 Woodbine Street, Leamington Spa, Warks CV32 5BG ☎ 01926 427222

WALKDEN Thomas (*T Sax*): 27 Manor Court Road, Nuneaton CV11 5HU ☎ 024 7638 4623

WARES Alec (*Saxes, Per*): 29 Springclough Drive, Worsley, Manchester M28 3HS ☎ 0161 799 1397

WARR Noel (*Sax*): 45 Coniston Avenue, Solihull, West Midlands B92 7NS ☎ 0121 742 3908

WESTBROOK Nicola (*Sax, Clt*): 11 Leys Drive, Westlands, Newcastle-Under-Lyme, Staffs ST5 3JG ☎ 01782 610574

WHITTAKER Ronald (*A Sax, Clt*): Flat 2, Birvell Court, Northcote Road, Rugby CV21 3EL

WILKINSON Derek (*T Sax, Clt*): 21 Finnemore Close, Styvechale Grange, Coventry, West Midlands CV3 6LR ☎ 024 7641 5481

WILLIAMS Clifford (*T Sax, Clt*): 2 Faulkner Close, Hill Street, Stourbridge, Worcs DY8 1AP ☎ 01384 372000

WILLIAMS John (*Saxes, Flt, A Flt, B Flt, Pic*): Leasowes Bank Farm, Ratlinghope, Shrewsbury SY5 0SW ☎ 01743 790769

WILLIAMS Richard (*Br Sax, A Sax, T Sax, Clt, S Sax, T*): 25 Melrose Avenue, Stourbridge, West Midlands DY8 2LE ☎ 01384 395575

WILSON John (*T Sax, Clt*): 60 Denison Street, Beeston, Nottingham NG9 1AX ☎ 0115 9222608

WITHERS Alan (*A Sax, T Sax, Br Sax, Clt, Fl*): 3 Elmstone Close, Hunt End, Redditch, Worcs B97 5UR ☎ 01527 543253

WITHINGTON David (*Sax*): Flat 2, 321 Lightwood Road, Longton, Stoke-on-Trent, Staffs ST3 4JT ☎ 01782 331892

WOOD Paul (*Sax, Kbds, Voc, Per*): 21 High Street, Great Glen, Leicester LE8 9FJ ☎ 0116 259 2064, 0378 890190, 0116 271 8128 fax

WORTHINGTON James (*A Sax, Br Sax*): 17 Wallis Road, Kettering NN15 6NX ☎ 01536 514415

WRIGHT Charles (*T Sax, Saxes, Clt, Flt*): 13 Broadfields Road, Wylde Green, Birmingham B23 5TL ☎ 0121 382 8191

SOUTH EAST

AL-MAHROUQ Amonn (*Sax*): Pantiles, 11 Eastern Parade, Southsea, Hants PO4 9RB ☎ 023 9275 0504, 0860 883313, 023 9229 7600

ALDERSON Geoffrey (*Saxes, Clt, Flt, Pic, Arr*): 23 Underwood Close, Poole, Dorset BH17 7EX ☎ 01202 602928

ALFRED Marcus (*T Sax*): The Oaks Annexe, Roundabout Lane, Winnersh, Berks RG11 5AE

ALLEN Norman (*T Sax, Clt*): Longview, Hartley Road, Cranbrook, Kent TN17 3QU ☎ 01580 712549

ANDREWS Victoria (*Sax, Clt, Flt*): 27 Coombe Avenue, Ensbury Park, Bournemouth BH10 5AA ☎ 01202 546751, 0374 699825

ARNOLD Bert (*Sax, Clt*): 91 Loder Road, Brighton, Sussex BN1 6PL ☎ Brighton 552094

ASKEM Tracey (*Saxes, B Clt, Flt*): 39 Meadow Way, Old Windsor, Berkshire SL4 2NX ☎ 01753 866518

ATCHINSON Mark (*A Sax, T Sax, Br Sax, Flt, Pi*): 275 Whaddon Way, Bletchley, Milton Keynes MK3 7LL ☎ 01908 372909, 0402 853 209 mob

ATTWOOD Jacqueline (*A Sax, Clt, Pf*): Westmoor, London Road, Dunton Green, Sevenoaks Kent TN13 2TJ ☎ 01732 462847

AUSTIN Michael (*Sax, Clt*): 84 Wickham Close, Newington, Sittingbourne, Kent ME9 7NT ☎ 0966 547248

BAILEY Bill (*Br Sax, A Sax, T Sax, S Sax*): 45 Hobb Lane, Hedge End, Southampton SO30 0GG ☎ 01489 690239

BAILEY Gerald (*A Sax, T Sax, Clt*): 136 Lynwood Drive, Wimborne, Dorset BH21 1UT ☎ 01202 889556

BAILEY John (*T Sax*): 53 Springfield Road, Brighton, E Sussex BN1 6DF ☎ 01273 508033

BARDEN Ronald (*A Sax, T Sax, B Sax*): 21 St Georges Road, Bexhill, East Sussex TN40 2BG ☎ 01424 212568

BOOTH Paul (*Sax, Pf, Flt, Wi Synth, Clt*): 39 Spencer Square, Ramsgate, Kent CT11 9LD ☎ 01843 589180, 0973 453203 mob

BRANCH Gary (*Saxes, Flt, Clt, B Clt, Pic*): Glebe Cottage, Rushmoor, Tilford, Farnham, Surrey GU10 2EN ☎ 01252 792014, 0831 462348 mob

BROADWAY Grahame (*T Sax, Clt, Flt, Vln, B Ldr*): 22 Avenue Road, Christchurch, Dorset BH23 2BY ☎ 01202 482030

BROWN Katherine (*Sax, Flt, Clt, Pf*): 1 Patchings, Horsham, West Sussex RH13 5HT ☎ 01403 262179, 07970 677803, 01403 250922

BRYANT Colin (*Saxes, Clt, Flt, B Ldr*): 24 Bushmead Drive, Ashley Heath, Ringwood, Hants BH24 2HU ☎ 01425 461 400

BUTTERWORTH Derek (*T Sax, S Sax, A Sax, Clt, Voc*): 16 Old Garden Close, Locks Heath, Southampton, Hants SO31 6RN ☎ 01489 582634, 07801 669586 mob, 01489 575965

CADDY Phillipa (*Saxes, Tbn, Tba*): 43 Withdean Court, London Road, Brighton BN1 6RP ☎ 01273 505732

CAINES Ronald (*A Sax, T Sax*): 36 Titian Road, Hove, East Sussex BN3 5QS ☎ 01273 387457

CAMPBELL Colin (*Br Sax, T Sax*): Berc Farm Cottage, 78 Dorchester Road, Lytchett Minster, Poole, Dorset BH16 6ER ☎ 01202 624389

CARTER Anthony (*T Sax, A Sax, Flt, Clt*): 7 Badgers Walk, Dibden Purlieu, Hants SO45 4BU ☎ 023 8084 5354

CARVISIGLIA Anna (*A Sax, Vln, Pf*): 27 Oakengates, Hanworth, Bracknell, Berks RG12 7QJ ☎ 01753 853289

CHAMBERS James (*A Sax, Clt*): Brentor Henfield Road, Cowfold, Horsham, West Sussex RH13 8DR ☎ 01403 864307

CHANDLER Ronald (*A Sax, A Sax, Br Sax, Clt, Fl*): 7 Whitecross Avenue, Shanklin, Isle Of Wight PO37 7EB ☎ 862761

CHIMES Tim (*Sax, Clt*): 8 Norfolk Road, Claygate, Esher, Surrey KT10 0RS ☎ 01372 470252

CLAPSON Michael (*Sax*): 4 South Close, Kidlington, Oxford OX5 1DF ☎ 01865 376850

CLARK Dugald (*Sax, Clt, Flt*): 16 Old Farm Gardens, Blanford, Dorset DT11 7UU ☎ 01258 454635

CONEY Patrick (*T Sax, Clt, Tbn, Flt, B Ldr*): Mount Joy, 8 Ford, Dartmouth, South Devon TQ6 9DT ☎ 018043 2786

COOPER Charly (*Sax, Flt, Gtr, Pf, Dms*): 26 Cavendish House, Kings Road, Brighton BN1 2JH ☎ 01273 203634

COOPER Derek (*A Sax, Clt, Flt, Org, Voc*): 1 Albert Road, New Milton, Hants BH25 6SP ☎ 01425 612595

CORCORAN John (*T Sax, A Sax, Clt, Flt*): 43 Thames Close, Ferndown, Dorset BH22 8XA ☎ 01202 871225

CORSBY David (*Saxes, Clt, Flt, Kbds*): 8 Lincoln Gardens, Birchington, Kent CT7 9SW ☎ 01843 41501

COSTELLO John (*T Sax, A Sax, Clt*): 18 Montague Road, Bournemouth BH5 2EP ☎ 01202 428722

COX David (*Sax, Clt, Flt*): 8 Green Close, Old Alresford, Hants SO24 9DJ ☎ 01962 735388

CRAWFORD Neill (*A Sax, S Sax, Flt, Clt*): 45 Dewlands Way, Verwood, Wimborne, Dorset BH31 6JN ☎ 01202 813646

CROOKS Dick (*A Sax, T Sax, Clt*): 29 Nichol Road, Chandlers Ford, Eastleigh, Hampshire SO53 5AY ☎ 023 8026 0395

CURRIE Simon (*Saxes, Flt, Clt*): Walnut Tree Cottages, 23 Donnington Square, Newbury, Berks RG14 1PJ ☎ 01635 38214, 01635 38908

CURTIS Michael (*Sax*): 17 Havelock Road, Tonbridge, Kent TN9 1JE ☎ 01732 357921, 07957 428018

DAVIES Noel (*Saxes, Clt*): Tamarak, 15 Landon Road, Herne Bay, Kent CT6 6HP ☎ Herne Bay 37555

DAVIES Stephen (*S Sax*): 39 Dale Crescent, Brighton BN1 8NT ☎ 01737 762646

DAVIS Ernest (*T Sax, Clt*): 135 Handsworth House, Quinton Close, Southsea, Hants PO5 4NE ☎ 023 9234 1598

DAVIS Granville (*A Sax, T Sax, Clt, Flt*): 83 The Copse, Oaktree Park, St Leonards, Ringwood, Dorset BH24 2RH

DAVIS Michael (*A Sax, Clt*): Prelude, 17 Nash Court Gardens, Margate, Kent CT9 4DG ☎ 0184 329 3669

DENNISON Richard (*Sax*): 145 The Grove, Christchurch, Dorset BH23 2EZ ☎ 01202 484442

DOWDING William (*T Sax*): Flat 10, Springbourne Court, 130 Windham Road, Bournemouth BH1 4RD

DUDZIK Bogdan (*Sax, Acc*): 49 The Grove, Sholing, Southampton SO19 9LT ☎ 023 8042 2015

DUNKLEY James (*A Sax, Clt, Vln*): 21 Beaulieu Road, Bournemouth, Dorset BH4 8HY ☎ 01202 764097

FARRENDEN Bernard (*Sax, Clt*): 8 Vecta Close, Friars Cliff, Christchurch, Dorset BH23 4EJ ☎ 01425 276471

FERGUSON Robert (*T Sax, Br Sax*): 43 Sandyhurst Close, Darbys Corner, Poole, Dorset B17 9JS ☎ 01202 601423

FISH Kate (*Sax, Clt, Flt*): 7 Lower Road, Meadvale, Redhill, Surrey RH1 6NN ☎ 01737 243801, 0973 746124

FORSYTH Alexander (*Saxes, Flt*): 14 Beacan Close, Badshot Lea, Farnham, Surrey GU10 4PA ☎ 01252 792221

FOWLER Robert (*T Sax, Clt, S Sax, A Sax*): 7 Pevensey Close, Bedgrove, Aylesbury, Bucks HP21 9UB ☎ 01923 445597

GAIR Martin (*T Sax*): 314 Park Road, Loughborough, Leicester LE11 2HL

GEE Paul (*A Sax, T Sax, S Sax, Gtr*): 23 Newbridge Court, Elmbridge Road, Cranleigh, Surrey GU6 8LP ☎ 01483 267581, 0802 817557 mob

GEE Roy (*T Sax*): 'Dunbuskin', 16 Hastings Road, Brighton BN2 3AF ☎ 01273 674661

GILBERT Jack (*Sax, Clt*): 34 Janes Lane, Burgess Hill, Sussex RH15 0QR ☎ 01444 244801

GLASSON Charlotte (*Br Sax, T Sax, A Sax, Vln, Vl*): 39 Freshfield Road, Brighton, East Sussex BN2 2BJ ☎ 01273 685669

GRIMSTER Alan (*B Sax, A Sax*): 22 Connaught Crescent, Brookwood, Woking, Surrey GU24 0AN ☎ 01483 476127

HALL Bob (*Sax, Pf*): 9 Philip Road, Blandford Forum, Dorset DT11 7NR ☎ 01258 456549

HARDING David (*Saxes, Clt, Flt, Org, Pic*): 4 Boreham Road, Bournemouth, Dorset BH6 5BW ☎ 01202 433616

HARMAN Martin (*Sax, Ob, Clt, Flt, Pf*): 1 Birkdale Court, Cardwell Crescent, Sunninghill, Berkshire SL5 9BT ☎ 01344 843345, 0468 878091

HARRIS Paul (*A Sax, T Sax*): Mulberry Lodge, 101 Kiln Ride, Finchampstead, Wokingham RG40 3PD ☎ 0118 9735131

HARRISON David (*A Sax, T Sax, Sax, Clt, Gtr*): 29A Cecilia Road, London E8 2ER ☎ 020 7254 1192

HASELIP John (*T Sax, Clt, Flt, A Sax*): 20 Herne Gardens, Rustington, Littlehampton, West Sussex BN16 3EF ☎ 01903 786978

HASLAM George (*T Sax, Br Sax, So Sax, Clt*): 3 Thesiger Road, Abingdon, Oxon OX14 2DX ☎ 01235 529012

HEATHORN Ron (*Saxes, Clt, Kbds, B Gtr*): 1 Barnstaple Road, Devon Park, Bedford MK40 3AJ ☎ 01234 215005, 07970 305854 mob

HINVES Neville (*Saxes*): Nanoon, Green Bottom, Colehill, Wimborne Dorset BH21 2LW ☎ 01202 885730

HOLLAND Peter (*Sax, A Sax, Clt*): Flat 1, 17 Trinty Road, Folkestone, Kent CT20 2RQ ☎ 01303 220056

HOPKINS Mike (*Ob, Clt*): 3 Bramley Road, Kinson, Bournemouth, Dorset BH10 5LU ☎ 01202 242213, 0831 724861

HOWE Ronald (*T Sax*): 7 Wentworth Aurum Close, Horley, Surrey RH6 9BE ☎ 01293 783452

HOY Stephen (*T Sax, Kbds, Gtr*): 28 Station Road, Woburn Sands, Bucks MK17 8RW ☎ 01908 281135

HUME Alastair (*Sax, Flt, Pf, Kbds*): 86 Seafield Road, Southbourne, Bournemouth, Dorset BH6 3JH ☎ 01202 425015

IRELAND Frank (*T Sax, Clt*): Lynmara, Ballinphellie, Ballinhassig, Co. Cork, Eire ☎ 0121 888 287

JONES Dick (*T Sax, Clt*): 9 Montrose Drive, Bournemouth, Dorset BH10 4AY ☎ 01202 527509

JONES Sandy (*T Sax, A Sax, Clt, Flt*): 40-42 Cliffe Road, Strood, Kent ME2 3DR ☎ 01634 710344

JUDGE Barry (*Sax, Clt, Flt*): 22 Hockeredge Gardens, Westgate, Kent CT8 8AN ☎ 01843 836395

KAIGHIN Jeff (*Saxes*): 10 Putnoe Heights, Bedford MK41 8EB ☎ 01234 353522, 0403 476063

KEENE Ronnie (*Sax, Pf, B Ldr*): 24 Clyde Road, Worthing, Sussex BN13 3LG ☎ 01903 266837

KNIGHT Duncan (*T Sax, A Sax, Br Sax, Clt, Fl*): 6 Arabian Gardens, Whiteley, Fareham, Hants PO15 7HE ☎ 01489 880607

LAY Pete (*Sax, Flt, Voc, B Gtr*): 43 Elton Road, Banbury, Oxon OX16 9UB ☎ 01295 250561

LEWIS Brynley (*Saxes, Flt, Clt, Com, Arr*): 75 Swanfield Drive, Chichester PO19 4TQ ☎ 01243 785203

LEWIS Geoffrey (*A Sax, T Sax, S Sax, Clt, Flt*): 20 Forest Road, Broadwater, Worthing, W Sussex BN14 9NB ☎ 01903 201817, 01903 201817

LITCHFIELD Mary (*A Sax, T Sax, Clt, Voc*): 4 Wythering Close, Lagoon Road, Pagham, Bognor Regis PO21 4XX ☎ 01243 263236

LOCOCK Duke (*Saxes, Clt, Cel*): 51 Palmerston Road, Lower Parkstone, Poole BH14 9HQ ☎ 01202 744831

LOWE Charles (*A Sax, Clt*): 5 Little Barrs Drive, New Milton, Hants BH25 5RW ☎ 01590 621605

LOWE Peter (*T Sax, Flt, A Flt, S Sax, Br*): Cleomone, Tenterden Road, Biddenden, Ashford, Kent TN27 8BL ☎ 01580 291024

LUCKHURST Joanna (*Sax, Ob, Clt*): 3 Firglen Drive, Yateley, Hants GU46 7TR ☎ 01252 870534

LYNALL Eleanor (*T Sax, S Sax, Clt*): 55 Pennywell Gardens, Ashley, New Milton, Hampshire BH25 5YB ☎ 01625 611923, 01425 655456, 01425 657740

MADER Bill (*Saxes, Clt, Flt*): 14 Bridle Crescent, Iford, Bournemouth, Dorset BH7 6SJ ☎ 01202 484472

MALCOMSON Inge (*A Sax, Br Sax, Voc*): 1 Cranbourne Road, Gosport, Hants PO12 1RJ ☎ 023 9258 5388, 0860 478624

MARSH Cecil (*Sax, Clt*): 18 Brackley, Queens Road, Weybridge, Surrey KT13 0BJ ☎ Weybridge 43510

MARSHALL Terry (*T Sax, Clt*): 129 High Street, Stony Stratford, Milton Keynes MK11 1AT ☎ 01908 565626

MARTIN Neil (*T Sax*): 45 Sandlands Road, Walton-on-The Hill, Tadworth, Surrey KT20 7XB ☎ 01737 814386

MASSEY Jack (*Saxes, Clt, Org, B Ldr*): West Winds, 20B Crossmead Avenue, New Milton, Hants BH25 6NF ☎ 01425 619545

MAURICE Brian (*A Sax, T Sax*): 19 Alma Road, Eton Wick, Berkshire SL4 6JZ ☎ 01753 861272

MCGIRR Priscilla (*A Sax, Voc*): Houseboat, YC74 "Port Werburgh", Vicarage Lane, Hoo, Rochester, Kent ME39 9TW ☎ 01634 254000

MELLY Alan (*Saxes, Clt, Flt, Pic, B Clt*): 9 Maundeville Road, Christchurch, Dorset BH23 2EN ☎ 01202 483577

MIDDLETON Julia (*S Sax, A Sax*): 22 Meadow View, Water Eaton Road, Oxford OX2 7QS ☎ 01865 316582

MILLS John (*Sax, Flt*): 40 Holly Hill, Bassett, Southampton SO16 7EW ☎ 023 8076 6560

MORPHEW Leonard (*T Sax, Flt*): 23 Beech Close, Faringdon, Oxon SN7 7EN ☎ 01367 20732

MORRIS Andrew (*A Sax, T Sax, So Sax, Clt, Fl*): 25 Nelson Road, Bognor Regis, West Sussex PO21 2RY ☎ 01243 860332

NEW Clive (*T Sax, Clt, B Gtr*): 21 Woodfield Avenue, Farlington, Portsmouth, Hants PO6 1AN ☎ 023 9237 6659

NEWTON Tony (*Sax, Clt*): 253 Fairmile Road, Christchurch, Dorset BH23 2LH ☎ 01202 484702

NIBLOCK Simon Mark (*Sax, Flt, Clt, Synth, Kbds*): 34 Donaldson Road, Cosham, Portsmouth, Hants PO6 2SZ ☎ 023 9261 8498, 023 9261 8498

NICHOLAS Julian (*T Sax, S Sax*): 8A Powis Square, Brighton, East Sussex BN1 3HH ☎ 01273 724515, 01273 328810

O'DONNELL James (*A Sax, S Sax*): Handon Cottage, Markwick Lane, Hascombe, Nr Godalming, Surrey GU8 4BD ☎ 01483 208295

O'NEILL Michael (*A Sax, T Sax, Clt*): 19 The Willows, Newington, Sittingbourne, Kent ME9 7LS ☎ 01795 842918

ODY John (*A Sax, Vln*): Northbourne, 2 Magnolia Avenue, Margate, Kent CT9 3DS ☎ Thanet 20365

PASHLEY Don (*Sax, Clt, Flt*): Flat 3, 18 Grantham Road, Brighton, Sussex BN1 6EE ☎ 01273 501902

PATON Philip (*Saxes, Clt, Flt, Kbds, Voc*): 9 Oak Tree Court, Uckfield, East Sussex TN22 1TT ☎ 01825 761298

PEPLOE Brian (*A Sax, T Sax, Br Sax*): 7 Denton Close, Kempton, Bedford MK42 8RY ☎ 01234 856973

PLATEROTI Achille (*Saxes, Clt*): 456 Ashley Road, Parkstone, Poole, Dorset BH14 0AD ☎ 01202 743654

POLLARD John (*T Sax, A Sax, Clt*): 10 Gilbert Close, Hempstead, Gillingham, Kent ME7 3QQ ☎ 01634 232638

PONTIN David (*Sax, Dms, Per, Kbds*): Rosehill, Bedbury Lane, Freshwater Bay, Isle Of Wight PO40 9PD ☎ 01983 752990

POTTER David (*Sax, Clt, Flt*): 4 Ribble Close, Broadstone, Dorset BH18 8JT ☎ 01202 697849

PRIMMETT Denis (*T Sax, Flt*): Flat 1, 31 St Michaels Place, Brighton BN1 3FU ☎ 01273 323307

QUINCY David (*T Sax, S Sax*): Flat 2, Napier Court, 1 Croft Road, Christchurch, Dorset BH23 3QQ ☎ 01202 474126

RANCE Denis (*Sax, Clt*): 25 Painters Pightle, Hook, Basingstoke, Hampshire RG27 9SS ☎ 01256 761613

READING John (*Sax, Clt*): 72 Beach Green, Shoreham, Sussex BN43 5YA ☎ Shoreham 2356

REED Oliver (*Sax, Pf, Synth*): 25 Woodland Vale Rd, St. Leonards-on-Sea, East Sussex TN37 6JJ ☎ 01424 460485

REEVES Jeff (*Sax*): Pitmore Cottage, Boyatt Lane, Eastleigh, Hants SO5 4LJ ☎ 023 8025 2752

REIDY John (*T Sax*): 86 Percy Avenue, Kingsgate, Broadstairs, Kent CT10 3LE ☎ 01843 64178

RIDOUT Beverley (*Saxes, Clt, Flt*): 151 Shelbourne Road, Bournemouth, Dorset BH8 8RD ☎ 01202 529669

RILEY Paul (*Sax*): 31 Cecil Avenue, Queens Park, Bournemouth, Dorset BH8 9EZ ☎ 01202 533466

ROBBINS Geoffrey (*Sax, Clt*): 9 Audley Road, Folkestone, Kent CT20 3QA ☎ 01303 254406

ROBINSON Eddie (*Saxes, Flt, Clt, Kbds, B Gtr*): 20 Aston Mead, St Catherines Hill, Christchurch, Dorset BH23 2SR ☎ 01202 471914

RYDER Allan (*Saxes, Clt, B Clt, Flt, Arr*): 24 Stuart Road, Gillingham, Kent ME7 4AB ☎ 01634 851646

SALT Jack (*A Sax, Clt, Br Sax, Vln*): 32 Lansdowne Avenue, Portchester, Portsmouth, Hants PO16 9NN ☎ 023 9271 1473

SANDOE Cliff (*Saxes, Clt, Flt, Cop*): 9 Whitecliff Road, Poole, Dorset BH14 8DU ☎ 01202 730465

SAYER Raymond (*T Sax, Clt, Flt*): 523 Canterbury Street, Gillingham, Kent ME7 5LG ☎ 01634 854189

SEAGROATT Jon (*Sax, Vib, Kbds, Pf*): 5 New Place, Cropredy, Oxfordshire OX17 1NY ☎ 01295 750437

SHEPHERD David (*Sax, Clt, Flt*): 14 Nursery Close, Hook, Basingstoke RG27 9QX

SIMKINS Geoffrey (*A Sax, Br Sax*): 35 Park Crescent Road, Brighton, Sussex BN2 3HT ☎ 01273 671097

SMETHURST-EVANS Hilary (*A Sax, S Sax, Clt, Flt*): 24 Shepherds Mount, Compton, Newbury, Berkshire RG20 6QZ ☎ 01635 578209, 0973 371286

SPANGLECOCK Zack (*Sax, Flt, Gtr*): Ecclesden Mill, High Street, Angmering, West Sussex BN16 4AW ☎ 01273 454641, 01903 782061, 01273 462440

SPEARE Paul (*Saxes*): 1 Butts Hill, Old London Road, Wrotham, Kent TN15 7DJ ☎ 01732 885611

STACEY Paul (*T Sax, Dms, Brass*): 59 Stansfield Road, Bournemouth, Dorset BH9 2NN ☎ 01202 242897, 0831 401061

STACEY Peter (*T Sax*): 10 Elmstead Place, Folkestone, Kent CT20 1QU ☎ 01303 253760

STEVENS Michael (*Sax, Kbds, Md*): 32 Friary Gardens, Newport Pagnell, Bucks MK16 0JZ ☎ 01908 618859, 0374 413700

STILES Paul (*T Sax, Flt, Flt*): 10 Phillimore Road, Swaythling, Southampton SO2 2NR ☎ 023 8055 6529

SWEET Peter (*Sax*): 29 Cattistock Road, Strouden Park, Bournemouth, Dorset BH8 9PQ ☎ 01202 534475

TAYLOR John (*Sax, Flt, Vln, Vla, Pf*): 5B Victoria Street, Gosport, Hants PO12 4TX ☎ 023 9242 0881, 07887 520559

TAYLOR Syd (*Saxes, Clt*): 29 Eastbourne Avenue, Southampton SO15 5HU ☎ 023 8077 0459

THOMAS Keith (*T Sax, S Sax, Flt, Clt*): Appledown, Hambrook Hill South, Hambrook, Chichester, West Sussex PO18 8UJ ☎ 01243 572763

THOMPSON Martyn (*Sax, Gtr, B Gtr, Hmca*): 41 Hag Hill Lane, Taplow, Berks SL6 0JW ☎ 01628 543741

TISBURY Stan (*T Sax, S Sax, A Sax, Vib, Arr*): 52 Bedford Road, Houghton Conquest, Bedford MK45 3NE ☎ 01234 741381

TODD William (*Saxes, Clt*): 80 Pinewood Avenue, Crowthorne, Berkshire RG45 6RP ☎ 01344 77212424

TOUHEY Andre (*Saxes, A Sax, S Sax, T Sax*): 33 Watts Lane, Old Town, Eastbourne, East Sussex BN21 2LN ☎ 01323 739961

VINE Lionel (*A Sax, T Sax, Clt*): 76 Pilsdon Drive, Canford Heath, Poole, Dorset BH17 9HS ☎ 01202 697769

WALDMANN Adam (*A Sax, S Sax, Kbds*): 4 Apsley Road, Oxford OX2 7QY ☎ 01865 553822, 01865 311836

WALLACE Jimmy (*Saxes, Clt*): 38 Alder Road, Parkstone, Poole, Dorset BH12 2AE ☎ 01202 736460

WARD Tamsin (*Saxes, Voc, Kbds*): 63 Winchester Road, North End, Portsmouth, Hants PO2 7PS ☎ 023 9267 7734

WATMOUGH John (*Saxes, Clt*): 39 Romney Road, Bournemouth, Dorset BH10 6JR ☎ 01202 527456

WATT Robin (*T Sax, A Sax*): 74 Hanover Street, Brighton, East Sussex BN2 2SS ☎ 01273 685160

WATTS Trevor (*A Sax, S Sax, Com*): 20 Collier Road, Hastings, East Sussex TN34 3JR ☎ 01424 443424

WELCH Colin (*A Sax, Clt*): Clap Hill House, Clap Hill, Aldington, Nr Ashford, Kent TN25 7DG ☎ 01233 720074

WHEALING Ted (*A Sax, Clt, Vln*): 4 Christopher Way, Emsworth, Hants PO10 7QZ ☎ 01243 374446

WHITE Brian (*Sax, Flt, Clt*): 4 Clifton Road, Bognor Regis, Sussex PO21 2HH ☎ 01243 821281

WILCOCK Stephen (*A Sax, Clt*): 14 Cloisterham Road, Rochester, Kent ME1 2BW ☎ 01634 402524

WILLIAMS Elaine (*Sax, Clt*): 40 Romney Road, Redhill, Bournemouth, Dorset BH10 6JR ☎ 01202 526789

WILLIAMS Paul (*Sax, Flt, Clt*): 14 Epsom Close, West Malling, Kent ME19 6NX ☎ 01732 845166

WILSON Tim (*Sax, Flt*): High Banks, Green Lane, North Leigh, Witney Oxon OX8 6TN ☎ 01993 883111

WYVER Nicolas (*Sax, Clt*): 24 Park Road, Sittingbourne, Kent ME10 1DR ☎ 01795 470598

SOUTH WEST

ANDRE David (*S Sax, A Sax, T Sax, Flt*): St Quai, Rue De Causie, St Clements, Jersey JE2 6SQ ☎ 01534 855166

ANSELM John (*A Sax*): 17 Cole Mead, Bruton, Somerset BA10 0DL ☎ 01749 812674

BABER Kenneth (*A Sax, T Sax, Clt, Flt*): Appledene, Iford Close, Saltford, Bristol BS18 3BD ☎ 01225 872519

BAGLEY Stephen (*Br Sax, A Sax, T Sax*): 12 Bedford Mews, Deptford Place, North Hill, Plymouth, Devon PL4 8JL ☎ 01752 229165

BAKER Eric (*A Sax, B Sax*): 26 Manor Road, Bishopsworth, Bristol BS13 8EP ☎ 0117 9782572

BEAVIS Ray (*Saxes, Flt*): 76 Wrefords Lane, Exeter EX4 5BS ☎ 01392 214918

BELLAMORE Joanne (*A Sax, Clt, Rec, Flt*): 5 West Park Road, Newport, Gwent NP9 3EH ☎ 01633 220718

BETTLE Peter (*Br Sax, Clt*): Windwood, The Cross, Okeford Fitzpaine, Dorset DT11 0EG

BOND Roger (*T Sax, Clt, Db*): 23 Bere Lane, Glastonbury, Somerset BA6 8BD ☎ 01458 835026

BOWLES Geoffrey (*Sax, Clt, Flt*): 22 Hollis Gardens, Cheltenham, Glos GL51 6JQ ☎ 01242 236482

BROWN Dennis (*Saxes, Clt, Db, B Gtr*): Rockall, Dicq Road, St Saviour, Jersey, Channel Islands JE2 7PD ☎ 01534 34062

BRUCE Leslie (*A Sax, S Sax, Br Sax, Clt*): 14 Brookfield, Highworth, Swindon, Wiltshire SN6 7HY ☎ 01793 766129

BUDD Graeme (*Sax, Kbds, B Gtr, Gtr, Tpt*): 18 Long Cross, Shaftesbury, Dorset SP7 8QP ☎ 01747 853733

BURKE Vicki (*T Sax, A Sax, S Sax*): 47 Allington Road, Southville, Bristol BS3 1PT ☎ 0117 963 9380

CARPENTER Victor (*Sax, Clt*): 2 Lawrence Close, Shudington, Cheltenham, Glos GL51 5SZ

CARPENTIERI Giovanni (*Sax, Cl Gtr, Flt, Com*): 1 Delvin Road, Westbury-on-Trym, Bristol BS10 5EJ ☎ 0117 9409572

CARTER Paul (*Sax, Clt, Flt*): 4 Vellanhoggan Mews, Gulval, Penzance, Cornwall TR18 3DN ☎ 01736 333270

CHANNON Sydney (*T Sax, Clt, Flt*): 7 Heanton Terrace, Millbrook, Torpoint, Cornwall PL10 1EF ☎ 01752 822203

CHESSER John (*Sax, Clt, Kbds, Acc*): Glenkiln, North Newton, Bridgwater TA7 0BD ☎ 01278 662639

CLARKE Eric (*A Sax, Flt, Clt, S Sax*): 107 Beechwood Road, Port Talbot, West Glamorgan SA13 2AF ☎ 01639 883218

CLARKE Frank (*Sax, Clt*): The Baker Arms, Beechcroft Road, Nr Swindon, Wilts SN2 6RE

CLARKE Jack (*Saxes, Org, B Gtr*): Address Unknown

CLEVELAND Trevor (*Saxes, Clt*): La Girouette, Rouge Rue, St Peter Port, Guernsey C.I. GY1 1ZE ☎ 01481 727637

COLLIER Cliff (*Sax, Clt, Vln*): 38 Priory Drive, Plympton, Plymouth, Devon PL7 1PU ☎ 01752 333062

CRAIG Thomas (*A Sax, T Sax, Clt*): Manor Eifed Farm, Llandygwyd, Llechryd, Cardigan Dyfed SA43 2QN ☎ 0123987480

CRAIG William (*Sax, Clt*): 14 St Hilary Terrace, St Judes, Plymouth, Devon PL4 8SA ☎ 01752 20695

CRONIN James (*Saxes*): 154 Arabella Street, Roath Park, Cardiff CF2 4SY ☎ 029 2048 5271

CROWE Mark (*Saxes, Clt, Flt, Ob, Kbds*): 10 Trentham Close, Paignton, Devon TQ3 3GF ☎ 01803 525584, 0385 752609 mob

DAVIES Donald (*A Sax, Clt*): 19 Dalton Road, Port Talbot, Glam SA12 6SF

DAVIES Kathleen (*Sax, Clt, Flt*): 32 Thornhill Way, Mannamead, Pylmouth PL3 5NP ☎ 01752 668042

DAVIES Terry (*A Sax, T Sax, Clt, B Ldr*): 18 Three Oaks Close, Bedwas Park, Bedwas, Newport, Gwent NP1 8HF ☎ 029 2086 7420

DE ST CROIX Chris (*A Sax*): 24 Ville Des Chenes, St. John, Jersey JE3 4BG ☎ 01534 861847

DOBBINS David (*Saxes, Tbn*): 31 Loughor Road, Kingsbridge, Gorseinon, Swansea W Glam SA4 2AY ☎ 01792 893857

DODSON Kenneth (*Saxes, Clt, Voc, Org*): 22 Cornwall Road, Salisbury, Wilts SP1 3NL ☎ 01722 27030

DORFMAN Dave (*T Sax, Flt, Clt*): 56 Greville Road, Southville, Bristol BS3 1LE ☎ 0117 9636779

DRISCOLL Ray (*A Sax, Clt, S Sax*): 97 Cemetery Road, Porth, Mid Glamorgan CF39 0BH ☎ Porth 683323

DU FEU Avril (*A Sax, T Sax*): 1 Apple Tree Court, Plat Douet Road, St Saviour, Jersey JE2 7PT ☎ 01534 639459

DUNLOP Thomas (*Saxes*): 4 Highfield Crescent, Kings Ash, Paignton, Devon TQ3 3TP ☎ 01803 556032

EGGLESTON John (*T Sax, S Sax*): 34 Forester Avenue, Bathwick, Bath BA2 6QD ☎ 01225 448852

ELLAM David (*B Sax, T Sax, A Sax, Flt, Clt*): The Crows Nest, Greve De Lecq, St Ouen, Jersey, Channel Islands JE3 2DN ☎ 01534 83802

FEAR Jack (*T Sax, Clt, Flt*): Flat B, Crathorne House, 19 Hermosa Road, Teignmouth, Devon TQ14 9JZ ☎ Teignmouth 7735

FIGES Kevin (*A Sax, Flt*): 64 Robertson Road, Eastville, Bristol BS5 6JT ☎ 0117 9855346

FOX Derek (*A Sax, T Sax, Clt, Flt, B Clt*): 10 Camrose Drive, Waunarlwydd, Swansea, West Glam SA5 4QE ☎ 01792 872186

FRANCOME Henry (*T Sax, Clt*): 190 Cheney Manor Road, Swindon, Wilts SN2 2NZ ☎ 01793 534986

FULCHER Harry (*Sax, Clt, Pf*): Lulworth, Grenville Road, Salcombe, S Devon TQ8 8BJ ☎ 0154 884 2869

GAMBLE Patsy (*Sax*): Hendy, Butterrow Lane, Stroud, Glos GL5 LX ☎ 01453 753501

GLANFIELD John (*A Sax, Tpt, Clt*): 70 Velwell Road, Exeter, Devon EX4 4LD ☎ 01392 73930

GOODLIFFE Ivor (*Saxes, Clt, B Clt, Flt, A Flt*): 17 Burrows Park, Braunton, N Devon EX33 1EU ☎ 01271 812622

GOODSELL Denys (*Saxes, Clt, Vln*): 25 Channel View Road, Easton, Portland, Dorset DT5 2AY ☎ 01305 822144

GORBUTT Tom (*Sax, Gtr*): Moor Lane House, North Street, Langport, Somerset TA10 9RH ☎ 01458 250194

GREEN Michael (*Sax, S Sax, A Sax, T Sax, Flt*): 1 Mount Pleasant, Old Road, Harbertonford, Totnes TQ9 5SX

GREGORY William (*Sax, Br Sax, Com*): 24 Morford Street, Bath BA1 2RT ☎ 01225 469235

GRIFFIN Donald (*T Sax*): 83 Maple Road, Horfield, Bristol BS7 8RF ☎ 0117 947215

GRIFFITHS Harold (*S Sax, A Sax, T Sax, Clt, B C*): 119 Oldbury Orchard, Churchdown, Glos GL3 2NX ☎ 01452 713195

GUEST Paul (*Sax, Pf*): Badgers Sett, Lower Turners Barn Lane, Yeovil, Somerset BA20 2JH ☎ 01935 20752

HAIGH Gordon (*Sax*): 4 The Orchard, Westfield Park South, Newbridge, Bath BA1 3HT ☎ Bath 463255

HAMER Dick (*Sax, Flt, Clt*): 124 Manor Way, Whitchurch, Cardiff CF4 1RN ☎ 029 2052 2702

HARRIS Roy (*Sax, Clt*): Ferncot, Oldmixon Road, Oldmixon, Weston Super Mare BS24 9PD

HERBERT Paul (*T Sax, A Sax, Br Sax*): 9 Portmore Close, Sparcells, Swindon, Wiltshire SN5 9FB ☎ 01793 877950, 0370 483495

HILLIER Ernie (*A Sax, Clt, T Sax*): 13 Lickhill Road, Calne, Wilts SN11 9DE ☎ Calne 814528

HITCHINGS Michael (*A Sax, Clt, Tbn*): 6 Hartington Park, Bristol 6 BS6 7ES ☎ 0117 920941

HORNSBY Paul (*Saxes, Flt, Clt*): 18 Beauford Road, Newport, Gwent NP9 7ND ☎ 01633 212373

HUGGETT Brian (*Saxes, Clt, Flt*): 2 Little Headley Close, Bristol BS13 7PJ ☎ 0117 9646421

HUGGETT Jeremy (*T Sax, S Sax, Br Sax, Clt, Fl*): 10 Oak Crescent, Willand Cullompton, Devon EX15 2SS ☎ 01884 35563, 0411 865009

HUGHES John (*Saxes, Vln*): Address Unknown ☎ 01792 201524

HUGO Adam (*A Sax, S Sax, Clt, Pf*): 3 Sound View, St Anns Chapel, Gunnislake, Cornwall PL18 9JD ☎ 01822 833927

HUTCHINGS Carreen (*Saxes, Clt*): 4 Claremont Lane, Exmouth EX8 2LE

JEFFCUTT Francis (*T Sax, Clt*): 12 Merrivale Grove, Swindon, Wiltshire SN3 1EH ☎ 01793 694291

JELITKO Patrick (*Sax, Clt, Flt*): 24 Hughville Street, Camborne, Cornwall TR14 8TR ☎ 01209 716584

JOHN Gwilym (*Sax, Clt, Hmca*): Isgaer, Tafarngrisiau, Y Felin Heli, Gwynedd LL56 4NZ

JONES John (*A Sax, Br Sax, Clt, Flt*): Harmonie, 4 Rowan Court, Landare, Nr Aberdare, Mid Glam CF44 8HB ☎ 01685 870705

KNOX Frederick (*Saxes, Clt*): 6 Marine Parade, Paignton, Devon TQ3 2NU ☎ 01803 523347

LAMBETH Zoe (*Br Sax, A Sax, Clt*): 12 Orchard Terrace, Buckfastleigh, Devon TQ11 0AH ☎ 01364 642493

LAWRENCE John (*Saxes, Org*): 80 Laura Grove, Paignton TQ3 2LN ☎ 01803 550601

LEWIS Iorie (*A Sax, Flt*): 19 New Road, Grovesend, Swansea SA4 4WE ☎ 01792 896048

LEWIS Jonathan (*T Sax, S Sax*): 11 Madingley, Bracknell, Berks RG12 7TF ☎ 01344 427801

MANBY Glen (*A Sax*): 104 Marlborough Road, Roath, Cardiff CF2 5BY ☎ 029 2048 7624

MAY Charlotte (*A Sax*): 1 Middlefield Close, Latchbrook, Saltash, Cornwall PL10 4UY ☎ 01752 840539

SAXOPHONES - SOUTH WEST

MCBRIDE Sean (*A Sax, T Sax, Flt*): 9 Tidenham Way, Patchway, Bristol BS12 5LA ☎ 0117 9690565

MCMURCHIE Jacob (*T Sax, A Sax, S Sax, Pf*): c/o Mrs S Mcmurchie, 1 Byrd Farm Cottages, Byrd Farm Lane, Saffron Walden, Essex CB10 1XN ☎ 0468 634825 mob, 0117 973 7653

MCWILLIAM Fiona (*Sax, Pf, Vln, B Gtr*): Treban, St Ive Road, Pensilua, Liskeard, Cornwall PL14 5RB ☎ 01579 362513

MENTER Ian (*A Sax*): 6 Christchurch Lane, Downend, Bristol BS16 5TQ

MEREDITH Allan (*A Sax, T Sax, S Sax*): Whiteways, 14 Inner Loop Road, Beachley, Cheapstow Gwent NP6 7HF ☎ 01291 622556

MONAN Peter (*A Sax*): 56 Broad Street, Swindon, Wiltshire SN1 2DU ☎ 01793 528514, 01793 528514

MONK Jimmy (*Saxes, Vln, Acc, Pf, Man*): 17 Stafford Close, St Columb Minor, Newquay, Cornwall TR7 3HT ☎ 01637 873648

MOORE Ollie (*T Sax, B Sax, S Sax, Flt, Mld*): 19 Pembroke Road, Clifton, Bristol BS8 3BA ☎ 0117 973 1416

MORRIS Ronald (*Sax*): Dolphin House, Westbury, Sherborne, Dorset DT9 3EJ

MORTON James (*Sax*): Gables, Round Oak Road, Cheddar, Somerset BS27 3BN ☎ 01934 743927

MURPHY Geoffrey (*T Sax, A Sax*): 60, Mynachdy Road, Gabalfa, Cardiff, Glam CF4 3EA ☎ 029 2052 2945

PARFITT Rex (*Sax, T Sax, B Ldr, B Gtr*): Kinvarra, Highbury Street, Coleford, Bath BA3 5NS ☎ 01373 812454

PARR Kenneth (*Sax, Clt, Flt*): 10 Burnley Close, Bradley Valley, Newton Abbot, South Devon TQ12 1YB ☎ 01626 60931

PERRY David (*T Sax, Clt*): 5 Greenmore Road, Upper Knowle, Bristol BS4 2LA

PETERS Steve (*T Sax, A Sax, Flt, Pic, S Sax*): Highfields, Three Burrows, Blackwater, Truro TR4 8HT

PLACE Adrian (*Sax*): 30 Eldon Terrace, Windmill Hill, Bristol BS3 4NZ ☎ 0117 907 6410

PLANT Steve (*Sax, Gtr, Kbds*): Flat 4, 68 Esplanade, Burnham-on-Sea, Somerset TA8 2AH ☎ 01278 795604, 01278 795604

PURCELL Don (*Saxes, Clt, Voc*): 114 Walton Street, Heywood, Gtr Manchester OL10 2BD

RAY Clifford (*Saxes*): 209 Kensington Cresc., Swansea, Glam. ☎ 01792 462108

ROBERT Peter (*Saxes, Flt, Clt, Vln*): 58 Barley Close, Warminster, Wilts BA12 9LX ☎ 01985 217379

ROGERS Derek (*Saxes, Clt, Acc, Acc*): 4 Clarendon Road, St Helier, Jersey, Channel Islands JE2 3YS ☎ 01534 21228

ROSE Tim (*Saxes, Clt, Voc*): 68, Field Barn Drive, Southill, Weymouth, Dorset DT4 0EE ☎ 01305 774678

SALT David (*A Sax, Clt*): Calle Can Cosi 1, Capdella, Calvia, Mallorca, Balearics, Spain ☎ +34 71 10 33 21, +34 71 10 33 47

SAMPSON Mary (*T Sax, A Sax, Clt, Flt, Harp*): Rockside, 28 Gaston Avenue, Keynsham, Bristol BS31 1LR ☎ 0117 986 9447

SERCOMBE Rex (*Sax, T Sax, Voc*): Orleigh, 58 Upper Morin Road, Paignton TQ3 2HY ☎ 01803 550285

SHERLOCK Howard (*Saxes, Clt*): El Cueto, Fresneda 37, Lieres, 33580 Siero, Asturias Spain ☎ +34 8 5724718

SMITH Robert (*Sax, Pf, Per, Rec, Kbds*): 26 Burlington Terrace, Cardiff CF5 1GG ☎ 029 2034 3814

SNELLING Michael (*T Sax, Clt*): The Ponderosa, 92A Radipole Lane, Weymouth, Dorset DT4 9RT ☎ 01305 775962

STABBINS Larry (*T Sax, S Sax, Flt*): Primrose Cottage, Carlidnack Lane, Mawnan Smith, Falmouth, Cornwall TR11 5HE ☎ 01326 250752

STOCKMAN John (*Sax, A Sax, Vln*): 60 Barton Hill Road, Torquay TQ2 8JD ☎ 01803 327983

STONE Tony (*Saxes, Clt, Org, Db, Arr*): 22 Wellington Hill, Horfield, Bristol BS7 8SR ☎ 0117 9756021

THOMAS Gary (*T Sax, Voc*): 11 Victoria Park Road, East Canton, Cardiff CF5 1EG ☎ 029 2023 6427

THOMAS Gwyn (*Sax, Clt*): 13 Ael Y Bryn Drive, Llanelli, Dyfed SA15 4GE ☎ 01554 772081

THOMAS Stanley (*Sax, Clt*): 13 Colebrook Lane, Plympton, Plymouth PL7 4BN ☎ 01752 330707

TOMKINS Peter (*A Sax, T Sax, Clt, Flt, Pic*): Woodwynd Cottage, Devauden Green, Nr Chepstow, Gwent NP6 6NT ☎ 01600 860859

TREVETT Julie (*Sax, Flt, Clt, Bsn, Pf*): 2 Milton Mead, West Milton, Bridport, Dorset DT6 3SQ ☎ 01308 485319

TREVETT Rex (*A Sax, T Sax, Tpt, Clt, Flt*): 7 St Katherines Avenue, Bridport, Dorset DT6 3DF ☎ 01308 456646

UNDERHILL Ian (*Sax, Flt, Kbds*): Address Unknown ☎ 01242 575925

WAGHORN Ben (*Saxes, Clt, Flt*): 316 Wick Road, Brislington, Bristol, Avon BS4 4HU ☎ 01179 776754

WEBBER Kenneth (*Sax*): Glendarach, Ugborough Road, Bittaford, Devon PL21 0ER ☎ 0175 54 3231

WELLINS Bobby (*T Sax*): 30 Frith Road, Bognor Regis, West Sussex PO21 5LL ☎ 01243 863882

WESTCOTT Geof (*T Sax, Clt*): 14A Station Road, Wellington, Somerset TA21 8JZ ☎ 01823 665199

WILDY Thomas (*Saxes, Hrp, Voc*): 11 Napier Street, Stoke, Plymouth PL1 4QX ☎ 01752 567964

WILKINS Michael (*Sax, Clt, Flt*): 46 Castle Street, Thornbury, Bristol BS12 1HB ☎ 01454 418573

WILLIAMS Alf (*T Sax, Clt, Flt*): 16 Stow Park Avenue, Newport, Gwent NP9 4FL ☎ 01633 62578

WILLIAMS Keith (*A Sax, T Sax, Flt, Clt*): 12 Llys Nant, Pandy, Caerphilly, Glam CF8 3JB ☎ 029 2086 8252

WILLIAMS Nicola (*A Sax*): 30 Everest Road, Leckhampton, Cheltenham, Glos GL53 9LG ☎ 01242 227328, 01242 227328

WILLIAMS Percy (*A Sax, Clt, Flt*): Imber, Boddington Road, Staverton, Glos GL51 0TN ☎ Cheltenham 6802

WILLIAMSON Andrew (*T Sax, A Sax, Voc, Br Sax, Ti*): 26 Ambra Vale East, Cliftonwood, Bristol BS8 4RE ☎ 0117 929 2861, 0378 309922 mob

WINTER Christopher (*Saxes, Kbds, Gtr*): 28 Chichester Way, Yate, Bristol BS17 5TA ☎ 01454 318268

WOODING Rob (*A Sax, S Sax, Clt*): Woodcott, Dashpers, Brixham, Devon TQ5 9LJ ☎ 01803 856511, 01803 866264 day

WRAFTER Tony (*T Sax, A Sax, Flt, Tpt, B Gtr*): 277 Newfoundland Road, Bristol BS2 9NS ☎ 0117 9351149

WRIGHT Victoria (*A Sax, Clt, Voc*): 12A St Katherines Drive, Bridport, Dorset DT6 3DQ ☎ 01308 423350

YATES John (*Saxes*): 7 Osborne Road, Weston-Super-Mare BS23 3EJ ☎ 01934 641925

LONDON

AARON Dave (*A Sax, T Sax, S Sax, Clt, Flt*): 135 Fulwell Park Avenue, Twickenham, Middx TW2 5HG ☎ 020 8898 2006

ADAMS Alyson (*Sax, Clt, Flt*): 12 Exeter Road, Kilburn, London NW2 4SP ☎ 020 8452 3833

ADAMS Bob (*Sax, Flt, Clt*): 50 Brick Farm Close, Richmond, Surrey TW9 4EG ☎ 020 8878 2344

AIRTH Graeme (*T Sax, Flt*): 88A The Chase, Clapham, London SW4 0NF ☎ 020 7622 1453

AKINTAYO Ola (*Sax, B Gtr, Voc*): 6 Morant House, Stockwell Gardens Estate, London SW9 9AA ☎ 020 7738 6929

ALBU Ben (*T Sax, S Sax, A Sax, Flt, Pf*): 447 Cockfosters Road, Barnet, Herts EN4 0HJ ☎ 020 8449 8481

ALEXANDER Kevin (*A Sax, T Sax*): Flat 2, 41 Temple Street, Brighton BN1 3BH ☎ 01273 748247

ALLAWAY David (*A Sax, Clt, Flt*): 26 Memory Close, Maldon, Essex CM9 6XT ☎ 01621 842 153

ALLAWAY Stephen (*A Sax, Flt*): 268, Fencepiece Road, Hainault, Ilford, Essex IG6 2ST ☎ 020 8500 6802

ALLEN Susanna (*A Sax, Vln*): 118 Benhill Road, Camberwell, London SE5 7LZ ☎ 020 7708 5628 & fax

ALTMAN John (*B Sax, Clt, Pf, Arr, Com*): Denton Dene, 42 The Drive Sth, Woodford E18 2BJ ☎ 020 8530 2244

AMSTELL Billy (*Sax, Clt, Com, Arr*): 40 Ebrington Road, Kenton, Middlesex HA3 0LT ☎ 020 8907 9241

ANDERSON Jamie (*Sax, Clt, Pf, Flt*): Flat 1, 4 Dickenson Road, Crouch End, London N8 9EN ☎ 020 8348 3292, 0976 743191 mob

ANDRADE Marcelo *(Sax, Flt, Gtr, Vln)*: 6 Raveley Street, London NW5 2HU ☎ 020 7209 9184, 0956 109140 mob

ANGWIN Benjamin *(Sax, Pf)*: 147 Crouch Hill, London N8 9QH ☎ 020 8341 4322, 020 8341 5480

ANNESLEY Luke *(Saxes, Clt, Pf, Kbds)*: Flat 3, 6 Montague Avenue, London SE4 1YP ☎ 020 8694 6911

ARGUELLES Julian *(T Sax, A Sax, S Sax, Br Sax)*: 12B Balchier Road, London SE2 1QN ☎ 020 8480 0492 & fax

ARNOLD Benedict *(T Sax, Pf, Voc)*: 74 Oxenholme, Harrington Square, London NW1 2JN ☎ 020 7209 0437

ARNOLD Jack *(T Sax, Clt)*: 23 Croftdown Road, London NW5 1EL ☎ 020 7485 6227

ARNOPP Tony *(Sax, Clt, Flt, Pic, A Flt)*: 61 Sheen Park, Richmond, Surrey TW9 1UN ☎ 020 8940 4380

ASH Vic *(Sax, Clt, Flt, B Clt)*: 15 White Hart Close, Back Lane, Chalfont St Giles, Bucks HP8 4PH ☎ 0149487 2054, 01494 873618

ASHE Brian *(Sax, Clt, Cop, Arr, Flt)*: 16 Meadvale Road, London W5 1NP ☎ 020 8997 8503

ASHTON Bill *(Saxes, Md)*: 11 Victor Road, Harrow, Middlesex HA2 6PT ☎ 020 8863 2717, 020 8863 8685 fax

ASPERY Ronald *(Sax, Flt, Com)*: 57 Wivelsfield Road, Saltdean, Brighton, East Sussex BN2 8FP ☎ 01273 304824

B.M Elvin *(A Sax, Clt, Gtr)*: Flat 1, 2 Stepney Green, London E1 3JU ☎ 020 7265 9305

BAGWELL Anthony *(Sax, Clt, Flt)*: Les Destres Nord, Le Luc-En-Provence, 83340, France ☎ +33 (0)4 94998049

BAKER David *(Saxes, Clt, B Clt)*: 2 Rolfe Close, New Barnet, Herts EN4 9QU ☎ 020 8440 5763

BALCON Gordon *(T Sax, Flt, B Ldr, Md)*: Ashlea, Wrights Green, Lt Hallingbury, Herts CM22 7RL ☎ 01279 722566

BALDWIN L *(Sax, Ob, Cor, Clt, Flt)*: Address Unknown

BALLAMY Iain *(Saxes, Clt, Com)*: Flat 4, Old Queen Anne Hse, 63 Aylesbury Road, London SE17 2EQ ☎ 020 7708 5853 & fax, 0973 940 020

BANKS James *(Sax, Pf, Cel)*: 117C Queens Drive, London N4 2BE ☎ 020 8809 4782

BAPTISTE Denys *(T Sax)*: 46 Montague Road, Hounslow, Middlesex TW3 1LD ☎ 020 8572 8899, 0956 129271

BARLOW Thomas *(Sax, Voc)*: 64 Westwood Park, Forest Hill, London SE23 3QH ☎ 020 8699 6351

BARNACLE Gary *(Sax, Flt, Gtr, Kbds)*: 241 Bedford Hill, Streatham, London SW16 1LB ☎ 020 8677 9237

BARNES Alan *(Saxes, Clt, Flt, B Clt)*: 146 Kings Avenue, London SW12 0BA ☎ 020 8674 5239

BARNES Lester *(A Sax, T Sax, Kbds)*: 21 Lower Camden, Chislehurst, Kent BR7 9HY ☎ 020 8467 4520

BARRATT Elisabeth *(S Sax, Br Sax, Com, Arr)*: 106 Erlanger Road, New Cross, London SE14 5TH ☎ 020 7277 5055

BARRY Ged *(T Sax, S Sax, Pf, Kbds)*: Flat 1, 11 Colworth Grove, London SE17 1LR ☎ 020 7701 7539

BARTHOLOMEW Paul *(Br Sax)*: 22 Bousfield Road, London SE14 5TR ☎ 020 7277 8714

BARTLETT Michael *(T Sax, E Gtr, Pf)*: 26 Highfield Drive, Bromley, Kent BR2 0RX ☎ 020 8460 6456

BARTLETT Rachel *(T Sax, S Sax, A Sax, Br Sax,)*: 21A Navarino Rd, London E8 1AD ☎ 020 7254 2829

BATES Simon *(Saxes, Clt, Flt, Wi Synth)*: 1 Erin Close, Bromley, Kent BR1 4NX ☎ 020 8464 9301, 0468 406080 mob

BATES Will *(A Sax, T Sax, S Sax)*: 48 Barrowgate Road, Chiswick, London W4 4QY ☎ 020 8994 0592

BAYTON George *(T Sax, Clt, Cop)*: 26 Stembridge Way, Norton, Fitzwarren,Taunton, Somerset TA2 6SX ☎ 01823 252560

BEADLE Bud *(T Sax)*: 186 Sunnyhill Road, Streatham, London SW16 2UN ☎ 020 8677 5661

BECK Christian *(Sax)*: 32 St Martins Road, Dartford, Kent DA1 1UJ ☎ 01322 228575

BEESON Andre *(Sax, Clt)*: 43 Bisterne Avenue, London E17 3QR ☎ 020 8520 4221

BEEVER J *(Saxes, Clt, Flt)*: 61A Rodmell Avenue, Saltdean, Brighton, Sussex BN2 8PG ☎ 01273 306473

BEINING Elmar *(Sax, Gtr)*: 48 Victoria Avenue, London E6 1EY ☎ 020 8552 9041

BEKKER Harold *(Sax, Clt, Flt)*: Address Unknown

BELLINGHAM Anthony *(A Sax, Clt)*: 52 Kingsley Grove, Woodhatch, Reigate, Surrey RH2 8DX ☎ 01737 43828

BENNETT Alan *(Sax, Clt, Flt)*: 55 Milwell Crescent, Chigwell, Essex IG7 5HX ☎ 020 8500 4459

BENNETT Paul *(Saxes, Clt, Flt, Ob, Heck)*: 75 Silverbirch Avenue, Stotfold, Hitchin, Herts SG5 4BB ☎ 01462 732184

BENSON Jeffrey *(T Sax, A Sax, S Sax)*: 96 Ramsden Road, London SW12 8QZ ☎ 020 8673 4439, 020 8675 5543 fax

BENTON Marie *(T Sax, A Sax)*: 95 Whitworth Way, Wilstead, Bedford MK45 3EF ☎ 01234 740971

BESTON Nick *(Sax, Flt, Clt, Kbds)*: 52 Hillcrest Road, Orpington, Kent BR6 9AL ☎ 01689 828120

BEWLEY Linus *(S Sax, T Sax, Clt)*: 17 Marius Road, Balham, London SW17 7QU ☎ 020 8673 6115

BIANCHI Mike *(Sax)*: 12 Mattison Road, London N4 1BD

BIBBY Arnold *(Saxes, Flt, Clt)*: 21 Mansfield Road, Chessington, Surrey KT9 2PJ ☎ 020 8397 1028

BIELBY Laurie *(A Sax, Clt, T Sax, Br Sax, S)*: 71 Greenfield Gardens, London NW2 1HU ☎ 020 8458 2321

BIRCH John *(A Sax, T Sax, S Sax, Clt, Flt)*: 48 The Fairway, North Wembley, Middlesex HA0 3LP ☎ 020 8908 0587

BIRD Ian *(A Sax, T Sax, S Sax)*: 12 Vancouver Road, Forest Hill, London SE23 2AF ☎ 020 8699 0778, 020 8699 4505

BISCOE Christopher *(Saxes, A Clt, Flt, Pic)*: 27A Crescent Road, Kingston-upon-Thames, Surrey KT2 7RD ☎ 020 8549 4465, 020 8547 3701

BISHOP David *(Saxes, Clt, B Clt, Flt, A Flt)*: 27 Radlett Park Rd, Radlett, Herts WD7 7BG ☎ 0192385 5344, 0956 317874 mob, 020 8549 1706 day

BISSONNETTE Sarah *(T Sax, Br Sax)*: 65 Ellsworth Street, Unit 307, Bridgeport, Connecticut, USA 06605 ☎ +1 203 336 9014 & fax

BITELLI David *(Saxes, Clt, Flt, B Clt, Arr)*: 020 8965 2624

BLACKMORE David *(Saxes, Br Sax, Clt, B Clt, Fl)*: 76 Powerscroft Road, London E5 0PP ☎ 020 8533 0152

BLACKMORE Judith *(A Sax, Br Sax, B Clt, Clt, Pf)*: 76 Powerscroft Road, Hackney, London E5 0PP ☎ 020 8533 0152

BLAKE Julie *(Sax, Clt)*: 5 Thorn Drive, George Green, Bucks SL3 6SA ☎ 01753 512191

BLANDAMER Stewart *(A Sax, Voc, Gtr, Com)*: 86 Kings Road, Berkhampstead, Herts HP4 3BP

BLATCHLY Duke *(Saxes, Clt)*: Palfreymans, Duddenhoe End, Saffron Walden, Essex CB11 4UU ☎ 01763 838552

BONGA Ntshukumo *(A Sax, Gtr, Clt)*: 5 Chiltern Court, Avonley Village, Avonley Road, London SE14 5EZ ☎ 020 7277 9588, 07971 260524

BONSER Jack *(Sax, Clt, Flt)*: 288 Portland Road, London SE25 4SL ☎ 020 8654 4106

BOOMER Simon *(Sax, Bsn, Kbds)*: 56 Brightwell Crescent, Tooting, London SW17 9AE ☎ 020 8672 8842, 0976 283413 mob

BORRELL Paula *(A Sax, Br Sax, Flt, T Sax, Pi)*: 43 Peverl House, Stow Road, Dagenham, Essex RH8 1DH ☎ 020 8592 1888

BOSTOCK David *(T Sax, S Sax, A Sax, Clt)*: 61 Bond Road, Surbiton, Surrey KT6 7SG ☎ 020 8391 5249

BOSTON Bill *(A Sax, B Sax, T Sax, Clt)*: 243 Dartmouth Road, London SE26 4QY ☎ 020 8291 7049

BOURNE Robin *(T Sax, A Sax, Vln, Dms)*: Leylands Orchards, Nr Meopham Green, Meopham, Kent DA13 0PZ ☎ 01474 812008

BOUSTEAD Peter *(A Sax, Clt)*: 13 Middleham Road, Edmonton, London N18 2SA ☎ 020 8807 0363

BRADBURY Dave *(Sax)*: Flat 5, 2/6 Summit Road, Walthamstow, London E17 9LR ☎ 020 7215 0761, 020 8520 3779 eve

BRADFIELD Colin *(Saxes, Clt, Flt, Pic)*: Diggers, Half Moon Lane, Redgrave, Diss, Norfolk IP22 1RX ☎ 01379 890299

BRAGGINS Belinda *(A Sax, Pf)*: 62 Rolkbourne Road, London SE23 2DD ☎ 020 8699 5613

BRAY Ned *(T Sax, Clt)*: 60 Burrard Road, West Hampstead, London NW6 1DD ☎ 020 7435 2939, 020 7794 7589

BREWER Christian (*A Sax, Clt*): 13 Southwood Mansions, Southwood Lane, Highgate, London N6 5SZ ☎ 020 8340 7409

BRIEN Sydney (*A Sax, Clt*): 42 Strathfield Gardens, Barking, Essex IG11 9UL ☎ 020 8594 7770

BRIGGS Simon (*Sax, Clt, Flt*): 11 Farmers Road, Staines, Middlesex TW18 3JE ☎ 01784 450701 & fax

BRIMMER Paul (*Sax*): 18 Follingham Court, Drysdale Place, London N1 6LZ ☎ 020 7739 0128

BROADLEY Gerald (*A Sax, T Sax, Br Sax, Clt, Fl*): 290 Northumberland Avenue, Welling, Kent DA16 2QG ☎ 020 8303 0792

BROOKER Scott (*Sax, Clt, Flt, Pf*): 43 Ford Close, Rainham, Essex RM13 7AU ☎ 01708 559941, 0976 757578 mob

BROOKS John (*Br Sax, S Sax, A Sax, A Flt*)

BROUGHTON Philip (*Sax, Clt, Flt, Pic*): 39 Dudley Gardens, Harrow-on-the-Hill, Middx HA2 0DQ ☎ 020 8422 5801

BROWN Ali (*Saxes, Clt, B Clt, Flt*): 9 Wexfenne Gardens, Pyrford, Woking, Surrey GU22 8TX ☎ 01932 349998, 0973 211217

BROWN Katherine (*Saxes, Clt, Flt*): 67 Castlewood Road, London N16 6DJ ☎ 020 8809 4807

BROWN Michael (*A Sax, T Sax, B Gtr*): 66A Ashley Road, London N19 3AF ☎ 020 7281 5727

BROWN Morris (*Sax, Clt*): Address Unknown ☎ 020 7402 5979

BROWNING Peter (*Sax, Clt, Flt, Rec, Tpt*): 244 Grange Road, South Norwood, London SE25 6TB ☎ 020 8653 2467

BRUER Jason (*Saxes*): 29 Woodlands Park Road, London N15 3RU ☎ 020 7284 2755

BRUTON Thomas (*A Sax, S Sax, Br Sax, Clt, B*): 58 Camborne Road, Morden, Surrey SM4 4JJ ☎ 020 8542 1060

BUCKLEY Michael (*T Sax, Flt, S Sax, B Sax*): 288 St Attracta Road, Cabra, Dublin 7, Ireland ☎ 01 8686 174

BULLEY Alan (*A Sax, T Sax, S Sax, Clt*): The Chapel, Silver Street, Witcham, Ely, Cambs CB6 2LF ☎ 01353 778065

BURCH Paul (*Sax, Clt, Flt*): 68 Ida Road, Tottenham, London N15 5JN ☎ 020 8292 7110

BURLING George (*T Sax, Clt*): 58 East Street, Rochford, Essex SS4 3ER ☎ 01702 62395

BURNS Robert (*Sax, Clt*): 124 Pearl Street, Sarnia, Ontario N7T5Gs, Canada ☎ 020 8519 3446/47

BUTCHER John (*T Sax*): 28 Aylmer Road, London W12 9LQ ☎ 020 8740 1349

BUTCHER Ken (*Br Sax, A Sax, S Sax, B Clt,*): 32B Lynn Road, Balham, London SW12 9LA ☎ 020 8673 6290

BYRD Byron (*Sax, Kbds, B Gtr*): Century Vista Comm. Ltd, Maurice Drummond House, Catherine Grove, Greenwich, London SE10 8JH ☎ 020 8855 2907, 0958 761071, 020 8855 7330

BYRNE Lennie (*Saxes, Clt*): 68 Woodville Road, Thornton Heath, Surrey CR7 8LJ ☎ 020 8653 3538

BYWATER Kay (*Sax, Clt, Flt, Pic*): 24 Eaton Close, Stanmore, Middlesex HA7 3BT ☎ 020 8954 1515

CAFFREY Jason (*Sax, Flt, Clt, Kbds*): 2 Studholme Court, Finchley Road, London NW3 7AE ☎ 020 7794 5226

CAISLEY Robert (*A Sax, Br Sax, Clt*): 20 Repton Road, Orpington, Kent BR6 9HS ☎ 01689 29428

CALDWELL Christopher (*Saxes, Clt, Flt, Pic*): 79 Royal Hill, Greenwich, London SE10 8SE ☎ 020 8692 3795, 0468 076687, 020 8692 6524

CALLAND Beverley (*Sax, Clt, Flt*): 44 Victoria Road, Abingdon, Oxfordshire OX14 1DQ ☎ 01235 520613

CAMPANALE Franco (*T Sax, A Sax, Clt, A Flt, Flt*): Grove Hill Villas, 4 Hampton Road, Hampton-on-Hill, Middx TW12 1NY ☎ 020 8943 1537

CARDEW Horace (*T Sax, Saxes, Clt, B Clt*): 5 Tell Grove, London SE22 8RH ☎ 020 8299 1826

CARLESS Raymond (*T Sax, A Sax, Br Sax, S Sax*): 147 Rendlesham Road, Clapton, London E5 8PA ☎ 020 8985 6146

CARMICHAEL Anita (*Saxes, Voc, Pf, Gtr*): 49E St Pauls Road, London N1 2LT ☎ 020 7354 2595

CARTER Geoff (*T Sax, Clt, Flt*): 64 Murray Crescent, Pinner, Middlesex HA5 3QE ☎ 020 8866 5842

CASEY Howie (*T Sax*): 36 Robert Louise Stevenson Ave, Westbourne, Bournemouth, Dorset BH4 8EG ☎ 01202 767918

CASTLE Ben (*Sax, Flt*): 21 South Park View, Gerrards Cross, Buckinghamshire SL9 8HN ☎ 01753 882571

CAWKWELL Roger (*Sax, Clt, Kbds, Gtr, Voc*): 4 Chatsworth Court, Powerscroft Road, London E5 0PS ☎ 020 8986 4758 & fax

CAWTHORNE Stuart (*Sax*): 12 Montgomery Road, Edgware, Middx HA8 6NT ☎ 020 8952 1756

CHADWICK Beverley (*T Sax, Br Sax*): 11 Walton Terrace, Woking, Surrey GU21 5EL ☎ 01483 833499

CHAMBERLAIN Ronald (*Saxes, Clt, Flt*): 509 High Road, Harrow Weald, Middx HA3 6HL ☎ 020 8954 2525

CHAMBERS Dave (*T Sax*): 4 Cleve Road, London NW6 3RR ☎ 020 7624 6626

CHARLES Nicholas (*Saxes, Flt, Clt*): 21 Woodstock Road, Finsbury Park, London N4 3ET ☎ 020 8292 4514, 0468 774377

CHARMAN Colin (*Sax, Clt, Flt, Arr, Com*): 47 Rochester Avenue, Bromley, Kent BR1 3DN ☎ 020 8289 7696, 0973 179799

CHILKES Jack (*T Sax, Clt*): 12A Vista Drive, Ilford, Essex IG4 5JE ☎ 020 8550 4122

CHRISTIANE Kelvin (*Sax, Flt, Clt, Kbds*): 43A Grove Road, Eastbourne, East Sussex BN21 4TX ☎ 01323 721 741

CHURCH Jimmy (*Sax, Clt*): 2 Lancaster Close, Kingston, Surrey KT2 5NH ☎ 020 8549 5431

CLACKETT Matthew (*A Sax, T Sax*): 21 Warwick Gdns Hse, Azenby Road, London SE15 5AJ ☎ 020 7708 5896

CLAHAR Patrick (*Sax, S Sax*): 85 Dyers Lane, Putney, London SW15 6JP ☎ 020 8785 9243

CLARK Charles (*Sax, Kbds, Per*): 156A Queens Road, London SW19 8LX ☎ 020 8241 1217

CLARK Norman (*T Sax, A Sax, Clt*): Avalon, Carlton Road, South Godstone, Surrey RH9 8LG ☎ 01342 892140

CLARKE Simon (*Saxes, Flt, Rec*): 44A Upland Road, East Dulwich, London SE22 9EF ☎ 020 8693 5991

COATES Michael (*Saxes, Flt, Clt*): 6 Bromleigh Court, Sydenham Hill, London SE23 3PW ☎ 020 8693 4028

COE Peter (*Sax*): 15 St.Barnabas Road, Sutton, Surrey SM1 4NL ☎ 020 8661 1219

COHEN Jonathan (*Sax*): 45 Fraser House, Green Dragon Lane, Brentford, Middx TW8 0DQ ☎ 020 8847 0835

COLLINS John (*Sax, Clt, A Sax, Flt*): 2 Effingham Close, Sutton, Surrey SM2 6AG ☎ 020 8643 3904

COLLINS Mel (*T Sax, A Sax, S Sax, Br Sax,*): c/o Linden Cottage, Woodland Way, Kingswood, Surrey KT20 6NU

CONDON Chris (*Sax, Flt, Pic, Clt*): 26 Chester Close, Off Pixham Lane, Dorking, Surrey RH4 1PP ☎ 01306 886186

CONN Harry (*Sax, Clt*): Flat 1, 122 Southampton Row, London WC1B 5AE ☎ 020 7405 8217

COOK Peter (*Saxes*): Flat 3, 101 Whitehart Lane, Barnes, London SW13 0JL ☎ 020 8878 8171

COPPEN John (*Br Sax, Cel*): ☎ 020 7378 1952

CORNISH Pete (*Saxes, Flt, Clt*): Ailies Buildings, Whitesmith Lane, East Hoathly, Lewes, East Sussex BN8 6QP ☎ 01825 873033, 01825 873044

CORRY Paul (*T Sax, A Sax, Flt, Clt*): 1 Norfolk Street, Fairfield, Hebden Bridge, West Yorkshire HX7 6HY ☎ 01422 846380

COUSSEE Pol (*Sax, Flt, Clt*): 15 Beaulieu Avenue, London SE26 6PN ☎ 020 8659 8798

COVEY Rachael (*A Sax, Clt, Pf, Voc*): 6 Winterbrook Road, Herne Hill, London SE24 9JA ☎ 020 7274 8672, 0585 848 188

COX Jonathan (*Sax, Flt*): 53 St Marys Tower, Fortune Street, London EC1Y 0SD ☎ 020 7490 2905

COXHILL David (*Br Sax, A Sax, Flt, Clt, T Sa*): 29 Beverley Road, West Wimbledon, London SW20 0RL ☎ 020 8946 7320, 0973 674779

COXHILL Lol (*S Sax, T Sax, A Sax*): 17 Laney House, Portpool Lane, London EC1N 7UL ☎ 020 7831 9400

CRAIG Jay (*Br Sax, Clt, Flt*): 3 Park Way, Ruislip, Middx HA4 8PJ ☎ 01895 632289, 0468 076726

CRAWFORD Adrian (*T Sax, A Sax, S Sax, Flt, Clt*): 81A Ballater Road, Brixton, London SW2 5QX ☎ 020 7274 3214

CRAWLEY Colin *(Sax, Flt, Gtr)*: 28 Branscombe Court, 111 Westmoreland Road, Bromley, Kent BR2 0UL ☎ 020 8460 1430

CRAYDEN Jim *(T Sax)*: 22 Forest Edge Drive, Ashley Heath, Ringwood, Hampshire BH24 2ER ☎ 01425 479998

CRUMLY Pat *(Saxes, Flt, Clt)*: 94 Samuel Lewis, Vanston Place, London SW6 1BU ☎ 020 7381 3233

DALY Jeff *(Saxes, Pic, Flt, A Flt, Clt)*: 37 Willow Grove, Middlesex HA4 6DG ☎ 01895 622892, 020 8549 1706 day, 0585 144963 mob

DANIELS David *(A Sax, Clt, B Gtr)*: 1 Sheridan Crescent, Chislehurst, Kent BR7 5RZ ☎ 020 8467 9745

DANIELS Jack *(Sax, Clt, Flt, Pf, Acc)*: 139 Downton Avenue, London SW2 3TX ☎ 020 8674 3826

DARLINGTON Steve *(A Sax, T Sax, Flt)*: 19 Minard Road, London SE6 1NP ☎ 020 8244 3610

DAVIS Gregory *(T Sax)*: 44 Montrell Rd, London SW2 4QB ☎ 020 7436 8584, 0378 641 067 mob, 020 7436 8584

DAVIS Snake Chris *(Saxes, Flt)*: Jive Cottage, Akeley Wood, Buckingham MK18 5BN ☎ 01280 812061

DAWKES Jack *(Sax, Clt)*: 20 Thornhill Road, Ickenham, Middlesex UB10 8SG ☎ 01895 678228

DAWSON Stacey *(A Sax, T Sax, S Sax, Clt, Flt)*: 17 Half Acre Road, Hanwell, London W7 3JH ☎ 020 8840 0653, 0831 151321 mob

DAY Philip *(T Sax, A Sax, Clt)*: 29 Buckingham Close, Enfield, Middlesex EN1 3JQ ☎ 020 8363 6597

DEAN Elton *(A Sax, Sax, Pf)*: 7 Farleigh Road, London N16 7TB ☎ 020 7249 3342

DEAN Julian *(A Sax, Clt)*: 123 Cann Hall Rd, Leytonstone, London E11 3NH ☎ 020 8555 2463

DIAMOND Alison *(T Sax, A Sax, S Sax)*: 12 Hulme Square, Macclesfield, Cheshire SK11 7SG ☎ 01625 611556

DICKATY Raymond *(Sax, Flt, Clt)*: Flat 4, 210-212 Deptford High Street, Deptford, London SE8 3PR ☎ 020 8691 2365

DILLEY Alan *(T Sax, Br Sax, S Sax, Clt, Fl)*: 18 Derwent Drive, Purley, Surrey CR2 1EQ ☎ 020 8660 1578

DINSLEY Brian *(A Sax, Clt, Flt, Cop)*: 78 Edgecombe, South Croydon, Surrey CR2 8AB ☎ 020 8657 5141

DOBSON Martin *(Saxes, Wood W, Wi Synth)*: 8 Brick Kiln Close, Coggeshall, Colchester CO6 1SQ ☎ 01376 562689, 0378 160837

DOLMAN Sally *(Sax, A Sax, T Sax, Clt)*: Address Unknown ☎ 020 8800 3934

DONE Julian *(T Sax, S Sax)*: 66B Fairlawn Park, London SE26 5RX ☎ 020 8659 4762

DOWLASZEWICZ Ewa *(A Sax, Pf)*: Flat 2, 63 Tennyson Road, Kilburn, London NW6 7RU ☎ 020 7372 1669

DOWNER Stan *(Saxes, Clt, Flt)*: 93 Sewardstone Road, North Chingford, London E4 E4 7PA ☎ 020 8529 8549

DOWNING Robert *(T Sax, A Sax, Clt, Gtr, B Gtr)*: 7 Cranbrook Drive, Gidea Park, Romford, Essex RM2 6AP ☎ 01708 741 251

DREW Denny *(T Sax, Voc)*: 33 Windmill Hill, Enfield, Middlesex EN2 7AE ☎ 020 8367 8729

DRISCOLL Geoff *(Saxes, Clt, Flt)*: 6 Mulgrave Hall, Mulgrave Road, Sutton, Surrey SM2 6LG ☎ 020 8661 6028

DUNCAN Molly *(Sax)*: Apartado De Correos 139, Andraitx 07150, Mallorca, Baleares, Espana ☎ +34 71 67 15 76

DUNMALL Paul *(Sax, Flt, Clt)*: 1 Pidgeon House Cottage, Dingle Road, Leigh, Nr Worcester WR6 5JX ☎ 01886 32046

DUNSDON Martin *(T Sax, A Sax, S Sax, Flt, Clt)*: 85 Meadfield Road, Langley, Slough, Berks SL3 8HY ☎ 01753 593149

EDE Terence *(T Sax, A Sax, S Sax, Clt, B C)*: 7 Church Farm Lane, Cheam, Surrey SM3 8PT ☎ 020 8643 2784, 0378 384 215

EDWARDS Ricky B *(Sax, Flt, B Clt)*: 46 Witcombe Point, Peckham High St, Clifton Estate, Peckham. London SE15 5EH ☎ 020 7635 8646

EDWARDS Terry *(A Sax, Br Sax, Gtr, Tpt, Arr)*: 43 Parfett Street, London E1 1JR ☎ 020 7377 9734

ELBOZ John *(A Sax, T Sax, Clt)*: 94 Ferndene Road, Herne Hill, London SE24 0AA ☎ 020 7274 3456

ELLINGWORTH Allan *(S Sax, A Sax, T Sax, Flt)*: 7, Madden Avenue, Davis Estate, Chatham, Kent ME5 9TJ ☎ 01634 301101

ELLIOTT Louise *(Sax, Flt)* ☎ 020 7609 6489

ELLIS Ian *(T Sax, A Sax, S Sax)*: 119 Tynemouth Road, Mitcham CR4 2BR ☎ 020 8648 3608

EVANS James *(Sax, Clt, Tbn, Pf)*: 181 Portnall Road, West Kilburn, London W9 3BN ☎ 020 8968 9132

EVANS John *(Sax, Clt, Flt, Voc)*: Lark Rise, 30A The Inlands, Daventry, Northants NN11 4DE ☎ 01327 879875

EVANS Leslie *(Sax, Clt)*: 275 Colney Hatch Lane, London N11 3DH ☎ 020 8368 4137

EVANS Phil *(T Sax, Kbds, La Per, Voc, Gtr)*: Ground Floor Flat, 42 Ridley Road, Wimbledon, London SW19 1EU ☎ 020 8544 0230, 0403 502 623 mob

EXALL Richard *(Saxes, Clt, Flt)*: 19 Warren Road, London SW19 2HY ☎ 020 8540 0963

FAHEY William *(Saxes, Clt, Flt)*: 219 West End Road, Ruslip, Middlesex HA4 6QG ☎ 020 8845 1338

FAIR Frederick *(A Sax, Clt, T Sax, Br Sax, Fl)*: 90 Third Walk, Canvey Island, Essex SS8 9SZ ☎ 01268 691883

FARRUQUE Syeeda *(Sax, Kbds, Dms)*: 34D Hermon Hill, Wanstead, London E11 2AP ☎ 020 8530 6975

FILBY Brian *(Saxes, Flt, Clt, Ob)*: 4 St Johns Terrace, Clay Hill, Enfield, Middx EN2 9AQ ☎ 020 8363 3289

FINDON Ronald *(Saxes, Clt, Flt, Ob, Bsn)*: 87 Brook Avenue, Edgware, Middx HA8 9UZ ☎ 020 8958 5331

FITZGERALD David *(Saxes, Flt, Wi Synth)*: 48 Avenue Road, Norwich, Norfolk NR2 3NN ☎ 01603 632444 & fax, 0468 573284 mob

FLETCHER James *(Sax, Com, Arr)*: 20 Westbrook House, Victoria Park Sq, London E2 0PB ☎ 020 8980 4174

FLETCHER Raymond *(T Sax, A Sax, Clt)*: 70 Blenheim Gardens, Wallington, Surrey SM6 9PS ☎ 020 8647 4818

FOLEY Brian *(Saxes, Gtr)*: 82 Cranbrook Rd, Deptford, London SE8 4EJ ☎ 020 8692 8280

FORAN John *(T Sax, Pf)*: 39 Sussex Road, Carshalton Beeches, Surrey SM5 3LT ☎ 01426 248931

FORDHAM John *(T Sax, Br Sax, Pf)*: c/o Jive Aces, Saint Hill Manor, East Grinstead, West Sussex RH19 4JY ☎ 01342 300075 & fax

FORDHAM Kenneth *(T Sax, Flt, Clt)*: 21 Castle Rise, Ridgewood, East Grinstead TN22 5UN ☎ 01825 764060

FORSHAW Christian *(Sax, Clt, Flt)*: 66 Dangan Road, Wanstead, London E11 2RF ☎ 020 8989 6567

FOSTER Mick *(B Sax, A Sax, S Sax, T Sax, C)*: The Garden Flat, 102 Jerningham Road, London SE14 5NW ☎ 020 7771 8416, 0831 810264

FRANCHI John *(Saxes, Flt, Pic, Clt, Rec)*: The Manse, Innes Street, Plockton, Ross-Shire, Scotland IV52 8TW ☎ 01599 544442

FRANCIS Chris *(A Sax, S Sax, Flt)*: 10A Putney High Street, London SW15 1SL ☎ 020 8788 2551

FRANCIS Joe *(Sax, Clt, Flt)*: 12C Albert Road, London N4 3RW ☎ 020 7281 4735, 07970 209458

FRANCIS John *(Sax, Clt, Flt, Pic, Arr)*: Woodstock, 57 Grove Farm Park, Northwood, Middlesex HA6 2BQ ☎ 01923 827067, 0385 563804

FRANK Samuel *(A Sax, T Sax, S Sax)*: 133A Ladbroke Grove, London W11 1PR ☎ 020 7243 8147

FRITH Martin *(Sax, Clt, Rec, Flt)*: Hunters Lodge, 29 Lynch Hill Park, Whitchurch, Hants RG28 7NF ☎ 01256 895556, 0860 755107 mob

GAFFIN Ivor *(A Sax, T Sax, Br Sax, Clt)*: 81 Hamilton Avenue, Barkingside, Essex IG6 1AD ☎ 020 8554 9086

GALDEZ Claudio *(T Sax, S Sax, Flt)*: 278, North Circular Road, Neasden, London NW10 0JR ☎ 020 8459 8374

GALLAGHER James *(A Sax, T Sax, So Sax, Clt, Wi)*: c/o 63 Balfour Road, Ealing, London W13 9TW ☎ 020 8678 0811

GAMLEN Amy *(A Sax, S Sax)*: 19 Manchester Road, Tottenham, London N15 6HP ☎ 020 8802 3526

GARLAND Scott *(Saxes, Flt, Clt, Wi Synth)*: 37C Underhill Road, East Dulwich, London SE22 0QZ ☎ 020 8693 2602, 0374 611875 mob

GARLAND Tim *(Sax, Com, Arr)*: 65 Birchen Grove, London NW9 8RY ☎ 020 8201 3518

GARNETT Alex *(T Sax, A Sax, S Sax, Flt)*: 145 Sutherland Avenue, Maida Vale, London W9 1ES ☎ 020 7289 0486, 0973 241061

GARNETT William *(Sax)*: 145, Sutherland Avenue, Maida Vale, London W9 1ES ☎ 020 7289 0486

GEGESHIDZE Aleksandr *(T Sax, S Sax, Kbds, Synth)*: 76B Gascony Avenue, London NW6 4NE ☎ 020 7916 3407, 0797 1324427, 020 7916 3407

GELLY Dave *(T Sax, Clt, B Clt)*: 16 Poplar Walk, Herne Hill, London SE24 0BU ☎ 020 7733 0564

GEMMELL Keith *(Saxes, Clt, Flt, Arr)*: 15 Burlington Drive, Beltinge, Herne Bay, Kent CT6 5ER ☎ 01227 375261

GEORGE Eric *(Sax, Clt, Arr)*: Flat 9, North Mount, High Road, London N20 0PH ☎ 020 8445 6635

GERKE Gerald *(A Sax, T Sax, Br Sax, Clt, Fl)*: Apt 404, Ed, "Nova Iii", 8 Avda Magalluf, Magalluf, Mallorca, Baleares ☎ +34 71 131467

GIBBS Gerry *(Saxes, Flt, Pic, Clt, B Clt)*: 60 Little Bushey Lane, Bushey Heath, Herts WD2 3JX ☎ 020 8950 1738

GIBBS Ralph *(T Sax, Acc)*: 7 Charlesfield, Mottingham, London SE9 4NX ☎ 020 8857 2301

GILBY Simon *(Sax)*: Flat 4, Pinner Hill Court, 22 Pinner Hill Road, Pinner, Middx HA5 3SB ☎ 020 8581 3804

GILCHRIST Eric *(Sax, Clt)*: 61 Grove Park Road, London W4 3RU ☎ 020 8995 9911

GILL Michael *(A Sax, T Sax, Clt, Flt, Kbds)*: 95 Chippenham Road, Harold Hill, Romford, Essex RM3 8HP ☎ 014023 75496, 01708 375496

GILLIERON Andre *(Saxes)*: 61 Fairmount Road, London SW2 2BJ ☎ 020 8674 0436

GLEDHILL Simon *(A Sax, Clt, Flt)*: 1 Cumberland Drive, Hinchley Wood, Esher, Surrey KT10 0BG ☎ 020 8398 3494

GODDARD Peter *(Sax, Clt)*: 21 Radlyn Park, West End Avenue, Harrogate, North Yorkshire HG2 9BZ

GODIN Peter *(Saxes, Flt, Com, Arr)*: 90 Latymer Road, London N9 9PW ☎ 020 8807 8839

GOFF Ken *(A Sax, T Sax, Clt, B Clt, Flt)*: 13 Fulwell Park Avenue, Twickenham, Middlesex TW2 5HF ☎ 020 8894 4348

GOLDSTEIN Lloyd *(T Sax, A Sax, Clt, Flt)*: Flat 6 Number 25, James Hilton House, Woodford Road, South Woodford, London E18 ☎ 020 8989 7743, 07971 104906

GORDON Jeff *(T Sax, S Sax, A Sax, Flt, Clt)*: 54 St George House, Charlotte Despard Avenue, Battersea, London SW11 5HN ☎ 020 7720 2609, 0956 972743

GOULD Bunny *(Saxes, Clt, B Clt, Bsn, Flt)*: 32 Kinfauns Road, Goodmayes, Essex IG3 9QL ☎ 020 8590 0883

GRAHAME Lisa *(Saxes, Flt, Cel, Pf)*: 6 Bell Lane, Northchurch, Berkhampstead, Herts HP4 3RD ☎ 01442 875414, 0374 991504 mob

GRANT Bradley *(Sax, Clt, Flt, Pf)*: 1 Redwood Gardens, Chingford, London E4 7NZ ☎ 020 8524 8304, 07050 040462

GRANT Sandra *(T Sax, Flt, A Sax)*: West Lodge, 2 Harmer Green Lane, Digswell, Welwyn, Herts AL6 0AD ☎ 0143871 4440

GRAY Nicholas *(T Sax, Gtr, B Gtr)*: 100 Lindsay Road, Worcester Park, Surrey KT4 8LE ☎ 020 8330 2832, 0378 848 000

GRAY Ron *(A Sax, Clt)*: 45 Therfield Court, 28 Brownswood Road, London N4 2XL ☎ 020 7503 7461

GREAVES Julian *(Saxes, Pf, Hmca)*: 110A Coborn Road, Bow, London E3 2DG ☎ 020 8980 4435

GREEN Alby *(T Sax)*: 103 Plevna Crescent, London N15 6DY ☎ 020 8809 7490

GREEN David *(Saxes, Clt, Flt, Pic, Vln)*: 8 The Vista, London SE9 5RQ ☎ 020 8859 0848, 0966 227936 mob

GREENWAY Sue *(A Sax, T Sax, Flt, Clt)*: 3 Park Way, Ruislip, Middlesex HA4 8PJ ☎ 01895 632289, 0961 381416

GREENWOOD Ben *(Sax, Flt, Pic, Clt, B Clt)*: 88 Mowbray Road, Edgware, Middx HA8 8JH ☎ 020 8958 8279

GREGORY Steve *(Sax, Flt, A Flt)*: 60 Tilehurst Road, London SW18 3ET ☎ 020 8870 4528, 0973 123547 mob

GRIFFIN John *(Saxes, Clt, Flt)*: 58 Bear Road, Hanworth, Middlesex TW13 6RA ☎ 020 8898 9065

GRIFFITH Frank *(T Sax, Clt, A Sax, Flt, Br Sa)*: 99 Eastcote Lane, Northolt, Middlesex UB5 5RH ☎ 020 8842 3217 & fax, 0976 313224 mob

GRIFFITHS M 'Eddie' *(T Sax, Flt, Voc)*: Flat 2, 7 Kellino Street, Tooting, London SW17 8SY ☎ 020 8767 2011

GROSSMITH Derek *(A Sax, Saxes, Flt, Pic, Ob)*: Laurelhurst, Pinner Hill, Pinner, Middx HA5 3XT ☎ 020 8866 0921

GROVES Roy *(T Sax, A Sax, Br Sax, Flt, Cl)*: Address Unknown ☎ 01277 653477

GUEST Keith *(T Sax, A Sax, Clt, Flt)*: 1 A, Tudor House, Tenterden Grove, London NW4 1TN ☎ 020 8203 4800

GUTTRIDGE Derek *(Sax, Flt)*: 14 Cairn Avenue, London W5 5HX ☎ 020 8567 3510

GUY Chris *(T Sax, Flt, Arr, Com)*: 19 Thurlestone Avenue, Friern Barnet, London N12 0LP ☎ 020 8368 0848

HACKER Jane *(Saxes, Clt, Flt, Arr, Com)*: 14 Birchwood Road, Tooting, London SW17 9BQ ☎ 020 8677 8304, 020 8681 8834

HAGLEY Bernard *(Sax, B Gtr, Voc)*: 97 Broomwood Road, Battersea, London SW11 6JT ☎ 020 7228 8282

HALL Tony *(T Sax, A Sax, S Sax)*: 41 Gledwood Gardens, Hayes, Middlesex UB4 0AT ☎ 020 8573 1258

HAMER George *(T Sax, Clt, Flt, Cntrc)*: Gordhayes Farm, Upottery, Nr Honiton, E. Devon EX14 9QT ☎ 01404 861477

HAMILTON Andrew *(Sax)*: 4 Churchill Road, Edgeware, Middx HA8 6FY ☎ 020 8952 4968

HAMILTON Andy *(T Sax, A Sax, S Sax, Kbds)*: 392 Upper Richmond Road West, East Sheen, London SW14 7JU ☎ 020 8876 9040

HAMMOND Ruth *(T Sax, Pf, Org)*: 13 Stewartsby Close, Edmonton, London N18 1AN ☎ 0966 541170 mob

HANSON Al *(T Sax, Clt)*: Flat 95, 11 New Crane Place, London E1 9TU ☎ 020 7702 4394

HARAM Simon *(Saxes, Clt)*: Flat 1, 49 Gipsy Hill, Upper Norwood, London SE19 1QH ☎ 020 8670 5447

HARRIS Hugh *(Sax, Kbds, Arr)*: 25 Champion Grove, London SE5 8BN ☎ 020 7737 2655

HARRIS Syd *(Sax, Clt, Flt)*: 15 Buckland Gardens, Ryde, Isle Of Wight PO33 3AG ☎ 01983 611067

HARRISON Mike *(A Sax)*: 70 Ollgar Close, London W12 0NG ☎ 020 8740 7875

HARTWELL Alan *(Saxes, Clt, Flt, Org)*: 183 Craddocks Avenue, Ashtead, Surrey KT21 1NT ☎ 01372 73767

HARVEY Ray *(Saxes, Clt)*: 34 Riefield Road, Eltham, London SE9 2QA ☎ 020 8850 5788

HASTINGS Jimmy *(Sax, Clt, Flt)*: 185 Albert Drive, Sheerwater, Woking, Surrey GU21 5RD ☎ 01483 823 282, 0956 236 164 mob, 01483 823 282

HATHAWAY Martin *(T Sax, A Sax, Clt, Pf)*: 95 Chignall Road, Chelmsford, Essex CM1 2JA ☎ 01245 263540 & fax

HATHAWAY Tina *(T Sax, A Sax, S Sax)*: 95 Chignall Road, Chelmsford, Essex CM1 2JA ☎ 01245 263540 & fax, 0973 155223 mob

HATHERILL Robert *(A Sax, Br Sax, T Sax, Clt, Fl)*: 41 Harris Lane, Shenley, Radlett, Herts WD7 9EF ☎ 01923 855311

HAUGHTON Michael *(S Sax, A Sax, T Sax, Flt)*: 20 Barnfield Avenue, Kingston, Surrey KT2 5RE ☎ 020 8546 8646

HAYNES Kevin *(Sax, Per)*: 11A Sevington Street, Maida Vale, London W9 2UD ☎ 020 7289 4734

HEATH Greg *(Sax, Flt)*: 13 Hales Prior, Calshot Street, London N1 9JW ☎ 020 7713 7006 & fax

HECKSTALL-SMITH Dick *(T Sax, S Sax, Br Sax)*: 5 Eden Mansions, Gondar Gardens, London NW6 1HE ☎ 020 7794 9243

HENRY Melanie *(Saxes, Flt, Pic, Clt)*: 40 Church Hill Road, Walthamstow, London E17 5EU

HENRY Neville *(Sax, Kbds)*

HENRY Simon *(A Sax, Clt, Flt, Pf)*: 34 Albert Road, London N4 ☎ 020 7272 3248

HENZELL Derek *(T Sax, A Sax)*: 50 Gloucester Crescent, Laleham Estate, Staines, Middlesex TW18 1PS ☎ 01784 258409 & fax, 0831 510674 mob

HERNIMAN Tim *(Saxes, Kbds, Vln, Gtr, B Gtr)*: 44 Bramber Road, Fulham, London W14 9PB ☎ 020 7460 8897, 0797 126 2136

HEYES Edward *(A Sax, Clt, Flt)*: 18 Sycamore Lane, Ely, Cambs CB7 4TW ☎ 01353 663680

HICKMAN Colin *(A Sax, Br Sax, Clt, Flt, T Sa)*: 58, Alers Road, Bexleyheath, Kent DA6 8HT ☎ 020 8306 1376

HIGHAM Stanley *(T Sax, Clt, Flt)*: Windrush, Ellwood, Nr Coleford, Glos GL16 7LY ☎ 01594 833634

HIGNELL Lauren *(Saxes, Clt, Flt)*: 70C Glengall Road, Peckham, London SE15 6NH ☎ 020 7277 9635

HINGSTON Rod *(Br Sax)*: 47 Oakways, London SE9 2PD ☎ 020 8859 2655

HIRST Clare *(Sax, Kbds)*: 146 Kings Avenue, Clapham, London SW12 0BA ☎ 020 8674 5239

HITCHCOCK Clive *(T Sax, A Sax, Clt, Flt)*: 36 Grove Walk, Norwich NR1 2QH ☎ 01603 663083

HITCHCOCK Nigel *(Sax, Clt, Flt)*: 6 Lindsay Court, Felpham, West Sussex PO22 8JQ ☎ 020 7630 1150

HJERT Gerry *(A Sax, T Sax, Br Sax)*: Willow Barn, Upper Farm, Taynton, Oxfordshire OX18 4UH ☎ 01993 823697

HOBAN Lynne *(Sax, Flt)*: 34 Cowper Road, Hanwell, London W7 1EH ☎ 020 8579 3609

HOBART Michael *(Sax, Flt)*: 14 Olinda Road, London N16 6TL ☎ 020 8809 0643

HODGKINSON Timothy *(Sax, Clt, Kbds)*: 46 Spenser Road, London SE24 0NR ☎ 020 7207 0719

HOLBROW Pauline *(Saxes, Ob, Rec)*: 44C Fermoy Road, London W9 3NH, 0958 782 505 mob

HOLLIDAY James *(A Sax)*: 87 Ardrossan Gardens, Worcester Park, Surrey KT4 7AY ☎ 020 8224 3882, 020 8873 3843

HOLMES Alan *(T Sax, A Sax, Flt, Clt)*: 37 Corbylands Road, Sidcup, Kent DA15 8JG ☎ 020 8300 8803 & fax

HOLMES Tim *(Sax, Clt)*: 129 Cambridge Road, Hitchin, Herts SG4 0JH ☎ 01462 454360

HONE Frederick *(Sax, Vln)*: Address Unknown

HOOPER Lew *(Saxes)*: 59 Albany Park Road, Kingston-upon-Thames, Surrey KT2 5SU ☎ 020 8287 3279

HORCH Kyle *(Sax, Clt)*: 9 Uffington Road, London SE27 0RW ☎ 020 8761 8201

HORTON Robert *(Sax)*: 44 Selkirk House, Bemerton Street, London N1 0AB

HOWELL Arthur *(T Sax, A Sax, Clt)*: 96 Park Avenue East, Stoneleigh, Surrey KT17 2PA ☎ 020 8394 2326

HOYLE Minnie *(Sax, Flt, Pf)*: 5 Wheathill Road, Penge, London SE20 7XQ ☎ 020 8778 9631

HUGHES Brian *(T Sax, A Sax, Clt)*: 25 West Road, Royal Hospital Chelsea, London SW3 4SR ☎ 020 7730 0161

HUGHES Nathan *(Sax, Clt, Flt, Pf, Gtr)*: 2 Yorkton Street, London E2 8NH ☎ 020 7729 5087

HUGHES Peter *(Sax, Flt, Clt, B Clt, Pic)*: 16A Weald Rise, Harrow Weald, Middx HA3 7DG ☎ 020 8954 4282

HUGHES Robert *(Sax, Clt, Flt)*: Basement Flat, 40 Erlanger Road, New Cross, London SE14 5TG ☎ 020 7652 1192, 0802 420599 mob

HUGHES Stevie *(T Sax, B Clt, Flt, Clt, Arr)*: 223 Harvist Road, London NW6 6HE ☎ 020 8668 1250

HUGHES Ted *(Sax, Clt)*: Avenell, 14 Sandilands Close, Sea Lane,Sandilands, Sutton-on-Sea Lincs LN12 2EY

HULL Peter *(Sax, Clt, Flt, Pic)*: 31 Dukes Wood Drive, Gerrards Cross, Bucks SL9 7LJ ☎ 01753 883518

HULME Kathy *(A Sax)*: 7 Navarino Grove, London E8 1AJ ☎ 020 7241 1255

HUMPHRIES Colin *(Saxes, Clt)*: Flat 2, 68 Wickham Road, London SE4 1LS ☎ 020 8469 0352

HUNT James *(T Sax, A Sax, Flt)*: 17A Tower Terrace, Wood Green, London N22 6SX ☎ 020 8352 4238, 0958 342465

HUNT Robert *(T Sax)*: 98 Blanmerle Road, Eltham, London SE9 2DZ ☎ 020 8850 6564

HUNTE Rupert *(T Sax, Clt, B Ldr)*: 33 Rostella Road, London SW17 0HY ☎ 020 8672 1490

HURT Peter *(Saxes, Flt, Clt, Arr, Cop)*: 1 Princes Road, Richmond, Surrey TW10 6DQ ☎ 020 8948 4942

IRWIN Raymond *(Sax)*: 40B Drayton Gardens, Ealing, London W13 0LQ ☎ 020 8998 8247, 020 8930 3901

JACKSON Richard *(Sax, Flt)*: 606A Hertford Road, Enfield, Middlesex EN3 5SX ☎ 020 8443 1851, 0467 706177

JAFFA Nina *(Br Sax, A Sax, Flt, Pic, Arr)*: 24B Colless Road, Seven Sisters, London N15 4NR ☎ 020 8808 4290, 0956 395018 mob

JENKINS Lyle *(T Sax, Br Sax, A Sax, Clt, Fl)*: 23 Water Lane, Seven Kings, Ilford, Essex IG3 9HE ☎ 020 8597 0436

JENNINGS Maurice *(Sax, Clt, Flt)*: 31, Latchmere Road, Kingston-on-Thames, Surrey KT2 5TP ☎ 020 8546 2355

JENSEN Andor *(Sax, Clt, Flt)*: 1 Courtenay Mews, Walthamstow, London E17 7PP ☎ 020 8503 7736

JEWELL Jimmy *(T Sax, A Sax, So Sax, B Sax,)*: 105 Britton Street, Gillingham, Kent ME7 5ES ☎ 01634 300626

JILLY-B *(T Sax)*: 74 Cranmer Avenue, Northfields, West Ealing, London W13 9XU ☎ 020 8567 2045

JONES Simeon *(Sax, Hmca, Flt)*: 105 Taybridge Road, London SW11 5PX ☎ 020 7652 6647

KANE Christopher *(Saxes, Kbds)*: 26 Northumberland Avenue, Wanstead Park, London E12 5HD ☎ 020 8530 7103

KARUZAS Jason *(T Sax, A Sax, Clt, Flt)*: c/o The Old Dairy, 1-3 Crouch Hill, London N4 4AP ☎ 07977 275363

KEEGAN Jesse *(Sax, Pf)*: 42 Coppetts Road, Muswell Hill, London N10 1JX ☎ 0956 961162 mob

KELMANSON Michael *(T Sax, Clt)*: Little Hatch, Partridge Green, Sussex RH13 8HF ☎ 01403 710439

KIDDIER Kenneth *(Saxes, Flt, Clt)*: 29 Barley Lane, Hastings, E Sussex TN35 5NX ☎ 01424 430256

KING Peter *(Sax)*: 15 Oak Hill Place, London SW15 2QN ☎ 020 8874 8646

KLEIN Harry *(Sax, Clt)*: 8 Bowling Green House, Cremorne Estate, London SW10 0DN ☎ 020 7352 8942

KNIGHT James *(A Sax, S Sax, Clt, Flt, Voc)*: 6 Temple Terrace, Vincent Road, Wood Green, London N22 6ND ☎ 020 8888 4887, 0976 949 830

KRAABEL Caroline *(A Sax, Br Sax, Voc)*: 59 Lucey Way, St. James Road, London SE16 3UD ☎ 020 7237 1564 & fax

KUSABBI Kemal *(A Sax, S Sax)*: Garden Flat, 29 Queensdown Road, London E5 8NN ☎ 020 8986 0523

KYLE Patrick *(Saxes, Flt, Pic, Clt)*: 49 Cambridge Road, Mitcham, Surrey CR4 1DW ☎ 020 8540 7109

LA ROSE Orlando *(T Sax, A Sax, Flt)*: 70 Durnsford Road, Bounds Green, London N11 2EJ ☎ 020 8889 5428

LACEY Roland *(T Sax, Flt)*: 9 Emanuel Avenue, Acton, London W3 6JG ☎ 020 8993 4875

LAMMIN Dennis *(T Sax, A Sax, Flt)*: 29 Eden Road, Walthamstow, London E17 9JS ☎ 020 8503 7491

LAMOND Bruce *(A Sax, T Sax, Pf)*: 129 Ferme Park Road, London N8 9SG ☎ 020 8348 0560

LAMONT Duncan *(Sax, Clt, B Clt, Flt)*: 2 Cadmer Close, New Malden, Surrey KT3 5DG ☎ 020 8949 5608

LAMONT JNR Duncan *(Sax, Flt, Clt)*: 56 Mount Pleasant Close, Lightwater, Surrey GU18 5TR ☎ 01276 452381

LAMPI James *(Sax)*: 9 Mulberry Way, Barkingside, Essex IG6 1ET ☎ 020 8551 4557

LASCELLES James *(A Sax, T Sax, S Sax)*: 55 Knightleas Court, 111 Brondesbury Park, London NW2 5JQ ☎ 020 8459 4997

LAUBROCK Ingrid *(Sax, A Sax, T Sax, Kbds)*: 5 Sandringham Road, London NW2 5EP ☎ 020 8459 6610

LEAKE Robert *(A Sax, T Sax, Clt)*: 37 Streatleigh Court, Streatham High Road, London SW16 1EG ☎ 020 8769 3028

LEE John *(T Sax, Clt, A Sax)*: 57 Crown Woods Way, Eltham, London SE9 2NL ☎ 020 8850 4661

LEVY Gerald *(Saxes, Clt, B Clt, Flt)*: 33 Forestdale, Southgate, London N14 7DY ☎ 020 8886 9376

LEWINGTON Ian *(Sax, Flt)*: 109 High Street, West Wickham, Kent BR4 0LT ☎ 020 8776 2675, 0961 413 522

LEWIS David *(T Sax, A Sax, Flt, Kbds)*: Garden Flat, 90 Coniston Road, Muswell Hill, London N10 2BN ☎ 020 8444 1346

LEWIS Richard *(Sax, Gtr, Kbds, Com)*: Birdland, 23 East Street, Osney Island, Oxford OX2 0AU ☎ 01865 248732

LIPMAN Daniel (*Sax, Flt*): The Attic, 4Th Floor, Imperial Works, Perren Street, London NW5 3ED ☎ 020 7485 0601

LITTLE Martin (*S Sax, A Sax, Clt*): 154 Southwark Bridge Road, London SE1 0DG ☎ 020 7803 0791, 0973 629229

LOCKETT Mornington (*T Sax, A Sax, Clt*): 4 Cornwall Mansions, 228 Blythe Road, London W14 0HF ☎ 020 7371 4527, 0468 490143 mob

LOCKHEART Mark (*A Sax, T Sax, Clt*): 8 Stephens Road, Tunbridge Wells, Kent TN4 9JE ☎ 01892 525108 & fax, 0976 228020

LODGE Gilly (*Saxes, Flt, Clt, Kbds*): 88 Chiswick Village, London W4 3BZ ☎ 020 8742 1528, 0956 436384 mob

LODGE William (*Sax, Clt, Vln*): 81 Millmark Grove, London SE14 6RN ☎ 020 8692 3428

LONG Peter (*Sax, Clt, Flt, Ob*): 126 Moyser Road, London SW16 6SH ☎ 020 8677 2867, 020 8769 1682

LOPEZ-REAL Carlos (*Saxes, Pf, Ob*): 31 Sanders Lane, Mill Hill East, London NW7 1BX ☎ 020 8346 5533, 0956 814219

LORD Stan (*A Sax, T Sax, Br Sax, Clt, Fl*): 24 Chestnut Drive, Harrow Weald, Middx HA3 7DJ ☎ 020 8954 3118

LOWE Kevin (*T Sax*): 120 Broadfield Road, Catford, London SE6 1TH ☎ 020 8695 0636

LUCK Brian (*A Sax, Clt*): 4 The Avenue, Hornchurch, Essex RM12 4JL ☎ 01708 442870

LUKAS Peter (*A Sax, T Sax*): Top Flat, 21 Muswell Road, London N10 2BJ ☎ 020 8372 8467

LUMSDON Des (*A Sax, T Sax, Clt, Flt*): 72 The Ridgeway, Chingford, London E4 6PU ☎ 020 8529 0212

LUNT Nicholas (*Br Sax*): 63 Desford Way, Ashford, Middlesex TW15 3AS

MACKENZIE Henry (*Sax, Clt, Flt*): 27 The Glade, Stoneleigh, Epsom, Surrey KT17 2HN ☎ 020 8393 4860

MACKIE Ronnie (*Sax, Flt, Clt*): Victoria Lodge, 144 Shirehall Road, Hawley,Dartford, Kent DA2 7SN ☎ 01322 287196

MACKINTOSH Andy (*A Sax, T Sax, Flt, Pic, Clt*): 27 Station Road, South Norwood, London SE25 5AH ☎ 020 8653 7478

MAIN Stephen (*Saxes, Clt, Flt*): 2 Elliott Road, Chiswick, London W4 1PE ☎ 020 8742 8863, 0802 246 089

MANZIN Roberto (*A Sax, Clt, Kbds*): 50 Rathmore Road, Charlton, London SE7 7QW ☎ 020 8853 0501

MARKS Robert (*Saxes, Flt, Clt, Md*): 66 Nightingale Crescent, West Horsley, Leatherhead, Surrey KT24 6PD ☎ 01483 284355

MARLEYN John (*Saxes, Flt, Pic, Clt, B Clt*): 15 Fairford Court, Grange Road, Sutton, Surrey SM2 6RY ☎ 020 8642 6486

MARRION Dave (*Saxes, Clt, Flt, Pic, Md*): 9 Hampton Road, Worcester Park, Surrey KT4 8EU ☎ 020 7330 3327

MARSTON Steven (*A Sax, Flt, Per*): 19 Ford Square, Whitechapel, London E1 2HS ☎ 020 7702 7972, 020 7702 7972

MARTIN Bob (*A Sax, Clt, Flt*): Flat 1 26-30 Battersea Court, Battersea Park Road, London SW11 ☎ 020 7622 2655

MASON Jeffrey (*Saxes, Clt, Flt, Voc*): 137 Laleham Road, Staines, Middlesex TW18 2EG ☎ 01784 451089, 07788 670218 mob

MASON Paul (*Saxes, Clt*): 21 Courtnell Street, London W2 5BU ☎ 020 7727 0191

MATTHEWS John (*Sax, Arr, Tpt*): 2 Kimberley Gardens, Enfield, Middlesex EN1 3SW ☎ 020 8366 1010

MATTHEWS Paul (*Saxes*): 27 Holmes Court, Paradise Road, London SW4 6QJ ☎ 020 7627 3989

MAY K (*A Sax, T Sax, Br Sax*): 11 Dartford Road, Dartford, Kent DA1 3EF ☎ 01322 224904

MCB Dan (*A Sax, Clt, T Sax, Gtr*): 7 Hylda Court, St Albans Road, London NW5 1RE ☎ 01784 451089, 0956 899893

MCCARROLL Leonard (*A Sax, Clt*): 23 New Street Hill, Bromley, Kent BR1 5AU ☎ 020 8857 8102

MCCHRYSTAL Gerard (*Sax, Clt*): 24 Leas Close, High Wycombe, Bucks HP13 7UW ☎ 01494 464831

MCCOOKWEIR Caroline (*A Sax, Voc, Clt, Pf*): 31 Oakhill Court, Oakhill Road, Putney, London SW15 2QH ☎ 020 8870 3864

MCCORMICK Tony (*A Sax, T Sax, S Sax, Clt, Pic*): 1 Wayfield Avenue, Hove, East Sussex BN3 7LW ☎ 01273 323788, 0976 243363

MCCULLOCH Adam (*T Sax, A Sax*): 27A Adamsrill Road, London SE26 4AJ ☎ 020 8291 1945

MCDONALD Sian (*T Sax, A Sax*): 72 Andalus Road, Stockwell, London SW9 9PF ☎ 020 8761 7544

MCGILL Howard (*Saxes, Clt, Flt*): The Station House, Woodside Park Underground, Woodside Park Road, North Finchley, London N12 8SE ☎ 020 8492 0014, 0860 850596 mob

MCGUIRE Alan (*Br Sax, B Clt*): 19 Leighton Place, London NW5 2QL ☎ 020 7482 4527

MCKAY Bob (*Sax, Flt, Clt*): 96 Clifton Road, Kingston-upon-Thames, Surrey KT2 6PN ☎ 020 8549 3901

MCLOUGHLIN Diane (*Sax, Pf*): 230 Evering Road, Clapton, London E5 8AJ ☎ 020 8806 6946

MCMAHON John (*Sax, Clt*): 139 Street Lane, Denby, Derbyshire DE5 8NF

MCMAHON Kevin (*T Sax, A Sax, S Sax*): Flat L Block 5, Taransom Close, Plough Way, Surrey Quays SE16 1FH ☎ 07970 866463

MEAD Frank (*Sax*): 22 Bexhill Road, Crofton Park, Brockley, London SE4 1SL ☎ 020 8690 7403

MENDHAM Tracey (*T Sax, Br Sax, A Sax, Clt, Fl*): 27 Thackary Avenue, Tilbury, Essex RM18 8HS ☎ 01375 844666, 0958 548 284 mob

MICAH Paul (*Sax*): 22 Taplow House, Thurlow Street, London SE17 2UQ ☎ 020 7701 0585

MILLER Morris (*Sax, Clt, Arr*): 7 Hawthorn Drive, Sway, Hampshire SO41 6DX ☎ 01590 682235

MITCHELL Alexander (*A Sax, Flt, Clt, Pf*): 360 Nelson Road, Twickenham, Middx TW2 7AH ☎ 020 8893 9822

MITCHELL Donald (*Sax, Kbds*): 99 Chelmsford Road, Walthamstow, Essex E17 8NP ☎ 020 8520 7536

MOLE Charlie (*Sax, Vln, Kbds*): 31 Mall Road, London W6 9DG ☎ 020 8563 7044

MOORE Kathleen (*T Sax, Br Sax, Kbds*): 8 Alconbury Road, London E5 8RH ☎ 020 8806 6031

MOORE Sarha (*Saxes, Cong*): 31 Weymouth Mews, London W1N 3FN ☎ 020 7580 4055

MORDUE Eddie (*Sax, Clt, Flt*): 6 Coverdale Road, London NW2 4BU ☎ 020 8459 3779

MORRIS Andrea (*Sax, Clt, Flt*): Pilgrim Lodge, Ennerdale Road, Richmond, Surrey TW9 3PE ☎ 020 8332 2577, 0860 317216 mob

MORRIS Rex (*Sax, Flt, Pic, B Clt*): 19 Leonard Road, London SW16 2SJ ☎ 020 8764 4851

MORRISSEY Dick (*Sax*): 15 Princes Street, Deal, Kent CT14 6DH ☎ 01304 363607

MOSS Nicholas (*Saxes, Clt, Flt*): Post Office Cottage, 3 Holland Road, Hurst Green, Oxted, Surrey RH8 9AU ☎ 01883 714061

MOSS Paul (*A Sax, Flt, Clt, Pf, Gtr*): Flat 5, 49/51 Daventry Street, London NW1 6TD ☎ 020 7723 6410

MOWER Michael (*Saxes, Flt, Pic, Clt*): 26 Hainthorpe Road, London SE27 0PH ☎ 020 8670 6691

MOYES Crawford (*A Sax, Clt, Pf, Flt, Voc*): 1/6 Sir John Cass Hall, 150 Well Street, London E9 7LQ ☎ 0839 689218 pager

MR NUTTY (*Sax*): c/o CC Young & Co, Chesham House, 150 Regent Street, London W1R 5FA ☎ 020 7432 0337

MULLIGAN Steve (*Sax, A Sax, S Sax, B Clt*): 47 Davenant Road, London N19 3NW ☎ 020 7281 5340

MURPHY Gordon (*A Sax, T Sax, Flt, Clt*): 16B Gillingham Road, London NW2 1RT ☎ 020 8452 0881, 020 7449 1263

MURRAY Noel (*T Sax, A Sax, Clt, Flt*): 1 Petersfield Crescent, Coulsdon, Surrey CR5 2YQ ☎ 020 8645 0803

MUTANT Matthew (*Sax*): 2 Lambolle Road, Belsize Park, London NW3 4HB ☎ 020 7433 3720

NASH Derek (*A Sax, T Sax, S Sax, Flt*): 85 Summerhouse Drive, Joydens Wood, Bexley, Kent DA5 2EF ☎ 01322 557720

NASH Nigel (*T Sax, A Sax, Clt, Flt*): The Manse, Laburnum Walk, Stonehouse, Glos GL10 2NR ☎ 01453 824951, 0831 731794 mob

NATHANIEL Paul (*Saxes, Clt*): 44 Magpie Close, Enfield, Middx EN1 4JB ☎ 020 8342 1487, 0973 144024

NEVILLE Edward (*T Sax, Clt, Tpt*): 9 Aquila Place, Leatherhead, Surrey KT22 8TY ☎ 01372 77915

NEWALL Nick *(A Sax, T Sax, Br Sax, Clt, Fl)*: 6 Lowndes Lodge, Hadley Road, Barnet, Herts EN5 5QW ☎ 020 8440 9502

NEWMAN Al *(Sax, Clt, Flt)*: 24 Hocroft Avenue, London NW2 2EH ☎ 020 7435 0920

NICHOLLS Al *(Sax, Arr)*: 23 University Mansions, Lower Richmond Road, Putney, London SW15 1EP ☎ 020 8789 2755

NICHOLS Colin *(Sax, Clt, Vln)*: The Hobbits, 42 High Street, Shanklin, Isle Of Wight PO37 6JN

NOVE Susan *(T Sax, A Sax, Clt)*: 27 Chesterton Road, Ladbroke Grove, London W10 5LY ☎ 020 8968 5329

O'HIGGINS David *(Saxes, Flt)*: Flat 3, 13 Thirlmere Road, Streatham, London SW16 1QW ☎ 020 8677 2505

O'NEILL John *(Sax, Clt, Flt, Voc, Gtr)*: 103 South View Road, London N8 7LX ☎ 020 8341 2819

OATES Niall *(Sax, Flt, Gtr)*: 17A Church Terrace, Blackheath, London SE13 5BT ☎ 020 8265 6563

OLIVER George *(T Sax, Clt, Ob, Cor)*: Address Unknown

ONISSI Marino *(T Sax, Flt, Voc)*: 36 The Woodlands, Southgate, London N14 5RN ☎ 020 8366 2316, 0958 371465 mob

OSBORN Sarah *(A Sax, Clt, Br Sax, Pf)*: 121 Shardeloes Road, New Cross, London SE14 6RU ☎ 020 8692 5834

OXLADE Roy *(Sax)*: 63 Sedlescombe Gardens, St Leonards-on-Sea, East Sussex TN38 0YT

PACKHAM Kit *(Saxes, Voc, Hmca, Flt, Gtr)*: 2 Wadhurst Court, Wadhurst Close, Anerley, London SE20 8TA ☎ 020 8659 9263

PAICE Michael *(Sax, Harm)*: 90 Barriedale, London SE14 6RG ☎ 020 8694 2035

PAINE Charles *(Sax, Clt, Flt)*: 78 Streatham Road, Mitcham, Surrey CR4 2AB ☎ 020 8648 5788

PARDY Richard *(T Sax, Saxes, Clt, Flt, Per)*: 33 Lauderdale Road, Hunton Bridge, Abbots Langley, Hertfordshire WD4 8QA ☎ 01923 265366, 0468 146200 mob

PARFETT Jez *(A Sax, Br Sax)*: Flat 3, 4 Birchington Road, London N8 8HR ☎ 020 8348 1073

PARK Benjamin *(B Sax, T Sax, S Sax)*: 32 Castellain Road, London W9 1EZ ☎ 020 7289 1863, 01523 164 289, 020 7289 4266

PARKER Evan *(T Sax, S Sax)*: 112 Hounslow Road, Twickenham, Middlesex TW2 7HB ☎ 020 8898 4095

PARKER Kelvin *(Sax, Clt, Flt, B Ldr)*: 48 Apeldoorn Drive, Wallington, Surrey SM6 9LG ☎ 020 8773 1645, 0411 020449

PARLETT Michael *(Saxes, Per, Flt, Voc, Wi Synt)*: 61 Howland Way, Surrey Quays, London SE16 1HW ☎ 020 7231 2553, 0973 146379

PARRIS Bernard *(Sax, Clt)*: Southfield House, Wangford Road, Reydon, Southwold, Suffolk IP18 6BP ☎ 01502 723493

PARRY Dick *(Saxes)*: 14 Herringswell Road, Kentford, Newmarket, Suffolk CB8 7QS ☎ 01638 750404

PAYN Nicholas *(T Sax, Br Sax, A Sax, S Sax,)*: 3A Kingdon Road, West Hampstead, London NW6 1PJ ☎ 020 7794 5069

PAYNE Alan *(T Sax, B Gtr)*: 33 Stoke Road, Walton-on-Thames, Surrey KT12 3DD ☎ 01932 229937

PAYTON Nik *(A Sax, Br Sax, Clt, Pf)*: Ground Floor Flat, 48 Alexandra Road, Wimbledon SW19 7JZ ☎ 020 8406 8630

PEAKE Jacko *(T Sax, A Sax, S Sax, B Sax, V)*: 101 Lady Margaret Road, London N19 5ER ☎ 020 7700 2671

PENFOLD *(A Sax, S Sax)*: Flat 16, 28 Westcourt, Churchill, London E17 9SG ☎ 020 8509 2489, 0958 440364 mob

PENTELOW Nicholas *(T Sax, S Sax, Flt, Clt)*: 12 Windermere Road, Muswell Hill, London N10 2RE ☎ 020 8444 1668

PERRY Frederick *(Sax, Flt, Clt)*: 2 Roscrea Close, Bournemouth, Dorset BH6 4LX

PICKERING Brian *(Sax, Clt, Flt, Con)*: Arundel, 2 Dukes Ride, Ickenham, Uxbridge, Middlesex UB10 8DA ☎ 01895 811458

PICKERING Michael *(Saxes, Arr)*: 27 St Marks Crescent, London NW1 7TU

PINE Courtney *(T Sax, S Sax, Clt, Flt, Pf)*: c/o Tickety -Boo Ltd, The Boathouse, Crabtree Lane, London SW6 6TY ☎ 020 7610 0122

PINTER John *(Saxes, Flt, Pic, Clt, B Clt)*: Katherine Beales, 48 Dalberg Road, London SW2 1AN ☎ 020 8299 2985 & fax, 0973 405451

PITT Philip *(A Sax, B Sax, Clt)*: 74 Denmark Hill, Camberwell, London SE5 8RZ ☎ 020 7274 7927

PLUMLEY Gary *(Sax, Clt, Flt)*: 132 Pall Mall, Leigh-on-Sea, Essex SS91 1RA ☎ 01702 482073

POLLARD Corinne *(T Sax, Pf)*: 12 Oxford Crescent, Corfton Park, London SE4 1RD ☎ 020 8699 8647

POOLE Ken *(Sax, Clt, Flt, Kbds)*: 15 Lavender Gdns, Battersea, London SW11 1DH ☎ 020 7228 2602

PORTER Terence *(Sax, Clt, Flt)*: 8 Rutlands Crescent, Ormskirk, West Lancs L39 1LD ☎ 01695 580865

POTTER Sally *(Sax, Pf, Voc)*: 7 Blackbird Yard, Ravenscroft Street, London E2 7RP ☎ 020 7613 2233

POTTS Andrew *(Sax, Flt, Clt)*: 55 High Street, Wealdstone, Middlesex HA3 5DQ ☎ 020 8427 8873, 0958 642070 mob

POVEY Bill *(Sax, Clt, Flt, Pic)*: 45 Glebemount, Wicklow Town, County Wicklow, Ireland ☎ 00353 404 69292

POVEY Scott *(Sax, Wood W)*: 105 Digby Avenue, Mapperley, Nottingham NG3 6DT ☎ 0410 425512

PRETTY Adam *(Sax, Gtr, Cong)*: 59A Prince George Road, London N16 8DL ☎ 020 7241 6366

PREZ Taurus *(T Sax)*: 22 Mayfield Road, Wimbledon, London SW19 3NF ☎ 020 8543 2607

PRICE Ian *(Sax)*: 22 Mayfield Gardens, Staines, Middlesex TW18 3LG ☎ 01784 453310

PRINCE Manny *(Sax, Clt, Flt)*: 4 St Aubyns, Snaresbrook Road, London E11 1PQ ☎ 020 8989 2745

PRITCHARD Maurice *(Saxes, Flt, Clt)*: 34 Beeches Walk, Carshalton Beeches, Surrey SM5 4JT ☎ 020 8642 8807

PURVES Ross *(T Sax, Kbds, Flt, Clt)*: 165 Elderfield Road, Hackney, London E5 0AY ☎ 020 8985 9637, 04325 269208 pager

QUAYLE Chrissy *(A Sax, Flt, Pic)*: Flat B, 10 Durham Terrace, London W2 5PB ☎ 020 7221 6067

QUINN David *(Sax)*: 150 Powerscroft Road, London E5 0PR ☎ 020 8986 1400

RAE Sandy *(A Sax, T Sax)*: Lamer Cottage, 81C Villiers Road, Willesden, London NW2 5PG ☎ 020 8451 2734

RAMSDEN Mark *(A Sax, S Sax, Flt)*: 45B Kingsmead Road, London SW2 3HY ☎ 020 8671 5609

REDMOND Andrew *(T Sax, A Sax, S Sax, Flt, Clt)*: 12 Bromley Gardens, Bromley, Kent BR2 0ET ☎ 020 8460 7264, 0966 133174 mob

REINHARDT Thierry *(Saxes, Clt, Flt)*: 58 Chesterton Road, London W10 6ER ☎ 020 8960 1900

RENDELL Donald *(Saxes, Clt, Flt)*: 23 Weir Hall Gardens, London N18 1BH ☎ 020 8807 7831

REUBEN Cyril *(Saxes, Clt, B Clt, Flt)*: Woodwind, Derek Road, Maidenhead, Berks SL6 8NT ☎ 01628 21488

REVELL Adrian *(Saxes, Clt, Flt)*: Cherry Tree Cottage, 26 Robinson Avenue, Goffs Oak, Waltham Cross, Herts EN7 5NY ☎ 01707 876707, 0850 605085 mob

REYNOLDS Kevin *(A Sax, T Sax, Voc, Kbds, Dms)*: 3 Wilmot Close, Peckham Park Road, London SE15 6UA ☎ 020 7732 1813, 0831 542136

REYNOLDS Victor *(T Sax, Vln, B Ldr)*: 13 Wadhurst Drive, Goring By Sea, Sussex BN12 4XA ☎ 01903 242951

RICHMOND Jim *(Sax, Flt)*: 86 Kneller Gardens, Isleworth, Middx TW7 7NW ☎ 020 8898 5369

RIDDING Neale *(Saxes, Flt, Kbds)*: 204 Portway, Stratford, London E15 3QW ☎ 020 8552 6563, 0402 330831

RILEY Barry *(Saxes, Clt, Flt, Voc)*: 7 Vanburgh Gardens, Hatch Warren, Basingstoke, Hants RG22 4UQ ☎ 01256 55154

RIPPER Peter *(Sax, Clt, Flt, Pic)*: 33 Furze Platt Road, Maidenhead, Berks SL6 7NE ☎ 01628 624514

RITCHIE Ian *(Saxes)*: 16 Gay Close, Kenneth Cres, Willesden Green, London NW2 4PR ☎ 020 8452 1684

RIVERS Tony *(Saxes, Clt, Flt, Pic)*: 60 Sunnyside Road, Teddington, Middx TW11 0RT ☎ 020 8977 2375

ROACH David *(Saxes, Ea Wnd, Flt, Clt, Ob)*: 16 Church Vale, London N2 9PA ☎ 020 8883 1699, 020 8883 9964, 0976 847739

ROACH Paul *(Saxes, Flt, Clt)*: 105 Lime Grove, Eastcote, Middlesex HA4 8RW ☎ 020 8866 8933

ROBERTSON Ernest (*A Sax, Br Sax*): 42 Haynes Park Court, 5 Lewins Close, Hornchurch, Essex RM11 2DF

ROBERTSON Hilary (*Br Sax, Clt, B Clt, Flt, Voc*): St.Crispin, 25 Blackhorse Lane, Hitchin, Herts SG4 5EG ☎ 01462 451268, 01462 459407 fax

ROBERTSON Martin (*Saxes, Clt, B Clt*): 134 Elthorne Avenue, London W7 2JW ☎ 020 8579 7534, 020 8840 0682

ROBINSON Barry (*A Sax, Flt, Clt*): Marvells, Moor Garden, Ardeley, Stevenage Hertfordshire SG2 7AT ☎ 01438 861709

ROBINSON Douglas (*Sax, Clt, Flt*): Vivenda Primervera, Cama/Da/Vaca, Burgau, Lagos 8600, Algarve, Portugal ☎ 020 8549 4667

ROBINSON Jeff (*Sax, Clt, Flt, Pic*): 2 Fyfield Avenue, Wickford, Essex SS12 0PD ☎ 01268 73 4079

ROBSON Stephen (*Sax, Kbds, Clt, Vln*): Flat 1, 30 Cheniston Gardens, Kensington, London W8 6TH ☎ 020 7937 1182, 0976 376172 mob

ROSE D (*T Sax, Clt, Wh*): 40 Queenswood Avenue, Wallington, Surrey SM6 8HS ☎ 020 8647 6711

ROSE Mike (*Sax, Flt*): 26 Blincoe Close, Queensmile Road, London SW19 5PP ☎ 020 8789 9160

ROSE Winston (Saxton) (*T Sax, A Sax, S Sax, Clt*): 36 Harper House, Angel Road, London SW9 7LN

ROSS Andrew (*Saxes, Flt*): 140 Stanford Road, Norbury, London SW16 4QB ☎ 020 8679 4562

ROSSETTI-BONELL Adrian (*Sax*): 60 Burghley Road, London NW5 1UN ☎ 020 7267 6988, 020 7485 1117

RUBIE Michael (*A Sax, Br Sax*): 43 Oakdene Park, Finchley, London N3 1EU ☎ 020 8346 0353

RUBIE Steve (*T Sax, Flt*): 10A Stadium Street, London SW10 0PT ☎ 020 7351 0941

RUDNICK Marius (*T Sax, Flt, S Sax, A Sax, Voc*): 4 Birchdale Road, Forest Gate, London E7 8AR ☎ 020 8470 1600

RUTTLEY Rex (*Sax, Clt, Flt, Pic*): 19 North Way, Kingsbury, London NW9 0RD ☎ 020 8204 2017

RYAN Eric (*Sax, Acc, Clt*): 3B Philpot Path, Eltham, London SE9 5DL ☎ 020 8850 7418

RYVES Martin (*T Sax, Clt*): 84 Misbourne Road, Hillingdon, Middlesex UB10 0HW ☎ 01895 59651

SADLER Richard (*Br Sax, S Sax, B Gtr*): 112 Station Road, Chertsey, Surrey KT16 8BT ☎ 01932 429389

SADLER Stephen (*A Sax, T Sax, Flt, Clt*): 28 Watermill Lane, Bengeo, Hertford, Herts SG14 3LB ☎ 01992 500114

SAGE Norman (*T Sax, Clt*): Rookery Lodge, Preston Deanery, Northants NN7 2DY ☎ 01604 870737

SANDERS Timothy (*Saxes*): 2 Firbank Road, London SE15 2DD ☎ 020 7732 2889

SANDS John (*Sax, Clt, Flt, Pic, A Flt*): 102 Whitton Dene, Hounslow, Middx TW3 2JU ☎ 020 8894 5997

SANDY (*Sax, Per*): 54 Herber Road, Cricklewood, London NW2 6AA ☎ 020 8452 9122 & fax

SAPSFORD Gordon (*A Sax, Clt*): 70 The Mead, Carpenters Park, Watford, Herts WD1 5BU ☎ 020 8428 6142

SAUNDERS Andy (*Saxes, Gtr, Pf*): Flat 1, 54 Dulwich Road, London SE24 0PA ☎ 020 7733 8360

SCANNELL James (*Sax, Clt, Flt*): 6 Edward Temme Avenue, Stratford, London E15 4BE ☎ 020 8534 9138

SCHAUERMAN Julia (*A Sax, S Sax*): 104 Bronte House, Poynders Gardens, Clapham SW4 8PE ☎ 020 8673 7166

SCHMID Bettina (*T Sax, A Sax, S Sax*): 6 Oldhill Street, London N16 6LB ☎ 020 8806 9725

SCHMOOL Barak (*Saxes, Flt*): Studio 6, 31 Ridge Hill, London NW11 8PR ☎ 020 8458 5731

SHACKLETON Geraldine (*A Sax, T Sax, Clt, Rec*): 42 Havelock Road, Bromley, Kent BR2 9NZ ☎ 020 8289 8051

SHEAN Russell (*T Sax*): Quince Tree House, Quince Tree Close, South Ockendon, Essex RM15 6NR ☎ 01708 851248

SHEANE Ronald (*T Sax, B Clt, Clt, Flt*): The Links, 31 Linden Road, Aldeburgh, Suffolk IP15 5JH ☎ 01728 452 3048

SHEEHAN Peter (*A Sax, T Sax, Flt*): Ground Floor, 67 Idmiston Road, Stratford, London E15 1RG ☎ 020 8555 0550

SHELDON Camilla (*A Sax, Br Sax, S Sax, T Sax*): 361 Wendover, Thurlow Street, London SE17 2UR ☎ 020 7708 3260, 0973 794494 mob

SHEPHERD Jack (*A Sax, T Sax, S Sax*): 9 Clapham Mansions, London SW4 9AQ ☎ 020 8673 3508

SHERWOOD (*A Sax, T Sax, Clt*): 4 Valley Mushroom Farm, Ricketts Hill Road, Tatsfield Nr Westerham, Kent TN16 2NG ☎ 01959 575368

SHEWAN Doug (*Saxes, Clt, Vln, Ob, Flt*): 15 Lowfield Road, Acton, London W3 0AY ☎ 020 8992 7216

SHOHAM Jeremy (*A Sax, S Sax, T Sax, Clt*): 14 Lancaster Gardens, London N2 9AJ

SHRUBSHALL Catherine (*Sax, Clt*): 76 Selby Road, Leytonstone, London E11 3LR ☎ 020 8519 7825, 01255 861626

SIDWELL Roy (*Sax, Clt, Cop*): 34 The Woodlands, London N14 5RN ☎ 020 8368 2440

SIEGEL Julian (*Saxes, Clt, Flt, Db, Com*): 63 Harcombe Road, Stoke Newington, London N16 0RX ☎ 020 7254 2438, 0973 833428

SILCOX John (*A Sax*): 45 Stapleton Road, Bexleyheath, Kent DA7 5QE

SIMMONDS John (*Saxes, Flt, Com, Arr*): 67 Tollington Park, London N4 3QW ☎ 020 7272 1312

SIMONS Les (*A Sax, T Sax, Clt, B Ldr, Voc*): 43 Camden Road, Bexley, Kent DA5 3NU ☎ 01322 527803

SIMPSON Phil (*Saxes, Clt*): 31A Childeric Road, London SE14 6DQ ☎ 020 8692 3314, 0976 563896 mob

SKIDMORE Alan (*T Sax, Flt, A Flt, S Sax*): 9 Badminton Close, Boreham Wood, Herts WD6 1UL ☎ 020 8953 0533 & fax

SKINNER Colin (*Saxes, Bsn, Clt, Flt*): 26B Warrington Road, Harrow, Middx HA1 1SY ☎ 020 8863 6867

SMITH Betty (*Sax, Voc*): 26 Ratcliffe Road, Sileby, Loughborough, Leics LE12 7PZ ☎ 0150981 6808

SMITH Harrison (*T Sax, S Sax, Flt, B Clt*): 1 Crescent Rise, London N22 4AW ☎ 020 8888 4844

SMITH Michael (*Saxes, Flt*): 29 Arthur Henderson House, Fulham Park Road, London SW6 4JU ☎ 020 7731 1640 & fax, 0973 731149

SMITH Nicholas (*Saxes, Flt, Clt, Wi Synth*): 40 Broomwood Road, Battersea, London SW11 6HT ☎ 020 7350 1737, 0976 930605 mob

SMITH Philip (*Sax, Kbds, Per*): 6 Lansdowne Road, South Woodford, London E18 2AX ☎ 020 8530 5484

SMITH Rodney (*Saxes, Clt, Flt*): 14 Friends, Priory Way, Haywards Heath, Sussex RH16 3SZ ☎ 01444 416800

SMITH Ruthie (*Saxes, Voc, Cel*): 63 Lothair Road South, London N4 1EN ☎ 020 8341 5438

SMUTS Pat (*Sax, Clt*): 188 Pullman Court, London SW2 4TA ☎ 020 8674 2551

SNACK Phil (*A Sax, Clt, Flt, Voc*): 27 Earlswood Gardens, Ilford, Essex IG5 0DF ☎ 020 8550 0400

SPALL Hubert (*T Sax, S Sax*): 8 Priolo Road, Charlton, London SE7 7PT ☎ 020 8473 2015

SPANNERMAN (*Saxes, Clt, Flt*): 14A Cathcart Hill, Tufnell Park, London N19 5QW ☎ 020 7281 4243

SPEAKE Martin (*Sax, Com*): 90B Hadley Highstone, Barnet, Herts EN5 4PY ☎ 020 8449 2844, 020 8440 1675

SPRAGUE Jack (*B Sax, Saxes, Clt*): 33 Malthouse Road, Selsey, Nr Chichester, West Sussex PO20 0GU ☎ 01243 606261

STEELE Jan (*Saxes, Flt, Md, Com, Clt*): 1 St Anne's Road, Caversham, Reading RG4 7PA ☎ 0118 947 7170, 020 8533 1372 day, 0403 304944 mob

STEVENS Paul (*Sax, Clt, Flt, Wi Synth*): 52 Rope Street, Surrey Quays, London SE16 1TF ☎ 020 7237 6481 & fax, 0850 539738 mob

STEWARD Terry (*A Sax, T Sax, S Sax, Br Sax*): The Turntable, 223 Broad Walk, London SE3 8NG ☎ 020 8319 1760, 0860 644250 mob

STOBART Kathleen (*Saxes, Flt, Clt*): Lichens, Church Street, Axmouth, Devon EX12 4AF ☎ 01297 21984

STREET Karen (*Saxes, Clt, Flt, Pic, Acc*): 4 Elm Park Road, Winchmore Hill, London N21 2HN ☎ 020 8350 7139 & fax, 0973 692497

STREVENS Eddie (*T Sax, Vln*): 3 Cobay Close, Hythe, Kent CT21 6AA ☎ 01303 69178

STUART Alan (*T Sax*): 11 Knowle Park, Cobham, Surrey KT11 3AB ☎ 01932 863651 & fax, 0836 231129

STUART Donald (*T Sax, Flt, Clt*): 44 Windsor Road, Worcester Park, Surrey KT4 8EW ☎ 020 7330 3075

SUBRA-BIEUSSES Jean-Pione (*Sax*): 5 Kingsfield House, Victorian Grove, London N16 8EY ☎ 020 7219 4192, 07680 18376

SULZMANN Stanley (*Saxes, Flt, Clt*): 36 Richmond Park Road, East Sheen, London SW14 8JT ☎ 020 8878 8494, 020 8549 1706 day

SUMMERBELL Fred (*Saxes, Clt*): 84 Woodlands Road, Isleworth, Middlesex TW7 6JY ☎ 020 8847 4770

SUMMERS Paul (*A Sax, Br Sax, T Sax, Clt, Fl*): Flat 4, 1 Hunting Gate Drive, Chessington, Surrey KT9 2DQ ☎ 020 8391 0054

SWINFEN Fred (*T Sax, A Sax, S Sax*): 53 Wakefield Street, Edmonton, London N18 N18 2AG ☎ 020 8807 1220

SWINFIELD Raymond (*Saxes, Flt, Pic, Clt, A Flt*): Flat 12, New River Head, 173 Rosebery Avenue, London EC1R 4UJ ☎ 020 7837 9530

SWINGLER Val (*Sax, Flt, Clt, Pf*): 16 Ladycroft Walk, Stanmore, Middlesex HA7 1PE ☎ 020 8951 4297

SYDOR Bob (*Sax, Clt, Flt*): 12 Meadway Court, Meadway, London NW11 6PN ☎ 020 8458 5799, 0976 982372 mob

SYMES Anthony (*Sax, Clt*): 69 Burntwood Grange Road, London SW18 3JY ☎ 020 8870 1401

TALBOT Jamie (*Saxes, Clt, Flt, B Clt*): 41 St. Leonards Road, Claygate, Esher, Surrey KT10 0EL ☎ 01372 812952

TANTRUM Peter (*Saxes, Flt, Clt*): Sampaquita, 2 Troughton Place, Tewkesbury, Glos GL20 8EA ☎ 01684 293419

TAYLOR Laurie (*Sax, Clt, Voc*): 6 Broadstrood, Loughton, Essex IG10 2SE ☎ 020 8508 7744

TAYLOR Simon (*A Sax, S Sax*): Address Unknown ☎ 020 8870 1832

TELFER John (*Br Sax, Flt*): 29 Hunsdon Road, London SE14 5RD ☎ 020 7652 1734

TELFORD Jake (*Sax*): 41 The Homestead, Waterfall Road, London N11 1LH ☎ 020 7281 7113

TEMPLE David (*Sax, Clt*): 6 Beresford Drive, Woodford Green, Essex IG8 OJH ☎ 020 8505 7408

TEMPLE Harry (*Sax, Clt, B Ldr*): 140 Bethune Road, London N16 5DS ☎ 020 8800 0509

THEMEN Art (*T Sax, S Sax*): Whitley Glebe, 11 Glebe Road, Reading, Berkshire RG2 7AG ☎ 01734 312707, 01734 752097

THISTLETHWAITE Anthony (*Sax, B Gtr, Man*): Top Floor, 14 York Road, London W3 6TP ☎ 020 8993 8131

THOMAS Kevin (*A Sax*): 9 Muswell Road, Muswell Hill, London N10 2BJ ☎ 020 8444 9122

THOMAS Owen (*T Sax, A Sax, S Sax, Flt*): Flat 1, 1 Compton Terrace, London N1 2UN ☎ 020 7354 8447

THOMAS Peter (*Saxes*): 127 Ferndale Road, Brixton, London SW4 7RN ☎ 020 7737 8011, 020 7733 5903 fax

THOMAS Philip (*A Sax, T Sax, Flt, S Sax*): 27A Powis Terrace, London W11 1JJ ☎ 020 7727 1892

THOMAS Vincent (*T Sax*): 265C The Vale, Acton, London W3 7QA

THOMPSON MBE, Barbara (*Saxes, Com, Flt*): 48 The Ridgeway, Sutton, Surrey SM2 5JU ☎ 020 8642 3210

THOMPSON Gail (*T Sax, Clt, Flt, B Gtr*): 5 St Faiths Road, West Dulwich, London SE21 8JD ☎ 020 8674 5926, 020 8674 5926

THOMPSON James (*Sax, Clt, Flt*): 16 Bramley Crescent, Gants Hill, Ilford, Essex IG2 6DA ☎ 020 8554 7379

THOMPSON Sheik (*Sax, Flt, Voc*): 37 Hamilton Close, Chesnut Road, Tottenham, London N17 9EG ☎ 020 8808 6294 & fax

THOROGOOD David (*Sax, B Gtr, Gtr, Org*): The Old Forge, Dunmow Road, Fyfield, Essex CM5 0NN ☎ 01277 899550, 01277 899319

TOBIAS Sarah (*Sax, Clt, B Gtr, Per, Voc*): 3 Navarino Road, Hackney, London E8 1AD ☎ 020 7241 1864

TODD Phillip (*Sax, Clt, Flt*): 21 Church Drive, North Harrow, Middx HA2 7NP ☎ 020 8427 0888

TOMLINSON Jim (*Sax, Clt, Flt*): 52 Albert Road, Alexandra Park, London N22 7AH ☎ 020 8889 6740

TOMPSON Mike (*A Sax, Clt, Voc*): 17 York Road, Brentford, London, Middx TW8 0QP ☎ 020 8568 4517

TORRANCE Albert (*Sax*): 18A Chepstow Road, London W2 5BD ☎ 020 7727 6835

TOUSSAINT Jean (*Sax, Com*): 50 Crouch Hall Road, London N8 8HS

TOWNSEND Rob (*A Sax, A Sax, T Sax, Flt*): 109 Whittington Road, London N22 4YR ☎ 020 8881 5398

TRATT David (*A Sax, Pf, Kbds*): 15A Woodfield Hill, Coulsdon, Surrey CR5 3EL ☎ 01737 556287

TRAVIS Theodore (*T Sax, S Sax, Flt*): 20 Strathmore Gardens, Finchley, London N3 2HL ☎ 020 8349 3059

TRIMMER Ian (*Sax*): 13 Outram Road, Alexandra Park, London N22 7AB ☎ 020 8881 7510, 07970 532311 mob

TUCKER Julian (*Saxes, Flt, Kbds*): 1A Pineapple Road, Amersham, Bucks HP7 9JN ☎ 01494 764734, 0976 723384

TURLEY William (*A Sax, Clt*): 286 Malden Road, New Malden, Surrey KT3 6AT ☎ 020 8942 6822

TWEED Andrew (*Saxes, Flt, Clt*): 4 Elm Park Road, Winchmore Hill, London N21 2HN ☎ 0973 692497, 020 8350 7139 & fax

ULITZKA Ivan (*Sax, Pf*): 153 Flora Gardens, Dalling Road, Hammersmith, London W6 0HS ☎ 020 8746 3530

UNDERWOOD Jerry (*T Sax*): 35 Frederick Street, Kingscross, London WC1X 0NB ☎ 020 7833 0090

VAS Olavo (*Sax*): 30 Sanderstead Court Ave, Sanderstead, S Croydon CR2 9AG ☎ 020 8657 3744

VEACOCK Philip (*Sax, Clt, Pf*): 54 Wyndcliff Road, Charlton, London SE7 7JX ☎ 020 8858 2723

VELTMEIJER Angele (*Sax, Flt*): 74B Canterbury Road, Leyton, London E10 6EE ☎ 020 8558 7300

VENTURINI Marina (*Sax*): 33 Kellett Road, London SW2 1DX ☎ 020 7733 4413

VERNON Felicity (*A Sax, T Sax, Br Sax, Flt*): 28 Whitworth Road, Plumstead, London SE18 3QB ☎ 020 8855 3999

VICKERS Michael (*A Sax, Clt*): 6 Fender Orchard, Combwich, Nr Bridgewater, Somerset TA5 2JD ☎ 01278 653488, 01278 653405

WADE Michael (*A Sax, Br Sax*): 13 Mentmore Terrace, London Fields, London E8 3PN ☎ 020 8533 4111

WAKEMAN Alan (*Saxes, Clt, B Clt, Flt*): 2 Sanders Lane, Potterspury, Northants NN12 7QF ☎ 01908 542841

WALDRON Reginald (*T Sax, A Sax, Clt*): 40, Rutherwyk Road, Chertsey, Surrey KT16 9JD ☎ 01932 570851

WALLACE John (*Sax, Clt*): 34 Parkstone Avenue, Lower Parkstone, Poole, Dorset BH14 9LA ☎ 01202 721689, 0421 830989

WALTON Dennis (*Sax, Clt, Flt, Pic, Cntrc*): 8 Redhill Court, Palace Road, London SW2 3NP ☎ 020 8674 2672

WAREHAM Pete (*Saxes, Flt, Pf*): Ground Floor Flat, 73 Rye Hill Park, Peckham, London SE15 3JS ☎ 020 7640 0570, 0973 957641 mob

WARGENT Richard (*T Sax, Flt, A Sax*): 15 Palmerston Court, Royal Victor Place, Bow, London E3 5SA ☎ 020 8980 5776

WARLEIGH Raymond (*Saxes, Pic, Flt, Clt, B Clt*): 11 Chancellors Street, London W6 9RN ☎ 020 8741 2128

WARNER Peter (*T Sax, Flt, Clt*): The Midlands, 15 Broadwater Gdns, Farnborough, Kent BR6 7UQ ☎ 016 8985 3334

WATERHOUSE Percy (*Sax, Clt*): Water House, Watery Lane, Goulcedy, Lincolnshire LN11 9UR ☎ 01507 343784

WATES Matt (*A Sax, S Sax, Flt*): The Lodge, Riverview Gardens, London SW13 9QY ☎ 020 8741 4667

WATSON Jason (*Sax, Clt, Hmca*): Flat B, 21 Millman Street, Bloomsbury, London WC1N 3EP ☎ 0958 569199 mob

WATTS George (*A Sax, Clt, Flt, Pic, So Sax*): Bloque 3/2C, Calpe Park, 03710 Calpe (Alicante), Spain ☎ +34 96 583 6737

WEARNE Sarah (*Sax, Flt, Clt*): 58 Quaker Court, Banner Street, London EC1 8QB ☎ 0966 539585

WEBB David (*Sax, Clt, Flt, Kbds*): 229 Marlborough Road, Romford, Essex RM7 8AP ☎ 01708 760925

WEBB Tony (*T Sax, Clt*): 17 Lustrells Close, Saldean, Sussex BN2 8AS ☎ 01273 304075

WEIMAR Paul (*T Sax, A Sax, S Sax, Br Sax,*): 38 Woodmans Croft, Fairford Leys, Aylesbury, Bucks HP17 8FU ☎ 0370 977337

WELLER Don *(T Sax, S Sax)*: 9 Upwood Road, London SW16 5RB ☎ 020 8764 2623

WELLINGS George *(Saxes, Clt, Flt, Pic)*: 33 Chapel Avenue, Brownhills, Walsall, W Midlands WS8 7NT ☎ 01543 375921

WELLMAN Jim *(Sax, Gtr, B Gtr, Per)*: 9 Barwell House, Chester Street, Bethnal Green, London E2 6HZ ☎ 020 7613 1052

WESTON John *(Sax, Clt, Flt, Pf, Acc)*: 180 London Road, Twickenham, Middx TW1 1EX ☎ 020 8892 1696

WHELAN John *(A Sax, B Sax, Flt, Cntrc)*: Wilden, Kiln Road, Prestwood, Great Missenden, Bucks HP16 9DG ☎ 01494 865258

WHITE Christopher *(Saxes, Flt, Clt)*: Irish Hill House, Irish Hill, Hamstead Marshall, Newbury, Berkshire RG20 0JB ☎ 01488 657221, 01488 608718

WHITE Frank *(Saxes, Clt, Flt, Pic, B Clt)*: 16 Bramley Crescent, Gants Hill, Ilford, Essex IG2 6DA ☎ 020 8554 7379

WHITEHEAD Tim *(Saxes, Flt)*: 5 Willow Bank, Richmond, Surrey TW10 7QY ☎ 020 8948 0687

WHITLOCK Gavin *(Sax, Clt)*: 16 Springfield, Clapton, London E5 9EF ☎ 020 8806 8879, 0976 942 578 mob

WHITTER Winston *(Sax)*: 23 Gordon Road, Leyton, London E15 2DD ☎ 020 8539 5477, 07957 208 687 mob

WHITTLE Tommy *(Saxes, B Clt, Flt, A Flt, Pic)*: 29 Oundle Avenue, Bushey, Hertfordshire WD2 3QG ☎ 020 8950 5338

WICKS Brian *(Sax)*: Address Unknown

WIGFIELD Leslie *(Saxes, Clt, Flt)*: 24 Elmfield Road, Tooting, London SW17 8AL ☎ 020 8673 6392, 0403 43 784

WILBER Bob *(S Sax, A Sax, Clt)*: M'Dina, Park Rd, Chipping Campden, Glos. GL55 6EA ☎ 01386 841217, 01386 841517 fax

WILCOX Mike *(A Sax, Br Sax, Clt, T Sax, Fl)*: Laurel Lodge, Perry Hill, Worplesdon, Surrey GU3 3RB ☎ 01483 233989

WILKINSON Alan *(A Sax, Br Sax, S Sax)*: 36 Arbor Court, Queen Elizabeths Walk, London N16 0QU ☎ 020 8809 6891

WILLIAMS Barry *(T Sax)*: 18 Essex Court, Station Road, Barnes, London SW13 0ER ☎ 020 8876 8167

WILLIAMS Geoff *(Sax, Flt, Clt)*: 7 Amberley Way, Morden, Surrey SM4 5QP ☎ 020 8648 6092, 0976 206545 mob

WILLIAMS Martin *(Sax, Wood W, Arr, Wi Synth)*: 350A Headstone Lane, Harrow, Middx HA3 6NS ☎ 0973 690588, 020 8621 6592

WILLIAMS Michael *(A Sax, Flt, Dms)*: 12A Cromwell Avenue, Highgate, London N6 5HL ☎ 020 8348 1409

WILLIAMS Sean *(Sax)*: 27 Burwash Road, Plumstead, London SE18 7QY ☎ 020 8854 5908, 020 8855 5054

WILLIAMS, BMUS (HONS) Caroline *(Saxes, Clt, Pf)*: Ground Floor Flat, 6 Exeter Road, London NW2 ☎ 020 8452 7064

WILLIS Dave *(A Sax, Br Sax, Clt)*: 23 Chestnut Road, West Norwood, London SE27 9EZ ☎ 020 8670 3020

WILLOX Roy *(Sax, Clt, Flt)*: 6 Hawtrees, Watford Road, Radlett, Herts WD7 8LP ☎ 01923 855305

WILLSON Tony *(T Sax, Kbds)*: 10 Campion Drive, Deeping St James, Peterborough PE6 8TB ☎ 01778 345157

WILSON Andrew *(T Sax, A Sax, S Sax, Tbn)*: Flat 64 Victoria Wahrf, 46 Narrow Street, Limehouse, London E14 8DD ☎ 020 7987 2762

WILSON Roger *(Saxes, Clt, Flt)*: 14 Tormount Road, London SE18 ☎ 020 8317 9749, 0831 391019

WINDLEY Roy *(T Sax, Br Sax, Clt)*: 51 Courtlands Avenue, Lee Green, London SE12 8JJ ☎ 020 8852 7177

WINN Matthew *(Sax)*: 39 Church Hill, London N21 9PZ ☎ 020 8886 6213

WOOD Diana *(A Sax, Voc, T Sax, S Sax)*: 10 Kenmara Close, Three Bridges, Crawley, West Sussex RH10 2AN ☎ 01293 546322, 01293 404745

WOODCOCK Neil *(T Sax, A Sax, Flt, Clt)*: The Lilacs, 26 Willow Lane, Amersham, Bucks HP7 9DW ☎ 01494 721840

WOODS Anthony *(Saxes, Clt, Flt, Pf)*: 73 Isobel House, Staines Road West, Sunbury-on-Thames, Middlesex TW16 7BD ☎ 01932 780657

WOODS Laurie *(A Sax, Clt)*: 12 Hollybush Hill, Highstone, Leytonstone, London E11 1PP ☎ 020 8989 1366

WRATHALL William *(A Sax)*: 6 Carville Crescent, Brentford, Middlesex TW8 9RD

WRIXTON Maurice *(T Sax, A Sax, Br Sax, Pic, Fl)*: 353 Sandycombe Road, Kew, Surrey TW9 3PR ☎ 020 8948 2964

YARDE Jason *(Saxes, Kbds)*: 19 Rowden Road, Beckenham, Kent BR3 4NA ☎ 020 8658 1479

YEOMANS William *(Sax, Flt, Clt, Pf, Gtr)*: 14 Worsley Road, Leytonstone, London E11 3JN ☎ 020 8519 3172

YORK Clive *(T Sax, S Sax)*: 72 North Hill, London N6 4RH ☎ 020 8348 7561

ZEC Paul *(A Sax, S Sax)*: 139 Eastcombe Avenue, London SE7 7LL ☎ 020 8858 1269

SCRATCHER

NORTH WEST

DAVE THE RUF *(Kbds, Voc)*: c/o Ruf Beats, PO Box 118, Altringham, Cheshire WA15 6AX ☎ 0161 286 0935

DJ PRESSURE *(Rapper)*: 24 Police Street, Eccles, Patricroft, Manchester M30 0RD ☎ 0161 661 9383

EAST

RAYNER Peter: 181 Thornbury Road, Isleworth, Middlesex TW7 4QG ☎ 020 8560 5805

MIDLANDS

DE SALVO Joe *(Club Dj, Kbds, Dms)* ☎ 01952 289470

SOUTH WEST

WALDRON Tim *(Dms, Kbds)*: 31 All Halows Road, Easton, Bristol BS5 0HL ☎ 0117 939 8961

LONDON

CLEMENTS Joel *(Dms)*: Flat 7 Chestnut House, Chestnut Road, London SE27 9EZ ☎ 020 8670 1388, 0956 302240

DJ AWE *(Kbds)*: 5 Coombe Lodge, Charlton, London SE7 7PE ☎ 020 8853 1451

KAYE Richard *(Club DJ)*: Estbury, Talbot Road, Lyme Regis, Dorset DT7 3BB ☎ 01297 445675, 0958 900702

SHAKUHACHI

LONDON

BELL Clive *(Flt, Acc)*: 1 Clyde Circus, London N15 4LF ☎ 020 8802 9839

HIROTA Joji *(Per, Com)*: 242 Worton Road, Isleworth, Middx TW7 6EF ☎ 020 8568 0240

SHEHANAI

LONDON

DURVESH Kadir *(Flt)*: 96 Studley Grange Road, Hanwell, London W7 2LX ☎ 020 8579 9450

SHOZYGS

LONDON

DAVIES Hugh: 25 Albert Road, London N4 3RR ☎ 020 7272 5508

SITAR

SOUTH WEST

PERKINS John *(Tabla, Gtr, Clt)*: The Convent, Old Exeter Road, Chudleigh, Newton Abbot Devon TQ13 0LD ☎ 01626 853387, 01626 854066

ROMAIN Ricky *(Surb, Tabla)*: The Flat, 1 West Street, Axminster, Devon EX13 5NU ☎ 01297 35807

LONDON

FARRELL Gerard *(Gtr)*: 41 Drayton Gardens, London W13 0LG ☎ 020 8997 7621 & fax

GUPTA Punita *(Tamp)*: 88 Kingsfield Avenue, North Harrow, Middlesex HA2 6AS ☎ 020 8427 3530, 020 8248 5138

MARKANDAY Sheila (*Harm, Tamp, Kbds*): 64 Colin Park Road, Colindale, London NW9 6HS ☎ 020 8205 8942

MAYER Jonathan (*Com*): 27 Hermitage Road, London N4 1DF ☎ 020 8802 2421

SRIVASTAV Baluji (*Tabla, Voc*): 33 Northolme Road, London N5 2UU ☎ 020 7226 2094

SONGWRITER

SCOTLAND

MCLAUGHLIN John: c/o Backlash, 54 Carlton Place, Glasgow G5 9TW ☎ 0141 418 0053

TREANOR Tam: The Point Management, 132 Royal College Street, London NW1 0TA ☎ 020 7424 9410, 020 7424 9401 fax

NORTH WEST

CLARE Peter (*Kbds, Pf*): Flat 3, 8 St Pauls Road, Salford, Lancs M7 3NY ☎ 0161 792 2891

JAMAC: 17 Mozart Close, Ancoats, Manchester M4 6JU ☎ 0161 205 9871, 0973 690710 mob

LEGH Tara (*Voc*): 30 West Avenue, Altrincham, Cheshire WA14 4JG ☎ 0161 941 1687

SEARLE James: Carthagena, Ruff Lane, Ormskirk, Lancashire L39 4QX ☎ 01695 575671

NORTH EAST

MARVELOUS: 17 Louis Grove, Leeds 7 LS7 4RJ ☎ 01132 374396, 0961 833846

EAST

HEATH Michael (*Voc, Gtr, B Gtr*): 19 Lords Robert Avenue, Leigh-on-Sea, Essex SS9 1ND ☎ 01702 75377

MIDLANDS

HARD-KAUR (*Rapper*): 29 Stafford Road, Handsworth, Birmingham B21 9DU ☎ 0121 551 9400, 0956 629676 mob

HOWELL Patrick: Flat 17/124 Sycamore Road, Stapenhill, Burton-on-Trent DE15 9NX ☎ 01283 530260, 07970 779481

PICKERING Ian: 50 Bournbrook Road, Selly Oak, Birmingham B29 7BT ☎ 0121 472 2316

SKILLMASTER: 14 Longmead Close, Edwards Lane, Arnold, Nottingham NG5 6EF ☎ 0115 9263081, 07971 567197

SOUTH EAST

ALLARDYCE Gavin: 23 North Park, Richings Park, Iver, Buckinghamshire SL0 9DH

EADE Winston (*Com*): 8 Upper Bourne Lane, Boundstone, Farnham, Surrey GU10 4RQ ☎ 01252 792152, 0802 277133 mob

HIGGINS Brian: The Old Cottage, Beadles Lane, Old Oxted, Surrey RH8 9JG ☎ 01883 714 158

PHILLIPS Elliott (*Voc*): 11 Devereux Place, Rose Hill, Oxford OX4 4RP ☎ 01865 395307

SOUTH WEST

ALLEN Rob (*Gtr, Voc, Dms*): 23 Wauntreoda Road, The Philog, Whitchurch, Cardiff, South Glamorgan CF4 1HS ☎ 029 2021 8362

BLOY Graham: 3Mthe Quadrant, Bristol, Avon BS6 7JI ☎ 0117 973 5984

DAVIES Jonathan (*Kbds*): Flat 2, 242 Newport Road, Roath, Cardiff CF2 1RR ☎ 029 2030 7779

DAVIES Martin: 5 Windy Ridge, Manorbier, Tenby, Pembrokeshire SA70 7TX ☎ 01834 871196

SHAKEY: 33 Lower Redannick, Truro, Cornwall TR1 2JW ☎ 01872 260167

VEE J. (*Lyric*): 20 Elm Close, Broadclyst, Nr Exeter, Devon EX5 3LT ☎ 01392 461479

LONDON

AUSTEN Michael (*Arr*): 71 Westcottcrescent, Hanwell, Middx W7 1PL ☎ 020 8575 8160

BARRY Kenneth (*Gtr*): 9 Mapledene Estate, Mapledene Road, Hackney, London E8 3LM ☎ 020 7254 4881

BEATTIE Cheryl ☎ 020 8964 0404, 020 8969 5231

BIRCH Gina (*Voc, Gtr*): 27A Monmouth Road, London W2 4UT ☎ 020 7229 3622

BROWN Castell: 26B Buchnan Gdns, Kensall Rise, London NW10 5AE ☎ 020 8969 8495

BRULEY David (*Voc, Gtr*): 62 Belmont Road, Belmont, Surrey SM2 6DW ☎ 020 8661 1486

BULL Irene: 18 The Bramblings, Chingford, London E4 6LU ☎ 020 8529 5807 & fax

CATTO James (*Voc, Dms*): Flat 2, 5 Denning Road, London NW3 1ST ☎ 020 7435 9774

CHAPMAN Richard: 100 Reddown Road, Coulsdon, Surrey CR5 1AL ☎ 01737 554356, 01737 361060

COPELAND Valerie (*Voc*): 11 Halliwell Road, Brixton Hill, London SW2 5HB ☎ 020 7207 4153

CRAY Marianne (*Voc*)

CUFFY Christine (*Voc*): 44 Radnor Road, Peckham, London SE15 6UR ☎ 020 7635 9426

D Mikey: 44 Warner Road, Walthamstow, London E17 7DZ ☎ 0956 872763 mob

DUVOISIN Michel (*B Gtr, Gtr, Pf, Tpt*): 1 Broomfield Cottages, Broomfield Road, London W13 9AT ☎ 020 8840 2753, 020 8566 2375 fax

ETTI Tunde (*Kbds, Pf*): 53 Blaydon Close, Northumberland Park, London N17 0TW ☎ 020 8808 9013

EVELYN Alison (*Com, Voc*): 13 Welshpool House, Broadway Market, Hackney, London E8 4PE

FOSTER Robert (*Voc, Kbds, Rh Gtr, B Gtr*): 79 Wharfedale Gardens, Thornton Heath, Surrey CR7 6LE ☎ 020 8684 4625 & fax, 0410 212821 mob

GACHET Dr. S.: 31 Empire House, Gt Cambridge Road, Edmonton, London N18 1EA ☎ 0831 399177

GREENWOOD Alan: 18A Lawford Road, Kentish Town, London NW5 2LN ☎ 020 7424 0172

HENRY Jason (*Com, Voc*): 110A Ringstead Road, Catford, London SE6 2BS ☎ 020 8698 6342

INNISS David (*Kbds*): 456 North Circular Road, Neasden, London NW10 1SP ☎ 020 8450 9241

JACOBS St.Clair: 3 Milton House Mansions, Shacklewell Lane, London E8 2EH

JOHNSON Holly (*Voc*): PO Box 425, London SW6 3TX, 020 7736 9212

JOHNSON Robb (*Voc, Gtr*): P O Box 72, Hounslow, Middlesex TW5 0YB ☎ 0958 236 103 mob

LEAHY Terence (*Kbds*): 30 Ardleigh, Basildon, Essex SS16 5RA ☎ 01268 412673

LLOYD Eddie (*Voc*): 96 Gassiot Road, Tooting, London SW17 8LA ☎ 020 8672 5137, 0973 728817

MACHIN Timothy (*Rh Gtr, Voc*): 2A Hercules Street, London N7 6AS ☎ 020 7272 4703

MARCH Neil (*Kbds, Gtr, B Gtr, Vla*): 1 Romborough Way, Lewisham, London SE13 6NS ☎ 020 8488 0158

MASHITER Peter H.: 1-7-3-404 Sakuragi, Tada, Kawanishi-Shi, Hyogo 666-01, Japan ☎ 0727 92 6481

NICHOLAS Nicholas: Flat 7, 60 Warwick Gardens, London W14 8PP ☎ 020 7602 8061

POWELL Teresa: 14 Schofield Walk, Blackheath, London SE3 7DA ☎ 020 8305 2591, 0411 342736

Q-DOT (*Rapper*): 25 Bay Court, North Parade, Chessington, Surrey KT9 1QN ☎ 020 8397 2169, 0956 908829 mob

RUSSELL Mark (*Com, B Gtr, Gtr, Pf*): 25 Witham Road, Isleworth, Middlesex TW7 4AJ

SINGH Bakhshish (*Voc*)

TAUBER Simon (*Voc*): 18 Manor Rd, Richmond, Surrey TW9 1YB ☎ 020 8940 4604

WALCOTT Mark (*Com, Pf, Kbds, Sax*): 10 Eastlea Mews, London E16 4NY ☎ 020 7473 1514

WRIGHT Jonathan: Flat 5, 3 Alexandra Grove, Finsbury Park, London N4 2LG ☎ 020 8802 3511

WUSU Metonu *(Voc, Per)*: 27 Lister Court, Pasteur Close, London NW9 5HZ ☎ 0958 618045

SOPRANO CORNET
NORTH WEST

THOMAS Sylvia *(Clt, Pf)*: Trefin, Hill Street, Rhosllanerchrugog, Wrexham LL14 1LW ☎ 01978 845909

SOUSAPHONE
NORTH WEST

MORRIS James *(Tba, B Gtr)*: 14 Wickenby Drive, Sale, Cheshire M33 7UY ☎ 0161 962 5785

SMITH Pete *(Tba, V Tbn, Eup, Br Hrn)*: 6 Sandiway, Shirebrook Park, Glossop, Derbyshire SK13 8SS ☎ 01457 869795

EAST

FULLALOVE Robert: Adelaide Cottage, Swallows Cross, Brentwood, Essex CM15 0SS ☎ 01277 352522

HOUSTON Andrew: 13 The Causeway, Burwell, Cambridge CB5 0DU

PRING Derek *(Tba)*: 9 Hillary Close, Chelmsford, Essex CM1 7RR ☎ 01245 266637

MIDLANDS

BALE Maurice *(Saxes, Tbn)*: 18 Raleigh Rd, Coventry CV2 4AA ☎ 024 7645 9409

SKED Malcolm: Barn Cottage, Brook End, Chastleton, Moreton In Marsh Glos GL56 0TA ☎ 01608 74496

WESTON Bryan *(Tbn, Bjo, Gtr)*: May Cottage, 41 Park Road, Moira, Swadlincote DB12 6BJ ☎ 01283 760348

SOUTH EAST

HEATH Jim: 126 Hillside, Brighton, East Sussex BN2 4TE ☎ 01273 694450

JONES Martin *(Tba, Eup, Tbn, V Tbn)*: 18 Porteous Crescent, Chandlers Ford, Eastleigh, Hampshire SO53 2DH ☎ 023 8026 9508, 0589 968830 mob, 023 8025 5225

WATERS Chris: Trewurzel, 258 Main Road, Southbourne, Emsworth Hants PO10 8JL ☎ 01243 379330

SOUTH WEST

WILLEY Richard: 16 Suffolk Crescent, Galmington, Taunton, Somerset TA1 4JN ☎ 01823 278039

LONDON

HART Laurie *(Tba)*: 188 Nether Street, Finchley, London N3 1PE ☎ 020 8343 1803

HILL David: 16 Priory Hill, Wembley, Middlesex HA0 2QF ☎ 020 8904 8887

KINLOCH Alice *(Tbn, Tba, Eup)*: The Garden Flat, 291A Stanstead Rd, London SE23 1JB ☎ 020 8690 9175, 0410 387087

PITE Richard *(Tba, Db, B Sax, Dms)*: 26 Harold Road, Leytonstone, London E11 4QY ☎ 020 8539 5229, 020 8556 9545 fax

PRESMAN Dini *(Db, Tbn)*: 7 St.Olaves Gardens, Walnut Tree Walk, London SE11 6DR ☎ 020 7735 8104

TOMES Francis *(Bjo)*: 25 Church Path, Merton Park, London SW19 3HJ ☎ 020 8542 4942

STEEL PAN
NORTH EAST

EDWARDS David John *(Gtr, B Gtr, Man)*: Aynucks Lodge, 20 Glendale Avenue, Whitley Bay, Tyne & Wear NE26 1RX ☎ 0191 253 4981

MIDLANDS

JAMMA: 105 Well Street, Newtown, Birmingham B19 3AZ ☎ 0121 554 3413, 0121 554 3413

O'LOUGHLIN William *(Saxes, Clt, B Ldr, Flt)*: 133 Boyne Road, Sheldon, Birmingham B26 2QG ☎ 0121 628 9931

SOUTH EAST

GIBSON Wayne *(Flt, B Gtr)*: 4A Beresford Gardens, Christchurch, Dorset BH23 3QW ☎ 01202 474698

HAYWARD Rachel: 19B Hampstead Road, Brighton BN1 5NG ☎ 01273 553943

SOUTH WEST

CLARKE Toussaint: c/o 5 Charmouth Road, Bath BA1 3LJ ☎ Bath 28872

FIELDS Roger: c/o 5 Charmouth Road, Bath BA1 3LJ

HAREWOOD Andy: c/o 5 Charmouth Road, Bath BA1 3LJ

IFILL Hallam: 5 Charmouth Road, Lower Weston, Bath, Avon BA1 3LJ ☎ 01225 311952

IFILL Melvin *(Dms)*: 5 Charmouth Road, Lower Weston, Bath, Avon BA1 3LJ ☎ Bath 311952

SKINNER Nigel: c/o 5 Charmouth Road, Bath BA1 3LJ

SOBERS Richard: c/o 5 Charmouth Road, Bath BA1 3LJ ☎ Radstock 35236

LONDON

BRAVO Bravo *(Djembe, Cong)*: 17 Therene Court, Tooting Bec Road, London SW17 8BJ ☎ 020 8767 7958

CARTY Joseph: 22 Kings Avenue, Hounslow, Middlesex TW3 4BL ☎ 020 8572 0427

DIAS Clyde: 17 A Wotton Road, London NW2 6PU

GUNNING Hugo *(La Per)*: 24A Furness Road, London NW10 4QD ☎ 020 8965 1965

PELTIER Richard *(Dms, Per)*: 155 Capel Road, Forest Gate, London E7 0JT ☎ 020 8478 2318, 0956 524777

TROTMAN Gary *(Dms, Kbds)*: 24 Saint Johns Road, Southall, Middlesex UB2 5AN ☎ 0973 325822 mob

STRINGS
LONDON

VENEGAS Maurigo *(Flt, Gtr, Pan P, Per)*: 19 Crossbow Road, Chigwell, Essex IG7 4EY ☎ 020 8500 3044

SYNTHESISER
SCOTLAND

FORD Andy: Flat 8, 21 Sloan Street, Edinburgh EH6 8PN ☎ 0131 467 6824, 0131 467 7375

GILL Michael *(Pf)*: Wester Jaw Cottage, Slammanan, Falkirk FK11 1DS ☎ 01324 851507

LIVINGSTON David *(Kbds, Song W, Com, Per)*: 596 Pollockshaws Road, Glasgow G41 2PJ ☎ 0141 423 4535 fax, 0385 536 980

REID Alan *(Org)*: 9 Dundas Avenue, Torrance, Scotland G64 4BD ☎ 01360 622114

SEATH Ian: 8 Havelock Street, Hawick, Scotland TD9 7BB ☎ 01450 376822

UNIVERSAL EAR *(E Gtr)*: 52 Penicuik Road, Roslin, Midlothian EH25 9LH ☎ 0131 440 1690

NORTH WEST

ASHCROFT Nicholas *(Gtr, Kbds)*: 70 Millbrook Lane, St. Helens, Merseyside WA10 4QY ☎ 01744 25409

CUBBON Philip *(Kbds)*: 2 College Green, Castletown, Isle Of Man IM9 1BE ☎ 01624 822464

TIMONEY Michael *(Acc, Cord, Md)*: Ty'N Twll Cottage, Llanrwst Road, Glan Conwy, Colwyn Bay Clwyd LL28 5SR ☎ 01492 573451

NORTH EAST

AVERY John ☎ 0114 268 2359, 0973 310645 mob

COLLINS David *(Pf, Org)*: 701 Leeds & Bradford Road, Stanningley, Pudsey, West Yorkshire LS28 6PE ☎ 0113 2568789

FOX Robert *(Dms, Club Dj)* ☎ 0113 2781656, 0113 2781656

SOAR Andrew *(Kbds)*: 70 Springfield Road, Grantham, Lincs NG31 7BE ☎ 01476 65407

WILSON Richard *(Pf, Voc)*: 11 Greenwood Mt, Meanwood, Leeds LS6 4LG ☎ 0113 2755244

WRAY John *(Pf, Org)*: 13 Green Lane, Spennymoor, Co Durham DL16 6HE ☎ 01388 814632

WRIGHT Tim *(Pf)*: 6 Finsbury Street, York YO23 1LT ☎ 01904 629570, 01904 629570

EAST

BUNTING Stephen *(Kbds, Tpt, Per, Gtr)*: 24 Layston Park, Royston, Herts SG8 9DS ☎ 01763 246122

J. Michael: 19 Back Church Lane, London E1 1LQ ☎ 020 7709 0792

RAMIREZ John *(Mldn, Voc)*: 3 Faraday Road, Ipswich, Suffolk IP4 1PU ☎ 01473 446018

MIDLANDS

JOYCE Paul *(Pf)*: 25 Burlington Road, Sherwood, Nottingham NG5 2GR ☎ 0115 9620131

KRISTY Andrew *(Kbds, Pf, Org)*: Cream Cottage, 4 Church Lane, Martin Hussingtree, Worcs WR3 8TQ ☎ 01905 755421

LANGELAAN Stuart: 21 Northwood Road, Belvidere Paddocks, Shrewsbury, Shropshire SY2 5LH ☎ 01743 350040

REVEAL K M A: 29 Kent Road, Mapperley, Nottingham NG3 6BE ☎ 0973 414197

STANLEY Sean *(Gtr)*: 9 Dog Lane, Netherseal, Swadlincote, Derbys DE12 8DE ☎ 01283 760564 & fax

STEWART Malc: 39 Nauls Mill House, Middleborough Road, Radford, Coventry CV1 4BZ ☎ 024 7655 9728

SOUTH EAST

ATRILL Peter *(Gtr)*: 2 Castle Lane, Carisbrooke, Newport, Isle Of Wight PO30 1PH ☎ 01983 526847

COX Chris: 45 Rivermead, Pulborough, West Sussex RH20 2DA

EDWARDS Steven *(Kbds)*: 8A Poole Road, Upton, Poole, Dorset BH16 5JA ☎ 01202 776612, 07970 794463

FERGUSON David *(Md, Com)*: 62 Roupell Street, London SE1 8SS ☎ 020 7620 1202

FRYER Nicholas: 20 Loxwood Road, Lovedean, Waterlooville, Hants PO8 9TU ☎ 023 9259 9767

GEESIN Ron *(Hmca, Pf, Gtr, Bjo)*: Headrest, Street End Lane, Broadoak, Heathfield E. Sussex TN21 8TU ☎ 01435 863994

GILLESPIE Oliver: 17 Canada Road, Woolston, Southampton, Hampshire SO19 9DQ ☎ 023 8042 2506

HARTNOLL Phillip: 187 London Road, Dunton Green, Sevenoaks, Kent TN13 2TB ☎ 01732 462 392

MARTIN Stanley: Top Flat, 176 Rock Avenue, Gillingham, Kent ME7 5PF ☎ 01634 281599

MCCARTHY Kevin *(Pf, Gtr)*: 134 St. Georges Crescent, Chippenham, Slough, Berkshire SL1 5PD ☎ 01628 663980, 01628 603252

WEIR Daniel: 29 Ferndene Way, Midanbury, Southampton SO18 4SZ ☎ 023 8090 5613

SOUTH WEST

LEYSHON Stephen *(Kbds, Gtr)*: 3 Ffordd Afan, Cwmafan, Port Talbot, West Glamorgan SA12 9BR ☎ 01639896845, 0585 890481

MARK Jodie *(Gtr)*: The White Heron, Old Polzeath, Nr Wadebridge, Cornwall PL27 6TJ ☎ 01208 863623

LONDON

ATTIKOURIS Theodore *(Gtr)*: 14 Corringham Road, Wembley, Middlesex HA9 9PZ ☎ 020 8904 1537

BARBER David *(Pf, Kbds, Md, Cop)*: Flat 2, 11 Oak Road, Ealing, London W5 3SS ☎ 020 8840 2446, 020 8840 2446

BLAKE Tim *(Hmca, Gtr)*: Le Moulin A, Vent De Coet-Bihan, 56230, Questembert, France ☎ +33 97 26 15 02

BLISS Paul Steven: 70 Park Road, New Barnet, Herts EN4 9QF ☎ 020 8440 3652

COCKBAIN Garry: Keith Webb, Freedom Management, 19 Brunswick Terrace, Brighton, Sussex BN3 1HL ☎ 01273 748599

COTTLE Richard *(Clt)*: 44 Lower Road, Higher Denham, Bucks UB9 5EB ☎ 01895 832186

COX Tim *(Gtr, Dms)*: c/o Liz Roberts, Sgo Music Management, The Old Brewery, Church Street Tisbury, Salisbury Wiltshire SP3 6NH ☎ 01747 871563, 01747 871564 fax

DOUGANS Brian: Keith Webb, Freedom Management, 19 Brunswick Terrace, Brighton, Sussex BN3 1HL ☎ 01273 748599

ENIAC *(Kbds, Dms, Club Dj)*: 160 New Cross Road, New Cross, London SE14 5AA ☎ 020 7732 8663

ENO Brian: Opal Ltd (Attn.Jane Geerts), 3 Pembridge Mews, London W11 3EQ ☎ 020 7727 8656, 020 7221 4901

FISHMAN Paul *(Kbds, Flt, Com, Arr)*: 34 Hampstead Lane, London N6 4NT ☎ 020 8340 2925

FROST Stephen *(Vln)*: 16A Darell Road, Kew, Richmond, Surrey TW9 4LQ ☎ 020 8878 3845

GI *(Dms)*: 20 Kellington Road, Canvey Island, Essex SS8 8EH

GILBERT Mark *(Voc, Kbds, Gtr, Sax)*: 41A Woodhouse Road, North Finchley, London N12 9ET ☎ 020 8445 1225

GRAY Andy *(Kbds)*: 37 High Street, Codicote, Hitchin, Herts SG4 8XB ☎ 01438 821676 & fax, 01850 457780

HARPER Cloff *(Dms)*: 60 Sedgeford Road, Shepherds Bush, London W12 0NB ☎ 020 8743 4064, 020 8743 8741 day

HUGHES Gary: 7 Whitecroft Street, Monmouth, Wales NP5 3BY ☎ 01600 715967

KENNERDALE Caspar *(Per)*: Ground Floor, 41 Victoria Crescent, London SE19 1AE ☎ 020 8670 4450

LAWSON Dave *(Kbds)*: 12 St Lawrence Avenue, Bidborough, Tunbridge Wells TN4 0XB ☎ 01892 41993

LEMER Peter *(Pf, Com, Arr, Md)*: Glebe House, Gt Hallingbury, Nr Bishops Stortford, Herts CM22 7TY ☎ 01279 654025

LEONARD John *(Kbds, Per)*: 10 Belsize Park, Hampstead, London NW3 4ES ☎ 020 7794 5942

MARSH Henry *(Pf, Gtr)*: The Red Cottage, Rood Ashton, Trowbridge, Wilts BA14 6BL ☎ 01380 870489

MEHTA Vikesh *(Kbds)*: 24 Greenway Gardens, Colindale, London NW9 5AX ☎ 020 8931 0001, 0956 975566 mob

MITCHELL Dennis *(Pf, Gtr)*: 142 625 6744 pager, 020 8993 8875

OAKLEY Barrington *(Scratch)* ☎ 020 8797 9883, 0956 501142

OSBORNE Douglas: 41B British Grove South, Chiswick, London W4 2PU ☎ 020 8741 0519, 020 8748 1729

PLASTIKMAN: c/o Novamute Records, 429 Harrow Road, London W10 4PE ☎ 020 8969 8866

RAMM David *(Hpsd, Acc)*: 2 Shrewsbury Lane, Shooters Hill, London SE18 3JF ☎ 020 8856 7112

REYNOLDS Carl *(Gtr)* ☎ 020 8482 2368

RICHARDS Andrew *(Kbds)*: 11 Burlington Road, Chiswick, London W4 4BQ ☎ 020 8400 9018, 020 8742 0267

RICHARDSON Christopher *(Org, Pf, Acc, Arr)*: 60 Claremont Road, Lonson W13 0DG ☎ 020 8997 4181

SMYTH Damian *(Kbds, Voc, Gtr, B Gtr)*: 5 Mandeville Court, Finchley Road, London NW7 6HB ☎ 020 7431 9168

SPENCER Lee: 1 Cowcross Street, London EC1M 6DR ☎ 020 7251 2538, 0956 504747 mob, 020 7490 3684

STARKS Gavin *(Pf, Sax, Clt)*: 95K Westbourne Terrace, London W2 6QT ☎ 020 7262 4565

STEELE Richard *(Org, Kbds, Pf, E Gtr)*: 5 Craig House, 75 Belsize Road, London NW6 4AX ☎ 020 7624 0619

SUTHERLAND Kevin *(Kbds)*: 169 Farmilo Road, Walthamstow, London E17 8JP ☎ 020 8539 3964

SWANSTON Nigel: c/o Liz Roberts, Sgo Music Management, The Old Brewery, Church Street Tisbury, Salisbury Wiltshire SP3 6NH ☎ 01747 871563, 01747 871564 fax

TEE-BIRDD Jamaka *(Gtr, B Gtr, Voc, Per)*: 7 Carlisle Avenue, Kingston 8, Jamaica, West Indies WI ☎ 809 924 6695

TERRY Ian *(Org, Pf)*: 12 Orlando Road, Clapham, London SW4 0LF ☎ 020 7622 0469

THORNE Michael: 15 Buckingham Court, Kensington Park Road, London W11 3BP ☎ 020 7727 1194

WRIGHT Daniel: 45 Baker Street, Enfield, Middx EN1 3EU ☎ 020 8363 0951

YASEEN Wajid *(B Gtr, Gtr)*: Flat 3, 65 Linden Gardens, London W2 4HJ ☎ 020 7727 5334

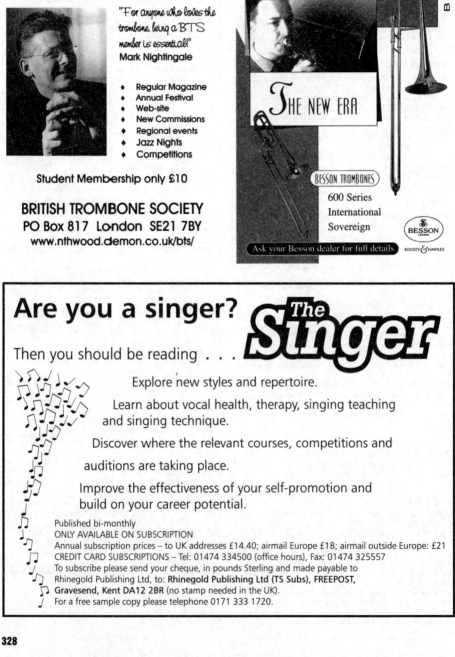

TABLA

MIDLANDS

SABRI G (*Ind Per*): 25, Mark House, Wake Green Road, Moseley, Birmingham B13 9HA ☎ 0121 449 2529

SINGH Harjit (*Dholak*): 21 Argyle Road, Blakenhall, Wolverhampton WV2 4NY ☎ 01902 342831

SINGH Mohinder (*Dholak*): 48 Park Road, Moseley, Birmingham B13 8AH ☎ 0121 449 9768

LONDON

KHAN Yousef (*Harm, Dholak*): 30 Chalfont Green, Edmonton, London N9 9RF ☎ 020 8803 7536, 0956 474398, 020 8372 0991

KOTHARE Madhukar (*Dholak*): 118 Watling Avenue, Burnt Oak, Edgware, Middlesex HA8 0NN ☎ 020 8906 2323

MAHMOUD Mohammad: 121 Greenland Crescent, Sothall, Middlesex UB2 5ET ☎ 020 8574 6686

MILLAR Jhalib (*Ind Per, Jaw H, Berimbau, Dje*): 65 Bayham Street, London NW1 0AA ☎ 020 7388 8205

NATHEKAR Abdul (*Naal, Dholak*): 126 Oakridge Road, High Wycombe, Bucks HP11 2PN ☎ 01494 525235

RAVAL Sandeep (*Dholak, Per*): 22 Mountbel Road, Stanmore, Middlesex HA7 2AF ☎ 020 8863 7215, 0956 576 239

SEHRA Jagdeep (*Per, Voc*): 10 Lincoln Road, Wembley, Middlesex HA0 4SU ☎ 020 8903 6353

SHEIKH Esmail (*Per*): 34 Shackleton Road, Southall, Middlesex UB1 2JB ☎ 020 8574 0202

TARSEM (*Dholak, Dms*): 55 Wallis Rd, Southall, Middx UB1 3LB

TAIKO DRUMS

SCOTLAND

CONNOLLY Shane (*Dms*): 3 Cameron Cresent, Carmunock, Glasgow G76 9DX ☎ 0141 644 4971

KURUMAYA Masaaki: 3 Cameron Crescent, Carmunnock, Glasgow G76 9DX ☎ 0141 644 4971

MACKIE Neil (*Dms, Per*): 3 Cameron Crescent, Carmnunnock, Glasgow G76 9DX ☎ 0141 644 4971

WILLIAMS Miyuki: 3 Cameron Crescent, Carmunnock, Claggow G76 9DX ☎ 0141 644 6971

SOUTH EAST

ALCOCK Mark: Barn House, Broomfield Hill, Great Missenden, Bucks HP16 9HT ☎ 01494 862027

BARROW James (*Flt, E Gtr, Hmca, Kbds*): 34 Scott Close, Emmer Green, Reading, Berkshire RG4 8NY ☎ 0118 946 3317 fax

TAMPURA

NORTH WEST

GUNSTONE Christopher (*Bzk, Dms, Flt, Bag*): Salkeld Cottage, Priest Hutton, Carnforth, Lancs LA6 1JP

LONDON

FARMER Harry (*Per*)

GUPTA Shambhu: 88 Kingsfield Avenue, North Harrow, Middlesex HA2 6AS ☎ 020 8427 3530, 020 8248 5138

TENOR HORN

NORTH EAST

BATHGATE Melvyn: 17, The Laurels, Earlsheaton, Dewsbury WF12 8JN ☎ 01924 452220

LOWE Mark: 27 Longdike Lane, Kippax, Leeds, Yorks LS25 7BP ☎ 01132 320175, 0378 644268, 01757 289609

THEORBO

LONDON

QUINTEIRO Elisio (*Lute, Vih, Gtr*): 30 Forest Drive East, Leytonestone, London E11 1JY ☎ 020 8558 7853

THERAMIN

LONDON

WOOLLEY Bruce (*Gtr, Pf*): Kings Ride House, Kings Ride, Camberley, Surrey GU15 4HU ☎ 01276 685987

TIN WHISTLE

SCOTLAND

MCCANN Thomas: 2F1 21 Royal Park Tce, Edinburgh EH8 8JB ☎ 0131 652 1613, 01426 114314 pager

LONDON

SHENTON James (*Vln*): 51 Whichelo Place, Brighton, East Sussex BN2 2XE ☎ 01273 673158

TROMBONE

SCOTLAND

ANDERSON Kevin (*Sack, Hrn*): 16 Glengyle Terrace, Edinburgh EH3 9LN ☎ 0131 229 4067

ARMSTRONG James (*Db*): 44 Highcroft Avenue, Glasgow G44 5RW ☎ 0141 569 6784

BARKER Andrew: 51 Longstone Avenue, East Linton, East Lothian EH40 3BS ☎ 01620 861638

BATCHELOR David: The Old Manse, Scotlandwell, Nr Kinross KY13 7HY ☎ 01592 840233

BISHOP Derek (*B Tbn*): 680 Anniesland Road, Scotstounhill, Glasgow G14 0XR ☎ 0141 954 8757

BOYD Mark (*Eup*): 2 Polbeth Ave, Polbeth, West Calder, West Lothian EH55 8TZ ☎ 01506 871767

BRACKPOOL Marion: 32 Burnhead Road, Balloch, Cumbernauld G68 9BT ☎ 01236 729171

BURNS Dugald: 101 Main Street, East Kilbride, Glasgow G74 1JE ☎ 01355 231832

COOPER Albert (*B Gtr*): Auchenvale, 23 Invergowrie Drive, Dundee, Angus DD2 1RB ☎ 01382 660820

COX Nigel: 154 Dormanside Road, Crookston Wood, Glasgow G53 5XU ☎ 0141 882 6042

DEANS Brian: 45 Buchanan Drive, Cambuslang, Glasgow G72 8BD ☎ 0141 641 0055

FERNIE Alan (*Com, Arr*): 11 Tenth Street, Newtongrange, Dalkeith, Midlothian EH22 4JF ☎ 0131 660 5782

FRASER Andrew (*A Tbn, B Tpt*): 27 Broughton Place, Edinburgh EH1 3RW ☎ 0131 556 4209, 0378 946629 mob

GIBSON Evatt (*Eup*): 22A Main Street, Callander, Perthshire FK17 8BB

GRAY Jack: 46 Lade Braes, Dalgety Bay, Fife KY11 5SS ☎ 01383 822956

GREEN Lance (*A Tbn, B Tpt*): Hillview Cottage, Kippen Road, Fintry, Stirlingshire G63 0YH ☎ 01360 860563

HANKIN David (*Arr*): 51 Nethan Gate, Hamilton ML3 8NH ☎ 01689 281573

JOHNSON Edwin (*Org, Arr, B Ldr*): 34 Highburgh Drive, Burnside, Glasgow G73 3RZ ☎ 0141 647 6699

KANE Denis: 2 Culzean Drive, Newarthill, Motherwell, Scotland ML1 5AS ☎ 01698 269248

KEIR Davy (*Tpt, Clt, Sax*): 35 Echline, South Queensferry EH30 9SW ☎ 0131 331 1670

KENNY John (*Sack, Alp Hrn, Rec, Com*): 69 Spottiswoode Street, Edinburgh EH9 1DL ☎ 0131 447 3707

MACNIVEN Ronnie: 60 Woodside Avenue, Rutherglen, Glasgow G73 3JG ☎ 0141 647 6273

MANN Jimmy: 47 Glen Esk, St Leonards, East Kilbride G74 3UR ☎ East Kilbride 3

MCGOVERN Edward: 1 Hutchison Terrace, Mannofield, Aberdeen AB10 7NN ☎ 01224 316516

MCGUFF John (*Tpt*): The Willows, 8 The Saughs, Newtongrange, Dalkeith, Midlothian EH22 4PA ☎ 0131 663 2612

MILNE John (*A Tbn, Sack, Com*): Flat 1, 215 Paisley Road West, Kinning Parr, Glasgow G51 1NE ☎ 0141 427 9105

The Musician's Handbook

Edited by Trevor Ford

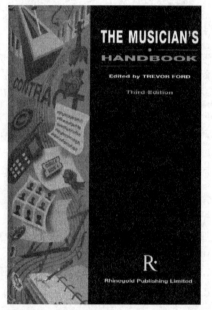

Forty-one chapters of essential advice for aspiring and established professional classical musicians covering career options, auditioning, competitions, concert management, finding an agent, marketing, health problems, insurance, forming a charity, income tax, NI and VAT, copyright and contract law and more.

Hardback 318 pages

HOW TO ORDER

Please send a cheque for **£16.95** (inc. p&p) payable to *Rhinegold Publishing Ltd* to: **TMHB Sales, Rhinegold Publishing, FREEPOST, London WC2H 8BR.**

TELEPHONE:	**0171 333 1721** (or 020 7333 1721 after 22 Apr 2000)
FAX:	**0171 333 1769** (or 020 7333 1769 after 22 Apr 2000)
EMAIL:	**sales@rhinegold.co.uk**
WEBSITE:	**www.rhinegold.co.uk**

NIEL David: 40-3 Mitchell Way, Alexandria, Dunbartonshire G83 0LW ☎ 01389 757388

ORAM Peter (*A Tbn*): 11 North Erskine Park, Bearsden, Glasgow G61 4LZ ☎ 0141 942 7956

PHILLIPS William (*Eup*): 18 Lansdowne Crescent, Edinburgh EH12 5EH ☎ 0131 538 7140, 0802 408125 mob, 0131 313 0281

POWER John (*Tba, Org, B Ldr*): 43 Marwick Street, Dennistoun, Glasgow G31 3NE ☎ 0141 556 6985

REECE David (*Pf*): 3 Main Road, Millarston, Paisley PA1 2TG ☎ 0141 889 9922

SCOATES Richard: 1/R 53 Landerdale Gardens, Hyndland, Glasgow G12 9QT ☎ 0141 400 0987, 07775 854 354

SERVICE John (*B Gtr, Db*): 1 Moor Road, Ayr KA8 9EW ☎ 01292 263535

SIGOUIN Toby (*Sack, Pf*): 12 Dalhousie Terrace, Edinburgh EH10 5NE ☎ 0131 447 7191, 0370 275 976 mob

STARK John (*Eup, Tba*): 143 Elderslie Street, Glasgow G3 7AW ☎ 0141 564 5896, 0141 567 4632

STEELL Robert: 14 Claremont Bank, Edinburgh EH7 4DR ☎ 0131 556 5721

STONE Paul (*Eup*): 2/G Garnet Court, Shamrock Street, Glasgow G4 9NT

THOMPSON Kevin: 8 Durley Dene Crescent, Bridge Of Earn, Perth PH2 9RD ☎ 01738 812802

TORBETT James: 811 Cumbernauld Road, Glasgow G33 2EG ☎ 0141 770 6965

WELSH David: 1 Endfield Avenue, Glasgow G12 0JX ☎ 0141 339 5447

WHELDON Philip: 37, Baronald Drive, Kelvindale, Glasgow G12 0HN ☎ 0141 334 3059

WHITTAKER John (*Con*): 48 Gartymore, Helmsdale, Sutherland, Scotland KW8 6HJ ☎ 01431 821380

YOUNG Andrew: 41 Manderston Court, Edinburgh EH6 8NL ☎ 0131 553 5391

NORTH WEST

APPLETON Ian (*B Tbn*): 25 Blinco Road, Urmston, Manchester M41 9NF ☎ 0161 718 9592, 0161 286 2702 fax, 0589 150675

AUTY Susan (*Eup, Cong, Per*): Flat 2, 35, Demesne Road, Whalley Range, Manchester M16 8HJ ☎ 0161 273 5175

BARKER John (*Tpt*): 3 Bramble Close, Wesham, Preston, Lancashire PR4 3EB ☎ 01772 685034, 0973 318877, 01772 685034

BASON Bill: 44 Chestnut Street, Southport PR8 6QG ☎ 01704 41448

BERRYMAN Andrew: 1 Helmclough Way, Ellenbrook, Worsley, Manchester M28 7XY ☎ 0161 703 9237

BREEZE Arthur (*B Tbn*): 24 Wychwood Avenue, Lymm, Cheshire WA13 0NE ☎ 01925 755129

BRIERLEY Eric (*Voc, Org*): 5 The Bearpits, Hayfield, Derbyshire SK12 5EW ☎ 01663 45396

BRIERLEY Frank: 47 Waterside Mews, Cyril Bell Close, Lymm, Cheshire WA13 0JU ☎ 01925 757232

BRUNT Terry: 20 Seymour Road, Cheadle Hulme, Cheadle SK8 6LR

BUTLER Eddie: 22 St Davids Square, Rhyl, Denbighshire LL18 2ER ☎ 01745 337298

CHATTERTON Timothy (*A Tbn, Eup*): 53 Heaton Road, Withington, Manchester M20 4PU ☎ 0161 434 8056

COOPER Laurence (*B Tbn, Sou*): 70 Collingtree Avenue, Winsford, Cheshire CW7 3UH ☎ 01606 860718

CUTTS Marcus (*Eup, T Tba, Tba*): 68 Wood Street, Glossop, Derbyshire SK13 8NL ☎ 01457 852866

DAVIES John: 3 Hareswood Close, Winsford, Cheshire CW7 2TP ☎ 01606 558787

DAVIES John (*A Tbn, B Tbn*): 30 Alnwick Drive, Moreton, Wirral, Merseyside L46 6ET ☎ 0151 678 2143

DAVIES Rosalyn (*A Tbn, Eup*): 15 Parsonage Way, Cheadle, Cheshire SK8 2JS ☎ 0161 286 6949

DAVIS Paul (*A Tbn*): 16 Foxcover Road, Heswall, Wirral L60 1YB ☎ 0151 342 6566, 0336 794224

DAYKIN Barry (*V Tbn, Eup, A Tbn, B Tpt*): 22 Hayburn Road, Offerton, Stockport, Cheshire SK2 5DB ☎ 0161 456 4739, 0973 740315

DEVLIN Frederick: 13 Lawns Avenue, Off Raby Drive, Raby Mere, Wirral, Cheshire L63 0NF ☎ 0151 334 3495

DIGBY Andrew (*Pf*): 9 Peterborough Close, Lodge Moor, Sheffield S10 4JA ☎ 0114 2304041

DONOHOE David: 72 High Street, Uppermill, Oldham, Lancs OL3 6AH ☎ 01457 871454, 01457 875099

DUNLEAVY Anthony: 39 Highbury Avenue, Irlam, Manchester M30 6BU ☎ 0161 775 5174

EGAN Ronald: 9 Warwick Close, Alkrington, Middleton, Manchester M24 1HY ☎ 0161 643 6321

FITTON Simon: Shore Barn Cottage, 26 Ribble Avenue, Shore, Littleborough, Lancs OL15 8EX ☎ 01706 376341

FOX Daniel (*Per*): 43 Union Street, Dalton In Furness, Cumbria LA15 8RT ☎ 01229 468282

FRYER Peter: 17 Brooke Avenue, Upton Heath, Chester CH2 1HQ ☎ 01244 383837

GALLOWAY Derek (*Voc*): 53 Glebelands Road, Sale-Cheshire, Manchester M33 1LH ☎ 0161 962 0932

GOODWIN Philip (*A Tbn, Eup, B Tpt*): 1 Rosslyn Road, Heald Green, Cheadle, Cheshire SK8 3DJ ☎ 0161 499 0755

GREENWOOD Anthony: 315 Stockport Road, Denton, Manchester M34 1AZ ☎ 0161 320 8496

GRIFFIN Thomas: 21 Barnacre Close, Hala, Lancaster LA1 4JZ ☎ 01524 381078

HAMBLETON Robert: 56 Cliff Road, Acton Bridge, Northwich, Cheshire CW8 3QY ☎ 01606 854694

HAWORTH Matthew (*Pf*): 2 The Dene, Hurst Green, Clitheroe, Lancashire BB7 9QF ☎ 01254 826069, 0113 2170211

HOLLIDAY Robert P (*A Tbn*): 103 Macclesfield Road, Whaley Bridge, High Peak SK23 7DH ☎ 01663 735201, 0468 404376 mob

JENNINGS Eric (*A Tbn, Vln*): 9 Hillside Rd, Frodsham, Via Warrington, Cheshire WA6 6AW ☎ 01928 733209

JOHNSON Simon (*Sack*): 12 Ingleton Mews, Valley Avenue, Bury, Lancs BL8 1UT ☎ 0161 763 5756 & fax, 0973 861623 mob

JONES Nick: 80 Byrom Street, Hale, Altrincham, Cheshire WA14 2EL ☎ 0161 929 0453, 0585 881075, 0161 929 0453

KEMPSTER Stuart: 24 Abington Road, Sale, Cheshire M33 3DL ☎ 0161 962 8696

LEARY T: 24 Fawns Keep, Wilmslow, Cheshire SK9 2BQ ☎ 01625 520243

LEWIS Hywel: 23, Rowan Avenue, Brooklands, Sale, Cheshire M33 3NG ☎ 0161 962 7117

LEWIS John (*Hmca*): 3 Ecclestone Close, Locking Stumps, Warrington, Cheshire WA3 7NL ☎ 01925 850042

LINDSAY James: 13 Westbank Avenue, New Brighton, Merseyside L45 1NA ☎ 0151 639 9411

LOWE Sidney: 41 Witham Street, Ashton-Under-Lyne, Lancs OL6 9RN ☎ 0161 330 4770

MANN Kenton: 3 Oakwood Avenue, Walkden, Manchester M28 3HW ☎ 0161 702 9290

MATHEWS Alan: 58 Rydal Road, Lancaster LA1 3HA ☎ 01524 35098

NELSON Ian: 134 High Street, Uppermill, Oldham, Lancs OL3 6BT ☎ 01457 875752

NIEL Keith: 87 Canon Hussey Court, Silington Way, Salford M3 5JA ☎ 0161 835 3635

NURSE Gwyneth (*A Tbn, Sack, Eup*): 72 Chinnbrook Road, Billesley, Birmingham B13 0LZ ☎ 0121 608 5309

PATON Reginald: 18, Marlcroft Avenue, Stockport, Cheshire SK4 3LZ ☎ 0161 432 8997

PEDDER Arthur (*Tba*): 19 Warren Lane, Hartford, Northwitch, Cheshire CW8 1RQ ☎ 01606 784161

PEPPERELL Alan (*B Tbn*): Flat 2, Regent Court, 277 Wellington Road North, Stockport, Cheshire SK4 5BP ☎ 0161 432 8809

PERRY Kenneth: 4 Winston Place, Blackpool, Lancs FY4 4SJ ☎ 01253 64874

PETCH Christopher (*Pf*): 61 Ullswater Road, Handforth, Wilmslow, Cheshire SK9 3NG ☎ 01625 535740

QUAYLE Terry: Howe Farm House, Clay Head, Baldrine, Isle Of Man IM4 6DL ☎ 01624 861352

REYNOLDS Paul: Ashworth House, Belfield Mill Lane, Rochdale, Lancs OL16 2UB ☎ 01706 525388

SIMONS Harry (*B Ldr*): 34 Woodhall Avenue, Whitefield, Manchester M45 7QF ☎ 0161 766 5151

TAYLOR David (*Pf, Org*): 21 Glebe Lane, Distington, Workington, Cumbria CA14 5SQ ☎ 01946 831624

WARREN Antony: Flat 6, 86 Palatine Road, West Didsbury, Manchester M20 3JW ☎ 0161 434 8815, 0839 058300

WHITE Alistair (*Pf*): 23 Eastbourne Close, Preston, Lancashire PR2 3YR ☎ 01772 732030 & fax, 0421 095753 mob

WILLIAMS Carole (*Pf*): 254 Green Lane, Heaton Moor, Stockport, Cheshire SK4 2NA ☎ 0161 442 1396

WILLIAMSON John (*A Tbn, Sack, Pf*): 32 Mersey Road, Aigburth, Liverpool L17 6AD ☎ 0151 281 0317, 0151 794 3095, 0151 280 2388

WINFIELD Duncan: 14 Oaklands Road, Swinton, Manchester M27 0ED ☎ 0161 728 2568

WRIGLEY Thomas (*B Tbn, B Tpt*): Calle La Marina 24, Urb. Marina, 03738 San Fulgenico, Alicante, Spain

NORTH EAST

ASHLEY Carolyn: 22 Clarence Street, Bowburn, Durham DH6 5BB ☎ 0191 377 2719

ATKINSON Arthur: 21 The Cote, Farsley, Leeds LS28 5BU ☎ 0113 2564449

BACON Robert: 105 Tenter Lane, Warmsworth, Doncaster, South Yorkshire ND4 9PE ☎ 01302 851217

BAKER Frank (*Pf*): 76 Oxford Street, Cleethorpes, N. E. Lincs DN35 8RG ☎ 01472 694060

BAXTER Steve (*B Tbn, Tba*): 5 Race Terrace, Great Ayton, Middlesbrough TS9 6NS ☎ 01642 723563

BAYLEY Timothy (*Clt*): Laundry Cottage, 21 Sand Hutton, York YO41 1LB ☎ 01904 468571

BEATTY Jonathan (*Pf*): 8 Slaithwaite Road, Meltham, Huddersfield HD7 3NY ☎ 01484 854251

BRADSHAW George: 20 Sunnybank Avenue, Thornbury, Bradford BD3 7DH ☎ 01274 665610

BROCKLESBY David (*Kbds, Pf*): 21 Buck Beck Way, Cleethorpes, N. E. Lincs DN 35 0RJ ☎ 01472 291678

BULLAS Phillip (*Voc, Wood W*): 33 Rythergate, Cawood, Selby, North Yorks YO8 3TP ☎ 01757 269321

BURNETT Ronald (*Voc, B Ldr*): 10 Holly Terrace, York YO10 4DS ☎ 01904 622498

BURTENSHAW Robert: Upper Laithe Farm, Ogden Lane, Denholm, West Yorkshire BD13 4JZ ☎ 01274 833319

CHIVERS Derek (*Clt*): Prospect House, The Old Village, Huntington, York YO32 9RB ☎ 01904 768801

DWYNELL Andre (*Pf, Kbds*): Flat 303 Garrow House, 190 Kensal Road, London S10 5BN ☎ 020 8964 4149

FAIRLEY Don: Copperfield, Lockhaugh Road, Rowlands Gill, Tyne & Wear NE39 1AW ☎ 01207 543083 & fax

FARLEY Paul: Mountain Ash, Staintondale, Scrborough, North Yorks YO13 0EL ☎ 01723 870580

FLETCHER Paul (*Tba, St Pan, Jav Gam*): 40 Rothbury Terrace, Heaton, Newcastle-upon-Tyne NE6 5XH ☎ 0191 265 0304

FLOOD John: 9 Garsdale Road, Whitley Bay, Tyne & Wear NE26 4NT ☎ 0191 252 2087

FORTE Remo (*Kbds*): 15 Hide Hill, Berwick-on-Tweed, Northumberland TD15 1EQ ☎ 01289 306412

GRAY Stuart (*A Tbn, Eup, Tba, Con*): 14 The Precinct, Tunstall, Sunderland SR2 9DN ☎ 0191 525 1676

GUDE Ian (*Kbds, Pf*): 67 Middlesex Street, Barnsley S70 4JS ☎ 01246 290886, 0374 161401

GURNHILL Andrew: 25 Lunbreck Road, Warmsworth, Doncaster, South Yorkshire DN4 9QU ☎ 01302 851691

HELLIWELL Julie (*Pf, Ac Gtr, B Gtr*): 66 Greystones Road, Sheffield S11 7BN ☎ 01377 257971

HORSLEY Rob (*Kbds, Eup, Tba*): 16 St Marys Avenue, Whitley Bay, Tyne & Wear NE26 1TA ☎ 0191 2525289

HOULDING Christopher: 32 Heaton Grove, Heaton, Bradford BD9 4DZ ☎ 01274 487078

JAMES Daniel (*B Tbn*): 125 North Street, Lockwood, Huddersfield HD1 3SQ ☎ 01484 514842

LEADBEATER Michael (*Voc*): 17 Quarmby Road, Quarmby, Huddersfield, West Yorkshire HD3 4HQ ☎ 01484 640896

LOCKER James: 22 Bothal Cottages, Ashington, Northumberland NE63 8NS ☎ 01670 813337

MACKINDER Michael (*Eup*): 6 Cromford Close, Cantley, Doncaster, South Yorks DN4 6PT ☎ 01302 371219

NORRIS Keith: 32 Corscombe Close\, Ferryhill, Co Durham DL17 8DB ☎ 01740 651989

O'DONNELL Ed (*Bjo*): 56 Cliff Road, Leeds LS6 2EZ ☎ 0113 216 1396

PARKER Brian (*Flt, Pic*): 9 Moatfield, Osbaldwick, York YO10 3PT ☎ 01904 411723

PUGSLEY Simon: 5 Dale Villas, Hawksworth Road, Leeds LS18 4JN ☎ 0113 259 1440

REYNOLDS Marcus: 38A Main Road, Marsh Lane, Eckington S21 5RH ☎ 01246 433647

SCOTT Robert: 158 Bishopthorpe Road, York YO23 1LF ☎ 01904 656262

SELWYN Frederick (*Tba*): 17 Hangmanstone Lane, High Melton, Doncaster DN5 7TB ☎ 01709 589031

SUNNERS Derek: 3 Hickory Road, Lincoln LN6 0PG

THOMPSON John (*B Tbn*): 14 Coquet Way, Warkworth, Northumberland NE65 0TY ☎ 01665 711856

TITCHBURN (*Voc, B Gtr*): Dog Kennel Farm, Woodhed, Burley In Wharfedale, Ilkley, West Yorkshire LS29 7BH ☎ 01943 864676, 0378 396234 mob

TURTON Richard: Hartendale Farm House, West Street, Flamborough, Bridlington, E Yorks YO15 1PH ☎ 01262 850839

WARD Patrick: 9 Lascelles Hall Road, Kirkheaton, Huddersfield HD5 0AT ☎ 01484 535066

WEATHERLEY Thomas (*Pf, Arr*): 20 Holland Pk, Park Lands, Wallsend, Tyne & Wear NE28 8UJ ☎ 0191 262 5355

WILKIE Peter (*Eup, Sack, R Wnd*): 6 Glebeside, Witton Gilbert, Durham DH7 6SD ☎ 0191 371 1754

WITTMANN Neil (*Eup*): 12 Gladstone Road, Rawdon, Leeds LS19 6HZ ☎ 0113 2501884

WRIGHT Stanley (*Dms, Arr*): 51 Seamer Road, East Ayton, Nr Scarborough, Yorks YO13 9HN ☎ 01723 864210

EAST

BATES Bob (*Sou*): 1 Bloomfield Road, Harpenden, Herts AL5 4DD ☎ 01582 760858

BRENNER Jonathan (*Acc, B Gtr*): 20 Hasketon Road, Woodbridge, Suffolk IP12 4JS ☎ 01394 385799

BRITTON Norman: 1 Poors Lane, Hadleigh, Essex SS7 2LA ☎ 01702 558334, 01702 558334

BROWN Duncan: 35 Rochford Road, Bishops Stortford, Herts CM23 5ET ☎ 01442 230858

CARMICHAEL Archie (*Pf*): 151 Church Road, Shoeburyness, Essex SS3 9EZ ☎ 01702 296776

COLE David: Ruskins, Rectory Road, Wrabness, Manningtree, Essex CO11 2TR ☎ 01255 880175

COLLINGE John (*Org, Con*): 6 Kingsmill Court, Hatfield, Hertfordshire AL10 8XW ☎ 01707 251565

ELLISTON Geoff: 47 Edinburgh Gardens, Braintree, Essex CM7 6LQ ☎ 01376 341536

FULCHER Byron: 25 Kirtle Road, Chesham, Buckinghamshire HP5 1AD ☎ 01494 794 395, 0976 401130 mob

GEORGE Neil: 17 Park North, Ipswich, Suffolk IP4 2XT ☎ 01473 251259

GRIFFITHS Michael: 17 Regents Court, 92 Randolph Avenue, London W9 1BG ☎ 020 7286 1393

HARVEY Eddie (*Pf, Arr*): 64 Parkhouse Gardens, East Twickenham, Middx TW1 2DE ☎ 020 8892 6709

HEMMINGS John: Ashe Cottage, Lower Hacheston, Woodbridge, Suffolk IP13 0PB ☎ 01728 746002

JAGO David: 44 Ditton Court Road, Westcliff-on-Sea, Essex SS0 7HF

JOUGHIN Raymond: 23 Becket Wood, Newdigate, Surrey RH5 5AQ ☎ 01306 631165

JUDGE Philip (*Eup, B Tpt*): 31 Brighton Road, North Watford, Hertfordshire WD2 5HN ☎ 01923 333434, 0976 243028 mob, 01483 451700

KEELY G (*Pf*): Address Unknown

LEACH Richard: 4 Campion Road, Westoning, Beds MK45 5LB ☎ 01525 718430

MAYHEW Richard: 30 Newton Road, Ipswich, Suffolk IP3 8HE ☎ 01473 414418

MCDERMOTT Scott (*B Tbn, Tba*): 7 Phillips Crescent, Needham Market, Ipswich IP6 8TF ☎ 01449 722640

PALSER Barry (*Dms, Voc*): 36 Dunmowe Road, Fulbourn, Cambridge CB1 5HW ☎ 01223 512007

QUICK Matthew (*Dms, Per*): Lindgren, 41 Grange Close, Linslade, Leighton Buzzard, Bedfordshire LU7 7PW ☎ 01525 852 272, 0374 708 423

RANDALL Johnathan (*A Tbn*): 18 Perry Hill, Chelmsford, Essex CM1 7RD ☎ 01245 347517

RENVOIZE Robert: 64, Kings Road, Glemsford, Suffolk CO10 7QZ ☎ 01787 280851

RUSHTON Gordon: The Bury, 129 Hempstead Road, Kingslangley, Hertfordshire WD4 8AJ ☎ 01923 265467

SEYMOUR Michael: 112 St Andrews Road, Boreham, Chelmsford CM3 3DL ☎ 01245 467399

SHEPHERD Paul: 7 Gladstone Road, Ipswich, Suffolk IP3 8AT ☎ 01473 423 694

SLOCOMBE Rob: 21 Hawthorn Close, Spixworth, Norwich NR10 3RD ☎ 01603 891563

T BONE

TURBERVILLE Richard: 22 Batford Road, Harpenden, Herts AL5 5AT ☎ 01582 760432

WARBURTON Janine: 72 High Street, Needingworth, Huntingdon, Cambs PE17 3SB ☎ 01480 66376

WELLS Michael: 12 Cheviot Close, Bushey, Hertfordshire WD2 3QW ☎ 020 8950 6123

WILLIAMS Roy: 5 Trowbridge Gardens, Luton, Bedfordshire LU2 7JY ☎ 01582 27208

WILLSON John (*Sou, Per*): 82 Beech Road, Hadleigh, Benfleet, Essex SS7 2AG ☎ 01702 556329

WOODCOCK Christine ☎ 01582 422845

WYATT Jonathan (*Eup*): 6 Ullswater Drive, Hethersett, Norwich NR9 3QD ☎ 01603 812965, 0802 770359 mob

MIDLANDS

ADAMS Ian: 54 Buckmaster Avenue, Clayton, Newcastle, Staffs ST5 3AN ☎ 01782 713585

ALLSOPP Clive (*Com, Con, Kbds, B Gtr*): 144 Wednesbury Road, Walsall, West Midlands WS1 4JJ ☎ 01922 448320

BAYLISS Pat: 433 Birchfield Road, Redditch, Worcs B97 4NF ☎ 01527 546102

BENNETT Bob (*Arr, Com, Md, Pf*): Musicians' Union, Benson House, Lombard Street, Birmingham B12 0QN ☎ 0121 622 3870

BIRCH Bramwell: 5 Milldale Road, Long Eaton, Nottingham NG10 3JB ☎ 0115 973 2701

BODEN Paul: 17 Wrekin Drive, Stourbridge, West Midlands DY9 7HB ☎ 01384 422367

BRADLEY Alan: 24 Wetherel Road, Stapenhill, Burton-on-Trent, Staffordshire DE15 9GW ☎ 01283 46119

BRAILSFORD Ian (*Tbn*): 54 Windsor Gardens, Castlecroft, Wolverhampton WV3 8LZ ☎ 01902 764706

BROOKES Martha: 2 Station Road, Kings Heath, Birmingham B14 7SB ☎ 0121 444 5655

BUXTON Donald: 36 Normandy Road, Perry Barr, Birmingham B20 3BD ☎ 0121 356 6620

CAMPBELL Ellen: Lower Southlowe Farm, Leek Road, Wetley Rocks, Staffordshire ST9 0AR ☎ 01782 551107

CLEWES David: 40 Beeston Road, Dunkirk, Nottingham NG7 2JR ☎ 0115 9701363

CLIFT Mick: 77 The Ridge, Great Doddington, Wellingborough NN29 7TT ☎ 01933 274739

COOK John: Kloof Cottage, Main Street, Caunton, Newark-on-Trent, Nottingham NG23 6AB ☎ 01636 636483, 0468 597970 mob, 01636 636736

COOPER William: 106 Colleys Lane, Willaston, Nantwich CW5 6NT ☎ 01270 664637

CUNNINGHAM David (*Pf, Arr, Com*): Minton House, 263 Hartshill Road, Hartshill, Stoke-on-Trent ST4 7NQ ☎ 01782 410237

DOBSON Peter: 33 Dower Road, Four Oaks, Sutton, Coldfield Warks B75 6TX ☎ 0121 308 2767

DOUGLAS Arthur (*Pf*): 16 Roderick Street, Old Basford, Nottingham NG6 0BP ☎ 0115 9760935

DUERDEN Quentin (*A Tbn, T Sack*): Hermes Place, 81 Hassall Road, Winterley, Sandbach, Cheshire CW11 4RT ☎ 01270 767857

FLETCHER Carl: 3 Margaret Road, Harborne, Birmingham B17 0EU ☎ 0121 426 5834

FOWLES Michael: 26 Beever Street, Old Trafford, Manchester M16 9JR ☎ 0161 877 6698, 0976 232446

HARRISON Phillip: 14 Park Lane, Bewdley, Worcestershire DY12 2ER ☎ 01299 402420

HINDLEY Frank (*Pf*): Fern Hill, Cropwell Bishop, Notts NG12 3BW ☎ 0115 9893189

HOBSON Nancy: 7 South Road, Northfield, Birmingham B31 2RB ☎ 0121 477 2311, 0976 272244 mob

HOGG Simon (*Eup*): Holloway House, The Holloway, Market Place, Warwick CV34 4SJ ☎ 01926 497887

HORREY Ted: 48 Dewsbury Avenue, Styvechale, Coventry, West Midlands CV3 6LF ☎ 024 7641 3494

HORTON Ashley: 106 Tresham Road, Great Barr, Birmingham B44 9UD ☎ 0121 360 9794

HUGHES Ted (*T Sax*): Address Unknown ☎ 01203 86532

JAEGER Penelope: The Old Infants School, The Hurst, Cleobury Mortimer DY14 8JU ☎ 01299 271008

JAMES Michael: 17 Lawn Close, Heanor, Derbyshire DE75 7TR ☎ 01772 760989

JOHNSON John T S: 263 Goodman Street, Burton-on-Trent, Staffs DE14 2RQ ☎ 01283 61123

JOHNSON Philip (*Md*): 14, Apse Close, Wombourne, Wolverhampton, West Midlands WV5 8BW ☎ 01902 892768

LACEY Peter (*Eup*): 98 Haymoor, Boley Park, Lichfield, Staffs WS14 9SS ☎ 01543 301 381, 0973 789256, 01543 300545

LEWIS Philip (*Db, Vln, Gtr*): 1115 Bristol Road South, Birmingham, West Midlands B31 2QP ☎ 0121 475 2079

LONGSTAFF Danny: 77 Mariner Avenue, Edgbaston, Birmingham B16 9DF ☎ 0121 452 1781, 0831 532342

MERCER Frederick (*Eup, B Ldr, Com*): 61 Charles Road, Solihull, Warks B91 1TT ☎ 0121 705 0550

MILLER Helen: 104 Amos Lane, Wednesfield, Wolverhampton WV11 1LZ ☎ 01902 738 240

MORRELL Alfred: 37 Seven Oaks Crescent, Bramcote, Nottingham NG9 3FP ☎ 0115 9229074

MORRISON John: 21 Morse Road, Whitnash, Leamington Spa, Warwicks CV31 2LH ☎ 01926 336288

MOSELEY Ian (*A Tbn*): 20, Freshfields, Harlescott Lane, Shrewsbury, Salop SY1 3JB ☎ 01743 240531

MUNNERY Paul: The Stores, Arthur Street, Montgomery, Powys SY15 6RA ☎ 01686 668617

NEWTON Brian: 65 Stonerwood Avenue, Birmingham B28 0AX ☎ 0121 777 2944

NEWTON Robert (*B Ldr*): 23 Windmill Avenue, Blisworth, Northants NN7 3EQ ☎ 01604 858549

NIELD Richard (*A Tbn, B Tpt*): 35 The Ridgeway, Hammerwich, Staffordshire WS7 8SP ☎ 01543 686002

PAYNE Donald: 38 Waterfield Road, Cropston, Leicester LE7 7HN ☎ 0116 236 4507

PEARCE David: 21 Mikado Road, New Sawley, Long Eaton, Nottingham NG10 3GN ☎ 0115 9731647

PERRIN Donald (*Bjo*): Seymour Cottage, 16 Church Street, Bingham, Notts NG13 8AL ☎ 01949 39846

PITT Kevin: 20 Oakleigh Road, Stratford-on-Avon, Warks CV37 0DW ☎ 01789 415954

POULTON Geoffrey *(Com)*: Harlequin Recording, Elgar House, Rufford, Tamworth, Staffs B79 7UT ☎ 01827 53553 & fax

RAE Ian *(A Tbn, B Tpt, Arr, Com)*: 1257 Bristol Road South, Longbridge, Birmingham, B31 2SW ☎ 0121 476 8049, 0374 957748

RAE Roger *(B Tbn, B Gtr, Md, B Ldr)*: 45 Grange Crescent, Halesowen, West Midlands B63 3ED ☎ 0121 550 6515

REID Paul *(A Tbn, Cop)*: 77 Southfield Road, Edgbaston, Birmingham B16 0JP ☎ 0121 420 4026, 0973 744505

REID Reginald *(Pf)*: 11 Herondale Crescent, Wollaston, Stourbridge, Worcs DY8 3LH ☎ 01384 372370

RICHARDSON Bill *(A Tbn, Cop)*: 8 Bramble Close, Nuneaton, Warks CV11 6XA ☎ 024 7638 4613

RIMAN Peter: 140 Kent Road, Mapperley, Notts NG3 6BS ☎ 0115 960 6365

SANDERS Carl: 71, Sharmans Cross Road, Solihull, West Midlands B91 1RQ ☎ 0121 705 0327

SHIFRIN Ken *(A Tbn, Eup, B Tpt)*: 47 Cole Bank Road, Hall Green, Birmingham B28 8EZ ☎ 0121 778 4912

SINCLAIR Eric: 54 Comberford Road, Tamworth, Staffs B79 8PF ☎ 01827 64086

SIVITER David: 58 Sandringham Road, Wordsley, Stourbridge, West Midlands DY8 5HL ☎ 01384 279924

SMITH Andrew: 19, Fullwood Avenue, Hurst Green, Halesowen, West Midlands B62 9SA ☎ 0121 423 2457

SPENCER William *(Pf)*: Dale End House, 14 Yeoman Street, Bonsall Matlock, Derbyshire DE4 2AA ☎ 01629 823501

STEPHENS Stanley: 33 Church Road, Netherton, Dudley, West Midlands DY2 0LY ☎ 01384 255304

SYMON Peter *(Sack)*: 30 King Edward Road, Birmingham B13 8HR ☎ 0121 449 9924

TURNBULL Allan *(Sack, B Tbn, Eup)*: 14 South Park, Rushden, Northants NN10 9LY ☎ 01933 317528

TURNER John: 88 Hassall Road, Sandbach, Cheshire CW11 0HN ☎ 01270 767272

VICKERS Dave: 12 Butterley Drive, Loughborough, Leks LE11 0PX ☎ 01509 230551

WALTERS Tavis *(Eup, Kbds)*: 8 Middlemore Road, Northfield, Birmingham B31 3UP ☎ 0121 478 0844, 07654 318129 pager

WEDGE James *(Pf, Arr)*: 46 Kemsley Road, Maypole, Birmingham, West Midlands B14 5DW ☎ 0121 430 8331

WHITE Bernard: Flat 110, Brown Court Brindley St, Pemberton Wigan, Lancs WN5 8ET ☎ 0942 701200

WHITEHOUSE Leslie: 53 Beachroft Road, Wall Heath, Kingswinford, West Midlands DY6 0HX ☎ 01384 830692

WILSON Bob *(Dms)*: 19 Southwell Road, Lowdham, Nottingham NG14 7DQ ☎ 0115 9663884

SOUTH EAST

ADAMS Charles: 80, Hangleton Way, Hove, Sussex BN3 8EQ ☎ Brighton 419956

ALLEN Catherine *(Voc)*: 26 Charborough Close, Lytchett Matrangers, Poole, Dorset BH16 6DH ☎ 01202 625075

AUSTIN Gary: Flat 3 Esmond, 18 Northbrook Road, Swanage, Dorset BH19 1PT ☎ 01929 427371

AYRES Bobi: 21 Easter Road, Bournemouth, Dorset BH9 1SW ☎ 01202 531531

BAILEY Sid: 104 Beach Green, Shoreham By Sea, Sussex BN43 5YA ☎ 01273 461222

BAKER Charlotte *(Tba)*: Balmoral House, Castlewood, Davids Lane, Ringwood BH24 2AW ☎ 01425 470969

BANNISTER Donal *(Eup, Sack)*: 2 Fairfield Road, Blandford Forum, Dorset DT11 7BZ ☎ 01258 454662

BARNBY Stuart *(Acc, Con, Com, Arr)*: 19 Beverley Gardnes, Maidenhead, Berks SL6 6SN ☎ 01628 789536, 0976 907581

BAXTER Eric *(Sax)*: 18 Ashleigh Drive, Beeford, Nr Driffield, East Yorkshire YO25 8AU ☎ 01262 88 706

BAXTER Fats *(Voc)*: Flat 1A, 4, Third Avenue, Hove, Sussex BN3 2PD ☎ Brighton 770818

CADDY Phillipa *(Saxes, Tba)*: 43 Withdean Court, London Road, Brighton BN1 6RP ☎ 01273 505732

CLARKE Paul *(Pf)*: 17 Millway, Barnby, Nr Beccles, Suffolk NR34 7PS ☎ 01502 475253, 07788697595

COLLIER Michael: Les Jardins De Janval, Les Erables Apt. 97, Rue Louis Fromager, Dieppe 76200, France ☎ +33 72 35 82 34 17

COTTON Brian: Address Unknown ☎ 01273 679982

D'CRUZE Rupert: 31 North Walls, Winchester, Hants SO23 8DB ☎ 01962 867682

DAVIS Michael *(Md, Arr, Cop)*: 30 Elms Road, Fareham, Hants PO16 0SQ ☎ 01329 232665

DUNGEY Peter: 149 Buckswood Drive, Gossops Green, Crawley, Sussex RH11 8JB ☎ 01293 527322

DURRANT David: 56 Hilary Avenue, Cosham, Portsmouth, Hants PO6 2PR ☎ 023 9238 4980

FRANCIS Colin *(B Gtr)*: 28 Bradpole Road, Bournemouth, Dorset BH8 9NX ☎ 01202 515415

FRANKLIN Jasper *(Tba, Tpt)*: 26 Hartfield Avenue, Hollingbury, Brighton BN1 8AE ☎ Brighton 508518

FRY Adrian *(Kbds, Arr)*: 65 Northfield Road, Townhill Park, Southampton SO2 2QQ ☎ 023 8058 1883

FULLBROOK Mark: 2 Bailie Close, Abingdon, Oxon OX14 5RF ☎ 01235 521992

GOLDER David: 36 Westcote Close, Witney, Oxon OX8 5FF ☎ 01993 705710

GRIFFITHS Griff *(Voc, Gtr)*: 59 Westmead, Windsor, Berks SL4 3NN ☎ 01753 831860, 0831 198875

HAWES William: 9 St Richards Close, Tarrant Keyneston, Blandford Forum, Dorset DT11 9JD ☎ 01258 451343

HAYES Rodney: 3 Primrose Avenue, Wigmore, Gillingham, Kent ME8 0TD ☎ 01634 374130

HAYES Stephen: 40 Westbourne Park Road, Bournemouth, Dorset BH4 8HQ ☎ 01202 760336

HEWSON Daniel *(Pf, Kbds)*: Walnut Tree Cottage, The Pike, Washington, West Susssex RH20 4AA ☎ 01903 892 889, 01798 813991

HILL Adam *(Ld Gtr, B Gtr, Cel)*: 133 Tukes Avenue, Bridgemary, Gosport, Hants PO13 0SB ☎ 01329 283968

HOWARD Keith: 20 Greensmeade, Woodfalls, Salisbury SP5 2NL ☎ 01725 21328

HYDE Phillip *(Eup, Per)*: Zilaross, 109 Alpine Road, Redhill, Surrey RH1 2LE ☎ 0173 7768493

JONES Stephen: 4 Broom Grove, Sandy Lane, Wokingham RG11 4TX

KENNY Patrick *(Kbds)*: 10 Hammond Crescent, Willen Park, Milton Keynes, Bucks MK15 9DH ☎ 01908 664295

KNOCK John: 12 Lealands Avenue, Leigh, Tonbridge, Kent TN11 8QU ☎ 01732 833158

LLEWELLYN Gareth: 37 Waverley Road, Freemantle, Southampton, Hants SO15 1JF ☎ 023 8032 6715

LLOYD Robert: 2 Setley Gardens, Bournemouth, Dorset BH8 0HQ ☎ 01202 532154

LONGCROFT Roger: Lambton, High Street, Shirrell Heath, Southampton Hants SO3 2JN ☎ 01329 832424

LOWE Christopher *(Dms)*: Birch Cottage, 5 High Street, Horsell, Surrey GU21 4XA ☎ 01483 714121, 01523 769 136 pager

MANSFIELD Peter *(Pf, Per, Cong, Gtr)*: 3 St Aubyns Road, Portslade, Brighton BN41 1AB ☎ 01273 424752

MAPLE John: 18, The Horshams, Beltinge, Herne Bay, Kent CT6 6PF ☎ Herne Bay 2833

MELBOURNE Andrew *(A Tbn, Eup)*: 10 Meon Close, Clanfield, Hants PO8 0PH ☎ 023 9275 4503

MINCHIN Francis: 52 St Lawrence Avenue, Worthing, West Sussex BN14 7JG ☎ Worthing 30855

MITCHELL Christopher: 3 Delamere Road, Earley, Reading, Berks RG6 1AP ☎ 01734 267754

MORGAN Harold: Church Cottage, West Street, Winterbourne Stickland, Blandford, Dorset DT11 0NJ ☎ 01258 881206

NICHOLLS George: 62 Gorran Ave, Gosport, Hants PO13 0NF ☎ 01329 288581

PENFOLD Gary (*Sax, B Gtr, Tpt*): 15 Bath Street, Flat B, Brighton, East Sussex BN1 3TB

PORTER Colin: Courts Yard, Windfall Wood, Jobsons Lane, Haslemere, Surrey GU27 3BX ☎ 01428 708004

PRITCHARD Bryan: 35 Guildhill Road, Bournemouth, Dorset BH6 3EX ☎ 01202 429540

QUINN John: Address Unknown

RHODES Phil (*Org, Pf*): Merrydown, 89 Mead Lane, Chertsey, Surrey KT16 8PA ☎ 01932 560438

RICKETTS Christopher: 43 Bugle Street, Southampton SO14 2AG ☎ 023 8033 9333

RIXON Pat: 44 Victoria Road, Wargrave, Berks RG10 8AB ☎ 0118 940 2959

ROLASTON Geoffrey: Flat 4, Marston Court, St Mary's Road, Poole, Dorset BH15 2LG ☎ 01202 672339

ROSE David (*Pf, Com*): 57 Woodlands Road, Witney, Oxon OX8 6DR ☎ 01993 703049, 04325 701010

SEYMOUR Alan (*Pf*): 34 Gower Road, Haywards Heath, West Sussex RH16 4PN ☎ 01444 413817

SMITH Douglas (*B Gtr*): 56 Huntly Road, Bournemouth, Dorset BH3 7HJ ☎ 01202 513462

STROUD Martyn: 55 Mill Hill Road, Cowes, Isle Of Wight PO3 7EG ☎ 01983 292952

SYKES Paul: 201 Pinewood Park, Cove, Farnborough, Hants GU14 9LQ ☎ 01252 520363

THORNE Mike (*Dms*): 36 Knights Croft, New Ash Green, Longfield, Kent DA3 8HT ☎ 01474 873570 & fax, 0421 382623 mob

WADE Timothy: Flat 2, New Steine Mansions, Devonshire Place, Brighton Sussex BN2 1QJ ☎ 01273 677664

WATERER Richard: Solent View, 2 Alvercliffe Drive, Alverstoke, Gosport, Hants PO12 2NB ☎ 023 9250 2431 eve

WATT William: 10 Crookhorn Lane, Purbrook, Waterlooville, Hants PO7 5QE ☎ 023 9226 2512

WHEELER Douglas: 3 Redwood Way, Southampton, Hants SO16 3PU ☎ 023 8076 8904

WHITE Philip (*A Tbn*): 69 Earlshall Road, Eltham, London SE9 1PP ☎ 020 8859 4651

WILLIAMS Donald: 12 Freshfield Close, Lancing, West Sussex BN15 9LS ☎ 01903 761345

WISE Denis: 39 Jameson Road, Winton, Bournemouth, Dorset BH9 2QG ☎ 01202 527591

YORK Norton: 44A St Dunstans Road, Barons Court, London W6 8RB

SOUTH WEST

AUSTIN Garfield: 11 Prior Park Cottages, Widcombe, Bath, Avon BA2 4NR ☎ 01225 336695, 0976 711540

BERRY John: 16 Elton Road, Bishopston, Bristol BS7 8DA

BOWDITCH Simon (*B Tbn*): 73 Behind Berry, Somerton, Somerset TA11 6JY ☎ 01458 273448

BOWEN Glyn: 43 Kingsway, Taunton, Somerset TA1 3YD ☎ 01823 253027

BOWEN Win: Cherry Tree House, Princes Hill, Redlynch, Salisbury, Wilts SP5 2HG ☎ 01725 511173

CHADD Nicholas (*Tba*): Trethew, Crackington Haven, Bude, Cornwall EX23 0JP ☎ 01288 354667

CHAMBERLAIN Sydney: 17 Hilltop Close, Bisley Old Road, Stroud, Glos GL5 1PZ ☎ 01453 757913

CHAPELL Brian (*Pf*): 3 Green Park Avenue, Mutley, Plymouth, Devon PL4 6PG ☎ 01752 366428

CLEMENTS Philip: 14 Mill Lane, Swindon, Wiltshire SN1 4HG ☎ 01793 695442

CLOUGH Wendy: A Cappella, 15 Byron Road, St Helier, Jersey, C.I. JE2 4LQ ☎ 01534 38265

COOMBS Timothy: 13 Chestnut Way, Dorchester, Dorset DT1 2PU ☎ 01305 263005

CUTTS Roger ☎ 029 2070 6961

DANIELS Gwyn (*Pf*): 9 Castle Close, Creigiau, Cardiff CF4 8NJ

DAVIS Bob (*Br Hrn*): 16 Ebbw View Terrace, Newbridge, Newport, Gwent NP1 4FB ☎ 01495 245702

DORE Andrew (*Eup*): 119 Salisbury Road, St Judes, Plymouth, Devon PL4 8TB ☎ 01752 302091

EVANS Anthony (*Kbds, Tba, Gtr, Md*): 12 Delaware Court, Drakewalk, Gunnislake, Cornwall PL18 2BH ☎ 01822 832903

EVANS Gary (*Pf*): Ty Miaren, 1 Ferry Road, Pennar, Pembroke Dock, Pembrokeshire SA72 6RD ☎ 01646 686502, 0966 387592

FORD Vincent (*B Tbn*): 54 Canterbury Road, North Worle, Weston-Super-Mare BS22 0TT ☎ Wsm 515966

GILL Thomas: 15 Marldon Road, Shiphay, Torquay, Devon TQ2 7EE ☎ 01803 400725

GREAVES John: The Old Post Office, Rose, Truro, Cornwall TR4 9PG ☎ 01872 573127

GRENFELL Kevin (*Voc*): 57 Exwick Road, Exeter EX4 ☎ 01392 253039

GRIBBLE Robert (*Tba, Bjo*): 16 East Street, Baneswell, Newport, Gwent, Wales NP9 4BR ☎ 01633 211391

HANNABY Daniel: 2 Maplewalk, Dan Y Craig, Porthcawl, Mid Glam CF36 5AY ☎ 065671 3067

HAWKINS Paul: The Well House, 6 Fore Street, St Erth-Hayle, Cornwall TR27 6HT ☎ 01736 752375

HENDY John (*Tbn*): Pwysty, George Street, Llantrisant, Pontyclun, Mid Glamorgan CF72 8EE ☎ 01443 224783

HOCKIN Keith: The Elms, The Square, Stow-on-The Wold, Cheltenham, Glos GL54 1AF ☎ 01451 831058

HUTCHINGS John: 8 Belle Vue Road, Exmouth, Devon EX8 3DR ☎ 01395 271632

HUXHAM Owen: 51 Sweetbriar Lane, Exeter, Devon EX1 3AQ ☎ 01392 55759

INCLEDON Chris (*B Gtr, T Sax*): 13 Ernesettle Crescent, Higher St Budeaux, Plymouth, Devon PL5 2ET ☎ 07732 361434

ISLEY Maxwell: 48 Homelands Road, Rhiwbina, Cardiff CF4 1UJ ☎ 029 2069 1195

LATHAM Sarah (*T Sax*): Lower Caerddu, Howey, Llandrindod Wells, Powys, Wales LD1 5PP ☎ 01597 824222

LEACH John (*Eup*): 5 The Terrace, Cregiau, Cardiff CF4 8NG ☎ 029 2089 1231

LEGGE Steven: 44 Fairwater Grove West, Llandaff, Cardiff CF5 2JQ ☎ 029 2056 4717

LETTEN Andrew: 77 Ashleigh Mount Road, Redhills, Exeter EX4 1SW

LOCKE Peter: 4 Groves Road, Newport, Gwent NP9 3SP ☎ 01633 267472

LOMAS Michael: The Brow, Avebury Trusloe, Nr Marlborough, Wilts SN8 1QY ☎ 01672 539646

MARKS Roger: 7 Seven Stars Lane, Tamerton Foliot, Plymouth PL5 4NN ☎ 767766

MEDLAND Gerald: 31 Berea Road, Ellacombe, Torquay TQ1 1JP ☎ 01803 214207

MORGAN Gregory: 11 Alfreda Road, Whitchurch, Cardiff CF4 2EH

MORGAN Jonathan (*Bq Flt, Rec*): 31 Middle Street, Stroud, Glos GL5 1DZ ☎ 01453 753078

NORMINGTON Brian: 13 Causie Drive, St Clement, Jersey, Channel Islands JE2 6SR ☎ 01534 854705

PALSER Geoffrey: 34 Insole Grove East, Llandaff, Cardiff CF5 2HP ☎ 029 2040 7512

PAWLBY Arwood: 14 Hopton Close, Eggbuckland, Plymouth, Devon PL6 5JJ ☎ 01752 771958

PEARCE Kenneth (*Dms*): 20, St Julien Crescent, Broadwey, Weymouth, Dorset DT3 5DT ☎ 01305 813258

PIPPEN Jonathan: The Vicarage Trevethin, Pontypool, Gwent NP4 8JF ☎ 01495 762228, 0410 237255 mob

POCKETT Kenneth (*Db*): 18 Milbourne Park, Milbourne, Malmesbury, Wilts SN16 9JE ☎ 01666 826342

PRICE David (*Eup*): 29 Ash Grove, Whitchurch, Cardiff CF4 1BD ☎ 029 2062 3519

PRISCOTT M (*B Tbn*): Dalestones, Lansdown Road, Bath, Avon BA1 5TB ☎ 01225 316788

PURNELL Elizabeth: 11 Sandford Road, Bristol BS8 4QG ☎ 0117 963 5747 & fax, 0458 498646 mob

SAMPSON Len: 9 St Annes Terrace, Tower Road, St Helier, Jersey, Channel Island JE2 3HU ☎ 01534 509892, 0979 720411 mob

SHINER Colin (*Tba*): 4 The Ridge, Blonsdon, Swindon, Wilts SN2 4AD ☎ 01793 721545

SMITH Kenneth: 39 Chamberlain Road, Llandaff North, Cardiff, S.Glam. CF4 2LW ☎ 029 2055 3941

STEPHENS Kevin: Jericho, Grande Rue, Vale, Guernsey, C.I. GY3 5HJ ☎ 01481 47818

THICK Ian: The Old Shop, 85 Chelynch, Shepton Mallett, Somerset BA4 4PY ☎ 0468 506179

UPTON Christian: 12 Les Parquetss, Maufant, St Martin, Jersey JE3 6UP ☎ 01534 852139

WALPOLE-BROWN George: Netherby, Shaw Green Lane, Prestbury, Cheltenham, Glos GL52 3BP ☎ 0124 252 7115

WHITTINGHAM Tom (*Sou, Dms*): 16 Queen's Road, St George, Bristol BS5 8HR ☎ 0117 9551976

WILLIAMS Daryl: Rustington, 8 Orchard Rise, Pwllmeyric, Chepstow, Gwent NP6 6JT ☎ 01291 628681

WILLIAMS Terry (*Dms, Kbds, Pf*): 50 Keedwell Hill, Long Ashton, Bristol BS41 9DR ☎ 01275 393493

YOUNG Gordon (*B Tbn*): The Powder Magazine, Bouley Bay, Jersey, Channel Islands JE3 5AS ☎ 01534 873333 day, 01534 62018 eve

LONDON

ADDISON Susan (*A Tbn, Sack*): 7 Parsonage Lane, Enfield EN2 0AL ☎ 020 8367 8182, 020 8533 1372 day, 020 8367 0946 fax

ADLAM Michael: 52 Spruce Drive, Paddock Wood, Lightwater, Surrey GU18 5YX ☎ 01276 451297

ALCOE John (*Tpt*): 1 Weathervane Cultages, Braintree Road, Gt. Bardfield, Essex CM7 4SW ☎ 01371 810466

ALLAN Alistair: The Old Stores, The Street, Willingale, Essex ☎ 01277 896214

ARMSTRONG Jackie (*B Tbn, Eup, Tba*): 19 Leyfield, Worcester Park, Surrey KT4 7LS ☎ 020 8337 2114

BAKER Andrew (*A Tbn, Eup*): 109A Mount Pleasant Road, London SE13 6HX ☎ 020 8852 7811, 0966 267427

BAKER Edwin: 31 Croft Close, Chislehurst, Kent BR7 6EY ☎ 020 8467 4004

BALDWIN Russell: 10 Dorchester Court, Buckingham Road, South Woodford, London E18 2NG ☎ 020 8504 4799

BARBER Chris (*Tpt*): 517 Yeading Lane, Northolt, Middlesex UB5 6LN ☎ 020 8842 4044, 020 8842 8810 fax

BARKER Ted: 19 Husseywell Crescent, Hayes, Bromley, Kent BR2 7LN ☎ 020 8462 6624

BARRETT Paul (*Eup*): Flat 3, 121 Long Acre, London WC2E 9PA ☎ 020 7836 7288, 01306 880669

BASSANO Peter (*Sack*): North Lodge, Potter Row, Great Missenden, Bucks HP16 9NT ☎ 01494 868240, 01494 868250 fax, 0831 805537 mob

BASSEY Mark (*Arr, Com, Cop*): 63 Upper Tollington Park, London N4 4DD ☎ 020 7263 9791

BATES Stuart (*Pf, Org*): 49 Broadhurst Gardens, West Hampstead, London NW6 3QT ☎ 020 7419 4120

BAYLE Jack: 6 Lawson Spinney, Malahide, C. Dublin, Ireland ☎ 01 8451128

BEACHILL Peter (*V Tbn, Eup*): 16 Coniston Road, Muswell Hill, London N10 2BP ☎ 020 8444 3019, 01483 723644 day, 0370 914928 mob

BEECHAM John (*Tba, Sou*): 143 Acton Lane, Chiswick, London W4 5HW ☎ 020 8742 8667

BEER Paul (*A Tbn, Eup, Sack*): 168 Effra Road, Wimbledon, London SW19 8QA ☎ 020 8543 3557, 01306 880669

BELSHAW Warren (*Com, Arr*): 9 Dunsmore Road, Hall Green, Birmingham B28 8EA ☎ 0121 777 9005, 01589 479621

BENNETT Trevor (*Tba, Kbds*): 28, Bayston Road, Stoke Newington, London N16 7LT ☎ 020 7249 2341

BENTON E: Address Unknown ☎ 020 8346 2064

BEVAN Paul (*Rec, Eup*): 57 Belsize Park Gardens, London NW3 4JN ☎ 020 7722 5779

BISSONNETTE Big Bill (*Dms*): 585 Pond Street, Bridgeport, Connecticut, USA 06606 ☎ +1 203 372 0597, +1 203 371 4330

BLEASDALE Keith: 26 Waldegrave Gardens, Upminster, Essex RM14 1UX ☎ 01708 222096

BOLTON Graham (*A Tbn, Sack*): 35 Cannonside, Fetcham, Leatherhead KT22 9LE ☎ 01372 375939

BOTTERELL Jack: 3 Roundwood, Moorhead Lane, Shipley, W Yorks BD18 4JP ☎ 01274 595888

BOTTING Stephen (*Pf, Eup*): 12 Ploughmans Way, Rainham, Gillingham, Kent ME8 8LH ☎ 01634 233276

BOUSFIELD Ian: 161 Herkomer Road, Bushey, Herts WD2 3LH ☎ 020 8420 5480

BOYD Graeme (*Eup, Cop*): Ground Floor Flat, 122 Farley Road, London SE6 2AR ☎ 020 8461 5444 & fax, 0374 758888

BRAITHWAITE Nicholas (*Con*): Taringa Park, Mount Barker Road, Hahndorf, South Australia 5245 ☎ +61 8 388 7683

BRAND Paul (*Com*): 81 Osbaldeston Road, London N16 6NP ☎ 07970 980595, 020 8880 0474

BRENNER Roger: 52 Bellingham Road, Catford, London SE6 2PT, 020 8549 1706

BRIDGE John (*Sou*): 3 Heath Road, Oxhey, Watford, Herts WD1 4HE ☎ 01923 248340

BRIGHT Dudley: 14 Lancaster Avenue, South Woodford, London E18 1QF ☎ 020 8989 2322

BROOKS Reg: 13 Martin Close, Warlingham, Surrey CR6 9AD ☎ 01883 622438

BROWN Bill (*Eup, Sou*): Address Unknown

BROWN Philip: 98 Crockford Park Road, Addlestone, Surrey KT15 2LP ☎ 01932 848431

BROWNE Hayden (*Sax, Voc, Per*): 5 Rochester Road, London NW5 9JH ☎ 020 7482 1855

BUNKER Andrew (*A Tbn, Eup*): 25 Hogarth Court, Fountain Drive, London SE19 1UY ☎ 020 8761 1119, 07771 781615 mob

BURNAP Campbell: 36 Glengarry Road, London SE22 8QD ☎ 020 8693 8914

BURTON Tim (*Per*): 213 Wangford House, Loughborough Park, Briston, London SW9 8TF ☎ 020 7274 1318, 04325 229881

BUSBY Colin: 103 Ashley Gardens, Thirleby Road, London SW1P 1HJ ☎ 020 7828 9150

BUTCHER Andrew: 17 Clovelly Road, London W5 5HF ☎ 020 8579 7448

BUTTONS (*Arr, Com*): 19 Bredinghurst, Overhill Road, London SE22 ☎ 0956 238973

CAMERON Calvin (*Com, Arr, Cop*): 4 St Raphael Road, Windward Rd, P/O Kingston 2, Jamaica

CAMPBELL Gordon: 16 Priory Road, High Wycombe, Buckinghamshire HP13 6SL ☎ 01494 449948, 020 8549 1706 day

CARE Melvyn: 12 Hallowell Road, Northwood, Middlesex HA6 1DW

CASEY James (*A Tbn*): 38 Aylesbury Street, Neasden, London NW10 0AS ☎ 020 8208 2748, 01306 880669

CHAMBERLAIN Lawrence: 32 Oak Grove, Eastcote, Ruislip, Middx HA4 8UE ☎ 020 8866 3693

CHANDLER David (*A Tbn*): Flat H, 40 Earlham Street, London WC2H 9LA ☎ 020 7240 5010

CLARKE Jim: 33 Springwell Road, Tonbridge, Kent TN9 2LH ☎ 01732 770920

CLIFFORD Jonathan (*Eup*): 6 Newhall Court, Blessington Road, Dublin 24, Eire ☎ 01 462 0753, 020 8533 1372 day

COCKER Peter (*Eup*): 41 Manor Way, Petts Wood, Orpington, Kent BR5 1NN ☎ 01689 825752

COLE Chris (*Eup*): 36 Bell Lane, Hendon, London NW4 2AD ☎ 020 8202 3270

COLE Geoffrey: 4 Chestnut Court, Chesnut Grove, New Malden, Surrey KT3 3JR ☎ 020 8949 5256

COLEMAN W: Address Unknown

COLLIE Max: 26 Wendover Road, Bromley, Kent BR2 9JX ☎ 020 8460 1139

COLMAN Matthew: 77 Hartham Road, Islington, London N7 9JJ ☎ 0956 510112 mob

CREES Eric *(Arr, Com, Con)*: 62 De Frene Road, London SE26 4AG ☎ 020 8699 7109

CROMPTON Andy *(Eup)*: 54 Station Road, Long Marston, Tring, Hertfordshire HP23 4QS ☎ 01296 661181, 0589 600450 mob

CROMPTON Dan *(Flt)*: 14 Wesussex House, Wedmore Street, London N19 4EG ☎ 020 7281 1925

CRONIN Robert *(B Tpt)*: 5 Holly Drive, Stoke Mandeville, Aylesbury, Bucks HP21 8TZ ☎ 01296 422299, 0468 254186, 01296 331954

CROWTHER Michael: 124 Pepys Road, London SW20 8NY ☎ 020 8946 4009

DARRIBA Michael *(B Tbn)*: 15 Beryl Avenue, Beckton, London E6 5JT ☎ 020 7473 3625, 0370 878748

DAVIES Gary: 33 Marler Road, Forest Hill, London SE23 2AE ☎ 020 8699 1218, 0961 3000199 mob

DAVIES Peter: 27 Bethcar Road, Harrow, Middlesex HA1 1SE ☎ 020 8427 6317, 020 8549 1706

DAVIES Ros *(Flt, B Gtr, Pf)*: 107 Crownstone Road, Brixton, London SW2 1LY ☎ 020 7326 0097

DE.JESUS Joe *(Tpt, Flt, Br Hrn, Per)*: 18D Eversley Park Road, London N21 1JU ☎ 020 8882 6015, 0802 484698 mob

DEAN Christopher *(Cel)*: 6 Orchard Leigh, St Nicholas Hill, Leatherhead, Surrey KT22 8NF ☎ 01372 360510, 020 8549 1706 day

DEARNESS Magnus *(Sack, Eup)*: 169A Coldharbour Lane, London SE5 9PA ☎ 020 7978 8043, 01426 293268

DI PIETRO Mario: Pantiles, 10 Greenfields, Gosfield, Essex CO9 1TR ☎ 01787 477965

DICKINSON Barnaby *(Pf)*: 172 Malpas Road, Brockley, London SE4 1DH ☎ 020 8691 8355, 0973 388141

DOWSE Matt: 96 Shenley Road, Camberwell, London SE5 8NQ ☎ 020 7701 6653

DUDLEY Roger *(Voc, Voc)*: Orchard House, The Green, Sarratt, Herts WD3 6BS ☎ 01923 66664

EAGER Mark: Hundred House, Church Street, Llysworney, S. Glamorgan CF7 7NQ ☎ 01446 775126, 0850 374018 mob

EDNEY John *(Eup, A Tbn)*: 35 Albemarle Park, Albemarle Road, Beckenham, Kent BR3 5XG ☎ 020 8658 0405 & fax, 020 8549 1706, 0973 538689 mob

EDWARDS Johnny *(B Tbn, Eup)*: Orchard Cottage, Hazel Way, Chipstead, Surrey CR5 3PJ ☎ 01737 833853

EDWARDS Richard: 39 Haywards Road, Haywards Heath, West Sussex RH16 4HX ☎ 01444 412993, 020 8549 1706

EMENY Andrew: 3 Lindley Close, Harpenden, Herts AL5 4HS ☎ 01582 768 661, 0976 796410

ENRIGHT Jonathan: Flat 1 The Lines, 35 Highbury Grove, London N5 1HL ☎ 020 7704 1737

FAWBERT Andrew *(Eup, B Tpt, Sack)*: 4 Meadow Cottages, Little Kingshill, Great Missenden, Bucks HP16 0DX ☎ 01494 864 521, 020 8549 1706

FELTHAM Michael: Flat 1, 13 Polworth Road, London SW6 2ET ☎ 020 8696 0843, 07775 915 956

FINCH John *(Tba)*: 1 Hartley Road, Longfield, Kent DA3 7PF ☎ 01474 702842

FLACK John: 91 Crescent Road, Leigh-on-Sea, Essex SS9 2PG ☎ 01702 76196

FLAXMAN Andrew: 51 Mint Close, Hillingdon, Middlesex UB10 0TL ☎ 020 8569 0838, 0973 839 707

FRAMMINGHAM Malcolm: 27 Inchmery Road, Catford, London SE6 2NA ☎ 020 8698 1042

FRASER Noel: 1 Rochester Terrace, London NW1 9JN ☎ 020 7485 6816

FREE Jackie: 34 Rahn Road, Epping, Essex CM16 4JB ☎ 01992 573667

GELDARD Bill *(B Tbn, Eup, Arr)*: 5 Newlands Avenue, Thames Ditton, Surrey KT7 0HD ☎ 020 8398 1870

GIBBS Michael *(Com, Arr)*: 101 Alexandra Road, London N8 0LG ☎ 020 8881 1330

GLOVER Jason *(A Tbn, Kbds, Synth)*: 86 Newark Street, Whitechapel, London E1 2ES ☎ 020 7426 0340, 0850 757587

GODDARD Mark: 11 Lancaster Close, Bromley, Kent BR2 0QF ☎ 020 8290 5147

GOLDING Ian *(A Tbn, Pf)*: 2 Courtfield House, Baldwins Gardens, London EC1N 7SB ☎ 020 7916 8461, 020 7916 8462, 020 8533 1372

GOSLYN Roger *(Pf, Flt, Acc)*: 14 Harefield Road, London SE4 1LR ☎ 020 8692 9231

GOSTICK Bethan *(Hrp, Pf, Vla, B Gtr)*: 7 Woodland Way, Purley, Surrey CR8 2HT ☎ 020 8660 5810, 020 8660 5737

GOUGH Jeremy: 74 Carlton Park Avenue, Raynes Park, London SW20 8BL ☎ 020 8543 1731

GOWER Chris: c/o 10 Brocas Street, Eton, Windsor, Berks ☎ 020 8896 1883, 0468 082 586 mob

GRIFFITHS Malcolm: 20 Archery Square, Walmer, Kent CT14 7HP ☎ 01304 375722

GROVES Roger *(Sack)*: 55 Albany Road, London W13 8PQ ☎ 020 8998 0214, 01306 880669

GUMMER Colin: 5 Aspen Green, Denton, Mancester M34 6LW ☎ 0161 320 0208

GUNTON Simon *(A Tbn, B Tpt, Eup)*: 43 Sydenham Park, Sydenham, London SE26 4EE ☎ 020 8699 1008, 0585 706456

GUY Christopher: 11 Drake Road, Chessington, Surrey KT9 1LQ ☎ 020 8397 9425

HALL Caroline *(Vib, Clt, Pf)*: 10B Groveway, London SW9 0AR ☎ 020 7587 1246

HAMMOND Thomas *(A Tbn, Sack, Con)*: 1st Floor Flat, 100 Adelaide Avenue, Ladywell, London SE4 1YR ☎ 0976 307423 mob, 020 8691 9229

HARBORNE John *(Bzk, Cav, Kbds, Per)*: 226 Amelia Street, London SE17 3AS ☎ 020 7703 3315

HARRISON Keith: Flat 1, 6 Exeter Road, Kilburn, London NW2 4SP ☎ 020 8452 7064, 0973 654841, 020 7624 7627 fax

HARTLEY Patrick: 73A Chambersbury Lane, Hemel Hempstead, Herts HP3 8BB ☎ 01442 247949

HARVEY Roger: Chantilly, Duton Hill, Nr Gt Dunmow, Essex CM6 2DZ ☎ 0956 292750 mob, 020 8549 1706 day, 01371 870762

HENRY Melvyn: 10 Beauchamp Terrace, Putney, London SW15 1BW ☎ 020 8785 9272

HERBERT Trevor *(Sack)*: 26 St Margarets Road, Whitchurch, Cardiff CF4 7AB ☎ 029 2062 6280

HEXT Michael *(A Tbn, Eup)*: 69 Salisbury Road, Barnet, Herts EN5 4JL ☎ 020 8449 5054

HILL Colin *(V Tbn, Eup)*: 11 Alexandra Gardens, Knaphill, Woking, Surrey GU21 2DG ☎ 01483 486633, 020 8549 1706

HISSEY David *(Sack, Eup)*: 62 Mill Hill Road, Acton, London W3 8JH ☎ 020 8993 3223

HODGE Peter: 20 Church Rd, Farnborough, Kent BR6 7DB ☎ 01689 818318

HOGH Mike: 235 Petersham Road, Richmond, Surrey TW10 7AW ☎ 020 8940 6469

HOLLOWAY Tracy *(T Tba, A Tbn)*: 75A Pellatt Road, East Dulwich, London SE22 9JD ☎ 020 8299 6658

HOLT David *(Eup, A Tbn)*: 35 Ewhurst Road, Crofton Park, London SE4 1AG ☎ 020 8690 3708, 01523 183127 pager

HORLER David: Kirchstrasse 17, Kudinghoven, 53227 Bonn, Germany ☎ +49 228 463691, 0228 468517 fax

HOWARTH Russell: 3A Castlefields, Stoke Mandeville, Aylesbury, Buckinghamshire HP22 5XY ☎ 01296 614327

HOWE Anthony: 4 Cranmer Road, Croydon CR0 1SR ☎ 020 8688 4522

HOWLETT John: 103 Headcorn Road, Thornton Heath, Surrey CR7 6JS ☎ 020 8684 4607

HUCKRIDGE Roy: 21 Sugden Road, Thames Ditton, Surrey KT7 0AB ☎ 020 8398 4808

HUGHES Robert: Hardwick Court Farm, Hardwick Lane, Chertsey, Surrey KT16 0AD ☎ 01784 248943, 01932 561082, 0831 492798

HUMPHRIES Philip *(Sack, Serp, Rec, R Wnd)*: Hillside Cottage, Pound Lane, Dewlish, Dorchester, Dorset DT2 7LZ ☎ 01258 837034

HUNT Digby: 139 Grange Road, South Norwood, London SE25 6TQ ☎ 020 8241 6676

HYAMS Richard: 1 Pevensey Avenue, New Southgate, London N11 2RB ☎ 020 8368 6160, 0973 385748 mob

INNES Michael (*Eup, Tba*): 84 Hampden Road, Harrow Weald, Middlesex HA3 5PR ☎ 020 8427 7429

IVORY Stewart (*Didj, Sack*): 3 St Marys Close, Wavendon, Milton Keynes MK17 8LN ☎ 01908 582744

JACKSON Ellis: Address Unknown

JAMES Derek: 39 Bromley Road, London N18 1LF ☎ 020 8482 1623

JASKULSKI Clive (*Vln*): 23 Compton Road, London N21 3NU ☎ 020 8350 4627, 0956 152647 mob

JENKINS Dan (*Com, A Tbn, E Gtr, Sack*): 28 Priors Mead, Enfield, Middx EN1 3LS ☎ 020 8366 3119, 01306 880669 day

JONES Cliff: 85 Whitchurch Gardens, Edgware, Middx HA8 6PG ☎ 020 8952 6319

JONES Marcus (*Eup*): 143 Dressington Avenue, Brockley, London SE4 1JQ ☎ 020 8690 4494

KEARSEY Mike (*Eup, B Tbn*): 22 Bousfield Road, London SE14 5TR

KEECH David (*Voc*): 46A Foyle Road, Blackheath, London SE3 7RH ☎ 020 8853 1957

KELLY Martin: 11 Upper Paddock Road, Oxhey, Watford, Herts WD1 4DY ☎ 01923 225104

KENNEDY Martin (*Eup*): 28 Chestnut Grove, East Barnet, Herts EN4 8PU ☎ 020 8449 7608

KENNEDY Ric: 4 Oak Avenue, Enfield, Middx EN2 8LB ☎ 020 8363 7346

KERSHAW Brian (*Eup*): 183 Merryhill Road, Bushey Heath, Herts WD2 1AP ☎ 020 8386 0955

KETCHEN James: 31 Hillwood Road, Madeley Heath, Nr Crewe, Cheshire CW3 9JY ☎ 01782 750469

KILLIPS Robert (*Tpt, Tba*): 23 Kenilworth Gardens, Shooters Hill, London SE18 3JB ☎ 020 8319 0924, 0468 141172 mob

KINCH Malcolm (*Db*): 23 Beechcroft Avenue, North Harrow, Middlesex HA2 7JD ☎ 020 8868 9595

KING Alastair (*Eup*): 259/261 Luton Road, Chatham, Kent ME4 5BN ☎ 01634 844260

KIRBY Alan (*B Ldr*): 127 Ellerman Avenue, Twickenham, Middx TW2 6AB ☎ 020 8894 3301

KIRK Mark (*B Tbn, B Gtr*): 341A Chiswick High Road, London W4 4HS ☎ 020 8742 2588, 0585 113847

LAMB Bob: 15 Arkwright Road, Sanderstead, Surrey CR2 0LN ☎ 020 8657 6760

LANE Adrian: 9 The Lawns, Tylers Green, Bucks HP10 8BH ☎ 01494 817145, 0973 427987 mob, 020 8533 1372 day

LANGSDALE Peter: 3 Craven Road, Addiscombe, Surrey CR0 7JH ☎ 020 8654 3899

LAWES John (*Pf, Md*): 7 Fairmead Road, Shinfield, Reading, Berks RG2 9DL ☎ 01734 882526

LEES Tom (*Sack*): Flat 7, 29 Cambridge Park, East Twickenham, Middlesex TW1 2JL ☎ 020 8891 0977

LIDDELL David: 25 Hillhead Crescent, Belfast, Ireland BT11 9FS ☎ 0966 373131 mob

LLOYD Nicholas (*B Tbn, Eup, A Tbn, Tba*) ☎ 0589 600810

LOGAN Doug (*Eup, Arr, Cop, Md*): 41 Elizabeth Avenue, Hove, East Sussex BN3 6WA ☎ 01273 507 227, 0468 778840 mob, 01273 507 267

LORKIN Eddie: 6 Green Lane, Croxley Green, Rickmansworth, Herts WD3 3HR ☎ 01923 772654

LUSHER Don (*Eup*): The Old Rectory, 104 Burdon Lane, Cheam, Surrey SM2 7DA ☎ 020 8643 0749

LYNCH Thomas: 32 Huntfield Road, Bournemouth, Dorset BH9 3HN ☎ 01202 547 457

MANDEL Dave: 61 Parliament Hill Mansions, Lissenden Gardens, London NW5 1NB ☎ 020 7485 1483

MANSON Donald: 52A Geldeston Road, Hackney, London E5 8SB ☎ 020 8806 9954, 07970 984563

MASKELL Roy: 32 Sladedale Road, Plumstead, London SE18 1PY ☎ 020 8317 9791

MATHIESON Stephen: 3 Abbey Lodge, Wydeville Manor Road, Grove Park, London SE12 0ES ☎ 020 8851 1920, 0589 159 792

MCCAW Shirley (*Pf*): 35 Limesford Road, Nunhead, London SE15 3BX ☎ 020 7964 4219

MCDONALD Nigel (*Eup, A Tbn*): 2 Church Mews, Rainham, Kent ME8 8LB ☎ 01634 376235, 0976 433125 mob

MCGREGOR Kenneth: Flat 3, 23 Parkhill, Carshalton, Surrey SM5 3SA ☎ 020 8669 1211, 0973 705980 mob

MESSENGER Roger: West Thorn Cottage, Millers Lane, Outwood, Surrey RH1 5PU ☎ 01342 842570

MILLER Amos (*B Tpt*) ☎ 020 7624 4599, 020 8549 1706 day, 020 7624 4599

MIRES Trevor: Flat 325A, Brockley Road, London SE4 2QZ ☎ 020 8469 2060, 0956 424349 mob

MOFFAT Ian (*A Tbn, Eup, Voc*): 184 Cottimore Lane, Walton-on-Thames, Surrey KT12 2BJ ☎ 01932 221 969, 01306 880 669

MOSES Jake (*Voc*): 6 Pankhurst Close, Isleworth, Middx TW7 6SA ☎ 020 8560 4479

MOWAT Christopher: 115 Claygate Lane, Hinchley Wood, Esher, Surrey KT10 0BH ☎ 020 8398 0057

MULLEY Mark John (*A Tbn, Sack*): 29 Stuart Road, Ham, Richmond, Surrey TW10 7QU ☎ 020 8948 5928

MURRILL Jayne (*T Tba, B Tpt*): 16 Rothsay Road, London E7 8LY ☎ 020 8471 5512

NASH Geoffrey (*B Tpt, A Tbn*): 27 Wellfield Road, Streatham, London SW16 2BT ☎ 020 8769 0873

NASH Harold (*B Tpt, A Tbn*): Barn House, Urchfont, Devizes, Wiltshire SN10 4QH ☎ 01380 848193 & fax

NASH Michael (*A Tbn*): 122 Bray, Fellows Road, London NW3 3JT ☎ 020 7586 7944

NEAL Antony (*A Tbn, Eup*): 432 Waterside, Chesham, Bucks HP5 1QE ☎ 01494 774723

NELL Philip (*A Tbn, Pf*): 16 Jubilee Close, Pinner, Middlesex HA5 3TB ☎ 020 8866 5732, 0403 285468

NEWLANDS Archie: 12 Field End Road, Eastcote, Pinner, Middlesex HA5 2QL ☎ 020 8866 6317

NEWMAN Abigail (*Sack*): 57 Waverley Avenue, Wembley HA9 6BO ☎ 020 8902 2318, 0976 769658 mob

NICHOLLS-BENNETT John (*Eup, Com, Arr, Cop*): 61 Hampton Road, Forest Gate, London E7 0NX ☎ 020 8522 0058

NIEMAN Paul (*T Sack*): 36 Exeter Street, Brighton, East Sussex BN1 5PG ☎ 07050 608962, 07050 604890, 0958 484122 mob

NIGHTINGALE Mark (*V Tbn, Arr, Com, Cop*): 9 Wexfenne Gardens, Pyrford, Woking, Surrey GU22 8TX ☎ 01932 349998

NORRIS James: 12 Brinklow Crescent, Shooters Hill, London SE18 3BP ☎ 020 8855 3587

ODELL Rex: 5 Brookhouse Gardens, Highams Park, London E4 6LZ ☎ 020 8531 0791

OSWALD George (*V Tbn*): 2 Wattisfield Road, London E5 9QH ☎ 020 8985 7019

OYESIKU Julian: 12F Peabody Buildings, Wild Street, London WC2B 4DD ☎ 0961 301014

PARKER Stuart: The Bungalow, 8 The Crescent, Sidcup, Kent DA14 6NW ☎ 020 8300 0021

PARSONS Anthony (*A Tbn*): 3 Christchurch Road, London N8 9QL ☎ 020 8340 4109

PATERSON James: 175 Wilkinson Way, Chiswick, London W4 5XF ☎ 020 8740 8915

PATTERSON Scott (*A Tbn, Sack, Voc*): 11 Jeymer Street, Willesden Green, London NW2 4PJ ☎ 020 8830 2948

PAUL Alexandra (*Voc, Pf*): 2 Alleyne Crescent, West Dulwich, London SE21 8BN

PEARCE Robert: 14 Old Downs, Hartley, Longfield, Kent DA3 7AA ☎ 01474 708788

PERKINS Geoff: Stumps Cottage, 111 Ledbury Road, Hereford HR1 1RQ ☎ 01432 279461

PETTER Chris (*Pf*): 7 Undercliff Road, Lewisham, London SE13 7TU ☎ 020 7928 7234

PHILLIPS Stuart: 28, Sevenoaks Road, Orpington, Kent BR6 9JJ ☎ 01689 824155

POINTON Mike: 11 Kings Court, Kings Road, Wimbledon, London SW19 8QP ☎ 020 8542 7193

POWELL Simon (*Eup, Pf*): 19 Rutland Road, Wanstead, London E11 2DY ☎ 020 8530 3340

PRATT Maurice (*B Tbn*): 88 Brunswick Road, London W5 1AE ☎ 020 8997 9028

PRICE Jeremy: 38 Falkland Road, Harringay, London N8 0NX ☎ 020 8340 5429, 0850 685784

PRICE Robert: 10 Killearn Road, Catford, London SE6 1BT ☎ 020 8695 1976

PRIEST Philip (*B Tbn*): 12 Bank Lane, Denby Dale, Huddersfield, W.Yorkshire HP8 8QP ☎ 01484 861124

PRIOR James (*A Tbn, B Tbn*): Address Unknown ☎ 020 7652 3282

PURSER David (*B Tpt*): 42 Norbiton Avenue, Kingston, Surrey KT1 3QR ☎ 020 8549 9178

PYWELL Richard (*A Tbn, V Tbn*): 16 Ash Road, Shirley, Croydon, Surrey CR0 8HU ☎ 020 8777 9902, 0973 254938

RABY Brian: Bronwydd, 4 Tyfica Road, Pontypridd, South Wales CF37 2DA ☎ 01443 402178

RAJAH Lyn (*Gtr*): 120 Sherwood Avenue, Streatham Vale, London SW16 5EJ ☎ 020 8764 8048

RAWBONE Martyn (*Kbds*): 49 Monkton Road, Minster, Ramsgate, Kent CT12 4ED ☎ 01843 822280, 0402 434615 mob

RECKLESS David: 81 Kings Road, Brentwood, Essex CM14 4DP ☎ 01277 226519

REES Owen (*A Tbn, B Gtr*): 60 St Asaph Road, Brockley, London SE4 2EL ☎ 020 7639 9892, 020 7639 3331

RINGHAM Maisie (*Eup*): 28 Moor Park Road, Northwood HA6 2DJ ☎ 01923 829889

ROBINSON Melvyn (*Eup, A Sax, Pf*): 28B St Philips Road, London E8 3BP ☎ 020 7254 0616

ROBSON James (*Pf*): 126 Manor Road, Chigwell, Essex IG7 5PR ☎ 020 8500 5233

RODRIQUEZ Rico: 64 Wiltshire Close, Draycott Avenue, Chelsea, London SW3 2NT

ROLLINS Dennis: 147 Sterling Gardens, Sanford Street, London SE14 6DU ☎ 020 8691 9717

ROSEBERRY Robert: 13 Hillside Road, Cheam, Surrey SM2 6ET ☎ 020 8661 1749

RUSHTON Mark (*Pf, Kbds, Gtr*): 24 Wilma Close, Kingston-upon-Thames, Surrey KT2 5LX ☎ 020 8549 3777

RUTHERFORD Paul: Flat 2, 67A Shooters Hill Road, London SE3 7HS ☎ 020 8858 3806 fax

SCOTT Daniel (*A Tbn*): 11 Haslemere Close, Wallington, Surrey SM6 8LT ☎ 020 8680 8645

SEAGO Frank (*B Gtr, Tpt, Eup*): 65 Pontefract Road, Bromley, Kent BR1 4RB ☎ 020 8698 2154

SEYMOUR Mark (*B Gtr, Voc*): 37C Oakhurst Grove, London SE22 9AN ☎ 020 8299 3071

SHARMAN Dave: 61 Rushmore Road, London E5 0EX ☎ 020 8985 7777

SHAW Steve (*V Tbn, Eup*): 18 Fishermans Way, Bourne End, Bucks SL8 5LY ☎ 01628 528278

SHEEN Colin: Jingles, Parkfields, Oxshott, Surrey KT22 0PW ☎ 01372 842862

SHEPHERD Jeremy (*B Sax*): 186, Church Road, Hanwell, London W7 3BP ☎ 020 8567 0676/4

SHEPHERD Kenneth: 24 Holly Close, Buckhurst Hill, Essex IG9 6HT ☎ 020 8504 3899

SHILLING Lindsay: 23A Woodlands Park Road, London SE10 9XE ☎ 020 8858 0743, 01483 723644

SIBLEY John: 6 St Edmunds Road, Gantshill, Ilford, Essex IG1 3QL ☎ 020 8554 6386

SIDWELL Neil: 22 Clifton Road, Finchley, London N3 2AR ☎ 020 8346 0627

SINGLETON John: 5 Cranmore Way, London N10 3TP ☎ 020 8442 1898

SLATER Ashley (*Voc, B Tbn, Tba*): Flat 12, 85 Marine Parade, Brighton BN2 1AJ ☎ 01273 600021, 0374 884467 mob, 01273 884467 fax

SLIDE Fred: 48 Felbridge Avenue, Stanmore, Middlesex HA7 2BH ☎ 020 8427 5133

SMITH Chris: 13 Letchmore Road, Radlett, Herts WD7 8HU ☎ 01923 854363

SMITH Malcolm (*Voc, Com, Arr*): 11C White Hart Lane, Wood Green, London N22 5SL ☎ 020 8881 6867

SMITH Peter (*Arr*): 89 Eden Way, Beckenham, Kent BR3 3DW ☎ 020 8650 5331

STOWE David (*A Tbn, B Tpt, Eup*): 12 Fairlie Gardens, London SE23 3TE ☎ 020 8699 4612, 01306 880669

STRANGE Peter (*Arr*): 11 Yewland Close, Banstead, Surrey SM7 3DB ☎ 01737 211582

STROMAN Scott (*Voc*): 91 Wilberforce Road, London N4 2SP ☎ 020 7354 5539

SULLIVAN Vincent: 46 Ellison Road, Streatham, London SW16 5BY ☎ 020 8679 3968, 0973 165973 mob, 020 8944 8842

SWAN Malcolm (*Pf*): 25 Heather Glen, Romford, Essex RM1 4SX ☎ 01708 42190

TAYLOR Leon (*A Tbn*): 28 The Grove, Teddington, Middx TW11 8AS ☎ 020 8943 1577

TAYLOR Paul: 91 Brook Drive, London SE11 4TU ☎ 020 7820 0878

THOMAS David: Mole Cottage, Highmolewood, Hertford, Herts SG14 2PL ☎ 01992 589291

THOMS Peter: 29, Leppoc Road, Clapham Common, London SW4 9LS ☎ 020 7622 1661

THOMSON Nichol D: 46 Hawthornes Road, Edmonton, London N18 1EZ ☎ 020 8373 8836, 0976 356289

THORLEY Peter: 8 Dorset Road, Wood Green, London N22 7SL ☎ 020 8889 7234

THORNETT David: 56 Clavering Road, London E12 5EX ☎ 020 8989 8932

TOMLINSON Alan (*B Tbn*): 47 Seldon House, Savona Estate, Stewarts Road, London SW8 4DP ☎ 020 7720 6949

TOWNEND Mark: 57 Wood Common, Hatfield, Hertfordshire AL10 0UE ☎ 01707 270965, 0973 615946 mob

TRAVES Christopher (*Pf*): 46 Kenilworth Road, London SE20 7QG ☎ 020 8402 9036, 0370 231091 mob

VIRJI Fayyaz (*Kbds, Com*): 150 Fairlawn Park, Sydenham, London SE26 5SD ☎ 020 8699 9748, 0973 118410 mob

VOLLAM Helen (*A Tbn, Sack, Eup*): 2 High Street, Chrishall, Royston, Herts SG8 8RP ☎ 01763 838167

WADSWORTH Derek (*Md, Cntrc*): 22 Gerard Road, Barnes, London SW13 9RG ☎ 020 8748 5868

WALTERS Mark: 23 Bendysh Road, Bushey, Herts WD2 2HZ ☎ 01923 224872

WARD Bob: 57 Oxford Road, West Harrow, Middlesex HA1 4JH ☎ 020 8427 3770

WATMOUGH Sam (*Cntrc*): Westwynds, Laleham Reach, Chertsey, Surrey KT16 8RT ☎ 019325 61107

WATSON Johnny: 7 Lexington Way, Bells Hill, High Barnet, Herts EN5 2SN ☎ 020 8440 4322

WHITE Ian (*A Tbn, Sack*): 13 Tugela Road, West Croydon, Surrey CR0 2HB ☎ 020 8689 9280, 020 8549 1706 day

WHITEHEAD Annie (*Eup*): 22 Richford Road, Stratford, London E15 3PQ ☎ 020 8519 1398, 020 8522 1957 fax

WHITSON David (*A Tbn, Sack*): 302 Reigate Road, Epsom Downs, Surrey KT17 3LX ☎ 01737 359791, 01306 880669 day, 0973 620522 mob

WICK Denis: 8 The Wilderness, East Molesey, Surrey KT8 0JT ☎ 01590 642152

WILLEY Roger: 27 Tharp Road, Wallington, Surrey SM6 8LG ☎ 020 8773 9526

WILLS Simon (*A Tbn, B Tpt, Eup*): 6 Abbey View Road, St Albans, Herts AL3 4QL ☎ 01727 832352, 01306 880669

WILSON Arthur (*A Tbn*): 21 Grasmere Road, London N10 2DH ☎ 020 8444 8316

WILSON Carey (*Voc*): 50 Kingswood Road, Ilford, Essex IG3 8UD ☎ 020 8599 8264

WILSON James (*B Tbn*): 46 Crouch Hall Road, London N8 8HJ ☎ 020 8340 5279, 020 8549 1706

WINTHORPE Tom: 31 Neal Street, Covent Garden, London WC2H 9PR ☎ 020 7379 6529

WOOD Andrew (*Pf, A Tbn, V Tbn, Cc⌐*): 12A Hibbert Road, Wealdstone, Harrow, Middx HA3 7JS ☎ 020 8930 8611, 0973 196 156 mob

WOOD Ken: 57 Leighton Road, London W13 9EL ☎ 020 8567 5740

WORDSWORTH Ray (*Pf*): 4A Harewood Road, South Croydon, Surrey CR2 7AL ☎ 020 8688 2430

WORKMAN Robert (*A Tbn*): 334 Oxbridge Road, Hatch End, Middlesex HA5 4HR ☎ 020 8428 8400, 0976 710881 mob

WRIGHT Nigel (*Kbds, Db*): Lockerbie, St Annes Hill Road, Chertsey, Surrey KT16 9NN ☎ 01932 567847

TRUMPET
SCOTLAND

ANDERSON Dave: The Manse, 84 Wardneuk Drive, Kilmarnock KA3 2EX ☎ 01563 521815

BAILLIE James (*Flgl*): 26 Belvidere Crescent, Bishopsbriggs, Glasgow G64 2JP ☎ 0141 762 4924

BAXTER Robert (*N Tpt, Ea Wnd*): 3/L, 24 Ancroft Street, Woodside, Glasgow G20 7HU ☎ 0141 332 7561

BENNETT Michael: 199 The Oval, Clarkston, Glasgow G76 8LU ☎ 0141 637 6717, 0378 447924 mob

BEYNON Darren (*Pf*): 64 Glencorf Avenue, Uddingston, Glasgow, Scotland G71 6EF ☎ 01698 813878

BOULT Geoffrey (*Cnt*): 71 Earlspark Avenue, Newlands, Glasgow G43 2HE ☎ 0141 649 5847

CARRICK Jillian: 26 Jordanhill Drive, Glasgow, Scotland G13 1SA ☎ 0141 959 6725

CLANCY Edmund (*Pf*): Cecilia Cottage, Baunogues, Castleblakeney, Ballinasloe, Co. Galway

CLUCAS Anthony: 184 Waverley Crescent, Livingston EH54 8JT ☎ 01506 416788

COWIESON Lorne: Flat 200, 367 Argyle Street, Glasgow G2 8LT ☎ 0141 221 1836, 0403 177673

DALY Michael (*Cnt*): 54 Main Road, Coylton KA6 6JD ☎ 01292 570348, 07775 768269 mob

FORSHAW Brian: 40 Cheviot Drive, Newton Mearns, Glasgow G77 5AS ☎ 0141 616 0941

FRANKS Peter: 29 West Bankton Place, Murieston West, Livingston EH54 9ED ☎ 01506 415514

FRIEL Alan: 53 Underwood Road, Paisley, Renfrewshire PA3 1TU ☎ 0141 889 7344

GARGAN Laurie (*Cnt*): 23 Sannox View, Ayr, Ayrshire KA8 0PR ☎ 01292 269533

GILLIES Gary: 58 Double Hedges Road, Neilston, Glasgow G78 3JH ☎ 0141 571 5372, 0141 881 5576

GRACIE John: 12, Broomvale Drive, Newton Mearns, Glasgow G77 5NN ☎ 0141 639 7173, 070500 92119 mob

GREER Charles (*Acc*): Address Unknown

HAGGART Alan (*Cnt, Sack*): 72 Walker Road, Aberdeen AB11 8BP ☎ 01224 249396

HARKIN C. (*Pf, Org*): The Limes, 1, Newark Street, Greenock PA16 7UH ☎ 01475 721183

JOHNSTON Graeme (*Flgl, Dms*): 20 Craigs Avenue, Edinburgh EH12 8HS ☎ 0131 334 4802

KERR Brian (*Flgl*): 26 E Stoneyholm Road, Kilbirnie, Ayrshire KA25 7DT ☎ 01505 684804

LAYCOCK Ivor (*Flgl*): 84 Cardowan Drive, Stepps, Glasgow G33 6HH ☎ 0141 779 3748

LOWE Thomas (*Flgl, Pf*): First Floor Left, 20 White Street, Partick, Glasgow G11 5RP ☎ 0141 576 0409, 0966 158425 mob

LYNN Andrew: 44 Queen's Drive, Glasgow G42 8DD ☎ 0141 424 4253

MACDONALD Alan: 9 Dalry Road, Kilbirnie, Ayrshire, Scotland KA25 6HZ ☎ 01505 682769

MACNIVEN Tom (*Flgl*): 60 Woodside Ave, Rutherglen, Glasgow G73 3JG ☎ 0141 647 6273

MARTIN William (*Dms*): 1 Seafield Road East, Edinburgh EH15 1EB ☎ 0131 669 8807

MATHEW David: 11 Garscadden Road, Old Drumchapel, Glasgow G15 6UW ☎ 0141 944 1734

MCCOMB James: 11 Croftpark Road, Hardgate, Clydebank, Dumbartonshire G81 6NN ☎ 01389 874505

MCCRACKEN Kenneth: 56 D Galston Road, Hurlford, Kilmarnock, Ayrshire KA1 5HY ☎ 01563 20069

MCGRATTAN Alexander (*N Tpt, Cntt Zin*): 7 West Ferryfield, Edinburgh EH5 2PT ☎ 0131 552 4803

MCKAY James (*Flgl*): 1C Dunlop Crescent, Renfrew, Renfrewshire PA4 8PQ ☎ 0141 562 5261

MCKENZIE Swanson: 10 Beechgrove Gardens, Aberdeen AB15 5HG ☎ 01224 632683

MCQUEEN Ross: 53 Kingston Road, Bishopton, Renfrewshire PA7 5BA ☎ 01505 862380

MITCHELL Brian (*Kbds, Arr, Com*): 34 Redburn Avenue, Culloden, Inverness IV1 2AG ☎ 01463 794002

MUIRHEAD Iain (*N Tpt, Pictpt, Flgl, Cnt*): 45 Craighill Drive, Clarkston, Glasgow G76 7TD ☎ 0141 639 2702, 0403 197013

MUNDAY Ray (*Pictpt, N Tpt, Cnt, Ea Wnd*): 15 Cairnpark Street, Dollar, Clackmannanshire FK14 7ND ☎ 01259 742143

MUNDIE Gordon (*Per, Pf*): Ty-Mawr, Squarepoint, Castle Douglas DG7 2LL

OWEN William: 68 Wedderburn Crescent, Dunfermline, Fife KY11 4SE ☎ 01383 734573

POPE Marcus: 79 Fotheringay Road, Glasgow G41 4LQ ☎ 0141 423 3600

PRENTICE David (*Pictpt, Flgl*): Address Unknown ☎ 0141 332 2164, 0973 862973 mob

PRICE Kevin (*Con*): Fingarry, Campsie Road, Milton Of Campsie, Glasgow G65 8EH ☎ 01360 311 215

PYE Nicholas (*Flgl, H Bag*): Beannach Aonguais, Balquhidder, Nr Lochearnhead, Perthshire FK19 8NY ☎ 01877 384277, 0402 002403, 01786 458021

SAMPSON John (*Rec, M Inst*): 54 Gilmore Place, Edinburgh EH3 9NX ☎ 0131 229 1519, 037 470 8933

SEVERN Eddie (*Flgl, Kbds, Arr*): Glen View, 12 Lady Brae, Gorebridge, Mid Lothian EH23 4HT ☎ 01875 20426

SHANNON William: Address Unknown

SHARP Paul (*N Tpt, Cntt, Ea Wnd*): 36A Main Road, Castlehead, Paisley, Renfrewshire, Scotland PA2 6AW ☎ 0141 889 4878, 0410 020012 mob

SHIELDS George: Address Unknown

STEELE Colin (*Flgl*): 55 Corbiehill Place, Edinburgh EH4 5AX ☎ 0131 539 5114

STEVENSON Thomas: 58 Glencairn Street, Stevenston, Ayrshire KA20 3BJ ☎ 01294 602570

THOMSON Gary (*Flgl, Kbds, Per, Tbn*): The Manor House, Rempstone, Leicestershire LE12 6RH ☎ 01509 880351

VAN DER WALT J Simon (*Tbn, Flgl, Gtr, Com*): 124 Dumbarton Road, Glasgow G11 6NY ☎ 0141 357 5743

WEIR Hugh: 96 Hillview Drive, Clarkston, Glasgow G76 7JD ☎ 0141 638 4243

WHITEFORD Roy (*Flgl*): 8A Lilybank Road, Port Glasgow PA14 5AN ☎ 01475 741122

WILSON Ruari (*Flgl, Pictpt, Voc, B Gtr*): 4/9 May Court, Pennywell Medway, Edinburgh EH4 4SD ☎ 0131 336 3503

YOUNG William (*Flgl*): Douglasdale, 6 Ingerbeck Avenue, Burnside, Rutherglen G73 5DH ☎ 0141 634 1502

NORTH WEST

ABBOTT Gary (*Cnt, Flgl*): 57 Albert Street, Barrow In Furness, Cumbria LA14 2JS

ADDISON Mark: Flat 7, Camergue Court, Candleford Road, Withington, Manchester M20 3JH ☎ 020 7277 4707, 0973 601911 mob

ANDERSON Keiron (*Md*): 2 Lynton Grove, Bradshaw, Halifax, W Yorks HX2 9XN ☎ 01422 247162

ANDREWS Christopher (*Cnt*): Meadowside, 119 Whittingham Lane, Broughton, Preston PR3 5UD ☎ 01772 862765

BARLOW Bob (*Flgl*): 30, Goyt Road, Lower Brinnington, Stockport, Cheshire. SK1 2EZ ☎ 0161 480 9829

BELL Jack: 16 West End Avenue, Gatley, Cheadle, Ches SK8 4DR ☎ 0161 428 5699

BROWN John: 67 Alder Road, Failsworth, Manchester M35 0QJ ☎ 0161 681 2567

BROWN Kenneth (*Cnt, Flgl*): Homestead, Chapel Milton, Chapel-En-Le-Frith, Stockport, Cheshire SK12 6QQ ☎ 01298 813371

BROWN Peter (*V Tbn, Eup*): 26, Tarragon Drive, Larks Hollow, Meir Park, Stoke-on-Trent, Staffs. ST3 7YE ☎ 01782 399521

BROWNING David (*Cnt, Flgl, Pictpt*): The White House, Rotherwood Road, Wilmslow, Cheshire SK9 6DR ☎ 01625 527756

BUTTERWORTH Ian (*Flgl, Cnt*): 2 Union Terrace, Penrith, Cumbria CA11 9DY ☎ 01768 892464, 01768 863175

CARSTAIRS David: 49 Hurst Lea Road, New Mills, High Peak, Derbyshire SK22 3HP ☎ 01663 750294

CHAPMAN John: 1 Barnes Avenue, Dalton In Furness, Lancs LA15 8NB ☎ 01229 63115

COLVIN Colin (*Cnt*): Greenwood, Ballaugh Curraghs, Isle Of Man IM7 5BG ☎ 01624 897754

COPPERWAITE David: 3 Kimberley Avenue, Romiley, Stockport, Cheshire SK6 4AB ☎ 0161 430 5067

CORKILL Roy: 49 Waterloo Road, Ramsey, Isle Of Man IM8 1DZ ☎ 01624 814652

CORNELL Andrew (*Flgl, Pictpt, Cnt*): 15 Prince George Street, Oldham, Lancashire OL1 4HW ☎ 0161 652 6848, 07931 748556

COULL Christopher (*Flgl, Pf*): 2 Broadoak Road, Bramhall, Stockport, Cheshire SK7 3BW ☎ 0161 440 0764

CROPPER Frank (*Flgl*): 11 Manor Farm Close, Ashton Under Lyne, Lancs OL7 9LS ☎ 0161 292 7648

DALLIMORE Andrew (*Cnt*): 26 Beever Street, Old Trafford, Manchester M16 9JR ☎ 0161 877 6698

DARLINGTON Ronald (*Flgl, Voc*): 94 Park Lane, Macclesfield, Cheshire SK11 6UA ☎ 01625 423443

DARRINGTON Ian (*Flgl, Pf, Md*): 139 Wigan Lane, Wigan, Lancs WN1 2NB ☎ 01942 243974, 0385 982524

DAS-GUPTA Luke: 5 Peverill Crescent, Chorlton, Manchester M21 9WR ☎ 0161 861 9650

DAVY Kevin (*Flgl, Cnt, Voc, Kbds*): 1A 31 Balham Hill, London SW12 9DX ☎ 020 8675 7124, 0585 514893

DEAN Robert (*Per*): 14 Barkhill Road, Liverpool L17 6AZ ☎ 0151 427 2228

DIAZ Julian (*Flgl, Per*): 3-5 Pedder Street, Morecambe, Lancs LA4 5DY ☎ 01524 410927

DICKINSON John (*Cnt*): 8 Wyngate Road, Hale, Altrincham, Cheshire WA15 0LZ ☎ 0161 980 4622

DINN Robert (*Flgl, Per, Pf, Kbds*): 5 Osborne Road, Levens Hulme, Manchester M19 2DU ☎ 0161 224 8211

DIPPLE Laura: 30 Wyverne Road, Chorlton, Manchester M21 0ZN ☎ 0161 881 4314

ECCLES Vaughan: Threeways, Charnleys Lane, Banks, Southport / Merseyside PR9 8HH ☎ 01704 29060

EDWARDS David (*Pf*): 2 Belfield Drive, Oxton Birkenhead L43 5SJ ☎ 0151 652 9624

ELLIOTT Don: White House Cottage, New Road, Laxey, Isle Of Man IM4 7HS ☎ 01624 861461

ENGLAND James (*Pf*): Hodder View Cottage, Chipping Road, Chaigley Nr Clitheroe, Lancs BB7 3LP ☎ 01254 826770

FARR Gary (*Flgl, Cnt*): 13 Clifton Road, Chorlton, Manchester M21 8UX ☎ 0161 881 4590, 0498 558342 mob

FORD Robert (*Kbds, E Gtr*): 6 Park Meadow, Westhoughton, Bolton, Lancs BL5 3UZ ☎ 01942 819685

FRANCE Leonard (*Md, Voc*): 44 St. George's Avenue, Thornton Cleveleys, Lancashire FY5 3JW ☎ 01253 854844

FREEMAN Roy: 11 Rose Terrace, Ashton, Preston PR2 1EB ☎ 01772 726459

FROHLICK Ashley (*Flgl*): Timbers, Pool Foot Lane, Singleton, Poulton-Le-Fylde, Lancs FY6 8LY ☎ 0976 625037

FRYER Neil: 6 Whitegates, Whitemoor, Congleton, Cheshire CW12 3ND ☎ 01782 513148

FULTON Neil: Flat 10 Manfield Mansions, 20 Alexandra Road, Manchester M16 8EZ ☎ 0161 226 4665, 0467 275561

GIBSON, GLCM Stephen (*Kbds*): 6 Bramley Road, Norden, Rochdale, Lancs OL11 5QN ☎ 01706 44628

HARRIS Leslie: Erindale Mews, Carriage Drive, Frodsham, Cheshire WA6 6EG ☎ 01928 731194

HEARNSHAW Colin (*Flgl*): 19 Mostyn Street, Dukinfield, Cheshire SK16 5JS ☎ 0161 303 0618

HEROD Gordon (*Flgl, Dms*): 35 Bakers Lane, Southport PR9 9RN ☎ 01704 26715

HIGHAM J: 5 Queens Road, St Helens, Lancs WA10 3HZ ☎ 01744 26932

HOLT William: 19 Luxor Grove, Denton, Manchester M34 2NR ☎ 0161 223 8957

HONE Ged: 37 Lower Fold, Marple Bridge, Cheshire SK6 5DU ☎ 0161 427 7992

HUGHES Gareth: 13 Cartmel Drive, Moreton, Wirral, Merseyside L46 0TE ☎ 0151 677 6355

HULME John D (*Flgl, Pf*): 43 Southwood Road, Great Moor, Stockport, Cheshire SK2 7DJ ☎ 0161 456 7667

JONES Graham (*Cnt*): 7 Brickfields, Spon Green, Buckley, Clwyd CH7 3BE ☎ 01244 546606

JONES Kris (*Pf*): Flat 2, 8 Mayfield Road, Whalley Range, Manchester M16 8FT ☎ 0161 232 9315

KELLETT Timothy (*Pf*): Trinity Parsonage, Hardwick Square East, Buxton, Derbys SK17 6PT ☎ 01298 27346

KELLY Fred: Wimereux, Kinders Crescent, Greenfield, Nr Oldham Lancs OL3 7JQ ☎ 01457 875218

KNOCK Richard (*Clt, Cnt*): 18 The Hawthorns, Eccleston, Chorley, Lancs PR7 5QW ☎ 01257 451362

LAIRD Jayne: 20 Beach Grove, Wallasey, Wirral, Merseyside L45 7QY

LANCASHIRE David (*Cnt, Con*): 40, Berry Drive, Great Sutton, South Wirral, Cheshire L66 4LT ☎ 0151 339 8484

LAWRENCE John: 22 Arno Road, Oxton, Birkenhead, Cheshire L43 5UX ☎ 0151 652 4759

LEE David: 2 Humber Avenue, Layton, Blackpool, Lancs FY3 7HY ☎ 01253 398954

LEWIS Bunny: 1 Belmore Avenue, Crumpsall, Manchester M8 6ED ☎ 0161 740 4435

LIDDLE Bob: 1 St Michael's Close, Bury, Lancs BL8 2JN ☎ 0161 761 5916

MACMURRAY John: 11 Summerfield Place, Wilmslow, Cheshire SK9 1NE ☎ 01625 533986

MAINWARING Peter (*Flgl*): Flat 2, 8 Mayfield Road, Whalley Range, Manchester M16 8FT ☎ 0161 232 9315, 0973 483633

MARGERSON Derrick: Prospect Cottage, Blaze Hill, Rainow, Macclesfield SK10 5BZ ☎ 01625 573550

MARKS Paul (*Flgl, Cnt*): 1 St Annes Road, Southport, Merseyside PR9 9TQ ☎ 01704 213411

MCGRORTY Joseph: 18 Gill Court, Harrowside, Blackpool, Lancashire FY4 1PS ☎ 01253 405835

MOORE Keith: Rokineath, Crosthwaite, Kendal, Cumbria LA8 8HT ☎ 015395 68492

MORRIS Andrew: Stanley House, 39 Stanley Gardens, London W3 7SY

MOSLEY Mark: 4 Wickham Drive, Astley, Manchester M29 7BX ☎ 01942 887794

MOSS Phil (*B Ldr*): 262 Middleton Road, Manchester M8 4WA ☎ 0161 740 2917

O'HARA Cy (*Gtr*): Cherry Grove, Pen-Y-Bont Road, Llangwstenin, Conwy LL31 9JJ ☎ 01492 545999

OWENS Rhys: 32 Earlston Road, Wallasey, Merseyside L42 5DY ☎ 0151 637 0537

PARRY Kevin: 14 Marsden Drive, Timperley, Altrincham, Cheshire WA15 7XF ☎ 0161 904 9046

PATTERSON Craig (*Cnt, Flgl*): 12 Colwyn Road, Cheadle Hulme, Cheadle, Cheshire SK8 6BX ☎ 0161 485 1393

POTTS Roy (*Flgl*): Farthings, Rivacre Road, Hooton Park, S. Wirral Cheshire L65 1AS ☎ 0151 339 3367

REID Gavin: 75 Moor End Road, Mellor, Stockport, Cheshire SK6 5PT ☎ 0161 427 5482, 0411 306793

ROBERTSON Elaine (Pf): 58 Macclesfield Road, Whaley Bridge, High Peak SK23 7DH ☎ 0189682 2802

ROYLE Ian: 3, Parsonage Road, Flixton, Manchester M41 6PZ ☎ 0161 747 4073

SASSOON Jeremy (Pf, Kbds): 45 High Grove Road, Cheadle, Cheshire SK8 1NW ☎ 0161 428 4765, 0385 933165 mob

SCOTT Clive: 23 Springfield Road, Gatley, Cheadle, Cheshire SK8 4PE ☎ 0161 428 8195

SHEPHERD Kenneth: 4 Southfield Drive, Normoss, Blackpool, Lancs FY3 0AN ☎ 01253 892217

SMALL Gareth (Pic, Cnt): 9 Wilton Street, Whitefield, Manchester M45 7FT ☎ 0161 796 8015, 0973 197148

SMITH Christopher (Flgl, V Tbn, B Gtr, E Gtr): 3 Micklegate, Thornton, Cleveleys FY5 1RG ☎ 01253 822008

SMITH Graham: 103 Bristol Avenue, Farington, Leyland PR5 2QZ ☎ 01772 431995

SMITH Martin: 26 Fir Grove, 40-42 Percy Street, Liverpool L8 7SE ☎ 0151 709 4325

STOREY Benjamin: 11 Mayfield Mansions, 20 Alexandra Road, Manchester M16 8EZ ☎ 0161 232 7296, 0421 097485 mob

STRINGER Alan: El-Carim, Bridges, Luxulyan, Nr Bodmin, Cornwall PL30 5EF ☎ 01726 851388

TAYLOR Bob: 41 Oldham Road, Delph, Oldham, Lancs OL3 5EB ☎ 01457 874264

TOMLINSON Alan (Flgl, Tbn, Hrn): 23 Fifth Avenue, Burnley, Lancs BB10 1YA ☎ 01282 422842

WADDINGTON Frank: 34 Elmfield Street, Church, Accrington, Lancs BB5 4DZ ☎ 01254 235703

WHALEY Doug: 37 Turnstone Road, Offerton, Stockport, Cheshire SK2 5XT ☎ 0161 456 9646

WILLAN Eric: Park View House, Newbold Street, Elton, Bury, Lancs BL8 2RR ☎ 0161 797 7991

WILLIAMS Wyn (Hrn, Flgl): Ysgubor Wen, Trefor, Caernarfon, Gwynedd LL54 5AA ☎ 01286 660532

WILSON Charles (Cnt): Brookside, Queen Street, Llangollen, Denbighshire, North Wales LL20 8LH ☎ 01978 860381

WORTHINGTON Desmond (Cnt): 7 Lugard Road, Liverpool L17 0BA ☎ 0151 280 3818

YATES Neil: 1541A London Road, Norbury, London SW16 4AD ☎ 020 8679 2195, 0468 748368

NORTH EAST

ACASTER Andrew (Pf, Gtr, Dms): 31 Swarthdale, Haxby, York YO32 3NZ

ALLEN Keith (Flgl, Cnt): Park House, Back Lane, Easingwold, York YO61 3BP ☎ 01347 822497

BARKER John (Flgl, Cnt, Pf): Woodside, 9 School Close, Darley Dale, Derbyshire DE4 2TQ ☎ 01629 734 540, 01629 734 540

BARKER Leslie: 6 Woodbine Terrace, Idle BD10 9JJ ☎ 01274 613865

BAXTER Ken (Flgl, Tbn, Tba, Arr): Burnside House, 10 Burns Court, Birstall, West Yorkshire WF17 9JB ☎ 01924 441441 & fax, 0850 319689 mob

BEADNELL Brian (B Gtr, Voc, Pf, Cnt): 61 Wilton Bank, Saltburn-By-Sea, Cleveland TS12 1PD ☎ 01287 622952

BELL Peter: 17 Grange Road, Oxhill, Stanley, Co Durham DH9 7RQ ☎ 01207 238151

BENSON Hedley (Cnt): 22 Cherry Tree Crescent, Farsley, Pudsey, Leeds LS28 5SR

BIGGINS John (Flgl): 32 Whitehill Road, Brinsworth, Rotherham S60 5HZ ☎ 01709 374620

BLOOD Christopher: 19 Greencliffe Drive, Clifton, York YO30 6NA ☎ 01904 622069

BOSWELL Peter (Cnt, Tbn): 3 Bankwell Close, Giggleswick, N. Yorks BD24 0BX ☎ 01729 822400

BRADY Oliver: 3 Second Avenue, Heworth, York YO31 0RS ☎ 01904 421369, 0411 267452

BURTON Trevor: 29 Kenilworth Close, Saxilby, Lincoln LN1 2FQ ☎ 01522 704710

COATES William: 17 South View, Annfield Plain, Stanley, Co Durham DL15 0JW ☎ 01207 234506

COLLINS Ed (Flgl, Pf): 11 Moorfield Avenue, Armley, Leeds, Yorkshire LS12 3RZ ☎ 0113 279 7248

CRAWFORD Barry (Cnt): 29 Lintzford Road, Hamsterley Mill, Rowlands Gill, Tyne & Wear NE39 1HG ☎ 01207 542830

CROOK Colin (Flgl): 300 Redmires Road, Redmires, Sheffield S10 4LD ☎ 0958 453145 mob

CROSS Michael (Voc, B Ldr): 37 Boothferry Road, Hessle, Hull HU13 9AZ ☎ 01482 3643252

CUTHELL John (Flgl): 33 Newton Court, Oakwood Grange Lane, Leeds LS8 2PH ☎ 01132 402273

DAVIES Nigel (Hrn, Clt, A Sax, Flt): 8 Pollit Avenue, Sowerby, Sowerby Bridge, Yorkshire HX6 1LF ☎ 01422 831935, 0802 583560

DE VERE Kenneth: Grangefield, 20 Cade Hill Road, Stocksfield, Northumberland NE43 7PT ☎ 01661 842556

DINSDALE George (Flgl): 4 Otterwood Lane, York YO24 3JR ☎ 01904 331951

DOCHERTY Alan: 12 Sharnford Close, Backworth, Tyne & Wear NE27 0JY ☎ 0191 2685805

DURHAM Michael: 60 Highbury, Newcastle-upon-Tyne NE2 3LN ☎ 0191 281 2935

ELSE Duncan (Cnt): 2 Sedley Close, Harrogate, North Yorkshire HG1 3LB ☎ 01423 521658

FIRTH Tony (Cnt): 56 Rotherham Road, West Melton, Rotherham, South Yorks S63 6AE ☎ 01709 872772

GARVEY Edward (Org, B Ldr): 12 Low Haugh, Ponteland, Newcastle-upon-Tyne NE20 9XN ☎ 01661 871481, 0976 872786 mob

GILBERT John (Dms): 96 Greenhill Avenue, Sheffield S8 7TE ☎ 0114 2748392

GILL Raymond (Db): 5 North Grain, Wearhead, Weardale, Co Durham DL13 1JE ☎ 01388 5375146

GRAY Malcolm (Flgl): 56 Earnshaw Way, Whitley Bay, Tyne & Wear NE25 9UN ☎ 0191 253 4698

GREENWOOD Nigel (Flgl, T Sax, S Sax, St Pan): 12 Ridge Grove, Woodhouse, Leeds, West Yorkshire LS7 2LN ☎ 0113 2341882

GREIG Murray: Keesholme, Sowood Green, Sowood, Nr Stainland, Halifax HX4 9JJ ☎ 01422 371428, 0966 282632 mob

GUY Ronald: 32 Whitwell Acres, High Shincliffe, Durham DH1 2PX ☎ 0191 386 9303

HAMMERTON Dan (Tbn, Saxes, Arr): 27 Highfield Range, Darfield, Nr Barnsley, South Yorkshire S73 9PQ ☎ 01226 752276, 0378 632463

HEMMINGHAM John (Pf): 98 Acorn Drive, Stannington, Sheffield S6 6ES ☎ 0114 232 5672, 01924 380900 & fax

HILL Michael: 2 Peterborough Road, Newton Hall, Durham DH1 5QX ☎ 0191 384 6403

HOLMES Timothy: 302 Fulford Road, York YO10 4PE ☎ 01904 639044

HORN Adrian (Pf): Stone Corft, Southview, Jackson Bridge, Huddersfield HD7 7HT ☎ 01484 683711, 0976 369153

HUMPHRIES Mark (Tbn, Clt): Sunny Dene, Whiphill Top Lane, Branton, Doncaster, South Yorkshire DN3 3NU ☎ 01302 535450

HUNTER Jack: 8 Whitby Crescent, Longbenton, Newcastle-upon-Tyne, Tyne & Wear NE12 8LQ ☎ 0191 266 2924

HUTTON Malcolm (Flgl, Cnt): 9 Trentham Avenue, Benton Lodge, Newcastle-on-Tyne, Tyne & Wear NE7 7NQ ☎ 0191 266 6151

IRWIN Darren (Flgl): 4 Briar Lane, Throckley, Newcastle-upon-Tyne, Tyne & Wear NE15 9AP ☎ 0191 2645360

JACKSON Andrew (Gtr, Acc, Md): 13 West Road, Bishop Auckland, County Durham DL14 7PP ☎ 0191 373 0772

JONES Arthur: 53 Tithe Barn Avenue, Woodhouse, Sheffield S13 7LG ☎ 0114 2694568

JONES Martin (Flgl, Voc): 126 Compass Road, Beverley High Road, Hull HU6 7BE ☎ 01482 448581

JONES Raymond (Tbn, B Gtr): 4 Ludlow Crescent, Redcar, Cleveland TS10 2LQ ☎ 01642 482583

LARDER Richard (Cnt): 7 Towers Close, Crofton, Wakefield, W. Yorks WF4 1JB ☎ 01924 864646

LAWTY F: 20 Rawcliffe Croft, Shipton Road, York YO30 5UT ☎ 01904 629084

LEADBEATER David (*Voc*): 143 Side Lane, Longwood, Huddersfield, West Yorkshire HD3 4SR ☎ 01484 650283

LEESON Mike (*N Tpt, Bq Tpt*): 21 Launds, Rochdale Road, Golcar, Huddersfield, W. Yorks HD7 4NN ☎ 01484 659455 & fax, 0850 062820 mob

LEWIS Alexander (*Pictpt*): 16 Aykley Green, Whitesmocks, Durham City DH1 4LN ☎ 0191 3849667

LONG Paul (*Tbn, Clt*): 27 Acre Lane, Bramhall, Cheadle Hulme, Stockport SK8 7PL

LUDLAM Bob (*Flgl, V Tbn, Tba, Hrn*): 8 Cumberland Way, Bolton-upon-Dearne, Rotherham, South Yorkshire S63 8NB ☎ 01709 896777

MACKFALL Derek: Hendwick Hall, Scoreby, Gate Helmsley, York YO41 1NP ☎ 01759 371900

MARSHALL Gordon: 11 Fieldfare Close, Ayton Village, Washington, Tyne & Wear NE38 0DQ ☎ 0191 4171519

MARTIN Alison: 11 Longridge Avenue, Cochrane Park, Newcastle NE7 7LB ☎ 0191 266 4035

MARTIN Anthony (*Flgl*): 36 Meadowhead Drive, Sheffield S8 7TQ ☎ 0114 2746705

MARTIN Pete: Styes Farm, Styes Lane, Sowerby Bridge, W Yorks HX6 1NF ☎ 01422 882442

MARTIN Richard (*Cnt*): 11 Longridge Ave, Newcastle-upon-Tyne NE7 7LB ☎ 0191 266 4035

MCEWEN Niall (*Pf, Cnt*): 38 Colleridge Grove, Beverley, North Humberside HU17 8XD ☎ 01482 864834

MORRISON Alan (*Cnt*): 25 Acaster Drive, Garforth, Leeds LS25 2BH ☎ 0113 286 3374

MORRISON Arthur (*A Sax, T Sax, Br Sax, Clt*): 6 Brookdale Road, Marton, Middlesbrough, Cleveland TS7 8HB ☎ 01642 326161

MORRISON John (*Cnt*): 40 Nursery Road, Silksworth Lane, Sunderland, Tyne & Wear SR3 1NT ☎ 0191 528 5173

NOOT Rebekah (*Pf*): Glen View, 111 Wheatley Road, Halifax, West Yorkshire HX3 5AA ☎ 01422 354089

O'BRIEN Patrick (*Tbn*): 19 Horseman Avenue, Copmanthorpe, York YO23 3UF ☎ 01904 706034

O'CONNOR Graham (*Cnt*): 29 Halton Court, Hackenthorpe, Sheffield S12 4ND ☎ 0114 248 1932

ORNSBY Clifford: 143 Louth Road, Grimsby DN33 2JU ☎ 01472 825956

ORNSBY Glenn (*Cnt, Tbn*): 22 Craven Road, Cleethorpes, N.E. Lincolnshire DN35 7SQ ☎ 01472 353448, 0860 123112

PASHLEY John (*Db, Gtr, Tba*): 30 Nab Wood Drive, Shipley, Yorks BD18 4EL ☎ 01274 583073

PEARSON Colin: 23 Earlsdon Avenue, Acklam, Middlesbrough, Cleveland TS5 8JH ☎ 01642 592942

POOLE Ray: West View, High Heworth Lane, Felling, Gateshead Tyne & Wear NE10 9XD ☎ 0191 469 5232

PRATT Alan: 20 Tintagel Drive, North Dene Park, Seaham, Co. Durham SR7 7AL ☎ 0191 581 3017

RICHARDS Bob (*Flgl, Cnt*): 6C Low Green, Berwick-upon-Tween, Northumberland TD15 1LZ ☎ 01289 303218

RITSON Gary (*Pictpt*): 7 Portland Mews, Sandyford, Newcastle-upon-Tyne NE2 7RW ☎ 0191261 0069, 0411 544 706, 0191 261 0069

ROBINSON Dave (*Pic*): 45 Spital Fields, Yarm, Co. Cleveland TS15 9HN

SIMS Richard (*Flgl, Dms*): 16 Pleasandt Place, Holbeck, Leeds LS11 9NX ☎ 0113 242 9857

SMITH Lindsey (*Flgl*): Flat 25, The Cedars, Park Road, Cruddas Park, Newcastle-upon-Tyne NE4 7DY

SNOWDON Jonathan: Greenlee, Bardon Mill, Hexham, Northumberland NE47 7AS ☎ 01434 344014

SPENCER George (*Flgl*): 20 Noster Hill, Leeds LS11 8QE ☎ 0113 270 2588

STEPHENSON Alfred (*Hrn*): The Gate House, 67 Westwood Road, Beverley HU17 8EN ☎ 01482 3861069

STRETTON Jim (*Pictpt, Flgl*): 22 Morrison Street, Castleford West, Yorkshire WF10 4BE ☎ 01977 731266

STUBBS Paul (*Cnt*): 26 Brecks Lane, Kirk Sandall, Doncaster, South Yorkshire DN3 1NQ ☎ 01302 880207

TANN Brian (*Cnt, Flgl*): Gerine House, 100A Moor Lane, Netherton, Huddersfield, West Yorks HD4 7JB ☎ 01484 665007

TEMPLE Robert: 11 Burnyng Hill Close, School Aycliffe, Co Durham DL5 6TQ ☎ 01325 316891

THOMSON Peter: 30 Ruswarp Lane, Whitby, Yorkshire YO21 1ND ☎ 01947 606094

TONKIN David: 218 Broadwater Drive, Hatfield, Doncaster DN7 4NR ☎ 01302 841359

TOWSE John: 22 Derwent Road, Dronfield, Derbyshire S18 6FN ☎ 01246 414789

TOWSE Kelvin (*Pf, Arr, Com, Cop*): 22 Derwent Road, Dronfield, Nr Sheffield S18 6FN ☎ 01246 414789

WADMAN Gregory (*Cnt, Flgl*): 21 The Old Village, Huntington, York YO32 9RA ☎ 01904 761673

WALTON Michael (*Pf, Org, B Gtr*): West Lodge, Beamish Burn, Stanley, Co. Durham DH9 0RJ ☎ 01207 237653

WEBB Mark (*Flgl*): 1 Wanlock Close, Southfield Lea, Cranlington, Northumberland NE23 6LS ☎ 01670 714146

WEEKS Geoffrey (*Flgl, Cnt, Pictpt, Pst H*): 59 Church Street, Heckington, Sleaford, Lincs NG34 9RJ ☎ 01529 460666

WILLIAMS Barry (*Cnt, Flgl, Clt, Flt*): Wayside, Main Street, Garton-on-The Wolds, Nr Driffield YO25 3ET ☎ 01377 255783

WILSON Marion: North Farm House, Killingworth Village, Newcastle-upon-Tyne NE12 0BL ☎ 0191 268 4356

WINCKLESS Richard (*Hrn, Per*): 428 Meanwood Road, Meanwood, Leeds LS7 2LP ☎ 0113 2623830

WOODHEAD Michael: 13 Holly Bank, Ackworth, Pontefract WF7 7LE ☎ 01977 613611

WRIGHT Adam: Estate Cottage, Cold Kirby, Thirsk, N Yorks YO7 2HL ☎ 01845 597 464

YATES Joanna (*Vln, Pf, Vla, Rec*): 49 Thornville Street, Hyde Park, Leeds LS6 1JL ☎ 0113 275 5039

EAST

ALDRED Clifford: 25 Grove Avenue, New Costessey, Norwich NR5 0JD

ALMOND Peter: Avon, Highland Road, Taverham, Norwich NR8 6QP ☎ 01603 867352

BARRETT Dave: 85 Stonefield, Bar Hill, Cambridge CB3 8TE ☎ 01954 789 670

BATSON Ray (*B Gtr*): 26 Broadacres, Luton, Bedfordshire LU2 7YF ☎ 01582 453419

BELL Billie (*Md*): 12 John Clarke Court, Milton Road, Cambridge CB4 1XS ☎ 01223 425068

BENWELL Tim (*Cnt, Flgl, Md*): 43 Chapel Close, Watford WD2 7AR ☎ 01923 671213, 0385 772333

BOLTON David (*Arr*): 55 Broomknoll, East End, East Bergholt, Suffolk CO7 6XN ☎ 01206 393500

BROWN Rachel (*N Tpt, Cntt*): 43 Eidefield, Letchworth, Herts SG6 4BW ☎ 01480 352789

BURRELL Eric: 1 Allens Lane, Sprowston, Norwich NR7 8EL ☎ 01603 426713

CHESTERMAN Chez: 116 Belswains Lane, Hemel Hempstead, Herts HP3 9PP ☎ 01442 256856

COLLINS Tom: Storyville, Birch Road, Layer-De-La-Haye, Nr Colchester Essex CO2 0EL ☎ 01206 734384

COOK John (*Flgl*): 3 Warren Way, Digswell, Welwyn, Herts AL6 0DG ☎ 0143 871 4786

CORBETT Jon (*Cnt, V Tbn, Hrn, Pf*): Lime Kiln House, Old Ipswich Road, Claydon, Suffolk IP6 0AB ☎ 01473 830334, 01473 833236 fax

COX Philip (*Flgl*): 15 Croft Close, Chipperfield, Herts WD4 9PA ☎ 01923 291633, 01923 291633

CRABB Alfred: 152 Valley Road, Clacton-on-Sea, Essex CO15 6LX ☎ 01255 425154

CUTTING Robert (*Cnt*): 88 Farm Road, Abingdon, Oxfordshire OX14 1NA ☎ 01235 528071

DANIELS Mike: 8 Lyndhurst Close, Milton, Cambridge CB4 6DH ☎ 01233 861798

ELLIS Mike: 17 Newlands Avenue, Radlett, Herts WD7 8EH ☎ 01923 856285, 0961 308888

FOX Andrew (*Flgl, Voc*): 34 Kings Road, Dovercourt, Essex CO12 4DS ☎ 01255 503639

GARNER Alfred: 15 Varvel Avenue, Sprowston, Norwich NR7 8JH ☎ 01603 409886

GODSILL John: 39 Tyrone Road, Thorpe Bay, Esssex SS1 3HX ☎ 01702 586178

GREGORY Brian: 'Selborne', Langley Road, Abbots Langley, Herts WD5 0EJ ☎ 01923 263031

GRUNNILL Chris (*Flgl, Cnt, Pic, Kbds*)

HACON Derek: 50 St Julian Road, Caister-on-Sea, Great Yarmouth, Norfolk NR30 5BY

HAMER Rod (*Pf*): Dunsmore Leaf, Dunsmore, Wendover, Buckinghamshire HP22 6QJ ☎ 01296 622992

HAMMOND John (*Flgl, Cnt*): 19 Peaslands Road, Saffron Walden, Essex CB11 3ED ☎ 01799 524346, 0410 803730

HEGARTY Kevin: Meadow Cottage, Rectory Road, Tivetshall St Mary, Norfolk NR15 2AL ☎ 01379 676426

HIGHAM Benedict (*Tba*): 70 York Street, Norwich NR2 2AW ☎ 01603 460393

HILL Nick (*Flgl, Voc*): 18 Dovehouse Close, St Neots, Huntingdon, Cambs PE19 1DS ☎ 01480 212332

HINDLEY Anthony (*Pic, Flgl*): 36 West Way, Harpenden, Herts AL5 4RD ☎ 01582 713 723

HODGSON Michael: 7 Hampstead Avenue, Clacton-on-Sea, Essex CO16 7HE ☎ 01255 428974

HOLDOM Colin (*Flgl*): 1 Bourne End Lane, Bourne End, Hemel Hemstead, Herts HP1 2RL

HUMPHREYS John: 39 Beechwood Avenue, Bottisham, Cambridge CB5 9BG ☎ 01223 811598

HUNTER Graham (*Kbds, Flgl, V Tbn, B Gtr*): 41 Weir Pond Road, Rochford, Essex SS4 1AH ☎ 01702 540010

JERMY John: 83 Chatsworth Crescent, Ipswich, Suffolk IP2 9BY ☎ 01473 691787, 0976 217 295

JONES David (*Pf, Org*): Lydian, 2 Dorian Drive, Watersplash Lane, Ascot Berkshire SL5 7QL ☎ 01344 24127

KIRK Chris (*Flgl*): 60 Bexwell Road, Downham Market PE38 9LH ☎ 01366 383794, 0468 983624

LAND Dave (*Flgl*): 'Soots Willow', Greenways Close, Flordon, Norwich NR15 1QP ☎ 01508 471800, 020 7489 0658, 01508 471800

LANDYMORE John (*Flgl*): 16 Sadler Road, Hellesdon, Norwich NR6 6PQ ☎ 01603 402457

LORENZ Gordon (*Gtr, Com, Cop, Arr*): 2 Windermere Court, Alexandra Road, Nascot Wood, Watford, Herts WD1 3UA ☎ 01492 549759, 01492 541482

MALAM John (*Flgl, Pic, Tpt, Arr*): 2 John Ray Street, Braintree, Essex SM7 9DL ☎ 01376 329958

MARTIN Raymond (*Flgl*): 32 Robert Avenue, St Albans, Herts AL1 2QP ☎ 01727 833204

MAYES Paul (*Flgl*): 8 Elin Way, Meldreth, Nr Royston SG8 6 ☎ 01763 261096

MCALLISTER Kevin: 19 Grove Gardens, Tring, Herts HP23 5PX ☎ 0144 282 7562

MUNCEY Ian (*Flgl*): 92 Heathcote Avenue, Hatfield, Herts AL10 0RJ ☎ 01707 267044

PARRY Laurence (*Cnt, Flgl, V Tbn*): 66 Golden House, Bullen Street, Battersea, London SW11 3HQ ☎ 020 7978 7997

PAYNE Donald (*Flgl*): 56 The Crescent, Haversham, Milton Keynes, Buckinghamshire MK19 7AW ☎ 01908 313509

PICKETT John: 53 Parkfield Cres, Kimpton, Hitchin, Herts SG4 8EQ ☎ 01582 763133, 01582 762595

RHODES Andrew: 42 Hilltop Avenue, Hullbridge, Nr Hockley, Essex SS5 6BN ☎ 01702 231459

SAPWELL Brian (*Flgl, Arr*): 13 White House Close, Houghton Regis, Dunstable, Bedfordshire LU5 5DU ☎ 01582 865581

SCALES Rosemary: 48 Briarhayes Close, Ipswich, Suffolk IP2 9AZ ☎ 01473 603342, 0410 989051 mob

SCARFF George: 82 Heatherway, Queensway, Hemel Hempstead, Hertfordshire HP2 5HF ☎ 01442 256654

SMITH Barry: 75 Sandridge Road, St Albans, Herts AL1 4AG ☎ 01727 55608

TAYLOR Paul: 21 Woodland Road, Maple Cross, Rickmansworth, Hertfordshire WD3 2ST ☎ 01923 775876, 0589 580338 mob

TETLEY Bert: 32 Paddock Close, Belton, Great Yarmouth, Norfolk NR31 9NT

THIRKELL John (*Flgl, Voc*): 39 Bournehall Avenue, Bushey, Watford WD2 3AU ☎ 020 8950 8426, 0468 684723 mob

THURLBOURN Philip (*B Gtr*): Wentone, 29 Green End, Fen Ditton, Cambridge CB5 8SX ☎ 012205 3205

TITCHENER Stephen (*Flgl, Kbds*): c/o Alan Titchener, Arts Ed School, Tring, Herts HP23 5LX ☎ 01442 891228

WATSON Thomas (*Flgl, Cnt*): 38 Cassiobury Park Avenue, Watford, Herts WD1 7LB ☎ 01923 254522, 07970 028057, 01923 249869

WATSON William (*Cnt, Flgl*): 38 Cassiobury Park Avenue, Watford, Herts WD1 7LB ☎ 01923 234522, 01923 249869

WEITZ Daniel (*N Tpt, Cnt*): Glenmore House, The High Street, Foulsham, Dereham, Nirfolk NR20 5RT ☎ 01362 683244, 01426 169619

WILKINS Geoff: 1 Glebe House, Fitzroy Mews, London W1P 5DQ ☎ 020 7388 7943

WINCH Matthew (*Flgl*): 42 Charles Street, Tring, Herts HP23 6BD ☎ 01442 822908, 0976 750025

WYNDHAM Janet (*Flgl, Cnt, Pf*): 67 Parkside Drive, Watford, Herts WD1 3AU ☎ 01832 274676, 01923 227995 mob, 0402 013156 mob

MIDLANDS

ADAMS Richard (*Cnt*): Head Of Wind, Brass & Per, Welsh College Of Music, Castle Grounds, Cathays Park, Cardiff CF1 3ER ☎ 029 2034 2854, 0585 861909 mob

ADDINELL Roy (*Flgl*): 98 Primrose Avenue, Wolverhampton, West Midlands WV10 8AR ☎ 01902 782915

ALLEN Bryan (*Cnt*): 62 Oxford Road, Moseley, Birmingham B13 9SQ ☎ 0121 442 4375, 0121 449 6167

ALLISON Mark Blair: 8 All Saints Road, Withybrook, Nr. Coventry CV7 9LS ☎ 024 7671 1149

BAILEY Deborah (*Cnt, Tbn, Tba, Hrn*): 14 Witley Crescent, Oldbury, Warley, West Midlands B69 1FF ☎ 0121 544 6960, 0802 761802

BAILEY Phillip (*Cnt, Con*): 14 Witley Crescent, Oldbury, Warley, W. Midlands B69 IFF ☎ 0121 544 6960, 0802 761802

BAILEY Stephen (*Bq Tpt, Cnt*): 165A Elm Terrace, Tividale, Warley, W Midlands B69 1TG

BASS Garth (*Flgl*): 48 Alwyn Road, Old Bilton, Rugby, Warwicks CV22 7QX ☎ 01788 812715

BATEMAN Peter: 19 Westcliffe Avenue, Westbury Park, Newcastle Under Lyne, Staffordshire ST5 4JS ☎ 01782 638352

BATES Brian: Wentworth, Common Lane, Corley Moor, Coventry CV7 8AQ ☎ 01676 40609

BENNETT Paul (*Flgl*): 104 Amos Lane, Wednesfield, Wolverhampton WV11 1LZ ☎ 01902 738 240

BENNETT Robert: 46 Brittania Road, Burbage, Hinckley, Leics LE10 2HF ☎ 01455 239477

BICKERDIKE John (*Cnt*): 14 Birch Lane, Oldbury, Warley, West Midlands B68 0NZ ☎ 0121 422 2464

BIRCH Robert (*Arr*): Fox Cottage, St Kenelms Road, Romsley, West Midlands B62 0NE ☎ 01562 710346

BLACKADDER David: 8 Northampton Road, Earls Barton, Northamptonshire NN6 0HA ☎ 01604 812357

BLAKEMORE Karen (*Pf*): 127 Walhouse Road, Walsall, West Midlands WS1 2BE ☎ 01922 22229

BOFFY Jack (*Flgl*): 7 Heather Road, Great Barr, Birmingham B43 5BX ☎ 0121 357 6658

BOND Gary (*Pictpt, Cnt, Flgl*): Archway Cottage, Yorton Heath, Shrewsbury SY4 3EU ☎ 01939 210502

BOYD James: 23 Mckey Hill, Ashby-De-La-Zouch, Leics LE65 1JA ☎ 01530 413618

BRADLEY George (*Flgl, Cnt*): 9 Rakestone Close, East Hunsbury, Northampton NN4 0TX ☎ 01604 661 910

BROWN Arthur *(Flgl)*: 9 Verstone Croft, Northfield, Birmingham B31 2QE ☎ 0121 475 6275

BUCKBERRY Russell *(Flgl)*: South View, Vicarage Road, South Clifton, Newark, Notts NG23 7AQ ☎ 01522 778492

BURNETT John *(Voc)*: 139 Queslett Road, Great Barr, Birmingham, West Midlands B43 6DS ☎ 0121 325 1305

BUTCHER Raymond *(Pf)*

BUTTERS Dennis *(Eup, T Hrn)*: 1 Target Close, Talke Pits, Stoke-on-Trent ST7 1RE ☎ 01782 784664

CADMAN.B.A.(HONS) Mark: 68 Plymouth Place, Leamington Spa, Warks CV31 1HW ☎ 01589 489601

CLEAVER Mark *(Flgl)*: 114 Mayswood Road, Solihull, West Midlands B92 9JE ☎ 0121 688 1924, 0976 836015 mob

COOMBS Nicolas *(Pf, Com, Arr)*: 15 Constance Road, Birmingham B5 7RB ☎ 0121 440 0710

CORBETT Bryan ☎ 0121 242 3592, 0411 601567 mob

COX Brian: 14 The Butts, Warwick CV34 4SS ☎ 01926 491595, 01926 403147

COX Colin: 260 Wilford Lane, Wilford, Nottingham NG11 7AW ☎ 0115 9815607

CRAMPTON Jeremy: Drift In, Nurses Lane, Wymondham, Melton Mowbray, Leics LE14 2AS ☎ 01572 787598

CROSBY Roy *(Flgl, B Ldr)*: 20 Norgetts Lane, Melbourn, Cambs SG8 6HS ☎ 01763 261283

CULSHAW Andrew *(Cnt)*: 122 Yardley Close, Oldbury, Warley, West Midlands B68 9DG ☎ 0121 552 4345

DARBY Trevor *(B Gtr)*: 1 Pullman Close, Glascote, Tamworth, Staffs B77 2DR ☎ 01827 250240

DARLOW Dennis *(Arr, Cop)*: 182 Penns Lane, Walmey, Sutton Coldfield, West Midlands B76 8JT ☎ 0121 373 7728

EDGAR James: 19 Ascot Close, Saxon Head, Bedworth, Nuneaton, Warwickshire CV12 8TB ☎ 024 7649 0257

EDWARDS Alec: Redesdale, Westgate, Bridgnorth, Shropshire WV16 5BL ☎ 01746 762379

ELLIS Mark: 295 Alcester Road, Stratford-on-Avon, Warwickshire CV37 9JG ☎ 01789 294578, 0403 712 186 mob

ENO Jonathan: 33 Queen Street, Waingroves, Ripley, Derby DE5 9TJ ☎ 01773 745734, 0402 416415 mob

FALLOON John *(Flgl)*: 31 Hill Morton Road, Rugby, Warwicks CV22 5AB ☎ 01788 535930

FISHER Peter *(Cnt)*: 80, Grove Road, Kings Heath, Birmingham B14 6ST ☎ 0121 443 5112

FRASER Laurence: Kintyre, 5 Lucknow Court, Mapperley Park, Nottingham NG3 5EG ☎ 0115 9621476

FULLICK Teddy *(Flgl)*: Flat 10 Windsor House, Redcliffe Gardens, Mapperley Park, Notts NG3 5AX ☎ 0115 9603450

GARRATTY Laurence *(Pf)*: 26 Alexandra Avenue, Mansfield NG18 5AB ☎ 01623 649784

GARRETT Sidney *(Cnt)*: 15 Vicarage Lane, Elworth, Sandbach, Cheshire CW11 9LB ☎ 01270 764449

GASSON Chris: 8 Park Mews, Selly Oak, Birmingham B29 5JQ ☎ 0121 472 8302, 07775 691173

GIBBON Nigel: Cobscot Hey, Adderley, Market Drayton, Shropshire TF9 3TJ ☎ 01630 658183

GODFREY David: Holly House, Meadow Lane, Fulford, Stoke-on-Trent ST11 9RZ

HALLAM Richard: 16 Eynsham Road, Botley, Oxford OX2 9BP ☎ 01865 863656

HARCOURT Kevin *(Flgl)*: 188 Balmoral Road, Wordsley, Stourbridge, West Midlands DY8 5JZ ☎ 01384 278510, 0956 898235, 01384 440086 fax

HARCOURT Stephen *(Flgl, Cnt)*: 188 Balmoral Road, Wordsley, Stourbridge, West Midlands DY8 5JZ ☎ 01384 278510

HARRIS Bill: 46 Lode Lane, Solihull, Warks B91 2AE ☎ 0121 705 2501

HARRIS John: 40 Five Fields Road, Willenhall, Wolverhampton WV12 4PA ☎ 01902 609507

HARRIS Martyn *(Pictpt, Flgl, Cnt)*: Upper Moat Farm, Stapleton, Dorrington, Shrewsbury SY5 7EW ☎ 01743 718866

HARRISON Tanya *(Vln)*: 29 Earles Road, Shavington, Crewe CW2 5EZ ☎ 01270 661391

HATTERSLEY Ian *(Pictpt, Flgl, Cnt, Pf)*: Broadacres, Mappleborough Green, Redditch, Worcs B80 7BH ☎ 0152 785 2762

HAYWARD Cecil *(Cnt, Flgl, Pictpt)*: Terraine, Worthen, Shrewsbury SY5 9HT ☎ 01743 891294

HIGHAM Mark: 74 The Avenue, Acocks Green, Birmingham B27 6NE ☎ 0121 708 2637

HOLLAND Jonathan: 71 Heathcote Road, Cotteridge, Birmingham B30 2HU ☎ 0121 689 1959

HOOKE Shaun: Flat 4, 43 Anderton Park Road, Moseley, Birmingham B13 9DU ☎ 0121 442 4450, 0966 165385 mob

HOPKINS Peter: 89 Palmerston Road, Earlsdon, Coventry CV5 6FH ☎ 024 7667 2764

HORTON Lyndley: 8 Thorncliffe Road, Great Barr, Birmingham B44 9DB ☎ 0121 360 9794

HURD Tony: 62 Manor Road, Littleover, Derby DE23 6BR ☎ 01332 605973

JACKSON Mark N W: 42 Kingsley Road, Kingswinford, West Midlands DY6 9RX ☎ 01384 296770

JAMES Bob *(Pictpt, Flgl, Cnt)*: Groes, Llanfyllin, Powys, West Midlands SY22 5JA ☎ 01691 648316

JARRATT-KNOCK David *(Pictpt, Bq Tpt, Cntt Zin)*: 12 Besbury Close, Dorridge, Solihull, West Midlands B93 8NT ☎ 01564 773532

JENNINGS Andrew *(Pictpt, Cnt)*: 8 The Island, Mile Oak, Tamworth, Staffs B78 3PP ☎ 01827 289112, 0850 820130 mob

JONES Christopher *(Flgl, Kbds, B Gtr, Gtr)*: 42 Heath Street, Stourbridge, West Midlands DY8 1SA ☎ 01384 820595

JONES Simon: 10 Blenheim Road, Moseley, Birmingham B13 9TY ☎ 07970 688259

JONES Wendy *(Pf)*: Bank House, Chapel Lane, Exfords Green, Shrewsbury SY5 8HG ☎ 01743 718417

KING Stephen *(Flgl, Arr, Com, Cop)*: 73, Woburn Drive, Lodgefield Park, Halesowen, West Midlands B62 8TQ ☎ 0121 559 5306

LAMBERT Frank *(Kbds)*: Kitridding, Lupton, Via Carnforth, Lancashire. LA6 2QA ☎ 015395 67724

LEITHEAD David: 6 Rudge Close, Wollaton, Nottingham NG8 1HF ☎ 0115 9289948

LENTON Simon: 13 Watling Street, Nuneaton, Warwickshire CV11 6JJ ☎ 024 7637 1990, 0973 312450

LUNN Simon *(Clt)* ☎ 0121 643 2285

MCCOY Alan *(Cnt)*: 57 Colebrook Road, Shirley, Solihull B90 2JZ ☎ 0121 744 0401, 0121 744 9848 fax

MCEWAN Gregon: Flat 6, 17 York Road, Edgbaston, Birmingham B16 9HX ☎ 0121 455 9948, 0976 267551

MOORE Richard *(Flgl)*: Gatesgarth, 14 Forest Close, Seabridge, Newcastle, Staffs ST5 3BG ☎ 01782 631865, 01426 267945 pager

MORRIS Stewart *(Flgl)*: 6 Trafford Road, Hinckley, Leics LE10 1LY ☎ 01455 230317

NARBETH Cyril: 76 St Christians Road, Coventry, West Midlands CV3 5GX ☎ 024 7650 2849

NEVINS Angela *(Pf)*: Ashton House, Ash Lane, Yarnfield, Stone, Staffs ST15 0NJ ☎ 01785 760432

NEVINS Paul *(Cntt Zin, Pictpt)*: Ashton House, Ash Lane, Yarnfield, Stone, Staffs ST15 0NJ ☎ 01785 760432

NICKEL Michael: 63 Gloucester Road, Walsall, West Midlands WS5 3PL ☎ 01922 36557

NUNN Jack *(Flgl)*: 57 Grange Road, Dorridge, Solihull, West Midlands B93 8QS ☎ 01564 772806

O'CONNOR Michael *(Flgl)*: 16 Wallinger Drive, Shenley Brook End, Milton Keynes, Bucks MK5 7BP ☎ 01908 522694, 0799957 422405

OWEN Donald *(Flgl, Cnt)*: 23 Birklands Avenue, New Ollerton, Notts NG22 9SA ☎ 01623 835969, 0850 587222

PARKER Kevin *(Cnt, Flgl)*: 44 Gaulby Road, Billesdon, Leicester LE7 9AF ☎ 0116 2596312

PAWSON Dan *(Vln)*: 4 Cropthorne Court, Calthorpe Road, Birmingham B15 1QP ☎ 0121 454 2340

PEATE Andrew *(Flgl, Kbds, B Ldr)*: 40, Poole Crescent, Harborne, Birmingham B17 0PB ☎ 0121 472 4483

PEPPER Len: 26 Newington Close, Coundon, Coventry, West Midlands CV6 1PP ☎ 024 7659 3460

PIPKIN Anthony *(Flgl)*: 97 Barclay Road, Bearwood, Smethwick, West Midlands B67 5JY ☎ 0121 429 8374

POTTS John: Heather View, Banky Fields, Congleton, Cheshire CW12 4BZ ☎ 01260 276810

PURSGLOVE Andrew *(Flgl)*: 145 Shawhurst Lane, Hollywood, Birmingham B47 5JR ☎ 01564 200679

QUIRK Jonathan: 18 Rush Lane, Church Hill North, Redditch B98 8RY ☎ 01527 65708

RAISHBROOK Frank: 316 Woodway Lane, Walsgrave, Coventry CV2 2LF ☎ 024 7661 0031

RATTENBURY Ken *(Pf)*: Way Down Yonder, 299 Birmingham Road, Walsall, West Midlands WS5 3QA ☎ 01922 26624

REDFERN Tracey *(Cnt)*: 7 Hoskins Close, Belle Vue, Manchester M12 4JX ☎ 0161 223 2356

ROBERTS-MALPASS Edward *(N Tpt)*: 38 Farmer Way, Gospel Oak, Tipton, West Midlands DY4 0BE ☎ 0121 556 1507, 0498 854783

ROLINSON Peter: 35 Humphrey Burtons Road, Coventry CV3 6HW ☎ 024 7650 3537

ROWLAND Phillip *(Flgl)*: 347 Hipswell Highway, Wyken, Coventry, Warks CV2 5FQ ☎ 024 7645 7759

ROYAL Jos *(Flgl, Eup, Voc, B Ldr)*: 76 Valley Road, Solihull, Warks B92 9AX ☎ 0121 743 4337

RUDDICK John *(Arr, Flgl)*: The New House, Marsh Lane, Hampton In Arden, Warks B92 0AH ☎ 01675 442050

RUDDICK John *(Flgl)*: New House, Marsh Lane, Hampton-In-Arden, Solihull, West Midlands B92 0AH ☎ 01675 442050

RUSBY Jack: The Stables, 101A Bagnall Road, Milton, Stoke-on-Trent ST2 7AY ☎ 01782 545562

SAUNDERS John *(Flgl, Tbn, Db)*: 24 Charfield Close, Bournville, Birmingham B30 1QS ☎ 0121 458 3108

SEARLE Benjamin *(Pf, Per)*: Flat 1, 44 Glenfield Road, Leicester LE3 6AQ ☎ 0116 299 2664

SHEPHERD Mark *(Flgl, V Tbn, Kbds)*: 148 Dominion Road, Glenfield, Leicester LE3 8JA ☎ 0116 223 4733, 0976 229541

SIMMONDS Robert: 2 Elm Drive, Halesowen, W. Midlands B62 9HT ☎ 0121 561 5136

SIMPSON Michael: 18 Guarlford Road, Malvern, Worcs WR14 3QP ☎ 01684 574844

SIVITER Roger: 7 Tamar Place, Cotswold Rise, Evesham, Worcs WR11 6FD ☎ 01386 765134

SMITH David *(Flgl, Pf)*: 20 King Edward Road, Moseley, Birmingham B13 8HR ☎ 0121 449 6079, 0966 449782 mob

SMITH Sydney: 87 Gloucester Crescent, Northampton NN4 9PP ☎ 01604 764353

SPEEDY David *(Flgl, V Tbn, Kbds, Arr)*: 3 Newlyn Close, Horeston Grange, Nuneaton CV11 6GG ☎ 024 7634 6836

SPRECKLEY Leslie: 43, Villiers Street, Leamington Spa, Warwickshire CV32 5YA ☎ 01926 428625

STONE-FEWINGS Andrew: 70 Glendon Way, Dorridge, Solihull, West Midlands B93 8SY ☎ 01564 771 569, 0860 376 774 mob

STORR Christopher *(Flgl, Pictpt)*: 13 Holloway Bank, Hill Top, West Bromwich, West Midlands B70 0QQ ☎ 0973 425417

STUBBS Frank *(Cnt)*: 289 St Pauls Road, Smethwick, Warley, West Midlands B66 1HF ☎ 0121 532 3152, 0973 828947

SUTTON Richard *(Flgl, Cnt, Pf)*: 123 Crewe Road, Alsager, Stoke-on-Trent ST7 2JE ☎ 01270 874 206

TAGGART Richard: 52 Bristol Road, Earlsdon, Coventry CV5 6LH ☎ 024 7667 0958

TAYLOR Martin: 14 Grampian Road, Pennfields, Stourbridge DY8 4UE ☎ 01384 376077

TISSINGTON Andrew *(Flgl)*: 11, The Square, Harborne, Birmingham B17 9EH ☎ 0121 471 4196

TUNDERVARY Justin *(Flgl)*: 11 Collings House, Huntley Road, Ladywood, Birmingham B16 8JR ☎ 0121 455 8061, 0831 892043 mob

VENN Jimmy: 42 Heather Road, Great Barr, Birmingham, West Midlands B43 5BY ☎ 0121 358 1272

VIVIAN Robert *(Pictpt)*: 6 The Russells, Off Russell Road, Moseley, Birmingham B13 8RT ☎ 0121 449 0031

WADKIN Frank *(Pf)*: Priory Cottage, Baswich Lane, Stafford ST18 0YD ☎ 01785 242319

WALKDEN Eric: 6 Dorchester Way, Nuneaton, Warwickshire CV11 6XB ☎ 024 7638 3149

WARREN Wesley *(Cnt)*: 12 Falstaff Close, Walmley, Sutton Coldfield, West Midlands B76 8YG ☎ 0121 351 5768

WELLS Derek *(A Sax, B Sax)*: 150 Pershore Road, Hampton, Evesham, Worcs WR11 6PJ ☎ 01386 446054, 01386 442819 day

WELLS Gavin *(Pictpt, Cnt, Flgl)*: The Willows, Lower Flat, Cold Slad Lane, Witcombe, Glos GL3 4UQ ☎ 01452 864062

WHELAN Angela *(N Tpt)*: 13 Watling Street, Nuneaton, Warwickshire CV11 6JJ ☎ 024 7637 1990, 0973 899597

WHITEHEAD Alan: 75 Castle Road West, Oldbury, Warley, Worcs B68 0EN ☎ 0121 422 4937

WHITWORTH Gordon: 16 Elder Lane, Burntwood, Walsall, Staffs WS7 9BT ☎ 01543 675636

WILD Bev *(Org, Pf)*: 4 Rooley Drive, Sutton In Ashford, Notts NG17 2EY ☎ 01623 650864

WILDE Peter *(Flgl)*: 109 Gertrude Road, West Bridgford, Notts NG2 5DA ☎ 0115 974 9885

WILLIAMS Jason *(Flgl)*: 20 De Moram Grove, Hampton Coppice, Solihull, West Midlands B92 0PZ ☎ 0121 243 6564

WILSON Terence: Fernscan Limited, No.1. Andover Street, Digbeth, Birmingham B5 5RG ☎ 0121 633 4742

WRAIGHT Peter *(Flgl)*: 25 The Terrace, Mayfield, Ashbourne, Derbyshire DE6 2JL ☎ 01335 346635

SOUTH EAST

ADCROFT Hylton *(Con)*: Bevirs, Wellington College, Crowthorne, Berks RG11 7PU ☎ 01344 775352

ALEMANY Jesus *(Per)*: 3 Church Lane, Brightwell Cum Sotwell, Nr Wallingford, Oxon OX10 0DS ☎ 01491 835832

ALEXANDER Ian: 17 Heath Farm Way, Ferndown, Dorset BH22 8JR ☎ 01202 892520, 0498 690460 mob

BAKER David: 4 Bankside, Alverstoke, Gosport, Hants PO12 2NH ☎ 023 9252 6457

BAKER Richard *(Cnt)*: 9 Poplar Avenue, Hove, East Sussex BN3 8PU ☎ 01273 321929, 01273 323440

BARNACLE Arthur: 38, Bewsbury Cross Lane, Whitfield, Dover, Kent CT16 3EZ ☎ 01304 820442

BARRETT Nicholas *(Flgl, Pf)*: Copthorne, The Close, Kings Road, Lancing, West Sussex BN15 8EE ☎ 01903 767072, 0705 0050635, 01903 751773

BERGLUND Kjell *(Flgl)*: 22 Westdene Drive, Brighton, Sussex BN1 5HF ☎ 01273 558474

BIRCH Michael *(Flgl)*: 2 School Lane, Sheet, Petersfield, Hampshire GU32 2AS ☎ 01730 266744

BOWER Roy *(Pf)*: 8 Reynolds Road, Hove, East Sussex BN3 5RJ ☎ Brighton 725215

BREEZE Nicholas *(B Gtr, Db, Pf, Org)*: Keepers Cottage, 6 Warleigh, Nr Bathford, Bath BA1 8EE ☎ 01225 852444

BREWER Edwin: 37 Limes Avenue, Horley, Surrey RH6 9DG ☎ 01293 772363

BRIGGS Nicholas: 2 Bakery Cottage, 320 Bournemouth Rd, Charlton Marshall, Blanford Forums, Dorset DT11 9NH ☎ 01258 456320

BROWN Gerald: 16 Kings Avenue, Poole, Dorset BH14 9QG ☎ 01202 749491

BROWN Graham *(Cnt, Pic, Bq Tpt, Pst H)*: 27 Aston Road, Southsea, Hants PO4 9BH ☎ 023 9279 0551

BROWN Richard *(Pf)*: 78 Victoria Road, Chichester, West Sussex PO19 4HZ ☎ 01243 776374

BUCKLEY Juls *(Flgl, Pf, Dms, Voc)*: 9 Bramcote Close, Aylesbury, Bucks HP20 1QE ☎ 01296 395507, 07775 904787, 01296 395507

BURCHELL James *(Pf)*: 7 Yew Tree Road, St Marys Bay, Romney Marsh, Kent TN29 0SU ☎ 01303 873708, 01523 148911

BURGOYNE Dennis: 11, Alpine Close, Barton-on-Sea, New Milton, Hants BH25 7HE ☎ 01425 612745

BURROWS Rodney: 146, Ridgeway, Woodingdean, Brighton, East Sussex BN2 6PA ☎ Brighton 32916

CHAPMAN Martin: 17 Buttsbridge Road, Hythe, Southampton SO45 3HF ☎ 023 8084 7692

CHAPPLE Michael: 6 West Avenue, Heath End, Farnham, Surrey GU9 0RH ☎ 01252 724418

CHISLETT Andy *(Flgl)*: 4 Priestley Road, Bourenmouth, Dorset BH10 4AS ☎ 01202 547502

CHISLETT Stephen *(Voc, Con)*: 7 Laburnam Close, Ferndown, Winborne, Dorset BH22 9TX ☎ 01202 891852

CLARK Christopher *(Cnt, Flgl)*: 6 Meads Close, Milton Bryan, Bedfordshire MK17 9HP ☎ 01525 210018

CLARKE Billy: Lapstone Farmhouse, Botley Road, Horton Heath, Nr Eastleigh Hants SO5 7AN ☎ 023 8069 3737

COLLARBONE Barry *(Pictpt, Bq Tpt)*: 40 Tamworth Stubb, Walnut Tree, Milton Keynes, Bucks MK7 7DT ☎ 01908 671440, 0802 367038, 01908 236371

COX Mark *(Pic, Flgl, Cnt)*: 50 Nursery Road, Taplow, Maidenhead, Berkshire SL6 0JZ ☎ 01628 602793

CRAEN Joseph: 7 Vandyke Close, Woburn Sands, Milton Keynes MK17 8UU ☎ 01908 582426

CRAIG Brian: 7 Gainsborough Gardens, Tonbridge, Kent TN10 4AD ☎ 01732 365104, 01732 365104

CURTIS Peter *(Flgl, Cnt)*: 21 Matlock Road, Ferndown, Wimborne, Dorset BH22 8QT ☎ 01202 894249

DAVIS Anthony: Gaston Cottage, Church Lane, Aston, Bampton, Oxon OX18 2DY ☎ 01993 852441, 01993 850164 fax

DEACON Andrew *(Vln)*: 11 Old Crossing Road, Westbrook, Margate, Kent CT9 5JH ☎ Thanet 291955/6

DEACON Christopher *(Cnt, N Tpt)*: 11 Old Crossing Road, Westbrook, Margate, Kent CT9 5JH ☎ 01843 291955, 020 7631 8300

DICKENS Andrew *(Gtr, Db)*: 6 Flexford Close, Chandlers Ford, Hants SO53 5RZ ☎ 023 8025 1301

EDWARDS Marc *(Pic, N Tpt, Cntt Zin)*: 30 Elm Road, Reading, Berks RG6 2TR ☎ 01734 863671

EDWARDS Michael: 295 Desborough Avenue, High Wycombe, Bucks HP11 2 TL ☎ 01494 523452

EMPTAGE Stanley: 5 Clegg Road, Southsea, Hants PO4 9DQ ☎ 023 9273 3892

FINLEY Campbell *(Flgl)*: 1 Elm Grove, Farnham, Surrey GU9 0QU ☎ 01252 725253, 01256 862342

FISH Nigel *(Cnt, Pictpt)*: 7 Lower Road, Meadvale, Redhill, Surrey RH1 6NN ☎ 01737 243801, 0973 257705 mob

FLOOD Alan *(Flgl)*: 22 Brackley Avenue, Fair Oak, Eastleigh, Hants SO50 8FJ ☎ 023 8060 1395

GALLAGHER Steven: 9 Ravenscourt Road, Bournemouth, Dorset BH6 5EF ☎ 01202 421743

GILMORE Peter: 5 Mount Grace Drive, Poole BH14 8NB ☎ 01202 708020

HAMES James *(Acc, Arr)*: Seasons, 67A Marine Parade East, Lee-on-Solent, Hants PO13 9BJ ☎ 023 9255 0270

HAMMOND Roger *(Flgl)*: 36 St Davids Road, Southsea, Hants PO5 1QN ☎ 023 9286 2957

HARTLEY Mark *(Flgl)*: 79 Northcourt Road, Abingdon, Oxfordshire OX14 1NN ☎ 020 7628 1680, 01235 524928

HATTON Jef *(Tbn, Voc)*: Chimneys, Station Road, Winchelsea, East Sussex TN36 4JX ☎ 01707 226606, 07957 814590 mob

HAWKINS Tony *(Flgl, Voc)*: 52 Bergholt Road, Colchester, Essex CO4 5AB ☎ 0976 253074 mob

HEMMING Bob *(Flgl)*: Bramble Cottage, Dibles Road, Warsash, Hants SO3 6JL ☎ 01489 575766

HENDERSON Gavin: Trinity College Of Music, 11-13 Mandeville Place, London WIM 6AQ ☎ 020 7935 5773

HENDERSON Stuart *(Flgl, Cnt, Pictpt, Pst H)*: 73 Donnington Road, Reading, Berks RG1 5NE ☎ 01734 610087

HILLIER Gordon *(Flgl, Voc)*: 4 Malderek Avenue, Preston, Paignton TQ3 2RP

HOLDSWORTH David: Flat 1, 7 Arundel Terrace, Kemp Town, Brighton BN2 1GA ☎ 01273 605808

HOLLINGSWORTH Paul *(Flgl, Cnt)*: 27 Junstion Road, Warley, Brentwood, Essex CM14 5JH ☎ 01277 263896, 01277 261407, 0498 721301

HORLER Ronnie *(Flgl)*: 13-14 St Thomas Street, Lymington, Hants SO4 9ND ☎ 01590 673134

HOWELL Kenneth: 15 Greenwood Avenue, Cosham, Portsmouth, Hants PO6 3NP ☎ 023 9237 1673

HULTMARK Torbjorn: 29 Roundfield, Upper Bucklebury, Berks RG7 6RA

HUNTER Jolyon: 17 Clarke Avenue, Hove, Sussex BN3 8GD ☎ Brighton 776722

INGS Martin: 'Greenfields', Balls Lane, Sturminster Marshall, Dorset BH21 4BG ☎ 01258 857893

JENKINS Albert: 50A Alton Road, Bournemouth, Dorset BH10 4AF ☎ 01202 536407

JONES Kevin *(Cnt, Flgl)*: 3 Oxford Road, Gosport, Hants PO12 3LP ☎ 023 9252 3146

KAVANAGH Gary *(Flgl, Pf)*: 119 Hollingbury Road, Brighton BN1 7JN ☎ 01273 330992

KELLY Dorian *(Flgl, Com)*: 11 Hill Brow, Reading, Berks RG2 8JD ☎ 0118 967 3461, 0976 358 722

KESEL Mark: 35 Pimento Drive, Lower Earley, Reading, Berkshire RG6 5GZ ☎ 01734 755621

KITCHEN Steven *(Flgl, Cnt)*: 50 Avenue Road, Winslow, Bucks MK18 3DJ ☎ 01296 714306

LAKE Andrew *(Kbds, Pf)*: Flat 4, 13A Granville Road, Hove, East Sussex BN3 1TG ☎ 01273 323 064

LATCHEM Barrington *(Cnt, Flgl)*: 14 Wetherby Close, Broadstone, Dorset BH18 8JB ☎ 01202 694840

LEESE Winston: Tumlyn, Spetisbury, Blandford, Dorset DT11 9DF ☎ 01258 455151

LINFORD Anthony *(B Ldr)*: Bluebells, 15 Hound Road, Netley Abbey, Southampton SO31 5FZ ☎ 023 8045 4706

MAPLE Paul *(Cnt, Flgl)*: 19 Torridon Close, Goldsworth Park, Woking, Surrey GU21 3DB ☎ 0421 457511 mob

MARLOW John *(Flgl)*: 27 Devonshire Place, Basingstoke, Hants RG21 8UU ☎ 01256 53327

MCGOVERN Peter: 36 Bonnar Road, Selsea, Chichester, West Sussex PO20 9AU ☎ 01243 606126

MCKENZIE Jock *(Cnt, Flgl, Pf, Con)*: 28 Lichfield Road, Titchfield Common, Fareham, Hants PO14 4QN ☎ 01489 574058

MOFFAT Shaun *(Cnt, Flgl, Pf)*: Poppies, Manor Land, Timsbury, Romsey, Southampton SO51 0NE ☎ 01794 367523

MOUNTER Michael: 77 Applesham Avenue, Hove, East Sussex BN3 8JN ☎ 01273 388139

O'CONNELL Pat *(Flgl, Cnt, Arr, Cop)*: 47 Waterton Avenue, Gravesend, Kent DA12 2PY ☎ 01474 743 569, 01474 743745

O'NEALE Robert *(Pf)*: 48 Parklands, Great Linford, Milton Keynes MK14 5DZ ☎ 01908 674585, 0958 520352 mob

OSULLIVAN Anthony: Court Cottage, Stodmarsh, Canterbury CT3 4BD

PAGE III (JNR) Widgeon *(Flgl, Triangle, Mar)*: 12 Fairoak Court, High Street, Tarring, Worthing, West Sussex BN14 7NT ☎ 01903 821036

PAINE Reginald *(Dms)*: Address Unknown

PAYNE Stanley *(N Tpt)*: Boyne Mead, Nations Hill, Kings Worthy, Winchester SO23 7QY ☎ Winchester 8821

PEEL Jonathan *(Flgl, Com, Arr)*: Landsdowne House, 24 Hartlip Hill, Hartlip, Kent ME9 7PA ☎ 01795 843441 fax

PHILLIPS William: 11 Howton Road, Bournemouth, Dorset BH10 5LN

PLANT Marcus *(Pictpt, Flgl)*: 66 Oxendean Gardens, Lower Willingdon, Eastbourne, East Sussex BN22 0RS ☎ 01323 508399

POTTS Mike *(Flgl)*: 26 Garden Road, Burley, Ringwood, Hants BH24 4EA ☎ 01425 403364

RAYMONDE Monty *(Flgl)*: 34 Nea Road, Highcliffe, Christchurch, Dorset BH23 4NB ☎ 01425 273575

RICHARDS Donald: 2 Ashton Villas, Lower Chase Road, Swanmore, Southampton Hants SO3 2PB ☎ 014893 893805

ROBINSON Simon: Garden Cottage, Main Street, Charlton, Banbury, Oxon OX17 3DP ☎ 01295 811207, 01295 811499

SAMWAYS Gordon: 473 Wimborne Road, Poole, Dorset BH15 3EE ☎ 01202 673606

SENIOR Rodney: 11 Osborne Road, Parkstone, Poole, Dorset BH14 8SD ☎ 01202 747707

SHAWCROSS Ian (*Flgl*): 19 Blenheim Road, Deal, Kent CT14 7AJ ☎ 01304 374755

SIBLEY Norman (*B Ldr*): 306 Winchester Road, Southampton SO1 2SH ☎ 023 8078 8766

SINGLETON Philip (*Flgl, Pictpt*): 91 Monmouth Road, Hayes, Middlesex UB3 4JJ ☎ 020 8848 9041

SMETS Andrew: Tymbal Lodge, Tubbs Lane, Highclere, Nr Newbury Berks RG20 9PR ☎ 01635 254789

SMITH Hal: 46 Monkswood Avenue, Bare, Morecombe, Lancs LA4 6TW ☎ 01524 414250

SMITH Lucy (*Tbn, Clt, Sax, Flt*): Orchard Cottage, The Green, Combe, Nr Witney, Oxon OX8 8NT ☎ 01993 891300, 01993 891300

SMITH Ronnie (*B Ldr*): 11 Elmhurst Close, Angnering Village, Sussex BN16 4BT ☎ Rustington 7845

SPAIN Stephen: 1 St Georges Avenue, Newbury RG14 5NX ☎ 01635 582 680

SPEARS Nigel (*Flgl*): 5 Heydon Hill Close, Farnham, Surrey GU9 8PA ☎ 01252 721913

SPENCER Stephen (*Flgl, Voc*): 57 Shakespeare Road, Eastleigh, Hants S050 4FY ☎ 023 8064 4275

STEVENSON Nicholas: 23 Alderbert Terrace, London SW8 1BH ☎ 020 7642 8282

STONE Jon (*B Gtr*): Blair Cottage, Church Street, Somerton, Oxfordshire OX6 4NB ☎ 01869 345674

SUMMERS Frank: 60 Uppleby Road, Parkstone, Poole, Dorset BH12 3DE ☎ 01202 733381

TAIT Jack (*V Tbn, Sou*): 50 North Street, Ventor, Isle Of Wight PO38 1NJ ☎ 01983 854403

TANNOCK Fraser (*Pictpt, Flgl*): 1 Hillside Close, Headley Down, Bordon, Hants GU35 8BL ☎ 01428 714039

TATAM Derek (*Cnt, Mel, Voc, B Ldr*): Little Croft, Stanton Road, Forest Hill, Oxford OX33 1DT ☎ 01865 873226

TELLICK Keith (*Cnt, Hrn*): 5 Hobart Close, Worthing, Sussex BN13 3HL ☎ 01903 268914

THE BASS MAN (*B Gtr, Dms, Pf*): 5 Challoners Hill, Steeple Claydon, Bucks MK18 2PD ☎ 01296 738090, 0976 226927 mob

THOMAS Ashley: Conifers, Trapfield Lane, Bearsted, Kent ME14 4EH ☎ 01622 738773, 0802 859171 mob, 01795 428546

THOMAS Thomas (*Sax, B Ldr*): 10 Southsea Avenue, Goring By Sea, Worthing, West Sussex BN12 4BN ☎ 01903 247868

TROTMAN David (*Flgl, Cnt*): The Anchorage, 1 Smugglers Lane South, Highcliffe-on-Sea, Christchurch Dorset BH23 4NF ☎ 01425 275214

TUNGAY T Paul (*Flgl, T Hrn, Cnt, Arr*): 87 Iveagh Court, Nightingale Crescent, Bracknell, Berks RG12 9PZ ☎ 01344 51938

TURNBULL Peter (*Cnt, Flgl*): 107 Lambs Green Lane, Corfe Mullen, Wimborne, Dorset BH21 3DN ☎ 01202 848119

URQUHART Andrew (*Flgl, Cnt, Pf, Voc*): 35 St Catherines Road, Wimborne, Dorset BH21 1BG ☎ 01202 849022

WALLER Tony: Rosewood, 48 Lodge Road, Holt, Wimborne, Dorset BH21 7DW ☎ 01202 881406, 0370 751837 mob

WALSH Francis: 10 Ferringham Lane, Ferring, West Sussex BN12 5NQ ☎ 01903 242998

WESTERMAN Martyn (*T Hrn, Br Hrn, Eup, Flgl*): 139 Arlington Drive, Carshalton, Surrey SM5 2EU ☎ 020 8715 5713

WHARTON Terence: 600 Blandford Road, Poole, Dorset BH16 5EQ ☎ 01202 623868

WHITE Nick (*Flgl*): 105 Shaftesbury Drive, Maidstone, Kent ME16 0JY ☎ 01622 756454

WHITE Peter H: 9 Chatsworth Road, Bitterne, Southampton, Hants SO2 7NL ☎ 023 8039 6175

WHITE Simon: 18 Hart Street, Oxford OX2 6BN ☎ 01865 436361

WHITWELL Christopher (*Flgl*): Owl & Dove Cottage, 461/3 Upper Shoreham Road, Shoreham, West Sussex BN43 5WQ ☎ 01243 463894

WILKINSON Peter (*Pf*): 13 Shanklin Crescent, Shirley, Southampton, Hants SO15 7RB ☎ 023 8078 1012

WOODING George: 158 Snodhurst Avenue, Chatham, Kent ME5 0TN ☎ 01634 862088

WOODS Alfred: 42 Lambs Farm Road, Horsham, Sussex RH12 4DQ

WOOLER Andrew: 7 Elm Drive, Hove, East Sussex BN3 7JS ☎ 01273 882539

WOON Andrew (*Flgl*): 15 Surrenden Crescent, Brighton, Sussex BN1 6WE ☎ 01273 884193

WRIGHT Brian: Eastlands Croft, Wheelers Lane, Bear Wood, Bournemouth BH11 9QJ ☎ 01202 581073

YATES Jon (*Flgl*): 24 Clifton Road, Lee-on-The-Solent, Hampshire PO13 9AT ☎ 023 9261 0657, 0976 388579 mob

ZAWADA Jan (*Pic, Cnt, Flgl, Pst H*): 2 Glendale, Locks Heath, Southampton, Hants SO31 6UL ☎ 01489 589896, 0585 114480 mob

SOUTH WEST

ANDREWS Alan (*N Tpt*): 19 Frobisher Avenue, Portishead, Bristol BS20 9XB ☎ 01275 848842

ARMSTRONG Dennis (*Cnt*): 16 Manworthy Road, Brislington, Bristol BS4 4PR ☎ 0117 971 7952

AUSTIN John (*B Gtr*): Cardueville, Higher Road, Breage, Helston Cornwall TR13 9PL ☎ 01326 573195

AYEAR Mike: Culverhayes, Wembury Point, Plymouth PL9 0AY ☎ 01752 863231

BAILEY Michael (*Flgl, Arr*): Overstream, Perrancoombe, Perranforth, Truro, Cornwall TR6 0HX ☎ 01872 572289

BATEMAN Alan (*A Sax, Clt, S Sax*): 73 Yiewsley Crescent, Stratton St Margaret, Swindon SN3 4LX ☎ 01793 824489

BETLEY Peter (*Cnt, Flgl, Con*): 15 King Street, Honiton, Devon EX14 8AB ☎ 01404 44501

BLAKE Michael: 9 Nottage Mead, Nottage, Porthcawl CF36 3SA ☎ 0165 671 2427

BRINKLEY David (*Pf*): 27 Severn Avenue, Greenmeadow, Swindon, Wilts SN2 3LF ☎ 01793 641914, 0411 345 096 mob

CHATFIELD Wally (*Tbn, Eup, Flgl, Efl Bass*): 9 Weirside Avenue, Wroughton SN4 9AL ☎ 01793 813084

COVENTRY Kenny (*Pf*): 6 Fitzroy Terrace, Stoke, Plymouth, Devon PL1 5PX ☎ 01752 550679

COWLEY Francis (*Cnt*): 28 St Andrews Close, Wroughton, Swindon SN4 9DW ☎ 01793 813115

CREECH David: 6 Beechmount Grove, Hengrove, Bristol BS14 9DN ☎ 0117 9774312

DAVIES David (*Gtr*): 33 Clive Terrace, Ynysybwl, Nr Pontypridd, Mid Glam CF37 3LD ☎ 01443 790372

DAVIES Ivor (*Flgl*): 40 Myddynfych, Tirdaill, Ammanford, Dyfed SA18 2EA ☎ 01269 592285

DAVIES Lawrence: 2 Bennett Street, Blana, Gwent NP3 3HY ☎ 01495 290037

DAVIES Roy (*B Gtr*): 18 Castle Lee, Caldicot, Monmouthshire NP6 4HR ☎ 01291 421534

DENTON Stephen (*Flgl*): 10 George Nuttall Close, Cambridge CB4 1YE ☎ 01223 425936

DOUGHTY Thomas (*Flgl*): 73 Sladebrook Road, Bath BA2 1LP ☎ Bath 337174

DURRANT Peter: 37 Argyle Street, St.Pauls, Bristol BS2 8UU

ELLSMORE Stuart: Mount Pleasant, Whiteshill, Stroud, Glos GL6 6AU ☎ 01453 758538

EVANS Haldon: 9 Squirrel Walk, Fforest, Pontardulais, Swansea, West Glam SA4 1UH ☎ 01792 884394

FORD David (*Flgl*): 18A Cadbury Heath Road, Warmley, Bristol BS15 5BX ☎ 0117 9609039

FROST David (*Org, Con*): Truck Cottage, Probus, Truro, Cornwall TR2 4JA ☎ 01872 520655

GRAY Simon (*Cnt, Flgl*): 4 Ynysbryn Close, Llantrisant, Ponty Clun, Mid Glamorgan CF72 8AX ☎ 01443 224102, 0410 386098 mob

GREATREX Joe: 91 Broadley Drive, Livermead, Torquay TQ2 6LT ☎ 01803 690 335

GURNER John (*Tbn*): 21 Sirowy View, Pont Llanfraith, Blackwood, Gwent

HAGUE Andrew (*Flgl, Dms*): 14 Church Road, Bedminster, Bristol BS3 4NF ☎ 0117 9669344

HAINES Cris (*Flgl*): 14 Felinfach, Cwmtwrch Uchaf SA9 2XR ☎ 01639 830501

HAM Bernard: The Willows, Quarry Rd, Treboeth, Swansea SA5 9DJ ☎ 01792 50968

HARPIN J W (*Pf*): 2 Chalfont Close, Trowbridge, Wiltshire BA14 9TE ☎ 01225 768873

HARRIES Martyn: 20 Somerset Road, Portishead, Avon BS20 8EE ☎ 01275 844492

HARRIS Christopher (*Db, Con*): 12 Brentry Road, Fishponds, Bristol BS16 2AA ☎ 0117 9651796

HARRIS Clifford (*Voc*): Bahaven, Siginstone, Nr. Cowbridge, Vale Of Glamorgan CF71 7LP ☎ 01446 771 069, 01446 735 048

HARRISON James (*Flgl, Cnt*): 1 Belle Vue Court, Longueville Road, St Saviour, Jersey JE2 7WG ☎ 01534 852430 & fax

HAWKES David (*B Gtr*): 101 Browning Road, Milehouse, Plymouth, Devon PL2 3AW ☎ 01752 53804

HAZELL Tony: 4 Archer Road, Penarth, S Glam CF64 3LS ☎ 029 2070 5471

HEMPSTEAD Catherine: 'Laburnums' 1 Ashley Road, Uffculme, Cullompton, Devon EX15 3AH ☎ Craddock 40843

HUXHAM Anthony: 3 Pinwood Lane, Exeter, Devon EX4 8NQ ☎ 01392 468537

HUXHAM Francis: 35 Gill Park, Efford, Plymouth PL3 6LX ☎ 01752 223037

JENKINS Rhys (*Gtr, Pf, Cnt, Flgl*): Langdon Brake, Begelly, Kilgetty SA68 0NJ ☎ 01834 891684 & fax

JENNER Robert (*Flgl*): 4 Sheppards Walk, Chilcompton, Somerset BA3 4FF ☎ 01761 233982, 0973 843615

JOHNSON Brahma Barry A (*Flgl*): Flat 1A, Claire Court, Higher Erith Road, Torquay, Devon TQ1 2NQ ☎ 01803 291770

JONES Andrew (*Flgl, Cnt*): 32 Llwyn Onn, Tyla Garw, Pontyclun, Rhondda Cynon Taff CF72 9ET ☎ 0973 869621 mob

JONES Paul (*Cnt, Flgl*): 42 Banc-Yr-Allt, Cefn Glas, Bridgend, Mid Glam CF31 4RH ☎ 01656 665160

JONES William: L'Heritage, La Rue De La Pointe, St Brelade, Jersey, C.I. JE3 8EN ☎ 68657

JOSEPH Max (*Flgl, Org*): 1 Redbrook Court, St Martins Road, Caerphilly, Mid Glamorgan, South Wales CF83 1ED ☎ 029 2086 6233, 0589 082087 mob

KIMBER Derek (*Org*): 17 Estcourt Crescent, Devizes, Wilts SN10 1LR ☎ 01380 721268

KING Ron: 5 East Clevedon Triangle, Clevedon BS21 6BQ ☎ 01275 871848

LE GOUPIL Fiona (*Flgl, T Hrn, Pf*): Meadow View, Rue Des Vallees, St Martin, Jersey C.I. JE3 6BB ☎ 01534 852548

LEE Linda: La Rochelle, Mawgan, Helston, Cornwall TR12 6AJ ☎ 01326 221201

LEE Steven: 126 Couzens Close, Chipping Soobury, South Glos BS17 6BU ☎ 01454 323704

LEWIS Roddy (*Flgl, Arr, Com, Cop*): 16 Beechwood Road, Newport, Gwent NP9 8AA ☎ 01633 272489

LIDDINGTON Gethin (*Cnt*): 22 Clos Powys, Yorkdale Estate, Beddaw, Pontypridd CF38 2SY ☎ 01443 201204

LINSKEY Michael: 6 Wyndham Road, Canton, Cardiff CF1 9EJ ☎ 029 2037 4994

LOCK Michael (*Flgl*): 45 Boness Road, Wroughton, Swindon, Wilts SN4 9DX ☎ 01793 812201

MACGOWAN Roger (*Voc*): 43 Hill View, Gaer Road, Newport NP9 3HY ☎ 01633 222817

MAINWARING Jonathan (*Pictpt*): 14 Bars Rest, Tyler Hendy, The Retreat, Miskin Nr. Pontyclun, Wales CF72 8QU ☎ 01443 237966

MARSH Anne (*Clt*): Tedworth Villa, 34 Trevarnon Lane, Connor Downs, Hayle, Cornwall TR27 5DL ☎ 01736 753661, 0589 018513 mob

MARTIN Neil (*Flgl, Arr, Com, Cop*): Woodbine Cottage, Hafodyrynys Road, Crumlin, Gwent NP1 5EQ ☎ 01495 249370

MARTIN Peter (*B Ldr*): 21 Powlett Road, Bathwick, Bath BA2 6QL ☎ 01225 61645

MAY Steve: 10 Trinity Place, Merchants Road, Hotwells, Bristol BS8 4PZ ☎ 0117 9299869

MITCHELL Reginald: 9 Southwood Court, Middle Warberry Road, Torquay TQ1 1RIT ☎ 01803 23740

MORRIS Philip: 5 Coed-Ty-Maen, Llangewydd Court, Bridgend, Mid Glamorgan CF31 4TG ☎ 01656 669045

MORRIS Philip (*Cnt*): 13 The Paddocks, Penarth, South Glam CF64 5BW ☎ 029 2070 1246, 029 2066 6150, 029 2022 7537

MORTON Adrian (*Cnt, Flgl*): 47 Cardiff Road, Taffs Well, Cardiff CF4 7RD ☎ 029 2081 0884

MOWAT David (*Flgl*): C/ 25 Manor Road, Alcombe, Minehead, Somerset TA24 6EJ

NABB Philippa (*Pf*): Lynwood, Brinsea Road, Congresbury BS49 5JQ ☎ 01934 833945

NEWMAN Tim: Newlands Farm, Grittleton, Chippenham, Wilts SN14 6AS ☎ 01249 782437

NICHOLAS Philip (*Flgl*): 4 Cluden Close, Alphington, Exeter, Devon EX2 8TX ☎ 01392 275396

NICHOLS Geoff (*Vib*): 62 Egerton Road, Bishopston, Bristol BS7 8HL ☎ 0117 9243981

OLIVER John (*B Ldr*): Catsash House, Catsash, Newport, Gwent NP6 1JG ☎ 01633 423234

PEARCE Ben (*Flgl*): Whitecroft, Millhayes, Stockland, Honiton, Devon EX14 9DB ☎ 01404 881 543

PEGG E: 20 Oakfield Road, Cwmbran, Gwent NP44 3EX ☎ 01633 868579

PROCTER Thomas: Wood Cottage, Georgetown, Gwaelod Y Garth, Cardiff CF4 8HF ☎ 029 2081 3346

PURVER Ron: 12 Haldon Close, Buckland, Newton Abbot, S Devon TQ12 4BQ ☎ 01626 365504

REES Gareth (*Flgl*): 149 Pwllmelin Road, Fairwater, Cardiff, South Glamorgan CF5 3QB ☎ 029 2056 3390

REYNOLDS Thomas (*Org, Flgl, Cnt*): The Bungalow, 11 Neath Abbey Road, Neath, West Glamorgan SA10 7BD ☎ 01639 52712

ROWELL Kenneth (*B Gtr*): Trafalgar Hotel, High Street, St Aubyn, Jersey, C.I. JE3 8BR ☎ 01534 499220

SHARP Joseph (*Gtr, Kbds, Voc*): 9 Clifton Terrace, Portcatho, Truro, Cornwall TR2 5HR ☎ 01872 580512, 07775 774341

SHEAD David (*Pictpt, Cnt*): 19 The Meads, Milborne Port, Nr Sherborne, Dorset DT9 5DS ☎ 01963 251589, 07775 805881 mob

SHIELDS Martin (*Flgl*): Hunters Moon, La Rue Ville Es Gazeaux, St Lawrence, Jersey, Channel Islands JE3 1HU ☎ 01534 45644

SHILLITO John: 5 Kirkstall Close, Plymouth PL2 2SD ☎ 01752 3604953

SMALL David: Maesgwyn, 42 Gowerton Road, Penclawdd, Swansea SA4 3XA ☎ 01792 850707

SMITH Clive (*Cnt*) ☎ 0297 34169

SMITH Leslie: Trees, Chapel Road, Osmington, Weymouth Dorset DT3 6ET ☎ 01305 833778

STEPHEN Andrew (*Cnt, Flgl, Pf*): 8 Crowther Park, Horfield, Bristol BS7 9NT ☎ 0117 9086 776

STEPHENSON Gordon: 15 Bardley Park Road, St Marychurch Road, Torquay TQ1 4RD ☎ 01803 325807

STRETTON Bill (*S Sax, Tbn, Flgl, Clt*): 20 Harlech Drive, Rhiwderin, Newport, Gwent NP1 9QS

TAIT Ronald (*Voc, Arr*): Address Unknown

TAYLOR David (*Eup, T Hrn*): 12 Quennevais Gardens, St Brelade, Jersey, Channel Islands JE3 8FQ ☎ Jersey 43492

THATCHER Norman (*Dms, Db, Tbn*): 15 Moorhouse Park, Moorhouse Lane, Hallen, Bristol BS10 7RU ☎ 01633 251043

THOMAS Christopher: Summerfields, New Road, West Huntspill, Highbridge, Somerset TA9 3QD ☎ 01278 783076

TINKER Bob (*Flgl, Mel, Kbds, Voc*): 33 St Leonards Road, Launceston, Cornwall PL15 8LQ ☎ 01566 777855

TRIGG Stephen (*Hrn, Cnt*): 7 Badgers Way, Forest Green, Nailsworth, Stroud, Glos GL6 0HE ☎ 01734 507005

WARD George (*Cnt, Flgl*): Georgia, 1 Greenclose Court, Colyton, Devon EX24 6RG ☎ 01297 553443, 07971 016183 mob

WARREN Ernest (*Flgl*): 25 Valletort House, Union Place, Plymouth PL1 3HY ☎ 01752 212972

WATKEYS John (*Pic, Pf*): 38 Verwood Drive, Bitton, Bristol BS15 6JP ☎ 324516

WATKINS Gareth (*Cnt, Flgl, Pf*): 3 Isca Mews, Caerleon, Newport NP6 1AS ☎ 01633 423138

WHEELER Harvey (*Flgl, B Gtr*): Severnside, High Street, Newnham, Gloucester GL14 1AA ☎ 01594 516203

WHITTINGHAM Clive: 16 Queens Road, St George, Bristol BS5 8HR ☎ 0117 9551976

WILKINSON Ken (*Arr*): 38 East Street, Ashburton, Devon TQ13 7AQ ☎ 01364 53020

WILLIAMS Edward (*Bjo, Br Sax*): 50 Conway Cresent, Toteg, Mid Glamorgan CF38 1HP ☎ 01443 204846

WILLIAMS Stephen (*Cnt, Pst H, Flgl*): 8 Barton Ave, Keyham, Plymouth PL2 1NY ☎ 01752 560800, 0378 578051 mob

WOODROFFE Alan (*Flgl, Hrn*): The Firs, Bridges, Luxulyan, Bodmin, Cornwall PL30 5EF ☎ 01726 851127

LONDON

AARONS Anthony: 47 Boscombe Road, Wimbledon, London SW19 3AX ☎ 020 8715 8123 & fax, 0402 186332

ADAMS Bruce (*Flgl*): 17 Carlisle Close, Sandy, Bedfordshire SG19 1TY ☎ 01767 691634

ADOO Clarence: 10 Lilly Avenue, Jesmond, Newcastle-upon-Tyne NE2 2SQ ☎ 0191 281 0637

AGUIRRE Pablo (*Flgl*): 50 Braxfield Road, Brockley, London SE4 2AN ☎ 020 8692 6449

ALAN Barbara (*Cnt, Voc*): 11 Leaf Close, Thames Ditton, Surrey KT7 0YQ ☎ 020 8398 0696

ALLEN Michael (*Cnt*): 16 Vaughan Ave, Vaughan Gdns, Ilford, Essex IG1 3NZ ☎ 020 8554 0182

ANDRE Denis (*Cnt, Flgl, Pic*): 72 Wilshere Avenue, St Albans, Herts AL1 2PH ☎ 01727 32981, 0850 209763 mob

APPLEYARD David: 6 South Hill Park, London NW3 2SB ☎ 020 7794 3623

ARCHER David (*Cnt, Flgl*): Holly House, 90 Grove Road, Tiptree, Essex CO5 0JG ☎ 01621 816581, 01306 880669

ARCHIBALD Norman: 48 Micawber Ave, Hillingdon, Middlesex UB8 3NZ ☎ 01895 814393

ARCHIBALD Paul (*Pf*): Flat 1, 3 Rodway Road, Roehampton, London SW15 5DN ☎ 020 8788 9613, 020 8780 1768 fax, 0973 731866 mob

ARMSTRONG Mark (*Flgl, Arr*): 49 Hillreach, London SE18 4AL ☎ 020 8855 3467, 0831 090693 mob

ARTHUR Edward: 109 Caxton Road, Hoddesdon, Herts EN11 9NX ☎ 01992 442790

ATKINS Joe: 58 Lower Road, High Denham, Bucks UB9 5EB ☎ 01895 834526, 01895 835013 fax, 0973 502089 mob

ATKINSON Joseph (*Pf*): 57 Welling Way, Welling, Kent DA16 2RN ☎ 020 8856 3583

BACHE Ken (*Cnt, Rec*): 9 Whitton Drive, Greenford, Middlesex UB6 0QX ☎ 020 8902 5843

BAILEY Jonathan (*Flgl*): Willetts Cottage, Muddles Green, Chiddingly Lewes, East Sussex BN8 6HR ☎ 01825 872574

BAKER Clive (*Flgl, Pic*): The Little Cottage, Brook Street, Elsworth, Cambridge CB3 8HX ☎ 01954 267637

BAKER John (*Cop*): 34 Guinness Court, Lever Street, London EC1V 3TR ☎ 020 7490 2430, 020 7251 5242 fax, 0973 508337 mob

BAKER Kenny (*B Ldr, Flgl, Cnt*): 6 Crossbush Road, Felpham, Bognor Regis, W Sussex PO22 7LS ☎ 01243 584932

BAKER Nicholas (*Flgl*): 52 Fawnbrake Avenue, Herne Hill, London SE24 0BU ☎ 020 7738 6348, 0973 796783 mob

BALDWIN Petra: 9 Alwyne Avenue, Shenfield, Essex CM15 8QT ☎ 01277 228381

BALL Brendan (*Cnt, Pictpt, N Tpt, Flgl*): 26 Walwyn Avenue, Bromley, Kent BR1 2RD ☎ 020 8464 9952, 020 8549 1706, 0976 423097

BALL Kenneth (*B Ldr*): Warmans Farm, Burton End, Stansted, Essex CM24 8UQ ☎ 01279 817148

BALL Mick (*Pf*): 31A Homerton Road, Kingston, Surrey KT1 3PL ☎ 0973 116396

BALMAIN Ian: 20A Bishopsthorpe Road, Sydenham, London SE26 4NY ☎ 020 8659 4878

BANKS Jeremy: 49 Burtons Road, Hampton Hill, Middlesex TW12 1DE ☎ 020 8941 4284

BANKS John: 207 Bourne Vale, Bromley, Kent BR2 7LX ☎ 020 8462 2611, 0973 179 909 mob

BARBER Trevor: 30 Knole Road, Dartford, Kent DA1 3JW ☎ 01322 287491

BARCLAY John: Southlands, 15 Elmwood Avenue, Kenton, Middx HA3 8AJ ☎ 020 8907 2287

BARKER Guy (*Flgl*): Flat 3, 54 Church Crescent, Muswell Hill, London N10 3NE ☎ 020 8883 8859 fax, 01483 541700 day

BARNARD Scott (*B Gtr*): 88A Swaby Road, Earlsfield, London SW18 3QZ ☎ 0976 885836, 0976 885836

BARNES Dylan: 21 Lower Camden, Chislehurst, Kent BB7 5HY ☎ 020 8467 4520

BARNETT Pat (*Mel*): 129 Highbury Grove, London N5 1HR ☎ 020 7226 5928

BARON Cohen Erran (*Pf*): 760A Finchley Road, London NW11 7TH ☎ 020 8381 4431

BARTON Jim (*Flgl, Pictpt, Cnt, Md*): 13 Ruskin House, Erasmus Strret, London SW1P 4HU ☎ 020 7821 6866

BATEMAN Donald (*Flgl, Pictpt*): 3 Kemble Drive, Keston, Bromley, Kent BR2 8PY ☎ 01689 851382

BATES Howard (*Flgl*): 33 Boxgrove Gardens, Aldwick, Bognor Regis, W Sussex PO21 4BB ☎ 01243 267471

BAXTER Malcolm (*Flgl, Cnt*): 29 Candover Close, Hammondsworth, Middlesex UB7 0BD ☎ 020 8897 7670

BEAVIS Peter (*Flgl, V Tbn*): 5 Thayers Farm Road, Beckenham, Kent BR3 4LY ☎ 020 8325 8681

BECKETT Harold (*Flgl, Arr*): 118 Nevill Road, Stokenewington, London N16 0SX ☎ 020 7254 9113

BELL Bob (*Flgl, T Hrn, Cnt, B Ldr*): 45 Bracken Drive, Chigwell, Essex IG7 5RD ☎ 020 8500 7242

BENISTON Paul: 12 Laurie Gray Avenue, Bluebell Hill, Chatham, Kent ☎ 01634 670410

BENN Maurice (*Sou*): 51 Blakes Lane, New Malden, Surrey KT3 6NS ☎ 020 8949 3488

BENNETT Mark: 222 Nelson Road, Whitton, Middlesex TW2 7BW ☎ 020 8898 1014, 01306 880669, 01459 101369 pager

BERLYN Alan (*Md, Flgl, A Sax, Kbds*): 20 Copthorne Avenue, Hainault, Ilford, Essex IG6 2SQ ☎ 020 8559 9898, 07979 936653 mob, 020 8559 9898

BETTS Nicholas: 11A Mansfield Road, Wanstead, London E11 2JN ☎ 020 8530 6474

BILHAM Roy: 26, Cartmel Road, Bexleyheath, Kent DA7 5EA ☎ 01322 430779, 01322 448416

BIMSON Gareth: 5 Lynwood Road, Hinchley Wood, Surrey KT7 0DN ☎ 020 8398 4239

BINCH Barry (*Gtr, Bjo, Voc*): 52 Nightingale Road, South Croydon, Surrey CR2 8PT ☎ 020 8651 4210

BLORE Simon: 148 Craneford Way, Twickenham, Middlesex TW2 7SQ ☎ 020 8744 2011

BOA David (*Flgl, Voc*): 57A Stapleton Road, London SW17 8AY ☎ 020 7767 1013, 0411 066932

BOLWELL Tim (*B Gtr*): 48 Seely Road, Tooting, London SW17 9QS

BONNER Paul (*Flgl*): 102 East Hill, Wandsworth, London SW18 2QB ☎ 020 8871 9008

BONNEY Alex (*Flgl*): 138 Mount Pleasant, Cockfosters, Barnet EN4 9HG ☎ 020 8441 6590, 0958 715218

BOOTH Matthew: 37A Leathwaite Road, Battersea, London SW11 1XG ☎ 020 7223 1414

BOTSCHINSKY Allan (*Flgl*): 64 Gilbey House, 38-46 Jamestown Road, London NW1 7BY ☎ 020 7284 1177, 020 7284 1179

BOWEN Greg: Storm Strasse 4, 14050, Berlin, Germany ☎ Berlin 302 1146

BREWER Julian (*Flgl, Pictpt, N Tpt, Bq Tpt*): 13 Kings Way, Woking, Surrey GU21 1NU ☎ 01483 725416

BRIAN Antony: Flat 3, 34 Woodside Park Rd, North Finchley, London N12 8RP ☎ 020 8446 4159

BROOK David: 99A King Henrys Road, Primrose Hill, Camden, London NW3 3QX ☎ 020 8854 4748

BROOKS Stuart (*Flgl*): 9 Northampton Road, Croydon, Surrey CR0 7HB ☎ 020 8654 8648, 020 8549 1706, 0976 765688 mob

BROUGH Neil (*N Tpt, Pictpt, Flgl*): 18 Bedford Court, Mowbray Road, Upper Norwood, London SE19 2RW ☎ 020 8771 9793, 0976 375168

BROUGHALL Sharon: 43 Fernbrook Drive, Harrow, Middlesex HA2 7EE ☎ 020 8248 0814, 0976 670045

BROWN Annette Sox (*Flgl, Pictpt, Cnt*): 75A Pellatt Road, East Dulwich, London SE22 9JD ☎ 020 8299 6658

BROWN Damon (*Flgl, Kbds*): The Garden Flat, 75 Lothair Road North, London N4 1ER ☎ 020 8348 0898

BROWN Ian: 9 Eversley Way, Shirley, Croydon, Surrey CR0 8QR ☎ 020 8777 2035

BRYAN Harry (*Flgl*): 9 Cranleigh Avenue, Rottingdean, Sussex BN2 7GT ☎ 01273 302490

BUCKENHAM Gemma (*Pf, Voc, Gtr*): 2 Arlington Court, Arlington Road, St Margarets, Middlesex TW1 2AU ☎ 020 8715 8625, 0589 200358

BUNCE Martin (*Flgl, B Ldr*): 18 State Farm Avenue, Farnborough, Kent BR6 7TN ☎ 01689 861627, 0956 224492

BURGESS Norman (*Cnt, Pst H, Flgl*): 61 Quickley Lane, Chorleywood, Herts WD3 5AE ☎ 01923 283028

BURKE Nicola (*Pf*): 78 Runnemeade Road, Egham, Surrey TW20 9BL ☎ 0468 698354 mob

BURNETT Roderick: 66 Hydeway, Hayes, Middlesex UB3 4PB ☎ 020 8848 9065, 0973 735089 mob

BUSH Andy: 240A Blythe Road, West Kensington, London W14 0HJ ☎ 020 7602 5227, 0860 920954

CALDER Mark: 18 Mead Road, Cranleigh, Surrey GU6 7BG ☎ 01483 278148, 0973 324067

CALLARD Andrew: 86 Bexhill Road, Crofton Park, London SE4 1SL ☎ 020 8690 9951, 0976 430295 mob, 0306 880669 day

CALVERT Leon (*Flgl*): 5 Great North Road, Brookmans Park, Hatfield, Herts AL9 6LB ☎ 01707 658222

CAMERON Ian: 29 North End Road, Golders Green, London NW11 7RJ ☎ 020 8455 4707

CAMERON Peter: 194 Muswell Hill Road, London N10 3NG ☎ 020 8444 0246

CAMPBELL Duncan (*Flgl, Cnt, E Tpt*): Field Gates, 29 Long Lane, Ickenham, Middx UB10 8QU ☎ 020 8868 4932

CARE Nicholas: 1 North Cottages, Stockgrove, Leighton Buzzard, Beds LU7 0BB ☎ 01525 237401

CARLESTON Tim (*Flgl, Tpt*): 10 Holyoake Court, Bryan Road, Rotherhithe, London SE16 1HJ ☎ 020 7394 8842, 0976 988 830

CARR Ian: Flat 1, 34 Brailsford Road, London SW2 2TE ☎ 020 8671 7195

CARTER Nigel: 191 Verity Way, Stevenage, Herts SG1 5PS ☎ 01438 354208

CASWELL David (*Flgl*): 124 Longmead Drive, Albany Park, Sidcup, Kent DA14 4NZ ☎ 020 8300 0250

CATT Arthur (*Flgl*): 10E Randolph Crescent, Maida Vale, London W9 1DR ☎ 020 7286 1370

CESAR Phil: 144 Crampton Street, London SE17 3AE ☎ 020 7703 0708, 01234 358450

CHARITY Karl: 59 Woodmansterne Road, Couldson, Surrey CR5 2DH ☎ 020 8660 5346

CHARLTON Kay (*Flgl*): 19A Glenarm Road, London E5 0LY ☎ 020 8985 2200, 0402 817994 mob

CHENEY John (*Gtr, Hmca, Voc*): 33 Silchester Court, London Road, Thornton Heath CR7 6HT ☎ 020 8689 8399

CHENEY Simon: 22 Davids Road, Forest Hill, London SE23 3EX ☎ 020 8291 9045

CHILTON John: 3 Great Ormond Street, London WC1N 3RA ☎ 020 7404 0016

CLAGUE Colin: 47 Courtlands Avenue, Hampton, Middx TW12 3NS ☎ 020 8941 4357

CLEWLOW David (*Cnt, Flgl*): 35 Caversham Avenue, Palmers Green, London N13 4LL ☎ 020 8886 0723

CLOTHIER Michael: C/Cristobal Alarcon 19/25, Mijas (Pueblo), Malaga 29650, Spain ☎ 010 3452 485662

COHEN Benjamin: 8 Pepys Close, Ickenham, Uxbridge, Middlesex UB10 8NL ☎ 01895 638185

COKER Eric (*Flgl, Pictpt, N Tpt*): 3 Conniston Court, Hangar Hill, Weybridge, Surrey KT13 9YR

COLE Gracie (*Flgl, Cnt*): 5 Newlands Avenue, Thames Ditton, Surrey KT7 0HD ☎ 020 8398 1870

COLEMAN Jamie (*Flgl*): 20 Homefield Road, Chiswick, London W4 2LN ☎ 020 8995 6642

COLES Toby: 21 Alconbury Road, Stoke Newington, London E5 8AG ☎ 020 7502 0316, 0958 597662, 01306 880669

COLLINS Henry (*Pf*): 4 Beaconsfield Road, Friern Barnet, London N11 3AB ☎ 020 8368 4354, 0956 445 206

COLLINS Michael: 35 Glebe Road, Bromley, Kent BR1 3AT ☎ 020 8466 1061

CONDON Peter (*Flgl*): 160 Swakeleys Road, Ickenham, Middx UB10 8AZ ☎ 01895 672354

CORNISH Eric: 2 Romford Road, Aveley, Essex RM15 ☎ 01708 866348

COSH Paul (*Cnt, Flgl*): 2F The Limes, Chase Side, Enfield, Middlesex EN2 6NB ☎ 020 8363 5224

COTTON Michael (*Hmca*): 10 Woodlea Lodge, 72 Wellington Road, Enfield EN1 2NW ☎ 020 8360 6855

CRAFT Colin: 58 Woodland Way, West Wickham, Kent BR4 9LR ☎ 020 8777 4786

CRAMP Alan: 1 Mount View, London Colney, Herts AL2 1AT ☎ 01727 821 389, 01483 451 700 day

CROMWELL Alex: 16 Merewood Road, Bexleyheath, Kent DA7 6PG ☎ 01322 332421, 01306 880669 day

CROWLEY Andrew: 131 Repton Road, Orpington, Kent BR6 9HY ☎ 01689 603644

CUMBERLAND Mark (*Flgl, Arr, Cop*): 325D Richmond Road, East Twickenham, Middlesex TW1 2PB ☎ 020 8744 1782, 0973 316556

CURLETT Denis: 16 Birchdale Road, Wimborne, Dorset BH1 1BY ☎ 01202 886 552

CUSS Andy: 6 Bell Lane, Northchurch, Berkhampstead, Herts HP4 3RD ☎ 01442 875414, 0385 918383 mob

CUTHBERT Jon: 28 Montcalm House, Millwall Estate, Westferry Road, Isle Of Dogs, London E14 3SD ☎ 020 7987 6285

CUTHELL Dick (*Flgl, Cnt, T Hrn, Arr*): 65 Shoot Up Hill, Cricklewood, London NW2 3PS ☎ 020 8450 9536

CUTLER David (*Cnt, Pictpt*): 5 Weymouth Street, Hemel Hempstead, Herts HP3 9SL ☎ 01442 251962, 0370 843085

D'OLIVEIRA Raul (*Flgl, Vib, B Gtr, Per*): 3 Flamstead Heights, Eddington Hill, Broad Field, Crawley, Sussex RH11 9JS ☎ 0421 535364 & fax, 01403 265798 mob

DA SILVA Simon (*Flgl*): 56 Salisbury Rd, Harrow, Middlesex HA1 1NZ ☎ 020 8427 2311, 0585 185533

DAVID Mark (*Cnt, Pic*): 16 Northcroft Road, West Ewell, Surrey KT19 9TA ☎ 020 8394 1570

DAVIES Hugh (*N Tpt*): 379 Fulham Palace Road, London SW6 6TA ☎ 020 7731 3779, 0306 880669

DAVIES Jerome (*Flgl, B Gtr, Cl Gtr*): 18 Horace Road, Forest Gate, London E7 0JG ☎ 020 8257 5739, 0411 268 633 mob

DAVIS Paul (*Flgl*): 57 Chestnut Road, London SE27 9EZ ☎ 020 8670 5343

DAVIS Paul (*Flgl*): 21 Chesham Road, Bovingdon, Herts HP3 0ED ☎ 01442 833670

DAWSON Stephen (*Flgl, Cnt*): 54 Durham Road, Bromley, Kent BR2 0SW ☎ 020 8464 5446 & fax

DAWSWELL John: 69 Southover, London N12 7HG ☎ 020 8446 0460

DE FLON John: 33 Kinnoul Road, London W6 8NG ☎ 020 7381 5858

DESMOND Peter (*Kbds, B Gtr, Arr*): 145 Ladysmith Road, Enfield, Middx EN1 3AH ☎ 020 8367 8449

DIAGRAM Andy ☎ 020 8533 5095

DICKSON John (*Flgl, Pf, Kbds*): 1st Floor Flat, 221 Ashmore Road, Queens Park, London W9 3DB ☎ 020 8968 3623

DILLEY Harry: Yew Tree Cottage, Hammonds Lane, Ropley, Alresford Hants SO24 0DZ ☎ 0196277 3609

DIPROSE Michael *(Cnt, Flgl, Pictpt, Com)*: Flat 3, 48A Chatsworth Road, Brondesbury, London NW2 4BT ☎ 020 8450 9449, 020 8451 4396, 0468 298343

DIXON Antony: 14 Roper Close, Parkwood, Rainham, Kent ME8 9QX ☎ 01634 373802

DOBSON Colin *(Voc)*: 17 Rosedene Avenue, London SW16 2LS ☎ 020 8769 2492

DOLEY Colin *(Pictpt, Flgl)*: Address Unknown ☎ 020 8520 4408, 020 8444 3657

DORSEY Jack *(Com, Arr)*: Shannon House, 45 Dyke Road Avenue, Hove, Sussex BN3 6QA ☎ 01273 508 588

DOUGLAS Anthony *(Flgl, Tbn, Arr, Com)*: 18A Belgrave Gardens, St Johns Wood, London NW8 0RB ☎ 020 7624 6217, 0374 801705 mob

DOWNEY Alan *(Flgl, Arr)*: 188 Malden Road, New Malden, Surrey KT3 6DS ☎ 020 8949 4289

DROVER Martin *(Flgl)*: 44 Durham Road, London SW20 0TW ☎ 020 8642 0913

DUDLEY Tony *(Flgl)*: 9 Bostall Road, St Pauls Cray, Orpington, Kent BR5 3DN ☎ 020 8302 9531

DUIZEND Matthew *(Kbds, Sitar)*: 14 Rowfant Road, London SW17 7AS ☎ 020 8488 0790

DUMAS Charles: 31 Cite Des Fleuiz, 75017, Paris, France ☎ 0958 455832

DUNCAN Peter *(Flgl)*: 88 Pirbright Road, London SW18 5NA ☎ 020 8874 0851

DUNN Andrew: 18 Weavers Green, Sandy, Beds SG19 2TR ☎ 01767 681 795, 0306 880669

DURRANT John *(Pictpt, Com, Arr, Cntt)* ☎ 020 8523 5363, 0976 580062 mob

DVORAK James *(Flgl)*: 43B Mulkern Road, London N19 3HQ ☎ 020 7281 1153

EBDON John *(Flgl)*: 10 Maple Close, Swanley, Kent BR8 7YN ☎ 01322 614253

EDEM Eddie *(Cong, Bong)*: 99B Ledbury Rd, London W11 2AG ☎ 020 7792 1743

EDEN David: 7 Windsor Close, Cheshunt, Herts EN7 5LW ☎ 01992 636065

EDWARDS Benjamin *(Flgl, Cnt)*: 68B Upper Tollington Park, London N4 4LS ☎ 020 7281 6788, 0795 713 9074 mob

EDWARDS Denis: 219 Salmon Street, Kingsbury, London NW9 8ND ☎ 020 8205 6308

ELDRED John *(Flgl)*: 20 Oakfield Lane, Dartford, Kent DA1 2SW ☎ 01322 228387

ELLIS Bob: 2 Ashcombe Court, 31 Carlton Drive, London SW15 2BW ☎ 020 8789 1423

ELLIS Cynthia: 17 Kewferry Road, Northwood, Middlesex HA6 2NS ☎ 01923 821237

ELLISON Sidney: West Lodge, Coxhill, Narberth, Pembs Dyfed SA67 8EH ☎ 01834 860625

ELLWOOD John: 122 New Road, North Ascot, Berks SL5 8QH ☎ 01344 885136 & fax, 0421 863330 mob

ELMS Simon *(Flgl)*: 46 Highgate Hill, London N19 5NQ ☎ 020 7272 1307

ELSDON Alan *(B Ldr)*: 29 Dorchester Road, Northolt Park, Greenford, Middx UB5 4PA ☎ 020 8422 1055

EMBLISS Will *(V Tbn)*: 61 Kitchener Road, London N17 6DU ☎ 020 8801 8830

ESHELBY Paul: Cranleigh, 118 Preston Hill, Harrow, Middx HA3 9SJ ☎ 020 8204 1032

ETHERIDGE Martin *(Pic, Flgl)*: 5 Pilgrims Way, Shere, Guildford, Surrey GU5 9HR ☎ 01483 203233, 0441 027306 mob

EVANS David: 8 Queens Road, Bromley, Kent BR1 3EA ☎ 020 8402 0326

EVANS Howard *(Cnt, Flgl)*: 23 Beeches Ave, Carshalton Beeches, Surrey SM5 3LJ ☎ 020 8669 1735

EVANS Laurie: Flat 3, 15 The Avenue, Eastbourne, East Sussex BN21 3YA ☎ 01323 644109, 0831 217218

EVANS Martin *(N Tpt)*: 12 Collingtree Grove, Sydenham, London SE26 4QG ☎ 0976 878406

EZARD Bert *(Flgl, Cnt)*: 40 Mulgrave Road, Whitby, North Yorkshire YO21 3JS ☎ 01947 603172

FAIRWEATHER Digby *(Cnt)*: The Upper Flat, 41 Cobham Road, Westcliff-on-Sea, Essex SS0 8EG ☎ 01702 435727

FARLEY Robert *(N Tpt)*: 334 Norton Way South, Letchworth, Herts SG6 1TA ☎ 01462 624363, 020 8549 1706

FERGUSON Simon: 11 Beaufort Road, Reigate, Surrey RH2 9DQ ☎ 01737 244046

FERRIMAN Robert: 46 Southern Down Ave, Mayals, Swansea SA3 5EL ☎ 01792 406438

FIELD Dominic *(Pf)*: 18 Pearl Gardens, West Ealing, London W13 0BA ☎ 020 8991 1270, 0378 027601 mob

FIELD Sarah *(Sax, Pf, Clt)*: Apartment 6, Trinity Hall, 6 Durward Street, London E1 5BA ☎ 020 7247 6816, 01426 180872, 020 7873 7374

FIGGIS Michael *(Pf, Gtr)*: 30 Percey Street, London W1P 9FF ☎ 020 7299 1080

FINCH Simon *(Flgl, Pf)*: 86 Newark Street, Whitechapel, London E1 2ES ☎ 020 7426 0340

FINDON Julia: 59 Brook Avenue, Edgware, Middlesex HA8 9UZ ☎ 020 8958 9359

FISHER Pauline: 82 Fernleigh Rise, Ditton, Maidstone, Kent ME20 6BS ☎ 01732 845659

FISHER Tony: Casa Bianca, 26 Higher Drive, Banstead, Surrey SM7 1PF ☎ 020 8393 4580, 020 8786 7884 fax

FISHWICK Steven: 221 Ashmore Road, Queens Park, London W9 3DB ☎ 020 8969 4381, 0797 0415581

FOMISON Richard *(N Tpt)*: 32 Adelaide Gardens, Ramsgate, Kent CT11 9HH ☎ 01843 597540, 0973 132588

FONE Michael: 59 Edward Road, Walthamstow, London E17 6PB ☎ 020 8521 7322

FRANKS Roderick *(Md, Con, Arr)*: 8 Berkley Close, St Albans, Herts AL4 9TS

FREEMAN William: 48 Marina Gardens, Cheshunt, Herts EN8 9QY ☎ 01992 633244

FRERE-SMITH Dennis *(Flgl, Cnt, Kbds, Rec)*: 3 Sackville House, Gracefield Gardens, Streatham, London SW16 2TP ☎ 020 8769 8769, 0411 13 89 44, 020 8796 6777

FULKER Martin *(B Gtr, Gtr, Kbds)*: 86 Lowerbarn Road, Riddlesdown, Purley CR8 1HR ☎ 01737 358740, 01523 186724, 01202 317331

FURNESS Alan *(Com, Arr, Con, Md)*: Upways, Long Lane, Ashcombe, Dawlish, Devon EX7 0QR ☎ 01626 864291

GABRIEL Simon: 18 Stamford Road, London N1 4JS ☎ 020 7923 2399, 0831 665886 mob

GARDNER Simon *(Flgl, Cnt, Pictpt)*: 31 Tudor Road, New Barnet, Herts EN5 5NW ☎ 020 8441 5335, 020 8549 1706 day

GARMAN Roy *(Tbn, Arr, Com)*: 7 The Meadway, Orpington, Kent BR6 6HH ☎ 01689 854657

GARSIDE Ernie: 2 Musbury Avenue, Cheadle Hulme, Cheshire SK8 7AT ☎ 0161 485 6538 & fax

GATHERCOLE Andrew *(Flgl, Pictpt)*: 17 Lascelles Avenue, Harrow, Middlesex HA1 4AW ☎ 020 8864 5934

GAULD Sidney *(Flgl)*: 15 New Farm Avenue, Bromley, Kent BR2 0TX ☎ 020 8460 0539, 0831 758 393 mob

GAY Bramwell: 20 Pasture Close, Warboys, Huntingdon, Cambridgeshire PE17 2RB ☎ 01480 469636

GHIGI James *(Bq Tpt)*: Flat 1, 1 Leggatts Wood, Watford, Herts WD2 5RS ☎ 01923 239799, 01306 880669

GIBSON Andy *(Flgl)*: 52 Beresford Road, Kingston-upon-Thames, Surrey KT2 6LR ☎ 020 8549 9086

GIFFORD Katherine *(N Tpt)*: 1 North Cottages, Stockgrove, Leighton Buzzard, Beds LU7 0BB ☎ 01525 237401

GLOVER Dominic *(Cnt, Pf, Flgl)*: 86 Newark Street, Whitechapel, London E1 2ES ☎ 020 7426 0340, 0850 757587

GODDARD Norman *(Flgl)*: 70 Broadlawn, New Eltham, London SE9 3XD ☎ 020 8857 2067

GOLD Gerald *(Flgl, Hmca)*: Blaenegwad, Nantgaredig, Carmarthen SA32 7PL ☎ 01558 668136 & fax

GOMM Nigel: 16 Halliwick Road, Muswell Hill, London N10 1AB ☎ 020 8883 1909

GOSDEN Malcolm *(Pic, Flgl, Cnt, Bq Tpt)*: 19 Multon Road, West Kingsdown, Sevenoaks, Kent TN15 6DB ☎ 01474 854102, 020 8533 1372 day, 0973 658075 mob

GOULDEN Mick *(Flgl, Dms)*: 35 Hunter Close, Gosport PO13 9XY ☎ 023 8023 1973

GOY Peter: 52 Bishopsgate Walk, Spitalfield Lane, Chichester, West Sussex PO19 4FQ ☎ 01243 783700

GRAHAM Colin *(Flgl)*: 40A Woodstock Road, London NW11 8ER ☎ 020 8455 9801

GRANT Ian: 111 Old Bedford Road, Luton, Beds LU2 7PF ☎ 01582 424497

GRESTY Alan: 10 Saffron Meadow, Standon, Ware, Herts SG11 1RE ☎ 01920 823522

GRIFFITH Len *(Flgl)*: 19, Juniper Way, Harold Wood, Essex RM3 0XL ☎ 01708 373548

GRIFFITH Shaun *(Flgl)*: 42 Sherrard Road, Forest Gate, London E7 8DW ☎ 020 8471 5253

GROCUTT Matthew: 4 Crestbrook Place, Green Lanes, London N13 5SB ☎ 020 8882 4657, 0973 796933 mob

GUMPERT Alice: 22 Acato Road, Clapham, London SW4 7TX ☎ 020 7622 3772, 07971 556 483

GUTTU Yngvil *(Gtr, Kbds, Hmca, Per)*: Top Flat, 42 Saltoun Road, Brixton, London SW2 1ET ☎ 020 7733 5292

HAINES Cliff *(Cnt, Flgl)*: 11 Tarrant Wharf, Arundel, West Sussex BN18 9NY ☎ 01903 884065

HALCOX Pat: 15 Brunswick Road, Ealing, London W5 1BB ☎ 020 8997 2152

HALL Malcolm *(Cnt)*: 43C Kenton Road, Harrow, Middlesex HA3 0AD ☎ 020 8907 5196

HAMER Ian *(Flgl, Arr, Com)*: 68 Rosehill Terrace, Brighton, East Sussex BN1 4JL ☎ 01273 600002

HAMER Stu *(Pf, Dms, Com, Arr)*: Flat B, 72 Bonnington Square, London SW8 1TG ☎ 020 7735 8031

HAMMOND Richard: 15 Jerome Court, 59-65 The Limes Avenue, New Southgate, London N11 1RF ☎ 020 8368 8223, 0973 327569 mob

HANCOCK David *(Flgl)*: Plum Tree Cottage, Goatsfield Road, Tatsfield, Kent TN16 2BU ☎ 01959 577540, 07957 707410

HANSON Dick *(Flgl, Hrn, Cong)*: 10 Brocas Street, Eton, Windsor, Berks SL4 6BW ☎ 01753 853650

HARDY John: 42 Ducks Hill Road, Northwood, Middlesex HA6 2SB ☎ 01923 825722

HARRIS John *(Flgl)*: 4 Clarence Road, Stratford-on-Avon CV37 9DL ☎ 01789 262151

HARRISON Ken *(Flgl, Pst H)*: 71 Langley Park Road, Sutton, Surrey SM2 5HA ☎ 020 8642 3543

HARRISON Michael: 33 Hillfield Park, Muswell Hill, London N10 3QT ☎ 020 8444 8404, 01306 880669 day

HART Arden *(Kbds, B Gtr, Dms)*: 188 Nether Street, Finchley, London N3 1PE ☎ 020 8346 9336, 0973 507785 mob

HART Edgar: 31 Dollis Road, Finchley Central, London N3 1RB ☎ 020 8346 6627

HASEMAN Nick *(Flgl)*: 55 Aplin Way, Osterley Road, Isleworth, Middlesex TW7 4RJ ☎ 020 8568 3509, 0956 409143 mob

HAWES Timothy *(Pic, N Tpt)*: 15 Cherington Gate, Pinkneys Green, Maidenhead, Berks SL6 6RU ☎ 01628 781094, 020 8549 1706

HAYNES Graham: 229 Grangehill Road, London SE9 1SS

HAYWARD Tim *(N Tpt, Pic, Flgl)*: 37 Chalk Cottages, Cray Road, Crockenhill, Kent BR8 8LP ☎ 020 8291 7434

HEADLEY Adrian: Flat 1, 73 Devonshire Road, Colliers Wood, London SW18 2EQ ☎ 020 8542 4081

HEALEY Derek *(Flgl, Cnt)*: 22 Cotsford Avenue, New Malden, Surrey KT3 5EU ☎ 020 8949 4201

HENDERSON Diane: 29 Egmont Road, Sutton, Surrey SM2 5JR ☎ 020 8643 1844

HENDRY David *(N Tpt)*: 5 Cowley Road, Mortlake, London SW14 8QD ☎ 020 8876 9149, 0802 974924

HENRY Michael *(Con, Flgl)*: 71 Lysia Street, London SW6 6NF ☎ 020 7381 3318, 0378 153114

HERBERT Nigel *(Flgl)*: 34 Glendale Road, Tadley, Hants RG26 4JN ☎ 01189 820901

HIGGS Paul *(Gtr, Pf)*: 91 Manor Road, Dagenham, Essex RM10 8BE ☎ 020 8517 5934

HIGHAM Robert *(Flgl)*: 6 Woolden House, 11 Connaught Avenue, London E4 7AF ☎ 020 8529 6594

HINCH John *(Flgl)*: 38 Belmont Close, Cockfosters, Herts EN4 9LT ☎ 020 8440 6227, 0402 253310

HINTON Michael *(Cnt, Flgl)*: 56 Nutfield Road, Coulsdon, Surrey CR3 3JN ☎ 020 8668 2784

HOBART Ted *(Flgl, Pictpt, Cnt)* ☎ 01462 433186, 0976 243368 mob

HOBBS Lesley: Upways, Long Lane, Ashcombe, Dawlish, Devon EX7 0QR ☎ 01626 864291

HODGKINS Chris: 41 Bedford Road, Ealing, London W13 0SP ☎ 020 8840 4643

HOGAN Ruth: Address Unknown ☎ 01708 764224

HOLLAND Chris *(Flgl)*: 9 Anthony Close, Billericay, Essex CM11 2QD ☎ 01277 624071

HOLLAND Matt *(Flgl, Per, Pf)*: 39 Colemans Moor Road, Woodley, Reading, Berks RG5 4DG ☎ 0118 954 0987, 0831 464346 mob

HOLMES James: Heather Cottage, 9 Tamar Mews, East Street, Bridport, Dorset DT6 3UL ☎ 01308 427 418

HOOK Christopher *(Cnt, Flgl)*: 57 Parkhill Road, Sidcup, Kent DA15 7NJ ☎ 020 8302 8137

HORN Christopher *(Flgl, Pictpt, N Tpt)*: 64 Greystead Road, Forest Hill, London SE23 6SD ☎ 020 7732 6696, 0973 889068, 01306 880669 day

HORNETT Michael *(Cop)*: 163 Friern Road, East Dulwich, London SE22 0AZ ☎ 020 8693 2548

HOSKINS Andrew: 10 Rheidol Terrace, London N1 8NT ☎ 020 7359 9955

HOSKINS Mark: 10 Rheidol Terrace, Islington, London N1 8NT ☎ 020 7359 9955

HOUGHTON William *(Cnt)*: Post Office Cottage, Ballinger Common, Gt Missenden, Bucks HP16 9LF ☎ 01494 837390

HOWARTH Elgar: 27 Cromwell Avenue, Highgate, London N6 5HN ☎ 020 8348 7800

HOWELL David *(Flgl)*: 20 Ewhurst Road, Crofton Park, London SE4 1AQ ☎ 020 8690 8415

HUCKRIDGE John *(Flgl, Cnt)*: 5 Oldfield Farm Gardens, Greenford, Middx UB6 8QA ☎ 020 8578 4186

HUDSON Roger(Butch): 19 Carrington Lane, Milford-on-Sea, Lymington, Hants SO41 0RA ☎ 01590 644225

HUGHES Ronnie *(Flgl)*: 144 Banstead Road, Ewell, Surrey KT17 3HN ☎ 020 8393 4834

HUMPHRIES Ronald *(Flgl, Cnt)*: 3 Cottage Close, Ruislip, Middlesex HA4 7JE ☎ 01895 638554

HUNT Derek: 175 Mortlake Road, Kew, Richmond, Surrey TW9 4AW ☎ 020 8878 8268

HUNT Ronald *(Flgl, Cnt)*: 10 Hermitage Close, Claygate, Surrey KT10 0HH ☎ 01372 463941

HURRELL Martin *(Cnt, Pictpt, Flgl, Con)*: 103 Salisbury Road, High Barnet, Herts EN5 4JL ☎ 020 8440 8746, 020 8449 5217

HURST David: 33 Broomfield Road, Bexleyheath, Kent DA6 7PD ☎ 01322 556827

HUTCHINS David *(Flgl)*: Bridge Cottage, Darenth Way, Shoreham, Sevenoaks, Kent TN14 7SE ☎ 01959 523305

HUTCHINSON Simon *(N Tpt)*: 45 Ashcombe Road, London SW19 8JP ☎ 020 8545 0876, 0958 288402

JACKSON Tim *(Flgl)*: 79 Nevill Road, Stoke Newington, London N16 0SU ☎ 020 7249 7872

JACOBS George: Address Unknown

JAMESON Frederick *(Vib)*: 15 Binns Road, Chiswick, London W4 2BS ☎ 020 8995 4274

JAYASINHA Paul *(Flgl, Cel, Synth)*: 11 Langbourne Way, Claygate, Surrey KT10 0DZ ☎ 01372 463 747, 0705 0037226

JENKINS Stuart *(Cnt, Flgl, Pictpt)*: 3 Torr Road, Penge, London SE20 7PS ☎ 020 8776 8127, 0973 796784

JENNER Stephen: 5 Brockwell Shott, Walkern, Nr Stevenage, Herts SG2 7PJ ☎ 01438 861400

JOHNSON Ron: 5 Longlands Avenue, Coulsdon, Surrey CR5 2QY ☎ 020 8660 5219

JONES Matthew (*Gtr*): 34 Little Gaynes Lane, Upminster, Essex RM14 2JJ ☎ 01708 223508

JONES Philip: 14 Hamilton Terrace, London NW8 9UG ☎ 020 7286 9155

JONES Richard: Valerian, Ravenslea Road, London SW12 8SB ☎ 020 8673 5589

JONES Stephen ☎ 0976 391556, 020 7813 9815

JORDAN Marc: Golf Lodge, 55 Hichisson Road, London SE15 3AN ☎ 020 7639 4078, 0956 423 487 mob

KEAVY Stephen: 4 Ludlow Drive, Thame, Oxfordshire OX9 3XS ☎ 01844 261384

KELLER Lesley: 8 Hampton Rise, Kenton, Middlesex HA3 0SB ☎ 020 8933 1228, 0421 610624 mob

KELLY Lance (*Flgl*): 129 Lancaster Road, East Barnet, Herts EN4 8AJ ☎ 020 8441 8005, 0976 263766 mob

KENWORTHY James (*Pf, Gtr*): 154 Malpas Road, Brockley, London SE4 1DH ☎ 020 8691 6211

KEOGH Steven: 151 Camborne Road, Morden, Surrey SM4 4JN ☎ 020 8395 6142

KERBY Philip: 35 Wandle Bank, South Wimbledon, London SW19 1DW ☎ 020 8543 4429

KILBORN Inigo (*Cnt, Flgl*): 6 Rue Galilee, 83610 Collobrieres, France ☎ +33 494 48 07 09

KING Tony (*Flgl, B Ldr*): 15 Haven Close, Istead Rise, Northfleet, Kent DA13 9JR ☎ 0147 483 2604

KLUBBEN Kristine: 6A Bowl Court, Plough Yard, London EC2A 3LJ ☎ 020 7247 0683, 020 7375 3233

LACEY Paul: The Croft, Lamberhurst Down, Lamberhurst, Kent TN3 8HD ☎ 01892 890 039

LAIRD Michael (*Bq Tpt, Cntt Zin*): 4 Hunter Road, Wimbledon, London SW20 8NZ ☎ 020 8946 2700, 01306 880669 day

LANGLEY Noel (*Flgl, Arr*): 21 Poets Road, Upper Flat, London N5 2SL ☎ 020 7226 3011, 0976 267507

LAW James: 160 Rectory Road, Little Thurrock, Grays, Essex RM17 5SJ ☎ 01375 370808

LAW Mark (*Pictpt, Cnt, Flgl*): 6A St James Street, Walthamstow, London E17 7PF ☎ 020 8520 8619, 0976 820749 mob

LAWRENCE Phillip: Addiscombe, 10 Empress Ave, Aldersbrook, Wanstend E12 5ES ☎ 020 8518 8629 & fax, 0956 275554 mob

LEE Christopher (*St Pan*): 46 Ferndale Road, Leytonstone, London E11 3DN ☎ 020 8923 5021

LEE Jonathan (*Dms*): 1 Heathside Place, Epsom Downs, Surrey KT18 5TX ☎ 01737 355535, 0374 167352 mob

LEON Andreas (*Flt, Kbds, Com*): 17 Charlton Road, Edmonton N9 8HP ☎ 020 8804 3748

LEWINGTON Martyn: 8 Lorne Road, London E17 7PX ☎ 020 8509 1419, 0973 123040

LEWIS Alan (*Flgl*): 172 Landells Road, London SE22 9PP ☎ 020 8693 6811

LIDDIARD Giles (*N Tpt*): 21B Ommaney Road, New Cross, London SE14 5NS ☎ 020 7732 6696, 079718 39781

LINSLEY Adam (*Flgl, Cnt*): 68 Herne Hill, London SE24 9QP ☎ 020 7274 3375, 07970 924 421 mob

LLOYD Darren (*Flgl, Cnt*): 383A Holmesdale Road, South Norwood, London SE25 6PN ☎ 020 8653 4351, 0973 899132

LOPEZ VALLE Omar (*Flgl, Timb, Cong, Per*) ☎ 020 7373 6838, 0410 457 337

LORIMER Roddy (*Flgl*): 74 Dallinger Road, Lee, London SE2 0TH ☎ 020 8851 5736

LOVATT Michael (*Flgl*): 75 New Road, Brentford, Middx TW8 0NU ☎ 020 8560 2920, 0973 882701 mob, 01483 723644 day

LOWE Lindsey: 34 Albert Road, Finsbury Park, London N4 ☎ 020 7272 3248

LOWTHER Henry (*Flgl, Pictpt, Com, Arr*): 61 Springfield Avenue, Muswell Hill, London N10 3SX ☎ 020 8883 5005, 01306 880669

LUFF Harold (*Flgl, Db, Pst H*): 52 Chaucer Road, London E11 2RE ☎ 020 8989 5236

LUSHER David (*Mel*): 25 Markwells, Elsenham, Nr Bishops Stortford, Herts CM22 6LT ☎ 01279 812943

LYNCH James (*Pictpt, Flgl, Cnt*): Flat 4, 92 East Dulwich Road, London SE22 9AT ☎ 020 8299 4730, 0468 082535, 07070 713028

LYTTELTON Humphrey: Alyn Close, Barnet Road, Arkley, Herts EN5 3LJ ☎ 01883 742474

MABBETT Tony (*Flgl, Cnt*): 158 New Barn Street, Plaistow, London E13 8JW ☎ 020 7476 7417

MACDOMNIC John (*Cnt, Flgl, N Tpt*): 4 Bowls Close, Stanmore, Middlesex HA7 3LF ☎ 020 8954 4882

MACKIE Alistair: One Way Cottage, College Lane, Hook Heath, Woking, Surrey GU22 0HP ☎ 01483 760100

MACNICOL John: 90 Brondesbury Rd, London NW6 6RX ☎ 020 7624 8201

MACPHERSON Richard (*Flgl*): 12 Roskell Road, London SW15 1DS ☎ 020 8788 3576

MADDEN David: 29 Grove Manor Drive, Kingston 8, Jamaica, West Indies ☎ 809 925 4552

MALLETT Gavin (*Flgl, Cnt, Pic*): 58 Queen's Walk, South Ruislip, Middlesex HA4 0LU ☎ 020 8841 3116 & fax, 0468 078714 mob

MARCHANT David (*Hmca*): 8 Gilder Close, Luton, Beds LU3 4AX ☎ 01582 580815

MARSDEN Daniel (*Flgl*): 6 Beaconsfield Court, Beaconsfield Road, London N11 3AF ☎ 020 8361 1860, 0976 819 343

MARSDEN Karl (*Pf*): 89B Earlanger Road, New Cross, London SE14 5TQ ☎ 020 7639 0469

MASON David: Deepfield, Orley Farm Road, Harrow-on-the-Hill, Middlesex HA1 3PE ☎ 020 8864 9056

MASON John: Flat 7, 1 Edge Hill, London SW19 4LR ☎ 020 8946 6760

MAXWELL Edward: 5A Chilworth Court, Windlesham Grove, London SW19 6AL ☎ 020 8789 9560

MCANENEY Anne (*Flgl, Cnt*): Chantilly, Duton Hill, Nr Gt Dunmow, Essex CM6 2DZ ☎ 0467 830952 mob, 01306 880 669 day, 01371 870762

MCCALLUM David (*Cnt, Pictpt, Kbds*): 42 Victoria Road, Barnet, Herts EN4 9PF ☎ 020 8449 8944, 0976 237921 mob

MCCARTHY Patrick (*Pictpt, Cnt, Kbds*): 119 Shepherds Bush Road, London W6 7LP ☎ 0421 364356

MCDERMID Jason (*Flgl, Voc, Kbds, Arr*): 6 Heber Road, London SE22 9LA ☎ 0705 0054898

MCDONNELL Stephen (*Flgl*): 51 Thornhill Meadows, Celbridge, Co. Kildare, Ireland ☎ Dublin 593206

MCINTOSH Kaye: 119 St Johns Road, Cannock, Staffs WS11 3AG ☎ 01543 578142

MCLEVY John: c/o 41 Woodland Road, Maple Cross, Rickmansworth, Hertfordshire WD3 2ST

MCNAUGHTON Duncan: 17 Stockmore Street, Oxford OX4 1JT ☎ 01865 722 042, 0860 836595

MCQUATER Thomas: 68 Lynwood Road, London W5 1JG ☎ 020 8997 5840

MERCER Jean (*Tbn*): 96 Hitchin Road, Stotfold, Nr Hitchin, Herts SG5 4HT ☎ 0370 585132

MIAN David (*Pf*): 13A Ferme Park Road, London N4 4DS ☎ 020 8348 9776

MILLER Geoff (*Flgl, Vln, Cop*): 19 Sunnyfields Close, Rainham, Gillingham, Kent ME8 9HW ☎ 01634 371871

MILLER John: 31-D New North Road, London N1 6JB ☎ 020 7336 0179, 020 7336 0415 fax, 0973 786002 mob

MITCHELL Andrew: Wychcombe, Onslo Crescent, Woking, Surrey GU22 7AU ☎ 01483 832545, 07971 526471 mob

MOFFAT George (*Flgl, Cnt, Pst H, Vla*): 43 Albany Road, Enfield Wash, Middx EN3 5UB ☎ 020 8804 2693

MOISEY Avelia (*Flgl, Voc*): 48 Woodlands Park Road, Haringay, London N15 3RX ☎ 020 8800 7295

MONTGOMERY Ronald: 82 Sunningvale Avenue, Biggin Hill, Westerham, Kent TN16 3TT ☎ 01959 572049

MOORE Alan (*Flgl, Cnt*): 21 Cornwell Road, Old Windsor, Berks SL4 2RF ☎ 01753 856801

MOORE Colin: 29 Egmont Road, Sutton, Surrey SM2 5JR ☎ 020 8643 1844

MOORE Jeremy: 11A Nibthwaite Road, Harrow, Middlesex HA1 1TB ☎ 020 8861 6346

MOORE Kate *(Cnt, Flgl, Pictpt, N Tpt)*: 39 Clarence Road, Walthamstow, London E17 6AG ☎ 020 8531 5281, 0468 506021 mob, 01306 880669 day

MORGAN Don *(Flgl, Cop, B Ldr)*: I Manor Park, Oakworth, Keighley, West Yorkshire BD22 7PW ☎ 01535 645 804

MORRIS Sonny: 221 Waye Avenue, Cranford, Hounslow, Middlesex TW5 9SJ ☎ 020 8759 0367

MOURANT Paul *(N Tpt)*: Berry House, 13 Berry Green Road, Finedon, Northamptonshire NN9 5JL ☎ 01933 682 064, 0850 066 885 mob

MOXON Peter: 4 Beehive Close, Uxbridge, Middx UB10 9QP ☎ 01895 252338

MUNDEN David *(Cnt)*: 12 Byron Court, Parkleys, Ham Common, Richmond, Surrey SW19 6PF ☎ 020 8546 5417, 01306 880669

MURPHY Maurice: 93 Birbeck Road, Mill Hill, London NW7 4BJ ☎ 020 8959 1372, 020 8906 9310 fax

MURRAY Gerry *(Flgl)*: 5 Brendon Gardens, South Harrow, Middlesex HA2 8NE ☎ 020 8422 4648

NEWELL Daniel *(Pf)*: Flat 1, 57 Christchurch Hill, Hampstead, London NW3 1JJ ☎ 020 7435 6935, 0966 198884

NEWTON Paul *(Flgl, Pictpt, N Tpt)*: 10 Connell Court, 13 Myers Lane, London SE14 5RZ ☎ 020 7732 6582, 0973 867107

NEWTON William: Ranworth, Church Road, Bulmer, Sudbury Suffolk CO10 7EL ☎ 01787 373451

NICHOLAS Robert *(Cnt)*: 162 Torridon Road, Catford, London SE6 1RD ☎ 020 8698 4215

NOCKLES Bruce *(Pf, Com)*: 108 Waller Road, New Cross, London SE14 5LU ☎ 020 7732 3067

NORRIS Noel *(Flgl)*: 45 Compayne Gardens, London NW6 3DB ☎ 020 7328 2314

ORCHARD Derek: 66 Radnor Avenue, Welling, Kent DA16 2BX ☎ 020 8304 2969

OSBORNE Robert: 113 Chestnut Avenue South, Walthamstow, London E17 9EJ ☎ 020 8520 2937

OSULLIVAN William *(Cnt, Flgl, N Tpt)*: 39 Common Lane, Harpenden, Herts AL5 5BT ☎ 01582 767195, 0802 435855 mob

OWEN Peter *(Cnt, Flgl, Pst H, Cnt)*: 25 Lonsdale Road, London SW13 9JP ☎ 020 8563 7775, 020 8563 7778 fax

PALMER Neil: 149 Merryhill Road, Bushey, Watford WD2 1DF ☎ 020 8950 1678

PARKER Phil: Mill House, Rowfant, Crawley, West Sussex RH10 4TB ☎ 01293 882226

PARKES Peter *(Flgl, Pf)*: 23 Laleham Road, Staines, Middlesex TW18 2DS ☎ 01784 455363

PATERSON Geo N *(Flgl, Arr, Voc)*: 39 Livingstone Road, Thornton Heath, Surrey CR7 8JX ☎ 020 8771 6911

PERIN Bernard: 17 Cranley Gardens, Palmers Green, London N13 4LT ☎ 020 8886 3003

PICKERING Philip: 26 Rambler Lane, Slough, Berks SL3 7RR ☎ 01753 538129

PICKLES John *(Cnt)*: 21 Barchester Road, Harrow Weald, Middlesex HA3 5HH ☎ 020 8427 4129

PICKSTOCK Stan: 24 Beach Drive, Penrhyn Bay, Llandudno, Gwynedd LL30 3PG ☎ 01492 540403

PIGRAM Christopher: 1 Railway Cottages, Holland Lane, Hurst Green, Surrey RH8 9AZ ☎ 01883 723072 & fax

PIKE Graham *(Pf, Voc)*: 1 Harrow Road, Ilford, Essex IG1 2XB ☎ 020 8527 2374

PLEWS David: 191A Streatfield Road, Harrow, Middx ☎ 020 8204 7497

POORE Julian *(Cnt)*: 37 Holbein Close, Black Dam, Basingstoke, Hants RG21 3EX ☎ 01256 467207 & fax, 020 8533 1372 day

POOTS Alexander: 55 Amber Road, London N4 2QS ☎ 020 7226 5090, 0973 361988, 020 7503 7525

PREECE Oliver *(Cnt, Flgl, Pictpt)*: 39 Sandlands Road, Walton-on-The Hill, Tadworth, Surrey KT20 7XB ☎ 01737 814831, 0973 262965 mob

PRICE David *(Cnt, Pic, Flgl)*: Bryanston School, Blandford Forum, Dorset ☎ 01258 484680, 0860 575075

PRICE David *(Flgl, Pictpt)*: 64 Mallock Road, Leyton, London E10 6DJ ☎ 020 8556 4313, 01523 110813 pager

PRISEMAN David *(Flgl, Dms)*: 132 Amhurst Road, London E8 2AG ☎ 020 7254 8447

PROSSER Stewart *(Flgl)*: 74 Arthur Road, Wimbledon, London SW19 7DS ☎ 020 8404 02994

RADFORD Jonathan: Sassoon Hall, Room S123, Trent Park, Cockfosters Road, Barnet, Herts EN4 0PT ☎ 020 8449 8540, 0976 702922 mob

RAE Colin *(Cnt, Flgl)*: 26 Colyton Road, London SE22 0NP ☎ 020 8693 3855, 0860 397797

RAMANAN Roland: 81 Nottingham Road, London E10 6EP ☎ 020 8558 9829

RANDALL Freddy: 1 Oakley Close, Teignmouth, Devon TQ14 8RX ☎ 01626 775154

RANKINE Brian *(Flgl, Cnt, Pic)*: 50 Clare Road, Prestwood, Gt. Missenden, Bucks HP16 0NS ☎ 01494 862072

REES-JONES Daniel *(B Gtr)*: 39 Slough Road, Datchet, Berks SL3 9AL ☎ 01758 581413, 07801 494454, 01753 581413

REEVE Peter *(Arr, Cop)*: Elder House, Ravensdowne, Berwick-upon-Tweed TD15 1DQ ☎ 01289 307533

REID Allan *(Flgl)*: 35 Harraden Road, London SE3 8BZ ☎ 020 8856 4573

REID Patricia: 124 Pepys Road, London SW20 8NY ☎ 020 8946 4009

REID Peter *(N Tpt)*: 220 Grasmere Ave, Wembley, Middlesex HA9 8TW ☎ 020 8904 3142, 0802 273 615

REVENS Philip: 15 East Ridgeway, Cuffley, Herts EN6 4AW ☎ 01707 875851

REYNOLDS George *(Cor)*: Knowles Cottage, Great Horkesley, Colchester, Essex CO6 4BU ☎ 01206271512

REYNOLDS Stanley *(Flgl)*: 3 Teazle Court, 16 Little Queens Road, Teddington, Middx TW11 0HP ☎ 020 8943 9823

RHIND-TUTT Mortimer *(N Tpt)*: Oldfield, Moor Road, Sutton Mallet, Somerset TA7 9AR ☎ 01278 723059, 0956 862926 mob

RICHES Edgar *(Cnt, Flgl)*: 28 Croham Park Avenue, Croydon, Surrey CR2 7HH ☎ 020 8680 1480

RICHMOND Joe: 16 Bushnell Road, Tooting Bec, London SW17 8QP ☎ 020 8673 2187

RICKARD Anthony *(Cop)*: Flat 4, 53 The Drive, Ilford, Essex IG1 3HD ☎ 020 8518 2816

RIGGS Nick *(Flgl, Cnt)*: 129 Union Street, Maidstone, Kent ME14 ☎ 01622 677800, 0585 141306

RINGHAM Paul *(Cnt)*: 2 Woodcroft Avenue, Mill Hill, London NW7 2AG, 01306 880669

RINGHAM Warren *(Cnt, Flgl)*: 40 Cherry Way, Shepperton, Middlesex TW17 8QF ☎ 01932 789841, 07930 364702

RIVA Andrew: 16 Lancaster Road, London W11 1QP ☎ 020 7221 4643

ROBINSON Kevin J *(Flgl, Kbds, Per)*: 45B The Grove, Biggin Hill, Westerham, Kent TN16 3TA ☎ 01959 571707 eve, 0976 401902 mob, 01959 572873 fax

RUDDOCK Gerald: 63 Lower Icknield Way, Chinnor, Oxon OX9 4EA ☎ 01844 352894, 01306 880669

RUDEFORTH Peter: 78 Jacksons Drive, Cheshunt, Herts EN7 6HW ☎ 01992 637180, 0589 434203 mob

RUSSELL Graham: 58 Grosvenor Avenue, Carshalton Beeches, Surrey SM5 3EW ☎ 020 8773 9901, 0860 283736 mob

RYAN Julie: 16 Vaughan Gardens, Ilford, Essex IG1 3NZ ☎ 020 8554 0182

SALMON Colin *(Dms, Per)*: 47 Barlby Road, N Kensington, London W10 6AW ☎ 020 8968 8889

SAMS Alison *(Flt)*: 103 Friern Barnet Road, London N11 3EU ☎ 020 8361 6470, 0976 432465 mob

SAMUEL Robert *(N Tpt)*: 11 Llwynhen Road, Cwmgors, Ammanford, Carns SA18 1RG, 0976 423984

SHADDOCK John: 30 Woodfield Drive, Gidea Park, Essex ☎ 01708 764224, 01306 880 669

SCOTT Jon: 19 Drakefell Road, London SE14 5SL ☎ 020 7639 8883 RM2 5DH

SHAKESPEARE John: 134 Tanbridge Park, Horsham, West Sussex RH12 1SF ☎ 01403 241785

SHAW Frederick (*Cnt*): 27 Clarendon Drive, Putney, London SW15 1AW ☎ 020 8788 2780

SHAW Martin (*Flgl, Pf*): 15 Burlington Road, Chiswick, London W4 4BQ ☎ 020 8994 7832

SHAW Michael (*N Tpt*): 21 Alconbury Road, London E5 8RG ☎ 020 8806 8705, 0958 522644 mob, 01306 880669 day

SHEARSMITH Paul: 7 Mornington Terrace, Camden, London NW1 7RR ☎ 020 7387 7962

SIDWELL Richard (*Flgl*): Ground Floor Flat, 233 Victoria Road, London N22 7XH ☎ 020 8889 9375, 0956 275954

SIDWELL Stephen (*Flgl, Cnt*): Hayling, 10 Crescent East, Hadley Wood, Barnet, Herts EN4 0EN ☎ 020 8441 4196, 020 8549 1706 day

SIMMONDS Ray: 27 Sandy Way, Walton-on-Thames, Surrey KT12 1BN ☎ 01932 223206

SIMMONS Ray (*Cnt, Flgl*): Mill Cottage, Uggeshall, Beccles, Suffolk NR34 8EN ☎ 01502 578316

SIMS Ken: 138 Sketty Road, Enfield, Middlesex EN1 3SQ ☎ 020 8363 5631

SINCLAIR Ken: 29 Oakland Park, Fforestfach, Swansea, West Glamorgan SA5 4BY ☎ 01792 581621

SKINNER John: 36 Chandos Road, East Finchley, London N2 9AP ☎ 020 8444 9958

SMART Nick (*Flgl, Cnt*): c/o 1 Dale Close, Toddington, Beds LU5 6EP ☎ 01525 872825, 0468 963508 mob

SMITH Colin: 42 Hillfield Road, London NW6 1PZ ☎ 020 7435 2499

SMITH Donald: Flat B, 38-44 Broadway Market, London E8 4QJ ☎ 020 7923 2567

SMITH Ian (*Flgl*) ☎ 020 8655 7124

SMITH John (*Cnt, Flgl*): 75 Marvels Lane, Grove Park, London SE12 9PH ☎ 020 8857 9384

SMITH Malcolm (*N Tpt, Flgl, Cnt*): Beech House, 6 Sydenham Park Road, London SE26 4ED ☎ 020 8291 5939, 020 8291 2205 fax

SMITH Neil (*Flgl, Cnt*): 14 Rubens Street, Catford, London SE6 4DH ☎ 020 8699 4458

SMITH Robin (*Flgl, Cnt*): 17 Crofton Gate Way, Crofton Park, London SE4 2DL ☎ 020 8691 7311, 0966 288989 mob

SMITH Ron (*Flgl*): 5 Stratton Close, Sutton Lane, Heston, Middx TW3 4JP ☎ 020 8570 6954

SMITH Simon (*Cnt, Pictpt*): 95 Meadway, Barnet, Herts EN5 5JZ ☎ 020 8449 8039

SNEDDON Robert (*Cop*): 55 Elmfield Way, Sanderstead, Surrey CR2 0EJ ☎ 020 8657 6950 fax, 0973 789894 mob

SNOW Barbara: 283 Holmesdale Road, London SE25 6PR ☎ 020 8653 1715

SPEED Paul: 24 Mallet Road, Hither Green, London SE13 6SP ☎ 020 8265 3789, 0976 269567 mob

SPENCE David (*Flgl*): 12 Chestnut Avenue, Forest Gate, London E7 0JH ☎ 020 8555 9629

SPENCER Ian (*Flgl*): 108 Hardy Road, Wimbledon, London SW19 1HZ ☎ 020 8543 3102

SPEYER Loz (*Flgl*): 26 Montague Road, London E8 2HW ☎ 020 7923 0943

SPIERS Andrew (*Flgl*): 105 Outlands Drive, Hinckley, Leicester LE10 0TN ☎ 01455 230615

STAFF Freddy (*Flgl, Arr*): 40 Milton Road, Ickenham, Middlesex UB10 8NJ ☎ 01895 672167

STEELE Donald (*Flgl*): 14 Hayesford Park Drive, Bromley, Kent BR2 9DB ☎ 020 8460 5952

STEELE-PERKINS Crispian (*Cnt, Pic, Flgl*): Random House, Sutton Place, Abinger Hammer, Nr.Dorking, Surrey RH5 6RN ☎ 01306 730 018, 01306 730013 fax

STEWART Stephen: 48 Albatross Street, London SE18 2SA ☎ 020 8854 4748, 0976 910241

STOKES William: Weathery Crook, Agden, Nr Malpas, Cheshire SY13 4RG ☎ 01948 666833, 01948 665 040

STREET Kevin (*Acc, Kbds, Md, Arr*): 221 Kent House Road, Beckenham, Kent BR3 1JZ ☎ 020 8776 6431, 0956 537802 mob

STUART Colin (*Flgl*): 139B Ashley Gardens, London SW1P 1HN ☎ 020 7834 7580

SUMMERS Mike (*Cnt, Pf, E Pf, B Ldr*): 45 Kilross Road, Bedfont, Feltham, Middlesex TW14 8SB ☎ 020 8893 1094

TEARLE Roderick: 5 Langley Hill, Kings Langley, Herts WD4 9HA ☎ 01923 264448

TEBBITT Jack: 9 Quinton Close, Wallington, Surrey SM6 7JZ ☎ 020 8647 1478

THOMAS Richard: 10 Kings Highway, Plumstead, London SE18 2NL

THOMAS Ruth Louise (*Pf, Flt*): 20A Castle Street, Kingston, Surrey KT1 1SS ☎ 020 8546 7590

THOMPSON Anthony David (*Pictpt, Cnt, Flgl, N Tpt*): Stonelea, Badsworth Court, Badsworth, Pontefract WF9 1NW ☎ 01977 645467, 0402 214210

THOMPSON Nicholas (*Cnt, Flgl*): 16 Kinch Grove, Wembley, Middlesex HA9 9TF ☎ 020 8904 0910, 01306 880669 day

THOMPSON William: 150 Englands Lane, Loughton, Essex IG10 2NS

THOMSON Brian: 15 Wynan Road, Isle Of Dogs, London E14 3AF ☎ 020 7987 9452 & fax, 0976 690621 mob

THORNTON Edward: 71 Noel Road, Acton, London W3 0JG ☎ 020 8992 9081

THORNTON Paul (*Pictpt, Flgl, Cnt, Pf*): 29 Cadogan Road, Surbiton, Surrey KT6 4DQ ☎ 020 8339 9220, 0468 241957 mob

THROWER Harold: 204 Markfield, Courtwood Lane, Forestdale, Croydon CR0 9HN ☎ 020 8651 2110

TOMASSO Enrico (*Flgl*): 443 Chiswick High Road, London W4 4AU ☎ 020 8995 3009

TRUMAN Gordon: 46 Peakview Road, Loudsley Green, Chesterfield, Derbyshire S40 4NN ☎ 01246 204104, 0976 266991

TUNNEY Luke (*Flgl, Kbds*): 76 Greenbank Road, Watford, Herts WD1 3JP ☎ 01923 239917

TURNER Joanne: 98 Chambers Lane, Willesden, London NW10 2RP ☎ 020 8459 3457, 01306 880 669 day

TWELFTREE Paul (*N Tpt, Cnt*): 2 Durham Row, Stepney, London E1 0NP ☎ 020 7790 3288, 01926 172833, 020 7790 3288

TYDEMAN Mark (*Flgl*): 46 Rosslyn Avenue, Dagenham, Essex RM8 1JP ☎ 020 8595 7139

VAUGHAN Brian (*Cop*): 1 Lovekyn Close, Kingston-on-Thames, Surrey KT2 6RY ☎ 020 8974 5602

VEASEY Terence (*Flgl, Hmca*): 38 Dacre Road, Hitchin, Herts SG5 1QJ ☎ 01462 421468

WALKER Alistair (*Voc*): 15 Swinford Gardens, Brixton, London SW9 7LG ☎ 020 7733 1302, 0973 834481 mob

WALKER David (*Flgl*): 154 Murchison Avenue, Bexley, Kent DA5 3LL ☎ 01322 528360

WALLACE John (*Arr, Com*) ☎ 020 7873 7302, 020 7873 7355 fax

WALLEN Byron (*Pf, Kbds*): 42 Commonwealth Way, London SE2 0JZ ☎ 020 8516 7633, 0961 306 627 mob

WALTON Bob (*Cnt*): Keeper's Cottage, Alciston, Near Polegate, Sussex BN26 6UH ☎ 01323 811517

WARD David (*Pic, Cnt, Flgl*): 22 Tudor Road, Hampton, Middlesex TW12 2NQ ☎ 020 8979 6318, 0973 738753, 01306 880669 day

WATERMAN Stephen (*Hrn*): 29 Valley Road, Henley-on-Thames, Oxfordshire RG9 1RL ☎ 01491 576180 & fax, 0831 564371 mob, 020 8549 1706 day

WATERSTON Douglas: 6A St James Street, Walthamstow, London E17 7PF ☎ 020 8520 8619, 0976 272474 mob

WATKINS Derek (*Flgl, Gtr, Cnt*): 17 St Leonards Road, Claygate, Esher, Surrey KT10 0EL ☎ 01372 467378, 01372 800681 fax

WATSON Ian (*Cnt, Gtr*): 14 Raleigh House, Albion Avenue, Stockwell SW8 2AF ☎ 020 7627 3583

WATSON James: 28 Cassiobury Park Avenue, Watford, Herts WD1 7LB ☎ 01923 234522

WEAVER Michael (*Flgl*): 38 Derwent Drive, Purley, Surrey CR2 1EQ ☎ 020 8660 7570

WEBB A (*Cnt*): 5 Wraysbury Road, Staines, Middlesex TW18 4TX ☎ 81 50171

WELLINGTON Canute *(Flgl, Kbds, Gtr)*: 87 Lewey House, Joseph St, London E3 4HW ☎ 020 8981 9487, 0956 476405

WELLS Matthew *(Dms, Pf)*: 14 Cameron Close, Myddelton Park, Whetstone, London N20 0HU ☎ 020 8446 9569, 0973 630927 mob

WHEELER Kenny: 141 Wallwood Road, Leytonstone, London E11 1AQ ☎ 020 8556 0639

WHELAN Stephen *(Flgl)*: 118A Wimbledon Hill Road, Wimbledon, London SW19 7QU ☎ 020 8946 6417

WHITE Barbara *(Flgl, Voc)*: 16 Bramley Crescent, Gants Hill, Ilford, Essex IG2 6DA ☎ 020 8554 7379, 020 8554 7378 fax

WHITE Kevin: 3 Derwent Grove, East Dulwich, London SE22 8DZ ☎ 020 8693 9678

WHITE Mark *(Flgl, Pictpt)*: 39A Quernmore Road, London N4 4QT ☎ 020 8347 5982, 0973 636652

WHITE Patrick *(Flgl)*: 61B Cranbrook Park, Wood Green, London N22 5NA ☎ 020 8881 1341, 0973 814940

WICKHAM Alan: 17 Beaufort Gardens, Ilford, Essex IG1 3DB ☎ 020 8518 5547

WILLIAMS Bryan *(Flgl, Clt, A Sax, Tbn)*: 45 Mascotts Close, London NW2 6NS ☎ 020 8450 2670

WILSON Allan *(Cntrc)*: 1 Northampton Road, Croydon, Surrey CR0 7HB ☎ 020 8656 4049

WILSON Iaan: 69 Leachcroft, Chalfont St. Peter, Gerrards Cross SL9 9LD ☎ 014945 80847, 0705 0107 573 mob

WILSON Jim *(Flgl)*: 27 Beech Grove, New Malden, Surrey KT3 3HR ☎ 020 8942 9399 & fax

WINSTON Henry *(Flgl)*: 1 Hillway, Highgate, London N6 6QB ☎ 020 8348 7210

WOOD David: 103 Vernon Crescent, East Barnet EN4 8QQ ☎ 020 8449 6749

WOOD Joanna *(Kbds)*: Flat 2, 66 Thicket Road, Penge, London SE20 8DR ☎ 020 8778 2216

WOODHEAD David *(Cnt)*: Flat B, 25 Sydenham Park, London SE26 ☎ 020 8291 5617

WOODS Stanley *(Pf, Com, Arr, Md)*: 150 Verulam Court, Woolmead Avenue, West Hendon, London NW9 7AW ☎ 01273 477053, 020 8202 0956

WOODWARD Adrian *(N Tpt, Cnt)*: 11 Jeymer Ave, Willesden Green, London NW2 4PJ ☎ 020 8452 7972, 0973 733997 mob

WRIGHT Dean: 4 Byron Place, Penarth, Cardiff

WRIGHT Leo: 35 Fencepiece Road, Barkingside, Essex IG6 2LY ☎ 020 8501 0998

WRIGHT Peter: 262 Haggerston Road, London E8 4EP ☎ 020 7241 3032, 01306 880669 day

WYNETTE Al *(Flgl)*: 77 Naylor Road, Whetstone, London N20 0HE ☎ 020 8445 5961

WYNTER Max *(Pf, Synth, Vln)*: Pulse House, 7A Palace Road, London N8 8QH ☎ 020 8341 4713, 0956 806184 mob

YOUNG John: Forres, 30 Wentworth Road, Barnet, Herts EN5 4NT ☎ 020 8449 6471, 0973 383017 mob, 01306 880669 day

YOUNG Neville *(Cop)*: 49 Muswell Avenue, London N10 2EH ☎ 020 8444 0499

TUBA

SCOTLAND

DOUGLAS Martin: The Whins, 33 Lower Breakish, Isle Of Skye, Inverness IV42 8QA ☎ 01426 282089

HORE Philip: 8, Drymen Place, Lenzie, Glasgow G66 5HL ☎ 0141 776 1798

MAGEE Francis: 36 Coolamber Drive, Rathcoole, Co. Dublin ☎ 00353 1 458 9413

MCKREEL Andrew: 3 Crum Crescent, St. Ninians, Stirling, Scotland FK7 0EX ☎ 01786 814934

MCSHANE Chris *(Eup, Sou)*: 41 Skaterigg Drive, Glasgow G13 1SR ☎ 0141 959 8319

SWAINSON Anthony: 96 Spiers Road, Glasgow G61 2LB ☎ 0141 563 7730

WALKER Thomas *(Voc)*: 586 Edinburgh Road, Carntyne, Glasgow G33 3QA ☎ 0141 764 1146, 0411 241194 mob

NORTH WEST

ANSTEE Ian: 21 Elmsett Close, Great Sankey, Warrington, Cheshire WA5 3RX ☎ 01925 729996, 0860 119299

BLAIR Sandy *(Con)*: 4 Diploma Drive, Middlewich, Cheshire CW10 9RA ☎ 01606 836132

BOOTH V Gerard: 18 Cheviot Close, Milnrow, Rochdale, Lancs OL16 3HH ☎ 01706 527101, 07970 700876

BREEN Ryan *(Pf)*: 10 Crummock Drive, Goose Green, Wigan WN3 6RX ☎ 01942 826055, 0976 538476 mob

CATTANACH Andrew *(B Tbn)*: Higher Nabs Head Farm, Nabs Head Lane, Samlesbury, Preston PR5 0UQ ☎ 01254 853941

DUNCAN Andrew: 31 Kearsley Road, Crumpsall, Manchester M8 4GH ☎ 0161 795 7118

GOLIGHTLY David Frederick *(Tbn, Kbds)*: 41 Parlklands Way, Poynton, Cheshire SK12 1AL ☎ 01625 875389

HAGGART Robin: 17 Colville Road, Wallasey, Merseyside L44 2AS ☎ 0151 513 6586, 0973 722141 mob

JOHNSON Michael *(Cimbasso, B Gtr)*: 62 Higher Croft, Barton, Eccles, Manchester M30 7ET ☎ 0161 281 2169, 0973 836858

KORNHAUSER David *(Serp)*: 13 Hanover Gardens, Salford M7 4FQ ☎ 0161 795 6785, 0705 098166, 0161 661 3205

MINSHALL Helen *(Sou, B Tbn, B Gtr)*: 11 Haweswater Avenue, Astley, Tyldesley, Manchester M29 7BL ☎ 01942 875626

REES Emyr *(B Gtr)*: 12 Lon Arfon, Caernarfon, Gwynedd LL55 2ER ☎ 01286 677140

WOODS Gavin: 57 Fields Road, Haslingden, Rossendale, Lancs BB4 6QA ☎ 01706 230208, 0468 360464 mob

NORTH EAST

DAVIES Paul: 23 Ansdell Road, Bentley, Doncaster, S Yorks DN5 0ET ☎ 01302 873716

GROSVENOR David *(Rec, Pf, Org)*: 98 Byland Avenue, Muncaster, York YO31 9AF ☎ 01904 656019

HALLAM John Carstairs *(Db, B Ldr, Arr, Bjo)*: 46 Belsay Avenue, Whitley Bay, Tyne & Wear NE25 8PZ ☎ 0191 252 3512

NESBITT David: 5 South View Otley, West Yorkshire LS21 1RZ ☎ 01943 467923

RAYNER Darryl *(Eup)*: Invicta, 9 Beagle Ridge Drive, Acomb, York YO24 3JH ☎ 0370 428958 mob, 01904 781519, 01904 331926

ROWELL Alan *(Pf, Kbds, Brass)*: 1 Argyle Terrace, Hexham, Northumberland NE46 1QB ☎ 01434 605676

SHAW Norman *(Db, B Gtr)*: 74 Swinnow Gardens, Bramley, Leeds LS13 4PQ ☎ 0113 2576213

WARRINER Andrew: 47 Ashworth Lane, Bolton, Lancs BL1 8RD ☎ 01204 303133

WHITAKER Andrew *(B Tba)*: 169 Longley, Huddersfield HD5 8LB ☎ 01484 431855

EAST

FITZHUGH Kenneth: 109 Beechfield Road, Hemel Hempstead, Herts HP1 1PH ☎ 01442 65657

NORMAN Robin: 32 The Beeches, Out Risbygate, Bury St Edmunds, Suffolk IP33 3RD ☎ 01284 705362, 0467 373254 mob

MIDLANDS

BANKS Ronald *(Tpt, Tbn, Clt)*: 49 Wetherel Road, Buton-on-Trent, Staffordshire DE15 9GW

BIRNIE Stuart *(Eup, Pf, Serp)*: 15 Bordeaux Close, Milking Bank, Dudley, West Midlands DY1 2UY ☎ 01384 252052

EVANS Christopher: 7 Longden Gardens, Belle View, Shrewsbury SY3 7EG ☎ 01663 743298

HALL Matthew P: c/o M Kyriakou, Rheindahlen Music Centre, Windsor School, Bfpo 40 ☎ +49 2434 24328 & fax

HODKIN Jon: PO Box 13, Ashbourne, Derbyshire DE6 1NR ☎ 01335 361087

INGLIS Alan: 16 Barrie Avenue, Kidderminster, Worcestershire DY10 3QN ☎ 01562 820 737, 0976 283 654 mob, 01562 820 737

MATTHEWS Philip *(Pf, B Gtr)*: 30 Launceston Close, Park Hall, Walsall, West Midlands WS5 3EG ☎ 01922 31022

PAWLUK Ronnie: 46 Hazelmere Road, Hall Green, Birmingham B28 8HZ ☎ 0121 604 5488

ROBERTS Simon: 52 Westfield Road, Kings Heath, Birmingham B14 7ST ☎ 0121 444 4624, 0966 193 418 mob

SANDLAND Richard: The Lilac Time, 68, Sion Hill, Broadwaters, Kidderminster, Worcs. DY10 2XS ☎ 01562 515403

SMITH George: 163 Barnby Gate, Newark, Notts NG24 1RJ ☎ 01636 671639

SNEADE Colin: 15 Welbeck Gardens, Toton Beeston, Nottingham NG9 6JD ☎ 0115 972 5600

SOUTH EAST

CRANHAM Christopher: 67A Coniston Road, Kempshott, Basingstoke, Hants RG22 5HT ☎ 01256 476083, 01256 476083

MOORE Geoffrey (*Eup*): 60 Springfield Road, Guildford, Surrey GU1 4DP ☎ 01483 304 399, 0956 207764 mob

MUTTER David (*Cel*): 27 Tile Kiln Hill, Blean, Canterbury, Kent CT2 9EE ☎ 01227 457089

PROUD Edward: 82 Frensham Road, Frensham, Surrey GU10 3AQ ☎ 01483 259691 day, 01252 794262 eve

SIMMONS Cathy (*Sax*): 6 Steadman Court, 165 Old Street, London EC1V 9ND ☎ 020 7251 2667, 0973 861280

THORNE Andrew: 16 Ivy Close, St Leonards, Ringwood, Hampshire BH24 2QZ ☎ 01425 475872, 01202 317331 & fax

WILKINSON Peter: 24 Gainsborough Road, Bournemouth BH7 7BD ☎ 01202 397351

SOUTH WEST

ALEXANDER Eilir: 88 Heol Giedd, Cwmgiedd, Ystradgynlais, Swansea SA9 1LS ☎ 01639 843669

DAVIS Stephen (*B Gtr*): 28A Moira Terrace, Adamsdown, Cardiff CF2 1EJ ☎ 029 2048 0710

HUDSON David: 45 Southdown Road, Bath, Avon BA2 1HJ ☎ 01225 444282

HUMPHRIES Shaun (*B Tbn, Kbds*): 4 Hertford Close, Walcot East, Swindon SN3 3AU ☎ 01793 611730

LAMMIN Lee (*B Gtr, Db*): 75 Kemble Drive, Cirencester, Gloucestershire GL7 1WZ ☎ 01285 655417

MCCURRIE Peter (*B Gtr*): Vinstone Cottage, 212 Mannameud Road, Hartley, Plymouth PL3 5RF ☎ 01752 783520

O'NEILL Sean: 6 Springfield Lane, Parklands, Rhiwderin, Newport Gwent NP1 9QZ ☎ 01633 894390

SEAMAN Nigel: The Old Stables, Crowfield Court, Llantillio Pertholey, Abergavenny, Gwent NP7 8NH ☎ 01873 852061

SHERRY Jo (*Eup*): 37 Bronhaul, Pentyrch, Cardiff CF4 8TA ☎ 029 2089 2161, 0113 2302273

THISTLEWOOD Matthew: 2 Richard Lewis Close, Llandaff, Cardiff CF5 2TB ☎ 029 2056 0141, 0976 723157 mob

LONDON

BEAL Michael: 112 Ashgrove Road, Goodmayes, Ilford, Essex IG3 9XD ☎ 020 8599 1593

BEVAN Clifford (*Eup, Tbn, Com, Arr*): 10 Clifton Terrace, Winchester, Hants SO22 5BJ ☎ 01962 864755, 020 7724 3250

DANIEL Mike (*B Tba, Sou, Eup, B Tbn*): 84 Brockenhurst Avenue, Worcester Park, Surrey KT4 7RF ☎ 020 8337 1646, 0374 112778 mob

DOHERTY James: Pleasant Lodge, 4 Mount Pleasant, Guildford, Surrey GU2 5HZ ☎ 01483 570772

EASENER Marc (*Eup*): 18 Fraser Close, Laindon West, Essex SS15 6SU ☎ 01268 546194, 0966 518399 mob

ELLIOTT John (*Sou, Db, Didj, Oph*): 223 Manor Lane, Lee, London SE12 0TZ ☎ 020 8851 6482, 01306 880669 day

FARR Paul: 446 Streatham High Road, London SW16 3PX ☎ 020 8679 4368, 0958 739326

FOX Richard: 40A Parkland Grove, Ashford, Middlesex TW15 2JR ☎ 01784 252388, 0956 431768 mob

GOULDING Ron (*Sou*): Oakridge, Knatts Valley, Sevenoaks, Kent TN15 6XY ☎ 01474 853855

GRAHAM Roger (*Eup, Pf*): 100 Lanes Avenue, Northfleet, Kent DA11 7HS ☎ 01474 355520, 0976 789049 mob

HALLIDAY Richard (*Oph*): 52 Pymers Mead, West Dulwich, London SE21 8NH ☎ 020 8244 5036, 0973 956 079, 020 8244 5036

HARRILD Patrick: 80 Honor Oak Road, London SE23 3RR ☎ 020 8699 2526, 020 8549 1706

HASSAN Joseph: 20 Halons Road, London SE9 5BS ☎ 020 8859 8530, 0973 833482

HEWINS Thomas (*Db, B Gtr*): 82 Roding Road, Hackney, London E5 0DS ☎ 020 8533 2314, 0973 460975, 07970 506378

HITCHENS Nicholas: 43 Cowley Road, Ilford, Essex IG1 3JL ☎ 020 8518 2304

IRVINE Nigel (*B Tba, Db*): 89 Strathdon Drive, Tooting, London SW17 0PR ☎ 020 8946 5349, 0860 683140

IZOD Joseph: Highway House, Main Road, Stickney, Boston Lincolnshire PE22 8AY ☎ 01205 480440, 0468 513738

JARVIS Martin (*Eup, Hrn, Tbn*): 50 Spencer Road, Wealdstone, Harrow, Middlesex HA3 7AR ☎ 020 8427 0411, 020 8533 1372

JENKINS John: 30 The Squirrels, Bushey, Watford, Herts WD2 3RT ☎ 020 8386 1097

JONES Huw (*Eup*): 25 The Mead, Carpenders Park, Watford, Herts WD1 5BX ☎ 020 8428 8876, 0973 418559

KNOWLES Martin: 2 Amiens Place, Bath Road, Paulton, Somerset BS39 7PB ☎ 01306 500022 day, 0374 729163 mob

LAWRENCE Paul (*Eup, Tbn*): 30 The Avenue, Radlett, Herts WD7 7DW ☎ 01923 855108

LOFTUS David: 72 Nelson Road, Whitton, Twickenham, Middx TW2 7AU ☎ 020 8898 5509 & fax, 0378 401942 mob

MARSHALL Oren (*Rec, Sou, Per, Rec*): 40 Springbank Road, London SE13 6SN ☎ 020 8318 9607

MARTIN Andrew (*Db*): 139 Mutton Lane, Potters Bar, Herts EN6 2HD ☎ 01707 655231

MASON Benjamin (*Tbn, Pf*): 20 Plantagenet Road, New Barnet EN5 5JG ☎ 020 8441 5983

MILLER Jeffrey (*C B Tbn, B Tbn*): 17 Mitford Buildings, Dawes Road, London SW6 7EW ☎ 020 7381 6160

MORGAN Kevin (*Eup*): 24 St Albans Avenue, Chiswick, London W4 5JP ☎ 020 8994 3086

MUSSETT Andrew: 92 Abbey Street, Faversham, Kent ME13 7BH

OWEN John (*Bjo, Gtr*): 9 Shortgate, London N12 7JP ☎ 020 8445 6732

PEARCE Andrew (*Vln*): 56A Church Road, London SE19 2EZ ☎ 020 8768 0062 & fax

POWELL David (*Sou, Serp*): 62 Sharsted Street, London SE17 3TN ☎ 020 7587 1324, 01306 880669

REECE Alf (*B Tbn, Eup*): Flat 29, Beech Spinney, Lorne Road, Warley Hill, Brentwood, Essex CM14 5HH

SIBLEY Graham (*Cimbasso*): 41 Brockhurst Road, Chesham, Bucks HP5 3JB ☎ 01494 792684, 01306 500022 day, 0976 721554 mob

SLADE Owen: 22 Boston Manor Road, Brentford, Middlesex TW8 8DR ☎ 020 8568 5333, 01306 880669

SMITH Matthew (*Pf*): Flat 1, 57 Christchurch Hill, Hampstead, London NW3 1SS ☎ 020 7435 6935, 0958 439 440

SMITH Paul (*Pf*): 63 Cardy Road, Boxmoor, Hemel Hempstead, Herts HP1 1SQ ☎ 01442 214400

TSARMAKLIS Eleftherios: 40A Cranley Gardens, London N13 4LS ☎ 020 8447 9227, 0966 486803, 020 8447 9229

WALL Ashley: Kingsley Cottage, Little Mill, East Peckham, Tonbridge Kent TN12 5JP ☎ 01622 871978

WASSELL Steven (*Eup*): 4 Hatch Lane, Chartham Hatch, Nr Canterbury, Kent CT4 7LP ☎ 01227 738518

WICK Stephen (*Cimbasso, Oph, Serp*): 22 Methuen Park, Muswell Hill, London N10 2JS ☎ 020 8442 0589, 0973 119762 mob, 020 8482 5399 fax

TUMBI

MIDLANDS

SINGH Malkit (*Harm*): 65 Cross Ways Lane, Kingstanding, Birmingham B44 8DL ☎ 0121 356 6649, 0831 261375

TYMPANI

SCOTLAND

CORBETT Heather (*Per, Cimb, Pf*): 33 Faskally Avenue, Bishopbriggs, Glasgow G64 3PJ ☎ 0141 772 3152, 07050 168772 mob, 0141 772 3152 fax

DONALDSON Ruari (*Per, Pf*): 84 Iona Way, Kirkintilloch G66 3PY ☎ 0141 776 3336, 0860 940442

EVANS Peter (*Timb*): 17 Duncrub Drive, Bishopbriggs, Glasgow G64 2EP ☎ 0141 563 0076

GIBSON Martin: 9 School Wynd, Kinross, Scotland KY13 7EJ ☎ 0411 834886

GUNNEE Dorothy (*Per*): 14 Penryn Gardens, Mount Vernon, Glasgow G32 9NY ☎ 0141 778 4458

JOHN Isabel (*Per*): Awel-Y-Mor, Alvah Terrace, Banff, Aberdeenshire AB45 1BG ☎ 01261 815121

NAISH Sarah (*Per*): 51 Lauderdale Street, Edinburgh EH9 1DE ☎ 0131 447 2068, 07050 154853 mob

NEWLAND Leslie (*Sax*): Bruce Buildings, West Port, Falkland, Fife KY7 7BL ☎ 01337 57199

OVERTON Chris (*Per*): Gardeners Cottage, Home Farm, Kemnay, Aberdeenshire AB51 5LH ☎ 01467 643 041

POULTER John (*Per*): Flat 0/1, 54 Carnarvon Street, Glasgow G3 6HP ☎ 0141 332 7940, 07957 871078

ROACH Simon (*Per, Dms, La Per*): 10 Kildrumme Court, 96 Buccleuch Court, Glasgow G3 6DY ☎ 0141 331 1729, 07654 575081 pager

SANDILANDS Iain (*Per*): 28 Cameron Avenue, Bishopton, Renfrewshire, Scotland PA7 5ES ☎ 01505 862411, 01523 728257

NORTH WEST

CERVENKA Edward (*Per, Cimb*): 30 Wyverne Road, Chorlton-Lym-Hardy, Manchester M21 0ZN ☎ 0161 881 4314, 0976 710175 mob

FORGRIEVE Ian (*Per, Cimb*): 27 Boothstown Drive, Worsley, Manchester M28 1UF ☎ 0161 799 6437, 0973 548588

HERBERT Jonathan (*Per*): 67 Dean Drive, Wilmslow, Cheshire SK9 2EY ☎ 01625 535378

HOOD Ian (*Per*): 21 Southern Crescent, Bramhall, Stockport, Cheshire SK7 3AQ ☎ 0161 439 2410

HUNT Jayne (*Per, Flt, Dms, Pf*): Flat 4, 17 Sandon Street, Liverpool L8 7NS ☎ 0151 512 5797

HYDE Jill (*Pf, Per, Md, Rep*): 15 Crondall Grove, Liverpool L15 6XD ☎ 0151 722 37541, 0151 738 0260

LOMAX Raymond (*Per, Md, Con*): 23 The Moorings, Middlewich, Cheshire CW10 9ER ☎ 01606 836292, 07887 556916

MOATE John (*Per*): 2 Oak Drive, Denton, Manchester M34 2JS ☎ 0161 337 9243

PEADAR (*Per, Vln, Clt*): Flat 2, 8 Mayfield Rd, Whalley Range, Manchester M16 8FT ☎ 0161 232 9315, 0421 366376 mob

WEBSTER Jean (*Per*): 56 Meadow Road, Newton, West Kirby, Wirral Cheshire L48 9XL ☎ 0151 625 5307

WILLIAMS Timothy (*Per*): 57 Ingleton Road, Edgeley, Stockport, Cheshire SK3 9NN ☎ 0161 480 5922

WOOD Sarah (*Per*): 2 Wycombe Drive, Astley, Tydlesly, Manchester M29 7BX ☎ 01942 892222

WOOLLISCROFT Eric (*Per*)

WRIGHT Ian (*Per*): 10 Chalkwell Drive, Barnston, Wirral, Merseyside L60 2UE ☎ 0151 342 1852

NORTH EAST

BANISTER John (*Per, Pf, Vln*): 11 Boston Place, Lower Boston Road, Hanwell, London W7 3UA ☎ 0385 731446

BRADLEY Christopher (*Per, Cimb*): Upper Red Brink Farm, Red Brink Lane, Hubberton, Halifax HX6 1PA ☎ 01422 839700

FULTON Janet (*Per, Pf*): Ivy House, Coxwold, York YO61 4AD ☎ 01347 868385

HALL Graham (*Per*): 48 King Street, Pinxton, Nottingham NG16 6NL ☎ 01773 810273

HILL Sally (*Per*): 129 York Road, Tadcaster LS24 8AU ☎ 01937 531545

JACKSON Heather (*Dms, Per*): Jacksonville, Kingsway Moorgate, Rotherham, South Yorkshire S60 3AU ☎ 01709 369189, 0585 809976 mob

KINDLEYSIDES Judy (*Per, Vln*): 185, Scalby Road, Scarborough, North Yorkshire YO12 6TB ☎ 01723 371 765

O'SULLIVAN Marney (*Per, Kbds*): 4 Pasture Crescent, Chapel Allerton, Leeds LS7 4QS ☎ 0113 2697936

EAST

BEUTTLER Francis (*Per*): 32 Long Plough, Aston Clinton, Aylesbury, Bucks HP22 5HB ☎ 01296 631787

PICKFORD James (*Per*): Strathmore, 78A Nightingale Rd, Rickmansworth, Herts WD3 2BT ☎ 01923 720616

TAIT Richard (*Tnd Per, Cong*): 8 Barry Close, Chiswell Green, St Albans, Herts AL2 3HN ☎ 01727 872487, 01306 500022 day, 01426 211811 pager

MIDLANDS

DAVIS Mary (*Per*): 2, Treetops, Carhampton, Minehead, Somerset TA24 6LP ☎ 01643 821075

FOWKES Chris (*Per*): 27 Littlewoods, Hunt End, Redditch, Worcs B97 5LF ☎ 01527 545211

HILL Peter (*Per*): 38, Springfield Glade, Malvern, Worcs WR14 1LN ☎ 01684 892266

HOOD James (*Per, Dms*): Flat 5, 6 Avenue Road, Compton, Wolverhampton WV3 9JR ☎ 01902 427783

MARSDEN Jennifer (*Per, Xyl, Pf*): 38 Red Lion Street, Alvechurch, Worcs B48 7LF ☎ 0121 4456131, 0121 4477390 fax

NICKLIN Christine (*Per, Pf*): 20 Arnos Grove, Nuthall, Nottingham NG16 1AQ

PARKER Norman (*Vib, Xyl*): 1 Corbett Road, Hollywood, Wythall, West Midlands B47 5LL ☎ 0121 430 6643

PERRY Matthew (*Per*): 3, Lovell Close, Selly Oak, Birmingham B29 4LH ☎ 0121 604 2119, 0421 067803 mob, 020 8444 6725

SHEPPARD Janet (*Per*): 28 Hampton Avenue, Fringe Green, Bromsgrove, Worcs B60 2AL ☎ 01527 872239

STREBING James (*Per, Dms*): 25 Grove Avenue, Moseley, Birmingham B13 9RU ☎ 0121 449 4677

THOMAS Huw (*Per*): 26 Coton Grove, Solihull Lodge, Shirley, Solihull B90 1BS ☎ 0121 430 3570

SOUTH EAST

DAY Shirley (*Per*): 51 Great Close Road, Yarnton, Oxford OX5 1QN ☎ 018675 5526

LAWRENCE Arthur (*Per*): New Cottage, Manor Road, Towersey, Nr Thame Oxon OX9 3QS ☎ 0184 421 4756

LAWRENCE Susan (*Per*): New Cottage, Manor Road, Towersey, Nr Thame Oxon OX9 3QS ☎ 0184 421 4756

PARIKIAN Levon (*Per*): Address Unknown

SOUTH WEST

BARNARD Steven (*Per*): Flat 5, 91 Cathedral Road, Cardiff CF1 9PG ☎ 029 2066 8399, 0410 212838

CHALKLIN Paul (*Per, Clst*): Southern Cross, The Ridgeway, Chiseldon, Wilts SN4 0HT ☎ 01793 740132

FOWLER Harry (*Per, Dms*): 18 Ninian Road Top Flat, Roath, Cardiff CF2 5EF ☎ 029 2049 2134, 0411 808 521

GIDDINGS John (*Per*): 23 Woodland Grove, Westbury-on-Trym, Bristol BS9 2BD ☎ 0117 9681315

HARRISON Giles (*Per*): Windmill Cottage, North Curry, Taunton TA3 6LY ☎ 01823 490498

HILEY Michelle (*Per*): Cedilla, 1 The Old Smithy, Cockwood, Dawlish, Exeter EX6 8RA ☎ 01626 890676

JONES Michael (*Per*): 15 Bernard Street, Uplands, Swansea SA2 0HU ☎ 01792 250756

LITTLE Jeremy (*Per*): The Green, Temple Cloud, Somerset BS39 5BW ☎ 01761 452812

SARGEANT Kim (*Per*): 69 Warden Hill Road, Cheltenham, Glos GL51 5EE ☎ 01242 236782

SEACOME Diggory (*Per*): 7A Queens Parade, Cheltenham, Glos GL50 3BB ☎ 01242 230794

STOCK Christopher (*Per*): 16 Southcourt Road, Penylan, Cardiff CF23 9DA ☎ 029 2049 7754

WALKER Mark (*Per*): 2 Kings Road, Radyr, Cardiff CF4 8EB ☎ 029 2084 4002

LONDON

APPLEWHITE Joe (*Per, Dms, La Per*): 60 Heath Hurst Road, Sanderstead, Surrey CR2 0BA ☎ 020 8657 1039

BENDING Adrian (*Per, Bq Tym*): ☎ 020 8579 9834, 01306 500022 day, 07669 006333 pager

BLUNDELL Christopher (*Per, Dms, Pf*): 5 Mornington Close, Biggin Hill, Kent TN16 3UL ☎ 01959 570237, 01306 880669

BOOTH Brian (*Per, Dms*): 40 Butterfield Road, Wheathampstead, Herts AL4 8QH ☎ 01582 832425, 01582 629484

BYWATER Scott (*Per, Dms*): 8 Millfield Road, Edgware, Middx HA8 0DJ ☎ 020 8952 7890, 01306 500022 day

CHIMES John (*Per*): Hunters Rest, Weedon Hill, Hyde Heath, Amersham Bucks HP6 5RN ☎ 01494 786701, 01494 771208

COLE Nicholas (*Per*): 110 Norfolk House Road, London SW16 1JH ☎ 020 8769 0722 & fax

COLLIS E.Anne (*Per*): Dragon Lodge, Jumps Road, Churt, Nr Farnham, Surrey GU10 2JY ☎ 01252 792315

CORNES Jeremy (*Per*): 33 St.Marks Road, Old Hanwell, London W7 2PN ☎ 020 8840 9437, 01306 880669

EYRE Kate (*Per*): 59 Snaresbrook Road, Wanstead, London E11 1PQ ☎ 020 8518 89820976 43, 01306 500022

GOEDICKE Kurt-Hans: 39 Harlyn Drive, Pinner, Middx HA5 2DF ☎ 020 8866 1845

GREENLEAVES Thomas (*Per*): 137 Barnes Wallis Court, Barnhill Road, Wembley, London HA9 9DP ☎ 020 8621 5166, 0973 666870, 01306 880 669

HACKETT Dominic (*Per*): Ground Floor Flat, 5 Hurstbourne Road, Forest Hill, London SE23 2AA ☎ 020 8699 7589, 01306 880669

HALL Anthony (*Per*): 15A Caversham Road, Kentish Town, London NW5 2DT ☎ 020 7267 4874

HIND Christopher (*Per*): 2 Stanmount Road, Chiswell Green, St Albans, Herts AL2 3AG ☎ 01727 843568 & fax, 01306 880669 day, 0973 183006 mob

HOCKINGS David (*Per*): Trelawney, 2 Hampden Close, Stoke Poges, Bucks SL2 4JF ☎ 01753 522850, 01753 573495 fax

HOFFNUNG Benedict (*Per*): The Old House, Market Place, Box, Wiltshire SN14 9NZ ☎ 01225 744320, 01306 880669

HORNE Richard (*Per*): 10 Mountain Ash Close, Hailsham, East Sussex BN27 3XN ☎ 01323 846508, 01306 880669 day

JORDAN Russell (*Per*): 35 Somerset Road, London W4 5DW ☎ 020 8747 3013

KESZEI Janos (*Per*): 6 Cottage Grounds, Upper Hartwell, Stone, Bucks HP17 8NQ ☎ 01296 748838, 0468 017189 mob

KING Grahame: 4 Mount Pleasant View, Dalmally Road, Croydon CR0 6LU ☎ 020 8654 3974, 01306 880669

LOCKHART William (*Per*): 86 Stanley Road, Bounds Green, London N11 2LG ☎ 020 8368 6441 & fax, 0973 185294 mob

LUCAS Tony (*Per*): 75 Vicarage Wood, Harlow, Essex CM20 3HG ☎ 01279 419637, 01306 880669, 0973 768484 mob

MCATOMINEY Aidan (*Per, Dms, Pf*): 69 Whitehouse Avenue, Borehamwood, Herts WD6 1HA ☎ 020 8953 7185

MCCUTCHEON John (*Per*): 7 Birchend Close, South Croydon, Surrey CR2 7DS ☎ 020 8681 7446, 0802 428161

MCDONAGH Gillian (*Per*): 47 Rosendale Road, West Dulwich, London SE21 8DY ☎ 020 8766 6164, 01306 880669

OWENS Martin (*Per, Flt*): 3 Molesford Road, Fulham, London SW6 4BU ☎ 020 7736 8520, 01306 880669

PERCY Neil (*Per*): 76 Ormond Ave, Hampton-on-Thames, Middx . TW12 2RX

PHILBERT Paul (*Per*): 42 Wood End Way, Northolt, Middx UB5 4QD ☎ 020 8426 9996, 020 8426 9996

READER Graham (*Per*): Mayleigh, 71 High Road, Ickenham, Uxbridge, Middlesex UB10 8HQ ☎ 01895 636541, 0831 829730 mob, 01895 678483

ROCKLIFFE John (*Per*): 122 Southridge Rise, Crowborough, East Sussex TN6 1LL ☎ 01892 653414, 0468 901329, 01892 653414

SMITH Andy (*Per*): The Acacias, 4 Higher Drive, Purley, Surrey CR8 2HE ☎ 020 8645 9459

SOUPER Richard (*Per*): 38A Dunsmure Road, Stamford Hill, London N16 5PW ☎ 020 8809 5518

STIRLING David (*Per*): 11A Montague Road, Dalston, London E8 2HN ☎ 020 7241 4689, 0956 574127

THOMAS Christopher (*Per*): 6 Wessex Court, West End Lane, Barnet, Herts EN5 2RA ☎ 020 8441 3096

TOLANSKY Jonathan (*Per*): 15 Matthew Arnold Close, Cobham, Surrey KT11 1JD ☎ 01932 860472 & fax

VALLIS Paul (*Per*): The Corn Exchange, 10 Forbury Road, Reading, Berks RG1 1SE ☎ 01189 512340

UILLEANN

SCOTLAND

HACKETT Liam: 10A Lefroy Street, Coatbridge, Lanarkshire, Scotland ML5 1PN ☎ 01236 428974

NORTH WEST

LIM David (*Rec*): 5 Hazel Avenue, Whalley Range, Manchester M16 8DY ☎ 0161 881 2796

MCGOLDRICK Michael (*Flt*): 8 Beechurst Close, Whalley Range, Manchester M16 8EP ☎ 0161 881 6896

NORTH EAST

DONOCKLEY Troy (*Gtr, Wh*): Ludhill Cottage, Warter, Pocklington, York YO4 2 1XW ☎ 01759 306657

EAST

O'GRADY James (*Vln, Wh*): 2 Havelock Rise, Luton, Bedfordshire LU2 7PS ☎ 01582 876583

MIDLANDS

CONCANNON Kieron (*Wh, Bod*): 15 Woodcote Road, Leamington Spa, Warks CV32 6PZ ☎ 01926 833460, 0385 544576, 01286 833460 fax

SOUTH EAST

CAMPBELL Dirk (*H Bag, Ney, Ne Wnd, Or Wnd*): Stoneywood Cottage, Greenwoods Lane, Punnetts Town, Nr Heathfield, East Sussex TN21 9HU ☎ 01435 830336

LONDON

FUREY Finbar (*Bjo, Flt, Wh, Gtr*): Banshee Music Ltd, 251 Moyville, Rathfarnham, Dublin 16, Eire ☎ 003531 4946271

MOLONEY Paddy (*Wh*): The Stores, Milltown Bridge, Dundrum Road, Dublin 14, Ireland ☎ +35 31 6674171, +35 31 6673920

SPILLANE Davy (*Wh, Gtr*): Cnocaobhinn, Luogh South, Liscannor, Co Clare, Ireland ☎ +35 65 81151

UKELELE

SCOTLAND

BAYNES Peter (*Pf, Kbds*): 24 Argyle Place, Edinburgh EH9 1JJ ☎ 0131 229 5675

EAST

DERRICK Jon (*Voc*): 4 Rosbrook Close, Bury St Edmunds, Suffolk IP33 3QP ☎ 01284 3308

MIDLANDS

LEWIS Luke (*Hmca*): The Grove, Manor Lane, Newnham Daventry, Northants NN11 3EU ☎ 01327 706737

SOUTH EAST

CROFTS David ☎ 0973 406984

LONDON

LUX Kitty *(Voc)*: 31A Larcom Street, London SE17 1NJ ☎ 020 7252 4096

VALVE TROMBONE

LONDON

BROWN Franklin *(Tba)*: 99 Hanworth House, London SE5 0XL ☎ 0403 678 243, 020 8655 2977, 020 8654 8787

MAYS Patsy *(Flgl, Mel)*: 93 Crown Woods Way, Eltham, London SE9 2NJ ☎ 020 8850 6943, 0831 255220 mob

PERROTTET Dave *(B Gtr, Sou, Arr, Com)*: 336 High Street, Berkhamsted, Herts HP4 1HT ☎ 01442 878377

VEENA

LONDON

SIVANESAN Sivanesan *(Voc)*: Flat A Basement, Barons Court House, Barons Court Road, London W14 9DS ☎ 020 7386 0924, 020 7381 8758 fax

VIBRAPHONE

NORTH WEST

GRESCH David *(Org)*: 58 Hereford Street, Werneth, Oldham, Lancs OL9 7RE ☎ 0161 652 1872

EAST

PYNE Martin *(Dms, Per)*: 38 Strode Street, Egham, Surrey TW20 9BX ☎ 01784 438521

MIDLANDS

RANDALL Alan *(Uke, Bjo, Pf)*: 104 Hinckley Road, Nuneaton, Warkwickshire CV11 6LS ☎ 024 7638 2185, 024 7632 6720 fax

WALTON Harry *(Dms)*: 128 Westcotes Drive, Leicester LE3 0QS ☎ 0116 2548609

WEBBER Michael: Field View, Pages Lane, Hornton Nr Banbury, Oxon OX15 6BX ☎ 01295 87 552

WILKINS Peter *(Vib)*: 20 Ferrers Avenue, Tutbury, Nr Burton-on-Trent, Staffs DE13 9JR ☎ 01283 812423

WILLETS Colin *(Pf, B Ldr)*: 32 Marsh Lane, Hampton In Arden, Solihull, West Midlands B92 0AJ ☎ 01675 442585

SOUTH EAST

BLAIR Derek *(Pf)*: Croft, 3 Hackington Road, Tyler Hill, Canterbury, Kent CT2 9NF ☎ Canterbury 4713

JONES Dave *(Pf)*: 341 Kingsway, Hove, East Sussex BN3 4PD ☎ 01273 414559

SMART Tan *(Pf)*: 51 Maclean Road, Bournemouth, Dorset BH11 8EN ☎ 01202 577233

SOUTH WEST

DOUGLAS-STEWART Jim *(Kbds, Org, Gtr, B Gtr)*: The Cedars, 14 Newlands Avenue, Exmouth, Devon EX8 4AX ☎ 01395 222482/276869, 01395 222483 fax

LONDON

BALLANTINE Ian *(Per, Pf, Flt)*: 49A Victoria Crescent, Upper Norwood, London SE19 1AE ☎ 020 8761 1079

BEAUJOLAIS Roger *(Mrba, Xyl, Glck)*: Basement Flat, 12A Lower Clapton Road, London E5 0PD ☎ 020 8533 4178

BERESFORD Peter: 20 Reydon Avenue, Wanstead, London E11 2JD ☎ 020 8989 5551

CALLINGHAM Robin *(Pf, Kbds)*: 33 Sherwood Park Rd, Sutton, Surrey SM1 2SG ☎ 020 8642 2734

CROUCH Richard *(Pf, Per)*: 55 Wykeham Way, Haddenham, Bucks HP17 8BU ☎ 01844 291445

FORD Patrick *(Dms)*: 41, Grosvenor Avenue, Carshalton Beeches, Surrey SM5 3EJ ☎ 020 8647 8609

KERR Anthony *(Mrba)*: 3 Priory Walk, St. Albans, Hertfordshire AL1 2JA ☎ 01727 859400

LYLE Teena *(Cong, Per, Kbds, Voc)*: 6 Corrib Heights, 30 Crescent Road, London N8 8DA ☎ 020 8347 9997, 0802 157305

MANJA Captain *(Song W, Cong, Voc, Per)*: 20 Leicester House, Loughborough Estate, Loughborough Road, London SW9 7LN ☎ 020 7924 0217

MOULE Frank *(Voc, Kbds, Acc)*: 6 Metha Parc, Newlyn East, Near Newquay, Cornwall TA8 5LT ☎ 01872 510931

PALMER Poli *(Per, Kbds)*: 5 Munster Road, London SW6 4ER ☎ 020 7731 0481

SHADE Peter *(Acc)*: Water Hythe, Hampton Court Road, East Molesey, Surrey KT8 9BP ☎ 020 8941 3994

VIOLA

SCOTLAND

ALBURGER Mary *(Vla, Vln, Cop)*: New House, Ballachulish, Argyll PA39 4JR ☎ 01855 811507

AMON David *(Vla)*: 19 Burns-Begg Crescent, Balfron, Glasgow G63 0NR ☎ 01360 440 822

BEATTIE Alistair *(Vla)*: 113 Southbrae Drive, Glasgow G13 1TU ☎ 0141 402 5344, 0141 402 5346 fax

BEESTON Michael *(Vla)*: 119 Craigleith Road, Edinburgh EH4 2EH ☎ 0131 332 8691

BLASDALE Susan *(Vla)*: 3 Balvicar Street, Glasgow G42 8QF ☎ 0141 423 4099

BLUE John *(Vla)*: 30 Kensington Court, Kensington Road, Glasgow G12 9LQ ☎ 0141 339 1976

BUDD Ian *(Vla)*: 33 Teviot Avenue, Bishopbriggs, Glasgow G64 3NA ☎ 0141 563 1983 & fax

CAMPBELL Mairi *(Vla, Vln, Voc)*: 34 Prince Regent Street, Edinburgh EH6 4AT ☎ 0131 554 3092

CASSELLS Linda *(Vla)*: 43 Millview, Barrhead, Glasgow G78 1AN ☎ 0141 881 8985

CLARK Olwen *(Vla)*: 7 Kirkmichael Gardens, Hyndland, Glasgow G11 7QP ☎ 0141 357 4254

COOPER Veronica *(Vla, Vln, Pf, Hpsd)*: 10 Braid Avenue, Edinburgh EH10 6DR ☎ 0131 447 6359

CROSBIE Christine *(Vla)*: 29 Allan Road, Killearn G63 9QF ☎ 01360 551 173

CUTHBERTSON George *(Vla)*: 2/1 1032 Pollokshaws Rd, Glasgow, Scotland G41 2HG ☎ 0141 636 1773, 0468 565541 mob

DAVIS Rachel *(Vla)*: 158 Niddrie Road, Glasgow G42 8QP ☎ 0141 433 2715

DICK Emily *(Vla)*: 50 Kelvin Drive, Glasgow G20 8QN ☎ 0141 946 3069

DUNN Claire *(Vla)*: Glenview Cottage, 9 Neilston Road, Uplawmoor, Glasgow G78 4AB ☎ 01505 850506

DURRANT R *(Vla)*: 3 Victoria Circus, Glasgow G12 9LB ☎ 0141 334 4867

FIELD Patricia *(Vla)*: 30 Ancaster Drive, Anniesland, Glasgow G13 1NB ☎ 0141 959 1018

GALBRAITH Alexis *(Vla)*: 18 Ashgrove, Maybole, Ayrshire KA19 8BG ☎ 01655 883333

GALBRAITH Joanna *(Vla, Pf)*: 7 Langour, Devonside, Tillicoultry, Clackmannanshire FK13 6JG ☎ 01259 752350, 0370 898554 mob

GILLIES Alison *(Vla, Vln)*: 5 Wilton Drive, North Kelvinside, Glasgow G20 6RW ☎ 0141 402 1077

GREEN Jan *(Vla, Vln)*: Cedar Cottage, Aberfoyle Road, Balfron Station, Glasgow G63 0SQ ☎ Balfron 40701

HAGGART Kevin *(Vla)*: 2/1 Sinclair Close, Shandon Appartments, Edinburgh EH11 1US ☎ 0131 337 5560

HALL Yvonne *(Vla, Bq Vla, Vln)*: G/L 104 Glencoe Street, Anniesland, Glasgow G13 1YR ☎ 0141 954 9800

HAMILTON Claire *(Vla, Vln, Bq Vla, Bq Vln)*: 16 Kirkpatrick Street, Girvan, Ayrshire KA26 0AD

HAMILTON Joanna *(Vla, Voc, Gtr)*: Dos Mhucarain, Achanalt, By Garve, Ross Shire IV23 2QD ☎ 01445720 224

HARRINGTON John *(Vla, Vln, Pf)*: Deep Stones, Boquhan, Balfron, Nr Glasgow G63 0RW ☎ 01360 440619

HARRIS Susan *(Vla)*: 30 Ancaster Drive, Glasgow G13 1NB ☎ 0141 959 1018

HASTIE Alison *(Vla, Vln)*: 1 Lomond View Cottages, Westfield, Bathgate, West Lothian EH48 3DE ☎ 01506 652455

HUNTER Joel *(Vla)*: 58 Derwent Road, Honley, Huddersfield, W Yorks HD7 2EL ☎ 01484 663458

JOHNSON Simon *(Vla)*: 4 Oakbank Road, Earlston, Berwickshire TD4 6BL ☎ 01896 849311

KELL Bill *(Vla, Vln, Pf, Bod)*: 1/L No.4 South Park Avenue, Hillhead, Glasgow G12 8HY ☎ 0141 357 3660

KETTERINGHAM Charles *(Vla, Vln)*: Flat 1/R, 29 Havelock Street, Glasgow G11 5HA ☎ 0141 357 0893

LUCAS Alison *(Vla)*: 10 Featherhall, Crescent North, Edinburgh EH12 7TY ☎ 0131 334 1848

MACLEAN Gillian *(Vla, Vln, Pf)*: Flat 3, 385 Victoria Road, Glasgow G42 8RZ ☎ 0141 423 8776

MARTIN David *(Vla)*: 101 Broomhill Drive, Glasgow G11 7NA ☎ 0141 357 2685

MARX Julian *(Vla, Vln)*: 50 Gordon Road, Mannofield, Aberdeen AB15 7RL ☎ 01224 317458

MCCOLL Elizabeth *(Vla, Voc, Pf)*: 74/4 Leamington Terrace, Edinburgh, Scotland EH10 4JU ☎ 0131 622 0751

MCMURDO Stewart *(Vla)*: 46 Glamis Road, Kirriemuir, Angus DD8 5BU ☎ 01575 574704, 01698 816181

MCWHIRTER Nicola *(Vla)*: 9 Calderwood Road, Newlands, Glasgow G43 2RP ☎ 0141 637 3939

MIDGLEY Cynthia *(Vla)*: 10 Regent Terrace, Edinburgh EH7 5BN ☎ 0131 557 4783

MILLER Margaret *(Vla)*: Greenside, 7 Albert Place, Stirling FK8 2QL ☎ 01786 463163

NORMAN Heather *(Vla)*: Flat 2/1, 69 West End Park Street, Woodlands, Glasgow, Scotland G3 6LJ ☎ 0141 332 7466, 0374 224037 mob

PELLY Mysie *(Vla, Bq Vln)*: 7 Granton Park Avenue, Edinburgh EH5 1HS ☎ 0131 552 2068

PENFOLD Jacqui *(Vla)*: 3 Cawder Way, Carrickstone Meadows, Cumbernauld, Glasgow G68 0AN ☎ 01236 737381

REID Nan *(Vla, Vln)*: 4 Lawson Place, Banchory, Kincardineshire AB31 5TY ☎ 013302 3254

ROBERTSON Fiona *(Vla)*: 18 Woodend Drive, Glasgow G13 1QS ☎ 0141 959 4013, 01523 796448, 0141 402 1347

SADLER Sarah *(Vla, Vln, Flt)*: 111 Connel Crescent, Mauchline, Ayrshire KA5 5AU ☎ 01290 551695

SNYDER Paula *(Vla, Pf)*: 2 Chesham Street, Brighton, East Sussex BN2 1NA

SPAREY-GILLIES Carolyn *(Vla, Bq Vln, Bq Vla)*: Woodside, 36 Station Road, Bearsden, Glasgow G61 4AL ☎ 0141 249 0239

SPENCE Claire *(Vla, Vln)*: 281 Southbrae Drive, Glasgow G13 1TR ☎ 0141 954 9098

STUBBS Michael *(Vla)*: 9 Queensberry Terrace, Cummertrees, Annan, Dumfriesshire, Scotland DG12 5QF ☎ 01461 700 420

SUTHERLAND Jenny *(Vla, Pf)*: 2/2 Buccleuch St, Cowcaddens, Glasgow G3 6SL ☎ 01426 210444

SWIFT Ian *(Vla, Vln)*: 29 Allan Road, Killearn, Glasgow G63 9QF ☎ 0141 632 1029, 07050 189555 mob

THORNTON Hilary *(Vla, Vln)*: Keepers Cottage, Blackcraig, Ballintuim, Perthshire PH10 7PX ☎ 01250 886225

TURBAYNE Hilary *(Vla, Vln)*: 163 Dundee Street 2F3, Edinburgh EH11 1BY ☎ 0131 228 1083

WARRACK Janet *(Vla)*: 26 Bankhead Road, Waterside, Kirkintilloch G66 3LQ ☎ 0141 578 1082

WARRENDER Colin *(Vla, Vln)*: 10 Harrowden Road, Inverness IV3 5QN ☎ 01463 241853

WEST (MCPHERSON) Fiona *(Vla, Pf, Gtr)*: 1 Floors Road, Eaglesham, Glasgow G76 0EP ☎ 0141 644 2100

WIGGINS Martin *(Vla, Bq Vla)*: 3/1 58 Park Road, Kelvinbridge, Glasgow G4 9JF ☎ 0141 334 8020, 0410 390664 mob, 0141 357 5687 fax

WORTHINGTON Judith *(Vla)*: The Blue House, South Street, Elie, Fife KY9 1DN ☎ 01333 330424

WREN Katherine *(Vla)*: 6 Coneyhill Road, Bridge Of Allan, Stirling FK9 4RH ☎ 01786 831008, 0585 020442

NORTH WEST

ADAMS John *(Vla)*: 93 Fog Lane, Didsbury, Manchester M20 6SL ☎ 0161 434 7240

AMBROSE Jean *(Vla, Bq Vla)*: 3 Woodfield Grove, Sale, Cheshire M33 6JW ☎ 0161 976 1925

ANSTEY Kathryn *(Vla, Vln)*: 15, Victoria Road, Timperley, Altrincham, Cheshire WA15 6PP ☎ 0161 980 7023

ANTHONY Jacqueline *(Vla)*: 5 Stanton Gardens, Stanton Avenue, Didsbury, Manchester M20 8PT ☎ 0161 434 8291

ATHERTON Jack *(Vla, Tpt)*: 31 Parsonage Road, Worsley, Manchester M28 5SJ ☎ 0161 790 5467

BATEMAN Anthony *(Vla, Vln)*: Flat C, Stanton Grange Mews, 160 Palatine Road, Manchester M20 2QH ☎ 0161 448 0953

BIGLEY Roger *(Vla)*: 78 Kingsway, Manchester M19 2DA ☎ 0161 224 9522

BLOOR Martin *(Vla)*: 80B Royle Green Road, Northendon, Manchester M22 4WB ☎ 0161 881 9428, 0958 276825 mob

BOYD Georgia *(Vla)*: 30 Neale Road, Chorlton, Manchester M21 9DQ ☎ 0161 881 9428

BRAGA Robert *(Vla)*: 20 Southwood Road, Liverpool L17 7BQ ☎ 0151 727 4982

BUTLER Joan *(Vla)*: The Old Joiners Shop, Low Street, Austwick, Via Lancaster LA2 8BN ☎ 01524 251445

CABOT Rosalyn *(Vla)*: 21 Southern Crescent, Bramhall, Stockport, Cheshire SK7 3AQ ☎ 0161 439 2410

CARLILE Brian *(Vla, Vln, Tba)*: 249/251 Rossendale Road, Burnley, Lancs BB11 5BZ ☎ 01282 451578, 0973 864109

CASHIN Janice *(Vla, Vln)*: 24 Salisbury Road, Cressington Park, Liverpool L19 0PJ ☎ 0151 427 3289, 0151427 3289

CHIVERS Mark *(Vla)*: Craigie Cottage, 1A Mill Lane, Northenden, Manchester M22 4HJ ☎ 0161 998 5013, 0860 678805 mob

COMPTON Matthew *(Vla, Pf)*: 10 Denmark Road, Sale, Cheshire M33 7JP ☎ 0161 976 3628

CONSTABLE Caitlin *(Vla, Pf, Vln)*: 16 Grains Road, Delph, Nr Oldham, Lancs OL3 5DS ☎ 01457 877063

COYLE Jayne *(Vla)*: 23 Wood Road, Whalley Range, Manchester M16 8BH ☎ 0161 881 1719, 07775 756015

CRISWELL Robert *(Vla)*: 35 Poplar Grove, Sale, Manchester M33 3AX ☎ 0161 286 1543

CROPPER Paul *(Vla)*: 9 Sandileigh Avenue, Withington, Manchester M20 3LN ☎ 0161 445 4450

CURTEIS Jason *(Vla)*: Combs Head Farm, Combs, High Peak SK23 9XA ☎ 0129 825981

CURTEIS Patricia *(Vla, Vln)*: Combs Head Farm, Combs, Chapel En Le Frith, Stockport Ches SK12 6XA ☎ 01298 25981

DALE Michael *(Vla)*: 15 Princes Road, Heaton Moor, Stockport, Cheshire SK4 3NQ ☎ 0161 432 8885

DAVIES Pip *(Vla, Vln, Pf)*: Craig-Y-Don, St.David's Road, Caernarfon, Gwynedd LL55 1EL ☎ 01286 673401

DEAN Matthew *(Vla, Ac Gtr, E Gtr)*: 8 Mayfield Road, Timperley, Altrincham, Cheshire WA15 7SZ ☎ 0161 980 3655

DOBSON Elizabeth *(Vla)*: Fron Hyfryd, Marian-Glas, Anglesey, North Wales LL73 8PE ☎ 01270 67636

ERTZ Simon *(Vla)*: 910 Abbott, Apt. #301, East Lansing, Michigan 48823, USA ☎ +517 337 7861

FERREIRA Jon *(Vla)*: 6 Cross Street, Broadbottom, Hyde, Cheshire SK14 6EF ☎ 01457 765321

FISHER Janet *(Vla)*: 15 Victoria Road, Timperley, Altrincham, Cheshire WA15 6PP ☎ 0161 980 7023

FOX Penelope *(Vla, Clt)*: 29 Beech Road, Cale Green, Stockport, Cheshire SK3 8HL ☎ 0161 476 4773

GAFFNEY John *(Vla)*: Philadelphia Chapel House, Llanarmon-Yn-Ial, Nr Mold CH7 4QN ☎ 01824 780281

GASPARINI Piero *(Vla)*: 22 Knights Court, Canterbury Gardens, Eccles New Road, Manchester M5 2AB ☎ 0161 789 0023

GENIN Jacqueline *(Vla, Vln)*: 2 Rundle Road, Liverpool L17 0AG ☎ 0151 727 5448

GILLIATT Andrea *(Vla)*: 22 Grangethorpe Drive, Burnage, Manchester M19 2LG ☎ 0161 225 1651

GREENLEES David *(Vla)*: Flat 5, 5 St. Aidan's Terrace, Birkenhead, Merseyside L43 8ST ☎ 0151 652 6884, 0410 912078 mob

GRIFFITHS Arfona *(Vla, Vln)*: 8 Moorland Avenue, Crosby, Liverpool 23 L23 2SW ☎ 0151 924 8849

HICKEY Della *(Vla)*: 18 Bucklow Avenue, Fallowfield, Manchester M14 7AR ☎ 0161 256 2453

HOLMES Jill *(Vla, Vln)*: 1 Cranford Court, Off Lache Lane, Chester CH4 7LN ☎ 01244 676507

HOWITT Tricia *(Vla)*: 20 Clough Lane, Little Hayfield, High Peak, Derbyshire SK22 2NL ☎ 01663 746754

JANES Rachel *(Vla)*: 3 Reuben Street, Stockport SK4 1PS ☎ 0161 429 9423

JENNINGS Anne *(Vla)*: 9 Hillside Road, Frodsham, Via Warrington, Cheshire WA6 6AW ☎ 01928 733209

JONES Stephen *(Vla)*: 69 Broadwalk, Wilmslow, Cheshire SK9 5PN

KING Fiona *(Vla)*: 5 Sandon Road, Wallasey, Merseyside L44 8BZ ☎ 0151 630 1289

KIRBY Emma *(Vla, Vln)*: 4 Yew Close, Carlisle, Cumbria CA2 6RT ☎ 01228 511803

LACEY Joanna *(Vla)*: c/o R.L.P.O, Hope Street, Liverpool L1 9BP

LANE Alison *(Vla)*: 28 Eshton Terrace, Clitheroe, Lancs BB7 1BQ ☎ 01200 425876

LITTLE Owen *(Vla)*: 64 Nicolas Road, Chorlton, Manchester M21 9LR ☎ 0161 881 4802, 07970 956575

MACLAREN Andrew *(Vla)*: 28 Beech Grove, Ashton, Preston, Lancs PR2 1DX ☎ 01772 726414

MARKS Sarah *(Vla)*: Ground Floor Flat, 61 Scarisbrick New Road, Southport, Merseyside PR8 6PA ☎ 01704 542056

MARSHMAN Aled *(Vla)*: 5 Maes Derw, Rhewl, Ruthin, Clwyd LL15 1TX ☎ 01824 707 369

METCALFE John *(Vla)*: 6 Tunley Road, London SW17 7QJ ☎ 020 8675 0285

MILES Bethan *(Vla, Vln, Man)*: Plas Hendre, Ffordd Clarach, Aberystwyth SY23 3DG ☎ 01970 623473

MOORE Maxine *(Vla)*: 42 Birch Road, Oxton, Birkenhead, Wirral L43 5UA ☎ 0151 734 1636, 0802 535723

MORRISSEY Clare *(Vla, Pf)*: 27 Frankby Grove, Upton Wirral L49 6LU ☎ 0151 522 0263

MOTTRAM Julian *(Vla)*: 18 Hale Road, Hale, Altrincham, Cheshire WA14 2EW ☎ 0161 929 8345

MUNCEY Richard *(Vla)*: Rodwell Head Farm, Cross Stone, Todmorden, Lancs OL14 8RG ☎ 01706 819668

NADEN Adele *(Vla, Pf)*: 3 Wood View, Carr End Lane, Stalmine, Lancashire FY6 0LH ☎ 01253 702019

NEEDHAM Frank *(Vla, Md)*: 20 Vaudrey Drive, Timperley, Altrincham, Cheshire WA15 6HQ ☎ 0161 973 6165

NEWTON Ingrid *(Vla, Vln, Pf)*: 17 Brookleigh Road, Withington, Manchester M20 4NZ ☎ 0161 434 3648

NEWTON Pamela *(Vla, Vln)*: 6 Braemar Close, Vicars Cross, Chester CH3 5HT ☎ 01244 347895

OSBORNE B *(Vla, Vln)*: 7 Stowell Place, Castletown, Isle Of Man IM9 1HF

PARKER Ruth *(Vla)*: Bowden Hall Cottage, Bowden Lane, Chapel-En-Le-Frith, High Peak SK23 0QP ☎ 01298 812711

PARTRIDGE Christopher *(Vla)*: 49 Post Street, Padfield, Glossop, Derbyshire SK13 1EF ☎ 01457 869742

POOLEY Timothy *(Vla)*: 43 Clothorn Road, Didsbury, Manchester M20 0BP ☎ 0161 445 6896

REDGRAVE Rose *(Vla)*: 34 St. Werburghs Road, Chorlton, Manchester M21 0TJ ☎ 0161 861 8088 & fax, 0966 381126 mob

RUBY David *(Vla)*: 9 Warwick Drive, Wallasey, Merseyside L45 7PJ ☎ 0151 637 0246

SCHEPENS Avril *(Vla)*: 2 Farndon Hall, Church Lane, Farndon, Cheshire CH3 6QF ☎ 01829 271449

SHAW Linda *(Vla)*: 82 Oak Street, Burnley, Lancs BB12 6QU ☎ 01282 436806, 0973 861376

SHEPLEY Rob *(Vla, Gtr, Bjo, Man, B Gtr)*: 6 The Spur, Crosby L23 3BT ☎ 0151 924 3582

SILVERMAN Katy *(Vla)*: 37 Rippingham Road, Withington, Manchester M20 3FX ☎ 0161 434 2922

SINCLAIR Fiona *(Vla)*: 9 Carlton Street, Old Trafford, Manchester M16 7QU ☎ 0161 226 9330

SONI Jean *(Vla)*: Crabmill Old Farmhouse, Crabmill Lane, Moston, Sandbach, Cheshire CW11 9QT ☎ 0127 077 244, 01270 526 244

SOOTHILL Fiona *(Vla, Vln, Pf, Sax)*: 48 Ash Tree Grove, Fir Tree Meadow, Croxteth, Liverpool L12 0PL ☎ 0151 548 1862

TAYLOR Esther *(Vla, Vln)*: 51 Bamford Road, Didsbury, Manchester M20 2QP ☎ 0161 446 1169

TRELOAR Ruth *(Vla, Vln)*: Address Unknown ☎ 0161 431 5517

VOYSEY Susan *(Vla)*: 5 Marina Close, Handforth, Wilmslow, Cheshire SK9 3JP ☎ 01625 524741

WALLACE Richard *(Vla)*: 30 Pinewood Avenue, Formby, Merseyside L37 2HZ ☎ 01704 874934

WALLINGTON Heather *(Vla)*: 3 Austin Drive, Didsbury, Manchester M20 6EB ☎ 0161 448 2649

WALLINGTON Martin *(Vla)*: 5 Wilford Avenue, Brooklands, Sale, Cheshire M33 3TH ☎ 0161 973 9526

WALTERS Rebecca *(Vla)*: 30 Neal Road, Chorlton, Manchester M21 9DQ ☎ 0161 881 9428, 0976 728725

WARRILOW Kenneth *(Vla)*: 8 Church View, Church Lane, Aughton, Lancs L39 6TQ ☎ 01695 423312

WEBB Margaret *(Vla, Pf, Vln)*: 14 Heatherfield, Edgworth, Turton, Bolton Lancs BL7 0DJ ☎ 01204 853188

WELCH Alison *(Vla, Vln, Pf)*: Hall Floor Flat, 26 Durdham Park, Redland, Bristol BS6 6XB

WERTHEIMER Fay *(Vla)*: 45 High Grove Road, Cheadle, Cheshire SK8 1NW ☎ 0161 428 4765

WILKINSON Joan *(Vla)*: Calinda, 14 Overhill Lane, Wilmslow, Cheshire SK9 2BG ☎ 01625 530895

WILLIAMS Dorothy *(Vla, Vln)*: 35 Cronk Drean, Douglas, Isle Of Man IM2 6AU ☎ 01624 672881

WILLIAMSON Richard *(Vla)*: 2 Ivy Road, Poynton, Cheshire SK12 1PE ☎ 01625 858802

WILSON Meta *(Vla)*: 17 Western Drive, Grassendale, Liverpool L19 0LX ☎ 0151 427 8823

WOLLEY Anne *(Vla, Vln)*: Dyffryn Nechtyd, Efenechtyd, Ruthin, Clwyd LL15 2PW ☎ 01824 702753

NORTH EAST

BREAKSPEAR Howard *(Vla)*: 27 Airedale Mount, Bagley Lane, Rodley, Leeds LS13 1JD ☎ 0113 2553005

BYRON Freda *(Vla)*: 4 West View, Littlethorpe, Nr Ripon, North Yorkshire HG4 3LN ☎ 01765 603404, 0370 623522 mob

CAMPBELL Vivienne *(Vla)*: Lane Side Farm, Helme Lane, Meltham, Hudds HD7 3RL ☎ 01484 850699

CRAWSHAW Frederick *(Vla)*: 1 Rothbury Avenue, Gosforth, Newcastle-upon-Tyne NE3 3HH ☎ 0191 285 7240

CULLEN Anthony *(Vla)*: 5 Collingwood Terrace, Jesmond, Newcastle/Tyne NE2 2JP ☎ 0191 281 7945

CUNDALL John *(Vla)*: 2 Orchard Gardens, York YO31 9EB ☎ 01904 624596

DEWAR Hilary *(Vla)*: Howe Green Cottage, Old Road, Kirbymoorside, North Yorkshire YO62 6LP ☎ 01751 432 364

DIKE Giovanna *(Vla, Vln)*: 1 Relly Path, Nevilles Cross, Durham DH1 4JG ☎ 0191 384 7565

DIKE Gordon *(Vla, Vln)*: 1 Relly Path, Nevilles Cross, Durham DH1 4JG ☎ 0191 384 7565

ELSE Pam *(Vla)*: 2 Sedley Close, Harrogate, North Yorkshire HG1 3LB ☎ 01423 521658

ENGELBRECHT Eileen *(Vla)*: Cornerstone House, 81 North Drive, Woodcroft Green, Hebburn,Tyne & Wear NE31 1EW ☎ 0191 483 5619

FLEETCROFT Martin *(Vla, Vln)*: 149 Sleaford Road, Boston, Lincs PE21 7PE ☎ 01205 352283

GARDINER Sheila *(Vla, Vln)*: 1 Queens Drive Lane, Ilkley, West Yorks LS29 9QS ☎ 01943 609581

GEORGE Alan *(Vla)*: 10, Bootham Terrace, York, Yorkshire YO30 7DH ☎ 01904 685189

GILCHRIST Alison (*Vla*): 38 Welton Mount, Leeds LS6 1ET ☎ 0113 275 1583

GLASS Clare (*Vla, Clt, Pf*): 17 Conowl Close, Helmsley, York YO62 5DU ☎ 01439 771730

GODDARD Caroline (*Vla, Vln*): 4 Vernon Avenue, Gledholt, Huddersfield, West Yorkshire HD1 4ED ☎ 01484 516859

HALL Diana (*Vla*): 1 Beechwood Walk, Leeds LS4 2LS ☎ 0113 2743114, 07801 473603

HARRISON Angela (*Vla*): Wath Farm, Slingsby, York, North Yorkshire YO62 4AS ☎ 01653 628261

HARRISON Sheila (*Vla*): 28 Claremont Avenue, South West Denton, Newcastle-upon-Tyne NE15 7LD ☎ 0191 2675959

HEARTFIELD Sarah (*Vla, Pf*): 1 Ash Grove, Greengates, Bradford BD10 0BP ☎ 01274 616080

HITCHINSON Gayle (*Vla*) ☎ 0191 258 7523

HOARE Christine (*Vla, Vln*): 28 Benomley Drive, Almondbury, Huddersfield, West Yorkshire HD5 8LX ☎ 01484 512691

KILLIK Ian (*Vla*): Flat 23, Highgate Edge, Gt North Road, London N2 0NT ☎ 020 8341 1721, 0378 158024

LEE Michael (*Vla, Vln, Pf*): 17 Cliff Terrace, The Headland, Hartlepool, Cleveland TS24 0PU ☎ 01429 232000

MORRIS Catherine (*Vla*): 11 St Oswald's Drive, Farewell Hall, Durham City DH1 3TE ☎ 0191 386 9049 & fax, 0402 907097 mob

NEWTON Laura (*Vla*): Welbury, 5 Preston Park, North Shields, Tyne & Wear NE29 9LJ ☎ 0191 257 4515

PACEY Fiona (*Vla*): 4 Dyson Houses, Argie Avenue, Leeds LS4 2QW ☎ 0113 2757831

PARHAM Barbara (*Vla*): 3 Pasture Close, Leconfield, Beverley, North Humberside HU17 7NL

PARSONAGE Vincent (*Vla, Vln, Pf*): 12 Chestnut Avenue, Crossgates, Leeds LS15 8ED ☎ 0113 295 6427

PRESCOTT Cordelia (*Vla*): 3 Stoney Croft Lane, Barkisland, Halifax HX4 0JD ☎ 01422 825162

ROBINSON Anne (*Vla, Pf*): 3 Heather Road, Meltham, Huddersfield HD7 3EY ☎ 01484 850457

SHORROCKS Robert (*Vla*): 24 Lodge Lane, Saughall, Chester CH1 6DT ☎ 01244 880319

SNOWDON Andrea (*Vla, Vln*): Greenlee, Bardon Mill, Hexham, Northumberland NE47 7AS ☎ 01434 344014

STILES Frank (*Vla, Com, Con*): 43 Beech Road, Branston, Lincoln LN4 1PP ☎ 01522 791662

TAYLOR Bruce (*Vla, Vln*): 6 Hadleigh Close, Sedgefield, Stockton-on-Tees, Cleveland TS21 2JL ☎ 01740 621247

TRENCHARD Sara (*Vla, Ob*): 28 Manor Street, Newsome, Huddersfield, W. Yorkshire HD4 6NN ☎ 01484 453899

WHEELER Shula (*Vla, Flt, Pf*): Manor House, Main Street, Newton-upon-Derwent, York YO41 5DA ☎ 01904 608 557

WILKS Diana (*Vla, Vln, B Viol, Reb*): 'Oaklea House', Front Street, Ingleton, Darlington, Co. Durham DL2 3HL ☎ 01325 730 831

WILSON Rona (*Vla*): 10 Mornington Road, Sale, Cheshire M33 2DA ☎ 0161 969 0710

WYLY Elizabeth (*Vla, Pf, Vln*): 17 Ingledew Crescent, Leeds LS8 1BP ☎ 0113 225 9286

EAST

APPEL Susan (*Vla*): 62 Woodstock Road South, St Albans, Herts AL1 4QH ☎ 01727 836522

BRIEN Juliet (*Vla*): 3 The Walks North, Huntingdon, Cambs PE18 6AX ☎ 01480 352528

CARLSON Marna (*Vla, Vln*): 65 Westgarth Gardens, Bury St Edmunds, Suffolk IP33 3LG ☎ 01284 704667

CLIFF Frank (*Vla*): 127 Chediston Street, Halesworth, Suffolk IP19 8BJ ☎ 01986 874324

ELMERS Ralf (*Vla*): 17 High Street, Berkhamsted, Herts HP4 2BX ☎ 01442 384 317

FRASER Nicolette (*Vla, Pf*): 11 Elm Tree Lane, Leavenheath, Colchester, Essex CO6 4UL ☎ 01206 262990

GEHAMMAR Anne (*Vla*): 119 Ashdon Road, Saffron Walden, Essex CB10 2AJ ☎ 01799 516484

GISKE Mari (*Vla*): 27A Upper Lattimore Road, St. Albans, Herts AL1 3UA ☎ 01727 861817 & fax, 0468 890443 mob

GRESWELL John (*Vla, Vln, Db*): 36 Don Phelan Close, Camberwell, London SE5 7AZ ☎ 020 7701 3745

HILL Kevin (*Vla, Con*): 8 Templars Court, Haverhill, Suffolk CB9 9AJ ☎ 01440 763799

JONES Rebecca (*Vla, Vln*): The Old Church, Queen Adelaide, Nr Ely, Cambs CB7 4TZ

LIEPA Janet (*Vla, Vln*): Carlsberg House, The Licensed Victuallers Sch., London Road, Ascot, Berks SL5 8DR

LIM Tze-Chian (*Vla, Vln*): 8 Brampton Close, Harpenden, Herts AL5 5SL ☎ 01582 460 382

MAGUIRE Tricia (*Vla, Vln*): Manor Farm, Benhall Green, Saxmundham, Suffolk IP17 1HN ☎ 01728 603245

MURPHY David (*Vla, Vla, Con*): 60 Cowper Road, Harpenden, Herts AL5 5NG ☎ 01582 462137

PAYNE Georgina (*Vla*): 334 Norton Way South, Letchworth, Herts SG6 1TA ☎ 01462 624363, 0831 095278

TREVELYAN Peter (*Vla*): 3 Abbey Hill End, St. Albans, Herts AL3 4HN ☎ 01727 843656 & fax

WILLIAMS Paul (*Vla, Pf*): 114B Ilford Lane, Ilford, Essex IG1 2LE ☎ 020 8514 5338

MIDLANDS

ADAMS Isobel (*Vla*): 27 Cottage Avenue, Whatton, Notts NG13 9FS ☎ 01949 50143

ARTUS Margaret (*Vla, Vln*): 43 Manor Road, Edgbaston, Birmingham B16 9JS ☎ 0121 454 4010

ASPIN David (*Vla*): 2 Avon Drive, Moseley, Birmingham B13 9PS ☎ 0121 449 2566, 0956 286359 mob

ASTON Shirley (*Vla*): 18, Lighton Close, Hampton Park, Hereford HR1 1UH ☎ 01432 268477

BLANTHORN Susan (*Vla, Vln*): 15 Albany Terrace, Leamington Spa, Warks CV32 5LP ☎ 01926 889192

BOWER Catherine (*Vla*): 21 Ashfield Road, Kings Heath, Birmingham, B14 7AS ☎ 0121 449 1171

BROOKES Ellen (*Vla, Vln*): 6 Coplow Cottages, Edgbaston, West Midlands B16 0DG ☎ 0121 558 9559, 0966 186347 mob

BROOKS Roy (*Vla*): 52 Tanfield Lane, Northampton NN1 5RN ☎ 01604 622986

CARTMELL Jean (*Vla*): 205 Turves Green, West Heath, Birmingham B31 4BS ☎ 0121 476 8956

CEREDIG Elizabeth (*Vla, Vln*): 20 Ombersley Road, Droitwich, Worcestershire WR9 8JE ☎ 01905 779736

CHAMBERLAIN Ian (*Vla, Vln*): 11, Rectory Gardens, Oldswinford, Stourbridge, West Midlands DY8 2HB ☎ 01384 440712

CHAPMAN Andrea (*Vla, Vln, Pf*): 62 Warren Road, Stirchley, Birmingham B30 2NY ☎ 0121 451 2914

CHIPPENDALE Anna (*Vla, Pf*): 282 Penns Lane, Sutton Coldfield, West Midlands B76 1LG ☎ 0121 313 1837

CLARKE Neil (*Vla*): 80 Ripley Road, Heage, Derbys DE56 2HU ☎ 01773 853270

COLE Peter (*Vla*): 36 Balsall Street East, Balsall Common, Coventry, West Midlands CV7 7FR ☎ 01676 535604

COLLINS Trevor (*Vla, Vln*): Minstead, 9 Mucklow Hill, Halesowen, West Midlands B62 8NT ☎ 0121 422 5251

CRANE Alice (*Vla, Vln*): Bankside Cottage, Marlcliff, Bidford-on-Avon, Warwickshire B50 4NT ☎ 01789 772671

CURTIS David (*Vla*): 66 West Street, Stratford-upon-Avon, Warks CV37 6DR

DOIDGE Gary (*Vla, Vln, Pf*): 36 Anton Drive, Walmley, Sutton Coldfield B76 1XG ☎ 0121 351 1107

DUGGAN Geoffrey (*Vla, Vln*): 27, Ashlawn Crescent, Solihull, West Midlands B91 1PR ☎ 0121 711 2706

FRYER Elizabeth (*Vla*): 14 Grove Avenue, Moseley, Birmingham B13 9RU ☎ 0121 449 0411

GILLHAM Graham (*Vla, Vadam*): 30 Wadham Road, Woodthorpe, Notts NG5 4JB ☎ 0115 9266340

HAYES Ian (*Vla, Vln*): 58, Christchurch Lane, Lichfield, Staffordshire WS13 8AN ☎ 01543 253 827

HEATHER Elizabeth (*Vla*): 12 Grayfield Avenue, Moseley, Birmingham B13 9AD ☎ 0121 449 6267

HENDERSON Malcolm (*Vla*): Pear Tree Cottage, East Street, Long Compton, Warks CV36 5JT ☎ 01608 684810

HISCOX Pamela (*Vla*): 51A Avenue Road, Queniborough, Leicestershire LE7 3FB ☎ 0116 2601870

HORTON Hannah (*Vla*): 106 Tresham Road, Great Barr, Birmingham B44 9UD ☎ 0121 360 6967, 0966 461896 mob

JAMES Pat (*Vla*): 39, Waterloo Road, Birmingham B14 7SD ☎ 0121 443 3810

JENKINSON Micheal (*Vla*): 27 Hunstanton Avenue, Harborne, Birmingham B17 8SX ☎ 0121 420 4675

JESSOP Mary (*Vla, Vln*): The Byre, Main Street, Smisby, Ashby-De-La-Zouch, Leics LE65 2TY ☎ 01530 411 113

JONES Frances (*Vla, Vln*): 73 Oxford Road, Moseley, Birmingham B13 9SG ☎ 0121 449 7139

KNIGHT Bernard (*Vla*): Apple Trees, Salford, Chipping Norton, Oxon OX7 5YW ☎ 01608 642939

LAW Cheryl (*Vla, Vln, Pf*): 11 Clive Road, Balsal Common, Warwickshire CV7 7DW ☎ 01676 533393

MAYNE Helen (*Vla, Vln*): 76 Poplar Road, Bearwood, Warley, West Midlands B66 4AN ☎ 0121 429 9740

MILLWARD Carol (*Vla*): 57, Greenhill Road, Moseley, Birmingham B13 9SU ☎ 0121 449 5400

MORRISON Aileen (*Vla*): 20 Grove Avenue, Moseley, Birmingham B13 9RU ☎ 0121 449 0668

PERKIN Janet (*Vla, Pf*): The Cottage, Breach Lane, Totmonslow, Nr Tean, Stoke-on-Trent Staffs ST10 4JJ ☎ 01538 723432

POPESCU Eugen-Doreanu (*Vla, Arr*): 54, Teme Road, Halesowen, West Midlands B63 2LU ☎ 01384 836566

RATCLIFFE Derek (*Vla*): 4 Grasmere Avenue, Sutton Coldfield, West Midlands B74 3DG ☎ 0121 353 9830

RICE Cecily (*Vla*): Mill Pond Cottage, Golden Valley, Castlemorton, Worcs WR13 6AA ☎ 01684 833607, 0402 568493

ROBERTS Helen (*Vla*): 65 Carless Avenue, Harborne, Birmingham B17 9BN ☎ 0121 426 3711

ROBINSON Julian (*Vla*): 108 Northfield Road, Kings Norton, Birmingham B30 1JG ☎ 0121 459 1522 & fax

ROSE Peter (*Vla*): 8 The Square, Oakthorpe, Swadlincote, Derby DE12 7QS ☎ 01530 272425, 01530 270106

SALMON Amanda (*Vla, Vln*): The Hatch, Lindridge, Tenbury, Worcester WR15 8JT ☎ 01584 881207, 01584 881564

SAUNDERS Francis (*Vla, Pf*): 18 Station Road, Kenilworth, Warwickshire CV8 1JJ ☎ 01926 53175

SUDLOW Paul (*Vla, Pf, Vln, Com*): 48 Price Road, Cubbington, Leamington Spa, Warks CV32 7LQ ☎ 01926 429607

SWANSON Angela (*Vla*): Emmanuel Villa, 102 Olton Boulevard East, Acocks Green, Birmingham B27 7ND ☎ 0121 680 9218

TATTERSDILL Rona (*Vla*): 57 Russell Road, Moseley, Birmingham B13 8RB ☎ 0121 449 0252

THOMAS Janet (*Vla, Vln*): 22 Patricia Avenue, Birmingham, West Midlands B14 4ES ☎ 0121 474 6784

WATSON Joy (*Vla*): 95 St Marys Road, Stratford-upon-Avon, Warwickshire CV37 6TL ☎ 01789 294946

WHITELAW Jennifer (*Vla*): 101, Malthouse Lane, Earlswood, Solihull, West Midlands B94 5RZ ☎ 01567 03695

WILEMAN Eric (*Vla, Vln*): 26 Silverwood Avenue, Ravenshead, Nottingham NG15 9BU ☎ 01623 793923

WILLIAMS Gwyn (*Vla*): 16 Swanfold, Wilmcote, Stratford-upon-Avon, Warks CV37 9XH ☎ 01789 294200

WILLIAMS Helen (*Vla, Vln*): 21 Union Road, Shirley, Solihull, West Midlands B90 3BU ☎ 0121 745 6587, 0411 251091

WILSON Bruce (*Vla, Vln*): 40 Edith Road, Smethwick, West Midlands B66 4QX

YATES Christopher (*Vla*): 93 Wood Lane, Harborne, Birmingham B17 9AY ☎ 0121 426 3052

SOUTH EAST

ANDREWES Virginia (*Vla*): 3 Beaulieu Court, Sunningwell, Oxon OX13 6RQ

ANDREWS Elizabeth (*Vla*): The Orangery, Hascombe Road, Godalming, Surrey GU8 4AE ☎ 01483 208207 & fax, 01483 208301

BAYLEY Sophie (*Vla, Vln, Voc, Theory*): 15 Hamilton Court, Lymington, Hants SO41 0PR

BENTLEY Jean (*Vla, Pf*): 5 Chancellor Way, Sevenoaks, Kent TN13 3LA ☎ 01732 455076

BLACK Susan (*Vla, Pf*): Flat 1, Mortimer House, 48 Eastern Avenue, Reading, Berkshire RG1 5RY ☎ 01734 351617

BLEW Douglas (*Vla, Org, Vln, Pf*): Allerton, Hawley Road, Hawley, Dartford Kent DA2 7RB ☎ 01322 229837, 0973 303967 mob

BRICE Judith (*Vla, Pf*): 84 Nortoft Road, Charminster, Bournemouth, Dorset BH8 8PZ ☎ 01202 467001

BROWN Sally A (*Vla*): 29 Hawthorne Drive, Creekmoor, Poole, Dorset BH7 7YG ☎ 01202 381598

CUMMING Oonagh (*Vla, Bq Vla*): 9 Pinewood Gardens, Bagshot, Surrey GU19 5ES ☎ 01276 472700, 0956 118940

DAVIES Paul (*Vla*): 70 Benmead Road, Kidlington, Oxford OX5 2AX ☎ 0186 75 3633

DOIDGE Marguerite (*Vla, Vln*): 54 Hatley Road, Bitterne, Southampton SO18 6NU ☎ 023 8032 6008

FORESTER Helen (*Vla, Vln*): Flat 10 Edmondsham House, Terrace Road, Bournemouth, Dorset BH2 5NJ ☎ 01202 780259

GALE Jacoba (*Vla*): 45 New Road, Lower Bryanston, Blandford, Dorset DT11 0DR ☎ 01258 455809

GEORGIADIS Andrew (*Vla*): North Rise, Martineau Lane, Guestling, Hastings, East Sussex TN35 5DS ☎ 01424 814105

GILES Gawin (*Vla*): 13 Cumberland Court, West Cliff Gardens, Bournemouth, Dorset BH2 5HL ☎ 01202 555968

GRAYER Christopher (*Vla, Vln*): 49 St Andrews Road, Lower Bemerton, Salisbury SP2 9NT ☎ 01722 331856

GREEN Stuart (*Vla*): Haere Mai, Hinton Martell, Wimborne, Dorset BH21 7HE ☎ 01258 840886

GRIFFIN Elizabeth (*Vla*): 21 Wing Road, Linslade, Leighton Buzzard, Beds LU7 7NG ☎ 01525 381156, 0402 270429 mob

KAY Alison (*Vla, Pf*): 54 Upton Way, Poole, Dorset BH18 9LZ ☎ 01202 602336

KING Paul (*Vla*): 44 Elphick Road, Newhaven, East Sussex BN9 9SY ☎ 01273 513268

MACKENZIE Jacqui (*Vla, Vln, Pf*): Old Cross House, Coscote, Didcot, Oxon OX11 0NP ☎ 01235 519304

MASTERS Sally (*Vla, Pf*): 27 Tilsworth Road, Beaconsfield, Bucks HP9 8TR

MAUDE-ROXBY Phyllida (*Vla, Pf*): Bay Tree House, 64 Warblington Road, Emsworth, Hants PO10 7HH ☎ 01243 379248

PERCY Rebecca (*Vla, Vln, Pf*): 5 Cheseldon Road, Guildford GU1 3SB ☎ 01483 506556

PILLOW Ian (*Vla*): c/o Bournemouth Symp Orch, 2 Seldown Lane, Poole, Dorset

PRIDGEON-HELLER Tanya (*Vla, Vln*): 82 Freshfield Bank, Forest Row, East Sussex RH18 5HN ☎ 01342 82 2590

PYE Sylvia (*Vla*): Old Castle House, 50 Old Bath Road, Speen, Newbury, Berks RG14 1QL ☎ 01635 40113

QUILLEN Jean (*Vla, Vln*): 13 Oakthorpe Road, Summertown, Oxford OX2 7BD ☎ 01865 553683

SECRET Robert (*Vla, Con*): 1 Poplars Close, Preston Bissett, Buckingham MK18 4LR ☎ 01280 848275

SMITH Michael (*Vla, Vln*): 26 Fairfield Road, Wimborne, Dorset BH21 2AJ ☎ 01202 880256

STAMMERS Janet (*Vla*): 11 Cranedown, Lewes, Sussex BN7 3NA ☎ Lewes 5544

STEVENS Cathy (*Vla*): 95 Albert Road, Poole, Dorset BH12 2BX ☎ 01202 740379

TURNER Adrian (*Vla*): 119 Cleavers Avenue, Milton Keynes, Bucks MK14 7DQ ☎ 01908 671922

WARE Rebecca (*Vla, Vln, E Vln*): St Catherines, Off Main Street, Gawcott, Bucks MK18 4HX ☎ 01280 822 270

WEARNE Amelia (*Vla, Vln*): 15C Boyne Park, Tunbridge Wells, Kent TN4 8EL ☎ 01892 540577

WESTRUP Gunnar (*Vla*): 37 Caledon Road, Poole, Dorset BH14 9NL ☎ 01202 741692

WILLETTS Samuel (*Vla*): Orchard House, Orchard Street, Blandford, Dorset DT11 7QZ ☎ 01258 451493

YOUNG Alice *(Vla, Vln)*: 17 Harland Road, Southbourne, Bournemouth, Dorset BH6 4DN ☎ 01202 525923

SOUTH WEST

ALLUM Cheremie *(Vla)*: 50 Tangmere Drive, Fairwater, Cardiff CF5 2PQ ☎ 029 2056 9019

ATTWOOD Nicola *(Vla, Vln)*: 32 Shilton Road, Carterton, Oxon OX18 1EH ☎ 01993 844667

BALKWILL Lilian *(Vla, Vln)*: 4 Parc Briwer, Penryn, Cornwall TR10 8LF ☎ 01326 72099

BENNETT Christina *(Vla, Vln, Pf)*: Bank House, 53 Fore Street, Hartland, Nr Bideford, North Devon EX39 6BD

BENNETT Kathryn *(Vla, Vln)*: 16 Ffordd Trecastell, Llanharry, Mid Glamorgan CF72 9ND ☎ 01443 228693

BRODRICK Louise *(Vla, Pf)*: 18 Machen Street, Penarth, South Glamorgan CF64 1UB ☎ 029 2071 2028

BULL Christine *(Vla, Pf, Vln)*: Glanville Lodge, Glanville Road, Wedmore, Somerset BS28 4AD ☎ 01934 712742

CLARKE Robert *(Vla, Vln)*: 20 Meadway Avneue, Nailsea, Bristol BS19 2DU

COHEN Ross *(Vla)*: 1 Tyrwhitt Crescent, Roath Park, Cardiff CF2 5QP ☎ 029 2076 3892

DANDO Nerissa *(Vla, Vln, Pf)*: 17 High Street, Chipping Sodbury, Bristol BS17 6BA ☎ 01454 313114

DAVIES Trevor *(Vla)*: Bryn Tawel, Wesley Close, Old Cwmbran, Gwent NP44 3ND ☎ 01633 838701

DRUMMOND James *(Vla, Vln)*: Plot 2, Westbury Homes, Miskin, Pontyclun, Mid Glamorgan CF72 9AJ

GAFFNEY Naomi *(Vla)*: 4 St Andrews Road, Wenvoe, Cardiff CF5 6AF ☎ 029 2059 3202

GILLETT Andrew *(Vla, Pf)*: 72 Heavitree Road, Exeter, Devon EX1 2LP ☎ 01392 211242

GRAVELLE Eirlys *(Vla, Pf, Vln)*: 74 Llanfteffan Road, Johnstown, Carmarthen, Dyfed SA31 3NR ☎ 01267 235 979

GRIBBLE David *(Vla)*: Brookside The Terrace, Creigau, Cardiff, S.Glamorgan CF4 8NG ☎ 029 2089 2135

HADFIELD Verity *(Vla, Vln, Pf)*: 34 Orchard Castle, Thornhill, Cardiff, S Glam CF4 9BA ☎ 610466

HEDGES David *(Vla, Vln)*: 1 Southwell, Trull, Taunton, Somerset TA3 7HU ☎ 01823 337466

HEYMAN Philip *(Vla)*: 2 Hastings Place, Penarth, Vale Of Glamorgan CF64 2TD ☎ 029 2030 7294

HOOLEY Patrick *(Vla)*: Hope Cottage, Winsford, Somerset TA24 7HS ☎ 01643 851500

HUGHES-JONES Catherine *(Vla, Vln)*: The Old Meeting House, The Green, Olveston, Bristol BS35 4EJ ☎ 01454 610056

JONES Simon *(Vla, Vln)*: Woodside, Broadclyst, Exeter, Nr Devon EX5 3BE ☎ 01392 461326

JONES Tegwen *(Vla)*: 139 Fairwater Road, Fairwater, Cardiff CF5 3JR ☎ 029 2056 0870

LEADBEATER Ania *(Vla)*: 34 Tymawr Road, Llandaff North, Cardiff CF4 2FN ☎ 029 2056 7720

LIPMAN Domini *(Vla, Bq Vla)*: 30B Syr David's Avenue, Llandaff, Cardiff CF5 1GH ☎ 029 2022 7578

LLOYD Stephen *(Vla, Vln)*: 31 St Michaels Road, Llandaff, Cardiff CF5 2AL ☎ 029 2040 8117

LYNCH Margaret *(Vla)*: Wayside House, Mill Road, Ynysybwl, Ponty Pridd CF37 3LS ☎ 01443 799176

MCKELVAY David *(Vla)*: 7 Grantham Close, Radyr Way, Llandaff, Cardiff CF5 2EX ☎ 029 2055 4664

MEYRICK Morfydd *(Vla)*: 4 Avonlea Court, Cloverdale Road, Longwell Green, Bristol BS15 6XZ ☎ 0117 9329153

MONTGOMERY Alison *(Vla, Vln, Pf)*: 55B Pen-Y-Peel Road, Canton, Cardiff CF5 1QY ☎ 029 2034 0720, 0973 187145 mob

MORGAN Annette *(Vla, Vln)*: 10 Spencer Street, Brynhyfryd, Swansea, West Glamorgan SA5 9JE ☎ 01792 650927

MOUNTAIN January *(Vla, Vln, Pf)*: 21 Ellerncroft Road, Wotton-Under-Edge, Gloucestershire GL12 7AX ☎ 01453 521082, 0860 722036 mob

MURRAY Sarah *(Vla)*: 10 Ty Mynydd Close, Radyr, Cardiff CF4 8AS ☎ 029 2084 3651

MUTTER James *(Vla, Vln, Pf, Db)*: Les Butiers Cottage, Rue De Basacre, St Martin, Jersey, Channel Islands JE3 6DN ☎ 01534 856432

PATRICK Anne *(Vla, Vln, Pf)*: 19 Karen Close, Backwell, Bristol BS19 3JE ☎ Flax Bourton 34

PATTENDEN Jacqueline *(Vla, Vln)*: 4 The Willows, Highworth, Swindon SN6 7PG ☎ 01367 244 921

SCHLIFFKE Joan *(Vla, Vln)*: Berrio Mill, South Hill, Callington, Cornwall PL17 7NL ☎ Liskeard 62592

SCHRECKER Patricia *(Vla, Vln, B Viol)*: Linden Cottage, Weston Road, Bath BA1 2XU ☎ Bath 312663

SIDGREAVES Joan *(Vla, Vln, Pf)*: Grooms Yard, Litfield Road, Clifton, Bristol BS8 3LL ☎ 0117 9742780

SKINNER William *(Vla)*: 5 Spowart Avenue, Llanelli, Dyfed SA15 3HY

TASNEY Laura *(Vla, Vln, Pf)*: ☎ 01452 552734

TAYLOR Peter *(Vla)*: Tyr Alswm, Dyffryn Crawnon, Llangynidr, Nr Crickhowell, Powys NP8 1NT ☎ 01874 730693

THOMAS Linda *(Vla, Vln)*: Pen-Y-Bryn, Duffryn Road, Abertillery, Gwent NP3 1HJ ☎ 01495 212135

TOMKINS Philip *(Vla)*: 8 St Johns Crescent, Canton, Cardiff CF5 1NX ☎ 029 2034 2138

VAN-WEEDE Benedict *(Vla, Vln)*: 98 Orchid Vale, Kingsteighton, Newton Abbot, Devon TQ12 3YS ☎ 01626 333211

WALKER Rachael *(Vla)*: c/o 5 Blakeney Grove, Nailsea, Bristol BS19 2RG ☎ 01275 855492

WILKS Rachel *(Vla, Vln)*: 8 Ashford Way, Kingswood, Bristol BS15 2YP ☎ 0117 9609986

WILLIAMS Gethin *(Vla, Vln)*: Diwedd Lon, St Dials Road, Greenmeadow, Cwmbran Gwent NP44 4BJ ☎ 01633 866294

WILSON Edmund *(Vla, Vln)*: 4 Cyncoed Rise, Cyncoed, Cardiff CF2 6SF ☎ 029 2075 9460

YORK Geoffrey *(Vla)*: Shenstone, 16 Heol Esgyn, Cyncoed, Cardiff CF2 6JJ ☎ 029 2075 2808

YOUNG Keith *(Vla, Vln)*: 33 Hathaway Road, Upper Stratton, Swindon, Wilts SN2 6TX ☎ 01793 826857

LONDON

AKEROYD Nicola *(Vla, Bq Vla)*: 3 Connor Street, Hackney, London E9 7LG ☎ 020 8985 0719, 0976 425891, 020 8985 0719

ALABASTER Moira *(Vla, Vln)*: 89 The Keep, Kingston-upon-Thames, Surrey KT2 5UD ☎ 020 8974 9568

ALEXANDER Marina *(Vla)*: 43 Blakesware Gardens, London N9 9HX ☎ 020 8360 6945

APPLEYARD Paul *(Vla)*: 27 Kendal Steps, St Georges Fields, London W2 2YE ☎ 020 7402 7860, 020 7354 2711

ASCHERSON Marina *(Vla)*: 15C Muswell Road, London N10 2BJ ☎ 020 8883 0064 & fax, 020 8549 1706 day

ATKINS Jane *(Vla)*: 46 Macoma Road, London SE18 2QP ☎ 020 8854 8491 & fax

AZULEK Celi *(Vla, Vadam, Vln)*: 2 Wilton Grove, New Malden, Surrey KT3 6RG ☎ 020 8942 1746, 020 8549 1706

BAKER Lynne *(Vla)*: 60 Broomfield Avenue, Palmers Green, London N13 4JP ☎ 020 8882 4760, 0976 426850

BALLARDIE Quintin *(Vla)*: 9 North Side, London SW4 0QW

BANNISTER Julius *(Vla)*: The Coach House, Church Road, Chelsfield, Kent BR6 7SN ☎ 01689 873617, 020 8533 1372 day, 01689 833141

BANNISTER Lori *(Vla)*: 15 Greenfinches, New Barn, Longfield, Kent DA3 7ND ☎ 01474 705265, 01306 880669 day

BARR Nicholas *(Vla)*: 3 Dalberg Road, London SW2 1AJ ☎ 020 7733 4848

BARRITT Jonathan *(Vla)*: 10 Queens Avenue, Finchley, London N3 2NP ☎ 020 8346 7071

BEAZLEY Andrew *(Vla, Vln)*: 58 Dolphin Rd, Slough, Berks SL1 1TA ☎ 01753 773585

BELL Elizabeth *(Vla)*: 72A George Lane, South Woodford, London E18 1JJ ☎ 020 8530 8520

BELL Sally *(Vla, Pf, Vln)*: 13 Hutton Court, Benson Row, Penrith, Cumbria CA11 7YJ ☎ 01768 863 206

BELLMAN David *(Vla)*: 18 The Brookdales, Bridge Lane, London NW11 9JU ☎ 020 8731 6173

BENEDICT Roger *(Vla, Vln)*: 2 Holly Bank, Primrose Lane, Forest Row, East Sussex RH18 5LT ☎ 01342 824463

BENJAMIN Rachel *(Vla)*: Flat 7, 272 Cold Harbour Lane, Brixton, London SW9 8SE

BERREEN Angela *(Vla, Pf)*: 18 Glenure Road, Eltham, London SE9 1UF ☎ 020 8859 8986

BEST Roger *(Vla)*: 75 Grove Lane, Camberwell, London SE5 8SP ☎ 020 7703 2014

BICKNELL Susan *(Vla, Bq Vla)*: 14 Whitehall Gardens, London W3 9RD ☎ 020 8992 5375 & fax, 0585 366509 mob

BIELBY Nigel *(Vla)*: 1 Springfield Road, North Chingford, London E4 7DJ ☎ 020 8524 8173

BIRKS Heather *(Vla)*: 22 Marriott Road, Barnet, Herts EN5 4NJ ☎ 020 8449 1860

BIRNBAUM Leo *(Vla)*: 49 Hodford Road, Golders Green, London NW11 8NL ☎ 020 8458 5954

BISHOP Sean *(Vla)*: 7 Dalkeith Road, West Dulwich, London SE21 8LT ☎ 020 8424 0056

BLEE Michael *(Vla, Vln)*: 239 Portnall Road, London W9 3BL ☎ 020 8969 3596

BLUME Norbert *(Vla)*: 31 Pond Street, Hampstead, London NW3 2PN ☎ 020 7794 7260

BOLT Rachel *(Vla)*: 34 Beeches Close, Genoa Road, London SE20 8ED ☎ 020 8659 8674, 01306 880669

BONDS Fiona *(Vla)*: 12 Winding Shott, Bramfield, Hertford SG14 2QP ☎ 01992 504049, 0836 259090 mob

BONETTI Angela *(Vla)*: 1 Newton Road, Barton-on-Sea, Hampshire BH25 7AS ☎ 01425 638664, 01306 500011 day

BONHAM-CARTER Amber *(Vla)*: 7 Fleur Gates, Princes Way, London SW19 6QQ ☎ 020 8788 1230

BORTHWICK Sophia *(Vla)*: Greenbank, 12 Crow Lane, Middle Herrington, Sunderland, Tyne & Wear SR3 3TE ☎ 0191 511 0330

BOSWORTH Norris *(Vla)*: 62 Mountfield Road, London N3 3NP ☎ 020 8346 2862

BOULTON Tim *(Vla)*: 18 Tulsemere Road, West Dulwich, London SE27 9EJ ☎ 020 8670 3086, 0976 390931 mob, 01306 880 669 day

BOYD James *(Vla)*: 82 Salcott Road, London SW11 6DF ☎ 020 7738 9479, 01306 880669 day, 020 7207 9969 fax

BOYD Jessamy *(Vla)*: 78A Idmiston Road, West Dulwich, London SE27 9HQ ☎ 020 8670 9915 & fax, 01306 500011

BRADLEY Karen *(Vla)*: 60 West End Lane, Chipping Barnet, Herts EN5 2SA ☎ 020 8441 4328

BRADLEY Sarah *(Vla, Pf)*: 21 Whaley Road, Potters Bar, Herts EN6 2RA ☎ 01707 57085

BRADSHAW Catherine *(Vla)*: 73 Maury Road, London N16 7BT ☎ 020 8806 7241

BREARLEY John *(Vla, Vln)*: 15 Marriott Road, Barnet, Herts EN5 4NJ ☎ 020 8449 7324

BROOKER David *(Vla, Bq Vla)*: 17E Barry Road, East Dulwich, London SE22 0HX ☎ 020 8693 8097

BROOM Stephen *(Vla)*: 53 Lemsford Village, Lemsford, Welwyn Garden City, Herts AL8 7TR ☎ 01707 331367

BROTHERS Brenda *(Vla, Pf)*: 7 Upper Paddock Road, Oxhey, Watford, Herts WD1 4DY ☎ 01923 232958

BROWN Andrew *(Vla)*: Timbers, Woburn Hill, Weybridge, Surrey KT15 2QG ☎ 01932 853172

BROWN Harvey *(Vla)*: 29 East Point, Avondale Square, Old Kent Road, London SE1 5NS ☎ 020 7252 0475

BROWN Nancie *(Vla)*: 6 Devon Court, Links Road, Acton, London W3 0EH ☎ 020 8992 5205

BROWN Naomi *(Vla)*: 35 Ewhurst Road, Crofton Park, London SE4 1AG ☎ 020 8690 3708

BROWN Penelope *(Vla)*: 86 Argyle Street, Cambridge CB1 3LS ☎ 01223 411809

BUCKNALL Joan *(Vla)*: 83 Dora Road, London SW19 7JT ☎ 020 8946 6690

BULCOCK Maritza *(Vla)*: 23 Chadwick Road, Peckham Rye, London SE15 4RA ☎ 020 7639 4597, 0976 852158 mob

BULLOCK Judy *(Vla)*: 126 Fernbank Road, Ascot, Berkshire SL5 8JP ☎ 01344 882029

BURGESS Kathryn *(Vla)*: North Lodge, Great Missenden, Bucks HP16 9NT ☎ 020 8549 1706 day, 07775 948509 mob

BURNS Duff *(Vla)*: 87 Mayfield Avenue, Orpington, Kent BR6 0AG ☎ 01689 828178

BURT Jean Robertson *(Vla)*: 6 Heathside Gardens, Woking, Surrey GU22 7HR ☎ 01483 740256

BURTON Oliver *(Vla, Vln)*: 131 Chesterton Road, Ladbroke Grove, London W10 6ET ☎ 020 8968 5615, 0850 896782

BUSBRIDGE Judith *(Vla)*: 48 Middle Lane, London N8 8PG ☎ 020 8348 2745, 020 8245 5067

BUTLER Elizabeth *(Vla)*: 42 Patterson Road, London SE19 2LD ☎ 020 8653 9788, 01306 880669

BUTLER Holly *(Vla)*: ☎ 0956 318 260

BYRNE Anthony *(Vla)*: Lindisfarne, 6 Downs View Road, Hassocks, West Sussex BN6 8HJ ☎ 01273 844488

BYRT Rachel *(Vla, Pf, Bq Vla)*: 50 Crouch Hall Road, London N8 8HG ☎ 020 8347 7161, 01306 880669 day

CAREY Bridget *(Vla)*: 55A Ferme Park Road, London N8 9RY ☎ 020 8341 4085, 020 8533 1372

CARNEY Adele *(Vla, Hrp, Vln, Pf)*: ☎ 01232 667458, 0966 183267

CARRINGTON Diana *(Vla, Org)*: 14 Limesford Road, London SE15 3BX ☎ 020 7639 1087

CARRINGTON Rebecca *(Vla)*: 131 Repton Road, Orpington, Kent BR6 9HY ☎ 01689 603644, 01306 880669 day

CASSIDY Paul *(Vla)*: 31 Park Avenue South, London N8 8LU ☎ 020 8348 2603

CHALLONER Moira *(Vla)*: 28 Hereford Road, Wanstead, London E11 2EA ☎ 020 8530 3237

CHAMBERS Stephanie *(Vla)*: Flat 1, Onslow House, Giddylake, Wimborne, Dorset BH21 2QT ☎ 01202 848285, 0976 691348 mob

CHASE Roger *(Vla)*: 41 Wrentham Avenue, London NW10 3HS ☎ 020 8960 3516

CHASSON Barbara *(Vla)*: 111 Barry Road, London SE22 0HW ☎ 020 8693 0357

CHILD Alan *(Vla, Vln)*: 54 Whitmore Close, New Southgate, London N11 1PB ☎ 020 8368 1720

CHIVERS Martin *(Vla)*: 25 Goldsmid Road, Tonbridge, Kent TN9 2BX ☎ 01732 356770

CLARK William *(Vla)*: 10 Ash Grove, Allington, Maidstone, Kent ME16 0AA ☎ 01622 677873

CLARKE Brian *(Vla)*: 23 Crescent Wood Road, Sydenham Hill, London SE26 6SA ☎ 020 8693 9988

CLEMENTS Samantha *(Vla, Vln)*: 29A Buchan Road, London SE15 3HQ ☎ 020 7564 6782, 01438 727826

CLISBY Donald *(Vla)*

COATES-SMITH Mark *(Vla)*: 48 Rothschild Road, Chiswick, London W4 5HT ☎ 020 8994 0919, 020 8533 1372

COCHRANE Christopher *(Vla, Vln)*: 10 Harvey Gardens, Loughton, Essex IG10 2AD ☎ 020 8502 4977

COCHRANE Lisa *(Vla, Bq Vla)*: 4 St Augustines Road, London NW1 9RN ☎ 020 7916 4824

COHEN Ruth *(Vla)*: 13 Stanhope Road, London N12 9DX ☎ 020 8445 9288, 01306 880669

COLLYER Peter *(Vla)*: 26 Merry Hill Mount, Bushey, Herts WD2 1DJ ☎ 020 8950 3947, 0585 578436 mob

COOKSON Michael *(Vla)*: 186 Mutton Lane, Potters Bar, Herts EN6 2AW ☎ 01707 656178

COOKSON Richard *(Vla)*: 12A Honor Oak Park, London SE23 1DY ☎ 020 8699 3445

COOPER Judith *(Vla)*: 73 Acacia Grove, New Malden, Surrey KT3 3BU ☎ 020 8942 2711

CORNFORD Daniel *(Vla, Vln)*: 9D Hopton Road, Streatham, London SW16 2EH ☎ 020 8673 7521

COTTRELL J *(Vla)*: Address Unknown

COULDRIDGE Simon *(Vla, Vln, Pf, B Gtr)*: 24 Hornbeams Rise, Poplar Grove, Friern Barnet, London N11 3PB ☎ 020 8368 3912, 0956 270735

COULLING John *(Vla, Con)*: Picketts Cottage, Newlands Lane, Glanvilles Wooton, Sherbourne Dorset DT9 5QG ☎ 01300 345450

CRESSWELL Pamela *(Vla, Bq Vla, T Viol)*: 30 Melrose Ave, Potters Bar, Hartfordshire EN6 1TA ☎ 01707 656686

CROSS Charles *(Vla)*: 16 Falkland Road, London NW5 2PX ☎ 020 7267 2395, 0958 259 268

D'ARCY Philip *(Vla, Bq Vla, Vln, E Vln, E Vl)*: 42 Stillness Road, London SE23 1NQ ☎ 020 8690 1302, 0973 128 971

DANFORD David *(Vla)*: 75 Annandale Road, Greenwich, London SE10 0DE ☎ 020 8853 0780

DANKS Harry *(Vla)*: 12 Beverley Gardens, Wembley Park, Middx HA9 9QZ ☎ 020 8904 7271

DAVIES Carolyn *(Vla)*: 2 Vallance Road, Alexandra Park, London N22 4UB ☎ 020 8888 0605

DAVIES Julia *(Vla, Vln)*: 37 Chapel Road, Bexley Heath, Kent DA7 4HW ☎ 020 8298 1525, 0966 539948 mob

DAVIS John *(Vla, Vadam)*: 27 Clifden Road, Twickenham, Middx TW1 4LU ☎ 020 8892 1690

DAVIS Miranda *(Vla)*: 27 Clifden Road, Twickenham, Middx TW1 4LU ☎ 020 8892 1690

DE GRAAL Christoffer *(Vla, Vln, Synth)*: 7A Kirchen Road, West Ealing, London W13 0TY ☎ 020 8579 3626

DEL MAR Antonia *(Vla)*: Appalachian Spring, Coplands Corner, Dartington, Totnes, Devon TQ9 6DJ ☎ 01803 862484

DEL MAR Robin *(Vla)*: 3 Hambalt Road, London SW4 9EA ☎ 020 8673 1061

DEMMEL Karen *(Vla)*: 72 Verdant Lane, London SE6 1LF ☎ 020 8461 5353

DENBIN Nat *(Vla)*: Address Unknown

DENCH Susan *(Vla)*: 3 Royal Cottages, The Common, Cookham Dean, Berks. SL6 9PA ☎ 016284 73912

DENLEY Amanda *(Vla)*: 256 Sirdar Road, Wood Green, London N22 6QX ☎ 020 8881 7256

DICKINSON Scott *(Vla)*: 264 Kirkdale, Sydenham, London SE26 4RS ☎ 020 8778 9407, 0956 865939

DICZKU Ferencz *(Vla, Pf, Org)*: 188A Squires Lane, Finchley, London N3 2QT ☎ 020 8346 0203

DODD Helen-Mary *(Vla)*: 34 Southlands Drive, London SW19 5QB ☎ 020 8944 2813

DRAYCOTT Stephen *(Vla)*: 20 Westhaven Court, Station Road, Market Bosworth, Nuneaton Warwickshire CV13 0PR ☎ 01455 291840

DRISCOLL Elizabeth *(Vla)*: 6 Lyndhurst Avenue, Mill Hill, London NW7 2AB ☎ 020 8959 2010

DRUMMOND Amanda *(Vla, Pf)*: Flat 4, 225 Archway Road, London N6 5BS ☎ 020 8374 8703, 0966 204959

DUFFIELD Michael *(Vla)*: Flat 6, 8 Pembridge Villas, London W11 2SU ☎ 020 7727 3337

DUKES Philip *(Vla)*: 116 Melrose Ave, London NW2 4JX ☎ 020 8450 2018

DUMRESE Maria *(Vla)*: 48 Princes Avenue, London N22 4SA ☎ 020 8889 9826

DUNCAN Robert *(Vla)*: 16 Gander Hill, Haywards Heath, West Sussex RH16 1QX ☎ 01444 453197

EDWARDS Gwynne *(Vla)*: 111 Bargates, Leominster, Herefordshire HR6 8QS ☎ 01568 613053

EDWARDS Myrna *(Vla, Pf)*: 91 Lyonsdown Road, New Barnet, Herts EN5 1JT ☎ 020 8440 4775

EMANUEL Elizabeth *(Vla, Vln)*: 10 Manygate Lane, Shepperton, Middx TW17 9ED ☎ 01932 223869

ERDELYI Csaba *(Vla)*: 2420 Boston Road, Bloomington, IN 47401, USA

ESSEX Ken *(Vla)*: 6 Creighton Avenue, Muswell Hill, London N10 1NU ☎ 020 8883 2025

FAIRHURST Naomi *(Vla)*: 26 Lidfifeld Road, London N16 9LX ☎ 020 7241 5727

FENN Martin *(Vla)*: 7 Fernleigh Road, Winchmore Hill, London N21 3AN ☎ 020 8886 5290, 020 8533 1372

FENTON Daniel *(Vla, Kbds, Pf)*: 78 North Grove, London N15 5QP ☎ 020 8800 4414

FENTON Sebastian *(Vla)*: Flat 2, 26 Grove Hill Road, London SE5 8DG ☎ 020 7274 0085

FERGUSON Duncan *(Vla)*: 90C Jerningham Road, Telegraph Hill, London SE14 5NW ☎ 020 7732 3803, 0976 329051 mob

FILER Penny *(Vla)*: 18 Carew Road, London W13 9QL ☎ 020 8579 3372, 020 8533 1372

FINNIMORE Clare *(Vla, Vla)*: East Cottage, Edworth, Biggleswade, Bedfordshire SG18 8QY ☎ 01767 314055

FLEETCROFT Jack *(Vla)*: 78 Windermere Avenue, London N3 3RA ☎ 020 8346 2036

FLYNN Janice *(Vla)*: 122 New Road, North Ascot, Berks SL5 8QH ☎ 01344 885136 & fax, 0831 385324 mob

FORRESTER John *(Vla)*

FRITH Emily *(Vla)*: 1 Fernbrook Road, Hither Green, London SE13 5NG ☎ 020 8318 1696, 0973 858153 mob

FRYE Robert *(Vla)*: Old Rectory Cottage, Mill Lane, Monks Risborough, Princes Risborough, Bucks HP27 9LG ☎ 01844 273253

FUSE Kenji *(Vla)*: 44A Queens Gardens, London W2 3AA ☎ 020 7402 1323

GELDARD Esther *(Vla)*: 48B Garthorne Road, Honor Oak Park, London SE23 1EW ☎ 020 8699 1631 & fax, 0973 713203 mob, 01306 880669 day

GILES Stephen *(Vla)*: 180 Olney Road, Walworth, London SE17 3HR ☎ 020 7701 6353

GLASSPOOL Wrayburn *(Vla)*: 11 Arlesey Close, Lyttongrove, London SW15 2EX ☎ 020 8788 1788

GLEDSETZER Almut *(Vla)*: 5 Deck Close, Rotherhithe, London SE16 1BU ☎ 020 7252 0209

GLOVER Jason *(Vla)*: 1 Grovefield House, Coppies Grove, New Southgate, London N11 1NS ☎ 020 8361 1349, 0976 418122

GODLEE Rachel *(Vla)*: Deepfield, Orley Farm Road, Harrow-on-the-Hill, Middlesex HA1 3PE ☎ 020 8864 9056

GODSELL David *(Vla)*: 73 Crofters Mead, Addington, Surrey CR0 9HT ☎ 020 8657 0199

GOLDSCHEIDER Christopher *(Vla, Vln)*: 77B Dyne Road, London NW6 7DR ☎ 020 7625 9463 & fax, 0956 557715 mob

GOODWIN Nigel *(Vla)*: 10 Danvers Road, Tonbridge, Kent TN9 1TR ☎ 01732 359643, 01306 880669 day

GORDON Owen *(Vla, Pf)*: 6 Swan Court, Agnes Court, London E14 7DG ☎ 020 7537 2886

GRANT Timothy *(Vla, Vln)*: 12 Winding Shott, Bramfield, Herts SG14 2QP ☎ 01992 504049 & fax, 020 8549 1706 day, 0956 449634 mob

GREEN Rosemary *(Vla, Vadam)*: 5 Bron Y Gader, Abergynolwyn, Tywyn, Gwynedd LL36 9YH ☎ 01654 782631

GREENE Vincent *(Vla)*: 113 Waverley Road, London SE18 7TH ☎ 020 8244 8354

GRIFFITH Fiona *(Vla)*: 2 Farley Drive, Ilford, Essex IG3 8LT ☎ 020 8597 1659, 0802 276980 mob

GRIFFITHS Graham *(Vla)*: Back In Tune, 48 Village Road, London N3 1TJ ☎ 020 8346 5472, 0958 476082 mob

GROUT Keith *(Vla)*: 14 The Crescent, South Harrow, Middlesex HA2 0PJ ☎ 020 8864 1802

GUNES Rusen *(Vla)*: 15 Cressy Road, London NW3 2NB ☎ 020 7485 2888

HALL John *(Vla)*: 58 Avenue Road, Erith, Kent DA8 3AS ☎ 01322 332192

HALL Philip *(Vla)*: 15 Victiora Road, Erith, Kent DA8 3AW ☎ 01322 359743

HALLETT Jonathan *(Vla)*: 163 London Road, Hertford Heath, Hertford SG13 7PN ☎ 01992 589961

HANNINGTON Kenneth *(Vla)*: 8 Hillside Road, Northwood, Middx HA6 1QA ☎ 01923 824916

HARPER Elizabeth *(Vla)*: 2 The Lodge, 80 Parkside, London SW19 5LL ☎ 020 8785 7114, 0976 260211

HARRIOTT Harold *(Vla)*: 156 Lancaster Road, London W11 1QU ☎ 020 7727 5763

HARRIS Amelia *(Vla, Vln)*: 1 Aragon Road, Kingston-on-Thames, Surrey KT2 5QA ☎ 020 8546 6984

HARRISON Caroline *(Vla)*: Flat 5, 103 Thornlaw Road, West Norwood, London SE27 0SQ ☎ 020 8761 0186

HART Katharine *(Vla)*: 28 Lonsdale Square, London N1 1EW ☎ 020 7607 7773

HAWKES William *(Vla, Vln)*: 311 Ivydale Road, London SE15 3DZ ☎ 020 7639 7874, 01306 880669 day

HAWKINS Brian *(Vla)*: The Old Vicarage, 129 Arthur Road, London SW19 7DR ☎ 020 8946 4511, 020 8946 9183 fax

HAXELL Andrew *(Vla)*: 156 Glenesk Road, Eltham, London SE9 1RE ☎ 020 8859 3681

HELLER Kate *(Vla, Bq Vla)*: 3 Reservoir Road, Brockley, London SE4 2NU ☎ 020 7732 7389, 020 8533 1372 day

HENNING Audrey *(Vla)*: 20 Midland Terrace, Cricklewood, London NW2 6QH ☎ 020 8450 0299

HILL Lucy *(Vla)*: 11 Foxenden Road, Guildford, Surrey GU1 4DL ☎ 01483 537382

HILTON Terry *(Vla)*: 16 Dukesthorpe Road, Sydenham, London SE26 4PB ☎ 020 8778 5433

HIRSCHMAN David R. *(Vla)*: 57 Maidstone Road, London N11 2JS ☎ 020 8368 2527, 020 8533 1372

HODGES Laura *(Vla, Vln)*: 51 Longford Road, Whitton, Twickenham, Middlesex TW2 6EB ☎ 020 8893 1642, 01306 880669

HOHMANN-BARKER Patricia *(Vla, Vln)*: 55 Hilmartin Avenue, Norbury, London SW16 4RA ☎ 020 8679 1151

HOLDSWORTH Sheila *(Vla)*: 93 Burnt Ash Road, London SE12 8RF ☎ 020 8852 4413

HOLTTUM Richard *(Vla)*: Upper Blackmoor, Four Elms, Edenbridge, Kent TN8 6PG ☎ 01732 700332

HOOLEY Martin *(Vla)*: 95 Chobham Road, Sunningdale, Ascot, Berkshire SL5 0HQ ☎ 01344 624192, 01306 880669 day

HOWARD Clive *(Vla)*: 13 The Crescent, London E17 8AB ☎ 020 8520 9392

HOWSON Nicholas *(Vla)*: 347 Ivydale Road, London SE15 3ED ☎ 020 7640 2172, 07970 977595 mob, 020 8533 1372 day

HULTMARK Carol *(Vla)*: 29 Roundfield, Upper Bucklebury, Berks RG7 6RA ☎ 01635 862932

HUMBEY Martin *(Vla)*: 2 Chandlers Lane, All Cannings, Devizes, Wiltshire SN10 3PG ☎ 01380 860480, 01306 880669

HUME David *(Vla)*: 34 Arnison Road, East Molesey, Surrey KT8 9JP ☎ 020 8941 3974

HUMPHREYS Patricia *(Vla)*: Almondwood, The Way, Reigate, Surrey RH2 0LD ☎ 01737 247262

HUNT Margaret *(Vla)*: 29 Welsby Court, Eaton Rise, London W5 W5 2EY ☎ 020 8998 6702

HURWITZ Kay *(Vla)*: 25 Dollis Avenue, London N3 1DA ☎ 020 8346 3936

INOUE Yuko *(Vla)*: 106 Hounslow Road, Twickenham, Middx TW2 7HB ☎ 020 8894 5381

IORIO Luciano *(Vla)*: 44 Gondar Gardens, London NW6 1HG ☎ 020 7435 5408, 020 7431 6843 fax

ISSERLIS Annette *(Vla)*: 6 Bottlehouse Cottages, Smarts Hill, Penshurst, Kent TN11 8EU ☎ 01892 870 510

JACKSON Ellen *(Vla)*: 77 Fowlers Walk, Ealing, London W5 1BQ ☎ 020 8998 8950

JACKSON Garfield *(Vla, Vln)*: 39 New Road, Croxley Green, Herts WD3 3EN ☎ 01923 773899, 01306 880669

JAMES Benedict *(Vla)*: 40 Mead Crescent, Sutton, Surrey SM1 3QS ☎ 020 8643 7532

JENKINS Anthony *(Vla)*: 25 Old Kerry Road, Newtown, Powys, Wales SY16 1BP ☎ 01686 626075

JEWEL Ian *(Vla)*: 49 Exeter Road, London NW2 4SE ☎ 020 8452 6843

JEZARD John *(Vla)*: Flat 3, 137 Gloucester Avenue, London NW1 8LA ☎ 020 7586 5740

JOHN Delyth *(Vla)*: Garden Maisonette, 157 Devonshire Road, Forest Hill, London SE23 3NB ☎ 020 8291 0336, 01306 880669

JOHNSTON Malcolm *(Vla)*: 4A York Mansions, Earls Court Road, London SW5 9AF ☎ 020 7373 1259

JOHNSTONE Duncan *(Vla)*: 19A Sydenham Road, Sydenham, London SE26 5EX ☎ 020 8488 7307

JONES Bill *(Vla)*: 68 Swakeleys Drive, Ickenham, Uxbridge, Middx UB10 8QF ☎ 01895 238117

JONES Harry *(Vla)*: Boundary Cottage, 21 Church Hill, Hythe, Kent CT21 5DW ☎ 01303 237 319

JONES Sara *(Vla)*: 3 Ash Court, 113/115 Burntash Hill, Lee, London SE12 0AH ☎ 020 8851 3310, 0976 215233 mob

JONES Wendy *(Vla)*: 12 Toulmin Drive, St Albans, Herts AL3 6EE ☎ 01727 842 624, 020 8533 1372, 0973 382 912 mob

KAMMINGA Helen *(Vla)*: 16A Somerfield Road, London N4 2JJ ☎ 020 7704 1273

KEILLER Pearl *(Vla, Vln)*: Keswick, St Nicolas Avenue, Cranleigh, Surrey GU6 7AQ ☎ 01483 272769

KELLY Martin *(Vla)*: 14 Thorncliffe Road, London SW2 4JQ ☎ 020 8671 3208 & fax

KELLY Matthew *(Vla, Vln)*: 90 Mornington Road, London E11 3DX ☎ 020 8558 6768

KELLY Wendi *(Vla, Bq Vla)*: 28 Valliere Road, London NW10 6AJ ☎ 020 8964 4552, 0378 671798

KING Leon *(Vla)*: 3 Dogsthorpe Road, Peterborough PE1 3AY ☎ 01733 319921, 020 8533 1372

KITCHING Colin *(Vla)*: 28 Barnes Avenue, Chesham, Bucks HP5 1AP ☎ 01494 778117, 01494 771728

KNIEF Helen *(Vla)*: 42A Manor Park Road, London N2 0SJ ☎ 020 8444 3753

KNIGHT Julia *(Vla)*: 20 Ardgowan Road, Hither Green, London SE6 1AJ ☎ 020 8461 3193

KNIGHT Susan *(Vla)*: 19 Grange Hill, London SE25 6XX ☎ 020 8771 3770

KNOX Garth *(Vla)*: 30 Rue Montg_ueil, Paris, France, 75001 ☎ +331 4026 7006

KNUSSEN Bernardine *(Vla)*: The Londesborough Arms, Middle Street, Metheringham, Lincoln ☎ 01526 320637

LALE Peter *(Vla)*: 3 Royal Cottages, The Common, Cookham Dean, Berks SL6 9PA ☎ 016284 73912

LAMB Margaret *(Vla)*: 18 Petersway, York YO3 6AR ☎ 01904 652526

LAU JONG On *(Vla)*: 30 Home Close, Sharnbrook, Bedfordshire MK44 1PQ ☎ 01234 781 960, 0973 294 216, 01234 781 960

LEAVER Michael *(Vla, Vln)*: 68 Deanery Close, East Finchley, London N2 8NT ☎ 020 8365 2676, 04325 31661

LEEK Katharine *(Vla)*: 71 Marlborough Road, London N22 4NJ ☎ 020 8881 3021

LEGGAT Fiona *(Vla, Vln, Pf)*: Address Unknown ☎ 020 8221 0738, 07970 368884

LEGGE Harry *(Vla)*: Garden Flat, 62 Messina Avenue, London NW6 4LE ☎ 020 7624 1221

LEIGHTON Robert *(Vla)*: 36 Oaklands Chase, Weybridge, Surrey KT13 9BT ☎ 01932 226275

LESLIE Joanna *(Vla)*: Manor Farm, Molesworth, Huntingdon, Cambs PE18 0QF ☎ [080 14] 315

LEWIS Eryl Bronwen *(Vla)*: Mill Cottage, Kings Thorn, Hereford HR2 8AW ☎ 01981 540407

LEWIS Peter *(Vla)*: 6 Pasture Close, North Wembley, Middx HA0 3JE ☎ 020 8904 3133

LICHTENSTERN Dorit *(Vla, Vln)*: 11 Leigh Gardens, London NW10 5HN ☎ 020 8969 3135

LLOYD Jacqueline *(Vla)*: 14 Hadley Road, New Barnet, Herts EN5 5HH ☎ 020 8440 2334

LLOYD Michael *(Vla)*: 12 Barham Close, Chislehurst, Kent BR7 6JA ☎ 020 8468 7693

LOGIE Nicholas *(Vla)*: Lotts End, Highgate, Forest Row, East Sussex RH18 5BE ☎ 0134 282 4536

LOVELL Keith *(Vla)*: 3 Beacon Hill, Newton Ferrers, Plymouth PL8 1DB ☎ 01752 873186

LUNDBERG Rosemary *(Vla)*: Tree Tops, 13 New Road, Aston Clinton, Buckinghamshire HP22 5JD ☎ 01296 630046

LYNESS Daniel *(Vla, Vln, Pf)*: 4 Berwyn Road, London SE24 9BD ☎ 020 8265 9436

MACK Brian *(Vla)*: 59 Ribblesdale Avenue, Northolt, Middx UB5 4NG ☎ 020 8864 6497

MACK Pauline *(Vla)*: Hope Cottage, Livery Road, W. Winterslow, Salisbury SP5 1RF ☎ 01980 863 172

MACK Sharada *(Vla)*: Flat 2, 55 Mount Avenue, Ealing, London W5 1PN ☎ 020 8991 0786

MAJOR Margaret *(Vla)*: 97 North Bersted Street, White Barn, Bognor Regis, West Sussex PO22 9AF ☎ 01243 829802

MANNING Gerald *(Vla)*: Three Gables, 68 Manor Road, North Lancing, West Sussex BN15 0HG ☎ 01903 461391

MANNING Judy *(Vla, Voc)*: 23 Wolvesmere, Woolmer Green, Knebworth, Herts SG3 6JW ☎ 01438 813494, 020 8549 1706

MARTELLI Carlo *(Vla, Com)*: 215 Burrage Road, London SE18 7JZ ☎ 020 8316 7905

MARTIN Paul *(Vla)*: Flat 10, 150 Randolph Avenue, Maida Vale, London W9 1PG ☎ 020 7286 1644, 01306 880669 day, 07971 387002 mob

MASKEY Elizabeth *(Vla)*: 99 The Pastures, Chells Manor Village, Stevenage, Herts SG2 7DF ☎ 020 8930 1918

MASTERS Brian *(Vla)*: 29 Pyrford Close, Nyetimber, Bognor Regis, W Sussex PO21 3NL ☎ 01243 261517

MAYES Patricia *(Vla, Cntrc)*: 6 Park Road, Chesham, Bucks HP5 2JE ☎ 01494 786315, 01306 880669

MCCOURT Vincent *(Vla)*: 89 Allenby Road, Southall, Middlesex UB1 2EZ ☎ 020 8575 1041

MCCRACKEN Cathryn *(Vla)*: 26 Fieldhead Gardens, Bourne End, Bucks SL8 5RN ☎ 01628 526469

MCGILLIVRAY Katherine *(Vla, Bq Vla, Vadam)*: 72A Melrose Avenue, London NW2 4JT ☎ 020 8208 0421 & fax

MCKEAN Graeme *(Vla)*: 100 Jerningham Road, London SE14 5NW ☎ 020 7652 5895, 0468 667447 mob

MCVAY Donald *(Vla)*: 16 Beresford Road, New Malden, Surrey KT3 3RQ ☎ 020 8949 7425

MEDROW Alan *(Vla, Vln, Pf)*: 51A Steele Road, Tottenham, London N17 6YJ ☎ 020 8801 0128 & fax

MEEK John *(Vla)*: 56 Montague Close, Walton-on-Thames, Surrey KT12 2NQ ☎ 01932 242818

MELLIARD David *(Vla)*: 54 Sunningfields Road, Hendon, London NW4 4RL ☎ 020 8203 1314

METCALFE Jane *(Vla, Bq Vla)*: 124 St.Anns Hill, Wandsworth, London SW18 2RR ☎ 020 8870 1732

MILLION Esther *(Vla)*: 26 Orchard Gate, Sudbury Hill, Greenford, Middlesex UB6 0QW ☎ 020 8900 1226

MITCHELL Richard *(Vla)*: Highfield West, 188 Cumnor Hill, Oxford OX2 9PJ ☎ 01865 863007

MOORE Jennifer *(Vla)*: Leechpits Cottage, Renby Farm, Eridge Green, Tonbridge Wells, Kent TN3 9LL ☎ 01892 664748

MORRISON Anne *(Vla, Vln)*: 98 Bramshot Avenue, Charlton, London SE7 7JN ☎ 020 8858 6650, 0378 192105

MULDER Berend *(Vla)*: 38 Trossachs Road, London SE22 8PY ☎ 020 8299 9965, 0410 784 914

MURPHY John *(Vla)*: 49 Bristow Road, London SE19 1JX ☎ 020 8670 2484

MURRAY Gillian *(Vla, Vln)*: 131 Farnborough Road, Heath End, Farnham, Surrey GU9 9AW ☎ 01252 325855

MUSKER Catherine *(Vla)*: ☎ 020 8533 1372 day, 020 8766 6966

MYERSCOUGH Henry *(Vla)*: 15 Salterton Road, London N7 6BB ☎ 020 7272 7513

NALDEN Rosemary *(Vla, Bq Vla)*: 27 Willow Road, London NW3 1TL ☎ 020 7435 3040

NELSON Richard *(Vla)*: 46 Macoma Road, London SE18 2QP ☎ 020 8854 8491

NEWLAND David *(Vla)*: 27 Liphook Crescent, Forest Hill, London SE23 3BN ☎ 020 8699 4227

NEWMAN Michael *(Vla)*: 72 Verdant Lane, London SE6 1LF ☎ 020 8461 5353, 020 8533 1372

NEWNHAM Arnold *(Vla)*: 35 Selwyn Crescent, Hatfield, Hertfordshire AL10 9NL

NI CHONAILL Niamh *(Vla)*: 24 Lacon Road, East Dulwich, London SE22 9HE ☎ 020 8299 1253

NORRIS Susan *(Vla, Bq Vla, Vadag, Rec)*: 76 Mowbrays Road, Romford, Essex RM5 3EL ☎ 01708 720134

NORRISS Peter *(Vla)*: 15 Greenfinches, New Barn, Longfield, Kent DA3 7ND ☎ 01474 705265

O'NEILL Caroline *(Vla)*: 32 Earlsthorpe Road, London SE26 4PD ☎ 020 8244 3203, 0976 275030

ORSLER Claire *(Vla)*: 2 Willow Corner, Bayford, Nr. Hertford, Herts SG13 8PN ☎ 01992 511392

OUTRAM Martin *(Vla)*: 12 Broad Green Wood, Bayford, Herts SG13 8PS ☎ 01992 511486

OWEN Gruffydd *(Vla, Pf)*: 57 Park Avenue, London N13 5PG ☎ 020 8882 2551

PADEL William *(Vla, Vln)*: 54 Queenscourt, Wembley, Middx HA9 7QU ☎ 020 8902 2063

PAGE Stella *(Vla, Vln)*: Flat 1, 34 Milton Avenue, Highgate, London N6 5QE ☎ 020 8374 0614

PARFITT Sarah *(Vla, Viol)*: 7 Yerbury Road, London N19 4RN ☎ 020 7281 5794, 0378 194803, 020 8533 1372 day

PARKER Andrew *(Vla)*: 85 Muswell Avenue, Muswell Hill, London N10 2EH ☎ 020 8444 3822

PEAKE Richard *(Vla)*: Flat K, Heather Court, 150 Leigham Court Road, London SW16 2RJ ☎ 020 8769 1241

PEARCE Christopher *(Vla)*: 7 Grove Terrace, North Road, Southall, Middlesex UB1 2JG ☎ 020 8571 2524

PEERLESS Mary *(Vla)*: 2 Ashburton, 118 Richmond Hill, Richmond, Surrey TW10 6RJ ☎ 020 8940 0578

PENDLEBURY Nicholas *(Vla)*: 21 Hamlet Road, Upper Norwood, London SE19 2AP ☎ 020 8771 8163 eve, 020 8533 1372 day, 0410 328 046 mob

PERKINS Jeremy *(Vla)*: Flat 2, 42 Hermons Hill, Wanstead, London E11 2AP ☎ 020 8530 3506, 0402 018660

PESKETT Elisabeth *(Vla)*: 72 Felpham Way, Felpham, Bognor Regis, West Sussex PO22 8QU ☎ 01243 822922, 0973 326936 mob

PITSILLIDES Chris *(Vla, Vln)*: 10 Viewland Road, London SE18 1PE ☎ 020 8854 4965 & fax, 0973 415927 mob, 01306 500011

POLLANI Benedetto *(Vla)*: 19A Becondale Road, London SE19 1QJ ☎ 020 8766 8483, 0850 510245 mob

PONDER Michael *(Vla)*: 55 Lincoln Road, London N2 9DJ ☎ 020 8444 2541

POOK Jocelyn *(Vla)*: 131 Tottenham Road, London N1 4EA ☎ 020 7254 1434

POPE Sarah *(Vla)*: 55 Fulwood Walk, Augustus Road, London SW19 6RB ☎ 01 788 8803

POSNER Michael *(Vla)*: 46 Harold Road, London SE19 3PL ☎ 020 8653 9446, 0958 902081 mob

PRENTICE Thomas *(Vla)*: 38 Sandhurst Road, Catford, London SE6 1XE ☎ 020 8858 3054, 0468 808732 mob

PRESLY Maura *(Vla)*: 178 Gloucester Terrace, London W2 6HT ☎ 020 7262 2661

PRETTEJOHN Beryl *(Vla)*: 72 Ellwood Avenue, Peterborough PE2 8LY ☎ 01733 566564

PUGH Richard *(Vla)*: Cowpen Cottage, Selborne, Alton, Hants GU34 3JA ☎ 01420 511342

PULLMAN James *(Vla)*: Basement Flat, 5 Templar Street, Camberwell, London SE5 9JB ☎ 020 7263 4847, 0958 693322

PUZEY Robert *(Vla, Vln)*: 47 Miranda Road, London N19 3RA ☎ 020 7263 3560, 01306 880669

QUENBY Matthew *(Vla)*: 65 Ashcombe Road, Wimbledon, London SW19 8JP ☎ 020 8543 0871, 01306 880669

RAMSAY Francis *(Vla, Kbds, Pf)*: Flat 9, 37 Sussex Square, Brighton BN2 5AD ☎ 01273 620176

RATHBONE Ian *(Vla)*: 38 Hermiston Avenue, London N8 8NP ☎ 020 8340 3693, 0973 832416 mob, 020 8533 1372 day

RAWSON Irmeli *(Vla)*: 21 Leopold Avenue, London SW19 7ET ☎ 020 8946 0290

RAYSON John *(Vla)*: 502 Thames Tunnel Mill, 113 Rotherhithe Street, London SE16 4NJ ☎ 020 7231 5060, 01523 125509 mob

REECE Eilen *(Vla, Vln, Pf)*: 160 Copleston Road, East Dulwich, London SE15 4AF ☎ 020 8693 5072, 0797 7501726

RENSHAW Sophie *(Vla, Vln)*: 181C Belsize Road, West Hampstead, London NW6 4AB ☎ 020 7624 4592 & fax

RICH Gerald *(Vla)*: Address Unknown

RICHARDSON Geoffrey *(Vla, Vln, Man, Gtr)*: 13 Cromwell Road, Whitstable, Kent CT5 1NW ☎ 0410 256 374 mob

Musical Instruments at Auction

- Six Annual Sales

- Reduced Vendors Commission for MU members

- Free Auction Valuations

- Unique 'Try Before you Buy' Service

For further information about buying or selling at Bonhams, please call **Peter Horner or Elisabeth Tölken** on

0171 393 3958

or visit our Internet Site www.bonhams.com for more details

A fine Cello by Giovanni Grancino, Cremona, c. 1700. Sold for £177,500

BONHAMS
—— AUCTIONEERS & VALUERS SINCE 1793 ——

Montpelier Street, London SW7 1HH. U.K.
Tel: 0171 393 3900 Fax: 0171 393 3959
Internet: www.bonhams.com

ROBERTSON George (Vla): Flat 30, Brookfield, 5 Highgate West Hill, London N6 6AT ☎ 020 8341 0076

RODDAM Catherine (Vla, Vln, Pf): 4 Cranmer Road, Croydon, Surrey CR0 1SR ☎ 020 8688 4522

ROGERS John (Vla): 86B Brixton Hill, London SW2 1QN ☎ 020 8671 6078, 020 8671 6078

ROWBOTHAM Ian (Vla, Arr): 21 Hewitt Road, London N8 0BS ☎ 020 8347 8174, 0370 416 158, 01483 451700 day

ROWLANDS Nigel (Vla, Vln): 6A Norwich Road, Forest Gate, London E7 9JH ☎ 020 8555 0627, 0836 547837 mob, 020 8534 2570

RUSE Kathleen (Vla): 20A Bishopsthorpe Road, Sydenham, London SE26 4NY ☎ 020 8659 4878

RYCROFT Anne (Vla, Pf): Old Tyles, Western Road, Hailsham, East Sussex BN27 3EJ ☎ 01323 841025

SALTER Susan (Vla): Lawn Cottage, 23A Brackley Road, Beckenham, Kent BR3 1RB ☎ 020 8658 6771

SAMUEL Anna (Vla): Stream Farm, Battle, East Sussex TN33 0HJ ☎ 01424 772538, 01306 880669

SANDERSON Rosemary (Vla): 9 Munts Meadow, Weston, Herts SG7 6DA ☎ 01462 491378, 01306 880669

SARGON Eric (Vla): 29 Hartland Drive, Edgware, Middx HA8 8RJ ☎ 020 8958 5263

SCAHILL Alistair (Vla): 36 Ridgeway Crescent, Tonbridge, Kent TN10 4NR ☎ 01732 351616

SCHIELE Brian (Vla): 14 Buckstone Hill, Edinburgh EH10 6TH ☎ 0131 445 3084, 0131 445 7969

SCHLAPP Jan (Vla): 1 Malvern Road, London E8 3LT ☎ 020 7249 3123

SCHOFIELD Michael (Vla, Vln): 12 Haslemere Avenue, Ealing, London W13 9UJ ☎ 020 8579 4624, 01306 880669 day

SCOTT Carolyn (Vla, Pf): 12 Laurie Gray Avenue, Blue Bell Hill, Chatham, Kent ME5 9DF ☎ 01634 670410

SCOTT Graeme (Vla): 9 Byron Hill Road, Harrow-on-the-Hill, Middx HA2 0JE ☎ 020 8423 0067, 01306 880669

SCOTT Ian (Vla): 3 Tilsworth Road, Beaconsfield, Buckinghamshire HP9 1TR ☎ 01494 675168

SERMON Peter (Vla): 42 Avenue Gardens, Mill Hill Park, London W3 8HB ☎ 020 8248 9198

SEYMOUR Marion (Vla): 105 Perryfield Way, Ham, Richmond, Surrey TW10 7SN ☎ 020 8940 4640

SHAKESHAFT Stephen (Vla): 26 Common View, Rusthall, Tunbridge Wells, Kent TN4 8RG ☎ 01892 540576, 020 8549 1706

SHARP Elizabeth (Vla, Vln): 8 Pine Grove, Maidstone, Kent ME14 2AJ ☎ 01622 763503

SHAVE Katherine (Vla, Vln): 5 Lymington Close, Beckton, London E6 5YW ☎ 01206 298795, 0956 680928

SHAW Julian (Vla): 62 Chestnut Road, West Norwood, London SE27 9LE ☎ 020 8761 4221

SILVERTHORNE Paul (Vla): 22 Merton Rise, London NW3 3EN ☎ 020 7419 7228, 0831 276403 mob, 020 7586 7268

SIPPINGS Andrew (Vla): 69 Friern Watch Avenue, London N12 9NY ☎ 020 8445 0116

SIROTA Sophie (Vla, Voc): 27 Ordnance Hill, St John's Wood, London NW8 6PR ☎ 020 7483 1174

SLEIGH James (Vla): 91 Wiverton Road, London SE26 5JB ☎ 020 8776 8695, 01306 880669, 0860 692132

SMISSEN Robert (Vla): 12 Yorke Road, Croxley Green, Hertfordshire WD3 3DN ☎ 01923 896911

SMITH Adrian (Vla): 103 Petts Wood Road, Petts Wood, Orpington, Kent BR5 1JX ☎ 01689 835278

SMITH Andrew (Vla): 61 Littell Tweed, Chelmer Village, Chelmsford, Essex CM2 6SH ☎ 01245 465885

SMITH Claire (Vla): 11 Oxdowne Close, Cobham, Surrey KT11 2SZ ☎ 0498 528069

SMITH Isabel (Vla, Gtr, Man): 37 Estelle Road, London NW3 2JX ☎ 020 7267 0388

SOUTER Matthew (Vla): Friars Cottage, Friars Farm, Wimbish, Saffron Walden, Essex CB10 2XT ☎ 01799 586 377, 01306 880669 day

SPENCER Sheila (Vla): 1 Peterborough Road, Collingham, Newark, Notts NG23 7SP ☎ 01636 892183

SPRIGGS Robert (Vla): 37 Temple Gardens, Golders Green, London NW11 0LP ☎ 020 8458 4933

ST LEON Josephine (Vla): 75 Jackson Road, Bromley Common, Kent BR2 8NT ☎ 020 8462 0042, 0306 880669

STAPLES Andrew (Vla): 92 Chatham Road, London SW11 6HG ☎ 020 7228 3901

STIRLING Dittany (Vla): 11A Montague Road, Dalston, London E8 2HN ☎ 020 7241 4689, 0956 574127 mob

STOBBART David (Vla): 91 Moss Lane, Pinner, Middlesex HA5 3AT ☎ 020 8866 0139

STURT Merlyn (Vla): 27 Cambridge Road, North Harrow, Middlesex HA2 7LA ☎ 020 8427 2120, 01426 289462

STUTZER Ernestine (Vla, Vln): c/o Gerner, Karolinenstr.12, D- 14165, Berlin, Germany W4 2QT ☎ +49 30 8013013

SUMPTON William (Vla, Vln): Flat 2, 25 Cheyne Place, London SW3 4HJ ☎ 020 7352 5412

SWAINSON James (Vla): Mount Pleasant, 20 Main Street, Long Preston, Nth Yorkshire BD23 4PH ☎ 01729 840883, 01729 840843 fax

SWEET Fay (Vla): 9 Croxley Road, London W9 3HH ☎ 020 8969 0456

TAYLOR Natalie (Vla): 113 Pembury Road, Tottenham, London N17 8LY ☎ 020 8808 1294

TAYLOR Susan (Vla): Dundale, 1A Oakland Way, Flackwell Heath, Bucks HP10 9ED ☎ 01628 524551

TEES Stephen (Vla, Per): 88 High Street, Kimpton, Hitchin, Herts SG4 8QW ☎ 01438 832531

THEO Lucy (Vla): 51 Hertford Road, East Finchley, London N2 9BX ☎ 020 8444 4065, 0966 528 931

THOMAS Allen (Vla): 115 Leicester Road, New Barnet, Herts EN5 5EA ☎ 020 8440 4504

THOMPSON Penelope (Vla): 103 Salisbury Road, High Barnet, Herts EN5 4JL ☎ 020 8440 8746

TIR Kayleigh (Vla): 72 Brecknock Road, Islington, London N7 0DB ☎ 020 7609 1518

TOPHAM James (Vla, Man, Vln, Hmca): 219 Portnall Road, London W9 3BL ☎ 020 8968 4654

TREDENNICK Joy (Vla): 5 Conical Corner, Enfield, Middx EN2 6SL ☎ 020 8367 6284

TUCKER Helen (Vla): 70 Cricklade Avenue, Streatham Hill, London SW2 3HQ ☎ 020 8674 3649, 020 8533 1372

TURNER Michael (Vla): 49 Rayleigh Road, Wimbledon, London SW19 3RE ☎ 020 8540 9498

TURNER Robert (Vla): 42 Patterson Road, Crystal Palace, London SE19 2LD ☎ 020 8653 9788

TURNLUND George (Vla): Wansum End, The Street, St Nicholas At Wade, Birchington. Kent CT7 0NT ☎ 01843 847493

TURRELL Robert (Vla): Bradbourne Farmhouse, Bradbourne Vale Road, Sevenoaks, Kent TN13 3DH ☎ 01732 455641

TYLER Jane (Vla, Vln): 10 Meadow Close, Catford, London SE6 3NW ☎ 020 8695 6004, 01306 880669

ULLMANN Ania (Vla): 19 Roxeth Hill, Harrow-on-the-Hill, Middlesex HA2 0JY ☎ 020 8422 1235, 01306 500011 day

UNDERWOOD John (Vla): Mashay Hall, Belchamp Road, Little Yeldham, Halstead, Essex CO9 4JY ☎ 01787 237284, 020 8549 1706 day, 01787 237970 fax

VALDIMARSDOTTIR Asdis (Vla): 69 Landcroft Road, East Dulwich, London SE22 9JS ☎ 020 8693 7414, 020 8299 0750

VAN DER WERFF Ivo (Vla): College House, 56 Nethercote Road, Tackley, Oxford OX5 3AT ☎ 01869 331273, 020 8549 1706 day

VANDERSPAR Edward (Vla): 20 Earlsthorpe Road, Sydenham, London SE26 4PD ☎ 020 8778 7190

VARLOW Elizabeth (Vla): 211 Friern Road, East Dulwich, London SE22 0BD ☎ 020 8693 8479, 020 8693 8479

VIJTOVITCH Andreij (Vla): 45 Seymour Court, Eversleigh Pk Road, Winchmore Hill, London N21 1JQ ☎ 020 8447 8301 & fax

VOGEL Dorothea (Vla, Bq Vla): 23 Ingham Road, London NW6 1DG ☎ 020 7431 2021

WADE Rebecca (Vla): 1 Almington Street, London N4 3BP ☎ 01 272 9860/207

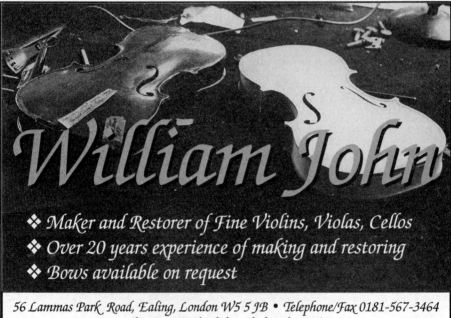

WALKER Jake *(Vla)*: 32 Upper Mall, Hammersmith, London W6 9TA ☎ 020 8563 7253 & fax, 0956 578335 mob

WALKER James *(Vla)*: 10 The Chase, Ton Road, Llangybi, Usk, Gwent NP5 1TY ☎ 01633 450358, 020 7207 0007

WARD Justin *(Vla)*: 7 Cavendish Drive, Claygate, Surrey KT10 0QE ☎ 01372 464984, 01306 880669

WARD Sally *(Vla, Vln)*: 4 Rosebery Road, Ground Floor Flat, London N10 2LH ☎ 020 8444 2107, 0831 583537

WARDMAN Vicci *(Vla)*: 31 Thornhill Square, Islington, London N1 1BQ ☎ 020 7607 2105, 020 7607 2105

WATSON Elizabeth *(Vla, Vadag, Bq Vla, Vln)*: 3 Ormonde Road, London SW14 7BE ☎ 020 8876 1445, 01306 880669 day

WEBBERLEY Judith *(Vla)*: 6 Northway Court, Litchfield Way, London NW11 6NX ☎ 020 8458 7859

WELCH Jonathan *(Vla)*: 44 Burton Road, Kingston-upon-Thames, Surrey KT2 5TF ☎ 020 8287 3063

WELCH Timothy *(Vla)*: 16 Highfield Road, Bushey, Nr Watford, Herts WD2 2HD ☎ 01923 222796

WELLINGTON Christopher *(Vla, Vadam)*: 13 Cambridge Road, New Malden, Surrey KT3 3QE ☎ 020 8949 6621

WEXLER Rebecca *(Vla)*: 14 Buckstone Hill, Edinburgh EH10 6TH ☎ 0131 445 3084, 0131 445 7969

WHIPPLE Teresa *(Vla, Ob, Pf)*: 2 Red Lion Place, Shooters Hill, London SE18 3RN ☎ 020 8856 5971

WHITE Bruce *(Vla)* ☎ 0973 882819 mob, 020 7433 3216

WHITE Ian *(Vla, Vadam)*: 4 Constable Road, Felixstowe, Suffolk IP11 7HH ☎ 01923 28 3526

WHITE Jeremy *(Vla)*: Castle Moat, Clun, Craven Arms, Shrops SY7 8JA ☎ 01588 640212

WHITTLE Mary *(Vla, Pf, Vln)*: 14 Maxwelton Close, London NW7 3NA ☎ 020 8906 3226

WILEMAN Alan *(Vla)*: 11 St James Road, Carshalton, Surrey SM5 2DT ☎ 01 773 4908 eve, 0973 502339 mob

WILKINSON Katie *(Vla)*: 24 Rosenthorpe Road, London SE15 3EG ☎ 020 7358 9259, 0973 399554 mob, 01306 880669 day

WILLIAMS Andrew *(Vla)*: 256 Sirdar Road, Wood Green, London N22 6QX ☎ 020 8881 7256, 0410 352082 mob, 01483 451700 day

WILLIAMS Louise *(Vla, Vln)*: 10A Paultons Street, London SW3 5DP ☎ 020 7352 8588

WILLIAMS Shani *(Vla)*: 78B Clarendon Road, Walthamstow, London E17 9AZ ☎ 020 8520 4408, 020 8444 3657

WILLIAMSON Felicity *(Vla, Vln, Pf)*: 3 Townshend Terrace, Richmond, Surrey TW9 1XJ ☎ 020 8940 1537

WILLIAMSON Malcolm *(Vla)*: 3 Townshend Terrace, Richmond, Surrey TW9 1XJ ☎ 020 8940 1537

WOODS Jacquelyn *(Vla)*: 10 Queens Avenue, Finchley, London N3 2NP ☎ 020 8346 7071, 0956 299306

WORN Philippa *(Vla)*: 84 Ferme Park Road, London N8 9SD ☎ 020 8347 6630/1, 020 8533 1372 day

WRIGHT Mary *(Vla, Pf)*: Flat 1, 31 Castlebar Road, Ealing, London W5 2DJ ☎ 020 8998 0158

WRIGHT Stephen *(Vla)*: 1 Newton Road, Barton-on-Sea, Hampshire BH25 7AS ☎ 01425 638664, 01306 500011, 0973 193029

WYNNE Lesley *(Vla)*: 2 Midland Terrace, London NW2 6QH ☎ 020 8452 4261

YENDOLE Lucy *(Vla)*: 197 Lymington Avenue, London N22 6JL ☎ 020 8881 7229

YOUNG Wendy *(Vla)*: 97 Kirkton Road, London N15 5EY ☎ 020 8809 7268

ZAGNI Gina *(Vla, Org, Pf)*: 2 Stoney Lane, Thaxted, Essex CM6 2PF ☎ 01371 830802, 0958 543093

ZAGNI Madeleine *(Vla)*: Address Unknown ☎ 020 7733 6872

ZARB Nikos *(Vla)*: 59 Empress Avenue, Ilford, Essex IG1 3DG ☎ 020 8554 9052

ZINGALE Licia *(Vla)*: Flat C, 50 Woodstock Road, London NW11 8QE ☎ 020 8201 8156

VIOLIN
SCOTLAND

AITCHISON Duncan: Neverland, Livera Street, Evanton, Ross & Cromarty IV16 9XZ ☎ 01349 830966

AITKEN I: Address Unknown

ALEXANDER James *(Org, Pf)*: 1 Auchenhalrig Cotts, Speybay, Fochabers, Moray IV32 7PP ☎ 01343 820870

ALLAN Alister *(Voc, Pf, Md)*: 18 Castle View, Letham, Perth PH1 2JW ☎ 01738 633979

ANGUS John: 5 Westholme Crescent South, Aberdeen AB15 6AF ☎ 01224 318084

BAILIE Kathryn *(Bq Vln)*: 6 Dalmellington Drive, Crookston, Glasgow G53 7GD ☎ 0141 883 4793, 07771 550872

BAIN Aly: Whirlie Records, 14 Broughton Place, Edinburgh EH1 3RX ☎ 0131 557 9099

BAMPING Elizabeth: Flat 2/3, 173 Deanston Drive, Glasgow G41 3JZ ☎ 0141 632 7165

BAXTER William: Drumcarrow, 7 Bonfield Road, Strathkinness, Fife KY16 9RR ☎ 01334 85787

BEALES Jon *(Kbds)*: 2 Salmond Place, Edinburgh EH7 5ST ☎ 0131 661 9154

BEATON Willie: Bay View, Erbusaig, By Kyle Of Lochalsh, Ross Shire IV40 8BB ☎ 01599 4648

BENNETT-KNIGHT Martyn *(Vla, Bag, Flt, Kbds)*: Address Unknown ☎ 0131 229 6016

BERRY William: 24 Westbourne Drive, Bearsden, Glasgow G61 4BH ☎ 0141 942 6911

BERTELLI Carlo: Address Unknown

BIRSE Moira: 12 Turnberry Crescent, Bridge Of Don, Aberdeen AB22 8PD

BLYTHE Astrid: 39 Henderson Street, Lansdowne Court, Glasgow G20 6HP ☎ 0141 334 1158, 01259 760207

BOHONEK Vaclav: 23 Dunellan Road, Milngavie, Glasgow G62 7RE ☎ 0141 956 6288

BOLTON Malcolm: 18 Ferryhill Terrace, Aberdeen AB1 2SQ

BRADLEY Hugh: 33 Alexandra Road, Lenzie, Kirkintilloch G66 5BA ☎ 0141 776 4139

BROGAN (NEE OMMER) Andrea: 26 Blane Drive, Milngavie, Glasgow G62 8HG ☎ 0141 956 2841

BROWN Eric: 100 Essex Drive, Jordanhill, Glasgow G14 9LX ☎ 0141 954 4736, 0850 623266 mob

BROWN Jane Susan: 7, Orleans Avenue, Jordanhill, Glasgow G14 9LA ☎ 0141 959 1825

BROWN Marie: 85 Westerton Avenue, Glasgow G61 1HR ☎ 0141 942 8142

BRUCE Arthur *(Vla)*: 39 Countesswells Crescent, Aberdeen AB15 8LN ☎ 01224 313792

BUCHANAN Lesley *(Pf)*: 56 Cartvale Road, Top Right, Langside, Glasgow G42 9SW ☎ 0141 632 5874

BURRIN Philip *(Vla)*: 283 Crow Road, Glasgow G11 7BQ ☎ 0141 357 2944

BUTTERWORTH Alexandra *(Pf, Bq Vln)*: 19 Queen Street, Stirling FK8 1HL ☎ 01786 478685

BUTTON Philip: 69 Curling Hall, Largs, Ayrshire KA30 8LB ☎ 01475 689129

BUURMAN Bernardus: 74 Norse Road, Scotstoun, Glasgow G14 9EF ☎ 0141 959 2797

CALDWELL Nan: Address Unknown ☎ Irvine 216372

CALVERT Robin *(Vla)*: Riedchalmai, Rogart, Sutherland IV28 3XE ☎ 01408 641451

CAMPBELL-KELLY Peter: 107 Woodhall Road, Colinton, Edinburgh EH13 0HP ☎ 0131 441 4247

CARPENTER Julia: 32 Gowanlea Drive, Giffnock, Glasgow G46 6HN ☎ 0141 637 7204

CHALMERS T *(Cel, Clt, Saxes)*: Address Unknown

CHRISTIE Robert: 204 Cultenhove Road, St Ninians, Stirling FK7 9EF ☎ 01786 461235

CLARK Justine: Address Unknown

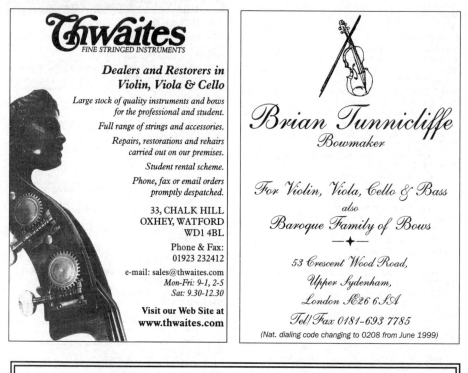
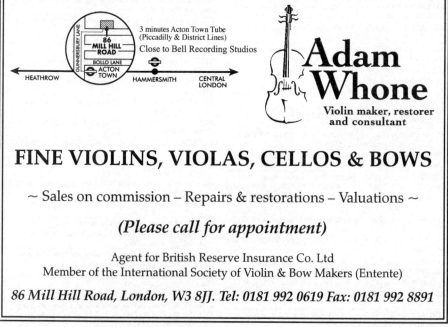

CLARK Pete *(Fo Fdl, Vla)*: The West Wing, Wester Auchnaguie, Tulliemet, Perthshire PH9 0PA ☎ 01796 482 549

CLEMENT Elizabeth *(Vla)*: 96 Morningside Drive, Edinburgh EH10 5NT ☎ 0131 447 3113

COWAN Lucy *(Bq Vln, Vla, Bq Vla, Mando)*: 12A Tower Road, Tweedmouth, Berwick-upon-Tweed TD15 2BD ☎ 01289 303982

CROCKETT Cheryl: 310 Holburn Street, Aberdeen, Scotland AB10 7GX ☎ 01224 592294, 0958 545818

CROSSAN John: Baligarve Schoolhouse, Isle Of Lismore, Oban, Argyll PA34 5UR ☎ 01631 760262

CRUICKSHANK Brian *(Db, B Gtr)*: Morven, Main Road, Lumphanan AB31 4PX ☎ 013398 83582, 013398 83587 fax

CURRIE Leslie: 41 Bayne Drive, Dingwall, Inverness IV15 9UB ☎ 01349 864650

CURTIS Robert: Little Logie, Newlands Of Delnies, Moss Side, Nairn, Scotland IV12 5NZ ☎ 01667 54971

DALGLEISH David James: 35 Penicuik Road, Roslin, Midlothian EH25 9LJ ☎ 0131 440 0519

DARGIE Bryan: 37 Mile-End Avenue, Aberdeen, Scotland AB15 5PT ☎ 01224 635792

DEPETTES Gloria: East Malletsheugh, Newton Mearns, Glasgow G77 6PR ☎ 0141 639 6375

DESSON-MURRAY Patricia: Trinity House, West Linton, Peebleshire EH46 7EA ☎ 01968 60638

DICKIN Robert: 12 Hillfoot Drive, Bearsden, Glasgow G61 3QQ ☎ 0141 942 8805

DICKSON Penelope: 71A Partickhill Road, Glasgow G11 5AD ☎ 0141 357 3537 & fax

DIGNEY Janette: Creagmhor Lodge, Lochard Road, Aberfoyle, Stirling FK8 3TD ☎ 01877 382636

DOCHERTY Bernard: Albany, 19 Iain Road, Bearsden G61 4PA ☎ 0141 943 1563

DOHERTY Gerard: 28 Brackenrig Crescent, Waterfoot, Glasgow G76 0HF ☎ 0141 644 4243, 0973 717013 mob

DOIG John *(Pf, Con)*: Endrick Mews, Killearn, By Glasgow G63 9ND ☎ 01360 550588

DUDDING Hilary: 15 Queen Street, Helensburgh G84 9QJ ☎ 01436 671969

DUFFIN Lesley: 73 Dunchurch Road, Oldhall, Paisley PA1 3EX ☎ 0141 882 5024

DUNCAN Mary J: Gfl 20 Wardlaw Place, Edinburgh EH11 1UF ☎ 0131 346 2371

DUNN Lawrence *(Vla, Bq Vln, Bq Vla)*: 5 St Marks Lane, Portobello, Edinburgh EH15 2PX ☎ 0131 669 3394

DYER Muriel: Nether Lyleston, Cardross, Argyll G82 5HF ☎ 01389 841261

EDWARD Robert: Address Unknown ☎ 01382 88765

ELDER Morag-Anne *(Vla)*: 5 Provost Road, Tayport, Fife DD6 9JE

ELLIS John: Isla Cottage, Wellbank, Dundee DD5 3PE ☎ 0182 625 304

EMSLIE Susan: 70 Comiston Road, Edinburgh EH10 5QQ ☎ 0131 447 7002

FERGUSON Jane: 3 Denovan Crescent, Kippen, Stirling FK8 3HJ ☎ 01786 870432, 0973 769186 mob

FFOULKES Christopher: 2 Hyndland Avenue, Glasgow G11 5BW ☎ 0141 334 9018

FIELD Christopher *(Ea Stg, Rec)*: 2 Maynard Road, St Andrews, Fife KY16 8RX

FLACK Elizabeth: 4 Islay Avenue, Burnside, Glasgow G73 5NH ☎ 0141 649 4592

FLEMING Vincent *(Vla)*: Flat 2/L, 49 Park Road, Glasgow G4 9JD ☎ 0141 334 4162, 04325 189140 pager

FOLEY Edward: Flat 1/1, 3 Barnwell Terrace, Glasgow G51 4TP ☎ 0141 445 4080, 0141 332 8676

FOWLIE Marjory *(Vla)*: Esdaile, Sandyhill Road, Banff AB45 1BE ☎ 01261 818962

FRAYLING-KELLY Frederick *(Vla, Tbn, Tba, Org)*: 2 Wellington Place, Leith, Edinburgh EH6 7EG ☎ 0131 554 0568

GASCOINE Alexander: 16 Lindsay Place, Kelvindale, Glasgow G12 0HX ☎ 0141 357 1826 & fax

GENEVER Norman *(Sax)*: 13 Tressilian Gardens, Edinburgh EH16 6YS ☎ 0131 664 2608

GIBSON Jerre: 66 Leicester Avenue, Glasgow G12 0ND ☎ 0141 357 0835

GILLIES Archibald *(Vla)*: 17 Crown Circus, Inverness IV2 3NU ☎ 01463 232646

GLOVER Mabel: 57 Bellshaugh Place, Kelvinside, Glasgow G12 0PF ☎ 0141 357 1748

GODSON Daphne *(Ea Stg)*: 48/11 Learmonth Avenue, Edinburgh EH4 1HT ☎ 0131 343 1556

GOSKIRK Donald *(Vla, Con, Md)*: 7 Camore Gardens, Dornoch, Sutherland IV25 3HX ☎ 01862 810547

GOULD Edna: 25 Forth Reach, St Davids Bay, Dalgety Bay, Fife KY11 5FF ☎ 01383 820810

GOURDIE Isabel: 10 Alwyn Avenue, Craigends Estate, Houston, Renfrewshire PA6 7LH ☎ 01505 612636

GOVE Laura *(Pf)*: Top Right, 98 Raeberry Street, Glasgow G20 6EG ☎ 0141 946 5683

GRAHAM John *(Gtr, Man, Bjo)*: 52 Munro Road, Glasgow G13 1SF ☎ 0141 954 5235

GRAHAM William: 15 Cheviot Place, Grangemouth FK3 0DE ☎ 01324 484801

GRANT Donald: 2 Brae Roy Road, Roybridge, Inverness-Shire PH31 4AJ ☎ 07957 110714

GRAY Hebbie *(Sax)*: 46 Mar Court, Keith, Banffshire AB55 3DH ☎ 01542 882210

HAINEY Wilson: 5 Devonshire Terrace, Dowan Hill, Glasgow G12 0XE ☎ 0141 334 6446

HALE Brian: 71 Morningside Drive, Edinburgh EH10 5NJ ☎ 0131 446 0305

HARDIE Alastair *(Pf, Vla)*: 35 Mountcastle Terrace, Edinburgh EH8 7SF ☎ 0131 657 2097

HARKESS Lynda *(Pf)*: Friarton Bank, Rhynd Road, Perth PH2 8PT ☎ 01738 643435

HASLAM Sharon *(Bq Vln)*: Flat 4, 37 Glencairn Drive, Pollokshields, Glasgow G41 4QW ☎ 0141 423 2679

HASTIE Alison *(Vla)*: 1 Lomond View Cottages, Westfield, Bathgate, West Lothian EH48 3DE ☎ 01506 652455

HASTIE Stephen *(Tbn)*: 13 Craigleith Hill Green, Edinburgh EH4 2ND ☎ 0131 332 6851

HATRICK Sara *(Pf)*: 22 Heron Court, Clydebank, Glasgow G81 6BB ☎ 01389 890760, 01389 384016 fax, 07931 959307 mob

HAYNES Esme: Address Unknown

HAYWARD Mark: 9 Garrioch Quadrant, Glasgow G20 8RT ☎ 0141 946 5270, 0966 181522 mob

HEIDECKER Ursula: Flat 2, 1 Broomhill Terrace, Glasgow G11 7AG ☎ 0141 334 6114

HESS Gabrielle: 4A Chalmers Crescent, Edinburgh EH9 1TR ☎ 0131 668 3278

HOPE Anne *(Pf)*: 6 Weir Avenue, Prestwick, Ayrshire KA9 2JY ☎ 01292 70400

HOWELLS Jean: 8 Salisbury Road, Edinburgh EH16 5AB ☎ 0131 667 5963

HUGHES Martin: 1 The Gables, Shandon, Helensborough G84 8NR ☎ 01436 821634

HULL Katie: 32 Duncan Ave, Scotstoun, Glasgow G14 9HN ☎ 0141 954 2959

ISAACS Peter: 32 Woodend Drive, Jordanhill, Glasgow G13 1QT ☎ 0141 954 1627

JAMES Diane: Dunstaffnage, 5 Mount Pleasant Drive, Old Kilpatrick, Glasgow G60 5HJ ☎ 01389 890 426, 0802 856 717 mob

JENNINGS Robert: 24 Buchanan Drive, Causewayhead, Stirling FK9 5HD ☎ 01786 475985

JOLLY Louise *(Vla, Ea Stg)*: Glenview, Finzean, Banchory, Kincardineshire AB31 6LY ☎ 01330 850 323

JONES Elizabeth: 32 Barrington Drive, Glasgow G4 9DT ☎ 0141 334 9775

JONES Peter *(Con)*: 28 Hawick Street, Yoker, Glasgow G13 4EJ ☎ 0141 951 1070

KEIR Douglas *(Vla, B Ldr, Con, Md)*: 7 Pitfirrane Park, Crossford, Fife KY12 8NU ☎ 01383 725359

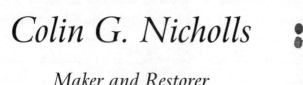

KELMAN Wilson (Db): 17 Forest Park, Stonehaven AB3 2GF

KENNEDY Eleanor: 48 Melville Gardens, Bishopbriggs, Glasgow G64 3DE ☏ 0141 772 2497

KERR Elaine (Pf): 11 Demorville Place, Beith, Ayshire, Scotland KA15 1AT ☏ 01505 504205, 0966 539169

KNIGHT Andrew (Vla): 34 The Square, Newtongrange, Dalkeith, Midlothian EH22 4PW ☏ 0131660 1926

LARKIN Michael: 4 Grantley Gardens, Glasgow G41 3QA ☏ 0141 649 1348

LATHAM Christopher (Flt): 24 Juniper Drive, Milton Of Campsie, Nr Glasgow G65 8HL ☏ 01360 310265 & fax

LAWRENCE Douglas: 86 Deanston Drive, Shawlands, Glasgow G41 3LH ☏ 0141 649 7666

LAWSON Margaret: Address Unknown

LEITCH Lorna: 6 Leven Street, Pollokshields, Glasgow G41 2JQ ☏ 0141 422 1598, 0411 343 259

LIBERSON Jack: 12 Cairndow Court, Muirend, Glasgow G44 3BU ☏ 0141 637 8824

LINDSAY Douglas (B Gtr, Ac Gtr): 3/1 28 Egunton Court, Glasgow G5 9NF ☏ 0141 429 3835

LINKLATER Andrew (Vla): 4 Eastwood Terrace, Aboyne, Aberdeenshire AB34 5AW ☏ 013398 86923

LINTON Judith (Fo Fdl): Barnside Farm, Abbey St Bathans, Duns, Berwickshire TD11 3TX ☏ 01361 840238

MACDONALD Anne: Castlelaw, West Linton, Peebleshire EH46 7EA ☏ 01968 660921

MACKISON Rachel (Vla, Pf): Linn Brae, Dinlugas, Turriff AB53 7NJ ☏ 01888 63242

MARTIN Andrew: Treeholm, Byars Road, Kirkintilloch G66 1DR ☏ 0141 777 7179

MARTIN John: 4 Bernard Terrace, Top Flat, Newington, Edinburgh EH8 9NX ☏ 0131 667 3268

MARTIN Sarah (Sax): 6 Caird Drive, Partickhill, Glasgow G11 5DS ☏ 0141 339 8123

MASON Nigel: 102 Speirs Road, Bearsden, Glasgow G61 2LA ☏ 0141 942 2658

MATASOVSKA Susan (Vla, Pf, Tr Viol): 66 Cranston Street, Penicuik, Midlothain EH26 9BW ☏ 01968 674760

MATTNER Audrey (Pf, Vla): St Aidans, New Road, Rattray, Blairgowrie, Perthshire PH10 7DJ ☏ 01250 872306

MAUNDER Guera ☏ 0141 636 9267

MAWSON Jane (Pf): 17 Beaconsfield Road, Glasgow G12 0PJ ☏ 0141 339 0606

MCCREATH Stewart: 3 Torridon Avenue, Glasgow G41 5LA ☏ 0141 427 1536

MCCULLOCH Alistair (Fo Fdl): 65 St Phillans Avenue, Ayr, Scotland KA7 3DD ☏ 01292 287083

MCFALL Robert: 9 Morningside Place, Edinburgh EH10 5ES ☏ 0131 447 1343

MCGARVA Andrew (Pf): 5 Shavin Brae, Ayr, Ayrshire, Scotland KA7 3NQ ☏ 01292 260290

MCGREGOR Sheila: 13 Corbiehill Grove, Davidsons Mains, Edinburgh EH4 5DU ☏ 0131 336 2298

MCINTYRE Alison: 21 Douglasmuir Drive, Milngavie, Glasgow G62 ☏ 0141 956 1950

MCLAREN Lorna: 1 Beechgrove Terrace, Perth PH1 1HZ ☏ 01738 624378

MCNAB William (Vla): 29 Gillbrae Crescent, Georgetown, Dumfrieshire, Dumfries DG1 4DJ ☏ 01387 267952

MCNEILL Brian (Citt, Ctna, Gtr, Bzk): 3 Cooperative Terrace, High Handenhold, Pelton, County Durham DH2 1QB ☏ 0191 3701910

MERSONJONES Diane: Bryn Corach, 32 Barlae Avenue, Waterfoot, Eaglesham Glasgow G76 0BD ☏ 0141 644 2863

MONTGOMERY James: Greenside, 7 Albert Place, Stirling FK8 2QL ☏ 01786 463163

MONTGOMERY Pat (Vla): Address Unknown ☏ Gourock 30587

MORONEY Helena: 12 Beechlands Drive, Clarkston, Glasgow, Scotland G76 7XB ☏ 0141 6203921

MORRICE Dave (Gtr, B Gtr): Beachview, Blairton, Balmedie AB23 8WY ☏ 01358 743182

MORRIS Andrew: 3 Coltpark Ave, Bishopbriggs, Glasgow G64 2AT ☏ 0141 563 2563

MUIR Susan: 96 Hammerfield Avenue, Aberdeen AB10 7FE ☏ 01224 313285

MURPHY Thomas: 43 Learmonth Grove, Edinburgh EH4 1BX ☏ 0131 332 9732

NEIL Renee: Northurst, Druids Park, Murthly, Perthshire PH1 4ES ☏ 01738 710574

NORTON Julia: 145 Cleveden Road, Kelvindale, Glasgow G12 0JU ☏ 0141 334 1564

O'RIORDAN Colin: 13 Leven Terrace, Edinburgh EH3 9LW ☏ 0131 229 8318

O'ROURKE Aidan: 2Fl, 21 Royal Park Terrace, Edinburgh EH8 8JB ☏ 0131 652 1613, 0780 114 0263

PARRY Caroline: 48 Duncan Avenue, Scotstoun, Glasgow G14 9HS ☏ 0141 954 4442

PATERSON Barbara: 21 Main Street, Fintry, Stirlingshire G63 0XA ☏ 01360 860429

PAYNE Fiona (Pf): Flat1/1, 88 Queensborough Gardens, Hyndland, Glasgow G12 9RY ☏ 0141 334 1471

PEAKE Alexandra: 4F2 16 Springhill Gardens, Glasgow G41 2EX ☏ 0141 649 6101, 0374 483 114

PERRICONE Sarah: 2 Skateringg Drive, Jordanhill, Glasgow G13 1SR ☏ 0141 959 3730

PRYCE Frances: 1 Whitefield Terrace, Croft Road, Cambuslang G72 8PP ☏ 0141 641 7885

RAMSAY Angus (Vla): 2 Staikhill, Lanark ML11 7PW ☏ 01555 662645

REEVES Elizabeth: Flat T/R, 105 Dundrennan Road, Glasgow G42 9SL ☏ 0141 649 6146

REID Jane: 11 Cairngorm Rd, Glasgow G43 2XA ☏ 0141 637 8654

REID Shelagh (Rec, Pf, Vla): South House, 17 Kirk Brae, Cults, Aberdeen AB1 9QP ☏ 01224 869615

RENNIE Jean: Address Unknown

REYNOLDS Julie: 37 Athole Gardens, 1/2, Dowanhill, Glasgow G12 9BQ ☏ 0141 357 0603

RHIND Gavin (Pf): T/L 50 Melville Street, Pollokshields, Glasgow G41 ☏ 0141 424 0834

RIGG Michael: 33 Greenbank Park, Edinburgh EH10 5SP ☏ 0131 447 5819

RITCH Lindsay (Kbds, Vla): 7 Elmwood Manor, Bothwell, Glasgow G71 8EA ☏ 01698 854468, 0370 832562

ROBERTSON Mhairi (Vla, Pf): 51A Oswald Avenue, Grangemouth, Scotland FK3 9AX ☏ 01324 482659

ROBERTSON Sheena (Pf): 13 Borestone Place, St Ninians, Stirling, Scotland FK7 0PP ☏ 01786 472267

ROBINSON John (Man, Bq Vln): Flat 4, 37 Glencairn Drive, Pollokshields, Glasgow G41 4QW ☏ 0141 423 2679

RODDEN Andrew: 6 Netherton Grove, Whitburn, West Lothian EH47 8JG ☏ 01501 741321, 0831 800407

ROLFE Joanna: 41 Carmichael Place, Langside, Glasgow G42 9UE ☏ 0141 632 8616

ROSS Debbie: 11 Lindley Bank, Alness, Ross-Shire, Scotland IV17 0TN ☏ 01349 884704

ROSS Malcolm: Flat G/1, 18 Burgh Hall Street, Glasgow G11 5LY ☏ 0141 579 2962

SAVAGE Alastair: Flat 1/2, 28 Ashley Street, Glasgow G3 6DR ☏ 0141 332 0238

SCOTT Hector: 3 Craiglockhart Ave, Edinburgh EH14 1DQ ☏ 0131 455 8393

SCOTT Thomas: 5 Colquhown Square, Flat 1, Helensburgh G84 8AD

SCULLION John: 530 Crookston Road, Glasgow G53 7TY ☏ 0141 883 4169

SHAW Ronald (Cel, Pf): 3C Friarsbank Terrace, Dunbar, East Lothian EH42 1BX ☏ 01368 864471

SIMANS Kathleen: 301 Churchill Drive, Glasgow G11 7HE ☏ 0141 339 1911

SIMANS Robert: 301 Churchill Drive, Glasgow G11 7HE ☏ 0141 339 1911

SIMPSON Anne: 54 Cawder Road, Cumbernauld, North Lanarkshire G68 0BF ☎ 01236 730375

SIMPSON Susan: 9 Cairn Park, Cults, Aberdeen AB15 9TG ☎ 01224 862011

SINCLAIR Christine *(Vla)*: Canton Cottage, 5, Suffolk Street, Helensburgh, Scotland G84 8EJ ☎ Helensburgh 463

SMITH Angela: 5 Duncryne Terrace, Gartocharn, Dunbartonshire, Scotland G83 8NU ☎ 01389 830604

SMITH Brenda *(Vla)*: 15 Lindston Place, Alloway, Ayr KA7 4UJ ☎ 01292 443923

SMITH David: 109 Essex Drive, Glasgow G14 9LX ☎ 0141 959 5786

SMYTH Hilary: 10 Striven Gardens, North Kelvinside, Glasgow G20 6DZ ☎ 0141 9453931

SPEIRS Jacqueline: Elrig, Main Street, Gartmore, Stirling FK8 3RW ☎ 01877 382247

STEVEN Yla: 101 Warrender Park Road, Edinburgh EH9 1EW ☎ 0131 229 6439

STEVENSON Anna-Wendy *(Pf)*: 4F1, 16 Johnston Terrace, Edinburgh, Scotland EH1 2PR ☎ 0131 225 3385

STEWART David: 38 Moray Place, Edinburgh EH3 6BT ☎ 0131 225 8102

STEWART Joyce *(Pf)*: 29 Woodhill Crescent, The Woodlands, Irvine KA11 1QR

STEWART Lois: 48 Moss Road, Tillicoultry, Clackmannanshire FK13 6NS ☎ 01259 750828

STEWART Roy *(Com, Man, Synth, Bjo)*: Juniper Bank House, Thurso, Caithness KW14 7EF ☎ 01847 894122

STOUT Christopher *(Fo Fdl, Pf, Kbds)*: 4/1 Buccleuch Street, Cowcaddens, Glasgow G3 6SL ☎ 0141 332 1380

STRACHAN Andrew *(Pf)*: Flat 1/1, 23 Hathaway Lane, Maryhill, Glasgow G20 8ND ☎ 0141 946 0186

SUTHERLAND Rhona *(Pf, Man)*: Brae Cottage, Dalchalm, Brora, Sutherland, Scotland KW9 6LP ☎ 01408 621 560

TASKER Alistair: 6 The Beeches, Craigends, Houston, Renfrewshire PA6 7DQ ☎ 01505 613847

THOMAS Clive: 21 Deaconsbank Avenue, Glasgow G46 7UN ☎ 0141 638 9005, 0141 638 9006 fax

TURNBULL George: 8 Highfield Place, Kelvindale, Glasgow G12 0LB ☎ 0141 357 3048

TYRE Ian *(Md)*: 55 The Loaning, Alloway, Ayrshire KA7 4UW ☎ 01292 42193

WALTON Janis: Wraysbury, Watt Road, Bridge Of Weir, Renfrewshire PA11 3DN ☎ 01505 612981

WARREN Caroline: 22 Buckstone Rise, Edinburgh EH10 6UW ☎ 0131 445 4377

WATSON Kitty *(Per, Voc)*: 30 Thistle Street, Aberdeenshire AB10 1XD ☎ 01224 641709, 07803 141467

WATTS Justine: Hillview Cottage, Kippen Road, Fintry G63 0YH ☎ 01360 860563

WEBB Liza *(Bq Vln)*: Flat 1/2, 145 Broomhill Drive, Glasgow, Scotland G11 7ND ☎ 0141 3373912

WEBBER Julie: Claddoch, Gartocharn, Dunbartonshire G83 8NQ ☎ 01389 830210

WILSON Sally *(Vla, Pf)*: 'Foveran', Crossbasket Estate, Stoney Meadow Road, High Blantyre G72 9UE ☎ 01698 828749

WINFIELD Catriona: 33 Hamilton Drive, Glasgow G12 8DN ☎ 0141 334 0985

YEAMAN James: 10 Winnock Court, Drymen, Glasgow G63 0BA ☎ 01360 60987

YELLAND David: 51 Drymen Road, Bearsden, Glasgow G61 2RN ☎ 0141 942 7698

YELLOWLEES Alex: Oleander, Cairney Hill Road, Bankfoot, Perth PH1 4AG ☎ 01738 787268

YOUNG Patricia: The Bothy, Fauldribbon, Girvan, Ayrshire KA26 9PH ☎ 01465 715367

NORTH WEST

ABBOTT Caroline: 17 Moorland Road, Didsbury, Manchester M20 6BB ☎ 0161 434 5702

ADAMSON Gerald: 5 Westway, Hightown, Merseyside L38 0BT ☎ 0151 929 2617

ALZAPIEDI Dania: Flat 3, 31 Parsonage Road, Withington, Manchester M20 4PE ☎ 0161 448 2209

ANDERSON Gerard: 21 Lon Goed, Llandudno Junction, Conwy LL31 9PE ☎ 01492 581005

ANDERSON Mary: 1 Ballbrook Avenue, Didsbury, Manchester M20 0AB ☎ 0161 445 3092

ANDREWS Helen *(Vla)*: 'Meadowside', 119 Whittingham Lane, Broughton, Preston, Lancs PR3 5DD ☎ 01772 862765

ANDREWS Wynford: 49 Doric Avenue, Frodsham, Cheshire WA6 7RB ☎ 01928 732138

ARMITAGE Shahla *(Pf)*: 1 Matlock Road, Heald Green, Cheadle SK8 3BU ☎ 0161 437 1599

ATHERTON Duncan: 108 Higher Road, Liverpool L26 1TH

AUGUST Frederick: 52 Goulden Road, Withington, Manchester M20 4YF ☎ 0161 448 1812

AUGUST Sally: 52 Goulden Road, Withington, Manchester M20 4YF ☎ 0161 448 1812

AUTY Karen: 11 Mayfield Mansions, 20 Alexandra Road, Manchester M16 8EZ ☎ 0161 232 7296, 0421 783925 mob

AYLWARD Samuel James: 11 Spring Road, Rhosddu, Wrexham, N. Wales LL11 2LU ☎ 01978 352373

BADEN Barbara: 9 Victoria Avenue, Blundellsdands, Liverpool L23 8UH

BAILEY Elizabeth *(Pf)*: 32 South Grove, Sale, Cheshire M33 3AU ☎ 0161 283 2326, 0421 883 843 mob

BANKS Anthony: 14 Yewtree Avenue, Northenden, Manchester M22 4DX

BARKER Baz: 247 Greenmount Lane, Heaton, Bolton, Lancs BL1 5JB ☎ 01204 841210

BARNES Charles *(Pf, Com)*: 33 Lower Lane, Chinley, Stockport, Cheshire SK12 6BE ☎ 01663 751108

BARNFIELD (GASCOYNE) Sheila: 9, Marlborough Road, Sale, Cheshire M33 3AF ☎ 0161 969 2364

BASS Elizabeth: Flat 3, 31 Parsonage Road, Withington, Manchester M20 4PF ☎ 0161 448 2009

BAYLEY Paulette *(Pf)*: 34 St Werburghs Road, Chorlton, Manchester M21 0TJ ☎ 0161 861 8088

BECK David *(Arr, Com, Cop)*: 4 Cambridge Close, Sale, Cheshire M33 4YJ

BELLINGHAM Valerie: 38 Truro Road, Liverpool, Merseyside L15 9HW ☎ 0151 733 7071

BIBBY Clifford: 96 South Mossley Hill Road, Liverpool L19 9BJ ☎ 0151 427 7636

BIRD Mary: 33 Lower Lane, Chinley, High Peak, Stockport, Cheshire SK23 6BE ☎ 01663 751108

BLINKHORN Anna: The Cairns, Caton Green, Brookhouse, Lancaster, Lancashire LA2 9JG ☎ 01524 770382

BOARDMAN Helen: 29 Freshfield Road, Wavertree, Liverpool L15 5BR ☎ 0151 733 2507

BONE Ian: 18 Cartwright Road, Chorlton Green, Manchester M21 9EY ☎ 0161 860 6641

BOOCOCK Kathleen: 25 Rowsley Road, St Annes-on-Sea, Lancs FY8 2NS ☎ 01253 724631

BOOTHROYD Edward: 18 Oaklea Way, Old Tupton, Chesterfield, Derbys S42 6JD ☎ 01246 863829

BOX Carol: 49 Appleton Road, Hale, Altrincham, Cheshire WA15 9LP ☎ 0161 928 5616

BRADLEY Jeremy: 28 Seymour Road, Cheadle Hulme, Cheshire SK8 6LR ☎ 0161 485 2887

BRANDWOOD-SPENCER Sarah *(Pf)*: 26 The Aspels, Penwortham, Preston PR1 9AL ☎ 01772 746390

BRATHERTON John: Grosvenor House, Talbot Road, Oxton, Birkenhead, Merseyside L43 2HJ ☎ 0151 652 5218

BRIDGES Helen *(Pf, Man)*: 45 Printers Bold, Padiham, Burnley, Lancs BB12 6PH ☎ 01282 777406

BRITTON Amanda: Flat 2, 12 York Road, Chorlton, Manchester M21 1HP ☎ 0161 881 2210

BURRAGE Martin: 6 Rosemont Road, Aigburth, Liverpool L17 6BZ ☎ 0151 724 3244

BUTLER Lucy: Craigie Cottage, 1A Mill Lane, Northenden, Manchester M22 4HJ ☎ 0161 998 5013

CALLING Joyce (*Pf, Vla*): 20 Silverthorne Drive, Hesketh Park, Southport, Lancs PR9 9PF ☎ 01704 228645

CAMPEY Fay: 14 Lees Road, Bramhall, Stockport, Cheshire SK7 1BT ☎ 0161 439 1156

CARLESTON Gerry: Naworth, Rossall School, Fleetwood, Lancs FY7 8JW ☎ 01253 774217

CARTER Owen: 176 Parklands, Little Sutton, Cheshire L66 3QE ☎ 0151 339 4802

CAUNCE Peter: Corner House, Croscombe, Nr Wells, Somerset BA5 3QS ☎ 01749 342400

CHASEY Vivien: 99 Clough Avenue, Sale, Cheshire M33 4HT ☎ 0161 962 0469

CHRISTIE David (*Voc*): Flat 11 Mayfield Mansions, 20 Alexandra Road South, Whalley Range, Manchester M16 8EZ ☎ 0161 232 7296

CLARK Graham (*E Gtr*): 2 Marlow Street, Buxton, Derbyshire SK17 7DP ☎ 01298 70802, 07977 806927

CLARK Martin: 20 Church Street, Horwich, Bolton, Lancs BL6 6AD ☎ 01204 693187

CLARK Nicola (*Pf*): 20 Church Street, Horwich, Bolton, Lancs BL6 6AD ☎ 01204 693187

COCHRAN Wendy: 3 Sark Road, Chorlton, Manchester M21 1NT ☎ 0161 881 8759

COWDY Judith: 37 Thistleton Close, Macclesfield, Cheshire SK11 8BE ☎ 01625 426328

CRIPPS Dennis: 191 Longhurst Lane, Mellor, Stockport, Cheshire SK6 5PN ☎ 0161 427 2959

CROPPER Brenda: 9 Sandileigh Avenue, Withington, Manchester M20 3LN ☎ 0161 445 4450

CROUCH Sarah: 45 Moorland Road, Didsbury, Manchester M20 6BB ☎ 0161 434 3110

DAVIES Avril: 2 Ffordd Cunedda, Ruthin, Clwyd LL15 1JF ☎ 01824 703699

DAVIES Edward (*Vla*): 7 Grianan, Menai Ville, Menai Bridge, Ynys Mon, Gwynedd LL59 5ES ☎ 01248 713336

DAVIES Gareth: 33 Portree Drive, Holmes Chapel, Cheshire CW4 7JB ☎ 01477 534393

DAVIES John: 2 Ffordd Cunedda, Ruthin, Clwyd, Debighshire LL15 1JF ☎ 01824 703699

DE COGAN Dara: Wayside House, Hargate Hill Lane, Glossop, Derbyshire SK13 9JL ☎ 0973 820779 mob

DIXON Clare (*Pf*): 8 Hey Cliff Road, Holmfirth, W. Yorks HD7 1XD ☎ 01484 689489

DONNELLY Patricia: 9 Westway, Hightown, Merseyside L38 0BT ☎ 0151 929 2375

DUFFY Gerald: 47 Mauldeth Road West, Withington, Manchester M20 8AA ☎ 0161 434 1693

DUFFY Margaret: 32 South Grove, Sale, Cheshire M33 3AU ☎ 0161 969 5772

EATON Sarah (*Pf*): 21 Berbice Road, Allerton, Liverpool L18 0HU ☎ 0151 734 0219, 0468 895300

EVANS Emlyn (*Vla*): 4 Westminster Drive, Wrexham, Clwyd LL12 7AU ☎ 01978 364096

EVANS James: 6 Ashburton Road, West Kirby, Wirral L48 ☎ 0151 625 5120

EVANS Katharine (*Pf*): Flat 4, 19 York Road, Chorlton, Manchester M20 6AZ ☎ 0161 448 0413

FERGUSON Alexander: 28 Childwall Crescent, Liverpool L16 7PQ ☎ 0151 722 6704

FIELD Thomas (*Vla*): 23 Rostrevor Road, Davenport, Stockport, Cheshire SK3 8LQ ☎ 0161 456 9552

FINN Vin (*Fo Fdl*): 27 Hollybank Road, Liverpool L18 1HP ☎ 0151 733 7253, 0498 737031 mob

FLOWER Ian (*Pf*): 8 Lloyd Street South, Fallowfield, Manchester M14 7HY ☎ 0161 226 8806, 0973 287931

FOSTER John (*Vla*): 196 Fleetwood Road (South), Thornton, Blackpool, Lancs FY5 5NR ☎ 01253 822278

FOXWELL Roger: 32 Fistral Avenue, Heald Green, Cheadle, Cheshire SK8 3HB ☎ 0161 499 9382

GARRIDO Victor (*T Sax*): 71 Oakland Avenue, Offerton, Stockport SK2 5RD ☎ 0161 456 4149

GAZDER Rohi: 19 College Drive, Manchester M16 0AD ☎ 0161 881 2447

GELL John: 66 Fitzwarren Court, Rosehill Close, Salford M6 5LN ☎ 0161 745 9071

GIBBON Susanna (*Kbds*): 12 Cartwright Road, Chorlton-Cum-Hardy, Manchester M21 9EY ☎ 0161 862 9865

GIBBS Anthony: 1 Brow Top, Friezland Lane, Greenfield, Oldham, Lancs OL3 7EY ☎ 01457 873858

GLEESON Jane: 74 Swinley Lane, Wigan WN1 2EF ☎ 01942 201308, 0973 283194 mob

GOODWIN Celia (*Pf*): Railway Cottage, 8 Riverbank Close, Lower Heswall, Wirral L60 8PP ☎ 0151 342 3577

GOODWIN Sian: 1 Rosslyn Road, Heald Green, Cheadle, Cheshire SK8 3DJ ☎ 0161 499 0755

GORDON-SMITH Richard (*Com, Cop*): 10 Dahlia Close, Walton Hall Park, Liverpool L9 1JJ ☎ 0151 523 1225

GREENWOOD Beverley (*Pf, Kbds*): 13 Grasmere Road, Frodsham, Cheshire WA6 7LP ☎ 01928 731254, 0421 932908 mob

GREGORY Julian: 26 Linglongs Avenue, Whaley Bridge, High Peak, Derbys SK23 7DT ☎ 01663 733331

GWYNN Ceredig: Lluest, 58 Vale Street, Denbigh, Clwyd LL16 3BW ☎ 01745 815701

GWYTHER Lesley: 14 Birch Road, Oxton, Birkenhead L43 5UA ☎ 0151 653 8626

HALL Michael: 115 Atwood Road, Didsbury, Manchester M20 6JW ☎ 0161 434 6916

HALL Susan: Holly House, Southport Road, Scarisbrick, Nr. Ormskirk, Lancashire L40 9RH ☎ 01704 840145, 0468 642919 mob

HAMILTON Annemauraide: 3 Stow Gardens, Withington, Manchester M20 1HL ☎ 0161 445 8065

HANCOCK Emma: 34 Holme Head Way, Denton Holme, Carlisle, Cumbria CA2 6AJ ☎ 01228 527106

HANDY Thelma: Spring House, Briardale Road, Willaston, South Wirral L64 1TB ☎ 0151 327 4774

HANNAH Frances (*Pf*): 1 Lawler Avenue, Salford, Lancs M5 3FW ☎ 0161 872 6257

HANSON Julia: 32 Clarendon Road West, Chorlton, Manchester M21 0RW ☎ 0161 881 2781

HARGREAVES Brenda: Newland, 12 Portland Road, Bowdon, Cheshire WA14 2JW ☎ 0161 928 1240

HARRIS Noreen: 12 Aigburth Hall Road, Liverpool L19 9DQ

HAWKINS Clare (*Pf*): 16 Primrose Close, Freshfield, Formby, Liverpool L37 3LL ☎ 01704 832906

HAYES Victor: 3 West Street, Prestwich, Manchester M25 3FB ☎ 0161 798 4160

HEALD Sarah: 22 Anerley Road, Didsbury, Manchester M20 2DJ ☎ 0161 434 0056

HEBBRON Celia: 34 Beresford Road, Oxton, Birkenhead, Merseyside L43 1XJ ☎ 0151 652 5833

HEBBRON John: 34 Beresford Road, Oxton, Birkenhead, Merseyside L43 1XJ ☎ 0151 652 5833

HECHT Philip: Address Unknown

HERBERT Colette: 67 Dean Drive, Wilmslow, Cheshire SK9 2EY ☎ 01625 535378

HITCHEN Janet (*Pf, Vla*): Sea View, Chorley Road, Hilldale, Parbold Lancs WN8 7AL ☎ 01257 464437

HOLDING Sian ☎ 0161 860 4171, 07970 748976

HOLLAND Benedict (*Pf*): 39 Moorland Road, Didsbury, Manchester M20 6BB ☎ 0161 434 2109

HOLLIDAY Cecily: 40 Morville Road, Chorlton, Manchester M21 1UR ☎ 0161 881 7132

HORNE Gabrielle: 57 Escolme Drive, Greasby, Wirral, Merseyside L49 1SF ☎ 0151 677 5603

HOWARTH Richard: 4 Kingston Road, Handforth, Wilmslow, Cheshire SK9 3JN ☎ 01625 530792 & fax

HOYLE Julia: Mill View, Old Mill Farm, Wilshaw Mill Road, Meltham, Huddersfield HD7 3EB ☎ 01484 854736

HUNT Alison: 7 Stratford Avenue, West Didsbury, Manchester M20 2LH ☎ 0161 445 9936

HUNTER Jane *(E Vln)*: Flat 11 Mayfield Mansions, 20 Alexandra Road South, Whalley Range, Manchester M16 8FZ ☎ 0161 232 7296, 0336 784606

HUTHNANCE John M: 53 Upland Road, Upton, Wirral, Merseyside L49 6LW ☎ 0151 677 9664

HUTTON James: 22 Harrier Drive, Halewood, Liverpool L26 7WQ ☎ 0151 475 5232

HYDEN Don: Address Unknown

JACKSON Thomas: 93 Whitby Road, Fallowfield, Manchester M14 6GJ ☎ 0161 286 3574

JACOBS Rachel *(Pf)*: 38 Matheson Drive, Worsley Hall, Wigan WN5 9SR ☎ 01942 207320

JARVIS Paul *(Vla)*: 9 Gatefield Close, Radcliffe, Manchester M26 3UY ☎ 0161 280 3804

JAY Nigel *(Vla)*: 3 Puffin Avenue, Poynton, Stockport, Cheshire SK12 1XJ ☎ 01625 876791

JAY Pamela: 3 Puffin Avenue, Poynton, Stockport, Cheshire SK12 1XJ ☎ 01625 876791

JENKINS Arthur *(Pf)*: Llwyn Palis, Pentrefelin, Llangollen, Denbighshire LL20 8EE ☎ 01978 861682

JERMAN Joan *(Pf)*: Tryfan, Trefor, Holyhead, Anglesey LL65 3YT ☎ 01407 720856

JOHNSON Kenneth: 61 Salisbury Road, Liverpool L19 0PH ☎ 0151 427 0220

JONES Christine: 22 Arthog Drive, Hale, Altrincham, Cheshire WA15 0NB ☎ 0161 980 2481

JORDAN Susanna *(Pf)*: 4 Farlands Drive, East Didsbury, Manchester M20 5GB ☎ 0161 445 9050, 0410 483993

KIRBY Susan *(Vla)*: 4 Yew Close, Carlisle, Cumbria CA2 6RT ☎ 01228 514123

KNOWLES Dianne: 31 Southwold, Little Weighton, North Humberside HU20 3UQ

LANCH Deborah: 8 South Bank Close, Heyes Lane, Alderley Edge, Cheshire SK9 7LQ ☎ 01625 58567

LANGFORD Lynda: 12 Hallville Road, Mossley Hill, Liverpool L18 0HR ☎ 0151 475 1361

LANSOM Mark *(Com)*: 63 Borras Park Road, Wrexham, Clwyd LL12 7TF ☎ 01978 350758

LATHAM Louise: 13 Copley Road, Chorlton, Manchester M21 9WT ☎ 0161 881 7907

LAYFIELD Malcolm: 1 Rowsley Avenue, West Didsbury, Manchester M20 8XD ☎ 0161 445 8634

LEACH Peter: 13 Grassendale Road, Liverpool L19 0LY ☎ 0151 427 1652

LEE Hai *(Vla, Voc)*: 40 Goldbourne Avenue, Wrexham LL13 9HQ ☎ 01978 356 352

LEE Susan: 11 Rock Bank, Whaley Bridge, High Peak, Derbyshire SK23 7LE ☎ 01663 733980

LEIGHTON-JONES Peter: 5 Stanton Gardens, Stanton Avenue, Didsbury, Manchester M20 2PT ☎ 0161 434 8291, 0973405833

LEVEY Philip: 1 Lincoln Road, Blackpool, Lancashire FY1 2LL

LEVY Edward: 85 Burnside Drive, Burnage, Manchester M19 2NA ☎ 0161 224 6167

LONG Andrew: 80 Ullswater Road, Astley, Manchester M29 2AQ ☎ 01942 892907, 0402 555876 mob

MARKS Alexander: Ground Floor Flat, 61 Scarisbrick New Road, Southport, Merseyside PR8 6PA ☎ 01704 542056

MCFARLANE Clare: 12 Moorside Road, Salford, Lancs M7 3PJ ☎ 0161 792 3370

MCINALLY Sian *(Vla)*: Flat 3, 23 Old Road, Mottram, Hyde, Cheshire SK14 6LG ☎ 0113 262 8763

MCKEOWN Bridget: 6 Kings Road, Old Trafford, Manchester M16 7SD ☎ 0161 226 4098

MELONEY Sheron: 24 Eatock Way, Daisy Hill, Westhoughton, Bolton Lancs BL5 2RB ☎ Westhoughton 81

MOFFAT Anthony: 22 Brixton Ave, Withington, Manchester M20 1JF ☎ 0161 374 2705, 0976 239028 mob

MORE Sylvia: 1 Red Lane, Frodsham, Cheshire WA6 6QZ ☎ 01928 735059

MORGANS Kathleen: 12 Rainford Avenue, Timperley, Altrincham, Cheshire WA15 7TH ☎ 0161 980 7681

MORLEY Sarah: 42 North Park Road, Bramhall, Stockport, Cheshire SK7 3JS ☎ 0161 439 5143

MORRIS Lucy: 59 Bainbridge Road, Sedbergh, Cumbria LA10 5AU ☎ 015396 20467

MUNCEY Catherine *(Vla)*: Rodwell Head Farm, Cross Stone, Todmorden, Lancs OL14 8RG ☎ 01706 819668

MUTH Stephen: Fernhole Farm, Brandside, Buxton, Derbyshire SK17 0SD ☎ 01298 72287

NASH Sonia: 11 Thorns Drive, Greasby, Wirral, Merseyside L49 3PU ☎ 0151 677 4213

NOAKES Claire *(Cel)*: 50 Mauldeth Road, Manchester M20 4WF ☎ 0161 445 9652

NOSSEK Jane *(Pf)*: 22 Woodside Road, Whalley Range, Manchester M16 0BT ☎ 0161 881 2176

PANKHURST Henry *(Vla)*: 38 St Clements Road, Harrogate, North Yorkshire HG2 8LX ☎ 01423 884309

PEACOCK Louise: Beny-Cot, Southey Street, Keswick, Cumbria CA12 4HH ☎ 017 687 74226

PEARCE Irene: 5 Patton Close, Unsworth, Bury, Lancashire BL9 8PY ☎ 0161 766 5524

PIGOTT Jonathan: 39 Ballantrae Road, Calderstones, Liverpool L18 6JG ☎ 0151 724 6724

POCKLINGTON Valerie: 6 Kirklands, Brooklands, Sale, Cheshire M33 3SG ☎ 0161 973 7644

PONSFORD Raymond: Address Unknown ☎ 0161 431 4071

PORTEOUS Rachel: 215 Old Chapel Street, Stockport SK3 9LR ☎ 0161 477 9714

RADCLIFFE Gillian *(Vla)*: Plas-Penrhyn, Penrhyndudraeth, Gwynedd LL48 6HY ☎ 01766 770242

RANKINE Sarah *(Pf)*: 75 Kestrel Road, Moreton, Wirral, Merseyside L46 6BW ☎ 0151 677 8287

REID Doug: Swindale House, Hilton, Nr. Appleby, Cumbria CA16 6LU ☎ 017683 52399

RICHARDSON Martin: 9 Keates Lane, Wincham, Cheshire CW9 6PP ☎ 01565 733716

RIDLEY Anthony *(Con)*: 40 Caulfield Drive, Greasby, Wirral, Merseyside L49 1SW ☎ 0151 677 8708

RILEY Ann: 2 Regents Way, Higher Bebington, Wirral, Merseyside L63 5QP ☎ 0151 608 7467

ROBERTSON Fiona: Flat 5, 103 Gatley Road, Cheadle, Cheshire SK8 1LX ☎ 0161 491 5937

ROCHFORD Mary-Rose *(Pf, Org, Flt)*: 26 Whalley Grove, Whalley Range, Manchester M16 8DN ☎ 0161 881 5245

ROGERS Elen *(Pf, Voc)*: Croes Iolyn, Garth, Llangollen, Clwyd LL20 7YP ☎ 01978 823245

ROSSI Liz *(Pf)*: Flat 5, 11 Derby Road, Fallowfield, Manchester M14 6UN ☎ 0161 224 3681

ROUTLEDGE David: 19 Lingard Raod, Nothenden, Manchester M22 4EW ☎ 0161 998 6987

ROYCE Grania *(Pf)*: 242 Ryebank Road, Chorlton, Manchester. M21 9LW ☎ 0161 862 9902

SALEH Morris: 7 Mosswood Park, Didsbury, Manchester M20 0QW ☎ 0164 445 8614

SCRIVENER Andrew: 30 Kings Hill Road, Chorlton, Manchester M21 1FY ☎ 0161 860 6951

SHARPLES Joyce: 22 Mottram Old Road, Gee Cross, Hyde, Ches SK14 5NG ☎ 0161 368 5987

SIDEBOTTOM Isobel *(Tbn)*: 5 Woodhouse Cliff, Leeds LS6 2HF

SIDEBOTTOM Jane: 5 Woodhouse Cloff, Leeds LS6 2HF ☎ 0113 2751597

SIDEBOTTOM Raymond: 5 Woodhouse Cliff, Leeds LS6 2HF

SMART Helena: Hartley Hall, Alexandra Road South, Manchester M16 8NH ☎ 0483 630268

SMEATON Adam: 15 The Yett, Kirk Yetholm, Kelso TD5 8PL ☎ 01573 420670

SPENCER David *(Pf)*: Flat 14, Oxford Place, 7 Oxford Road, Manchester M1 6EY ☎ 0161 273 2704

STACEY Peter: 28 Eshton Terrace, Clitheroe, Lancs BB7 1BQ ☎ 01200 425876

STEMP Morris: 12 Heaton Street, Prestwich, Manchester M25 1HP ☎ 0161 798 8087

STEPHENS Peter: 4 Kingsley Road, Dentons Green, St Helens, Merseyside WA10 6JN ☎ 01744 754864

STEWART M: 50 Greendale Road, Port Sunlight Village, Wirral L62 5DG

STOKES Helen: 14 Linden Avenue, Sale, Cheshire M33 6RS ☎ 0161 969 7223

STONEBRIDGE Peter (*Vla*): Tan-Yr-Allt, Pont Ystrad, Denbighshire, 464908 LL16 3HE ☎ 01745 815600

STOVELL Diana (*Pf*): 41 Moorside Road, Heaton Moor, Stockport, Cheshire SK4 4DS ☎ 0161 432 9970

SYKES Thomas (*Pf, Kbds, Vla*): 4 The Avenue, Halsall Lane, Ormskirk, Lamcashire L39 3BA ☎ 01695 571699

TAYLOR Frank: 6 Winchester Avenue, Ashton Under Lyne, Lancs OL6 8BU ☎ 0161 330 8930

TAYLOR Robert: 133 Walton Road, Sale, Cheshire M33 4DR ☎ 0161 973 3624

TAYLOR Sheila: 133 Walton Road, Sale, Cheshire M33 4DR ☎ 0161 973 3624

THIRLWALL Richard: 341 Stockport Road, Cheadle Heath, Stockport, Cheshire SK3 0PP ☎ 0161 428 3936

THOMPSON R: 24 Charles Berrington Road, Liverpool L15 9HQ ☎ 0151 722 3330

THOMPSON Rebecca: 53 Heaton Road, Withington, Manchester M20 4PU ☎ 0161 434 8056

THOMSON Shelagh: 16 Broomville Ave, Sale, Chesire M33 3DD ☎ 0161 969 7098

THOMSON William (*Vla, Pf*): Tower House, Station Road, Kirk Michael, Isle Of Man IM6 1EZ ☎ 01624 878380

TRUNDLE Anthony (*Fo Fdl*): 31 St Annes Road, Chorlton, Manchester M21 2TQ ☎ 0161 881 5418

TUNSTALL Geraldine (*Vla*): 4 Aspen Close, South Wirral, Merseyside L66 2YR ☎ 0151 608 9158

TURNBULL Donald: 40 Princes Court, Croxteth Road, Liverpool L8 3UJ ☎ 0151 727 7500

VAN-INGEN Judith: 1 Blakeley Brow, Raby Mere, Bromborough, Wirral Merseyside L63 0PS ☎ 0151 334 1956

VANCE Simon (*Pf*): 29 Cleveland Drive, Milnrow, Rochdale OL16 3HY ☎ 0151 355285

WADSWORTH Sonya (*Vla*) ☎ 0161 287 7783, 0777 1758962, 0161 287 7783

WAINWRIGHT Anne: 59 Seal Road, Bramhall, Stockport, Cheshire SK7 2LB ☎ 0161 440 9198

WEBB William: 14 Heatherfield, Edgworth, Turton, Bolton Lancs BL7 0DJ ☎ Turton 853188

WHITE Kathleen (*Vla*): 140 Waterloo Road, Birkdale, Southport, Merseyside PR8 3AL ☎ 01204 853188

WHITEHEAD David: 39 Catherine Street, Liverpool L8 7NE ☎ 0151 708 0330

WHITFIELD Peter (*Voc*): 169 Leamington Road, Blackburn BB2 6HJ ☎ 01254 583892

WILDE Richard (*Vla, Pf*): 'Richmond', 13 Hazel Crove, Irby, Wirral L61 4UZ ☎ 0151 648 7764

WILKIE Steven James: 1 Major Street, Ramsbottom, Bury, Lancashire BL0 9JH ☎ 01706 827 909

WILSON Anne (*Pf*): 8 Moorland Road, Didsbury, Manchester M20 6BD ☎ 0161 445 4393

WOOD Edouard (*Pf*): Address Unknown ☎ 0151 733 8712

WOODS Joanna: 21 Berbice Road, Liverpool, Merseyside L18 0HU ☎ 0151 734 0219, 0374 937560

WORRELL Peter: 84 Urban Road, Sale, Cheshire M33 7TU ☎ 0161 962 3775

WRIGHT Judi (*Per*): Brookholme Farm, Willow Lane, Lancaster LA1 5LW ☎ 01524 388326

WRIGHT Lucy: Stancil House, Barn Furlong, Great Longstone, Bakewell, Derbyshire DE45 1TB ☎ 01629 640136

YATES Catherine: 14 Yew Tree Avenue, Northenden, Manchester M22 4GX ☎ 0161 902 9412

YOUNG Isabel: 80 Brooklawn Drive, Withington, Manchester M20 3GZ ☎ 0161 445 1480

ZUNTZ Alyson: 31 Brighton Avenue, North Reddish, Stockport, Cheshire SK5 6LS ☎ 0161 431 8539

NORTH EAST

ADAMS David: Erin House, Nightingales Lane, Chalfont St Giles, Buckinghamshire HP8 4SR

ALLISON Susan (*Pf, Vla*): 159 Bennetthorpe, Doncaster, S. Yorks DN2 6AH ☎ 01302 367811

ARDRON Michael: 4 Riversway, Gargrave, Skipton, North Yorks BD23 3NR ☎ 01756 749459

BENNET John: 53 Haven Road, Barton-on-Humer, North Lincolnshire DN18 5BS ☎ 01652 632038

BERRIDGE Andrew (*Vla, Pf*): 61 Wensley Drive, Chapel Allerton, Leeds, West Yorkshire LS7 3QP ☎ 0113 269 3940

BIDDLE Georgina (*Pf, Kbds, Vla*): 110 Audley Road, South Gosforth, Newcastle-upon-Tyne NE3 1QX ☎ 0191 285 3510

BITHEL Karen: 10 Beech Dale Road, Alferton, Derbyshire DE55 7QH ☎ 01773 521898

BOOTH Trevor: 25 Ridgeway, Southwell, Nottinghamshire NG25 0DU ☎ 01636 816970

BOWMAN Jill (*Vla*): Little Court, Boltby, Thirsk, York Y07 2DY ☎ 01845 537227

BOYFIELD Rachel (*Pf*): 11 Millfield Gardens, Hexham, Northumberland NE46 3EG ☎ 01434 601692

BRACKLEY JONES Helen (*Pf, Vla*): Broadwood, 12A Wyncroft Grove, Bramhope, Leeds LS16 9DG ☎ 0113 2672476, 07970 036560

BRAGANZA Angelo: 198 Mount Vale, York YO24 1DL ☎ 01904 630454

BROOME Noel (*Vla*): Leadgate Farm, Dryburn, Allendale, Hexham, Northumberland NE47 9PR ☎ 01434 345 071

BROWN Christine (*Vla*): 40 Gledhow Wood Avenue, Leeds LS8 1NY ☎ 0113 293 2511

BROWN Iona: 93 Addycombe Terrace, Heaton, Newcastle-upon-Tyne NE6 5NB ☎ 0191 224 2510

BROWN Joanne: 28 Rose Terrace, Horsforth, Leeds LS18 4QA

BRUNTON Leonard (*Vla*): Alexandra Court, 333 Spen Lane, Leeds LS16 5BB ☎ 0113 274 3661

CAMPBELL Clare (*Man, Bjo*): 235 Western Road, Crookes, Sheffield S10 1LE ☎ 0114 2660319

CHALLONER Peter (*Bjo, Man, Voc*): 130 Brighton Grove, Newcastle-upon-Tyne NE4 5NT ☎ 0191 2724635

CHAMBERS Catherine (*Pf*): 5 Dobcroft Close, Ecclesall, Sheffield S11 9LL ☎ 0114 236 5804

CHANDLER Olive: 1 Kensington Avenue, Grange Park, Newcastle-upon-Tyne 3 NE3 2HP ☎ 0191 285 4369

CHATTERTON Josephine: Flat 4, 152 Trinity Street, Huddersfield HD1 4DT ☎ 01484 316098

CHIDSEY Anita: 117 Lascelles Hall Road, Kirkheaton, Huddersfield HD5 0BE ☎ 01484 546341

CHISHOLM Barbara (*Vla, Pf*): 22 Hallam Grange Road, Sheffield S10 4BJ ☎ 0114 2306639

CLARK Peter (*Vla*): The Old Manse, Market Place, Tetney, Grimsby DN36 5NN

CLEGG Philip ☎ 0161 231 7261, 0976 227671 mob

COATES Thomas (*Vla*): 2 Eslington Terrace, Jesmond, Newcastle-upon-Tyne NE2 4RJ ☎ 0191 281 6448

COOK Adrian: 46 George Street, Cleethorpes, Lincs DN35 8PX ☎ 01472 692331

COOLEY Catherine (*Vla, Pf*): 6 Littlefield Lane, Grimsby, Ne Lincs DN31 2LG ☎ 01472 318819

COOPER David (*Pf*): Oak Villa, Dunswell Road, Cottingham, Kingston-upon-Hull, East Yorkshire HU16 4JF ☎ 01482 876441

COOPER Joan: 41 Hastings Road, Millhouses, Sheffield S7 2GT ☎ 0114 236 8038

CORCORAN Tony: 26 Lesbury Road, Newcastle-upon-Tyne, Tyne & Wear NE6 5LB ☎ 0191 266 4497, 0191 427 3636

CRESWICK Bradley (*Clt, Pf*): 13 Stratford Grove Terrace, Heaton, Newcastle-upon-Tyne NE6 5BA

CROPPER Peter: Peppertree Lodge, 19 Canterbury Crescent, Sheffield S10 3RW

DAVIES Diane (*Vla*): 18 The Crescent, Heslington, York YO10 5EF ☎ 01904 415454

DAWSON Ralph *(Pf, Voc)*: 68 Norfolk Road, Sheffield S2 2SY ☎ 0114 2723558

DIXON Alison: 6 Oakwood Ave, Roundahay, Leeds LS8 2HZ ☎ 0113 240 9831

DODDS James: 16 Oak Grove, Wallsend-on-Tyne, Tyne And Wear

DUNN Robin *(Man)*: 1020 Sheilds Road, Newcastle-upon-Tyne, Tyne & Wear NE6 4SQ ☎ 0191 2955851

DYSON Wendy: 39 Westcombe Avenue, Leeds LS8 2BS ☎ 0113 266 4373

EATON Susan *(Vla)*: 5 Collingwood Tce, Jesmond, Newcastle-upon-Tyne 2, Tyne & Wear NE2 2JP ☎ 0191 281 7945

EDMUNDS Catherine *(Vla)*: 5 Waldron Street, Bishop Auckland, Co Durham DL14 7DS ☎ 01388 608815

EDWARDS Helen *(Pf)*: 171 Columbia Road, Grimsby, Lincolnshire DN32 8EE ☎ 01472 340044

EDWARDS Julie: 42 Myrtle Road, Golcar, Huddersfield, W. Yorks HD7 4EF ☎ 01484 646156

EKE Jonathan *(Vla)*: Maristowe, Belton Road, Beltoft, Nr Doncaster DN9 1NN ☎ 01724 782924

ELLISON Frank: 329 Millhouse Lane, Sheffield S11 9HY ☎ 0114 326 6070

FISHER Sarah *(Pf)*: 59 Meldon Terrace, Heaton, Newcastle-upon-Tyne NE6 5XQ ☎ 0191 240 1451, 01665 575111

FLEMING Charles *(Man)*: 8 Hill Top, Esh, Co Durham DH7 9RL ☎ 0191 373 0921

FLETCHER Jean: 55 Woodhouse Road, Wheatley, Doncaster DN2 4DG ☎ 01302 349002

FORBES Richard *(A Sax)*: 71 Beckett's Park Drive, Leeds LS6 3PJ ☎ 01132 745 765

FOSTER Jill *(Vla, Pf)*: 117 Welholme Avenue, Grimsby, N.E Lincoln DN32 0BP ☎ 01472 879628

FOX-GAL Eva *(Pf)*: The Hall, 67 The Village, Osbaldwick, York YO10 3NP

GOMERSALL Barry: 1 Wheatlands Way, Harrogate, N Yorkshire HG2 8PZ ☎ 01423 886292

GOULD Ronald *(Vla, Vln)*: 12 Fell View, Shires Lane, Embsay Nr Skipton, Yorks BD23 6RX ☎ 01756 794422

GREED David: 12 Grove Lane, Leeds LS6 2AP ☎ 0113 225 6934

GUMBO Gabrielle: 25 Hamilton Terrace, Otley LS21 1AN ☎ 01943 465436

HALL Gwen: 1A Nottingham Road, Somercotes, Derby DE55 4HQ ☎ 01773 540001

HALLIDAY Craig: 29 Apperley Road, Idle, Bradford BD10 9SH ☎ 01274 419764

HARDING Rachel: Cambridge House, 6 Tennyson Avenue, Chesterfield, Derbyshire S40 4SW ☎ 01246 277786

HENDERSON Eleanor: Address Unknown

HERRING Margaret *(Pf, Voc)* ☎ 01845 523056

HICKMAN Victor *(Vla, T Sax, B Ldr)*: Saddlers Rest, Market Place, Easingwold, York YO61 3AD ☎ 01347 823866

HILLIER Marion: Leadgate, Allendale, Hexham NE47 9PA ☎ 01434 345 071

HILTON Christopher: 15 Ash Grove, Ilkley, West Yorkshire LS29 8EP ☎ 01943 608330, 0402 322948 mob

HODGSON David: 77 Main Street, Wheldrake, York YO19 6AA

HOLMES Patricia *(Vla, Saxes, B Gtr)*: 302 Fulford Road, York YO10 4PE ☎ 01904 639044

HOROBIN Susan *(Pf, Flt)*: Rosegarth, Chapel Street, Nawton, York YO62 7RE ☎ 01439 771664

HORSEY Stephen *(Pf, Flt, Org, Per)*: 45 Neville Greove, Swillington, Leeds LS26 8QP ☎ 0113 2871362, 0930 760535

HOWARD Clare *(Pf)*: 61 Fountayne Street, York YO31 8HN ☎ 01904 640926

HOWES Charlotte: Skinner Cottage, Gilesgate, Hexham, Northumberland NE46 3QD ☎ 01434 608648

HUBY Mary: 14 Burley Wood View, Burley, Leeds LS4 2ST ☎ 0113 278 2832

HUGHES Christopher: 8 Blenheim Walk, Leeds LS2 9AQ ☎ 0113 234 9048

HUMPAGE John *(Vla, Kbds, Per, Gtr)*: The Church, Toft-Next-Newton, Market Rasen, Lincs LN8 3NE

HUNTER James: Fairleas Farm, Daddry Shields, Weardale DL13 1NB ☎ 01388 517231

HYDES Sarah J *(Vla, Pf)*: 54 Stakesby Road, Whitby, North Yorkshire ☎ 01947 603999, 07801 384995 mob

INGRAM Michael: 8 Leven Road, Guisborough, Cleveland TS14 8AH ☎ 01287 636188

INGRAM Sheila: 8 Leven Road, Guisborough, Cleveland TS14 8AH ☎ 01287 636188

INNES Susan: 21 Orchard Drive, Durham City, Co. Durham DH1 1LA ☎ 0191 384 9935

IONS Hilary *(Vla)*: 5 Burnside, Witton Gilbert, Durham DH7 6SE ☎ 0191 3711 575

IRELAND Robin *(Vla)*: 47A Westbourne Road, Sheffield S10 2QT ☎ 0114 2660781

JAMES Cath: 14 Bosville Road, Crookes, Sheffield, South Yorkshire S10 5FW ☎ 0114 268 0880

JOB Gillian: 126 Green Oak Road, Totley, Sheffield S17 4FS ☎ 0114 2360122

JOHNS Antony: 84 Westgate, Tranmere Park, Guiseley, West Yorkshire LS20 8HJ ☎ 01943 875311

JOHNSON Amanda *(Vla, Theory)*: Rose Tree Cottage, 26 The Barrow, Barrow Hill, Rotherham S62 7TT ☎ 01226 740592

JORYSZ Walter: 88 Becketts Park Drive, Headingley, Leeds LS6 3PL ☎ 0113 2758495

JOWETT Claire: The Basement Flat, 10 Bootham Terrace, York YO30 7DH ☎ 01904 621382

KING Bridget *(Vla)*: 31 Ibbotson Road, Walkley, Sheffield S6 5AD ☎ 0114 233 1928

KING Diane *(Voc)*: 6 Hesketh Avenue, Kirkstall, Leeds LS5 3EU ☎ 0113 278 7985

KITCHEN Rosamund: Town Foot, Main Street, Acomb, Hexham, Northumberland NE46 4PT ☎ 01434 605845

KOCO Raimonda: 106 Church Avenue, Leeds LS6 4JT ☎ 0113 278 0512

KUROSINSKI Margaret *(Pf)*: Seaview Cottage, The Parade, Sandsend, Whitby, North Yorkshire YO21 3SZ ☎ 01947 893360

LAWRANCE Nicholas: 17 Louisa Street, Darlington, Co. Durham DL1 4ED ☎ 01325 480953

LAWSON Sarah: 28 Spa Hill, Kirton In Lindsey, Gainsborough, Lincolnshire DN21 4BA ☎ 01652 648608

LEARY Valerie: Eden House, Sutton, Under Whitestone Cliffe, Thirsk, North Yorkshire YO7 2PS ☎ 01845 597111

LEARY William: Eden House, Sutton, Under Whitestone Cliffe, Thirsk, North Yorkshire YO7 2PS ☎ 01845 597111

LEFAUX Georgina *(Vla, Man, Gtr)*: 359 Salterhebble Hill, Salterhebble, Halifax, West Yorkshire HX3 0QA ☎ 01422 362634

LOVE Fiona *(Pf)*: 21 Hollin Drive, Headingley, Leeds LS16 5NE ☎ 0113 226 1876

LOVELL Jonathan *(Vla, Db, B Gtr)*: Almery Garth, Marygate Lane, York YO3 7BJ ☎ 01904 622000

MARRISON Frank *(Vla)*: 14 Lundhill Road, Wombwell, Barnsley S73 0RB ☎ 01226 754256

MARSDEN Harvey: 38 Ashleigh Avenue, Wakefield WF2 9DA ☎ 01924 376819

MARSHALL Mary: 12 Woodsome Drive, Fenay Bridge, Huddersfield, Yorks HD8 0JR ☎ 01484 602460

MASLIN Peter: 17 Broomhill Drive, Leeds LS17 6JW ☎ 0113 2668164

MATLEY Edward: 70 Wreyfield Drive, Scarborough, Yorks YO12 6NP ☎ 01723 362201

MATTHEWS Jeremy *(Pf)*: 25 Whitwell Acres, High Shincliffe, Durham DH1 2PX ☎ 0191 386 8293

MCALISTER Alison: 4 Kyme Street, Bishopshill, York YO1 1HG ☎ 01904 652448

MCCONVILLE Thomas *(Voc)*: 24 Lewisham Road, Slaithwaite, Huddersfield HD7 5AL ☎ 01484 847614

MCCOOL Annamaria: 5 Gosforth Terrace, Gosforth, Newcastle-upon-Tyne, Tyne & Wear NE3 1RT ☎ 0191 285 4200

MCINTYRE W: 7 Onslow Gardens, Low Fell, Gateshead, Tyne & Wear NE9 6HL ☎ 0191 487 5268

MEREDITH Nicholas (*Pf*): 14 Kendal Lane, Burley, Leeds LS3 1AY ☎ 0113 2459760

MEREDITH Rachel (*Vla, Pf*): 107 East Parade, Heworth, York YO31 7YD ☎ 01904 422058

MIDDLETON Nigel (*Vla*): Southey Bank, Lower Pilley, Tankersley, Barnsley S75 3BJ ☎ 01226 742593

MORTIMER Neville: Kirby Cottage, Market Place, Easingwold, N Yorks YO6 3AD ☎ 01347 821646

MOSELEY Margaret (*Vla*): 8 Brooklands, East Keswick, Leeds LS17 9DD ☎ 01937 72487

MOULE Graham: Aberlady, 14 Parkside, Nettleham, Lincoln LN2 2RZ ☎ 01522 751802

MOUNTAIN Paul (*Vla, Con*): 13 Huby Park, Strait Lane, Huby, North Yorks LS17 0EE ☎ 01423 734361 & fax, 0802 713707 mob

MOUNTAIN Peter: 93 Park Road, Bingley, West Yorkshire BD16 4BY

MULDOON Zechariah (*Pf, Tpt*): 1 Peak View, Moor End Lane, Dewsbury, West Yorks WF13 4PY ☎ 01924 401285

MURTHWAITE Carol (*Vla*): 10 Pond Side, Wootton, Ulceby, North Lincolnshire DN39 6SD ☎ 01469 588777

NORTON Fiona (*Pf*): Mir House, Hall Lane, Elsham, North Lincolnshire DN20 0QY ☎ 01662 688759, 0411 80 33 22

OLIVER Robert (*Vla*): East Moor, Trimdon Station, Co Durham TS29 6DU ☎ 01429 880340

OSTYN Mark (*Gtr*): Full Moon Cottage, Main Street, Cliffe, Selby, North Yorkshire YO8 7NL ☎ 0113 2585007

PEARCE Roslyn: 76 Harold Terrace, Leeds LS6 1LD

PEARSON Gill (*Acc, Pf, Gtr*): 7 Conway Avenue, Leeds LS8 5JE ☎ 0113 2405318

PIGOTT Raymond: 37 Rushley Drive, Dore, Sheffield S17 3EL ☎ 0114 236 4078

PIGOTT Sheila (*Vla, Pf*): 37 Rushley Drive, Dore, Sheffield S17 3EL ☎ 0114 236 4078

PRICE Chereene (*Pf*): 62 Carr Hill Road, Upper Cumberworth, Huddersfield, West Yorkshire HD8 8XN ☎ 01484 606593, 01523 103511

PUENTE Omar (*B Gtr, Kbds*): 4 Airedale Crescent, Bradford BD3 0JX ☎ 01274 781257, 0421 098953, 01274 404849

RAFFERTY Mary (*Pf*): 6 Hill Grove, Huddersfield, Yorks HD3 3TL ☎ 01484 653100

RAGSDALE John (*Vla*): 242 East Bawtry Road, Rotherham S60 3LS

REGAN Valerie (*Gtr*): Flat A1, 3 Summersfield, Ashdell Road, Sheffield S10 3DD ☎ 0114 232 6952

REILLY Brian: 7 Pasture Parade, Chapel Allerton, Leeds LS7 4QT ☎ 0113 268 9219

RENHARD Jack: 186 Leadwell Lane, Rothwell, Leeds LS26 0SH ☎ 0113 2828347

RICHARDSON Joanna: 14 Broomfield Place, Headingley, Leeds, W Yorkshire LS6 3DG ☎ 0113 2785107

RICHARDSON Nancy (*Vla, Pf*): 9 Queens Drive, Whitley Bay, Tyne & Wear NE26 2JU ☎ 0191 251 4068

RILEY David: 3 Cavendish Drive, Guiseley, Leeds LS20 8DR ☎ 01943 873060

ROBERTS Bransby: Sunnyside, 37 Woolsington Gdns, Wollsington, Newcastle-upon-Tyne NE13 8AP ☎ 0191 286 0949

ROBERTS Sarah: 61 Tosson Terrace, Heaton, Newcastle-upon-Tyne NE6 5LY ☎ 0191 265 5398, 0411 667 882

ROBINSON Paul (*Com*): 5 Box House, Luddenden, Halifax HX2 6QA ☎ 01422 883408

ROBINSON Sally (*B Gtr*): 23 Manor House Road, Wilsden, Bradford, W Yorks BD15 0EB ☎ 01535 273033

ROSSER Dick (*Vla, Db*): 3 Grove Park Gardens, Settle, N Yorks BD24 9QS ☎ 01729 823383 & fax

ROWDEN-MARTIN Amanda Jane (*Hpsd, Pf*): Corner Cottage, The Nook, Stoney Middleton, Hope Valley S32 4TU ☎ 01433 631150

ROWDEN-MARTIN Laurence: Corner Cotage, The Nook, Stoney Middleton, Hope Valley S32 4TU ☎ 01433 631150, 01433 631150

SAWYER Margaret (*Vla*): 25 Barmby Road, Pocklington, Nr York YO42 2DL ☎ 01759 304916

SCOTT Rupert: 4 Kyme Street, Bishophill, York YO1 1HG ☎ 01904 652448

SCURFIELD Joseph (*Man, Tbn, Gtr*): 2 Wellesley Terrace, Newcastle-upon-Tyne 4, Tyne & Wear NE5 5NL ☎ 0191 272 3867

SHULMAN Carol (*Vla*): 8 Gledhow Park Crescent, Leeds LS7 4JY ☎ 0113 2622302

SIRIWARDENA Caroline: North Dene, Langworth Road, Scothern, Lincoln LN2 2UP ☎ 01400 72306

SLADE Andrew (*Vla, Pf*): 48 Hermiston, Whitley Bay, Tyne + Wear NE25 9AN ☎ 0191 2526872

SPENCER Eileen: 12 Grove Hall Avenue, Leeds LS11 7EX ☎ 0113 2774717

STAGGS Katherine (*Vla, Pf*): 38 Kendal Gardens, Tockwith, York YO26 7QR ☎ 01423 359157

STEPHENSON Irene: Address Unknown

STRANGER-FORD Claire: 83 St James Road, Bridlington, East Yorks YO15 3PQ ☎ 01262 673944, 0467 830864 mob

STUBBS Christine (*Vla*): 5 Carnoustie, Waltham, Grimsby DN37 0EJ ☎ 01472 823822

SUTTON Sylvia (*Pf*): 24 Lansdowne Gardens, Jesmond, Newcastle NE2 1HE ☎ 0191 281 0496

SWALLOW Douglas (*A Sax*): 12 Leyburn Road, North Hykeham, Lincoln LN6 8SP ☎ 01522 684934

SYMONS Tamsin (*Vla, Pf*): 35 Oakwood Ave, Leeds LS8 2HZ ☎ 0113 240 5206, 0976 669343 mob

TAYLOR Rod (*Gtr*): 51 Bayswater Place, Leeds LS8 5LS ☎ 0113 248 8575

THOMPSON Hazel: 26 Northdale Mount, Bradford 5 BD5 9AP ☎ 01274 574746

THOMPSON Michael (*Vla*): 92 Colwyn Road, Hartlepool, Cleveland TS26 9BE ☎ 01429 298956

THOMPSON Pamela: 92 Colwyn Road, Hartlepool, Cleveland TS26 9BE ☎ 01429 262517

TODD Angela (*Vla*): 14 Hesketh Road, Leeds LS5 3ET ☎ 0113 274 8911, 0113 294 3071

TOMPKINS Alison (*Pf, Vla*): 18 Nairn Close, Darlington DL1 3RH ☎ 023 8048 5642, 0411 326340

TONSON-WARD Maxwell (*Vla, Vadam, Pf, Org*): 8 Norton Street, Grantham NG31 6BY ☎ 01476 77554

TORDOFF Helen (*Pf, Rec*): 22 Station Road, Holywell Green, Halifax, West Yorkshire HX4 9AW ☎ 01422 371851

UDLOFF Paul (*Vla*): Flat 6, 20 Parish Ghyll Drive, Ilkley, Leeds LS29 9PT ☎ 01943 609964

VERICONTE Maria: Richmond House, 49 Cowpasture Road, Ilkley, W. Yorks LS29 8SY ☎ 01943 430 135

WALKER Barry (*Pf*): 46 Cromer Avenue, Low Fell, Gateshead, Tyne & Wear NE9 6UL ☎ 0191 421 9848

WALTON Michael (*Pf*): 93 Station Road, Norton, Stockton-on-Tees TS20 1NN

WATKINSON Andrew (*Vla*): 58 Gaisby Lane, Shipley, Bradford BD18 1AX ☎ 01274 584556

WATMOUGH Katherine (*Pf, Vla*): Chestnut Farm, Heapham, Gainsborough, Lincolnshire DN21 5PT ☎ 01427 838285, 0411 284576 mob

WAUGH Thomas: 50 Cheviot View, Ponteland, Newcastle-upon-Tyne, Tyne & Wear NE20 9BW ☎ 01661 825229

WEST Helen (*Vla, Hrn*): 24 The Gardens, Whitley Bay, Tyne & Wear NE25 8BG ☎ 0191 252 1199

WHITE Robert: 'Two Hoots', 38 Wentworth Road, Thorpe Hesley, Rotherham S61 2RL ☎ 0114 245 1599

WHITFORD Dorothy: 1 Halcyon Hill, Leeds LS7 3PU ☎ 0113 2686830, 0113 268 8308 fax

WHONE George: 46 Duchy Road, Harrogate, Yorks HG1 2ER ☎ 01423 563255

WILSON Michael (*Gtr*): 5 Littlewood, Cragg Vale, Hebden Bridge, West Yorkshire HX7 5TL ☎ 01904 634750

WOLSTONHOLME Edward (*Vla, Man*): 34 Dale Street, Longwood, Huddersfield, West Yorks HD3 4TG ☎ 01484 649544, 0378 676370

WRIGHT Janet: 1 Wigfull Rd, Sheffield S11 8RJ ☎ 0114 266 4801

EAST

ADDENBROOKE David: Address Unknown

AITCHISON Andy: 18 Poets Chase, Hemel Hempstead, Herts HP1 3RN ☎ 01442 232427

AKROYD Karen (*Rec, Pf*): 82A Hastings Street, Luton, Beds LU1 5BH ☎ 01582 459008

BASS David (*Vla*): 89 Hurst Park Avenue, Cambridge CB4 2AA ☎ 01223 361927

BENNETT Emily: Marsh Cottages, The Ferry, Felixstowe, Suffolk IP11 9RZ ☎ 01394 670614, 01394 270384

BERGERSEN Elisa (*Flt*): 112A Leigh Road, Leigh-on-Sea, Essex SS9 1BU ☎ 01702 471726

BLAY Bernard: 7 The Avenue, Hitchin, Herts SG4 9RQ ☎ 01462 451060

BOME Helen (*Pf*): 27A Pierce Lane, Fullbourn, Cambridge CB1 5DJ ☎ 01223 880287

BORGES Matthew (*Gtr, Man*): 31 Victory Road, West Mersea, Colchester, Essex CO5 8LX ☎ 01206 382265

BROWN Andy: 21 Sandfield Road, St Albans AL1 4JZ ☎ 01727 839229

CANTLON Jane (*Pf*): 47 St Pauls Road, Hemel Hempstead, Herts HP2 5DD ☎ 01442 232964

CLARKE Barbara: 48 Bolton Lane, Ipswich IP4 2BT ☎ 01473 231402

CLEMENT-SMITH Helen: 61 Poplar Hill, Stowmarket, Suffolk IP14 2AU ☎ 01449 615634

COOMBS Catherine (*Cel, Wh*): 2A Carlow, St. Matthew's Street, Cambridge CB1 1QH ☎ 01223 360179

CROOKE Elizabeth: Brook House, Wortham, Diss IP22 1PX ☎ 01379 783229

CURIEL Jennifer (*Pf*): 10 Kirklands, Welwyn Garden City, Herts AL8 7RD ☎ 01707 328160

CURNOW Lucy: 114 Glenmore Gardens, Norwich, Norfolk NR3 2RN ☎ 01603 410914

FAELBER Kathleen: 54 Woodlands Way, Mildenhall, Suffolk IP28 7JE ☎ 01638 714284

FELL Carolyn (*Pf*): Holly Lodge, Friston, Saxmundham, Suffolk IP17 1PW ☎ 01728 688714

FERRIMAN Caroline: 65 Apton Road, Bishop's Stortford, Herts CM23 3ST ☎ 01279 461281, 0385 534256 mob

FLEET Myrna: 10 Kestrel Way, Watermead, Aylesbury, Bucks HP19 3GH ☎ 01296 888010

FORSDYKE Tina (*Pf*) ☎ 01462 671 572, 0961 819 201, 01462 623374

FRAPE Julia: 46 Drove Road, Biggleswade, Beds SG18 8HD ☎ 01767 317222, 0402 117646 mob

GERADINE Kay: The Star & Garter, 147 High Street South, Dunstable LU6 3SQ ☎ 01582 661044

GOULD Christopher (*Dms, Per*): 193 Lexden Road, Colchester, Essex CO3 4BH ☎ 01206 578990, 0973 600127 mob, 01206 563084

GREELEY Kathryn: 11C Lauriston Gardens, Edinburgh EH3 9HH ☎ 0131 228 3258, 0836 370 263, 0131 228 3410

GREENSILL Mark: 13 Park Crescent, Westcliff-on-Sea, Essex SS0 7PG ☎ 01702 430 211

HAYLEY Nicholas (*Bq Vln, Reb, Lira*): Violet Cottage, 5 Deben Lane, Waldringfield, Woodbridge, Suffolk IP12 4QN ☎ 01473 736500

HEAD Rosemary: 2 Stansfield Gardens, Fulbourn, Cambridge CB1 5HX ☎ 01223 882049

HEMMING Katherine (*Pf*): 8 Canterbury Close, Kempston, Beds MK42 8TU ☎ 01234 302185, 0958 680321

HODGES Joanne (*Vla, Man, Pf*): First Floor Flat, 2 Grosvenor Road, Norwich, Norfolk NR2 2PY ☎ 01603 615716

HUMPHREY Alan (*Md*): Newlands, Framsden, Stowmarket18, Suffolk IP14 6LR ☎ 01728 860308

KERR Emma (*Pf, Voc*): 19 Calder Avenue, Brookmans Park, Hatfield, Herts AL9 7AH ☎ 01707 653 954, 07771 860319

KINDELL Gene (*Sax, Pf*): 55 Great Lane, Bierton, Nr Aylesbury, Bucks HP22 5DE ☎ 01296 437114

KITCHEN Robert: Rowans, 14 Roydon Road, Diss, Norfolk IP22 3LW ☎ 01379 642468

LAYTON Elizabeth: 47 Westway, Rickmansworth, Hertfordshire WD3 2EH ☎ 01923 770445

LEVITAS Diana: 25 Bedford Road, Hitchin, Herts SG5 2TP ☎ 01462 458296

LEWIS-LIM Claire (*Pf*): 8 Brampton Close, Harpenden, Herts AL5 5SL ☎ 01582 460382

MARSEN Elizabeth (*Pf*): 249 Woodbridge Road, Ipswich, Suffolk IP4 2RA ☎ 01473 252186

MCCAGUE Catherine (*Pf*): 77 The Footpath, Coton, Cambridge CB3 7PX ☎ 01954 211122 & fax, 0467 836340 mob

MCINTOSH Robert: 3 Haddon Road, Chorley Wood, Herts WD3 5AW ☎ 01923 285415, 0860 377000, 01923 286097 fax

MESSENGER Mark (*Pf*): 16 East Hill, Colchester, Essex CO1 2QX ☎ 01206 520292, 0973 622985

MORRIS Andrea: 21 Wing Road, Leighton Buzzard, Bedfordshire LU7 7NG ☎ 01525 381156, 0850 800288 mob, 01525 381156

MUNKS Pamela: Tudor Cottage, 29 Benton Street, Hadleigh, Suffolk IP7 5AR ☎ 01473 823071

OLIVER Lance (*Theory, Aural*): St Leonards, Wensley Road, Thundersley, Essex SS7 3DS ☎ 01702 553538

PARLE Mike (*Bjo, Gtr*): 73 City Road, Norwich NR1 3AS ☎ 01603 618109

PASKE Katy (*Vla, Pf*): 10 Watercress Close, Stevenage, Herts SG2 9TN ☎ 01438 223520, 07771 520028

PEARCE Lesley: 185 Pinner Road, Watford, Herts WD1 4EP ☎ 01923 460293, 01923 817574

POULSTON Wendy (*Flt, Vla*): 28 Halliwell Road, Ipswich, Suffolk IP4 5LS ☎ 01473 271694

PYNN Nick (*Gtr, App Dulc, Bzk*): 43 Roundhill Crescent, Brighton, Sussex BN2 3FQ ☎ 01273 687980

RAPHAEL Prudence (*Vla*): 4 Ivy Field, Barton, Cambridge CB3 7BJ ☎ 01223 263012

RATCLIFFE Lynne (*Pf*): 22 Rosabelle Avenue, Wivenhoe, Essex CO7 9NX ☎ 029 2049 2267

ROBINSON Gideon: 14 Mill Street, Gamlingay, Sandy, Bedfordshire SG19 3JW ☎ 01767 651634

ROBY Peter (*Kbds, Gtr*): 29 Cassiobridge Road, Watford, Herts WD1 7QL ☎ 01923 236724

ROWE Janet (*Vla*): 24 Ivry Street, Ipswich, Suffolk IP1 3QW ☎ 01473 216410

SCHMIDT Gerhard (*Vla*): 52 Seymour Road, St Albans, St Albans, Herts AL3 5HW ☎ 01727 865420

SMITH Martin: 60 Holyrood Crescent, St Albans, Herts AL1 2LN ☎ 01727 864048, 020 7354 2711 day

TATTERSALL Elizabeth (*Clt, Pf*): Chase End, Abington Pigotts, Royston, Herts SG8 0SD ☎ 01763 852504, 01763 853305 fax

TERRY Diane (*Vla, Pf, Gtr*): 3 Abbey Mill End, St Albans, Herts AL3 4HN ☎ 01727 843 656, 01727 843 656

THOMPSON Tommy (*T Sax, Sax*): 56 Outwell Road, Emneth, West Norfolk PE14 0DU ☎ 01945 588685

WALKER Jayne: 74 Kimbolton Crescent, Hertford Road, Stevenage, Herts SG2 8RL ☎ 01438 232740

WARBURTON Timothy: Courtyard Cottage, Southwick Hall, Southwick, Nr Oundle, Northants PE8 5BL ☎ 01832 274011

WEALE Stephen: 47 Beverly Road, Ipswich, Suffolk IP4 4BU ☎ 01473 271740

WILLIAMS Dorothy: 5 Leyside, Bromham, Bedford MK43 8NE

WILSON Elisabeth: 38 Hartington Grove, Cambridge CB1 4UE ☎ 01223 511887, 01223 566639

MIDLANDS

ALLEN-SMITH Catherine (*Pf*): 16 Silvermead Road, Boldmere, Sutton Coldfield B73 5SR ☎ 0121 241 9504

ALLIN Ralph: 24 Hobson Road, Selly Park, Birmingham B29 7QH ☎ 0121 471 4693

ARLAN David: 16 Clewley Grove, Quinton, Birmingham B32 1QZ ☎ 0121 422 6737

ARLIDGE Catherine: 45 Greenfield Road, Harborne, Birmingham B17 0EP ☎ 0121 426 2074

VIOLIN - MIDLANDS

ASKEW Katy (*Pf, Kbds, Gtr*): Flat 1, 12 Douglas Road, Nottingham NG7 1NW ☎ 0966 219128 mob

ASTON Susan (*Pf*): 49 Whitemoor Drive, Monkspath, Solihull, West Midlands B90 4UL ☎ 0121 733 8918

AVERY Dennis (*Vla*): 5 Westbourne Avenue, Hodge Hill, Birmingham B34 6AN ☎ 0121 783 8038

BADDELEY Jonathan: 36 Bala Grove, Cheadle, Staffs ST10 1SY ☎ 01538 752013

BADDELEY Raymond: 36 Bala Grove, Cheadle, Staffs ST10 1SY ☎ 01538 752013

BALLARD Jeremy: 26 St Agnes Road, Moseley, Birmingham B13 9PW ☎ 0121 449 0692

BARFIELD Kate (*Tbn*) ☎ 01782 632962

BATTEN Edward: 47 Coleridge Road, Enderby, Leicester LE9 5QF ☎ 0116 2863705

BEAUMONT Enid: First Floor Flat, 5, Vicars Close, Lichfield, Staffs WS13 7LD ☎ 01543 253893

BEST Joan: 14 Summervale Close, West Hagley, Stourbridge, West Midlands DY9 0LZ ☎ 01562 883980

BILSON Robert: 11 Park Avenue, Worcester WR3 7AT ☎ 01905 27625

BIRCH Henry: 36 Bertha Road, Greet, Birmingham B11 2NN ☎ 0121 773 2561

BIRD John (*T Sax, A Sax*): 90 Lubbesthorpe Road, Braunstone, Leicester LE3 2XE ☎ 0116 289 0263

BOCHMANN Michael: The Barns, Village Farm, Ford, Nr Cheltenham GL54 5RU ☎ 01905 763071

BODIMEAD Caroline: 43 Milcote Road, Bearwood, Warley, West Midlands B67 5BJ ☎ 0121 429 6031, 0966 541881

BOUNFORD Isobel: 19 King Edward Avenue, Mansfield, Notts NG18 5AE ☎ 01623 653354

BOWRON Leslie: 95 Langleys Road, Selly Oak, Birmingham B29 6HR ☎ 0121 472 2493

BRADLEY Martin: 15 Repington Road South, Annington, Tamworth, Staffordshire B77 4AA ☎ 01827 51461

BRADSHAW Heather: 27 Corbett Street, Smethwick, Warley, West Midlands B66 3PU ☎ 0121 601 5216

BRIDLE Peter (*Vla*): 280 Moor Green Lane, Birmingham B13 8QL ☎ 0121 449 1826

BRITTEN John (*Vla*): 5 Misterton Crescent, Ravenshead, Nottingham NG15 9AX ☎ 01623 798801

BROOKS Vyvyan: Quarry Bank, Ross Road, Huntley, Glos GL19 3EX ☎ 01452 830398, 0973 223936 mob

BROWNLOW Erick: 18 Garden Lane, Melton Mowbray, Leics LE13 0SJ

BUCKLEY Sylvia (*Vla*): 37 Meremore Drive, Chesterton, Newcastle-U-Lyme, Staffs ST5 7SE ☎ 01782 560139

BULL Geoffrey (*Vla*): 64 Olive Hill Road, Halesowen, West Midlands B62 8JN ☎ 0121 559 5877, 0958 781881

BURGESS Jane (*E Vln, Pf*): Scrubby Oaks, Lordsley, Ashley, Nr Market Drayton, Shropshire TF9 4EQ ☎ 01630 673353 & fax, 0370 600060 mob

BURNS Catriona (*Pf*): 16 Main Street, Desford, Leicester LE9 9JP ☎ 01455 828054

BURNS Leo: 5 Frank Walsh House, Jenner Street, Coventry CV1 4HU ☎ 024 7622 1894

CAREY Louise: 11 Bond Street, Stirchley, Birmingham B30 2LB ☎ 0121 458 3274

CARTLIDGE Christopher (*Bjo*): Ovenshall Cottage, Great Gate, Tean, Stoke-on-Trent, Staffs ST10 4HF ☎ 01889 507339, 07970 325504

CHALK Simon: 17 Willow Coppice, Bartley Green, Birmingham B32 3JA ☎ 0121 475 6491

CHATER Jennifer (*Pf*): 25, Stonepits Lane, Hunt End, Redditch, Worcs B97 5LX ☎ 01527 24287

CLARKE David: 45 Crossway, Didsbury, Manchester M20 6PU ☎ 0161 445 9764

CLARKE Sheila: 7, Birches Close, Moseley, Birmingham B13 9TR ☎ 0121 449 9196

CLIFT Christopher: 449 Reddings Lane, Tyseley, Birmingham B11 3DF ☎ 0121 778 1336 & fax

COHEN Mary: 110 Willow Avenue, Birmingham B17 8HE ☎ 0121 429 6857

COLLINGE-HILL Lucy (*Vla, Pf*): 6 Albert Road, Kings Heath, Birmingham B14 7HE ☎ 0121 444 0070

COOKE Eleanor: 97 Frankley Beeches Road, Northfield, Birmingham B31 5LN ☎ 0121 476 4680

CRABB Elizabeth: 41 West Drive, Edgbaston, Birmingham B5 7RR ☎ 0121 472 3845, 0121 472 0269

D'SOUZA Fiona (*Pf*): 9 Derwent Road, Stirchley, Birmingham B30 2UY ☎ 0121 689 1725

DAVIDSON Ian (*Pf*): 34 Shenley Lane, Weoley Castle, Birmingham B29 5PL ☎ 0121 476 3990, 0973 796331

DAVIS Hazel: Wilcroft, Bartestree, Hereford HR1 4BB ☎ 01432 850409

DAVIS James (*Arr, Com, Cop*): 61 Somers Road, Malvern, Worcs WR14 1JA ☎ 01684 576538

DAWKINS Rita (*Pf, Accom*): Tudor House, Long Itchington, Nr Rugby, Warks CV23 8QN ☎ 01926 81 2429

DAYMAN Louise: 28 Loughborough Road, Thringstone, Leicester LE67 8LP ☎ 01530 223241

DE JESUS Elena (*Pf*): 2 Springbank Farm Cottage, Bradwall, Nr Sandbach, Cheshire CW11 1RB ☎ 01270 753558

DEAN Joan (*Vla, Voc*): 4 Carrwood, Knutsford, Cheshire WA16 8NG ☎ 01565 52838

DODD Mairi (*Bq Vln*): 64 Rednall Mill Drive, Rednall, Birmingham B45 8XY ☎ 0121 453 7669, 07971 914 378 mob

DOWNHAM Patricia: 71 Halton Road, Sutton Coldfield B73 6NU ☎ 0121 354 5711

DRYER-BEERS Anna (*Vla*): 187 Jackmans Place, Letchworth, Herts SG6 1RG ☎ 01462 673531

ELDRIDGE Christopher (*Vla*): 88 Avenue Road, Astwood Bank, Redditch B96 6AT ☎ 0152789 3577

EWART George: 186 The Mallards, Ridgemoor Road, Leominster, Herefordshire HR6 8UJ ☎ 01568 613027

FALLOWFIELD Nicholas (*Con*): 88 Brook Street, Stourbridge, West Midlands DY8 3UX ☎ 01384 835457

FEATHERSTONE Richard (*Vla*): 11A Riley Crescent, Penn Fields, Wolverhampton WV3 7DR

FLINT John: 97 Limes Road, Tettenhall, Wolverhampton WV6 8RD ☎ 01902 742884

FORSTER Anne: 42 St Judes Road West, Wolverhampton, Staffs WV6 0DA ☎ 01902 423879

GANDY Judith: Hillcroft, Blythe Bridge Bank, Kingstone, Uttoxeter, Staffs ST14 8QP ☎ 01889 500515

GILLETT Tania (*Pf*): The Vicarage, Butleigh, Glastonbury, Somerset BA6 8SH ☎ 01458 850409

GITTINGS Katharine (*Pf*): 86, Oxford Road, Moseley, Birmingham B13 9SQ ☎ 0121 449 5902

GOLDING Elizabeth (*Vla*): 14 Yelverton Drive, Edgbaston, Birmingham B15 3NT ☎ 0121 454 8308

GOODGER Arnold: Haslington, 106 Wells Road, Malvern Wells, Worcs WR14 4PG ☎ 01684 572392

GOUGH Colin: 44 School Road, Moseley, Birmingham B13 9SN ☎ 0121 449 1164

GRAFF-BAKER Eleanor: 50A Main Street, Peckleton, Leicester LE9 7RE ☎ 01455 828434, 0973 411737 mob, 01455 828693 fax

GREENWOOD Rachel (*Vla*): 8, Birch Tree Road, Bewdley, Worcestershire DY12 2HB ☎ 01299 402513

GREENWOOD Susan: 38 Springfield Glade, Malvern, Worcs WR14 1LN ☎ 01684 892266

GREGORY David (*Voc*): 43 Springfield Road, Kings Heath, Birmingham B14 7DU ☎ 0121 444 2339

HADWEN David (*Vla*): 43 Monsom Lane, Repton, Derbyshire DE65 6FX

HADWEN Richard (*Vla*): 168 Claremont Road, Moss Side, Manchester M14 4TU ☎ 0161 226 2527

HALL Leslie: 48 King Street, Pinxton, Nottingham NG16 6NL ☎ 01773 810273

HALLAM Mandy (*Pf*): 89 Hillwood Road, Madeley Heath, Nr Crew CW3 9JZ ☎ 01782 751287

HAMER Catherine: 3 Rear Cottage, Withy Bed Green, Alvechurch, Worcs B48 7PN ☎ 0121 445 3876

HARPER Villia: Address Unknown ☎ 01902 23497

HARRISON Debbie (Pf): 14 Park Lane, Bewdley, Worcestershire DY12 2ER ☎ 01299 402420

HAYES Hazel (Pf): 58, Christchurch Lane, Lichfield, Staffordshire WS13 8AN ☎ 01543 253 827

HEAD Philip: 72 Pereira Road, Harborne, Birmingham B17 9JN ☎ 0121 427 1017

HEMERY Anna (Pf, Per): 75 Byne Road, London SE26 5JG ☎ 020 7354 2711 day

HESS Gisela: 84 Robin Hood Lane, Hall Green, Birmingham B28 0JX ☎ 0121 745 2154

HILL Jackie (Pf): 15A Alexandra Road, Halesowen, Birmingham B63 4DJ ☎ 0121 550 1918

HISCOX David: 51A Avenue Road, Queniborough, Leicester LE7 3FB ☎ 0116 2601870

HOLLIMAN Andrew (Vla): 22 Nicholson Street, Newark, Notts NG24 1RD ☎ 01636 677416

HOLLOWAY Julia: Trenwyth, Mill Street, Aston-on-Clun, Shropshire SY7 8EN ☎ 01588 660 422, 0973 783506

HORGAN Brian: Rose Cottage, Haughton, Shrewsbury TF6 6BU ☎ 01743 709264

HORGAN Clare: Rose Cottage, Haughton, Shrewsbury TF6 6BU ☎ 01743 709264

HORNE Cyril: 2 Howard Avenue, Bromsgrove, Worcs B61 8PP ☎ 01527 73993

HUGHES James: 17 Newport Drive, Alcester, Warks B49 5BL ☎ 01789 763277

JACOBS Susan: 11 Knighton Park Road, Leicester LE2 1ZA ☎ 0116 2700028

JOHNSON Thelma: 14 Petersfield Road, Birmingham B28 0AR ☎ 0121 777 1281

JONES Lesley (Pf): 3 Sandon Avenue, Newcastle, Staffs ST5 3QB ☎ 01782 616174

JONES Levin: Nesscliff House, Malthouse Bank, Little Wenlock, Telford, Shropshire TF6 5BN ☎ 01952 505046

JOYCE David: 8 Chepstow Grove, Rednal, Birmingham B45 8EG ☎ 0121 453 6689, 0374 144938

KEMPTON Laurence: 12 Grove Road, Churchdown, Gloucester GL3 2SN ☎ 01452 714175

KOK Felix: 3 The Manor, Trusley, Sutton-on-The Hill, Derby DE6 5JG ☎ 028 373 4145

KYRIAKOU Maria (Pf): Rheindahlen Music Centre, Windsor School, Bfpo 40 ☎ +49 2434 24328 & fax

LAMBERT Chris (Org, Pf): 21 Edwal Road, Weston Coyney, Stoke-on-Trent, Staffs ST3 5HH ☎ 01782 319997

LAWRENCE Della K (Vla): 25A, Union Street, Stourbridge, West Midlands DY8 1PJ ☎ 01384 375874

LAWRENCE Ruth: 76 Kingsway, Wollaston, Stourbridge, West Midlands DY8 4TG ☎ 01384 372040

LEACH Sarah (Pf, Synth, Voc): 181 Springfield Road, Walmley, Sutton Coldfield, West Midlands B76 2SY ☎ 0121 378 2272 & fax, 0802 410834 mob

LEONARD Eric: 46 Orchard Road, Hockley Heath, Solihull, West Midlands B94 6QR

LEWIS Elizabeth: 23 Victoria Road, Malvern, Worcs WR14 2TE ☎ 01684 568848

LEWIS Philip (Rec): Flat 1, 9 Calrendon Street, Chapel Ash, Wolverhampton, West Midlands WV3 9PP ☎ 01902 830409

LIPMAN Amanda: 7 The Paddock, Northfield, Birmingham B31 2BU ☎ 0121 477 2183

LITTLEWOOD Graeme: 60, Oxford Road, Moseley, Birmingham B13 9ES ☎ 0121 449 0710

LLOYD Maria: 12 Dawes Close, Armitage, Rugeley, Staffs WS15 4BE ☎ 01543 307145

LOMBARD Freddy: 5, Baxter Close, Tile Hill, Coventry, West Midlands CV4 9EH ☎ 024 7646 6308

LOVINI Gary (Pf): 68 Gillway Lane, Tamworth, West Midlands B79 8PL ☎ 01827 68577

LYCETT David (Vla): 25 Chester Crescent, Westlands, Newcastle Under Lyme, Staffs ST5 3RT ☎ 01782 616852

LYNNE Deborah (Vla): 7 Leonard Street, London EC2A 4AQ ☎ 0370 522395 mob, 01523 181616 pager

MAJOR Willett: 34 Parkview Apartments, Abbey Road, Malvern, Worcs WR14 3HG ☎ 01684 563717

MANTELL Christopher (Vla, Tpt): Hammerwich Hall, 105 Burntwood Road, Hammerwich, Staffs WS7 0JL ☎ 01543 686873

MARJORAM Elizabeth: Butterley Brook Cottage, Wacton, Nr Bromyard, Herefordshire HR7 4NG ☎ 01885 488233

MARSHALL Robert: 314 Ombersley Road, Worcester WR3 7HD ☎ 01905 756959

MASON Samuel: 340 Selly Oak Road, Kings Norton, Birmingham B30 1HP ☎ 0121 451 1412

MASTERS Janet: 4 Bellosquardo, 29 St Annes Road, Great Malvern, Worcs WR14 4RG ☎ 01684 567522

MATARASSO Veronique (Pf): Manor Farm, Fenny Compton, Leamington Spa, Warwicks CV33 0YY ☎ 01295 770525

MATTHEWS Sarah (Pf, Bod, Man, Vla): 10 Hamblin Crescent, Sinfin, Derby DE24 9PL ☎ 01332 273383

MCAUSLAN Judith: 3 Mardale Close, Congleton, Cheshire CW12 2DQ ☎ 01260 279 000

MCCUSKER Kelly (Pf, Voc): 5 Weston Road, Bearwood, Warley, West Midlands B67 5HH ☎ 0121 420 2461, 0498 828 701 mob

MCNULTY John (Vla): 59 Briar Close, Evesham, Worcs WR11 4JJ ☎ 01386 49033

MOORE Andrew (Vla, Pf): 436 Bromford Road, Hodge Hill, Birmingham B36 8JH ☎ 0121 783 3114, 04325 228 701

MOORE Elizabeth: 42 Porthill Road, Shrewsbury, Shropshire SY3 8RN ☎ 01743 350738, 0467 660993

NAGLE Susan: 12 Rotton Park Road, Birmingham 16 B16 9JJ ☎ 0121 454 2136

NOBLE Bethan (Vla, Voc): 21 St Judes Avenue, Mapperley, Nottingham NG3 5FG ☎ 0115 9605249

ORSMAN Jc: Flat One, 8 Priory Street, Cheltenham, Glos. GL52 6DG ☎ 01242 572 705

OSBORN Gordon (Vla): 136 All Saints Road, Kings Heath, Birmingham B14 6AT ☎ 0121 444 1811

PACEY Stephen: 78 Greenhill Road, Winchester, Hampshire S022 5DX ☎ 01962 864563

PAGE Rosalind: 15 Cashmore Road, Kenilworth CV8 2SJ ☎ 01926 513063

PARISH Byron: 18 Berrow View, Bromsgrove, Worcestershire B61 7HF ☎ 01527 577195

PARKES Hazel: 41 Broad Elms Lane, Sheffield S11 9RQ ☎ 0114 2361276

PARKIN Anne: 506 Litchfield Road, Four Oaks, Sutton Coldfield, West Midlands B74 4EJ ☎ 0121 323 3833

PELLING Kate: 7 Springfield Close, Leek, Staffs ST13 6PJ ☎ 01538 381180

PERKES Kate (Vla): 23, Witton Street, Norton, Stourbridge, West Midlands DY8 3YF ☎ 01384 441745

PERKINS Timothy (Vla, Gtr, Rec, Kbds): 33 Margaret Street, Northampton NN1 3BW ☎ 01604 231281

PERRY Adrian: 41 Fallowfield, Ampthill, Bedfordshire MK45 2TS ☎ 01525 402503

PHILLIP Diane (Bq Vln): 5 Castle Terrace, Bridgnorth, Shropshire WV16 4AH ☎ 01746 764097

PITCHFORD Clare (Pf): 69 Winster Crescent, Melton Mowbray, Leicestershire LE13 0EH ☎ 01664 61569, 0589 081095

QUIRK Wendy (Pf): 18 Rush Lane, Church Hill North, Redditch B98 8RY ☎ 01527 65708

REID John: 14, Upper Bar, Newport, Salop TF10 7EJ ☎ 01952 825235

RHODES Linda: 88 Brook Street, Stourbridge, West Midlands DY8 3UX ☎ 01384 835457

RICHEY Angela: Harborough Bank, Shelsley Beauchamp, Worcester WR6 6RA ☎ 01886 812282

RILEY Andrew (Vla): 7 The Paddock, Northfield, Birmingham B31 2BU ☎ 0121 477 2183

ROBINSON Mark (Man): 6 Hayfield Road, Moseley, Birmingham B13 9LF ☎ 0121 449 3525

ROWLANDS Austin: 26 Sandhurst Avenue, Pedmore, Stourbridge, Dudley, West Midlands DY9 0XL ☎ 01384 376837

SANDERS Ric: PO Box 37, Banbury, Oxon OX16 8YN

SAULL Maggie: 2 Woodman's Cottage, Bromsgrove Road, Clent DY9 9PY ☎ 01562 882999

SCHEUER Betty (Vla): 10 Blenheim Road, Birmingham B13 9TY ☎ 0121 449 1218

SCOTT Catherine: 46 Bow Fell, Rugby, Warks CV21 1JF ☎ 01788 536558 & fax, 0973 779787 mob

SCOTT Ernest: Millbeck, Newbiggin-In-Bishopdale, Leyburn, North Yorks DL8 3TD

SCOTT Kirsteen: 194 Hay Green Lane, Bournville, Birmingham B30 1HR ☎ 0121 458 7789

SCOTT Sarah (Vla): Address Unknown

SEAL Michael: 30 Galton Road, Bearwood, Birmingham B67 5JU ☎ 0121 434 5215

SHARP Louise (Vla, Pf): Tile Cottage, Far Forest, Nr Kidderminster, Worcs DY14 9UE ☎ 01299 266085, 0802 473181 mob

SHAW Michael: 15 Dunsmore Close, Beeston Rylands, Nottingham NG9 1LU ☎ 0115 9224980, 0966 163760

SILVERBROOKE Ceinwen (Vla): 6 Murray Road, Rugby CV21 3JN ☎ 01788 572722

SMITH Abigail: 26 Moyston Road, Edgbaston B16 9DU ☎ 0121 456 2123

SMITH Anthony: 2 Milcote Way, Kingswinford, West Midlands DY6 9DE ☎ 01384 288232

SMITH Paul: 50 Station Road, Kings Norton, Birmingham B30 1DA ☎ 0121 694 4201

SMITH Stanley: 96 Oxford Road, Moseley, Birmingham B13 9SQ

SNAPE Richard: 18 Lenthall Avenue, Congleton, Cheshire CW12 3BE ☎ 01260 271447

SNOWDEN Joy: The Large Thatched Cottage, Church Street, Eynsham, Oxfordshire OX8 1UG ☎ 01865 881039

SPRINGATE G: The Old Court House, Sibford Ferris, Banbury, Oxon OX15 5RG ☎ 0129 578 340

SPRINGATE Richard: The Old Court House, Sibford Ferris, Banbury, Oxon OX15 5RG ☎ 0129 578 340

SPURRELL Jill: 46 Rockford Close, Oakenshaw South, Redditch, West Midlands B98 7SZ ☎ 01527 45134

STRONG Roger (Vla): Dormer House, Main Street, Cotesbach, Lutterworth LE17 4HZ ☎ 01455 553221

STUBBS Nigel: 8, Antler Drive, Etching Hill, Rugeley, Staffs WS15 2XS ☎ 01889 576010

SUTTON John: 144 Middleton Hall Road, Kings Norton, Birmingham B30 1DL ☎ 0121 243 9299

SUTTON P Anne: 144 Middleton Hall Road, Kings Norton, Birmingham, B30 1DL ☎ 0121 243 9229

SWANN Peter: 3 Fernwood Close, Littleover, Derby DE23 6JB ☎ 01332 766890

SWARBRICK David (Man): Address Unknown ☎ 01544 231313 & fax

TANN Elsie (Vln): 1268 Stratford Road, Hall Green, Birmingham B28 9BQ ☎ 0121 778 2409

TAYLOR Jane: 43 Grayswood Park Road, Quinton, Birmingham B32 1HF ☎ 0121 422 4884

THODAY Janet: Styche Close, Chesterton, Leamington Spa, Warwcolsjore CV33 9LD ☎ 01926 613464, 0402 941088

THOMAS Peter: 16 Yew Tree Road, Edgbaston, Birmingham B15 2LX ☎ 0121 440 5164

TINLEY Stella (Db): 58 Willenhall Road, Bilston, West Midlands WV14 6NW ☎ 01902 498327

TONEY Elizabeth (Bq Vln): 34 Upper St Mary's Road, Smethwick, West Midlands B67 5JR ☎ 0121 420 2336

TRANTER Malcolm (Pf): 132 The Beeches, Holly Green, Upton-on-Severn WR8 0QQ ☎ 01684 592018

TWIGG Colin (Vla): 58, Grayshott Close, Erdington, Birmingham B23 6JU ☎ 0121 382 8021

ULLMANN Louis: 18 Wentworth Road, Harborne, Birmingham, West Midlands B17 9SG ☎ 0121 427 1302

WARBURTON Paul: 88, Plymouth Place, Leamington Spa, Warks CV31 1HW ☎ 01926 831236

WHEELER Geoffrey: 89 Hungerford Road, Crewe, Cheshire CW1 1EY ☎ 01270 582032

WHITE Alison: 23 Frobisher Close, Hinckley, Leicestershire LE10 1UP ☎ 01455 449280

WHITE Paul: 23 Frobisher Close, Hinckley, Leicester LE10 1UP ☎ 01455 449280

WHITE Rosemary (Rec, Gtr): 44 Church Lane, Crewe, Cheshire CW2 8HA ☎ 01270 665742

WILLIAMS David: 1 Malanlay Road, Rugby, Warks CV22 6HR ☎ 01788 815763, 0973 134340 mob

WILSON Marjorie: Address Unknown

WOODS Amanda (Pf): 11 Park Avenue, Worcester WR3 7AT ☎ 01905 27625

YOUNGMAN Dianne: 22 Dean Road, Erdington, Birmingham B23 6QF ☎ 0121 382 6864

SOUTH EAST

ARSENAULT Terry (Gtr, Man, Bod): 10 Penrith Road, Basingstoke, Hampshire RG21 8XW ☎ 01256 329702, 01256 475381

ASHTON Charlotte: Flat 3, 337A West End Lane, West Hampstead, London NW6 4RS ☎ 020 7435 3752

BACHE Jeremy: 5 Ilkley Road, Caversham, Reading, Berkshire RG4 7BD ☎ 01734 477943

BAILEY Sarah-Jane (Vla, Hpsd, Pf): 7 The Close, Reigate, Surrey RH2 7BN ☎ Reigate 240707

BARNARD Nicholas (Vla): Wychway Cottage, Headley Fields, Headley, Nr Bordon, Hants GU35 8PX ☎ 01428 712093, 0860 164358 mob

BARTER Mary: Willow Cottage, 5 Bassett Heath Avenue, Bassett, Southampton SO1 7GP ☎ 023 8076 6108

BARTON Philippa (Pf): 3 Rhyl Road, Perrivale, Middlesex UB6 8LD ☎ 020 8997 8273

BEDFORD Beatrice: 100 Malvern Road, Moordown, Bournemouth, Dorset BH9 3DE ☎ 01202 529659

BELLMAN Frederick: 1 Berdonna Court, 2 Copper Beech Drive, Farlington, Portsmouth Hants PO6 1AZ ☎ 023 9238 6728

BERTHOUD Caroline H: 26 Sandecotes Road, Poole, Dorset BH14 8NZ ☎ 01202 741472

BISHOP Julia (Bq Vln): Rykehurst House Flat, Rotton Row, Lewes, East Sussex BN7 1TN ☎ 01273 474463

BOCKING Katherine: 21 Minster View, Wimborne, Dorset BH21 1BA ☎ 01202 882200

BORG WHEELER Philip (Clt): 8 Lanchards, Shillingstone, Blandford, Dorset DT11 8BT ☎ 01258 860392

BOYDEN Phillip: Flat 4, Princes Court, 320 Poole Road, Branksome, Poole BH12 1AN ☎ 01202 763607

BROWN Nicolette: 68 Vale Road, Parkstone, Poole, Dorset BH14 9AU ☎ 01202 734168

BULTZ Jane: 118 Seafield Road, Southbourne, Bournemouth, Dorset BH6 3JL ☎ 01202 425 564

BURSTON Barbara: 233 Goldstone Crescent, Hove, Sussex BN3 6BG ☎ Brighton 502329

CARTER Lara: 16 Florence Road, Poole, Dorset BH14 9JF ☎ 01202 739548

CASTLE Peter: 79 Alexandra Road, Parkstone, Poole, Dorset BH14 9EW ☎ 01202 773294

CHAPPELL Kay: Flat 6C, 6 Eldon Place, Westbourne, Bournemouth BH4 9AZ ☎ 01202 762329, 01202 762329

CHILD Leslie: 14 Hillbrow Road, Southbourne, Bournemouth, Dorsett BH6 5NT ☎ 01202 433561

CLARK Jane: 259 Tonbridge Road, Little Mill, East Peckham, Kent TN12 5LA ☎ 01622 871506

CLARKSON John: 119 Hankinson Road, Bournemouth, Dorset BH9 1HR ☎ 01202 777278

CLEMENTS Heather: 18 Codrington Road, Ramsgate, Kent CT11 9SP ☎ 01843 584514

COLMAN Robert: 20A,Broadway Lane, Bournemouth, Dorset BH8 0AA ☎ 01202 510330

COLYER Ronald: 39 Green Road, Reading, Berks RG6 7BS ☎ 0118 926 1600

COOK Gillian: 4 Felday Houses, Holmbury St Mary, Dorking, Surrey RH5 6NJ

COOKE Stephen (*Vla, Kbds*): Flat 1, 5 Laton Road, Hastings TN34 2ET ☎ 01424 423738

COURSE Gail (*Vla*): 103 Nutley Cres, Goring-By-Sea, Worthing, W. Sussex BN12 4LB ☎ 01903 506902

COURT Andrew: 93 Church Road, Ferndown, Dorset BH21 6RQ ☎ 01202 896036

COURTNEY Neil (*Vla*): 3 Hollis Drive, Brighstone, Isle Of Wight PO30 4AS ☎ 01983 740608

COWEN Andrew: 6 Sinclair Court, Pascoe Close, Lower Parkstone, Poole BH14 0NU ☎ 01202 718506

CUTTER Michael (*Vla*): 57, Caledon Road, Parkstone, Poole, Dorset BH14 9NL ☎ 01202 743861

DANCEY Sonia: 3 Orchard Close, Edmondsham, Wimborne, Dorset BH21 5RG ☎ 0172 54 251

DAVID Eluned: Flat 4, 320 Poole Road, Branksome, Dorset BH12 1AN ☎ 01202 765607

DAVIDSON William: 6 Shepherds Walk, Tunbridge Wells, Kent TN2 3QR ☎ 01892 534620

DAVIES Adrian: 34 Montacute Road, Lewes, East Sussex BN7 1EP ☎ Lewes 471608

DAVIES William (*A Sax, Clt*): 38 Westways, Havant, Hants PO9 3LN ☎ Havant 471292

DAVIS Peter: Willowbrook Cottage, Willowbrook, Eton Windsor, Berkshire SL4 6HL ☎ 01753 866120

DAVISON Beverley (*Voc, Vla*): Primrose Cottage, Pishill, Henley-on-Thames, Oxfordshire RG9 6HJ ☎ 01491 638903, 01491 638939

DEAN Vernon: 1 Dovas Cottages, Well Roiad, Crondall, Farnham, Surrey GU10 5PW ☎ 01252 851210

DELLA-VERDE Guy (*A Sax, T Sax, Br Sax, Clt*): 85 Shadwell Road, North End, Portsmouth, Hants PO2 9EH ☎ 023 9269 8995

DENLEY Paul (*Vla, Viol, Bq Vln*): Firwood, Victoria Road, Bishops Waltham, Hampshire SO32 1DJ ☎ 01489 892730

DOE Rebecca: Mount St. Laurence, High Street, Cranbrook, Kent TN17 3EW ☎ 01580 712330

DOIDGE Sydney (*Vla*): 54 Hatley Road, Bitterne, Southampton SO18 6NU ☎ 023 8057 8068

DREW Jacqueline: French's Riverside, Long Wittenham, Oxon OX14 4QQ ☎ 01865 407952

DUFFY Bernard: Windene, Manor Farm Road, Bournemouth, Dorset BH10 7LF ☎ 01202 573601

DYTOR Sarah: St Edwards School, Woodstock Road, Oxford OX2 7NN ☎ 01865 319257

ELLIS Katherine: Mayfield, 5 Ticknell Piece Road, Charlbury, Oxon OX7 3TN ☎ 01608 810877

ERAUT Cynthia: 49 St Annes Crescent, Lewes, Sussex BN7 1SD ☎ Lewes 5955

FAIRMAN Matthew: 13 Beehive Green, Welwyn Garden City, Herts AL7 4BE ☎ 01707 323083, 01306 880669

FISHER Timothy: 10 Mansfield Close, Lower Parkstone, Poole, Dorset BH14 0DH ☎ 01202 749381

FLEETCROFT Anne: 4 Locksley Drive, Ferndown, Dorset BH22 8JY ☎ 01202 893564

FORBES Stuart: 1 Renault Road, Woodley, Reading RG5 4EY ☎ 01734 694135 eve, 071 583 6666 ext3251

FORDYCE Emily: 2 Langton Farm, Langton Long, Blandford Forum, Dorset DT11 ☎ 01258 454791

FRASER Rosemary: 4 Kennart Road, Poole, Dorset BH17 7AP ☎ 01202 668525

FRENCH Rita: 84 Nevill Avenue, Hove, Sussex BN3 7NA ☎ 01273 730411

FRENCH Zoe: Flat 5 Surrey Towers, 2 Ipswich Road, Bournemouth BH4 9HZ ☎ 01202 762858

FROOMES Janet: 17 Aldrich Road, Sunnymead, Oxford OX2 7SS ☎ 01865 515946 & fax, 0976 545011

FULKER John: 70 Alexandra Road, Parkstone, Poole, Dorset BH14 9EW ☎ 01202 740157

GALLAGHER Charlotte (*Pf*): 9 Ravenscourt Road, Bournemouth, Dorset BH6 5EF ☎ 01202 421743

GILLARD Roy: Lansdowne Villa, Goldhill North, Chalfont St Peter SL9 9JH ☎ 01753 880009

HALL Sylvia (*Vla, Pf*): 6 Ripley Close, High Wycombe, Bucks HP13 5LF ☎ 01249 713587

HARDING Jean (*Pf*): 61 Willowbed Drive, Chichester, Sussex PO19 2HY ☎ 01243 783835

HARTE Benjamin: 122 Wilton Road, Southampton SO15 5JT ☎ 0958 361 832

HAXWORTH Jessica: Pigotts, North Dean, High Wycombe, Bucks HP14 4NF ☎ 01494 565871

HEACOCK Richard (*Pf, Gtr*): 1 Manor Farm Cottages, Baulking, Faringdon, Oxon SN7 7QE ☎ 01367 820794

HEATH Eric: 16 Redhill Drive, Bournemouth, Dorset BH10 6AL ☎ 01202 514145

HENRY Leah (*Pf, Kbds, Org, Voc*): 57 Mayhew Crescent, High Wycombe, Bucks HP13 6DF ☎ 01494 443854

HERBERT Martin (*Flt, Wi Synth, Didj*): 14 Station Road, Loudwater, High Wycombe HP10 9TX ☎ 01494 438620, 0802 516 922

HEWITT Michael (*Vla, Cel*): Fir Tree House, Steel Cross, Crowborough, E. Sussex TN6 2XA ☎ 01892 661537

HOLLAND Nick (*Cel*): 19 Fairfield Road, Winchester, Hants SO22 6SF ☎ 01962 851953, 0306 880669

HOOPER Barbara (*Voc*): 5 Hannams Close, Lytchett Matravers, Poole, Dorset BH16 6DN ☎ 01202 624554

HOWELLS Brian: 19 Castlemain Avenue, Bournemouth, Dorset BH6 5EH ☎ 01202 420168

HUMPHREYS Sydney: 1259 Hewlett Place, Victoria Bc, Canada, V8S 4Pg

INGS Elizabeth: 'Greenfields', Balls Lane, Sturminster Marshall, Dorset BH21 4BG ☎ 01258 857893

ISAAC Kathleen: 15 Sandford Rise, Charlbury, Oxon OX7 3SZ ☎ 01608 810544

JAMES Philip (*Vla, Pf*): 16, Stephen Langton Drive, Bournemouth, Dorset BH11 9PF ☎ 01202 571118

JEWEL Dominic: 10 St. Paul's Road West, Dorking, Surrey RH4 2HU ☎ 01306 886863, 0958 583530 mob

JOHNSON Benjamin: Flat 1, 30 George Street, Ryde, Isle Of Wight PO33 2EN ☎ 01983 564121

JOHNSTON Brian: 17 Morrison Avenue, Poole, Dorset BH12 4AD ☎ 01202 715961

JONES Derek: 33 West Avenue, Heath End, Farnham, Surrey GU9 0RB ☎ 01252 727434

JOSEPH Eric (*Vla*): 61 Branksome Wood Road, Bournemouth, Dorset BH4 9JU ☎ 01202 761806

JOUBERT Pierre: 33 Abinger Place, Lewes, East Sussex BN7 2QA ☎ 01273 480023

KELLETT Michael: 4 Jarvis Drive, Kings Green, Twyford, Reading, Berkshire RG10 9EW ☎ 01189 321 725, 0410 455851

KING Barbara: 10 Oliver Road, Swaythling, Southampton SO2 2JP ☎ 023 8055 8599

KINGHAM Suzanne: 39 Kings Road, Charminster, Bournemouth BH3 7LE ☎ 01202 257 162

KIRBY Molly: Flat 19, Belle Vue Mansions, Belle Vue Road, Bournemouth, Dorset BH6 3ET ☎ 01202 433156

KNOWLAND Isabel (*Vla*): 31 Borrowmead Road, Headington, Oxford OX3 9QP ☎ 01806 763834

LARGE Jonathan (*Vla*): 68 St Peters Road, Reading, Berks RG6 1PH ☎ 0118 926 2634

LE GOOD Rosemary: 17 Meades Lane, Chesham, Buckinghamshire HP5 1ND ☎ 01494 774310

LEACH Karen: 25 Old Farm Road, Oakdale, Poole, Dorset BH15 3LL ☎ 01202 668406

LEADBETTER Nicola: Four Winds, Bryanston, Blandford, Dorset DT11 0PU ☎ 01258 484692

LESLIE Chris (*Man, B Gtr*): Grange Cottage, High Street, Adderbury, Oxon OX17 3LS

LEVY Mark (*Bq Vln*): Flat 4, Wick Hall, Radley Abingdon, Oxon OX14 3NF ☎ 01235 450524

LEWIS Phyllis (*Acc*): 24 Park Rise, Hove, Sussex BN3 8PG ☎ 01273 737065

MACDONALD Donald: 83 The Avenue, Bournemouth, Dorset BH9 2UT ☎ 01202 520850

MAGUIRE Jack: 1A St Clements Gardens, Bournemouth, Dorset BH1 4ED ☎ 01202 399114, 020 8207 0007

MAHER Joseph: Fairbank, Bolney Road, Ansty, West Sussex RH17 5AW ☎ 01444 413258

MALLET Arthur (*Sax, Clt*): 11 Brixley Close, Bournemouth, Dorset BH12 3PE ☎ 01202 70658

MAYOR Simon (*Man, Gtr*): 2 Talfourd Avenue, Reading, Berkshire RG6 2BP ☎ 01734 68615

MCCONNELL Arthur: 51 East St Helens Street, Abingdon, Oxon OX14 5EE ☎ 01235 523484

MCNICHOLAS Steve (*Gtr, Man, Kbds*): Yes/No Productions Ltd, 8 Pavilion Parade, Brighton BN2 1SF ☎ 01273 673634

MEYER Gloria: 1 Bath Court, Kings Esplanade, Hove, Sussex BN3 2WP ☎ Brighton 204274

MILLER Hugh (*Vla*): 22 Frankland Crescent, Poole, Dorset BH14 9PX ☎ 01202 746356

MILLER Marisa (*Vla*): 46 Cherry Tree Close, Southmoor, Abingdon, Oxon OX13 5BE ☎ 01865 820815

MITCHELL Cynthia: 38 Richmond Park Avenue, Bournemouth, Dorset BH8 9DP ☎ 01202 515412

MITCHELL Emma (*Pf*): 105 Wellington Street, Thame, Oxon OX9 3BW ☎ 01844 260851, 0973 360203 mob

MORGAN Peter (*Pf, B Gtr*): 7 Cartwright Road, Charlton, Banbury, Oxon OX17 3DG ☎ 01295 811404, 0802 855856

MOULD Cheryl (*Pf*) ☎ 01908 679670, 0403 164 381

NALL Peter: Flat 5 Surrey Towers, 2 Ipswich Road, Bournemouth BH4 9HZ ☎ 01202 762858

NEWGARTH Sam (*Md, Com, Arr*): 32 Barnes Close, Sturminster Newton, Dorset DT10 1BN ☎ 01258 473073

NORRIS Thomas (*Vla*): The Old Coach House, Barn Hill, Hunton Maidstone, Kent ME15 0QT ☎ 01622 820323

OBRIEN Anita: 24 Cassel Avenue, Poole, Dorset BH13 6JD ☎ 01202 760960

OBRIEN Brendan: 24 Cassel Avenue, Poole, Dorset BH13 6JD ☎ 01202 760960

PALEY Ben: 35 Coombe Terrace, Brighton, East Sussex BN2 4AD ☎ 01273 626 366

PALMER Martin: Flat 1 Fernbank, 33 Rushams Road, Horsham, West Sussex RH12 2NU ☎ 01403 242046

PARSONS David: 196 Belle Vue Road, Bournemouth, Dorset BH6 3AH ☎ 01202 432527

PATIENCE Elaine: 3 Ambleside Avenue, Telscombe Cliffs, Nr Newhaven, East Sussex BN4 7LS ☎ 01273 587384

PERRY Vicky: 14 Highland View Close, Wimborne, Dorset BH21 2QX ☎ 01202 887696

PHILLIPS David (*B Gtr*): 4 Harvey Road, Langley, Berks SL1 8JB ☎ 01753 544475, 01753 711554

PLUMMER Sarah: Flat 2, 37 The Goffs, Eastbourne, East Sussex BN21 1HF ☎ 01323 723516

POLLARD Clare (*Vla*): 40 Bourlon Wood, Abingdon, Oxfordshire OX14 1LF ☎ 01235 521585

POOLE Penelope: 74 Elder Road, Bere Regis, Wareham, Dorset BH20 7NB ☎ 01929 472541, 0374 139159

POWELL Derek (*Vla*): 8 Bruce Close, Deal, Kent CT14 9BU ☎ 01304 375989

PRIDDLE Anita (*Vla, Pf*): 110 Springfield Road, Southborough, Tunbridge Wells, Kent TN4 0RA ☎ 01892 548483

PRYCE Melody: 105 Queen Street, Broadwater, Worthing, Sussex BN14 7BH ☎ 01903 212144

REED Ashley (*Vla*) ☎ 01202 881711, 0958 310058

REED Elizabeth: 10 Minster Road, Oxford OX4 1LX ☎ 01865 726919

ROBERTSON Kirstie: 45 Nightingale Road, Southampton SO15 3EL ☎ 023 8078 9868

SANDERSON Sally: 22 Bramley Road, Worthing, West Sussex BN14 9DR ☎ 01903 237086

SCHMEISING Evelyn: 34 Mill Road, Salisbury, Wilts SP2 7RZ

SCHWARM Christa: 13 Kirk Court, Mount Harry Road, Sevenoaks, Kent TN13 3JW ☎ 01732 452645

SECRET Gillian: 1 Poplars Close, Preston Bissett, Buckingham MK18 4LR ☎ 01280 848275

SEPHTON Eileen: 1 Romney Road, West Worthing, West Sussex BN11 5ES ☎ 01903 248770

SHEAN David: 13 Mansfield Avenue, Parkstone, Poole, Dorset BH14 0DQ ☎ 01202 743642

SHERRAH-DAVIES Helen (*Pf*): Cairnhill, 7 Birch End, West Chiltington, Pulborough, West Sussex RH20 2QF ☎ 01798 812 069, 0498 810 705

SHORT William: 37 Swainstone Road, Reading, Berkshire RG2 0DX

SMITH Ian (*Vla*): 44 Beverley Crescent, Bedford MK40 4BY ☎ 01234 353762

SMITH Keith (*Bag*): 35 Selwyn Gardens, Cambridge CB3 9AY ☎ 01223 357703

SMITH Keith: The Stable House, Chapel Lane, Ratley Nr Banbury, Oxon OX15 6DS ☎ 0129 587 540

SONNEVELD Martin (*Vla*): 20 Dallaway Gardens, East Grinstead, West Sussex RH19 1AR ☎ 01342 315575, 01342 324769

SPONG Richard (*Gtr*): 47 Freshfield Road, Brighton BN2 2BJ ☎ 01273 603633

STAIT Brien (*Vla*): 31 Kidmore End Road, Emmer Green, Reading, Berkshire RG4 8SN ☎ 0118 947 4547

STEAD Gillian (*Cel, Voc*): 8 Ashburn Garth, Hightown, Ringwood, Hampshire BH24 3DS ☎ 01425 476350

STEAR Kate: 6 Edward Street, Blandford, Dorset DT11 7QJ ☎ 01258 454772

STEEL Barbara (*Voc*): Fairbanks, Alfold Road, Cranleigh, Surrey GU6 8NB ☎ 01483 274838

STILWELL Jane: 12 Rowlands Road, Roffey, Horsham, Sussex RH12 4LH ☎ Horsham 52914

STUDT Richard: 101 Queens Park Avenue, Bournemouth, Dorset BH8 9LJ ☎ 01202 394955

SUMMERBELL Ros (*Pf, Voc, Theory*): 84 Woodlands Road, Isleworth, London TW7 6JY ☎ 01722 330012

TAYLOR Jonathan (*Vla*): 176 West Way, Broadstone, Dorset BH18 9LN ☎ 01202 692770

TAYLOR Susan: 176 West Way, Broadstone, Dorset BH18 9LN ☎ 01202 692770

TENDLER Ronald: 25 Woodruff Avenue, Burpham, Guildford, Surrey GU1 1XT ☎ 01483 533544

THORGILSON Charles: 45 West Morden, Wareham, Dorset BH20 7EA ☎ 01929 459631

THORGILSON Janice: 45 West Morden, Wareham, Dorset BH20 7EA ☎ 01929 459631

TOMKINS Saskia (*Fo Fdl, Vla*): 190 Church Street, Wolverton, Milton Keynes MK12 5JS ☎ 01908 222966

TOPPING John (*Vla*): 30 Beeches Avenue, Worthing, Sussex BN14 9JF ☎ Worthing 38484

TURNBULL Kate (*Pf*): 107 Lambs Green Lane, Corfe Mullen, Wimborne, Dorset BH21 3DN ☎ 01202 848119

UNDERWOOD James: Holme Wood Bungalow, Chisbridge Cross, Marlow, Bucks SL7 2RH ☎ 01494 881260, 0378 388393

VERRALL Colin: 116 Carberry Avenue, Bournemouth, Dorset BH6 3LH ☎ 01202 424328

WATSON George: 59 Bannings Vale, Saltdean, Sussex BN2 8DF ☎ 01273 331464

WHITE Alison: 158 Hilmanton, Lower Earley, Reading, Berks RG6 4HJ ☎ 0118 986 1005, 0860 316072 mob

WHITE Lesley: 16 Prichard Road, Habberton Mead, Oxford OX3 0DG ☎ 01865 243936

WHITMORE Sheila: 48 Victoria Road, Poole, Dorset BH12 3BB ☎ 01202 742999

WILKINSON Ann: 24 Gainsborough Road, Bournemouth BH7 7BD ☎ 01202 397351

WILLETTS Annabelle: Orchard House, Orchard Street, Blandford, Dorset DT11 7QZ ☎ 01258 451493

WILLIAMSON Heather: 13 Longfellow Road, Worthing, Brighton BN11 4NU ☎ 01903 238861

WINDASS Christopher (*Vla*): 17 Whittall Street, Kings Sutton, Banbury, Oxon OX17 3RD ☎ 01295 810683 & fax

WITHAM Peter: 9 Woods View Road, Bournemouth, Dorset BH9 2LL ☎ 01202 519098

WOOD Beverley (*Kbds, Arr, Com*): 9 Baxter Road, Thornhill, Southampton SO19 6HZ ☎ 023 8049 3516

WOOD Christopher (*Gtr, Ac Gtr, E Gtr*): 40 Whitstable Road, Faversham, Kent ME13 8DL ☎ 01795 537906

WYATT Ellie (*Pf, Kbds, Voc, Dul*): 17 Linton Road, Hastings, East Sussex TN34 1TW ☎ 01424 446275

YOUCHENG: 31 Egerton Road, Bournemouth, Dorset BH8 9AY ☎ 01202 396448

SOUTH WEST

ABERCROMBY Jillian (*Pf*): La Primavera, Village De Putron, St Peter Port, Guernsey,Channel Islands GY1 2TG ☎ 01481 37496

ADAMS Kevin (*Pf*): Murmur-Y-Mor, 6 Somerset View, Ogmore-By-Sea, Bridgend Mid Glam CF32 0PP ☎ 01656 880337

AIRD Philip (*Vla*): 3 Llanbedr Road, Fairwater, Cardiff CF5 3BU ☎ 029 2057 6338

ALLAN Andrew (*Kbds, Flt, Gtr, Voc*): 27 Clare Avenue, Bishopston, Bristol BS7 8JF ☎ 0117 9425472

ALLEN Miranda (*Voc, Pf*): 5 Archer Terrace, North Rd West, Plymouth, Devon PL1 5HD ☎ 01762 260401

ASHBY Dawn (*Pf*): Flat 2, 2 Sussex Place, Plymouth, Devon PL1 2HT ☎ 01752 260201

ATKINSON Jane (*Pf*): 99 Marlborough Road, Roath, Cardiff CF2 5BW ☎ 029 2049 9433

ATTWOOD Stewart (*Db*): 32 Shilton Road, Carterton, Oxon OX18 1EH ☎ 01993 844667

BAKER Robert (*Vla*): Treetops, Firgrove Lane, Lower Peasedown, Nr Bath Avon BA2 8AJ ☎ 01761 432982

BALFOUR-PAUL Alison: 84 Fairwater Grove East, Llandaff, Cardiff, S.Glamorgan CF5 2JU ☎ 029 2056 0673

BARBER Andrew (*Pf*): Laxton Cottage, Milton Road, Oundle, Nr Peterborough PE8 4AQ ☎ 01832 274049 eve, 01832 272227 day

BARBER Carmel: 5 Fairfield Avenue, Victoria Park, Cardiff CF5 1BR ☎ 029 2055 3806

BARRETT Sarah (*Pf, Flt*): Flat 1, Norfolk House, Rushcroft Road, London SW2 1JX

BASKERVILLE James (*Vla*): New Beaupre House, St Hilary, Nr Cowbridge CF7 7DP

BASS Ruth: 131 Kings Road, Canton, Cardiff CF1 9DE ☎ 029 2021 3601

BENNETT Andrea (*Pf*): 31 Doulting, Shepton Mallet, Somerset BA4 4QD ☎ 01749 880508

BENNETT Bob (*Saxes*): 1, Heath Walk, Downend, Bristol, Avon BS16 6EY ☎ 0117 9569282

BENNETT Frances: 24 Valley Close, Newbridge, Truro, Cornwall TR1 3UN ☎ 01872 275058

BERGIN John: 33 St Johns Crescent, Whitchurch, Cardiff CF4 7AF ☎ 029 2061 5797

BERRY Gillian (*Com*): 2 Pyrland Avenue, Taunton, Somerset TA2 7BD ☎ 01823 326200

BETTERIDGE Lisa: 56 Shakespeare Avenue, Bath BA2 4RG ☎ 01225 337489

BIRD Robert: 97 Graham Avenue, Penyfai, Bridgend, Mid Glamorgan CF31 4NP ☎ 01656 725790

BLACK Catherine (*Pf, Voc*): Orchard House, 6 Clevedon Road, Tickenham, N Somerset BS21 6QT ☎ 01275 858607

BLADEN Anthony: 31, Abbey Close, Curry Rivel, Langport TA10 0EL ☎ 01458 251552

BODGER Ruth: Castle View, 15 Lower Castle Street, Abergavenny, Gwent NP7 5EE ☎ 01873 858239

BOOTH Jeffrey: 25 Cambourne Close, Highlight Park, Barry, South Glamorgan CF62 8AL ☎ 01446 744459

BOOTHROYD Ralph: Tremyra, 36 Gog Road, Sully, South Glamorgan CF64 5TD ☎ 029 2053 0554

BOTT Douglas (*Vla, B Gtr, Kbds*): Kew House, 23 Anchor Road, Calne, Wiltshire SN11 8DY ☎ 01249 813021, 0117 924 3484

BURNARD Stephen (*Vla*): The Granary, Gwern-Y-Saint, Wonaston, Monmouth, Gwent NP5 4DW

BURNETT Jonathan: 6 Langstone Cottages, Langstone, Newport NP6 2LY ☎ 01633 411107, 0467 716851

BURNS Edward (*Vla*): The Rocks Old Ditch, Westbury-Sub-Mendip15, Wells, Somerset BA5 1HA ☎ 01749 870221

BUTLER Rosalind: 16 Southcourt Road, Penylan, Cardiff CF23 9DA ☎ 029 2049 7754

CARSON Mary: Yew Trees, Comeytrowe Rise, Taunton, Somerset TA1 5JA ☎ 01823 2722764 & fax

CHADWICK Robert: 24 Station Road, Winterbourne Down, Bristol BS17 1EP ☎ Winterbourne 77

CHAPPELL Clare (*Pf*): Rock Villa, Crowlas, Penzance, Cornwall TR20 8DP ☎ 01736 740605

CHEW Robert (*Vla*): 19 Whitecross Square, Cheltenham, Glos GL53 7AY ☎ 01242 233049

COCKROFT Anna (*Pf*): 1 Bartholomew Street West, Exeter, Devon EX4 3AJ ☎ 01392 433748

COLE Dennis: 367 Locking Road, Weston Super Mare, Somerset BS22 8NH ☎ 01934 22519/237

CONSTABLE Jennifer (*Pf*): 23 Archer Road, Penarth, South Glamorgan CF64 3HJ ☎ 029 2070 3180

COULTAS Michael: 3 Primrose Way, The Foxgloves, Rogerstone, Newport NP1 9BB ☎ 01633 891058

COX Tony: Philton, St Mabyn, Bodmin, Cornwall PL30 3DF ☎ 01208 841557

CRABTREE Richard (*Vla*): Chaceley, 34 Station Road, Backwell, Bristol BS19 3LN ☎ 01275 462494

CRAWFORD Janet (*Vla, Bq Vln*): 137 High Street, Yatton, N. Somerst BS49 4DB ☎ 01934 876491

CROALL Neill: 9 Gabalfa Road, Sketty, Swansea SA2 8NF ☎ 01792 205318

CROOKS Margaret (*Pf*): 5 Godsitch, Ashton Keynes, Swindon, Wilts SN6 6NZ ☎ 01285 861205

D'ALMEIDA Dale (*Vla*): Address Unknown ☎ 029 2088 3868

DATSON Roger: 21 Widham, Purton, Swindon, Wilts SN5 9HP ☎ 01793 770503

DAVIES Angharad: Sycamore, 3 Elysiah Grove, Aberystwyth, Ceredigion, Wales SY23 2EZ ☎ 01970 615494

DAVIES John (*Pf*): 18 Woodbury Avenue, Wells, Somerset BA5 2XN ☎ 01749 675724

DAVIES Rhiannon (*Pf*): Flat 1, Aquilla Court, Conway Road, Pontcanna, Cardiff CF1 9PA ☎ 029 2037 7393, 0595 262165

DE MONTET Rolette: 8 Greenclose Road, Whitchurch, Cardiff CF4 1QP ☎ 029 2062 5269

DE ST PAER Wendy: 10 Blosse Road, Llandaff North, Cardiff CF4 2JB ☎ 029 2057 5468

DEARNLEY Helen (*Pf*): 'Lynton', 12 Ham Road, Upper Wanborough, Swindon, Wilts SN4 0DF ☎ 01793 790852

DEBLEY Margaret: 11 Canowie Rd, Redland, Bristol BS6 7HP ☎ 0117 9730935

DEWAR Beverley: Knowle Cottage, Lamyatt, Somerset BA4 6NP ☎ 01749 813226

DEWAR Frances (*Pf*): Walnut Cottage, Canada Coombe, Hutton, Weston Super Mare, Avon BS24 9US ☎ 01934 812542

DRISCOLL Kim (*Flt*): Address Unknown ☎ 01643 702198

DU FEU Elizabeth: 2 Highfield Mews, La Pouquelaye, St Helier, Jersey C.I. JE2 3GF ☎ 01534 38017

EALES Adrian: 20 Manton Hollow, Marlborough, Wilts SN8 1RR ☎ 01672 514381

ELDRIDGE Kathryn (*Pf*): First Floor Flat, 33 Brock Street, Bath, Avon BA1 2LN ☎ 01225 464486

ELLERINGTON Iris (*Pf*): 15 Priorsgate, Oakdale, Blackwood, Caerphilly, Gwent NP2 0EL ☎ 01495 223475, 0831 091585

ELMS Samantha: Curzon House, 12 Lodway, Easton-In-Gordano, North Somerset BS20 0DH ☎ 01275 371213

EVANS Michael *(Vla, Voc)*: The Old Manse, Bath Road, Beckington, Somerset BA3 6SW ☎ 01373 830806

FARNON John *(Vla)*: 32 High Street, Market Lavington, N Devizes, Wilts SN10 1AT ☎ 0138 081 2237

FRANCIS Alison: 19 Water House Drive, City Gardens, Cardiff CF1 8AY ☎ 029 2066 6067

GARNER Robert: Plot 18, Whitsand Bay View, Portwrinkle, Cornwall PL11 3DB ☎ St Germans 3089

GEE Peggy: Davenport, Bracken Rise, Broadsands, Paignton Devon TQ4 6JU ☎ 01803 842826

GORDON David *(Voc)*: Flat 4 - Steepholm, 17 Randall Road, Clifton, Bristol BS8 4TP ☎ 0117 9292777

GREENSLADE Rebecca Marie: 26 St Clears Close, St Martins Est, Caerphilly, Mid Glamorgan CF8 1DU ☎ 029 2086 3443

GRIBBLE Olivia: Brookside The Terrace, Creigian, Cardiff, S.Glamorgan CF4 8NG ☎ 029 2089 2135

HAMER Jill Meredith: 19 Lon Werdd, St Fagans Court, Cardiff CF5 4SS ☎ 029 2059 3873

HARLOCK John *(Per)*: 35B Point Terrace, Exmouth, Devon EX8 1EF ☎ 01395 275675

HASKEY Barry: 5 Llyn Close, Lakeside, Cardiff CF2 6LG ☎ 029 2075 6003

HEAD George: Le Marche-Pied, Route De Carteret, Castel, Guernsey, Channel Islands GY5 7YU ☎ 01481 53801, 01481 51298

HEARD John: Lockengate Farm, Bugle, St Austell, Cornwall PL26 8RY ☎ Lanivet 831730

HEWITT Helen: Darkes Farm, Noverton Lane, Prestbury, Cheltenham, Glos GL52 5DD ☎ 01242 244541, 0976 396322

HIGGINS Norman *(Db)*: 13 Well Street, Tywardreath, Par, Cornwall PL24 2QH ☎ Par 2110/5919

HINGS Catherine: 2 Hillside View, Craigwen, Pontypridd, Mid Glam CF37 2LF ☎ 01443 402262

HOLMES Sophia *(Vla)*: Wisnan, Ludgvan, Penzance, Cornwall TR20 8BN ☎ 01736 740450

HORNER Christopher: 17 Fairwood Road, Llandaff, Cardiff CF5 3QF ☎ 029 2056 5525, 029 2088 4445

HOWARD Francis *(Clt)*: 63 St Michaels Road, Llandaff, Cardiff CF5 2AN ☎ 029 2056 3294

HOWELLS Jonathan: Grey Tiles, Paynters Lane, Illogan, Redruth TR16 4DR ☎ 01209 842331, 0378 736910 mob

HUCKLE Roger: 29 Holmes Grove, Henleaze, Bristol BS9 4ED ☎ 0117 962 4289

HUGHES Edward: 146 Vicarage Road, Morriston, Swansea SA6 6DR

HYMAN Robert: Camelot House, Tunley, Nr Bath BA3 1DZ ☎ 01761 471232

IZZETT Sarah: 21 Andrews Rd, Llandaff North, Cardiff, Wales CF4 2JN ☎ 029 2057 7990

JACKSON Jeremy: 5 Uchel Dre, Kerry, Newtown, Powys SY16 4PS ☎ 01686 670714

JAMES Alexander *(Gtr, Man)*: 17 Landor Drive, Loughor, Swansea SA4 6QL ☎ 01792 897510

JAMISON Shelley *(Vla, Pf, Gtr, Voc)*: Winters Lodge, Wirr Road, Winterslow, Salisbury, Wilts SP5 1PL ☎ 01980 862 167, 07775 827907

JESSE David *(Vla, Pf)*: 7A Pentreath Terrace, Lanner, Redruth, Cornwall TR16 6HP ☎ 01209 315190

JOHNSON Tom *(Gtr, Vla, Kbds, Voc)*: 43 Gwilliam Street, Windmill Hill, Bristol BS3 4LT ☎ 0117 9665489

JONES Ann: 10 Kirton Close, Radyr Way, Llandaff, Cardiff CF5 2NB ☎ 029 2056 5151

JONES Iolo: 14 Llanbradach Street, Grangetown, Cardiff CF1 7AD ☎ 029 2022 8324

JUTTON Maureen *(Vla)*: 5 Hunters Wood, Torrington, Devon EX38 7NX

KASSIER Hans *(Vla)*: 26 Higher Port View, Saltash, Cornwall PL12 4BX

KEGELMANN Martin: 124 Plassey Street, Penarth, South Glamorgan CF64 1EQ ☎ 029 2035 0302 & fax

KERSHAW Elizabeth: 20 Castlecroft Road, Westminster Park, Chester CH4 7QD

KILBRIDE Gerard ☎ 029 2022 5737

KILPATRICK Elizabeth *(Vla)*: 209 Whitchurch Road, Tavistock, Devon PL19 9DQ ☎ 01822 2229

KIRKLAND-WILSON Brigid: Twinell Farm, Spaxton, Bridgewater, Somerset TA5 1DQ ☎ 01278 671261

LAKEMAN Seth: The Firs, Crapstone, Yelverton, Devon PL20 7PJ ☎ 01822 852274

LATHAM Katy *(Voc, Pf)*: 21 Robin Lane, Clevedon, Nr. Bristol BS21 7ES ☎ 0117 9873798

LILLEY George: Afondel, Falcondale Drive, Lampeter, Dyfed SA48 7JW ☎ 01570 422883

LILLEY Peter: Flat 4, 143 Stanwell Road, Penarth, South Glamorgan CF6 1HQ ☎ 029 2070 8996, 01308 488344

LLOYD Jeff *(Vla, Con)*: 24 Dunraven Crescent, Talbot Green, Mid Glamorganshire CF7 8JD ☎ 01443 222841

LOCKWOOD Ronald *(Vla)*: 45 Pencoedtre Road, Cadoxton, Barry, South Glam CF6 7SE ☎ 01446 739489

LUCCHESI Dudley: 27 Aberdeen Road, Redland, Bristol BS6 6HX ☎ 0117 9734324

LUCK Rupert: Abbels House, Elkstone, Cheltenham, Glos GL53 9PB ☎ 01242 870483, 01242 870368 fax

MAINWARING Richard *(Vla, B Gtr, Dms)*: 71 Lansdown Lane, Weston, Bath BA1 4ND ☎ 01225 336848, 0411 291942

MAISEY Rachel: 4 Bryon Place, Penarth, Vale Of Glamorgan CF64 2SS ☎ 029 2021 6709, 0973 818322

MANN Paul: 48 Kyle Avenue, Whitchurch, Cardiff CF4 1SS ☎ 029 2061 5997

MAPLESTONE Trevor: 19 Salisbury Court, Greenmeadow, Cwmbran, Gwent NP44 3EN ☎ 01633 866780

MARKS Anne-Marie: Cerddfan, 6 College Square, Llanelli, Dyfed SA15 1DT ☎ 01554 772594

MARSHALL Kay: Woodland House, Twyneyn, Dinas Powys, South Glamorgan CF64 4AS ☎ 0122 515333

MATTHIAS John *(Gtr, Pf, Voc)*: 16 Bellevue Crescent, Clifton Wood, Bristol BS8 4TE ☎ 0117 926 8711

MAXWELL Vera: Apartment C, The Sackville, Delawarr Parade, Bexhill, East Sussex TN40 1LS

MCCONVILLE Dermott *(Gtr, H Gtr)*: 41 Oakbury Drive, Preston, Weymouth, Dorset DT3 6JD ☎ 01305 832158

MCKINNON Andrew *(Pf, Hrn)*: 55 Trenos Gardens, Llanharan, Pontyclun, Mid Glam CF72 9SZ ☎ 01443 228438

MCNAUGHT Donald: 6 King Street, Penarth, Cardiff CF6 1HP ☎ 029 2070 9527

MEARE Annabelle *(Pf)*: St Breock, Butleigh Road, Glastonbury, Somerset BA6 8AQ ☎ 01458 831823, 01523 701301 pager

MINTO Hilary: 19 Pontcanna Place, Pontcanna, Cardiff CF1 9JY ☎ 029 2039 7040

MONTGOMERY-SMITH Philip *(Vla)*: 3 Greenbank Close, Grampound Road, Truro, Cornwall TR2 4TD ☎ 01726 883397

MOODY Daphne: Lodge Farm House, Elm Close, Pitton, Salisbury, Wilts SP5 1EU ☎ 01722 72645

MORRIS Alan: 101 Milton Road, Yate, Bristol BS37 5ES ☎ 01454 315498

MORSE Jane *(Vla)*: 32 Cory Crescent, Peterston-Super-Ely, Ely, S.Glamorgan CF5 6LS ☎ 01446 760722

MUNRO Margaret: 6 Queens Gardens, Magor, Newport, Gwent NP6 3BU ☎ 01633 881041

MURRAY David: 10 Tymynydd Close, Radyr, Cardiff CF4 8AS ☎ 029 2084 3651

NEATH Deborah *(Pf)*: Address Unknown ☎ 029 2055 4783

NELSON Ruth *(Pf)*: 18 Beatrice Avenue, Saltash, Cornwall PL12 4NF ☎ 01752 843042

NEWINGTON Richard: 50 Kyle Avenue, Whitchurch, Cardiff, South Glamorgan CF4 1SS ☎ 029 2062 4967

NICHOLS David: 2 West Rocke Avenue, Coombe Lane, Westbury-on-Trym, Bristol BS9 2AW ☎ 0117 9685278

NICOLIN Bernadette: Flat A, 70 Stanwell Road, Penarth, Vale Of Glamorgan CF64 3LQ

OGDEN Sarah *(Pf)*: 12 Hill View, Clifton, Bristol BS8 1DF ☎ 0117 9292150

OLIVE Sybil: Cawdor, 3 Greenwood Lane, St Fagans, Cardiff CF5 6EL ☎ 029 2055 4145

OSBON Lorna: 52 St. Kilda's Road, Oldfield Park, Bath BA2 3QL ☎ 01225 337722

PARTINGTON Sydney: Mumlus Mutton Dingle, New Radnor Presteigne, Powys LD8 2TL ☎ 0154 421 606

PATTENDEN Jacqueline (*Vla*): 4 The Willows, Highworth, Swindon SN6 7PG ☎ 01367 244 921

PHILLIPS Sian: The Coach House, Station Road, St Clears, Carmarthenshire SA33 4DF ☎ 01994 231376

PINNIGER Robert: 31 West Town Lane, Brislington, Bristol BS4 5DA ☎ Bristol 773974

PLESSNER Susan: 15 Plasturton Avenue, Cardiff CF1 9HL ☎ 029 2023 3809

POOLEY Anthony (*Vla*): Longpath Cottage, Moor Road, Sutton Mallet, Bridgwater, Somerset TA7 9AW ☎ 01278 723256

PORTER Catherine: 2 Ovington Terrace, Cardiff, South Glamorgan CF5 1GF ☎ 029 2023 1813

PORTEUS Terry (*Vla*): 9 Victoria Square, Penarth, South Glam CF6 2EW ☎ 029 2070 9541

PREECE George: Address Unknown ☎ 01792 893312

PRESTON Joyce (*Vla*): Fawn Glen, Bosworlas Moor, St Just, Nr Penzance, Cornwall TR19 7RQ ☎ 01736 788258

PRICE Helina (*Pf*): 30 Lidmore Road, Barry, Vale Of Glamorgan CF62 7NF ☎ 01446 740 484

PRICE Jane: The Vicarage, 42 Vicarage Road, Twyardreath, Par, Cornwall PL24 2PH ☎ 01726 812775

RAFFERTY Michael: Splott Cottage, Colwinston, Nr Cowbridge, S Glamorgan CF71 7NJ ☎ 01656 767128

REES Stephen (*Acc*): Gwenlais, 8 Bron Arfon, Llanllechid, Gwynedd LL57 3LW

RICHARDSON Elizabeth: Mimulus, Mutton Dingle, New Radnor Presteigne, Powys LD8 2TL ☎ 0154 421 606

RIDOUT Jane (*Gtr*): 3 St Hildas Road, Griffiths Town, Ponty Pool, Gwent NP4 5HN ☎ 014955 51005

RIDSDALE Peter (*Kbds*): 1 Canowie Road, Redland, Bristol BS6 7HP ☎ 0117 9737324

RILEY Bethan (*Bq Vln*): 3 Londonderry Terrace, Machynlleth, Powys SY20 8BG ☎ 01654 702220 & fax, 0410 209627 mob

RINGGUTH Vickie: 9 Victoria Square, Penarth, Cardiff CF6 2EJ ☎ 029 2070 9541

ROBB Michael (*Vla*): 48 First Avenue, Oldfield Park, Bath, Avon BA2 3NW

ROBERTS Lucy (*Vla, Crum*): 4 Allington Mead, Bridport, Dorset DT6 5HF ☎ 01308 425173

ROBLIN Louise: 87 Mackworth Drive, Cimla, Neath, West Glamorgan SA11 2QA ☎ 01639 851606

ROLT Heather: 24 Ash Crescent, Galmington, Taunton, Somerset TA1 5PW ☎ 01823 283734

ROSKAMS Luke: 14 Alfreda Road, Whitchurch, Cardiff CF4 2EH ☎ 029 2062 5316

ROSSI Davide (*Vla, Pf, Kbds*): 2 West Street, Warminster, Wiltshire BA12 8JJ ☎ 01985 215 757

RUTLAND Gillian (*Voc*): 27 Gabalfa Road, Llandaff, Cardiff CF4 2JJ

SANDERSON Richard (*Man, Gtr, Kbds, Per*): 64 Foxdown, Wadebridge, Cornwall PL27 6BD ☎ 01208 812285, 01208 863022

SAUER C: 72 Laura Grove, Paignton, Devon TQ3 2LN ☎ 01803 550523

SAUNT Lucy (*Pf*): 5 Spring Gardens, Britton, Westbury, Wiltshire BA13 4SD ☎ 01380 830916

SCHLAIFFER Don (*Vla*): 9 Ducie Road, Staple Hill, Bristol BS16 5JZ ☎ 0117 957 5759 & fax, 0336 720484 pager

SCHRECKER Peter: Linden Cottage, Weston Road, Bath BA1 2XU ☎ 01225 312663

SEARS John (*Vla, Rec*): Flat 1, 12 Walcot Buildings, London Road, Bath BA1 6AD ☎ 01225 312341

SEGAL Joel (*Vla*): 57 Fore Street, Topsham, Nr Exeter EX3 0HW ☎ 01392 875239

SELDIS Francesca: 29 Templeway, Lydney, Glos GL15 5HU ☎ 01594 844895

SHAW Hazel (*Vla, Pf*): 6 Croft Street, Cowbridge, South Glamorgan CF7 7DH ☎ 01446 775540

SHEARMAN Thomas: 39 Farm Road, Weston Super Mare BS22 8BA ☎ 01934 627792

SHEWRING Marilyn: 134 Parc-Y-Fro, Creigiau, Cardiff, South Glamorgan CF4 8SB ☎ 029 2089 2107

SILVERSTON Anita: 18 Stockwell Close, Downend, Bristol BS16 6XB ☎ 0117 957 2153

SINCLAIR Jane: 6 Mill Road, Tongwynlis, Cardiff CF4 7JP ☎ 029 2081 1051

SMITH Graham: 84 Cobourg Road, Montpelier, Bristol BS6 5HX

SMITH Shirley: Oakland, Trevanion Road, Wadebridge, Cornwall PL27 7NZ ☎ 01208 814356

SMYTH Julia: 27B Great George Street, Bristol BS1 5QT ☎ 0117 9213311

STACEY Brenda (*Vla*): 118 Brampton Way, Portishead, Avon BS20 9YT

STANBURY Rosemary (*Vla*): Highleaze, Mill Lane, Swindon SN1 4HG ☎ 01793 522798

STEIN John: 28 Westbourne Road, Penarth, South Glam CF6 2HF

STEPHEN Rosahund: 32 Raleigh Road, Southville, Bristol BS3 1QR ☎ 0117 9668048

STOWELL Robin (*Vla, Bq Vln*): 43 Woodvale Avenue, Cyncoed, Cardiff, S Glamorgan CF2 6SP ☎ 029 2075 2001

STRIKE Sarah (*Vla*): 6 St Thomas Hill, Launceston, Cornwall PL15 8BL ☎ 01566 775159

SWARBRICK Simon (*Gtr, B Gtr, Man*): 21 Lorne Road, Dorchester, Dorset DT1 2LQ ☎ 01305 263118

SWEENEY Katherine: Melindwr, Ponterwyd, Aberystwyth, Dyfed SY23 3JY ☎ 01970 85603

TARLTON Anthony: The Old Surgery, Church Street, Llantwit Major, South Glamorgan CF61 1SB ☎ 01446 796733

THOMAS George (*Vla*): 13 Queen Street, Tongwynlais, Cardiff CF4 7NL ☎ 029 2081 0404

THOMAS Leslie: Sunningdale, 137 Pontardawe Road, Clydach, Swansea SA6 5PB ☎ 01792 843368

THOMAS Vivian: 1 Trossachs Drive, Bath BA2 6RP ☎ 01225 465421

THOMPSON Billy (*E Vln, Fo Fdl, Man*): 26 Lower Cathedral Road, Riverside, Cardiff CF1 8LT ☎ 029 2039 7150, 07666 77 2300 pager

THOMPSON Stanley: 12 Gooch Way, Worle, Nr West Super Mare, Avon BS22 0YH ☎ 01934 521570

TONKIN Robert: 1 Heal St Denys, Lisvane, Cardiff CF4 5RU ☎ 029 2075 2057

TOPPING Michael: 98 Colthester Ave, Penylan, Cardiff CF3 7AZ ☎ 029 2045 1759

TORPY Helena (*Pf, Rec, T Viol*): 18 South View, Staple Hill, Bristol BS16 5PJ ☎ 0117 9571341

TREHARNE Eric: 18 Hendre Close, Llandaff, Cardiff CF5 2HT ☎ 029 2056 4655

TUNLEY Jane: 69 Pontcanna Street, Pontcanna, Cardiff CF1 9HR ☎ 029 2038 2468

VAN DER VLIET Victoria: Penlan, St Germans, Nr Saltash, Cornwall PL12 5LT ☎ 01503 230808, 0378 935 085

VOS Josephine: 18 Salop Place, Penarth, S. Glam CF6 1HP ☎ 029 2070 9624

WAY Darryl: Ackmans, South Huish, Nr Kingsbridge, Devon TQ7 3EH ☎ 01753 42918

WAY David (*Vla*): 25 Hartley Park Gardens, Plymouth PL3 5HU

WEINMANN Simon: 1 Ovington Terrace, Llandaff, Cardiff, S Glamorgan CF5 1GF ☎ 029 2038 8226

WESTCOTT Lois: 60 Llandaff Road, Cardiff, South Glam CF1 9NL ☎ 01222 28916

WHITE Andrew: Greenfields, Forthay, North Nibley, Dursley Glos GL11 6DY ☎ Dursley 2228

WILLIAMS Eileen (*Bq Vln*): Diwedd Lon, St Dials Road, Greenmeadow, Cwmbran Gwent NP44 4BJ ☎ 01633 866294

WILLIAMS Helen: 2 Clenavon Crescent, Porthcawl, Mid Glamorgan CF36 3LP

MUSICAL INSTRUMENTS

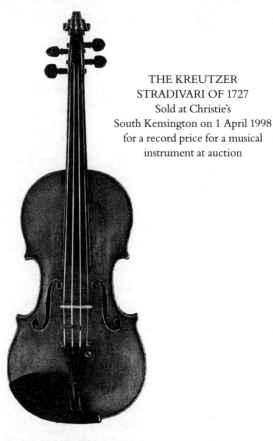

THE KREUTZER
STRADIVARI OF 1727
Sold at Christie's
South Kensington on 1 April 1998
for a record price for a musical
instrument at auction

Members of the musical profession are eligible for special rates of commission if
they wish to include items in auctions of Musical Instruments on their own behalf.

For further information please contact Christie's
Musical Instruments Department on (44 171) 321 3470

CATALOGUES: (44 171) 321 3152/(44 171) 389 2820

CHRISTIE'S
SOUTH KENSINGTON
85 Old Brompton Road, London SW7 3LD
Tel: (44 171) 581 7611 Fax: (44 171) 321 3321 www.christies.com

WILLIAMS Kathleen *(Vla)*: 133 California Road, Oldland, Bristol BS15 6PP ☏ 0117 932 4370

WILLIAMS Rosemary: Greenhill Lodge, Greenhill Road, Moseley, Birmingham B13

WILLIAMS Sharon *(Pf)*: 48 Primrose Road, Neath, West Glam SA11 2AS ☏ 01639 644952

WILLIAMS Wynephred: Address Unknown ☏ 029 2056 3078

WILLOUGHBY Brenda *(Vla)*: Pear Tree Court, Old Road, Harbertonford, Totnes, Devon TQ9 7TA ☏ 01803 732198

WILSON Amy C.E. *(Vla)*: 4 Cyncoed Rise, Cyncoed, Cardiff CF2 6SF ☏ 029 2075 9460

WINTER Caroline *(Pf, Gtr, Rec)*: 'Rehobath', 5 Parr Close, Swindon SN5 6JY ☏ 01793 877662

WOODBURN Veronica: Agar, Fore Street, Probus, Truro, Cornwall TR2 4LZ ☏ 01726 882580

WOODSFORD Patricia: 5 Darwell House, La Route Du Petite Clos, Mont Au Pretre, St Helier, Jersey C. I. JE2 3FD ☏ 01534 626861

LONDON

AARONS Ivan: Address Unknown ☏ 020 7328 5107

ACOSTA Gonzalo: Casa Blanca, 214 Chase Side, London N14 4PH ☏ 020 8441 8248, 0973 143777 mob

ACTON Jonathan: 48 Moorymead Close, Watton-At-Stone, Herts SG14 3HF ☏ 0956 132989

ADAMS David *(Vla, Pf)*: Flat 1, 238 Nether Street, Finchley, London N3 1HU ☏ 020 8343 4221

ADAMS J: 7 Cavendish Gardens, Trouville Road, London SW4 8QW

ADAMS Katharine: 14 Eton Road, Worthing, West Sussex BN11 4RA ☏ 01903 234926, 01306 885411

ADAMS Margaret: Address Unknown

ADDISON Trevor: 34 Windsor Road, Church End, Finchley Central, London N3 3SS ☏ 020 8349 0437

ADLAM Adrian: 9 Pimlico House, Ebury Bridge Road, London SW1W 8SN ☏ 020 7730 5717

ALBERMAN David: 14 Fairmead Road, London N19 4DF ☏ 020 7272 5579

ALDERTON Stuart: 1 Huddlestone Road, London E7 0AW

ALEXANDER Fred: 2 The Rowans, Grand Avenue, Worthing, Sussex BN11 5AT ☏ 01903 245879

ALLAN John *(Cop)*: 5-15-8 Henara Corinthian, Jalan Binjai, Off Jalan Ampane, 50450 Kuala Lumpa, Malaysia ☏ +1 603 261 5534 fax

ALLEN Jeremy: 63 Thorpe Avenue, Tonbridge, Kent TN10 4PR ☏ 01732 369 364

ALLEN Rachel: 10 Beecroft Road, London SE4 2BS ☏ 020 8694 6538, 0973 627438 mob, 01306 880669 day

ALLEN Susan *(Gtr)*: 140C Anerley Road, Anerley, London SE20 8DL ☏ 020 8289 9922, 020 7314 6120 day

ALLISON Camilla: 136 Connaught Road, Brookwood, Woking, Surrey GU24 0AS ☏ 01483 481524, 207 0007

ALLPORT Helen: 1 Alston Close, Long Ditton, Surrey KT6 5QS ☏ 020 8398 6774

ALTER Tim: 35 Buckthorne Road, London SE4 2DG ☏ 020 8699 3458, 07050 192160

ALVANIS Adonis: 95 Oxford Gardens, London W10 6NF ☏ 020 8968 7767 & fax

ALVARES Enrico *(Vla)*: 56 Normanhurst Road, Walton-on-Thames, Surrey KT12 3EQ ☏ 01932 224415

AMBERG Marie-Luise: 69 Oakington Avenue, Wembley, Middlesex HA9 8HY ☏ 020 8904 2389

ANDERSON Angus: 47 Hamlet Square, The Vale, London NW2 1SR ☏ 020 8450 5977

ANDRADE Frances: 11 South Parade, Bedford Park, London W4 1JU ☏ 020 8994 4125, 020 8742 7735

ANDRADE Levine *(Vla)*: High Winkworth, Hascombe Road, Godalming, Surrey GU8 4AE ☏ 01483 208 502, 0941 114 738 pager, 01483 208 504

ANDREWS Alan: 4 Fletcher Road, Chiswick, London W4 5AY ☏ 020 8995 4627

ANGEL David: 4 Brickmakers Lane, Hemel Hempstaed, Herts HP3 8NY ☏ 01442 214252

ANNER Naomi: 29 Alston Road, Barnet, Herts EN5 4EU ☏ 020 8441 1107

ANSTEE Karen: 4 Valentine Mansions, The Green, Winchmore Hill, London N21 1BA ☏ 020 8886 7844

APEL George ☏ +1 61 08 944 82140 & fax

ARCHARD Joanna *(Pf)*: 4 Garbutt Place, London W1M 3HQ ☏ 020 7487 4615, 0973 735132

ARCHER James: Barnabey Arms Hotel, Bredenbury, Nr Bromyard, Herefordshire HR7 4TF ☏ 01885 482233

ARDITTI Irvine: 12 Dukes Avenue, Finchley, London N3 2DD ☏ 020 8343 2112, 020 8343 2166, 01708 379505/506 fax

ARMON Vaughan: 74 Anyards Road, Cobham, Surrey KT11 2LG ☏ 01932 865704

ASHBY Claire: 53 Klea Ave, London SW4 9HY ☏ 020 8673 6620, 07887 643964

ATCHISON Robert: 16 Clacton Road, Walthamstow, London E17 8AR ☏ 020 8503 7098

ATHERTON Joan: 12, Addison Way, London NW11 6AJ ☏ 020 8455 0658

ATKINSON Julia: 13 Fermor Road, Forest Hill, London SE23 2HW ☏ 020 8699 2147

AUGAR Phillip: 32 Ernald Ave, East Ham, London E6 3AL ☏ 020 8470 5529, 020 8533 1372

AUTY Beryl: 44 Southfields Road, West Kingsdown, Kent TN15 6LE ☏ 01474 852425

AXON Lisa: 41 Chinnor Crescent, Greenford, Middlesex UB6 9NZ ☏ 020 8578 7172

AYLWIN Richard *(Vla, Pf, Com)*: 16 West Hill Way, London N20 8QP ☏ 020 8445 1975

BABYNCHUK Andrew: 29A Greencroft Gardens, London NW6 3LN ☏ 020 7624 2977

BAILEY Gillian: 37 Huntingdon Road, East Finchley, London N2 9DX ☏ 020 8444 7589

BAILEY Kate *(Pf)*: 53 Stapleton Road, Headington, Oxford OX3 7LX ☏ 01865 66565

BAKER Susan *(Man, Hrp)*: Beckington Abbey, Beckington, Nr Bath BA3 6TD

BALANESCU Alexander: 78 Sussex Way, London N7 6RR

BALCON Raymond *(Vla, A Sax, Clt)*: 33 Redbridge Court, Ilford, Essex IG4 5DG ☏ 020 8550 7398

BALDEY Elizabeth: 20 Robertson Road, Brighton, Sussex BN1 5NL ☏ 01273 503306, 01306 880669

BALDING Caroline: 25 Stephen Road, Headington, Oxford OX3 9AY ☏ 01865 751598, 01865 751591 fax

BALL Gini *(Voc)*: Flat 7, 63 Carlton Hill, London NW8 0EN ☏ 020 7328 1873

BALL Howard: Whitemays, Rowley Green Road, Arkley, Herts EN5 5HH ☏ 020 8441 3842 & fax, 020 8549 1706 day

BALLARA Carlo: Address Unknown ☏ 020 8520 1904

BALLARD Philippa: Green Cottage, 17 The Greenway, Gerards Cross, Bucks SL9 8LX ☏ 01753 886158

BALLENGER Carol: Highfield, Culver Lane, Rattery, South Brent, Devon TQ10 9LJ ☏ 01364 72312

BALMER Paul: 55 Barrington Road, Hornsey, London N8 8QT ☏ 020 8245 8820

BALTAIAN Aroussiak *(Pf)*: 283 Nether Str, London N3 1PD ☏ 020 8922 7857, 020 8922 0383

BANWELL Margaret: 28 Kemplay Road, London NW3 1SY ☏ 020 7794 7400

BAREAU Suzanne: Mount Pleasant, 20 Main Street, Long Preston, Nth Yorkshire BD23 4PH ☏ 01729 840883, 01729 840843 fax

BARKER Kaye *(Pf)*: 70 Midhurst Road, Ealing, London W13 9XR ☏ 020 8579 1740

BARKHAM Gwyneth: Five Bells Cottage, 132 St Leonards Street, West Malling, Kent ME19 6PD ☏ 01732 874285, 020 8549 1706 day

BARLOW Frances: 2 Shirlock Road, London NW3 2HS ☏ 020 7485 1362

BARNES Caroline: Rouselle Cottage, Mount Gardens, Sydenham, London SE26 4NG ☏ 020 8291 0325

BARNES Katherine (*Pf*): 29 Greystoke Court, Hanger Lane, London W5 1EN ☎ 020 8810 9423, 0973 498632

BARRY Edward: 99 Stradella Road, London SE24 9HL ☎ 020 7326 4853, 01306 880669

BARTEL-BROWN Justin: Leyhill, Tortworth, Wooton-Under-Edge, Glouestershire GL12 8BT

BARTON Fenella: 16B Warneford Street, London E9 7NG ☎ 020 8533 1744, 01483 451 700 day, 01523 447011 pager

BATES Dylan: 81 Osbaldesto Road, Stoke Newington, London N16 6NP ☎ 0336 739036

BAUMEISTER Meike (*Tpt*): 70A Acton Lane, Harlesden, London NW10 8TU

BAWDEN Rupert: 17 Clapham Common Sth Sde, London SW4 7AB ☎ 020 7720 0756

BEALE Marcus (*E Vln, Vla, Per*): 87 Graham Road, London SW19 3SP

BEAMAN David (*Pf, Con*): Angel Cottage, High Street, Redbourn, Herts AL3 7LN ☎ 01582 792123, 0585 878147 mob

BEAN Hugh: 30 Stone Park Ave, Beckenham, Kent BR3 3LX ☎ 020 8650 8774

BEATTY Alison: 20 Shrubbery Road, Windmill Hill, Gravesend, Kent DA12 1JW ☎ 01474 325361

BECKENSALL Sheila: Bull River Farm, Chiddingly, Lewes, East Sussex BN8 6HQ ☎ 01825 872369

BEDDOW Carl: 1St Andrews Close, Isleworth, Middlesex TW7 4PG ☎ 020 8232 8842, 020 8533 1372

BELDOM Charles: 124 Falloden Way, London NW11 6JD ☎ 020 8455 6415

BELL Martin (*Gtr, Bjo, Man, Kbds*): 39B Anson Road, Tuffnel Park, London N7 0AR ☎ 020 7700 7257, 020 7700 7257 fax

BELTON Catherine (*Vla*): 2 Churchill Road, Guildford, Surrey GU1 2AX ☎ 01483 304142

BELTON Ian: 2 Churchill Road, Guildford, Surrey GU1 2AX ☎ 01483 304142

BEN-NATHAN Ruth: 32 Farm Avenue, London NW2 2BH ☎ 020 8450 1811

BENHAM Bill (*Vla*): 6 Inlands Close, Pewsey, Wilts SN9 5HD ☎ 01672 562406, 01306 880669 day

BENNETT Shirley: 270 Blenheim Chase, Leigh-on-Sea, Essex SS9 3HQ ☎ 0170 271 0189

BENSON Peter: 56 Worple Way, Harrow, Middx HA2 9SR ☎ 020 8866 3674

BENSON Ruth: 12 Heathfield Gardens, London NW11 9HX ☎ 020 8455 9166

BENTLEY Lionel (*Vla*): 47 Mayflower Way, Farnham Common, Bucks SL2 3UA ☎ 0128 14 3807

BENTLEY-KLEIN Steve (*Tpt*): 15 Alderney Road, Stepney Green, London E1 4EG ☎ 020 7790 0706

BERCOVITCH J: Address Unknown

BERE Georges: 49 Leadale Road, Stamford Hill, London N16 6DG ☎ 020 8800 3525

BERNARDI Andrew (*Vla*): The Plat, Thakeham Road, Coolham, West Sussex RH13 8QD ☎ 01403 741685 & fax, 020 8533 1372 day, 0140 0246 08 mob

BERROW Mark: 27 Willows Avenue, Morden, Surrey SM4 5SG ☎ 020 8640 5738

BETTANEY Stephen (*Pf*): 78 Harrowes Mead, Edgware, Middlesex HA8 8RP ☎ 020 8958 9806

BEUKES Gina: 37B Patshull Road, Kentish Town, London NW5 2JX ☎ 020 7485 3438 & fax, 0973 197449 mob

BEVAN Christopher (*Kbds*): 25 Strafford Road, Barnet, Herts EN5 4LR ☎ 020 8449 1028, 0306 880669

BEVAN Louise: 44 Edenvale Street, Fulham, London SW6 2SF ☎ 020 7371 5666

BEZKORVANY Sergei: 61 Coval Road, London SW14 7RW ☎ 020 8876 8603

BIALAS Antonina: Hailes House, Hailes, Nr Winchcombe, Cheltenham.Glos GL54 5PB ☎ 01242 602379

BICKEL Maya: 30 Pembroke Gardens, London W8 6HU ☎ 020 7602 2318, 0467 818778

BIDDULPH Frank: 165 Clapham Road, London SW9 0PU ☎ 020 7587 1487

BINKS Elizabeth (*Pf*): 13 Sussex Gdns, Chesington, Surrey KT9 2PU ☎ 020 8397 1716

BIRCHALL Kate: 103 Lee Park, Blackheath, London SE3 9HG ☎ 020 8463 0256

BISHOP Caroline: 197 Lymington Ave, Wood Green, London N22 6JL ☎ 020 8881 7229

BISHOP Robert: 72 Vaughan Road, Harrow, Middlesex HA1 4ED ☎ 020 8864 6146

BISS Hannah (*Vla*): 19 Fitzjohns Avenue, London NW3 5JY ☎ 020 7794 5119, 0966 177551, 020 7435 1523

BLAIR Ellen: Flat A, 163 Streatham High Road, London SW16 6EG ☎ 020 8769 3676

BLAYDEN Richard: 22 Hogarth Court, Phanton Drive, London SE19 1UY ☎ 020 8761 1697

BLEACH Julian (*Kbds*): 18 Dalebury Road, Tooting Bec, London SW17 7HH ☎ 020 8672 2490

BLENDIS Simon: 95C Ferme Park Road, Crouch End, London N8 9SA ☎ 020 8372 3802, 020 8341 9730

BLUNT Alison (*Pf*): 65 Springdale Road, London N16 9NT ☎ 020 7690 4529

BOENDERS Elizabeth: Glen Lyn Cottage, Lynmouth, North Devon EX35 6ER ☎ 01598 52477

BOGLE David: 1 The Bottle Factory, Hanbury Mews, London N1 7DW ☎ 020 7359 3134

BONHAM CARTER Thomas: 46 Kempshott Road, London SW16 5LQ ☎ 020 8764 8915

BONNER Natalia (*Bq Vln, Pf*): Station House, Woodside Park Underground, Woodside Park Road, London N12 8SE ☎ 01234 354374, 0468 892488

BOROS Tomi (*Pf*): 357 Kenton Road, Harrow, Middlesex HA3 0XS ☎ 020 8907 7953, 020 8907 7953

BOUCHER Paul: Flat 2, 5 Kensington Park Gardens, London W11 3HB ☎ 020 7792 8027, 020 7243 8305 fax

BOURGEOIS Jean (*Vla*): 43 Bute Gardens, London W6 7DR ☎ 020 8748 6027 fax

BOWE Ella: 38 Curzon Road, Muswell Hill, London N10 2RA ☎ 020 8444 7402

BOWERS-BROADBENT Nicholas: Fox Cottage, Didmarton, Glos GL9 1DT ☎ 0973 473977

BOWES Thomas: 166 Bethnal Green Road, London E2 6DL ☎ 020 7729 8362, 01306 880669

BOWIE Eric: Address Unknown ☎ 0475373766

BOWLES Tina: 9 Higham Hill Road, London E17 6EA ☎ 020 8531 4962, 0468 570 384 mob

BOWN Stefan: 50, Alric Avenue, New Malden, Surrey KT3 4JN ☎ 020 8949 3668

BOWRAN Susan: 130 Broad Street, Chesham, Bucks HP5 3ED ☎ 01494 771158, 01306 880669, 0966 409978 mob

BOYLE Rebecca: Bankside, The Chase, Pinner, Middlesex HA5 5OP ☎ 020 8866 9615

BRADBURY John: The White Cottage, Sudbury Hill, Harrow-on-the-Hill,The Hill, Middlesex HA1 3NA ☎ 020 8422 1456, 01306 880669

BRADLEY Anna ☎ 020 8291 2410

BRANDON John: 32 Pikes Hill, Epsom, Surrey KT17 4EA ☎ 01372 741668, 0976 796695

BRETT Fiona: Hampden House, 17 Couchling Street, Watlington, Oxfordshire OX9 5QF ☎ 01491 612 565

BRETT Maurice: 7 Dunstall Road, Wimbledon Common, London SW20 0HP ☎ 020 8947 4156

BRETT Reginald (*Saxes*): Arthur House, 110 Arthur Road, Wimbledon Park, London SW19 8AA ☎ 020 8946 8989

BRIGHTMAN Robin: 95 Barn Hill, Wembley Park, Middx HA9 9LW ☎ 020 8933 1009

BRIGHTWELL Gillian: 70 Selkirk Road, London SW17 0EP ☎ 020 8672 5271, 01306 880669

BRIGNALL Ian: 7 Durham Road, East Finchley, London N2 9DP ☎ 020 8883 4944, 0831 200474 mob

BRIND Alan: Address Unknown ☎ 020 7371 7034

Healthy Practice for Musicians

by Elizabeth Andrews

Elizabeth Andrews

Healthy Practice for Musicians

FITNESS TO PLAY ♪ POSTURE ♪ EYES AND EARS
MUSICIAN VS THE ENVIRONMENT ♪ DIETARY MATTERS AND
ALLERGIES ♪ SURVIVING ON TOUR ♪ ADDICTION
BURNOUT AND SAYING NO ♪ STAGE FRIGHT ♪ STRESS
PSYCHOSOMATIC ACHES AND PAINS ♪ PHOBIAS
THE NERVES ♪ ARTHRITIS ♪ HOW THE LIMBS WORK
HOW TO TEST MUSCLES ♪ THE MUSCLES OF THE BODY
MID-CONCERT SELF-HELP ♪ INJURY REVERSAL
REFLEXOLOGY POINTS ♪ REHABILITATION LADDERS

Rhinegold Publishing Limited

R·

Hardback 432 pages

Packed full of practical advice covering every aspect of a musician's physical and mental well-being. The book suggests ways of adapting the performing world to fit you and is a treasure trove for those who, despite the occupational hazards, want to go on doing their job successfully, and look after themselves in an environment that is physically, mentally and chemically as benign as possible.

"...it should be required reading for anyone considering a career as a perfomer - as well as ALL music teachers...the best source I've ever seen for finding out which foods are rich in which vitamins, and which vitamins do what". BRITISH SUZUKI INSTITUTE

HOW TO ORDER

Please send a cheque for **£19.70** (inc. p&p) payable to *Rhinegold Publishing Ltd* to: **Book Sales, Rhinegold Publishing, FREEPOST, London WC2H 8BR.**

TELEPHONE:	**0171 333 1721** (or 020 7333 1721 after 22 Apr 2000)
FAX:	**0171 333 1769** (or 020 7333 1769 after 22 Apr 2000)
EMAIL:	**sales@rhinegold.co.uk**
WEBSITE:	**www.rhinegold.co.uk**

BRISCOE Helen: 16A Hawarden Grove, Herne Hill, London SE24 9DH ☎ 020 7652 1751

BRISCOE Susan: 13 Astrope Lane, Long Marston, Nr Tring, Herts HP23 4PL ☎ 01296 661056

BROADBENT Giles (*E Vln*): 17 Gathorne Road, Wood Green, London N22 5ND ☎ 0498 821920

BROADBENT Nigel: 25 Victoria Road, London N4 3SH ☎ 020 7272 0043

BROADBRIDGE Aidan (*Pf*): 55A Elliscombe Road, London SE7 7PF ☎ 020 8853 2711, 0956 326267

BROCKLEHURST Julia (*Bq Vln*): 1 Fox Hill Gardens, Upper Norwood, London SE19 2XB ☎ 020 8653 3716, 0378 453395 mob, 01483 723644 day

BROOK Bernard: 4, Fen Grove, Sidcup, Kent DA15 8QN ☎ 020 8850 5014

BROOK Ruth: 4, Fen Grove, Sidcup, Kent DA15 8QN ☎ 020 8850 5014

BROOKE-PIKE Sally (*Vla*): 123 Woodwarde Road, London SE22 8UP ☎ 020 8693 5434

BROOME Marcus (*Pf*): 59 Princes Avenue, Alexandra Park, London N22 7SB ☎ 020 8889 5205

BROWDER Risa (*Bq Vln, Vla*): 814 N.Daniel Street, Arlington, VA 22201, USA ☎ +1 703 351 7852 & fax

BROWN Abigail (*Voc*): Address Unknown ☎ 020 7226 6247

BROWN Amanda: 7 Cricklade Court, Nailsea, Bristol BS19 2ST ☎ 01275 858529, 0589 386488

BROWN Andrew: Address Unknown

BROWN Helen: Forres, 30 Wentworth Road, Barnet, Herts EN5 4NT ☎ 020 8449 6471, 0973 214378 mob, 020 8533 1372 day

BROWN Jimmie (*T Sax, Clt, Flt*): 178 Sherwood Avenue, London SW16 5EG ☎ 020 8679 3758

BROWN John: Long Meadows, Harewood Road, Collingham, Weatherby, W Yorks LS22 5BZ ☎ 01937 572 541

BROWN Susan: 133 Clarence Avenue, Northampton NN2 6NY ☎ 01604 711618

BROWN William: 4 Queen Elizabeths Drive, London N14 6RB ☎ 020 8886 5597, 01306 880669 day

BROWNE Cormac: 24 Hollingbourne Road, London SE24 9ND ☎ 020 7733 3564

BROWNING Catherine: 7 Chatterton Road, London N4 2EA ☎ 020 7359 7677

BRYANT Stephen (*Pf*): 8 Station Road, Claygate, Esher, Surrey KT10 9DH

BRYANT Toni: 8 Station Road, Claygate, Surrey KT10 9DH ☎ 01372 465682

BRYCE Morven ☎ 020 8556 5758, 0976 943666 mob

BUCHAN Gordon: 23 Egerton Gardens, London W13 8HG ☎ 020 8998 7788, 01306 880669

BUCKTON Benjamin (*Vla*): 8 Wolseley Road, London N22 4TW ☎ 020 8881 1134

BULL Stephen: 17A High Road, London N15 6LT ☎ 020 8809 1464

BUNT Belinda: Address Unknown ☎ 310 471 0054, 01306 880669

BURCHELL Judith: 2 Whitethorn Avenue, Coulsdon, Surrey CR5 2PP ☎ 020 8660 0063

BUREAU Richard (*Con*): 120 Belmont Rise, Sutton, Surrey SM2 6EE ☎ 020 8642 5714

BURGESS Martin: 13 Astrope Lane, Long Marston, Nr Tring, Herts HP23 2PL ☎ 01296 661056, 0860 693678

BUROV Sergei: Hesper House, Wells Park Road, Sydenham, London SE26 6RQ ☎ 020 8699 5242, 0385 365495, 020 8473 5262

BURROWS Grace: Address Unknown

BURROWS Lester: Address Unknown

BURTON David: 10 Meadow Close, Catford, London SE6 3NW ☎ 020 8695 6004

BURTON William: 212 Alexandra Park Road, London N22 4UQ ☎ 020 8889 0470

BURY Alison: 27 Grange Road, Lewes, East Sussex BN7 1TS ☎ 01273 475200

BUSSEREAU Peter: 18 Windsor Road, Barton-Le-Clay, Beds MK45 4LX ☎ 01582 882159

BUTLER David (*Vla*): Little Orchard,The Avenue, Hitchin, Herts SG4 9RQ ☎ 01462 432813

BUTLER Mark: 2 Condover Crescent, London SE18 3LZ ☎ 020 8854 6049, 01306 880669 day

BUTT Edmund: 7 Downsway, Berwick, East Sussex BN26 6TD ☎ 01323 870673, 0956 276794

BUTTERFIELD Adrian: 14 Oxford Gardens, London N21 2AP ☎ 020 8360 0232

BUTTON Brigid: 34 Glenilla Road, London NW3 4AN ☎ 020 7916 7360, 020 7722 3587

BUTTON Sarah: Flat 2, 47 Stanhope Road, London N12 9DX ☎ 020 8446 9178, 0498 872651

BUXTON Jennifer: 26 Meadway, Epsom, Surrey KT19 8JZ ☎ 01372 720807

BUXTON Paul: 26 Meadway, Epsom, Surrey KT19 8JZ ☎ 01372 720807

CAESAR Angela: 11 Aldwick Avenue, Didsbury, Manchester M20 6JL ☎ 0161 445 0730

CALDI Claudia (*Vla*): 287 Bethnal Green Road, London E2 6AH ☎ 020 7613 3204, 020 7240 9816

CALLOW Colin: 19 The Crescent, London N11 3HN ☎ 020 8368 1609

CALNAN Patricia: 30 Brookfield Mnsns, 5 Highgate West Hill, London N6 6AT ☎ 020 8347 6788, 020 8549 1706 day

CALORES Carole (*Acc*): 48 Pellipar Close, Palmers Green, London N13 4AG ☎ 020 8886 1921

CALTHORPE Emer: Bearsden, 25 Hampstead Lane, London N6 4RT ☎ 020 8348 8498, 01306 880669, 0976 830306 mob

CAMPBELL Jane: 67 The Rise, Sevenoaks, Kent TN13 1RL ☎ 01732 455385

CAMPTON Rosemary: 3D Bushey Hill Road, Camberwell, London SE5 8QF ☎ 020 7277 1831, 0958 791503

CANTER John (*Pf, Vla*): Brynteg, Brynawel, Aberdare CF44 7PF ☎ 01685 877951

CANTONI Michele: Flat 5, 287 Bethnal Green Road, London E2 6AH ☎ 020 7613 3204, 020 7240 9816

CANTRILL Lucy: 42 Arthurdon Road, Brockley, London SE4 1JU ☎ 020 8690 5957, 0956 847180

CARMALT Averil: 59 Christchurch Road, Winchester, Hants SO23 9TE ☎ 01962 869309

CARNEY Jonathan: 46 Mountfield Road, Finchley, London N3 3NP ☎ 020 8346 9433

CARPENTER Elizabeth (*Pf*): 6 Claremont Road, Tunbridge Wells, Kent TN1 1SZ ☎ 01892 526921

CARPENTER-JACOBS Susan (*Bq Vln, Vla*): 21 Manor Gardens, Merton Park, London SW20 9AB ☎ 020 8540 6795

CARTER Karen (*Pf*): 111 Church Road, Bexleyheath, Kent DA7 4DN ☎ 020 8303 5422

CARTHY Eliza (*Pf*): Hillcrest, Mount Pleasant East, Robin Hoods Bay, Whitby, N.Yorks YO22 4RF ☎ 01947 880622

CARVELL Susan: 100 College Road, Kensal Rise, London NW10 5HL ☎ 020 8964 1175

CARWARDINE Jane: Hathaway, Surrey Gardens, Effingham Junction, Surrey KT24 5HF ☎ 01483 282445

CASBOLT Jason: 33 Orford Gardens, Strawberry Hill, Twickenham, Middlesex TW1 4PL ☎ 020 8892 1762

CASEY Michael: 1 Minster Road, Bromley, Kent BR1 4DY ☎ 020 8464 4032

CASEY Nollaig (*Tin Wh*): 51 Lios Mor, Cappagh Road, Bearna, Co. Galway, Ireland ☎ 00 35391 590908

CASS Helen: 11 Woodhall Close, Bengeo, Hertford, Herts SG14 3ED ☎ 01992 554344, 01306 880669

CASTLE Olwen (*Vla*): 13 Thornsett Road, London SE20 7XB ☎ 020 8659 0639

CASTLE Stanley: High Ridge, Prior's Frome, Dormington, Hereford HR1 4EP ☎ 01432 850429

CAVANAGH Maurice: 24 Chiltern Court, Pages Hill, London N10 1EN ☎ 020 8883 0550

CHANDRU (*E Vln, Com, Arr, Man*): 11 Albon House, Nevill Gill Close, Wandsworth, London SW18 4BS ☎ 020 8874 3447 & fax, 0956 987313 mob

CHAPMAN Donna: 124 Falloden Way, Hampstead Garden Suburb, London NW11 6JD ☎ 020 8455 6415

CHARLESWORTH Adrian: 10 Parsons Mead, East Molesey, Surrey KT8 9DT ☎ 020 8979 4655

CHEW Robert: 28 Dalmore Avenue, Claygate, Surrey KT10 0HQ ☎ 01372 462 463

CHILINGIRIAN Levon: 7 Hollingbourne Road, London SE24 9NB ☎ 020 7978 9104

CHURCHILL Caroline: 22 Tavistock Terrace, London N19 4DB ☎ 020 7272 0888

CLARK Robert (*Vla, Con*): 27 Foxglove Close, Burgess Hill, W Sussex RH15 9TB ☎ 01444 239648, 01273 473278

CLARKE Norman: 10A Wavel Mews, London NW6 3AB ☎ 020 7328 5996

CLARKSON Gustav (*Vla*): 15 Elm Park Road, London N3 1EG ☎ 020 8346 7490, 01306 880669

CLEVELAND Anthony: Flat 1 The Rolle, Budleigh, Salterton, Devon EX9 6NG ☎ 01395 445434

CLISSOLD Helen: 30 The Heights, Charlton, London SE7 8JH ☎ 020 8853 0826, 0973 390268 mob

CLOONAN Fay (*Pf*): 19 Cuckoo Hill Road, Pinner, Middx HA5 1AS ☎ 020 8866 7751

COATES Emily: 100 Gifford Street, Islington, London N1 0DF ☎ 020 7607 7752

COCHRANE Helen: 8 Ashbourne Rise, Orpington, Kent BR6 9PZ ☎ 01689 851267, 01306 880669

COCHRANE Laura: 13A Kingsdown Road, London N19 4LD ☎ 020 7272 9427

COHEN Gillian: 55 Lincoln Road, London N2 9DJ ☎ 020 8444 9810, 01483 723644

COHEN Raymond: 38 Keyes Road, London NW2 3XA ☎ 020 8452 3493

COLEMAN Blanche (*Clt, Sax*): 68 Golders Manor Drive, London Nw11 NW11 9HT ☎ 020 8455 8751

COLEMAN Rebecca: 26C Ringstead Road, Catford, London SE6 2BP ☎ 020 8461 5854

COLES James: Cornmill, Compton Abdale, Cheltenham, Glos GL54 4DT ☎ 01242 890316

COLLEN Paul: 216 Meadowview Road, London SE6 3NH ☎ 020 8698 7376

COLLIER Daniel (*Fo Fdl, Gtr, Kbds*): 34A Maury Road, London N16 7BP ☎ 020 8442 4099

COLLIER Derek: 9 Cambridge Road, Frinton-on-Sea, Essex CO13 9HN ☎ 01255 852038

COLLIER Susan: 96 Queens Avenue, Finchley, London N3 2NP ☎ 020 8349 3045

COLMAN Anna: 4 Gordon Road, Sevenoaks, Kent TN13 1HE ☎ 01732 463921

COLMAN Timothy (*Pf*): 135A Hamilton Terrace, St Johns Wood, London NW8 9QR ☎ 020 7624 9931

COMBERTI Micaela: 15 Elm Park Road, London N3 1EG ☎ 020 8349 3580

COMFORT Marianne (*Vla*): 21 Osborne Road, Kingston-upon-Thames, Surrey KT2 5HB ☎ 020 8541 0456

CONCANNON HODGES Nicholas: 16A Stonor Road, West Kensington, London W14 8RZ ☎ 020 7603 7022, 01426 110365 pager

CONNORS Clare (*Vla, Pf*): 78 Sussex Way, London N7 6RR ☎ 020 7272 8889

CONSTANTINE Benjamin: 254 Wellington Flats, Peabody Estate, Ebury Bridge, London SW1 8RY ☎ 020 7730 1868

COOK Lynn: 12 Taylors Lane, London SE26 6QL ☎ 020 8291 1376

COOPER Helen: 71 Barclay Road, Walthamstow, London E17 9JH ☎ 020 8520 6888

COOPER Pete (*Man*): 86 Eleanor Rd, London E8 1DN ☎ 020 7249 2770

COOPER Robert: 86 Woodhouse Road, London E11 3NA ☎ 020 8519 4094

COPELAND Sybil: 221 Watford Way, Hendon, London NW4 6SL ☎ 020 8203 1165

COPPERWHEAT Elizabeth: 15 Alderley Close, Woodley, Reading, Berks RG5 4TG ☎ 0118 969 6903

CORMICAN Karen (*Fo Fdl*): 561 Kenton Lane, Harrow Weald, Middlesex HA3 7LB ☎ 020 8427 5918, 020 8863 7826 fax

COSTELLO Gillian: 25 Huddlestone Rd, Forest Gate, London E7 0AW ☎ 020 8519 1631

COSTIN Paul Alexander: 72 Hounsden Road, London N21 1LY ☎ 020 8360 2743

COTTRELL Erica: 59 Marion Crescent, Orpington, Kent BR5 2DF ☎ 01689 877586, 01306 880669

COULDRIDGE Richard (*Pf, E Gtr*): 40 Bywater House, Harlinger Street, Woolwich, London SE18 5SP ☎ 020 8855 2629

COULL Roger: Haseley Cottage, 15 Lower Ladyes Hills, Kenilworth, Warwickshire CV8 2GN ☎ 01926 54151

COUNSELL Eos: 59 Bennerley Road, Battersea, London SW11 6DR ☎ 020 7350 2844, 0976 407851

COWDELL Alexander: 8 Blendon Terrace, Plumstead Common, London SE18 7RR ☎ 020 8854 5167

COWDREY Elizabeth (*Bq Vln, Bsn*): 1 South Street, Middle Barton, Oxon OX7 7BU ☎ 01869 340951

COWEN Margaret: 9A Findon Road, London W12 9PY ☎ 020 8743 7715

COWEY Elspeth (*Vla*): 16 Ennis Road, Plumstead Common, London SE18 2QT ☎ 020 8854 5736

COX Helen: Amberlea, Glebe Road, Ashtead, Surrey KT21 3NT ☎ 0137 227 5855

COXON Edmund: Nina Villas, 67A Laureiston Road, London E9 7HA ☎ 020 8986 9556

CRACKNELL Graham: 211 Sheepcot Lane, Garston, Watford, Herts WD2 7DD ☎ 01923 449259

CRAFER Rachel (*Pf*): 38 Hillcrest Road, Whyteleafe, Surrey CR3 0DJ ☎ 020 8668 4920

CRAIG Catherine: 53 Brightfield Rd, Lee, London SE12 8QE ☎ 020 8318 1159

CRAIG Charles: 2 Grove Crescent, South Woodford, London E18 2JR ☎ 020 8530 6580

CRAWFORD John: 28 Wrentham Road, London NW10 3HA ☎ 020 8969 2880

CRAYFORD Marcia: 14 Azalea Walk, Old Eastcote, Pinner, Middlesex HA5 2EJ ☎ 020 8868 0477

CREESE Geoff: Flat 1, 48 Surrey Square, Walworth, London SE17 2JX ☎ 020 7708 0149

CREHAN Dermot (*Fo Fdl*): 22 Kent Gardens, Ealing, London W13 8BU ☎ 020 8997 7126, 01306 880669

CRIDA Quentin: 23 Clitherow Road, Brentford, Middlesex TW8 9KT ☎ 020 8400 6853, 0966 175601

CRISCUOLO Ann: 13 Goring Road, Bounds Green, London N11 2BU ☎ 020 8889 7087

CROOT Susan: 27 Dunmore Road, Wimbledon, London SW20 8TN ☎ 020 8947 3238, 01306 880669 day, 0973 616557 mob

CROSS David: 69 Avondale Avenue, Finchley, London N12 8ER ☎ 020 8446 7697

CROWLEY Regan: All Saints Vicarage, Twyford Avenue, London N2 9NH ☎ 020 8883 9315

CROXFORD Peggy: 7 Rockley Court, Rockley Road, London W14 0DB ☎ 020 7603 9550

CRUFT Benedict: 23 Dorset Road, London SW8 1EF ☎ 020 7735 4203

CUCCHIARA Antonio: 90 Keslake Road, London NW6 6DG ☎ 020 8964 5122, 07970 914670 mob

CULLITY Brenda: 11 Sandringham Road, London NW11 9DR ☎ 020 8458 2607

CUMMINGS Diana: 44 Gondar Gardens, London NW6 1HG ☎ 020 7435 5408

CUMMINGS Julian: 10 Trinity Avenue, East Finchley, London N2 0LX ☎ 020 8883 8013, 01306 880669

DA-COSTA Josephine: Old Rectory Cottage, Mill Lane, Monks Risborough, Princes Risborough, Bucks HP27 9LG ☎ 01844 273253

DALBY Julia: 8 Edward Street, Southborough, Tunbridge Wells, Kent TN4 0HP ☎ 01892 549211

DALE Miranda: 25 Park Avenue North, Hornsey, London N8 7RU ☎ 020 8347 9697, 020 8347 9697

DALE Peter: 3-4 Yew Tree Cottages, Shortfield Common, Frensham, Farnham, Surrey GU10 3BG ☎ 01252 793491, 01306 880 669 day

DALLY Angela: 22A South Avenue, Egham, Surrey TW20 8HG ☎ 01784 453347

DALTON Christine: 8 Barrett Road, Walthamstow, London E17 9ET ☎ 020 8520 6690, 020 8509 5004

DALY Declan (*Pf*): 72 Crofton Road, Camberwell, London SE5 8NB ☎ 020 7564 4579

DAMERELL Benjamin (*Voc, Pf*): 28 Venn Street, London SW4 0AT ☎ 020 7720 8887, 020 7622 3801

DARBY Nicholas: 12 Watcombe Cottages, Kew Green, Richmond, Surrey TW9 3BD ☎ 020 8948 2910

DAVEY Bridget: 100 Roydene Road, London SE18 1QA ☎ 020 8244 9400, 0976 721 548

DAVID Vanessa: 44 New River Crescent, London N13 5RF ☎ 020 8882 0690, 0586 330834

DAVIES Celia (*Con*): Michaelmas, Peckelton, Leicester LE9 7RE ☎ 01455 822604, 0831 531 835

DAVIES Harriet: 311 Ivydale Road, London SE15 3GJ ☎ 020 7639 7874

DAVIES Hywel (*Con*): 2B Florence Road, Ealing, London W5 3TX ☎ 020 8567 8708

DAVIES Iona: 33A Esmond Gardens, Sth Parade, Chiswick, London W4 1JT ☎ 020 8995 6264

DAVIES Janet (*Vla*): 16 Abbotts Green, Addington, Croydon, Surrey CR0 5BH ☎ 020 8656 1732

DAVIES John J (*Vla, Con*): Meadowdale, The Street, Rickinghall, Diss, Norfolk IP22 1BN ☎ 01379 890140

DAVIES Rachel: 1 Warwick Court, Bounds Green Road, Bounds Green, London N11 2EB ☎ 020 8881 4878

DAVIES Sally (*Hrn, Pf, Rec*): 19 Mount Pleasant Cres., London N4 4HP ☎ 020 7281 4480

DAVIES Timothy (*Pf*): 32 Clissold Crescent, London N16 2AR ☎ 020 7254 0825, 0378 449797

DAVIES William: 12A Halliwick Road, Muswell Hill, London N10 1AB ☎ 020 8444 1732

DAVIS Caroline: 14 Fairmount Road, London SW2 2BL ☎ 020 8674 9573

DAVIS Emily: 1 Pembury Court, Cobham Close, London SW11 6SP ☎ 020 7978 5893

DAVIS Howard: Charlotte Cottage, 123 Sheering Road, Harlow, Essex CM17 0JP ☎ 01279 431337

DAVIS Michael: 1303A High Road, Whetstone, London N20 9HX ☎ 020 8445 3253

DAWSON Russell: 5 Moat Drive, Harrow, Middlesex HA1 4RY ☎ 020 8723 2911

DAWSON Ruth: 12 Newton Road, Westbourne Grove, London W2 5LS ☎ 020 7229 6070

DE CAMILLIS Julia: 32 Delta Court, Coles Green Road, London NW2 7HB ☎ 020 8208 3976

DE LA MARE Calina: 62 Princess May Road, London N16 8DG ☎ 020 7254 8368, 0966 291677 mob

DE SAULLES Michael: 31 Mount Park, Carshalton, Surrey SM5 4PR ☎ 020 8647 8915, 01306 880669

DE SAULLES Teresa: 6 Park Hill Road, Wallington, Surrey SM6 0SB ☎ 020 8647 7577

DE SOUZA Ralph (*Vla*): 73 Maury Road, London N16 7BT ☎ 020 8806 7241

DEAKIN Richard: Ings Cottage, Berrier, Greystoke, Penrith, Cumbria CA11 0XD ☎ 017684 83443

DECUYPER Ginette: 63C Newlands Park, London SE26 5PW ☎ 020 8659 6995

DENMAN Mark: 14 Babbacombe Road, Bromley, Kent BR1 3LW ☎ 020 8313 0051

DENNENT Antony: 37 Stepney Green, London E1 3JY ☎ 020 7780 9421

DENTON Sarah (*Vla*): 30 Netherton Road, St. Margarets, Twickenham, Middlesex TW1 1LZ ☎ 020 8891 0727 & fax

DEROME Manon: 3 Bells Hill, Barnet, Herts EN5 2SE ☎ 020 8449 1160

DESCH Corinna: 91B Englefield Road, London N1 3LY ☎ 020 7226 3922

DESIMPELAERE Barbara: 10 Campion Place, Waterfield Gardens, London SE28 8EN ☎ 020 8311 4372

DEVI Susheela: 23 Woodbastwick Road, London SE26 5LG ☎ 020 8778 7685

DINWOODIE Stephen: 44B Graham Road, Mitcham, Surrey CR4 2HA ☎ 020 8646 0954, 01306 880 669

DITTMER Petronella (*Vla*): 10 Pembroke Mews, London W8 6ER ☎ 020 7937 0684 & fax, 01249 730781 & fax, 0802 324292 mob

DIXON Vivien: The Coach House, 1A Woodstock Road, London W4 1DR ☎ 020 8995 0121

DJACHENKO Yuri (*Vla, Bq Vln*): 17 Pickwick Place, Harrow-on-the-Hill, Middlesex HA1 3BG ☎ 020 8426 4498, 0966 395183 mob

DOBBINS Clive: 49 Aberdare Gardens, London NW6 ☎ 020 7625 5224, 01306 880669

DODD Edwin: 30 Cromer Villas Road, London SW18 1PN ☎ 020 8874 5446

DODS Alison: 44 Carlton Hill, London NW8 0ES ☎ 020 7372 0645

DODWELL Charlotte ☎ 020 8643 6009

DOFF Kenneth: 13 Heath Close, Wokingham, Berks RG41 2PG ☎ 01189 783777

DOLAN Michael: 33 Abbotts Drive, Wembley, Middx HA0 3SB ☎ 020 8908 1149/20

DOLBY Claire: 57 St Albans Avenue, Chiswick, London W4 5JS ☎ 020 8994 7473

DOODY Jane: 33 Seagry Road, Wanstead, London E11 2NQ ☎ 020 8530 1022

DOWDING Nicolas: Flat 7, 12 Thicket Road, London SE20 8DD ☎ 020 8778 6618

DOWNS Marilyn: 307 Leigham Court Road, Streatham, London SW16 2RX ☎ 020 8677 9627

DRANE Jacqueline: 62 Hatherleigh Road, Ruislip Manor, Middlesex HA4 6AU

DROUGHT Geraldine (*Vla*): 39 New Road, Croxley Green, Herts WD3 3EN ☎ 01923 773899, 01306 880669

DRUCE Duncan (*Bq Vln, Vla, Vadam*): Westfield House, 155 West End, Netherthong, Huddersfield HD7 2YJ ☎ 01484 683158, 01484 689408 fax

DRURY Sarah: 42 Tulsemere Road, London SE27 9EJ ☎ 020 8761 1620, 020 8533 1372

DUDLEY Stephen: 37 Cecile Park, London N8 9AX ☎ 020 8340 6071

DUFFY Kevin: 4 Avondale Avenue, London N12 8EJ ☎ 020 8445 1921

DUKOV Bruce: 28 Gresham Gardens, London NW11 8PB ☎ 020 8455 2544

DUNCAN Fiona (*Vla, Bq Vln*): 42 Hatfield Road, Watford, Herts WD2 4DB ☎ 01923 221 707, 01923 237261 fax

DUNN Adrian: 5 Calais Street, London SE5 9LP ☎ 020 7733 6609 & fax, 01306 880669 day, 0973 753498 mob

DUSSEK Sarah: Weissensteinweg 5, Ch-4852 Rothrist, Switzerland

EADEN Eric: 3 Braithwaite Gardens, Stanmore, Middx HA7 2QG ☎ 020 8907 4487

EAST Denis: The Old Chapel, Stoke Road, Nayland, Suffolk CO6 4JD ☎ 01206 263291

EAST Imogen: The Acacias, 4 Higher Drive, Purley, Surrey CR8 2HE ☎ 020 8645 9459

EASTWOOD Gillian: Newholme, 45 Baker Street, Potters Bar, Herts EN6 2DZ ☎ 01707 850028

EDDOWES Rita: Flat 4, 28 Silverdale Road, Eastbourne, East Sussex BN20 7EY ☎ 01323 430494

EDE Stephanie: First Floor Flat, 64 Leighton Road, West Ealing, London W13 9DS ☎ 020 8566 5945

EDWARDS Alan: 116 Regal Way, Kenton, Harrow, Middx HA3 0SQ ☎ 020 8907 0652

EDWARDS Charlotte: Dunvegan, St Nicholas Avenue, Great Bookham, Surrey KT23 4AY ☎ 01372 450936

EDWARDS David: 16 Oak Hall Road, Wanstead, London E11 2JT ☎ 020 8989 1031

EDWARDS Elizabeth: 41 Dorking Road, Tunbridge Wells, Kent TN1 2LN ☎ 01892 538893

EDWARDS George: 34 Elm Drive, North Harrow, Middlesex HA2 7BS ☎ 020 8427 1085

EDWARDS Gudrun: 55 Marksbury Avenue, Kew, Surrey TW9 4JE ☎ 020 8876 9318

EDWARDS Juliet: 143 Hydethorpe Road, London SW12 0JF

EDWARDS Nigel: 3 Elliswick Road, Harpenden, Herts AL5 4TP ☎ 01582 762905

EHRLICH Ruth: 4 Fortismere Avenue, London N10 3BL ☎ 020 8444 4899, 01306 880669

EISNER Thomas: 7 Leinster Avenue, London SW14 7JW ☎ 020 7794 0545

EITLER Marta: 9 Rowlands Avenue, Hatch End, Middx HA5 4DF ☎ 020 8428 6000

ELAN Nancy: Flat 4, 42 Fellows Road, London NW3 3LH ☎ 020 7722 2452

ELDERTON Ann: 33 Weald Road, Brentwood, Essex CM14 4TH ☎ 01277 223881

ELLIS David: 32 Ernest Gdns, London W4 3QU ☎ 020 8995 5896, 020 8549 1706 day

EMANUEL Christina (*Pf*): 24 Goodwyn Avenue, Mill Hill, London NW7 3RG ☎ 020 8201 0407, 020 8549 1706

EMANUEL David (*Hpsd, Pf, Vla*): 24 Goodwyn Avenue, Millhill, London NW7 3RG ☎ 020 8201 0407, 020 8549 1706

EMERSON Mark (*Pf, Vla*): Lower Panpwnton, Kinsley Road, Knighton, Powys LD7 1TN ☎ 01547 528112

ENGLAND Richard: 57 Ullswater Crescent, London SW15 3RG ☎ 020 8546 6370

ESSEX-HILL Christopher: Address Unknown ☎ 020 8878 8137, 0956 288958 mob

ESTRUCH-LORAIN Ernesto (*Pf, Kbds*): 167D Kent House Road, Beckenham, Kent BR3 1JZ ☎ 020 8402 1402, 0802 729785

EVANS Elizabeth: Moor End, Horsell Rise, Woking, Surrey GU21 4BD ☎ 01483 763324

EVANS Marjorie: 156 London Road, Wembley, Middx HA9 7HG ☎ 020 8902 8467

EVANS Susan (*Voc*): 163 London Road, Hertford Heath, Herts SG13 7PN ☎ 01992 589961

EVANS-JONES Jonathan (*Vla*): 114 Queen Mary Road, London SE19 3NP ☎ 020 8761 8411

EWINS Sarah: Brooklands Cottage, Ripe, Lewes, East Sussex BN8 6AR ☎ 01323 811320, 01483 723644 day

EYRES Rachel: 41 Onslow Gardens, South Woodford, London E18 1ND ☎ 020 8989 7421, 020 8207 0007

FAGG Stella: 35 Redstone Hill, Redhill, Surrey RH1 4AW ☎ 01737 772428

FAIRBAIRN Sonya: 103 Whitehall Gardnes, Chingford, London E4 6EJ ☎ 020 8524 3898, 0839 623637 pager, 0306 880669 day

FAULKNER Jane: Victoria House, The Green, Sarratt, Nr Rickmansworth, Herts WD3 6AY ☎ 01923 265066

FAULTLESS Margaret: Brown's Cottage, Alton Barnes, Marlborough, Wilts SN8 4JZ ☎ 01672 851322 & fax, 020 8444 5092

FAUX Steven (*Pf*): Fleetlands, Weston Park, Bath BA1 4AL ☎ 01225 313145

FERGUSON Ruth: 25 Thurlstone Road, Ruislip, Middlesex HA4 0BT ☎ 01895 633161

FERRAR Susanna: 4/19 Morden Road, London SE3 0AD ☎ 020 8852 8379

FINDLAY Gillian: 55 Albany Road, London W13 8PQ ☎ 020 8998 0214, 01306 880669

FINDLAY Mary: 9 Mount Harry Road, Sevenoaks, Kent TN13 3JJ ☎ 01732 452642

FISCHER Simon: Flat 3, 46 Fitzroy Road, Primrose Hill, London NW1 8TY ☎ 020 7722 1889, 01306 880669 day

FISHER Joshua: 58 Okehampton Road, London NW10 3EP ☎ 020 8830 2892, 0956 229003 mob, 020 8459 7058

FISHER Peter: 187A Devonshire Road, London SE23 3TA ☎ 020 8291 1670

FISKE Jean: 11 Malpas Drive, Pinner, Middlesex HA5 1DG ☎ 020 8868 6626

FITCHETT Rosemary: 50 Grosvenor Road, Leyton, London E10 6LQ ☎ 020 8558 6434

FITZSIMONS Geraldine: ROSO, PO Box 18, Code 121-Seeb, Sultanate Of Oman

FLEMING Cynthia (*Vla*): 3 Middlebrook Road, High Wycombe, Bucks HP13 5NH ☎ 01494 526350 & fax, 0831 206405, 01494 445364

FLEMING Robert: 80 High Street, Montrose, Angus DD10 8JF ☎ 01674 74719

FLETCHER Lyn: Orchard Cottage, Offley Rock, Eccleshall, Staffordshire ST21 6ES ☎ 01785 280348

FORD Catherine (*Bq Vln*): 49 Cheverton Road, London N19 3BA ☎ 020 7263 8721

FOSTER Cindy: 20 Peckarmans Wood, Sydenham Hill, Dulwich, London SE26 6RY ☎ 020 8693 1912, 01306 880669

FOSTER Claire: 14 Manor Grove, Richmond, Surrey TW9 4QF ☎ 020 8392 1553, 0966 503160, 020 8392 4553

FOURMY Ruth: 7 Swinton Close, Wembley Park, Middlesex HA9 9HW ☎ 020 8904 9106

FOX Ivan: 2 Sotheby Road, Highbury, London N5 2UR ☎ 020 7226 2987

FRANCIS David (*Vla, Bq Vln*): Hawkstone Hall, 1A Kennington Road, London SE1 7QP ☎ 020 7401 7892, 0958 430811

FRANCIS Emily: 1/180 Gloucester Place, London NW1 6DS ☎ 020 7724 5041, 0468 475632 mob

FRANCIS John (*Vla*): 17 Whitehorse Hill, Chislehurst, Kent BR7 6DG ☎ 020 8467 2427

FRANKS Carolyn: 8 Princes Avenue, London N3 2DB ☎ 020 8346 2225, 020 8533 1372 day

FRANZ Beth: 44 Clarence Terrace, Regents Park, London NW1 4RD ☎ 020 7724 3306

FRASER Joyce: 18 Upper Street, Rusthall, Tunbridge Wells, Kent TN4 8NX ☎ 01892 521910, 020 8533 1372

FRENCH George: 20 Dorset Road, Ashford, Middlesex TW15 3BY ☎ 01784 258906

FRENCH Nancy: 13 Wheatland House, Dog Kennel Hill, London SE22 8AG ☎ 020 7564 5157, 0973 553752 mob

FROHLICH Josef: 53 Oakleigh Avenue, London N20 9JE ☎ 020 8445 3768

FROWDE Paul: Dove Cottage, High Street, Markyate, St Albans Herts AL3 8PD ☎ 01582 840753, 020 8549 1706

FUCHS Antonia (*Pf*): 72 Oxford Gardens, London W10 5UW ☎ 020 7727 8403, 01306 880669

FULLER Louisa: 6 Tunley Road, London SW17 7QJ ☎ 020 8675 0285

FUNNELL Ruth: The Rectory, 9 Church Crescent, London E9 7DH ☎ 020 8985 5145, 0966 471227

FURMANEK-HALBERDA Susanna (*Clt*): 1037 Forest Road, Walthamstow, London E17 4AH ☎ 020 8523 2613

FURNISS Rosemary (*Vla*): Collins Farm, The Vachery Estate, Cranleigh, Surrey GU6 8EF ☎ 01483 274668, 0976 392644

GABY: 10 Point Close, Blackheath Hill, London SE10 8QS ☎ 020 8691 8318

GAILLARD Julien: 57 Elthorne Avenue, Hanwell, London W7 2JY ☎ 020 8840 3987

GALE Gwendoline: 1 Green Lanes, West Ewell, Epsom, Surrey KT19 9TW ☎ 020 8393 0393

GALEONE Marie: 107 Hendon Way, Finchley, London NW2 2LY ☎ 020 8455 5647

GALEONE Pierrette: 44 Greenfield Gardens, London NW2 1HX ☎ 020 8455 3217

GALLAGHER Frank (*Wh, Vla*): 10 Richmond Crescent, Derry, N.Ireland BT48 7PQ ☎ 028 7126 4269

GALLAWAY Philip: 23 Rouncil Lane, Kenilworth, Warwickshire CV8 1FF ☎ 01926 852755

GARCIA Sige: 17 York Avenue, London SW14 7LQ ☎ 020 8876 5066, 020 8876 9633 fax

GARLAND Roger (*Pf*): 2A Chapel Close, Shephards Way, Brookmans Park, Hatfield, Herts AL9 6NY ☎ 01707 642244 & fax

GARRICK Christian (*E Vln*): 35 Normanby Road, London NW10 1BU ☎ 020 8208 0406, 020 8452 1600

GARVIN Phillip *(Gtr)*: Appletree Cottage, Crays Hill Road, Crays Hill, Billericay Essex CM11 2YP ☎ 01268 20871

GAULT Patricia: 238 Hagden Lane, West Watford, Hertfordshire WD1 8LS ☎ 01923 219 273

GAULTON Brian: 17 Cotsford Avenue, New Malden, Surrey KT3 5EU ☎ 020 8942 8493

GEDULD Ron *(Pf)*: 1499 High Road, Whetstone, London N20 9PJ ☎ 020 8445 2626

GEE Penelope *(Pf, Rec)*: 27 Royston Park Road, Hatch End, Pinner, Middlesex HA5 4AA ☎ 020 8421 4584

GEORGE Christopher *(Pf)*: 196 Meavdale Road, London W5 1LT ☎ 020 8997 8049

GEORGE Richard: 54 Aylmer Road, Shepherds Bush, London W12 9LQ ☎ 020 8740 9125, 07970 666 985 mob, 01306 500011 day

GEORGIADIS John *(Con)*: Purton Corner, Purton Lane, Farnham Royal, Bucks SL2 3LY ☎ 01753 647447, 01753 647363

GERADINE Thomas: 250 Eastwood Road North, Leigh-on-Sea, Essex SS9 4LU ☎ 01702 525696

GIARDINO David: 43 The Grove, Finchley, London N3 1QT ☎ 020 8371 9958

GIBBON Angus: 64 Linden Road, Hampton, Middlesex TW12 2JB ☎ 020 8979 8112, 0589 655535 mob

GIBBS Jeniffer: 28 Pemberton Road, Lyndhurst, Hants SO43 7AN ☎ 023 8028 2376

GIBBS Robert Whysall: 10 St Margarets Drive, Twickenham, Middlesex TW1 1QN ☎ 020 8891 2174

GIBSON Philip *(Con)*: 25 Roy Road, Northwood, Middlesex HA6 1EQ ☎ 01923 828055

GIBSON Wilfred *(Arr, Com, Fo Fdl)*: 33 Cotterill Road, Surbiton, Surrey KT6 7UW ☎ 020 8390 3908

GIDDEY Anna: 38A Abbeville Road, Clapham South, London SW4 9NG ☎ 020 8673 3596

GILCHRIST Eleonor *(Bq Vln)*: 17 Mitford Buildings, Dawes Road, London SW6 7EW ☎ 020 7381 6160, 0976 938368

GILES David *(Vla)*: 125 Beckford Road, Addiscombe, Croydon, Surrey CR0 6HZ ☎ 020 8656 8697

GILES Isabel: 39 Worsley Road, Leytonstone, London E11 3JL ☎ 020 8536 0704

GILL Martin: 1St Floor Flat, 35 Rosebery Gardens, Crouch End, London N8 8SH ☎ 020 8340 5872, 01306 880669 day

GILL Trevor: The Music Box, 1 Bramley Way, Ashill, Cullompton, Devon EX15 3MJ ☎ 01884 841 753

GILLIE Jane *(Bq Vln, Vla)*: 13C Mortimer Terrace, Off Wesleyan Place, London NW5 1LH ☎ 020 7284 1737

GLICKMAN John *(Vla)*: 96 Bridge Lane, London NW11 0EL ☎ 020 8458 7812

GODDEN Emilie *(Pf)*: 130 Algernon Road, Lewisham, London SE13 7AW ☎ 020 8690 7848, 0973 693384

GODDEN Jo: 6 Hambalt Road, London SW4 9EB ☎ 020 8675 1916, 020 8772 9742

GODRICH Vic *(Fo Fdl)*: 62 Huddleston Road, Tufnell Park, London N7 0AG ☎ 020 7607 8975

GODSON Jennifer: 15 Friern Road, East Dulwich, London SE22 0AU ☎ 020 8693 2039, 07970 210502 mob

GODWIN-GREER Merith: 25 Aspen Square, Oatlands Drive, Weybridge, Surrey KT13 9ZA ☎ 07971 009450

GOLDBERG Nigel: 28 Leicester Road, London N2 9EA ☎ 020 8444 5891

GOLDBERG Rachelle *(Vla, Pf)*: Flat 11 Vine Cottage, Tentelow Lane, Norwood Green, Southall Middx UB2 4LG ☎ 020 8571 6614

GOLDING Miles: 21 Tennyson Road, Harpenden, Herts AL5 4BE ☎ 01582 461572, 01582 762405 fax

GOLDSCHEIDER Nicola: 84 Rushgrove Ave, Colindale, London NW9 6RB ☎ 020 8205 3765

GOLDSTEIN Jennie: 14A Kingswood Road, London SW2 4JH ☎ 020 8674 7792

GOMM Jane: 26 Common View, Rusthall, Tunbridge Wells, Kent TN4 8RG ☎ 01892 540576, 01306 880669

GOOD Timothy: 20 Morley Court, 78 The Avenue, Beckenham, Kent BR3 5EY, 01306 880669

GOODALL David *(Vla)*: 83 Woodland Rise, London N10 3UN ☎ 020 8883 2334

GOODALL Janet: 8 Charlton Court, Knaresborough, N.Yorks HG5 0BZ ☎ 01423 864630

GOODMAN Roy *(Kbds, Con)*: 97 Mill Lane, Lower Earley, Reading, Berks RG6 3UH ☎ 0118 935 2595, 0385 362595 mob, 0118 935 2627 fax

GOODWIN Nicola: 10 Danvers Road, Tonbridge, Kent TN9 1TR ☎ 01732 359643

GOTT Howard *(Gtr)*: 1 Grovefield House, Coppies Grove, New Southgate, London N11 1NS ☎ 020 8361 1349

GOTTLIEB Ruth *(Vla)*: 39A Medina Road, London N7 7LA

GOULD Clio: 1 Needham Terrace, London NW2 6QL ☎ 020 8452 4959

GOULD Lucy: 8A Berners Road, Wood Green, London N22 5NB ☎ 020 8881 7584 & fax

GOW Jane: Wayfarers, Bramble Lane, Wye, Kent TN25 5EE ☎ 01233 812979

GRAHAM Breta: 17A Gloucester Avenue, London NW1 7AU ☎ 020 7485 2795

GRAHAM Janice: 11 Malpas Drive, Pinner, Middlesex HA3 9PD ☎ 020 8868 6626

GRAJNER Erica *(Pf)*: 4 Water Eaton Mews, 98 Duncombe Street, Bletchley, Bucks MK2 2LY ☎ 01908 377276

GRANT Barbara *(Reb, Bq Vln, Voc)*: 5A Borneo Street, Putney, London SW15 1QQ ☎ 020 8789 1266

GRANT Miriam: 39 Lindal Crescent, Enfield, Middlesex EN2 7RP ☎ 020 8355 4142

GRATTAN Louise *(Vla)*: 12 Woodstock Road, London W4 1UE ☎ 020 8995 1231

GRAUDINA Anete *(Pf)*: 32 Osterley Road, Isleworth, Middlesex TW7 4PN ☎ 0958 462787 mob

GRAY Michael Antony *(Vla)*: 71 Belgrave Road, London E11 3QP ☎ 020 8989 4515

GREAVES Hilary: 1 Castle House, 46 - 48 Old Bath Road, Speen, Newbury, Berkshire RG14 1QL ☎ 01635 38136

GREELEY Liz: 61 Cranbury Road, Reading, Berks RG30 2XE ☎ 01734 478834

GREEN Andrew: 29 Roger Dowley Court, Parmiter Street, London E2 9NJ ☎ 020 8981 6855

GREEN Deborah: 136 Fairbridge Road, Archway, London N19 3HU ☎ 020 7272 1840

GREENSTONE Jack: 11 Roding Close, Elmbridge Village, Cranleigh, Surrey GU6 8TE ☎ 01483 272592

GRIEVE Pamela: 35 Needwood House, Woodberrydown Estate, Manor House, London N4 2TN ☎ 020 8671 7375

GRIFFIN Claire *(Pf)*: 64 Matlock Road, Leyton, London E10 6DJ ☎ 020 8556 4313

GRIFFITHS Barry: The Shealing, 56 Bayham Road, Sevenoaks, Kent TN13 3XE ☎ 01732 53779

GRIFFITHS Dominic: 40 Pellatt Road, East Dulwich, London SE22 9JB ☎ 020 8516 1042, 0956 218 475

GRIFFITHS Jane: 33 The Glebe, Blackheath, London SE3 9TG ☎ 020 8318 7359

GROVES Rosalyn *(Com, Arr)*: 227 Cassiobury Drive, Watford, Herts WD1 3AN ☎ 01923 236680

GRUCA-BROADBENT Magdalena: 22 Fordyke Road, Dagenham, Essex RM8 1PJ ☎ 020 8592 2258, 01306 880669

GRUENBERG Erich: 22 Spencer Drive, Hampstead Garden Suburb, London N2 0QX ☎ 020 8455 4360

GRUENBERG Tina: 17 Ildersly Grove, London SE21 8EU ☎ 020 8761 8202

GRUN Gundula *(Voc, Pf, Man, Per)*: 10 Clare Gardens, Ladbroke Grove, London W11 1NX ☎ 020 7243 4295 & fax, 0956 824953 mob

GUEST Elizabeth *(Pf)*: 5 Weymouth Street, Hemel Hempstead, Herts HP3 9SL ☎ 01442 251962

GULLAN Richard: 98 Woodvale, Forest Hill, London SE23 3ED ☎ 020 8299 0896

GUNNER Imogen *(Flt, Pf, Voc, Bsn)*: Flat 6, 6 Palmerston Villas, Upper Rathmines, Dublin 6, Eire ☎ +353 14940116

GURRY Keith: Belgrave House, 20 Belgrave Road, Wanstead, London E11 3QN ☎ 020 8530 5228

HABGOOD Gillian: 9 Loudhams Road, Little Chalfont, Bucks HP7 9NY ☎ 01494 762785

HAGUE Stephen: 23 Roseholme Road, Abington, Northampton NN1 4TQ ☎ 01604 24623

HAIGH Chris (*Gtr*): 232 Sebert Road, Forest Gate, London E7 0NP ☎ 020 8534 3887

HALLAM George: 86 The Ridgeway, London NW11 9RU ☎ 020 8455 8700

HALLETT Sylvia (*Pf, Arr, Com*): 33 Summerhill Road, London N15 4HF ☎ 020 8802 0094

HALLING Patrick: 14 Cherry Orchard Gardens, West Molesey, Surrey KT8 9QY ☎ 020 8979 5707

HALSTEAD Christian (*Bq Vln*): 2 Clovelly Road, Hornsey, London N8 7RH ☎ 020 8348 0447

HAMERTON Susan: 6 Draxmont, Wimbledon, London SW19 7PG ☎ 020 8947 6255

HAMLIN Julian: 135 St Thomas Road, Finsbury Park, Islington, London N4 2QJ ☎ 020 7704 6790

HANESWORTH David: 57 Osmond Gardens, Wallington, Surrey SM6 8SX ☎ 020 8395 6270

HANLEY Aoife: Lissaniska, Foxford, Co Mayo, Eire

HANSON Peter: 138 Severalls Avenue, Chesham, Buckinghamshire HP5 3EN ☎ 01494 771137

HARPER Andrew: 12 Hillyfields Crescent, London SE4 1QA ☎ 020 8692 2546

HARPER Beatrice: 11 Elmwood Road, Chiswick, London W4 3DY ☎ 020 8994 9528, 020 8994 9595

HARPER Laurence (*B Gtr, Man*): 11B Cheverton Road, London N19 3BB ☎ 020 7263 9787

HARRIES Andre: 31 Pagoda Avenue, Richmond, Surrey TW9 2HQ ☎ 020 8948 4448

HARRIS Drusilla (*Pf*): 48C Onslow Gardens, Muswell Hill, London N10 3JX ☎ 020 8444 3797

HARRIS Jayne (*E Vln*): 59 Moring Road, London SW17 8DN ☎ 020 8682 4533, 0956 290810, 01483 723644

HARRIS Jenny: 27 Willows Avenue, Morden, Surrey SM4 5SG ☎ 020 8640 5738

HARRIS Louis: 8 Tudor Close, London NW9 8SU ☎ 020 8205 7595

HARRIS Pippa: 16A Burnt Ash Lane, Bromley, Kent BR1 4DH ☎ 020 8325 8016

HARRISON Susan: Flat 3, 23 Park Hill, Carshalton, Surrey SM5 3SA ☎ 020 8669 1211

HARRITT Gillian: 7 Matham Road, East Molesey, Surrey KT8 0SX ☎ 020 8979 2275

HART Catherine: 53 Lower Street, Stansted, Mountfitcher, Essex CM24 8LN ☎ 01279 814198, 01306 880669

HART Charlie (*Acc, Db, B Gtr*): 140 Tressillian Road, London SE4 1XX ☎ 020 8691 0715

HARTLEY Jacqueline: Sydenham Farm House, Aynho Road, Adderbury, Oxfordshire OX17 3NJ ☎ 01295 811524

HARTLEY John ☎ 01702 710189

HASTINGS Eric: 16 Buckhurst Mead, Baldwins Hill, East Grinstead, West Sussex RH19 2AN ☎ 01342 322991

HAVERON Andrew: 78A Idmiston Road, West Dulwich, London SE27 9HQ ☎ 020 8670 9915, 020 8670 9915

HAYES Clare: Burnside Cottage, Munden Road, Dane Lane, Ware, Herts SG12 0LP ☎ 01920 438165

HEANUE Teresa (*Tin Wh*): 95 Nightingale Lane, Hornsey, London N8 7QY ☎ 020 8348 6646

HEARD Robert: Orchard Cottage, Offley Rock, Eccleshall, Staffordshire ST21 6ES ☎ 01785 280348

HEATH Desmond: 60 Esmond Road, London W4 1JF ☎ 020 8994 3046

HEATH Juliette (*Pf, Voc, Gtr, Flt*): 22A Grove Road, New Barnet, Herts EN4 9DE ☎ 020 8441 2705

HEDGER Susan: Flat 3, 214 Burrage Road, Woolwich, London SE18 7JU ☎ 020 8854 9376

HEICHELHEIM Stefanie: 15 Hampstead Gardens, London NW11 7EU ☎ 020 8458 1432

HEIN George: 55 Rylett Crescent, London W12 9RP ☎ 020 8743 4055

HEMBROUGH Peter: 1 Alexander Road, Brentwood, Essex CM14 4HH ☎ 01277 232532, 01306 880669 day

HENBEST Rosemary: 10 Viewland Road, Plumstead, London SE18 1PE ☎ 020 8854 4965 & fax, 01306 880 669 day, 0973 415927 mob

HERBERT Sarah: 10 Lambert Street, London N1 1JE ☎ 020 7607 0246

HERD David: 258 Rosendale Road, London SE24 9DL ☎ 020 8671 5284

HERMAN Elaine (*Pf*): 2 Forlease Drive, Maidenhead, Berks SL6 1UD ☎ 01628 22437

HESS Rachel (*Vla*): 63 Judd Road, Tonbridge, Kent TN9 2NJ ☎ 01732 358223, 0468 047161 mob

HICKMAN Rachael (*Pf, Org*): Flat 3.08/B, Francis Rowley Court, 16/17 Brisket Street, London EC1M 5RN ☎ 020 7505 5699 ext 774, 04325 339 838

HICKS Janet: 10 Trevor Road, Hitchin, Herts SG4 9TA ☎ 01462 451338

HIGGS Robert (*Vla*): 148 Blandford Road, Beckenham, Kent BR3 4NQ ☎ 020 8658 5033, 01306 880669

HIGHAM Fiona: 1 Lyme Street, Camden Town, London NW1 0EH ☎ 020 7485 2702, 020 7813 0994

HILL Jonathan G (*Pf*): 35 Oakwood Park Road, Southgate, London N14 6QD ☎ 020 8350 4501 & fax, 020 8313 0010 mob

HILL Warwick: The Gate House, Old Park, Slaugham Lane, Warninglid, West Sussex RH17 5TJ ☎ 01444 461194

HILTON Christine: 28 Bellew Street, London SW17 0AD ☎ 020 8947 5814

HIND Evelyn: St Georges Retreat, Burgess Hill, Sussex RH15 0SQ

HIND Vivien: 4 Dunbar Court, Woodside Grange Road, London N12 8SU ☎ 020 8445 4094

HINDLEY Joanne: c/o Sigmund Shalit & Ass, Cambridge Theatre, Seven Dials, Covent Garden, London WC2H 9HU ☎ 020 7379 3282, 020 7379 3238

HIRONS Christopher: 99 Wimbledon Hill Road, Wimbledon, London SW19 7QT ☎ 020 8946 6967, 020 8946 6966 fax

HIRSCH Deborah(Miffi) (*Vla*): Flat 2, 15 Nightingale Road, Rickamansworth, Herts WD3 2DE ☎ 01923 771633, 01306 880669

HIRSCH Rebecca (*Vla*): 47 Love Lane, Pinner, Middx HA5 3EY ☎ 020 8429 3453, 020 8549 1706

HIRST Bridget: 20 Townley Road, London SE22 8SR ☎ 020 8693 1086

HITCHENOR Joseph: 3 Thame Park Road, Thame, Oxon OX9 3JA ☎ 0184 421 3970

HOBDAY Clive: 134 Locket Road, Harrow Weald, Middlesex HA3 7NR ☎ 020 8427 6280

HODGE Marjorie (*Vla*): Flat 6, 6 Collingham Gardens, London SW5 0HW ☎ 020 7373 8810

HODGES Laura (*Vla*): 51 Longford Road, Whitton, Twickenham, Middlesex TW2 6EB ☎ 020 8893 3672, 01306 880669

HOFFMAN Clare (*Vla*): 25 Strafford Road, Barnet EN5 4LR ☎ 020 8449 1028

HOLTER Margaret: 18 Villiers Crescent, St Albans, Herts AL4 9HY ☎ 01727 839609

HONEYMAN Susie: 284 Globe Road, Bethnal Green, London E2 0NS ☎ 020 8983 3825

HONORE Philippe: 131A Westbourne Park Road, London W2 5QL ☎ 020 7243 3238 & fax, 0973 653542 mob

HOOLEY Ann: 29 Chadwick Road, Peckham, London SE15 4RA ☎ 020 7639 1203

HOOSON Gwilym: 58 Selbourne Road, London N14 7DG ☎ 020 8886 3580

HORSMAN Simon: 27A Red Lion Lane, Farnham, Surrey GU9 7QN ☎ 01252 726850 & fax, 01426 205658 pager

HOULDSWORTH Simon (*Vla*): 49G Chesterton Road, London W10 6ES ☎ 020 8969 4641

HOUNAM John-Lawrence (*Bq Vln*): 3A St. Mary's Road, Oxford OX4 1PX ☎ 01865 790748

HOUSTON Dudley: Hotel Lindsey (25), 4 Lindsey Street, London EC1A 9HP

HOWARD Lucy: 28 Stanley Avenue, Chesham, Bucks HP5 2JG ☎ 01494 776202

HOWICK Clare: 15 Seymour Gardens, Surbiton, Surrey KT5 8QE ☎ 020 8390 1561

HOWSON Michael: 22 Hallam Gardens, Hatch End, Pinner, Middlsex HA5 4PR ☎ 020 8421 1269

HUBER Colin: 78 Puller Road, High Barnet, Herts EN5 4HD ☎ 020 8441 4825

HUDSON Ruth: 16 West Hill Way, London N20 8QP ☎ 020 8445 1975

HUGGETT Monica: 87 Lancaster Road, London N4 4PL ☎ 020 7263 2644, 020 7263 2644

HUGGETT-LING Fiona (*Vadag*): 25 Cleveland Road, Barnes, London SW13 0AA ☎ 020 8876 1274

HUGHES Neville: The Cottage, 28 Watercroft Road, Halstead, Nr Sevenoaks Kent TN14 7DP ☎ 01959 534514

HUGHES Vanessa: Willow Cottage, 32 Pikes Hill, Epsom, Surrey KT17 4EA ☎ 01372 741668, 0976 796695 mob

HUMPHREY Michael: 10 Wheelers Orchard, Chalfont St Peter, Gerrards Cross, Bucks SL9 0HL ☎ 012407 5579

HUMPHREYS Fenella (*Pf*, *Voc*): 94 Kings Avenue, Greenford, Middlesex UB6 9DD ☎ 020 8575 0367

HUMPHREYS Kyra: 53 Shortridge Terrace, Newcastle-upon-Tyne NE2 2JE ☎ 0191 281 3456, 01306 50011 day

HUMPHRIES Ian (*Pf*, *Vla*): Marglao, Mill Lane, Gerrards Corss, Bucks SL9 8AU ☎ 01753 886124

HUNKA Alison: 61 Erpingham Road, London SW15 1BH ☎ 020 8788 1031

HUNKA Katherine: 61 Erpingham Road, Putney, London SW15 1BH ☎ 020 8788 1031

HUNT Angela: 1 Leighton Road, Enfield EN1 1XH ☎ 020 8364 4637

HUNTER Ailsa: 40 Birkbeck Road, London N12 8DZ ☎ 020 8445 0344

HURN Ruby: 31 Hesketh Close, Cranleigh, Surrey GU6 7JB ☎ 01483 271204

HURWITZ Emanuel: 25 Dollis Avenue, Finchley, London N3 1DA ☎ 020 8346 3936, 020 8343 1595 fax

HUSSEY Stephen (*Kbds, Arr, Con*): 10 Leff House, 2-12 Winchester Avenue, London NW6 7UB ☎ 020 7625 6335, 0956 421184 mob, 020 7604 3444

HUTCHINGS Nicola: 35 Bury Road, Old Harlow, Essex CM17 0EE ☎ 01279 635848, 020 8533 1372 day

IBBOTSON Philippa: 121 Roydene Road, Plumstead Common, London SE18 1PZ ☎ 020 8855 1980

ICHINOSE Yasuo: 2 Vallance Road, London N22 4UB ☎ 020 8888 0605

INNES Grahame (*Vla, Cel, Pf*): 12 Blythe Hill Lane, Catford, London SE6 4UH ☎ 020 7520 0708 ext42028

IRBY Carol: 2 Ravens Court, 23 Uxbridge Road, Kingston-upon-Thames, Surrey KT1 2LS ☎ 020 8549 9899, 0777 5531641

ISAACS Maurice: 84 Sutton Road, London N10 1HG ☎ 020 8444 9628

ISSERLIS Rachel: 39 Chandos Road, London NW2 4LT ☎ 020 8208 3398

JACKSON Laurence: 36 Southwold, Roman Wood, Bracknell, Berks RG12 8XY ☎ 01344 4816608, 0973 501 833

JACKSON Rachel: 25 Rothschild Road, Chiswick, London W4 5HT ☎ 020 8742 7430, 0973 758493

JACKSON Simon: 8 Weardale Road, Lewisham, London SE13 5QB ☎ 020 8297 0353

JAMES Stuart: 19 Roxeth Hill, Harrow-on-The-Hill, Middlesex HA2 0JY ☎ 020 8422 7767, 020 8422 7767

JENKINS Peter: 32 Foxglove Way, Dunston Park, Thatcham, Berkshire RG18 4DL ☎ 01635 861661

JENKINSON Maeve: The Swallows, 4 Washere Close, Berwick, Polegate, East Sussex BN26 6TB ☎ 01323 871273

JESSOPP Angela (*Vla*): 5 Station Road, Hanwell, London W7 3JD ☎ 020 8840 2752

JOHNSON Alexandra: 333 Norwood Road, Tulse Hill, London SE24 9AH ☎ 020 8480 7831, 0411 704145

JOHNSON Susan (*Pf*): School House, High Lorton, Nr Cockermouth, Cumbria CA13 9UL ☎ 01900 85601

JONES Alison: 79 Brighton Road, London N16 8EQ ☎ 020 7254 9500

JONES Justin: 14 Maxwelton Close, London NW7 3NA ☎ 020 8906 3226

JONES Martyn: Lawn Cottage, 23A Brackley Road, Beckenham, Kent BR3 1RB ☎ 020 8658 6771

JONES Mary: 137 Priory Road, Crouch End, London N8 8NA ☎ 020 8347 7482

JONES Michael: 10 Churchfield Court, Girton, Cambridge CB3 0XA ☎ 01223 277471

JONES Rebecca (*Pf*): 18C Cheverton Road, London N19 3AY ☎ 020 7272 5480, 0966 416 771 mob

JONES Stephen (*Bq Vln, Ea Stg, Reb, Erhu*): 29 Priory Road, London W4 5JA ☎ 020 8995 5976

JONES Vaughan (*Pf*): 20 Brook Avenue, Wembley Park, Middlesex HA9 8PH ☎ 020 8908 4484

JOSEPHS Jonathan: 23 Foxbury Road, Bromley, Kent BR1 4DG ☎ 020 8464 8542

JURITZ David (*Vla*): 106 Woodstock Road, London W4 1EG ☎ 020 8747 4869, 020 8742 0377 fax

KAHAN Jonathan: 9 West Cottages, Off West End Lane, West Hampstead, London NW6 1RJ ☎ 020 7433 3204, 0976 848424 mob

KAMINSKI Michael (*Kbds*)

KANGA Homi: 14 Orchard Gate, London NW9 6HU ☎ 020 8205 4973

KANTROVITCH Vera (*Vla*): Address Unknown ☎ 020 8346 3434

KATZ David: 11 Larken Close, Bushey Heath, Herts WD2 1AY ☎ 020 8950 9494

KAVINA Vabiz: 55 Thurlow Park Road, London SE21 8JP ☎ 020 8333 2763

KEAR Stephen: 19 Theobalds Avenue, London N12 8QG ☎ 020 8445 1122, 020 8549 1706

KELLY Alison: Flat 4, 214 Burrage Road, London SE18 7JU ☎ 020 8855 1040, 01306 880669

KELLY Judith (*Vla*): 12 Fairlie Gardens, Forest Hill, London SE23 3TE ☎ 020 8699 4612, 01306 880669

KEMP Thomas: Address Unknown ☎ 020 8342 8619

KENT Gillian: 6 Oldbury Place, London W1M 3AN ☎ 020 7935 3182

KERR Harry: 27A Lakeside Road, Shepherds Bush, London W14 0DX ☎ 020 7602 5970

KERSHAW Harold: 18 Froghall Drive, Wokingham, Berkshire RG40 2LF ☎ 0118 978 3542

KHAN Nawazish (*Harm, Voc*): 30 Pikestone Close, Yeading Hayes, Middlesex UB4 9QT ☎ 020 8841 5893

KIERNAN Patrick: 3 Shalimar Road, Acton, London W3 9JD ☎ 020 8896 9986, 0467 980948 mob

KINCH Linda: 23 Beechcroft Avenue, North Harrow, Middlesex HA2 7JD ☎ 020 8868 9595

KING Iain: 202A Brockley Road, London SE4 2SU ☎ 020 8659 7670

KING Jenny (*Bq Vln*): 72 Uphill Drive, Kingsbury, London NW9 0BX ☎ 020 8206 2319, 0976 292618, 020 8206 2319

KING Katharine: 8 Prior Bolton Street, London N1 2NX ☎ 020 7226 3032

KING Kenneth: 71 Lansdowne Road, London W11 2LG ☎ 020 7229 8025

KING Marjory: 10 Sheepfold Lane, Amersham, Bucks HP7 9EL ☎ 01494 728349

KINNERSLEY Sue (*Bq Vln, Vla*): 138 Riverdale Road, London SE18 1PB ☎ 020 8854 5891, 020 8549 1706

KIRBY Anne-Marie (*Ob, Pf*): Flat 2, 329 Caledonian Road, Islington, London N1 1DW ☎ 020 7607 2072, 0958 426310 mob

KIRKLAND John: 1491 High Road, Whetstone, London N20 9PJ ☎ 020 8445 7773

VIOLIN - LONDON

KITCHEN John: 18 Defoe Avenue, Richmond, Surrey TW9 4DL ☎ 020 8878 0563

KITCHEN Leonard: 8 Wykeham Hill, Wembley Park, Middlesex HA9 9RZ ☎ 020 8904 6969

KLEE Andrew: 2 Dover House, 100 Westwood Hill, London SE26 6TD ☎ 020 8659 1084

KLEMPERER Erika: 23 The Park, London NW11 7ST ☎ 020 8458 1025

KLINGELS Kirsten: 25 Gabriel Street, Forest Hill, London SE23 1DW ☎ 020 8699 2838

KNELL Ruth: Echo Cottage, 31 Parrock Road, Gravesend, Kent DA12 1QE ☎ 01474 352148, 0850 001189 mob

KNIGHT Mark (Vla, Md): The Penthouse Flat, 56 Bow Road, London E3 4DH ☎ 020 8981 7156

KNIGHTS Charles: 69 Oaklands Grove, Shepherds Bush, London W12 0JE ☎ 020 8740 4745, 0956 579868 mob

KOK Darrell: 11 Bridgman Road, Chiswick, London W4 5BA ☎ 020 8742 0314, 020 8533 1372 day, 0410 350586 mob

KONII Eri (Pf): 40 Basing Hill, London NW11 8TH ☎ 020 8455 4272, 020 8455 4272

KOSTECKI Bogustav: 17A Longton Avenue, Sydenham, London SE26 6RE ☎ 020 8659 1481

KOSTECKI Zofia: 17A Longton Avenue, Sydenham, London SE26 6RE ☎ 020 8659 1481

KOSTER Richard (Vla): 41 Sulina Road, Brixton, London SW2 4EL ☎ 020 8671 7024

KRAMER-GABREL Miriam: 3 Stuart Tower, 105 Maida Vale, London W9 1UE ☎ 020 7266 3596

KUNSTLER Tibor (Sax, Clt, Md): Address Unknown ☎ 020 8205 7959

KUO Nicolette: Marglo, Mill Lane, Gerrards Cross, Bucks SL9 8AU ☎ 01753 886124, 0374 936 533 mob

LAING Andrew: 63 Judd Road, Tonbridge, Kent TN9 2NJ ☎ 01732 358223, 0468 047160 mob

LANDER Clive: 4 Blackmore's Grove, Teddington, Middlesex TW11 9AF ☎ 020 8977 9701, 0973 722309 mob

LANGDON Sophie: Stream Cottage, 4 Laurel Grove, Farnham, Surrey GU10 4AU ☎ 01252 795234, 01306 500011

LANGFORD Oliver (Vla, E Vln): 341B Kentish Town Road, London NW5 2TJ ☎ 020 7482 0516, 0956 845618 mob

LASSERSON David (Vla): Flat 3, 2 Brondesbury Villas, London NW6 6AA ☎ 020 7625 4800

LATCHEM Malcolm: Station House, Staverton, Totnes, Devon TQ9 6AG ☎ 01803 762670

LAULUND Jorge: 21 Connaught Gdns, London N10 3LG ☎ 020 8883 0403

LAURICELLA Remo: Trinacria, 10 Brondesbury Road, London NW6 6AS ☎ 020 7328 1046

LAVIGNE Berenice: 4 Square Saint Roch, 78150, Le Chesnay, France N7 0RB ☎ +331 39540380

LAWRENCE Alwin: 51A Northumberland Park Road, London N17 0TB

LAWRENCE Kenneth: 97 Dutton Street, Greenwich, London SE10 8TB ☎ 020 8691 5195

LAYTON Richard: 20 Lower Hill Road, Epsom, Surrey KT19 8LT ☎ 01372 721658

LE FERVE J: 22 Mill Lane, Amersham, Bucks HP7 0EH ☎ 012403 7459

LEAF Mary: 11 London Road, Harrow-on-The-Hill, Middx HA1 3JJ ☎ 020 8422 1292

LEAPER Julian (Pf): Middle Oak, Chapel Croft, Chipperfield, Kings Langley, Hertfordshire WD4 9EQ ☎ 01923 262468, 01306 885411, 0374 252115 mob

LEAVER Richard: 10 Lightwoods Hill, Bearwood, Warley, West Midlands B67 5EA ☎ 0121 429 8577

LEDERMAN Norman: Monks Cottage, 34 Northbridge Street, Robertsbridge, East Sussex TN32 5NY ☎ 01580 880363

LEE Joanna (Pf, Theory): 10 Penny Mews, Balaham, London SW12 8PU ☎ 020 8675 2066

LEE Pan: 11 Sydmons Court, Netherby Road, Forest Hill, London SE23 3AJ ☎ 020 8291 9270 & fax, 020 8549 1706 day

LEE Philip (Pf): Address Unknown ☎ 01932 248559

LEIGHTON Lindsay: 4A Homecroft Road, Sydenham, London SE26 5QG ☎ 020 8778 2331, 0467 835922 mob

LEIGHTON-JONES Juliet: Holly Mount, 21 Llanthewy Road, Newport, Gwent NP9 4RJ ☎ 01633 243700 & fax

LEISHMAN Karin: Friars Cottage, Friars Farm, Wimbish, Saffron Waldon, Essex CB10 2XT ☎ 01799 586 377, 01306 880669 day

LEOPOLD Reginald: 74 Chiltington Way, Saltdean, Brighton, Sussex BN2 8HB ☎ 01273 307897

LETT Catherine: 5A Merton Road, Walthamstow, London E17 9DE ☎ 020 8503 6494, 01306 880669

LEVINE Adrian (Vla): 27 Leicester Road, London N2 9DY ☎ 020 8444 5905, 020 8549 1706 day

LEVINE Stephen: 24 Cyprus Gardens, London N3 1SP ☎ 020 8371 9770, 0958 380873 mob, 01306 880669 day

LEVY Debra: 83 Latchmere Lane, Kingston-upon-Thames, Surrey KT2 5SF ☎ 020 8974 8984

LEVY Nicholas: 83 Latchmere Lane, Kingston-upon-Thames, Surrey KT2 5SF ☎ 020 8974 8984

LEWCOCK Robert: 9 Cowdray Close, Little Common, Bexhill-on-Sea, E Sussex TN39 3NL ☎ 01424 843599

LEWIS Carl: 5 Castle Court, Waterford Place, Highcliffe, Dorset BH23 5HT ☎ 01425 278780

LEWIS David (Bq Vln): 28 Swallow Close, Brackley, Northampton NN13 6PQ ☎ 01280 840595

LEWIS Keith: 17 Flanders Road, London W4 1NQ ☎ 020 8994 6315

LEWIS Laurie: 2 Osborne House, Courtlands, Sheen Road, Richmond Surrey TW10 5BE ☎ 020 8948 3429

LEWIS Oliver: 14 Woodmansterne Road, Carhsalton Beeches, Surrey SM5 4JL ☎ 020 8643 6154, 01306 880669, 0411 285150 mob

LEWIS Paul: 3 Springwood Way, Romford, Essex RM1 2BD ☎ 01708 755710

LEWIS Simon: 81 Pickwick Road, Corsham, Wilts SN13 9BY ☎ 01249 714081 & fax

LIDDELL Nona: 28B Ravenscroft Park, Barnet, Hertfordshire EN5 4NH ☎ 020 8441 7703

LIEW Sarah (Pf): 42 Birley Road, London N20 0EZ ☎ 020 8445 9055

LILLY Rosemary: Oaklands, Poundsbridge Lane, Penshurst, Tonbridge Kent TN11 8AE ☎ 01892 870242

LIN Malu R: 2B Radcliffe Avenue, London NW10 5XS ☎ 020 8961 4031

LINDER-DEWAN Kerstin: 190 Andrewes House, Barbican, London EC2Y 8BA ☎ 020 7638 3256 eve

LISHAK Bertha (Pf): 33 Elm Park Road, Winchmore Hill, London N21 2HP ☎ 020 8360 6245

LISHAK Rosalyn: 75 Conway Road, Southgate, London N14 7BD ☎ 020 8886 6588, 0378 029099 mob

LISSAUER Peter (Bq Vln): 173 Canbury Park Road, Kingston-upon-Thames, Surrey KT2 6LG ☎ 020 8541 5716

LOCK Simon: Ground Floor Flat, 100 Adelaide Avenue, London SE4 1YR ☎ 020 8691 6161, 0976 442729

LONGFORD Tina (Voc): 95 Wolfington Road, London SE27 0RH ☎ 020 8670 9821

LOSTON Dale (Cel): c/o 53 Dalisbury Avenue, Cheam, Surrey SM1 2DD

LOVEDAY Alan: 184 Holland Park Avenue, London W11 4UJ

LOVEDAY Bob (E Vln, B Gtr, Rec, Man): 159 Casewick Road, London SE27 0TA ☎ 020 8670 1228

LOVEDAY Martin: 41 Summerfield Avenue, Queens Park, London NW6 6JT ☎ 020 8933 7615, 020 8969 1975

LOVEJOY Michael: C-O English Nat Opera Orch, The London Colliseum, London WC2N 4ES

LOVELL John: 16 The Crescent, Friern Barnet, London N11 3HN ☎ 020 8368 5955

LOVELL Kolbrun: 16 The Crescent, Friern Barnet, London N11 3HN ☎ 020 8368 5955

LOVELL Pat: 8 Fitzwilliam Mews, Britannie Village, Royal Victoria Dock, Silvertown, London E16 1SH ☎ 020 7511 8448

413

LOVERIDGE Kitty: Cooks Cottage, Plummers Plain, Horsham, West Sussex RH13 6PB ☎ 01444 400536

LOW Rebecca (*Vla*): 16 Highmans Road, East Dulwich, London SE22 9NF ☎ 020 8693 3562, 0468 878416

LOWBURY Pauline: 6 Colebrooke Avenue, Ealing, London W13 8JY ☎ 020 8991 5975, 01306 880669

LOYNES Katherine (*Vla*): Flat 2, 17 Cardigan Road, Richmond, Surrey TW10 6BJ ☎ 020 8940 4575 & fax, 0973 147970 mob

LUDLOW John: 11 Arbour Close, Fetcham, Surrey KT22 9DZ ☎ 01372 378481

LUPIN Mark: 628 West 13th Avenue, Apt. 203, Vancouver, British Columbia, Canada,V5Z 1N9 ☎ +604 879 5504

LYDON Christopher: c/o Royal Oman Symphony Orchestra, PO Box 18, Seeb 121, Sultanate Of Oman ☎ +96 8694581 & fax

LYNN Geoffrey: 29 Hawes Road, Bromley, Kent BR1 3JS ☎ 020 8460 9064

LYON David (*Vla*): 86 Taymount Grange, Taymount Rise, London SE23 3UJ ☎ 020 8291 6042

LYONS Harry (*Md*): 55 King's Court, King Street, London W6 0RW ☎ 020 8748 5324

MABY Lewis: 24 The Glen, Pinner, Middlesex HA5 5AY ☎ 020 8868 4020

MACDONALD Andrew: 104 Nelson Road, London N8 9RT ☎ 020 8348 9485

MACKAY Gordon: 9 Algiers Road, London SE13 7JD ☎ 020 8314 0984, 01306 880669 day

MACKENZIE Lennox: 83 St Josephs Vale, Blackheath, London SE3 0XG ☎ 020 8852 6844

MACKIE Douglas: 349C Liverpool Road, London N1 1NL ☎ 020 7609 7830

MACKINNON Iain (*Md*): 18 Newland Court, Forty Ave, Wembley Park, Middx. HA9 9LZ ☎ 020 8904 6558

MACKINTOSH Catherine (*Vla, Bq Vln*): 15 Ranelagh Road, London W5 5RJ ☎ 020 8840 2659, 020 8579 0571 fax

MACKRELL Elliet (*Didj*): 69B Barnsdale Road, London W9 3LL ☎ 0958 680885

MACNAGHTEN Anne: 23 Wymondley Road, Hitchin, Herts SG4 9PN ☎ 01462 451053

MADDOCKS James (*Vla, Con*): 37 St David's Road, Clifton Campville, Nr Tamworth, Staffs B79 0BA ☎ 01827 373586

MAGUB Maya: 85 Nightingale Road, Bounds Green, London N22 8PT ☎ 020 8881 6981

MAGUIRE Hugh (*Con*): Manor Farm, Benhall Green, Saxmundham, Suffolk IP17 1HN ☎ 01728 603245

MAGUIRE Teresa (*Man*): 22 Wembley Way, Wembley, Middlesex HA9 6JJ ☎ 020 8902 8385

MAHER Rachel: 45 Gondar Gardens, West Hampstead, London NW6 1EP ☎ 020 7461 6459

MALLOCK Sarah (*Vla*): 11D Theatre Street, Battersea, London SW11 5NE ☎ 020 7223 7805

MANLEY Paul: Horseshoe Barn, Cobbarn Farm, Groombridge Lane, Eridge, Tunbridge Wells TN3 9LA ☎ 01892 864069, 01306 880669

MANN Jeanne: 135 The Downs, Harlow, Essex CM20 3RQ ☎ 01279 415186, 0378 149866 mob

MANNING Peter: 17 Oakden Street, Kennington, London SE11 4UQ ☎ 020 7793 9615, 020 7793 8625 fax

MANNING Rita: 23 Woodberry Crescent, Muswell Hill, London N10 1PJ ☎ 020 8883 7342

MANSON Catherine (*Vla*): 15 Twisden Road, London NW5 1DL ☎ 020 7485 2199 & fax

MARCUS Marshall: Greenways, Long Wittenham, Nr.Abingdon, Oxon OX14 4PZ ☎ 0186 540 7286, 0186 540 7287

MARGESON Jane: 16 High Street, Sydling St. Nicholas, Dorchester, Dorset DT2 9PB ☎ 01300 341719

MARGO Sidney: 5 Fairgreen Court, Fairgreen, Cockfosters, Herts EN4 0QT ☎ 020 8449 6173

MARLEYN Denise: c/o 9 Glenavon Court, St Philips Avenue, Worcester Park, Surrey KT4 8JY ☎ 020 8337 0303, 01306 880669 day

MARQUIS Paul (*Man, Mando, Dom*): 80 Temple Grove, Bakers Lane, West Hanningfield CN2 8LH ☎ 01277 841008

MARRINER Neville: 67 Cornwall Gardens, London SW7 4BA ☎ 020 7937 2330

MARSHALL Davina: Moyns, Christchurch Road, Virginia Water, Surrey GU25 4PJ ☎ 01344 842118

MARTIN Anne: 33 Gables Close, Lee, London SE12 0UD ☎ 020 8857 9857, 020 8533 1372 day, 0378 549178 mob

MARTIN Catherine: 85D Brondesbury Villas, London NW6 6AG ☎ 020 7372 1714

MARTIN Ellen: 38 Corringham Road, Hampstead Garden Suburb, London NW11 7BU ☎ 020 8458 5724

MARTIN Jeremy: 53 Salisbury Road, Banstead, Surrey SM7 2DP ☎ 01737 362906

MARTIN June: 139 Mutton Lane, Potters Bar, Herts EN6 2HD ☎ 01707 655231

MARTIN Mary: 328 Kennington Road, London SE11 4LD ☎ 020 7582 7778, 0966 540926

MARTIN Nina: Pepertree Lodge, 19 Canterbury Cres, Sheffield S10 3RW ☎ 0114 2302516

MARTIN Wilhelm (*Pf, Vla*): 33 Brownlow Court, Oak Lane N11 2BH ☎ 020 8889 5376

MASARACHI Robert (*Vla*): 67 Woodrow, London SE18 5DH ☎ 020 8854 1020

MASON Frances: 16 Stonehill Road, East Sheen, London SW14 8RW ☎ 020 8876 3156

MASTRANDREAS Carla (*Rec*): The Eaves, 14 Mill Street, Gamlingay, Sandy, Bedfordshire SG19 3JW ☎ 01767 651634

MATHEWS Catherine: Meon Hall Cottage, High Street, Meonstoke, Hants SO32 3NH ☎ 01489 877 804

MATHIESON Eleanor (*Pf*): Garden Flat, 1B Woodsome Road, London NW5 1RX ☎ 020 7482 1263, 020 8533 1372 day, 0956 997467 mob

MATTHEWS Janet: 12A Halliwick Road, Muswell Hill, London N10 1AB ☎ 020 8444 1732, 0973 293088

MAXTED-JONES Nicholas: The Byre, Gadbridge Lane, Weobley, Hereford HR4 8SN ☎ 01544 319083

MAYER Gillian (*Pf*): 27 Hermitage Road, London N4 1DF ☎ 020 8802 2421

MAYER John (*Com*): 27 Hermitage Road, London N4 1DF ☎ 020 8802 2421

MAYES Peter: 9 Old Park Road, Palmers Green, London N13 4RG ☎ 020 8882 0604

MAYHEW Judy: 3 Shelton Road, Merton Park, London SW19 5AT ☎ 020 8540 9062

MAYO John: 2 Sinnock Square, High Street, Hastings, Sussex TN34 3HQ ☎ 01424 434 944

MCASLAN Lorraine: 10 Hillside Gardens, Barnet, Herts EN5 2NJ ☎ 020 8440 0574, 07771 743227, 020 8440 0632

MCCAPRA Fiona: 89 Waller Road, London SE14 5LB ☎ 020 7639 1382

MCCONKEY Elizabeth: Flat B, 4 St Georges Road, Mitcham, Surrey CR4 1EB ☎ 020 8640 1770, 0976 280526 mob

MCCORMACK Gina: 136 Rosendale Road, London SE21 8LG ☎ 020 8761 7637

MCDADE Annmarie: 45A Queen Mary Road, Upper Norwood, London SE19 3NN ☎ 020 8670 2950, 0468 082344 mob

MCDONALD Anna: Flat 11, 147-149 Gloucester Terrace, London W2 6DX ☎ 020 7723 6608, 020 7723 6608

MCDONOUGH Ian (*Pf*): 12A Phoenix Lodge Mansions, Brook Green, London W6 7BG ☎ 020 7602 9343

MCEVOY Eleanor (*Pf, Kbds, Gtr*): 21 Vernon Street, Dublin 8, Ireland ☎ +353 1 478 0709

MCEVOY Mark (*Kbds, B Gtr, Dms, Per*): 26B Tressillian Road, London SE4 ☎ 020 8692 6253

MCFARLANE Belinda: 16 Halliwick Road, Muswell Hill, London N10 1AB ☎ 020 8883 1909

MCGEE Andrew: The Croft, Farm Lane, Loudwater, Rickmansworth Herts WD3 4JX ☎ 01923 773585

MCGOWAN Marion: 70A Camborne Road, Southfields, London SW18 4BJ ☎ 020 8874 2514, 0850 162875

MCGUINNESS Yvonne: 58 Grasmere Road, Muswell Hill, London N10 2DJ ☎ 020 8883 1293, 01483 723 644 day

MCINTOSH Rosalind: 19 Crawford Road, Camberwell, London SE5 9NF ☎ 020 7733 3702, 07803 124683

MCLAREN David: 9 Mountcombe Close, Upper Brighton Rd, Surbiton, Surrey KT6 6LJ ☎ 020 8399 5695

MCLAREN Linda: 42 North Road, Kew, Surrey TW9 4HA ☎ 020 8878 8320

MCLEOD Iain: Ground Floor Flat, 44 Church Lane, Crouch End, London N8 7BT ☎ 020 8347 9484, 01306 880669

MCLEOD James: 150A Church Lane, London SW17 9PU ☎ 020 8682 0518, 01306 880669

MCMENEMY Michael: 37 Huntingdon Road, East Finchley, London N2 9DX ☎ 020 8444 7589, 01306 880669

MCVEIGH Simon (Bq Vln): 13 Oakwood Road, Orpington, Kent BR6 8JH ☎ 01689 861594

MEADER Rosemary: 6 Westwick, Chesterton Terrace, Kingston-upon-Thames, Surrey KT1 3JE ☎ 020 8549 1930

MEASURES Ann (Vla): Garden Flat, 56 Belsize Park Gardens, London NW3 4ND ☎ 020 7586 7160

MEINARDI Charles: 13 Rodney Gardens, West Wickham, Kent BR4 9DD ☎ 020 8462 7177

MELHUISH Laura: 98 Hindmans Road, East Dulwich, London SE22 9NG ☎ 020 8693 8319, 0973 334642 mob, 01306 880669 day

MELVILLE Elizabeth: 83 Stoke Lane, Westbury-on-Trym, Bristol, Avon BS9 3SN ☎ 01378 610138, 020 8207 0007

MENDELSSOHN Cecily: 3 Dresden Road, London N19 3BE ☎ 020 7263 2800

MERNICK Nick: 62 Townshend Road, Subiaco, Perth, W.Australia 6008, Australia 291098 ☎ +61 9 381 6493

MERRICK Alan: 1 Fox Hill Gardens, London SE19 2XB ☎ 020 8653 3716

MERSON Stephen: 7 Westmere Drive, Mill Hill, London NW7 3HG ☎ 020 8906 0367

METCALFE Jeremy: Westleton, Old London Road, Knockholt, Kent TN14 7JR ☎ 01959 532360, 01306 880669

MEYER Daniel: 142 Haliburton Road, St Margarets, Twickenham TW1 1PH ☎ 020 8744 0078

MEYER Maurice (Vla): 80 Geary Road, London NW10 1HR ☎ 020 8452 6291

MILES Jacqueline (Pf): 9 Eversley Way, Shirley, Croydon, Surrey CRO 8QR ☎ 020 8777 2035

MILLER Julie (Bq Vln): 7 Kingsbury Avenue, St Albans, Herts AL3 4TA ☎ 01727 869786

MILLER Nicholas: Rutland House, The Ridge, Woking, Surrey GU22 7EE ☎ 01483 771361

MILLMAN David (Vla): 16 Nicholas Road, Elstree, Boreham Wood, Herts WD6 3JY ☎ 020 8207 0007, 020 8207 4554

MILLWARD R: Woodleigh, Woodhill Avenue, Gerrard Cross, Bucks SL9 8DS ☎ 01753 883578

MILNE Julia: 37 Chapel Road, Bexleyheath, Kent DA7 4HW ☎ 020 8298 1525

MILONE Richard: 28 Brandreth Road, Tooting Bec, London SW17 8ER ☎ 020 8767 3768

MITCHELL Dianna (E Vln): 62A Barrow Road, Streatham, London SW16 5PG ☎ 020 8677 6360

MITCHELL Madeleine: 41 Queens Gardens, London W2 3AA ☎ 020 7402 0014

MONNINGTON Ann (Bq Vln): 56 Lower Luton Road, Harpenden, Herts AL5 5AH ☎ 01582 467187

MONTAGUE John: 58 Collyer Avenue, Beddington, Croydon, Surrey CR0 4QW ☎ 020 8688 4624

MONTAGUE-MASON Perry: Dragon Lodge, Jumps Road, Churt,Nr Farnham, Surrey GU10 2JY ☎ 01252 792315, 01306 880 669

MONTE Lionel: 22 The Pines, 40 The Avenue, Branksome Park, Poole Dorset BH13 6HJ ☎ 01202 763237

MONUMENT Julie: 19 Wyndham Road, Kingston-upon-Thames, Surrey KT2 5JR ☎ 020 8546 8427

MOONEN Julia: 83 Marlborough Road, London N22 4NL ☎ 020 8889 6284

MOORE Dominic (Pf): 18 Marrowells, Weybridge, Surrey KT13 9RN ☎ 0973 416533

MOORE Jeff (Vla, Pf): 5 Oakridge Drive, London N2 8DF ☎ 020 8442 0324

MOORE Kenneth: 1 Milton Place, Clapton Row, Bourton-on-The Water, Cheltenham Glos GL54 2LA ☎ 01451 820130

MORFEE Ann: 75 New Road, Brentford, Middx TW8 0BA ☎ 020 8560 2920

MORGAN Catherine: 16 Ruston Mews, London W11 1RB ☎ 020 7229 3989, 01306 880669

MORGAN Tomas: Upper Flat, 56 Martell Road, West Dulwich, London SE21 8EE ☎ 020 8473 2815, 0956 916510 mob, 01306 880669

MORIARTY Dean (Gtr, B Gtr): 98 Moore Avenue, Grays, Essex RM20 4XW ☎ 01375 371937, 0839 059991 pager

MORLEY Joanna: 80 Lewis Road, Sidcup, Kent DA14 4NA ☎ 020 8302 6046, 07050 114072, 0142 625 2401

MORRIS Jeremy: 29 Legard Road, London N5 1DE ☎ 020 7354 3281, 020 7503 7693 fax

MORRIS Stephen: Bakers Diary Service ☎ 0432 5232892

MORRISON James (Vla, Man): 98 Copleston Road, London SE15 4AG ☎ 020 7732 5661

MORRISON Joe: 56 Queenswood Rd, Forest Hill, London SE23 2QS ☎ 020 8473 5234

MORRISON Kirsten (Pf, Voc): The Bungalow, Brook Road, London NW2 7NH ☎ 020 8450 1524

MORTON Jonathan (Vla): 1 Raleigh Gardens, Brixton Hill, London SW2 1AB ☎ 020 8674 1678, 0498 656 375

MOSLEY Raymond: 4 The Mallows, Ickenham, Uxbridge, Middx UB10 8BX ☎ 01895 672186

MOWATT Roy (Bq Vln): 62 Fountayne Road, London N16 7DT ☎ 020 8806 0962

MOYES Brian: 25 Southwell Grove Road, Leytonstone, London E11 4PP

MULLIGAN Hazel: 20 Cassland Road, London E9 7AN ☎ 020 8986 7452

MULLIN Daniel (Pf): 4 Barrington Road, Crouch End, London N8 8QS ☎ 020 8348 2617, 0973 178549 mob

MURPHY Aubrey: 58 Oxford Close, Mitcham, Surrey CR4 1OZ ☎ 020 8685 0841, 07970 103523

MURRAY Rona: 35 Danecroft Road, London SE24 9PA ☎ 020 7733 2117

MUSIKANT Jack: 35 Green Acres, Hendon Lane, London N3 3SF ☎ 020 8346 2290

MUTTER Charles (Pf, Vla): 6 Grange Walk, London SE1 3DT ☎ 020 7232 0787

MYALL Timothy: 39B Fairlawn Park, Sydenham, London SE26 5SA ☎ 020 8676 8060

MYERSCOUGH Clarence: 17 Salterton Road, London N7 6BB ☎ 020 7272 2547

MYERSCOUGH Nadia: 68 Denning Point, Commercial Street, London E1 6DJ ☎ 020 7375 2602

NAKIPBEKOVA Elvira: 4 Portsmouth Road, Camberley, Surrey GU15 1LA ☎ 01276 685022

NANCARROW Charles (Vla, Man): 55 Ambler Road, London N4 2QS ☎ 020 7226 5090

NASH Jacqueline (Pf): 148 Craneford Way, Twickenham, Middlesex TW2 7SQ ☎ 020 8744 2011

NEAMAN Yfrah: 11 Chadwell Street, London EC1R 1XD ☎ 020 7837 4455

NEIL Elizabeth-Anne: 157 Devonshire Road, Forest Hill, London SE23 3NB ☎ 020 8291 0356, 070500 39803

NELLER Dawn (Pf): 58 Dolphin Rd, Slough, Berkshire SL1 1TA ☎ 01753 773585

NELSON Claire (Bq Vln): 1St Floor Flat, 71 Perham Road, West Kensington, London W14 9SP ☎ 020 7610 2076

NELSON Everton (Vla, Flt): Flat 2, 188 Camberwell Grove, London SE5 8RJ ☎ 020 7737 0818 & fax, 0973 815263

NEWCOMBE Karin (Vla, Pf): 9 Thompson Way, Shepherds Lane, Rickmansworth, Herts WD3 2GP

NEWLAND Bernard: 137 Balls Pond Road, London N1 4BG ☎ 020 7684 0547

NEWMAN Peter: 66C Cavendish Road, Harringay, London N4 1RS ☎ 020 8341 7993

NICHOLSON Ralph *(Vla, Con, Com)*: 9 Barton Green, Trull, Taunton, Somerset TA3 7NA ☎ 01823 353240

NICHOLSON Vanessa-Mae: 34 Phillimore Walk, London W8 7SA ☎ 020 7937 2869, 020 7938 1983 fax

NICKSON Jennifer: 17 South Cottage Gardens, Chorleywood, Herts WD3 5EH ☎ 01923 282412

NICOLAIDES Kimon: 63 Rowstock Gardens, Camden Road, London N7 0BH ☎ 020 7607 5088, 01306 880669 day

NIEMIRA Stephanie: 82 Bensham Lane, West Croydon, Surrey CR0 2RZ ☎ 020 8689 3760

NIXON Joyce: 20 Denning Road, London NW3 1SU ☎ 020 7431 0998

NOBES Pauline: 18B Christchurch Hill, London NW3 1LG ☎ 020 7794 2998 & fax

NOLAN Charles: 91 Sudbury Court Drive, Harrow, Middx HA1 3SS ☎ 020 8904 7988

NOLAN Charles: 14 Marlborough Avenue, Edgware, Middx HA8 8UH

NOLAN David: 126 Turney Road, Dulwich, London SE21 7JJ ☎ 020 7733 1653

NOLEY: 45 Rockingham Street, London SE1 ☎ 020 7407 4544, 020 8533 1372 day, 0973 815763 mob

NORMAN Helen: 71 Pevensey Road, Forest Gate, London E7 0AR ☎ 020 8519 6491

NORMAN Jane *(Bq Vln, Vla)*: 4 Ludlow Drive, Thame, Oxon OX9 3XS ☎ 01844 261384, 01844 261814 fax

NUTTING Peter: 109 Riefield Road, Eltham, London SE9 2RB ☎ 020 8850 1332

O'BRIEN Melanie *(Bq Vln)*: 21 Anley Road, West Kensington, London W14 0BY ☎ 020 7603 2508, 0973 971322 mob

O'CONNOR Mary *(Vla, Pf)*: 40 Pinkham Mansions, Brooks Road, Chiswick W4 3BQ ☎ 020 8742 0860

O'DELL Ellen *(Bq Vln)*: 2 Clovelly Road, London N8 7RH ☎ 020 8347 8621

O'LEARY Jessica: Flat 5, St Lukes Church, 42 Mayfield Road, London N8 9LP ☎ 020 8347 7341, 020 8533 1372 day, 0956 503084 mob

O'REILLY Brendon: 61 Wandsworth Bridge Road, London SW6 2TB ☎ 020 7736 6714

OFFENBERG Bogdan: Flat 3, 92 Fellows Road, London NW3 3JG ☎ 020 7586 5995

OGDEN David *(Vla)*: Fair Rig, Little Thurlow Green, Thurlow, Suffolk CB9 7JH ☎ 01440 783260, 01306 880669

OLYVER Marianne: 77 Nunnery Street, Castle Hedingham, Essex CO9 3DP ☎ 01787 460296

OSAHN Prabjote: 6 Craneswater, Bath Road, Harlington, Middlesex UB3 5HP ☎ 020 8897 1104

OVENDEN Elizabeth: The Barraclough, Oakham School, Ashwell Road, Oakham, Rutland LE15 6QG ☎ 01572 722606

OVENS Raymond: 10 Recreation Road, Shortlands, Bromley, Kent BR2 0DZ ☎ 020 8464 9059

OWEN Martin: 119 Leslie Road, Leytonstone, London E11 4HF ☎ 020 8556 0676, 01426 251640

OXER Peter: 46 Havelock Road, Wealdstone, Harrow, Middlesex HA3 5SA ☎ 020 8427 7233, 01483 451700

PAGULATOS Antonia: 20 Calvert House, Australia Road, White City, London W12 7QD ☎ 020 8740 7059

PALM Anna *(Voc)*: 30 Knighthead Point, West Ferry Road, Millwall, London E14 8SR ☎ 020 7987 4849

PALMER Geoffrey: Wendela Cottage, Holmbury Hill, Holmbury St Mary, Dorking, Surrey RH5 6NS ☎ 01483 271386

PALMER Rebecca: 23A Bennerley Road, London SW11 6DR ☎ 020 7223 3972, 01306 880669 day

PANTIN Rachel: 113 Ridley Road, London E8 2NH ☎ 020 7249 0121

PARFITT Claire: Holly House, 90 Grove Road, Tiptree, Essex CO5 0JG ☎ 01621 816581

PARKER Hilaryjane: 5 Glebe Court, The Glebe, London SE3 9TH ☎ 020 8318 9127, 0306 880669

PARKER Joanna *(Bq Vln)*: 1 The Laurels, Kingsway Avenue, Woking, Surrey GU21 1NX ☎ 01483 721639

PARKIN Claire: 76 Church Street, Bollington, Macclesfield, Cheshire SK10 5QD ☎ 01625 576328

PARRINGTON Fred: 14 Ballingdon Street, Sudbury, Suffolk CO10 6BT ☎ 01787 74166

PARTRIDGE Bernard: Hailes House, Hailes, Nr Winchcombe, Glos. GL54 5PB ☎ 01242 602379

PARTRIDGE Elizabeth: 30 Selborne Road, London N14 7DH ☎ 020 8886 4950

PASCOE Keith *(Pf, Vla, Con)*: 12 Streatham Common South, London SW16 3BT ☎ 020 8679 0202

PATERSON Helen: 141 Inderwick Road, Crouch End, London N8 9JR ☎ 020 8245 6851, 01306 880 669

PATERSON Jean *(Bq Vln)*: Hawkley Cottage, Highclere Street, Highclere, Newbury, Berkshire RG20 9QB ☎ 01635 255141

PATSTON Edward: Oakmere, 11 Pole Barn Lane, Frinton-on-Sea, Essex CO13 9NJ ☎ 012556 78689

PATTINSON Susannah *(Vla, Tpt)*: Flat 3, Hillside, 6 Egham Hill, Egham, Surrey TW20 0BD ☎ 01784 436132, 0958 295877 mob

PAYNE Leo *(Vla)*: Finmere House, Mere Lane, Little Tingwick, Buckingham MK18 4AG ☎ 01280 847489

PEET Joe B *(B Gtr, Db, Com)*: 130 Hewitt Road, London N8 0BN ☎ 020 8340 7095

PENFOLD Emma: 2 East Common, Harpenden, Herts AL5 1BJ ☎ 01582 712808, 01306 880669 day, 0385 242924 mob

PERCIVALL Mabel: 20 Aultone Way, Sutton, Surrey SM1 3LE ☎ 020 8644 7584

PERKINS Simon: 17 Fairfield Close, Harpenden, Hertfordshire AL5 5RZ ☎ 01582 765322 & fax

PERRETT Rowan *(Bq Vln)*: 26 Orchard Gate, Sudbury, Greenford, Middlesex UB6 0QW ☎ 020 8900 1226

PETERS Alan: 97 Heath Road, Hounslow, Middlesex TW3 2NP ☎ 020 8560 2573

PETERSEN Bjorn: 187A Devonshire Road, London SE23 3NJ ☎ 020 8291 1670

PETITCLERC Alain: Flat 1, 133 Victoria Way, Charlton, London SE7 7NX ☎ 020 8858 7384

PHAROAH Mark *(Vla)*: 16 Ennis Road, Plumstead Common, London SE18 2QT ☎ 020 8854 5736, 01306 880669

PHILLIPS Andrew *(Vla, Pf)*: 61 Bellclose Road, West Drayton, Middlesex UB7 9DF ☎ 01895 421673

PIGGOTT Michael *(Gtr, Man)*: 3A Park Terrace East, Horsham, West Sussex RH13 5DJ ☎ 01403 256064

PIGRAM Elizabeth: 1 Railway Cottages, Holland Lane, Oxted, Surrey RH8 9AZ ☎ 01883 723072, 01883 714481

PITSTOW Helen: 35 Gilpin Green, Harpenden, Hertfordshire AL5 5NP ☎ 01582 766685

PODGER Rachel: 33 Erskine Hill, London NW11 6EY ☎ 020 8458 6037, 020 8458 6037

POLLOCK Andrew: The Old Forge, 49 High Street, Bridge, Canterbury CT4 5LA ☎ 01227 832507

POOK Alan: 63 Wiverton Road, Sydenham, London SE26 5JB ☎ 020 8778 6689

POOL Robert: 15 Hamlet Road, Upper Norwood, London SE19 2AP ☎ 020 8289 1567

POOLE Peter: 19 Peckarmans Wood, Sydenham Hill, Dulwich, London SE26 6RY ☎ 020 8549 1706, 020 8693 3059

POOLEY Alison: 30 Bennett Park, Blackheath, London SE3 9RA ☎ 020 8244 7684, 020 8533 1372

POPLE Peter: 95 Herons Wood, Harlow, Essex CM20 1RS ☎ 01279 433000, 01279 305658

POPLE T M: 95 Herons Wood, Harlow, Essex CM20 1RS ☎ 01279 433000, 020 8533 1372

PORTER Brian: 55 Acacia Grove, New Malden, Surrey KT3 3BU ☎ 020 8942 9775

POUND Megan *(Pf)*: 7 Fernleigh Road, Winchmore Hill, London N21 3AN ☎ 020 8886 5290

PRATLEY Alice (*Pf*): 219 Noel Road, West Acton, London W3 0JL ☎ 020 8932 4911, 0966 262385

PREECE Deborah: 24 Maclean Road, Forest Hill, London SE23 1PD ☎ 020 8699 4992

PRESCOTT Raymond: 192 Elgar Avenue, Surbiton, Surrey KT5 9JY ☎ 020 8399 5146

PRICE Arthur: Copper Beeches, Waterend Lane, Redbourn, St. Albans, Herts AL3 7JZ ☎ 01582 794896, 0973 538355 mob, 01582 794511

PRICE Geoffrey: Sussex Cottage, 4 The Spinney, Epsom Downs, Surrey KT18 5QU ☎ 017373 54665

PRING Martin: 7 Cricklade Court, Nailsea, Bristol BS19 2ST ☎ 01275 858529, 0370 302375

PROTHEROE Anthony: 13 Lennard Road, Bromley, Kent BR2 8LN ☎ 020 8402 5183

PRYCE Nicholas: 9 Oswin Street, Kennington, London SE11 4TF ☎ 020 7735 8056

PULSFORD Angela: 10 Dalkeith Road, Harpenden, Herts AL5 5PW ☎ 01582 769278

PURNELL Donald (*Org, Pf, Clst*): 38 Chase Road, London N14 4EU ☎ 020 8886 3948

PURNOMOHADI Tri (*Gtr*): 29 The Greenway, Uxbridge, Middlesex UB8 2PJ ☎ 01895 257090, 0402 336578 mob

PUTTERILL Sylvia: 60 Esmond Road, Chiswick, London W4 1JF ☎ 020 8994 3046

QUINN Sarah: 105 Woodcock Hill, Kenton, Harrow, Middlesex HA3 0JJ ☎ 020 8907 2112, 0958 406 447

RAINEY Alyson: 21 Wilton Place, Gayton Road, Harrow Middlesex, Middlesex HA1 2HJ ☎ 020 8933 1820, 0956 387758

RAKOWSKI Maciej: 51 Tennyson Avenue, Twickenham, Middx TW1 4QX ☎ 020 8892 5035

RANDALL Rebecca: 44 Rosecroft Drive, Watford, Herts WD1 3JQ ☎ 01923 223 581

RASMUSSEN Jette: Flat 5, 7 Heathfield Park, Willesden Green, London NW2 5JE

RAYBOULD Clare (*Vla*): 7 Theatre Street, Battersea, London SW11 5NE ☎ 020 7223 2773, 0973 631242 mob

RAYFIELD Harriet: 14 Highview Road, Ealing, London W13 0HB ☎ 020 8566 8767 & fax

REA Jake: 39 Torrington Gardens, London N11 2AB ☎ 020 8361 9249

READ Christine: 123 Redston Road, Hornsey, London N8 7HG ☎ 020 8348 4938

REAGAN Samantha: 58D Vanburgh Park, Blackheath, London SE3 7JQ ☎ 020 8853 2365, 07957 367774 mob

REDGATE Roger: 29 Ladas Road, West Norwood, London SE27 0UP ☎ 020 8670 5761 & fax

REED Adrian: 6 Drake Road, London SE4 1QH ☎ 020 8692 7529

REES Jonathan: 42 Railway Side, London SW13 0PN ☎ 020 8392 8980, 01306 880669

REID Caroline (*Pf*): 20 Thorn Close, Bromley, Kent BR2 8DH ☎ 020 8468 7794

REID Edmund: 6 Angel Hill Court, Sutton, Surrey SM1 3EE ☎ 020 8644 1579

REID William: Yew Tree Cottage, Post Office Road, Knodishall, Saxmundham, Suffolk IP17 1UG ☎ 01728 830881

REMNANT Mary (*Pf, Rec*): 15 Fernshaw Road, Chelsea, London SW10 0TG ☎ 020 7352 5181

RENWICK Charles: 7 Southwold Mansions, Widley Road, Maida Vale, London W9 2LE ☎ 020 7289 9488

RENWICK Clare: 83 Woodland Rise, London N10 3UN ☎ 020 8883 2334

RETALLICK Robert: 54 Kings Road, London SW19 8QW ☎ 020 8542 0617

RHODES Ian: 8 Tower Mews, Ashenden Road, London E5 0ES ☎ 020 8533 7390

RICHARDS Frances: 11 Alexandra Gardens, Knaphill, Woking, Surrey GU21 2DG ☎ 01483 486633, 020 8549 1706

RICHARDS Jack: 132 Hammeison House, The Bishops Ave, London N2 0BE ☎ 020 8905 5149

RICHMOND David: 10 Woodford Place, Wembley, Middx HA9 8TE ☎ 020 8908 1924

RICHTER Mariette (*Pf*): Windrush Cottage, 2 Chilswell Path, South Hinksey, Oxon OX1 5AP ☎ 01865 730242

RIDDELL Duncan: Harvieston, Hollybank Road, Hook Heath, Woking, Surrey GU22 0JP ☎ 01483 762524

RIDDOCH Christina: 7 Beach Street, Deal, Kent CT14 7AH

ROBERTS Andrew: 12A Pellatt Road, London SE22 9JA ☎ 020 8693 2314, 020 8549 1706

ROBERTS Edward: 8 Ashbourne Rise, Orpington, Kent BR6 9PZ ☎ 01689 851267 & fax, 01306 880669

ROBERTS Roland: 46A Fairlawn Grove, London W4 6EH ☎ 020 8987 8611, 020 8995 5581

ROBERTS Rosemary: Paddock House, 1 Copse End, Camberley, Surrey GU15 2BP ☎ 01276 29875

ROBERTS Winifred: The Long House, Arkley Lane, Barnet, Herts EN5 3JR ☎ 020 8449 0303

ROBERTSON Stuart: 86 Capri Road, Addiscombe, Surrey CR0 6LF ☎ 020 8654 3364

ROBINSON Helen: Flat 6, 26 Minster Road, London NW2 3RB ☎ 020 8452 7937

ROBINSON William (*Gtr, Kbds, Vla, Cel*): 47 Dahomey Road, London SW16 6NB ☎ 020 8677 9980

ROBSON Paul: 95 Wolfington Road, London SE27 0RH ☎ 020 8670 9821

RODGERS Glenda: 16 Gladesmore Road, Stamford Hill, London N15 6TB ☎ 020 8809 3395

ROGERS William (*Vla*): Ripple Sands, Beadon Road, Salcombe, South Devon TQ8 8JT ☎ 01548 843325

ROMERO Cecilia: 27 The Avenue, West Wickham, Kent BR4 0DX ☎ 020 8777 7459

RONAYNE John: 44 Vineyard Hill Road, London SW19 7JH ☎ 020 8946 5557

RONCHETTI Viviane (*Vla*): 7 Scotgrove, Pinner, Middx HA5 4RT ☎ 020 8428 7174

ROSEBERRY Margaret: 119 Clifden Road, Hackney, London E5 0LW ☎ 020 8985 7361

ROSEN Joe: 33 Tenterden Gardens, London NW4 1TG ☎ 020 8203 3814

ROSENBERG Norman: 15 Farm Avenue, Cricklewood Lane, London NW2 2EE ☎ 020 8452 3857

ROSENBERG Sylvia: 98 Riverside Drive, Appt. 12D, New York, NY 10024, USA

ROSS Jayne: 29 Fitzjohn Avenue, Chipping Barnet, Herts EN5 2HH ☎ 020 8449 4237

ROSSI Eric (*A Sax*): Address Unknown

ROSSI Lawrence: 50 Lillie Road, Fulham, London SW6 1TN ☎ 020 7385 7037

ROTH David: 16 Oman Avenue, London NW2 6BG ☎ 020 8452 7376

ROTHSTEIN Jack: 4 Chelmsford Square, London NW10 3AR ☎ 020 8459 1475

ROWE Elizabeth: 219 Noel Road, West Alton, London W3 0JL ☎ 020 8932 4911, 0973 685334

ROWLINSON Stephen: 13 Mortimer Terrace, Off Wesleyan Place, London NW5 1LH ☎ 020 7284 1737

ROZSA Suzanne: 24 Redington Gardens, London NW3 7RX ☎ 020 7794 9898

RUMSEY Michael: 81 Rounton Road, Waltham Abbey, Essex EN9 3AP ☎ 01992 761952

RUSH Celeste (*Vla*): Flat 1, 133 Victoria Way, Charlton, London SE7 7NX ☎ 020 8858 7384

RUSHWORTH Abigail: 83 King Henrys Road, London NW3 3QU ☎ 020 7722 8368

RUSMANIS Margot: Wycombe End House, Wycombe End, Beaconsfield, Bucks HP9 1NB ☎ 01494 673192

RUSSELL John (*Vla, Pf*): 9 Marine Gardens, Selsey, Chichester, Sussex PO20 0LJ ☎ 01243 604376

RUSSELL Lucy (*Bq Vln, Pf, Ob*): 9 Ritchings Avenue, London E17 6LD ☎ 020 8521 7657

RUTLAND Louis: 18 Stratton Avenue, Wallington, Surrey SM6 9LL ☎ 020 8647 5984

RYAN Cliodhna (Pf): 5 Foster Lane, Priests Court, Cheapside, London EC2V 6HH ☎ 020 7606 1103

RYAN John (Vla): 92 Hallowell Road, Northwood, Middlesex HA6 1DS ☎ 01923 821494

RYE Anthony: 23 Thorney Hedge Road, Chiswick, London W4 5SB ☎ 020 8747 0939

SADLER Mary (Pf): Ground Floor Flat, 3 Hillfield Park, Muswell Hill, London N10 ☎ 020 8444 3723

SALINGER Anne (Vla): 4 Corby Crescent, Oakwood, Enfield, Middlesex EN2 7JT ☎ 020 8363 3421, 0973 361673

SALMON Godfrey (Md): 63 Harland Road, London SE12 0JB ☎ 020 8851 6534, 01306 880669

SALPETER Max: 26 Long Lodge Drive, Walton-on-Thames, Surrey KT12 3BY ☎ 01932 220559

SALTER Robert: 35 Cecile Park, London N8 9AX ☎ 020 8340 1542, 0976 428515 mob

SAMPSON Jeremy: 14 High Street, North Crawley, Bucks MK16 9LH ☎ 01234 391671

SAMUEL Jill: Beechwood, 66 Harrow Lane, Maidenhead, Berkshire SL6 7PA ☎ 01628 782806

SANKEY Claire-Louise: 193 Springbank Road, Hither Green, London SE13 6ST ☎ 020 8461 1340, 0802 644220 mob

SANSOM Claire: 3 Connor Street, London E9 7LG ☎ 020 8533 3909

SAUNDERS Harry (Vla): 31 Rose Street, Tonbridge, Kent TN9 2BN ☎ 01732 358896

SAUNDERS Penelope: 79 Foyle Road, London SE3 7RQ ☎ 020 8858 2543

SAWYERS Philip: 55 Erlanger Road, New Cross, London SE14 5TF ☎ 020 7639 8985

SAX Sidney: 7 Lowlands, Eton Avenue, London NW3 3EJ ☎ 020 7722 1078

SAXL Julian: 34 Stuart Road, Wimbledon Park, London SW19 8DH ☎ 020 8947 6687

SCHAY Eva: 2 Nedahall Court, Golders Green Crescent, London NW11 8LB ☎ 020 8458 4057

SCHLENTHER Deborah (Pf): 13 Caversham Avenue, London N13 4LL ☎ 020 8886 4694

SCHOFIELD Catherine: 12 Haslemere Avenue, Ealing, London W13 9UJ ☎ 020 8579 4624

SCHWEINBERGER Silvia: 2B Tulsmere Road, London SE27 9EJ ☎ 020 8488 2350, 0958 714136 mob

SCOTT Farran: Garden Flat, 9 Lyndhurst Road, London NW3 5PX ☎ 020 7794 6877

SCOTT Rebbecca: 9 Bryon Hill Road, Harrow-on-the-Hill, Middlesex HA2 0JE ☎ 020 8423 0067

SCOTT Shirley: 31 Chiltern Road, Hitchin, Herts SG4 9PJ ☎ 01462 457731

SCRIVENER Matthew ☎ 07957 430714 mob, 01306 500011 day

SEATON Sylvia (Pf): 135 Dunlace Road, Homerton, London E5 0NG ☎ 020 8986 6316

SEDGWICK Prunella: 26 Sutton Road, Muswell Hill, London N10 1HE ☎ 020 8883 7524, 01306 880669

SELLSCHOP Ingrid: 47C Bounds Green Road, Wood Green, London N22 4HB ☎ 020 8881 7370, 01306 880669

SEWART Charles (Vla): 22 Rommany Road, Gipsy Hill, London SE27 9PX ☎ 020 8244 8177, 0850 154673

SHACKELTON Louise: 22 Chalcot Square, London NW1 8YA ☎ 020 7586 .2117

SHAROVA Alla: Flat 2, 81 Shepherds Hill, Highgate, London N6 5RG ☎ 020 8340 5207

SHARPE Nigel: 51 Princes Plain, Bromley, Kent BR2 8LF ☎ 020 8325 9634

SHAVE Jacqueline (Pf): 12 Park Avenue, Peper Harow, Godalming, Surrey GU8 6BA ☎ 01483 414740

SHAVE Katherine: The Cedars, Church Road, Lyminge, Kent CT18 8HZ ☎ 020 8854 9806

SHAW Briony (Vla): Clockhouse, Hartshill Wharf, Atherstone Road, Nuneaton, Warks. CV10 0TB ☎ 024 7639 3629

SHEEN Celia (Theramin): Jingles, Parkfields, Oxshott, Surrey KT22 0PW ☎ 0137284 2862

SHELDON Glen: 104 Nelson Road, Crouch End, London N8 9RT ☎ 020 8348 9485, 01306 500011 day

SHELVER Graham (Citt, Man, Bod): 110 Warrington Road, Paddock Wood, Tonbridge, Kent TN12 6JR ☎ 01892 832936

SHENTON David (Pf, Bq Vln, Vla, Com): Flat 1, 180 Gloucester Place, London NW1 6DS ☎ 020 7724 5041, 0956 430342 mob

SHERMAN Les (A Sax, Clt): 13, Elliot Close, Oakington Avenue, Wembley HA9 8AJ ☎ 020 8908 4344

SHORROCK Rebecca: 64 Godley Road, London SW18 3HD ☎ 020 8333 1487, 0976 702991 mob

SIENKIEWICZ Yvonne: 3 Copeland Road, Walthamstow, London E17 9DB ☎ 020 8923 1495

SILLITO Kenneth: 13 Wordsworth Walk, London NW11 6AU ☎ 020 8458 1476

SILLS Helen: 22 Peaks Hill, Purley, Surrey CR8 3JE ☎ 020 8660 7204

SILVER Geoffrey: 111 East Dulwich Grove, London SE22 8PU ☎ 020 8693 6235, 0973 626 180 mob

SILVERSTONE Phil: Elstree Lawns Nursing Home, Barnet Lane, Elstree, Herts WD6 3RD ☎ 020 8207 3255

SILVESTER Thomas (Vla, B Gtr, Kbds)

SIMON Richard (Vla): 309 West 104th St., Apt. 4B, New York, NY 10025, USA

SINGLETON Emlyn (Com, Arr): c/o 20 Kingly Street, London W1R 5LB ☎ 020 7434 4313, 0831 715158 mob, 01306 880669 day

SINGLETON Julia: Garden Flat, 48 Carysfort Road, London N8 8RB ☎ 020 8341 7189

SKEAPING Lucie (Reb, Vielle): 19 Patshull Road, London NW5 2JX ☎ 020 7485 3957, 020 7267 2957

SKEWES Hilary (Cel): 40A Norland Square, London W11 4PZ ☎ 020 7243 3881, 0973 968599 mob

SLADE Roy (Tbn, Vla): 51 Shinglewell Road, Erith, Kent DA8 1NF ☎ 01322 31944

SLANY Sonia: 100 Village Road, Enfield, Middlesex EN1 2EX ☎ 0973 159563 mob, 020 8360 4975, 01306 880669 day

SLATER Carol: 49 Exeter Road, London NW2 4SE ☎ 020 8452 6843

SLATER Ruth: 231B Blackstock Road, London N5 2LL ☎ 020 7704 1330

SLOAN Alan: 20 Holroyd Road, Claygate, Surrey KT10 0LG ☎ 01372 465807

SMALLS Julie E: 8 Abbott Close, Hampton, Middlesex TW12 3XR ☎ 020 8941 2406

SMART Basil (Pf): Suttons, Brown Bread Street, Ashburnham, East Sussex TN33 9NX ☎ 01424 892410

SMITH Amanda: 165 Brakespeares Road, London SE4 1UA ☎ 020 8691 7683

SMITH Andrew James Thomas: 277 Jersey Road, Osterley, Middlesex TW7 4RF ☎ 020 8568 7262

SMITH Beverley: 58 Medesenge Way, Palmers Green, London N13 6DZ ☎ 020 8889 6739

SMITH Brian (Bq Vln, Cntrc): 105 Woodgrange Avenue, London N12 0PT ☎ 020 8445 4091, 01306 880669

SMITH Deirdre (Pf): 2 Doune Gardens, Glasgow G20 6DG ☎ 0973 626062, 0141 945 3061

SMITH Esther: 49 Perry Street, Crayford, Kent DA1 4RB

SMITH Francesca: 10 Scawfell Street, London E2 8NG ☎ 020 7729 5850

SMITH Hazel: 23 Westfield Terrace, Longford, Gloucester GL2 9BA ☎ 01452 522379

SMITH Judith (Vla, Pf): 125 Haydon Park Road, London SW19 8JH ☎ 020 8542 5043, 0976 282497 mob

SMITH Katie: Ivy Cottages, 44 Several Avenue, Chesham, Bucks HP5 3EL ☎ 01494 775577

SMITH Maureen: 8 Heath Close, London NW11 7DX ☎ 020 8458 4827

SMITH Pauline (Bq Vln): 51 Oakhurst Grove, East Dulwich, London SE22 9AH ☎ 020 8693 0581

SMITH Roger: 5 The Avenue, Tonbridge, Kent TN9 1JG ☎ 01732 355229

SMITH Sidney *(Vla, Sax, Clt)*: 20 Coburg Close, Greencoat Place, London SW1 1DX ☎ 020 7828 9241

SMITH Simon: Burnside Cottage, Munden Road, Dane End, Ware, Herts SG12 0LP ☎ 01920 438165

SNELL Brent *(Con)*: 29 Nelgarde Road, London SE6 4TA ☎ 020 8690 6048

SNELL Juliet: 99 Hampden Road, Hornsey, London N8 0HU ☎ 020 8341 4877

SNEYD Will *(Fo Fdl, Vla)*: 3 Sovereign Mews, Pearson Street, Hackney, London E2 8ER ☎ 020 7729 5861

SNOW Ursula: Forge House, River Street, Westbourne Nr.Emsworth, Hants PO10 8TG ☎ 01243 375841

SOLAREK Marina *(Pf)*: 30 Chandos Road, Willesden Green, London NW2 4LU ☎ 020 8208 0277, 020 8549 1706

SOLODCHIN Galina: Mashay Hall, Belchamp Road, Little Yeldham, Halstead, Essex CO9 4JY ☎ 01787 237284, 020 8549 1706 day, 01787 237970 fax

SOLOMON Anne: 73 Staverton Road, London NW2 5HA ☎ 07931 955268

SOLOMONS Derek: 33 Foundry Street, Brighton, Sussex BN1 4AT ☎ 01273 673327

SPECK Linda: 32 Ernest Gardens, London W4 3QU ☎ 020 8995 5896

SPENCER Jayne: 16C Cecile Park, Crouch End, London N8 9AS ☎ 020 8340 7647, 0973 720421 mob

SPENCER Michael *(Cntrc)*: Flat 4, 20 Gloucester Drive, Finsbury Park, London N4 2LN ☎ 020 8809 6624

SPENDLOVE Beth: Oxford House, 2 Lexden Road, Colchester, Essex CO3 3NE ☎ 01206 576686

SPIER Irene: 69 Golders Gardens, London NW11 9BS ☎ 020 8455 8394

SPURRELL Elizabeth: 16 Berestede Road, Hammersmith, London W6 9NP ☎ 020 8748 9327

ST GEORGE Eleanor: 65 Holdenhurst Avenue, London N12 0HY ☎ 020 8346 8273

ST JOHN WRIGHT Robert: Four Aces, Chapel Lane, Pirbright, Surrey GU24 0JY ☎ 01483 476226

STAIT Anya: 47 Ruskin Walk, London SE24 9NA ☎ 020 7737 4938

STANDAGE Simon: 106 Hervey Road, Blackheath, London SE3 8BX ☎ 020 8319 3372

STANLEY Albert *(Vla)*: Address Unknown

STANLEY Helen B: 60 Julian Avenue, London W3 9JF ☎ 020 8248 6328 & fax

STAPLES Julie *(Pf)*: 92 Chatham Road, London SW11 6HG ☎ 020 7228 3901

STARKE Gordon *(Clt, Rec, Sax)*: 25 Tormount Road, London SE18 1QD ☎ 020 8473 7817

STARKE Jean *(Vla)*: 25 Tormount Road, London SE18 1QD ☎ 020 8473 7817

STAVELEY Colin: 4 Homersham Road, Norbiton, Kingston-on-Thames KT1 3PN ☎ 020 8546 8765

STEADMAN Jack: 2 Parc Eglos, Helston, Cornwall TR13 8UP ☎ 01326 562744

STEPHENSON Anne *(Voc)*: 5 Haddington Court, Tarves Way, Greenwich, London SE10 9QR ☎ 020 8355 6036

STEVENS Ashley *(Vla)*: 50C Granville Park, Lewisham, London SE13 7DX ☎ 0973 834365

STEVENS Dayle: 34 Arnison Road, East Molesey, Surrey KT8 9JP ☎ 020 8941 3974

STEVENS Peter *(Vla)*: 10 The Rise, Ewell, Epsom, Surrey KT17 1LY ☎ 020 8393 2579

STEWART Julia *(Vla)*: Ashlea Cottage, 50 Dollis Avenue, London N3 1BU ☎ 020 8343 1337

STEWART Simon *(B Gtr, Man, Gtr)*: First Floor, 1 Heyford Terrace, Vauxhall, London SW8 1XT ☎ 020 7820 8914

STEWART Stephen *(Pf)*: 54 Ronalds Road, London N5 IXG ☎ 020 7609 6623, 01306 880669

STOREY Andrew ☎ 0976 329074 mob

STRANGE Alison: 9 Cambridge Road, Carshalton, Surrey SM5 3QP ☎ 020 8643 0104, 0585 634127, 01306 880669

STRANGE Jonathan: 113 Park Lane, Wembley, Middx HA9 7SF ☎ 020 8902 2572, 01306 880669

STRATTON Craig *(Pf)*: 39 Ledborough Lane, Beaconsfield, Bucks HP9 2DB ☎ 0149 467 4114, 0149 467 0104

STRAWSON Virginia *(Pf, Accom)*: 17 Cecilia Road, London E8 2EP ☎ 020 7249 6519

STREATFEILD Sarah: 62 Fountayne Road, London N16 7DT ☎ 020 8806 0962

STURDY Adrienne: High View, Milton Avenue, Badgers Mount, Sevenoaks, Kent TN14 7AU ☎ 01959 534459

STURDY Kathleen: 3 Woodville Court, Woodville Road, London NW11 9TR ☎ 020 8458 2983

STURT Hilary *(Vla)*: 10 Vyner Court, Rossington Street, London E5 8SF ☎ 020 8806 8520, 0881 830 994 pager

SUTTIE Alexander *(Vla)*: 3 Tilsworth Road, Beaconsfield, Bucks HP9 1TR ☎ 01494 675168, 0468 936058 mob

SVENHEDEN Joakim: Flat 1, 156 Haverstock Hill, London NW3 2AT ☎ 020 7483 0453

SWAN Jenny: 1 Strafford Gate, Potters Bar, Herts EN6 1PW ☎ 01707 655896

SWEENEY Nicola: 6 Lyttleton Road, Hornsey, London N8 0QB ☎ 020 8881 2612

SWIFT Thomas: 10 Eversley Avenue, Wembley Park, Middx HA9 9JZ ☎ 020 8904 2959

T Johnny *(E Vln, B Gtr, Kbds, Voc)* ☎ 020 7637 1357, 0956 816 118, 020 7637 1357

TANFIELD Peter

TARLTON Gillian *(Vla)*: Stable Cottage, 116A Weir Road, Balham, London SW12 0ND ☎ 020 8673 6427

TAWEEL Neville: 56 Cottenham Drive, London SW20 0ND ☎ 020 8946 0388, 020 8549 1706

TAYLOR Adrian: 1 Sylvan Road, Wellington, Somerset TA21 8EG ☎ 01823 667805

TAYLOR Charles: Address Unknown

TAYLOR Imogen ☎ 020 8947 4321

TAYLOR Marilyn *(Ea Stg)*: 11 Arbour Close, Fetcham, Leatherhead, Surrey KT22 9DZ ☎ 01372 378481 & fax

TAYLOR Morris: 2 York Court, Aldermans Hill, London N13 4QG ☎ 020 8882 1494

TEAR Julian: 62 Annandale Road, Greenwich, London SE10 0DB ☎ 020 8858 8596 & fax

TELFER Ian *(Ctna)*: 49 Cavendish Road, London N4 1RP ☎ 020 8341 5595

TELLEM Geraint: 157 Devonshire Road, Forest Hill, London SE23 3NB

TENNANT Sophia: 12 Morpeth Mansions, Morpeth Terrace, London SW1P 1ER ☎ 020 7834 6597, 01426 281 270 pager, 020 8533 1372 day

TEO-WA *(Voc)*: 52 Crofdown Road, London NW5 1EN

TEPPICH Miriam *(Pf)*: 7 Meadow Gardens, Edgware, Middlesex HA8 9LQ ☎ 020 8958 5826

THACKER Louise: Flat 310, The Colonnades, Porchester Square, Bayswater, London W2 6AU ☎ 020 7723 8022

THEAKER Roy *(Vla)*: 53A Foxberry Road, London SE24 2SR, 0976 749771

THOM Jayne: 68 Puller Road, High Barnet, Herts EN5 4HD ☎ 020 8449 3009

THOMAS Alun: Flat 11, 66-68 St Michaels Road, Westcliff, Bournemouth, Dorset BH2 5DZ ☎ 01202 314025 & fax

THOMAS David: 6 Marsworth Avenue, Pinner, Middx HA5 4UB ☎ 020 8428 9990

THOMAS Francis *(A Sax, T Sax)*: 10, Albert Road, Hythe, Kent. CT21 6BP ☎ 01303 265530

THOMAS Kenneth *(Gtr, Man, Bjo)*: 74 Vivian Avenue, London NW4 3XG ☎ 020 8202 4935

THOMAS Michael: 6 Baden Road, Crouch End, London N8 7RJ ☎ 020 8341 3930

THOMAS Ronald: Unit 1, 54A Darling Point Road, Darling Point, Sydney 2027 NSW, Australia

THOMAS-MURLIS Lexey: 22 Summerfield, West Farm Avenue, Ashted, Surrey KT21 2LF ☎ 01372 276675

THOMPSON Cathy: 195 Amyand Park Road, St. Margarets, Twickenham TW1 3HN ☎ 020 8744 9460

THOMPSON Clare: 91A Heathwood Gardens, Charlton, London SE7 8ET ☎ 020 8316 1933, 01306 880669

THOMPSON Karen: 93 Ravenshaw Street, West Hampstead, London NW6 1NP ☎ 020 7431 4616

THOMPSON Rosalind (Pf): Barnyard House, 6 Harpers Lane, Great Linford, Milton Keynes MK14 5BA ☎ 01908 694996

THORMAHLEN Wiebke (Vla): 16 Leigh Street, London WC1H 9EW ☎ 020 7387 6911

THORN Jennifer: 80D Cambridge Gardens, London W10 6HS ☎ 020 8969 9403

THORP William (Vadam, Bq Vln, Vla, Arr): 34 Milman Road, London NW6 6EG ☎ 020 8960 7322

THURGOOD Andrew: Honeysuckle Cottage, 25 Paddockhall Road, Haywards Heath, West Sussex RH16 1HQ ☎ 01444 413432

THURSTON Jennifer: 99 Wellington Road, Wanstead, London E11 2AS ☎ 020 8530 3250 & fax, 01306 880669 day, 0976 266734 mob

TILCH Karen: 53 The Drive, London NW11 9UJ ☎ 020 8209 0867

TILLEY Sarah: 26B Tressillian Road, London SE4 1YB

TIMONEY Therese: 40 St Marys Crescent, Osterley, Middx TW7 4NA ☎ 020 8560 5220

TOMBLING Christopher: 42 Michael Cliffe House, Skinner St, Finsbury Estate, London EC1R 0LN ☎ 020 7278 3546, 0956 269354 mob

TOMS Thomas (Pf): 3 Chalfont Court, 34 Northwick Park Rd, Harrow, Middx HA1 2ES ☎ 020 8424 0056

TOO Sarah: 30 Crown Lodge, 12 Elystan Street, London SW3 3PP ☎ 020 7584 4674, 020 7589 6388 fax

TORCHINSKY Yuri: 14 Ellery Road, Upper Norwood, London SE19 3QG ☎ 020 8653 6660

TOWNLEY Alison: 'Woodview', 6 Lower Mount Pleasant, Sharpstone, Freshford, Avon BA3 6DB ☎ 01225 723629

TOWNSEND Joe (Gtr): Flat 12 Inner City House, 165-169 Lewisham Way, London SE4 6QP ☎ 020 8694 1663, 0370 771719

TOWSE David: 47 Abbotswood Road, London SW16 1AJ ☎ 020 8769 7673

TRAEGER Stuart: 4 Westlands Court, Bridge Road, East Molesey, Surrey KT8 9HQ ☎ 020 8783 1364, 020 8783 1829

TRAFFORD Julian: 38 Breakspeare Road, Abbots Langley, Watford, Herts WD5 0EP ☎ 01923 446754, 01306 880669

TRAUBE Sally (Voc): 40 Oakwood Court, London W14 8JX ☎ 020 7603 6821, 0973 185362 mob

TRENTHAM Julie (Pf): 30 Imperial Close, North Harrow, Middlesex HA2 7LN ☎ 020 8866 4412

TUBAN Joseph: 27 Langley Park, London NW7 2AA ☎ 020 8959 4989

TUCKER Mardyah: 8 Charles Simmons House, Margery Street, Islington, London WC1X 0HP ☎ 020 7837 0961, 0802 986 530

TURNER Julia: 69 Whitehouse Avenue, Borehamwood, Herts WD6 1HA ☎ 020 8953 7185

TURNER Katharine: 91 Elmgrove Road, Harrow, Middlesex HA1 2QW ☎ 020 8863 7915

TURNER Rachel (Cel): 70 Pearcroft Road, London E11 4DR ☎ 020 8231 3255, 07970 166697

TURNER Rebecca: 62 Tycehurst Hill, Loughton, Essex IG10 1DA ☎ 020 8508 1255

TURNER Shirley: 13 St.Peters Square, London W6 9AB ☎ 020 8563 2075, 020 8533 1372 day

TURNLUND Martin (Vla): 17 Balmoral Road, Gillingham, Kent ME7 4BY ☎ 01634 307187, 0973 627753 mob, 01634 310090

TYSALL Paula: 2 Ashington Court, Westwood Hill, Sydenham, London SE26 6BN ☎ 020 8778 5955, 01306 880669

UENO Michiko: 10 St Margarets Drive, Twickenham, Middlesex TW1 1QN ☎ 020 8891 2174

UNDERHILL Jennifer (Pf): 64B Station Road, Harrow, Middlesex HA1 2SQ ☎ 020 8863 6719, 01277 626661

UNDERWOOD Brian: Flat 2, 81 Shepherds Hill, London N6 5RG ☎ 020 8340 5207

UNSWORTH Meryl (Vla): Rosemary Cottage, Chapel Road, Old Newton, Stowmarket Suffolk IP14 4PP ☎ 01449 673223

URBAINCZYK Tony: 63 St Andrews Road, Malvern, Worcs WR14 3PT ☎ 01684 562433

VAANDRAGER Neti: 101 Mellitus Street, London W12 0AU ☎ 020 8749 9803

VALENTE Anthony: 8 Green Court Road, Petts Wood, Kent BR5 1QW ☎ 66 29870

VAN DER WERFF Rosemary: 56 College House, Nethercote Road, Tackley, Oxford OX5 3AT ☎ 0186983 273, 01869 331273

VAN LOEN Shelley: 104 Valley Road, Streatham, London SW16 2XR ☎ 020 8677 1500, 020 8664 7183 fax

VAN MENTS Elizabeth: 64 Linden Road, Hampton, Middx TW12 2JB ☎ 020 8979 8112, 0589 655535

VANDERSPAR Fiona: 309 West 104St, Flat 4B, New York, NYC 10025, USA

VASSEUR Sylvain: Flat 5, College Heights, 246-252 St John Street, London EC1V 4PH ☎ 020 7251 0016

VAUGHAN Kerry: 51 Palace Gardens, Buckhurst Hill, Essex IG9 5PQ ☎ 020 8506 2252, 0973 701 511

VINCE Carina: 13 River Court, Station Road, Sawbridgeworth, Herts CM21 9PX ☎ 01279 726 960

VOIGT Sarah (Pf): 12 B Delamere Road, Wimbledon, London SW20 8PS ☎ 020 8947 3455

VOSS Katrin: 39 Keighley Close, London N7 9RT ☎ 020 7700 3162

WACHSMANN Philipp: 3 Beverley Path, London SW13 0AL ☎ 020 8876 0429

WADE Richard (Bq Vln, Vla, Pf): 10A Heathfield Park, London NW2 5JD ☎ 1081 459 6199, 0976 238902 mob

WAKEFIELD Audrey: Olin, 63 Foxdell Way, Chalfont St Peter, Gerrards Cross, Bucks SL9 0PL ☎ 01494 872487

WAKEFIELD Jeffrey: Olin, 63 Foxdell Way, Chalfont St Peter, Gerrards Cross, Bucks SL9 0PL ☎ 01494 872487

WAKEHAM Daphne: Flat 1, 12 Marine Road, Walmer, Deal, Kent CT14 7DN ☎ 01304 369597

WAKELAM Susan: 95 Chobham Road, Sunningdale, Ascot, Berkshire SL5 0HQ ☎ 01344 624192

WALKER Frances (Pf): 55 Coleshill Road, Teddington, Middlesex TW11 0LL ☎ 020 8977 1901

WALLACE Bridget: 10 The Rise, Ewell, Epsom, Surrey KT1 1LY ☎ 020 8393 2579

WALLACE Derek (Clt): 91, Moordown, London SE18 3NA ☎ 020 8856 8384

WALLFISCH Elizabeth: 24 Versailles Road, London SE20 8AX

WALSH Howard: 30 Marks Avenue, Ongar, Essex CM5 9AY ☎ 01277 365694

WALTERS Helena (Pf): 38 Aylesbury Street, London NW10 0AS ☎ 020 8208 2748

WALTERS Louise (Voc, Pf, Flt): Flat 1, 39 Troutbeck Road, London SE14 5PN ☎ 020 7652 2687

WALTON Andrew: 10 Hillside Gardens, Barnet, Herts EN5 2NJ ☎ 020 8440 0574, 020 8440 0632

WALTON Mark: 44 Hermead Road, London W9 3NQ ☎ 0930 714517

WALTON Sarah: 92 Norbury Crescent, Norbury, London SW16 4LA ☎ 020 8764 2663

WARBURTON Jillian (Vla): 3 Purley Bury Avenue, Purley, Surrey CR8 1JE ☎ 020 8660 0730

WARD Helen: 159 More Close, St Pauls Court, West Kensington, London W14 9BW ☎ 01483 723644

WARD Matthew: Top Flat, 112 Belsize Road, Swiss Cottage, London NW6 4BG ☎ 020 7372 2633, 0777 5521207

WARD Nicholas: 34 Long Lane, London N3 2PU ☎ 020 8922 0961

WARREN Wilson Gregory: 25 Cranbrook Park, London N22 5NA ☎ 020 8881 0609

WARREN-GREEN Christopher: Collins Farm, Teh Vachery Estate, Nr Cranleigh, Surrey GU6 8EF ☎ 01483 274668, 01483 274668

WASTNAGE Patrick: 38 Midland Terrace, Cricklewood, London NW2 6QH ☎ 020 8450 8419

WATERHOUSE Celia *(Vla)*: 111 Talbot Road, London W11 2AT ☎ 020 7243 1123, 020 7402 4986

WATERWORTH Kate: 22A Broomhill Road, Woodford Green, Essex IG8 9HA ☎ 020 8559 2357

WATKINS Julia: 53 Lemsford Village, Lemsford, Welwyn Garden City, Herts AL8 7TR ☎ 01707 331367

WATKINSON Andrew *(Vla)*: 8 The Quadrangle, Welwyn Garden City, Herts AL8 6SG ☎ 01707 336422

WATSON Neil: 40 Wentworth Avenue, London N3 1YL ☎ 020 8371 9554

WATTS Joanna: Flat 3, 19 Gleneagle Road, Streatham, London SW16 6AY ☎ 020 8677 4286, 0973 289377

WEBER Alwin: 81 St Edmunds Drive, Stanmore, Middx HA7 2AT ☎ 020 8427 0800

WEEKES Donald: 164 Broom Road, Teddington, Middx TW11 9PQ ☎ 020 8977 1403, 01306 885411

WEEKS Sally-Ann *(Pf)*: 17 Pickwick Place, Harrow-on-the-Hill, Middlesex HA1 3BG ☎ 020 8426 4498, 0966 395183 mob

WEISS Catherine *(Bq Vln)*: 24 Elm Park Road, London N3 1EB ☎ 020 8346 4175

WELCHMAN Donna: 5 Albert Road, London E10 6NU

WEST Derek: 42 Robin Hood Way, Greenford, Middx UB6 7QN ☎ 020 8903 0074

WEST Joanna: 49 Gt Ormond Street, London WC1N 3HZ ☎ 020 7242 1049

WEXLER Elizabeth: 109 Rosendale Road, London SE21 8EZ ☎ 020 8761 4808

WHELAN Sarah: 112 Cranbrook Road, Chiswick, London W4 2LJ ☎ 020 8995 9525

WHISTON David: Buchzelgstrasse 91, 8053 Zurich, Switzerland ☎ 01382 4342

WHITE Gil: 7 Princes Road, Wimbledon, London SW19 8RQ ☎ 020 8542 2791

WHITE Janice: 54 Sycamore Road, Wimbledon, London SW19 4TP ☎ 020 8879 1921, 0958 361687 mob

WHITE Nicola ☎ 01494 721917

WHITE Pamela: 50 Elborough Street, Southfields, London SW18 5DN ☎ 020 8870 1197

WHITE Sarah *(Pf)*: 55 Ulleswater Road, Southgate, London N14 7BN ☎ 020 8886 1029

WHITEHEAD Elaine: 9 Phyllis Avenue, New Malden, Surrey KT3 6LA ☎ 020 8949 5667

WHITEHOUSE Ruth: Top Flat, 13 Chapel Market, London N1 9EZ ☎ 020 7837 9667

WHITEHURST Nina: 51 Tresco Road, London SE15 3PY ☎ 020 7635 7688, 020 7635 6211

WHITELAW Madeleine *(Pf)*: 28 Mayfields, Wembley Park, Middlesex HA9 9PS ☎ 020 8904 4109

WHITFIELD Lawrence: 9 Cambridge Road, Charshalton, Surrey SM5 3QP ☎ 020 8643 0104, 0976 835512 mob

WHITING Nick: Address Unknown ☎ 020 8343 0209 & fax

WHITTALL Margaret: 17 Cotsford Avenue, New Malden, Surrey KT3 5EU ☎ 020 8942 8493

WHITTAM Elizabeth: 51 Linden Gardens, London W4 2EH ☎ 01306 880669 day

WICKENS Andrew: 4 Church Close, Lower Beeding, Horsham, West Sussex RH13 6NS ☎ 01403 891 432

WICKENS Barry *(E Vln)*: 44 St Albans Crescent, Wood Green, London N22 5NB ☎ 020 8881 9019

WIDDUP Deborah: 22 Tudor Road, Hampton, Middlesex TW12 2NQ ☎ 020 8979 6318, 01306 880669 day, 0973 191757 mob

WIGGINS Gaye *(Pf)*: 122 Brockley Rise, Honor Oak Park, London SE23 1NH ☎ 020 8690 7652

WILDE Peter: 4 Montague Road, Wimbledon, London SW19 1SY ☎ 020 8542 0310

WILFORD Tim: 23 Alexandra Road, East Twickenham, Middlesex TW1 2HE ☎ 020 8892 1038

WILKINS Lucy: 282 Muswell Hill Broadway, London N10 2QR ☎ 020 8444 8208, 0589 107239 mob

WILKINS-OPPLER Nancy *(Vla)*: Apple Acre, Garlinge Green, Petham, Nr Canterbury Kent CT4 5RP ☎ 01227 700805

WILKINSON Eleanor: 31 Lincoln Road, London N2 9DJ ☎ 020 8444 7230

WILLEY Paul: 14 Vineyard Hill Road, Wimbledon, London SW19 7JH ☎ 020 8947 4245, 01306 880 669

WILLIAMS Hildburg: 17 Asmuns Place, London NW11 7XE ☎ 020 8455 1434

WILLIAMS Jeremy *(Vla)*: 143 Kinveachy Gardens, Charlton, London SE7 8EQ ☎ 020 8854 6977

WILLIAMS Laura *(Vla)*: 2 Wilton Way, Hackney, London E8 3EE ☎ 020 7241 3713, 0958 354 560

WILLIAMS Liz: 131B Whittington Road, Bounds Green, London N22 8YR ☎ 020 8826 0760 & fax, 0958 710366 mob

WILLIAMS Robin *(E Vln)*: 25 Hollies Road, Ealing, London W5 4UU ☎ 020 8568 4960, 020 8560 9965 fax

WILLIAMS Sioni: 44 Church Lane, London N8 7BT ☎ 020 8347 9484, 0976 420556 mob, 01306 880669 day

WILLIAMS Trevor: 3 Ravenscourt Place, London W6 0UN ☎ 020 8748 7774

WILLIAMSON Dean: 13 Caversham Avenue, Palmers Green, London N13 4LL ☎ 020 8886 4694

WILLS Anne: 30 Cromer Villas Road, London SW18 1PN ☎ 020 8874 5446

WILSON Alexa: 136 Erlanger Road, New Cross, London SE14 5TJ ☎ 020 7639 2806

WILSON Brian Lloyd *(Bq Vln, Vla, Vadam, Ea Stg)*: 18 Burnt Hill Way, Boundstone, Farnham, Surrey GU10 4RP ☎ 01252 795047 & fax

WILSON Claire: 447 Baker Street, Enfield, Middlesex EN1 3QY ☎ 020 8350 5806, 0973 678527 mob

WILSON Katherine: 28 Wrentham Avenue, London NW10 3HA ☎ 020 8969 2880

WILSON Marina: 13B Howard Road, London N15 6NL ☎ 020 8880 1955

WILSON Miranda: 93 Nasmyth Street, Hammersmith, London W6 0HA ☎ 020 8741 3686

WILSON Nicole *(Pf, Vla)*: 18 Connaught Road, Ealing, London W13 ☎ 020 8579 1231

WILSON Rolf: 92 Hempstead Road, Watford, Herts WD1 3LA ☎ 01923 235950

WILSON-DICKSON Sovra *(Dms)*: 61 Wyllen Close, Cambridge Heath Road, Stepney, London E1 4HQ ☎ 07970 381055 mob

WINTER Philip: 43 Briton Hill Road, Sanderstead, South Croydon, Surrey CR2 0JJ ☎ 020 8657 1662

WINWOOD John *(Con)*: Game Farm House, Bovingdon, Herts HP3 0NL ☎ 01442 832163

WITKOWSKY Mario: 65 Chesterton Road, London W10 6ES ☎ 020 8969 6440

WOOD Anne *(E Vln, B Gtr)*: 79 Royal College Street, London NW1 0SE ☎ 020 7681 7974, 0378 616 744

WOOD Catherine: 129 Mitcham Road, East Ham, London E6 3NG ☎ 020 8471 2185

WOOD George *(Sax)*: Flat 317, Vivian Court, Maida Vale, London W9 1PY ☎ 020 7624 2163

WOOD Jonathan *(Kbds, B Gtr, Per)*: 45B Hilldrop Road, Tufnell Park, London N7 0JE ☎ 020 7700 3960

WOODCOCK David: 41 Nassau Road, London SW13 9QF ☎ 020 8748 3978

WOODHALL John *(Vla, Pf)*: 44 Arundel Drive, South Harrow, Middlesex HA2 8PR ☎ 020 8864 6677

WOOLDRIDGE Yvonne: 4 Rockways, Barnet, Herts EN5 3JJ ☎ 020 8440 1718, 01483 723644

WOOLF John *(Pf)*: Rose Bank, Florence Road, London N4 4BU ☎ 020 7263 3563

WORSLEY Len: 105 Woodwarde Road, London SE22 8UP ☎ 020 8693 3950

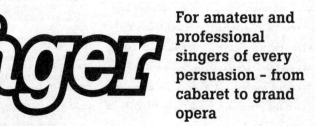

WRAY Gina: 242 Friern Road, Dulwich, London SE22 0BB ☎ 020 8693 1565

WRIGHT Brian *(Vla)*: 28 Thurlow Park Road, London SE21 8JA ☎ 020 8670 8820

WRIGHT Gavyn *(Cntrc)*: Wood Cottage, Smugglers Way, The Sands, Nr. Farnham, Surrey GU10 1NA ☎ 020 7435 8960

WYBURN Carla *(Pf, Clt)*: 99 Fountains Crescent, Southgate, London N14 6BD ☎ 020 8882 6812, 0956 848 806

YANG Min: 6 Marlborough Crescent, Chiswick, London W4 1HF ☎ 020 8747 4855

YEELES Philip *(Bq Vln)*: Rua Isadora Duncan 8. Cv Esq., Vila Nova De Caparica, 2825 Caparica, Portugal ☎ +3511 2958364, +351 936 459466 mob

YEOMANS-MARTIN Freda *(Vla)*: 8 The Paragon, Ramsgate, Kent CT11 9JX ☎ 01843 591412

YOUNG Abigail: 8 Michelle Court, Torrington Park, London N12 9TD ☎ 020 8446 0498

YOUNG Marsha *(Pf, Db)*: 37 Clandon Close, Stoneleigh, Surrey KT17 2NH ☎ 020 8393 2656

YOUNG Sara *(Pf)* ☎ 020 8466 7736

ZABLUDOW Michael: 57 Bramley Road, Southgate, London N14 4IIA ☎ 020 8449 8357

VOICE

SCOTLAND

ANDERSON Craig *(Voc)*: Rustic Cottage, Braefindon, Culbokie, Conon Bridge Highland Region IV7 8JY ☎ 0134 987 449

ANTHONY Gaye *(Voc, Gtr)*: Dalherrick Croft, Sauchen, Inverurie, Aberdeenshire AB3 7RP ☎ 01330 833883 & fax

BANCROFT Sophie *(Voc, Gtr, Com)*: Rock House, 26 Calton Hill, Edinburgh EH1 3BJ ☎ 0131 558 3586

BANNON Lorna *(Voc)*: 3 Coastal Road, East Preston, West Sussex BN16 1SJ ☎ 01903 785006

BELLO Nerea *(Voc)*: T/R 97 Otago Street, Glasgow G12 8NS ☎ 0141 334 6386

BLAIR Robert *(Voc, Gtr, Ctna)*: 8 Melford Avenue, Giffnock, Glasgow G46 6NA ☎ 0141 638 6589

BOLAM Sharon *(Voc, Gtr, Man, Per)*: 19 Noble Place, Edinburgh EH6 8AX ☎ 0131 554 3443

BORLAND Denise *(Voc, Clars)*: 35 Frogston Road West, Edinburgh EH10 7AB, 0131 445 7491, 0131 445 7492 fax

BRAITHWAITE Tracey *(Voc)*: Flat 4, 41 Candlemaker Row, Edinburgh EH1 2QB ☎ 0131 220 5921

BREBNER, D.R.S.A.M Alexander *(Voc)*: 21 Silverknowes View, Edinburgh EH4 5PT ☎ 0131 538 6392

BRENNAN Lee *(Voc, Kbds, Sax, Tpt)*: 54 Carleton Place, Glasgow G5 9TW ☎ 0141 248 9109

BROOKS Lorna *(Voc, Pf, Gtr, Tpt)*: R/L 28 Heriot Hill Terrace, Edinburgh EH7 4DY ☎ 0131 558 9843

BROWN Jim *(Voc, Gtr, Kbds)*: 7 Ryehill Grove, Edinburgh EH6 8ET ☎ 0131 467 9742

BURNS Alison *(Voc, Vln, Vla)*: Drumglass, Balmaghie, Castle Douglas DG7 2LZ ☎ 01644 450660, 01556 504775

BURNS Gary *(Voc)*: Glenlea Cottage, Kirkfieldbank, Lanark ML11 9UJ ☎ 01555 661523

CAL *(Voc, Gtr)*: 14 Bank Street, Grangemouth, Central Region FK3 8EY ☎ 01324 474967

CALLAN Margaret *(Voc, Bag)*: Medrox Villa, Gain Road, Annathill, By Glenboig, Lanarkshire ML5 2QG ☎ 01236 879460, 0141 7791470

CHISHOLM Colin *(Voc, Dms)*: 49 Chesser Crescent, Edinburgh EH14 1SP ☎ 0131 539 9366

CLARK Christopher *(Voc, Pf, Per, Hmca, Sax)*: 12 Bellefield Avenue, 3rd Floor Left, Dundee, Tayside, Scotland ☎ 01382 643 780

CLARK Steven J *(Voc, Gtr, Dms)*: Bis Nation Ltd, Unit 14, Firhill Business Centre, 76 Firhill Road, Glasgow G20 7BA ☎ 0141 945 5515, 0141 945 5585

CONDIE Philip *(Voc, Gtr, Dms, Per)*: 12 Hadfast Road, Cousland, Mid Lothain, Scotland EH22 2NU ☎ 0131 660 2180

CONSTABLE James *(Voc, Gtr, Kbds, Dms, Per)*: 54 Carelton Place, Glasgow G5 9TW

CORMACK Arthur *(Voc, Gtr)*: Quay Brae, Portree, Isle Of Skye IV51 9DE ☎ 01478 612990, 01478 613263 fax

COTTON Del *(Voc)*: 6 Kilmeny Court, Ardrossan, Ayrshire, Scotland KA22 8DJ ☎ 01294 470820

COWIE Elspeth *(Voc, Per)*: 3 Rockville Terrace, Bonnyrigg, Midlothian EH19 2AG ☎ 0131 663 7647, 0131 663 7647

CURSITER Maureen *(Voc)*: 8 Old Scapa Road, Kirkwall, Orkney KW15 1BB ☎ 01856 861210 & fax, 01856 873604

D'ARCY Margaret *(Voc)*: 2 Bourock Square, Barrhead, Renfrewshire G78 2NQ ☎ 0141 571 4212

DANUSIA *(Voc)*: 2 Berwick Crescent, Cairnhill Estate, Airdrie ML6 9RW ☎ 01236 769625 & fax

DAWBARN Simon *(Voc, Kbds, Gtr, B Gtr)*: 54 Carleton Place, Glasgow G5 9TW

DICKOV Caroline *(Voc, Pf)*: Oakmoor, 10 Orchard Drive, Giffnock, Glasgow G46 7NR ☎ 0141 638 7673, 0961 156141 mob

DOROTHEA Fiona *(Voc, Tpt)*: 1B Brights Crescent, Edinburgh EH9 2DA ☎ 0131 466 1076

DOVASTON Isabella *(Voc)*: 2 Queens Terrace, Ayr, Scotland KA7 1DU ☎ 01292 286156

DUFFY Stephen *(Voc, Pf, Arr)*: 5 Hughenden Terrace, Glasgow G12 9XN ☎ 0141 567 1207

DUNCAN Fionna *(Voc)*: The Nest, Portincaple, By Garelochead G84 0EU ☎ 01436 810752 & fax

EVANS Peter *(Voc, Gtr)*: 8 Trent Street, Townhead, Coatbridge ML5 2NT ☎ 01236 437225

FERAL Stephen *(Voc)*: 59 Fauldswood Crescent, Paisley, Renfrewshire PA2 9PB ☎ 01505 815651

FISH *(Voc)*: Main House, Spitalrig Farm, Nr Haddington, East Lothian, Scotland EH41 3SU

FISHER Cilla *(Voc)*: The Post House, Kingskettle, Cupar, Fife KY15 7PN ☎ 01337 831121, 01337 831374 fax

FORMAN Emma *(Voc, Gtr, Tpt, Cnt, Pf)*: 35F St Clair Street, Aberdeen AB24 5AL ☎ 01224 620707, 0411 574742, 01779 475960

FRANK Richard *(Voc, Gtr, B Gtr)*: 1 Christie Street, Dunfermline, Fife KY12 0AQ ☎ 01383 722893

FRASER Helenna *(Voc)*: 183 Meadowpark Street, Dennistoun, Glasgow G31 2TF ☎ 0141 554 5367

FRAYLING-KELLY Nigel *(Voc, Kbds, Dms, B Gtr, Gtr)*: 7/3 Dinshire House North, 87 Calder Crescent, Edinburgh EH11 4JH ☎ 0131 4584874, 0385 317117

GORMAN Christopher *(Voc)*: Ravenswood, Prieston Road, Bridge Of Weir, Scotland PA11 3AN ☎ 01505 615600, 0956 111777, 01505 615604

GRADY Matthew *(Voc, Gtr)*: 31 St Andrews Gardens, Dalry, North Ayrshire KA24 4JY ☎ 01294 832957, 0468 706659

GRANT Frances *(Voc, Pf)*: 2 Adelphi Villa, Nursery Lane, Oban, Argyll PA34 5JA ☎ 01631 563452, 0141 357 5127

GRANT Isla *(Voc, Gtr, Song W)*: Cleughhead Farmhouse, Charterhall, Duns, Berwickshire, Scotland TD11 3RE ☎ 01890 840722

GRANT Kirsteen *(Voc)*: 25 Gartconnell Road, Bearsden, Glasgow G61 3BZ

HARLEY Chris *(Voc, Kbds, Rh Gtr)*: 1 Waterloo Breakish, Isle Of Skye IV42 8QE ☎ 01471 822484, 0468 031060, 01471 822673

HARTE Ann *(Voc)*: 15 Lewis Rise, Broomlands, Irvine KA11 1HH ☎ 01294 215372

HAWLEY Keith *(Voc, Gtr, Kbds)*: 1/Left, 11 Camphill Ave, Glasgow G41 3AU ☎ 0141 632 0848 & fax

HOLLAND Margaret *(Voc, B Gtr, Ac Gtr, Bjo)*: 1 Fr, 13 Brunswick Road, Edinburgh EH7 5NQ ☎ 0131 556 6653

HORSE *(Voc, Ac Gtr)*: C/ O Kelso, 163 West Princes Street, Glasgow G4 9BZ ☎ 0141 333 9074

INNES Heather *(Voc, Bod)*: Auld Of Clunie Farmhouse, Blairgowrie, Perthshire PH10 6RH ☎ 01250 884265, 01250 884748 fax, 0411 583373 mob

JOE-ADIGWE Ciozie *(Voc)*: 6 Willowbank Crescent, Woodlands, Glasgow G3 6NB ☎ 0141 332 4406

JOHNSTON Sarah *(Voc)*: 40 Whitehill Avenue, Musselburgh EH21 6PE ☎ 0131 V665 3899, 04688 81089

JUDGE Christopher *(Voc)*: Brigaddon, Glensburgh, Grangemouth, Stirlingshire FK3 8XL ☎ 01324 485833, 0141 353 3070

KELMAN Laura *(Voc, Pf, Vln)*: Flat 12, 76 Eyre Place, Edinburgh EH3 5EZ ☎ 0976 522862 mob, 0131 558 3850

KERR Al *(Voc, Rh Gtr)*: 14 Cameron Way, Knightsridge, Livingston EH54 8HD ☎ 01506 437281

KERR James *(Voc)*: Simple Minds, c/o Mrs Sandra Dods, 7 Belford Gardens, Edinburgh EH4 3EP ☎ 0131 332 3165

KIANI Mary *(Voc)*: 39 Third Avenue, Auchinloch, Lenzie G66 5EB ☎ 0141 776 7991

KIDD Carol *(Voc)*: c/o Jazz Arena, 45 Milton Avenue, St Neot'S, Cambridgeshire PE19 3LH ☎ 01480 76325, 01480 215969

KYDD Christine *(Voc, Gtr)*: 54 East Claremont Street, Edinburgh EH7 4JR ☎ 0131 557 3215 & fax, 01523 143698 pager

LAULA Carol *(Voc, Gtr)*: C L Productions, c/o Millbank Cottage, Brewery Street, Johnstone PA5 8BQ

LEIGHTON Violet *(Voc)*: 14 White Street, Partick, Glasgow G11 5RT ☎ 0131 339 6908

LEONARD Aimee *(Voc, Bod, Wh)*: North Lodge, Livingstone Place, Galashiels TD1 1DQ

LEWIS Jenny *(Voc, Song W)*: 605 Great Western Road, Flat 2/Left, Glasgow G12 8HX ☎ 0141 334 6528

LINDSAY Fiona *(Voc)*: 103 Larkfield Road, Lenzie, Glasgow G66 3AS ☎ 0141 776 6635

LOTHIAN Eric *(Voc, Gtr, B Gtr)* ☎ 01592 759410

MACALAN Helen *(Voc)*: Flat 2F1, 170 Canongate, Edinburgh EH8 8DF

MACINNES Mairi *(Voc)*: Caledonia, Whiting Bay Road, Lamlash, Brodick, Isle Of Arran KA27 8NL ☎ 01770 600400

MACKAY Morag *(Voc, Pf, Cel)*: 2 Orchard Brae, Edinburgh EH4 1NY ☎ 0131 315 2665, 0973 181634

MACKAY Sandra *(Voc)*: 2 Kennoway Drive, Glasgow G11 7UB ☎ 0141 339 2508

MACKENZIE Talitha *(Voc, Kbds, Clars, Wh, Ctna)*: 33 Millar Crescent (Top Flat), Edinburgh EH10 5HQ ☎ 0131 447 0091

MACLEAN Douglas *(Voc, Song W, Gtr, Vln, Didj)*: Old Schoolhouse, Butterstone, Dunkeld, Perthshire PH7 0AH ☎ 01350 727686 day, 01350 728606 fax, 03747 61944

MAHONEY Linda *(Voc, Gtr, Dms)*: Address Unknown ☎ 0141 334 0988

MAHONNEY *(Voc)*: Flat 3/1, 6 Whitefield Road, Ibrox, Glasgow G51 2YD

MALARKEY Karen *(Voc, Gtr)*: 25 Balvaird Drive, Rutherglen, Glasgow G73 2PU ☎ 0141 634 6319

MANN Doug *(Voc, Gtr, Pf)*: Traquair Mill Cottage, Tweeddale, Scotland EH44 6PT ☎ 01896 830526

MARTIN Anne *(Voc)*: 19 Linicro, Kilmuir, Isle Of Skye IV51 9YN ☎ 01470 542414

MAULE Graham *(Voc)*: 416 Great Western Road, Glasgow G4 9HZ ☎ 0141 334 0688

MCALLISTER Colin *(Voc, Per)*: 18 Teith Place, Cambuslang, Glasgow G72 7YL ☎ 0141 641 8112

MCCAFFERTY Dan *(Voc)*: 27 Munro Street, Kirkcaldy, Fife, Scotland KY1 1PY ☎ 01592 641 778

MCCORMACK Alyth *(Voc)*: 13 Church Street, Partick, Glasgow G11 5JP ☎ 0141 334 3185

MCCRACKEN Frank *(Voc)*: 207 East Clyde Street, Helensburgh, Scotland G84 7AP ☎ 01436 671840

MCDONALD Derek *(Voc, Gtr, Kbds)*: 195 Millers Neuk Crescent, Glasgow G33 6PW ☎ 0141 418 0053

MCGREGOR Kerry *(Voc)*: 174 Uphall Station Road, Pumpherston, West Lothian, Scotland EH53 0PD ☎ 01506 494674

MCINTOSH Lorraine *(Voc)*: Cec Management, 4 Warren Mews, London W1P 5DJ ☎ 020 7388 6500, 020 7388 6522 fax

MCLAUGHLIN Paul *(Voc, Tba, Tbn)*: 90 Muirfield Cres, Dundee DD3 8QA ☎ 0191 260 2855, 01382 826369

MCLEAN Pamela *(Voc, Com)*: Address Unknown ☎ 0182 87 514

MCMILLAN Alistair *(Voc, Gtr, Hmca, Kbds)*: 14 Bertram Street, Glasgow G41 3XR ☎ 0141 632 4778, 0141 633 2229

MCMURDO Craig *(Voc, B Ldr)*: 5/5 Glenogle Road, Edinburgh EH3 5HW ☎ 0131 557 5767/5, 0410 557081 mob

MCQUEEN-HUNTER Douglas *(Voc, Gtr, Man)*: 36 Duncan Avenue, Scotstoun, Glasgow G14 9HS ☎ 0141 954 8180

MCVIE Ross *(Voc, Gtr)*: 7 Ewing Street, Penicuik, Mid Lothian EH26 0JY ☎ 01968 674101, 0802 765 897

MENZIES Laura *(Voc)*: 68 West Holmes Gardens, Musselburgh EH21 6QJ ☎ 0131 665 8959, 046 888 1089

MHOIREACH Anna *(Voc, H Bag)*: 24 Idrigil, Uig, Isle Of Skye, Scotland IV51 9XU ☎ 01470 542 463

MOBBS Charlotte *(Voc, Flt, Pf)*: 1/2 46 Bentinck Street, Kelvin Grove, Glasgow G3 7TT ☎ 0141 339 9441, 0410 488357

MOFFAT Aidan *(Voc, Dms)*: 2 Garthill Gardens, Falkirk, Scotland FK1 5SN

MOFFAT Alan *(Voc, Gtr)*: 154 Broomfield Road, Balarnock, Glasgow G21 3UE ☎ 0141 558 2787

MURDOCH James *(Voc, Kbds, Pf, Gtr, B Gtr)*: 47 Hillside Road, Greenock, Renfrewshire PA15 3LQ ☎ 01475 790806

MURPHY Marianne *(Voc)*: 27 Elm Crescent, Viewpark, Uddingston G71 5AD ☎ 01698 814544

MURRAY John *(Voc)*: G/R 33 Woodlands Drive, Glasgow G4 9DN ☎ 0141 400 0500

NEARY John *(Voc, Gtr)*: 109 Albert Drive, Flat 2-1, Glasgow G41 2SU ☎ 0141 401 0221

O'NEILL James *(Voc, Song W, Gtr, Kbds)*: 7 1/2 Laird Street, Coatbridge, Motherwell, Strathclyde, Scotland ML5 3LJ ☎ 01236 609113

O'REILLY Melanie *(Voc)*: 56 White Oaks, Clenskeagh, Dublin 14, Eire ☎ 003531 2985903

OSBORNE Alexander *(Voc, Gtr)*: 62 Drumsargard Road, Burnside, Glasgow G73 ☎ 0141 647 6406

PARK Darren *(Voc)*: 7 Baxter Street, Fallin, Stirling FK7 7ET ☎ 01786 817944

PATERSON Kenny *(Voc)*: Balquhidder Shore Road, Garelochhead, Dumbartonshire G84 0EJ ☎ 01436 810363, 01436 810363

PELLOW Marti *(Voc, Kbds)*: 1 Park Gate, Glasgow G3 6DL ☎ 0141 353 1515

PETTINGER Patricia *(Voc)*: Banavie, Broomknowe Road, Kilmacolm, Renfrewshire PA13 4HX ☎ Kilmacolm 2391

PRENTICE Scott *(Voc, Kbds, Dms, Per)*: 40 Traquair Avenue, Wishaw, Lanarkshire ML2 8QP ☎ 01698 386174

PROVEN Kim *(Voc)*: Treetops, 44A King Street, Bathgate, Edinburgh EH48 1AY ☎ 01506 656797

RAE Cathie *(Voc)*: The Nest, Portincaple, Nr Garelochead, Dumbartonshire ☎ 01436 810752 fax

RANKIN Mark *(Voc)*: c/o Gun, Parklane Studios, 974 Pollokshaws Road, Glasgow G41 2HA ☎ 0141 632 1111

REID Beverley *(Voc)*: 18 Main Street, Davidson's Mains, Edinburgh EH4 5BY ☎ 0131 336 4006

REID Craig *(Voc, Per, Pf)*: Address Unknown ☎ 0131 445 3317

REID Linda *(Voc)*: 38 Angus Avenue, Eastkilbride, Glasgow G74 3TU ☎ 013552 24333

RILEY Iain *(Voc, Pf, Rec)*: 18 Broompark East, Menstrie, Clackmannanshire, Scotland FK11 7AN ☎ 01259 769874

ROBB Frank *(Voc, Gtr, Hmca)*: 20 Newburgh Crescent, Bridge Of Don, Aberdeen AB2 8ST ☎ 01224 704648

ROBERTS Patricia *(Voc, Clars, Gtr)*: 113 Lothian Crescent, Causeway Head, Stirling FK9 5SE ☎ 01786 465065

ROWAN Michaela *(Voc)*: 2F2 30 Blackwood Crescent, Newington, Edinburgh EH9 1QX ☎ 0131 667 7921

RUSSELL Lady *(Voc)*: 114 Fulton Street, Anniesland, Glasgow G13 1DT ☎ 0141 959 7162

RUTKOWSKI Deirdre *(Voc)*: 38 Main Street, Howth, Co Dublin, Ireland ☎ +3531 8322339

SHANKS Andy *(Voc, Song W)*: Alverton Villa, Dalhousie Street, Edzell, Angus DD9 7UA ☎ 01356 647465

SHORTHOUSE Elaine *(Voc, Pf, Kbds)*: 7 Juniper Grove, Pitcorthie, Dunfermline KY11 ☎ 01383 620455

SLATER Judy *(Voc)*: 66 Elgin Ave, Maida Vale, London W9 2HA ☎ 020 7266 0229

SMITH Biff *(Voc, Gtr, B Gtr, Pf, Kbds)*: 2/R c/o Macaulay, 1 Holmbank Avenue, Shawlands, Glasgow G41 3JQ ☎ 0141 649 9720

SMITH Marilyn *(Voc, Md)*: 16 Westbourne Crescent, Bearsden, Glasgow G61 4HD ☎ 0141 943 0767

SPEIRS Sam *(Voc, Pf, Gtr)*: 3 Brigend, East Whitburn, West Lothian EH47 0JA ☎ 01501 742033

SPELLER Martin *(Voc)*: 81 East King Street, Helensburgh, Dunbartonshire G84 7RG ☎ 01436 676279

SPITERI Sharleen *(Voc)*: 974 Pollokshaws Road, Shawlands, Glasgow G41 2HA ☎ 0141 632 1111

STEVENS Terry *(Voc)*: Croc, Lamlash, Isle Of Arran, Scotland KA27 8NJ, 01770 600393

STEWART Christina *(Voc, Pf)*: 52 Kilnford Drive, Dundonald, South Ayrshire, Scotland KA2 9ET ☎ 01563 850486, 0498 751007

STRACHAN William *(Voc)*: Howford, 2 Moorfield Road, Cumnock, Ayrshire KA18 1BY ☎ 01290 420374

SWAPP Murray *(Voc, Gtr)*: 4 Merxland Road, Top Floor Left, Aberdeen AB24 3HR ☎ 01224 620867

THOMSON Inge *(Voc, Acc, Tin Wh, Per)*: Top Flat Right, 228 King Street, Aberdeen AB2 3BU ☎ 01224 630152

TREZISE Artie *(Voc)*: The Post House, Kingskettle, Cupar, Fife KY15 7PN ☎ 01337 831121, 01337 831374 fax

TURNER Ann *(Voc)*: Beechwood Cottage, Beeslack, By Peniciuk, Midlothian EH26 0QF ☎ 01968 678615

URE James *(Voc, Gtr, Kbds)*: C.M.O. Management, Unit 32, Ransomes Dock, 35/37 Parkgate Road, London SW11 4NP ☎ 020 7228 4000

WELLINGTON Sheena *(Voc, Com)*: 6 St Andrews Road, Largoward, Leven, Fife KY9 1HZ ☎ 0133 484 0297

WHITE Tam *(Voc)*: 1 Saughton Park, Edinburgh EH12 5TB ☎ 1031 313 3917

WILKIE James *(Voc, Gtr)*: 32 Mcnabb Street, Dollar, Clackmannanshire FK14 7DL ☎ 01259 43368

WILSON Kim *(Voc)*: 29 Orchard Drive, Giffnock, Glasgow G46 7AG ☎ 0141 638 7617

WILSON Ray *(Voc, Gtr, Song W)*: c/o Fundamental Ltd, 42 Southfields, East Molesey, Surrey KT8 0BP ☎ 020 8224 4900, 020 8224 6123 fax

WINTER Gwyn *(Voc, Ac Gtr)*: Achray Lodge, Trossachs, By Callander, Perthshire FK17 8HZ ☎ 01877 376257

X Karen *(Voc, Gtr, Kbds)*: 76 Eglinton Cres, Troon KA10 6LQ ☎ 01292 315 764

YOUNG John *(Voc, Gtr, Lute, Man)*: 47 Bainfield Road, Cardross G82 5JQ ☎ 01389 841772, 01389 841772

NORTH WEST

ADKINS Haydon *(Voc)*: 2 Riversdale, Woolston, Warrington WA1 4PZ ☎ 01925 817615

ALLEN Carol *(Voc)*: 36 Heversham Avenue, Fulwood, Preston, Lancashire PR2 4TD ☎ 01772 464112, 0802 841185

ALLEYNE-HUGHES Perri *(Voc, Song W)*: 49 Rosslyn Street, Liverpool L17 7DL ☎ 0151 283 1142

ALTINBAS Maria *(Voc, Song W, Gtr)*: 21 Croft Hill Road, Moston, Manchester M40 9GL ☎ 0161 681 2598

AMOO Christopher *(Voc, Gtr)*: Gables Brook, Mill Lane, Kingsley, Cheshire WA6 8HZ ☎ 01928 787562

AMOO Edward *(Voc, Gtr)*: 15 Alexandra Drive, Liverpool L17 8TA ☎ 0151 727 2436

ANDERSON Birgitte *(Voc, Pf, Gtr, Per, Song W)*: 11 Chiswick Road, Didsbury, Manchester M20 6RZ ☎ 0161 434 2591

ASTLEY Rick *(Voc, Sax)*: c/o Mike Astley, Earnmulti Ltd, 2 Shellingford Close, Appley Bridge, Lancs WN6 8DN ☎ 01257 255684

AUSTIN Steve *(Voc)*: 65 Mallard Crescent, Poynton, Cheshire SK12 1XG

BAILEY Louise *(Voc, Kbds, Gtr)*: 10 Torbay Road, Chorlton, Manchester M21 8XP

BAKER Lois *(Voc)*: 594 Halliwell Road, Bolton, Lancs BL1 8BY ☎ 01204 845596

BALL Fiona *(Voc)*: Flat 206, 41 Old Birley Street, Hulme, Manchester M15 5RE

BANKS Michael *(Voc, B Gtr, Gtr)* ☎ 01942 512138

BEARD Jason *(Voc, Gtr, B Gtr, Kbds)*: 10A Gawsworth Ave, East Didsbury, Manchester M20 5NF ☎ 0161 446 1017, 0976 893024 mob

BEC Monty *(Voc)*: 175 Mackets Lane, Woolton, Liverpool L25 9NG ☎ 0151 342 4490

BELSTEN Peter *(Voc, Gtr, Pf, Song W)*: 1175 Manchester Road, Castleton, Rochdale OL11 2XZ ☎ 01706 353161

BERNHARDT Oscar *(Voc, Tpt)*: 19 Dartmouth Road, Chorlton, Manchester M21 8XL ☎ 0161 881 2798

BERRY Colin *(Voc, Gtr, Dms)*: 36 Papermill Road, Eagley, Bolton, Lancs BL7 9DF ☎ 01204 594847

BHADURI Reba *(Voc, Harm, Tamp)*: 122 School Lane, Didsbury, Manchester M20 0BJ ☎ 0161 434 6276

BOOTH Timothy *(Voc, Gtr)*: C.C Young & Co, Chesham Hosue, 150 Regent Street, London W1R 5FA ☎ 020 7432 0337, 020 7432 0338

BORTHWICK Shirley *(Voc)*: 14 Patrick Avenue, Rhyl, North Wales LL18 4TU ☎ 01745 353264

BOYLAND Stephen *(Voc)*: 15 Alresford Road, Liverpool L19 3QZ ☎ 0151 727 1889

BRADSHAW Robert *(Voc, Gtr, B Gtr, Kbds)*: 59 George Lane, Bredbury, Stockport, Cheshire SK6 1AT ☎ 0161 612 8269, 0958 418827 mob

BREEN Joanne *(Voc)*: 5 Martindale Grove, Beechwood, Runcorn, Cheshire WA7 2TU ☎ 01928 566067

BRIDGWOOD Sarah *(Voc)*: 17 Littlegate, Westhoughton, Bolton BL5 2SD ☎ 01942 818728, 07970 623 288

BURROWS Leanne *(Voc)* ☎ 0161 832 8080, 0161 832 1613

BUTCHER Nina *(Voc, Song W)*: 65 Nettlesford Road, Whalley Range, Manchester M16 8NJ ☎ 0161 861 7450

BUTLER Stephen *(Voc)*: 28 Gaskell Road, Altrincham, Cheshire WA14 1WH ☎ 0161 941 3130

CAMPBELL REID Wayne *(Voc, Song W)*: 47 Haryington Ave, Bewsey, Warrington, Cheshire WA5 5AY

CANTY Clare *(Voc)*: 84 Whitefriar Court, Saint Simon Street, Salford, Lancs M3 7ER ☎ 0161 834 0920

CATTERALL Deborah *(Voc)*: 19 Conway Road, Hindley Green, Wigan, Lancs WN2 4PG ☎ 01942 255998, 0467 677914

CHESTER Andrew *(Voc, Gtr, Synth, Cong)*: 107 Fog Lane, Didsbury, Manchester M33 6SN ☎ 07971 300457

CLARKE Basil *(Voc)*: 44 Carlton Street, Old Trafford, Manchester M16 7GT

CLARKE Suzannah *(Voc)*: 5 Victoria Terrace, 147 Hathersage Road, Victoria Park, Manchester M13 0HY ☎ 0161 256 1126

COOKE John *(Voc, Gtr)*: 9 Parsonage Road, Withington, Manchester M20 4PB ☎ 0161 445 8829, 0161 952 4672

COOKSON Francesca *(Voc)*

COUTTS Jack *(Voc)*: Meadow Cottage, 7 Thomas Lane, Liverpool L14 5NR ☎ 0151 220 0152

CUNLIFFE Gary *(Voc, Dms)*: 30 Lythcoe Avenue, Fulwood, Preston, Lancs PR2 3SB ☎ 01772 727561

CURLEY Seamus *(Voc, Gtr, Mando, B Gtr)*: 72 Lowfield Road, Shaw Heath, Stockport SK3 8JS ☎ 0161 474 1263

DAVIES Daniel *(Voc, Gtr, Kbds)*: The Toft Studio, Toft Road, Knutsford, Cheshire WA16 9EH ☎ 01565 633790, 01565 633470

DAVIES Kimberley *(Voc, Kbds, Flt)*: 62A Kemble Street, Prescot, Merseyside L34 5SH ☎ 0151 289 1184

DAVIES Truly *(Voc, Kbds)*

DAYVE *(Voc, Gtr, Kbds, Pf)*: 14 Dove Close, Sandbach, Cheshire CW11 1SY ☎ 0127 076 6110

DEPASOIS Brenelda *(Voc)*: 26 Great Southern Street, Rusholme, Manchester M14 4EZ ☎ 0161 226 5556

DEWEY Clare *(Voc, Pf)* ☎ 0161 798 6690

DHAND Sabina *(Voc)*: C/0 Ms B Ahmed, Penny Wise, Corner Of Sherbourne St, Bury New Road, Manchester M8 8FN ☎ 0161 831 7550

DONALD Craig *(Voc, Pf)*: 2 Dodding House, Hunter Lane, Penrith, Cumbria CA11 7UY ☎ 01768 867775

DOUGHERTY Stephen *(Voc, Gtr, Kbds, Dms, Brass)* ☎ 0161 224 7495

EDWARDS Doreen *(Voc)*: 19 Dartmouth Road, Chorlton, Manchester M21 8XL ☎ 01523 717384

ELLISON Mark *(Voc)*: 2 Dodington Close, Alexandre Park Estate, Manchester M16 7LG

FATIMILEHIN Jonathan *(Voc)*

FERGUSSON-NICOL Avni *(Voc, Pf, Org, Per)*: 13 Kelvin Grove, Cheetham Hill, Manchester M8 0SX ☎ 0161 205 3927, 07970 343446

FINLAYSON Rhonda *(Voc)*: Flat 87, Lowton Court, Teddington Road, Moston Manchester M10 0DW

FLORCZAK Fiona *(Voc)*: 27 Parrswood Road, Withington, Manchester M20 4WJ ☎ 0161 374 1602, 07971 328461

FLOREK Jaki *(Voc)*: 11 Stanley Villas, Greenway Road, Runcorn, Cheshire WA7 4NW ☎ 01928 566261

FOX Catherine *(Voc)*: 52 Linden Avenue, Connahs Quay, Deeside, Flintshire CH5 4SW

FROST Karen *(Voc, Kbds, Sax)*: 55 Beech Lane, Macclesfield, Cheshire SK10 2DS ☎ 01625 615558

GARRITY Edmund *(Voc, Gtr, Kbds)*: 42 Redburn Road, Baguley, Manchester M23 1AJ ☎ 0161 374 1347

GHOSH Mala *(Voc)*: 12 Arden Court, Bramhall SK7 3NG

GIBB Robin *(Voc)*: Eatons, Solicitors, 22 Blades Court, Deodar Road, Putney, London SW15 2NU ☎ 020 8877 9727, 020 8877 9940 fax

GLASGOW Debbie *(Voc)*: 24 Stockholm Road, Edgeley, Stockport, Cheshire SK3 9QR ☎ 0161 718 1613

GORDON Alistair *(Voc, Kbds)*: 59 Westgate, Hale, Altrincham, Cheshire WA15 9BA ☎ 0161 928 3999

GOUGH Damon *(Voc, Gtr, Kbds)*: 26 Keppel Road, Chorlton, Manchester M21 0BW ☎ 07970 748226

GOVAN Rebecca *(Voc)*: 92 St Georges Avenue, Daisy Hill, West Houghton, Bolton, Lancs BL5 2EZ ☎ 01942 812834, 07887 548183

GRANT Damien *(Voc)*: 73 Darnley Street, Old Trafford, Manchester M16 9WD ☎ 0161 227 9709, 0161 374 6362

HAYES Richard *(Voc, Gtr, Dms)*: 24 Lichfield Road, Davyhulme, Urmston, Manchester M41 0RU ☎ 0161 748 7266

HEARN Samantha *(Voc)*

HIGGINS Yonah *(Voc, Song W)* ☎0161 661 9535

HINCHLIFFE Emma *(Voc)*: Address Unknown ☎ 01942 742920

HUCKNALL Michael *(Voc, Gtr, Hmca)*: Dream Productions, Lock Keepers Cottage, 9 Century Street, Manchester M8 4QL ☎ 0161 832 2111, 0161 832 2333 fax

HUMPHREYS Mary *(Voc, Bjo, Ctna, Gtr)*: 2 Belle Vue, Barkisland, Halifax HX4 0DW ☎ 01422 825 084

IKE *(Voc, Song W)* ☎ 0161 442 3088

ILGINNIS Debra *(Voc)*: 40 Haughton Drive, Northenden, Manchester M22 4EQ ☎ 0161 998 1943

JACKSON Nick *(Voc, Gtr, B Gtr, Man, Kbds)*

JOHN Jennifer *(Voc, Pf)*: Parr Street Studios, 33-45 Parr Street, Liverpool L1 4JN ☎ 0151 707 1050, 0151 709 8612

JOHNSON Dean *(Voc, Gtr)*: Flat 4, 23 Devonshire Place, Oxton, Wirral, Merseyside L43 1TX ☎ 0151 653 7541

JOHNSON Timothy *(Voc, Pf)*: 103 Compstall Road, Marple Bridge, Stockport, Cheshire SK6 5HE ☎ 0161 427 7294

JOHNSTON Jan *(Voc, Kbds)*: 218 Butterstile Lane, Prestwich, Manchester M25 8UN ☎ 0161 773 2774

JONES Elizabeth *(Voc)*: 28 Princes Street, Connahs Quay, Deeside, Flintshire CH5 4QE ☎ 01244 814727, 0370 660378

KHAN Mazaufar *(Voc)*: 49 Wellmead Close, Manchester M8 8BS ☎ 0161 833 9556 & fax

KHAN Tariq *(Voc)*: 8 Mull Avenue, Longsight, Manchester M12 4PR ☎ 0161 273 4438

KILL Jessica *(Voc, Sax, Flt)*: Flat 2, 234 Palatine Road, West Didsbury, Manchester M20 2WF ☎ 0161 7187331, 0956 941907

KIM *(Voc)*

KING Shirley *(Voc)*: 23 Kenilworth Road, Ainsdale, Southport, Merseyside PR8 3PE ☎ 01704 574003

KITTY *(Voc)*: 25 Thwaites Road, Oswaltwistle, Lancashire BB5 4QT ☎ 01254 237381, 0797 0911347

LA-VENE Debbie *(Voc)*: 95 Wilkinson Avenue, Little Lever, Bolton, Lancs BL3 1QP ☎ 01204 77377

LEE Jason *(Voc)*: 35 Crofton Street, Manchester M14 4DX, 0961 108624

LEE Michelle *(Voc)* ☎ 0161 832 8080, 0161 832 1613

LENNON Helen *(Voc)*: 116 St Bridgets Close, Fearnhead, Warrington, Cheshire WA2 0EP ☎ 01925 831680

LID *(Voc, Gtr, Hmca, B Gtr)*: 11 Culgarth Avenue, Cockermouth, Cumbria CA13 9PL ☎ 01900 823954

LLORENNA AATW Kelly *(Voc, Pf)*: 4-13 Penny Street, Blackburn, Lancs BL2 5RR ☎ 01254 264120

LLOYD Rachel *(Voc)*: 13 Berwyn Drive, St. Martins, Oswestry, Shropshire SY11 3AT ☎ 01691 777918

LOWE Christina *(Voc)*: 35 Church Road, West Kirby, Wirral L48 0RN ☎ 0151 625 9737, 07775 873111

MAHER Siobhan *(Voc)*: 11 Ilford Avenue, Crosby, Liverpool L23 7YE ☎ 0151 924 3972

MALONE Mae *(Voc)*: 57 Hulmes Road, Clayton Bridge, Manchester M40 1GP ☎ 0161 681 0658

MARITA *(Voc)*: 43 Buller Street, Bury, Lancs BL8 2BQ ☎ 0161 797 8976

MARSH Kimberley *(Voc)*: 16 Princess Avenue, Ashton In Makerfield, Wigan, Lancs WN4 9DF ☎ 01942 728817

MARTLEW Samantha *(Voc)*: 40 Bramcote Avenue, Laffak, St Helens, Merseyside WA11 9JQ ☎ 01744 602496, 07931 907024

MATTIS Audrey *(Voc)*: 23 Whitelake Ave, Flixton, Manchester M41 5GN ☎ 0161 748 5799

MCCLARNON Elizabeth *(Voc)*: 1 Rosewarne Close, Aigburth, Liverpool L17 5BX

MCDONNELL Sophie *(Voc)*: 26 Kingsday, Penworth, Preston, Lancashire PR1 0BJ ☎ 01772 744656, 0850 286160

MCFARLANE Rachelle *(Voc)*: 16 Crayfield Road, Manchester M19 3NX ☎ 0161 248 5742

MCIVER Lesley *(Voc, Gtr)*: 36 Pool Bank Street, Rhonde, Middleston, Manchester M24 4RN ☎ 0161 654 0685

MENZIES Stephen *(Voc, Kbds)*: 7 Limley Grove, Chorlton, Manchester M21 8UB ☎ 0161 881 4761

MINTA Ryland *(Voc)*: 297 Bolton Road, Radcliffe, Manchester M26 0QP ☎ 0161 723 4113

MOLYNEUX Tony *(Voc)*: 9 Hooton Road, Aintree, Liverpool L9 4SF ☎ 0151 521 5967

MORTON-SMITH Emma *(Voc)*: 41 Greave, Romiley, Stockport, Cheshire SK6 4PU ☎ 0161 494 1305

MULHOLLAND Gregory *(Voc, Song W, Rh Gtr)*: 15 Warwick Road, Hale, Altrincham, Cheshire WA15 9NS ☎ 0161 941 9170

MURPHY Dale *(Voc, Gtr, Pf, Kbds)*: 2A Downing Street, Ashton Under Lyne, Lancs OL7 9LR ☎ 0161 330 3922

MURRAY Jane *(Voc)* ☎ 0161 832 8080, 0161 832 1613

MYERS William *(Voc, Ac Gtr)*: 62 Ney Street, Ashton-U-Lyne, Lancs OL6 9NL ☎ 0161 343 5579

NEWTON Andrew *(Voc, Gtr, Dms)*: 27 Lowood Avenue, Davyhulme, Urmston, Manchester M41 8GD ☎ 0161 748 9120

NORFOLK Simon *(Voc)*: 58A North Road, Lancaster, Lancs LA1 1LT ☎ 01524 64073

O'TOOLE Stephen *(Voc, Gtr, Pf, B Gtr)* ☎ 0151 727 3693

PAL Michael *(Voc)*: Flat 6 Martin House, Conyngham Road, Victoria Park, Manchester M14 5SA ☎ 0161 225 1294

PARKER Andrew *(Voc, Sax)*: 23 Chepstow Avenue, Wallasey, Merseyside L44 0BA ☎ 0151 630 3226

PARRY Mark *(Voc, Dms, Gtr, B Gtr)*: 7B Linnet Lane, Aigburth, Liverpool L17 3BE ☎ 0151 728 7733

PEARSON Gary *(Voc, B Gtr, Dms)*: 9 Redwood Avenue, Leyland, Preston PR5 1RN ☎ 01772 516978

POSSIBLE Gilda *(Voc)*: 4 Grapes Court, Lord Street, Macclesfield, Cheshire SK11 6SY ☎ 01625 42 7856

PRANGE Maria *(Voc)*: 10 Sark Close, Lowry Hill, Carlisle, Cumbria CA3 0DX ☎ 01387 269977

PRIMATE Tomas *(Voc, B Gtr)*: 2 Handley Avenue, Fallowfield, Manchester M14 7AF

PURDY Martin *(Voc, Kbds)*: 163 Baguley Crescent, Rhodes, Middleton, Greater Manchester M24 4QU ☎ 0161 654 0790

QUIGLEY Ann *(Voc)*: 4 Grecian Street, Lower Broughton, Salford, Lancs M7 9JF ☎ 0161 792 3125

QUIGLEY Paul *(Voc, Gtr)*: 20 Silverdale Street, Manchester M11 1ET ☎ 0161 371 1892, 0161 371 0120

QUIN Sue *(Voc)*: 16 Dale Lane, Appleton, Warrington, Cheshire WA4 3DG ☎ 01925 602569

RAINBOW Katrina *(Voc, Gtr, Rec, Tamb)* ☎ 01539 88628

REID Neil *(Voc, Kbds)*: Flat 3, 3 Parkgate Avenue, Withington, Manchester M20 9DZ ☎ 0161 434 0985

RICHARDS Rosaline *(Voc, Kbds)*: 4 Cranford Avenue, Didsbury, Manchester M20 6EH

RIGG Laura *(Voc)*: 90 Partington Street, Castleton, Rochdale, Lancs OL11 3DG ☎ 01706 32687

RILEY Peter *(Voc)*: 156 Hilton Lane, Prestwich, Manchester M25 9QY ☎ 0161 798 7363

RUDGE Eleanor *(Voc, Pf)*: 8 Cote Lane, Hayfield, High Peak SK22 2HL ☎ 01663 746027

RUSSELL Elizabeth *(Voc, Pf)*

RUSSELL Juliet *(Voc)*: Sense Of Sound, Parr Street Studios, 33 45 Parr Street, Liverpool L1 4JN ☎ 0151 707 1050, 0151 709 8612

RUSSO Chuca *(Voc, Per)*: 19 Greendale Road, Port Sunlight, Wirral, Merseyside L62 5DF

SANDERS Bev *(Voc, Per)*: 34 Glen Park Drive, Hesketh Bank, Preston, Lancs PR4 6TA

SIREN Steve *(Voc, Gtr, Hmca, Pf, Flt)*: 39A Hope Street, Liverpool L1 9DZ ☎ 0151 707 1591

SIREN Sylvie *(Voc)* ☎ 0151 525 5685

SMITH Carrie *(Voc)*: 78 Mesnes Road, Wigan, Lancs WN1 2DE ☎ 01942 205900

SMITH David *(Voc)*: 2 Coney Grove, Brook Vale, Cheshire WA7 6BT ☎ 01928 719724

SMITH Sarah *(Voc)*: 20 Barlow Road, Stretford, Manchester M32 0RG ☎ 0161 282 6865, 0956 531214

SMITH Serena *(Voc)*: 20 Barlow Road, Stretford, Manchester M32 0RG ☎ 0161 282 6865, 0956 531 214

SMITH Stevie *(Voc, Gtr)*: 18 Burman Street, Higher Openshaw, Manchester M11 1EY ☎ 0161 371 7621

SOWERBY Aron *(Voc)*: 120 Cabul Close, Orford, Warrington, Cheshire WA2 7SE ☎ 01925 727411, 01925 571524

STARKIE Gerard *(Voc)*: 207 Chorley Road, Blackrod, Bolton BL6 5LJ ☎ 01257 480538

TABOR June *(Voc, Tamb)*: Lower Panpwnton, Kinsley Road, Knighton, Powys LD7 1TN ☎ 01547 528112

THOMPSON Doris *(Voc)*: 227 Kew Road, Birkdale, Southport PR8 4JE ☎ 01704 56877

THORNTON Sally *(Voc, Gtr, Vln, Rec, Pf)*: 9 Egerton Road, Whitefield, Manchester M25 7FU ☎ 0161 766 1129

UDDIN Ruqia *(Voc)*: 15 Queens Centre, Longsight, Manchester M12 4WL

VAN WIJNGAARDEN Paule *(Voc)* ☎ 01254 395189

WALKER Pamela *(Voc)*: The Beehive, Old Hutton, Kendal, Cumbria LA8 0LT ☎ 01539 740583

WALKER Sarah *(Voc)*

WALKLATE Mathew *(Voc, Hmca, Flt, Wh)*: 23 Brookfield Avenue, Chorlton-Cum-Hardy, Manchester M21 8TX ☎ 0161 881 0071 & fax

WALTERS Noel *(Voc)*: 105 Adelphi Court, North George Street, Salford M3 6HX ☎ 0161 839 5696 & fax

WAY Kathryn *(Voc)*: 21 Edenhurst Road, Mile End, Stockport, Cheshire SK2 6BT ☎ 0161 456 7470

WHITE Jennifer *(Voc, Gtr, Pf, Vln, Song W)*: 67 Dale Street, Lancaster LA1 3AP ☎ 04988 50150

WHITE Suzan *(Voc)* ☎ 01744 600563, 07775 604373

WILLIAMS Claire *(Voc, Pf)*: 31 Brushwood Avenue, Flint, Flintshire CH6 5TY ☎ 01352 763025, 0441 145599

WILLIAMS Emma *(Voc)*: 46 Chester Road, Wrexham, N. Wales LL11 2SD ☎ 01978 355985, 0831 817988 mob

WILLOUGHBY Mike *(Voc, Bzk, Mldn, Hmca)*: 17 Sun Street, Ulverston, Cumbria LA12 7BX ☎ 01229 581747 & fax

WOOD Miriam *(Voc)*: Flat 6, 3 Eliza Street, Hulme, Manchester M15 ☎ 0161 839 2799

WOODS Maria *(Voc)*: 2 Gladstone Road, Southport PR9 7AW ☎ 01704 86398

WYLIE Peter *(Voc, Gtr, B Gtr, Kbds, Hmca)*

YATES Abbi *(Voc)*: 35 Briar Bank Row, Fulwood, Preston, Lancashire PR2 9PF ☎ 01772 717446

YORKIE *(Voc, B Gtr, Kbds)*: 31 Prospect Vale, Fairfield, Liverpool L6 8PE ☎ 0151 228 5928

YVONNE *(Voc, Per)*: 175 Reddish Road, Reddish, Stockport, Cheshire SK5 7HR ☎ 0161 476 1415

NORTH EAST

ALLEN David *(Voc)*: 91 Wheldrake Road, Firth Park, Sheffield S5 6UE ☎ 07970 342107

ALLEN Jon *(Voc, Kbds, Fo Fdl, Man)*: 14 Prospect Place, Grantham, Lincs NG31 8DB ☎ 01476 561761

AMBLER Paul *(Voc)*: 41 Salisbury Road, Armley, Leeds, West Yorkshire LS12 2BH ☎ 0113 279 7207

ARCHER Tasmin *(Voc)*: c/o Martin Green Ravden, 55 Loudoun Road, St Johns Wood, London NW8 0DL ☎ 020 7625 4545, 020 7625 5265

ARMSTRONG Robert *(Voc, Com)*: 15 Fairview Terrace, Greencroft, Co Durham DH9 8NK ☎ 01207 235048 eve, 01207 239744 eve

B Sean *(Voc)*

BABINGTON Susan *(Voc, Pf)*: Broadheath, 3 Humber Crescent, Ashby, Scunthorpe, Lincs DN17 1JD ☎ 01724 868519, 0421 097219 mob

BAIYEWU Emmanuel *(Voc)*: Kitchenware Records, St Thomas Street Workshop, St Thomas Street, Newcastle-upon-Tyne NE1 4LE ☎ 0191 232 4895

BALMFORTH Melanie *(Voc)*: Flat C, 5 Park Holme, Chapeltown, Leeds LS7 4EX ☎ 0113 2620304

BARRY Jacqueline *(Voc, Per)*: 142 Main Street, Seahouses, Northumberland NE68 7UA ☎ 01665 720089

BEATTIE Neil *(Voc, Gtr, B Gtr)*: 33 Norman Terrace, Eccleshill, Bradford, W. Yorks BD2 2JJ ☎ 01274 630645

BLYTHE Hilary *(Voc, B Gtr)*: 5 Prospect Place, Totley Rise, Sheffield S17 4HZ ☎ 0114 236 3309

BOWER John *(Voc, Gtr)*: 53 Huddersfield Road, Barnsley S75 1DR ☎ 01226 219446

BOWKER Robert *(Voc, Gtr)*: 37 Lower East Avenue, Barnoldswick, Lancs BB8 6DN ☎ 01282 815138

BOYES Michael *(Voc, Gtr, Kbds)*: 42 Highfield Road, Darlington, County Durham DL3 0DY ☎ 01325 359157

BRADLEY Peter *(Voc, Gtr, Pf, Dms, B Gtr)*: Stokesley Glebe, 2A Station Road, Stokesley, North Yorkshire TS9 5AH ☎ 01642 713054

BROOKS Nick *(Voc, Gtr)*: 2 High Road, Londonthorpe, Grantham, Lincs NG31 9RU ☎ 01476 575708, 0378 216675

BROON Alvis *(Voc, Pf)*: 57 Nortumberland Avenue, Newbiggin-By-The-Sea, Northumberland NE64 6RL ☎ 01670 818233

BROWN Becky *(Voc)*: 14 Westwood Close, Tweendykes Road, Sutton, Hull HU7 4XH ☎ 01482 377131

BROWN Rosanna *(Voc)*: 50 Plymouth Road, Sheffield S7 2DE ☎ 0114 249 0436

BUNCALL Christopher *(Voc, Dms, B Gtr, Gtr, Kbds)*: Flat 2, 12 Beechill Road, Broomhill, Sheffield S10 2SB ☎ 0114 268 1440

CAIN Miles *(Voc, Gtr)*: 32 Saint Matthew Street, Boulevard, Hull HU3 2UA ☎ 01482 216084

CHERRY *(Voc)*: 45 Bowness Road, Walkley, Sheffield S6 2PQ ☎ 0114 234 2963

CLEGG Carole *(Voc)*: Tanfield, Durham Road, Annfield Plain, Stanley, Co.Durham DH9 7UF ☎ 01207 239977

COLEMAN Paul *(Voc, Dms, B Gtr, Sax, Flt)*: 84 Digby Street, Scunthorpe, Lincs DN15 7LU ☎ 01724 871833, 01724 866955

COOK Timothy *(Voc)*: Hakerley Bridge Farm, Frithville, Boston, Lincs PE22 7EB ☎ 01205 750292

CRAIG Lynnette *(Voc)*: 3 Elm Avenue, Whickham, Newcastle-upon-Tyne, Tyne & Wear NE16 4SR ☎ 0191 488 7249

CRAIG Munro *(Voc, Scratch)*: 3 Elm Avenue, Whickham, Newcastle-upon-Tyne, Tyne & Wear NE16 4SR ☎ 01941 488 7249

CUNNINGHAM Margaret *(Voc, Per)*: 148A Sprotbroughroad, Doncaster, S Yorkshire DN5 8BB ☎ 01302 783874

DALE Jaye C *(Voc)*: 5 Folly Hall Close, Wibsey, Bradford, West Yorkshire BD6 1UX ☎ 01274 405531

DALTON Paul *(Voc, Pf)*: 15 Coronation Avenue, Oatlands, Harrogate, North Yorkshire HE2 8BY ☎ 01423 873082

DARNILL James *(Voc)*: 17 Coronation Road, Stocksbridge, Sheffield S30 5AX ☎ 0114 288 7574

DAVIS *(Voc, Gtr, Pf, B Gtr, Kbds)*: c/o P Cass/Beautiful South, Cavendish House, St Andrews Court, St Andrews Street, Leeds LS3 1JY ☎ 0113 243 0898, 0113 234 0698

DAWSON Sally *(Voc)*: 22 Stoneyridge Road, Cottingley, Bingley, Bradford, W Yorkshire BD16 1UJ ☎ 01274 496792, 04410 26150

DICKSON Kelly *(Voc)*: ☎ 0113 240 8206, 0973 307370 mob

DIMOND Vanessa *(Voc)*: 28 Cloverdale Road, Cross Heath, Newcastle, Staffs ST5 9LE ☎ 01782 622502, 0976 715198 (M0, 01782 315275

DINNING Judy *(Voc, Pf, Gtr, Per)*: Stable Cottage, 4 The Manor House, Whalton, Northumberland NE61 3UT ☎ 01670 775456

DOHERRY Jade *(Voc)*: 6 Hustler Street, Undercliffe, Bradford BD3 0QA

DONOVAN Simon *(Voc)*: 10 Lydford House, Elizabeth Street, Bradford, W. Yorkshire BD5 0RX ☎ 01274 739622, 0411 100069 mob

EDWARDS Stephen *(Voc, B Gtr, Kbds, Per)*: 19 Holland Place, Sheffield S2 4US

EVERITT Craig *(Voc)* ☎ 01484 311694

FINCH Sean *(Voc, Gtr)* ☎ 01964 551757, 0468 050712

FINCH Vera *(Voc, Pf, Org)*: Cliffe House, 7 Hough Lane, Wombwell, Barnsley, Yorks S73 0DP ☎ 01226 258110

FIRTH Andrew *(Voc, Kbds, Gtr, B Gtr, Hmca)*: 6 Heaton Road, Upper Batley, West Yorkshire WF17 0AT ☎ 01924 470390

FORSE Mike *(Voc, Gtr)*: 254 Rectory Road, Gateshead, Tyne & Wear NE8 4RP ☎ 0191 420 1559

FREEMAN Sue-Lee *(Voc)*: 21 Roundhay View, Leeds, West Yorks LS5 4DX ☎ 0113 2289991

FRENCH Sally *(Voc, Pf)*: 10 Booth House, Holmfirth, West Yorkshire HD7 1QA ☎ 01484 687038

FURNESS Dawn *(Voc, Pf, B Gtr, Per)* ☎ 0956 176096

GRANVILLE-FALL Anthony *(Voc, Gtr, Kbds)*: 18 Orchard Gardens, Pocklington, East Yorks YO42 3EX ☎ 01759 306186

GUY Anthony *(Voc, Dms)*: 7 Western Hill, Off Chester Road, Sunderland SR2 7PH

HALL Maureen *(Voc)*: 1 Carnoustie Court, Rosemount, Whitley Bay, Tyne & Wear NE25 9EZ ☎ 0191 252 7482

HARKIN Holly *(Voc)*: 3 Broomfield Place, Headingley, Leeds LS6 3DG ☎ 0113 274 1785, 0113 278 6052

HART Michelle *(Voc, Pf)*: 11 Spurn Avenue, Scartho, Grimsby DN33 2LG ☎ 01472 327611

HEATON Paul *(Voc, Hmca, Gtr, Tbn, B Gtr)*: c/o P Cass/Beautiful South, Cavendish House, St Andrews Court, St Andrews Street, Leeds LS3 1JY ☎ 0113 243 0898, 0113 234 0698

HOBSON Jane *(Voc)*: Stagwood Cottage, 4 Cuttlehurst, Scissett, Huddersfield, West Yorkshire HD8 9LF ☎ 01484 863139

HOLMES Nicholas John *(Voc)*: 15 Groveville, Northedge Lane, Hipperholme, Halifax West Yorkshire HX3 8LO ☎ 01422 201139

HORSFALL Des *(Voc, Gtr)*: Four Winds, Stubbings, Mytholmroyd, Hebden Bridge, W Yorks ☎ 01422 884225

JACKSON Bridie *(Voc, Hrn, Gtr, Rec, Wh)*: 13 West Road, Bishop Auckland, Durham DL14 7PP ☎ 01388 607060

JACKSON-KANE Kit *(Voc, Gtr, Vla, Wh)*: 13 West Road, Bishop Auckland, Durham DL14 7PP ☎ 01388 607060

JAIMEE *(Voc)*: 80 Alverthorpe Road, Wakefield, West Yorks WF2 9PD ☎ 01924 201322, 0113 2307388

JAMES Mo *(Voc, Pf, Org)*: 18 Robert Street, Harrogate HG1 1HP ☎ 01423 541438

JAY Just *(Voc, Rapper)*: 5 Ned Lane, Slaithwaite, Huddersfield, West Yorkshire HD7 5HQ ☎ 01484 847096

JOHNSON Brian *(Voc)*: c/o Messrs Prager & Fenton, Accounts Dept, Midway House, 27/29 Cursitor Street London WC1 4SR

JONES Maxine *(Voc, Song W)*: 47 Weston Road, Balby, Doncaster, South Yorkshire DN4 8JS ☎ 0956 321953

KELLY Michael *(Voc, Gtr, Hmca, Kbds)*: 16 Mowbray Street, Durham DH1 4BH ☎ 0191384 5242

KENNY Leigh *(Voc)*: 2 Montreal Terrace, Swinnow, Leeds LS13 4QA ☎ 0113 246 9239, 0113 243 9328

LANGDON Christian *(Voc, Gtr)*: 40 Grove Lane, Headingley, Leeds LS6 2AP ☎ 0113 2307581

LARKIN Paul *(Voc, Gtr)*: 4 Walton Heath, Darlington, Co. Durham DL1 3HZ ☎ 01325 362422

LEIGHTON Michelle *(Voc)*: 2 Southwell Road, Linthorpe, Middlesbrough, Cleveland TS5 6QD

LESLIE Uriah *(Voc)*

LONE Johnny *(Voc)*: 26 Murgatroyd Street, West Bowling, Bradford, West Yorkshire BD5 5EB ☎ Bradford 404836

MALT David *(Voc, Pf)*: 5 Pine Court, Southcliffe Drive, Baildon Shipley, West Yorks BD17 5QW ☎ 01274 588626

MCKENDRICK Paul *(Voc, Gtr)*: 45 Leeds Road, Rawdon, Leeds, W. Yorks LS19 6NW ☎ 0113 239 1878

MILGATE Ken *(Voc, Dul, Tamb)*: 76 Plawsworth Road, Scariston, County Durham DH7 6PE ☎ 0191 371 1907

MILNER Edward *(Voc, Brass, Kbds)*: 15 Claremont Road, Newcastle-upon-Tyne NE2 4AD ☎ 0191 2602855, 01434 632566

MORRIS Annette *(Voc)* ☎ 0956 230652

MORRIS Paulette *(Voc)*: 41 Sholebroke Palce, Leeds, West Yorkshire LS7 3HJ ☎ 0956 218899

MORRISON Tom *(Voc, Gtr)*: 9 Clarney Place, Darfield, Barnsley, South Yorkshire S73 9EQ ☎ 01226 750923

MORTON John *(Voc, E Gtr, Rec, B Gtr, Cl Gt)*: Black Ox House, 3 Roman Road, Leeming, North Yorkshire DL7 9SB

MR TALKATIVE *(Voc)*: 5 Pennard House, Launton Way, Hutson Street, Bradford BD5 7PL ☎ 0958 726159

NUTTER Alice *(Voc, Per)* ☎ 0113 279 0739, 0860 797808 mob

PALLADINO Alice *(Voc, Per)*: 31 Markham Crescent, Rawdon, Leeds LS19 6NG

PATTISON Andrea *(Voc, Kbds)*: Flat F, 48 St Andrews Street, Newcastle-upon-Tyne NE1 5SF ☎ 0191 260 2966, 07801 548118 mob

PRESINEE Yasmin *(Voc)*: Address Unknown

ROBINSON Keith *(Voc, Song W, Gtr)*: 2 Stanley Street, Lockwood, Hudersfield, West Yorkshire HD1 3UQ

RUSBY Kate *(Voc, Gtr, Pf, Vln)*: 11 Darton Road, Cawthorne, Barnsley, South Yorkshire S75 4HR ☎ 01226 790536

RUSSELL Sandi *(Voc)*: 11 Tenter Terrace, Durham City, County Durham DH1 4RD ☎ 0191 386 0092

SCOTT Richard *(Voc, Flt, T Sax, Gtr)*: 10 Ravenswood Road, Heaton, Newcastle-upon-Tyne NE6 5TU ☎ 276 7036

SHERIDAN Mark *(Voc, Gtr)*: 50 Plymouth Road, Sheffield S7 2DE ☎ 0114 249 0436

SIMONS Jane *(Voc, Pf)*: 6 Caxton Road, Broomhill, Sheffield S10 3DE ☎ 0114 266 4428

SIMPSON Peter *(Voc, B Gtr, Hrp)*: 83 Castle Walk, Castle Court, Hyde Park Flat, St Johns Road, Sheffield S2 5JB ☎ 0114 279 8596

TAGGART David *(Voc, Gtr, Man, Hmca)*: 88 Rutherglen Road, Red House, Sunderland SR5 5LL ☎ 0191 549 4891

TAT *(Voc, Per, Gtr)*: 5 Drivers Row, Wakefield Road, Pontefract, West Yorkshire WF8 4HF ☎ 01977 792571

TILBROOK Lyn *(Voc, Pf)*: 9 Dunbar Drive, Eaglescliffe, Stockton-on-Tees, Cleveland TS16 9EG ☎ 01325 480807

TREVOR Anne *(Voc)*: 1 Claremont Road, Grimsby, Lincs DN32 8NU ☎ 01472 695177

VOCHL.85 Hsm *(Voc)*: Naracen Productions, Flat 2, 1 Park View Road, Bradford, West Yorkshire BD9 4PA ☎ 0113 269 6050

WALKER Edward *(Voc, Gtr)*: 33 The Grove, Brookfield, Middlesbrough, Cleveland TS5 8DT ☎ 01642 593780

WALLACE Susan *(Voc, Kbds)*: 40 Milton Street, York YO10 3EP ☎ 01904 411867

WALTERS Stephen *(Voc, Kbds, Tpt)*: 3 Lansdowne Ave, Lincoln LN6 7PU ☎ 01522 871514, 0973 369128 mob

WALTON Ian *(Voc, Kbds)*: 122 Bolling Road, Ben Rhydding, Ilkley, West Yorkshire LS29 8PN ☎ 01943 600725, 01943 600725

WATERSON Norma *(Voc)*: Hillcrest, Mount Pleasant East, Robin Hoods Bay, Whitby North Yorkshire YO22 4RF ☎ 01947 880622, 01947 880622

WATKINS Eleanor *(Voc, Cel, Pf)*: 36 Parkside Grove, Bradford, West Yorkshire BD9 5LL

WAUDBY James *(Voc, Gtr, Vln, Pf)*: 223 Ganstead Lane East, Bilton, Hull HU77 4BG ☎ 01482 813864

WEBB Mia *(Voc)*: 76 Cheshire Grove, South Shields, Tyne & Wear NE34 7HZ ☎ 0191 454 3878, 0831 534743

WIGHT Gary *(Voc, Gtr)*: 26 Westbourne Avenue, Gateshead, Tyne & Wear NE8 4NP ☎ 0191 477 0224, 0498 528776

WILKINSON Jennifer *(Voc)*: 2 Church Lane, Netherton, Wakefield, W Yorks WF4 4HE ☎ 01924 277636, 01294 250399

WILSON Elizabeth *(Voc, Pf, Kbds, Gtr)*: Greenacres, Pinfold Lane, Stickney, Boston, Lincoln PE22 8AN ☎ 01205 480922 & fax, 0374 989384 mob

WITTER Rick *(Voc, Gtr, Hmca)*: 2 Carleton Street, Leeman Road, York YO26 4XN

EAST

ARCHER Paul *(Voc, Gtr, Didj, Bod, Per)*: 12 Artillery Street, Wisbech, Cambridgeshire PE13 2QP ☎ 01945 655804

AYERS Lizzie *(Voc)*: 170 Woodland Drive, Watford WD1 3DB ☎ 01923 22910

BARNETT Mandie *(Voc, Pf)*: 12 Hillside Road, Thorpe, St Andrew, Norwich, Norfolk NR7 0QG ☎ 01603 431418

BARRETT Rosie Val *(Voc)*: 85 Stonefield, Bar Hill, Cambridge CB3 8TE ☎ 01954 789 670

BATTERBEE Robert *(Voc)*: Hannah Cottage, Winch Road, Gayton, Kings Lynn, Norfolk PE32 1QP ☎ 01553 636039

BERRIMAN Simonne *(Voc)*: 14 Bocking End, Braintree, Essex CM7 9AA ☎ 01376 323871

BROWN Ray *(Voc, Gtr)*: 113 Ambleside Drive, Southend-on-Sea SS1 2UP ☎ 0836 734 796

CAMPBELL Grace *(Voc)*: 88 Wexham Close, Marsh Farm, Luton, Bedfordshire LU3 3TX ☎ 01582 584352

CAMPBELL Stevie *(Voc)* ☎ 0850 674072

CARLOS Mexeena *(Voc, Fo Fdl, Man, Gtr, Kbds)*: Aviary Cottage, Briggate, Worstead, Norfolk NR28 9QZ ☎ 01692 536497

CARNE Geoff *(Voc, Gtr)*: 14 Courtlands Close, Watford, Herts WD2 5GR ☎ 01923 680690

CARROLL Dina *(Voc)*: c/o Simon Makepeace, Martin Greene Ravden, 55 Loudoun Road, London NW8 0DL ☎ 020 7625 4545, 020 7625 5265

CASSIDY Jennifer *(Voc)*: 79 Humber Doucy Lane, Ipswich, Suffolk IP4 3NU ☎ 01473 718811

CATTEN Paul *(Voc)*: 9 Tudor Street, Ross-on-Wye, Herefordshire HR9 5PS ☎ 01989 566864

CLARK Indy *(Voc, Gtr, B Gtr)*: 33 Oxford Road, Mistley, Manningtree, Essex CO11 1BW ☎ 01206 394 585

CONSCIOUS KEN *(Voc, Gtr)*: 68A Mill Hill Road, Norwich NR2 3DS ☎ 01603 765186

COOK James *(Voc, E Gtr)*: 24B Kirkstall Ave, London N17 6PH ☎ 020 8808 2189 & fax

DABROWSKI Peter *(Voc, Gtr)*: 8 Beecroft Way, Dunstable, Beds LU6 1ED ☎ 01582 472018

DAINES Maria *(Voc)*: 4 Audley Way, Horseheath, Cambs CB1 6QE ☎ 01223 890164

DANIELS Maxine *(Voc)*: 125 Bellmaine Avenue, Corringham, Essex SS17 7SZ ☎ 01375 642567

DARE Mark *(Voc)*: 106 Forresters Drive, Welwyn Garden City, Hertfordshire AL7 2JQ ☎ 01707 371479, 0839 618847 pager

DARREN Jenny *(Voc, Song W)*: 25 Wrights Way, Colchestetr, Leavenheath, Essex CO6 4VR ☎ 01206 263993

DAVIS Ginette *(Voc, Cel, Vln)*: 3 Faraday Road, Ipswich, Suffolk IP4 1PU ☎ 01473 446019

DEASON Barbara *(Voc, Flt, Gtr, Song W)*: 24 Garden Row, Hitchin, Herts SG5 1QD ☎ 01462 458902

DENNIS Catherine *(Voc, Kbds, Flt)*: c/o 19 Management, Unit 32, Ransomes Dock, 35-37 Parkgate Road, London SW11 4NP ☎ 020 7738 1919, 020 7738 1819 fax

DOBIE Allyson *(Voc, Pf, Gtr)*: 50 Mill Road, Ashley, Newmarket, Suffolk CB8 9ER ☎ 01638 731348

DOWNS Jeanne *(Voc)*: 34C Webbs Road, London SW11 6SF ☎ 020 7738 9627

DOYLE Amanda *(Voc, Gtr)*: 5 Chartridge, The Hoe, Carpenders Park, Watford, Herts WD1 5AT ☎ 020 8428 8144, 0956 446140

DR ROBERT *(Voc, Song W, B Gtr, Pf, Kbds)*: 18 Brewery Road, Pampisford, Cambridge CB2 4EW ☎ 01223 830510

DUFFY Pip *(Voc, Kbds)*: 11 Lancaster Road, Ipswich IP4 2NY ☎ 01473 280063, 07050 198025

EDEN Bill *(Voc, Gtr, B Gtr, Hmca)*: 7 Fir Tree Rise, Chelmsford, Essex CM2 9HS ☎ 01245 352476

ENGLISH Jane *(Voc)*: 1 Welland Road, Burnham-on-Crouch, Essex CM0 8TX ☎ 01621 783954

FAWCETT Mark *(Voc, Gtr)*: 45 Wells Road, Stiffkey, Wells Next The Sea, Norfolk NR23 1AJ ☎ 01328 830209

FEATHERSTONE Craig *(Voc)*: 23 Creighton Ave, St. Albans, Herts AL1 2LG ☎ 01727 862763

FENTON Paula *(Voc)*: 17 Poplar Avenue, Warden Hill, Luton, Beds LU3 2BP ☎ 01582 504785

FIELDS Tricia *(Voc)*: 29 Seller Street, Chester CH1 3NA ☎ 01244 319992

FLINT Keith *(Voc)*: Northend Farm Cottage, Northend, Dunmow, Essex CM7 3PQ ☎ 01376 551426

FULLER Graham *(Voc, Gtr, Sax, Clt, Hmca)*: 21, Russet Way, Melbourn, Near Royston, Herts SG8 6HF ☎ 01763 261295

FULLERTON Neal *(Voc)*: 137 Church Road, Potters Bar, Herts EN6 1EU ☎ 0973 342974, 01707 652532

G Rayan *(Voc)*: 62 Ratcliffe Court, Welland Estate, Peterborough PE1 4TY ☎ 01733 558249, 01733 208128

GARNER Sophie *(Voc)*: 7 Monmouth Road, Watford, Herts WD1 1QW ☎ 01923 220756, 07887 614825

GILBERT Brenda-Jean *(Voc)*: 1 Old Oak Gardens, Herons Elm, Northchurch, Hertfordshire HP4 3TD ☎ 01442 877668, 070500 44746

GLEAVE Delia *(Voc, Db, B Gtr, Gtr, Flag)*: 41 Golden Riddy, Linslade, Bedfordshire LU7 7RH ☎ 01525 375977

GONZALEZ Lily *(Voc, Per)*: 5A St Marys Close, Chilton, Sudbury, Suffolk CO10 0PN ☎ 01787 313348

GOODEY Stella *(Voc)* ☎ 01760 725876

GOODMAN Nanci *(Voc)*: 30 Broad Oak Walk, Rayleigh, Exxes SS6 8JU ☎ 01268 779159

GREEN Terrence *(Voc, Song W)*: 33 Dalton Street, St Albans, Herts AL3 5QH ☎ 01727 842955

GREENFIELD Charley *(Voc)*: 35 Rodeheath, Luton, Beds LU3 9XB ☎ 01582 584203

GRIMSHAW Marie *(Voc, Per)*: 89 Foxglove Ave, Barking Road, Needham Mkt., Suffolk IP6 8JJ ☎ 01449 721 048, 01449 721 678

HEMSWORTH Kathy *(Voc)*: 4 Kingsbury Gardens, Dunstable, Beds LU5 4PX ☎ 01582 670469, 01582 605465

HENDRICKS Joanna *(Voc)*: 8 Court Two, Bronte Road, Witham, Essex CM8 2QQ ☎ 01376 501047

HEYNE Rebecca *(Voc)*: 31A Ekin Road, Cambridge CB5 8PS ☎ 01223 515186

HILDIA *(Voc, Arr, Song W)*: 21 Clarendon Avenue, Luton, Bedfordshire LU2 7PQ ☎ 01582 561508, 01582 561508 fax

HILHAM Caroline *(Voc)*: 8 Benbow Road, Thetford, Norfolk IP24 2TN ☎ 01842 754124

HODGKIN Keyy *(Voc, Gtr)*: 20 Parkgate, Hitchin, Herts SG4 9BP ☎ 01462 437832

HOLLINGSWORTH Rachel *(Voc, Pf, Vln)*: The Cottage, Cromer, Nr Stevenage, Herts SG2 7QA ☎ 01438 861176 & fax

JONES Sianed *(Voc, Vln, Vadag, Kbds, A Sax)*: 85 London Road South, Lowestoft, Suffolk NR33 0AS ☎ 01502 512905

JORDAN David *(Voc)*: 2 Lapwing Drive, Whittlesey, Peterborough, Cambridge PE7 1PW ☎ 01733 202415, 01426 134003

KNIGHT John *(Voc, Gtr, Dms, Kbds)*: Flat 3, 33 Lyndhurst Road, Lowestoft, Suffolk NR32 4PD ☎ 01502 513959, 01502 517900

LAMBERT Mary Lou *(Voc)* ☎ 01379 741236

KT *(Voc, Rec)*: 67 Peterborough Road, Farcet, Peterborough, Cambs PE7 3BN ☎ 01733 241474

LEAPER Tasha *(Voc)*: 141 Fairfax Drive, Westcliffe-on-Sea, Essex SS0 9BQ ☎ 01702 433392, 0468 903443

LEIGHTON Jane *(Voc, T Sax, A Sax, Flt, Clt)*: 19 Camden Road, Ipswich, Suffolk IP3 8JW ☎ 01473 278054

LOW Patti *(Voc)*: 292 Brocklesmead, Harlow, Essex CM19 4QB ☎ 01297 453407, 01279 323199

LUNEDEI Ezio *(Voc)*: 3 Corona Road, Cambridge CB4 3EB

LUNNISS Amanda *(Voc)*: White Acres, Colchester Road, Chappel, Essex CO6 2AF ☎ 01206 240058, 0468 904028 mob

LYNDSEY *(Voc)*

MACK Jimmy *(Voc)* ☎ 07071 223271, 0374 170257

MALIK Samia *(Voc, Song W, Com)*: 61 Glebe Road, Norwich, Norfolk NR2 3JH ☎ 01603 503626

MARDI Dee *(Voc)*: 10B Langdale Gardens, Chelmsford, Essex CM2 9QH ☎ 01245 264524

MARTIN Syrus *(Voc, Gtr)*: 24 Fellowes Gardens, Peterborough PE2 8DH ☎ 01733 61529

MATTHEWS Georgina *(Voc)*: 122 Lynn Road, Ely, Cambs CB6 1DE ☎ 01353 669250

MAY Tina *(Voc)*: 8 Oliver Road, Bennetts End, Hemel Hempstead, Herts HP3 9PY ☎ 01442 243835, 0378 191551 mob

MCMAHON Geraldine *(Voc, Hrp, Pf)*: 27 Orchard Drive, Park Street, St Albans, Herts AL2 2HQ ☎ 01727 872372

MELOY Laure *(Voc)*: 8 The Squirrells, Welwyn Garden City, Herts AL7 2JH ☎ 0839 682855

MILLER John *(Voc)*: 16 Kitchner Avenue, Chatham, Kent ME4 5XS

MIRA Elisa *(Voc, Song W)*: 61 Warrengate Road, North Mymms, Herts AL9 7TT ☎ 01707 643121

MUDEKA Anna *(Voc, Per, Mbira, Mrba)*: c/o 9 Havant Close, Eaton, Norwich, Norfolk NR4 6NP, 0589 740928

MYERS Sharon *(Voc, Gtr)*: 49 St Georges Park Avenue, Westcliff-on-Sea, Essex SS0 9UE ☎ 01702 343707, 0468 073775

MYNOTT Terry *(Voc)*: 13 Hay Green, Therfield, Royston, Hertfordshire SG8 9QL ☎ 01763 287468, 01426 136989 pager

NICHOLS Ellie *(Voc, B Gtr)*: 33 Selwyn Road, Stamford, Lincs PE9 1JW ☎ 01780 55944

NORRIS George *(Voc, Gtr)*: 10 Barley Way, Putnoe Estate, Bedford MK41 8HY ☎ 01234 343810

OFFICER Gareth *(Voc)*: 116 Kings Road, London Colney, St. Albans, Herts AL2 1EP ☎ 01727 824030

ORBELL Candy *(Voc, Pf, Gtr, Clt)*: 69 Back Road, Linton, Cambridge CB1 6JF ☎ 01223 893738, 01223 893444

OVERMAN Arlette *(Voc, Pf, Vln)*: 24 Millers Close, Bishops Stortford, Herts CM23 4FJ ☎ 01279 658622

PANAYIOTOU Georgios *(Voc, Pf, Kbds, Gtr)*: 21 Pond Square, Highgate Village, London N6 6BA ☎ 020 8340 8840, 020 8340 9202 fax

PEARSON Andrew *(Voc, Gtr, Song W)*: Beech House, 20 Burgate Road, Felixstowe, Suffolk IP11 8DE ☎ 01394 271517

POWELL Heather *(Voc, Per)*: 109A Cambridge Street, Aylesbury, Buckinghamshire HP20 1BT ☎ 01296 630476

RAULT Odille *(Voc)*: Little Tallants, Kimpton Bottom, Kimpton, Herts SG4 8EU ☎ 01438 832364, 07971 469437, 01438 833892

RAYMOND Miss P *(Voc)*: 21 Oakfield Park Road, Dartford, Kent DA1 2SR ☎ 01332 229916

RENAE Louise *(Voc, Song W)*

RICE-MILTON Terence *(Voc)*: 8 Copthorn Avenue, Park Lane, Broxbourne, Herts EN10 7RA ☎ 01992 441096

ROBINSON Marc *(Voc)*: 91 Brook Road, Tolleshunt Knights, Nr Tiptree, Essex C05 0RH ☎ 01621 819553

ROGERS Sebastian *(Voc, Gtr)*: 23 Mount Pleasant, Diss, Norfolk IP22 3DT ☎ 01379 640290, 01379 651280, 01379 651280

ROSATO Tania *(Voc, Pf)*: 32B Garston Lane, Watford, Herts WD2 6QL ☎ 01923 671951, 0410 032297 mob

RYAN Ellen *(Voc)*: 8 Wilcox Close, Borehamwood, Herts WD6 5PY

SANDERSON Hayley *(Voc, Sax, Pf, Kbds)*: 100 Uplands Werington, Peterborough, Cambs PE4 5AF ☎ 01733 57720, 0402 595964

SARWAR Atif *(Voc, Kbds)*: 8 New House Park, St Albans, Herts AL1 1TJ ☎ 01727 842382, 01727 856750

SASHA *(Voc)*: 95 Copse Hill, Harlow, Essex CM19 4PP ☎ 01279 414859

SCOTT Russell *(Voc, Kbds)*: 30 Farm Close, Borehamwood, Herts WD6 4TX ☎ 020 8953 4600

SEWELL Niki *(Voc, B Gtr)* ☎ 01727 854982, 0370 812284

SHORT Aaron *(Voc, Gtr, Kbds, Song W)*: 3 Daneway Gardens, Goldings Lane, Leiston, Suffolk IP16 4XA ☎ 01728 830105, 01728 833281

STERN Christopher *(Voc, Gtr)*: Address Unknown ☎ 01778 342386, 0585 358 225

STOCKLEY Roslyn *(Voc, Pf, Gtr, Brass)*: 249 Queen Ediths Way, Cambridge CB1 8NJ ☎ 01223 248233

STRACHAN Louisa *(Voc)*: 4 Aberdeen Gardens, Leigh-on-Sea, Essex SS9 3RH ☎ 01702 558762

SUTHERLAND Irene *(Voc, Rec)*: 8 Manor Drive, Chiswell Green, St Albans, Herts AL3 3DH ☎ 01727 768451

TERRELONGE Wanda *(Voc)*: 34 Dunstable Road, Dagnall, Herts HP4 1RG ☎ 01442 842501

THORNTON *(Voc, Gtr, Song W, Per)*: 83 Huntley Grove, Peterborough PE1 2QW ☎ 01733 770 555, 0374 490526 mob

TROTMAN Beverley *(Voc)*: 64 Icknield Road, Luton, Bedfordshire SG4 0UD ☎ 01582 652764

VAN JUPP Richie *(Voc, Gtr, Song W)*: Pear Tree House, St Neots Road, Hardwick, Cambridge CB3 7QL ☎ 01954 212788

VAN SERTIMA Colette *(Voc)*: 25B Arcadian Gardens, Wood Green, London N22 3AG ☎ 020 8365 8234

VICARS Kathryn *(Voc)*: 3 Redwing Grove, Abbotts Langley, Herts WD5 0GJ, 0976 766880 mob

WALLIS Walter J *(Voc)*: 3 Alexandra Road, Hitchin, Herts SG5 1RB ☎ 01462 454004

WALSHE Katherine *(Voc, Pf)*: Sycamore, Beech Avenue, Radlett, Herts WD7 7DD ☎ 1923 855321, 0958 708760

WALTERS Caroline *(Voc, Pf)*: 50 Temple Road, Ipswich, Suffolk IP3 8PB ☎ 01473 720206

WARD Gill *(Voc)*: Sucris Lodge, Lower Road, Hockley, Essex SS5 5NL ☎ 01702 232653, 01702 202219

WEARE Juliet *(Voc)*: 17 Philpot Avenue, Southend-on-Sea, Essex SS2 4RS ☎ 01702 467031

WEBB Victoria *(Voc)*: The Vicarage, Manor Gardens, Saxmundham, Suffolk IP17 1ET ☎ 01728 604234

WEBBER David *(Voc, Ctna, Kbds)*: 68 Oxhey Avenue, Oxhey, Watford, Herts WD1 4HA ☎ 01923 228468

WELHAM John *(Voc)*: 4 Edgefield Avenue, Lawford, Manningtree, Essex CO11 2HD ☎ 01206 392540

WERNICK Rebecca *(Voc, Gtr, Pf, Per)*: The Lyches, Greenway, Hutton Mount, Brentwood, Essex CM13 2NR

WILDMAN Heather *(Voc)*: 3 Great Grove, Bushey, Watford, Herts WD2 3BQ ☎ 020 8386 1195

WILLIAMS Cuthbert *(Voc, B Gtr)* ☎ 0956 968844

MIDLANDS

AKIRA Shaz *(Voc, Pf, Kbds)*: 95A Park Lane, Aston, Birmingham B6 5DL ☎ 0121 359 0097

ALCOCK Colette *(Voc)*: 15 Lordshire Plack, Packmoor, Stoke-on-Trent, Staffordshire ST7 4QD ☎ 01782 851937

ALEXANDER Paul *(Voc)*: 333 Flat 1 Gillott Road, Edgbaston, Birmingham B16 0RP ☎ 0966 228467

ALEXANDER Yaz *(Voc, Song W)*: 10 Southacre Avenue, City Centre, Birmingham B5 7DE ☎ 0121 622 6180, 0961 415517, 0468 385517

ALLARD Marie-Louise *(Voc)*: 58 Milverton Road, Erdington, Birmingham B23 6ES ☎ 0121 350 5924, 0956 303973 mob

ARMII Garbi *(Voc, Didj)*: 26 Abbey Road, Malvern, Worcs WR14 3HD ☎ 01684 567418

ASHA-B *(Voc, Per, Song W)*: 11 Fladbury Place, Carpenters Road, Newtown, Birmingham B19 2BE ☎ 0121 328 1208

ASHTON Shirley *(Voc, B Gtr, Kbds, Gtr)*: 59 Assarts Road, Malvern Wells, Worcestershire WR14 4HW ☎ 01684 893108

BAIG Abid *(Voc, Gtr, Kbds)*: 1 Fenbourne Close, Walsall, West Midlands WS4 1XD ☎ 01922 685760, 0956 696758

BALL Jyllian *(Voc)*: 20 Sovereign Court, Queens Road, Beeston, Notts NG9 1HJ ☎ 0115 9251683

BANSAL Sanjay *(Voc)*: 1 Upper Villers Street, Blakenhall, Wolverhampton, West Midlands WV2 4NP ☎ 01902 659422

BARKER Sally *(Voc, Gtr)*: Hill Farm, Misterton, Nr Lutterworth, Leics LE17 4LD

BARRETT Annette *(Voc)*: 19 St Andrew Close, Hednesford, Staffs WS12 5FA ☎ 01543 426599

BATES Jo *(Voc, Kbds)*: Laarbruch, Doley Canny, Newchurch, Kington, Herefordshire HR5 3QT ☎ 01497 851232

BATES Martyn *(Voc, Gtr)*

BATSFORD Richard *(Voc, Pf)*: 2 Valentine Court, Kings Heath, Birmingham B14 7AN ☎ 0121 689 2402

BEECH Adrianne *(Voc)*: High View, Keele Road, Keele, Newcastle, Staffs ST5 5AL ☎ 01782 751203

BERESFORD Charlie *(Voc, Gtr, Ac Gtr)* ☎ 01547 530818

BERRIMAN James *(Voc, Gtr, B Gtr)*: 24 Ravens Lane, Bignall End, Stoke-on-Trent, Staffordshire ST7 8PS ☎ 01782 720368

BLYTHE Andrea *(Voc)*: Naseby House, Marlbrooke Lane, Sale Green, Nr Doritwich, Worcestershire WR9 7LW ☎ 01905 391570

BONGAY Hassan *(Voc, Cong)*: 13Th Redruth Close, Delapre, Northampton NN4 8PL ☎ 01604 765328, 0585 045599

BONZO Alanzo *(Voc, Kbds)*: 37 Keswick Drive, Brownsover, Rugby, Warwickshire CV21 1PN ☎ 01788 541216

BOWN Alison *(Voc, Gtr, B Gtr)*: 19 Fleetwood Road, Leicester LE2 1YA ☎ 0116 2448236

BRENNAN John *(Voc, Dms)*: 45 Hardwicke Road, Narborough, Leicester LE9 5LW ☎ 0116 2862650, 0850 931617

BROWN Beverley *(Voc)*: 1 Fearon Place, Regent Street, Smethwick , Warley, Birmingham B66 3BY

BROWNE Andrew *(Voc, Gtr, Dms)*: 67 Oak Road, West Bromwich, West Midlands B70 8HR ☎ 0121 553 0847, 0973 782721

BUTCHER Simon *(Voc, Gtr, Vln, Kbds)*: 96 George Street, Mansfield, Notts NG19 6SB ☎ 01623 624778

BUTLER John *(Voc, Gtr, Kbds)*: 27 Haddenham Road, Leicester LE3 2BH ☎ 0116 289 1029

BUTTOLPH Katharine *(Voc, Pf, Per)*: 11 The Worthings, Stirchley, Birmingham B30 3AE ☎ 0121 458 6664

CAMBRIDGE Emma-Jayne *(Voc)*: 8 Herbert Road, Aldridge, Walsall, West Midlands WS9 8JR ☎ 01922 865636, 07887 997460, 01922 865636

CAMPBELL Kibibi *(Voc)*: 1 Andover Street, Digbeth, Birmingham B5 5RG ☎ 0121 633 4742

CHARLES Peter *(Voc)*: 45 Margaret Grove, Harborne, Birmingham B17 9JJ ☎ 0121 427 4566

CHIOTIS Zoe *(Voc, Pf)*: 67 Orchard Road, Erdington, Birmingham B24 9JB ☎ 0121 373 0412

CLARKE Andy *(Voc, Gtr, Hmca)*: 14 Beaconside Court, Beaconside, Stafford, Staffordshire ST16 3QS ☎ 01785 605622

CLARKE Neil *(Voc, Gtr)*: 22 Sun Street, Derby DE22 3UL ☎ 01332 368 910

CLAYTON Vikki *(Voc, Gtr)*: 9 Fern Close, Thurnby, Leicester LE7 9QJ ☎ 0116 2433447

CLEO *(Voc)*: 64 Andrew Gardens, Handsworth, Birmingham B21 9PN ☎ 0121 241 0880, 0961 309 293

CLEWS Michael *(Voc, Gtr)*: 18 Elm Tree Way, Cradley Heath, West Midlands B64 6EN ☎ 01384 347895, 0956 146704

COLMAN Sara *(Voc, Pf)*: 18 Link Road, Edgbaston, Birmingham B16 0EP ☎ 0121 246 7773

CONNEALLY Paul *(Voc, Kbds, Dms, Per, B Gtr)*: Mallards, 161 Tuckers Road, Loughborough, Leics LE11 2PH ☎ 01509 232385

COOPE Barry *(Voc, Kbds)*: 10 Moor Rise, Holbrook, Derbyshire DE56 0TR ☎ 01332 883472

COWLISHAW Lynsey *(Voc)*: 2 Hall Leys, Quorn, Leics LE12 8HF ☎ 01509 414063, 0976 830673 mob

CRADDOCK Daniel *(Voc)*: 12 Roman Street, Leicester LE3 0BD

CRESSWELL Deborah *(Voc)* ☎ 0468 914114

DADDY WATTSIE *(Voc)*: 30 Parkstone Road, Scraptoft, Lane, Leicester LE5 1NN ☎ 07977 317406

DALZELL Sarah *(Voc)*: 35 Middleton Street, Aylestone, Leicester LE2 8LU ☎ 0116 283 1077, 0116 224 888 fax

DAVIES Kerry *(Voc, Per)*: 70 Pooley View, Polesworth, Nr Tamworth, Staffs B78 1BP ☎ 01827 899942, 0411 165168

DAVIES Lorna *(Voc, Auto Hrp, Rec, Per)*: Koinonia, Cheddleton Heath Road, Cheddleton, Staffs ST13 7DX ☎ 01538 360256

DAVIES Sara *(Voc, Pf)*: 5 Brookhus Farm Road, Walmley, Sutton Coldfield, West Midlands B76 1QP ☎ 0121 313 1619

DE LA POER Petra *(Voc, Pf, Gtr, Ob)* ☎ 0370 953126

DENE *(Voc, B Ldr)*: 2 Greswolde Park Road, Birmingham B27 6QD ☎ 0121 707 3062

DENNY *(Voc)*: 127 Sneyd Street, Cobridge, Stoke-on-Trent, Staffs ST6 2NY ☎ 01782 286693

DEVIT Tony *(Voc, Song W)*: 1 Hinstock Road, Handsworth Wood, Birmingham B20 2ET ☎ 0121 523 5608

DIAMOND Denise *(Voc, Vln)*: 37 Dunsford Road, Smethwick, Warley, West Midlands B66 4EH ☎ 0121 429 1490

DIESEL *(Voc, Gtr, Kbds, Sitar, Club D)* ☎ 01902 788428

DOUGLAS Ronald *(Voc, Gtr, Kbds)* ☎ 0121 328 4033, 0958 633554

DYER Peter *(Voc, Gtr)*: 25 Barnby Gate, Newark, Notts NG24 1PX ☎ 01636 605143

EARDLEY Janice *(Voc)*: 18 Garnett Road West, Porthill, Newcastle, Staffs ST5 8EQ ☎ 01782 617682, 01782 239036

EVANS Cathy *(Voc, Gtr)*: 39 Porter Road, Derby DE3 6QZ ☎ 01332 763763

EVANS Emi *(Voc, Cel, Pf, Gtr)*: 6 Keswick Close, Beeston, Nottingham NG9 3AR ☎ 0115 925 3249

EVANS Victor *(Voc)*: 10 Cleveland Tower, Holloway Head, Birmingham B1 1UB ☎ 0121 632 6679

EYE Shine *(Voc)*: 79 Allens Road, Winson Green, Birmingham B18 4QX

FARDA P *(Voc)*: Clevelys, 89B Belmont Road, Wolverhampton, East Midlands WV4 5UE ☎ 0190 262 0838

FLETCHER Annette *(Voc, Gtr)* ☎ 01332 862823

FLETCHER Kirsty *(Voc, Dms)*: 5 Wheatley Grove, Nottingham NG9 5AG ☎ 0115 925 8954

FORBES Roy *(Voc)*: 10, Highgate Close, Highgate, Birmingham B12 0YD ☎ 0121 440 6397

FORD Lornette *(Voc, Pf)*: 37 Balderstone Close, Rowlatts Hill, Leicester LE5 4EB ☎ 0116 276 3936, 0802 902287

FOSTER Gladston *(Voc, Af Dms, Per)*: 15 Albert Road, Handsworth, Birmingham B21 9LA ☎ 0956 150154

FREEMAN Marilyne *(Voc)*: 'Brokenhill', Abberley, Worcester WR6 6AR ☎ 01299 896279

GAIR Peter *(Voc)*: 94 St.Bernards Road, Whitwick, Coalville, Leics LE67 5GW ☎ 01530 812643

GAYLE Godfrey *(Voc)*: 167 Wattville Raod, Handsworth, Birmingham, West Midlands B21 0DN ☎ 0121 569 5803, 01523 123662 pager

GIBBONS Stephen *(Voc)*: 18 Yew Tree Road, Edgbaston, Birmingham B15 2LX ☎ 0121 440 3101

GIFT Roland *(Voc, Sax)*: 8 Tufnall Park Road, London N7 0DP ☎ 020 7485 0292

GILBODY Justin *(Voc)*: 11 Victoria Terrace, Mansfield Road, Tibshelf, Alfreton, Derbyshire DE55 5NF ☎ 01773 874275

GRAHAM Jaki *(Voc, Voc)*: G O Management, Brickhaven House, Pattingham Road, Wightwick, Wolverhampton, Staffs WV6 8DD ☎ 01902 710293

GRAHAM Melissa *(Voc)*: Fortuna, 13 Avon Street, Wyken, Coventry CV2 3GJ ☎ 024 7666 5657, 024 7665 0652

GREEN Anna *(Voc)*: 7 Claisdale Road, Wigston, Magna, Leicester LE18 3YN ☎ 0116 2889260, 0836 536965

GREEN Ewart *(Voc, B Gtr)*: 161 Horninglow Road North, Burton-on-Trent, Staffs DE13 0SZ ☎ 01283 61427

GREEN Paul *(Voc)*: 26 Carden Close, West Bromwich, Birmingham B70 8NP ☎ 0121 525 8009, 0958 405751 mob

HALFORD Robert *(Voc)*: c/o Martin Green Ravden, 55 Loudoun Road, St. John's Wood, London NW8 0DL ☎ 020 7625 4545

HALL Stephen *(Voc, Gtr, Pf)*: 37 Oxford Road, Leicester LE2 1TN ☎ 0116 270 5060

HARDY Kate *(Voc)*: The Barn, Wickton Court, Stoke Prior, Leominster HR6 0LN ☎ 01568 797089

HARLEY Dan *(Voc)* ☎ 07970 421761

HARVEY Steven *(Voc)*: 25 Bamford Road, Pennfields, Wolverhampton WV3 0AT ☎ 01902 340547

HEMUS Alan *(Voc, B Ldr, Arr, Com, Cop)*: 4 Rowallan Road, Four Oaks, Sutton Coldfield, Warks B75 6RJ ☎ 0121 308 6294, 0121 429 5603

HOPKINS Gary *(Voc, Pf, Kbds, Dms, Per)*: 264A Old Birmingham Road, Lickey, Bromsgrove, Worcestershire B60 1NU ☎ 0121 445 5274

HUGH Owen *(Voc, Gtr, Hmca, Wh)*: c/o Dr J Mackay, 27 Kings Road, Oakham, Leics LE15 6PB ☎ 01572 724341

HUNT Arthur *(Voc, Gtr, Song W)*: 106 Coleshill Road, Water Orton, Birmingham B46 1RD ☎ 0121 749 7178

HURLEY Lisa *(Voc, Sax)*: 11 The Pastures, Kingsthorpe, Northampton NN2 8DD ☎ 01604 454691

HUTCHINSON Delroy *(Voc, Dms, B Gtr)*: 23 Norton Close, Smethwick, Warley, West Midlands B66 3JE ☎ 0121 565 2471

HUTCHINSON Steff *(Voc, Gtr, B Gtr)*: 14 Northcote Street, Leamington Spa, Warks CV31 1DX

INNISS Stephen *(Voc)*: 74 Aubrey Road, Small Heath, Birmingham B10 9DF ☎ 0831 293166

ISRAEL-WHEELER Samuel *(Voc, Gtr, Dms, B Gtr, Per)*: 9 Edith Terrace, Radford, Nottingham NG7 3BD ☎ 0115 942 7176

JAMES John *(Voc)*: 43 George Street, Anstey, Leicester LE7 7DT ☎ 0116 2365153

JAY Angelina *(Voc)*: 14 St Marks Crescent, Ladywood, Birmingham B1 2PX ☎ 0121 456 2721, 0956 834 746

JONES Delyth *(Voc)*: 47 Mapletree Lane, Halesowen B63 2BT ☎ 0121 602 5758

JONES Marie *(Voc)*: 73D Sedgley Road West, Tipton, West Midlands DY4 8AD ☎ 0121 557 4222

JONES Oliver *(Voc, Pf)*: 57 Lickey Rock, Marlbrook, Bromsgrove, Worcs B60 1HF ☎ 0121 445 3514, 07971 561119, 0121 445 3514

KANG Avtar *(Voc)*: 6 Copthall Road, Handsworth, Birmingham B21 8JJ

KHAN Shaneeka *(Voc, Kbds, Tbn)*: 45 Brinklow Tower, Upper Highgate Street, Highgate, Birmingham B12 0XT ☎ 0121 440 2867

KHODA Nichelle *(Voc, Harm, Tamp)*: 23 Wanlip Road, Syston, Leicester LE7 1PA ☎ 0116 260 6775, 0976 258328 mob

KING Gwen *(Voc)*: 2 Leslie Road, Edgbaston, Birmingham B16 8HD ☎ 0121 454 3012

KING PLEASURE *(Voc, T Sax)*: 220 Yardley Road, Acocks Green, Birmingham B27 6LR ☎ 0121 244 5140

KNIGHT Jon *(Voc, Rh Gtr, Dms)*: 102 Danvers Road, Leicester LE3 2AB ☎ 0116 299 7962

KULLY *(Voc, Kbds, Harm)*: 22 Peartree Road, Great Barr, Birmingham B43 6HY ☎ 0973 189723

LATOUCHE Cleveland *(Voc)*: 112 Milverton Road, Erdington, Birmingham B23 6EY ☎ 0121 243 7486

LAW Tina *(Voc)*: 617 Bristol Road South, Northfield, Birmingham B31 2JS ☎ 0121 475 7524

LEEMING Carol *(Voc, Kbds, Dms)*: 28 Beckingham Road, Leicester LE2 1HB ☎ 0116 2540398

LEWIS Amanda *(Voc)*: Flat 40 Waltham Hosue, Overend Street, West Bromwich, Birmingham B70 6ER ☎ 0121 525 5736

LEWIS Melanie *(Voc, Gtr, Kbds)*: 119 Milner Road, Selly Park, Birmingham B29 7RG ☎ 0121 684 8135

LEWIS Paul *(Voc)*: 76 Rowley Street, Chuckery, Walsall, West Midlands WS1 2AY ☎ 01922 616378

LLOYD Andrew *(Voc, Gtr, Hmca)*: 26A Cadogan Terrace, Hackney, London E9 ☎ 020 8986 8905

LUPA *(Voc)*: 30 Waterside, Wheeleys Lane, Birmingham B15 2DW ☎ 0121 622 6640, 0121 772 2827 fax

MACHIN Ben *(Voc, Gtr)*: 38 Main Road, Austrey, Nr Atherstone, Warks CV9 3EH ☎ 01827 830445

MACKA.B *(Voc, Kbds)*: 6 Scafell Drive, Bilston, West Midlands WV14 7BD ☎ 01902 655926

MANSER Pat *(Voc)*: 5 Coleridge Walk, Daventry, Northants NN11 5AU ☎ 01327 78328

MARSH Lynn *(Voc)*: 36 Leighs Road, High Heath, Pelsall, Walsall, W. Midlands WS4 1BZ ☎ 01922 691371 & fax

MARSHALL Darren *(Voc)*: 244 Haydn Road, Sherwood, Nottingham NG5 2LG ☎ 0115 9109220, 0973 123143

MATTSON Daniel *(Voc, Gtr, B Gtr)*: 152 Westcotes Drive, Leicester LE3 0SP ☎ 0116 291 2040

MATTU Jaspal *(Voc, Hmca, Tabla, Gtr, B Gtr)*: 3 Postbridge Road, Stivichall, Coventry CV3 5AG ☎ 024 7669 0376, 0973 491628 mob

MCCALLA Subrina *(Voc)*: 125 Grestone Avenue, Handsworth Wood, Birmingham B20 1ND ☎ 0121 523 7794

MEEK Jessica *(Voc)*: 43 The Lea, Trentham, Stoke-on-Trent, Staffs ST4 8DY

MILES Debbie *(Voc)*: Larkspur, 12 Chestnut Close, Lower Moor, Pershore, Worcs WR10 2RE ☎ 01386 861281

MINELLI Geri *(Voc)*: c/o T.M.A., PO Box 7685, Birmingham B34 7BE ☎ 0121 749 7779

MORRELL Rachael *(Voc, Pf, Vln)*: 40 Hillwood Road, Madeley Heath, Near Crewe, Cheshire CW3 9JY ☎ 01782 751575

MOSAIC *(Voc)*: 36 Cardinals Walk, Humberstone, Leicester LE5 1LD ☎ 0116 241 6448, 07771 752175

MOULD Kelvin *(Voc, Kbds, Gtr)*: 8A High Street, Eccleshall, Stafford ST21 6BZ ☎ 01785 851573

NANTON Adele *(Voc)*: 47 Hornbeam, Amington, Tamworth, Staffordshire B77 4NB ☎ 01827 312605

NATACHA *(Voc, Per)*: 33 Kersley Road, London N16 0NT ☎ 020 7275 9235

NIEPER Wendy *(Voc)* ☎ 0421 054871 mob

NIX Zoe *(Voc)*: 8 Hillview Close, Belle Vale, Halesowen, West Midlands B63 3QW ☎ 01384 68471, 0973 939527

NOBLE Geoffrey Charles *(Voc, Kbds, Gtr)*: 357 Shobnall Street, Burton-on-Trent DE14 2HT ☎ 01283 543141

O'CALLAGHAN Sharyn *(Voc)*: 40 Waltham House, Overend St, West Bromwich, West Midlands B70 ☎ 0121 525 5736, 0966 366478

O'CONNELL Liam *(Voc, Song W, Ac Gtr)*: 22 Cornwallis Drive, Shipnal, Shropshire TF11 8UB ☎ 01952 462790, 0791 363205

O'DEA Gary *(Voc, Hmca, Per, Gtr)*: 12 Pear Tree Avenue, Tipton, West Midlands DY4 8NJ ☎ 0121 520 5259

OLIDIA *(Voc)*

PAPERDOLLS *(Voc)*: Address Unknown

PARDESI Silinder *(Voc)*: 32 Ashdown Close, Ernesford Grange, Coventry CV3 2PT ☎ 024 7644 0405, 0378 777992, 024 7644 0405 fax

PARKES Garry, *(Voc, Song W)*: 172, 7' Oxford Road, Moseley, Birmingham B13 9ES ☎ 0121 689 2552, 0958 320761

PENDLEBURY Marcia *(Voc, Per)*: Tyddyn Corn, Botwnnog, Pwllheli, Gwynedd OL53 8HA ☎ 0175873 0360

PENNEY Jonn *(Voc)*: 39 Union Street, Stourbridge, West Midlands DY8 1PR ☎ 01384 440790

POLACK Margaret *(Voc, Pf)*: 19 Barker Street, Lozells, Birmingham B19 1EL ☎ 0121 551 7772

PRICE Laura *(Voc, Gtr, Hmca)*

PROCTER Colin *(Voc, Kbds, Gtr)* ☎ 01536 725140

PROUDLOVE Kate *(Voc, Pf, Gtr)*: Terrick House, Whitchurch, Shropshire SY13 4JZ ☎ 01948 665964, 01743 365561

PRYOR Vicky *(Voc)* ☎ 020 7499 2634, 0958 776396

RANDELL Andrew *(Voc, Gtr)*: 51 Minehead Street, Leicester LE3 0SJ ☎ 01162 332425

REEVES Marion *(Voc)*: The Coach House, Danesmoor, Danescourt Road, Tettenhall, Wolverhampton, West Midlands WV6 9BG ☎ 01902 757984

RICHARDSON Paul *(Voc)*: Address Unknown

RITCHIE Derrick *(Voc, B Gtr, Ld Gtr, Rh Gtr)*: 15 Reapers Walk, Pendeford, Wolverhampton WV8 1TS ☎ 01902 839551

RODEN Julie *(Voc, Saxes)* ☎ 01785 612165

SABEDORIA Alison *(Voc, M Hrp, M Fid)*: 108, Wattville Road, Handsworth, Birmingham B21 0DR ☎ 0121 523 9424

SAFRI Balwinder *(Voc, Gtr)*: 43 Aylesford Road, Handsworth, Birmingham B21 8DN ☎ 0121 551 2783

SASSY *(Voc)*: The Queen Victoria, 192 Victoria Road, Fenton, Stoke-on-Trent ST4 2HQ ☎ 01782 883673, 01782 883679

SCOTT Brenda *(Voc, Arr, Com, Cop)*: 150 Poplar Avenue, Edgbaston, Birmingham B17 8ER ☎ 0121 420 4232

SEATON Dennis *(Voc)*: 38 Pargeter Road, Bearwood, Warley, West Midlands B67 5HY ☎ 0121 429 6867

SHIN *(Voc)* ☎ 0121 565 5249 & fax, 0374 651651 mob

SINGH Samiera *(Voc)*: 116 Brickhill Road, Wellingborough, Northants NN8 3JP ☎ 0115 9795272, 0973 711698

SINGH Sardara *(Voc)*: 4 George Bird Close, Smethwick, Warley, West Midlands B66 3BP ☎ 0121 558 3772

SMITH Cynthia *(Voc)*: 78 Langbank Avenue, Binley, Coventry CV3 2PN ☎ 024 7645 2821

SMITH Russell *(Voc, Gtr, Pf)*: 7 Brunswick Road, Earlsdon, Coventry CV1 3EX ☎ 024 7655 0215

SMITHYMAN Ernest *(Voc, Clt, Sax, Pf)*: 313 Littleworth Road, Hednesford, Staffs WS12 5HY ☎ 01543 871874

SPENCER Bonnie *(Voc)*

SPROSTON Trevor *(Voc, Pf, Con)*: 65 High Street, Alsagers Bank, Stoke-on-Trent, Staffs ST7 8BQ ☎ 01782 720956

ST CLARE Avis *(Voc, Kbds, B Ldr)*: 13 Walmley Ash Road, Sutton Coldfield, West Midlands B76 1HY ☎ 0121 351 1513

ST JOHN Genea *(Voc, Sax)*: 48 Leafield Gardens, Halesowen, West Midlands B62 8LX ☎ 0121 559 6784, 07775 855746, 0870 0560515

STORM Bob *(Voc, Gtr, Kbds)*: 40 Westbury Road, Nuneaton, Warwickshire CV10 8HG ☎ 024 7635 4606

SULLIVAN Robert *(Voc)*

SUMMERS Keith *(Voc, Kbds, Tpt)*: 43 The Chesils, Styvechale, Coventry CV3 5BD ☎ 024 7641 4290

SWEENEY Vee *(Voc, Kbds)*: 72, Salisbury Road, Moseley, Birmingham B13 8JU ☎ 0121 449 1711 eve

TAYLOR Helen *(Voc)*: 27 Highwood Avenue, Solihull, West Midlands B92 8QY ☎ 0121 684 5794

TERRY Richard *(Voc)*: 9, Browning Close, Coton Green, Tamworth, West Midlands B79 8NB ☎ 01827 55252

THOMSON Murray *(Voc, Gtr)* ☎ 01509 213902

TIGER Brandy *(Voc)*: 7 Twyning Road, Edgbaston, Birmingham B16 0HJ ☎ 0121 454 8092

TIVEY Cara *(Voc, Pf)*: Flat 1, 48, Somers Road, Malvern Link, Worcs WR14 1JB ☎ 01684 562549

TUDOR Alison *(Voc)*: 33 Uplands Road, Handsworth, Birmingham, West Midlands B21 8BU ☎ 0121 523 6156

TURNER Ruby *(Voc, Per)*: 8 Botteville Road, Acocks Green, Birmingham B27 7YD ☎ 0121 708 1349

ULLAH Jaimie *(Voc)*: 11 Collmead Court, Blackthorn, Northampton NN3 8QE ☎ 01604 413233, 079796 23982

VAN DYKE Chris *(Voc, Gtr, Pf)*

WALCOTT Degigha *(Voc)*: 81 Queslett Road, Great Barr, Birmingham B43 6DR ☎ 0121 360 8214

WALLACE Diane *(Voc)*: 49 Legge Street, West Bromwich, West Midlands B70 6HE ☎ 0121 553 4072

WHYTE Sharon *(Voc)*: 11 Homer Street, Balsal Heath, Birmingham B12 9RA ☎ 0121 440 0423, 0958 510532

WISEMAN Valerie *(Voc)* ☎ 0121 454 7020

WOODVINE-WEST Joyce *(Voc)*: 21 Davenport Avenue, Crewe, Cheshire CW2 6LG ☎ 01270 257224

WRIGHT David *(Voc, Gtr)*: 99 Derbyshire Lane, Hucknall, Nottingham NG15 7GF ☎ 0115 953 6320

YORK Alan James *(Voc, Gtr, B Gtr)*: 75 Kingston Road, Earlsdon, Coventry CV5 6LQ ☎ 024 7671 4362

ZARA *(Voc)*: 29 Castlecroft Road, Finchfield, Wolverhampton WV3 8BS ☎ 01902 823161, 07788 818803

SOUTH EAST

AHDDOUD Latifa *(Voc)*: 8 Frazer Gardens, Dorking, Surrey RH4 1HR ☎ 01306 882805, 0956 151887

ALSFORD Niki *(Voc, Pf)*: 5 Middle Road, Sholing, Southampton, Hampshire SO19 8FR ☎ 023 8043 8861, 07979 074120

AMBER LIGHT *(Voc, B Ldr)*: 75 Swanfield Drive, Chichester, West Sussex PO19 4TQ ☎ 01243 785203

ANDERSON Lindsay *(Voc)*: 2 Rose Cottage, 56 Poole Road, Upton, Poole, Dorset BH16 5JD ☎ 01202 632469

ASHTON-WILSON Genevieve *(Voc)*: No. 1 Elm Road, Hornscross, Greenhithe, Kent DA9 9DL ☎ 01322 370064

ASTA Sally *(Voc, Gtr)*: Top Floor Flat, Shurlock Row Garage, Broadmoor Road, Waltham St Lawrence RG10 0HX ☎ 01189 344535

AQUA LIVI *(Voc, Rh Gtr, Per, Dms)*: 22 Gloucester Road, Reading, Berks RG3 2TH ☎ 01734 622753

BARRINGTON Richard *(Voc, Gtr)*: Railton House, Queen Street, Gillingham, Dorset SP8 4DZ ☎ 01747 822375

BATH Jillian *(Voc)*: 85 Ruxley Lane, West Ewell, Surrey KT19 9JW ☎ 020 8391 0631, 0850 270886 mob

BECK Christopher *(Voc)*: 9 Meadowbrook Close, West Kingsdown, Sevenoaks, Kent TN15 6UB ☎ 0973 761712

BENTLEY Alison *(Voc, Gtr)*: 63 Hertford Street, Oxford OX4 3AL ☎ 01865 728275

BERNARD Richard *(Voc, Song W)*: 23 Paget Road, Langley, Slough, Berkshire SL3 7QP ☎ 01753 818486

BEST Bobbie *(Voc)*: 23 Severn Road, Ferndown, Dorset BH22 8XB ☎ 01202 896051

BLACKMAN Brenda *(Voc)*: 100 Central Avenue, Telscombe Cliffs, East Sussex BN10 7NE

BLACKMAN Sharon *(Voc)*: 5 Shenfield Way, Hollingdean, Brighton, Sussex BN1 7EX ☎ 01273 507415

BOLAND Gabriel *(Voc, Song W, Ac Gtr)* ☎ 023 8060 0115, 07930 651519 mob

BOLWELL Laurence *(Voc, Gtr, Arr, Com, Song W)*: 22 Higher Wood, Bovington Camp, Ware, Dorset BH20 6NF ☎ 01929 405226

BOUCHERAT Vivienne *(Voc)*: 74 Wooler Street, London SE17 2EF ☎ 020 7701 1927

BOURNE Josephine *(Voc, Per)*: Flat 4, 8 Wilbury Road, Hove, East Sussex BN3 3JN ☎ 01273 732870

BOWDLER Lenore *(Voc)*: Flat 5, 55 Festing Road, Southsea, Hants PO4 0NG ☎ 023 9243 1962

BROWN Michael *(Voc)*: 8 Farthing Court, Halfpenny Lane, Sunningdale, Berkshire SL5 0EH ☎ 01344 872032

BROWNING Michael *(Voc, Dms, Gtr, Pf)*: 9 Woodland Rise, 21 Richmond Way, East Grinstead, West Sussex RH19 4TG

BUNDY Rachel *(Voc)* ☎ 01273 604758

BURNETT Norrie *(Voc, Rh Gtr, Hmca)*: Oakwood, Cheapside, Ascot, Berkshire SL5 7QR ☎ 01344 624389, 01753 860441X6865

CAINE Angela *(Voc, Pf)*: The Voice Workshop, 436 Winchester Road, Southampton, Hants SO16 7DH ☎ 023 8039 0555

CAMERON Kate *(Voc, Pf)*: 139 Marine Parade, Brighton BN2 1DF ☎ 01273 570374

CANNELL Helen *(Voc, Tbn)*: 5 Corsair Drive, Dibden, Southampton, Hampshire SO45 5UE ☎ 023 8088 3795, 023 8088 3968

CARROLL Liane *(Voc, Pf)*: 47 Canute Road, Hastings, East Sussex TN35 5HT ☎ 01424 715675

CARTER Elinor *(Voc, Pf, Vln, Vla)*: 193 Thame Road, Warborough, Wallingford, Oxfordshire OX10 7DH ☎ 01865 858693, 0976 912514, 020 7385 7636

CARTNEY Jane *(Voc, Kbds)*: 16 Alexandra Road, Worthing, West Sussex BN11 2DX ☎ 01903 211471

CASEY Sheila *(Voc, Kbds)*: 36 R.L. Stevenson Avenue, Bournemouth, Dorset BH4 8EG ☎ 01202 767918

CHARLIE *(Voc)*: 38 Calluna Drive, Copthorne, West Sussex RH10 3XF ☎ 01342 716770

CHEZ *(Voc, Song W)* ☎ 01737 242064, 0468 201714 mob, 01737 225555

CHURCHILL Barbara *(Voc)*: 39 Romney Road, Bournemouth, Dorset BH10 6JR ☎ 01202 527456

CLARE Debbie *(Voc)*: Hewells House, Dorking Road, Kingsfold, Nr Horsham, West Sussex RH12 3SD ☎ 01306 627727, 0378 392689, 01306 627101

COLTHAM Mike *(Voc, Gtr, Kbds)*: 6 Highview Close, Loose, Maidstone, Kent ME15 6DQ ☎ 01622 670942, 0966 229552 mob

COOPER Dorothy *(Voc)*: 4 Medland, Woughton Park, Milton Keynes MK6 3BH ☎ 01908 670306

COSSINS Christabel *(Voc)* ☎ 01273 279565

COSTELLO Julie *(Voc)*: 'Brightlands', 7 The Lees, Dalbury Lees, Derby DE6 5BE

COWELL Emma *(Voc, Pf, Kbds)*: Randalls Farmhouse, Randalls Road, Leatherhead, Surey KT22 0AL ☎ 01372 377349, 0831 572 840, 01372 375183

DANCER Anthony *(Voc, Gtr, Dms)*: 8 Somerset Close, Bletchley, Milton Keynes MK3 7HJ ☎ 01908 649113

DARTNELL John *(Voc)*: Strawberry Theif House, 2 Rotherfield Lane, Mayfield, E Sussex TN20 6AR ☎ 01435 872431, 07801 544079 mob

DAVIS Rosie *(Voc, Auto Hrp, B Gtr, Song W)*: 2 Fairview Cottages, Balaclava Lane, Wadhurst, East Sussex TN5 6EQ ☎ 01892 88 2412

DEMARVLEST *(Voc, Pf, Kbds)* ☎ 0374 988979, 01295 268989

DENIS Dickie *(Voc, Clt)*: 21 Durrington Gardens, The Causeway, Goring By Sea, Worthing, West Sussex BN12 6BU ☎ 01903 700733

DIXON Martin *(Voc)*: 27 Yew Tree Rise, Calcot, Reading, Berkshire RG3 5RQ ☎ 01189 424568

DORAN Brian *(Voc, Gtr, Flt, Sax)*: 8 Smith Lane, Windsor, Berks SL4 5PD ☎ 01753 858003

DRAYTON Lucinda *(Voc)*: Yogi Barn, 2 Manor Farm Barns, Toot Baldon, Oxon OX44 9NG ☎ 0467 836903

DYER Chubb *(Voc)*: 19 Rubens Close, Black Dam, Basingstoke RG21 3EL ☎ 01256 22945

EAMES Judith *(Voc)*: Gaston Cottage, Aston, Bampton, Oxon OX18 2DY ☎ 01993 850164, 0860 177342, 01993 850164

EASTON Lydia *(Voc, Flt, Pic, Rec, Pf)*: Mews Cottage, 30 Park Road, Redhill, Surrey RH1 2AH ☎ 01737 765861 & fax

ELLINGHAM Anthony *(Voc)*: 635 Lordswood Lane, Chatham, Kent ME5 8RA ☎ 01364 863941

ELTHAM Rachel *(Voc, Sax, Rh Gtr)*: 52 Kings Court, Mill Lane, Crowborough, East Sussex TN6 1DY ☎ 01892 667044 0973 394832, 01892 867044

EPPS Stuart *(Voc)*: Huckenden Farm, Wheeler End, High Wycombe, Bucks HP14 3ND ☎ 016285 287762, 0468 602006, 016285 28762

EVANS Amanda *(Voc, Song W, Gtr)*: 146 Francis Avenue, Southsea, Hants PO4 0ER ☎ 023 9287 4454

EVANS Peter *(Voc, Gtr, Pf)*: 38 Islingword Street, Brighton, East Sussex BN2 2UR ☎ 01273 620529

EVELEIGH Deborah *(Voc, Rec)*: 10 Camden Road, Sevenoaks, Kent TN13 3LY ☎ 01732 459530

FEARN *(Voc)*: 27 St Marys Road, Golders Green, London NW11 9UE ☎ 020 8455 6633, 0589 961311, 020 7791 0171

FITNESS Julia *(Voc, Pf, Gtr)*: 16 Chelston Avenue, Hove East Sussex BN3 5SR ☎ 01273 418808, 07775 764957

FLEET Susan *(Voc)*: 147 London Road, Burgess Hill, West Sussex RH15 8LH ☎ 01444 230266, 01444 871577

FLETCHER Amelia *(Voc, Gtr)*: 8 Temple Street, Oxford OX4 1JS

FORD Christine *(Voc)*: 96 Puddletown Crescent, Canford Heath, Poolet, Dorset BH17 8AN ☎ 01202 773007

FRANCIS Neale *(Voc, Kbds, Gtr)*: 13 Saltbox Close, Barns Green, Nr Horsham, West Sussex RH13 7PN ☎ 01403 731860

FRATER Amanda *(Voc, Gtr, Rec, Wh)*: 55 Willow Drive, Bicester, Oxfordshire OX6 9XF ☎ 01869 249943

FREEMAN Janet *(Voc)*: 11 O'Connell Road, Eastleigh, Hants SO50 9FX ☎ 023 8061 1900, 023 8032 2417

GEE Anne *(Voc)*: Crystal Water, 77 Crossbush Road, Summerley, Felpham, Bognor Regis PO22 7LZ ☎ 01243 69 5567

GHAFFARI Farahnaz *(Voc)*

GILMORE Thea *(Voc, Gtr)*: The Green, North Aston, Bicester, Oxon OX6 4HX ☎ 01869 347480 & fax

GODEL Rowan *(Voc)*: 61A Preston Street, Brighton, East Sussex BN1 2HE ☎ 01273 739913

GODWIN Patricia *(Voc, Per)*: Winkton Lodge Cottage, Salisbury Road, Winkton, Christchurch Dorset BH23 7AR ☎ 01202 484185

GOOD Robert *(Voc, Hrn, Pf, Kbds, Gtr)*: Tinkers, Sweet Lane, Peaslake, Guildford, Surrey GU5 9SH ☎ 01306 730424

GRANT Dominic *(Voc)*: Waterford House, Irish Village, Whitstable, Kent CT5 4LS ☎ 01227 276164, 0031 6532 11432, 01227 264606

GRANT Jill Martin *(Voc)*: 9 Woodbridge Drive, Tovil Mill, Maidstone, Kent ME15 6FU ☎ 01622 208556, 0374 862486 mob

GREEN John *(Voc, B Gtr)*: 58 Westland Road, Faringdon, Oxfordshire SN7 7EY ☎ 01367 242601

GURR Nadine *(Voc)*: 46 Norn Hill, Oakridge, Basingstoke, Hampshire RG1 4RW ☎ 01256 471236, 07901 504983

HAMILTON Timothy *(Voc, Kbds, Flt)*: Flat 6, 69 Beaconsfield Road, Canterbury, Kent CT2 7LG ☎ 01227 788886, 07771 602312

HARDING-CHESTNEY Kaytie *(Voc, Tbn)*: Little Well Cottage, 264 Crawley Road, Horsham, West Sussex RH12 4HG ☎ 01403 242336, 0850 068326, 01403 254624

HARRIS Wendy *(Voc, Acc, Hmca)*: 6 Ireton Close, Chalgrove, Oxford OX44 7RZ ☎ 01865 890215

HARRISON Lynn *(Voc)*: 5 Osterley Close, Wokingham, Berkshire RG40 2LY ☎ 01734 782370

HARRISON Sarah *(Voc)*: 549 Portswood Road, Portswood, Southampton SO17 3SA ☎ 023 8032 5644

HATCHER Joanne *(Voc)*: 34 Regency Drive, West Byfleet, Surrey KT14 6EN ☎ 01932 345785, 0956 266124 mob

HAWKINS Lynne *(Voc)*: 9 Orchard Crescent, Horsmonden, Kent TN12 8LB ☎ 01892 724221

HAYLER Stephen *(Voc)*: 46 Nelson Road, Whitstable, Kent CT5 1EA ☎ 01227 263540

HAZE Hammy *(Voc, Song W, Gtr)*: 9 Exeter Road, Southsea, Portsmouth, Hants PO4 9PZ ☎ 023 9275 5707

HAZELTINE Deborah *(Voc)*: Byeways,Woodgate Road, Ryarsh, Nr West Malling, Kent ME19 5LH ☎ 01732 848285, 0378 773323, 01734 5675551

HENDERSON Gareth *(Voc, Kbds)*: 65 Salisbury Road, Totton, Hants SO40 3HY ☎ 023 8086 8922, 07775 910414

HEWITT Rachel *(Voc)*: 48 Wear Road, Bicester, Oxon OX6 8FF ☎ 01869 245253, 01908 844834, 01908 844888

HICKS Daisy *(Voc, Pf)*: 20 Freshfield Street, Brighton, E Sussex BN2 2ZG ☎ 01273 691625

HIGHAM Cynthia *(Voc, Pf)*: Monks Lea, Tilmore Gardens, Petersfield, Hants GU32 2JH ☎ 01730 264135

HILTON Paul *(Voc, Kbds, Hmca)*: 12 Malvern Close, Banbury, Oxon OX16 9EL ☎ 01295 258120, 0467 894110

HODSON Charlotte *(Voc)*: Beechwood House, Totteridge Common, High Wycombe, Bucks HP13 7QG ☎ 01494 529492, 01523 188180 pager

HUBBARD Christine *(Voc)*: The Pines, 7 Shaws Way, Rochester, Kent ME1 3DY ☎ 01634 848444 & fax, 01634 828275

HUMPHRYS Matthew *(Voc, Kbds)*: 72 Frogmore Park Drive, Blackwater, Camberley, Surrey GU17 0PJ ☎ 01276 33079

HUNT Frances *(Voc, Gtr)*: 7 Forest Dell, Winford, Isle Of Wight PO36 0LG ☎ 01983 867650, 01895 238644

JACKSON Amanda *(Voc, Gtr)*: 7 Southwood Avenue, Walkford, Christchurch, Dorset BH23 5RJ ☎ 01425 274052

JACKSON Nick *(Voc, Gtr)*: 59 The Crossways, Merstham, Redhill, Surrey RH1 3NA ☎ 01737 769349

JAMES Hilary *(Voc, Gtr)*: 2 Talfourd Avenue, Reading, Berkshire RG6 2BP ☎ 01734 68615

JAY Chad *(Voc, Kbds, Gtr)*: 32 Green Tiles Lane, Denham Green, Denham, South Buckingham UB9 5HU ☎ 01895 832671 & fax

JEFFERYS Derek *(Voc, Gtr, Kbds)*: 45 West Dumpton Lane, Ramsgate, Kent CT11 7DG ☎ 01843 588505, 07970 728157, 01843 588505

JENSEN Mark *(Voc, Gtr, Arr, Com, Md)*: 44 Carew Road, Eastbourne, Sussex BN21 2JN ☎ 01323 723368

JOHN-BAPTISTE Dave *(Voc)*: Flat 6, 75 Montpelier Road, Brighton, Sussex BN1 3BD ☎ 01273 720428

JONES Chris *(Voc, Gtr)*: Traygam, Bearwood Road, Sindlesham, Wokingham, Berks RG41 5BT ☎ 0118 977 6337, 0118 977 6414

JONES David *(Voc, Song W, Gtr)*: Lower Flat, 4 Wimbledon Park Road, Southsea, Hants PO5 2PD ☎ 023 9273 0159

JONES Gavin *(Voc)*: Manor Cottage And Stables, 7 Lansdowne Road, Worthing, Sussex BN11 4LY ☎ 01903 230773

JUAN Brandy *(Voc)*: 28 Hamilton Road, Whitstable, Kent CT5 1JX ☎ 01227 265384

KALDALONS Solveig *(Voc, Pf, Gtr)*: 4 Tansy Mead, Storrington, West Sussex RH20 4QS ☎ 01803 744039

KARIAN Karin *(Voc)*: 9 Green Road, Winton, Bournemouth BH9 1DU ☎ 01202 253704

KENNEDY Lynne *(Voc)*: Flat 2, 830 Wimborne Road, Bournemouth, Dorset BH9 2DT ☎ 01202 528314

KENT Simon *(Voc, Ld Gtr, Kbds, B Gtr)*: 267 Laburnum Grove, North End, Portsmouth, Hants PO2 0EY ☎ 023 9265 2007

KERSHAW 'Sneaky' Pete *(Voc, Gtr)*: 36 Settrington Road, Fulham, London SW6 3BA

KERSWELL Henry *(Voc, Vln, Vla)*: 16 Plotmore Road, Guilford, Surrey GU2 8PT ☎ 01483 567612

KNIGHT Kerry *(Voc, Pf)*: 223 St Helens Road, Hastings, East Sussex TN34 2NB ☎ 01424 431557

L'SAAZ Babod *(Voc, Kbds)*: 64 Hazlemere Road, Slough, Berks SL2 5PW ☎ 01753 522948, 0958 284684

LABBETT Julia *(Voc, Pf, Ob)*: 65 Victoria Road South, Southsea, Hants PO5 2BU ☎ 023 9279 6597, 0976 728 596 mob

LANE Annie *(Voc, B Gtr, Pf)*: Madrigal, 18 Ashburton Road, Alverstoke, Gosport, Hants PO12 2LJ ☎ 023 9252 1640

LARAWAY Simone *(Voc, Pf)*: Tamar House, 14 Beach Road, Southsea, Portsmouth PO5 2JH ☎ 023 9273 7549, 0411 705 373

LAWRENCE Denise *(Voc)*: 189 Loddon Bridge Road, Woodley, Reading, Berks RG5 4BP ☎ Reading 690625

LE SERVE Valerie *(Voc)*: Valspetrie, 4 Fourth Avenue, Worthing, Sussex BN14 9NY ☎ Worthing 211397

LEON Anna *(Voc)*: 65 Fairways, 192 Dyke Road, Brighton, East Sussex BN1 5AD ☎ 01273 506681

LEON Cassell *(Voc, Pf)*: Trendalls Cottage, Beacons Bottom, Nr High Wycombe, Bucks HP14 3XF ☎ 01494 483121, 01494 484303

LEWIS Jackie *(Voc)*

LISHMAN Anna *(Voc, Pf, Flt)*: 26 Red Lion Street, Chesham, Bucks HP5 1EZ ☎ 01494 775799, 0385 394996 mob

LOEHRY Adrienne *(Voc)*: 61A Parkwood Road, Southbourne, Bournemouth, Dorset BH5 2BS ☎ 01202 460472

LOVEMUSCLE Johnny *(Voc, Sax)*: 'Delabole', 28-30 Ecton Road, Addlestone, Weybridge, Surrey KT15 1UE ☎ 020 7703 2238

MAGGS Haydon *(Voc, Dms, Per, Kbds)*: 226A Hunts Pond Road, Titchfield Common, Fareham, Hants PO14 4PG ☎ 01329 317444

MARCHANT Bernard *(Voc, Gtr)*: 14 Mendip Avenue, Eastbourne, East Sussex BN23 8ER ☎ 01323 762362

MARTIN Kerry *(Voc, Kbds)*: 8 Pennine Way, Ashford, Kent TN24 8RD ☎ 01233 632384

MAZUMDER Sonia *(Voc)*: 16 Whichelo Place, Brighton, East Sussex BN2 2XF ☎ 01273 623163

MCEWAN Margaret *(Voc, Sax)*: 60 Constable Way, College Town, Sandhurst, Hants GU47 0FE ☎ 01276 609501, 0831 354029 mob

MCGLYNN Emma *(Voc, Gtr, Pf)*: Blasco De Garay, 8.1 E, Madrid 28015, Spain

MCNAUGHTON Elizabeth *(Voc)*: 79 Alexandra Road, Reading, Berkshire RG1 5PS ☎ 01734 264668

MCROBBIE Helen *(Voc)*: 2 Church Cottage, Ipsden, Wallingford, Oxon OX10 6AE ☎ 01491 681 809

MCSHEE Jacqui *(Voc)*: 37 Earlswood Road, Redhill, Surrey RH1 6HD ☎ 01737 210586, 01737 766626 fax

MILLAR Deborah *(Voc)*: 89 Alma Road, Bournemouth, Dorset BH9 1AE ☎ 01202 515253

MILLS Angie *(Voc)*: 89 Abinger Road, Portslade, East Sussex BN41 1SD ☎ 01273 419505

MINTRIM Shelley *(Voc)*: 26 Lavington Gardens, North Baddesley, Southampton SO52 9NR ☎ 023 8073 1461

MITCHELLE Johnny *(Voc)*: 15 Elm Tree Walk, West Parley, Ferndown, Wimborne, Dorset BH22 8TX ☎ 01202 594392

MOORE Nicholas *(Voc, Pf, Kbds)*: 82 Hardy Street, Maidstone, Kent ME14 2SJ ☎ 01622 765823, 01622 208633

MORRIS Lesley *(Voc, Vln)*: 3 Church Green, Witney, Oxfordshire OX8 6AZ ☎ 01993 776445

MOSELEY Dexter *(Voc)*: 76 Heath View, East Finchley, London N2 0QB ☎ 020 8883 7518

MOSS TALLON Sally-Anne *(Voc, Pf)*: Trulls Court, Trulls Hatch, Rotherfield, Nr Mayfield, East Sussex TN6 3QL ☎ 01892 853686

MUNNS Heather *(Voc)*: 1 Ormuz Cottages, Newchapel Road, Lingfield, Surrey RH7 6BD ☎ 01342 835005

NEWMAN David *(Voc)*: 37 Maplehurst Road, Chichester, West Sussex PO19 4QL ☎ 01243 527430, 0411 539975, 01243 527430

NEWTON Richard *(Voc, Gtr, Kbds)*: 115 Parkstone Avenue, Poole, Dorset BH14 9LP

NICHOLSON Stuart *(Voc, Per)*: 41 Amberwood, Ferndown, Dorset BH22 9JT ☎ 01202 896397, 01425 652646 day, 01202 896397

NOVA *(Voc)*: 105 Bennett Road, Charminster, Bournemouth, Dorset BH8 8RL ☎ 01202 309979

NUNAN Jennifer *(Voc, Pf)*: 29 Stourcliffe Ave, Southbourne, Bournemouth BH6 3PU ☎ 01202 250762

P.H.D *(Voc)*: 11 Penn Road, South Court, Aylesbury, Bucks HP21 8HN ☎ 01296 583999, 0467 890309, 01296 583999

PADLEY Bill *(Voc, Kbds, Gtr)*: Flat 3, 24 Lymington Road, West Hampstead, London NW6 4HY ☎ 01983 404506

PASHM Max *(Voc, Per, Kbds, Synth)*: ☎ 01273 278022

PENTECOST Stephanie *(Voc, Gtr, Pf)*: 50 Owen Street, Eastney, Southsea, Hampshire PO4 9PB ☎ 023 9279 9540

PEREIRA Clinton *(Voc)*: 6 Hyperion Court, Bewbush, Crawley, West Sussex RH11 6DB ☎ 01293 549017

PEREZ BENNETT Maria *(Voc)*: 16 Manning Avenue, Highcliffe, Christchurch, Dorset BH23 4PW ☎ 01425 275822

POLLARD David *(Voc)*: 36 Bramshaw Way, Barton-on-Sea, New Milton, Hants BH25 7ST ☎ 01425 628693

PRESCOTT Peter *(Voc)*: 157 Bulverhythe Road, St Leonards-on-Sea TN38 8AF ☎ 01424 440023

PRESLEY Reg *(Voc, B Gtr, Gtr)*: The Cedars, Andover Down, Andover, Hants SP11 6LJ ☎ 01264 354614, 01264 354614

PRINCE Nicky *(Voc)*: 120 Arncliffe Drive, Heelands, Milton Keynes, Bucks MK13 7LJ ☎ 01908 310814, 0956 635085, 01908 83311

PROUT Virginia *(Voc, Pf, Gtr)*: 18 Richington Way, Blue Haze Avenue, Seaford, East Sussex BN25 3HU ☎ 01323 891086

REED Stuart *(Voc, Gtr)*: 28 Colbourne Road, Hove, Sussex BN3 1TB ☎ 01273 776014

REYNOLDS Mandy *(Voc)*: Tall Trees, Seasalter Lane, Seasalater, Kent CT5 4BS ☎ 01227 265509, 0961 100204

ROBERTS Katherine *(Voc)*: 58 Arnewood Road, Southbourne, Bournemouth, Dorset BH6 5DL ☎ 01202 432554

ROBERTS Naby *(Voc, Pf)*: 2 Hamilton Road, Hlythe, Hants SO45 3PB ☎ 023 8084 4407, 0410 183123

ROBERTS Peter (Dowdall) *(Voc, B Gtr)*: 101 Nortoft Road, Bournemouth, Dorset BH8 8QB ☎ 01202 556599

RODGERS Stephen *(Voc, Gtr, Pf)*

ROPER Harold *(Voc)*: 37 Grove Road West, Christchurch, Dorset BH23 2DH ☎ 01202 483217

ROWSON Susanna *(Voc)*: 44 Burley Road, Harestock, Winchester SO22 6LJ ☎ 01962 620500

RUNCHMAN Mark *(Voc, Gtr, B Gtr)*: 60 Vale Road, Seaford, East Sussex BN25 3EZ ☎ 01323 892581

RUSHWORTH Daniel *(Voc)*: Dodsley Gate, Dodsley Grove, Midhurst, West Sussex GU29 9AB ☎ 01730 812874

SACRE Stephen *(Voc)*: ☎ 01483 836768, 0956 885721 mob, 020 7372 6370

SALWAY Colin J *(Voc, Tpt, Gtr)*: 105 Lynton Road, Chesham, Bucks HP5 2BP ☎ 01494 773126

SCHOFIELD Linda *(Voc)*: 6 Claremont Place, Canterbury, Kent CT1 3SU ☎ 01227 766636

SCOTT Alison *(Voc)*: 45 Teg Close, Downs Park, Portslade, East Sussex BN41 2GZ ☎ 01273 882072

SCRIVEN Lee *(Voc, Dms)*: 10 Swallowfield, Great Holm, Milton Keynes, Bucks MK8 9BH ☎ 01908 567824

SEAGRAVE PEARCE Susie *(Voc)*: 'Headland', 4 Cornfield Close, Falconers Wood, Chandlers Ford, Hants SO53 4HD ☎ 023 8027 6756

SHAW Teresa *(Voc)*: 131 Lowther Road, Charminster, Bournemouth BH8 8NP ☎ 01202 310389, 01202 310389

SHEA Elizabeth *(Voc, Pf, Vln, Rec)*: 18 Deanfield Road, Botley, Oxford OX2 9DW ☎ 01865 864448, 0976 869467

SHEPPARD Helen *(Voc, Pf, Gtr, Flt, Rec)*: Flat 5, 5 Eaton Gardens, Hove, East Sussex BN3 3TL ☎ 020 7229 7661, 020 7792 8300 fax

SHIRMAN Richard 'Hershey' *(Voc, Hmca)*: 126 Wrights Lane, Prestwood, Great Missenden, Bucks HP16 0LG ☎ 01494 863573

SIMPSON Catherine *(Voc, Gtr, Pf)*: Chivery Cottage, Chivery Hall Farm, St Leonards, Nr Tring HP23 6LD

SMITH Martin *(Voc, Gtr)* ☎ 01903 733031

SPARKES Richard *(Voc, Gtr, Kbds)*: 42 Jevington, Bracknel, Berks RG12 7ZD ☎ 01344 412568, 07775 727629

STACEY Kim *(Voc)*: Railton House, Queen Street, Gullingham, Dorset SP8 4DZ ☎ 01747 822375

STARBUCK Simone *(Voc)*: 2 Divinity Road, Oxford OX4 1LJ ☎ 01865 240717, 0831 394958

STEPHENS Carla *(Voc, Pf)*: 17 Huntingdon Close, Totton, Southampton, Hants SO40 3NX

STONE Russell *(Voc)*: 117 Forest Road, Liss Forest, Hants GU33 7BP ☎ 01730 895635

STRAWBERRY Sally *(Voc)*: 9 Guilford Park Road, Guilford GU2 5NA ☎ 01483 503411

SULLIVAN Christine *(Voc)*: 15 Nutley Avenue, Saltdean, Brighton BN2 8ED ☎ 01273 307318, 0410 938953 mob

SUNNY *(Voc, Gtr)*: 83 Varsity Drive, Twickenham, Middx TW1 1AH ☎ 020 8891 4877

SYLVI-D *(Voc)* ☎ 01243 830854, 01243 830854

TABITHA *(Voc, Song W)*: 15 Windlesham Gardens, Shoreham By Sea, West Sussex BN43 5AD ☎ 01273 463389

TAYLOR Patricia *(Voc, B Gtr)*: 14 Vicarage Way, Burton, Christchurch, Dorset BH23 7NE ☎ 01202 482323

THOMAS Elizabeth *(Voc)*: 25 Holly Hedge Road, Frimley, Camberley, Surrey GU16 5ST ☎ 01276 25760

THOMPSON-SMITH Mark *(Voc, Gtr)*: 34 Valley Park Road, Clanfield, Waterlooville, Hants PO8 0PB ☎ 023 9259 8731

THOMSON Tobin *(Voc, Gtr, Pf, Synth)*: Flat 2, 6 St Ronans Ave, Southsea, Hampshire PO4 0QE ☎ 01523 459162

TIKARAM Ramon *(Voc)*: Address Unknown ☎ 020 7722 4178

TOMLIN Stevie *(Voc)*: Address Unknown ☎ 01329 220245, 0850 570230, 01329 825402

TORR Pat *(Voc)*: Intermezzo, 45 Thornbury Road, Southbourne, Bournemouth, Dorset BH6 4HU ☎ 01202 419 239

TUNDI (2E) *(Voc)*: 4 Charlecote Road, Worthing, West Sussex BN11 1LX

TURNER Miles *(Voc)*: 24 Sandringham Close, Bournemouth, Dorset BH9 3QP ☎ 01202 533832

TWO-CAN *(Voc, Dms)*: 440 Bursledon Road, Sholing, Southampton SO19 8QQ ☎ 023 8049 5453

TWO-CAN *(Voc)*: 26 Redcote Close, Bitterne, Southampton, Herts SO18 5SU ☎ 023 8039 9557

TYNDALL Debby *(Voc)*: 71A Stanford Avenue, Brighton, East Sussex BN1 6FB ☎ 01273 556961

WAKELIN John *(Voc, Kbds)*: 24 Seaview Avenue, Peacehaven, East Sussex BN10 8PP

WARING Silas *(Voc, Gtr, B Gtr, Kbds)*: Park Farm House, Cots Green, Banbury Road, Kidlington, Oxford OX5 1AH ☎ 01865 372330

WARREN Jacqueline *(Voc, Tamb)*: c/o 10 Priestlands Lane, Pennington, Lymington, Hants SO41 8HZ

WASNIEWSKI Andrew *(Voc)*: 90 Southend Road, Andover, Hants SP10 3DT ☎ 0958 588143

WEBB Lori *(Voc)*: Windrush, 15 Marshall Avenue, Worthing, West Sussex BN14 0ES ☎ 01903 873105, 0973 465154 mob, 01903 873105

WEBSTER Claire *(Voc)*: 40 York Avenue, Sidcup, Kent DA15 7LH ☎ 020 8300 1675, 01732 357240

WERTH Howard *(Voc, Gtr, B Gtr, Hmca)*: Norman House, 92 Manor Road, Deal, Kent CT14 9DB ☎ 01304 369053

WHATLEY Kevin *(Voc, Gtr)*: 1 Harcourt Green, Wantage, Oxon OX12 7DJ ☎ 01235 223362, 0966 194850

WHEATLEY Adam *(Voc, Gtr)*: PO Box 103, Leatherhead, Surrey KT22 8YP ☎ 01372 372313

WHITELEY Kay *(Voc)*: Flat B, 50 Shooters Hill Road, Blackheath, London SE3 7BG ☎ 01580 241059, 020 8293 9037, 07971 208176 mob

WILKINS Neil *(Voc)*: 14 Cecil Court, Charminster Road, Bournemouth BH8 9RY ☎ 01202 527311

WOB *(Voc, Gtr, Man)*: PO Box 2684, Reading, Berks RG1 7WH ☎ 0118 959 9195 & fax

WOLF Jane *(Voc, Lyric)*: 47 Rochester Street, Brighton, East Sussex BN2 2EJ ☎ 01273 672132

WOOD Hadyn R *(Voc)*: 42 Tamar Way, Wokingham RG41 3UB ☎ 01734 629100

WOODHOUSE Elizabeth *(Voc, Gtr)*: 146 Maidstone Road, Chatham, Kent ME4 6EN ☎ 01634 840490

WOOLF Sharon *(Voc, Song W)*: Flat 3, 15 Devonshire Place, Brighton, East Sussex BN2 1QA ☎ 01273 699799

WORTHY Jean *(Voc)*: 89 Alma Road, Bournemouth, Dorset BH9 1AE ☎ 01202 515253

WORTHY Kathy *(Voc)*: 15 Thorncombe Close, Bournemouth, Dorset BH9 3QL ☎ 01202 521318

SOUTH WEST

ACKRILL Richard *(Voc, Gtr, Dms, B Gtr)*: 113 Wheeler Avenue, Swindon, Wilts SN2 6HL ☎ 01793 521685

ALEXANDER Jay *(Voc, Dms, Kbds)*: 8 Bishops Road, Whitchurch, Cardiff CF4 1LZ ☎ 01426 286360

ALLEN Renee *(Voc)*: 49 Ivy Avenue, Bath BA2 1AJ ☎ 01225 401793

AMIS Stephen *(Voc, B Gtr, Gtr)*: 87 Harbour Road, Seaton, Devon EX12 2NE ☎ 01297 21816

ANN *(Voc, Per, Kbds)*: 189 Portland Road, Wyke Regis, Weymouth, Dorset DT4 9BH ☎ 01305 789748

APPLEBY Bernadette *(Voc)*: Harmony Cottage, 1 The Square, Petrockstowe, Okehampton, Devon EX20 3HN ☎ 01837 811172

ASHLEY Steve *(Voc, Gtr, Bzk, Hmca, Wh)*: 87 Prestbury Road, Cheltenham, Glos GL52 2DR ☎ 01242 581965

BAKER Sioux *(Voc)*: 85 Swindon Road, Lower Stratton, Swindon, Wiltshire SN3 4PU ☎ 01793 826262, 01793 535220

BALE Paul *(Voc, Pf, Ac Gtr, Hmca)*: 21 Crown Street, Newport, Gwent. S. Wales NP9 8FU ☎ 01633 263597

BALEN Jude *(Voc)*: Sunnyhill Park, Polbathic, Torpoint, Cornwall PL11 3ET ☎ 01503 230653, 07801 956421

BEER Cheryl *(Voc, Gtr)*: 54 Park Street, Bridgend, S. Wales CF31 4AZ ☎ 01656 652366

BELLAMY Matthew *(Voc, Gtr, Pf, B Gtr)*: Dunstan House, Landscore Road, Teignmouth, Devon TQ14 9JU ☎ 01626 774403

BEST Lorraine *(Voc)*: Kelso House, Sion Road, Lansdown, Bath BA1 5SH ☎ 01225 466900

BLACKWELL Amanda *(Voc, Flt, Per)*: 36 Exmouth Street, Swindon, Wiltshire SN1 3PU ☎ 01793 491906

BRAMAH Teri *(Voc)*: 3 Islington Road, Southville, Bristol BS3 1QB ☎ 0117 966 2821

BRISTOL Mandy *(Voc, Vln, Gtr)*: 4 South Barn, Ryleys Farm, Gruttleton, Chippenham, Wilts SN14 6AF ☎ 01249 782702

BROOK Sheila *(Voc, Pf, Gtr, Clt, Sax)*: 4 The Old Baths, Siliwen Road, Bangor, Gwynedd LL57 2BT ☎ 01248 352102

BROWN Suzanne *(Voc, Gtr, T Sax, Clt)*: 11, Kents Road, Wellswood, Torquay, Devon TQ1 2NL ☎ 211140

CARLTON *(Voc)*: 7 Prudham Street, Greenbank, Bristol BS5 6ER ☎ 01179 522966

CARLYLE Mary *(Voc)*: 115 Don Road, St Helier, Jersey, C.I. JE2 7QD ☎ 01534 35185

CARRAHAR Elisa *(Voc, Song W)*: 45 Freemantle Gardens, Eastville, Bristol BS5 6SZ ☎ 0117 9420057

CARTER Diane *(Voc)*: 28 Meadow Close, Kingskerswell, Devon TQ12 5AS ☎ 2474

CARY *(Voc)*: Bakers Cottage, Butterleigh, Cullompton, Devon EX15 1PW ☎ 01884 855628, 0956 216146, 01426 242357 pager

CHALLONER Jack *(Voc, Pf, Gtr)*: 78 Raymend Road, Bristol BS3 4QW ☎ 017 914 6036, 0117 914 3069

CHIVERS Adrian *(Voc)*: 4 Mount Becon Row, Richmond Lane, Bath, Avon BA1 5QH ☎ 01225 332896

CHURCH Charlotte *(Voc, Pf)*: Shalit Entertainment, Cambridge Theatre, Seven Dials, Covent Garden, London WC2H 9HU ☎ 020 7379 3282, 020 7377 93238 fax

CIPOLLA Sebastiano *(Voc, Clt, Flt)*: 29 Spaines, Great Bedwin, Marlborough, Wiltshire SN8 3LT

CLUTSON Steven *(Voc, Flt, Per)*: 64 All Saints Road, Cheltenham, Glos. GL52 2HA

COLING Leo *(Voc)*: 126 Coronation Road, Southville, Bristol ☎ 0117 963 1298

COLLINS Steve *(Voc)*: Belle Vue Hotel, The Butes, Alderney, Channel Islands GY9 3HN ☎ 0481 822844

CROWLEY Eddy *(Voc, Song W, Gtr)*: Chestnut View, Durleigh Close, Headley Park, Bristol BS13 7NQ ☎ 0117 964 2323, 0117 978 1708 day

CURTIS Bj *(Voc, Ld Gtr, Kbds, B Gtr)*: 491 Topsham Road, Exeter, Devon EX2 7AQ ☎ 01392 876987

DAVIES Helen *(Voc, Kbds)*: 29 Grasmere Drive, Cwmbach, Aberdare, Rhondda Cynon Taff CF44 0HP ☎ 01685 881545

DAVIES Mary *(Voc, Pf, Theory, Harmony)*: 11 St Marys Close, Griffithstown, Gwent NP4 5LS ☎ 01495 752713

DAVIES Stephanie *(Voc)*: 39 Borough Close, Kings Stanley, Stonehouse, Glos GL10 3LJ ☎ 01453 824165

DECORDOVA Louise *(Voc)* ☎ 0117 955 0969

DEEP *(Voc, Kbds, B Gtr, Gtr)*: 44 Hill Park Crescent, Plymouth PL4 8JP ☎ 020 8851 2626

DILLON Cara *(Voc, Vln)*: 9 The Village, Buckland Monachorum, Yelverton, Devon PL20 7NA ☎ 01822 855507

DWYER Sally-Ann *(Voc, Kbds, Gtr)*: 8 Park Place, Eastville, Bristol BS5 6RG ☎ 0117 9512661

EATON Dave *(Voc, Gtr, Kbds)*: 39 Glandwr, Newtown, Powys SY16 1RE ☎ 01686 622530

EVANS Stephanie *(Voc, Pf)*: 1 Caerau Crescent, Newport, Gwent NP9 4HG ☎ 01633 764 712, 01633 764 713

FALKOUS Andrew *(Voc, Gtr)*: 88 Liwsuane Street, Cathays, Cardiff CF2 4LN ☎ 029 2064 0117

FARDELL Sandra *(Voc, Per, Gtr)*: 10 Upper Church Street, Exmouth, Devon EX8 2JA ☎ 01395 276206

FLANNERY Susan *(Voc)*: Three Gables, Frog Lane, Chilmark, Salisbury SP3 5BB ☎ 01722 716807, 0860 226112

FLETCHER Diana *(Voc, Sax, Kbds)*: 33 Plasturton Gardens, Cardiff CF1 9HG ☎ 029 2038 7671

FLETCHER Jeff *(Voc, Song W)*: Brymar Hillway, Charlton Mackrel, Somerton, Somerset TA11 6AN ☎ 01458 223104

FORNARA Tim *(Voc, Gtr, Dms)*: Garden House, Beckford, Nr. Cewkesbury, Glos GL2 7AD ☎ 01386 881424

GAIR Robin *(Voc)*: Coda House, Chichester Close, Salisbury, Wilts SP2 8AQ ☎ 01722 329487, 0370 774424

GANBERG Barry *(Voc, Pf, Kbds, Per, Dul)*: 68 Dixon Street, Swindon, Wiltshire SN1 3PJ ☎ 01793 491060

GARLAND Paul *(Voc)*: 131 St.Georges Road, Bristol BS1 5UW ☎ 0117 9293939

GAYLE Kris *(Voc)*: Springfield, 19 Penpol Road, Hayle, Cornwall TR27 4AD ☎ 01736 757351

GILES Gillian *(Voc)*: 16 Durham Avenue, St Judes, Plymouth PL4 8SP ☎ 01752 671572

GODDARD Lois *(Voc, Gtr)*: Redland Green Farm, Redland Green, Redland, Bristol BS6 7HF ☎ 0117 9420256

GREEN Godfrey *(Voc, B Gtr, Song W, Per)*: 19 Berkeley Gdns, Keynsham, Bristol BS31 2PN

GREGSON Anne *(Voc, Ctna)*: 24 St. Laurence Road, Bradford-on-Avon, Wiltshire BA15 1JQ ☎ 012216 3762

HAGGARD Mick *(Voc)*: 2 Glebe Cottages, North Stoke, Bath BA1 9AS ☎ 0117 9329627

HEATH Bob *(Voc, Gtr, Kbds)*: 23 Avenue Road, Swindon, Wiltshire SN1 4BZ ☎ 01793 611432, 0468 148 401 mob

HEMBROUGH Oliver *(Voc, Kbds, Gtr)*: 2 Abbey Park, Keynsham, Bristol BS31 2BT ☎ 0117 9868616

HETHERINGTON Charles *(Voc, Pf)*: Yew Tree, Donhead St Mary, Sahftesbury, Dorset SP7 9DG ☎ 01747 828398

HOLPIN Sue *(Voc, Flt, Sax)*: Grove House, Collafield, Cinderford, Glos GL14 3LG ☎ 01594 825557

HOWARD Tony *(Voc, Gtr, Kbds)*: 7 The Parade, Whitchurch, Cardiff, South Glam CF4 2EE

HUMPHREYS Pamela *(Voc)*: 24 Heol Don, Whitchurch, Cardiff, South Glamorgan CF4 2AU ☎ 61103

HURLOCK Josee *(Voc)*: 73 British Road, Bedminster, Bristol BS3 3BU ☎ 0117 983 2477

IFAN Gareth *(Voc, Pf)*: Crud-Alaw, 15 Castle Street, Maesteg, Mid Glamorgan CF34 9YH ☎ 01656 733034, 07970 940018

IRELAND Mary *(Voc, Vln, Pf)*: 112 High Street, Bidford-on-Avon, Warwks B50 4AQ ☎ 01789 490183, 0976 734985

JARLETT Dee *(Voc, Gtr)*: 27 Narroways Road, St. Werburghs, Bristol BS2 9XD ☎ 0117 9411440

JARVIS Caleb *(Voc, Gtr)*: Flat 3, 79 Abbotsham Road, Bideford, North Devon EX39 3AQ ☎ 01237 473804

JOHNSON Sally *(Voc)*: The Mount, Wadefrod, Chard, Somerset TA20 3AP ☎ 01460 65155

KENNEDY Wilma *(Voc, Clars)*: Top Flat Left, 23 Merrick Gardens, Ibrox, Glasgow G51 2TN ☎ 0141 427 7298

LARKIN Sally *(Voc)*: 18C Trenchard Street, Bristol BS1 5AN

LARSEN Victoria *(Voc)*: 27 Cross Street, Lynton, North Devon EX35 6HG ☎ 01598 7582724

LAWMAN Derek *(Voc, Gtr, Bjo)*: 25 Clifton Road, Paignton, Devon TQ3 3LQ ☎ 01803 526496

LONEY Rebecca *(Voc, Pf, Kbds)*: 27 Caen Street, Top Floor Flat, Braunton, Devon EX33 1AA

LONG Linda *(Voc, Gtr)*: Address Unknown ☎ 01225 463517

MARSHALL Steve *(Voc, Gtr, Kbds, Cong, Per)*: 'Sunnyside', Townsend, Curry Rivel, Langport, Somerset TA10 0HN ☎ 01458 253264, 01458 253280

MCCARTHY Martine *(Voc, Gtr)*: Ground Floor Flat, 10 Fremantle Square, Cotham, Bristol BS6 5TL ☎ 0117 944 2239, 0117 927 4570, 07788 684137

MCGOWAN Susan *(Voc)*: 82 Albion Road, Helston, Cornwall TR13 8JL ☎ 01326 565188

MCGREGOR Jane *(Voc)*: Marketing Enterprises, 16 Freeland Place, Hotwells, Bristol BS8 4NP ☎ 0117 9494527, 0117 9494527

MCKELL Jane *(Voc)*: Talbothays, 3 Osmington Lodge, Osmington, Weymouth, Dorset DT3 6EX ☎ 01305 835541, 03787 37700

MEUROSS Reg *(Voc, Gtr, Bjo)*: 43 Lyewater, Crewkerne, Somerset TA18 8BB ☎ 01460 73432

MEYLAN Pauline *(Voc)*: Flat 11, 25 Cheshire Road, Exmouth, Devon EX8 4BW ☎ 01395 274138

MICHAELS Shaun *(Voc, Gtr, B Gtr, Kbds, Dms)*: 38 Redbrooke Road, Camborne, Cornwall TR14 7AZ ☎ 01209 713253

MIGHTY BIJOU *(Voc)*: 24 Penfield Road, St Werburghs, Bristol BS2 9YG ☎ 01179 090582

MILLER *(Voc, Gtr)*: 29 Grenville Avenue, Locking, Weston Super Mare BS24 8AJ

MORGAN Marion *(Voc, Vla, Vln)*: 21 Meon Road, Mickleton, Chipping, Campden, Glos GL55 6TB ☎ 01384 438932

MORGAN Page *(Voc)*: 18 Trusthams, Broadwindsor, Beaminster, Dorset DT8 3QB ☎ 01308 868544

MORLEY Helen *(Voc)*: Woods Corner, Cliddesden, Nr Basingstoke, Hants RG25 2JF ☎ Basingstoke 466

MURPHY Julie *(Voc)*: Alltfechan, Pencader, Carmarthenshire, Wales SA39 9BU ☎ 01559 384962

OMORI Mark *(Voc, Gtr, B Gtr, Per, Kbds)*: New Hope, 4 Labour In Vain, St Just, Penzance, Cornwall TR19 7RY ☎ 01736 787892

OSBORN Patricia *(Voc)*: 17 Parkham Glade, Wren Hill, Brixham, Devon TQ5 9JS ☎ 07803 8558362

OTTER-BARRY Lisa *(Voc, Flt, Per)*: 61 Wooley Street, Bradford-on-Avon, Avon BA15 1AG ☎ 01225 863822

PARAMOR Susan *(Voc)*: Tinkers Cottage, Burcombe, Salisbury, Wilts SP2 0EN ☎ 01722 744196

PARSONS Aubrey *(Voc, Com)*: 12 Mill Park, Cowbridge, S. Glamorgan, S. Wales CF71 7BG ☎ 01446 773551

PORTER Mark *(Voc)*: 4 Harnhill Close, Hartcliffe, Bristol BS13 9NH ☎ 0117 987 0507, 0117 9732026

POWELL Sian *(Voc)*: 63C Ashley Road, Montpellier, Bristol BS6 5NJ ☎ 0117 914 9271

VOICE - SOUTH WEST

PRICE Richard (*Voc, Gtr, B Gtr, Kbds*): 66 Manselfield Road, Murton, Swansea SA3 3AP ☏ 01792 205253

RANDALL Amanda (*Voc*): Lar Feliz, Forge Lane, East Chinnock, Nr Yeovil, Somerset BA22 9EG ☏ 01935 863457

RANDLE Sarah (*Voc, Kbds*): Braewood, West Quantoxhead, Taunton, Somerset TA4 4DX ☏ 01984 632515, 0777 5847304, 01984 632758

RIPPON Carole (*Voc, Pf*): 5 Rustic Close, Tycoch, Swansea SA2 9LZ ☏ 01792 290238

RUSSELL Bella (*Voc, Pf*): The Shrubbery, Camden Road, Bath BA1 5HX ☏ 01225 423553

SIM Hazel (*Voc*): Springfield House, Springfield, Radsloch, Bath, Ne Somerset BA3 3JB ☏ 01761 414152, 0585 033866 mob

SMITH Oliver (*Voc*): 2 Locks Cross, Neston, Corsham, Wilts SN13 9TB ☏ 01225 811878

SOUTHORN Madeleine (*Voc, Pf, Kbds*): Courtenway House, Sampford, Courtnay Station, Okehampton, Devon EX20 2SP ☏ 01837 53250, 0802 311195

SPIRO (*Voc, Gtr*): Pound Cottage, 2 Meadow View, Longmeadow Road, Lympstone, Devon EX8 5LH ☏ 01395 224 919

STATTON Alison (*Voc, B Gtr*): 5 John Street, Penarth, S Glam CF6 1DN ☏ 029 2070 7443

STRATTON Cindy (*Voc, Gtr, Song W*): 18 Lansdown View, Twerton, Bath BA2 1BG ☏ 01225 460459

STUART-CLARK Derek (*Voc, Pf*): 38 Sidmouth Road, Bedminster, Bristol BS3 5HS

SWAN Karen (*Voc, Gtr*): 6 Nailsworth Terrace, Hereford Place, Cheltenham, Glos GL50 4BE ☏ 01242 244415

SWEETMAN Maxine (*Voc*): 29 Ash Grove, Seaton, Devon EX12 2TT ☏ 01297 23184

TANJY (*Voc, Cong, Gtr*): St Dunstans Cottage, St Dunstans Car Park, Magdelane St, Glastonbury, Somerset BA6 9EL ☏ 01458 830082

TATLOW Eily (*Voc*): 1 Lansdwone Road, Whiterock, Wadebridge, Cornwall PL27 7EE ☏ 01208 814355

THOMAS Rhys (*Voc*): 63A Queen Street, Newton Abbot, Devon TQ12 2AU ☏ 01626 354068

TIPPETTS Julie (*Voc*): The Cottage, Tortworth, Wooton-U-Edge, Gloucester GL12 8HG ☏ 01454 260757

TUCKER Marilyn (*Voc*): 38 Hillfield, South Zeal, Okehampton, Devon EX20 2NY ☏ 0183 784 219

TYLER Bonnie (*Voc*): Bandpick Ltd, Fernhill Annexe, 156 Mumbles Road, Blackpill, Swansea SA3 5AW ☏ 01792 403699 & fax

UPTON Eddie (*Voc, Ctna, Hmca, Mldn*): 2 Hayes Cottages, Stocklinch, Somerset TA19 9JQ ☏ 01460 55322, 01460 55311

WALCOTT-GORDON Celestine (*Voc*): 106 Stonebridge Park, Upper Eastville, Bristol BS5 6RW ☏ 07970 068357

WALTON Lydia (*Voc, Gtr, Wh*): Candyland Studios, Stapleton Farm, Langtree, Torrington, North Devon EX39 8NP ☏ 01805 601335, 01805 601620

WEATHERILL Raymond (*Voc, Gtr, Hmca, Kbds, B Gtr*): Penwern, Llandeilo Graban, Builth Wells, Powys, Wales LD2 3UZ ☏ 01982 560 710, 01982 560 770

WILLIAMS Ben (*Voc, Gtr*): 116 Mount Hill Road, Hanham, Bristol BS15 2OR ☏ 01275 512038, 0117 967 6734

WILSON-COPP Everest (*Voc, Song W, Kbds, Gtr*): Weavers Cottage, 1 Steanbridge Lane, Slad, Stroud, Glos GL6 7QE ☏ 01453 756918

WRIGHT David (*Voc, Gtr, Man, Kbds*): 110 Kennington Avenue, Bishopston, Bristol BS7 9ES ☏ 0117 9423715

LONDON

0.0.0.7 (*Voc*): 86 Frant Road, Thornton Road, Surrey CR7 7JR ☏ 020 8239 9618, 0956 272 455

ABDILLAHI Sahal (*Voc, Kbds*): 67 Dunloe Avenue, Tottenham, London N17 6LB ☏ 020 8880 9817, 0956 918020

ADAMS Kevin Paige (*Voc*): 181 Rivermill, Harlow, Essex CM20 1PA ☏ 01279 452722

ADAMS Richard (*Voc, Gtr, E Gtr, Ac Gtr*): 83 Racecourse Road, East Ayton, Scarborough YO3 9HT

ADAMS Victoria (*Voc, Song W*): Moody Productions Ltd, 66-68 Bell Street, London NW1 6SP ☏ 020 7724 0246, 020 7724 8050

ADE (*Voc, Dms*): 3 The Orchards, 28-30 Edgwarebury Lane, Edgware, Middlesex HA8 8LW ☏ 020 8958 6319 & fax, 0976 412093 mob

ADEBAYO Adesoji (*Voc, Com*): 20 Park Parade Mansions, Edgware Road, Colindale, London NW9 6NL ☏ 020 8201 3894, 020 8964 9818

AFRIKANSIMBA (*Voc, Per*): 15 Westdown Road, Leyton, London E15 2BZ ☏ 020 8923 0895, 0961 148150, 0956 878166 mob

AGARWAL Sangeeta (*Voc, Saxes, Com, Rec, Kbds*): 18 Valentine Rd, Hackney, London E9 7AD ☏ 020 8985 4238

AGBEBYI Adeola (*Voc, Gtr*): Flat 2, 147 Hertford Road, London N1 4LR

AGYEI Ben (*Voc*): 18 Charlemont Road, East Ham, London E6 4HL ☏ 020 8470 7519

AHMAD Vivienne (*Voc, Ac Gtr, Song W*): 73 Merriman Road, Blackheath, London SE3 8SB ☏ 020 8319 1590 eve, 020 7842 6827 day

AJANA Ayodele (*Voc*): 50A Belmont Hill, Lewisham, London SE13 5DN ☏ 020 8463 0061, 07957 466322

AJAYI Steve (*Voc*) ☏ 020 7281 7366, 0956 348828

AKHTAR Najma (*Voc, Harm*): 26 Berkeley Court, Baker Street, London NW1 5ND ☏ 020 7487 3583

AKINPELU Olu (*Voc*): Flat 3, Stoneleigh, Mosslea Road, Penge, London SE20 7BW ☏ 0956 932157, 020 8778 8464

AKPEWRENE Victoria (*Voc*): 5 Hallane House, Woodvale Estate, West Norwood, London SE27 0EX ☏ 020 8761 7389, 0956 994343 mob

ALBARN Damon (*Voc, Kbds*): c/o C.M.O., 35/7 Parkgate Road, London SW11 4NP

ALBUQUERQUE Sharon (*Voc, Kbds*): 53 Heathwood Gardens, London SE7 8ET ☏ 020 8855 1668

ALELE Henrietta (*Voc, Dms*): 15 Banyan House, Lithos Road, London NW3 6ES ☏ 020 7431 0441

ALIETA Joy (*Voc, Kbds*): 59 Carlton House, Albert Road, London NW6 5DX ☏ 020 7624 1048

ALLAIN Jan (*Voc, Gtr, Hmca*): 178B Elderfield Road, London E5 0AZ ☏ 020 8985 8403, 020 8985 8403

ALLAN Dawn (*Voc*): 62 Uvedale Road, Enfield, Middlesex EN2 6HD ☏ 020 8366 8401, 0976 930315, 020 8366 1338

ALLEN Lyn (*Voc*): 13 Cheval Court, 335 Upper Richmond Road, London SW15 6UA ☏ 020 8789 5652

ALLEN Ruth (*Voc*): 39 Mayfair Avenue, Worcester Park, Surrey KT4 7SH ☏ 020 8337 6887

ALLEN Sue (*Voc*): 59 Southway, West Wimbledon, London SW20 9JG ☏ 020 8543 1056, 0956 396569

ALYSA (*Voc, Kbds*): 20 Flat D, Anson Road, Willesden, London NW2 3UU ☏ 020 8208 3937, 0705 003 8895

AMA Shola (*Voc*): c/o 1.2. One Management, 20 Damien Street, London E1 2HX ☏ 020 7423 9993, 020 7423 9996

AMANZE Ronald (*Voc*): 69B Leyhorn Road, London NW10 4PJ ☏ 020 8961 5680, 0956 533906

AMES Keith (*Voc, Gtr*): 16 Longmead Close, Caterham, Surrey CR3 5HA ☏ 01883 345265, 0976 301775

ANDERSON Adele (*Voc*): 18A Vicarage Road, Stratford, London E15 4HD

ANDERSON April Joy (*Voc, Flt, Pf, Gtr*): 105A Blackheath Road, Greenwich, London SE10 8PD ☏ 020 8691 3757

ANDERSON Brett (*Voc*): c/o Interceptor Enterprises, First Floor, 98 White Lion Street, London N1 9PF ☏ 020 7278 8001, 020 7713 6298 fax

ANDERSON Liz (*Voc, Per*): 15B Granville Road, Southfields, London SW18 5SB ☏ 020 8871 1976

ANDERSON Shaun (*Voc*): 176 Ivorydown, Bromley, Kent BR1 5EF ☏ 020 8516 3415

ANDERSON Vicki (*Voc*): 52 Fenton Road, Southbourne, Bournemouth, Dorset BH6 5BU ☏ 01202 255485

ANDREW-SMITH Jenny (*Voc, Pf*): 12 Mavis Walk, Beckton, London E6 4LU ☏ 020 7474 7863 & fax

ANDREWS Lea *(Voc, Gtr, Kbds, B Gtr, Dms)*: 17 Ranelagh Road, Wood Green, London N22 4TJ ☎ 020 8881 2346

ANGELICA (THE REAL ANGELICA) *(Voc, Gtr)*: 13 Halstow Road, London NW10 5DB ☎ 020 8932 5888

ANGUS Caridad *(Voc, Sax, Gtr)*: 84B Ywca Park House, 227 Earls Court Road, London SW5 9BL ☎ 020 7373 2729, 020 7727 8684

ANN Vera *(Voc)*: Flat 2, 970 Garratt Lane, Tooting, London SW17 0ND ☎ 020 8672 7673

ANSELL Martin *(Voc, Gtr)*: Dureston Lodge, Durweston, Balandford Forum, Dorset DT11 0QA ☎ 01258 480631

ANT Adam *(Voc, Gtr)*: Willie & Blackwell, Ther Barleymaw Center, 10 Barleymaw Passage, London W4 4PH ☎ 020 8742 8600, 020 8742 7789

ANTHONI Mark *(Voc, Gtr)*: 43C Goldsmith Avenue, Acton, London W3 6HR ☎ 020 8932 2413, 020 8840 5001

ANYOGU Denyse *(Voc)*: 42 John Cornwell V.C House, Grantham Road, Manor Park, London E12 5LY ☎ 020 8478 2567, 0956 445826

AQUAMANDA *(Voc, Kbds, Per)*: 35 Playfield Crescent, Dulwich, London SE22 8QR ☎ 020 8299 1645

AQUILLA *(Voc)*: 40A St Marys Road, South Norwood, London SE25 6UT ☎ 020 8239 0592

ARCHER Yvonne *(Voc, Kbds)*: 82, Axminster Road, London N7 6BS ☎ 020 7263 1384

ARDEN-GRIFFITH Paul *(Voc, Pf)*: 138 Sandy Hill Road, London SE18 7BA ☎ 020 8854 2558

ARIKE *(Voc, Hmca, Hrp, Gtr)*: 14 Lind Street, St John, London SE8 4JE ☎ 020 8692 9573

ARMSTRONG Bernie *(Voc, Gtr, Kbds)*: 49 Kings Road, Walton-on-Thames, Surrey KT12 2RB ☎ 01932 886 322, 07775 626855

ARMSTRONG Lisa *(Voc)*: 20 Berry Close, Watlington Road, Cowley, Oxford OX4 5NB ☎ 01865 774523

ARNOLD Jamie *(Voc)*: 204 Ravenscroft Road, Beckenham, Kent BR3 4TE ☎ 020 8778 0624, 0958 396165 mob

ASHANTI *(Voc, Per, Cong)* ☎ 020 7281 5404

ASHER De'Borah *(Voc)*: 31 Risborough House, Mallory Street, Marylebone, London NW8 8TB ☎ 020 7706 2375

ASHIA *(Voc)*: Flat 4, 62 Wickham Road, Brockley SE4 1LS

ASHTON Adeen *(Voc, Pf)*: 80 Larden Road, London W3 7SX ☎ 020 8749 7748

ASKEW Caroline *(Voc)*: Hall Or Nothing, 11 Poplar Mews, Uxbridge Road, London W12 7JS ☎ 020 8749 0799

ASKEW Rebecca *(Voc)*: 52A Geldeston Road, London E5 8SB ☎ 020 8806 9952

ATKINSON Nigel *(Voc)*: 132A Acre Lane, Brixton, London SW2 5RJ ☎ 020 7978 8613, 01523 722328

AUSTIN Heather *(Voc)*: 5 Kangley Bridge Road, Sydenham, London SE26 5BA ☎ 020 8778 9176

AUSTIN Helen *(Voc, Flt, Pf, A Sax)*: 64 Albion Road, Stoke Newington, London N16 9PH ☎ 020 7275 9366, 0973 814013

AUSTIN Steve *(Voc, Gtr, Pf, Man, Wh)*: Church Flat, Urc Church, Joel Street, Northwood Hills, Middlesex HA6 1NL ☎ 01923 822210

AUTY Rachel *(Voc, Vla, Pf, B Gtr)*: 85 John Trundle Court, Barbican, London EC2Y 8DJ ☎ 020 7588 6230

AWORK Robert *(Voc, Kbds, Gtr)*: c/o Qmm Ltd, Suite 216, Saga Centre, 326 Kensal Road, London W10 5BZ ☎ 020 7565 4711, 020 7565 4712

AYERS Galen *(Voc)* ☎ 020 7286 3581

AZANIA Nya *(Voc)*: 10 Vestry Road, Camberwell, London SE5 8NX ☎ 020 7703 7885, 0973 344208 mob

B Johnnie *(Voc, Song W, Kbds)*: Address Unknown ☎ 0956 149373

BADON Tara *(Voc)*: 34 Johnson Road, Bromley, Kent BR2 9SN ☎ 020 8290 4180

BAILEY Jordan *(Voc)*: 87 Bargery Road, London SE6 2LP

BAILLIE D H *(Voc, Kbds)*: 73 Durdans House, Royal College Street, London NW1 9RD ☎ 020 7485 9368

BAKER Efua *(Voc, Per)*: 13A Mornington Place, London NW1 7RG

BALL Alison *(Voc)*: 36 Bonfield Road, Lewisham, London SE13 6BX ☎ 020 8852 2772

BAMIDELE Ayo *(Voc, Gtr)*

BANDO Salud *(Voc)*: 24 Lea Gardens, Wembley, Middlesex HA9 7SE ☎ 020 8902 2554

BANUGO Desiree *(Voc)* ☎ 020 8767 8645, 0956 121779 mob

BARAKAT Ashwak *(Voc)*: 144 Cotton Avenue, London W3 6YG ☎ 020 8993 0614, 020 8345 6789

BARNES Selina *(Voc, Vln)* ☎ 020 8525 0352

BARRETT Marcia *(Voc)*: 9663 Yardham Terrace, The Harbour. Hobe Sound, Martin County, Florida 33455 ☎ 407 546 3217

BARRON Jacqueline *(Voc)*: 37 Bourne Hill, London N13 4LJ ☎ 020 8886 8521

BARRON Tim *(Voc, Gtr)*: 27 Tresco Road, Nunhead, London SE15 3PY ☎ 020 7639 6753

BARRY Paul *(Voc, B Gtr, Kbds)*: 27 Balmoral Road, Kingston-on-Thames, Surrey KT1 2TY ☎ 020 8974 8123

BARSTAD Ingeborg *(Voc, Pf, Clt)*: 64 Ravenswood Road, London SW12 9PN ☎ 020 8675 4596

BARTLETT Curtis *(Voc, Song W, Gtr)*: 14 Kinver Road, Sydenham, London SE26 4NT ☎ 020 8659 5801, 0956 851 361

BARTON Claudia *(Voc, Pf, Gtr)*: 6 Provspence Villas, Brackenbury Road, L0Ondon W6 0BA ☎ 020 8740 1522

BASTICK Don *(Voc)*: 44 Elsindre Road, Forest Hill, London SE23 2SL ☎ 020 8291 6052

BATTISTESSA Catherine *(Voc)*: Brick House Farm, Cockgreen, Flested, Essex CM6 3JE ☎ 01371 821464, 04325 254171

BAYLEY Blaze *(Voc)*: c/o Paul Oxley, Focus Business Management, The Colonnades, 82 Bishopsbridge Road London W2 6BD ☎ 020 7243 0640

BEARD Alison *(Voc)*: 37 Torrington Drive, Loughton, Essex IG10 3TA ☎ 020 8502 0556

BEARD Louisa *(Voc)*: Flat 4, 22 Rodway Road, Bromley, Kent BR1 3JL ☎ 020 8249 0384

BEARD Susan *(Voc, Kbds, Ob)*: 16 Vandyke Road, Leighton Buzzard, Beds LU7 8HH ☎ 01525 379697

BECKFORD Melissa *(Voc, Pf)*: 8 Chandos Mansions, Albert Road, South Norwood, London SE25 4JF ☎ 020 8656 1948

BEE Sandra *(Voc, Song W)*: 17 Redfern Road, Harlesden, London NW10 9LA ☎ 020 8453 0607

BELL *(Voc)*: 13 Clock Court, Wanstead, London E11 1UJ ☎ 020 8989 3254

BELL Melissa *(Voc, Pf, B Gtr)*: 115 Bunning Way, Holloway, London N7 9UR ☎ 020 7700 8468, 0958 483482, 020 7700 8468

BELL Robbie *(Voc)*: 3 Bracken Drive, Chigwell, Essex IG7 5RG ☎ 020 8501 4824

BELL Saranella *(Voc, Kbds)*: 122 Guiness Court, Mansell Street, Aldgate, London E1 8AQ ☎ 020 7481 3121

BENNETT Easther *(Voc, Gtr)*: c/o Martin Greene Ravden, 55 Loudoun Road, St Johns Wood, London NW8 0DL ☎ 020 7625 4545, 020 7625 5265

BENNETT Rachel *(Voc, Per)*: 15 Camellia House, Idonia Street, Deptford, London SE8 4LZ ☎ 020 8692 7033

BENSON Lindsay *(Voc, Tbn, Clt, Pf)*: 26 Evesham Way, Clayhall, Ilford, Essex IG5 0EQ ☎ 020 8550 1880

BENSON Stephanie *(Voc)*: Broadlands, Leeds Road, Langley, Kent ME17 3JN ☎ 01622 843222

BERENYI Miki *(Voc, Gtr)*: 24 Mostyn Gardens, London NW10 5QX

BERLIN Maria *(Voc, Pf)*: 34 East India Dock Road, Limehouse, London E14 6JJ ☎ 020 7515 9135

BERN Deborah *(Voc, Gtr)*: Garden Flat, 34 Mountview Road, Stroud Green, London N4 4HX ☎ 020 8347 9160

BERNARD Paul *(Voc)*: 45 Vaughan House, Poynders Gardens, London SW4 8PB ☎ 020 8675 8486

BERNARDI Alessandro *(Voc, Gtr, Kbds)*: 14B Vicarage Grove, London SE5 7LW ☎ 020 7701 8393

BESSEM Theo *(Voc)*: 113 Sterry Road, Dagenham, Essex RM10 8NT ☎ 020 8593 3321, 020 7454 1787 fax

BEST Jane *(Voc)*: 211B Upper Street, London N1 1RL

BEST Martin (*Voc, Gtr, Lute, Psal, Arr*): 36A Gordon Place, London W8 4JE

BILLANY Martin (*Voc, Gtr*): 4 Park Hill, Richmond TW10 6HE ☎ 020 8948 5334

BINNS Anthony (*Voc, Gtr, Song W*): Ground Floor Flat, 265 Magdalen Road, London SW18 3NZ ☎ 020 8946 6903

BIOLA (*Voc*): 79 Lucas Court, Strasburg Road, Battersea, London SW11 5JG ☎ 020 7720 7879 & fax, 0956 390611 mob

BIRING Rena (*Voc*): 15 Okehampton Crescent, Welling, Kent DA16 1DG ☎ 020 8301 5115

BLACK Daniel (*Voc, Gtr, Kbds*)

BLACKBURN Jane (*Voc, Gtr*): 36 Winchester Court, Vicarage Gate, London W8 4AD ☎ 020 7937 4271

BLAKE Jacqueline (*Voc*): Hall Or Nothing, 11 Poplar Mew, Uxbridge Road, London W12 7JS ☎ 020 8749 0799

BLAKE Katharine (*Voc, Rec, Vln, Pf*): 43 Corinne Road, Tufnell Park, London N19 5EZ ☎ 020 7700 5840, 020 7700 0805 & fax

BLUE (*Voc, Song W, Gtr*) ☎ 020 8341 2253, 020 8341 2253

BOARDMAN Claire (*Voc, Ob*): 45 Grand Drive, Raynes Park, London SW20 0JB ☎ 020 8715 8690, 01523 148611 pager

BOATENG Wilson (*Voc, Gtr, Org, Arr, Com*): 6 Staveley Close, Hackney, London E9 6DY ☎ 020 8533 4058

BONFILS Khan (*Voc, Pf, Gtr*): Address Unknown ☎ 020 7791 3346, 0976 261479 mob

BONNER Sam (*Voc*): 37 Parkside, Mill Hill, London NW7 2LN ☎ 020 8906 4721, 020 8906 9989

BONO (*Voc*): Not Us Limited (U2), 30/32 Sir John Rogersons Quay, Dublin 2, Ireland ☎ Dublin 677 7330

BOOKER Stephen (*Voc, Gtr, Pf*): Basement Flat, 176 Camberwell Grove, London SE5 8RH ☎ 020 7737 1474

BOOTH Blair (*Voc, Pf, Kbds*): Address Unknown ☎ 020 8885 2532

BOOTH Maxine (*Voc*): Flat 10, Phoenix Court, Ingersoll Road, Enfield, Middx EN3 ☎ 020 8923 7228

BOSCA Kreama (*Voc*): 556A Lea Bridge Road, Leyton, London E10 7DT ☎ 020 8539 5590

BOWEN Lorraine (*Voc, Pf, Clt, Rec*): 6 Stannard Road, Dalston, London E8 1DB ☎ 020 7254 4237

BOWERS Dane (*Voc*): 14 Kingswood Way, Selsdon, South Croydon, Surrey CR2 8QP ☎ 020 8651 6450, 020 8741 9933, 020 8741 3938

BOWES Daniel (*Voc*): c/o Tony Medcalf, Garden Flat, 83 Cambridge Gardens, London W10 6JE ☎ 020 8960 3596, 020 8960 4330

BOWIE David (*Voc, Gtr, Kbds, Sax*): Isolar Enterprises Inc., 641 Fifth Avenue, Suite 22Q, New York, NY 10022, USA ☎ +1 212 308 9345, +1 212 308 2355 fax

BOWYER Charles (*Voc, Gtr*): 66 Glenbuck Court, Glenbuck Road, Surbiton, Surrey KT6 6BZ ☎ 020 8390 9891

BOZADJIAN Harry (*Voc*) ☎ 020 8904 0648, 0956 583221

BRADLEY Andrew (*Voc*): 137 Wallwood Road, London E11 1AQ ☎ 020 8539 0018, 0831 151944

BRADLEY Kate (*Voc, Pf, Flt*): 7 Overhill Road, East Dulwich, London SE22 0PQ ☎ 020 8693 1215

BRADLEY Peter (*Voc, Kbds, Gtr, B Gtr*): 24 Alwyns Lane, Chertsey, Surrey KT16 9DW ☎ 01932 568981

BRANSON Fiona (*Voc, Song W, Ac Gtr*): 22 Aragon Tower, Longshore, Peps Estate, Deptford, London SE8 3AH ☎ 020 8469 3110

BRICKLEBANK Claire (*Voc, Song W*): 216 Westbourne Park Rd, London W11 1EP ☎ 020 7792 2661

BRIGHT Annie (*Voc*): 16 Poplar Walk, Herne Hill, London SE24 0BU ☎ 020 7733 0564

BROMFIELD Rahsaan (*Voc*): 87 Greenrigg Walk, Wembley, Middlesex HA9 9UD ☎ 020 8908 1428

BROOKS Elkie (*Voc*): Trees, Woody Bay, Parracombe, North Devon EX31 4QX ☎ 020 7439 8442

BROWN Alex (*Voc, Gtr, Tpt*): 150A Ravensbury Road, Earlsfield, London SW18 4 RU ☎ 020 8947 7589

BROWN Errol (*Voc*): Phil Dale, A M G, 11-13 Broad Court, Covent Garden, London WC2B 5QN ☎ 020 7240 5052

BROWN Lisa (*Voc*): 1 Franklin House, Sandbourne Road, London SE4 2NT ☎ 020 7639 0056, 0966 374403 mob

BROWN Melanie (*Voc, Song W*): Moneyspider Productions Ltd, 66-68 Bell Street, London NW1 6SP ☎ 020 7724 0246, 020 7724 8050

BROWN Natalie (*Voc*): 5 Englefield Close, West Croydon, Surrey CR0 2TU

BROWN Peter (*Voc, Per*): 123 Mountview Road, London N4 4JH

BROWN Rachael (*Voc*): 13 Coulser Close, Gadebridge, Hemel Hempsted, Herts HP1 3NU ☎ 01442 262021

BROWN Sam (*Voc*): Old School House, Path Of Condia, Forgandenny, Nr Perth, Scotland PH2 9DW

BROWN Sarah (*Voc*): Flat 6, Verona Court, 68 St James Drive, London SW12 8SX ☎ 020 8672 0289, 0831 264853

BROWNE Anton (*Voc, Gtr*): 6 Clarendon Road, Croydon, Surrey CR0 3SG ☎ 020 8686 6369

BROWTON Richard (*Voc, Gtr*): 77A Endwell Road, Brockley, London SE4 2NF ☎ 020 7639 5746, 07970 672676

BRYAN Kelle (*Voc, B Gtr, Pf, Kbds*): First Avenue Mgmt, 42 Colwith Road, London W6 9EY ☎ 020 8741 1419

BRYANT Kelly (*Voc*): 43 Guiness Square, Pages Walk, London SE1 4HH ☎ 020 7232 1358, 0958 488828 mob

BRYCE Lindy (*Voc, Gtr*): 29 Cheyham Way, South Cheam, Surrey SM2 7HX ☎ 020 8661 0065

BRYDON-PHILLIPS Mary (*Voc, Clt, Sax, Pf*): 167 Chevening Road, Kilburn, London NW6 6DT ☎ 020 8968 7731

BUCHANAN Margo (*Voc*): 48 Dukes Avenue, Muswell Hill, London N10 2PU ☎ 020 8444 2007, 020 8444 6229 fax

BUCKLEY Jackie (*Voc*): Flat 1, 26 Woodside Road, Woodgreen, London N22 5HT ☎ 0958 767484

BULL Bernita (*Voc, Sax, Wood W, Kbds*): 26 Winton Avenue, London N11 2AT ☎ 020 8889 8161

BULL Linda (*Voc*): 65 Kingsbridge Road, Harold Hill, Romford, Essex RM3 8PA ☎ 01708 344592

BUNTON Emma (*Voc, Song W*): Monsta Productions Ltd, 66-68 Bell Street, London NW1 6SP ☎ 020 7724 0246, 020 7724 8050

BURGHER Richard (*Voc, Kbds*): 2 Curtisfield Road, London SW16 2TE ☎ 020 8664 7361

BURNS Lucie (*Voc, Song W, Pf, Kbds, Dms*): 23 Cornwallis Square, London N19 4LY ☎ 020 7281 1148, 0585 164938

BURROWES Margaret (*Voc*): 59 Diamond Terrace, Old Kentroad, London SE15 1DU ☎ 0976 640 737 mob, 020 7732 5274

BURTON Geoffrey (*Voc, Clt, Flt, Per, Gtr*): 15A Cathcart Hill, London N19 5QW ☎ 020 7272 5996

BURTON Lou (*Voc, Song W*): Green Arbour, 38 Westcar Lane, Walton-on-Thames, Surrey KT12 5ES ☎ 01932 241234, 0956 804805 mob

BYNOE Victor (*Voc, Dms*): 179C West Barnes Lane, New Malden, Surrey KT3 6HR ☎ 020 8336 0084

CAHILL Sarah (*Voc, Pf*): Hartismere House, Hartismere Road, Fulham, London SW6 7TS ☎ 020 7386 0338

CAICEDO Luz (*Voc*): 44 Fentiman Road, London SW8 1LF ☎ 020 7587 1322, 0956 495179 mob

CAINE Andy (*Voc, Gtr*): 2 Dudley Road, London NW6 6JX ☎ 020 8960 9855

CAMERON Lennox (*Voc, Kbds*): 26 Wager Street, Bow, London E3 4JE ☎ 020 8980 0795

CAMERON Tarnya (*Voc*) ☎ 020 8257 7404, 07801 658800

CAMILLE Chantal (*Voc*) ☎ 020 7737 6188, 0956 299 091 pager

CANALE Donna (*Voc*): 4 Wickham Road, Brockley, London SE4 1PB ☎ 020 8692 5670

CAPORASO Luciana (*Voc*): Frederick Cottages, 31 Sutton Grove, Sutton, Surrey SM1 4LR

CARGILL Margo (*Voc, Rec, Kbds*): 18 Bromley Street, Stepeny, London E1 0NB ☎ 020 7790 3422, 0966 448528

CARLILL Neil (*Voc, Gtr*): 288C Archway Road, London N5 5AU ☎ 020 8348 6016

CARMEL Heather (*Voc, Pf*): 1 Mortimer Road, East Ham, London E6 3QP ☎ 020 8552 4974

CARMICHAEL Challan (*Voc*): 5 Thicket Court, Thicket Road, Sutton, Surrey SM1 4PZ ☎ 07971 573 407

CASELLA Teresa *(Voc)*: 128 Priory Park Road, Kilburn, London NW6 7UU ☎ 020 7625 9495

CASHIN Chrissy *(Voc)*: 26 B, Thirsk Road, Battersea, London SW11 5SX ☎ 020 7228 2105

CASPER Nova *(Voc)*: 27A Basement Flat, Vartry Road, Stamford Hill, London N15 6PR ☎ 020 8802 0320

CASSELL Debbie *(Voc, Gtr, Kbds)*: Durweston Lodge, Durweston, Blandford Forum, Dorset DT11 0QA ☎ 020 8693 9786

CASSIDY Mary *(Voc)*: Address Unknown ☎ 020 8870 3513

CATO Lurine *(Voc)*: 6 Park Road, Edmonton, London N18 2UT ☎ 020 8807 6624, 0795 7401969

CAVE Suzanne *(Voc)*: 4 Darwin Street, Winkworth, Kennington, London SE17 1HB ☎ 020 7277 0581

CECIL Katherine *(Voc)*

CHACHIAN Liliana *(Voc, Per)*: 122B Croxted Road, London SE21 8NR ☎ 020 8761 7769

CHADWICK Guy *(Voc, Gtr)*: P O Box 333, London SE5 9HL

CHADWICK Helen *(Voc)*: 11 John Campbell Road, London N16 8JY ☎ 020 7241 3152, 020 7241 3152 fax

CHALMERS Valerie *(Voc, Song W, Per)* ☎ 020 7387 1779

CHANDLER Marianne *(Voc)*: 129 Queenswood Gardens, Wanstead, London E11 3SG ☎ 020 8518 8861

CHANNI *(Voc)*: 71 St Josephs Drive, Southall, Middlesex UB1 1RP ☎ 020 8574 5784

CHANTER Doreen *(Voc, Pf, Tamb)*: Flat 1, The Dowings, 21 Southey Road, Wimbledon SW19 1ND ☎ 0468 000356

CHAPLIN Brian *(Voc)*: 86 Chichester Road, Croydon, Surrey CR0 5NB ☎ 020 8688 6233

CHAPMAN Roger *(Voc)*: 18 Gordon Avenue, East Sheen, London SW14 8DZ ☎ 020 8876 6117

CHARLES Debbie *(Voc, Per)*: 19 The Green, Stratford, London E15 4ND ☎ 020 7265 8166

CHAZ *(Voc)*: 16 Burton Lane, Myatts Field, Brixton, London SW9 6NX ☎ 020 7924 0284, 0956 966004

CHISHOLM Melanie *(Voc, Song W)*: Red Girl Productions Ltd, 66-68 Bell Street, London NW1 6SP ☎ 020 7724 0246, 020 7724 8050

CHRISTOFI Andrianna *(Voc)*: 19 Devonshire Gardens, London N21 2AL ☎ 020 8360 4961

CHYNA *(Voc)*: 301A Thornton Road, Croydon, Surrey CR0 3EY ☎ 020 8239 9370

CITA *(Voc)*: 225 Southampton Way, London SE5 7EQ ☎ 020 7708 2657

CLARK Christina *(Voc, Gtr)*: 196 Lyndhurst Road, Wood Green, London N22 5AU ☎ 020 8888 3488

CLARK Nigel *(Voc, B Gtr, Ac Gtr)*: c/o 271 Royal College Street, Camden Town, London NW1 9LU ☎ 020 7482 0115, 020 7267 1169 fax

CLARKE Claire *(Voc, Gtr)*: 59 Harvesters Close, Isleworth, Middx TW7 7PS ☎ 020 8755 1049, 0378 290918

CLARKE Maurice *(Voc, Pf)*

CLARKE Sharon *(Voc)*: 102 Ranelagh Road, London N17 6XT ☎ 020 8808 8745

CLARKSON Ian *(Voc, Tpt, Gtr)*: c/o Jive Aces, St Hill Manor, East Grinstead, West Sussex RH19 4JY ☎ 01342 300075, 0589 155046

CLAYDEN Jonathan *(Voc)*: c/o Knightmare Mgmnt Ltd, Friars House, Suite 118, 1St Floor, 157-168 Blackfriars Road, London SE1 8EZ ☎ 020 7928 6755

CLEE Ginny *(Voc, Gtr)*: Flat 1, 83 Dartmouth Park Road, London NW5 1SL ☎ 020 7267 3876

CLEO *(Voc)*: 2 Clifton Road, London N22 4XN ☎ 020 8888 2289

CLIMIE Simon *(Voc, Kbds, Gtr, Song W, Per)*: c/o Newman & Co, Regent House, 1 Pratt Mews, London NW1 0AD ☎ 020 7267 6899, 020 7267 6746

COATALEN Diana *(Voc, Flt)*: 37 Beaconsfield Road, Surbiton, Surrey KT5 9AW ☎ 020 8399 6312, 0961 374287

COBBING Bob *(Voc, Per)*: 89A Petherton Rd, London N5 2QT ☎ 020 7226 2657

COE Melrose *(Voc)*: 25 Essex Close, Walthamstow, London E17 6JS ☎ 020 8521 8264

COFFEY Joan *(Voc, Gtr)*: 135 St Thomas's Road, Finsbury Park, London N4 2QJ ☎ 020 7704 6790

COKER Aduragbemi *(Voc, Song W, Pf, Gtr)*: 18 Inglewood Mansions, West End Lane, Hampstead, London NW6 1RE ☎ 020 8694 6464, 0966 195 336, 020 8694 6363

COLDWELL Terry *(Voc)*: 24 Harts Grove, Woodford Green, Essex IG8 ☎ 020 7613 2457, 020 7613 4395

COLE Travis *(Voc, Pf)*: 48 The Sandlings, Glynne Road, Wood Green, London N22 6XP ☎ 020 8889 0759

COLLINS Jo *(Voc, Pf, Gtr, Com)*: 28 Riverway, London N13 5LJ

COLLISTER Christine *(Voc, Gtr)*: 8 Rathlin Walk, Islington, London N1 2PD ☎ 020 7359 7624, 0976 710886 mob

COLMAN Anthony *(Voc, Gtr, Kbds, Per)*: 17 Barons Court Road, London W14 9DP ☎ 020 7386 8760

COMMEY-TAYLOR Samantha *(Voc, Com, Pf)*: 5 Dounesforth Gardens, London SW18 4QP ☎ 020 8871 1384

CONLAN Anita *(Voc)*: 5 Thornton Road, Carshalton, Surrey SM5 1NL ☎ 020 8641 1016, 0956 292131

CONNER Trevor James *(Voc, Sax)*: Ground Floor, 236 Portnall Road, Queens Park, London W9 3BJ ☎ 020 8964 5502

CONNETT Maureen *(Voc)*: 93 Moundfield Road, Stamford Hill, London N16 6TD ☎ 020 8802 8292

CONSTANTIN Virginie *(Voc)*: 190 St Barnabas Road, Woodford Green, Essex IG8 7DU

CONSTANTINE Helen *(Voc, Com)*: Flat D, 249 Uxbridge Road, London W12 9DS

COOK Carole *(Voc, Per)*: Address Unknown ☎ 01932 820955

COOKE Terence *(Voc, Gtr, Flt, Per)*: Flat A (Side Entrance), 130 Salusbury Road, London NW6 6PB ☎ 020 7328 3601

COOKMAN Louise *(Voc)*: 22 Hawley Road, Wilmington, Dartford, Kent DA1 1NR ☎ 01322 276409, 01227 264826

COOPER Mike *(Voc, Gtr, Kbds)*: 147A Hackney Road, London E2 8JL ☎ 020 7613 0670

CORNELL Katherine *(Voc)*: 5 Galsworthy Road, Cricklewood, London NW2 2SD ☎ 020 8452 2896, 0410 503000 mob

CORNWALL Lindel *(Voc, Per, B Gtr)*: 34 Howard House, Barrington Road, Brixton, London SW9 7JY ☎ 020 7924 9960

CORRINGHAM Viv *(Voc)*: 9 Brecknock Road, London N7 0BL ☎ 020 7267 8388

COSTER Pamela *(Voc)*: 55 Alexandra Park Road, Muswell Hill, London N10 2DG ☎ 020 8883 9418

COTTERILL Carlton *(Voc, B Gtr, Kbds)* ☎ 020 7735 4110

COTTERILL Marianne *(Voc, Pf)*: 307A Kingston Road, London SW20 8LB ☎ 020 8543 0166

COWAN Vinnette *(Voc)*: 50 Clanricarde Gardens, London W2 4JW ☎ 020 7792 3517

COWLING Zee *(Voc, Song W)*: 9 Elizabeth Mews, Headstone Road, Harrow, Middlesex HA1 1PF ☎ 020 8427 4008, 0973 134053

COX Doc *(Voc, Uke, Gtr)*: 72, Cranmer Avenue, Northfields, London W13 9XU

COX George *(Voc)*: 71A Granville Road, Walthamstow, London E17 5BS ☎ 020 8925 9400

CRAGG Eileen *(Voc)*: 165 Gunnersbury Lane, Acton, London W3 8LJ ☎ 020 8993 2111

CRAIG Robbie *(Voc)*: La Maison, Ash Green Lane East, Ash Green, Aldershot, Hants GU12 6JA ☎ 01252 314697

CREAM *(Voc)*

CREMER Patric *(Voc, Synth)*: Naunynstr 42, 10999 Berlin, Germany ☎ +49 30 614 2760

CROKER Joanne *(Voc, Pf)*: Basement Flat, 20 Grange Park, Ealing, London W5 3PS ☎ 020 8567 0781

CROSBY Carol *(Voc)*: 35 Rainham Road, Kensal Green, London NW10 5DL ☎ 020 8969 2805

CROUCH Stuart *(Voc, Hmca, Kbds)*: 258 Northumberland Ave, Welling, Kent DA16 2QG ☎ 020 8301 0056, 020 8237 5702, 0973 413567 mob

CRYER Karina *(Voc, Vln, Per)*: 135 Avenue Road, Acton, London W3 8QJ ☎ 020 8992 8268

CRYME *(Voc)*: 152B Malpas Road, Brockley SE4 1DH ☎ 0973 197183

CUBBON Germaine *(Voc)*: 106 Silverdale Road, Tunbridge Wells, Kent TN4 9HZ

CUMMINS Ross *(Voc, Hrp)*: 8 Hazlitt Rd, Olympia, London W14 0JY ☎ 020 7602 4950

CUNNINGHAM-REID Jane *(Voc)*: 24 Malbrook Road, London SW15 6UF ☎ 0831 378487

CURRAN Paul *(Voc, Rh Gtr, Kbds)*: 5 Crayle House, Malta Street, London EC1V 0BT ☎ 020 7251 0268

CURTIS Dee *(Voc)*: 152A Howard Road, Walthamstow, London E17 4SQ ☎ 020 8520 8370

CURTIS Yvonne *(Voc)*: 95 Greyhound Road, Tottenham, London N17 6XR ☎ 020 8885 5337

D Danny *(Voc, Per)*: c/o 19 Management Ltd, Unit 32, Ransomes Dock, Parkgate Road, London SW11 4NP ☎ 020 7228 4000

D'ORIO Gina *(Voc, Kbds)*: Naunynstr 42, 10999 Berlin, Germany ☎ +49 30614276

DADDY GEE (Voc, Kbds, Dms): c/o T Hancock, West, 6A Orde Hall Street, London WC1N 3JW ☎ 020 7405 7270, 020 7405 9834 fax

DAISICAL Laka *(Voc, Kbds)*: 14B Cricketfield Road, London E5 8NS ☎ 020 8985 1039, 0958 526201 mob

DAKAR Rhoda *(Voc, A Sax)*: 8 Dover Mansions, Canterbury Crescent, London SW9 7QF ☎ 020 7738 6468

DALE Josie *(Voc, Pf, Gtr)*: 105D Pepys Road, New Cross, London SE14 5SE ☎ 020 7639 7518

DALLAS Kat *(Voc, Gtr)*: K.L.D. Music, North London N16 ☎ 020 8802 0451

DALY Susan *(Voc)*: c/o 14 River Avenue, Palmers Green, London N13 5RU ☎ 020 8886 1772

DAN Richie *(Voc, Rapper, Club Dj)*: 64 Minet Avenue, Harlesden, London NW10 8AH ☎ 020 8965 2600, 0956 517514, 020 8838 0920

DANIEL David *(Voc, Kbds)*: 34 Ridge Road, Hornsey, London N8 9LH ☎ 020 8347 9116

DANIEL Donna *(Voc)*: 34 Ridge Road, Hornsey, London N8 9LH ☎ 020 8347 9116

DANIEL Lisa *(Voc)*: 111 Elspeth Road, London SW11 1DP ☎ 020 7978 5709

DANIELA *(Voc)*: 5 Girdlestone Walk, Bredgar Road, London N19 5DL ☎ 0958 554146

DANSE Nicolle *(Voc, Song W)*: 7 Diana Close, Chafford Hundred, Grays, Essex RM16 6PX ☎ 01375 480539

DANSER Mel *(Voc, B Ldr)*: 801 Eastern Avenue, Newbury Park, Ilford, Essex IG2 7RY ☎ 020 8590 2346

DANZIG Karen *(Voc, Theory)*: P O Box 1345, Ilford, Essex IG4 5FX ☎ 07970 213378 mob

DARENNTH Suzanne *(Voc, Kbds)* ☎ 020 8778 1132

DARKMAN *(Voc, Pf, Dms)*: 53 Mill Hill Road, Acton, London W3 8JF ☎ 020 8248 7183/4, 0831 223340, 0831 2487184

DARN Debbie *(Voc, Per)*: 4 Crabtree Court, Clays Lane, Stratford, London E15 2UG ☎ 020 8534 5810

DAVID Alison *(Voc, Kbds)*: 95 Hanover Road, London NW10 3DL ☎ 020 8459 1245

DAVID Matthew *(Voc)*: 27 Winter Garden, 2-4 Macklin Street, Covent Gdn, London WC2B 5ND ☎ 020 7831 6920

DAVID Paula *(Voc, Per)*: 4 Landsbury Road, Enfield, Middx EN3 5NB ☎ 020 8805 3885

DAVIES Claire *(Voc)*: 34 Greenford Avenue, Hanwell, London W7 3QP ☎ 020 8840 6753

DAVIES Claire *(Voc)*: 3 Cambourne Way, Harold Hill, Romford, Essex RM3 8RA ☎ 01708 744334, 0836 210868, 01708 762492

DAVIES Marian *(Voc)*: 45 Adelaide Road, Surbiton, Surrey KT6 4SR ☎ 020 8399 4724

DAVILA Beatrix *(Voc, Gtr, Xyl, Per)*: 28 Wandle Road, Beddington, Surrey CR0 4SD ☎ 020 8395 7980

DAVIS Colete *(Voc)*: Flat E, 8 Connaught Road, London NW10 9AG ☎ 020 8453 0391

DAVIS Laura *(Voc, Pf, Per)*: 112 Kilmorie Road, London SE23 2SR ☎ 020 8699 0844

DAVIS Neil *(Voc, B Gtr, Gtr, Dms)*: 2 Firestation Mews, 4A Bromley Road, Beckenham, Kent BR3 5JQ ☎ 020 8653 4843

DAVIS T.J. *(Voc, Pf, Kbds)*: Top Floor, 28 Sinclair Road, London W14 0NH ☎ 020 7603 8997

DAWE Judi *(Voc, Pf, Kbds)*: 28 Eastside Road, London NW11 0BA ☎ 020 8209 1833, 0973 385265

DE AZEVEDO Daniel *(Voc, Dms, Kbds, B Gtr)*: 31 Clarence Road, London E12 5BB ☎ 020 8478 2701

DE PEYER Lorrayn *(Voc, Pf, Gtr)* ☎ 020 8671 1286

DE SYKES Stephanie *(Voc)*: Nithsdale, Pembroke Road, Woking, Surrey GU22 7EB ☎ 01483 762493, 01483 751399

DE-MOOR Des *(Voc, Pf, Gtr)*: 84 Knoyle Street, London SE14 6JY ☎ 020 8692 6857

DE.PALMA Ghida *(Voc)*: 3 Linacre Road, Willesden, London NW2 5BD ☎ 020 8459 0471, 0958 723 371 mob

DEAN Gary *(Voc, Dms)*: 38 Oakdale Road, London SW16 2HL ☎ 020 8769 2673

DEAR Brian *(Voc, Gtr)*: 23 Mackenzie House, Ainsworth Close, London NW2 7EH ☎ 020 8208 2305

DEBENHAM Shelley *(Voc, Dms)*: 144 Haynes Road, Hornchurch, Essex RM11 2HU ☎ 01708 457471/452008, 0958 452139 mob

DEBOURG Daniel *(Voc, Gtr)*: 2 Alten Place, Standish Road, Hammersmith, London W6 9UN ☎ 020 8746 3936, 0410 536815 mob

DEDEWO Wynford *(Voc, Kbds)* ☎ 020 8809 3732

DEE Howard *(Voc, Kbds, Gtr)*: 429 Ewell Road, Tolworth, Surrey KT6 7ES ☎ 020 8390 5671, 546 1042 day

DEE-AN *(Voc)*: 31 Galway Road, Sheerness, Kent ME12 2QL ☎ 01795 661996, 01523 138020 pager

DEL ROSARIO Sonia *(Voc, Pf)*: 59 Holland Park, London W11 3SJ ☎ 020 7792 3403

DELL *(Voc, Dms, Kbds, Gtr, Tamb)*: 45 Butler House, Burdette Road, London E14 7AB

DELVINO Lorraine *(Voc)*: Ivydene, Dukesthorpe Road, Sydenham, London SE26 4PB ☎ 020 8776 7245

DEMETRIOU Demetrios *(Voc)*: 24A Hanover Park, London SE15 5HS ☎ 020 7277 6535

DENIS Carol *(Voc, Kbds, Gtr, Song W)*: 85 Kerridge Court, Balls Pond Road, London N1 4AN ☎ 020 7503 7192

DEPASS Michele *(Voc)*: 13 Tabley Road, London N7 0NA ☎ 020 7700 6934

DEWSON Edward *(Voc, Pf, Gtr, Vln, Sax)*: 50 Melbourne Avenue, London N13 4SX ☎ 020 8889 5377, 0973 110075

DEZZ *(Voc)*: 103 Broadwater Rd, Tottenham, London N17 6EP ☎ 020 8801 6568

DIAMOND Rae *(Voc, La Per, Tamb)*: 65 Elmsleigh Avenue, Kenton, Harrow, Middx HA3 8HY ☎ 020 8907 7523

DICKENS Frankie *(Voc)*: 65 Newark Street, Stepney, London E1 2ET ☎ 020 7375 2667

DICKINSON Bruce *(Voc)*: C-O Iron Maiden Ltd, The Colonnades, 82 Bishopsbridge Road, London W2 6BB ☎ 020 7631 3929

DICKINSON Philip *(Voc, Vln)*: 52 Beltran Road, London SW6 3AJ ☎ 020 7384 2566

DIETRICH Simone *(Voc, Pf)*: Strelitzer Str 18, 10115 Berlin, Germany ☎ +49 30 391 00 397, +49 30 391 00 398 fax

DITSEBE Joe *(Voc, Per, Mbira, Tkg Dms, Mrb)*: 40 Grasmere, Robert Street, Regents Park Estate, London NW1 3QL ☎ 020 7387 0338

DIXON Alexandra J *(Voc)*: Flat 1, 9 Station Parade, Kew Gardens TW9 3PS ☎ 020 8940 1438

DIXON Rebecca *(Voc)*

DIXON Ruth *(Voc)*: 5 Portrush Court, Whitecote Road, Southall, Middx UB1 3NR ☎ 020 8813 9916, 020 8771 4796

DIXON Shenton *(Voc, Gtr, B Gtr, Kbds, Pf)*: 93 Brecknock Road, London N7 0BZ ☎ 020 7482 1981, 0973 814438 mob

DODWA Gifty *(Voc)*: 7 Coronet Street, London N1 6HD ☎ 020 7613 2479

DOMINIC John *(Voc, Com, Gtr, Hmca)*: The Garden Flat, 11 Warwick Avenue, London W9 2PS

DORE Michael *(Voc, Pf)*: Flat D, 35 Central Hill, Upper Norwood, London SE19 1BW ☎ 020 8670 6901, 0973 386658 mob

DOUBLE Daniella *(Voc)*: 355 Grafton Road, Gospel Oak, London NW5 4BL ☎ 020 7482 0583, 0831 380 267

DOUGLAS Ellisha *(Voc)*: 36 Mandela Street, Vassal Road, Brixton, London SW9 6EL ☎ 020 7735 2395

DOUGLAS Stacey-Jane (*Voc, Gtr, Song W, Com*): 33 Arden House, Black Prince Road, Vauxhall, London SE11 5QH ☎ 020 7735 1720

DOWNS Richard (*Voc*): 45 Hillside Avenue, Gravesend, Kent DA12 5QN ☎ 01474 355772

DRAVEN Jay Eric (*Voc*): 89 Astbury Road, Peckham, London SE15 2NP ☎ 020 7732 1874, 0958 55 7275

DREWERY Corinne (*Voc*): c/o Chapel House, Gilling East, York YO6 4JL

DREZ (*Voc, Pf, Per*): 73 Barriedale, London SE14 6RP ☎ 020 8694 1343

DUCIL Roy (*Voc, Song W*): 70 Oakdale Road, Leytonstone, London E11 4DL ☎ 020 8558 9919

DUGGAN Linda (*Voc*): 66H Blomfield Road, Maida Vale, London W9 2PA ☎ 020 7289 9543

DUNCAN-SUTHERLAND Margaret (*Voc, Vln, Pf*): 29 Lawn Crescent, Kew, Richmond TW9 3NS ☎ 020 8940 4463

DUNN Julie (*Voc, Pf, Per*): 39 Caldbeck Avenue, Worcester Park, Surrey KT4 8BQ ☎ 020 8715 0368

DUNSFORD Yona (*Voc, Kbds*): 59 Bedford Road, Walthamstow, London E17 4PU ☎ 020 8531 2971

DURAND Jacqueline (*Voc*): 230 Morville Street, Bow, London E3 2EF ☎ 020 8880 6593

DURY Ian (*Voc, Dms*): c/o Harris & Trotter, 65 New Cavendish St, London WIM 7RD ☎ 020 7487 4393

DUVERNEY Michele (*Voc*): 65 East Walk, East Barnet, Herts EN4 8JU ☎ 020 8368 3002

DYER Sherene (*Voc*): 3 Langton Lodge, Palaitine Road, Stoke Newington, London N16 8SU ☎ 020 7241 0954

EARL 16 (*Voc, Kbds*): 95 Pilton Place, London SE17 1DP ☎ 020 8964 8440

EASTWOOD Al (*Voc, Gtr, Flt, Dms, Hmca*): 102 Maugham Court, Palmerston Road, Acton, London W3 8TW ☎ 020 8993 7983

EBUN (*Voc*): 52 Montacute Road, Catford, London SE6 4XJ ☎ 020 8314 0418

ECONOMOS Amalia (*Voc*): Flat 4, 174 Ladbroke Grove, London W10 5LZ ☎ 020 8723 8911, 0956 650612 mob

EDEN (*Voc, Pf*): 14 Prospect Place, 212-230 Evelyn Street, London SE8 5BZ ☎ 020 8691 1193, 05895 425978 mob

EDWARDS Glenton (*Voc, Gtr*)

EDWARDS Janet (*Voc, Kbds, Hpsd*): 37B Dartmouth Park Ave, London NW5 1JL ☎ 020 7263 6116, 020 7263 5995

EDWARDS Julie (*Voc*): ☎ 020 8926 8695, 0705 0188961

EDWARDS Robin (*Voc, Gtr, Kbds, Per*): ☎ 01708 401756, 0973 283013 mob, 01375 891107 fax

EDWARDS Zena (*Voc, Mbira*): ☎ 020 8801 6350

EDWIGE (*Voc, Song W*): c/o Quasar Music, PO Box 10269, London W2 5GD

EGBOH Anthony (*Voc, Song W*): 46B Filey Avenue, Stamford Hill, London N16 6JJ ☎ 020 8806 9826

ELIXIR Ouriel (*Voc*): Resid Diana, 71 Dd Alexandre 111, 06400 Cannes, France ☎ 0493 946815

ELLIOT (*Voc*): 80 Angell Road, Brixton, London SW9 7HP ☎ 020 7733 7607

ELLIOTT Rachel (*Voc*): 5 The Priory, Priory Park, Blackheath, London SE3 9XA ☎ 020 8318 9636

ELLIOTT Ryan (*Voc*)

ELLIS Katherine (*Voc, Song W, Gtr, B Gtr, Pf*): 8 Elfin Lodge, Elfin Grove, Teddington, Middlesex TW11 8RE

ELLIS Vivien (*Voc*): Flat 4, 12 Lancaster Drive, London NW3 4HA ☎ 020 7431 5326

ELTON Hugh (*Voc, Vln*): Garden Flat, 10-16A Stanlake Villas, Shepherds Bush, London W12 W12 7EX ☎ 020 8743 7495

EMMETT Christopher (*Voc*): 55 Gospatrick Road, London N17 7EH ☎ 020 8885 1305

ENEVER Cheryl (*Voc, Cel*): Top Flat, 139 Aldborough Road South, Seven Kings, Ilford, Essex IG3 8HT ☎ 020 8590 2851

ENGLAND Natasha (*Voc*): 26 Queens Avenue, Muswell Hill, London N10 3NR ☎ 020 8883 3369

ERASMUS Sarah (*Voc*): 24 Seal Road, Selsey, Chichester, West Sussex PO20 0HU ☎ 01932 865350

ESCOFFERY Michelle (*Voc, Song W, Arr*): 56 Peak Hill, Sydenham, London SE26 4LR ☎ 0468 892397

ESCOFFERY-THOMPSON Marcia (*Voc*): 34 Greenhurst Road, West Norwood, London SE27 0LH ☎ 020 8480 9104, 0961 320455 mob

ESJAE (*Voc*): 33E Avondale Park Road, London W11 4HG ☎ 020 7792 0050

ESSINGTON-BOULTON Olivia (*Voc*): 39 Freedom Street, Battersea, London SW11 5AQ ☎ 01225 480682, 020 7228 9350, 0411 309182

ETIENNE Valerie (*Voc, Gtr*): Address Unknown ☎ 020 7241 0621

EVANS Audrey (*Voc, Gtr*): 153 Stoke Newington, Church Street, London N6 0UH ☎ 020 7254 1496

EVANS Jenni (*Voc*): 1 Greenside Road, West Croydon, London CR0 3PP ☎ 020 8684 9500

EVANS Sara (*Voc, B Gtr, Vib*): 4, Clock House, St. Mary's Street, Nether Stowey, Bridgwater, Somerset TA5 1LJ ☎ 01278 732123, 01278 733205 fax

EVANS Sophie (*Voc, Sax, Gtr*): 40 Marvell House, Camberwell Road, Camberwell, London SE5 7JD ☎ 020 7708 0957, 0976 770831, 020 8885 6030

EVE Alison (*Voc, Gtr, Kbds*): Flat 2, 46 Chalk Hill, Oxhey, Herts WD1 4BX ☎ 01923 50758

EVELYN (*Voc*): 61 Highfield Towers, Hillrise Road, Collier Row, Romford , Essex RM5 3DQ ☎ 01708 25908

EXLEY Heather (*Voc, Ob*): Flat 3, 86 Burnt Ash Hill, London SE12 0HT ☎ 020 8851 5767

FAIRBRASS Richard (*Voc, B Gtr*): c/o Simon Makepeace, Martin Greene Ravden, 55 Loudoun Road, St Johns Wood, London NW8 0DL ☎ 020 7625 4545, 020 7625 5265 fax

FAIRLEY Liz (*Voc*): 2 Treverton Street, North Kensington, London W10 6DW

FAITHFIELD Rory (*Voc, Gtr*): 393 Clontarf Road, Dublin 3, Ireland ☎ +3531 8530780

FALLOON Beverley (*Voc*): 91 Lealand Road, Tottenham, London N15 6JT ☎ 020 8809 0583

FAR Sam (*Voc*): 43 Waddon Park Avenue, Croydon, Surrey CR0 4LW ☎ 020 8251 9809, 0958 68454

FARI Piper (*Voc, Song W, B Gtr, Pf, Dms*): 79 Lightfoot Road, Hornsey, London N8 7JF ☎ 020 8374 8289, 0956 900831 mob

FARR Henry (*Voc, B Gtr, Gtr, Dms, Kbds*): 141 Winchester Road, Four Marks, Alton, Hampshire GU34 5HY ☎ 01420 562992

FARWELL Antony (*Voc, Gtr*): 34 Southfield Road, High Wycombe, Bucks HP13 5LA ☎ 01494 471239

FEASEY Mia (*Voc*): Flat 26, 180 Acton Lane, Chiswick, London W4 5DL ☎ 0958 238311

FELLOWES Marcus (*Voc*): Flat 3, 30 Cintra Park, Crystal Palace, London SE19 2LQ ☎ 020 8771 0880, 07771 663301

FENTON Graham (*Voc*): 7 Byward Ave, Feltham, Middlesex TW14 OEY ☎ 020 8384 9864

FERGUS Lorna (*Voc*): 11 Medesenge Way, Palmers Green, London N13 6DZ ☎ 020 8889 0281, 0956 643230 mob

FERGUSSON Harriet (*Voc, Pf, Cell*): 31A Boscastle Road, Dartmouth Park, London NW5 1EE ☎ 020 7267 6260, 0961 140524, 020 7284 4554

FERNANDES Hazel (*Voc*): 296 Watford Way, Hendon, London NW4 4SH ☎ 0385 951 358 mob

FESTENSTEIN Iris (*Voc*): 11 Fairlawn Avenue, East Finchley, London N2 9PS ☎ 020 8883 0154

FIBI (*Voc, Gtr, Sax*): Garden Flat, 12 Gauden Road, Clapham, London SW4 6LT ☎ 020 7498 7291, 0956 696034 mob

FIELD Caroline (*Voc, Pf, Gtr*): 11 The Colonnades, 107 Wilton Way, London E8 1BH ☎ 020 8986 6222

FINDLEY Marie (*Voc*): 401 Hornsey Road, Upper Holloway, London N19 4DX ☎ 020 7272 9822

FINLAY Nadine (*Voc*)

FINNEY David (*Voc, Gtr*): 62 Walnut Way, Buckhurst Hill, Essex IG9 6HX ☎ 020 8506 1486

FISHER Rhoda (*Voc*): 52A Kempshott Road, Streatham, London SW16 5LH ☎ 020 8561 8868, 0958 420350

FITZGERALD Warren (*Voc*): 50 Cranbrook Park, London N22 5NA ☎ 020 8888 8166

FITZJOHN Ethel (*Voc*): 49 Laurel Gardens, London W7 3JG ☎ 020 8579 4486

FLETCHER Hilary (*Voc*): 18 Heath Gardens, Twickenham, Middlesex TW1 4LZ ☎ 020 8892 6175

FLETCHER Liz (*Voc, Kbds, Cong*): 5 Chiswick Mall, London W4 2QH ☎ 020 8747 8093, 0958 316129

FLOWERS Zowie (*Voc*): Address Unknown ☎ 020 7258 0547

FLYNN Fabian-Anna (*Voc*): 8 Castle Street, Ongar, Essex CM5 9SR ☎ 01277 363476 & fax

FOLEYCASH (*Voc*): 50 Cecil Road, Walthamstow, London E17 5DJ ☎ 020 8527 3071, 0961 301872

FOLLETT Marie-Claire (*Voc*): 92 Cheyne Walk, Chelsea, London SW10 0DQ ☎ 020 7351 5526, 020 7352 5168 fax

FONTAINE Claudia (*Voc*): 74 Latona Road, Unwin Estate, Peckham, London SE15 6RY ☎ 020 7639 2058

FORD Bill (*Voc*): 56 Northview, Swanley, Kent BR8 7BQ ☎ 01322 64010

FORD Lucy-Anne (*Voc*): 38 Springwood, Cheshunt, Herts EN7 6AZ ☎ 01992 638764, 07971 718503

FORDE Nadine (*Voc*): 59 Beechwood Road, Hornsey, London N8 7NE ☎ 020 8341 3205, 020 7829 1103, 020 7928 7625

FORDHAM Richard (*Voc, Vib, Org*): 91 Ledbury Road, London W11 2AG

FOSTER Weston B (*Voc, Dms*): 19 Blean Grove, Penge, London SE20 8QS ☎ 020 8659 8768

FOULCER Alexander (*Voc, Pf, Gtr, Dms, Per*): 41 Blackhorse Road, Walthamstow, London E17 7AS ☎ 020 8925 8421

FOX-LITTLE Debbie (*Voc*): 135 Canbury Park Road, Kingston-upon-Thames, Surrey KT2 6LH ☎ 020 8287 5279

FOXALL Emma (*Voc, Sax*): 11 Princes Road, West Ealing, London W13 9AS ☎ 020 8932 0441, 0850 898618

FRANCIS Louise (*Voc*): 13 Shearwater Court, Abinger Grove, Deptford, London SE8 5SR ☎ 020 8691 2912

FRANCIS Shireen (*Voc*): 16 Beattie House, Stewarts Road, London SW8 4LB ☎ 020 7627 3578

FRANCOMBE Peter (*Voc, Kbds, Gtr*): 36 Bedford Road, East Finchley, London N2 9DA ☎ 0956 801690

FRANKCOM Alan (*Voc*): 13 Beaconsfield Road, New Malden, Surrey KT3 3HY ☎ 020 8949 1466

FRANKLIN Ben (*Voc, Flt, B Gtr, Pf, Gtr*): 29 Foulden Road, London N16 7UU ☎ 020 7923 4527, 04325 309 834 pager

FRANKONYTE Loreta (*Voc, Kbds*): 70F Fellows Road, London NW3 3LJ ☎ 020 8960 1237

FRATER Josie (*Voc, Gtr, Per*): 59 Churchbury Road, Enfield EN1 3HP ☎ 020 8292 2160, 020 8373 7304

FREEDMAN Madelaine (*Voc, Gtr*): 49 Whitchurch Gardens, Edgware, Middlesex, London HA8 6PF ☎ 020 8952 6484, 0961 198865

FRENCH Ns (*Voc, Pf, Per*): 58 Queen's Walk, South Ruislip, Middlesex HA4 0LU

FROST Susan (*Voc, Pf, Gtr*): 39 Northfield House, Peckham Park Road, London SE15 6TL ☎ 020 7635 9303

FRUCTUOSO-MARTINEZ Isabel-Carmen (*Voc*): 41 Montefiore Court, Stamford Hill, London N16 5TY ☎ 020 8809 2876

FRY James (*Voc*): 7 Richborough Road, London NW2 3LU

FUGLER Jonathon (*Voc, Cel*): c/o Fluke, Rear Court Yard, Sagaland, 326 Kensal Road W10 5BZ ☎ 020 8964 4623

FUNKY MAC The (*Voc*): 18 Ditton Road, Norwood Green, Southall, Middlesex UB2 5RZ ☎ 020 8574 0789, 01523 198385 pager

FURLER Sia (*Voc*): Basement Flat, 85 Holland Road, Kensington, London W14 8HP ☎ 020 7603 2082, 0961 835163

FYFE James (*Voc, Gtr*): 18 Oakhall Drive, Sunbury, Middlesex TW16 7LG ☎ 020 8890 8797

GALDES Dorothy (*Voc*): 1 Perth Avenue, Kingsbury, London NW9 7JP ☎ 020 8459 8374

GALLAGHER Audrey (*Voc, Gtr, Kbds*): 65 Station Road, Maghera, Co Derry, Northern Ireland BT46 5EY ☎ 01648 45803

GALLOWAY Ruth (*Voc, Dms, Rec*): 43 Corinne Road, Tufnell Park, London N19 5EZ ☎ 020 7700 0805 & fax, 020 7700 5840

GANTZ Carrie-Ann (*Voc, B Gtr*): 49C Gondar Gardens, West Hampstead, London NW6 1EP

GARCIA Vincent (*Voc, Kbds*): 24A Thurlow Road, Hampstead, London NW3 5PP ☎ 020 7435 2811

GARDIER Donna (*Voc*): Unit 37 Buspace Studios, Conlan Street, London W10 5AP ☎ 020 8969 1600

GARRETT Julia (*Voc*): ☎ 020 7631 7859, 0956 497744

GAYNOR Dee (*Voc*): 58 The Spinney, Sidcup, Kent DA14 5NF ☎ 020 8300 7631

GBESEMETE Enyonam (*Voc*): 6 Wyborne House, Wyborne Way, London NW10 0TB ☎ 020 8961 7380, 020 8830 2787

GEARY Caron (*Voc, Per, Dms*): c/o 97 Lisson Grove, London NW1 6UP

GEE (*Voc*): 121 Shelley Avenue, Manor Park, London E12 6PX ☎ 020 8548 4284

GELDOF Robert (*Voc*): c/o Mick Owen, M.D.O., The Dawn, Northwood Lane, Bewdley, Worcs DY12 1AS ☎ 01299 404579, 0836 378224 mob

GELSTON Natasha (*Voc, Pf*): 34 Warren Road, Chingford, London E4 6QS ☎ 020 8529 8039

GEM (*Voc, Song W*): 12 Cluny Place, 30 Cluny Place, Bermondsey, London SE1 4QU ☎ 020 7357 8110

GEOFFO (*Voc, Gtr*): 9 Burr Close, St Katharines Dock, London E1 9NB

GEORGE Boy (*Voc, Pf*): c/o Wedge Music Ltd, 63 Grosvenor Street, London W1X 9DA ☎ 020 7493 7831

GERON Jos (*Voc*): 573 Chiswick High Road, Chiswick, London W4 4NF ☎ 020 8747 0009

GIBB Michelle (*Voc*) ☎ 020 8355 4364, 0370 836 632, 020 8355 4364

GIBBON Alani (*Voc*): Kleshay, PO Box 207, Wembley, Middx HA0 2YU ☎ 020 8741 1345

GIBBONS John (*Voc*): 86 Henley Road, Ilford, Essex IG1 2TX ☎ 020 8220 9182, 0958 386091

GIBBS Louise (*Voc, Pf*): 52 Gubyon Avenue, Herne Hill, London SE24 0DX ☎ 020 7733 0535

GIBBS Venessa (*Voc*): 158A Fore Street, Edmonton, London N18 2XA ☎ 020 7272 7648

GIBSON Lee (*Voc, Pf*): Garden Cottage, 48 New Road, Penn, High Wycombe, Buckinghamshire HP10 8DL ☎ 01494 817548

GILBERT Julie (*Voc*): 67 Plumtree Close, Exeter Road, Essex RM10 8UE

GILLAN Ian (*Voc*): c/o Peforming Artists Network, No 1 Water Lane, Camden Town, London NW1 8NZ ☎ 020 7267 5599, 020 7267 5663 fax

GINNY (*Voc*): 38 Camden Road, Chafford Hundred, Grays, Essex RM16 6PY ☎ 01375 480104 & fax

GODFREY Billie (*Voc*): Flat 2, 9 Brunswick Terrace, Hove, East Sussex BN3 1HL ☎ 01273 770199

GODFREY Graham (*Voc, Pf*): 17 Westcott Road, Kennington, London SE17 3QY ☎ 020 7735 2086, 0795 7227149

GODWIN Peter (*Voc, Gtr, Pf, Acc, Kbds*): 70B Kensington Mansions, Warwick Road, London SW5 9TB ☎ 020 7373 4761

GOLDEN John (*Voc*): 15 Vansittart Road, Forest Gate, London E7 0AS ☎ 020 8519 2273

GOLDEN LION The (D Mcquilkin) (*Voc, Song W*): 27A Princess Road, Kilburn Park, London NW6 5AT ☎ 020 7372 9778, 0958 362917

GOLDING Alex (*Voc, Gtr, B Gtr*): Flat 3, 4 Bolingbroke Road, London W14 0AL ☎ 020 7602 4292

GOLDING Ben (*Voc, Gtr, Kbds*): ☎ 020 8265 1990, 0956 825017

GOLDING Laura (*Voc, Kbds, Gtr*): 23 Picardy House, Cedar Road, Enfield, Middlesex EN2 0RD ☎ 0411 985 305

GOLDMAN Jill (*Voc, Song W*): Alvia Cottage, 2 Preston Waye, Kenton, Harrow, Middlesex HA3 0QG ☎ 020 8904 7122

GOLL Achemedes (*Voc, Song W, Kbds*): 58 Key House, Bowling Green Street, London SE11 5TY ☎ 020 7207 6550

GORDON Marlaine *(Voc)*: c/o Bonnymove Ltd, Manor Court, Manor Road, Loughton, Essex IG10 4RP ☎ 020 8502 2952, 020 8502 1037 fax

GORDON Shirley *(Voc, Song W)* ☎ 01707 852415, 0956 226606 mob

GRACE Tina *(Voc)*: 48A Cecilia Road, London E8 2ER ☎ 020 7254 0203, 07957 920756

GRAEME Jim *(Voc, Kbds, Clt, Arr)*: 8 Rythe Road, Claygate, Surrey KT10 9DF ☎ 01372 466 228, 0831 770 794, 01372 466 229

GRANGER Greta *(Voc, Gtr)*: 23 Thorndon Avenue, West Horndon, Brentwood, Essex CM13 3TT

GRANT Andrea *(Voc)*: 8 Southern Avenue, South Norwood, London SE25 4BT ☎ 0956 812715

GRANT Elaina *(Voc)*

GRANT Kenny *(Voc, Gtr, Wh, Cel)*: Flat 5, 52 Old Road, Lee, London SE13 5SR ☎ 020 8469 3393

GRANT Simon *(Voc, Kbds)*: 37 Bourne Hill, Palmers Green, London N13 4LJ ☎ 020 8886 8521

GRANVILLE Charles *(Voc, Cop)*: Address Unknown

GRATTON John *(Voc, Ac Gtr)*: 57D Ufford Street, London SE1 8QB ☎ 020 7928 8656

GRAVESON Jan *(Voc, Kbds, Gtr)*: 54 Coppetts Road, Muswell Hill, London N10 1JU ☎ 020 8883 2003, 0370 581116 mob

GRAY David *(Voc, Gtr)*: 32 Lordship Road, Stoke Newington, London N16 0QT

GRAY Elizabeth *(Voc)*: c/o Sublime, 65 Overdale Road, London W5 4TU ☎ 020 8840 2042, 020 8840 5001

GRAY Karim Beau *(Voc)*: 25 Sandhurst Road, Catford, London SE6 1UP ☎ 020 7413 6180, 020 7289 6846

GRAY Suzanne *(Voc)*: 63 Harcombe Road, Stoke Newington, London N16 0RX ☎ 020 7254 2438 & fax

GRAY Thomas *(Voc)*: 99 Wood Vale, London N10 3DL ☎ 020 8444 3325

GREEN Christina *(Voc)*: 55 Falcon Way, Clippers Quay, Isle Of Dogs, London E14 9UP ☎ 020 7515 5051

GREEN Earl *(Voc)*: 20 Pickhurst Rise, West Wickham, Kent BR4 0AL ☎ 020 8777 3175

GREENAWAY Da'Nelle *(Voc)*: 2B Victoria Road, New Barnet, Herts EN4 9PB ☎ 0973 748 447

GREGOIRE Sonia *(Voc)*: 105 Danebury Avenue, London SW15 4DQ

GREGORY Glenn *(Voc)*: 4 Elsworthy Terrace, London NW3 3DR

GRIFFIN Clive *(Voc, Kbds)*: Flat 1, 7 Sydenham Avenue, London SE26 6UL ☎ 020 8676 9756

GRIFFITHS Jo *(Voc, Ac Gtr)*: 247A West Green Road, London N15 5ED ☎ 020 8809 1292

GRIMM Douglas *(Voc)*: 238 Gipsy Road, South Norwood, London SE27 9RB ☎ 0441 221958

GRUNFELD Jean *(Voc)*: 404A Edgware Road, London W2 1EP ☎ 020 7724 5832

GUDGEON Ailsa *(Voc)*: 404/6B Edgware Road, London W2 1ED ☎ 020 7706 0188

GUDMUNDSDOTTIR Sara *(Voc)*: Address Unknown ☎ +354 5519267, +354 5617899

GUINNESS Valentine *(Voc, Gtr)*: 87 Hereford Road, London W2 5BB ☎ 020 7221 8485, 020 7243 2167 fax

GUIREY Kadir *(Voc)*: 60A Golborne Road, London W10 5PR ☎ 020 8969 8412

GUNNS Nikki *(Voc, Gtr, Dms)*: 2 Evelyn Avenue, Ruislip, Middlesex HA4 8AS

H.Q *(Voc)*: 86 Frant Road, Thornton Heath, Surrey CR7 7JR ☎ 020 8239 9618, 0958 236215

HABERMANN Robert *(Voc, Pf)*: 10 Orchard Court, Portman Square, London W1H 9PA ☎ 020 7486 3821

HADLEY Anthony *(Voc, Synth)*: Slipstream Music, 37 Ellington Road, Muswell Hill, London N10 3DD ☎ 020 7792 1040, 020 7221 7625 fax

HALES Matthew *(Voc, Kbds, Tbn)*: 17 Old Road, London SE13 5SU ☎ 020 8297 8259

HALL Linda *(Voc)*: 66 Westrow Drive, Barking, Essex IG11 9BN ☎ 020 8591 7601

HALLBERG Petra *(Voc, Pf)*: Flat 3 Park Mansions, 28 St Pauls Avenue, London NW2 5TD ☎ 020 8451 3479

HALLIDAY Toni *(Voc)* ☎ 020 8450 4270

HALLIWELL Geraldine *(Voc, Song W)*: Martin Schuitemaker Esq, Geri Productions Ltd, Hill House, 1 Little New Street, London EC4A 3TR ☎ 020 7303 4255, 020 7303 4784

HAMM June *(Voc, Kbds)*: 57B Bovill Road, Forest Hill, London SE23 1EX ☎ 020 8291 6614

HARA Yumi *(Voc, Pf, Kbds, Per, Tabla)*: 4 Chatsworth Court, Powerscroft Road, London E5 0PS ☎ 020 8986 4758 & fax

HARDISTY Christine *(Voc)*: 3 Hyrstdene, Bramley Hill, Croydon CR2 6NR ☎ 020 8688 5328

HARDY Caroline *(Voc)*: 2 Niagara House, Northfields Avenue, London W5 4UG ☎ 020 8567 7230, 0585 290085

HARDY Melanie *(Voc, Com, Song W)*: 33 Johns Ave, London NW4 4EN ☎ 020 8203 1993

HARKELL Gina *(Voc)*: 27 Connaught Road, London N4 4NT ☎ 020 7263 8369

HARKET Morten *(Voc, Gtr)*: c/o Delancey Business, Management Ltd, 220A Blythe Road, London W14 0HH ☎ 020 7602 5424

HARRIS Elana *(Voc)*: 25 Badsworth Road, Camberwell, London SE5 0JY ☎ 020 7701 9849

HARRIS Roy *(Voc, Kbds)*: 161 Tylecroft Road, Norbury SW16 4BJ ☎ 020 8764 0022

HARRIS Steve *(Voc, Rh Gtr)*: 46 Antrobus Road, Chiswick, London W4 5HZ ☎ 020 8747 0323

HASKARD Kathleen *(Voc, Gtr, Pf, Per)*: 176 Camberwell Grove, London SE5 8RH ☎ 020 7274 9518, 0976 255767, 020 7642 3218

HASKELL Gordon *(Voc, Gtr, B Gtr)*: 22 The Kingfishers, Verwood, Dorset BH31 6NP ☎ 01202 824206

HATHERLEY Beatrice *(Voc, Kbds, Gtr)*: Top Flat, 452 Hornsey Road, London N19 4EE ☎ 020 7263 3103

HAYES Lynda *(Voc, Gtr)*: 46 Longstone Ave, London NW10 3TX ☎ 020 8963 0392

HAYNES Rachael *(Voc, Flt)*: 12A Amersham Road, New Cross, London SE14 6QE ☎ 020 8244 9251

HAZE *(Voc, Ac Gtr)*: 111 Clarence Road, London SW19 8QB ☎ 020 8540 8122

HEADLEY Lisa *(Voc)*: 1 Brady House, Worsopp Drive, Clapham, London SW4 9RA ☎ 020 7498 0488

HEALY Francis *(Voc, Gtr)*: Unit F, 21 Heathmans Rd, Parsons Green, London SW6 4TJ ☎ 020 7371 7008, 020 7371 7708

HEATH Suzanne *(Voc)*: 19 Ardrossan Gardens, Worcester Park, Surrey KT4 7AU ☎ 020 8224 5894

HECTOR Wayne *(Voc)*: 101 Brookscroft Road, London E17 4JP ☎ 020 8523 1245, 0956 914817

HEDIN Jakob *(Voc, Gtr)*: Torgg. 25B, 64633 Gnesta, Sweden

HEDLEY Giles *(Voc, Hmca, St Gtr)*: 52A Springfield Road, Linslade, Leighton Buzzard, Beds LU7 7QS ☎ 01525 381373

HEINRICH Jasmine *(Voc)*: 14C Macroom Road, London W9 3HY ☎ 020 8968 1159

HENDRICKS Nimroy *(Voc, Song W)*: 12 Laughton House, Tulse Hill, London SW2 2EP ☎ 020 8255 6266

HENRY Annie *(Voc, Gtr)*: 4 The Grange, Wimbledon, London SW19 4PT

HENRY Cassie *(Voc, Song W, Kbds)*: 101 Alison Road, Hornsey, London N8 0AP ☎ 020 8348 9224

HENRY Christine *(Voc)*: 100 Parliament Hill Mansions, Lissenden Gardens, London NW5 1NB ☎ 020 7267 0092

HENRY Michael *(Voc, Clt, Com, Song W)*: 83A Lucien Road, Tooting, London SW17 8HS ☎ 020 8672 5977

HENRY Pauline *(Voc)*: 105 Beaufort Park, London NW11 6BY ☎ 020 8731 9513, 020 8201 8107

HENRY Tyrone *(Voc, Gtr)*: 34 Westbridge Road, London SW11 3PW ☎ 0956 470187 mob

HENSTOCK Mark *(Voc)*: 129 Mantilla Road, London SW17 8DX ☎ 020 8672 8549

HERAIL Caroline *(Voc, Pf, Flt)*: 312 Queenstown Road, Battersea Park, London SW8 4LT ☎ 020 7720 2536

HERBERT Simone *(Voc)* ☎ 07957 261 785

HERMAN Marilyn *(Voc, Pf, Gtr)*: 45 Suton Court Road, London W4 3EJ ☎ 020 8995 0604, 07970 837933

HERNEN Elaine *(Voc)*: 146 Westcombe Park Road, Blackheath, London SE3 7RZ

HIBBERT Rosemarie *(Voc)*: 61 Kings Grove, Peckham, London SE15 2NA ☎ 020 7642 8990, 0956 391188 mob

HICKLING Anna *(Voc)*: 122B Bathurst Gardens, Kensal Green, London NW10 5HX ☎ 020 8241 1217

HICKS Jacqueline *(Voc, Sax, Clt, Flt)*: 73A Chambersbury Lane, Hemel Hempstead, Herts HP3 8BB ☎ 01442 247949

HIGGINS Elaine *(Voc)*: 53 Stepney Green Court, Stepney Green, London E1 3LL ☎ 020 8981 9108

HIGGINS Julie *(Voc, Song W)*: 30 The Quadrangle, Ducane Road, Hammersmith, London W12 0EP ☎ 020 8809 1376

HIGGS Jessica *(Voc, Com, Pf)*: 41A Barnsbury St, London N1 1PW ☎ 020 7359 7848

HILDEBRAND Jacqi *(Voc, B Ldr)*: 8 Hill Top, Hampstead Garden Suburb, London NW11 6EE ☎ 020 8458 8958

HILL Judy *(Voc)*: 55 Cleveland Road, London SW13 0AA ☎ 020 8878 4123

HISEMAN Jill *(Voc)*: 16 Felhampton Road, New Eltham, London SE9 3NU ☎ 020 8851 6526

HOBBS Nick *(Voc, Dms)*: 46 Spenser Road, London SE24 0NR ☎ 020 7274 6618

HOLGATE Paul *(Voc)*: 76 Rowhurst Avenue, Addlestone, Surrey KT15 1NF ☎ 01932 224457

HOLLAND John *(Voc)*: 7 Ockley Road, Streatham, London SW16 1UG ☎ 020 8677 0793

HOLLAND Nicholas *(Voc, Org, Kbds)*: 1 Old Turnpike Cottages, Bartongate, Middle Barton, Chipping Norton, Oxfordshire OX7 7DB ☎ 01869 340943

HOLLIS Mark *(Voc)*: c/o Central London Branch, 60-62 Clapham Road, London SW9 0JJ

HOLLWEG Rebecca *(Voc)*: 14A Emu Road, London SW8 3PR ☎ 020 7978 2584

HOPKIN Mary *(Voc)*: c/o Gerry Maxin, Tudor Lodge, 11 Warren Road, Wanstead, London E11 2LU

HOPKINS Emily *(Voc, Flt, Pf)*: 301 Aldborough Road South, Newbury Park, Ilford, Essex IG3 8JE

HORLYCK Helene *(Voc)*: Flat 4, 32 Lithos Road, London NW3 6EE ☎ 020 7431 2400

HORNER Sally *(Voc)*: 25 Brook Drive, Kennington, London SE11 4TU ☎ 020 7582 8700

HOSSELL Peter *(Voc, Hmca, Gtr)*: 8 Holmdale Road, London NW6 1BP

HOUCHIN Joanne *(Voc)*: 54B Bellclose Road, West Drayton, Middlesex UB7 9DF ☎ 01895 435686, 0961 430388

HUBBARD Richard *(Voc, B Gtr, Ac Gtr, Kbds)*: 2 Springfield Crescent, Lynton Road, London W3 9EA ☎ 020 8993 6439 & fax

HUGO Tara *(Voc)*: 149 Casewick Road, London SE27 0TA ☎ 020 7284 2246

HUGO Vic *(Voc, Gtr, La Per, B Ldr, Com)*: PO Box 14303, London SE26 4ZH ☎ 07000 472 572, 0956 446342

HURLOCK Samantha *(Voc, Song W)*: 16 Topsfield Close, Wolseley Road, Crouch End, London N8 8DW ☎ 020 8374 6124

HYATT Marianne *(Voc, Gtr)*: 183 Lyndhurst Road, London N22 5AY ☎ 0958 981 149, 0839 454605 pager

IHEANACHO Lisa *(Voc, Song W)*: 216 Westbourne Park Rd, London W11 1EP ☎ 020 7792 2661

IKUSHIMA Yuka *(Voc, Kbds)*: 35B Chippenham Road, London W9 2AH ☎ 020 7286 1581

IMBRUGLIA Natalie *(Voc)*: c/o Brackman & Co, 8 Fairfax Mansions, Finchley Road, London NW3 6JY

IMMY *(Voc, Kbds)*: 45 Manchester Street, London W1M 5PE ☎ 020 7224 1140, 020 7323 9223

INDIGO Count *(Voc)*: 50 Larkhall Rise, London SW4 6JX ☎ 020 7498 7568

INGHAM David *(Voc, Ld Gtr, Rh Gtr)*: 39 Holdenby Road, Crofton Park, London SE4 2DA ☎ 020 8691 2928

INGRAM Leon *(Voc, Gtr, Kbds)* ☎ 0765 4250263

ISHERWOOD Carol *(Voc)*: 61 Bayham Street, Camden Town, London NW1 0AA ☎ 020 7388 4799

ISMAIL Yashmin *(Voc)*: 16 Pentland Close, The Vale, Golders Green, London NW11 8SP ☎ 020 8455 6391, 0956 955902, 020 8455 6391

JA'SELLE *(Voc)*: 9 Godstone Court, Holmleigh Road Estate, Stoke Newington, London N16 5QW ☎ 020 8800 4627

JACAS Eileen *(Voc)*: 26 Coniston House, Pitman Street, Cuyndham Road, London SE5 0UF ☎ 020 7708 4336

JACKSON Janine *(Voc)*: 2 Victoria Terrace, Ealing Green, London W5 5QN ☎ 020 8579 0130, 020 8810 0317

JACKSON Ryan *(Voc)*: 15 Dukes Thorpe Road, London SE26 4PR ☎ 020 8244 4546

JACKSON Tony *(Voc, Dms, Per)*: 59 Hunters Road, Chessington, Surrey KT9 1RY ☎ 020 8397 9728

JAGGER Mick *(Voc, Hmca)*: c/o Lucy Aubree, 5 Church Row, Wandsworth Plain, London SW18 1ES ☎ 020 8877 3100/3

JAMES Casey *(Voc, Per)*: 15 Lindsay Road, Worcester Park, Surrey KT4 8LF ☎ 020 8335 3817 & fax

JAMES Jayne *(Voc, Kbds)*: 45 Willes Road, Kentish Town, London NW5 3DN ☎ 0956 190619

JAMES Leroy *(Voc, Gtr, Kbds, B Gtr)*: 8 Salford Rd, Streatham Hill, London SW2 4BH ☎ 020 8671 3192

JAMES Michael *(Voc)*: 18 Harcourt Road, Brockley, London SE4 2AJ ☎ 020 8691 2157, 0973 506458 mob

JAMES (AKA YORATH) David *(Voc, Gtr, Kbds)*: c/o Surrey Sound Studios, 70 Kingston Road, Leatherhead, Surrey KT22 7BW ☎ 01372 379444, 01372 363360 fax

JAMIROQUAI *(Voc)*: c/o Long Lost Brother Mngt, First Floor Offices, 1A Chalk Farm Parade, Adelaide Road, London NW3 2BN

JANOBE *(Voc)*: 106 Chudleigh Road, London SE4 1HH ☎ 020 8690 0414, 0958 243763 mob

JAYMSON Drew *(Voc)*: 21 Hawthorn Close, Wallingford, Oxon OX10 0SY ☎ 01491 834085

JAYNE Tara *(Voc)*: Flat 47, Globe Wharf, 205 Rotherhithe Street, Rotherhithe, London SE16 1XS ☎ 020 7394 1928

JAZ *(Voc, B Gtr, Kbds)*: 190 Ribblesdale Road, Streatham, London SW16 6QY ☎ 0956 220681 mob, 020 8677 1480

JEAN-MARIE Lincoln *(Voc)*: 18 Trelawney Estate, Paragon Road, London E9

JEAN-PAUL-DENIS Patrick *(Voc)*: 203-213 Mare Street, Unit 307-308, Hackney, London E8 3QE ☎ 020 8533 7074, 020 8533 6156

JIMENEZ-GOMEZ Alfonso *(Voc, Per, Bong, Cong, Timb)*: Flat 5, 1 Avenue Road, London N6 5DJ ☎ 020 8374 4063

JINADU Simon *(Voc, Kbds)*: 93C Manor Avenue, Brockley, London SE4 1TD ☎ 020 8694 8556

JOEBEE *(Voc, Kbds, Dms, B Gtr, E Gtr)*: 2 Sark House, Clephane Road, London N1 2PR ☎ 020 7704 6324

JOHN Leee *(Voc, Per, Song W, Com, Arr)*: 14 Marlborough Avenue, Edgware, Middx HA8 8UH ☎ 020 8905 4370

JOHNSON Dee *(Voc)* ☎ 0121 686 4851

JOHNSON Rosalind *(Voc, Kbds)*: 9 Percy Rd, Canning Town, London E16 4RB ☎ 020 7222 9121 day

JOHNSON Spider *(Voc, Dms, B Gtr, Per, Rh Gtr)*: 3 Lee Conservancy Road, London E9 5HW ☎ 020 8985 4207

JOHNSON Yana *(Voc)*: 6 Walters Way, Honor Oak Park, Forest Hill, London SE23 3LH ☎ 020 8291 3971

JOHNSTON James *(Voc, Pf, Org, Gtr, Hmca)*: 37 Buxton Street, London E1 5EH ☎ 020 7247 0159, 01483 892464

JONES Joanna *(Voc, Gtr)*: 76 St Keverne Road, London SE9 4AL

JONES Mirelle *(Voc, Mar, Per)*: 44 Ashurst Road, Cockfosters, Herts EN4 9LF ☎ 020 8368 3323

JOOLZ *(Voc, Song W)*: 42 Berry Close, Church End, Neasden, London NW10 9NE ☎ 020 8459 6320, 0956 168438

JORDAN Clint *(Voc, Per, Tpt)*: St Annes, 20 The Drive, Coulsdon, Surrey CR5 2BL ☎ 020 8668 6221

JORDAN Deborah *(Voc, Flt)*: 310 Markhouse Road, Walthamstow, London E17 8EF ☎ 020 8556 3327

JOSHI Divya *(Voc)*: 18 Elmwood Avenue, Harrow, Middlesex HA3 8AH ☎ 020 8907 4466 & fax

JUNGR Barb *(Voc, Com)*: 69 Thomson House, Bessborough Place, London SW1V 3SL ☎ 020 7828 0455

KALLAGHAN *(Voc)*: 3 Risborough Close, Muswell Hill, London N10 3PL ☎ 020 8444 2614

KAMPTA Sharon *(Voc, Pf, Acc)*: 74 Roxeth Green Avenue, South Harrow, Middlesex HA2 8AG ☎ 020 8422 7270, 0958 713545

KAPELLE Frances *(Voc)*: 14 Green Leas, Chestfield, Whitstable, Kent CT5 3JY ☎ 01227 792775

KARPENKO Anna *(Voc)*: 64 Arthur Court, Queensway, London W2 5HW ☎ 0467 368 599

KAT *(Voc, Kbds)*: 35 Peter Avenue, Willesden Green, London NW10 2DD ☎ 020 8451 3189, 01523 741 603 pager

KATE *(Voc)*: 13 Ellis House, Brandon Street, London SE17 1EA ☎ 020 7703 7742

KAVANAGH Niamh *(Voc)*: 54 Willow Park Grove, Glasnevin, Dublin 11, Ireland ☎ 842 2057

KAY Sandra *(Voc)*: Cala Bassa, Stanhoe Road, Docking, Kings Lynn, Norfolk PE31 8NJ ☎ 01485 518375

KEENE Deanna *(Voc)*: 60 Clifton Avenue, Wembley, Middlesex HA9 6BW ☎ 020 8900 1052, 0468 686661

KELANI Reem *(Voc, Flt, Gtr, Pf, Per)*: 24 Twisaday House, 28 Colville Square, London W11 2BW ☎ 020 7792 9748

KELLY Juliet *(Voc)*: Flat 4, 143 Cromwell Road, London SW7 4DW ☎ 020 7373 2133, 0958 578020

KELLY Kin *(Voc, Gtr)*: 55 Ellesmere Road, Chiswick, London W4 3EA ☎ 020 8994 8048

KELLY Tracey *(Voc, Com)*: 127 Manor Park, London SE13 5RQ ☎ 020 8297 2123

KELSER Mark *(Voc, B Gtr, Kbds, Dms)*: 225 Ealing Road, Northolt Village, Middx UB5 5HS ☎ 020 8845 2124

KEMP Gary *(Voc, Gtr, Kbds)*: Dagger Entertainment, 14 Lambton Place, Notting Hill, London W11 2SH ☎ 020 7792 1040, 020 7221 7625 fax

KEMP Joanne *(Voc)*: 4 Alloa Road, Surrey Quays, London SE8 5AJ ☎ 07801 233753

KENNEDY Brian *(Voc, Pf, Gtr)*: 19 Management Ltd, Ransomes Dock, 35-37 Parkgate Rd, London SW11 4NP ☎ 020 7228 4000

KENNEDY K *(Voc)*: 28C London Road, Tooting, London SW17 9HW

KENNEY Gordon *(Voc, Gtr, Hmca)*: 7 Porter Road, Beckton, London E6 4PN ☎ 020 7474 3487

KENSIT Patsy *(Voc)*: c/o J Vickers, 14 Lambton Place, London W11 2SH ☎ 020 7792 1040, 020 7221 7625

KENT Stacey *(Voc)*: 52 Albert Road, Alexandra Park, London N22 4AH ☎ 020 8889 6740

KENTON-FORBES Meryl *(Voc)*: 78 Hornby House, Clayton Street, Kennington, London SE11 5DB ☎ 020 7207 3768

KENYON Carol *(Voc)*: Pez Promotions-Management, 15 Sutherland House, 137-139 Queenstown Road, London SW8 3RJ ☎ 020 7978 1503, 020 7978 1502 fax

KENYON Sam *(Voc, Pf, Flt)*: 122 Rectory Road, London N16 7SD ☎ 020 7249 8038, 0958 327118

KERR Trudy *(Voc)*: 93 Alderbrook Road, London SW12 8AD ☎ 020 8673 6043

KESTER Faye *(Voc)*: 28 Mountbatten Close, Upper Norwood, London SE19 1AP ☎ 020 8244 9796

KHAN Mark *(Voc, Gtr, Kbds)*: Flat 1, 222 Cricklewood Lane, London NW2 2PU ☎ 020 8452 2753

KHAN Michael *(Voc, Gtr, Pf)*: 32 Battledean Road, Highbury, Islington, London N5 1UZ ☎ 020 7704 9466

KHAN Ray *(Voc)* ☎ 0956 695364

KHWAJA Darius *(Voc)*: 26 Southfields Road, Wandsworth, London SW18 1QL, 0956 228734 mob

KING Lloyd *(Voc)*: 168 Navarino Mansions, Dalston Lane, Hackney, London E8 1LE ☎ 020 7923 1611

KING Simon *(Voc, Pf, Gtr, Dms, Com)*: 18 Orrdell Road, Bow, London E3 2DS ☎ 020 8981 2588 & fax

KINGTON Natalie *(Voc, Vln)*: Address Unknown ☎ 020 8363 3050, 0976 636451 mob

KLASS Myleene *(Voc, Hrp, Pf, Vln)*

KOKOT Estelle *(Voc, Pf)* ☎ 020 8340 7176

KOSTERIS Rafael *(Voc, Gtr)* ☎ 020 8884 1289

KOUTOUZI Katerina *(Voc, Pf, Acc, Hmca)*: 155B Drummond Street, London NW1 2PB ☎ 020 7388 0643

KRYSTIN *(Voc)*: 187 Essex Road, Leyton, London E10 6BT ☎ 020 8539 7354, 0958 217268 mob

KUMADA Jane *(Voc, Gtr, Pf)*: 56 Laleham Road, London SE6 2HX ☎ 020 8697 0665

KURIAN Anna *(Voc, Pf, Flt, Dms, Gtr)*: 25 Longcrofte Road, Edgware, Middlesex HA8 6RR ☎ 020 8952 9307

KYRIACOU Elizabeth *(Voc)*: 11 Belsize Avenue, Palmers Green, London N13 4TL ☎ 020 8888 1612

L'ESTRANGE Alexander *(Voc, Con, Db, Pf, B Gtr)*: 7 Mall Court, 30 The Mall, Ealing, London W5 2PZ ☎ 020 8567 5099, 0973 510235

LA *(Voc, Gtr)*: 76 Mount View Road, London N4 4JR ☎ 020 8348 7457

LAFFERTY Catrina *(Voc)*: 142 Totterdown Street, London SW17 8TA ☎ 020 8672 1563, 07970 818101

LAHIRI Anya *(Voc)*: 8 Temple Grove, London NW11 7OA ☎ 020 8458 5191

LALOU *(Voc, Pf)*: 141A Stroud Green Road, Finsbury Park, London N4 3PZ ☎ 020 7272 8033, 0956 988899 mob

LAMONTE-STONE Melayne *(Voc)*: 38 Edith Road, South Norwood, London SE25 5PQ ☎ 020 8665 9337

LANGAN Tony *(Voc, Gtr, B Gtr)*: 62 Earlswood Street, Greenwich, London SE10 9ES ☎ 020 8305 0919

LANGLEY John *(Voc, Arr, Vln)*: 16 Glazbury Road, London W14 9AS ☎ 020 7603 8796, 0468 491 368, 020 7602 1257

LANGTON James *(Voc, Clt, T Sax, A Sax)*: 11 St Matthew's Court, Coppetts Road, Muswell Hill, London N10 1NW ☎ 020 8341 6564

LANHAM Katherine *(Voc)*: 18C Pendrell Road, London SE4 2PB ☎ 020 7358 0589

LANI *(Voc, Gtr, Kbds)* ☎ 020 7274 9679

LANKAI *(Voc)*: 14 Evelyn Dennington Road, London E6 4YH ☎ 020 7511 9641 & fax

LARNIE Jane *(Voc, Gtr, Kbds, Per)*: 31 Soldene Court, Ringcross Est., Georges Road N7 8HQ

LAW Joanna *(Voc, Flt)*: 13 Lovell Place, Rotherhithe, London SE16 1QQ ☎ 020 7237 1035

LAW Michael *(Voc, Pf)*: 50 Albert Street, Windsor, Berkshire SL4 5BU ☎ 01753 855828, 0802 702232 mob, 01753 855802 fax

LAWRENCE Emma *(Voc)*: 64 Grengall Road, Woodford Green, Essex IG8 0DL ☎ 020 8559 0444

LAWRENCE Sandra *(Voc)*: 2 Greenways Court, Butts Green Road, Hornchurch, Essex RM11 2JL ☎ 01708 446789

LAWSON Ellie *(Voc, Kbds, Per)*: 126 Wellington Buildings, Ebury Bridge Road, London SW1W 8SA

LAZAR Natalie *(Voc)*: 8 The Farthings, Brunswick Road, Kingston Hill, Surrey KT2 7PT ☎ 020 8541 3462, 0956 598 778

LE POER POWER Cecilia *(Voc, Pf)*: 52 Dulwich Village, London SE21 7AJ ☎ 020 8693 3074

LEE Dee C *(Voc)*: 2 The Spinney, Dyke Road Avenue, Hove, Sussex BN3 6QT ☎ 01273 565223 & fax

LEE Kat *(Voc, Pf, Flt)*: 26 Barnes House, Warlterville Road, London N19 3AN ☎ 020 7263 0133

LEE Zeony *(Voc, Song W)*: 11A Treport Street, Wandsworth, London SW18 2BW ☎ 020 8877 3357

LEE-DAVID *(Voc, Pf, Kbds, Synth, Org)*: Address Unknown ☎ 020 7607 8031, 01523 153488 pager

LEGEE Chris *(Voc, Gtr)*: 81 Grove Lane, London SE5 8SP ☎ 020 7703 9648, 020 7701 6827 fax

LEIGH-WHITE Rebecca *(Voc, Pf)*: 2 Old Dairy Cottages, Grange Farm, Buttermere, Marlborough, Wiltshire SN8 3RQ ☎ 01488 668744

LENNARD Carrie *(Voc, Gtr)*: 5 Ferry Square, Brentford, Middx TW8 0AJ ☎ 020 8560 1738 & fax

LENNON Farrell *(Voc, Kbds, Song W)*: 30 Denham Drive, Gants Hill, Ilford, Essex IG2 6QU ☎ 020 8252 0282

LENNON Julian *(Voc, Kbds, Song W)*: c/o John Cousins, Cousins Brett, 20 Bulstrode Street, London WIM 5FR ☎ 020 7486 5791, 020 7224 7226

LEO Kevin *(Voc, Com)*: 162 Dowdeswell Close, London SW15 5RN ☎ 020 8878 6705

LESKANICH Katrina *(Voc, Gtr)*

LESLIE Grace *(Voc, Per, Dms)*: 91B Albion Road, Stoke Newington, London N16 9PL ☎ 020 7503 6992

LESSENBERRY William *(Voc)*: 120 Burnham, Adelaide Road, London NW3 3JN ☎ 020 7722 4814, 049 8844917

LEVENE Sarah *(Voc)*: 70 Devonshire Road, Colliers Wood, London SW19 2EF ☎ 020 8540 6639

LEVY Emma *(Voc)*

LEWIS Georgia *(Voc)* ☎ 020 8677 8443

LEWIS Lurleen *(Voc)*

LEWIS Melanie *(Voc)*: 53 Hatchlands Road, Redhill, Surrey RH1 6AP ☎ 0976 268442

LEWIS Paul *(Voc)*: 52 Wilmer House, Daling Way, Bow, London E3 5NW ☎ 020 8983 7642

LIEBERT Vikki *(Voc, Pf, Org, Kbds, Gtr)*: Niton, 12 Church Road, Aldingbourne, West Sussex PO20 6TT ☎ 01243 544635

LILLEY Mandy *(Voc)*: 8 Craddocks Avenue, Ashtead, Surrey KT21 1PB ☎ 0589 729834

LILLITOS Malachi *(Voc, Pf)*: 44 Park Avenue North, Crouch End, London N8 7RT ☎ 020 8340 3250

LIMERICK Alison *(Voc)* ☎ 020 7241 0833, 020 7351 4333

LINDVALL Helienne *(Voc, Gtr, Pf, Kbds)*: 65 Park Court, Battersea Park Road, London SW11 7LE ☎ 020 7738 8061

LIPSCOMBE William *(Voc)*: 11 Colyers Lane, North Heath, Erith, Kent DA8 3NG ☎ 01322 34868

LITTLE Matthew *(Voc, B Tbn)*: 94 Dawes Road, Uxbridge, Middlesex UB10 0RR ☎ 01895 812671

LLOYD Eddie *(Voc, Song W)*: 96 Gassiot Road, Tooting, London SW17 8LA ☎ 020 8672 5137, 0973 728817

LORD Victoria *(Voc, Tbn, Pf)*: 49B Esmond Road, Chiswick, London W4 1JG ☎ 0468 348790

LORDAN Erin *(Voc)*: 85A The Broadway, Mill Hill, London NW7 3TG ☎ 020 8201 0868

LORELEI *(Voc, Song W)* ☎ 020 7243 8143

LOREN *(Voc)*: 24 Pattenden Road, Catford, London SE6 4NQ ☎ 020 8690 1158, 0956 589930 mob

LORENZ V *(Voc)*: 154 Leaview House, Jessam Avenue, Hackney, London E5 9EA ☎ 020 8806 8232, 020 8219 2331

LOVE *(Voc)*: 143 Uvedale Crescent, New Addington, Croydon CR0 0BW

LOVE Danny *(Voc, Kbds, Song W)*: Flat B, 5-7 Penge Road, South Norwood, London SE25 4EJ ☎ 020 8778 2021, 0973 410135 mob

LOWE Pearl *(Voc)*: 27 Stratford Villas, London NW1 9SE ☎ 020 7267 2625

LOWE Virginia *(Voc)*: Top Flat, 42 Fentiman Road, London SW8 1LF ☎ 020 7735 4454

LUCAS Antonia *(Voc)*: 32 Watersplash Road, Shepperton, Middx TW17 0EX ☎ 01932 254715, 0956 664302, 01372 372728

LUCE Francine *(Voc, Tpt)*: 10B Newton Road, London W2 5LS ☎ 020 7727 9204

LUPTON Karen *(Voc, Clt)*: 43 Corinne Road, Tufnell Park, London N19 5EZ ☎ 020 7700 0805 & fax, 0468 391060 mob

LUYEYES Jean *(Voc)*: 58 Holloway Road, London N7 8JL ☎ 020 7700 3048, 0958 389927 mob

LYDON John *(Voc)*: C/0 Anna Fitzsimons, Martin Greene Ravden, 55 Loudoun Road, London NW8 0DL ☎ 020 7625 4545

LYNCH Catharine *(Voc)*: Apt 27, Waterloo Warehouse, Waterloo Road, Liverpool L3 0BG

LYONS Shara *(Voc, Vln, Clt)*: 13 Sunninghill Court, Bollo Bridge Road, London W3 8BB ☎ 020 8993 4253

LYRICS Leslie *(Voc)*: 3 Hopedale Road, Charlton, London SE7 7JH ☎ 020 8858 7058

M Johnny *(Voc)*: 101 Listria Park, London N16 5SP ☎ 020 8802 4688

MACCOLL Kirsty *(Voc, Gtr)*: c/o Harris & Trotter, 65 New Cavendish St, London W1M 7RD ☎ 020 7487 4393, 020 7935 1308

MACDONALD Neville *(Voc, Gtr)*: 30 Other Street, Ynysybwl, Pontypridd, Mid Glam CF37 3LN ☎ 01443 791354

MACHA Freddy *(Voc, Gtr, Per, Pf, Berimbau)*: Flat B, 44 Durley Road, London N16 5JS ☎ 020 8802 3732, 020 7281 6677

MACKELWORTH Anna *(Voc)*: 79 Russell Court, Ross Road, Wallington, Surrey SM6 8QT ☎ 020 8647 7476

MACKENDRICK Caroline *(Voc, Kbds, Ac Gtr)*: Flat 4, 75 Amwell Street, London EC1R 1UT ☎ 020 7837 3509

MACMAHON Bree *(Voc)*: 1A Randolph Gardens, London NW6 5EH ☎ 020 7328 8904

MACMANUS Ronan *(Voc, Gtr, Pf)*: 24 River Way, Twickenham, Middlesex TW2 5JP ☎ 020 8241 3363, 020 8894 3590

MADILYN *(Voc)*: 251 Old Kent Road, London SE1 5LU ☎ 0958 578482

MAGEE Belinda *(Voc, Pf)*: 3 Tanner Street, London SE1 3LE ☎ 020 7407 3280, 020 7357 7345

MAIR Stephanie *(Voc)*: Flat 2, 49 The Grove, London N3 1QT ☎ 020 8349 1277

MANAJAH *(Voc)*: 35 Tait Court, Lansdowne Green Estate, Stockwell, London SW8 2EU ☎ 020 7627 5420, 0961 350272

MANCIO Georgia *(Voc)*: 47A Dulwich Road, London SE24 0NJ ☎ 020 7733 9920

MANDAVY Francoise *(Voc, Pf)*: 117 Castlewood Road, London N16 6DJ ☎ 020 8880 1050, 07957 288 136

MANLY Gill *(Voc)* ☎ 020 8677 6905 & fax, 0956 636181 mob

MANZI Paul *(Voc, Ld Gtr, Rh Gtr, B Gtr, K)*: 54 Clarendon Gardens, Ilford, Essex IG1 3JW ☎ 020 8262 9879

MARCEL *(Voc)*

MARLENE Tania *(Voc)*: Amsterdam, Holland ☎ +31 0204 705120 & fax

MARNEY Josephine *(Voc)*: 20 Ashworth Mansions, Elgin Avenue, London W9 1JP ☎ 020 7286 9299

MARSH Barbara *(Voc, Gtr, Pf)*: 10C Porchester Square, London W2 6AN ☎ 020 7229 3915

MARSH Jon *(Voc, Kbds, Dms)*: PO Box 12251, London EC1V 0LA

MARSHALL Joanne *(Voc)*: 7 Mhind House, Harvest Estate, Hornsey Road, London N7 7NA

MARSHALL Lorna *(Voc)*: 64 Tavistock Avenue, Perivale, Greenford UB6 8AL ☎ 020 8723 9387, 0958 270063

MARSHALL Melanie *(Voc)*

MARSHALL Nadine *(Voc, Pf, Dms)*: 139 Holly Park Estate, Crouch Hill, London N4 4BJ ☎ 020 7486 7766, 020 8556 2937, 020 7486 7764

MARTIN Claire *(Voc)*: Lower Ground Floor Flat, 61 Brunswick Place, Hove, Sussex BN3 1NE

MARTIN Roger *(Voc, Pf, Gtr)*: 40 Hart Grove, Ealing Common, London W5 3NB ☎ 020 8993 4306

MASLEN Riz *(Voc)*: Flat 5, 42-44 Kingsland Road, London E2 8DA ☎ 020 7729 0579 & fax

MASON Myriam *(Voc)*: 6A Fairbourne Road, London N17 6TP ☎ 020 8801 6150

MASON Sylvia *(Voc)*: 57 Nova Road, West Croydon CR0 2TN ☎ 020 8686 1681, 020 8667 9802

MASRI Maria *(Voc, Pf, Kbds)*: 6 Atherlay Way, Hounslow, Twickenham, Middlesex TW4 5NG ☎ 020 8898 3540

MATTHEWS John *(Voc, Song W)*: 55 Mary Peters Drive, Greenford, Middlesex UB6 0SS ☎ 020 8423 1460

MATZDORF David *(Voc, Pf, Kbds, Com)*: 113 Seymour Buildings, Seymour Place, London W1H 5TU ☎ 020 7262 8131

MAXIMEN Luvain *(Voc)*: 11 Gulliver Street, London SE16 1LT ☎ 020 7237 6729, 0973 797306 mob

MAXINE *(Voc, Song W)*: P.O.Box 346, Caterham, Surrey CR3 6XX ☎ 01883 340005

MAXLOVE *(Voc, Song W, Gtr, Com)*

MAYFIELD Big Al *(Voc)*: 9 Almond Way, Mitcham, Surrey CR4 1LP ☎ 020 8679 5185, 0831 440772

MC SUZY Q *(Voc, Per)*: 86C Clarence Avenue, London SW4 8JR ☎ 020 8673 2130, 0831 411 690 mob

MC WEIRD *(Voc)*: 136 Edgehill, Woolwich, London SE18 3TQ ☎ 020 8317 9490, 0956 323660

MCANANEY Tony *(Voc, Gtr, B Gtr)*: 531A Old York Road, Wandsworth, London SW18 1TG ☎ 020 8870 0501

MCCOOK Barbara *(Voc)*: 21 Hollywood Road, Chingford, London E4 8JE ☎ 020 8524 4547

MCDONALD Helen *(Voc)*: 74 Mayall Road, Herne Hill, Brixton, London SE24 0PJ ☎ 020 7326 1249, 07666 758968

MCGOWAN Karen *(Voc)*: Flat 7, Forest House, St Germans Road, Forest Hill, London SE23 1RX ☎ 020 8690 9395

MCGUINN Nico *(Voc, Gtr)*: Top Floor Flat, 78 Langham Road, London N15 3LX ☎ 020 8889 9727

MCGUINNESS Tom *(Voc, Gtr)*: St Beunos, St Asaph, Denbigshire, North Wales LL17 0AS ☎ 020 7435 8534

MCINROY Mary *(Voc, Gtr, Kbds)*: 72 Carysfort Road, Stoke Newington, London N16 9AP

MCINTOSH Lauraine *(Voc, B Gtr)*

MCKENNA Mae *(Voc)* ☎ 020 8942 3892

MCKRIETH Jade *(Voc)*: 10 Highlands Close, Crough Hill, London N4 4SE ☎ 020 7263 9167

MCLAREN Malcolm *(Voc, Song W)*: 16 Scala Street, London W1P 1LU ☎ 020 7636 2687, 020 7580 9237 fax

MCLAUGHLIN Aileen *(Voc)*: Top Floor, 43 Blenheim Terrace, St Johns Wood, London NW8 0EJ ☎ 020 7625 6964, 0860 274351 mob

MCLEAN Beth *(Voc, Pf, Theory)*: Little Watermead, Reigate Road, Hookwood, Horley, Surrey RH6 0HD

MCPHERSON Caroline *(Voc, Pf, Kbds, Gtr, Dms)*: 169 Horns Road, Baritingside, Ilford, Essex IG6 1DF ☎ 020 8518 5684

MEDFORD Paul J *(Voc, Per)*: 159B Holland Road, London NW10 5AX ☎ 020 8930 3343

MEISTER Martin *(Voc, Kbds)* ☎ 020 7731 8219 & fax, 0410 475608 mob

MELHUS Marianne *(Voc)*: 71B Park Hall Road, London N2 9PY ☎ 020 8442 1162

MELLER Mark *(Voc, Gtr, B Gtr, Kbds)*: 20C Sutherland Street, London SW1V 4LA

MELLY George *(Voc)*: 81 Frithville Gardens, London W12 7JQ ☎ 020 8749 0433, 020 8740 7557 fax

MELO.D *(Voc)*: 189A Lanark Road, Maida Vale, London W9 1NX ☎ 020 7328 0569

MELODY Mr. *(Voc)*: Flat 1, 20 Beatrice Road, Finsbury Park, London N4 4PD ☎ 020 7561 1508

MELONE *(Voc)*

METCALFE Bridget *(Voc)*: P O Box 1, Chipping Ongar, Essex CM5 9HZ ☎ 01277 362916, 01277 366736

MICHAEL *(Voc, Song W)*: 64 Bickenhall Mansions, Bickenhall Street, London W1H 3LD ☎ 020 7486 5438 & fax

MICHAEL Darren *(Voc, B Gtr, Gtr, Kbds)*: 551 Green Lanes, Palmers Green, London N13 4DR ☎ 020 8886 3159, 020 8882 5983

MICHAEL Donna *(Voc)*: 129 Langdale Road, Thornton Heath, Surrey CR4 7PX

MICHAEL Kelsey *(Voc, Kbds, Pf)*: 60 Malpas Road, Brockley, London SE4 1BS ☎ 020 8469 2600

MICHAELS Christine *(Voc)* ☎ 020 8889 9186, 0956 248060 mob

MICHAELS Mia *(Voc, Pf, Kbds)*: 37 Cunnington Street, Chiswick, London W4 5ER ☎ 020 8742 0447, 0973 162131

MICHALISLES George *(Voc, Gtr, Pf, Kbds)*: 169 Cavendish Avenue, West Ealing, London W13 N0JZ ☎ 020 8933 3248, 0956 493032

MICHEL Hilary *(Voc, Accom, Pf, Rec, Gtr)*: 82 Greenway, London N20 8EJ ☎ 020 8343 7243

MILES John *(Voc, Gtr, Kbds)*: 10 Rectory Green, West Boldon, Tyne & Wear NE36 0QD ☎ 020 7240 7696

MILES Peter *(Voc)*: 35 Bradley Gardens, Ealing, London W13 8HE ☎ 020 8998 7778

MILLER Todd *(Voc, Con)*: Old Orchard, 39 Straight Bit, Flackwell Heath, Bucks HP10 9LT ☎ 020 8578 2594

MILLER Yvonne *(Voc)*: 49 Gunnell Close, Croydon, Surrey CR0 6YF ☎ 020 8654 8133

MILLS Miranda *(Voc, Kbds)*: 15A Sheen Lane, Mortlake, London SW14 8HY ☎ 020 8392 2755

MILLS Sandra *(Voc, Clt)*: 160 Sunnyhill Road, Streatham, London SW16 2UN

MILTON Richie *(Voc, Gtr, Sax)*: 59 Western Road, London E13 9JE ☎ 020 8470 4347

MINTON Phil *(Voc)*: 97 Hertford Road, London N2 9BX ☎ 020 8883 4758 & fax

MISTRI Sneha *(Voc)*: 153 Bethnal Green Road, London E2 7DG ☎ 0956 915566 mob

MISS L.A. *(Voc)*: 153 High Street, Cranford, Middlesex TW5 9PF ☎ 020 8897 0077, 020 8897 0077

MITCHELL Andrew *(Voc, Hmca, Pf)*: 35B Prince Of Wales Road, Kentish Town, London NW5 3LJ ☎ 020 7267 7276, 020 7482 6736

MITCHELL Susan *(Voc)*: 9 Chuters Grove, Epsom, Surrey KT17 4AS ☎ 01372 723381

MOGOTSI Joseph *(Voc, Com)*: 23 Windsor Crescent, Wembley Park, Wembley, Middlesex HA9 9AN ☎ 020 8904 5359

MOHAPI Laura *(Voc, Song W)*

MOIGNARD Daniel *(Voc, B Gtr, Gtr)*: 38 Durham Road, South Ealing, London W5 4JP ☎ 020 8567 1544

MOLLET Francis *(Voc, Pf, Kbds, Hmca, Tpt)*: Flat 6, West House, Rosemoor Street, London SW3 2LP ☎ 020 7584 7424

MOLLOY Ryan *(Voc, Song W)*: c/o 19 Management, Unit 32, 35-37 Parkgate Road, London SW11 4NP ☎ 020 7738 1919, 020 7738 1819

MONTANDON Mirjam *(Voc)*: 40 Argyle Square, London WC1 H8AL ☎ 0802 783684

MONTY *(Voc, Gtr, Kbds)*: 19 The Drive, Banstead, Surrey SM7 1DF

MOONEY Janet *(Voc)*: 10 Crescent East, Hadley Wood, Herts EN4 0EN ☎ 020 8441 4196, 020 8441 4197

MORRIS David Lyle *(Voc, Ac Gtr)*: P.O. Box 46, Beckenham, Kent BR3 4YR ☎ 020 8658 2153

MORRIS Hayley *(Voc)*: 2 Kenlford Way, Northolt, Middlesex UB5 5NG ☎ 020 8841 2131, 0797 0120613

MORRIS Isobel *(Voc, Gtr)*: 392B Finchley Road, Childs Hill, London NW2 2HR ☎ 020 7433 1632

MORRIS Martin *(Voc, Gtr, Acc)*: 5 Brockwell Park Gardens, London SE24 9BL ☎ 020 8488 5122

MORRIS Sarah *(Voc)*: The Old Post Office, Walton, Warwick CV35 9HX ☎ 01789 470112 & fax

MORRISON Julie *(Voc)*: 33 Seymour Court, Whitehall Road, London E4 6DZ

MORTON Charles *(Voc, Gtr, B Gtr, Dms, Kbds)*: 197 Arthur Road, Wimbledon, London SW19 8AG ☎ 020 8947 1026

MOSLEY Paul *(Voc, Pf, Clt, Sax, Eup)*: 139 Nevill Road, Stoke Newington, London N16 0SU ☎ 020 7734 1600, 020 7254 7627

MOSQUERA Luisito *(Voc)*: 25C Selwyn Road, Upton Park, London E13 0PY, 0958 356599

MOSS John *(Voc)*: 39 Morris Court, Ninefields, Honey Lane, Waltham Abbey Essex EN9 3DX ☎ 01992 713207

MOTTLEY Susan *(Voc)*: 18 Arnold Drive, Chessington, Surey KT9 2GD ☎ 020 8287 5861

MOULE Sarah *(Voc)*: 91 Albert Palace Mansions, Lurline Gardens, London SW11 4DH ☎ 020 7720 6812, 0336 779476, 020 7720 6812

MOYET Alison *(Voc, A Sax)*: 79 Parkway, London NW1 7PP ☎ 020 7482 7230, 020 7482 7286 fax

MTUNGWAZI Eska *(Voc, Pf, Vln)*: 156 Hither Green Lane, Lewisham, London SE13 6QA ☎ 020 8318 5493

MUFFETT Nicola *(Voc, Pf, Vla)*: 55 Cottesmore Avenue, Clayhall, Ilford, Essex IG5 0TG ☎ 020 8924 8907, 0958 737845

MULLEN Mary *(Voc, Kbds, Gtr)*: Flat C, 412 Seven Siters Road, London N4 2LX ☎ 020 8211 8931

MURALDO Caroline *(Voc)*: 48A Navarino Road, Hackney, London E8 1AD ☎ 020 7241 1753

MURGATROYD John *(Voc)*: 32 Kennington Park House, Kennington Park Place, London SE11 4JT ☎ 020 7735 6878

MURIEL Linda *(Voc)*: 121 Heigham Road, East Ham, London E6 2JJ

MURPHY Lisa *(Voc)* ☎ 020 8540 7948

MUSHROOM *(Voc)*: c/o Tracey Hancock, West, 6A Orde Hall Street, London WC1N 3JW ☎ 020 7405 7270, 020 7405 9834 fax

MYERS John *(Voc, Gtr, Kbds, B Gtr, Vln)*: 47 Wedmore Gardens, London N19 4SY ☎ 020 7263 9366

MYERS Patrick *(Voc, Per, B Gtr)*: 79 Riverdale Road, Erith, Kent DA8 1PU

MYKILA *(Voc, Kbds)*: 60A Stondon Park, Forest Hill, London SE23 1JZ ☎ 020 8291 7573, 0958 248553 mob, 020 7252 7180

MYLOVE *(Voc)*: Flat 4, 52 Elm Park Gardens, Chelsea, London SW10 9PA ☎ 020 7352 9852, 0956 607542, 020 7352 9852

NASH Russell *(Voc, Kbds, Gtr, B Gtr)*: 51 Sutton Square, Urswick Road, Hackney, London E9 6EQ ☎ 020 8985 0302

NAYLER Maria *(Voc, Kbds)*: Red Parrot Management, Phoenix House, 86 Fulham High Street, London SW6 3LF ☎ 020 7736 9676

NEALE Anthony *(Voc)*: 7 The Fentons, Vanbrugh Park Road, Blackheath, London SE3 7NJ ☎ 020 8305 1159

NEALE Joanna *(Voc, Sax, Kbds)*: 22 Gibbs Green, Beaumont Crescent, London W14 9NB ☎ 020 7386 7585

NEELAM *(Voc, Song W)*: 25 Zangwill Road, Blackheath, London SE3 8EH ☎ 020 8856 6326 & fax, 0956 456462 mob

NEIL Kirsten *(Voc, Gtr)*: 165 Lyham Road, Brixton, London SW2 5PY ☎ 020 8671 3155

NELSON Kendrick *(Voc)*: 32 Higham Street, London E17 6DA ☎ 020 8523 3620

NELSON Shara *(Voc)* ☎ 020 7514 5200

NELSON Suzanne *(Voc)*: 304A Holloway Road, London N7 6NR ☎ 020 7607 7943

NEUMAYR Elisabeth *(Voc, Sax)*: 22 Lansdowne Road, Walthamstow, London E17 8QU ☎ 020 8926 9182

NEVILLE Gordon *(Voc, Pf)*: 48 Friern Barnet Lane, London N11 3NA ☎ 020 8361 1100

NEW Howard *(Voc)*: Flat A, 151 Bravington Road, London W9 3AT ☎ 0973 540071

NEWBERY Philip *(Voc, Rh Gtr)*: 33 Sydney Road, Maywards Heath, West Sussex RM16 1QD ☎ 01444 453800

NEWTON Keechie *(Voc, Dms, Kbds)*: 9B Spencer Rise, London NW5 1AR ☎ 020 7485 2100

NEWTON Victoria *(Voc, Clt)* ☎ 020 8451 7342, 0973 422916

NIBLETT Zoe *(Voc)*: Flat 1, 27A Lymington Road, London NW6 1HZ ☎ 020 7794 0859

NICHOLL Phillip *(Voc)*: 105 Breton House, Barbican, London EC2Y 8PQ ☎ 020 7628 4995

NICHOLLS Helen *(Voc)*: Flat 2F, Shillington Old School, 181 Este Road, Battersea, London SW11 2TB ☎ 020 7924 3684, 0976 278638 mob

NICOLS Maggie *(Voc)*: 23 Nottingham House, Shorts Gardens, London WC2H 9AX ☎ 020 7379 6810

NICOLSON Claire *(Voc, Pf, E Gtr)*: First Floor Flat, 235 All Souls Road, London NW10 3AE, 07775 556305

NILES Tessa *(Voc, Gtr)*: 100 St Lukes Road, Old Windsor, Berkshire SL4 2QJ ☎ 01753 622623, 01753 621 992

NINA *(Voc, Gtr)*: 44 Linden Avenue, Thornton Heath, Surrey CR7 7DW ☎ 020 8684 2081, 0956 256721 mob

NISHIHARA Mayumi *(Voc, B Gtr, Rh Gtr)*: Flat 4, 197 Royal Collage Street, London0On NW1 0SG ☎ 020 7209 3813

NISHITANI GILLIAT Catherine *(Voc)*: Flat 2, 135 Highiever Rd, N. Kensington, London W10 6PH ☎ 020 8969 2086

NITU *(Voc)*: 30 Upcroft Avenue, Edgware, Middlesex HA8 9RB ☎ 020 8959 4498, 0956 446247

NLEWEDIM Stella *(Voc)*: 166 Malpas Road, Brockley, London SE4 1DH ☎ 020 8488 7806

NORRIS Richard *(Voc, Gtr, Sax)*: Address Unknown ☎ 020 8968 1723

NOVA Heather *(Voc, Song W, Ac Gtr)*: c/o Bedlam Management, 131 Holland Park Avenue, London W11 4UT ☎ 020 7610 4662

NURDING Louise *(Voc, Sax)*: First Avenue Mgmt, 42 Colwith Road, London W6 9EY ☎ 020 8741 1419

O'BRIEN Kevin *(Voc)*: 85 Kingsway, Mortlake, London SW14 7HH ☎ 020 8392 1022

O'CONNOR Andrew *(Voc, Gtr, Song W)* ☎ 0402 002181

O'DAY Teish *(Voc)*: 34A Madeira Road, Streatham, London SW16 2DE ☎ 020 8696 0983

O'DONOVAN Michael *(Voc, B Gtr, Gtr, Kbds)*: 51 St Thomas Road, Finsbury Park, London N4 2QH ☎ 020 7226 7097

O'GRADY Jenny *(Voc, Pf)*: 2 Queens Road, Barnet, Herts EN5 4DQ ☎ 020 8441 0045 fax, 0973 891306 mob

O'NEIL Lisa *(Voc, Kbds)*: 34B Westcroft Square, Hammersmith, London W6 0TD ☎ 020 8741 0250, 0336 781071 pager

O'SHEA Keavy *(Voc, Pf, Sax, Vln, Gtr)*: 53 Farm Road, London N21 3JD ☎ 020 8360 9608

O'SULLIVAN Eileen *(Voc, Gtr, Pf)*: Flat C, 176 Shooters Hill, Woolwich, London SE18 3HY ☎ 0973 443560

OBANO Erire *(Voc)*: 1St Floor Flat, 59 Warwick Gardens, London W14 8PL ☎ 020 7610 5073

ODURO-SINTIM Kwadwo *(Voc, Per)*: 8A Stock Orchard Crescent, London N7 9SL ☎ 020 7700 1412

OGDEN John *(Voc, Gtr)*: Flat 2, 72 Brixton Water Lane, London SW2 1QB ☎ 020 7207 0821

OGSTON Bruce *(Voc, Pf)*: 150A Shirland Road, London W9 2BT ☎ 020 7289 0620

OKASILI Martin *(Voc, Rh Gtr, B Gtr)*: Nok Kultcha, 51 Lexton Street, London W1R 41R ☎ 020 7434 3472, 020 7287 1403

OKIN Earl *(Voc, Com, Pf, Gtr, Arr)*: 248 Portobello Road, London W11 1LL. ☎ 020 7727 6375

OLAFSDOTTIR Alda *(Voc)*: Jamdown Lte, Research House Fraser Road, Perivale, Middlesex UB6 7AQ ☎ 020 8930 1070, 0973 423974

OLAOYE Adeola *(Voc, Gtr)*: 19 Swanley House, Kinglake Street, London SE17 2LF ☎ 020 7701 2205

OLAREWAJU Hastings *(Voc)* ☎ 020 8764 9929

OLIVIER Phil *(Voc, Ac Gtr)*: 79 Berrymead Gardens, Acton, London W3 8AB ☎ 020 8723 3729, 0911 293714

OMONUA Margaret *(Voc)* ☎ 020 7771 6019, 0956 983131

ONE Charlie *(Voc)*: 1 Weald Road, Brentwood, Essex CM14 4QU ☎ 020 7787 6127

OST Linda *(Voc)*: Torgg. 25B, 64633 Gnesta, Sweden

OSTENENGEN Monica *(Voc)*: 28 Galton House Royal, Herbert Pavilions, Shooters Hill, London SE18 7LN ☎ 020 8319 8546

OSTROFF Nadya *(Voc, Gtr, Kbds, Synth)*: 25 Woodlands Close, London NW11 9QR ☎ 020 8455 0097

OVA *(Voc, Ac Gtr)* ☎ 020 8469 3814, 0956 943529

OWEN Johathan *(Voc, Kbds, Gtr, Com)*: 41 Pinkham Mansions, Brooks Road, London W4 3BQ ☎ 020 8477 3358, 0860 813667 car

PACE Elio *(Voc, Pf, Kbds, Song W)*: 3 Elizabeth Way, Eastleigh, Hampshire SO50 4JJ ☎ 0976 740 451

PADDY *(Voc, Pf, Kbds, Gtr)*: 3 Western Court, Huntley Drive, Finchley, London N3 1NX ☎ 020 8346 9803

PAGE Felicity *(Voc)*: 10 Ranmore Road, Cheam, Surrey SM2 7LT ☎ 020 8393 4608, 0378 791875

PAINTER Simon *(Voc, Kbds, Gtr)*: The Old Joinery, Wishanger Lane, Churt, Farnham Surrey GU10 2QJ ☎ 01252 794001

PALLOT Nerina *(Voc, Pf)*: 24 Caldervale Road, Clapham, London SW4 9LZ ☎ 020 7720 8030

PALMER Keith *(Voc)*: c/o Interactive Psl, 120-124 Curtain Road, London EC2A 3SA ☎ 020 7426 5130

PAM *(Voc)*: 18B Ainworth Way, Abbey Road, London NW8 0SR ☎ 020 7624 0510

PANDIT John Ashok *(Voc)*: 59 Charles Rowan House, Margery Street, London WC1X 0GH ☎ 020 7713 7809

PANDIT Vishwa *(Voc, Harm)*: 28 Cranbrook Road, Hounslow West, Middx TW4 7BN ☎ 020 8572 9997

PANIZZO Emanuela *(Voc, Pf)*: 12 Stacey Path, Harris Street, London SE5 7SL, 0961 157411

PARKER Janet *(Voc)*: 5 Larkshall Road, Chingford, London E4 7HS ☎ 020 8529 7444 & fax

PARKINSON Michelle *(Voc)*: 23 Penistone Road, Streatham, London SW16 5LU ☎ 020 8679 7130, 0956 439743 mob

PARRIAH Ms Psilobye *(Voc)*: 38D Wray Crescnet, Finsbury Park, London N4 8LP ☎ 020 7281 5668

PARSONS Paul *(Voc)*: 4 Cranleigh Drive, Swanley, Kent BR8 8NX ☎ 01322 667782

PARTINGTON Gitika *(Voc, Kbds, Song W)*: 185A Tufnel Park Road, Islington, London N7 0PU ☎ 020 7700 4840

PATEMAN Matthew *(Voc)*: 23 Meriden Close, Bromley, Kent BR1 2UF ☎ 020 8466 8244

PATTERSON Jeff *(Voc, B Gtr, Kbds, Per)* ☎ 020 8506 2092

PATTERSON Patricia *(Voc)*: Flat B, 7 Blenheim Terrace, St Johns Wood, London NW8 0DD ☎ 020 7625 1747

PAUL Howard *(Voc, Gtr, B Gtr)*: 16 Blenheim Court, Wellesley Road, Sutton, Surrey SM2 5BW ☎ 020 8643 4394

PEARCE Mary *(Voc)*: 39 Ormanton Road, London SE26 6RB

PEARSON-THOMAS Kathleen *(Voc, Pf, B Gtr)*: 16 Athlone House, Wilkin Street, London NW5 4LS ☎ 020 7424 0701, 0956 187 144

PEDRO Elohor *(Voc, Per)* ☎ 020 7242 1448

PELLIUS Everis *(Voc)*: Global House, 92 De Beauvoir Road, London N1 4EN ☎ 0973 293189 mob

PEMBERTON Clare *(Voc)*: 41 St Leonards Road, Claygate, Esher, Surrey KT10 0EL ☎ 01372 812952

PEREZ Maria *(Voc)*: 41 Shacklewell House, Shacklewell Lane, London E8 2EQ ☎ 020 7254 0246

PERONA-WRIGHT Hilary *(Voc, Gtr, Rec)*: 9 Hillside Road, Ashtead, Surrey KT21 1RZ ☎ 01372 277703, 01372 278406 fax

PERRY John *(Voc, Gtr, B Gtr)*: PO Box 93, Walton-on-Thames, Surrey KT12 2RS ☎ 01932 252815 & fax

PERRY Nina *(Voc, Pf, Kbds)*: Flat A The Limes, 5 Massie Road, Dalston, London E8 1BY

PHILLIPS Carol *(Voc, Gtr)*: 20 Burnaby Street, London SW10 0PJ ☎ 020 7352 6497

PHILLIPS Michelle *(Voc)*: 21C Thicket Road, Anerley, London SE20 8DB ☎ 020 8249 0192, 0956 263735

PHILLIPS Ronald *(Voc)*: 2 Woodside Park, Attleborough, Norfolk NR17 2JL ☎ 01953 455330

PHILLIPSON Petra *(Voc, Gtr, Dms)*: 91A Hollaway Road, London N7 8LT ☎ 020 7607 1423, 01523 162850

PIERRE Marie *(Voc)*: 30 Bank Ave, Mitcham, Surrey CR4 3DU ☎ 020 8640 3715

PLANT Robert *(Voc, Hmca)*: C-O Joan Hudson & Co, 91 Tabernacle Street, London EC2A 4BA ☎ 020 7253 3107

PLUTO *(Voc)*: 18A St Lukes Road, London W11 1DP ☎ 020 7221 4226, 0956 485834

POPO Melissa *(Voc)*

PORTAL Kate *(Voc, Vln, Gtr, Pf, Per)*: 511 Redwood Housing Co-Op, Oxo Tower Wharf, South Bank, London SE1 9GY ☎ 020 7928 8221

POSNETT Martin *(Voc)*

POTTER Alison *(Voc)*: 57 Exeter Road, Southgate, London N14 5JT ☎ 020 8368 0778

PRESIDENT Fatz *(Voc)* ☎ 0958 427 201 mob

PRICE Helen *(Voc, Gtr, Kbds)*: 25 White House, Vicarge Crescent, Battersea, London SW11 3LJ ☎ 020 7223 2492

PRICE Richelle *(Voc, Song W)*: 67 Betterton Road, Rainham, Essex RM13 8NB ☎ 01708 526959

PRITCHARD Andy *(Voc, Gtr)*: 23 Slades Gardens, Enfield, Middlesex EN2 7DP ☎ 020 8366 4815

PRYCE Rose *(Voc, Gtr)* ☎ 020 7833 9435

PRYKE Wendy *(Voc, Pf)*: Flat 4, 72 Netherwood Road, London W14 0BG ☎ 020 7603 2361, 0973 267405 mob

PUPPINI Marcella *(Voc, Pf)*: 259 Kennington Lane, London SE11 5QU ☎ 020 7582 6012, 0956 376138

PUSHAUN *(Voc, Vln, Pf, Kbds)*: 139C Finborough Road, Chelsea, London SW10 9AW ☎ 020 7373 9503, 0958 273692

Q Susie *(Voc, Kbds)*: 25 Nasham House, Kale Road, Erith, Kent DA18 4RN ☎ 020 8310 0797

QUAYE Finley *(Voc, Gtr, B Gtr, Dms, Af Dms)*: c/o Helen Searle, Searles Solicitors, The Chapel, 26A Munster Road, London SW6 4EN ☎ 020 8563 2799, 020 8563 2788

QUICKE Anne *(Voc, Flt, A Sax)*: The Basement, 21 Spring Hill, London E5 9BE ☎ 020 8806 8071

QUINTILE Maria *(Voc)*: 44 Ada Lewis House, Empire Way, Wembley, London HA9 0RD ☎ 020 8795 1710

RAASAY Susan *(Voc, Gtr)*: 49G Milner Square, Islington, London N1 1TW ☎ 020 7607 1065

RACHEL *(Voc)*: Flat 4, 46 Foxglove Way, Hackbridge, Surrey SM6 7JU ☎ 020 8669 6164, 07979 960383

RALPH Seymour *(Voc)*: 53 Stoddart House, Meadow Road, London SW8 1ND ☎ 020 7582 3515, 0836 536684, 0956 202493

RAMELIZE Karen *(Voc)*: Flat 62, 153 Queenstown Road, London SW8 3RN ☎ 020 7652 3244

RANDIE *(Voc)*: 16 Burton Lane, Myatts Field, Brixton, London SW9 6NX ☎ 020 7924 0284, 0958 490495

RANKS Cutty *(Voc)*: C/0 Fashion Records Ltd, 17 Davids Road, Forest Hill, London SE23 3EP ☎ 020 8291 6253, 020 8291 1097 fax

RANSON John *(Voc, Gtr)*: Flat C, 31 Baring Road, London SE12 0JP

RAPPAPORT Danielle *(Voc, Song W)*: 52 Croftdown Road, London NW5 1EN ☎ 020 7267 3226, 020 7485 0086

RASMUSSEN Leah *(Voc, Jaw H, Per)*: 176B Lewisham Way, Brockley, London SE4 7UU ☎ 020 8692 6556

RATHBONE Lucy *(Voc)*: 101 Moore Park Road, London SW6 2DA ☎ 020 7736 2128, 0468 101772

RAVEL Claire *(Voc)*: 121 Kingsley Avenue, West Ealing, London W13 ☎ 020 7700 0805

RAVEN Mellie *(Voc, Kbds)*: 207A Camden Road, London NW1 9AA ☎ 020 7267 9476, 0421 646920

RAWE Jackie *(Voc)*: 72 Church Road, London W7 1LB ☎ 01276 452872

RAY Pennie *(Voc, Kbds, Gtr, B Gtr)*: Flat F, 119 Cambridge Gardens, London W10 6JA ☎ 020 8964 2331

RAYELLE *(Voc)*: 125A De Beuvoir Road, London N1 4DL ☎ 0961 378151

REA Christopher *(Voc, Gtr, Pf)*: The Sol Studios, Mill Lane, Cookham, Berkshire SL6 9QT ☎ 01628 533289

REBEL *(Voc, B Gtr, Pf)*: Address Unknown

RECKORD Rohan *(Voc)*: 16 Burlington Gardens, Burlington Road, London SW6 4NU ☎ 020 7731 0026

REDMOND Melanie *(Voc, Per)*: 61 Dysart Avenue, Kingston-on-Thames, Surrey KT2 5RA ☎ 020 8549 8322

REDMONDS Duncan *(Voc, Dms, Gtr)*: 65A Headstone Road, Harrow, Middlesex HA1 1PQ ☎ 020 8424 8191, 020 8427 7806

REDWOOD Clifton *(Voc)*: 19 Walton Heath, Pound Hill, Crawley, West Sussex RH10 3UE ☎ 01293 885115

REEVES Kevin *(Voc, Pf)*: 31 Dartmoor Walk, London E14 9WF ☎ 020 7537 0153

REEVES Madeline *(Voc)* ☎ 020 8954 0370 & fax

REGAL Gray *(Voc, Ac Gtr)*: End Unit 1E, Links Way (Off Links Road), Tooting, London SW17 9ED ☎ 020 8682 0202

REGAN Diane *(Voc)*: Flat 13, 1 Longton Avenue, Sydenham, London SE26 6RA ☎ 0468 074828

REID Angela *(Voc)*: 16 The Croft, Friday Hill, London E4 6EZ

REID Grace *(Voc)*: 9C Ranelagh Road, London SW1V 3EX ☎ 020 7976 6948

REID Nigel *(Voc, Gtr)*: 842 Garratt Lane, London SW17 0NA ☎ 020 8672 6539, 020 8640 3086

REID Sonia *(Voc)*: 30 Firshill Avenue, Firshill, Sheffield S4 7AA ☎ 0114 242 0163

REID Symone *(Voc)*: 30 Prince Henry Road, Charlton, London SE7 8PP ☎ 020 8473 2606, 0956 450804

REIDS *(Voc)*: 21 Miller House, New Park Estate, Forster Road, Brixton Hill, London SW2 4UY

REILLY Maggie *(Voc)*: c/o Fk Management, Dapoune Wharf, Guildford, Surrey GU1 4RF ☎ 01483 565010, 01483 457144 fax

REMEDEE *(Voc, Hmca)*: 40 Hambalt Road, London SW4 9EG ☎ 020 8673 2130, 0831 411 690 mob

REVELL Patti *(Voc, Pf)*: Cherrytree Cottage, 26 Robinson Avenue, Goffs Oak, Watlham Cross EN7 5NY ☎ 01707 876707, 01707 873047 fax

REYNOLDS Basil *(Voc)*: 18 Winterbourne Rd, Dagenham, Essex RM8 2JZ ☎ 020 8491 4091

REYNOLDS Susan *(Voc)*: 6 Woodland Way, Mitcham, Surrey CR4 2DY ☎ 020 8640 2664

RICHARDS Nicole *(Voc, Song W)*: ☎ 020 7564 4661, 07930 985282

RICHARDSON Susan *(Voc, Tpt, Pf)*: Flat 4, Malatia, 78 St Augustine, South Croyden, Surrey CR2 6JH ☎ 020 8680 9809

RIDER Marguerite *(Voc, Kbds)*: 50 The Avenue, Kew Gardens, Surrey TW9 2AH ☎ 020 8940 0067

RILEY David *(Voc)*: 33 Wilson Close, Preston Road, Wembley HA9 9SU ☏ 020 8908 3859, 020 8459 9775 day

RILEY Dee *(Voc, Dms, Per, Kbds)* ☏ 020 8520 0984, 0795 7498017

RILEY Mykaell *(Voc)*: 73 Bollingbroke Road, London W14 0AA ☏ 020 8995 0426

RISE Mark *(Voc, Gtr)*: Flat 3, 107 Selborne Road, Southgate, London N14 ☏ 0956 418739, 020 8346 1517

RIX Delrae *(Voc, Gtr)*: 13 Field Lane, Brentford, Middlesex TW8 8NA ☏ 020 8580 1585

ROBERSON Jane *(Voc)*: Fern Villa, 54 Derby Road, South Woodford, London E18 2PS ☏ 020 8504 5715, 09569 421894, 020 8518 0152

ROBERTIN Pamela *(Voc)*: 142 Pomeroy Street, Queens Road, London SE14 5BT ☏ 0958 763252 mob

ROBERTS Evelyne *(Voc)*: 1 Rosedale Road, Forest Gate, London E7 8AU ☏ 020 8552 6257, 0585 140511 mob

ROBERTS Jennifer *(Voc)*: 208 Camberwell New Road, London SE5 0RR ☏ 020 7582 5932 & fax, 0973 562445 mob

ROBERTS Miles *(Voc, Gtr)*: 7 Leconfield Avenue, London SW13 0LD ☏ 020 8287 9330

ROBERTS Sharon *(Voc)*: 44 Kemp Court, Hartington Road, London SW8 2BJ ☏ 020 7771 9244, 0958 202150, 020 7456 1400

ROBERTS Vicky Taylor *(Voc, Song W)*: 58 Hawley Road, London NW1 8RG ☏ 020 7485 0125

ROBINSON Carey *(Voc)*: 31 Venetian Road, Camberwell, London SE5 9RR ☏ 0961 344575

ROBINSON Zuleikna *(Voc)*: 34 Welford Place, Wimbledon, London SW19 5AJ ☏ 020 8947 4926

ROBSON Cathryn Victoria *(Voc)*: 51 Tottenham Lane, Hornsey, London N8 9BD

ROCHA Miranda Nina *(Voc)*: 3 Archibald Road, London N7 0AN ☏ 020 8357 6986, 0956 447885 mob

ROCHEFORT Damon *(Voc)*: c/o Serious Rope, 78 Wakehurst Road, London SW11 6BU ☏ 020 7738 1081

ROCHESTER Gregory *(Voc)*: 168 Merrow Street, Walworth, London SE17 2NP ☏ 020 7564 2174

ROCILLO Lani *(Voc)*: 53 Lapworth Court, Little Venice, London W2 6NN ☏ 0795 730 8071, 0795 730 8071

ROCK Donna *(Voc)*: 130 Linwood Crescent, Enfield, Off Carterhatch Lane EN1 4UR ☏ 020 8367 3903

ROCK J *(Voc)*: 23 Barville Close, St Norbert Road, Brockley, London SE4 2LL ☏ 020 7732 5058

RODGERS Jasmine *(Voc, Gtr, Wh, Pf, Santoor)*: 24 Willows Court, 7 Sir Cyril Black Way, Wimbledon, London SW19 1UE ☏ 020 8540 3171, 020 8540 5646

RODGERS Paul *(Voc, Gtr, Song W)*: c/o C Sampson, PO Box 1002, King's Lynn, Norfolk PE30 4US ☏ 01553 770455

ROGERS Ben *(Voc, Gtr, Pf)*: Top Flat, 83 Ferndale Road, London SW4 7RL ☏ 020 7733 8585

ROGERS Glenn *(Voc, Ld Gtr, Rh Gtr, Kbds)* ☏ 01708 731695, 0441 161798 mob, 020 8467 0808

ROGERSON Paul *(Voc, Tpt, Kbds)*: 327A The Coach And Horses, Lewisham High Street, Lewisham, London SE13 6NR ☏ 020 8488 5362, 0378 226938

ROKITA Tess *(Voc, Kbds)*: 21 Durban Road, Beckenham, Kent BR3 4EY ☏ 020 8658 9956

ROLLIN Lisa *(Voc, Vln)*: 106 Drayton Bridge Road, London W7 1EP ☏ 020 8840 6812

ROMAY Gyp *(Voc)*: 291 Western Road, Leigh-on-Sea, Essex SS9 2QU ☏ 01702 551347

ROMEO Jennifer *(Voc, Harmony)*: 6 Baird Close, Kingsbury, London NW9 8XU ☏ 020 8933 8089

RONALD Terry *(Voc)*: 72 B Granville Park, Lewisham, London SE13 7DX ☏ 020 8318 6980

RONSKI Rubber *(Voc, Kbds)* ☏ 020 7266 0331, 020 7284 0623, 020 7916 1262

ROQUETTE Suzanne *(Voc, Gtr)*: Craigieburn, Duppas Hill Road, Croydon, Surrey CR0 4BG ☏ 020 8686 9190

ROSE Janet *(Voc)*: 5 Undercliff Road, London SE13 7TU ☏ 020 8265 9357

ROSE Marcia *(Voc)*: The Basement, 4 Bellfield Road, Brixton, London SW9 9UQ ☏ 020 7274 9166, 020 8960 9051, 020 7274 9166

ROSS Caroline *(Voc, B Gtr, Gtr)* ☏ 020 8488 9351, 020 8675 1832 & fax

ROSS Leopold *(Voc, Ld Gtr)*: 16 Kelfield Gardens, London W10 6LS ☏ 020 7379 0038, 020 7497 8909

ROSS Milo *(Voc)*: 16 Kelfield Gardens, London W10 6LS ☏ 020 7379 0038, 020 7497 8909

ROSS Robert *(Voc, Gtr)*: 85 Battersea Rise, London SW11 1HW

ROSSELSON Daniela *(Voc, Per)*: 107 Camden Mews, London NW1 9AH ☏ 020 7482 3330

ROSSITER Martin *(Voc, Pf, Org)*: c/o Jerry Smith, Automatic, 3 Wansdown Place, London SW6 1DN ☏ 020 7386 7172, 020 7610 1250 fax

ROWLES Allyson *(Voc)*: Address Unknown ☏ 020 8255 9477

ROYCE CHANCELIER (Des Mbwese) *(Voc)*: 25 Goddards Way, Vicarage Lane, Ilford, Essex IG1 4BF ☏ 020 8514 2792, 0956 127100 mob

RUBY *(Voc)*: 47 Prout Grove, Neasden, London NW10 1PU ☏ 020 8450 5789

RUDD Hilary *(Voc, Pf, Vln, Rec)*: 43B Victoria Road, London N4 3SJ ☏ 020 7281 5923

RUFFELLE Louise *(Voc)*: 42 Dulverton Road, South Croydon, Surrey CR2 8PG ☏ 0973 420234

RUSO *(Voc, Gtr, B Gtr, Kbds, Dms)*: 8 Sandhurst Court, Acre Lane, London SW2 5TX ☏ 020 7733 2252

RUSSELL-WHITAKER Lynda *(Voc)*: Top Flat, 21 Ritherdon Road, London SW17 8QE ☏ 020 8767 1139

RUST Tom *(Voc, T Sax, Kbds)*: Ground Floor Flat, 24 Charleville Road, West Kensington, London W14 9JH ☏ 0956 53434609 mob

RYAN Dave *(Voc)*: 49 Regent Square, Belvedere, Kent DA17 6EP ☏ 01322 405380, 0956 591536

SADLER Jeremy *(Voice, Cel)*: 41A Station Road, Edgware, London HA8 7HX ☏ 020 8952 1901, 0976 658801

SALEEM Imaani *(Voc)*: 133 Roslyn Road, Tottenham, London N15 5JB ☏ 020 8880 2069

SAMMES Michael *(Voc)*: 1 Orchard Road, Reigate, Surrey RH2 0PA

SAMPSON Richard *(Voc, Gtr)*: 315A Brockley Road, (Above Florist), Brockley, London SE4 2QZ ☏ 020 8691 9514, 020 8691 9514

SAMUELS Jazante *(Voc)*: 13C Glenarm Road, London E5 0LY ☏ 020 8525 9146

SAMUELS Joyce *(Voc)*: 56 Samuel House, Clarissa Street, London E8 4HN

SAMY Michella *(Voc)*: 214 The Ridgeway, North Harrow, Middlesex HA2 7DB ☏ 020 8863 7976

SANDS Mick *(Voc, Flt)*: 21 Lancaster Avenue, West Norwood, London SE27 9EL ☏ 020 8761 0984

SANTANA Adriana *(Voc)*: 6 Lomley House, Tulse Hill Estate, London SW2 2EW ☏ 020 8265 4930, 0956 572694

SARLIN Paula *(Voc)*: 64 St Johns Villas, London N19 3EG

SAUL Pinise *(Voc)*: 33 Gillam House, Silwood Street, London SE16 2SJ ☏ 020 7237 6015

SAUNDERS Sue *(Voc)*: Address Unknown ☏ 020 7625 6032

SCHREIBER Arianne *(Voc)*: 10 Chamberlain Road, London N2 8JS ☏ 020 8346 7166

SCIALLA Janelle *(Voc, Flt, Kbds, Gtr, Rec)*: 118 Wilberforce Road, London N4 2SU ☏ 020 7354 2054, 0378 441073 mob

SCOTT Eileen *(Voc)*: 16 College Court, Hammersmith, London W6 9DY ☏ 020 8748 3559

SEAL *(Voc)*: c/o Martin Greene Ravden, 55 Loudoun Road, St John's Wood, London NW8 0DL ☏ 020 7625 4545

SEALY Denice *(Voc)*: 22 Magpie Close, Forest Lane, London E7 9DE ☏ 020 8519 4763, 0956 904601 mob

SEAMAN Caroline *(Voc)*: 75B Arcadian Gardens, London N22 5AG ☏ 020 8888 9431

SEBUNYA Charles *(Voc)*: 15 First Avenue, Walthamstow, London E17 9QG ☏ 020 7561 9949, 0958 253049, 020 8520 8255

SEGAL Lizzie *(Voc, Gtr, Flt)*: 131 Waltham Road, Woodford Bridge, Essex IG8 8DP ☏ 020 8444 4506, 020 8262 1834

SENIOR Victoria *(Voc)*: 2 Fleet House, Victory Place, Lime House, London E14 8BG ☎ 020 7987 0616, 0467 816104

SEWSANKER Erica *(Voc, Pf)*: 3 Orpington Road, Winchmore Hill, London N21 3PD

SHANOVITCH Linda *(Voc)*: 33 Northolme Road, London N5 2UU ☎ 020 7226 2094

SHARDA Anju *(Voc)*: 76C Rochester Row, Westminster, London SW1P 1JU ☎ 020 7931 7085

SHAW Craig *(Voc, Gtr, Hmca)*: 17 Goodhall Street, Park Royal, London NW10 6TT ☎ 020 8961 1757

SHAW Mark *(Voc, Gtr)* ☎ 020 8672 7757

SHAW Samantha *(Voc)*: 226 Queens Road, Buckhurst Hill, Essex IG9 5AY ☎ 020 8504 5379, 0973 321088

SHEARMUR Bryony *(Voc, Gtr)*: Flat 3, 1B Kenley Walk, London W11 ☎ 020 7370 7170, 0973 882 453

SHERIDAN Claire *(Voc)*: 31 Larch Close, Friern Barnet, London N11 3NU ☎ 020 8361 5742

SHERIDAN Jackie *(Voc)*: 47 Plimsoll Road, London N4 2EN ☎ 020 7354 4652

SHERIFF Bernadette *(Voc, Kbds)*: 14 Northcote Road, London NW10 9LJ ☎ 020 8965 4309

SHIJI *(Voc, Kbds, Per)*: 15 Reynardsons Court, High Road, London N17 9HX ☎ 020 8808 6943

SHOLA *(Voc)*: 11 Ujima Court, Sunnyhill Road, London SW16 2UG ☎ 020 8677 9170

SHORT Phillip *(Voc, Gtr, B Gtr, Kbds, Dms)*: 20 Melrose Road, Coulsdon, Surrey CR5 3JH ☎ 020 8660 5665, 0410 243389 mob

SHRIMPTON Hayley *(Voc)*: 194 Peterborough Road, Carshalton, Surrey SM5 1DP ☎ 020 8286 3934

SIEGER Lucinda *(Voc)*: 20 Hanover Flats, Binney Street, London W1Y 1RG ☎ 020 7409 1883

SIFFRE Labi *(Voc, Kbds, Gtr)*: PO Box 17, Abergavenny, Gwent NP8 1XA

SILVERSTONE Kezi *(Voc)*: c/o J Khan Management, Tunstall Studios, 34-44 Tunstall Road, London SW9 8DA ☎ 020 7924 9294, 0956 444260, 020 7924 9494

SIMEON *(Voc, Kbds)*: 28 Egbert House, Kingsmead Eastate, Hackney, London E9 5QF ☎ 020 8533 7870, 0958 275493

SIMNETT Derek *(Voc, Gtr, Dms)*: 148G Plumstead Road, London SE18 7DY ☎ 020 8317 0015

SIMONS Simone *(Voc, Pf)*: 28 Brinklow House, Warwick Estate, London W2 5EN ☎ 0402 128990 mob

SIMPSON Herma *(Voc)*: 27C Clifton Villas, Maida Vale, London W9 2PH ☎ 020 7266 0187

SIMPSON Olive *(Voc)*: 7 Emperors Gate, London SW7 4HH ☎ 020 7373 4453

SIMPSON Ray *(Voc, Kbds)*: 127 Knatchbull Road, Camberwell, London SE5 9QY ☎ 020 7737 2287

SIN Jimmy *(Voc)*: 2B Bristow Road, Hounslow, Middlesex TW3 1UP ☎ 020 8510 2134

SINGH Manohar *(Voc, Harm, Tabla)*: 8 Furness Road, West Harrow, Middlesex HA2 0RL ☎ 020 8248 0474, 020 8427 1291 day

SISTER.MIRIAM *(Voc)*: 6 Daubeney Road, Homerton, London E5 0EF ☎ 020 8985 3340

SKATES Anne *(Voc, Gtr, Flt, Pf)*: 8 Rythe Road, Claygate, Surrey KT10 9DF ☎ 01372 466228, 01372 466229 fax

SKYE Mel *(Voc, Ac Gtr)* ☎ 020 8671 4929

SLEET Nichole *(Voc, Tbn)*: 43 Corinne Road, Tufnell Park, London N19 5EZ ☎ 020 7700 5840

SMIKLE Esmina *(Voc, Song W)*: Address Unknown ☎ 020 7221 9611

SMITH David *(Voc)*: 242B London Road, Mitcham, Surrey CR4 3HD

SMITH Emma *(Voc, Sax, B Clt, Gtr)*: Top Flat, 158 Franciscan Road, Tooting, London SW17 8HH ☎ 020 8767 5169

SMITH Helen *(Voc, Song W, Kbds, Club Dj)*: 141C Hartford Road, London N1 4LR ☎ 020 7241 4265

SMITH Maureen *(Voc, Pf, Gtr)*: 3 Worple Court, Worple Road, Isleworth, Middlesex TW7 7AX ☎ 020 8568 0339, 0498 678315

SMITH Michael *(Voc)*: Freshwater House, Outdowns, Effingham, Surrey KT24 5QR ☎ 01483 281500/1, 01483 281502 fax

SMITH Pete *(Voc, Kbds, Gtr, Dms, B Gtr)*: 57 Hangar Lane, Ealing, London W5 3HL ☎ 020 8997 7474

SMITH Samantha *(Voc, Per)*: 52 Chewton Road, Walthamstow, London E17 7DW ☎ 020 8521 9625

SMITH Sheree *(Voc)*: 101 Northcote Road, Croydon, Surrey CR0 2HZ ☎ 020 8683 2710

SMITH Stephen *(Voc, Song W, Gtr)*: Flat 8, 14 Old Compton Street, London W1V ☎ 020 7494 0535, 020 7494 0535

SMITH TV *(Voc)*: 155 Hartswood Road, London W12 9NG

SMITH Vanessa *(Voc)* ☎ 020 8748 1708

SMOKIN' JO *(Voc)*: 49 Rosebank, Holyfort Road, London SW6 6LH

SMYTH John *(Voc, Song W)*: 38 Prince George Road, Stoke Newington, London N16 8BY ☎ 020 7249 5628

SOLID ROX *(Voc)*: 86 Biggerstaff Road, Stratford, London E15 2LX ☎ 0839 793699 mob

SOMERVILLE Jimmy *(Voc, Per)*: c/o Jess E Musique Ltd, Solar Management Ltd, 42/48 Charlbert Street, London NW8 7BU ☎ 020 7722 4175, 020 7722 4072 fax

SONI *(Voc, Com)* ☎ 020 7231 7616, 0956 494320

SORO Cia *(Voc, Synth, Gtr, Pf, Mldca)*: Ostgotagatan 41, 116 25 Stockholm, Sweden ☎ +46 707277700

SORRENTINO Daniela *(Voc, Gtr)*: 2 Somerfield Road, Finsbury, London N4 2JJ ☎ 020 7690 5278

SOUTH Zoe *(Voc)*: Flat 4, 29 Queen Annes Grove, Bedford Park, London W4 1HW ☎ 020 8995 2351 & fax, 01523 700526

SPARKS Andra *(Voc, Pf)*: 24 Ryland Road, London NW5 3EA ☎ 020 7284 0226

SPILLING James *(Voc, Pf, Vln)*: 1 Cambria Road, Camberwell, London SE5 9AB ☎ 020 7733 0724, 0467 353 854

ST HILL Carl *(Voc, Pf)*: 2 Dobell Road, Eltham, London SE9 1HE ☎ 020 8859 3824, 020 8969 7139 day

STEER Peter *(Voc, Gtr, Kbds)*: 7 Whitegates, Court Bushes Road, Whyteleafe, Surrey CR3 0BX ☎ 01883 626971

STEPHENSON Kate *(Voc, Dms)*: 28B Ormeley Road, London SW12 9QE ☎ 020 8673 2423

STEVENS Jonathan *(Voc, Gtr, B Gtr)*: 17 Havant Road, London E17 3JE ☎ 020 8521 9075

STEWART Helena *(Voc, Flt)*: 14 Hexham Road, Morden, Surrey SM4 6NH ☎ 020 8644 8314, 0411 392418 mob

STEWART Rod *(Voc)*: c/o Boulevard Mngt, 16130 Ventura Boulevard, Suite 550, Encino, California 91436, USA

STOCKER Catherine *(Voc, Gtr, Flt)*: 55D Stapleton Hall Road, London N4 3QF

STOCKLEY Miriam *(Voc, Kbds)*: 106 Copse Wood Way, Northwood, Middlesex HA6 2UB ☎ 01923 835606

STRAHAN Nadia *(Voc, Song W)* ☎ 020 7681 0833

STREDDER Maggie *(Voc)*: 48 Alpha Road, Surbiton, Surrey KT5 8PR ☎ 020 8399 6080

STRONGMAN Jay *(Voc)*: Flat 5, 61 Redcliffe Gardens, London SW10 9JJ

STUBBS Anthony *(Voc, Kbds, B Gtr)*: 516 Finchley Road, London NW11 8DD ☎ 020 8458 0149

STUBBS Donna *(Voc)*: 15 Durham Avenue, Gidea Park, Romford, Essex RM2 6JJ ☎ 01708 477253

SUBAN Ravelle *(Voc)*: 42 Kelvin Gardens, Cherry Trees, Croydon, Surrey CR0 4UR ☎ 07970 738002

SUGGS *(Voc, La Per)*: c/o Cc Young & Co, Chesham Rhouse, 150 Regent Street, London W1R 5FA ☎ 020 7432 0337

SUISSA Justine *(Voc)*: 84 Kensington Church St, London W8 4BY ☎ 020 7221 7101

SULIMAN *(Voc, Sax, B Gtr, Gtr, Kbds)*: 9 Pasfield Court, 6A Cleaver Street, London SE11 4DY ☎ 020 7582 1555

SUMMERFIELD Saffron *(Voc, Gtr, Pf, Man)*: 25 Ferndale Road, South Norwood, London SE25 4QR ☎ 020 8406 3175 & fax

SUMNER Tina *(Voc, Pf)*: 67 B Barnes High Street, Barnes, London SW13 9LD

SUPER FLEX *(Voc)* ☎ 0956 334578 mob

SUSAN *(Voc)* ☎ 020 7476 9525

SUTHERLAND-SYLVESTER Sherlyn *(Voc, Kbds)* ☎ 020 7385 9077

SWABY Courtney *(Voc, Song W, Arr)*: 23B Tresco Road, Nunhead, London SE15 3PY ☎ 020 7358 1567

SWALLOW Deborah *(Voc, Acc, Vln)*: 148B Westcombe Hill, Blackheath, London SE3 7DT ☎ 020 8858 6382

SWAN Rosemary *(Voc, Song W)*: 11A Albert Road, London N4 3RR ☎ 020 7263 9809, 020 7281 5233

TAPPER Natalie *(Voc)*: 295 Glyn Road, Clapton, London E5 0JP ☎ 020 8533 7301, 0956 168122

TAYLOR Dennis *(Voc, Gtr)*: 153A Sunningvale Avenue, Biggin Hill, Kent TN16 3TL ☎ 01959 72782

TAYLOR Linda *(Voc)*: 67 Sidney Road, Bedford MK40 2BQ ☎ 01234 301057, 0836 609335 mob

TAYLOR Pauline *(Voc)*: 20 The Crescent, Independent Place, 1 Downs Park Road, London E8 2HE

TAYUS *(Voc, Per)* ☎ 020 7274 1293

TAZ *(Voc, Bod, Gtr, Vln)*: 62 Iliffe Street, London SE17 3LL ☎ 020 7252 5902

TEE Shinri *(Voc, Gtr)* ☎ 0956 363656

TEEGO *(Voc, Pf, Tpt, Per, Gtr)*: 33 Colchester Road, Leyton, London E10 6HB ☎ 020 8539 5680, 0958 637336 mob

TELLA Sylvia *(Voc)*: 46 Pheonix Court, Wembley, Middlesex HA9 9XG ☎ 020 8908 0696

TENNANT Lorne *(Voc)*: Flat 3F3 Virginia Court, 70 Miller Street, Glasgow G1 1DT

TENNANT Peter *(Voc, Pf, Kbds)*: First Flor Flat, 194 Wightman Road, London N8 0BY ☎ 020 8341 7976

TERRI Caron *(Voc)*: 28A Inman Road, Harlesdon, London NW10 9JT ☎ 020 8961 8381

TERRY Helen C *(Voc)*: Address Unknown ☎ 020 8986 6222

THE REAL MAXINE *(Voc)*: 32 Rupert Gardens, London SW9 7TL ☎ 020 7738 3356 & fax

THOMAS David *(Voc, Acc)*: Flat 1B, 1 St Catherines Terrace, Kingsway, Hove, East Sussex BN3 2RR ☎ 01273 770376

THOMAS Dawn *(Voc)*: 23 Ellison Gardens, Southall, Middlesex UB2 4EW ☎ 020 8574 8073

THOMPSON Christopher *(Voc, Gtr)*: 58 Kinloch Drive, London NW9 7LH ☎ 020 8200 0499, 020 8200 0158 fax

THOMPSON Naomi *(Voc)* ☎ 020 8969 4219

THORN Tracey *(Voc)*: Unit 9, Acklam Workshops, 10 Acklam Road, London W10 5QZ ☎ 020 8968 7159, 020 8960 0298 fax

TIYEE *(Voc)*: 38 Arragon Road, Earlsfield, London SW18 4XH ☎ 020 8877 1790, 0961 306724, 677 8739

TOBIN Christine *(Voc, Pf)*: 20 Malvern House, Stamford Hill Estate, London N16 6RR ☎ 020 8442 4381

TOLMER Phobbe *(Voc, Lyric)*: 12 Station Rise, Tulse Hill, London SE27 9BW ☎ 020 8674 3048

TOOTH Anthony *(Voc, Rec)*: 64 Portland Road, Kingston-on-Thames, Surrey KT1 2SH ☎ 020 8541 0446

TOP Head *(Voc, Club Dj)*: 31 Phippes House, White City, London W12 7QE ☎ 020 8746 0496, 0958 405154

TOPLEY William *(Voc)*: 67 Marksbury Avenue, Richmond, Surrey TW9 4JE

TORMANN John *(Voc, Pf, Db)*: 7 Wendover Road, Bromley, Kent BR2 9JU ☎ 020 8460 0344 & fax, 020 8290 5205

TOTH Anita Maria *(Voc, Pf, Per)*: 10 Turner Close, Stevenage, Herts SG1 4AF ☎ 01438 361721

TOVEY Penni *(Voc, Pf)*: 38B Hindmans Road, East Dulwich, London SE22 9NF ☎ 020 8693 9526

TOZER Cathy *(Voc, Song W, Gtr)*: 7 The Quadrangle, London SE24 9QR ☎ 020 7733 6530

TRAQUAIR Nancy *(Voc)*: 56 Lordship Road, London N16 0QT ☎ 020 8809 0741

TRINDER Aaron *(Voc, Gtr, B Gtr, Ld Gtr, Kbds)*: Flat 2, 24 Alexandra Grove, London N4 2LF ☎ 020 7503 8183

TROMPETELER Andy *(Voc)*: 1 Pearson Court, Central Road, Morden, Surrey SM4 5RN ☎ 020 8648 4434

TROUBLESOME *(Voc)*: 14 Crawshay Court, Eythorne Road, Myattfield Estate, London SW9 7RJ ☎ 020 7582 0546

TROY Elisabeth *(Voc)*: c/o Sublime Mngt, 65 Overdale Road, London W5 4TU ☎ 020 8840 2042, 020 8840 5001

TRUJILLO Jorge George *(Voc, B Gtr, Gtr)*: 37 Fleeming Toad, Walthamstow, London E17 5ET ☎ 020 8527 2967

TSCHANZ Marc *(Voc, Gtr, Kbds)*: 1 Flat D, Hampstead Hill Gardens, Lodon NW3 2PH ☎ 020 7433 1733

TURNER Genneah-Eloise *(Voc, Gtr, B Gtr)* ☎ 020 8409 0656

TURNER Marc *(Voc, Gtr)*: 31 Addington Grove, Sydenham, London SE26 4JU

UBAKA Chinye *(Voc)*: Flat 10 Beech House, 215 Chinford Mount Road, London E4 8LP ☎ 020 8523 9942, 0956 476981

UNDERWOOD Claire *(Voc)*: 138 Springbank Road, London SE13 6SU ☎ 020 8698 7885, 0585 149601 mob

UPTON Anthony *(Voc, Gtr, B Gtr)*: Flat 8, Kensington Hall Gardens, Beaumont Avenue, London W14 ☎ 020 7385 6896

VAN ASCH Rachel *(Voc, Dms)*: 43 Corinne Road, Tufnell Park, London N19 5EZ ☎ 020 7700 5840 & fax, 020 7700 0805

VASCONCELOS Monica *(Voc)*: 53C Clapton Common, London E5 9AA ☎ 020 8806 9576

VELVART Marianne *(Voc, Song W, Gtr)*: 70 Oakley Road, South Norwood, London SE25 4XQ ☎ 020 8656 8080

VERNEY Francesca *(Voc)*: The Old Cottage, London Road, Bourne End, Herts HP1 2RJ

VINCENT Steve *(Voc, Hmca)*: Flat 1, 2 Coppermill Lane, Walthamstow, London E17 7HB ☎ 07931 915529

VISHAL *(Voc)* ☎ 020 8551 5522, 0958 783541 mob

VISKANT Joan *(Voc)*: 71 Lysia Street, London SW6 6NF ☎ 020 7381 3318

WADE David *(Voc, Per)*: PO Box 13232, Camberwell, London SE5 0ZL ☎ 0958 350588 mob

WADE Nik *(Voc)*: c/o Blue Crumb Truck, PO Box 416, Cardiff CF1 8XU ☎ 020 7833 4013

WAGER Henrik *(Voc, Vln)*: The Garden Flat, 6 Regents Park Road, Primrose Hill, London NW1 7TX ☎ 020 7267 0250

WALKER David *(Voc, Gtr)*: Handle Group Of Companies, Pinewood Studios, Pinewood Road, Iver Heath, Buckinghamshire SL0 0NH ☎ 01753 651 001, 01753 630 555/633

WALLACE Rachel *(Voc)*: 46 Holmewood Gardens, Brixton Hill, London SW2 3NA

WALTERS Hannelore *(Voc)*: c/o 8 Roberts Road, Belvedere, Kent DA17 6NP

WALTON Anna *(Voc)*: Flat B, 15 Hampstead Hill Gardens, London NW3 2PH ☎ 020 7431 6096, 020 7435 9636, 0374 123105 mob

WALWYN David *(Voc, Pf)*: 21 Nightingale Grove, Lewisham, London SE13 6EY ☎ 020 8355 4099, 0956 320472, 020 8355 4099

WANDER De'Jon *(Voc)*: 25A Nettleton Road, New Cross, London SE14 5UJ ☎ 0961 751702

WANGFORD Hank *(Voc)*: 30 Colville Terrace, London W11 2BU ☎ 020 7229 7107

WARCHAL Wendy *(Voc)*: 22 Parsonage Road, West Thurrock, Grays, Essex RM16 1AG

WARD Winston *(Voc)*: 73 Leathwaite Road, Battersea, London SW11 6RL ☎ 020 7787 0350, 0958 310214, 020 7642 1789

WARDALLY Rikki *(Voc)*: 222A Camberwell New Road, London SE5 0RR ☎ 020 7587 3671

WASSEY Cassandra *(Voc, Pf, Kbds)*: 21 Southview Close, Rectory Lane, Tooting, London SW17 9TU ☎ 020 8672 0794

WATES Rupert *(Voc, B Gtr, Gtr, Pf, Synth)*: 5 Chiswick Mall, London W4 2PF ☎ 020 8994 3830

WATKISS Cleveland *(Voc, Song W)*: 187 Fawcett Estate, Clapton Common, London E5 9DQ ☎ 020 8806 1051

WATSON Guy *(Voc, Gtr, E Gtr, Ac Gtr, Dms)*: Flat 5, 4 Hawes Road, Bromley, Kent BR1 3JR ☎ 020 8402 2718, 0410 794673 mob

WEAPON Lisa *(Voc, Club Dj)* ☎ 0973 821076 mob

WEBB Gary *(Voc, Gtr, Kbds)*: 86 Staines Road, Wraysbury, Berks TW19 5AA ☎ 01784 2111

WEBB Helen *(Voc, Flt, Cong)*: Flat 8, 15 Belsize Ave, London NW3 4BL ☎ 020 7916 7016

WEBB Sarah *(Voc)*: 19 Ford Square, London E1 2HS

WEBLEY Yvonne *(Voc, Pf)* ☎ 01523 106385 pager

WEDELL Rebekka *(Voc, Pf, Per)*: 63 Habington House, Notley Street, London SE5 7NW ☎ 020 7703 1611

WEEKES Desree *(Voc)*: S. Gor.93 Oakwood Crescent, Greenford, Middlesex UB6 0RG ☎ 020 8771 2600

WELCH Lizzy *(Voc, Gtr)*: Sheepwash House, Sheepwash Lane, West Wittering, W. Sussex PO20 8QN ☎ 0378 213378

WELDON Shelly *(Voc, Pf, Kbds, Gtr)*: 2 Arlington Close, East Twickenham, Middlesex TW1 2BE ☎ 020 8891 0595

WELLER Sarah *(Voc)*: Address Unknown ☎ 020 8556 8412

WELLS Fedd *(Voc, B Gtr, Kbds)*: 12 Woodstar House, Hereford Retreat, Bird In Bush Road, Peckham, London SE15 6RJ

WELMANS Nanette *(Voc)* ☎ 020 8575 3771

WESTBROOK Kate *(Voc, T Hrn, Pic)*: Brent House, Holbeton, Nr Plymouth, Devon PL8 1LX ☎ 01752 830589

WESTERHOUT Lisa *(Voc, Pf)*: 3 Wandle Road, London SW17 7DL ☎ 020 8672 0007

WHALLEY Tasmin *(Voc, Kbds)* ☎ 0421 890004

WHARMBY Denise *(Voc, Pf, Vln)*: Flat J, Welford House, 114 Shirland Road, Maida Vale, London W9 2BT ☎ 020 7286 1232

WHARMBY Tony *(Voc)*: 31 Kingsley Way, London N2 0EH ☎ 020 8455 4030, 020 8455 2700

WHEELER Alison *(Voc, Gtr)*: 2Nd Floor Flat, 75 Gunterstone Road, London W14 9BS ☎ 020 7602 9571, 0958 219375

WHEELER Caron *(Voc)*: 51A Beckwith Road, London SE24 9LQ ☎ 020 8299 3996

WHITE Peter *(Voc, Rh Gtr)*: 109 Hartswood Road, Brentwood, Essex CM14 5AG ☎ 01277 218 941, 0930 733 717

WHITE Richard *(Voc)*: 47 Malden Avenue, South Norwood, London SE25 4HR ☎ 020 8655 3897, 0956 154530 mob

WHITE Sherina *(Voc)*: 10 Parry Road, South Norwood, London SE25 6RJ ☎ 020 8409 0653, 0958 485 815

WHITNALL Timothy *(Voc, Gtr, Kbds, Bjo, B Gtr)*: 3 Clarence Street, Richmond, Surrey TW9 2SA ☎ 020 8948 4260, 0976 273305 mob, 020 8940 2335 fax

WHITTAKER Leo Heath *(Voc, Rapper, Gtr)*: 1 Roseleigh Avenue, London N5 1SG ☎ 020 7503 8498, 0956 432012

WHYNE Janice *(Voc)*: 32 Squarey Street, Tooting, London SW17 0AB ☎ 020 8488 1406, 0958 683320

WICKES Nicholas *(Voc, Gtr)*: 70 Endlesham Road, London SW12 8JL, 0958 393192 mob

WIDDUP Vanessa *(Voc, Pf, Gtr, Rec)*: 17A Vardens Road, London SW11 1RQ ☎ 020 7207 4968

WILBY Rosie *(Voc, Gtr, Kbds)*: 117A Upper Tollington Park, London N4 4ND ☎ 020 7607 7896, 0956 460372

WILCOCKS Lizie *(Voc, Kbds, Gtr)*: 454 Kings Road, London SW10 0LQ ☎ 020 7352 8223

WILDE Shane *(Voc, Ac Gtr, B Gtr, Dms, Synt)* ☎ 020 7233 8554, 07971 249299

WILKES Fiona *(Voc)*: c/o 6 Hillcrest View, Leeds LS7 4EB ☎ 0113 2622 483

WILKINSON Collette *(Voc)*: 46 Lots Road, London SW10 0QF ☎ 020 7352 9883

WILLIAMS David *(Voc, Gtr)*: 22 Devonshire Road, Palmers Green, London N13 4QX ☎ 020 8886 8789

WILLIAMS Donna *(Voc, Song W)*: Flat 1, 2A Flaxman Road, Camberwell, London SE5 9DH ☎ 020 7733 6516

WILLIAMS Esther *(Voc)* ☎ 020 7328 1520

WILLIAMS Geoffrey *(Voc)*: 16 Mcgregor Road, London W11 1DE ☎ 020 7792 3632

WILLIAMS Orville *(Voc, Song W)*: 32 Radley Road, Tottenham, London N17 6RL ☎ 0956 132870 mob

WILLIAMS Rob *(Voc, Gtr, B Gtr, Per)*: 129 Inderwick Road, Crouch End, London N8 9JR

WILLISON Nina J *(Voc)* ☎ 020 7722 6796, 0402 596359

WILLS Lucy *(Voc)*: 40 Oaklands Grove, Shepherds Bush, London W12 0JA ☎ 020 8743 3359

WILSON Amanda *(Voc)*: 19 Glover House, Nunhead Lane, Peckham, London SE15 3UR ☎ 020 7277 9514

WILSON Emma *(Voc)*: 62C Castellain Road, Maida Vale, London W9 1EX ☎ 020 7223 0670

WILSON John *(Voc, Gtr, B Gtr, Pf)*: 141 Wills Crescent, Whitton, Nr Twickenham, Middlesex TW3 2JF ☎ 020 8287 4131, 0973 153990 mob

WILSON Mari *(Voc)*: 14 Shanklin Road, London N8 8TJ

WILSON Rohan *(Voc, Kbds, B Gtr, Per)*: The Courtyard, 42 Colwith Road, London W6 ☎ 020 8741 1419

WINFIELD John *(Voc, Kbds)*: 11A Barry Avenue, Tottenham, London N15 6AD ☎ 020 8802 7722

WINSTONE Norma *(Voc)*: Tideway, Wellington Parade, Walmer, Deal, Kent CT14 8AA ☎ 01304 367840, 01304 382056

WINWOOD Julia *(Voc)*: 23 Nettleton Road, New Cross Gate, London SE14 5UJ ☎ 020 7277 5611

WISDOM Gillian *(Voc)*: 1B Celia Road, London N19 5ET ☎ 020 7609 2551

WITCHY *(Voc, Gtr)*: 58 Cranley Gardens, London N13 4LS ☎ 020 8886 6673

WOCKER Sebastian *(Voc, Gtr, Kbds, Per)*: 82A Hampstead High Street, London NW3 1RE ☎ 020 7435 5562, 0421 083874 mob, 020 7433 1443

WONDER Dennis *(Voc)*: 3 Esher House, Springfield Estate, Union Grove, Stockwell, London SW8 2QL ☎ 020 7498 8266 & fax

WONG Simon *(Voc, Gtr, B Gtr, Kbds, Dms)*: 30B Craven Park Road, Harlesden, London NW10 4AB ☎ 020 8965 6231

WOOD Diana *(Voc, T Sax, A Sax, S Sax)*: 10 Kenmara Close, Three Bridges, Crawley, West Sussex RH10 2AN ☎ 01293 546322, 01293 404745

WOOD Paul *(Voc)*: 97 Gordon Road, Ilford, Essex IG1 1SJ ☎ 020 8478 3771, 0468 122516

WOODS Marcella *(Voc, Db, Pf)*: 110 Luxborough Lane, Chigwell, Essex IG7 5AA ☎ 020 8504 6528 & fax, 0973 671332 mob

WORTLEY James *(Voc, Gtr)*: 98A Willesden Lane, London NW6 7TA ☎ 020 7625 4344

WRAY Viveen *(Voc)* ☎ 020 8896 0023, 0973 868265

WRIGHT Andrea *(Voc, Song W, Gtr)*: 47 Gaskarth Road, London SW12 9NN ☎ 020 8675 2566

XAN *(Voc)*: 14A Long Lane, London N3 2PT ☎ 020 8883 2654

Y *(Voc, B Gtr, Kbds, Dms)*: 29 Marcia Road, London SE1 5XE ☎ 020 7237 8901, 0956 218298

YAPP Phillip *(Voc)*: Top Fl At, 23 Drayton Road, West Ealing, London W13 0LD ☎ 020 8810 9245

YAWSON Helen *(Voc)*: 199 Charlton Road, Edmonton, London N9 8HJ ☎ 020 8805 7221

YAZZ *(Voc, Kbds)*

YIANNIS *(Voc, Kbds)*: 6 Pawleyne Close, Penge, London SE20 8JH ☎ 020 8402 1302, 0956 922864 mob

YOGESWARAN Manickam *(Voc, Com, Per, Flt)*: 29 Firdene, Tolworth, Surbiton, Surrey KT5 9QQ

YOUNG Anthony *(Voc)*: 188A Sely Road, Tooting, London SW17 9RD ☎ 020 8241 4683

YOUNG Sally *(Voc, Gtr, Vln, Kbds, B Gtr)*: 45 Howitt Close, London NW3 4LX ☎ 020 7586 0170

YOUNGER Virginia *(Voc, Gtr)*: 5 Abbey Close, Pinner, Middlesex HA5 2AW ☎ 020 8429 0494, 0956 574793, 020 8866 8799

ZAGORITIS Adrian *(Voc, Kbds, Dms, Song W)*: 2 Timber Close, Chislehurst, Kent BR7 5PA ☎ 020 8467 8716

ZAKIAN Laura *(Voc)*: 22 Bousfield Road, London SE14 5TR ☎ 020 7277 8714

ZION *(Voc, Song W, Kbds, B Gtr)*: The Annexe, Cleveland, Waterhouse Lane, Kingswood, Surrey KT20 6EB ☎ 01737 356853, 07000 255441

ZOZO *(Voc, Per, B Gtr, Dms)*: 8 Chancery House, Bewley Street, London E1 0BU ☎ 020 7790 2553

WASHBOARD

LONDON

SOFTLEY Beverley *(Per, Voc)*: 1 Ashendene Road, Bayford, Herts SG13 8PX ☎ 01992 511254

WHISTLE

SCOTLAND

GREEN Alexander: Greenfield Cottage, 1 Seafield Terrace, Portknockie, Banffshire AB56 4NA ☎ 01542 841 481

NORTH EAST

FLETCHER David *(Mldn, Voc)*: Amulree, Holme Road, Kirton Holme, Boston, Lincs PE20 1TB ☎ 01205 79562

MCNALLY James *(Bod, Voc, Acc, Kbds)*: New Nook Farm House, Newal Nook, Bradwell, Nr Sheffield S30 2HX ☎ 01433 620165

WALKER William: 2 Myrtle Place, Saltaire, Shipley, West Yorks BD18 4NB ☎ 01274 772731, 0140 659234

EAST

JAMES Trevor *(Bag, Bod, Bones, Psal)*: 7 Park Close, Markyate, St Albans, Herts AL3 8RG ☎ 01582 842178

LONDON

BREATNACH Cormac *(Flt)*: Mandala, Ballrd, Knockrath, Rathdrum, Co Wicklow, Eire ☎ +353 404 45218, +353 404 45516

KILDUFF Vinnie *(Gtr, Uill, Pf, Bod)*: 15 Rose Hill Court, Kilkenny, Co Kilkenny, Ireland ☎ +353 88 58868

ZITHER

LONDON

CRONSHAW Andrew *(Ctna, Eth Wnd, Kantele, Eth S)*: 51 Hainault Court, Forest Rise, London E17 3NW ☎ 020 8521 4649 & fax

NASER Ernest *(Com)*: 39 Southfields, London NW4 4LX ☎ 020 8203 3175

Index of Members

The following index is ordered alphabetically by name and should be used in conjunction with the National Directory of Members beginning on page 1.

Alan, Gary : *Guitars* (Lon)
Alancroft, Rick : *Bass Guitar* (E)
Albarn, Damon : *Voice* (Lon)
Alberga, Eleanor : *Composer* (Lon)
Albergaria-Savill, Oli : *Latin American Percu* (SE)
Alberman, David : *Violin* (Lon)
Alberts, Lionel : *Cello* (Lon)
Albery, Robbie : *Guitars* (SE)
Albrighton, Che : *Percussion* (Lon)
Albu, Ben : *Saxophones* (Lon)
Albuquerque, Sharon : *Voice* (Lon)
Alburger, Mary : *Viola* (Sco)
Alcock, Anthony : *Double Bass* (Sco)
Alcock, Colette : *Voice* (Mid)
Alcock, Douglas : *Percussion* (Mid)
Alcock, George : *Pianoforte* (NW)
Alcock, Gregory : *Guitars* (E)
Alcock, Helen : *Bassoon* (Sco)
Alcock, Mark : *Taiko Drums* (SE)
Alcock, Neil : *Keyboards* (Mid)
Alcock, Susan : *Clarinet* (Lon)
Alcoe, John : *Trombone* (Lon)
Alden, Timothy : *Percussion* (Lon)
Alderdice, Martyn : *Guitars* (NE)
Alderking, Seann : *Pianoforte* (Lon)
Aldersea, Jon : *Percussion* (Mid)
Aldersea, Rebecca : *Cello* (NW)
Alderson, Geoffrey : *Saxophones* (SE)
Alderton, Glenn : *Percussion* (SW)
Alderton, Stuart : *Violin* (Lon)
Aldis, Kathryn : *Melodeon* (E)
Aldis, Maddy : *Oboe* (NW)
Aldred, Clifford : *Trumpet* (E)
Aldred, Jude : *Guitars* (Lon)
Aldrich-Smith, V.J. : *Harp* (SW)
Aldridge, Chris : *Saxophones* (Mid)
Aldridge, Graham : *Guitars* (Lon)
Aldridge, Kenneth : *Percussion* (SW)
Aldridge, Luke : *Percussion* (Lon)
Aldridge, Mark : *Percussion* (Mid)
Aldwinckle, Robert : *Pianoforte* (Lon)
Alele, Henrietta : *Voice* (Lon)
Alemany, Jesus : *Trumpet* (SE)
Alexander : *Bass Guitar* (Lon)
Alexander, Andrew : *Keyboards* (Lon)
Alexander, Charles : *Guitars* (Lon)
Alexander, David : *Guitars* (NW)
Alexander, Dennis : *Guitars* (Sco)
Alexander, Drusilla : *Cello* (SE)
Alexander, Eilir : *Tuba* (SW)
Alexander, Evan : *Percussion* (Mid)
Alexander, Fred : *Violin* (Lon)
Alexander, Gill : *Double Bass* (Lon)
Alexander, Ian : *Trumpet* (SE)
Alexander, Jae : *Music Director* (Lon)
Alexander, James : *Violin* (Sco)
Alexander, Jay : *Voice* (SW)
Alexander, Jim : *Harmonica (Inc Bass* (NW)
Alexander, Kevin : *Saxophones* (Lon)
Alexander, Les : *Cornet* (Sco)
Alexander, Marina : *Viola* (Lon)
Alexander, Matthew : *Keyboards* (Mid)
Alexander, Meyrick : *Bassoon* (Lon)
Alexander, Mike : *Music Director* (Mid)
Alexander, Mike : *Pianoforte* (Mid)
Alexander, Paul : *Voice* (Mid)
Alexander, Peter : *Pianoforte* (Sco)
Alexander, Phil : *Mandolin* (Lon)
Alexander, Phil : *Pianoforte* (Lon)
Alexander, Philip : *Clarinet* (Sco)
Alexander, Ronnie : *Guitars* (Sco)
Alexander, Steve : *Percussion* (Lon)
Alexander, Tommas : *Percussion* (Lon)
Alexander, Yaz : *Voice* (Mid)
Alexander-Max, Susan : *Pianoforte* (Lon)

Alexandra, Janet : *Flute* (Lon)
Alford, Derek : *Bass Guitar* (SE)
Alford, Ruth : *Cello* (Lon)
Alford, Tim : *Guitars* (Mid)
Alfred, Marcus : *Saxophones* (SE)
Alfredsson, Vidar : *Horn* (Lon)
Algie, Ian : *Guitars* (Mid)
Ali, Cheb : *Darabouka* (Lon)
Ali, Linton : *Percussion* (NW)
Alieta, Joy : *Voice* (Lon)
Aliwell, Rick : *Guitars* (NE)
Alkema, Jan : *Percussion* (SE)
Alker, Martin : *Saxophones* (NE)
Allaby, Matthew : *Percussion* (NW)
Allain, Jan : *Voice* (Lon)
Allam, Roger : *Keyboards* (Lon)
Allan, Alistair : *Trombone* (Lon)
Allan, Alister : *Violin* (Sco)
Allan, Andrew : *Violin* (SW)
Allan, Christopher : *Cello* (Lon)
Allan, Dawn : *Voice* (Lon)
Allan, Dorothy : *Keyboards* (Lon)
Allan, Haydn : *Double Bass* (NE)
Allan, James : *Percussion* (Sco)
Allan, John : *Violin* (Lon)
Allan, Simon : *Bass Guitar* (NE)
Allard, Marie-Louise : *Voice* (Mid)
Allardyce, Darren : *Pianoforte* (NW)
Allardyce, Gavin : *Songwriter* (SE)
Allardyce, Michele : *Percussion* (SE)
Allardyce, Patricia : *Percussion* (Lon)
Allatson, Lee : *Percussion* (Mid)
Allaway, David : *Saxophones* (Lon)
Allaway, Mark : *Saxophones* (Lon)
Allcock, Garry : *Bandleader* (Mid)
Allcock, Garry : *Percussion* (Mid)
Allder, Robert : *Pianoforte* (Lon)
Alldis, Dominic : *Pianoforte* (Lon)
Allen, Alexander : *Clarinet* (Lon)
Allen, Anne : *Flute* (Lon)
Allen, Benjamin : *Guitars* (Lon)
Allen, Bryan : *Trumpet* (Mid)
Allen, Carol : *Voice* (NW)
Allen, Catherine : *Trombone* (SE)
Allen, Charles : *Guitars* (SW)
Allen, Christopher : *Percussion* (SE)
Allen, Clive : *Pianoforte* (SE)
Allen, Dave : *Organ* (SE)
Allen, David : *Voice* (NE)
Allen, Dennis : *Bass Guitar* (SE)
Allen, Edward : *Bass Guitar* (E)
Allen, Eric : *Percussion* (Lon)
Allen, Frank : *Clarinet* (Mid)
Allen, Freddie : *Percussion* (E)
Allen, George : *Pianoforte* (SW)
Allen, Geraldine : *Clarinet* (Lon)
Allen, Geraldine : *Pianoforte* (Lon)
Allen, Jay : *Percussion* (Sco)
Allen, Jeffrey : *Percussion* (Lon)
Allen, Jeremy : *Violin* (Lon)
Allen, John : *Percussion* (Lon)
Allen, John : *Clarinet* (NE)
Allen, Jon : *Voice* (NE)
Allen, Jude : *Music Director* (Lon)
Allen, Judith : *Oboe* (Lon)
Allen, Keith : *Trumpet* (NE)
Allen, Keith : *Pianoforte* (NW)
Allen, Kelly : *Keyboards* (Lon)
Allen, Leslie : *Clarinet* (Lon)
Allen, Lyn : *Voice* (Lon)
Allen, Mark : *Guitars* (SE)
Allen, Mark : *Accordion* (SW)
Allen, Martin : *Percussion* (Lon)
Allen, Michael : *Trumpet* (Lon)
Allen, Miranda : *Violin* (SW)

Allen, Norman : *Saxophones* (SE)
Allen, Paul : *Clarinet* (Lon)
Allen, Pete : *Clarinet* (SW)
Allen, Peter : *Clarinet* (Lon)
Allen, Rachel : *Violin* (Lon)
Allen, Renee : *Voice* (SW)
Allen, Richard : *Keyboards* (Lon)
Allen, Richard : *Percussion* (Lon)
Allen, Richard : *Pianoforte* (Mid)
Allen, Rob : *Songwriter* (SW)
Allen, Robert : *Keyboards* (E)
Allen, Roger : *Guitars* (SE)
Allen, Ronald : *Pianoforte* (E)
Allen, Ronald : *Organ* (Mid)
Allen, Ruth : *Voice* (Lon)
Allen, Sarah : *Flute* (Lon)
Allen, Sebastian : *Bass Guitar* (Lon)
Allen, Simon : *Percussion* (Lon)
Allen, Simon : *Percussion* (NE)
Allen, Stuart : *Clarinet* (Lon)
Allen, Sue : *Voice* (Lon)
Allen, Susan : *Violin* (Lon)
Allen, Susanna : *Saxophones* (Lon)
Allen, Thomas : *Bass Guitar* (SW)
Allen, William : *Guitars* (NW)
Allen-Smith, Catherine : *Violin* (Mid)
Allenby, Dave : *Saxophones* (NE)
Allerhand, Peter : *Guitars* (SW)
Allerton, Fred : *Saxophones* (NE)
Alley, John : *Pianoforte* (Lon)
Alleyne, Cheryl : *Percussion* (Lon)
Alleyne, Ian : *Guitars* (Lon)
Alleyne-Hughes, Perri : *Voice* (NW)
Allie, Yusef : *Guitars* (Lon)
Allin, Ralph : *Violin* (Mid)
Allis, Julie : *Harp* (Lon)
Allis, Mark : *Percussion* (Lon)
Allison, Camilla : *Violin* (Lon)
Allison, Christopher : *Clarinet* (Mid)
Allison, Darren : *Percussion* (Lon)
Allison, Finlay : *Folk Fiddle* (Sco)
Allison, Jack : *Bass Trombone* (NW)
Allison, John : *Percussion* (Lon)
Allison, Mark Blair : *Trumpet* (Mid)
Allison, Ralph : *Composer* (Lon)
Allison, Susan : *Violin* (NE)
Allman, Ben : *Guitars* (SE)
Allnatt, Michael : *Double Bass* (SW)
Allodi, Claudio : *Accordion* (Lon)
Allonby, Terry : *Guitars* (NE)
Allpass, Andrew : *Pianoforte* (SW)
Allport, Helen : *Violin* (Lon)
Allsopp, Clive : *Trombone* (Mid)
Allsopp, David : *Bass Guitar* (Mid)
Allsopp, Peter : *Pianoforte* (NE)
Allum, Cheremie : *Viola* (SW)
Allum, Robert : *Percussion* (Lon)
Allwood, Ralph : *Arranger* (SE)
Alman, Robert : *Pianoforte* (Lon)
Almond, David : *Percussion* (E)
Almond, Martin : *Pianoforte* (NW)
Almond, Peter : *Trumpet* (E)
Alo, Pete : *Keyboards* (Lon)
Alom, Samsul : *Percussion* (Lon)
Alp, Christine : *Pianoforte* (NE)
Alpert, Stephen : *Pianoforte* (Lon)
Alqueres, Gabriela : *Guitars* (Lon)
Alsaady, Ahmed : *Oud* (Lon)
Alsford, Niki : *Voice* (SE)
Alsop, Graham : *Pianoforte* (SW)
Alsop, Richard : *Double Bass* (Lon)
Alsop, Steve : *Keyboards* (NE)
Alston, Andrew : *Pianoforte* (Sco)
Alston, Pauline : *Pianoforte* (NW)
Alter, Tim : *Violin* (Lon)

Altinbas, Maria : *Voice* (NW)
Altman, Darren : *Percussion* (Lon)
Altman, John : *Saxophones* (Lon)
Alton, Tony : *Guitars* (SE)
Alty, Alison : *Oboe* (Lon)
Alvanis, Adonis : *Violin* (Lon)
Alvares, Enrico : *Violin* (Lon)
Alvey, Michael : *Pianoforte* (SW)
Alwyn, Kenneth : *Conductor* (Lon)
Alysa : *Voice* (Lon)
Alzapiedi, Dania : *Violin* (NW)
Ama, Shola : *Voice* (Lon)
Amadi, Cheru : *Keyboards* (Lon)
Amann, Timothy : *Pianoforte* (Mid)
Amanze, Ronald : *Voice* (Lon)
Amata, Karl : *Keyboards* (Lon)
Amazing Harry : *Pianoforte* (Lon)
Ambache, Diana : *Pianoforte* (Lon)
Amber Light : *Voice* (SE)
Amberg, Marie-Louise : *Violin* (Lon)
Ambler, Mark : *Pianoforte* (Lon)
Ambler, Paul : *Voice* (NE)
Ambrose, Jean : *Viola* (NW)
Ames, Keith : *Voice* (Lon)
Ames, Kenneth : *Bass Guitar* (SW)
Ames-Henderson, Brian : *Guitars* (Lon)
Amherst, Gabriel : *Cello* (Lon)
Amherst, Nigel : *Double Bass* (SW)
Amherst, Timothy : *Double Bass* (Lon)
Amick, Gabriel : *Guitars* (NW)
Amis, Stephen : *Voice* (SW)
Ammar, Morris : *Bass Guitar* (Lon)
Amon, David : *Viola* (Sco)
Amoo, Christopher : *Voice* (NW)
Amoo, Edward : *Voice* (NW)
Amos, Kevin : *Music Director* (Lon)
Amos, Richard : *Pianoforte* (Lon)
Amos, Roberta : *Horn* (SW)
Amstell, Billy : *Saxophones* (Lon)
Amu-Logotse, Gift : *African Drums* (Sco)
Andersen, Jens : *Guitars* (Sco)
Andersen, Toby : *Keyboards* (Lon)
Anderson, Adele : *Voice* (Lon)
Anderson, Alicia : *Bass Guitar* (Lon)
Anderson, Alistair : *Concertina (Inc Engl* (NE)
Anderson, Angus : *Violin* (Lon)
Anderson, April Joy : *Voice* (Lon)
Anderson, Archibald : *Guitars* (Lon)
Anderson, Billy : *Accordion* (Sco)
Anderson, Birgitte : *Voice* (NW)
Anderson, Brett : *Voice* (Lon)
Anderson, Chris : *Guitars* (E)
Anderson, Christopher : *Pianoforte* (Lon)
Anderson, Craig : *Voice* (Sco)
Anderson, D. Sutton : *Pianoforte* (Lon)
Anderson, Dave : *Trumpet* (Sco)
Anderson, David : *Guitars* (Lon)
Anderson, Emma : *Guitars* (Lon)
Anderson, Ewan : *Conductor* (NW)
Anderson, George : *Bass Guitar* (Lon)
Anderson, Gerard : *Violin* (NW)
Anderson, Graham : *Double Bass* (NE)
Anderson, Greg : *Guitars* (NE)
Anderson, Jack : *Pianoforte* (SW)
Anderson, Jamie : *Saxophones* (Lon)
Anderson, Jill : *Clarinet* (Lon)
Anderson, Jim : *Cimbasso* (Lon)
Anderson, John : *Oboe* (Lon)
Anderson, John : *Guitars* (Sco)
Anderson, Keiron : *Trumpet* (NW)
Anderson, Kevin : *Trombone* (Sco)
Anderson, Lindsay : *Voice* (SE)
Anderson, Liz : *Voice* (Lon)
Anderson, Marian : *Accordion* (Sco)
Anderson, Mary : *Violin* (NW)

Anderson, Molly : *Clarinet* (NW)
Anderson, Murray : *Percussion* (Lon)
Anderson, Paul : *Guitars* (Lon)
Anderson, Peter : *Percussion* (Sco)
Anderson, Robert (Bert) O : *Pianoforte* (Sco)
Anderson, Roderick : *Keyboards* (Lon)
Anderson, Ross : *Guitars* (Lon)
Anderson, Shaun : *Voice* (Lon)
Anderson, Stig : *Percussion* (SE)
Anderson, Stuart : *Accordion* (Sco)
Anderson, Vicki : *Voice* (Lon)
Anderson, Ziggy : *Guitars* (Lon)
Anderton, Terry : *Organ* (Mid)
Andrade, Frances : *Violin* (Lon)
Andrade, Levine : *Violin* (Lon)
Andrade, Marcelo : *Saxophones* (Lon)
Andre, David : *Saxophones* (SW)
Andre, Denis : *Trumpet* (Lon)
Andre, Eric : *Composer* (Lon)
Andreas, Louie : *Pianoforte* (E)
Andrew, Nick : *Guitars* (Lon)
Andrew, Philip : *Guitars* (Lon)
Andrew-Smith, Jenny : *Voice* (Lon)
Andrewes, Virginia : *Viola* (SE)
Andrews, Alan : *Clarinet* (Lon)
Andrews, Alan : *Violin* (Lon)
Andrews, Alan : *Trumpet* (SW)
Andrews, Andy : *Guitars* (NW)
Andrews, Christopher : *Guitars* (Lon)
Andrews, Christopher : *Trumpet* (NW)
Andrews, Darren : *Percussion* (Lon)
Andrews, Dave : *Pianoforte* (Lon)
Andrews, Edna : *Pianoforte* (SW)
Andrews, Elizabeth : *Cello* (Lon)
Andrews, Elizabeth : *Viola* (SE)
Andrews, Helen : *Voice* (NW)
Andrews, John : *Pianoforte* (Mid)
Andrews, John : *Guitars* (SE)
Andrews, Julie : *Bassoon* (Lon)
Andrews, Lea : *Voice* (Lon)
Andrews, Matthew : *Guitars* (Lon)
Andrews, Michelle : *Clarinet* (Lon)
Andrews, Peregrine : *Keyboards* (Lon)
Andrews, Stanley : *Guitars* (Lon)
Andrews, Stuart : *Pianoforte* (Lon)
Andrews, Victoria : *Saxophones* (SE)
Andrews, Wynford : *Violin* (NW)
Androvic, Stipo : *Voice* (Lon)
Andrusier, Tamar : *Pianoforte* (NW)
Anelay, Angela : *Oboe* (NE)
Angel, David : *Violin* (Lon)
Angel, Elizabeth : *Cello* (Lon)
Angelica (The Real Angelica) : *Voice* (Lon)
Angell, Frances : *Pianoforte* (Lon)
Angiama, Oroh : *Bass Guitar* (Lon)
Angilley, Neil : *Pianoforte* (Lon)
Anglim, Carlene : *Folk Fiddle* (Mid)
Anglim, Goretti : *Flute* (Lon)
Angress, Michael : *Clarinet* (Lon)
Angus, Caridad : *Voice* (Lon)
Angus, Colin : *Bass Guitar* (Lon)
Angus, John : *Violin* (Sco)
Angwin, Benjamin : *Saxophones* (Lon)
Ann : *Voice* (SW)
Ann, Vera : *Voice* (Lon)
Annand, Janet : *Harp* (Sco)
Anner, Naomi : *Violin* (Lon)
Annesley, Luke : *Saxophones* (Lon)
Ansell, Geoffrey : *Percussion* (SE)
Ansell, Martin : *Voice* (Lon)
Ansell, Peter : *Pianoforte* (E)
Ansell, Stephen : *Pianoforte* (Lon)
Ansell, Stuart : *Guitars* (Lon)
Anselm, John : *Saxophones* (SW)
Ansett, Jane : *Double Bass* (SE)

Anson : *Flute* (Lon)
Anstee, Ian : *Tuba* (NW)
Anstee, Karen : *Violin* (Lon)
Anstee, Stephen : *Cello* (Lon)
Anstee, Stuart : *Guitars* (SW)
Anstey, Kathryn : *Viola* (NW)
Anstice-Brown, Sam : *Percussion* (SW)
Anstis, Stuart : *Guitars* (Lon)
Anstiss, Hayley : *Pianoforte* (Lon)
Answer, Thomas : *Guitars* (SE)
Ant : *Guitars* (Lon)
Ant, Adam : *Voice* (Lon)
Antcliff, Andrew : *Horn* (Lon)
Antcliff, Catherine : *Bassoon* (Lon)
Anthoney, Douglas : *Guitars* (Sco)
Anthoney, Gordon : *Guitars* (Lon)
Anthoni, Mark : *Voice* (Lon)
Anthony, Charles : *Guitars* (Lon)
Anthony, Daniel : *Horn* (Lon)
Anthony, Darren : *Keyboards* (NE)
Anthony, David : *Bass Guitar* (SE)
Anthony, Gaye : *Voice* (Sco)
Anthony, Jacqueline : *Viola* (NW)
Anthony, Michael : *Percussion* (SE)
Anthony, Monica : *Composer* (Lon)
Anthony, Paul : *Keyboards* (Lon)
Anthony, Phil : *Bandleader* (E)
Antoine : *Bass Guitar* (E)
Antoine, Anita : *Guitars* (Lon)
Antonia, Philip : *Double Bass* (Lon)
Antoniades, Loucas : *Bass Guitar* (Lon)
Antonio, Trevor : *Percussion* (Lon)
Antoniou, Michael : *Pianoforte* (E)
Antrobus, Anthony : *Percussion* (NW)
Anyogu, Denyse : *Voice* (Lon)
Anzalone, Maurizio : *Voice* (Lon)
Ap Gwynedd, Peredur : *Guitars* (Lon)
Ap Gwynedd, Rheinallt : *Bass Guitar* (Lon)
Ap Sion, Pwyll : *Keyboards* (NW)
Apel, George : *Violin* (Lon)
Aphrodite : *Keyboards* (Lon)
Aplin, Albert : *Percussion* (SW)
Appapoulay, Eric : *Guitars* (Lon)
Appel, Susan : *Viola* (E)
Appleby, Bernadette : *Voice* (SW)
Appleby, Clare : *Flute* (NE)
Appleby, Colin : *Percussion* (NW)
Appleby, Kim : *Pianoforte* (Lon)
Appleby, Richard : *Bass Guitar* (SW)
Applegate, Simon J : *Conductor* (SW)
Appleton, Alan : *Percussion* (NW)
Appleton, Anna : *Cello* (E)
Appleton, Colin : *Copyist* (Lon)
Appleton, David : *Pianoforte* (Lon)
Appleton, Ian : *Trombone* (NW)
Appleton, Nigel : *Percussion* (Lon)
Appleton, Norman : *Saxophones* (E)
Appleton, Richard : *Guitars* (NE)
Applewhite, Joe : *Tympani* (Lon)
Appleyard, David : *Trumpet* (Lon)
Appleyard, Paul : *Viola* (Lon)
Apsley, Richard : *Conductor* (Lon)
Aptaker, Randolph : *Bass Guitar* (Lon)
Aqua Livi : *Voice* (SE)
Aquamanda : *Voice* (Lon)
Aquilla : *Voice* (Lon)
Arajs, Hazel : *Clarinet* (Lon)
Aralepo, Anthony : *Keyboards* (Lon)
Aram, Vicki : *Pianoforte* (Lon)
Arber, Ronald : *Percussion* (SE)
Arcari, David : *Guitars* (Sco)
Arch, David : *Keyboards* (Lon)
Archard, Joanna : *Violin* (Lon)
Archer, David : *Trumpet* (Lon)
Archer, James : *Violin* (Lon)

Archer, Martin : *Saxophones* (NE)
Archer, Mitchell : *Percussion* (Mid)
Archer, Paul : *Voice* (E)
Archer, Richard : *Pianoforte* (Mid)
Archer, Robert : *Cornet* (NE)
Archer, Tasmin : *Voice* (NE)
Archer, Yvonne : *Voice* (Lon)
Archibald, Margaret : *Clarinet* (Lon)
Archibald, Norman : *Trumpet* (Lon)
Archibald, Paul : *Trumpet* (Lon)
Ardagh-Walter, Catherine : *Cello* (Mid)
Arden, Jeremy : *Composer* (Lon)
Arden-Griffith, Paul : *Voice* (Lon)
Arden-Taylor, Paul : *Oboe* (Mid)
Ardill, Nony : *Guitars* (Lon)
Ardin, Antony : *Saxophones* (E)
Arditti, Irvine : *Violin* (Lon)
Ardley, Neil : *Composer* (Lon)
Ardron, Michael : *Violin* (NE)
Argent, Len : *Guitars* (Lon)
Argent, Rodney : *Pianoforte* (E)
Argente, Roger : *Bass Trombone* (Lon)
Argiros, Marios : *Oboe* (Lon)
Argondizza, Peter : *Guitars* (Sco)
Arguelles, Julian : *Saxophones* (Lon)
Arguelles, Steve : *Percussion* (Lon)
Arike : *Voice* (Lon)
Ariss, Nathan : *Pianoforte* (Lon)
Arkarna : *Guitars* (Lon)
Arksun : *Keyboards* (SW)
Arlan, David : *Violin* (Mid)
Arlan, F : *Bassoon* (NW)
Arlidge, Catherine : *Violin* (Mid)
Arlidge, Victoria : *Composer* (Lon)
Armatage, Justine : *Pianoforte* (Lon)
Armatrading, Joan : *Pianoforte* (Lon)
Armer, Derek : *Guitars* (SE)
Armer, Eddie : *Harmonica (Inc Bass* (Lon)
Armii, Garbi : *Voice* (Mid)
Armistead, Brian : *Guitars* (Lon)
Armistead, Paul : *Guitars* (Lon)
Armitage, David : *Clarinet* (NW)
Armitage, Shahla : *Violin* (NW)
Armon, Vaughan : *Violin* (Lon)
Armour, Bernard : *Flute* (NE)
Armour, Janie : *Pianoforte* (Lon)
Armour, Lynn : *Cello* (Sco)
Armstrong, Ann : *Clarinet* (SW)
Armstrong, Bernie : *Voice* (Lon)
Armstrong, Craig : *Pianoforte* (Sco)
Armstrong, Daniel : *Keyboards* (Mid)
Armstrong, David : *Bass Guitar* (NW)
Armstrong, Dennis : *Trumpet* (SW)
Armstrong, Jackie : *Trombone* (Lon)
Armstrong, James : *Trombone* (Sco)
Armstrong, Jason : *Guitars* (NE)
Armstrong, Kevin : *Guitars* (Lon)
Armstrong, Kevin : *Guitars* (SE)
Armstrong, Lisa : *Voice* (Lon)
Armstrong, Mark : *Trumpet* (Lon)
Armstrong, Niall : *Saxophones* (NE)
Armstrong, Norman : *Organ* (Sco)
Armstrong, Robert : *Voice* (NE)
Armstrong, Roger : *Flute* (SW)
Armstrong, Rosalie : *Pianoforte* (SW)
Armstrong, Sarah : *Saxophones* (NE)
Armstrong, Steve : *Bass Guitar* (Lon)
Armstrong, Warwick : *Oboe* (NW)
Armstrong-Wilson, Robert : *Cittern* (Sco)
Arnhold, Gerd : *Harmonica (Inc Bass* (SE)
Arnold, Alan : *Double Bass* (E)
Arnold, Benedict : *Saxophones* (Lon)
Arnold, Bert : *Saxophones* (SE)
Arnold, David : *Guitars* (E)
Arnold, David : *Music Director* (Lon)

Arnold, George : *Pianoforte* (Lon)
Arnold, Helen : *Harp* (Lon)
Arnold, Jack : *Saxophones* (Lon)
Arnold, Jamie : *Voice* (Lon)
Arnold, John : *Organ* (SE)
Arnold, Leslie : *Percussion* (E)
Arnold, Mark : *Percussion* (NE)
Arnold, Peter : *Guitars* (Mid)
Arnold, Peter : *Pianoforte* (SE)
Arnold, Simon : *Keyboards* (Mid)
Arnold, Thomas : *Percussion* (SE)
Arnold, Malcolm : *Composer* (Lon)
Arnopp, Tony : *Saxophones* (Lon)
Arnott, William : *Percussion* (Sco)
Arnouf, Jerome : *Horn* (Lon)
Arrow, Robin : *Guitars* (SW)
Arrowsmith, David : *Guitars* (Lon)
Arrowsmith, David : *Guitars* (Mid)
Arsenault, Terry : *Violin* (SE)
Artaud, Austin : *Guitars* (SE)
Arthey, Johnny : *Arranger* (Lon)
Arthur, Alan : *Guitars* (NW)
Arthur, Bruce : *Percussion* (NE)
Arthur, Edward : *Trumpet* (Lon)
Arthur, Frank : *Percussion* (NE)
Arthurs, Debbie : *Percussion* (SW)
Arthurs, Richard : *Guitars* (NE)
Arthurton, Ian : *Percussion* (Lon)
Arthy, John : *Double Bass* (Lon)
Artley, John : *Keyboards* (NE)
Artus, Margaret : *Viola* (Mid)
Ascherson, Marina : *Viola* (Lon)
Ash, Jacqueline : *Pianoforte* (SW)
Ash, Red : *Guitars* (SE)
Ash, Stephen : *Bass Guitar* (E)
Ash, Vic : *Saxophones* (Lon)
Asha-B : *Voice* (Mid)
Ashanti : *Voice* (Lon)
Ashanti, Makeeba : *Pianoforte* (Lon)
Ashby, Charles : *Percussion* (NE)
Ashby, Claire : *Violin* (Lon)
Ashby, Dawn : *Violin* (SW)
Ashby, Duncan : *Clarinet* (Lon)
Ashby, Jack : *Saxophones* (Mid)
Ashby, Rhiannon : *Cello* (SE)
Ashcombe, John : *Pianoforte* (Lon)
Ashcroft, Keith John : *Guitars* (NW)
Ashcroft, Nicholas : *Synthesiser* (NW)
Ashe, Brian : *Saxophones* (Lon)
Ashe-Roy, Hilary : *Flute* (Mid)
Ashenashae : *Percussion* (SE)
Asher, Deborah : *Voice* (Lon)
Asher, James : *Percussion* (Lon)
Asher, John : *Pianoforte* (Lon)
Asher, Peter : *Percussion* (Lon)
Ashford, Darren : *Percussion* (SE)
Ashford, Simon : *Pianoforte* (Lon)
Ashforth, S : *Bandleader* (NE)
Ashia : *Voice* (Lon)
Ashley, Carolyn : *Trombone* (NE)
Ashley, Ceri : *Saxophones* (Mid)
Ashley, Laurence : *Keyboards* (Lon)
Ashley, Steve : *Voice* (SW)
Ashman, Micky : *Double Bass* (Lon)
Ashmore, Larry : *Arranger* (Lon)
Ashmore, Richard : *Bass Trombone* (Lon)
Ashton, Adeen : *Voice* (Lon)
Ashton, Ann : *Cello* (Lon)
Ashton, Bill : *Saxophones* (Lon)
Ashton, Charlotte : *Voice* (Lon)
Ashton, David : *Bass Guitar* (Mid)
Ashton, Gwyn : *Guitars* (SE)
Ashton, Kenneth : *Accordion* (SE)
Ashton, Laura : *Oboe* (Sco)
Ashton, Peter : *Saxophones* (Mid)

Ashton, Richard : *Horn* (Lon)
Ashton, Shirley : *Voice* (Mid)
Ashton, Stephen : *Guitars* (NW)
Ashton-Wilson, Genevieve : *Voice* (SE)
Ashworth, David : *Guitars* (NE)
Ashworth, Dominic : *Guitars* (Lon)
Ashworth, Eric : *Double Bass* (SW)
Ashworth, John : *Pianoforte* (Lon)
Ashworth, Neyire : *Clarinet* (Lon)
Ashworth, Robert : *Horn* (NE)
Askem, Tracey : *Saxophones* (SE)
Askew, Caroline : *Voice* (Lon)
Askew, Katy : *Violin* (Mid)
Askew, Rebecca : *Voice* (Lon)
Askew, Roger : *Keyboards* (Lon)
Askew, Sophie : *Harp* (Sco)
Aslangul, Philip : *Cello* (Lon)
Aslin, Anita : *Harp* (NE)
Aspery, Ronald : *Saxophones* (Lon)
Aspin, David : *Viola* (Mid)
Aspinall, Norman : *Pianoforte* (SE)
Aspland, Robin : *Pianoforte* (Lon)
Asquith, Alan : *Clarinet* (NW)
Assheton, Robert : *Pianoforte* (NW)
Asta, Sally : *Voice* (SE)
Astbury, Ian : *Guitars* (Lon)
Astill, Norman : *Saxophones* (Mid)
Astle, Philip : *Early Strings* (Lon)
Astley, Carl : *Percussion* (Mid)
Astley, Jon : *Guitars* (Lon)
Astley, Rick : *Voice* (NW)
Aston, Mark : *Guitars* (Lon)
Aston, Peter : *Guitars* (SE)
Aston, Shirley : *Viola* (Mid)
Aston, Susan : *Violin* (Mid)
Astrovibe : *Bass Guitar* (Lon)
Atack, Keith : *Guitars* (Lon)
Atack, Timothy : *Keyboards* (NE)
Atar : *Pianoforte* (SE)
Atchinson, Mark : *Saxophones* (SE)
Atchison, Robert : *Violin* (Lon)
Atha, Graham : *Guitars* (Lon)
Atherton, Duncan : *Violin* (NW)
Atherton, Jack : *Viola* (NW)
Atherton, Joan : *Violin* (Lon)
Atherton, Mark : *Keyboards* (Sco)
Atherton, Naomi : *Horn* (NW)
Atherton, Paul : *Guitars* (NW)
Atkins, Andrew : *Music Director* (Lon)
Atkins, Anthony : *Guitars* (Lon)
Atkins, Jane : *Viola* (Lon)
Atkins, Joe : *Trumpet* (Lon)
Atkins, Lorraine : *Horn* (SE)
Atkins, Malcolm : *Pianoforte* (SE)
Atkins, Matthew : *Percussion* (Lon)
Atkins, Richard : *Non Playing Member* (Mid)
Atkins, Stephen : *Guitars* (SW)
Atkinson, Alistair : *Keyboards* (NE)
Atkinson, Arthur : *Trombone* (NE)
Atkinson, Christopher : *Clarinet* (Lon)
Atkinson, Cliff : *Pianoforte* (Lon)
Atkinson, Gary : *Guitars* (NW)
Atkinson, Georgina : *Pianoforte* (Lon)
Atkinson, Jane : *Violin* (SW)
Atkinson, Jonathan : *Percussion* (Lon)
Atkinson, Joseph : *Trumpet* (Lon)
Atkinson, Julia : *Violin* (Lon)
Atkinson, Julian : *Double Bass* (Mid)
Atkinson, Martin : *Guitars* (SE)
Atkinson, Neil : *Percussion* (NE)
Atkinson, Nigel : *Voice* (Lon)
Atkinson, Paul : *Bass Guitar* (SE)
Atkinson, Richard : *Pianoforte* (Lon)
Atkinson, Richard : *Bass Guitar* (SW)
Atkinson, Robert : *Pianoforte* (Mid)

Bergelodt, Rune : *Bass Guitar* (Lon)
Bergersen, Elisa : *Violin* (E)
Bergin, John : *Violin* (SW)
Bergin, Johnny : *Organ* (SE)
Bergin, Mary : *Cello* (Lon)
Berglund, Kjell : *Trumpet* (SE)
Berkley, Gerald : *Percussion* (SE)
Berkovitch, Valerie : *Pianoforte* (Lon)
Berlin, Maria : *Voice* (Lon)
Berlyn, Alan : *Trumpet* (Lon)
Bern, Deborah : *Voice* (Lon)
Bernard, Joe : *Bass Guitar* (E)
Bernard, Paul : *Voice* (Lon)
Bernard, Richard : *Voice* (SE)
Bernardi, Alessandro : *Voice* (Lon)
Bernardi, Andrew : *Violin* (Lon)
Bernardin, Jim : *Percussion* (NW)
Bernasconi, Justin : *Guitars* (E)
Bernez : *Guitars* (Lon)
Bernhardt, Oscar : *Voice* (NW)
Bernstein, Howard : *Percussion* (Lon)
Berown, Nico : *Mandolin* (Lon)
Berreen, Angela : *Viola* (Lon)
Berridge, Andrew : *Violin* (NE)
Berridge, Cara : *Cello* (NE)
Berridge, Mike : *Keyboards* (E)
Berriman, James : *Voice* (Mid)
Berriman, Michael : *Bass Guitar* (E)
Berriman, Simonne : *Voice* (E)
Berrow, Mark : *Violin* (Lon)
Berry, Alan : *Pianoforte* (Lon)
Berry, Alan : *Pianoforte* (Mid)
Berry, Alison : *Pianoforte* (Lon)
Berry, Colin : *Voice* (NW)
Berry, David : *Bass Guitar* (Lon)
Berry, Gillian : *Violin* (SW)
Berry, John : *Bass Guitar* (Lon)
Berry, John : *Trombone* (SW)
Berry, Joseph : *Double Bass* (Lon)
Berry, Richard : *Guitars* (Lon)
Berry, Richard : *Horn* (Lon)
Berry, Ronnie : *Guitars* (Sco)
Berry, Stephen : *Double Bass* (Lon)
Berry, Wendy : *Flute* (Lon)
Berry, William : *Violin* (Sco)
Berryman, Andrew : *Trombone* (NW)
Berryman, Evan : *Guitars* (Lon)
Berryman, Peter : *Guitars* (SW)
Bersey, James : *Composer* (Lon)
Bersey, William : *Cello* (Lon)
Bersin, Michael : *Guitars* (NE)
Bertelli, Carlo : *Violin* (Sco)
Berthon, Darell : *Percussion* (Sco)
Berthoud, Caroline H : *Violin* (SE)
Berthoud, Mahrey : *Folk Fiddle* (SE)
Berthoud, Philip : *Folk Fiddle* (SE)
Bertram, Simon : *Organ* (Sco)
Bespoke Music : *Guitars* (Lon)
Bessell, John : *Oboe* (Lon)
Bessem, Theo : *Voice* (Lon)
Best, Andrew : *Bass Guitar* (SW)
Best, Bobbie : *Voice* (SE)
Best, Hubert : *Organ* (Lon)
Best, Jane : *Voice* (Lon)
Best, Joan : *Violin* (Mid)
Best, Lorraine : *Voice* (SW)
Best, Martin : *Voice* (Lon)
Best, Matthew : *Percussion* (Lon)
Best, Roger : *Viola* (Lon)
Best, Steve : *Bass Guitar* (SE)
Beston, Nick : *Saxophones* (Lon)
Beswick, John : *Conductor* (SW)
Bethel, Mark : *Cello* (Lon)
Bethell, Brian : *Bass Guitar* (Lon)
Bethge, Deitrich : *Cello* (Lon)

Betley, Peter : *Trumpet* (SW)
Bettaney, Stephen : *Violin* (Lon)
Betteridge, Lisa : *Violin* (SW)
Betteridge, Stephen : *Pianoforte* (Lon)
Bettison, Michael : *Melodeon* (NE)
Bettle, Peter : *Saxophones* (SW)
Betton, Natasha : *Keyboards* (Lon)
Betts, Andrew : *Pianoforte* (Mid)
Betts, John : *Pianoforte* (Mid)
Betts, Kevin : *Guitars* (E)
Betts, Michael : *Clarinet* (SE)
Betts, Michaela : *Pianoforte* (Lon)
Betts, Nicholas : *Trumpet* (Lon)
Betts, Paul : *Bass Guitar* (SE)
Betts, Robert : *Bassoon* (E)
Beukes, Gina : *Violin* (Lon)
Beuttler, Francis : *Tympani* (E)
Bevan, Arthur : *Horn* (NW)
Bevan, Catriona : *Cello* (SE)
Bevan, Christopher : *Violin* (Lon)
Bevan, Clifford : *Tuba* (Lon)
Bevan, Cyril : *Percussion* (SE)
Bevan, Louise : *Violin* (Lon)
Bevan, Paul : *Trombone* (Lon)
Bevan, Sydney : *Pianoforte* (SE)
Beveridge, Tim : *Flute* (NE)
Bevir, Thomas : *Double Bass* (SW)
Bevis, Suzanne : *Harp* (SE)
Bewick, John : *Saxophones* (Mid)
Bewley, Linus : *Saxophones* (Lon)
Beynon, Catherine : *Harp* (Lon)
Beynon, Darren : *Trumpet* (Sco)
Beynon, Emily : *Flute* (Lon)
Bezer, Terry : *Bass Guitar* (Lon)
Bezkorvany, Sergei : *Violin* (Lon)
Beznosiuk, Lisa : *Early Wind* (Mid)
Bhaduri, Reba : *Voice* (NW)
Bhajihead, Bavid : *Guitars* (NE)
Bhamrah, Kulwant : *Keyboards* (Mid)
Bhattacharjee, Nicholas : *Flute* (NW)
Bialas, Antonina : *Violin* (Lon)
Bianchi, Mike : *Saxophones* (Lon)
Bianco, Anthony : *Percussion* (Lon)
Biancofiore, Michele : *Guitars* (Lon)
Bibby, Arnold : *Saxophones* (Lon)
Bibby, Clifford : *Violin* (NW)
Bibby, David : *Double Bass* (E)
Bibby, Robin : *Pianoforte* (SE)
Bibi, Robin : *Guitars* (Lon)
Bick, Mark : *Guitars* (SW)
Bickel, Maya : *Violin* (Lon)
Bickerdike, John : *Trumpet* (Mid)
Bickersteth, John : *Keyboards* (SW)
Bickerton, Wayne : *Guitars* (Lon)
Bicket, Harry : *Conductor* (Lon)
Bickford, John : *Folk Fiddle* (SW)
Bicknell, Susan : *Viola* (Lon)
Bidder, Helena : *Oboe* (NW)
Biddle, Georgina : *Violin* (NE)
Biddu-Biddu : *Guitars* (Lon)
Biddulph, Frank : *Violin* (Lon)
Biddulph, Richard : *Guitars* (Lon)
Bidmead, John : *Keyboards* (NW)
Bielby, Laurie : *Saxophones* (Lon)
Bielby, Nigel : *Viola* (Lon)
Big Steve : *Guitars* (Lon)
Bigden, Alf : *Percussion* (Lon)
Biggin, Peter : *Percussion* (NE)
Biggin, Tony : *Composer* (NW)
Biggins, John : *Trumpet* (NE)
Biggs, Brett : *Percussion* (NE)
Biggs, Mihaly : *Double Bass* (Lon)
Bigham, Edward : *Percussion* (Lon)
Bigley, Roger : *Viola* (NW)
Bignall, Wilton : *Guitars* (Lon)

Bigwood, Mark : *Guitars* (SE)
Bilbo : *Percussion* (Lon)
Bilbrough, Dave : *Guitars* (Lon)
Bilham, Colin : *Double Bass* (Lon)
Bilham, Roy : *Trumpet* (Lon)
Bilk, Acker : *Clarinet* (Lon)
Bill, Douglas : *Saxophones* (Mid)
Bill, Keith : *Pianoforte* (Mid)
Billany, Martin : *Voice* (Lon)
Billett, Adrian : *Guitars* (Lon)
Billing, Jane : *Pianoforte* (Lon)
Billingham, Edward : *Guitars* (SE)
Billingham, Tony : *Saxophones* (Mid)
Billington, Anna : *Flute* (Mid)
Bills, Heather : *Cello* (NW)
Bilson, Robert : *Violin* (Mid)
Bimson, Gareth : *Trumpet* (Lon)
Binch, Barry : *Trumpet* (Lon)
Binding, Judith : *Pianoforte* (SE)
Binding, Philip : *Keyboards* (Lon)
Binelli, Mickey : *Accordion* (Lon)
Bing, David : *Guitars* (Lon)
Bingham, Ruth : *Cello* (NW)
Bingham, Steve : *Bass Guitar* (Lon)
Bingley, Del : *Bandleader* (Lon)
Binks, Elizabeth : *Violin* (Lon)
Binks, Les : *Percussion* (Lon)
Binney, Helena : *Cello* (Lon)
Binnie, Anne : *Cello* (Sco)
Binns, Anthony : *Voice* (Lon)
Binns, Catherine : *Pianoforte* (NE)
Binns, Christopher : *Pianoforte* (NE)
Binns, Henry : *Keyboards* (Lon)
Binns, Kerry : *Guitars* (Lon)
Binns, Timothy : *Keyboards* (Lon)
Biola : *Voice* (Lon)
Bip, Mr : *Keyboards* (E)
Birch, Bramwell : *Trombone* (Mid)
Birch, Buster : *Percussion* (Lon)
Birch, Catherine : *Pianoforte* (E)
Birch, Gina : *Songwriter* (Lon)
Birch, Henry : *Violin* (Mid)
Birch, John : *Organ* (Lon)
Birch, John : *Saxophones* (Lon)
Birch, John : *Guitars* (Mid)
Birch, Lachie : *Percussion* (Sco)
Birch, Michael : *Trumpet* (SE)
Birch, Robert : *Trumpet* (Mid)
Birchall, Hamish : *Percussion* (Lon)
Birchall, Kate : *Violin* (Lon)
Bircher, Katy : *Early Wind* (Lon)
Bird, Adam : *Pianoforte* (Lon)
Bird, Anthony : *Keyboards* (SE)
Bird, Bobby : *Guitars* (Mid)
Bird, David : *Keyboards* (Lon)
Bird, Denise : *Organ* (Lon)
Bird, Diane : *Percussion* (NW)
Bird, Gillian : *Horn* (Lon)
Bird, Ian : *Saxophones* (Lon)
Bird, John : *Violin* (Mid)
Bird, Mary : *Violin* (NW)
Bird, Philip : *Pianoforte* (Lon)
Bird, Richard : *Guitars* (Mid)
Bird, Robert : *Pianoforte* (Lon)
Bird, Robert : *Violin* (SW)
Bird, Stephen : *Keyboards* (Mid)
Bird, Tim : *Percussion* (Mid)
Biring, Rena : *Voice* (Lon)
Birkby, Peter : *Percussion* (NW)
Birkett, Christopher : *Guitars* (Lon)
Birkett, James : *Guitars* (NE)
Birkinshaw, Celia : *Bassoon* (Lon)
Birkinshaw, Roy : *Accordion* (Lon)
Birks, Heather : *Viola* (Lon)
Birnbaum, Leo : *Viola* (Lon)

Birnie, Stuart : *Tuba* (Mid)
Birnstingl, Roger : *Bassoon* (Lon)
Biro, Daniel : *Keyboards* (Lon)
Birrane, James : *Guitars* (NW)
Birse, Moira : *Violin* (Sco)
Birt, Andrew : *Guitars* (SW)
Birtchnell, Una : *Cello* (Lon)
Birtles, Gary : *Saxophones* (Mid)
Birtles, Rachel : *Flute* (NW)
Birtwistle, Stephen : *Saxophones* (NW)
Birznieks, Robert : *Bass Guitar* (SE)
Biscoe, Christopher : *Saxophones* (Lon)
Bisengaliev, Stina : *Flute* (NE)
Bishop, Adrian : *Pianoforte* (Lon)
Bishop, Ann : *Bassoon* (NE)
Bishop, Anthony : *Bass Guitar* (E)
Bishop, Caroline : *Violin* (Lon)
Bishop, Charlotte : *Cello* (NE)
Bishop, Chiz : *Organ* (SE)
Bishop, David : *Saxophones* (Lon)
Bishop, David : *Pianoforte* (Mid)
Bishop, Derek : *Trombone* (Sco)
Bishop, Helen : *Clarinet* (Lon)
Bishop, Jake : *Guitars* (SE)
Bishop, John : *Saxophones* (Mid)
Bishop, Jonathan : *Guitars* (Lon)
Bishop, Julia : *Violin* (SE)
Bishop, Pamela : *Concertina (Inc Engl* (Mid)
Bishop, Paul : *Banjo* (SE)
Bishop, Robert : *Violin* (Lon)
Bishop, Roland : *Latin American Percu* (SE)
Bishop, Ronald : *Percussion* (Lon)
Bishop, Sean : *Viola* (Lon)
Bishop, Sharon : *Organ* (NE)
Bishop, Susan : *Clarinet* (Lon)
Biss, Hannah : *Violin* (Lon)
Bissell, Christine : *Pianoforte* (NW)
Bissill, Richard : *Horn* (Lon)
Bissonnette, Big Bill : *Trombone* (Lon)
Bissonnette, Sarah : *Saxophones* (Lon)
Biswas, Anup : *Cello* (Lon)
Biswas, Kingusk : *Bass Guitar* (Lon)
Bitelli, David : *Saxophones* (Lon)
Bithel, Karen : *Violin* (NE)
Bixley, Susan : *Percussion* (Lon)
Bizzi : *Keyboards* (Mid)
Black, Adrienne : *Harpsichord* (Lon)
Black, Barry : *Percussion* (NE)
Black, Bryony : *Horn* (NE)
Black, Catherine : *Cello* (Lon)
Black, Catherine : *Violin* (SW)
Black, Daniel : *Voice* (Lon)
Black, David : *Saxophones* (NE)
Black, David : *Percussion* (SE)
Black, Dominic : *Double Bass* (Lon)
Black, Donald : *Harmonica (Inc Bass* (Sco)
Black, Douglas : *Percussion* (NW)
Black, Emma : *Cello* (Lon)
Black, Ian : *Oboe* (Lon)
Black, Ian : *Pianoforte* (Sco)
Black, Jim : *Bass Guitar* (E)
Black, Julia : *Early Strings* (NW)
Black, Kenneth : *Double Bass* (Sco)
Black, Lindsay : *Percussion* (SW)
Black, Martin : *Percussion* (SE)
Black, Matt : *Keyboards* (NW)
Black, Matthew : *Guitars* (Mid)
Black, Neil : *Oboe* (Lon)
Black, Nigel : *Horn* (Lon)
Black, Susan : *Viola* (SE)
Blackadder, David : *Trumpet* (Mid)
Blackburn, Anthony : *Percussion* (Lon)
Blackburn, Jane : *Voice* (Lon)
Blackford, Norman : *Keyboards* (Lon)
Blackham, Robert : *Guitars* (Lon)

Blacklock, Ian : *Percussion* (Sco)
Blackman, Brenda : *Voice* (SE)
Blackman, Daniel : *Guitars* (E)
Blackman, Robert : *Guitars* (Lon)
Blackman, Sharon : *Voice* (SE)
Blackmark : *Keyboards* (Lon)
Blackmore, David : *Saxophones* (Lon)
Blackmore, Judith : *Saxophones* (Lon)
Blackmore, Julian : *Pianoforte* (NE)
Blackstock, Kenneth : *Percussion* (NW)
Blackwell, Amanda : *Voice* (SW)
Blackwell, John : *Guitars* (Lon)
Blackwell, Llewellyn : *Guitars* (E)
Blackwell, Mark : *Bass Guitar* (Mid)
Blackwell, Martin : *Pianoforte* (Lon)
Blackwell, Susan : *Bassoon* (NE)
Blackwood, Kenneth : *Horn* (Sco)
Blackwood, Peter : *Pianoforte* (Lon)
Blackwood, William : *Clarinet* (Sco)
Bladen, Anthony : *Violin* (SW)
Blades, Glenroy : *Percussion* (Lon)
Blades, James : *Percussion* (Lon)
Blades, Thomas : *Guitars* (Lon)
Blagrove, Stephen : *African Drums* (Lon)
Blaikley, Alan : *Composer* (Lon)
Blain, J : *Percussion* (E)
Blair, Christine : *Pianoforte* (Lon)
Blair, Derek : *Vibraphone* (SE)
Blair, Ellen : *Violin* (Lon)
Blair, Gerry : *Guitars* (Lon)
Blair, Robert : *Voice* (Sco)
Blair, Roger : *Percussion* (Lon)
Blair, Sandy : *Tuba* (NW)
Blair, Susan : *Harp* (Lon)
Blair, Walter : *Pianoforte* (Sco)
Blaisdon, Jim : *Guitars* (Mid)
Blak Spice : *Club DJ* (Mid)
Blake, Adam : *Guitars* (Lon)
Blake, Anna : *Bassoon* (Lon)
Blake, Brian : *Clarinet* (SE)
Blake, George : *Percussion* (SE)
Blake, Howard : *Pianoforte* (Lon)
Blake, Jacqueline : *Voice* (Lon)
Blake, Jerome : *Bass Guitar* (Lon)
Blake, Julie : *Saxophones* (Lon)
Blake, Karl : *Guitars* (Lon)
Blake, Katharine : *Voice* (Lon)
Blake, Michael : *Trumpet* (SW)
Blake, Peter : *Horn* (Lon)
Blake, Richard : *Guitars* (Lon)
Blake, Rod : *Guitars* (Lon)
Blake, Tim : *Synthesiser* (Lon)
Blake, Wayne : *Pianoforte* (Mid)
Blakely, John : *Percussion* (Sco)
Blakeman, Edward : *Flute* (E)
Blakemore, Karen : *Trumpet* (Mid)
Blanchard, Christine : *Pianoforte* (SW)
Blanchard, John : *Percussion* (Lon)
Blanchard, John : *Cello* (SE)
Blanchard, Lee : *Pianoforte* (SE)
Blanchard, Mark : *Bass Guitar* (Lon)
Blanchard, Richard : *Percussion* (NE)
Blanchflower, Oliver : *Double Bass* (Lon)
Bland, Bill : *African Drums* (Lon)
Bland, Richard : *Bass Guitar* (SW)
Blandamer, Stewart : *Saxophones* (Lon)
Blanden, Noel : *Percussion* (Lon)
Blank, Niklas : *Guitars* (Mid)
Blanken, Robert : *Clarinet* (SE)
Blannin, Peter : *Double Bass* (E)
Blanthorn, Susan : *Viola* (Mid)
Blasdale, Susan : *Violin* (Sco)
Blatchly, Duke : *Saxophones* (Lon)
Blay, Bernard : *Violin* (E)
Blayden, Alastair : *Cello* (Lon)

Blayden, Richard : *Violin* (Lon)
Bleach, Julian : *Violin* (Lon)
Bleasby, Keith : *Percussion* (Lon)
Bleasdale, John : *Pianoforte* (NW)
Bleasdale, Keith : *Trombone* (Lon)
Blee, Michael : *Viola* (Lon)
Blegvad, Peter : *Guitars* (Lon)
Blencowe, Ju : *Electric Piano* (Mid)
Blendis, Simon : *Violin* (Lon)
Blennerhassett, James : *Double Bass* (Lon)
Blew, Douglas : *Viola* (SE)
Blewett, Lorna : *Oboe* (SW)
Blewett, Suzanne : *Flute* (SW)
Blezard, William : *Music Director* (Lon)
Blinkhorn, Anna : *Violin* (NW)
Bliss : *Keyboards* (Lon)
Bliss, Paul Steven : *Synthesiser* (Lon)
Bliss, Vic : *Keyboards* (E)
Blissett, Andrew : *Pianoforte* (SE)
Blissett, Winston : *Bass Guitar* (Lon)
Bloch, Nicholas : *Guitars* (Lon)
Block, Brandon : *Percussion* (Lon)
Blockley, Dale : *Flute* (SW)
Bloggs, Steve : *Guitars* (SW)
Blomberg, David : *Guitars* (SE)
Blomberg, Philip Suen : *Bass Guitar* (Mid)
Blomeley, Mark : *Guitars* (NW)
Blomfield, Jim : *Pianoforte* (SW)
Blomiley, Nigel : *Cello* (Lon)
Blood, Christopher : *Trumpet* (NE)
Blood, Steven : *Keyboards* (Lon)
Bloom, Bernie : *Pianoforte* (Lon)
Bloomfield, Damian : *Bass Guitar* (NW)
Bloomfield, Steve : *Guitars* (Lon)
Bloor, Martin : *Viola* (NW)
Blore, Simon : *Trumpet* (Lon)
Blount, Matthew : *Pianoforte* (Mid)
Bloxwich, Janet : *Bassoon* (Sco)
Bloy, Graham : *Songwriter* (SW)
Blue : *Voice* (Lon)
Blue, Barry : *Bass Guitar* (Lon)
Blue, John : *Viola* (Sco)
Blue, Rikki : *Keyboards* (Lon)
Bluglass, Charles : *Guitars* (NW)
Blume, Norbert : *Viola* (Lon)
Blundell, Christopher : *Tympani* (Lon)
Blunn, Nick : *Pianoforte* (Mid)
Blunt, Alison : *Violin* (Lon)
Blyth, Terry : *Bass Guitar* (Lon)
Blythe, Andrea : *Voice* (Mid)
Blythe, Astrid : *Violin* (Sco)
Blythe, Hilary : *Voice* (NE)
Boa, David : *Trumpet* (Lon)
Boaden, Victoria : *Double Bass* (Lon)
Boag, David : *Folk Fiddle* (Sco)
Boakes, Stephen : *DiDJeridu* (Lon)
Boaks, Georgina : *Copyist* (Lon)
Boardman, Bruce : *Keyboards* (Lon)
Boardman, Claire : *Voice* (Lon)
Boardman, Dave : *Guitars* (NW)
Boardman, Helen : *Violin* (NW)
Boateng, Danny : *Bass Guitar* (Lon)
Boateng, Wilson : *Voice* (Lon)
Bobba Black Star : *Guitars* (Lon)
Bochmann, Michael : *Violin* (Mid)
Bocking, Katherine : *Violin* (SE)
Boddice, Nigel : *Conductor* (Sco)
Boddington, Joanne : *Flute* (NW)
Boddis, Walter : *Cello* (NW)
Boddy, Paul : *Keyboards* (SE)
Boddy, Suzi : *Saxophones* (E)
Boden, Daphne : *Harp* (Lon)
Boden, Paul : *Trombone* (Mid)
Bodenham, Harry : *Guitars* (Mid)
Bodger, Phil : *Percussion* (Lon)

467

Bodger, Ruth : *Violin* (SW)
Bodimead, Caroline : *Violin* (Mid)
Bodin, Jesper : *Guitars* (Lon)
Bodnar, Andrew : *Bass Guitar* (Lon)
Bodnar, Emese : *Cello* (Lon)
Body, Caroline : *Flute* (Lon)
Boenders, Elizabeth : *Violin* (Lon)
Boffey, Graham : *Percussion* (Mid)
Boffy, Jack : *Trumpet* (Mid)
Bogen, Joel : *Guitars* (Lon)
Bogie, Frank : *Guitars* (Lon)
Bogle, David : *Violin* (Lon)
Bogomas, Nina : *Harp* (Lon)
Bohling, Sue : *Oboe* (Lon)
Bohonek, Judith : *Cello* (Sco)
Bohonek, Vaclav : *Violin* (Sco)
Boita, Peter : *Percussion* (Lon)
Bolam, Frank : *Guitars* (Sco)
Bolam, Ken : *Pianoforte* (Lon)
Bolam, Sharon : *Voice* (Sco)
Bolan, Sean : *Cornet* (Mid)
Boland, Gabriel : *Voice* (SE)
Boland, Greg : *Guitars* (Lon)
Bold, Andrew : *Percussion* (NW)
Bold, David : *Guitars* (Lon)
Bolger, Leslie : *Guitars* (NW)
Bolger, Lorraine : *Cello* (Lon)
Bolingbroke, Paula : *Pianoforte* (SE)
Bolt, Rachel : *Viola* (Lon)
Bolte, Barbara : *Oboe* (Lon)
Bolton, Cecil : *Arranger* (Lon)
Bolton, David : *Trumpet* (E)
Bolton, Graham : *Trombone* (Lon)
Bolton, Ivor : *Harpsichord* (Lon)
Bolton, Malcolm : *Violin* (Sco)
Bolton, Norman : *Pianoforte* (NW)
Bolton, Richard : *Guitars* (Lon)
Bolton, Roger : *Guitars* (Lon)
Bolton, Steve : *Guitars* (Lon)
Boltz, Michael : *Pianoforte* (E)
Bolwell, Laurence : *Voice* (SE)
Bolwell, Tim : *Trumpet* (Lon)
Bomber, Ray : *Clarinet* (E)
Bome, Helen : *Violin* (E)
Bonacci, Cristina : *Guitars* (Lon)
Bond, Alexander : *Guitars* (Lon)
Bond, Christine : *Double Bass* (Lon)
Bond, Gary : *Trumpet* (Mid)
Bond, Geoffrey : *Percussion* (NW)
Bond, Gordon : *Bass Guitar* (Lon)
Bond, Paul : *Guitars* (Lon)
Bond, Peter : *Guitars* (NW)
Bond, Philip : *Guitars* (Lon)
Bond, Roger : *Saxophones* (SW)
Bond, Ronnie : *Guitars* (Lon)
Bond, Rupert : *Double Bass* (Lon)
Bondonno, Alessandro : *Clarinet* (Lon)
Bonds, Fiona : *Viola* (Lon)
Bone, David : *Bass Trombone* (Sco)
Bone, Ian : *Violin* (NW)
Bone, Steven : *Saxophones* (NE)
Bone, T : *Trombone* (E)
Bonett, Kevin : *Percussion* (SE)
Bonetti, Angela : *Viola* (Lon)
Bonfield, Neil : *Guitars* (Lon)
Bonfils, Khan : *Voice* (Lon)
Bonga, Ntshukumo : *Saxophones* (Lon)
Bongay, Hassan : *Voice* (Mid)
Bongo Billy : *Latin American Percu* (Lon)
Bonham, Jason : *Percussion* (Lon)
Bonham-Carter, Thomas : *Violin* (Lon)
Bonham-Carter, Amber : *Viola* (Lon)
Bonner, Natalia : *Violin* (Lon)
Bonner, Paul : *Trumpet* (Lon)
Bonner, Sam : *Voice* (Lon)

Bonney, Alex : *Trumpet* (Lon)
Bonney, Gordon : *Saxophones* (NW)
Bonney, Helen : *Pianoforte* (E)
Bono : *Voice* (Lon)
Bonodi, Lorenzo : *Guitars* (Lon)
Bonser, Jack : *Saxophones* (Lon)
Bonson, Lloyd : *Keyboards* (E)
Bonwick, Michael : *Bass Guitar* (NW)
Bonzo, Alanzo : *Voice* (Mid)
Boobyer, Keith : *Percussion* (SW)
Boocock, Kathleen : *Violin* (NW)
Booga : *Guitars* (E)
Bookbinder, Laura : *Flute* (E)
Booker, Jack : *Pianoforte* (NW)
Booker, Peter : *Keyboards* (Lon)
Booker, Stephen : *Voice* (Lon)
Bool, Helen P : *Percussion* (Mid)
Boole-Masterson, Naomi : *Cello* (Mid)
Boomer : *Saxophones* (Lon)
Boonham, John : *Organ* (Mid)
Boorer, Jeffrey : *Clarinet* (SW)
Boorer, Martin : *Guitars* (Lon)
Boorer, Steven : *Percussion* (Lon)
Boorman, Peter : *Organ* (Lon)
Booroff, Stephane : *Percussion* (SE)
Booth, Barry : *Pianoforte* (Lon)
Booth, Blair : *Voice* (Lon)
Booth, Brian : *Tympani* (Lon)
Booth, Donald : *Keyboards* (SW)
Booth, Elizabeth : *Cello* (Lon)
Booth, Jane : *Clarinet* (Lon)
Booth, Jeffrey : *Violin* (SW)
Booth, John : *Percussion* (NW)
Booth, Judith : *Guitars* (Lon)
Booth, Matthew : *Trumpet* (Lon)
Booth, Maxine : *Voice* (Lon)
Booth, Paul : *Saxophones* (SE)
Booth, Rick : *Guitars* (E)
Booth, Timothy : *Voice* (NW)
Booth, Trevor : *Violin* (NE)
Booth, V Gerard : *Tuba* (NW)
Boothby, Hannah : *Bass Guitar* (Mid)
Boothroyd, Edward : *Violin* (NW)
Boothroyd, Nicholas : *Cello* (Lon)
Boothroyd, Ralph : *Violin* (SW)
Booty, Jonathan : *Flute* (NW)
Boparai, Harjinder : *Keyboards* (Mid)
Boreham, Daniel : *Guitars* (SE)
Borenius, Louis : *Percussion* (SE)
Borez, William : *Keyboards* (Lon)
Borg Wheeler, Philip : *Violin* (SE)
Borges, Matthew : *Violin* (E)
Boris : *Balalaika* (NW)
Borjanic, Dusan : *Guitars* (Lon)
Borland, Denise : *Voice* (Sco)
Bornet, Adrian : *Double Bass* (Sco)
Boros, Gabor K : *Double Bass* (Lon)
Boros, Tomi : *Violin* (Lon)
Borowiecki, Teddy : *Pianoforte* (Lon)
Borowski, George : *Guitars* (Lon)
Borrell, Paula : *Saxophones* (Lon)
Borthwick, Dickie : *Organ* (SW)
Borthwick, John : *Double Bass* (Lon)
Borthwick, Margaret : *Flute* (NE)
Borthwick, Morgan : *Organ* (NW)
Borthwick, Shirley : *Voice* (NW)
Borthwick, Sophia : *Viola* (Lon)
Bortoft, Tim : *Organ* (NE)
Borzymowska, Izabela : *Pianoforte* (SE)
Bosca, Kreama : *Voice* (Lon)
Bosch, Leon : *Double Bass* (Lon)
Bose, Jonathan : *Percussion* (Lon)
Bosher, Edward : *Cello* (Mid)
Bosman, Andre : *Guitars* (E)
Bostock, David : *Saxophones* (Lon)

Boston, Bill : *Saxophones* (Lon)
Boston, Jonny : *Clarinet* (Lon)
Boswell, Peter : *Trumpet* (NE)
Bosworth, Norris : *Viola* (Lon)
Botham, Stephen : *Guitars* (NW)
Botschinsky, Allan : *Trumpet* (Lon)
Bott, Douglas : *Violin* (SW)
Botterell, Jack : *Trombone* (Lon)
Botterill, Michael : *Guitars* (SW)
Botting, Stephen : *Trombone* (Lon)
Bottom, Richard : *Guitars* (Lon)
Bottomley, David : *Pianoforte* (NE)
Bottomley, Lynne : *Horn* (Mid)
Bottomley, Ronald : *Percussion* (NE)
Bottrill, Andrew : *Pianoforte* (SE)
Botwright, Valerie : *Double Bass* (Lon)
Bouchaux, Axel : *Double Bass* (Lon)
Boucher, Alex : *Percussion* (E)
Boucher, Paul : *Violin* (Lon)
Boucherat, Vivienne : *Voice* (SE)
Bougie : *Double Bass* (Lon)
Bouic, Christian : *Guitars* (Lon)
Bould, Miles : *Percussion* (Lon)
Boult, Geoffrey : *Trumpet* (Sco)
Boult, Robin : *Guitars* (Lon)
Boulter, Ian : *Bass Trombone* (NW)
Boulton, David : *Northumbrian Pipes* (SE)
Boulton, Phil : *Organ* (Mid)
Boulton, Tim : *Viola* (Lon)
Bound, Andrew : *Cello* (Mid)
Bounford, Isobel : *Violin* (Mid)
Bourgeois, Jean : *Violin* (Lon)
Bourke, Stan : *Percussion* (Lon)
Bourke, Tony : *Percussion* (Lon)
Bourn, Richard : *Horn* (NW)
Bourne, Josephine : *Voice* (SE)
Bourne, Robin : *Saxophones* (Lon)
Bourne, Sue : *Flute* (NE)
Bourton, Robert : *Bassoon* (Lon)
Bousfield, Ian : *Trombone* (Lon)
Bousie, Mark : *Accordion* (Lon)
Boustead, Alan : *Copyist* (Lon)
Boustead, Peter : *Saxophones* (Lon)
Boutwood, Daniel : *Guitars* (Lon)
Bouvy, Yves : *Flute* (Lon)
Bouzida, Nasser : *Percussion* (SE)
Bowater, Ronnie : *Pianoforte* (Lon)
Bowden, Alex : *Saxophones* (SE)
Bowden, Colin : *Percussion* (E)
Bowden, Eric : *Saxophones* (NW)
Bowden, Graham : *Percussion* (Mid)
Bowden, James : *Percussion* (Lon)
Bowden, Richard : *Guitars* (SE)
Bowden, Ronald : *Percussion* (Lon)
Bowden, Thomas : *Bass Guitar* (SE)
Bowditch, Simon : *Trombone* (SW)
Bowdler, Bill : *Percussion* (Mid)
Bowdler, Heidi : *Horn* (Lon)
Bowdler, John : *Organ* (NW)
Bowdler, Lenore : *Voice* (SE)
Bowe, Ella : *Violin* (Lon)
Bowell, Mary : *Cello* (NE)
Bowen, Andrew : *Bass Guitar* (NE)
Bowen, Colin : *Bass Trombone* (Sco)
Bowen, David : *Clarinet* (SW)
Bowen, David : *Guitars* (SW)
Bowen, Gareth : *Keyboards* (Lon)
Bowen, Glyn : *Trombone* (SW)
Bowen, Greg : *Trumpet* (Lon)
Bowen, Jules : *Pianoforte* (Lon)
Bowen, Lorraine : *Voice* (Lon)
Bowen, Martin : *Bassoon* (SW)
Bowen, Win : *Trombone* (SW)
Bower, Catherine : *Viola* (Mid)
Bower, John : *Voice* (NE)

Index of Members - Breeze

Bower, Jon : *Bass Guitar* (Lon)
Bower, Nick : *Bass Guitar* (SE)
Bower, Roy : *Trumpet* (SE)
Bowers, Dane : *Voice* (Lon)
Bowers, Edward : *Pianoforte* (SE)
Bowers, Geoffrey : *Banjo* (Mid)
Bowers, Phillip : *Keyboards* (Mid)
Bowers-Broadbent, Christopher : *Organ* (Lon)
Bowers-Broadbent, Henry : *Percussion* (Lon)
Bowers-Broadbent, Nicholas : *Violin* (Lon)
Bowery, Al : *Guitars* (SW)
Bowes, Colin : *Guitars* (NW)
Bowes, Daniel : *Voice* (Lon)
Bowes, Thomas : *Violin* (Lon)
Bowie, David : *Voice* (Lon)
Bowie, Eric : *Violin* (Lon)
Bowker, Robert : *Voice* (NE)
Bowler, John : *Flute* (Lon)
Bowles, Geoffrey : *Saxophones* (SW)
Bowles, Robin : *Keyboards* (NE)
Bowles, Thomas : *Clarinet* (Lon)
Bowles, Tina : *Violin* (Lon)
Bowley, Martin : *Bass Guitar* (Lon)
Bowman, Aubrey : *Conductor* (Lon)
Bowman, Jill : *Violin* (NE)
Bowman, Ronald : *Pianoforte* (E)
Bown, Alison : *Voice* (Mid)
Bown, Andrew : *Guitars* (Lon)
Bown, Edward : *Saxophones* (NE)
Bown, Eileen : *Pianoforte* (NE)
Bown, Julian : *Percussion* (SE)
Bown, Stefan : *Violin* (Lon)
Bowran, Susan : *Violin* (Lon)
Bowring, Sarah : *Clarinet* (Lon)
Bowron, Leslie : *Violin* (Mid)
Bowser, Ian : *Double Bass* (SW)
Bowyer, Charles : *Voice* (Lon)
Bowyer, Geoffrey : *Keyboards* (Lon)
Bowyer, Keith : *Percussion* (NW)
Box, Carol : *Violin* (NW)
Box, Jeffrey : *Double Bass* (NW)
Box, Philip : *Horn* (Lon)
Boy, Chrissy : *Guitars* (Lon)
Boyce, Charlotte : *Cello* (SW)
Boyce, Edward : *Pianoforte* (SW)
Boyce, Gerry : *Percussion* (Lon)
Boyd, David : *Music Director* (Lon)
Boyd, Ed : *Guitars* (SW)
Boyd, Georgia : *Viola* (NW)
Boyd, Graeme : *Trombone* (Lon)
Boyd, James : *Viola* (Lon)
Boyd, James : *Trumpet* (Mid)
Boyd, Jessamy : *Viola* (Lon)
Boyd, Marian : *Cello* (Sco)
Boyd, Mark : *Trombone* (Sco)
Boyd, Martin : *Saxophones* (NE)
Boyd, Stuart : *Guitars* (NW)
Boyd, William : *Organ* (SE)
Boyde, Hugh : *Guitars* (E)
Boyden, Phillip : *Violin* (SE)
Boyes, Deborah : *Oboe* (Lon)
Boyes, Derrick : *Bass Guitar* (NE)
Boyes, James : *Guitars* (NE)
Boyes, Michael : *Voice* (NE)
Boyes, Paul : *Bassoon* (E)
Boyesen, Nicole : *Double Bass* (SE)
Boyfield, Rachel : *Violin* (NE)
Boyland, Stephen : *Voice* (NW)
Boyle, Conor : *Guitars* (Lon)
Boyle, Elizabeth : *Harpsichord* (Lon)
Boyle, James : *Bass Guitar* (Sco)
Boyle, Margaret : *Flute* (SW)
Boyle, Michael : *Bassoon* (Lon)
Boyle, Paul : *Keyboards* (Sco)
Boyle, Rebecca : *Violin* (Lon)

Boyle, Stewart : *Guitars* (Lon)
Boyle, Tommy : *Percussion* (Sco)
Boylett, Lynda : *Flute* (NW)
BozaDJian, Harry : *Voice* (Lon)
Brace, George : *Percussion* (SE)
Brace, Thomas : *Saxophones* (NW)
Bracegirdle, Nicholas : *Keyboards* (SE)
Bracewell, Alan : *Pianoforte* (NW)
Bracewell, Steve : *Keyboards* (SW)
Bracken, Ian : *Cello* (NW)
Brackenbury, Ian : *Pianoforte* (NE)
Brackley, Jane : *Pianoforte* (E)
Brackley Jones, Helen : *Violin* (NE)
Brackpool, James : *Keyboards* (SE)
Brackpool, Marion : *Trombone* (Sco)
Bradbeer, Robert : *Guitars* (E)
Bradbury, Adrian : *Cello* (Lon)
Bradbury, Colin : *Clarinet* (Lon)
Bradbury, Dave : *Saxophones* (Lon)
Bradbury, John : *Violin* (Lon)
Bradbury, John : *Clarinet* (NW)
Bradbury, Peter : *Percussion* (NW)
Braddock, John : *Flute* (SE)
Braddock, Phil : *Bass Guitar* (NW)
Braden, Alan : *Arranger* (Lon)
Bradfield, Colin : *Saxophones* (Lon)
Bradfield, James Dean : *Guitars* (SW)
Bradford, Colin : *Accordion* (NE)
Bradford, Peter : *Guitars* (SE)
Bradford, Terry : *Guitars* (Lon)
Bradford, Thomas : *Guitars* (Lon)
Bradley, Alan : *Guitars* (Lon)
Bradley, Alan : *Trombone* (Mid)
Bradley, Andrew : *Voice* (Lon)
Bradley, Anna : *Violin* (Lon)
Bradley, Billy : *Organ* (NW)
Bradley, Christopher : *Tympani* (NE)
Bradley, Clinton : *Guitars* (SE)
Bradley, George : *Trumpet* (Mid)
Bradley, Graham : *Percussion* (SW)
Bradley, Hugh : *Guitars* (NE)
Bradley, Hugh : *Violin* (Sco)
Bradley, Jan : *Percussion* (NW)
Bradley, Jeremy : *Violin* (NW)
Bradley, Joanne : *Double Bass* (NE)
Bradley, Karen : *Viola* (Lon)
Bradley, Kate : *Voice* (Lon)
Bradley, Laurence : *Pianoforte* (Lon)
Bradley, Martin : *Violin* (Mid)
Bradley, Michael : *Guitars* (Lon)
Bradley, Michael : *Percussion* (Lon)
Bradley, Paul : *Guitars* (Lon)
Bradley, Peter : *Voice* (Lon)
Bradley, Peter : *Voice* (NE)
Bradley, Philip : *Keyboards* (NW)
Bradley, Robert : *Guitars* (Lon)
Bradley, Sarah : *Viola* (Lon)
Bradley, Stuart : *Bass Guitar* (Lon)
Bradshaw, Catherine : *Viola* (Lon)
Bradshaw, George : *Trombone* (NE)
Bradshaw, Graham : *Cello* (Lon)
Bradshaw, Heather : *Violin* (Mid)
Bradshaw, Julia : *Cello* (NW)
Bradshaw, Larry : *Double Bass* (Mid)
Bradshaw, Martin : *Cello* (Lon)
Bradshaw, Nicholas : *Percussion* (Lon)
Bradshaw, Noel : *Cello* (Lon)
Bradshaw, Penny : *Cello* (Lon)
Bradshaw, Robert : *Voice* (NW)
Bradshaw, Susan : *Pianoforte* (Lon)
Bradshaw, Timothy : *Guitars* (Lon)
Brady, Colin : *Percussion* (E)
Brady, Conor : *Guitars* (Lon)
Brady, Gareth : *Clarinet* (Lon)
Brady, John : *Guitars* (Lon)

Brady, Leslie : *Percussion* (NW)
Brady, Oliver : *Trumpet* (NE)
Brady, William : *Keyboards* (Lon)
Braga, Robert : *Viola* (NW)
Braganza, Angelo : *Violin* (NE)
Braganza, Henry : *Guitars* (SE)
Bragen, Howard : *Guitars* (Lon)
Bragg, Billy : *Guitars* (Lon)
Bragg, Glyn : *Music Director* (Sco)
Bragg, Keith : *Flute* (E)
Bragg, Richard : *Keyboards* (E)
Braggins, Belinda : *Saxophones* (Lon)
Braham, Thomas : *Guitars* (Lon)
Brailey, Peter : *Guitars* (SE)
Brailsford, Ian : *Trombone* (Mid)
Brailsford, Murray : *Guitars* (Mid)
Braime, Hilary : *Double Bass* (Mid)
Brain, Reg : *Pianoforte* (SW)
Braine, Anthony : *Pianoforte* (SW)
Braithwaite, James : *Saxophones* (Mid)
Braithwaite, Nicholas : *Trombone* (Lon)
Braithwaite, Tracey : *Voice* (Sco)
Bramah, Teri : *Voice* (SW)
Bramley, Simon : *Bass Guitar* (Mid)
Brampton, Harry : *Clarinet* (Lon)
Bramson, Susanne : *Guitars* (Lon)
Bramwell, Jonathan : *Pianoforte* (NW)
Bran, Timothy : *Keyboards* (Lon)
Branch, Gary : *Saxophones* (SE)
Branch, Philip : *Bass Guitar* (Lon)
Brand, Gail : *Trombone* (Lon)
Brand, Graham : *Double Bass* (Lon)
Brand, John : *Organ* (E)
Brand, Neil : *Pianoforte* (Lon)
Brandon, John : *Violin* (Lon)
Brandwood-Spencer, Sarah : *Violin* (NW)
Brannick, Chris : *Percussion* (Lon)
Brannigan, Martin Sean : *Keyboards* (SE)
Branson, Fiona : *Voice* (Lon)
Branson, Peter : *Pianoforte* (SE)
Brant, Helen : *Percussion* (NE)
Brasher, Hugh : *Percussion* (SW)
Brasington, Damian : *Bassoon* (SE)
Bratherton, John : *Violin* (NW)
Brathwaite, Vibert : *Pianoforte* (Lon)
Bratkowski, Cheryl : *Pianoforte* (NE)
Bratt, Andrew : *Percussion* (Lon)
Bratton, Stephen : *Guitars* (Mid)
Bravo, Bravo : *Steel Pan* (Lon)
Brawley, Michael : *Saxophones* (Sco)
Brawn, Geoffrey : *Pianoforte* (SE)
Brawn, Victoria : *Oboe* (Lon)
Bray, Colin : *Saxophones* (E)
Bray, James : *Double Bass* (Lon)
Bray, Ned : *Saxophones* (Lon)
Bray, Nick : *Guitars* (Lon)
Bray, Pete : *Percussion* (Lon)
Brazier, Peter F : *Keyboards* (E)
Brazier, Philip : *Oboe* (SE)
Breadstill, John : *Accordion* (SE)
Breakspear, Howard : *Viola* (NE)
Breakspear, Julia : *Flute* (NE)
Brear, Jack : *Keyboards* (E)
Brearley, John : *Viola* (Lon)
Breatnach, Cormac : *Whistle* (Lon)
Brebner, Alexander : *Voice* (Sco)
Brechin, Sandy : *Accordion* (Sco)
Bree, Michael : *Electric Double Bass* (SE)
Bree, Patrick : *Guitars* (SW)
Breen, Abs : *Pianoforte* (Lon)
Breen, Joanne : *Voice* (NW)
Breen, Karl : *Guitars* (Lon)
Breen, Ryan : *Tuba* (NW)
Breese, Emma : *Pianoforte* (SW)
Breeze, Arthur : *Trombone* (NW)

Brownlow, Erick : *Violin* (Mid)
Brownridge, Angela : *Pianoforte* (Lon)
Brownson, Lee : *Guitars* (SW)
Browse, Paul : *Guitars* (Lon)
Browton, Richard : *Voice* (Lon)
Bruce, Arthur : *Violin* (Sco)
Bruce, Deborah : *Percussion* (Lon)
Bruce, Jo : *Bassoon* (SW)
Bruce, Keith : *Saxophones* (Sco)
Bruce, Leslie : *Saxophones* (SW)
Bruce, Malcolm : *Guitars* (Lon)
Bruce, Mike : *Bass Trombone* (Mid)
Bruce, Nichola : *Accordion* (Lon)
Bruce, Paul : *Bass Guitar* (Lon)
Bruce, Robert : *Saxophones* (Sco)
Bruce, Sheila : *Pianoforte* (Sco)
Bruce, William : *Cello* (Lon)
Bruce-Mitford, Myrtle : *Cello* (Lon)
Bruer, Jason : *Saxophones* (Lon)
Bruford, Alexander : *Percussion* (SE)
Bruford, William : *Percussion* (Lon)
Bruggemeyer, Cecelia : *Double Bass* (Lon)
Bruinsma, Cornelius : *Guitars* (Lon)
Bruley, David : *Songwriter* (Lon)
Brumby, James : *Percussion* (NE)
Brundan, Amanda : *Cello* (SE)
Brunner, Paul : *Cello* (Lon)
Brunt, Terry : *Trombone* (NW)
Brunton, John : *Clarinet* (NW)
Brunton, Leonard : *Violin* (NE)
Brunton, Phillip D : *Conductor* (E)
Brunton, Richard : *Guitars* (SW)
Bruschini, Angelo : *Guitars* (SW)
Brush, Andy : *Saxophones* (E)
Bruton, Roger : *Percussion* (Mid)
Bruton, Thomas : *Saxophones* (Lon)
Bryan, Fiona : *Bassoon* (Lon)
Bryan, Harry : *Trumpet* (Lon)
Bryan, John : *Early Renaissance* (NE)
Bryan, Joseph : *Accordion* (Mid)
Bryan, Kelle : *Voice* (Lon)
Bryan, Margaret : *Cello* (NE)
Bryan, Russ : *Percussion* (Lon)
Bryans, Ronald : *Bass Trombone* (Lon)
Bryant, Barry : *Pianoforte* (E)
Bryant, Colin : *Saxophones* (SE)
Bryant, David : *Percussion* (Lon)
Bryant, Jeffrey : *Horn* (Lon)
Bryant, Kelly : *Voice* (Lon)
Bryant, Mike : *Bass Guitar* (Lon)
Bryant, Richie : *Percussion* (Lon)
Bryant, Stephen : *Violin* (Lon)
Bryant, Terl : *Percussion* (Lon)
Bryant, Toni : *Violin* (Lon)
Bryar, Quentin : *Saxophones* (E)
Bryce, Alison : *Horn* (Lon)
Bryce, James : *Composer* (Sco)
Bryce, Lindy : *Voice* (Lon)
Bryce, Morven : *Violin* (Lon)
Bryden, Paul : *Guitars* (NW)
Brydon-Phillips, Mary : *Voice* (Lon)
Brymer, Jack : *Clarinet* (Lon)
Bryn-Parri, Annette : *Pianoforte* (NW)
Bryson, Una : *Accordion* (Sco)
Brzezicki, Mark : *Percussion* (Lon)
Buchan, Gordon : *Violin* (Lon)
Buchanan, Cameron : *Guitars* (Sco)
Buchanan, Kate : *Flute* (Lon)
Buchanan, Lesley : *Violin* (Sco)
Buchanan, Margo : *Voice* (Lon)
Buchanan, Robert : *Bass Guitar* (Lon)
Buchanan, Wallis : *DiDJeridu* (Lon)
Buck, Arthur : *Percussion* (NW)
Buck, Dennis : *Percussion* (E)
Buck, J : *Horn* (Lon)

Buck, Stanley : *Accordion* (Lon)
Buck, Stephen : *Percussion* (E)
Buckberry, Ivan : *Pianoforte* (Mid)
Buckberry, Russell : *Trumpet* (Mid)
Buckee, Robert : *Pianoforte* (Mid)
Buckenham, Gemma : *Trumpet* (Lon)
Buckeridge, Corin : *Pianoforte* (SE)
Buckingham, Bryan : *Percussion* (E)
Buckingham, Mark : *Bass Clarinet* (Lon)
Buckingham, Paul : *Bass Guitar* (Mid)
Buckland, David : *Bassoon* (SW)
Buckland, Robert : *Saxophones* (NW)
Buckland, Susan : *Flute* (SW)
Buckle, Ian : *Pianoforte* (NW)
Buckle, Jason : *Keyboards* (NE)
Buckle, Stuart : *Guitars* (E)
Buckley, Alan : *Percussion* (Mid)
Buckley, Gary : *Bass Guitar* (SW)
Buckley, Geoffrey : *Pianoforte* (SW)
Buckley, George : *Percussion* (SE)
Buckley, Graham : *Double Bass* (NW)
Buckley, Jack : *Harmonica (Inc Bass* (NW)
Buckley, Jack : *Bass Clarinet* (SW)
Buckley, Jackie : *Voice* (Lon)
Buckley, Juls : *Trumpet* (SE)
Buckley, Michael : *Saxophones* (Lon)
Buckley, Ronald : *Bassoon* (Mid)
Buckley, Steven : *Guitars* (NW)
Buckley, Sylvia : *Violin* (Mid)
Bucknall, Christopher : *Pianoforte* (Mid)
Bucknall, David : *Cello* (Lon)
Bucknall, Francis : *Cello* (Lon)
Bucknall, Joan : *Viola* (Lon)
Bucknall, Juliet : *Clarinet* (Lon)
Bucknall, Nicholas : *Clarinet* (Lon)
Buckoke, Peter : *Double Bass* (Lon)
Buckton, Benjamin : *Violin* (Lon)
Buckton, Malcolm : *Bass Guitar* (NE)
Budd, Graeme : *Saxophones* (SW)
Budd, Ian : *Viola* (Sco)
Budd, Iris : *Pianoforte* (Lon)
Budd, Matt : *Latin American Percu* (E)
Budd, Paul : *Percussion* (Lon)
Budd, Stephen : *Guitars* (Lon)
Budden, Roy : *Conductor* (Lon)
Budge, William : *Percussion* (E)
Budgen, Adrian : *Saxophones* (E)
Bugden, James : *Pianoforte* (Lon)
Built For Comfort : *Saxophones* (NW)
Bukic, Mirsad : *Guitars* (Lon)
Bulcock, Maritza : *Viola* (Lon)
Bull, Bernita : *Voice* (Lon)
Bull, Brian : *Guitars* (Lon)
Bull, Christine : *Viola* (SW)
Bull, Christopher : *Bass Guitar* (NE)
Bull, Geoffrey : *Violin* (Mid)
Bull, Irene : *Songwriter* (Lon)
Bull, Linda : *Voice* (Lon)
Bull, Naomi : *Saxophones* (NE)
Bull, Peter : *Hurdy-gurdy* (NE)
Bull, Richard Michael : *Guitars* (Lon)
Bull, Sarah : *Flute* (NW)
Bull, Stephen : *Violin* (Lon)
Bull, William : *Horn* (Mid)
Bullard, Martin : *Pianoforte* (NE)
Bullas, Phillip : *Trombone* (NE)
Bullen, Dennis : *Double Bass* (SW)
Bullers, Adrian : *Saxophones* (Mid)
Bulley, Alan : *Saxophones* (Lon)
Bulley, Denise : *Organ* (Mid)
Bullivant, Roger : *Harpsichord* (NE)
Bullock, Judy : *Viola* (Lon)
Bullock, Neil : *Percussion* (Mid)
Bullock, Richard : *Percussion* (Mid)
Bullock, Ron : *Organ* (Mid)

Bulmer, David : *Accordion* (NE)
Bulpitt, John : *Bass Guitar* (Lon)
Bulson, Philip : *Pianoforte* (SE)
Bultitude, Timothy : *Guitars* (Lon)
Bultz, Jane : *Violin* (SE)
Buncall, Christopher : *Voice* (NE)
Bunce, Christopher : *Guitars* (SE)
Bunce, Martin : *Bandleader* (Lon)
Bunce, Martin : *Trumpet* (Lon)
Bundrick (Rabbit), John : *Keyboards* (Lon)
Bundy, Rachel : *Voice* (SE)
Bune, Margaret : *Cello* (SW)
Bunkell, David : *Pianoforte* (Lon)
Bunker, Andrew : *Trombone* (Lon)
Bunker, Clive : *Percussion* (E)
Bunnett, Keith : *Percussion* (SE)
Bunt : *Bass Guitar* (NE)
Bunt, Belinda : *Violin* (Lon)
Bunt, Felicity Jane : *Flute* (Lon)
Bunting, Allan : *Percussion* (Sco)
Bunting, Catherine : *Cello* (Mid)
Bunting, Darren : *Bass Guitar* (NE)
Bunting, Stephen : *Synthesiser* (E)
Bunton, Emma : *Voice* (Lon)
Bunyan, Rachel : *Horn* (Lon)
Burbidge, David : *Accordion* (SE)
Burbidge, Victor : *Pianoforte* (Lon)
Burch, John : *Pianoforte* (Lon)
Burch, Paul : *Saxophones* (Lon)
Burchell, Anthony : *Bandleader* (Mid)
Burchell, Anthony : *Pianoforte* (Mid)
Burchell, James : *Trumpet* (SE)
Burchell, Judith : *Violin* (Lon)
Burchill, Charles : *Guitars* (Sco)
Burden, David : *Guitars* (E)
Burden, Elizabeth : *Pianoforte* (SE)
Burden, John : *Horn* (Lon)
Burden, Martin : *Bass Guitar* (Lon)
Burden, Oliver : *Guitars* (E)
Burden, Rachel : *Oboe* (E)
Burdett, Bryan : *Cello* (SE)
Burdett, Lesley : *Pianoforte* (Lon)
Burdge, Ian : *Cello* (Lon)
Burdis, Raymond : *Guitars* (Lon)
Bureau, Richard : *Violin* (Lon)
Burford, Geoffrey : *Pianoforte* (Lon)
Burford, Ian : *Guitars* (Mid)
Burgan, A : *Double Bass* (NE)
Burge, Harry : *Flute* (SW)
Burge, Richard : *Bass Guitar* (SW)
Burger, Richard : *Keyboards* (Sco)
Burgess, Anthony : *Keyboards* (NW)
Burgess, Chris : *Percussion* (Lon)
Burgess, Jane : *Violin* (Mid)
Burgess, John : *Double Bass* (SE)
Burgess, Jonathan : *Flute* (SW)
Burgess, Kathryn : *Viola* (Lon)
Burgess, Martin : *Violin* (Lon)
Burgess, Nancy : *Saxophones* (Mid)
Burgess, Norman : *Trumpet* (Lon)
Burgess, Paul : *Recorders* (SW)
Burgess, Peter : *Guitars* (Lon)
Burgess, Richard : *Percussion* (Lon)
Burgess, Rob : *Bass Trombone* (Lon)
Burgess, Samuel : *Double Bass* (Lon)
Burgess, Steven : *Keyboards* (NW)
Burgess, Timothy : *Percussion* (SE)
Burgher, Richard : *Voice* (Lon)
Burgin, Judith : *Cello* (NE)
Burgin, Lee : *Guitars* (Mid)
Burgoyne, Dennis : *Trumpet* (SE)
Burholt, Stephen : *Keyboards* (Lon)
Burke, Charlotte : *Horn* (SW)
Burke, David : *Clarinet* (NW)
Burke, Mark : *Guitars* (Lon)

Burke, Nicola : *Trumpet* (Lon)
Burke, Tony : *Copyist* (SW)
Burke, Vicki : *Saxophones* (SW)
Burley, David : *Guitars* (Lon)
Burley, Elizabeth : *Pianoforte* (Lon)
Burley, Imogen : *Cello* (Lon)
Burley, Philip : *Keyboards* (Lon)
Burley, Raymond : *Guitars* (SE)
Burley, Trevor : *Cello* (Lon)
Burling, George : *Saxophones* (Lon)
Burman, David : *Pianoforte* (Lon)
Burn, Christopher : *Composer* (Lon)
Burnage, Susan : *Oboe* (NE)
Burnap, Campbell : *Trombone* (Lon)
Burnard, Stephen : *Violin* (SW)
Burnby, Stephen : *Keyboards* (NE)
Burnby-Crouch, Christopher : *Keyboards* (Lon)
Burnell, Carol : *Bassoon* (NW)
Burnell, Donald : *Clarinet* (SW)
Burness, Jack : *Guitars* (NE)
Burnett, Barbara : *Percussion* (E)
Burnett, Barry : *Guitars* (E)
Burnett, Frank : *Saxophones* (Sco)
Burnett, John : *Trumpet* (Mid)
Burnett, Jonathan : *Violin* (SW)
Burnett, Norrie : *Voice* (SE)
Burnett, Paul : *Music Director* (Lon)
Burnett, Richard : *Pianoforte* (Lon)
Burnett, Roderick : *Trumpet* (Lon)
Burnett, Ronald : *Trombone* (NE)
Burnett, Sandy : *Double Bass* (Lon)
Burnett, Sandy : *Music Director* (Lon)
Burnett, Sarah : *Bassoon* (Lon)
Burney, Mike : *Saxophones* (Mid)
Burnham, Catherine : *Pianoforte* (SW)
Burnham, Don : *Percussion* (Mid)
Burnie, Angus : *Double Bass* (Sco)
Burns, Alison : *Voice* (Sco)
Burns, Catriona : *Violin* (Mid)
Burns, Cha : *Guitars* (Lon)
Burns, Colin : *Keyboards* (Lon)
Burns, Colin : *Double Bass* (SW)
Burns, David : *Mandolin* (SW)
Burns, Duff : *Viola* (Lon)
Burns, Dugald : *Trombone* (Sco)
Burns, Duncan : *Percussion* (Sco)
Burns, Edward : *Violin* (SW)
Burns, Elaine : *Pianoforte* (Mid)
Burns, Gary : *Voice* (Sco)
Burns, Gill : *Guitars* (NW)
Burns, Hugh : *Guitars* (Lon)
Burns, Keith W : *Percussion* (Sco)
Burns, Leo : *Violin* (Mid)
Burns, Lucie : *Voice* (Lon)
Burns, Neil : *Guitars* (SW)
Burns, Richard : *Percussion* (SW)
Burns, Robert : *Bass Guitar* (Lon)
Burns, Robert : *Saxophones* (Lon)
Burnside, Raymond : *Percussion* (NW)
Burov, Sergei : *Violin* (Lon)
Burr, James : *Pianoforte* (Lon)
Burrage, Martin : *Violin* (NW)
Burras, William : *Pianoforte* (SE)
Burrell, Alvin : *Bass Guitar* (Lon)
Burrell, Eric : *Trumpet* (E)
Burrell, Howard : *Music Director* (E)
Burrell, Paul : *Pianoforte* (Lon)
Burrell, Raymond : *Double Bass* (Lon)
Burrell, Richard : *Guitars* (Lon)
Burrin, Philip : *Violin* (Sco)
Burrow, Joan : *Oboe* (Lon)
Burrow, Richard : *Bass Guitar* (E)
Burrowes, David : *Cello* (Lon)
Burrowes, Margaret : *Voice* (Lon)
Burrows, Bryn : *Percussion* (Lon)

Burrows, Denise : *Oboe* (NW)
Burrows, Grace : *Violin* (Lon)
Burrows, Helen : *Pianoforte* (E)
Burrows, Jonathan : *Pianoforte* (SE)
Burrows, Kathryn : *Flute* (Lon)
Burrows, Leanne : *Voice* (NW)
Burrows, Lester : *Violin* (Lon)
Burrows, Matthew : *Keyboards* (Lon)
Burrows, Paul : *Bass Guitar* (E)
Burrows, Rodney : *Trumpet* (SE)
Burrows, Stephen : *Pianoforte* (NW)
Burston, Barbara : *Violin* (SE)
Burt, George : *Guitars* (Sco)
Burt, Jean Robertson : *Viola* (Lon)
Burt, Micky : *Percussion* (SE)
Burt, Nicholas : *Composer* (Mid)
Burt, Peter : *Guitars* (SE)
Burtenshaw, Leslie : *Pianoforte* (NE)
Burtenshaw, Robert : *Trombone* (NE)
Burton, Alan : *Irish Pipes* (Lon)
Burton, Cathy : *Guitars* (SE)
Burton, David : *Violin* (Lon)
Burton, Geoffrey : *Voice* (Lon)
Burton, Jonathan : *Arranger* (Lon)
Burton, Julian : *Melodeon* (SE)
Burton, Lou : *Voice* (Lon)
Burton, Mark : *Keyboards* (SE)
Burton, Oliver : *Viola* (Lon)
Burton, Patrick : *Banjo* (NE)
Burton, Susan : *Pianoforte* (Lon)
Burton, Tigger : *Bass Guitar* (Lon)
Burton, Tim : *Trombone* (Lon)
Burton, Tommy : *Pianoforte* (Mid)
Burton, Trevor : *Trumpet* (NE)
Burton, William : *Violin* (Lon)
Burvill, Mandy : *Clarinet* (Lon)
Burville, Eric : *Percussion* (SE)
Bury, Alison : *Violin* (Lon)
Bury, Julian : *Double Bass* (Lon)
Busbridge, Judith : *Viola* (Lon)
Busby, Colin : *Trombone* (Lon)
Busby, Paul : *Pianoforte* (SE)
Busby, Terry : *Clarinet* (SW)
Busch, Nicholas : *Horn* (Lon)
Buser, Felix : *Cello* (SE)
Bush, Andy : *Trumpet* (Lon)
Bush, Kate : *Composer* (Lon)
Bush, Lennie : *Double Bass* (Lon)
Bush, Marcus D : *Bass Guitar* (Lon)
Bush, Martin : *Pianoforte* (Lon)
Bush, Paddy : *Mandolin* (Lon)
Bushby, Adrian : *Bass Guitar* (Lon)
Bushell, Adam : *Percussion* (Lon)
Bushell, Hugh : *Double Bass* (SW)
Bushell, Jeremy : *Horn* (NW)
Bushell, Julian : *Bass Guitar* (SW)
Bushnell-Wye, Mairearad : *Clarinet* (NW)
Bushrod, Andrew : *Guitars* (SE)
Bushwaka B, Matthew : *Keyboards* (Lon)
Busiakiewicz, Richard : *Pianoforte* (Lon)
Bussereau, Peter : *Violin* (Lon)
Buswell, John : *Flute* (SE)
Butcher, Andrew : *Trombone* (Lon)
Butcher, Bill : *Saxophones* (Mid)
Butcher, Damon : *Keyboards* (Lon)
Butcher, John : *Saxophones* (Lon)
Butcher, Joseph : *Pianoforte* (Lon)
Butcher, Ken : *Saxophones* (Lon)
Butcher, Kevin : *Guitars* (E)
Butcher, Nina : *Voice* (NW)
Butcher, Philip : *Double Bass* (Lon)
Butcher, Raymond : *Trumpet* (Mid)
Butcher, Sarah : *Cello* (Lon)
Butcher, Simon : *Voice* (Mid)
Buterworth, Christian : *Keyboards* (SE)

Butler, Anthony : *Bass Guitar* (NE)
Butler, Bernard : *Guitars* (Lon)
Butler, David : *Violin* (Lon)
Butler, Eddie : *Trombone* (NW)
Butler, Elizabeth : *Viola* (Lon)
Butler, Gerald : *Pianoforte* (NE)
Butler, Gregg : *Cornet* (NW)
Butler, Holly : *Viola* (Lon)
Butler, Joan : *Viola* (NW)
Butler, John : *Pianoforte* (Lon)
Butler, John : *Voice* (Mid)
Butler, Lucy : *Violin* (NW)
Butler, Mark : *Violin* (Lon)
Butler, Matthew : *Percussion* (NE)
Butler, Nigel : *Keyboards* (Lon)
Butler, Rosalind : *Violin* (SW)
Butler, Stephen : *Voice* (NW)
Butler, Verity : *Clarinet* (SW)
Butlin, Matthew : *Percussion* (SW)
Butt, David : *Flute* (Lon)
Butt, Edmund : *Violin* (Lon)
Butt, Eric : *Bassoon* (SE)
Butt, Frances : *Keyboards* (SW)
Butt, Raymond : *Clarinet* (SW)
Butterfield, Adrian : *Violin* (Lon)
Butterfield, Stu : *Percussion* (Lon)
Butterly, Kevin : *Percussion* (Mid)
Butters, Dennis : *Trumpet* (Mid)
Butters, John : *Percussion* (E)
Butters, Nick : *Pianoforte* (Lon)
Butterworth, Alexandra : *Early Strings* (Sco)
Butterworth, Alexandra : *Violin* (Sco)
Butterworth, Chris : *Keyboards* (Lon)
Butterworth, Derek : *Saxophones* (SE)
Butterworth, Ian : *Trumpet* (NW)
Butterworth, Naomi : *Cello* (Lon)
Butterworth, Roy : *Clarinet* (SW)
Butterworth, Stephen : *Percussion* (NW)
Buttolph, Katharine : *Voice* (Mid)
Button, Brigid : *Violin* (Lon)
Button, Ian : *Bass Guitar* (Lon)
Button, Jean : *Pianoforte* (SE)
Button, Philip : *Violin* (Sco)
Button, Sarah : *Violin* (Lon)
Buttons : *Trombone* (Lon)
Buurman, Bernardus : *Violin* (Sco)
Buxton, Donald : *Trombone* (Mid)
Buxton, Jennifer : *Violin* (Lon)
Buxton, Paul : *Violin* (Lon)
Buxton, Ruth : *Clarinet* (Lon)
Byam-Grounds, Gabrielle : *Flute* (Mid)
Byatt, Martin : *Guitars* (Lon)
Bye, Peter : *Arranger* (Lon)
Bye, Tim : *Percussion* (Lon)
Byers, Roddy : *Guitars* (Mid)
Byng, Frank : *Percussion* (Lon)
Bynoe, Victor : *Voice* (Lon)
Byram-Wigfield, Timothy : *Organ* (Sco)
Byrd, Byron : *Saxophones* (Lon)
Byrne, Alan : *Percussion* (SE)
Byrne, Anthony : *Viola* (Lon)
Byrne, Daniel : *Percussion* (NW)
Byrne, Lennie : *Saxophones* (Lon)
Byrne, Lloyd : *Percussion* (Lon)
Byrne, Miki J : *Latin American Percu* (Mid)
Byrne, Peter : *Guitars* (Lon)
Byrom, Reginald : *Clarinet* (SE)
Byron, Freda : *Viola* (NE)
Byron, Graham : *Percussion* (Sco)
Byrt, Linda : *Oboe* (SW)
Byrt, Rachel : *Viola* (Lon)
Bywater, James : *Guitars* (NE)
Bywater, Kay : *Saxophones* (Lon)
Bywater, Scott : *Tympani* (Lon)

C

C-Lex : *Bass Guitar* (Lon)
C.B. : *Keyboards* (Lon)
Cable, Tom : *Guitars* (SE)
Cabot, Rosalyn : *Viola* (NW)
Cadbury, Richard : *Bass Guitar* (SW)
Caddick, Helen : *Keyboards* (Lon)
Caddle, Tony : *Bass Guitar* (SW)
Caddy, Joe : *Percussion* (SE)
Caddy, Phillipa : *Saxophones* (SE)
Caddy, Phillipa : *Trombone* (SE)
Cadman, Julia : *Saxophones* (NW)
Cadman, Mark : *Trumpet* (Mid)
Cadman, Steve : *Percussion* (Mid)
Cadore, Cosimo : *Percussion* (Lon)
Cadwallader, Neil : *Bass Guitar* (Mid)
Cadwallender, Muriel : *Horn* (NE)
Caesar, Angela : *Violin* (Lon)
Caesar, Julian : *Percussion* (SE)
Caesar, Pogus : *Keyboards* (Mid)
Caffelle, Anja : *Bassoon* (Mid)
Caffelle, Sandie : *Saxophones* (Mid)
Caffrey, Jason : *Saxophones* (Lon)
Cahen, Michael : *Guitars* (Lon)
Cahill, Sarah : *Voice* (Lon)
Caicedo, Luz : *Voice* (Lon)
Cain, Miles : *Voice* (NE)
Caine, Andy : *Voice* (Lon)
Caine, Angela : *Voice* (SE)
Caine, James : *Pianoforte* (NW)
Caines, Ronald : *Saxophones* (SE)
Caird, Alexander : *Bass Guitar* (Lon)
Caird, George : *Oboe* (Lon)
Cairn, Steve : *Composer* (Lon)
Cairney, Alan : *Double Bass* (Sco)
Cairney, Peter : *Guitars* (Lon)
Cairns, Alexander : *Pianoforte* (Sco)
Cairns, Forrest : *Clarinet* (Sco)
Cairo, Joel : *Guitars* (Lon)
Caisley, Robert : *Saxophones* (Lon)
Caister, Timothy : *Horn* (Lon)
Cal : *Voice* (Sco)
Calcutt, Sid : *Percussion* (SE)
Caldas, John : *Percussion* (Lon)
Calder, Mark : *Trumpet* (Lon)
Calder, Ronald : *Cello* (Lon)
Calder, Stephen : *Pianoforte* (Sco)
Calder, Thomas : *Pianoforte* (Sco)
Calderbank, Merle : *Bassoon* (Mid)
Calderwood, Neal : *Guitars* (NW)
Caldi, Claudia : *Violin* (Lon)
Caldicott, Anthony : *Percussion* (Mid)
Caldicott, Louise : *Oboe* (Lon)
Caldicott, Stephen : *Horn* (SE)
Caldwell, Christopher : *Saxophones* (Lon)
Caldwell, Nan : *Violin* (Sco)
Caldwell, Robert : *Saxophones* (Mid)
Cale, Mavis : *Clarinet* (Lon)
Callaghan, Ann : *Guitars* (Lon)
Callaghan, Bob : *Guitars* (Lon)
Callaghan, Raphael : *Harmonica (Inc Bass)* (NW)
Callaghan, Robert : *Percussion* (Lon)
Callaghan, Robert : *Saxophones* (NE)
Callan, Margaret : *Voice* (Sco)
Callan, Richard : *Guitars* (Lon)
Calland, Beverley : *Saxophones* (Lon)
Callard, Andrew : *Trumpet* (Lon)
Callard, Peter : *Guitars* (Lon)
Callender, Jon : *Percussion* (SE)
Calling, Joyce : *Violin* (NW)
Callingham, Robin : *Vibraphone* (Lon)
Callis, Jo : *Guitars* (Sco)
Callow, Colin : *Violin* (Lon)

Callow, Daren : *Guitars* (Lon)
Callow, Haydn : *Percussion* (Lon)
Callow, Penelope : *Cello* (NE)
Callow, Steven : *Cello* (NW)
Calnan, Anthony : *Pianoforte* (Lon)
Calnan, Patricia : *Violin* (Lon)
Calores, Carole : *Violin* (Lon)
Calthorpe, Emer : *Violin* (Lon)
Calver, Harold : *Saxophones* (NE)
Calverley, Anthony : *Cello* (Mid)
Calverley, Rachael : *Cello* (Mid)
Calvert, Bryan : *Pianoforte* (NW)
Calvert, Gillian : *Pianoforte* (NE)
Calvert, Leon : *Trumpet* (Lon)
Calvert, Rebecca : *Double Bass* (Sco)
Calvert, Robin : *Violin* (Sco)
Calvert, Stuart : *Pianoforte* (Lon)
Calvo, Robbie : *Guitars* (Lon)
Camara, Hatib : *Keyboards* (Lon)
Cambridge, Emma-Jayne : *Voice* (Mid)
Cambridge, John : *Guitars* (E)
Cambridge, Maurice : *Contractor* (Lon)
Camby, Norma : *Copyist* (Lon)
Camden, Kerry : *Bassoon* (Lon)
Camerata, Trio : *Flute* (SW)
Cameron, Alexander : *Cello* (Lon)
Cameron, Bruce : *Saxophones* (E)
Cameron, Calvin : *Trombone* (Lon)
Cameron, Chris : *Keyboards* (Lon)
Cameron, Hilary : *Pianoforte* (Lon)
Cameron, Ian : *Trumpet* (Lon)
Cameron, John : *Composer* (Lon)
Cameron, Kate : *Voice* (SE)
Cameron, Lennox : *Voice* (Lon)
Cameron, Neil : *Double Bass* (Sco)
Cameron, Peter : *Trumpet* (Lon)
Cameron, Sarah : *Clarinet* (E)
Cameron, Tarnya : *Voice* (Lon)
Camille, Chantal : *Voice* (Lon)
Camlin, David : *Guitars* (NW)
Camm, Howard : *Flute* (NE)
Camm, Tim : *Keyboards* (Lon)
Camp, Richard : *Guitars* (E)
Campanale, Franco : *Saxophones* (Lon)
Campbell, Adam : *Pianoforte* (Lon)
Campbell, Alistair : *Guitars* (Mid)
Campbell, Andrew : *Bass Guitar* (Mid)
Campbell, Brian : *Accordion* (NE)
Campbell, Clare : *Violin* (NE)
Campbell, Colin : *Bandleader* (Mid)
Campbell, Colin : *Pianoforte* (Mid)
Campbell, Colin : *Accordion* (Sco)
Campbell, Colin : *Pianoforte* (SE)
Campbell, Colin : *Saxophones* (SE)
Campbell, David : *Clarinet* (Lon)
Campbell, David : *Percussion* (Sco)
Campbell, Dirk : *Uillean* (SE)
Campbell, Douglas : *Guitars* (Lon)
Campbell, Douglas : *Pianoforte* (SE)
Campbell, Duncan : *Trumpet* (Lon)
Campbell, Duncan : *Guitars* (SE)
Campbell, Edward : *Keyboards* (Sco)
Campbell, Ellen : *Trombone* (Mid)
Campbell, Francis : *Pianoforte* (Lon)
Campbell, Gordon : *Trombone* (Lon)
Campbell, Grace : *Voice* (E)
Campbell, Hilary : *Percussion* (SW)
Campbell, Isobel : *Cello* (Sco)
Campbell, James : *Accordion* (Sco)
Campbell, James : *Keyboards* (Sco)
Campbell, Jane : *Violin* (Lon)
Campbell, Joel : *Keyboards* (Lon)
Campbell, John : *Double Bass* (Sco)
Campbell, John : *Pianoforte* (SE)
Campbell, Joseph : *Double Bass* (Lon)

Campbell, Junior : *Keyboards* (SE)
Campbell, Ken : *Guitars* (Sco)
Campbell, Kevin : *Percussion* (Lon)
Campbell, Kibibi : *Voice* (Mid)
Campbell, Laura : *Double Bass* (Lon)
Campbell, Lucy : *Clarinet* (E)
Campbell, Mairi : *Viola* (Sco)
Campbell, Margaret : *Flute* (Lon)
Campbell, Martyn : *Bass Guitar* (NW)
Campbell, Murray : *Early Wind* (Sco)
Campbell, Neil : *Guitars* (Sco)
Campbell, Patsy : *Early Strings* (Sco)
Campbell, Richard : *Early Strings* (Lon)
Campbell, Robert : *Oboe* (NW)
Campbell, Robert : *Saxophones* (Sco)
Campbell, Robin : *Guitars* (Mid)
Campbell, Rory : *Bagpipes* (Sco)
Campbell, Simon : *Guitars* (NW)
Campbell, Stephen : *Guitars* (NE)
Campbell, Stevie : *Voice* (E)
Campbell, Tony : *Guitars* (Lon)
Campbell, Vivienne : *Viola* (NE)
Campbell Reid, Wayne : *Voice* (NW)
Campbell Thornton, Peter : *Pianoforte* (NW)
Campbell-Kelly, Peter : *Violin* (Sco)
Campbell-Lyons, Patrick : *Keyboards* (Lon)
Campey, Fay : *Violin* (NW)
Campey, Mark : *Keyboards* (NW)
Campion, Beverley-Jane : *Copyist* (Lon)
Campling, Mark : *Guitars* (E)
Campton, Rosemary : *Violin* (Lon)
Can, Mehmet : *Harp* (Lon)
Canaan, Danny : *Bass Guitar* (Mid)
Canale, Donna : *Voice* (Lon)
Canavan, Emma : *Clarinet* (Lon)
Candler, Michael : *Cornet* (Lon)
Cane, Robin : *Horn* (Lon)
Canepa, Marco : *Early Wind* (Lon)
Cang, Gil : *Percussion* (Lon)
Cang, Matthew : *Guitars* (Lon)
Cann, Antoinette : *Pianoforte* (E)
Cann, Claire : *Pianoforte* (E)
Cann, Judith : *Keyboards* (Lon)
Cannam, Anthony : *Guitars* (Lon)
Cannell, Helen : *Voice* (SE)
Cannell, Laura : *Folk Fiddle* (E)
Cannelli, Tony : *Percussion* (NE)
Cannon, Fiona : *Keyboards* (Sco)
Cannon, Rachel : *Clarinet* (Lon)
Cannon, Vinny : *Guitars* (SW)
Canonici, Corrado : *Double Bass* (Lon)
Cansdale, Roy : *Double Bass* (NW)
Canter, John : *Violin* (Lon)
Canter, Robin : *Oboe* (Lon)
Cantlon, Jane : *Violin* (E)
Cantlon, Kelly : *Double Bass* (E)
Cantoni, Michele : *Violin* (Lon)
Cantor, Matthew : *Keyboards* (Lon)
Cantor, Rafi : *Percussion* (NE)
Cantrill, Lucy : *Violin* (Lon)
Cantrill, Simon : *Double Bass* (Lon)
Canty, Clare : *Voice* (NW)
Canty, Laurence : *Bass Guitar* (Lon)
Capaldi, Jim : *Percussion* (Lon)
Capaldi, Phil : *Percussion* (Mid)
Caplan, Stuart : *Organ* (Sco)
Capocci, Michael : *Pianoforte* (E)
Capocci, Nicholas : *Pianoforte* (SE)
Capone, Philip : *Guitars* (Lon)
Caporaso, Luciana : *Voice* (Lon)
Capp, David : *Double Bass* (NW)
Capricorn : *Guitars* (SW)
Capstick, Peter : *Percussion* (NW)
Carben, Barry : *Bassoon* (Lon)
Card, J G : *Percussion* (SE)

Cardall, Ralph : *Guitars* (Mid)
Cardew, Horace : *Saxophones* (Lon)
Cardwell, Richard : *Pianoforte* (Lon)
Care, Melvyn : *Trombone* (Lon)
Care, Nicholas : *Trumpet* (Lon)
Care, Simon : *Melodeon* (Mid)
Carey, Bridget : *Viola* (Lon)
Carey, Jadie : *Cello* (Mid)
Carey, Louise : *Violin* (Mid)
Carey, Patrick : *Bass Guitar* (Lon)
Carey, Timothy : *Pianoforte* (Lon)
Cargill, Margo : *Voice* (Lon)
Cargill, Rory : *Guitars* (Lon)
Cargill, Suzy : *Percussion* (Sco)
Caribe, Mario : *Double Bass* (Sco)
Caris, Tom : *Guitars* (Lon)
Carless, Raymond : *Saxophones* (Lon)
Carless, Timothy : *Guitars* (Lon)
Carleston, Gerry : *Violin* (NW)
Carleston, Tim : *Trumpet* (Lon)
Carleton, Iain : *Guitars* (Sco)
Carlile, Brian : *Viola* (NW)
Carlill, Neil : *Voice* (Lon)
Carlin, John : *Bass Guitar* (Mid)
Carling, Martin : *Percussion* (Lon)
Carlisle, Liz : *Percussion* (NW)
Carlos, Mexeena : *Voice* (E)
Carloss, Adrian : *Guitars* (Mid)
Carlson, Marna : *Viola* (E)
Carlson, Neil : *Oboe* (E)
Carlton : *Voice* (SW)
Carlton, Dennis : *Horn* (Lon)
Carlton, Malcolm : *Composer* (Mid)
Carlyle, Mary : *Voice* (SW)
Carlyon, Shaun : *Guitars* (SW)
Carmalt, Averil : *Violin* (Lon)
Carmel, Heather : *Voice* (Lon)
Carmen : *Guitars* (Mid)
Carmichael, Anita : *Saxophones* (Lon)
Carmichael, Archie : *Trombone* (E)
Carmichael, Challan : *Voice* (Lon)
Carmichael, George : *Accordion* (Sco)
Carmichael, Gregory : *Guitars* (Lon)
Carmichael, Jim : *Percussion* (Lon)
Carmichael, John : *Accordion* (Sco)
Carmichael, Paul : *Bass Guitar* (Lon)
Carnaby, Denis : *Guitars* (SW)
Carnac, Jon : *Clarinet* (Lon)
Carne, Geoff : *Voice* (E)
Carney, Adele : *Viola* (Lon)
Carney, Andrew : *Percussion* (NW)
Carney, Barbara : *Organ* (NE)
Carney, Jonathan : *Violin* (Lon)
Carney, Leonard : *Percussion* (Lon)
Carnochan, Ian : *Guitars* (Lon)
Caro, Benjamin : *Guitars* (SE)
Carolan, Lucy : *Harpsichord* (E)
Carouth, Joscelin : *Flute* (E)
Carpena, Francesco : *Percussion* (Lon)
Carpenter, Doug : *Percussion* (SE)
Carpenter, Elizabeth : *Violin* (Lon)
Carpenter, Julia : *Violin* (Sco)
Carpenter, Nicholas : *Clarinet* (Lon)
Carpenter, Raymond : *Clarinet* (SE)
Carpenter, Victor : *Saxophones* (SW)
Carpenter-Jacobs, Susan : *Violin* (Lon)
Carpentieri, Giovanni : *Saxophones* (SW)
Carpetbighter, Lord : *Guitars* (Lon)
Carpos, Francesca : *Bassoon* (Lon)
Carr, Carlina : *Pianoforte* (Lon)
Carr, Gordon : *Horn* (Lon)
Carr, Helen : *Percussion* (Lon)
Carr, Ian : *Trumpet* (Lon)
Carr, Jennifer : *Pianoforte* (Lon)
Carr, Julian : *Bass Guitar* (Lon)

Carr, Michael : *Pianoforte* (Lon)
Carr, Michael : *Guitars* (SW)
Carr, Nikki : *Flute* (Lon)
Carr, Roger : *Keyboards* (NE)
Carr, Sam : *Percussion* (NE)
Carr, Simon : *Oboe* (Lon)
Carr, Terry : *Bagpipes* (NW)
Carr, Tony : *Percussion* (Lon)
Carrack, Paul : *Keyboards* (Lon)
Carrahar, Elisa : *Voice* (SW)
Carre, Isabelle : *Flute* (Lon)
Carrera-Weatherley, David : *Bass Guitar* (SE)
Carrick, Andrew : *Pianoforte* (Sco)
Carrick, Brian : *Clarinet* (NE)
Carrick, Jillian : *Trumpet* (Sco)
Carrick, Lindsay : *Horn* (Sco)
Carrillo-Garcia, Roberto : *Double Bass* (NE)
Carrington, Christopher : *Percussion* (SE)
Carrington, Diana : *Viola* (Lon)
Carrington, Ian : *Keyboards* (NW)
Carrington, Rebecca : *Viola* (Lon)
Carrington, Simon : *Percussion* (Lon)
Carroll, Andy : *Bass Guitar* (Lon)
Carroll, Colin : *Bass Guitar* (Lon)
Carroll, David : *Guitars* (Mid)
Carroll, Dina : *Voice* (E)
Carroll, Johnny : *Percussion* (Mid)
Carroll, Liane : *Voice* (SE)
Carroll, Marc : *Guitars* (Lon)
Carroll, Richard : *Pianoforte* (Lon)
Carroll, Walter : *Percussion* (Lon)
Carruthers, Geoffrey : *Keyboards* (Mid)
Carsan, Paul : *Composer* (Lon)
Carson, Malcolm : *Guitars* (Lon)
Carson, Mary : *Violin* (SW)
Carstairs, David : *Trumpet* (NW)
Carter, Anthony : *Saxophones* (SE)
Carter, Bradley : *Keyboards* (E)
Carter, Charles : *Percussion* (SE)
Carter, Daniel : *Bass Guitar* (SE)
Carter, David : *Music Director* (Lon)
Carter, David S : *Clarinet* (E)
Carter, Dean : *Guitars* (Lon)
Carter, Diane : *Guitars* (SW)
Carter, Diane : *Voice* (SW)
Carter, Don : *Pianoforte* (E)
Carter, Elinor : *Voice* (SE)
Carter, Gareth : *Percussion* (Mid)
Carter, Geoff : *Saxophones* (Lon)
Carter, Gillian : *Oboe* (SE)
Carter, Ian : *Guitars* (Lon)
Carter, Jack : *Pianoforte* (Lon)
Carter, Jillian : *Flute* (Lon)
Carter, Jonathan : *Guitars* (Lon)
Carter, Karen : *Violin* (Lon)
Carter, Lara : *Violin* (SE)
Carter, Margot : *Pianoforte* (SE)
Carter, Michael : *Organ* (NE)
Carter, Nick : *Flute* (NE)
Carter, Nigel : *Trumpet* (Lon)
Carter, Owen : *Violin* (NW)
Carter, Paul : *Percussion* (Lon)
Carter, Paul : *Saxophones* (SW)
Carter, Peter : *Guitars* (E)
Carter, Peter : *Guitars* (Mid)
Carter, Peter : *Saxophones* (NE)
Carter, Platts Matthew : *Guitars* (SE)
Carter, Robert : *Pianoforte* (Lon)
Carter, Roy : *Pianoforte* (Mid)
Carter, Ruth : *Bassoon* (Lon)
Carter, Simon : *Pianoforte* (Lon)
Carter, Tim Nibbs : *Bass Guitar* (NE)
Carter, Trevor : *Guitars* (Mid)
Carter, Vince : *Guitars* (Lon)
Carthy, Eliza : *Violin* (Lon)

Carthy, Martin : *Guitars* (NE)
Cartledge, Lucy : *Flute* (Sco)
Cartledge, Nicholas : *Flute* (SE)
Cartledge, Sophia : *Harp* (Lon)
Cartlidge, Christopher : *Violin* (Mid)
Cartlidge, Glenn : *Guitars* (NW)
Cartlidge, Luke : *Keyboards* (Mid)
Cartmell, Jean : *Viola* (Mid)
Cartmell, Tom : *Pianoforte* (NE)
Cartney, Jane : *Voice* (SE)
Cartwright, Bernice : *Bass Guitar* (Lon)
Cartwright, Danny : *Guitars* (Mid)
Cartwright, David : *Guitars* (E)
Cartwright, Deirdre : *Guitars* (Lon)
Cartwright, Kenneth : *Pianoforte* (Mid)
Cartwright, Sally : *Clarinet* (SE)
Cartwright, Sarah : *Clarinet* (Mid)
Cartwright, Terry : *Guitars* (Lon)
Carty, Joseph : *Steel Pan* (Lon)
Caruana, Nicholas : *Clarinet* (Mid)
Carus-Wilson, Alan : *Cello* (Mid)
Caruso, Tony : *Guitars* (Lon)
Carvalho, Robert : *Bass Guitar* (Mid)
Carvalho, Santiago : *Cello* (Lon)
Carvell, Alan : *Guitars* (Lon)
Carvell, John : *Horn* (Mid)
Carvell, Susan : *Violin* (Lon)
Carver, Alison : *Percussion* (NW)
Carver, Jack : *Percussion* (SW)
Carvisiglia, Anna : *Saxophones* (SE)
Carwardine, Jane : *Violin* (Lon)
Cary : *Voice* (SW)
Casbolt, Jason : *Violin* (Lon)
Cascarino, Lidia : *Bass Guitar* (SE)
Case : *Keyboards* (E)
Case, Matthew : *Saxophones* (NE)
Casella, Teresa : *Voice* (Lon)
Casey, Charlie : *Guitars* (Lon)
Casey, Graham : *Clarinet* (Lon)
Casey, Howie : *Saxophones* (Lon)
Casey, James : *Trombone* (Lon)
Casey, Michael : *Violin* (Lon)
Casey, Neil : *Pianoforte* (Lon)
Casey, Neil : *Conductor* (Mid)
Casey, Nollaig : *Violin* (Lon)
Casey, Richard : *Pianoforte* (NW)
Casey, Sheila : *Voice* (SE)
Cash, Dave : *Guitars* (NE)
Cash, David : *Keyboards* (Lon)
Cash, Nicholas : *Percussion* (Lon)
Cashin, Chrissy : *Voice* (Lon)
Cashin, Janice : *Voice* (NW)
Cashmore, Catherine : *Guitars* (Mid)
Casper, Nova : *Voice* (Lon)
Cass, Dave : *Guitars* (E)
Cass, Dave : *Pianoforte* (NE)
Cass, Gregory : *Horn* (Lon)
Cass, Helen : *Violin* (Lon)
Cass, Ronnie : *Music Director* (Lon)
Cassell, Debbie : *Voice* (Lon)
Cassells, Linda : *Voice* (Sco)
Casserley, Lawrence : *Percussion* (Lon)
Cassidy, Carl : *Clarinet* (Lon)
Cassidy, Claudine : *Cello* (SW)
Cassidy, Eugene : *Percussion* (Lon)
Cassidy, James : *Pianoforte* (E)
Cassidy, Jennifer : *Voice* (E)
Cassidy, Mary : *Voice* (Lon)
Cassidy, Paul : *Viola* (Lon)
Casson, Sue : *Pianoforte* (Lon)
Casswell, Michael : *Guitars* (Lon)
Castellano, Michael : *Bass Guitar* (E)
Castle, Barry : *Horn* (Lon)
Castle, Ben : *Saxophones* (Lon)
Castle, Geoff : *Keyboards* (Lon)

Clark, Roger : *Horn* (Lon)
Clark, Simon (Andy) : *Keyboards* (Lon)
Clark, Stephen : *Bass Guitar* (NW)
Clark, Steven J : *Voice* (Sco)
Clark, William : *Viola* (Lon)
Clarke, Aaron : *Guitars* (E)
Clarke, Alan : *Percussion* (E)
Clarke, Alden : *Keyboards* (Lon)
Clarke, Allan : *Guitars* (Mid)
Clarke, Andy : *Voice* (Mid)
Clarke, Anthony : *Guitars* (NW)
Clarke, Barbara : *Violin* (E)
Clarke, Basil : *Voice* (NW)
Clarke, Billy : *Trumpet* (SE)
Clarke, Bob : *Organ* (Mid)
Clarke, Brian : *Viola* (Lon)
Clarke, Brynly : *Bassoon* (Lon)
Clarke, Claire : *Voice* (Lon)
Clarke, David : *Bass Guitar* (Lon)
Clarke, David : *Guitars* (Lon)
Clarke, David : *Keyboards* (Lon)
Clarke, David : *Violin* (Mid)
Clarke, Dean : *Bass Guitar* (SE)
Clarke, Duncan : *Keyboards* (Lon)
Clarke, Eric : *Saxophones* (SW)
Clarke, Frank : *Double Bass* (Lon)
Clarke, Frank : *Saxophones* (SW)
Clarke, Garry : *Early Strings* (Mid)
Clarke, Glen : *Percussion* (Mid)
Clarke, Helen : *Oboe* (Lon)
Clarke, Ian : *Flute* (Lon)
Clarke, Ian : *Bass Guitar* (SE)
Clarke, Jack : *Saxophones* (SW)
Clarke, Jane : *Pianoforte* (SE)
Clarke, Jim : *Trombone* (Lon)
Clarke, Jimmi : *Guitars* (E)
Clarke, John : *Pianoforte* (SE)
Clarke, Jonathan : *Pianoforte* (Mid)
Clarke, Ken : *Clarinet* (E)
Clarke, Lisa : *Percussion* (Lon)
Clarke, Louise : *Oboe* (SW)
Clarke, Marcus : *Bass Trombone* (Lon)
Clarke, Maurice : *Voice* (Lon)
Clarke, Michael : *Double Bass* (Lon)
Clarke, Miranda : *Pianoforte* (Lon)
Clarke, Neil : *Viola* (Mid)
Clarke, Neil : *Voice* (Mid)
Clarke, Norman : *Pianoforte* (Lon)
Clarke, Norman : *Violin* (Lon)
Clarke, Oliver : *Pianoforte* (Mid)
Clarke, Owain : *Celtic Harp* (SE)
Clarke, Paul : *Trombone* (SE)
Clarke, Peter Andrew : *Bass Guitar* (Lon)
Clarke, Ralph : *Saxophones* (Sco)
Clarke, Richard : *Double Bass* (NE)
Clarke, Richie : *Pianoforte* (Mid)
Clarke, Robert : *Guitars* (SE)
Clarke, Robert : *Viola* (SW)
Clarke, Sarah : *Clarinet* (Lon)
Clarke, Sean : *Guitars* (NE)
Clarke, Sharon : *Voice* (Lon)
Clarke, Sheila : *Violin* (Mid)
Clarke, Simon : *Saxophones* (Lon)
Clarke, Suzannah : *Voice* (NW)
Clarke, Sycuano : *Keyboards* (Lon)
Clarke, Terence : *Double Bass* (SE)
Clarke, Terry : *Pianoforte* (Lon)
Clarke, Timothy : *Bass Guitar* (Sco)
Clarke, Tina : *Percussion* (Sco)
Clarke, Toussaint : *Steel Pan* (SW)
Clarkin, Paul : *Guitars* (E)
Clarkson, Anthony : *Keyboards* (NW)
Clarkson, Gustav : *Violin* (Lon)
Clarkson, Ian : *Voice* (Lon)
Clarkson, John : *Violin* (SE)

Clarkson, Ransford : *Percussion* (Mid)
Clarvis, Paul : *Percussion* (Lon)
Class, Sarah : *Pianoforte* (SW)
Classen, Uschi : *Keyboards* (Lon)
Clatworthy, Gina : *Saxophones* (Mid)
Claxton, Andrew : *Composer* (Lon)
Clay, Neville : *Guitars* (NE)
Clayden, Jonathan : *Voice* (Lon)
Clayden, Mark : *Bass Guitar* (Lon)
Clayden, Roger : *Cello* (SE)
Claydon, Mark : *Percussion* (Lon)
Claydon, Steven : *Keyboards* (Lon)
Clayton, Adam : *Bass Guitar* (Lon)
Clayton, Anthony : *Guitars* (Lon)
Clayton, David : *Keyboards* (Lon)
Clayton, Eddy : *Percussion* (E)
Clayton, Justin : *Guitars* (Lon)
Clayton, Kenny : *Pianoforte* (Lon)
Clayton, Leon : *Double Bass* (Lon)
Clayton, Lynn : *Guitars* (Lon)
Clayton, Malcolm : *Bass Guitar* (NE)
Clayton, Robin : *Bass Guitar* (Lon)
Clayton, Stephen : *Percussion* (NE)
Clayton, Vikki : *Voice* (Mid)
Cleal, Carol : *Cello* (SE)
Cleall, Robert : *Percussion* (SE)
Cleary, Joseph : *Pianoforte* (E)
Cleary, Neil : *Music Director* (E)
Cleaver, Mark : *Trumpet* (Mid)
Cleaver, Michael : *Pianoforte* (NE)
Cleaver, Ron : *Pianoforte* (Mid)
Clee, Ginny : *Voice* (Lon)
Clegg, Carole : *Voice* (NE)
Clegg, Eric : *Clarinet* (NE)
Clegg, Philip : *Violin* (NE)
Clegg, Rachael : *Oboe* (NW)
Clemas, James : *Pianoforte* (Mid)
Clement, Elizabeth : *Violin* (Sco)
Clement-Evans, Huw : *Oboe* (Lon)
Clement-Evans, Peryn : *Clarinet* (Lon)
Clement-Smith, Helen : *Violin* (E)
Clements, Antony : *Recorders* (Lon)
Clements, Heather : *Violin* (SE)
Clements, Joel : *Scratcher* (Lon)
Clements, Matt : *Percussion* (Lon)
Clements, Philip : *Trombone* (SW)
Clements, Rod : *Bass Guitar* (Lon)
Clements, Samantha : *Viola* (Lon)
Clements, Stuart : *Keyboards* (SE)
Clementson, Diana : *Oboe* (NW)
Clemmow, Katie : *Oboe* (Lon)
Clemo, Dave : *Guitars* (Mid)
Clempson, Clem : *Guitars* (Lon)
Clennon, Ornette : *Clarinet* (Sco)
Cleo : *Voice* (Lon)
Cleo : *Voice* (Mid)
Clerici, Brenda : *Flute* (SE)
Cleveland, Anthony : *Violin* (Lon)
Cleveland, Ivan : *Pianoforte* (E)
Cleveland, Trevor : *Saxophones* (SW)
Cleverley, Nicholas : *Guitars* (Mid)
Clewes, David : *Trombone* (Mid)
Clewlow, Alf : *Keyboards* (E)
Clewlow, David : *Trumpet* (Lon)
Clews, Dave : *Keyboards* (Lon)
Clews, Jacqueline : *Keyboards* (SW)
Clews, Karl : *Bass Guitar* (SE)
Clews, Martyn : *Bass Guitar* (Mid)
Clews, Michael : *Voice* (Mid)
Clews, Paul : *Guitars* (SW)
Clews, Richard : *Horn* (Lon)
Cleyndert, Andrew : *Double Bass* (Lon)
Clibbens, Sylvia : *Organ* (Lon)
Cliff, David : *Guitars* (Lon)
Cliff, Frank : *Viola* (E)

Cliff, Penelope : *Cello* (Lon)
Cliff, Tony : *Composer* (SW)
Cliffe, Marcus : *Bass Guitar* (NE)
Clifford, Bob : *Bass Guitar* (Lon)
Clifford, John : *Saxophones* (Mid)
Clifford, Jonathan : *Trombone* (Lon)
Clifford, Matt : *Keyboards* (Lon)
Clifford, Winston : *Percussion* (Lon)
Clift, Christopher : *Violin* (Mid)
Clift, Mick : *Trombone* (Mid)
Clift, Roger : *Keyboards* (Mid)
Clift, Roger : *Percussion* (SW)
Clifton, David : *Guitars* (Lon)
Clifton, Jacqueline : *Harpsichord* (Lon)
Clifton-Welker, Fiona : *Harp* (Lon)
Climie, Simon : *Voice* (Lon)
Clinch, David : *Bones* (Lon)
Cline-Bailey, William : *Percussion* (SE)
Clipsham, Caroline : *Pianoforte* (Lon)
Clisby, Donald : *Viola* (Lon)
Clissold, Helen : *Violin* (Lon)
Clist, Donald : *Horn* (NE)
Cload, Peter : *Guitars* (Lon)
Cloonan, Fay : *Violin* (Lon)
Close, Geoff : *Percussion* (NE)
Clothier, Michael : *Trumpet* (Lon)
Clough, Allison : *Bass Guitar* (NE)
Clough, Diana : *Flute* (NE)
Clough, Wendy : *Trombone* (SW)
Cloughton, Roy : *Pianoforte* (Lon)
Clouston, Keith : *Oud* (Lon)
Clout, Tony : *Arranger* (Lon)
Clouts, Philip : *Pianoforte* (Lon)
Clow, Dionne : *Double Bass* (NE)
Clow, Jim : *Flute* (Lon)
Clubley, Tom : *Guitars* (SE)
Clucas, Anthony : *Trumpet* (Sco)
Clugston, Simon : *Non Playing Member* (Mid)
Clunies-Ross, Andrew : *Cello* (SE)
Clutson, Steven : *Voice* (SW)
Clutterbuck, Carl : *Bass Guitar* (SW)
Clutterbuck, Paul : *Pianoforte* (SW)
Clutton, Christine : *Cello* (Lon)
Clyde, Thomas : *Percussion* (Sco)
Clynch, Alistair : *Guitars* (NW)
Clyne, Jeff : *Double Bass* (Lon)
Clynes, Kenneth : *Saxophones* (Mid)
Coady, Alan : *Guitars* (Sco)
Coady, Phillip : *Keyboards* (E)
Coase, Los : *Guitars* (NW)
Coatalen, Diana : *Voice* (Lon)
Coates, Alan : *Guitars* (Lon)
Coates, Bruce : *Saxophones* (Mid)
Coates, Emily : *Violin* (Lon)
Coates, Ian : *Pianoforte* (Mid)
Coates, John : *Guitars* (NE)
Coates, Kevin : *Mandolin* (Lon)
Coates, Leon : *Harpsichord* (Sco)
Coates, Michael : *Saxophones* (Lon)
Coates, Richard : *Pianoforte* (Lon)
Coates, Simon : *Guitars* (Lon)
Coates, Stanley : *Saxophones* (NE)
Coates, Tamara : *Oboe* (Lon)
Coates, Thomas : *Violin* (NE)
Coates, William : *Trumpet* (NE)
Coates-Smith, Mark : *Viola* (Lon)
Cobbett, G : *Percussion* (Lon)
Cobbing, Bob : *Voice* (Lon)
Cobham, Jeffrey : *Keyboards* (Lon)
Coburn, Alexander : *Guitars* (Lon)
Coccia, Dominic : *Percussion* (Lon)
Cochran, Wendy : *Violin* (NW)
Cochrane, Christopher : *Viola* (Lon)
Cochrane, Diom : *Percussion* (Mid)
Cochrane, Guy : *Pianoforte* (E)

Cochrane, Helen : *Violin* (Lon)
Cochrane, Laura : *Violin* (Lon)
Cochrane, Lisa : *Viola* (Lon)
Cochrane, Lynda : *Pianoforte* (Sco)
Cochrane, Willie : *Bagpipes* (Lon)
Cockayne, David : *Percussion* (Mid)
Cockbain, Garry : *Synthesiser* (Lon)
Cocker, Jarvis Branson : *Guitars* (NE)
Cocker, Peter : *Trombone* (Lon)
Cockerill, Craig : *Pianoforte* (NE)
Cockle, Alexander : *Pianoforte* (Lon)
Cockram, Raymond : *Organ* (SW)
Cockroft, Anna : *Violin* (SW)
Cocks, Adam : *Percussion* (NE)
Cocks, Elaine : *Clarinet* (Lon)
Cocks, Stuart : *Keyboards* (E)
Codd, Jean Marsden : *Oboe* (SW)
Codd, Robert : *Bassoon* (SW)
Code D : *Keyboards* (Lon)
CodJoe, Samuel : *Rapper* (Lon)
Codling, Andrew : *Saxophones* (Mid)
Codling, Paul : *Percussion* (E)
Cody, Maurice : *Clarinet* (Lon)
Coe, Anthony : *Clarinet* (Lon)
Coe, Debbie : *Clarinet* (NW)
Coe, Jane : *Cello* (SE)
Coe, Melrose : *Voice* (Lon)
Coe, Pete : *Bouzouki* (NE)
Coe, Peter : *Saxophones* (Lon)
Coffey, Joan : *Voice* (Lon)
Cohen, Alan : *Composer* (Lon)
Cohen, Benjamin : *Trumpet* (Lon)
Cohen, Chase : *Keyboards* (Lon)
Cohen, Gillian : *Violin* (Lon)
Cohen, Jon : *Keyboards* (Lon)
Cohen, Jonathan : *Pianoforte* (Lon)
Cohen, Jonathan : *Saxophones* (Lon)
Cohen, Kenneth : *Pianoforte* (Lon)
Cohen, Leon : *Pianoforte* (Lon)
Cohen, Mary : *Violin* (Mid)
Cohen, Nicholas : *Bass Guitar* (Lon)
Cohen, Raymond : *Violin* (Lon)
Cohen, Ross : *Viola* (SW)
Cohen, Ruth : *Viola* (Lon)
Cohen, Susanna : *Bassoon* (Lon)
Coigley, James : *Guitars* (Lon)
Coker, Aduragbemi : *Voice* (Lon)
Coker, David : *Keyboards* (Lon)
Coker, Eric : *Trumpet* (Lon)
Cola, Nick : *Keyboards* (Lon)
Colam, Simon : *Pianoforte* (Lon)
Colbert, Laurence : *Percussion* (SE)
Colborne, W : *Double Bass* (Lon)
Colburn, Richard : *Percussion* (Sco)
Colburt, Peter : *Percussion* (SE)
Colchester, Sheila : *Pianoforte* (SE)
Coldrick, Mark : *Percussion* (Lon)
Coldwell, Terry : *Voice* (Lon)
Cole, Andrew : *Oboe* (NE)
Cole, BJ : *Guitars* (Lon)
Cole, Chris : *Trombone* (Lon)
Cole, David : *Trombone* (E)
Cole, Dennis : *Violin* (SW)
Cole, Elmer : *Flute* (Lon)
Cole, Geoffrey : *Trombone* (Lon)
Cole, George : *Percussion* (Lon)
Cole, Gracie : *Trumpet* (Lon)
Cole, Helen : *Harp* (Lon)
Cole, Joanne : *Cello* (Lon)
Cole, John : *Percussion* (SE)
Cole, Jonathan : *Bass Guitar* (E)
Cole, Kevin : *Bass Guitar* (SW)
Cole, Maggie : *Harpsichord* (Lon)
Cole, Michael : *Pianoforte* (E)
Cole, Michael : *Bassoon* (Lon)

Cole, Michael : *Double Bass* (Lon)
Cole, Michael : *Bass Guitar* (Mid)
Cole, Nicholas : *Tympani* (Lon)
Cole, Peter : *Viola* (Mid)
Cole, Stephen : *Pianoforte* (Lon)
Cole, Susan : *Flute* (SW)
Cole, Travis : *Voice* (Lon)
Cole, William : *Double Bass* (Mid)
Coleby, Grant : *Guitars* (Lon)
Coleman, Bill : *Double Bass* (Mid)
Coleman, Blanche : *Violin* (Lon)
Coleman, Colin : *Guitars* (E)
Coleman, David : *Pianoforte* (Lon)
Coleman, Hilary : *Clarinet* (SW)
Coleman, Jamie : *Trumpet* (Lon)
Coleman, Jazz : *Keyboards* (Lon)
Coleman, Jeffrey : *Guitars* (SW)
Coleman, John : *Music Director* (Lon)
Coleman, John : *Pianoforte* (Mid)
Coleman, Matthew : *Pianoforte* (Lon)
Coleman, Nicholas : *Mandolin* (E)
Coleman, Paul : *Voice* (NE)
Coleman, Peter : *Percussion* (Lon)
Coleman, Rebecca : *Violin* (Lon)
Coleman, Robert : *Guitars* (Lon)
Coleman, Stephen : *Pianoforte* (Lon)
Coleman, W : *Trombone* (Lon)
Coles, Andrew : *Guitars* (Lon)
Coles, Derren : *Clarinet* (Lon)
Coles, James : *Violin* (Lon)
Coles, Janet : *Cello* (Lon)
Coles, Richard : *Percussion* (Lon)
Coles, Richard : *Pianoforte* (Lon)
Coles, Toby : *Trumpet* (Lon)
Colin : *Guitars* (NE)
Coling, Leo : *Voice* (SW)
Collarbone, Barry : *Trumpet* (SE)
Collarbone, Winifred : *Cello* (Mid)
Collard, Esther : *Clarinet* (Lon)
Collcutt, Terence : *Keyboards* (Lon)
Collen, James : *Bass Guitar* (SE)
Collen, Paul : *Violin* (Lon)
Collen, Philip : *Guitars* (Lon)
Collett, Andrew : *Guitars* (Mid)
Collett, David : *Pianoforte* (SW)
Collett-Simpson, Reginald : *Arranger* (SE)
Collie, Max : *Trombone* (Lon)
Collier, Andrew : *Flute* (Lon)
Collier, Anne-Marie : *Guitars* (SW)
Collier, Cliff : *Saxophones* (SW)
Collier, Daniel : *Violin* (Lon)
Collier, Derek : *Violin* (Lon)
Collier, Graham : *Composer* (Lon)
Collier, J Jayne : *Cello* (SE)
Collier, Michael : *Trombone* (SE)
Collier, Susan : *Violin* (Lon)
Colling, Jonathan : *Keyboards* (NW)
Colling, Robert : *Keyboards* (NE)
Collinge, John : *Trombone* (E)
Collinge-Hill, Lucy : *Violin* (Mid)
Collingham, Ray : *Latin American Percu* (Lon)
Collingwood, Timothy : *Keyboards* (SW)
Collins, Andrew : *Double Bass* (SE)
Collins, Arthur : *Guitars* (Sco)
Collins, Billie : *Keyboards* (SE)
Collins, Charlie : *Saxophones* (NE)
Collins, David : *Synthesiser* (NE)
Collins, Ed : *Trumpet* (NE)
Collins, Edwin : *Guitars* (Lon)
Collins, Gerald : *Guitars* (Lon)
Collins, Henry : *Trumpet* (Lon)
Collins, Jo : *Voice* (Lon)
Collins, John : *Guitars* (Lon)
Collins, John : *Saxophones* (Lon)
Collins, Johnny : *Guitars* (Lon)

Collins, Leslie : *Double Bass* (Lon)
Collins, Mel : *Saxophones* (Lon)
Collins, Michael : *Bass Guitar* (Lon)
Collins, Michael : *Trumpet* (Lon)
Collins, Philip : *Percussion* (Lon)
Collins, Ronald : *Pianoforte* (SE)
Collins, Rosie : *Oboe* (NW)
Collins, Steve : *Voice* (SW)
Collins, Tom : *Trumpet* (E)
Collins, Trevor : *Viola* (Mid)
Collinson, Alex : *Pianoforte* (Lon)
Collinson, Christopher : *Bass Guitar* (SW)
Collinson, Francis : *Music Director* (Lon)
Collis, Bill : *Percussion* (Lon)
Collis, Christopher : *Pianoforte* (Mid)
Collis, E Anne : *Tympani* (Lon)
Collis, Peter : *Conductor* (Lon)
Collison, Dennis : *Percussion* (SE)
Collisson, Sacha : *Guitars* (Lon)
Collisson, Stephen : *Pianoforte* (Mid)
Collister, Christine : *Voice* (Lon)
Collumbine, Syd : *Guitars* (NE)
Collyer, Peter : *Viola* (Lon)
Colman, Anna : *Violin* (Lon)
Colman, Anthony : *Voice* (Lon)
Colman, Matthew : *Trombone* (Lon)
Colman, Robert : *Violin* (SE)
Colman, Sara : *Voice* (Mid)
Colman, Timothy : *Violin* (Lon)
Colquhoun, Andy : *Saxophones* (NW)
Colquhoun, David : *Guitars* (Lon)
Coltart, Robert : *Guitars* (SE)
Coltham, Mike : *Voice* (SE)
Colville, Donna : *Clarinet* (SW)
Colville, Randolph : *Clarinet* (SE)
Colvin, Colin : *Trumpet* (NW)
Colwell, Catherine : *Double Bass* (Lon)
Colwell, Richard : *Keyboards* (SE)
Colwyn, Lord Ian : *Percussion* (SW)
Colyer, Ronald : *Violin* (SE)
Coman, Matthew : *Double Bass* (Lon)
Comberti, Micaela : *Violin* (Lon)
Comberti, Sebastian : *Cello* (Lon)
Comer, Tex : *Bass Guitar* (Lon)
Comfort, Marianne : *Violin* (Lon)
Commey-Taylor, Samantha : *Voice* (Lon)
Compton, Chris : *Guitars* (Lon)
Compton, Daniel : *Guitars* (E)
Compton, Ernest : *Double Bass* (SW)
Compton, James : *Keyboards* (Lon)
Compton, Matthew : *Viola* (NW)
Conaghan, Stuart : *Pianoforte* (Sco)
Concannon, Kieron : *Uilleann* (Mid)
Concannon Hodges, Nicholas : *Violin* (Lon)
Condie, James : *Guitars* (Sco)
Condie, Philip : *Voice* (Sco)
Condliffe, Jacqueline : *Clarinet* (Mid)
Condliffe, Mary : *Double Bass* (SW)
Condon, Chris : *Saxophones* (Lon)
Condon, Martin : *Guitars* (SE)
Condon, Matthew : *Keyboards* (Lon)
Condon, Paul : *Bass Guitar* (Lon)
Condon, Peter : *Trumpet* (Lon)
Coney, John : *Horn* (Lon)
Coney, Patrick : *Saxophones* (SE)
Congdon, David : *Keyboards* (Lon)
Conibear, Peter : *Clarinet* (SE)
Conlan, Anita : *Voice* (Lon)
Conlon, Gerry : *Accordion* (Sco)
Conlon, John : *Bass Guitar* (Lon)
Conlon, Sean : *Keyboards* (NE)
Conn, Harry : *Saxophones* (Lon)
Connah, Lyndon : *Keyboards* (Lon)
Connaris, Michael : *Guitars* (Lon)
Conneally, Paul : *Voice* (Mid)

Conneff, Kevin : *Bodhran* (Lon)
Connell, Andrew : *Keyboards* (NW)
Connell, Marie : *Cello* (Sco)
Connell, Myles : *Pianoforte* (Lon)
Connell, Patrick : *Pianoforte* (NW)
Connell, Sean : *Guitars* (SW)
Connell-Hinkes, John : *Guitars* (SE)
Conner, Trevor James : *Voice* (Lon)
Connery, Sam : *Pianoforte* (Lon)
Connett, Maureen : *Voice* (Lon)
Connolly, Matthew : *Guitars* (Lon)
Connolly, Robert : *Bassoon* (NW)
Connolly, Shane : *Taiko Drums* (Sco)
Connolly, William : *Guitars* (Sco)
Connor, Bill : *Composer* (NW)
Connor, Charles : *Saxophones* (E)
Connor, Mary : *Percussion* (Sco)
Connor, Paul : *Accordion* (NW)
Connors, Clare : *Violin* (Lon)
Conomy, Sean : *Guitars* (NE)
Conor : *Keyboards* (Sco)
Conroy, Sean : *Guitars* (NW)
Conscious Ken : *Voice* (E)
Considine, Rachel : *Clarinet* (Sco)
Consoli, Pascal : *Percussion* (Lon)
Constable, Caitlin : *Viola* (NW)
Constable, Claire : *Cello* (Lon)
Constable, James : *Voice* (Sco)
Constable, Jennifer : *Violin* (SW)
Constable, John : *Pianoforte* (Lon)
Constable, Katharine : *Flute* (Lon)
Constance, Peter : *Pianoforte* (NE)
Constantin, Virginie : *Voice* (Lon)
Constantine, Benjamin : *Violin* (Lon)
Constantine, Helen : *Voice* (Lon)
Constantinou, Stace : *Pianoforte* (Mid)
Contogeorge, Peter : *Guitars* (Lon)
Contractor, Ruth : *Oboe* (Lon)
Conway, Christopher : *Pianoforte* (Mid)
Conway, David : *Guitars* (Lon)
Conway, Gerry : *Percussion* (Lon)
Conway, Shaun : *Guitars* (NE)
Conway, William : *Cello* (Sco)
Conway, William : *Conductor* (Sco)
Cook, Adrian : *Violin* (NE)
Cook, Alec : *Guitars* (NW)
Cook, Andrew : *Percussion* (NE)
Cook, Barry : *Percussion* (Lon)
Cook, Betsy : *Keyboards* (Lon)
Cook, Bobby : *Percussion* (Lon)
Cook, Carole : *Voice* (Lon)
Cook, Colin : *Organ* (NE)
Cook, Dick : *Clarinet* (Lon)
Cook, Don : *Percussion* (Lon)
Cook, Francesca : *Double Bass* (Lon)
Cook, Gillian : *Violin* (SE)
Cook, James : *Voice* (E)
Cook, Jez : *Guitars* (SE)
Cook, John : *Bass Guitar* (E)
Cook, John : *Trumpet* (E)
Cook, John : *Keyboards* (Lon)
Cook, John : *Trombone* (Mid)
Cook, John : *Keyboards* (NE)
Cook, John : *Cello* (NW)
Cook, John : *Percussion* (SE)
Cook, Kevin : *Percussion* (SW)
Cook, Lee : *Percussion* (SE)
Cook, Leonard : *Pianoforte* (SW)
Cook, Lisa : *Keyboards* (Mid)
Cook, Lynn : *Violin* (Lon)
Cook, Martin : *Pianoforte* (Lon)
Cook, Natasha : *Clarinet* (Lon)
Cook, Norman : *Bass Guitar* (SE)
Cook, Peter : *Saxophones* (Lon)
Cook, Sean : *Bass Guitar* (SW)

Cook, Simon : *Double Bass* (Lon)
Cook, Timothy : *Voice* (NE)
Cook Berendina, Jill : *Pianoforte* (SE)
Cooke, Alfred : *Saxophones* (Mid)
Cooke, Alistair : *Percussion* (Sco)
Cooke, David : *Guitars* (Lon)
Cooke, David : *Guitars* (NE)
Cooke, Eleanor : *Violin* (Mid)
Cooke, Jeremy : *Pianoforte* (E)
Cooke, John : *Keyboards* (E)
Cooke, John : *Voice* (NW)
Cooke, Matthew : *Horn* (NW)
Cooke, Michael : *Organ* (SE)
Cooke, Peter : *Pianoforte* (SE)
Cooke, Stephen : *Violin* (SE)
Cooke, Terence : *Voice* (Lon)
Cookhorn, Margaret : *Bassoon* (Mid)
Cookman, Louise : *Voice* (Lon)
Cooksley, Andrew : *Guitars* (SW)
Cookson, Andrew : *Percussion* (SE)
Cookson, Francesca : *Voice* (NW)
Cookson, Michael : *Viola* (Lon)
Cookson, Richard : *Viola* (Lon)
Cool, Johnny Ace : *Bass Guitar* (SW)
Cool, Ricky : *Harmonica (Inc Bass* (Mid)
Cooley, Catherine : *Violin* (NE)
Cooley, Jase : *Percussion* (Mid)
Cooling, Leslie : *Organ* (NE)
Cooling, Mike : *Guitars* (Mid)
Coombes, Douglas : *Pianoforte* (E)
Coombes, Jacqueline : *Bass Guitar* (Lon)
Coombes, Jarrod : *Double Bass* (SE)
Coombes, Joel : *Bass Guitar* (Mid)
Coombes, Nigel : *Clarinet* (Lon)
Coombes, Robert : *Keyboards* (SE)
Coombs, Catherine : *Violin* (E)
Coombs, Dominic : *Guitars* (Mid)
Coombs, George : *Percussion* (Lon)
Coombs, Mike : *Guitars* (E)
Coombs, Nicolas : *Trumpet* (Mid)
Coombs, Timothy : *Trombone* (SW)
Coombs, William : *Pianoforte* (SE)
Coope, Barry : *Voice* (Mid)
Cooper, Alan : *Double Bass* (NW)
Cooper, Albert : *Trombone* (Sco)
Cooper, Albert : *Percussion* (SE)
Cooper, Anna : *Oboe* (NW)
Cooper, Charly : *Saxophones* (SE)
Cooper, Clive : *Bass Guitar* (Lon)
Cooper, David : *Percussion* (NE)
Cooper, David : *Violin* (NE)
Cooper, Deirdre : *Cello* (Lon)
Cooper, Derek : *Saxophones* (SE)
Cooper, Dorothy : *Voice* (SE)
Cooper, Douglas : *Bandleader* (Lon)
Cooper, Douglas : *Percussion* (SW)
Cooper, Edward : *Keyboards* (Lon)
Cooper, Frank : *Cello* (NE)
Cooper, Freddie : *Percussion* (SW)
Cooper, Gary : *Harpsichord* (SE)
Cooper, Geoffrey : *Percussion* (Lon)
Cooper, Gordon : *Clarinet* (Lon)
Cooper, Helen : *Violin* (Lon)
Cooper, Henry : *Pianoforte* (Lon)
Cooper, Ian : *Double Bass* (SW)
Cooper, Jason : *Percussion* (Lon)
Cooper, Joe : *Voice* (Lon)
Cooper, John : *Double Bass* (Lon)
Cooper, John : *Keyboards* (Lon)
Cooper, John : *Violin* (NE)
Cooper, John : *Clarinet* (SW)
Cooper, Jonathan : *Keyboards* (E)
Cooper, Jonathan : *Clarinet* (Lon)
Cooper, Joseph : *Percussion* (Lon)
Cooper, Judith : *Viola* (Lon)

Cooper, Julian : *Guitars* (Lon)
Cooper, Julie : *Pianoforte* (Lon)
Cooper, Laurence : *Trombone* (NW)
Cooper, Lindsay : *Bassoon* (Lon)
Cooper, Lindsay : *Double Bass* (Sco)
Cooper, Marc : *Early Strings* (Lon)
Cooper, Mark : *Bass Guitar* (SE)
Cooper, Martyn : *Keyboards* (SE)
Cooper, Michael : *Keyboards* (Lon)
Cooper, Mike : *Voice* (Lon)
Cooper, Neville : *Guitars* (Mid)
Cooper, Nicholas : *Cello* (Lon)
Cooper, Pete : *Violin* (Lon)
Cooper, Peter : *Double Bass* (Lon)
Cooper, Philip : *Double Bass* (NE)
Cooper, Rachel : *Guitars* (NE)
Cooper, Ray : *Bass Guitar* (Lon)
Cooper, Raymond : *Saxophones* (NE)
Cooper, Robert : *Violin* (Lon)
Cooper, Sally : *Pianoforte* (Lon)
Cooper, Susan : *Cello* (Lon)
Cooper, Thomas : *Percussion* (E)
Cooper, Veronica : *Viola* (Sco)
Cooper, William : *Trombone* (Mid)
Cooper-Sherring, Mary : *Pianoforte* (SE)
Coote, Anthony : *Guitars* (Lon)
Coote, Heather : *Clarinet* (SW)
Coote, Nicholas : *Cello* (Lon)
Copas, Belinda : *Pianoforte* (Lon)
Copas, Paul : *Clarinet* (Lon)
Copeland, Stuart : *Percussion* (Lon)
Copeland, Sybil : *Violin* (Lon)
Copeland, Valerie : *Songwriter* (Lon)
Copland, Neil : *Accordion* (Sco)
Copland-Cale, R : *Euphonium* (Lon)
Copley, James : *Percussion* (SW)
Copp, Gillian : *Cello* (Sco)
Coppard, Sue : *Accordion* (SW)
Coppard, Tessa : *Pianoforte* (Lon)
Coppen, John : *Saxophones* (Lon)
Copperthwaite, James : *Pianoforte* (Lon)
Copperwaite, David : *Trumpet* (NW)
Copperwheat, Elizabeth : *Violin* (Lon)
Copus, Antony : *Horn* (Lon)
Coram, Jeremy : *Guitars* (NE)
Corbet, Alan : *Pianoforte* (Mid)
Corbett, Alan : *Saxophones* (Sco)
Corbett, Ben : *Bass Guitar* (Lon)
Corbett, Bryan : *Trumpet* (Mid)
Corbett, Daniel : *Guitars* (Lon)
Corbett, Dave : *Keyboards* (Mid)
Corbett, David : *Keyboards* (SE)
Corbett, Geoffrey : *Conductor* (Lon)
Corbett, Guy : *Accordion* (SE)
Corbett, Heather : *Cimbalon* (Sco)
Corbett, Heather : *Percussion* (Sco)
Corbett, Heather : *Pianoforte* (Sco)
Corbett, Heather : *Tympani* (Sco)
Corbett, Ian : *Guitars* (NE)
Corbett, Jon : *Trumpet* (E)
Corbett, Peter : *Pianoforte* (Lon)
Corbould, Graham : *Guitars* (Lon)
Corbyn, Michael : *Percussion* (E)
Corcoran, Chris : *Guitars* (SE)
Corcoran, Christopher : *Keyboards* (Mid)
Corcoran, John : *Saxophones* (SE)
Corcoran, Tony : *Violin* (NE)
Corcos, Nadia : *Cello* (SW)
Cordell, John : *Bass Guitar* (Lon)
Cordery, Jeanette : *Harp* (Lon)
Cordiner, A : *Pianoforte* (Sco)
Cordle, Matthew : *Pianoforte* (SE)
Core, Stephanie : *Flute* (Lon)
Corello, Paul : *Guitars* (Lon)
Cork, Peter : *Composer* (SE)

Drew, Martin : *Percussion* (Lon)
Drew, Paul : *Guitars* (Lon)
Drewery, Corinne : *Voice* (Lon)
Drez : *Voice* (Lon)
Driessen, Ellert : *Keyboards* (Lon)
Drinkall, Hilary : *Cello* (E)
Drinkall, Spencer : *Clarinet* (E)
Drinkwater, Neil : *Pianoforte* (Lon)
Driscole, Reginald : *Keyboards* (SW)
Driscoll, Elizabeth : *Viola* (Lon)
Driscoll, Geoff : *Saxophones* (Lon)
Driscoll, Kim : *Violin* (SW)
Driscoll, Ray : *Saxophones* (SW)
Driver, Fiona : *Folk Fiddle* (Sco)
Driver, Richard : *Double Bass* (Lon)
Drouet, Ben : *Saxophones* (Mid)
Drought, Geraldine : *Violin* (Lon)
Drover, Adrian : *Bass Trombone* (Sco)
Drover, Adrian : *Music Director* (Sco)
Drover, Martin : *Trumpet* (Lon)
Druce, Duncan : *Violin* (Lon)
Drucker, Gerald : *Double Bass* (Lon)
Drudy, Andy : *Guitars* (Lon)
Drum : *Percussion* (NW)
Drumhead : *Percussion* (Lon)
Drumm, Ian : *Guitars* (NW)
Drummond, Amanda : *Viola* (Lon)
Drummond, Jackie : *Percussion* (Lon)
Drummond, James : *Percussion* (Sco)
Drummond, James : *Viola* (SW)
Drummond, Pippa : *Flute* (Mid)
Drummond, Terry : *Guitars* (Lon)
Drury, Sarah : *Violin* (Lon)
Dryden, Dave : *Guitars* (NE)
Dryden, Kenneth : *Flute* (SE)
Dryer-Beers, Anna : *Violin* (Mid)
Dryer-Beers, Thomas : *Saxophones* (Mid)
Drysdale, Dainty : *Clarinet* (Lon)
Du Feu, Avril : *Saxophones* (SW)
Du Feu, Elizabeth : *Violin* (SW)
Du Valle, Cecil : *Pianoforte* (SW)
Du-Fresne, Graeme : *Pianoforte* (NE)
Duarl, Meena Louise : *Pianoforte* (NW)
Dubber, Godfrey : *Clarinet* (Lon)
Dubois, Lewis : *Bass Guitar* (Sco)
Dubroff, Julie : *Guitars* (E)
Ducil, Roy : *Voice* (Lon)
Duckers, Kenneth : *Saxophones* (NW)
Duckett, Catherine : *Bassoon* (Lon)
Duckworth, Ruth : *Flute* (NW)
Dudding, Hilary : *Violin* (Sco)
Dudding, Paul : *Horn* (Mid)
Duddington, Alan : *Double Bass* (SE)
Dudgeon, Gus : *Percussion* (SE)
Dudley, Roger : *Trombone* (Lon)
Dudley, Stephen : *Violin* (Lon)
Dudley, Tony : *Trumpet* (Lon)
Dudman, Colin : *Pianoforte* (Lon)
Dudman, Peter : *Keyboards* (Lon)
Dudzik, Bogdan : *Saxophones* (SE)
Duerden, Fred : *Music Director* (SW)
Duerden, Quentin : *Trombone* (Mid)
Duff, Jack : *Saxophones* (Sco)
Duff, Robert : *Organ* (Mid)
Duffield, Michael : *Viola* (Lon)
Duffin, Graeme : *Guitars* (Sco)
Duffin, Lesley : *Violin* (Sco)
Duffy, Bernard : *Violin* (SE)
Duffy, Billy : *Guitars* (Lon)
Duffy, Gerald : *Violin* (NW)
Duffy, Keith : *Bass Guitar* (Lon)
Duffy, Kevin : *Violin* (Lon)
Duffy, Liam : *Horn* (NW)
Duffy, Margaret : *Violin* (NW)
Duffy, Martin : *Pianoforte* (Lon)

Duffy, Melvin : *Guitars* (Lon)
Duffy, Pip : *Voice* (E)
Duffy, Robert : *Double Bass* (NW)
Duffy, Stephen : *Guitars* (Mid)
Duffy, Stephen : *Voice* (Sco)
Dufty, Nigel : *Double Bass* (NW)
Duggan, Daniel : *Percussion* (Sco)
Duggan, Geoffrey : *Viola* (Mid)
Duggan, Linda : *Voice* (Lon)
Duggan, Louisa : *Harp* (Lon)
Duggins, Paul : *Pianoforte* (Mid)
Dugmore, Geoffrey : *Percussion* (Lon)
Duguid, Irvin : *Pianoforte* (Lon)
Duhalde, Fernando : *Percussion* (Lon)
Duizend, Matthew : *Trumpet* (Lon)
Duke, Henry : *Pianoforte* (SE)
Dukes, Philip : *Viola* (Lon)
Dukov, Bruce : *Violin* (Lon)
Dulcimers, Dove : *Hammer Dulcimer* (SW)
Dumas, Andre : *Accordion* (NW)
Dumas, Charles : *Trumpet* (Lon)
Dummer, Stephen : *Conductor* (SE)
Dumrese, Maria : *Viola* (Lon)
Dunbar, Edward : *Bass Guitar* (Sco)
Dunbar, Frank : *Guitars* (Sco)
Dunbar, Patrick : *Highland Bagpipes* (SW)
Duncan, Alex : *Guitars* (SW)
Duncan, Andrew : *Tuba* (NW)
Duncan, Archibald : *Accordion* (Sco)
Duncan, Donald : *Keyboards* (NE)
Duncan, Fiona : *Violin* (Lon)
Duncan, Fiona : *Voice* (Sco)
Duncan, Helen : *Cello* (Sco)
Duncan, Mary J : *Violin* (Sco)
Duncan, Molly : *Saxophones* (Lon)
Duncan, Ossy : *Electric Double Bass* (Lon)
Duncan, Paul : *Cello* (Sco)
Duncan, Pete : *Bass Guitar* (Lon)
Duncan, Peter : *Trumpet* (Lon)
Duncan, Philip : *Bass Guitar* (NW)
Duncan, Robert : *Viola* (Lon)
Duncan, Robert : *Pianoforte* (Sco)
Duncan, Robin : *Guitars* (Sco)
Duncan-Sutherland, Margaret : *Voice* (Lon)
Duncombe, Leslie : *Accordion* (SE)
Dundas-Grant, Deirdre : *Bassoon* (Lon)
Dunford, John : *Guitars* (NW)
Dunford, Philip : *Bass Guitar* (SW)
Dungey, Peter : *Trombone* (SE)
Dunk, Roderick : *Conductor* (Lon)
Dunkley, James : *Saxophones* (SE)
Dunkley, Matthew : *Arranger* (Lon)
Dunkley, Michael : *Percussion* (Mid)
Dunleavy, Anthony : *Trombone* (NW)
Dunlop, Andrew : *Guitars* (Lon)
Dunlop, Thomas : *Saxophones* (SW)
Dunmall, Paul : *Saxophones* (Lon)
Dunmore, John : *Saxophones* (Mid)
Dunn, Adrian : *Violin* (Lon)
Dunn, Alan : *Accordion* (Lon)
Dunn, Andrew : *Trumpet* (Lon)
Dunn, Belinda : *Flute* (Lon)
Dunn, Christopher : *Pianoforte* (Lon)
Dunn, Claire : *Viola* (Sco)
Dunn, Gary : *Guitars* (NE)
Dunn, Geoffrey : *Percussion* (Lon)
Dunn, Jonathan : *Pianoforte* (NW)
Dunn, Julie : *Voice* (Lon)
Dunn, Lawrence : *Early Strings* (Sco)
Dunn, Lawrence : *Violin* (Sco)
Dunn, Marjorie : *Horn* (Lon)
Dunn, Martin : *Flute* (NE)
Dunn, Peter J : *Bass Guitar* (Mid)
Dunn, Robin : *Violin* (NE)
Dunne, Patrick : *Pianoforte* (Lon)

Dunne, Paul : *Guitars* (Lon)
Dunne, Ronan : *Double Bass* (Lon)
Dunning, Paul : *Guitars* (Sco)
Dunning, Ronald : *Double Bass* (Lon)
Dunning, Steve : *Bass Guitar* (Lon)
Dunning, Steve : *Guitars* (SE)
Dunsdon, Martin : *Saxophones* (Lon)
Dunsford, Yona : *Voice* (Lon)
Dunsmore, Allan : *Bagpipes* (Lon)
Dunsmore, John : *Clarinet* (Sco)
Dunstall, Clive : *Pianoforte* (Lon)
Dunstall, Ernie : *Pianoforte* (Lon)
Dunstan, Dunstan : *Guitars* (SE)
Dunstan, James : *Pianoforte* (Mid)
Dupin, Valerie : *Percussion* (Sco)
Duprez, John : *Horn* (Lon)
Dupuy, Nicki : *Double Bass* (NW)
Duran, Elena : *Flute* (Lon)
Durand, Jacqueline : *Voice* (Lon)
Durant, Bob : *Bass Guitar* (SE)
Durban, Andrew : *Double Bass* (Lon)
Durbin, Robin : *Guitars* (NE)
Durbin, Rose : *Pianoforte* (NW)
Durell, Matthew : *Bass Guitar* (Lon)
Durell, Mike : *Double Bass* (Lon)
Durell, Sarah : *Euphonium* (Lon)
Durham, Catherine : *Cello* (SW)
Durham, Christopher : *Percussion* (SE)
Durham, Michael : *Trumpet* (NE)
Durham, Peter : *Percussion* (SE)
Durkan, Jessie : *Horn* (Lon)
Durnford, Alexander : *Percussion* (Lon)
Durnford, Simon : *Bassoon* (NW)
Durrant, David : *Trombone* (SE)
Durrant, John : *Trumpet* (Lon)
Durrant, Jonathan : *Horn* (Sco)
Durrant, Peter : *Trumpet* (SW)
Durrant, R : *Viola* (Sco)
Durrant, Richard : *Guitars* (SE)
Durrent, Peter : *Pianoforte* (Lon)
Durvesh, Aref : *Dholak* (Lon)
Durvesh, Kadir : *Shehanai* (Lon)
Dury, Ian : *Voice* (Lon)
Dussek, Michael : *Pianoforte* (Lon)
Dussek, Sarah : *Violin* (Lon)
Dutfield, Gerald : *Percussion* (Mid)
Duthie, Joanna : *Horn* (Sco)
Dutiro, Chartwell : *Mbira* (Lon)
Dutson Bromley, Darren : *Guitars* (NE)
Dutton, Mark : *Percussion* (E)
Dutton, Owen : *Keyboards* (Mid)
Dutton, Richard : *Pianoforte* (SE)
Dutton, Roy : *Percussion* (Mid)
Duverney, Michele : *Voice* (Lon)
Duvoisin, Michel : *Songwriter* (Lon)
Duvoisin, Patrick : *Club DJ* (Lon)
Dux, Tim : *Guitars* (Lon)
Duxbury, Mark : *Bass Guitar* (SW)
Dvorak, James : *Trumpet* (Lon)
Dworniak, Joseph : *Bass Guitar* (Lon)
Dwyer, Adrian : *Double Bass* (SE)
Dwyer, Paul : *Bass Guitar* (Lon)
Dwyer, Sally-Ann : *Voice* (SW)
Dwynell, Andre : *Trombone* (NE)
Dyani-Akuru, Thomas : *Percussion* (Lon)
Dyball, Jeffrey : *Harp* (Lon)
Dye, Patrick : *Guitars* (NE)
Dyer, Andrew : *Pianoforte* (NE)
Dyer, Billy : *Bass Guitar* (E)
Dyer, Chubb : *Voice* (SE)
Dyer, Dave : *Guitars* (Lon)
Dyer, Graham : *Oboe* (SW)
Dyer, Jonathan : *Pianoforte* (E)
Dyer, Joye : *Keyboards* (E)
Dyer, Julie : *Percussion* (Lon)

Dyer, Muriel : *Violin* (Sco)
Dyer, Peter : *Voice* (Mid)
Dyer, Sherene : *Voice* (Lon)
Dyke, Jonathan : *Keyboards* (Mid)
Dyke-Smith, T J : *Pianoforte* (SE)
Dylak, Anthony : *Clarinet* (NE)
Dyne, Malcolm : *Keyboards* (SE)
Dyne, Marcus : *Keyboards* (Lon)
Dyson, George : *Double Bass* (SW)
Dyson, John : *Saxophones* (NW)
Dyson, Katherine : *Guitars* (NW)
Dyson, Lewis : *Percussion* (Mid)
Dyson, Mark : *Keyboards* (Lon)
Dyson, Norman : *Organ* (Mid)
Dyson, Peter : *Horn* (Mid)
Dyson, Sally : *Horn* (Mid)
Dyson, Wendy : *Violin* (NE)
Dytham, Nicholas : *Double Bass* (E)
Dytor, Sarah : *Violin* (SE)
Dzierzanowski, Udo : *Guitars* (SE)

E

E, Mr : *Keyboards* (Lon)
Eade, Winston : *Songwriter* (SE)
Eaden, Eric : *Violin* (Lon)
Eager, Mark : *Trombone* (Lon)
Eagles, Harvey : *Cello* (Lon)
Eaglesham, John : *Concertina (Inc Engl* (Sco)
Eaglestone, Robin : *Bass Guitar* (Lon)
Eales, Adrian : *Violin* (SW)
Eales, Ben : *Guitars* (Lon)
Eales, Geoff : *Pianoforte* (Lon)
Ealovega, Benjamin : *Guitars* (Lon)
Eames, Judith : *Voice* (SE)
Eames, Roger : *Double Bass* (SW)
Eames, Timothy : *Keyboards* (Lon)
Eames, Tudur : *Harp* (Lon)
Eardley, Aidan : *Cello* (SW)
Eardley, Ian : *Guitars* (Mid)
Eardley, Janice : *Voice* (Mid)
Earl : *Bass Guitar* (Lon)
Earl, Roderick : *Guitars* (SW)
Earl 16 : *Voice* (Lon)
Earle, Richard : *Oboe* (Lon)
Earley, Judith : *Pianoforte* (Lon)
Earley, Kevin : *Percussion* (Lon)
Easener, Marc : *Tuba* (Lon)
East, Angela : *Cello* (Lon)
East, Carol : *Flute* (Mid)
East, Denis : *Violin* (Lon)
East, Imogen : *Violin* (Lon)
East, Ruth : *Cello* (Lon)
Eastabrook, Cliff : *Bass Guitar* (Lon)
Eastaugh, Martin : *Bass Guitar* (Mid)
Eastaway, James : *Oboe* (Lon)
Eastbury, Jonathan : *Composer* (Mid)
Eastcott, John : *Double Bass* (SE)
Eastham, Stuart : *Bass Guitar* (NW)
Eastick, William : *Organ* (E)
Eastley, Max : *Arc* (Lon)
Eastman, Cyril : *Pianoforte* (SW)
Easto, Dave : *Guitars* (SW)
Easton, David : *Organ* (NE)
Easton, Lydia : *Voice* (SE)
Eastop, Pip : *Horn* (Lon)
Eastwood, Al : *Voice* (Lon)
Eastwood, CJ : *Percussion* (Lon)
Eastwood, Gillian : *Violin* (Lon)
Eastwood, Luke : *Keyboards* (Lon)
Eaton, Chris : *Guitars* (SE)
Eaton, Christopher : *Keyboards* (Mid)
Eaton, Dave : *Voice* (SW)
Eaton, Derek : *Organ* (Lon)
Eaton, James : *Pianoforte* (NW)
Eaton, Lynette : *Double Bass* (Lon)

Eaton, Nigel : *Hurdy-gurdy* (Lon)
Eaton, Sarah : *Violin* (NW)
Eaton, Susan : *Violin* (NE)
Eaton, Tim : *Oboe* (Lon)
Eaton, Wilfred : *Percussion* (NE)
Eaves, Michael : *Guitars* (Lon)
Ebbage, David : *Pianoforte* (Lon)
Ebben, Guy : *Pianoforte* (Lon)
Ebbinghouse, Bernard : *Music Director* (Lon)
Ebbutt, Lucinda : *Cello* (Lon)
Ebdon, John : *Trumpet* (Lon)
Ebsworth, Andrew : *Percussion* (Lon)
Ebun : *Voice* (Lon)
Eccles, Graham : *Organ* (NW)
Eccles, Noel : *Percussion* (Lon)
Eccles, Vaughan : *Trumpet* (NW)
Ecclestone, Daniel : *Pianoforte* (Lon)
Ecclestone, Malcolm : *Brass* (E)
Eccott, David : *Bass Trombone* (Lon)
Economides, Anthony : *Harmonica (Inc Bass* (Lon)
Economos, Amalia : *Voice* (Lon)
Eddie : *Bass Guitar* (NW)
Eddolls, John : *Percussion* (SE)
Eddowes, Peter : *Percussion* (NW)
Eddowes, Rita : *Violin* (Lon)
Eddy, John : *Percussion* (SW)
Ede, Stephanie : *Violin* (Lon)
Ede, Terence : *Saxophones* (Lon)
Edem, Eddie : *Trumpet* (Lon)
Eden : *Voice* (Lon)
Eden, Bill : *Voice* (E)
Eden, David : *Trumpet* (Lon)
Edgar, Helen : *Cello* (Lon)
Edgar, Jack : *Percussion* (NE)
Edgar, James : *Trumpet* (Mid)
Edgar, Kate : *Music Director* (Lon)
Edgar, Ronald : *Clarinet* (Lon)
Edge, Graham : *Percussion* (Lon)
Edge, Stuart : *Saxophones* (NE)
Edge, The : *Guitars* (Lon)
Edgoose, Simon : *Percussion* (Lon)
Edgson, Roger : *Percussion* (E)
Edington, John : *Pianoforte* (Lon)
Edis, Steven : *Music Director* (Lon)
Edmond, Edward : *Accordion* (Sco)
Edmondes, William : *Guitars* (Lon)
Edmonds, Gavin : *Pianoforte* (Lon)
Edmonds, Lu : *Guitars* (Lon)
Edmonds, Michael : *Bass Guitar* (Lon)
Edmonds, Rachel : *Bassoon* (Lon)
Edmondson, Andy : *Guitars* (Lon)
Edmondson, Stephen : *Bass Guitar* (NE)
Edmund-Davies, Paul : *Flute* (Lon)
Edmunds, Catherine : *Violin* (NE)
Edmunds, Chris : *Pianoforte* (SW)
Edmunds, David : *Cello* (NE)
Edmunds, Tony : *Keyboards* (Lon)
Edney, John : *Trombone* (Lon)
Edney, Phillip : *Pianoforte* (SE)
Edward, Robert : *Violin* (Sco)
Edwards, Alan : *Violin* (Lon)
Edwards, Alec : *Trumpet* (Mid)
Edwards, Alfred : *Clarinet* (Mid)
Edwards, Andrew : *Pianoforte* (Lon)
Edwards, Benjamin : *Trumpet* (Lon)
Edwards, Bryan : *Clarinet* (Lon)
Edwards, Carlo : *Guitars* (Lon)
Edwards, Carlton : *Pianoforte* (Lon)
Edwards, Catherine : *Pianoforte* (Lon)
Edwards, Catrin : *Guitars* (SW)
Edwards, Charlotte : *Violin* (Lon)
Edwards, Dan : *Guitars* (Lon)
Edwards, Daniel : *Horn* (SW)
Edwards, Darren Paul : *Bass Guitar* (Mid)
Edwards, David : *Violin* (Lon)

Edwards, David : *Keyboards* (Mid)
Edwards, David : *Horn* (NW)
Edwards, David : *Trumpet* (NW)
Edwards, David : *Cello* (Sco)
Edwards, David : *Bass Guitar* (SE)
Edwards, David John : *Steel Pan* (NE)
Edwards, Denis : *Trumpet* (Lon)
Edwards, Doreen : *Voice* (NW)
Edwards, Elizabeth : *Violin* (Lon)
Edwards, Emmanuel : *Keyboards* (Lon)
Edwards, Felicity : *Clarinet* (Lon)
Edwards, Gavin : *Horn* (Lon)
Edwards, Genene : *Composer* (Lon)
Edwards, George : *Violin* (Lon)
Edwards, Glenton : *Voice* (Lon)
Edwards, Gudrun : *Violin* (Lon)
Edwards, Gwynne : *Viola* (Lon)
Edwards, Helen : *Violin* (NE)
Edwards, Hilary : *Banjo* (SW)
Edwards, Ian : *Bass Guitar* (Lon)
Edwards, James : *Bass Guitar* (Lon)
Edwards, Janet : *Voice* (Lon)
Edwards, John : *Bass Guitar* (E)
Edwards, John : *Bass Guitar* (Lon)
Edwards, John : *Double Bass* (Lon)
Edwards, Johnny : *Trombone* (Lon)
Edwards, Jon : *Percussion* (Lon)
Edwards, Jonathan : *Guitars* (Lon)
Edwards, Julie : *Voice* (Lon)
Edwards, Julie : *Violin* (NE)
Edwards, Juliet : *Violin* (Lon)
Edwards, Karlos : *Percussion* (Lon)
Edwards, Lucy : *Guitars* (Lon)
Edwards, Luke : *Percussion* (SE)
Edwards, Lyn : *Percussion* (Lon)
Edwards, Marc : *Trumpet* (SE)
Edwards, Mark : *Pianoforte* (SE)
Edwards, Michael : *Trumpet* (SE)
Edwards, Michael : *Guitars* (SW)
Edwards, Morfen : *Harp* (Lon)
Edwards, Myrna : *Viola* (Lon)
Edwards, Nicola : *Flute* (NW)
Edwards, Nicola : *Composer* (SW)
Edwards, Nigel : *Violin* (Lon)
Edwards, Owen : *Saxophones* (Mid)
Edwards, Pamela : *Harpsichord* (Lon)
Edwards, Phillip : *Clarinet* (Lon)
Edwards, Phillip : *Music Director* (Lon)
Edwards, Rebecca : *Cello* (NW)
Edwards, Reginald : *Bass Guitar* (Lon)
Edwards, Richard : *Trombone* (Lon)
Edwards, Richard : *Guitars* (SW)
Edwards, Ricky B : *Saxophones* (Lon)
Edwards, Robin : *Voice* (Lon)
Edwards, Rod : *Music Director* (Lon)
Edwards, Rosemary : *Cello* (Lon)
Edwards, Ryan : *Organ* (Mid)
Edwards, Sam : *Keyboards* (Lon)
Edwards, Simon : *Bass Guitar* (Lon)
Edwards, Stephen : *Voice* (NE)
Edwards, Steven : *Guitars* (Lon)
Edwards, Steven : *Bass Guitar* (SE)
Edwards, Steven : *Synthesiser* (SE)
Edwards, Susan : *Oboe* (Lon)
Edwards, Terry : *Saxophones* (Lon)
Edwards, Thomas : *Double Bass* (SW)
Edwards, Warwick : *Early Strings* (Sco)
Edwards, Zena : *Voice* (Lon)
Edwige : *Voice* (Lon)
Egan, Christopher : *Keyboards* (Mid)
Egan, Raymond : *Pianoforte* (Lon)
Egan, Ronald : *Trombone* (NW)
Egboh, Anthony : *Voice* (Lon)
Eggington, Phillippa : *Cello* (SE)
Eggleston, James : *Pianoforte* (Mid)

Fife, Desmond : *Guitars* (E)
Fifield, Fraser : *Saxophones* (Sco)
Figes, Kevin : *Saxophones* (SW)
Figgis, Michael : *Trumpet* (Lon)
Filby, Anthony : *Flute* (Lon)
Filby, Brian : *Saxophones* (Lon)
Filer, Penny : *Viola* (Lon)
Filipe, Nuno : *Pianoforte* (Lon)
Filleul, Peter : *Keyboards* (SW)
Fillmore, Miriam : *Pianoforte* (SW)
Filmer, David : *Cello* (SE)
Filsell, Jeremy : *Pianoforte* (Lon)
Finch, Flora : *Composer* (Lon)
Finch, Greg : *Percussion* (NW)
Finch, John : *Trombone* (Lon)
Finch, Keith : *Keyboards* (Lon)
Finch, Matthew : *Pianoforte* (SW)
Finch, Peter : *Keyboards* (Lon)
Finch, Sean : *Voice* (NE)
Finch, Simon : *Trumpet* (Lon)
Finch, Stephen : *Percussion* (Lon)
Finch, Vera : *Voice* (NE)
Fincham, Alistair : *Percussion* (Lon)
Findlay, Alan : *Percussion* (Sco)
Findlay, Colin : *Percussion* (Sco)
Findlay, Duncan : *Guitars* (Sco)
Findlay, Gillian : *Violin* (Lon)
Findlay, Gordon : *Organ* (NE)
Findlay, Ian : *Organ* (Sco)
Findlay, Mary : *Violin* (Lon)
Findlay, Thomas : *Flugel Horn* (Lon)
Findlay, Valerie : *Cello* (SE)
Findley, Andi : *Composer* (Lon)
Findley, David : *Double Bass* (NE)
Findley, Marie : *Voice* (Lon)
Findon, Andy : *Flute* (Lon)
Findon, Julia : *Trumpet* (Lon)
Findon, Ronald : *Saxophones* (Lon)
Finlay, Nadine : *Voice* (Lon)
Finlay, Rick : *Percussion* (Lon)
Finlayson, Donald : *Flute* (Sco)
Finlayson, Rhonda : *Voice* (NW)
Finlayson, Tucker : *Double Bass* (Lon)
Finley, Campbell : *Trumpet* (SE)
Finlow, Nicolas : *Pianoforte* (Lon)
Finn, Micky : *Keyboards* (Lon)
Finn, Vin : *Violin* (NW)
Finnamore, Marina : *Clarinet* (SE)
Finnegan, Derbhail : *Harp* (Lon)
Finnemore, Audrey : *Harp* (SE)
Finney, David : *Voice* (Lon)
Finney, Nigel : *Horn* (Mid)
Finney, Stephen : *Guitars* (Mid)
Finnimore, Clare : *Viola* (Lon)
Finucane, Gavin : *Guitars* (Lon)
Finucane, Thomas : *Early Strings* (Lon)
Fiondella, Gennard : *Accordion* (SE)
Fioramonti, Javier : *Guitars* (Lon)
Fiorentini, Mario : *Bandleader* (Lon)
Fiorilo, Oliver : *Percussion* (Lon)
Fire, Ray : *Guitars* (Lon)
Firman, Andrew : *Keyboards* (Mid)
Firman, David : *Music Director* (Lon)
Firman, Robin : *Cello* (Lon)
Firman, Roger : *Organ* (Lon)
Firsht, Samuel : *Percussion* (SE)
Firth, Andrew : *Voice* (NE)
Firth, Deborah : *Double Bass* (Lon)
Firth, Nicholas : *Horn* (Mid)
Firth, Scott : *Bass Guitar* (Lon)
Firth, Tony : *Trumpet* (NE)
Fischbacher, Stephen : *Guitars* (Sco)
Fischer, Jessica : *Bass Guitar* (NE)
Fischer, Mark : *Saxophones* (E)
Fischer, Simon : *Violin* (Lon)

Fish : *Voice* (Sco)
Fish, Christopher : *Cello* (SE)
Fish, George : *Percussion* (NW)
Fish, Kate : *Saxophones* (SE)
Fish, Nigel : *Trumpet* (SE)
Fish, Rosalind : *Clarinet* (SE)
Fisher, Andy : *Pianoforte* (SE)
Fisher, Cilla : *Voice* (Sco)
Fisher, Damian : *Percussion* (Lon)
Fisher, Danny : *Guitars* (E)
Fisher, David : *Keyboards* (NE)
Fisher, Fay : *Oboe* (SW)
Fisher, Harold : *Percussion* (Lon)
Fisher, Howard : *Pianoforte* (NW)
Fisher, Ian : *Horn* (SW)
Fisher, Jane : *Flute* (Lon)
Fisher, Janet : *Viola* (NW)
Fisher, Jeremy : *Pianoforte* (Lon)
Fisher, John : *Bandleader* (Mid)
Fisher, John : *Percussion* (Mid)
Fisher, Jonty : *Bass Guitar* (Lon)
Fisher, Joshua : *Violin* (Lon)
Fisher, Judith : *Bass Guitar* (Lon)
Fisher, Mark : *Keyboards* (Lon)
Fisher, Martin : *Guitars* (Lon)
Fisher, Pauline : *Trumpet* (Lon)
Fisher, Peter : *Violin* (Lon)
Fisher, Peter : *Trumpet* (Mid)
Fisher, Peter : *Harp* (SW)
Fisher, Ray : *Guitars* (NE)
Fisher, Rhoda : *Voice* (Lon)
Fisher, Roger : *Organ* (Mid)
Fisher, Roy : *Pianoforte* (Mid)
Fisher, Sarah : *Violin* (NE)
Fisher, Stephen : *Bass Guitar* (Lon)
Fisher, Stuart : *Percussion* (SW)
Fisher, Susannah : *Cello* (Lon)
Fisher, Timothy : *Violin* (SE)
Fisher, Tony : *Trumpet* (Lon)
Fisher-Jones, Norman/Noko : *Guitars* (Lon)
Fishley, Anthony : *Percussion* (Mid)
Fishlock, Clive : *Pianoforte* (Mid)
Fishman, Paul : *Synthesiser* (Lon)
Fishwick, Mathew : *Percussion* (Lon)
Fishwick, Steven : *Trumpet* (Lon)
Fiske, Jean : *Violin* (Lon)
Fison, Rubina : *Flute* (Lon)
Fistein, Jonathan : *Cello* (NW)
Fitchett, Rosemary : *Violin* (Lon)
Fitkin, Graham : *Pianoforte* (SW)
Fitness, Julia : *Voice* (SE)
Fitton, Judith : *Flute* (Lon)
Fitton, Simon : *Trombone* (NW)
Fitzgerald, Barry : *Guitars* (NW)
Fitzgerald, Brendan : *Bassoon* (Lon)
Fitzgerald, David : *Akai Ewi 1000* (Lon)
Fitzgerald, David : *Cello* (Lon)
Fitzgerald, David : *Flute* (Lon)
Fitzgerald, David : *Saxophones* (Lon)
Fitzgerald, Helen : *Cello* (Mid)
Fitzgerald, Josephine : *Cello* (Lon)
Fitzgerald, Paul : *Double Bass* (E)
Fitzgerald, Warren : *Voice* (Lon)
Fitzgibbon, Martin : *Percussion* (SW)
Fitzhugh, Kenneth : *Tuba* (E)
Fitzjohn, Ethel : *Voice* (Lon)
Fitzmaurice, Tristan : *Guitars* (NE)
Fitzsimons, Geraldine : *Violin* (Lon)
Fitzsimons, Gerard : *Bass Guitar* (SW)
Flack, Elizabeth : *Violin* (Sco)
Flack, John : *Trombone* (Lon)
Flahant, Richard : *Keyboards* (SE)
Flaherty, Daniel : *Percussion* (Sco)
Flanagan, Lin : *Guitars* (SE)
Flanagan, Mark : *Guitars* (Lon)

Flannery, Mark : *Guitars* (Lon)
Flannery, Susan : *Voice* (SW)
Flatau, David : *Composer* (E)
Flavell, Roger B : *Bass Guitar* (SE)
Flavius, Terrince : *Bass Guitar* (Lon)
Flaxman, Andrew : *Trombone* (Lon)
Fleay, Robert : *Guitars* (Mid)
Fleck, Derek : *Clarinet* (NE)
Fleckney, Clive : *Pianoforte* (E)
Fleckney, Robin : *Guitars* (SE)
Fleeman, Jim : *Percussion* (Lon)
Fleet, Judith : *Cello* (Lon)
Fleet, Myrna : *Violin* (E)
Fleet, Susan : *Voice* (SE)
Fleetcroft, Anne : *Violin* (SE)
Fleetcroft, Jack : *Viola* (Lon)
Fleetcroft, Martin : *Viola* (NE)
Fleetham, David : *Guitars* (Lon)
Fleetwood, Joe : *Pianoforte* (Sco)
Fleetwood, Roger : *Saxophones* (NW)
Flegg, Chris : *Guitars* (SE)
Fleischer, Marion : *Pianoforte* (Mid)
Fleming, Andy : *Guitars* (E)
Fleming, Charles : *Violin* (NE)
Fleming, Cynthia : *Violin* (Lon)
Fleming, Ian : *Bagpipes* (Lon)
Fleming, Mike : *Double Bass* (NE)
Fleming, Robert : *Violin* (Lon)
Fleming, Vincent : *Violin* (Sco)
Flemming, Peter : *Bass Guitar* (Lon)
Fletcher, Alastair : *Percussion* (Lon)
Fletcher, Alistair : *Percussion* (NW)
Fletcher, Amelia : *Voice* (SE)
Fletcher, Andrew : *Horn* (Lon)
Fletcher, Annette : *Voice* (Mid)
Fletcher, C Jeremy : *Cello* (Sco)
Fletcher, Carl : *Trombone* (Mid)
Fletcher, Chris : *Latin American Percu* (Lon)
Fletcher, Clive : *Double Bass* (SE)
Fletcher, Colin : *Bass Guitar* (SE)
Fletcher, David : *Whistle* (NE)
Fletcher, Diana : *Voice* (SW)
Fletcher, Elizabeth : *Harp* (Lon)
Fletcher, Eric : *Oboe* (NW)
Fletcher, Gary : *Bass Guitar* (Lon)
Fletcher, Guy : *Percussion* (Mid)
Fletcher, Guy : *Keyboards* (SE)
Fletcher, Hilary : *Voice* (Lon)
Fletcher, James : *Saxophones* (Lon)
Fletcher, Jean : *Violin* (NE)
Fletcher, Jeff : *Voice* (SW)
Fletcher, Kirsty : *Voice* (Mid)
Fletcher, Liz : *Voice* (Lon)
Fletcher, Lyn : *Violin* (Lon)
Fletcher, Mark : *Percussion* (Lon)
Fletcher, Paul : *Trombone* (NE)
Fletcher, Paul : *Pianoforte* (NW)
Fletcher, Raymond : *Saxophones* (Lon)
Fletcher, Stephen : *Percussion* (NE)
Fletcher, Tim : *Bass Guitar* (E)
Fletcher-Campbell, Christopher : *Organ* (SE)
Flick, Vic : *Guitars* (Lon)
Flinders, John : *Pianoforte* (Lon)
Flinn, Peter : *Percussion* (NW)
Flint, James : *Pianoforte* (SE)
Flint, John : *Violin* (Mid)
Flint, Keith : *Voice* (E)
Flint, Mathew : *Bass Guitar* (Lon)
Fliszar, Dicki : *Percussion* (Lon)
Flood, Alan : *Trumpet* (SE)
Flood, John : *Trombone* (NE)
Flood, Mike : *Keyboards* (SE)
Florczak, Fiona : *Voice* (NW)
Florek, Jaki : *Voice* (NW)
Florides, Chris : *Pianoforte* (SE)

Flower, Ian : *Violin* (NW)
Flower, Miles : *Guitars* (SE)
Flower, Stephen : *Horn* (Lon)
Flowerdew, Sean : *Keyboards* (Lon)
Flowers, Frank : *Double Bass* (NW)
Flowers, Herbie : *Bass Guitar* (Lon)
Flowers, Mike : *Composer* (Lon)
Flowers, Zowie : *Voice* (Lon)
Floyd, Charles : *Horn* (Sco)
Floyd, Denzil : *Horn* (Lon)
Flush, Paul Kendal : *Pianoforte* (Sco)
Fly, T G : *Percussion* (Lon)
Flynn, Andrew : *Guitars* (Lon)
Flynn, B : *Pianoforte* (NW)
Flynn, Chris : *Percussion* (SW)
Flynn, Christopher : *Guitars* (NW)
Flynn, Declan : *Pianoforte* (Lon)
Flynn, Eamonn : *Mandolin* (Lon)
Flynn, Fabian-Anna : *Voice* (Lon)
Flynn, Janice : *Viola* (Lon)
Flynn, John : *Organ* (NE)
Foad, Paul : *Guitars* (Mid)
Foden, David : *Guitars* (NW)
Fogg, Rod : *Guitars* (Lon)
Foggin, Ellen : *Horn* (Lon)
Foggin, Susan : *Flute* (SW)
Folch, Laura : *Cello* (Lon)
Foley, Brian : *Saxophones* (Lon)
Foley, Dean : *Horn* (Lon)
Foley, Edward : *Violin* (Lon)
Foley, Graham : *Percussion* (SE)
Foley, Gregory : *Bass Guitar* (NW)
Foley, John : *Clarinet* (Sco)
Foley, Kenneth : *Guitars* (E)
Foley, Steven : *Guitars* (Lon)
Foleycash : *Voice* (Lon)
Follan, James : *Bass Clarinet* (Sco)
Follett, Emanuele : *Guitars* (Lon)
Follett, Marie-Claire : *Voice* (Lon)
Fomison, Richard : *Trumpet* (Lon)
Fonda, Quentin : *Guitars* (Sco)
Fone, Michael : *Trumpet* (Lon)
Fontaine, Claudia : *Voice* (Lon)
Foot, Richard : *Double Bass* (SE)
Foran, John : *Saxophones* (Lon)
Forbes, Alistair : *Accordion* (Lon)
Forbes, Ann E J : *Clarinet* (Sco)
Forbes, Cherry : *Oboe* (E)
Forbes, Derek : *Bass Guitar* (Sco)
Forbes, Ian : *Bassoon* (Lon)
Forbes, Ian : *Percussion* (NE)
Forbes, Janet : *Flute* (Lon)
Forbes, Jerry : *Pianoforte* (SW)
Forbes, Richard : *Violin* (NE)
Forbes, Roy : *Voice* (Mid)
Forbes, Stephen : *Oboe* (Lon)
Forbes, Stewart : *Saxophones* (Sco)
Forbes, Stuart : *Violin* (SE)
Forcione, Antonio : *Guitars* (Lon)
Ford, Allen : *Cello* (Lon)
Ford, Andrew : *Banjo* (Lon)
Ford, Andrew : *Pianoforte* (Mid)
Ford, Andy : *Synthesiser* (Sco)
Ford, Anthony : *Harpsichord* (NE)
Ford, Bill : *Voice* (Lon)
Ford, Billy : *Saxophones* (Sco)
Ford, Catherine : *Violin* (Lon)
Ford, Charles : *Cello* (Lon)
Ford, Christine : *Voice* (SE)
Ford, Dave : *Keyboards* (Lon)
Ford, David : *Trumpet* (SW)
Ford, Dorian : *Keyboards* (Lon)
Ford, Eric : *Percussion* (NW)
Ford, Gillian : *Pianoforte* (Lon)
Ford, James T : *Keyboards* (Lon)

Ford, John : *Guitars* (Sco)
Ford, Julia : *Clarinet* (E)
Ford, Kenneth : *Bass Guitar* (NE)
Ford, Lornette : *Voice* (Mid)
Ford, Luan : *Clarinet* (Mid)
Ford, Lucy-Anne : *Voice* (Lon)
Ford, Michael : *Bassoon* (Lon)
Ford, Patrick : *Vibraphone* (Lon)
Ford, Peter : *Pianoforte* (SE)
Ford, Rachel : *Cello* (Lon)
Ford, Robert : *Trumpet* (NW)
Ford, Tommy : *Accordion* (Sco)
Ford, Trevor : *Flute* (Lon)
Ford, Vincent : *Trombone* (SW)
Ford-Powell, Ken : *Guitars* (E)
Forde, Jermain : *Percussion* (E)
Forde, Nadine : *Voice* (Lon)
Fordham, Ian : *Bass Guitar* (Lon)
Fordham, John : *Saxophones* (Lon)
Fordham, Kenneth : *Saxophones* (Lon)
Fordham, Richard : *Voice* (Lon)
ForDJour, Robert : *Percussion* (Lon)
Fordree, John : *Percussion* (Lon)
Fordyce, Emily : *Violin* (SE)
Foreman, Alan : *Double Bass* (Lon)
Foreman, Brian : *Bass Guitar* (Lon)
Foreman, Kenneth : *Guitars* (Lon)
Forester, Helen : *Viola* (SE)
Forester, Thomas : *Guitars* (Lon)
Forgie, Barry : *Arranger* (Lon)
Forgrieve, Ian : *Tympani* (NW)
Forman, Emma : *Voice* (Sco)
Forman, John : *Saxophones* (Mid)
Formula, Dave : *Keyboards* (Lon)
Fornachon, Peter : *Guitars* (SE)
Fornara, Tim : *Voice* (SW)
Forrell, Gene : *Conductor* (Lon)
Forrest, John : *Double Bass* (Sco)
Forrest, Matt : *Keyboards* (Lon)
Forrester, John : *Viola* (Lon)
Forrester, John : *Bass Guitar* (SE)
Forsdyke, Tina : *Violin* (E)
Forse, Mike : *Voice* (NE)
Forsey, David : *Percussion* (E)
Forshaw, Alec : *Bassoon* (Lon)
Forshaw, Brian : *Trumpet* (Sco)
Forshaw, Christian : *Saxophones* (Lon)
Forster, Anne : *Violin* (Mid)
Forster, John : *Guitars* (NW)
Forster, Peter : *Percussion* (NE)
Forster, Robert : *Guitars* (Lon)
Forsyth, Alexander : *Saxophones* (SE)
Forsyth, Eric : *Guitars* (SE)
Forte, Remo : *Trombone* (NE)
Fortin, Antonio : *Guitars* (Lon)
Fortune, Douglas : *Double Bass* (NW)
Fossey, Robert : *Guitars* (Mid)
Foster, Anthony : *Guitars* (Mid)
Foster, Ben : *Music Director* (Lon)
Foster, Cindy : *Violin* (Lon)
Foster, Claire : *Violin* (Lon)
Foster, Dave : *Double Bass* (Mid)
Foster, Dominic : *Bassoon* (Lon)
Foster, Geoffrey : *Clarinet* (SE)
Foster, Gladston : *Voice* (Mid)
Foster, Jill : *Violin* (NE)
Foster, John : *Violin* (NW)
Foster, Justin : *Double Bass* (Mid)
Foster, Kevin : *Bass Guitar* (Lon)
Foster, Leonard : *Clarinet* (NW)
Foster, Lucy : *Oboe* (Lon)
Foster, Malcolm : *Bass Guitar* (Lon)
Foster, Mick : *Saxophones* (Lon)
Foster, Mo : *Bass Guitar* (Lon)
Foster, Neil : *Percussion* (Lon)

Foster, Nicholas : *Clarinet* (NW)
Foster, Nick : *Bass Guitar* (Lon)
Foster, Nick : *Keyboards* (Lon)
Foster, Nigel : *Pianoforte* (Lon)
Foster, Robert : *Songwriter* (Lon)
Foster, Stan : *Pianoforte* (Lon)
Foster, Stephen : *Bass Guitar* (Lon)
Foster, Weston B : *Voice* (Lon)
Fothergill, Lee : *Guitars* (Lon)
Fotheringham, Elizabeth : *Pianoforte* (Sco)
Foulcer, Alexander : *Voice* (Lon)
Fourmy, Ruth : *Violin* (Lon)
Fower, Chris : *Bass Trombone* (Lon)
Fowke, Jon : *Pianoforte* (Lon)
Fowkes, Edwin : *Tympani* (Mid)
Fowler, Charles : *Percussion* (SW)
Fowler, Emma : *Bass Clarinet* (Lon)
Fowler, Harry : *Percussion* (SW)
Fowler, Harry : *Tympani* (SW)
Fowler, James : *Keyboards* (Lon)
Fowler, Karen : *Pianoforte* (Mid)
Fowler, Lenny : *Guitars* (Lon)
Fowler, Matt : *Keyboards* (Lon)
Fowler, Michael : *Pianoforte* (Mid)
Fowler, Paul : *Percussion* (Lon)
Fowler, Robert : *Guitars* (Lon)
Fowler, Robert : *Saxophones* (SE)
Fowler, Samuel : *Double Bass* (SW)
Fowler, Tommy : *Composer* (Sco)
Fowles, Anthony : *Percussion* (SW)
Fowles, Michael : *Trombone* (Mid)
Fowlie, Marjory : *Violin* (Sco)
Fownes, Brandon : *Keyboards* (Lon)
Fox, Adam : *Guitars* (Lon)
Fox, Allie : *Guitars* (Sco)
Fox, Andrew : *Trumpet* (E)
Fox, Brian : *Double Bass* (E)
Fox, Catherine : *Voice* (NW)
Fox, Daniel : *Trombone* (NW)
Fox, Denis : *Pianoforte* (NE)
Fox, Derek : *Saxophones* (SW)
Fox, Dianne : *Guitars* (E)
Fox, Garney : *Accordion* (E)
Fox, Ivan : *Violin* (Lon)
Fox, John : *Arranger* (Lon)
Fox, Marc : *Percussion* (Lon)
Fox, Marcus : *Bass Guitar* (Lon)
Fox, Margaret : *Cello* (NE)
Fox, Matthew : *Dulcimer* (Lon)
Fox, Nigel : *Pianoforte* (Lon)
Fox, Oliver : *Clarinet* (Lon)
Fox, Penelope : *Viola* (NW)
Fox, Richard : *Tuba* (Lon)
Fox, Robert : *Synthesiser* (NE)
Fox, Steve : *Latin American Percu* (Lon)
Fox, Sylvia : *Pianoforte* (Mid)
Fox, The : *Percussion* (Mid)
Fox-Gal, Eva : *Violin* (NE)
Fox-Little, Debbie : *Voice* (Lon)
Foxall, Emma : *Voice* (Lon)
Foxley, Ray : *Pianoforte* (Lon)
Foxley, Simon : *Pianoforte* (Lon)
Foxton, Bruce : *Bass Guitar* (Lon)
Foxwell, Heather : *Oboe* (NW)
Foxwell, Roger : *Violin* (NW)
Foxworthy, Jane : *Bass Guitar* (Mid)
Foyle, Trevor : *Guitars* (SE)
Frame, Roddy : *Guitars* (Lon)
Frammingham, Malcolm : *Trombone* (Lon)
Frampton, Ashley : *Double Bass* (NW)
Frampton, Pauline : *Flute* (NW)
Frampton, Peter : *Guitars* (Lon)
France, Adrian : *Bass Trombone* (Lon)
France, Leonard : *Trumpet* (NW)
France, Martin : *Percussion* (Lon)

Index of Members - France

France, Nic : *Percussion* (Lon)
France, Phil : *Bass Guitar* (NE)
France, Timothy : *Saxophones* (NW)
Franchi, John : *Saxophones* (Lon)
Francis, Alison : *Violin* (SW)
Francis, Carolyn : *Folk Fiddle* (NW)
Francis, Charles : *Bass Guitar* (Lon)
Francis, Chris : *Saxophones* (Lon)
Francis, Colin : *Trombone* (SE)
Francis, Dave : *Guitars* (Sco)
Francis, David : *Music Director* (Lon)
Francis, David : *Violin* (Lon)
Francis, David : *Harpsichord* (NW)
Francis, Edward : *Percussion* (SE)
Francis, Emily : *Violin* (Lon)
Francis, George : *Music Director* (Lon)
Francis, Gregor : *Arranger* (Mid)
Francis, Gregor : *Bandleader* (Mid)
Francis, Gregor : *Conductor* (Mid)
Francis, Jeremy : *Keyboards* (NW)
Francis, Joe : *Saxophones* (Lon)
Francis, John : *Saxophones* (Lon)
Francis, John : *Violin* (Lon)
Francis, Karl : *Percussion* (Lon)
Francis, Kenneth : *Percussion* (Lon)
Francis, Louise : *Voice* (Lon)
Francis, Mark : *Guitars* (Lon)
Francis, Neale : *Voice* (SE)
Francis, Nic : *Guitars* (SE)
Francis, Paul : *Bass Guitar* (E)
Francis, Paul : *Percussion* (E)
Francis, Paul : *Percussion* (NE)
Francis, Paul : *Pianoforte* (SE)
Francis, Peter : *Bassoon* (Lon)
Francis, Rory : *Percussion* (SW)
Francis, Sarah : *Oboe* (Lon)
Francis, Sedley : *Bass Guitar* (Lon)
Francis, Shireen : *Voice* (Lon)
Francis, Susan : *Flute* (Mid)
Francis, Terence : *Percussion* (SE)
Franco, Fausto : *Harp* (SW)
Franco, Mariana : *Flute* (Sco)
Francolini, David : *Percussion* (Lon)
Francombe, Peter : *Voice* (Lon)
Francome, Henry : *Saxophones* (SW)
Franey, Kevin : *Percussion* (NE)
Frangos, Marco : *Bass Guitar* (Lon)
Frank, Evelyn : *Flute* (Lon)
Frank, Mary : *Pianoforte* (Lon)
Frank, Richard : *Voice* (Sco)
Frank, Samuel : *Saxophones* (Lon)
Frankcom, Alan : *Voice* (Lon)
Frankel, David : *Pianoforte* (Lon)
Frankel, Laurence : *Oboe* (Lon)
Frankish, Paul : *Percussion* (NE)
Franklin, Ben : *Voice* (Lon)
Franklin, Brian : *Guitars* (E)
Franklin, Harry : *Pianoforte* (Mid)
Franklin, Jasper : *Trombone* (SE)
Franklin, John : *Flute* (Mid)
Franklin, Keith : *Horn* (SE)
Franklin, Mark : *Keyboards* (E)
Franklin, Mark : *Percussion* (SE)
Franklin, Martin : *Percussion* (SE)
Franklin, Maxine : *Pianoforte* (Lon)
Franklin, Nikki : *Pianoforte* (SE)
Franklin, Stephen : *Pianoforte* (Lon)
Franklyn, Caroline : *Flute* (Lon)
Frankonyte, Loreta : *Voice* (Lon)
Franks, Carolyn : *Violin* (Lon)
Franks, Jeremy : *Guitars* (NE)
Franks, Peter : *Trumpet* (Sco)
Franks, Roderick : *Trumpet* (Lon)
Franks, Ronald : *Organ* (E)
Franks, Timothy : *Percussion* (NW)

Frantz, Christopher : *Guitars* (SE)
Franz, Beth : *Violin* (Lon)
Frape, Julia : *Violin* (E)
Fraser, Andrew : *Trombone* (Sco)
Fraser, Don : *Guitars* (Lon)
Fraser, Fi : *Folk Fiddle* (Mid)
Fraser, Helenna : *Voice* (Sco)
Fraser, Jo-Anne : *Pianoforte* (Lon)
Fraser, Jock : *Pianoforte* (Sco)
Fraser, Joyce : *Violin* (Lon)
Fraser, June : *Guitars* (Lon)
Fraser, Laurence : *Trumpet* (Mid)
Fraser, Lorraine : *Flute* (Sco)
Fraser, Mathew : *Percussion* (Lon)
Fraser, Nicolette : *Viola* (E)
Fraser, Noel : *Trombone* (Lon)
Fraser, Richard : *Guitars* (Lon)
Fraser, Rosemary : *Violin* (SE)
Fraser, Victor : *Copyist* (Lon)
Fraser-Hill, Gregory : *Organ* (SE)
Frater, Amanda : *Voice* (SE)
Frater, Josie : *Voice* (Lon)
Frayling-Cork, Isobel : *Harp* (Lon)
Frayling-Kelly, Frederick : *Violin* (Sco)
Frayling-Kelly, Nigel : *Voice* (Sco)
Frazer, Anna : *Cello* (SE)
Freaky Frog : *Percussion* (Lon)
Frechter, Colin : *Music Director* (Lon)
Freckleton, Cleve : *Organ* (NE)
Frederikse, Tom : *Keyboards* (Lon)
Free, Jackie : *Trombone* (Lon)
Freedman, Bob : *Guitars* (Lon)
Freedman, Jerry : *Keyboards* (Lon)
Freedman, Madelaine : *Voice* (Lon)
Freedman, Sara : *Oboe* (Lon)
Freeland, Joanne : *Clarinet* (Sco)
Freeman, Alan : *Percussion* (Mid)
Freeman, Bill : *Guitars* (NW)
Freeman, Christopher : *Double Bass* (Sco)
Freeman, Gerry : *Percussion* (Mid)
Freeman, Janet : *Voice* (SE)
Freeman, Julian : *Guitars* (SE)
Freeman, Kenneth : *Pianoforte* (Mid)
Freeman, Marilyne : *Voice* (Mid)
Freeman, Matthew : *Music Director* (Lon)
Freeman, Michael : *Composer* (NE)
Freeman, Roy : *Trumpet* (NW)
Freeman, Sophia : *Flute* (Mid)
Freeman, Sue-Lee : *Voice* (NE)
Freeman, William : *Trumpet* (Lon)
Freer, Anthony : *Oboe* (Lon)
Freeth, Naomi : *Guitars* (Mid)
Freke, Nicholas : *Saxophones* (NW)
French, David : *Percussion* (SE)
French, George : *Violin* (Lon)
French, Nancy : *Violin* (Lon)
French, NS : *Voice* (Lon)
French, Paul : *Arranger* (Lon)
French, Paul : *Bass Guitar* (NE)
French, Rita : *Violin* (SE)
French, Sally : *Voice* (NE)
French, Stephen : *Pianoforte* (Lon)
French, Zoe : *Violin* (SE)
Frere-Smith, Dennis : *Trumpet* (Lon)
Frew, James : *Guitars* (Sco)
Freya, Jo-Anne : *Pianoforte* (Mid)
Freyhan, Peter : *Cello* (Lon)
Fribbins, Peter : *Composer* (Lon)
Fricker, Simon : *Music Director* (SE)
Friedman, Aron : *Pianoforte* (Mid)
Friel, Alan : *Trumpet* (Sco)
Friend, Alistair : *Bass Guitar* (Lon)
Friend, Marion : *Oboe* (Lon)
Friesegreene, Timothy : *Pianoforte* (Lon)
Friesner, Andrew : *Music Director* (Lon)

Fripp, Robert : *Guitars* (Lon)
Frisby, Mark : *Guitars* (Mid)
Frisby, Sid : *Banjo* (SW)
Frith, Emily : *Viola* (Lon)
Frith, Mark : *Bass Guitar* (Lon)
Frith, Martin : *Saxophones* (Lon)
Frizell, Andy : *Bass Guitar* (NW)
Froggatt, Ian : *Bass Guitar* (NE)
Frohlich, Josef : *Violin* (Lon)
Frohlick, Ashley : *Trumpet* (NW)
Froomes, Janet : *Violin* (SE)
Frost, Brian : *Clarinet* (NE)
Frost, Christopher : *Pianoforte* (Lon)
Frost, Corinne : *Cello* (Mid)
Frost, David : *Trumpet* (SW)
Frost, Eleanor : *Guitars* (NE)
Frost, Emma : *Horn* (SW)
Frost, Karen : *Bass Guitar* (NW)
Frost, Karen : *Voice* (NW)
Frost, Mark : *Bass Trombone* (NW)
Frost, Norman : *Saxophones* (NW)
Frost, Ronald : *Organ* (NW)
Frost, Stephen : *Synthesiser* (Lon)
Frost, Susan : *Oboe* (Lon)
Frost, Susan : *Voice* (Lon)
Frowde, Paul : *Violin* (Lon)
Frucht, John : *Double Bass* (SE)
Fructuoso-Martinez, Isabel-Carmen : *Voice* (Lon)
Fry, Adrian : *Trombone* (Lon)
Fry, Alan : *Percussion* (NW)
Fry, Bridget : *Pianoforte* (NW)
Fry, Christopher : *Guitars* (SW)
Fry, James : *Voice* (Lon)
Fry, Michael : *Guitars* (Lon)
Fry, Pauline : *Flute* (Lon)
Fry, Peter : *Percussion* (Lon)
Fry, Peter : *Bass Guitar* (SE)
Fry, Peter J : *Double Bass* (SW)
Fry, Tristan : *Percussion* (Lon)
Fryatt, Glenn : *Percussion* (SE)
Frye, Robert : *Viola* (Lon)
Fryer, Dave : *Bass Guitar* (SW)
Fryer, Elizabeth : *Viola* (Mid)
Fryer, Neil : *Trumpet* (NW)
Fryer, Nicholas : *Synthesiser* (SE)
Fryer, Peter : *Trombone* (NW)
Fryer, Ruth : *Pianoforte* (SW)
Fryett, Kevin : *Keyboards* (E)
Fuchs, Antonia : *Violin* (Lon)
Fuest, David : *Clarinet* (Lon)
Fuest, John : *Clarinet* (NW)
Fuest, Wendy : *Oboe* (NW)
Fuge, Charles : *Bass Guitar* (Lon)
Fuge, Christopher : *Bass Guitar* (Lon)
Fugler, Jonathan : *Voice* (Lon)
Fujisawa, Reiko : *Pianoforte* (Lon)
Fukuoka, Yasuko : *Keyboards* (Lon)
Fulcher, Byron : *Trombone* (E)
Fulcher, Colin : *Double Bass* (Lon)
Fulcher, Harry : *Clarinet* (SW)
Fulcher, Harry : *Saxophones* (SW)
Fulcher, Seamus D : *Guitars* (Lon)
Fulker, John : *Violin* (SE)
Fulker, Martin : *Trumpet* (Lon)
Fulker, Nicola : *Clarinet* (Lon)
Fullalove, Robert : *Sousaphone* (E)
Fullard, Simon : *Oboe* (SW)
Fullarton, Andy : *Guitars* (Sco)
Fullbrook, Charles : *Percussion* (Lon)
Fullbrook, Mark : *Trombone* (SE)
Fullbrook, Richard : *Percussion* (Sco)
Fuller, Adrian : *Horn* (NW)
Fuller, Andrew : *Cello* (Lon)
Fuller, Darren : *Guitars* (SE)
Fuller, Gareth : *Pianoforte* (Mid)

Fuller, Graham : *Voice* (E)
Fuller, John : *Percussion* (Lon)
Fuller, Louisa : *Violin* (Lon)
Fuller, Michael : *Cello* (Lon)
Fuller, Stephen : *Bassoon* (Lon)
Fullerton, Henry : *Bass Guitar* (Sco)
Fullerton, Neal : *Voice* (E)
Fullick, Teddy : *Trumpet* (Mid)
Fulton, Arty : *Percussion* (Sco)
Fulton, Janet : *Tympani* (NE)
Fulton, Neil : *Trumpet* (NW)
Funky Mac, The : *Voice* (Lon)
Funnell, Ruth : *Violin* (Lon)
Furber, Paul : *Percussion* (Lon)
Furey, Finbar : *Uilleann* (Lon)
Furler, Sia : *Voice* (Lon)
Furmanek-Halberda, Susanna : *Violin* (Lon)
Furneaux, Joanna : *Pianoforte* (SW)
Furness, Alan : *Trumpet* (Lon)
Furness, Clive : *Guitars* (Lon)
Furness, Dawn : *Voice* (NE)
Furnish, Alfred : *Pianoforte* (Mid)
Furnish, Pete : *Double Bass* (SW)
Furniss, Rosemary : *Violin* (Lon)
Furuholmen, Magne : *Keyboards* (Lon)
Fuse, Kenji : *Viola* (Lon)
Fussell, Angela : *Clarinet* (Lon)
Fuster, Francis : *African Drums* (Lon)
Futter, George : *Electric Violin* (Sco)
Fuzz : *Percussion* (Mid)
Fyfe, Elizabeth : *Oboe* (Lon)
Fyfe, James : *Voice* (Lon)
Fyfe, Peter : *Mandolin* (Lon)
Fyffe, Nicholas : *Bass Guitar* (Lon)
Fyffe, Will : *Keyboards* (Lon)
Fyles, Kenneth : *Pianoforte* (NW)

G

G, Andy : *Guitars* (Lon)
G, Damian : *Guitars* (NW)
G, Rayan : *Voice* (E)
G-Ray : *Percussion* (Lon)
Gabbidon, Basil : *Guitars* (Mid)
Gabriel, Andrew : *Guitars* (Lon)
Gabriel, Ella : *Pianoforte* (SE)
Gabriel, Pascal : *Percussion* (Lon)
Gabriel, Peter : *Flute* (SW)
Gabriel, Simon : *Trumpet* (Lon)
Gabrielle, Anne : *Pianoforte* (Lon)
Gaby : *Violin* (Lon)
Gachet, Dr S : *Songwriter* (Lon)
Gad, Cristo : *Keyboards* (NE)
Gadhvi, Chandrashekhar : *Latin American Percu* (Lon)
Gadian, Wendy : *Pianoforte* (NW)
Gael Force : *Folk Fiddle* (NE)
Gaffin, Ivor : *Saxophones* (Lon)
Gaffney, John : *Viola* (NW)
Gaffney, Naomi : *Viola* (SW)
Gaffney, Stephen : *Bass Guitar* (Mid)
Gafsen, Adam : *Guitars* (Lon)
Gagon, Robert : *Guitars* (NW)
Gail-Louise : *Percussion* (SW)
Gaillard, Julien : *Violin* (Lon)
Gain, Stuart : *Percussion* (Lon)
Gainford, Claire : *Bassoon* (NW)
Gainham, Catherine : *Flute* (Lon)
Gair, Martin : *Saxophones* (SE)
Gair, Peter : *Voice* (Mid)
Gair, Robin : *Voice* (SW)
Gaisburgh-Watkyn, Dean : *Bass Guitar* (Lon)
Galbraith, Alexis : *Viola* (Sco)
Galbraith, Colin : *Pianoforte* (NW)
Galbraith, Joanna : *Viola* (Sco)
Galdes, Dorothy : *Voice* (Lon)

Galdez, Claudio : *Saxophones* (Lon)
Gale, Christopher : *Percussion* (Lon)
Gale, Christopher : *Bassoon* (SE)
Gale, David : *Clarinet* (Lon)
Gale, Derek : *Percussion* (Lon)
Gale, Frank : *Double Bass* (Sco)
Gale, Gwendoline : *Violin* (Lon)
Gale, Jacoba : *Viola* (SE)
Gale, Jocelyn : *Cello* (Lon)
Gale, Roy : *Percussion* (NE)
Galea, Andrew : *Keyboards* (SE)
Galeone, Marie : *Violin* (Lon)
Galeone, Pierrette : *Violin* (Lon)
Galey, Steve : *Double Bass* (Mid)
Gallacher, George : *Guitars* (Sco)
Gallagher, Audrey : *Voice* (Lon)
Gallagher, Charlotte : *Violin* (SE)
Gallagher, Frank : *Violin* (Lon)
Gallagher, James : *Saxophones* (Lon)
Gallagher, James : *Bass Guitar* (Mid)
Gallagher, Julian : *Bass Guitar* (Lon)
Gallagher, Micky : *Keyboards* (E)
Gallagher, Steven : *Trumpet* (SE)
Gallais, Lydie : *Percussion* (Lon)
Gallan, Anna : *Flute* (Mid)
Gallaway, Philip : *Violin* (Lon)
Galler, Steve : *Guitars* (Lon)
Gallery, Roland : *Guitars* (Lon)
Galley, Edward : *Accordion* (Sco)
Gallimore, Joseph : *Pianoforte* (SW)
Gallo, Ray : *Guitars* (Lon)
Galloway, Charles : *Bagpipes* (Lon)
Galloway, Derek : *Trombone* (NW)
Galloway, Jennifer : *Oboe* (NW)
Galloway, Ruth : *Voice* (Lon)
Galloway, Walter : *Double Bass* (Sco)
Gallup, Simon : *Bass Guitar* (Lon)
Galvin, Robert : *Keyboards* (NW)
Galway, George : *Flute* (NW)
Galway, James : *Flute* (Lon)
Gamal, El : *Organ* (Lon)
Gamba, Giangaleazzo : *Guitars* (Lon)
Gamble, Danny : *Pianoforte* (NE)
Gamble, Mary : *Pianoforte* (NW)
Gamble, Patsy : *Saxophones* (SW)
Gamblin, Paul : *Guitars* (Lon)
Game, Martin : *Accordion* (E)
Gamlen, Amy : *Saxophones* (Lon)
Gamley, John : *Pianoforte* (Lon)
Gammon, Aaron : *Percussion* (NE)
Gammon, Philip : *Pianoforte* (Lon)
Gammon, Vic : *Melodeon* (NE)
Gammons, Christian : *Guitars* (Lon)
Gammons, Rod : *Percussion* (Lon)
Gamon, Mark : *Guitars* (E)
Gamon, Mitt : *Harmonica (Inc Bass* (Lon)
Ganberg, Barry : *Voice* (SW)
Gandee, Clive : *Horn* (NW)
Gandy, Judith : *Violin* (Mid)
Ganeva, Daniella : *Percussion* (Lon)
Gangadeen : *Percussion* (Lon)
Ganley, Allan : *Percussion* (Lon)
Ganner, David : *Guitars* (SW)
Ganney, Paul : *Bass Guitar* (NE)
Gannon, Craig : *Guitars* (NW)
Gannon, Michael : *Guitars* (NW)
Gantz, Carrie-Ann : *Voice* (Lon)
Garabedian, Silva : *Keyboards* (Lon)
Garbett, Byron : *Guitars* (Mid)
Garbow, Geoffrey : *Guitars* (Lon)
Garbutt, Christopher : *Cello* (SE)
Garbutt, David : *Horn* (NW)
Garcia, Dean : *Bass Guitar* (Lon)
Garcia, Gerald : *Guitars* (SE)
Garcia, Jose : *Violin* (Lon)

Garcia, Nestor : *Guitars* (Lon)
Garcia, Victor G : *Guitars* (Lon)
Garcia, Vincent : *Voice* (Lon)
Gard, John-Paul : *Pianoforte* (SW)
Garden, Malcolm : *Cello* (Sco)
Garden, Michael : *Guitars* (Lon)
Garden, Stuart : *Pianoforte* (NE)
Garden, William : *Keyboards* (Sco)
Gardham, Paul : *Horn* (Lon)
Gardier, Donna : *Voice* (Lon)
Gardiner, Paula : *Double Bass* (SW)
Gardiner, Sheila : *Viola* (NE)
Gardner : *Harmonica (Inc Bass* (SE)
Gardner, Alan : *Pianoforte* (E)
Gardner, Christopher : *Clarinet* (SE)
Gardner, James : *Keyboards* (NW)
Gardner, Peter : *Keyboards* (NE)
Gardner, Simon : *Trumpet* (Lon)
Gardner, Thomas : *Cello* (Lon)
Gardner, Trevor : *Percussion* (NW)
Gareh, Daniel : *Guitars* (Lon)
Garfield, Laurence : *Clarinet* (SE)
Garforth, David : *Conductor* (Lon)
Gargan, Laurie : *Trumpet* (Sco)
Garland, Miranda : *Pianoforte* (SW)
Garland, Paul : *Voice* (SW)
Garland, Roger : *Violin* (Lon)
Garland, Scott : *Saxophones* (Lon)
Garland, Tim : *Saxophones* (Lon)
Garman, Julian : *Keyboards* (Lon)
Garman, Roy : *Trumpet* (Lon)
Garner, Alan : *Oboe* (Lon)
Garner, Alfred : *Trumpet* (E)
Garner, Paul : *Pianoforte* (NW)
Garner, Robert : *Violin* (SW)
Garner, Sophie : *Voice* (E)
Garner, Tim : *Percussion* (Lon)
Garner, Tyrone : *Guitars* (Mid)
Garnett, Alex : *Saxophones* (Lon)
Garnett, William : *Saxophones* (Lon)
Garnham, Phil : *Bandleader* (SE)
Garofalo, Enrico : *Saxophones* (NW)
Garrard, Stuart : *Guitars* (Lon)
Garratty, Laurence : *Trumpet* (Mid)
Garrett, John : *Keyboards* (Mid)
Garrett, Julia : *Voice* (Lon)
Garrett, Katherine : *Flute* (SE)
Garrett, Malcolm : *Percussion* (Mid)
Garrett, Sidney : *Trumpet* (Mid)
Garrety, Hugh : *Bass Guitar* (Lon)
Garrick, Christian : *Violin* (Lon)
Garrick, Michael : *Pianoforte* (Lon)
Garrido, Victor : *Violin* (NW)
Garrison, John : *Bass Guitar* (Mid)
Garrity, Edmund : *Voice* (NW)
Garside, Alison : *Organ* (SW)
Garside, Ernie : *Trumpet* (Lon)
Garside, Gus : *Double Bass* (SE)
Garson, Louis : *Double Bass* (Lon)
Garthwaite, Paul : *Bass Guitar* (NE)
Garvey, Edward : *Bandleader* (NE)
Garvey, Edward : *Trumpet* (NE)
Garvey, Nigel : *Percussion* (Lon)
Garvin, Phillip : *Violin* (Lon)
Garwood, Alan Robert : *Saxophones* (Mid)
Garwood, David : *Accordion* (Mid)
Gascoigne, Brian : *Arranger* (Lon)
Gascoine, Alexander : *Violin* (Sco)
Gaskell, Danny : *Guitars* (Lon)
Gaskell, Helen : *Oboe* (Lon)
Gaskin, Barbara : *Cello* (Lon)
Gasparini, Piero : *Viola* (NW)
Gasson, Chris : *Trumpet* (Mid)
Gate, Colin : *Keyboards* (Sco)
Gateley, Stephen : *Double Bass* (SW)

Index of Members - Gathercole

Gathercole, Andrew : *Trumpet* (Lon)
Gathern, Graham : *Keyboards* (E)
Gatt, Martin : *Bassoon* (Lon)
Gatti, Luca : *Pianoforte* (Lon)
Gaudi : *Keyboards* (Lon)
Gaughan, Dick : *Guitars* (Sco)
Gaughran, Philip : *Percussion* (NW)
Gauld, Sidney : *Trumpet* (Lon)
Gault, Patricia : *Violin* (Lon)
Gaulton, Brian : *Violin* (Lon)
Gaunt, Peter : *Organ* (NE)
Gaunt, Stephen : *Bass Guitar* (E)
Gauntlett, Neil R : *Guitars* (Mid)
Gavin, Alastair : *Keyboards* (Lon)
Gavin, Michael : *Guitars* (Lon)
Gay, Bramwell : *Trumpet* (Lon)
Gay, Elsie : *Pianoforte* (SW)
Gay, Robert : *Keyboards* (Lon)
Gaye, Althea : *Pianoforte* (Mid)
Gayle, Godfrey : *Voice* (Mid)
Gayle, Kris : *Voice* (SW)
Gayle, Roy : *Bass Guitar* (SE)
Gaynor, Dee : *Voice* (Lon)
Gaynor, Lascelles : *Guitars* (NW)
Gaytten, Robert : *Guitars* (Lon)
Gaywood, David : *Percussion* (SW)
Gazder, Rohi : *Violin* (NW)
Gbesemete, Enyonam : *Voice* (Lon)
Gbla, John : *Keyboards* (E)
Gearing, David : *Percussion* (SE)
Geary, Caron : *Voice* (Lon)
Geddes, Allan : *Bassoon* (Sco)
Geddes, Amy : *Folk Fiddle* (Sco)
Geddes, Christopher : *Keyboards* (Sco)
Geddes, Graham : *Music Director* (Sco)
Geddes, Helen : *Cello* (Lon)
Geddes, John : *Horn* (Mid)
Geddes, John : *Composer* (Sco)
Geddon, Alma : *Guitars* (Lon)
Geduld, Ron : *Violin* (Lon)
Gee : *Voice* (Lon)
Gee, Allegra : *Pianoforte* (SE)
Gee, Anne : *Voice* (SE)
Gee, Barrington : *Guitars* (Mid)
Gee, Danny : *Keyboards* (Lon)
Gee, Darryl : *Horn* (NE)
Gee, David : *Guitars* (SE)
Gee, Jon : *Double Bass* (Lon)
Gee, Jonathan : *Pianoforte* (Lon)
Gee, Michael : *Guitars* (SW)
Gee, Paul : *Saxophones* (SE)
Gee, Peggy : *Violin* (SW)
Gee, Penelope : *Violin* (Lon)
Gee, Roy : *Saxophones* (SE)
Gee, Stephen : *Pianoforte* (Mid)
Gee, Steve : *Bass Guitar* (Lon)
Gee, Susan : *Horn* (Lon)
Geen, Beverley : *Double Bass* (SE)
Geer, Christine : *Oboe* (Lon)
Geesin, Ron : *Synthesiser* (SE)
Gegeshidze, Aleksandr : *Saxophones* (Lon)
Gehammar, Anne : *Viola* (E)
Geldard, Bill : *Trombone* (Lon)
Geldard, Esther : *Viola* (Lon)
Geldard, Lois : *Flute* (Lon)
Geldof, Robert : *Voice* (Lon)
Geldsetzer, Christian : *Double Bass* (Lon)
Gell, John : *Violin* (NW)
Gellhorn, Peter : *Conductor* (Lon)
Gelly, Dave : *Saxophones* (Lon)
Gelston, Natasha : *Voice* (Lon)
Gem : *Voice* (Lon)
Gemmell, Keith : *Saxophones* (Lon)
Gendall, Luke : *Bass Guitar* (SW)
Gendler, Paul : *Guitars* (Lon)

Genever, Norman : *Violin* (Sco)
Geneves, Jean-Jacques : *Guitars* (Lon)
Genic : *Bass Guitar* (NW)
Genin, Winifred : *Viola* (NW)
Gennedy : *Flute* (NE)
Genockey, Liam : *Percussion* (SE)
Genockey, Sean : *Guitars* (Lon)
Genovesi, Alfredo : *Guitars* (Lon)
Gent, Alison : *Flute* (Lon)
Gentles, Malcolm : *Keyboards* (NW)
Geoff : *Percussion* (Lon)
Geoffo : *Voice* (Lon)
George : *Percussion* (SE)
George, Alan : *Viola* (NE)
George, Boy : *Voice* (Lon)
George, Christopher : *Violin* (Lon)
George, Dave : *Percussion* (SE)
George, Eric : *Saxophones* (Lon)
George, Lloyd : *Keyboards* (SW)
George, Neil : *Trombone* (E)
George, Richard : *Violin* (Lon)
George, Siwsann : *Guitars* (SW)
Georgiadis, Andrew : *Viola* (SE)
Georgiadis, John : *Violin* (Lon)
Georgie, Esther : *Clarinet* (E)
Gepff : *Pianoforte* (NE)
Geradine, Kay : *Violin* (E)
Geradine, Thomas : *Violin* (Lon)
Geraint, Martyn : *Keyboards* (SW)
Gerke, Gerald : *Saxophones* (Lon)
Germain, Roberto L. : *Guitars* (SE)
Gerolemou, Adrian : *Guitars* (Lon)
Geron, Jos : *Voice* (Lon)
Gerrand, Fergus : *Percussion* (Lon)
Gerrard, Gillian : *Oboe* (E)
Gerrard, Horace : *Early Strings* (NW)
Gerrard, James : *Guitars* (Mid)
Gerrelli, Kenneth : *Pianoforte* (E)
Gers, Janick : *Guitars* (Lon)
Gethin, Nicholas : *Cello* (Lon)
Gethin, Tony : *Guitars* (Lon)
Ghaffari, Farahnaz : *Voice* (SE)
Ghigi, James : *Trumpet* (Lon)
Ghiro, Yann : *Clarinet* (Sco)
Ghosh, Mala : *Voice* (NW)
Ghoshal, Neal : *Guitars* (Lon)
GI : *Synthesiser* (Lon)
Giardino, David : *Violin* (Lon)
Gibb, Michelle : *Voice* (Lon)
Gibb, Robin : *Voice* (NW)
Gibb, Steve : *Guitars* (Sco)
Gibbin, Hilary : *Pianoforte* (SW)
Gibbins, Christopher : *Bass Guitar* (Lon)
Gibbinson, Walter : *Percussion* (NE)
Gibbon, Alani : *Voice* (Lon)
Gibbon, Angus : *Violin* (Lon)
Gibbon, Frank : *Bass Guitar* (NE)
Gibbon, John : *Percussion* (Lon)
Gibbon, Matthew : *Double Bass* (NW)
Gibbon, Nigel : *Trumpet* (Mid)
Gibbon, Susanna : *Violin* (NW)
Gibbon, Westerby : *Bassoon* (Mid)
Gibbons, Beth : *Percussion* (Lon)
Gibbons, Graham : *Guitars* (Lon)
Gibbons, Ian : *Keyboards* (E)
Gibbons, John : *Voice* (Lon)
Gibbons, John : *Pianoforte* (SW)
Gibbons, Kenneth : *Organ* (SW)
Gibbons, Malcolm : *Guitars* (NW)
Gibbons, Richard : *Double Bass* (SW)
Gibbons, Stephen : *Voice* (Mid)
Gibbs, Anthony : *Violin* (NW)
Gibbs, Eric : *Double Bass* (Lon)
Gibbs, Gerry : *Saxophones* (Lon)
Gibbs, Jeniffer : *Violin* (Lon)

Gibbs, Karen : *Bass Guitar* (Lon)
Gibbs, Louise : *Voice* (Lon)
Gibbs, Margaret : *Pianoforte* (Lon)
Gibbs, Michael : *Trombone* (Lon)
Gibbs, Nathan : *Bass Guitar* (NW)
Gibbs, Ralph : *Saxophones* (Lon)
Gibbs, Robert Whysall : *Violin* (Lon)
Gibbs, Stephen : *Guitars* (SW)
Gibbs, Venessa : *Voice* (Lon)
Gibley, Carolyn : *Harpsichord* (Lon)
Gibley, Ruth : *Flute* (E)
Giblin, Clive : *Guitars* (Lon)
Giblin, John : *Bass Guitar* (Lon)
Gibson, Andy : *Trumpet* (Lon)
Gibson, Colin : *Bass Guitar* (Lon)
Gibson, Daniel : *Clarinet* (NE)
Gibson, Dave : *Guitars* (NE)
Gibson, David : *Conductor* (SE)
Gibson, Elliot : *Guitars* (Lon)
Gibson, Evatt : *Trombone* (Sco)
Gibson, Jerre : *Violin* (Sco)
Gibson, John : *Percussion* (Mid)
Gibson, John : *Mandolin* (SE)
Gibson, Lee : *Voice* (Lon)
Gibson, Mark : *Percussion* (E)
Gibson, Martin : *Tympani* (Sco)
Gibson, Matthew : *Double Bass* (Lon)
Gibson, Michael : *Percussion* (SE)
Gibson, Pearl : *Percussion* (E)
Gibson, Philip : *Violin* (Lon)
Gibson, Rachel : *Flute* (SE)
Gibson, Richard : *Bass Guitar* (NE)
Gibson, Roger : *Bassoon* (NW)
Gibson, Stephen : *Percussion* (SE)
Gibson, Stephen : *Trumpet* (NW)
Gibson, Tim : *Copyist* (Lon)
Gibson, Wayne : *Steel Pan* (SE)
Gibson, Wilfred : *Violin* (Lon)
Gibson, Will : *Bass Guitar* (SE)
Giddens, Richard : *Bass Guitar* (E)
Giddey, Anna : *Violin* (Lon)
Giddings, John : *Percussion* (SW)
Giddings, John : *Tympani* (SW)
Giddis-Currie, Joseph : *Horn* (Sco)
Gidman, Brian : *Saxophones* (Mid)
Gifford, Derek : *Guitars* (NW)
Gifford, Gerald : *Cello* (Sco)
Gifford, Jason : *Bass Guitar* (SE)
Gifford, Katherine : *Trumpet* (Lon)
Gifford, Robert : *Percussion* (Lon)
Gift, Roland : *Voice* (Mid)
Gilbert, Brenda-Jean : *Voice* (E)
Gilbert, Gillian : *Guitars* (NW)
Gilbert, Jack : *Saxophones* (SE)
Gilbert, John : *Trumpet* (NE)
Gilbert, Julie : *Guitars* (Lon)
Gilbert, Mark : *Synthesiser* (Lon)
Gilbert, Mary : *Oboe* (NW)
Gilbert, Nicholas : *Bass Guitar* (NW)
Gilbert, Simon : *Percussion* (Lon)
Gilbert, Simon : *Keyboards* (SW)
Gilbert, Steven : *Percussion* (NW)
Gilbert, William : *Bass Guitar* (Mid)
Gilbertson, Dorothy : *Harp* (NE)
Gilbody, Justin : *Voice* (Mid)
Gilbody, Paul : *Bass Guitar* (Sco)
Gilby, Simon : *Saxophones* (Lon)
Gilchrist, Adam : *Bass Guitar* (Mid)
Gilchrist, Alison : *Viola* (NE)
Gilchrist, Eleonor : *Violin* (Lon)
Gilchrist, Elizabeth : *Cello* (Lon)
Gilchrist, Eric : *Saxophones* (Lon)
Gilchrist, Margaret : *Oboe* (Mid)
Gilchrist, Neil : *Bassoon* (Lon)
Gilchrist, Stephen : *Percussion* (Lon)

Index of Members - Greenfield

Greenfield, Charley : *Voice* (E)
Greenhalgh, Darrell : *Guitars* (Mid)
Greenhalgh, George : *Organ* (NW)
Greenhalgh, Mark : *Pianoforte* (SW)
Greenham, Maurice : *Pianoforte* (Mid)
Greenham, Peter : *Percussion* (Lon)
Greenhill, Simon : *Percussion* (SE)
Greenhouse, Philip : *Percussion* (Mid)
Greening, William : *Cello* (Lon)
Greenlaw, Verina : *Pianoforte* (E)
Greenleaves, Thomas : *Tympani* (Lon)
Greenlee, Martin : *Pianoforte* (SW)
Greenlees, David : *Viola* (NW)
Greenlees, Robert : *Clarinet* (Mid)
Greenshields, Lynne : *Pianoforte* (SE)
Greensill, Mark : *Violin* (E)
Greenslade, David : *Composer* (Lon)
Greenslade, Rebecca Marie : *Violin* (SW)
Greensmith, Brian : *Cello* (NE)
Greensmith, Clive : *Cello* (Lon)
Greensmith, David : *Double Bass* (SW)
Greenstone, Jack : *Violin* (Lon)
Greenway, John : *Percussion* (Mid)
Greenway, Mike : *Keyboards* (Lon)
Greenway, Paul Charles : *Pianoforte* (SW)
Greenway, Rhiannon : *Recorders* (Lon)
Greenway, Sue : *Saxophones* (Lon)
Greenwood, Alan : *Songwriter* (Lon)
Greenwood, Alexander : *Percussion* (NE)
Greenwood, Andrew : *Repetiteur* (SW)
Greenwood, Anthony : *Trombone* (NW)
Greenwood, Ben : *Saxophones* (Lon)
Greenwood, Beverley : *Violin* (NW)
Greenwood, Chico : *Percussion* (SW)
Greenwood, David : *Percussion* (NW)
Greenwood, Gordon : *Organ* (NE)
Greenwood, Jane : *Cello* (SW)
Greenwood, John : *Guitars* (SE)
Greenwood, Michael : *Clarinet* (SW)
Greenwood, Nigel : *Trumpet* (NE)
Greenwood, Rachel : *Violin* (Mid)
Greenwood, Stan : *Guitars* (NE)
Greenwood, Susan : *Violin* (Mid)
Greenwood, Tom : *Guitars* (Lon)
Greer, Andrew : *Percussion* (SW)
Greer, Charles : *Trumpet* (Sco)
Greeve, Micky : *Percussion* (Lon)
Gregoire, Sonia : *Voice* (Lon)
Gregor-Smith, Bernard : *Cello* (NE)
Gregorig, Ian : *Guitars* (SW)
Gregory, Alfred : *Bandleader* (Mid)
Gregory, Alfred : *Saxophones* (Mid)
Gregory, Brian : *Trumpet* (E)
Gregory, Christian : *Pianoforte* (Lon)
Gregory, David : *Violin* (Mid)
Gregory, David : *Guitars* (SW)
Gregory, Glenn : *Voice* (Lon)
Gregory, Ian : *Percussion* (SW)
Gregory, James : *Early Wind* (Lon)
Gregory, James : *Flute* (Lon)
Gregory, Jayne : *Double Bass* (SW)
Gregory, John : *Composer* (Lon)
Gregory, John Brandon : *Pianoforte* (NE)
Gregory, Julian : *Violin* (NW)
Gregory, Michael : *Percussion* (Lon)
Gregory, Michael : *Bass Guitar* (NE)
Gregory, Rachel : *Flute* (Lon)
Gregory, Rob : *Percussion* (NE)
Gregory, Robert : *Organ* (NW)
Gregory, Roy : *Pianoforte* (Lon)
Gregory, Sam Paul : *Pianoforte* (Lon)
Gregory, Sean : *Composer* (Lon)
Gregory, Stephen : *Percussion* (NW)
Gregory, Steve : *Saxophones* (Lon)
Gregory, Terrence : *Bass Guitar* (Lon)

Gregory, William : *Saxophones* (SW)
Gregson, Anne : *Voice* (SW)
Gregson, Clive : *Guitars* (NW)
Gregson, James : *Clarinet* (NW)
Gregson, Keith : *Guitars* (NE)
Gregson-Williams, Rupert : *Keyboards* (Lon)
Greig, Michael : *Keyboards* (Sco)
Greig, Murray : *Trumpet* (NE)
Greig, Stanley : *Pianoforte* (Lon)
Grenfell, Kevin : *Trombone* (SW)
Gresch, David : *Organ* (NW)
Gresch, David : *Vibraphone* (NW)
Gresswell, Steve : *Keyboards* (Lon)
Gresty, Alan : *Trumpet* (Lon)
Greswell, John : *Viola* (E)
Grey, Alan : *Harmonica (Inc Bass)* (Lon)
Grey, Stanley : *Saxophones* (NE)
Gribble, David : *Viola* (SW)
Gribble, Olivia : *Violin* (SW)
Gribble, Robert : *Trombone* (SW)
Grieve, Pamela : *Violin* (Lon)
Griffin, Claire : *Violin* (Lon)
Griffin, Clive : *Voice* (Lon)
Griffin, Dirk : *Bass Guitar* (Mid)
Griffin, Donald : *Saxophones* (SW)
Griffin, Elizabeth : *Viola* (SE)
Griffin, Ian : *Keyboards* (SW)
Griffin, Jeffrey : *Percussion* (SE)
Griffin, John : *Saxophones* (Lon)
Griffin, Jonathan : *Keyboards* (Lon)
Griffin, Lee : *Guitars* (NW)
Griffin, Roger : *Percussion* (Lon)
Griffin, Thomas : *Trombone* (NW)
Griffith, Barrie : *Bass Guitar* (NW)
Griffith, Daryl : *Conductor* (Lon)
Griffith, Fiona : *Viola* (Lon)
Griffith, Frank : *Saxophones* (Lon)
Griffith, Len : *Trumpet* (Lon)
Griffith, Shaun : *Trumpet* (Lon)
Griffiths, Alan : *Guitars* (Mid)
Griffiths, Andrew : *Percussion* (SW)
Griffiths, Ann : *Harp* (SW)
Griffiths, Anthony : *Violin* (NW)
Griffiths, Arfona : *Viola* (NW)
Griffiths, Arthur : *Double Bass* (Lon)
Griffiths, Arthur : *Pianoforte* (SE)
Griffiths, Barbara : *Keyboards* (E)
Griffiths, Barry : *Violin* (Lon)
Griffiths, Benjamin : *Percussion* (Mid)
Griffiths, David : *Double Bass* (Lon)
Griffiths, David : *Double Bass* (SW)
Griffiths, David : *Percussion* (SW)
Griffiths, Debbie : *Double Bass* (SE)
Griffiths, Derek : *Guitars* (Lon)
Griffiths, Dominic : *Violin* (Lon)
Griffiths, Gareth : *Pianoforte* (SW)
Griffiths, Geraint : *Guitars* (SW)
Griffiths, Gordon : *Percussion* (Mid)
Griffiths, Graham : *Viola* (Lon)
Griffiths, Griff : *Trombone* (SE)
Griffiths, Harold : *Saxophones* (SW)
Griffiths, Huw : *Percussion* (SW)
Griffiths, Jane : *Violin* (Lon)
Griffiths, Jo : *Voice* (Lon)
Griffiths, Jonathan : *Pianoforte* (SW)
Griffiths, Leslie : *Pianoforte* (Lon)
Griffiths, M 'Eddie' : *Saxophones* (Lon)
Griffiths, Malcolm : *Trombone* (Lon)
Griffiths, Mark : *Guitars* (Mid)
Griffiths, Mark : *Guitars* (SW)
Griffiths, Matt : *Harmonica (Inc Bass)* (Lon)
Griffiths, Matthew : *Percussion* (SW)
Griffiths, Michael : *Trombone* (E)
Griffiths, Michael : *Organ* (SW)
Griffiths, Paul : *Pianoforte* (Lon)

Griffiths, Philip : *Percussion* (NW)
Griffiths, Richard : *Clarinet* (Mid)
Griffiths, Sharron : *Harp* (Lon)
Griffiths, Simon : *Saxophones* (SE)
Griffiths, Simon : *Guitars* (SW)
Griffiths, Simon : *Horn* (SW)
Griffiths, Spencer : *Guitars* (Lon)
Griffiths, Thomas : *Melodeon* (E)
Grigelis, Alexander : *Keyboards* (Sco)
Grigg, Michael : *Percussion* (Lon)
Griggs, Ross : *Keyboards* (E)
Grigue, Stephan Perez : *Guitars* (Lon)
Grime, Frank : *Bass Guitar* (NW)
Grimes, Alan : *Percussion* (NE)
Grimes, Ged : *Bass Guitar* (Sco)
Grimes, Stephen : *Guitars* (NW)
Grimm, Douglas : *Voice* (Lon)
Grimm, Nigel : *Cello* (NW)
Grimshaw, Marie : *Voice* (E)
Grimster, Alan : *Saxophones* (SE)
Grindell, John : *Pianoforte* (NW)
Grindley, John : *Guitars* (SE)
Gringras, Paul : *Guitars* (Lon)
Grint (Wharton), Sara : *Oboe* (Lon)
Grippa, Steve : *Guitars* (Lon)
Gripton, Sue : *Oboe* (Mid)
Grisi, Laura : *Flute* (Sco)
Grist, Raymond : *Organ* (SW)
Gritton, Robin : *Cello* (Lon)
Grocott, Stephen : *Guitars* (Lon)
Grocutt, Matthew : *Trumpet* (Lon)
Groenevelt, Benjamin : *Double Bass* (SW)
Grogan, Sheila : *Cello* (Lon)
Groom, Don : *Percussion* (SE)
Groovebug : *Keyboards* (E)
Grooves, T.C. : *Bass Guitar* (Lon)
Gross, Jose : *Keyboards* (Lon)
Grossart, Andy : *Bass Guitar* (Lon)
Grossart, James : *Percussion* (Sco)
Grossart, Steven : *Pianoforte* (Sco)
Grosse, Paul : *Double Bass* (NW)
Grossmith, Derek : *Saxophones* (Lon)
Grosvenor, David : *Tuba* (NE)
Groth, Michael : *Guitars* (Lon)
Grout, Keith : *Viola* (Lon)
Grove, Ben : *Guitars* (SE)
Grove, John : *Bassoon* (NW)
Grove, Neil : *Bass Guitar* (Lon)
Grove, Peter : *Pianoforte* (SW)
Grove, William : *Guitars* (SE)
Groves, Andrew : *Guitars* (Sco)
Groves, Chris : *Guitars* (Lon)
Groves, Jane : *Flute* (SW)
Groves, Peter : *Guitars* (Lon)
Groves, Roger : *Trombone* (Lon)
Groves, Rosalyn : *Voice* (Lon)
Groves, Roy : *Saxophones* (Lon)
Grower, Alexis : *Pianoforte* (Lon)
Gruca-Broadbent, Magdalena : *Violin* (Lon)
Gruenberg, Erich : *Violin* (Lon)
Gruenberg, Tina : *Violin* (Lon)
Grummett, Barry : *Pianoforte* (Mid)
Grun, Gundula : *Violin* (Lon)
Grundell, Richard : *Percussion* (SW)
Grundy, Dan : *Percussion* (SE)
Grundy, David : *Bodhran* (Mid)
Grundy, John : *Percussion* (SW)
Grundy, Liam : *Keyboards* (Lon)
Grundy, Neil : *Horn* (NW)
Gruner, Alan : *Bass Guitar* (Lon)
Grunfeld, Jean : *Voice* (Lon)
Grunnill, Chris : *Trumpet* (E)
Grunthal, Barbara : *Cello* (NW)
Guarare, Grupo : *Accordion* (Lon)
Guard, Barrie : *Percussion* (Lon)
Guard, Sebastian : *Percussion* (Lon)

Index of Members - Hall

Hall, Richard : *Guitars* (Mid)
Hall, Robert : *Clarinet* (E)
Hall, Ron : *Percussion* (NW)
Hall, Simon T : *Bass Trombone* (Mid)
Hall, Stephen : *Guitars* (Lon)
Hall, Stephen : *Voice* (Mid)
Hall, Steven : *Keyboards* (NW)
Hall, Stuart : *Guitars* (Lon)
Hall, Susan : *Violin* (NW)
Hall, Sylvia : *Violin* (SE)
Hall, Tony : *Saxophones* (Lon)
Hall, William : *Organ* (SW)
Hall, Yvonne : *Viola* (Sco)
Hallam, George : *Violin* (Lon)
Hallam, John : *Saxophones* (NW)
Hallam, John Carstairs : *Bandleader* (NE)
Hallam, John Carstairs : *Tuba* (NE)
Hallam, Mandy : *Violin* (Mid)
Hallam, Norman : *Clarinet* (SE)
Hallam, Richard : *Trumpet* (Mid)
Hallam, Timothy : *Percussion* (SE)
Hallawell, James : *Keyboards* (Lon)
Hallberg, Petra : *Voice* (Lon)
Hallett, Jane : *Cello* (NW)
Hallett, Jonathan : *Viola* (Lon)
Hallett, Simon : *Double Bass* (Lon)
Hallett, Sylvia : *Violin* (Lon)
Halliday, Craig : *Violin* (NE)
Halliday, James : *Pianoforte* (SE)
Halliday, Neil : *Percussion* (Sco)
Halliday, Richard : *Tuba* (Lon)
Halliday, Toni : *Voice* (Lon)
Halligan, Anthony : *Double Bass* (Lon)
Halling, Patrick : *Violin* (Lon)
Halliwell, Francis : *Guitars* (NW)
Halliwell, Geraldine : *Voice* (Lon)
Halliwell, Rick : *Saxophones* (NW)
Hallowell, Adrian : *Bass Trombone* (Lon)
Halm, Nana : *Rapper* (Lon)
Halsey, Denys : *Pianoforte* (NE)
Halsey, James : *Cello* (Lon)
Halsey, John : *Percussion* (E)
Halsey, Simon : *Conductor* (Mid)
Halstead, Anthony : *Horn* (Lon)
Halstead, Christian : *Violin* (Lon)
Halyburton, May : *Double Bass* (Sco)
Halyburton, May : *Early Strings* (Sco)
Ham, Bernard : *Trumpet* (SW)
Hambleton, Hale : *Clarinet* (Lon)
Hambleton, Robert : *Trombone* (NW)
Hambleton-Smith, Sandra : *Guitars* (Lon)
Hambrook, Helen : *Electric Violin* (Lon)
Hambrook, Stefan : *Percussion* (Lon)
Hamer, Catherine : *Violin* (Mid)
Hamer, Dick : *Saxophones* (SW)
Hamer, George : *Saxophones* (Lon)
Hamer, Ian : *Trumpet* (Lon)
Hamer, Jill Meredith : *Violin* (SW)
Hamer, Mick : *Pianoforte* (Lon)
Hamer, Philip : *Oboe* (Lon)
Hamer, Rod : *Trumpet* (E)
Hamer, Stu : *Trumpet* (Lon)
Hamerton, Susan : *Violin* (Lon)
Hames, James : *Trumpet* (SE)
Hames, Robin : *Cello* (SW)
Hamill, Andy : *Double Bass* (Lon)
Hamill, Drew : *Guitars* (Lon)
Hamilton, Andrew : *Saxophones* (Lon)
Hamilton, Andy : *Saxophones* (Lon)
Hamilton, Andy : *Saxophones* (Mid)
Hamilton, Annemauraide : *Violin* (NW)
Hamilton, Armour : *Double Bass* (Sco)
Hamilton, Claire : *Viola* (Sco)
Hamilton, Claire : *Harp* (SW)
Hamilton, Craig : *Guitars* (Sco)

Hamilton, Ian : *Bass Guitar* (NE)
Hamilton, Ian : *Oboe* (NE)
Hamilton, Joanna : *Viola* (Sco)
Hamilton, John : *Guitars* (E)
Hamilton, Laurie : *Bass Guitar* (Sco)
Hamilton, Peter : *Double Bass* (Mid)
Hamilton, Rachel : *Early Renaissance* (Lon)
Hamilton, Rachel : *Pianoforte* (SW)
Hamilton, Ross : *Bass Guitar* (Lon)
Hamilton, Ross : *Percussion* (SW)
Hamilton, Roy : *Pianoforte* (Lon)
Hamilton, Steve : *Pianoforte* (Lon)
Hamilton, Timothy : *Voice* (SE)
Hamilton-Box, Peter : *Double Bass* (Lon)
Hamlin, Gareth : *Percussion* (SW)
Hamlin, Julian : *Violin* (Lon)
Hamm, June : *Voice* (Lon)
Hamm, Ralf : *Keyboards* (Lon)
Hammer, Jeffrey : *Keyboards* (Lon)
Hammerton, Dan : *Trumpet* (NE)
Hammerton, Daniel : *Double Bass* (NW)
Hammett, Barry : *Guitars* (SW)
Hammett, Kirstie : *Guitars* (SW)
Hammill, Peter : *Keyboards* (Lon)
Hammond, Alan : *Bassoon* (Lon)
Hammond, Gary : *Percussion* (Lon)
Hammond, Graham : *Bass Guitar* (NW)
Hammond, Ian : *Bass Trombone* (SW)
Hammond, John : *Trumpet* (E)
Hammond, John : *Percussion* (SE)
Hammond, Mark : *Organ* (Lon)
Hammond, Paul : *Guitars* (SE)
Hammond, Richard : *Trumpet* (Lon)
Hammond, Richard : *Percussion* (SE)
Hammond, Roger : *Trumpet* (SE)
Hammond, Ruth : *Saxophones* (Lon)
Hammond, Scott : *Percussion* (Lon)
Hammond, Stan : *Bass Guitar* (Mid)
Hammond, Thomas : *Trombone* (Lon)
Hamper, Stephen : *Percussion* (E)
Hampshire, Christopher : *Keyboards* (SE)
Hampson, Leslie : *Percussion* (NW)
Han, Yi : *Double Bass* (NW)
Hanby, Chris : *Bass Guitar* (E)
Hancock, David : *Trumpet* (Lon)
Hancock, Emma : *Violin* (NW)
Hancock, Garrad : *Percussion* (Lon)
Hancock, Michael : *Pianoforte* (NW)
Hancock, Peter : *Guitars* (Mid)
Hancock, Robin : *Guitars* (Lon)
Hancock, Stephen : *Music Director* (Mid)
Hancock, Stephen : *Pianoforte* (Mid)
Hand, Jonathan : *Guitars* (Mid)
Hand, Raymond : *Pianoforte* (E)
Hand, Richard : *Guitars* (Lon)
Hand, Richard : *Saxophones* (Mid)
Handford, Greg : *Percussion* (SE)
Handle, Johnny : *Accordion* (NE)
Handley, Catherine : *Flute* (SW)
Handley, Mark : *Guitars* (SE)
Hands, David : *Guitars* (E)
Hands, Tim : *Bass Guitar* (Lon)
Handsome, Mikey : *Rapper* (Lon)
Handy, Allen : *Composer* (Lon)
Handy, Edmund : *Keyboards* (Lon)
Handy, James : *Horn* (Lon)
Handy, Lionel : *Cello* (SE)
Handy, Thelma : *Violin* (NW)
Hanesworth, David : *Violin* (Lon)
Hanesworth, Walter : *Cello* (SE)
Haney, Janet Elizabeth : *Pianoforte* (Lon)
Hankin, Christine : *Flute* (Lon)
Hankin, David : *Trombone* (Sco)
Hankin, Paul : *Latin American Percu* (Lon)
Hankin, Richard : *Guitars* (SE)

Hanks, Nicholas : *Bodhran* (SW)
Hanley, Aoife : *Violin* (Lon)
Hanley, Clare : *Cornet* (Sco)
Hanley, Francesca : *Flute* (Lon)
Hanna, Jane : *Horn* (Lon)
Hannaby, Daniel : *Trombone* (SW)
Hannaford, Richard : *Bass Guitar* (Lon)
Hannah, Frances : *Violin* (NW)
Hannah, Jayne : *Flute* (SW)
Hannah, Tom : *Guitars* (Lon)
Hannam, David : *Bass Guitar* (Lon)
Hannan, Lawrence : *Double Bass* (Mid)
Hannan, Patrick : *Percussion* (SE)
Hannigan, Derek : *Clarinet* (Lon)
Hannigan, Steafan : *Irish Pipes* (Lon)
Hannington, Kenneth : *Viola* (Lon)
Hanratty, Stewart : *Guitars* (Sco)
Hanson, Al : *Saxophones* (Lon)
Hanson, Dick : *Trumpet* (Lon)
Hanson, Julia : *Violin* (NW)
Hanson, Leonard : *Organ* (NE)
Hanson, Peter : *Violin* (Lon)
Hanson, Reginald : *Organ* (NE)
Hanson, Simon : *Percussion* (Lon)
Hanson-Usher, Moira : *Percussion* (NW)
Hanvey, J Neale : *Keyboards* (Lon)
Hara, Yumi : *Voice* (Lon)
Harada, Kuma : *Bass Guitar* (Lon)
Haram, Simon : *Saxophones* (Lon)
Harberd, Cyril : *Percussion* (SW)
Harborne, John : *Trombone* (Lon)
Harborne, Raymond : *Guitars* (Lon)
Harbour, Sidney : *Guitars* (Lon)
Harbron, Robert : *Concertina (Inc Engl* (Lon)
Harcourt, Kevin : *Trumpet* (Mid)
Harcourt, Stephen : *Guitars* (Lon)
Harcourt, Stephen : *Trumpet* (Mid)
Hard-Kaur : *Songwriter* (Mid)
Hardaker, Sam : *Keyboards* (Lon)
Hardcastle, Paul : *Keyboards* (Lon)
Hardie, Alastair : *Violin* (Sco)
Hardie, Ian : *Folk Fiddle* (Sco)
Hardin, Eddie : *Pianoforte* (SE)
Harding, Brian : *Guitars* (Mid)
Harding, Caroline : *Double Bass* (Lon)
Harding, Christopher : *Flute* (Lon)
Harding, David : *Saxophones* (SE)
Harding, Elizabeth : *Guitars* (Lon)
Harding, Eric : *Pianoforte* (Lon)
Harding, Jean : *Violin* (SE)
Harding, Kate : *Cello* (E)
Harding, Matthew : *Percussion* (SW)
Harding, Michael : *Guitars* (SE)
Harding, Mike : *Guitars* (NW)
Harding, Philip : *Keyboards* (Lon)
Harding, Rachel : *Violin* (NE)
Harding, Robert : *Electric Accordion* (SW)
Harding, Sam : *Pianoforte* (SE)
Harding, Stan : *Percussion* (E)
Harding, Timothy : *Music Director* (Mid)
Harding, Trevor : *Guitars* (SE)
Harding, Wendy : *Percussion* (Sco)
Harding-Chestney, Kaytie : *Voice* (SE)
Hardisty, Christine : *Voice* (Lon)
Hardman, Christopher : *Percussion* (Lon)
Hardwick, Andy : *Keyboards* (Mid)
Hardwick, Ian : *Oboe* (Lon)
Hardwick, James : *Pianoforte* (Lon)
Hardwick, Jamie : *Keyboards* (Lon)
Hardwick, Sheila : *Bassoon* (NE)
Hardy, Caroline : *Voice* (Lon)
Hardy, Christopher : *Guitars* (Lon)
Hardy, Craig : *Keyboards* (Lon)
Hardy, David : *Saxophones* (NE)
Hardy, John : *Trumpet* (Lon)

504

Hayes, Rodney : *Trombone* (SE)
Hayes, Stephen : *Trombone* (SE)
Hayes, Tony : *Bass Guitar* (Lon)
Hayes, Victor : *Violin* (NW)
Hayhurst, Alison : *Flute* (Lon)
Hayhurst, Oli : *Double Bass* (Lon)
Hayler, Richard : *Percussion* (NW)
Hayler, Stephen : *Voice* (SE)
Hayles, Martin : *Keyboards* (Lon)
Hayley, Nicholas : *Violin* (E)
Hayman, Keith : *Pianoforte* (SE)
Hayman, Steve : *Percussion* (SE)
Hayne, Christopher : *Keyboards* (Lon)
Haynes, Esme : *Violin* (Sco)
Haynes, Francis : *Pianoforte* (SE)
Haynes, Graham : *Trumpet* (Lon)
Haynes, Kevin : *Saxophones* (Lon)
Haynes, Rachael : *Voice* (Lon)
Haynes, Sarah : *Double Bass* (Lon)
Haynes, Tony : *Composer* (Lon)
Haysted, Ian : *Clarinet* (Lon)
Hayston, Nicola : *Early Strings* (Lon)
Hayto, James : *Guitars* (Lon)
Hayward, Albert : *Double Bass* (Lon)
Hayward, Cecil : *Trumpet* (Mid)
Hayward, David : *Guitars* (E)
Hayward, Dennis : *Bandleader* (Lon)
Hayward, Jack : *Harp* (Lon)
Hayward, John : *Oboe* (NE)
Hayward, Jonathan : *Guitars* (Lon)
Hayward, Justin : *Guitars* (Lon)
Hayward, Mark : *Violin* (Sco)
Hayward, Peter : *Pianoforte* (SE)
Hayward, Rachel : *Steel Pan* (SE)
Hayward, Robert : *Pianoforte* (NW)
Hayward, Russell : *Horn* (NW)
Hayward, Ruth : *Flute* (Mid)
Hayward, Tim : *Trumpet* (Lon)
Hayward, Valerie : *Cello* (NW)
Hayward, William : *Organ* (Mid)
Haywood, Beverley : *Percussion* (Mid)
Haywood, Cliff : *Composer* (Lon)
Haywood, John : *Pianoforte* (Lon)
Haywood, Mark : *Guitars* (SW)
Haywood, Tony : *Guitars* (E)
Haze : *Voice* (Lon)
Haze, Hammy : *Voice* (SE)
Hazelhurst-Howles, Damon : *Percussion* (SW)
Hazell, Gary : *Organ* (Lon)
Hazell, Tony : *Trumpet* (SW)
Hazeltine, Deborah : *Voice* (SE)
Hazle, Nicholas : *Harmonica (Inc Bass* (E)
Hazlehurst, Ronnie : *Arranger* (Lon)
Hazleton, Ben : *Double Bass* (Lon)
Heacock, Richard : *Violin* (SE)
Head, George : *Violin* (SW)
Head, John : *Banjo* (Lon)
Head, Philip : *Violin* (Mid)
Head, Raymond : *Pianoforte* (Lon)
Head, Rosemary : *Violin* (E)
Headey, Stuart : *Pianoforte* (Lon)
Headley, Adrian : *Trumpet* (Lon)
Headley, Lisa : *Voice* (Lon)
Headley, Nigel : *Guitars* (SE)
Heald, Mike : *Percussion* (NW)
Heald, Sarah : *Violin* (NW)
Healey, Derek : *Trumpet* (Lon)
Healey, Jane : *Double Bass* (Lon)
Healy, Francis : *Voice* (Lon)
Healy, Kevin : *Guitars* (Lon)
Heaney, Clare : *Flute* (SW)
Heanue, Teresa : *Violin* (Lon)
Heap, Steve : *Cornet* (SE)
Heape, Emma : *Hurdy-gurdy* (SE)
Heard, Gordon : *Conductor* (Lon)

Heard, John : *Violin* (SW)
Heard, Jonathan : *Percussion* (Mid)
Heard, Robert : *Violin* (Lon)
Heard, Roger : *Keyboards* (SW)
Hearn, Martin : *Percussion* (Lon)
Hearn, Samantha : *Voice* (NW)
Hearne, Anthony : *Guitars* (NE)
Hearnshaw, Charles : *Clarinet* (SW)
Hearnshaw, Colin : *Trumpet* (NW)
Heart, Andrew : *Bass Guitar* (Lon)
Heartfield, Jill : *Cello* (Mid)
Heartfield, Sarah : *Viola* (NE)
Hearton, Alan : *Pianoforte* (SE)
Heath, Antony : *Organ* (SE)
Heath, Bob : *Voice* (SE)
Heath, Bobby : *Pianoforte* (Lon)
Heath, Dave : *Flute* (Sco)
Heath, Desmond : *Violin* (Lon)
Heath, Elizabeth : *Percussion* (Lon)
Heath, Eric : *Violin* (SE)
Heath, Greg : *Saxophones* (Lon)
Heath, Jim : *Sousaphone* (SE)
Heath, Juliette : *Violin* (Lon)
Heath, Kate : *Pianoforte* (Lon)
Heath, Lucy : *Double Bass* (Lon)
Heath, Martin : *Cello* (Lon)
Heath, Michael : *Songwriter* (E)
Heath, Sally : *Pianoforte* (Lon)
Heath, Suzanne : *Voice* (Lon)
Heather, Elizabeth : *Viola* (Mid)
Heathorn, Ron : *Saxophones* (SE)
Heatley, Spike : *Double Bass* (Lon)
Heatlie, Robert : *Keyboards* (Sco)
Heaton, Paul : *Voice* (NE)
Heaton, Phil : *Percussion* (Mid)
Heaviside, Colin : *Pianoforte* (E)
Heawood, Marian : *Pianoforte* (E)
Hebblewhite, Bruce : *Horn* (NW)
Hebbron, Celia : *Violin* (NW)
Hebbron, John : *Violin* (NW)
Hebden, Kieran : *Guitars* (Lon)
Hecht, Philip : *Violin* (NW)
Heckel, Stefan : *Pianoforte* (Lon)
Heckstall-Smith, Dick : *Saxophones* (Lon)
Hector, Timothy : *Bass Guitar* (Lon)
Hector, Wayne : *Voice* (Lon)
Hedgecock, John Bernard : *Percussion* (SE)
Hedger, Geoffrey : *Keyboards* (SE)
Hedger, Susan : *Violin* (Lon)
Hedges, David : *Viola* (SW)
Hedges, William : *Guitars* (SW)
Hedin, Jakob : *Voice* (Lon)
Hedley, Adam : *Percussion* (SE)
Hedley, Giles : *Voice* (Lon)
Hedley-Miller, Sarah : *Cello* (Lon)
Heel, Christopher : *Bass Guitar* (SW)
Heeley, Brian : *Percussion* (SE)
Heeley, Roger : *Pianoforte* (Mid)
Heffernan, Seamus : *Guitars* (NW)
Hegan, Patrick : *Percussion* (NW)
Hegarty, Kevin : *Trumpet* (E)
Hegedus, Olga : *Cello* (Lon)
Heggart, William : *Cello* (Lon)
Heggarty, Leigh : *Guitars* (Lon)
Heggie, Kenneth : *Guitars* (NW)
Hehir, Michael : *Guitars* (NW)
Heichelheim, Stefanie : *Violin* (Lon)
Heidecker, Ursula : *Violin* (Sco)
Heighway, John : *Organ* (SE)
Hein, George : *Violin* (Lon)
Hein, Ricky : *Keyboards* (SE)
Heinen, Elaine : *Cello* (Mid)
Heinen, Ulrich : *Cello* (Mid)
Heinrich, Jasmine : *Voice* (Lon)
Heley, John : *Cello* (Lon)

Helion, Perl : *Guitars* (Lon)
Hellen, Marian : *Horn* (E)
Heller, Jana : *Guitars* (Lon)
Heller, Kate : *Viola* (Lon)
Hellier, Ruth : *Pianoforte* (Mid)
Helliwell, Donna : *Flute* (NE)
Helliwell, John : *Saxophones* (NW)
Helliwell, Julie : *Trombone* (NE)
Hellyer, Roger : *Bassoon* (Lon)
Hellyer Jones, Jonathan : *Harpsichord* (Lon)
Helm, Jonathan : *Percussion* (SW)
Helm, Nicholas : *Guitars* (Mid)
Helmore, Mark : *Percussion* (SW)
Helson, Robert : *Percussion* (SW)
Hembrough, Oliver : *Voice* (NW)
Hembrough, Peter : *Violin* (Lon)
Hemery, Anna : *Violin* (Mid)
Hemming, Bob : *Trumpet* (SE)
Hemming, John : *Pianoforte* (Mid)
Hemming, Katherine : *Violin* (E)
Hemming, Paul : *Guitars* (SE)
Hemmingham, John : *Trumpet* (NE)
Hemmings, Diana : *Clarinet* (E)
Hemmings, John : *Trombone* (E)
Hemmings, Karl Eric : *Guitars* (Mid)
Hemmings, Paul : *Guitars* (NW)
Hemmings, Ria : *Keyboards* (Lon)
Hemmingsley, Carl : *Percussion* (Mid)
Hempell, John : *Percussion* (SW)
Hempsall, R R : *Percussion* (NE)
Hempstead, Catherine : *Trumpet* (SW)
Hemsworth, Kathy : *Voice* (E)
Hemsworth, Ross : *Guitars* (E)
Hemus, Alan : *Bandleader* (Mid)
Hemus, Alan : *Voice* (Mid)
Henbest, Rosemary : *Violin* (Lon)
Henderson, Albert : *Percussion* (NE)
Henderson, Allie : *Pianoforte* (Lon)
Henderson, Andrew : *Percussion* (Lon)
Henderson, Andy : *Keyboards* (Sco)
Henderson, Colin : *Bass Guitar* (SE)
Henderson, David : *Guitars* (Sco)
Henderson, Diane : *Trumpet* (Lon)
Henderson, Eleanor : *Violin* (NE)
Henderson, Forbes : *Guitars* (Lon)
Henderson, Gareth : *Voice* (SE)
Henderson, Gavin : *Trumpet* (SE)
Henderson, Graham : *Pianoforte* (Lon)
Henderson, Guy : *Double Bass* (Lon)
Henderson, Kahl : *Keyboards* (Sco)
Henderson, Keith : *Composer* (SE)
Henderson, Kelvin : *Guitars* (SW)
Henderson, Malcolm : *Viola* (Mid)
Henderson, Martin : *Double Bass* (Lon)
Henderson, Martin : *Guitars* (Lon)
Henderson, Paul : *Guitars* (Sco)
Henderson, Peter : *Percussion* (Lon)
Henderson, Richard : *Percussion* (Lon)
Henderson, Robert : *Guitars* (Sco)
Henderson, Stephen : *Percussion* (Lon)
Henderson, Stewart : *Guitars* (Sco)
Henderson, Stuart : *Bass Guitar* (Sco)
Henderson, Stuart : *Trumpet* (SE)
Henderson, Tamasine : *Guitars* (Lon)
Henderson, Veronica : *Cello* (E)
Henderson, W : *Percussion* (NW)
Hendricks, Joanna : *Voice* (E)
Hendricks, Nimroy : *Voice* (Lon)
Hendricks, Roger : *Composer* (Lon)
Hendrickse, Jan : *Flute* (Lon)
Hendry, David : *Trumpet* (Lon)
Hendry, David : *Keyboards* (SE)
Hendry, Linn : *Pianoforte* (Lon)
Hendry, Robert : *Guitars* (Lon)
Hendy, John : *Trombone* (SW)

Hendy, Peter : *Bass Trombone* (SW)
Henery, Frank : *Guitars* (Sco)
Henesy, Charles : *Pianoforte* (NE)
Henesy, Paul : *Pianoforte* (Lon)
Henley, John : *Bass Guitar* (Mid)
Hennessey, Andrew : *Electric Violin* (Sco)
Hennessey, Bill : *Percussion* (Mid)
Hennessey, Brian : *Percussion* (SW)
Hennessey, Mike : *Pianoforte* (Lon)
Hennessy, Frank : *Guitars* (SW)
Hennessy, Gail : *Oboe* (Lon)
Hennin, Michael : *Organ* (Lon)
Henning, Audrey : *Viola* (Lon)
Henning, Douglas : *Bass Guitar* (Lon)
Henning, Martin : *Bass Guitar* (SW)
Hennings, Stephen : *Guitars* (Lon)
Henrit, Robert : *Percussion* (Lon)
Henry, Annie : *Voice* (Lon)
Henry, Brian : *Keyboards* (Lon)
Henry, Cassie : *Voice* (Lon)
Henry, Christine : *Voice* (Lon)
Henry, Errol : *Percussion* (Lon)
Henry, Frank : *Cello* (Lon)
Henry, James : *Guitars* (Sco)
Henry, Jason : *Songwriter* (Lon)
Henry, Leah : *Violin* (SE)
Henry, Melanie : *Saxophones* (Lon)
Henry, Melvyn : *Trombone* (Lon)
Henry, Michael : *Trumpet* (Lon)
Henry, Michael : *Voice* (Lon)
Henry, Neville : *Saxophones* (Lon)
Henry, Pauline : *Voice* (Lon)
Henry, Richard : *Bass Trombone* (Lon)
Henry, Simon : *Saxophones* (Lon)
Henry, Tyrone : *Voice* (Lon)
Hensel, Joanna : *Horn* (Lon)
Hensel, William : *Keyboards* (SE)
Henshaw, Elliott : *Percussion* (NW)
Henson, Elena : *Flute* (Lon)
Henson, Joe : *Bass Guitar* (Lon)
Henstock, Mark : *Voice* (Lon)
Henty, Timothy : *Percussion* (Lon)
Henzell, Derek : *Saxophones* (Lon)
Hepbir, Jonathan : *Guitars* (SE)
Hepburn, Donavan : *Percussion* (Mid)
Hepburn, Harold : *Percussion* (Sco)
Hepburn, Keith : *Guitars* (Lon)
Heppell, Martin : *Horn* (Lon)
Herail, Caroline : *Voice* (Lon)
Herbert, Andrew : *Percussion* (Mid)
Herbert, Brian : *Guitars* (NE)
Herbert, Colette : *Violin* (NW)
Herbert, Ian : *Clarinet* (Lon)
Herbert, Jonathan : *Tympani* (NW)
Herbert, Judith : *Cello* (Lon)
Herbert, Martin : *Violin* (SE)
Herbert, Nigel : *Trumpet* (Lon)
Herbert, Nuala : *Harp* (Lon)
Herbert, Paul : *Saxophones* (SW)
Herbert, Royston : *Accordion* (Lon)
Herbert, Sarah : *Violin* (Lon)
Herbert, Simone : *Voice* (Lon)
Herbert, Thomas : *Double Bass* (Lon)
Herbert, Trevor : *Trombone* (Lon)
Herbert, Vincent : *Bass Guitar* (SE)
Hercules, Carlos : *Percussion* (E)
Herd, David : *Violin* (Lon)
Herd, Judith : *Oboe* (Sco)
Herd, Neil Robert : *Guitars* (Lon)
Heredia, Tito : *Guitars* (Lon)
Heritage, Tom : *Saxophones* (NE)
Herman, Elaine : *Violin* (Lon)
Herman, Godfrey : *Double Bass* (Lon)
Herman, Marilyn : *Voice* (Lon)
Herman, Thomas : *Arranger* (Lon)

Hern, Martyn : *Keyboards* (SW)
Hernen, Elaine : *Voice* (Lon)
Herniman, Tim : *Saxophones* (Lon)
Herod, Gordon : *Trumpet* (NW)
Herold, Ian : *Guitars* (Lon)
Heron, James : *Guitars* (Lon)
Heron, Paul : *Percussion* (Lon)
Herridge, David : *Pianoforte* (Lon)
Herring, Duncan : *Bass Guitar* (Mid)
Herring, Margaret : *Violin* (NE)
Herriot, Alan : *Pianoforte* (Sco)
Herriott, Richard M J : *Pianoforte* (Lon)
Herrmann, Jill : *Harp* (Mid)
Herschmann, Heinz : *Pianoforte* (Lon)
Hersh, Benjamin : *Pianoforte* (Lon)
Hershman, Nick : *Pianoforte* (Lon)
Herson, Janet : *Clarinet* (Lon)
Hesketh, George : *Bass Guitar* (NW)
Heslewood, Alan : *Horn* (NW)
Heslop, Kathryn : *Electric Violin* (Lon)
Heslop, Thomas : *Double Bass* (NE)
Hess, Andrea : *Cello* (Lon)
Hess, Benjamin : *Cello* (Lon)
Hess, Gabrielle : *Violin* (Sco)
Hess, Gisela : *Violin* (Mid)
Hess, Rachel : *Violin* (Lon)
Hess, Ursula : *Cello* (Lon)
Hession, Edward : *Accordion* (Lon)
Hession, Paul : *Percussion* (NE)
Hester, Dieter : *Bassoon* (Lon)
Hester, Kate : *Pianoforte* (Mid)
Hetherington, Charles : *Voice* (SW)
Hetherington, Edward : *Accordion* (Lon)
Hetherington, George : *Organ* (NE)
Hetherington, Mariela : *Flute* (Lon)
Hetherington, Peter : *Double Bass* (Lon)
Hetherington, Ronald : *Percussion* (SE)
Hetherington, Simon : *Double Bass* (Lon)
Hewat, Corrina Dawn : *Harp* (Sco)
Hewerdine, Boo : *Bass Guitar* (E)
Hewett, Polly Jane : *Cello* (Lon)
Hewie, Christopher : *Pianoforte* (Lon)
Hewin, Simon : *Guitars* (Mid)
Hewins, Edwin : *Pianoforte* (NW)
Hewins, Mark : *Guitars* (Lon)
Hewins, Thomas : *Tuba* (Lon)
Hewinson, Colin : *Keyboards* (Lon)
Hewitt, Andy : *Percussion* (E)
Hewitt, Dave : *Guitars* (Lon)
Hewitt, Donald : *Guitars* (SE)
Hewitt, Edwin : *Bass Guitar* (E)
Hewitt, Helen : *Violin* (SW)
Hewitt, Keith : *Cello* (SW)
Hewitt, Mark : *Percussion* (Lon)
Hewitt, Michael : *Violin* (SE)
Hewitt, Miles : *Horn* (Lon)
Hewitt, Rachel : *Voice* (SE)
Hewitt, Richard : *Oboe* (NE)
Hewitt, Stephanie : *Cello* (NW)
Hewitt, Steven : *Percussion* (Lon)
Hewitt-Jones, Timothy : *Cello* (Lon)
Hewlett, Ben : *Harmonica (Inc Bass* (SW)
Hews, Richard : *Pianoforte* (SE)
Hewson, Daniel : *Trombone* (SE)
Hewson, David : *Pianoforte* (Lon)
Hewson, Richard : *Composer* (Lon)
Hext, David : *Percussion* (NW)
Hext, Joanna : *Cello* (NW)
Hext, Michael : *Trombone* (Lon)
Hey, Peter : *Bass Guitar* (Mid)
Heyat, Susan : *Guitars* (Lon)
Heyes, Edward : *Saxophones* (Lon)
Heyes, Nicola : *Cello* (NE)
Heyman, Paul : *Electric Violin* (Lon)
Heyman, Philip : *Viola* (SW)

Heyman, Preston : *Percussion* (Lon)
Heymerdinger, Tim : *Percussion* (SE)
Heyne, Rebecca : *Voice* (E)
Heyward, Mark : *Percussion* (SW)
Heyward, Nick : *Guitars* (Lon)
Heywood, Alison : *Accordion* (E)
Heywood, Barrington : *Bass Guitar* (NW)
Heywood, Brian : *Guitars* (E)
Heywood, David : *Clarinet* (NW)
Heywood, David : *Percussion* (NW)
Heywood, Derek : *Double Bass* (NE)
Heywood, Ian : *Guitars* (NE)
Heywood, Sandra : *Pianoforte* (SE)
Heywood, Susan : *Cello* (E)
Hibberd, Nick : *Guitars* (SE)
Hibbert, Fiona : *Harp* (Lon)
Hibbert, Ian : *Clarinet* (Mid)
Hibbert, Ian : *Music Director* (Mid)
Hibbert, Martin : *Keyboards* (Lon)
Hibbert, Rosemarie : *Voice* (Lon)
Hibbs, Colin : *Bass Guitar* (NE)
Hickey, Andy : *Keyboards* (NW)
Hickey, Darren : *Keyboards* (Lon)
Hickey, Della : *Viola* (NW)
Hickey, Michael : *Guitars* (NW)
Hickling, Anna : *Voice* (Lon)
Hickman, Colin : *Saxophones* (Lon)
Hickman, Rachael : *Violin* (Lon)
Hickman, Victor : *Violin* (NE)
Hicks, Anthony : *Guitars* (NW)
Hicks, Brian : *Horn* (SW)
Hicks, Clive : *Guitars* (Lon)
Hicks, Colin : *Keyboards* (Lon)
Hicks, Daisy : *Voice* (SE)
Hicks, David : *Guitars* (SE)
Hicks, Jacqueline : *Voice* (Lon)
Hicks, Janet : *Violin* (Lon)
Hicks, Malcolm : *Organ* (Lon)
Hicks, Robert : *Percussion* (SW)
Hickson, Andrew : *Percussion* (NW)
Hickson, Robert : *Bass Guitar* (Lon)
Hidson, Jean : *Celtic Harp* (Mid)
Hier, Carolyn : *Clarinet* (Lon)
Hier, Philip : *Cello* (SW)
Higginbotham, John : *Bass Trombone* (Lon)
Higginbottom, Christopher : *Percussion* (Lon)
Higginbottom, Craig : *Guitars* (Lon)
Higgins, Andrea : *Bassoon* (SW)
Higgins, Andy : *Bass Guitar* (Lon)
Higgins, Brian : *Songwriter* (SE)
Higgins, David : *Percussion* (SE)
Higgins, Elaine : *Voice* (Lon)
Higgins, Gerry : *Double Bass* (Lon)
Higgins, Janet : *Flute* (SE)
Higgins, John : *Guitars* (Sco)
Higgins, Julian : *Keyboards* (SE)
Higgins, Julie : *Voice* (Lon)
Higgins, Mike : *Keyboards* (NE)
Higgins, Norman : *Violin* (SW)
Higgins, Peter : *Guitars* (Lon)
Higgins, Richard : *Percussion* (Lon)
Higgins, Suzanne : *Saxophones* (NW)
Higgins, Thomas : *Oboe* (Lon)
Higgins, Yonah : *Voice* (NW)
Higginson, Colin : *Saxophones* (NW)
Higginson, Daniel : *Percussion* (SE)
Higginson, Jonathan : *Guitars* (SE)
Higginson, Victoria L : *Cello* (SW)
Higgs, David : *Bass Guitar* (SE)
Higgs, Jessica : *Voice* (Lon)
Higgs, Lindsay : *Bass Guitar* (SE)
Higgs, Martin : *Keyboards* (Mid)
Higgs, Nigel : *Guitars* (SE)
Higgs, Paul : *Trumpet* (Lon)
Higgs, Paul : *Northumbrian Pipes* (SE)

Higgs, Robert : *Violin* (Lon)
Higham, Benedict : *Trumpet* (E)
Higham, Cynthia : *Voice* (SE)
Higham, Darrel : *Guitars* (Lon)
Higham, Fiona : *Violin* (Lon)
Higham, J : *Trumpet* (NW)
Higham, Mark : *Trumpet* (Mid)
Higham, Michael : *Pianoforte* (SE)
Higham, Robert : *Trumpet* (Lon)
Higham, Stanley : *Saxophones* (Lon)
Highley, David : *Guitars* (NE)
Highton, Elizabeth : *Flute* (SW)
Hignell, Lauren : *Saxophones* (Lon)
Hilbert, Steven : *Guitars* (NE)
Hildebrand, Jacqi : *Voice* (Lon)
Hildia : *Voice* (E)
Hiley, Michelle : *Tympani* (SW)
Hiley, Paul : *Percussion* (SW)
Hilham, Caroline : *Voice* (E)
Hill, Adam : *Trombone* (SE)
Hill, Alan : *Guitars* (Lon)
Hill, Andrew : *Keyboards* (Lon)
Hill, Anthony : *Bass Guitar* (Lon)
Hill, Barbara : *Pianoforte* (Lon)
Hill, Colin : *Trombone* (Lon)
Hill, David : *Guitars* (Lon)
Hill, David : *Sousaphone* (Lon)
Hill, Derek : *Double Bass* (Sco)
Hill, Francis : *Guitars* (Lon)
Hill, Gary : *Bass Guitar* (E)
Hill, Gary Oliver : *Percussion* (Mid)
Hill, Gavin : *Bassoon* (Sco)
Hill, Ian : *Bass Guitar* (Mid)
Hill, Jackie : *Violin* (Mid)
Hill, Jason : *Guitars* (Mid)
Hill, John : *Double Bass* (Lon)
Hill, Jonathan G : *Violin* (Lon)
Hill, Judy : *Voice* (Lon)
Hill, Juliet : *Music Director* (Lon)
Hill, Kate : *Flute* (Lon)
Hill, Kathrine : *Pianoforte* (Mid)
Hill, Kevin : *Viola* (E)
Hill, Lisa : *Clarinet* (SE)
Hill, Lucy : *Viola* (Lon)
Hill, Marcus : *Keyboards* (Lon)
Hill, Matt : *Bass Guitar* (Sco)
Hill, Matthew : *Pianoforte* (Mid)
Hill, Mel : *Cornet* (Mid)
Hill, Michael : *Trumpet* (NE)
Hill, Nicholas : *Horn* (Lon)
Hill, Nick : *Trumpet* (E)
Hill, Nigel : *Double Bass* (SW)
Hill, Peter : *Tympani* (Mid)
Hill, Peter : *Clarinet* (NW)
Hill, Philip : *Oboe* (Sco)
Hill, Richard : *Bass Guitar* (NE)
Hill, Richard : *Composer* (Sco)
Hill, Richard : *Guitars* (SE)
Hill, Robert : *Clarinet* (Lon)
Hill, Sally : *Tympani* (NE)
Hill, Shane : *Guitars* (SE)
Hill, Stephen : *Pianoforte* (SE)
Hill, Steve : *Clarinet* (Lon)
Hill, Steve : *Pianoforte* (Lon)
Hill, Steve : *Guitars* (SW)
Hill, Thomas : *Pianoforte* (Lon)
Hill, Thomas : *Bass Guitar* (Mid)
Hill, Thomas Alan : *Double Bass* (Mid)
Hill, Timothy : *Horn* (Mid)
Hill, Vaughan : *Pianoforte* (SW)
Hill, Warwick : *Violin* (Lon)
Hill, William : *Percussion* (Lon)
Hill-Ahmad, Jennifer : *Early Wind* (Sco)
Hill-Ahmad, Jennifer : *Recorders* (Sco)
Hillard, Ross : *Bass Guitar* (Mid)

Hillary, David : *Keyboards* (NW)
Hillier, Ernie : *Saxophones* (SW)
Hillier, Gordon : *Trumpet* (SE)
Hillier, Marion : *Violin* (NE)
Hillier, Simon : *Guitars* (SW)
Hillman, George : *Keyboards* (SE)
Hillman, Hank : *Guitars* (SW)
Hillman, Mary : *Pianoforte* (Sco)
Hillman, Paul : *Bass Guitar* (SW)
Hills, Christopher : *Guitars* (Lon)
Hills, John : *Bass Guitar* (Lon)
Hilsum, Leonard : *Pianoforte* (Lon)
Hilton, Andrew : *Pianoforte* (NE)
Hilton, Christine : *Violin* (Lon)
Hilton, Christopher : *Violin* (NE)
Hilton, Derek : *Composer* (NW)
Hilton, Geoff : *Guitars* (Lon)
Hilton, Janet : *Clarinet* (NW)
Hilton, Michael : *Bass Guitar* (Lon)
Hilton, Paul : *Voice* (SE)
Hilton, Roy : *Music Director* (Lon)
Hilton, Stephen : *Keyboards* (Lon)
Hilton, Stuart : *Percussion* (Lon)
Hilton, Terry : *Viola* (Lon)
Hinch, John : *Trumpet* (Lon)
Hinchliffe, Emma : *Voice* (NW)
Hinchliffe, Keith : *Guitars* (NE)
Hinchliffe, Robert : *Oboe* (Lon)
Hind, Christopher : *Tympani* (Lon)
Hind, Evelyn : *Violin* (Lon)
Hind, Gary : *Music Director* (Lon)
Hind, Matthew : *Pianoforte* (NE)
Hind, Vivien : *Violin* (Lon)
Hinde, Bob : *Bassoon* (NW)
Hinde, Carl : *Double Bass* (NW)
Hinde, Neil : *Keyboards* (NE)
Hindes, Richard : *Bass Guitar* (E)
Hindle, Claire : *Flute* (SW)
Hindley, Aileen : *Accordion* (NW)
Hindley, Ann : *Banjo* (NW)
Hindley, Anthony : *Trumpet* (E)
Hindley, Frank : *Trombone* (Mid)
Hindley, Guy : *Accordion* (NW)
Hindley, Joanne : *Violin* (Lon)
Hinds, Camelle : *Bass Guitar* (Lon)
Hinds, David : *Guitars* (Mid)
Hinds, Jeremy : *Keyboards* (E)
Hinds, Peter : *Keyboards* (Lon)
Hine, Charles : *Clarinet* (Lon)
Hine, Keith : *Guitars* (Mid)
Hines, Gavin : *Guitars* (Mid)
Hines, Robert : *Guitars* (Mid)
Hings, Catherine : *Violin* (SW)
Hingston, Michael : *Saxophones* (E)
Hingston, Rod : *Saxophones* (Lon)
Hinnigan, Anthony : *Cello* (Lon)
Hinson, Amanda : *Bass Guitar* (Lon)
Hinton, Alistair : *Composer* (SW)
Hinton, Clare : *Cello* (Lon)
Hinton, Jonathan : *Keyboards* (SW)
Hinton, Michael : *Trumpet* (Lon)
Hinves, Neville : *Saxophones* (SE)
Hipkin, Murray : *Pianoforte* (Lon)
Hipkiss, Barry : *Pianoforte* (Mid)
Hipwell, Naomi : *Horn* (Lon)
Hird, Alison : *Contra Bassoon* (SW)
Hirons, Christopher : *Violin* (Lon)
Hirose, Taka : *Bass Guitar* (Lon)
Hirota, Joji : *Percussion* (Lon)
Hirota, Joji : *Shakuhachi* (Lon)
Hirsch, Deborah (Miffi) : *Violin* (Lon)
Hirsch, Jake : *Pianoforte* (Lon)
Hirsch, Rebecca : *Violin* (Lon)
Hirschman, David R. : *Viola* (Lon)
Hirsh, Paul : *Keyboards* (Lon)

Hirst, Bridget : *Violin* (Lon)
Hirst, Clare : *Saxophones* (Lon)
Hirst, Julian : *Guitars* (SE)
Hirst, Michael : *Flute* (Lon)
Hirst, Nigel : *Percussion* (Sco)
Hirst, Willie : *Saxophones* (NE)
Hiscock, Nigel : *Horn* (Lon)
Hiscock, Stephen : *Percussion* (Lon)
Hiscox, David : *Violin* (Mid)
Hiscox, Pamela : *Viola* (Mid)
Hiseman, Jill : *Voice* (Lon)
Hiseman, Jon : *Percussion* (Lon)
Hislam, Nicholas : *Percussion* (Mid)
Hislam, Nicholas : *Saxophones* (Mid)
Hissey, David : *Trombone* (Lon)
Hitchcock, Clive : *Saxophones* (Lon)
Hitchcock, Nigel : *Saxophones* (Lon)
Hitchell, William : *Guitars* (Sco)
Hitchen, Janet : *Violin* (NW)
Hitchenor, Joseph : *Violin* (Lon)
Hitchens, Nicholas : *Tuba* (Lon)
Hitchings, Michael : *Saxophones* (SW)
Hitchinson, Gayle : *Viola* (NE)
Hitchman, Nigel : *Pianoforte* (Lon)
Hjert, Gerry : *Saxophones* (Lon)
Hlela, Betty : *African Drums* (Lon)
Hoad, Paul : *Guitars* (Lon)
Hoare, Alan : *Double Bass* (SE)
Hoare, Brian : *Guitars* (Lon)
Hoare, Christine : *Viola* (NE)
Hoare, Simon : *Percussion* (Lon)
Hoarty, Peter : *Guitars* (NW)
Hoban, Christopher : *Berimbau* (Lon)
Hoban, Lynne : *Saxophones* (Lon)
Hoban, Peter : *Guitars* (Lon)
Hobart, Michael : *Saxophones* (Lon)
Hobart, Ted : *Trumpet* (Lon)
Hobbins, Darryl : *Cornet* (NE)
Hobbs, Jason : *Organ* (NE)
Hobbs, Lesley : *Trumpet* (Lon)
Hobbs, Martin : *Horn* (Lon)
Hobbs, Nick : *Voice* (Lon)
Hobbs, Paul : *Percussion* (SE)
Hobbs, Richard : *Guitars* (Lon)
Hobday, Clive : *Violin* (Lon)
Hobson, Andy : *Bass Guitar* (NE)
Hobson, Gregory : *Guitars* (E)
Hobson, Jane : *Voice* (NE)
Hobson, John : *Guitars* (SE)
Hobson, Lee : *Bass Guitar* (Lon)
Hobson, Nancy : *Trombone* (Mid)
Hociej, John : *Guitars* (Lon)
Hockin, Keith : *Trombone* (SW)
Hocking, Chris : *Pianoforte* (SE)
Hockings, David : *Tympani* (Lon)
Hockney, John : *Pianoforte* (SE)
Hockridge, David : *Percussion* (E)
Hockridge, Stephen : *Bass Guitar* (E)
Hodder-Williams, Susie : *Flute* (Lon)
Hodge, Al : *Guitars* (SW)
Hodge, Andrew : *Bass Guitar* (SW)
Hodge, Basil : *Pianoforte* (Lon)
Hodge, G : *Horn* (Sco)
Hodge, Iain : *Percussion* (Lon)
Hodge, Marjorie : *Violin* (Lon)
Hodge, Peter : *Trombone* (Lon)
Hodges, Alan : *Oboe* (Mid)
Hodges, Christopher : *Cello* (SW)
Hodges, Joanne : *Violin* (E)
Hodges, Laura : *Viola* (Lon)
Hodges, Laura : *Violin* (Lon)
Hodges, Maurice : *Recorders* (E)
Hodges, Peter : *Double Bass* (Lon)
Hodges, Valerie : *Clarinet* (SW)
Hodgkin, Keyy : *Voice* (E)

Index of Members - Hodgkins

Hodgkins, Chris : *Trumpet* (Lon)
Hodgkins, Tim : *Guitars* (Mid)
Hodgkinson, Stephen : *Bass Guitar* (NW)
Hodgkinson, Timothy : *Saxophones* (Lon)
Hodgson, Anne : *Flute* (Lon)
Hodgson, Brian : *Bass Guitar* (Lon)
Hodgson, David : *Violin* (NE)
Hodgson, G : *Percussion* (NE)
Hodgson, Janet : *Pianoforte* (SW)
Hodgson, Julia : *Early Strings* (Lon)
Hodgson, Lee : *Guitars* (E)
Hodgson, Michael : *Trumpet* (E)
Hodgson, Paul : *Copyist* (Lon)
Hodgson, Ron : *Saxophones* (NE)
Hodkin, Jon : *Tuba* (Mid)
Hodson, Charlotte : *Voice* (SE)
Hodson, Joseph : *Percussion* (Lon)
Hoe, Ivan : *Percussion* (Lon)
Hoetee, Yanuwn : *Pianoforte* (Lon)
Hoffman, Clare : *Violin* (Lon)
Hoffmeister, James : *Pianoforte* (SE)
Hoffnung, Benedict : *Tympani* (Lon)
Hofner, Paul : *Guitars* (Lon)
Hogan, Gerry : *Guitars* (Lon)
Hogan, Neil : *Percussion* (Lon)
Hogan, Nigel : *Keyboards* (Lon)
Hogan, Noel : *Guitars* (Lon)
Hogan, Ruth : *Trumpet* (Lon)
Hogan, Terry : *Pianoforte* (Lon)
Hogg, Jeremy : *Guitars* (SW)
Hogg, John : *Guitars* (Lon)
Hogg, John : *Guitars* (NE)
Hogg, Michael : *Guitars* (Sco)
Hogg, Norman : *Saxophones* (Mid)
Hogg, Robert : *Pianoforte* (NE)
Hogg, Rosemarie : *Pianoforte* (Sco)
Hogg, Simon : *Trombone* (Mid)
Hoggarth, Craig : *Percussion* (NW)
Hogger, Alan : *Pianoforte* (NW)
Hogger, John : *Percussion* (E)
Hogh, Mike : *Trombone* (Lon)
Hohmann-Barker, Patricia : *Viola* (Lon)
Holbrow, Pauline : *Saxophones* (Lon)
Holdaway, Marcus : *Keyboards* (Lon)
Holden, Bernard : *Clarinet* (Lon)
Holden, Ruth : *Harp* (Lon)
Holden, Timothy : *Percussion* (NW)
Holder, Henry : *Keyboards* (Lon)
Holder, Michael : *Pianoforte* (Lon)
Holder, Noddy : *Guitars* (Lon)
Holder, Peter : *Bass Guitar* (E)
Holder, Simon : *Percussion* (Mid)
Holding, Christopher : *Bass Trombone* (E)
Holding, Melissa : *Koto* (SE)
Holding, Sian : *Violin* (NW)
Holdom, Colin : *Trumpet* (E)
Holdsworth, Andrew : *Pianoforte* (NE)
Holdsworth, Andrew : *Guitars* (NW)
Holdsworth, Cyril : *Percussion* (Lon)
Holdsworth, David : *Trumpet* (SE)
Holdsworth, Gary : *Clarinet* (Lon)
Holdsworth, Sheila : *Viola* (Lon)
Holgate, David : *Double Bass* (E)
Holgate, Paul : *Voice* (Lon)
Hollamby, Stephen : *Arranger* (SE)
Holland, Alf : *Accordion* (NE)
Holland, Benedict : *Violin* (NW)
Holland, Bernie : *Guitars* (Lon)
Holland, Chris : *Trumpet* (Lon)
Holland, Christopher : *Keyboards* (Lon)
Holland, Gavin : *Keyboards* (Mid)
Holland, James : *Percussion* (Lon)
Holland, John : *Voice* (Lon)
Holland, Jonathan : *Trumpet* (Mid)
Holland, Jools : *Keyboards* (Lon)

Holland, Margaret : *Voice* (Sco)
Holland, Matt : *Trumpet* (Lon)
Holland, Nicholas : *Voice* (Lon)
Holland, Nick : *Violin* (SE)
Holland, Nicky : *Oboe* (Lon)
Holland, Nicola : *Pianoforte* (Lon)
Holland, Peter : *Saxophones* (SE)
Holland, Simon : *Bassoon* (Lon)
Holland, Steve : *Percussion* (Lon)
Holland, Tobe : *Guitars* (Lon)
Holland, Vincent : *Pianoforte* (Lon)
Holland-Hanbury, Nigel : *Percussion* (Mid)
Hollender, Phil : *Keyboards* (E)
Holler, Felix : *Pianoforte* (Lon)
Hollick, Kenneth : *Percussion* (SE)
Holliday, Cecily : *Violin* (NW)
Holliday, Claire : *Horn* (NW)
Holliday, David : *Guitars* (SE)
Holliday, James : *Saxophones* (Lon)
Holliday, John : *Bass Guitar* (Lon)
Holliday, Robert P : *Trombone* (NW)
Holliman, Andrew : *Violin* (Mid)
Hollingsworth, Catherine : *Saxophones* (Mid)
Hollingsworth, James : *Keyboards* (Lon)
Hollingsworth, Paul : *Trumpet* (SE)
Hollingsworth, Rachel : *Voice* (E)
Hollington, Donald : *Accordion* (Lon)
Hollingworth, Andrew : *Pianoforte* (Lon)
Hollingworth, Jane : *Percussion* (E)
Hollins, Clayton : *Percussion* (NW)
Hollinshead, Anji : *Guitars* (Mid)
Hollis, Mark : *Voice* (Lon)
Hollis, Paul : *Saxophones* (Mid)
Holloway, Anthony : *Double Bass* (SE)
Holloway, Julia : *Violin* (Mid)
Holloway, Keith : *Melodeon* (SE)
Holloway, Laurie : *Pianoforte* (Lon)
Holloway, Robert : *Pianoforte* (Lon)
Holloway, Tracy : *Trombone* (Lon)
Holloway, Yvonne : *Pianoforte* (Lon)
Hollowell, Allan : *Saxophones* (Mid)
Hollweg, Rebecca : *Voice* (Lon)
Holm, Jane : *Cello* (Lon)
Holman, Peter : *Harpsichord* (Lon)
Holman-Fox, Lynn : *Clarinet* (Lon)
Holmen, David : *Bass Guitar* (Lon)
Holmes, Alan : *Saxophones* (Lon)
Holmes, Alan : *Guitars* (SW)
Holmes, Alexandra : *Saxophones* (NE)
Holmes, Alison : *Pianoforte* (NW)
Holmes, Anna : *Cello* (Lon)
Holmes, Christopher : *Percussion* (NW)
Holmes, Daniel : *Electric Accordion* (NW)
Holmes, Dave : *Percussion* (Mid)
Holmes, David : *Guitars* (Lon)
Holmes, Edward : *Cello* (Lon)
Holmes, Graham : *Pianoforte* (E)
Holmes, Ian : *Accordion* (Sco)
Holmes, James : *Conductor* (Lon)
Holmes, James : *Trumpet* (Lon)
Holmes, Jill : *Viola* (NW)
Holmes, Joan : *Percussion* (NW)
Holmes, John : *Cello* (Lon)
Holmes, John : *Pianoforte* (Mid)
Holmes, Marie : *Cello* (Sco)
Holmes, Michael : *Organ* (NW)
Holmes, Nicholas John : *Voice* (NE)
Holmes, Nigel : *Bass Guitar* (NE)
Holmes, Patricia : *Violin* (NE)
Holmes, Richard : *Pianoforte* (Lon)
Holmes, Shaun : *Pianoforte* (Lon)
Holmes, Sophia : *Violin* (SW)
Holmes, Stephen : *Percussion* (NE)
Holmes, Tim : *Saxophones* (Lon)
Holmes, Timothy : *Trumpet* (NE)

Holmshaw, Andrew : *Guitars* (Lon)
Holoran, Jamie : *Guitars* (Lon)
Holpin, Sue : *Voice* (SW)
Holroyde, Geoff : *Percussion* (Lon)
Holt, Carl : *Bass Guitar* (SE)
Holt, David : *Trombone* (Lon)
Holt, Derek : *Bass Guitar* (Mid)
Holt, Helen : *Accordion* (Lon)
Holt, John : *Saxophones* (E)
Holt, John : *Double Bass* (Lon)
Holt, Richard : *Pianoforte* (SE)
Holt, Roger : *Percussion* (Lon)
Holt, Sian : *Cello* (Lon)
Holt, William : *Trumpet* (NW)
Holter, Margaret : *Violin* (Lon)
Holton, Chico : *Guitars* (SW)
Holttum, Richard : *Viola* (Lon)
Homburger, Maya : *Early Strings* (Lon)
Home, Matthew : *Percussion* (NE)
Homer, Sarah : *Clarinet* (Lon)
Hone, Frederick : *Saxophones* (Lon)
Hone, Ged : *Trumpet* (NW)
Honer, Dean : *Keyboards* (NE)
Honey, Paul : *Pianoforte* (E)
Honeyborne, Jack : *Pianoforte* (Lon)
Honeyman, John : *Double Bass* (SW)
Honeyman, Susie : *Violin* (Lon)
Honner, Derek : *Flute* (Lon)
Honore, Philippe : *Violin* (Lon)
Honour, Colin : *Clarinet* (NE)
Hood, Derek : *Percussion* (Sco)
Hood, Iain : *Harp* (Sco)
Hood, Ian : *Tympani* (NW)
Hood, J.F.T. : *Percussion* (Lon)
Hood, James : *Tympani* (Mid)
Hood, Victoria : *Clarinet* (Mid)
Hook, Christopher : *Trumpet* (Lon)
Hook, Heather : *Brass* (Sco)
Hook, Peter : *Bass Guitar* (NW)
Hook, Teddie : *Clarinet* (Lon)
Hooke, Shaun : *Trumpet* (Mid)
Hooker, Christopher : *Oboe* (Lon)
Hooker, Steve : *Guitars* (E)
Hookway, Tony : *Pianoforte* (Lon)
Hooley, Ann : *Violin* (Lon)
Hooley, George : *Saxophones* (NE)
Hooley, Martin : *Viola* (Lon)
Hooley, Patrick : *Viola* (SW)
Hooper, Barbara : *Violin* (SE)
Hooper, Chris : *Guitars* (Mid)
Hooper, David : *Pianoforte* (SW)
Hooper, Frederick : *Bass Guitar* (SE)
Hooper, Jon : *Saxophones* (Lon)
Hooper, Lew : *Saxophones* (Lon)
Hooper, Matt : *Bass Guitar* (Lon)
Hooper, Nicholas : *Guitars* (SE)
Hooper, Tom : *Percussion* (Lon)
Hooper, Tony : *Pianoforte* (Mid)
Hooson, Christopher : *Guitars* (NE)
Hooson, Edwin : *Double Bass* (Lon)
Hooson, Gwilym : *Violin* (Lon)
Hooson, James : *Bassoon* (NW)
Hooson, Vivienne : *Pianoforte* (NW)
Hope, Anne : *Violin* (Sco)
Hope, Carolyn : *Flute* (Lon)
Hope, Harvey : *Guitars* (Lon)
Hope, Margaret : *Melodeon* (NW)
Hope, Martyn : *Guitars* (Lon)
Hope, Mike : *Saxophones* (NW)
Hope, Philip : *Guitars* (Lon)
Hope, Richard : *Guitars* (Lon)
Hope-Evans, Peter : *Harmonica (Inc Bass* (Lon)
Hope-Taylor, Randy : *Bass Guitar* (Lon)
Hopes, Clifford : *Baritone Horn* (NE)
Hopgood, Adrian : *Saxophones* (E)

Hubbard, Neil : *Guitars* (Lon)
Hubbard, Richard : *Percussion* (E)
Hubbard, Richard : *Voice* (Lon)
Hubbard, Roy : *Clarinet* (Mid)
Hubbard, Ruth : *Horn* (SE)
Huber, Colin : *Violin* (Lon)
Huby, Mary : *Violin* (NE)
Huckle, Roger : *Violin* (SW)
Hucknall, Michael : *Voice* (NW)
Huckridge, John : *Trumpet* (Lon)
Huckridge, Roy : *Trombone* (Lon)
Hudson, Bert : *Organ* (NE)
Hudson, Colin : *Keyboards* (E)
Hudson, David : *Tuba* (SW)
Hudson, Eleanor : *Harp* (NW)
Hudson, Gary : *Bass Guitar* (Mid)
Hudson, John : *Organ* (Mid)
Hudson, Keith : *Percussion* (NE)
Hudson, Kristian : *Bass Guitar* (NE)
Hudson, Noel : *Double Bass* (Mid)
Hudson, Paul : *Percussion* (NE)
Hudson, Phillip : *Guitars* (Lon)
Hudson, Reg : *Percussion* (Lon)
Hudson, Richard : *Guitars* (Lon)
Hudson, Robert : *Pianoforte* (Mid)
Hudson, Roger (Butch) : *Trumpet* (Lon)
Hudson, Ruth : *Violin* (Lon)
Hudson, William : *Guitars* (Lon)
Hugall, Christopher : *Percussion* (Lon)
Hugg, Mike : *Keyboards* (Lon)
Huggett, Andrew : *Percussion* (Lon)
Huggett, Brian : *Saxophones* (SW)
Huggett, Jeremy : *Saxophones* (SW)
Huggett, Mark : *Percussion* (Lon)
Huggett, Monica : *Violin* (Lon)
Huggett, Roy : *Percussion* (SE)
Huggett-Ling, Fiona : *Violin* (Lon)
Huggins, Christopher : *Latin American Percu* (Sco)
Hugh, Owen : *Voice* (Mid)
Hughes, Adrian : *Pianoforte* (Mid)
Hughes, Alison : *Clarinet* (SE)
Hughes, Allan : *African Drums* (Sco)
Hughes, Brian : *Saxophones* (Lon)
Hughes, Brian : *Saxophones* (Mid)
Hughes, Brian : *Composer* (NW)
Hughes, Carys : *Harp* (Lon)
Hughes, Catherine : *Pianoforte* (SE)
Hughes, Chris : *Percussion* (SW)
Hughes, Christopher : *Organ* (E)
Hughes, Christopher : *Violin* (NE)
Hughes, David : *Guitars* (Lon)
Hughes, Edward : *Violin* (SW)
Hughes, Enid : *Flute* (Lon)
Hughes, Eric : *Pianoforte* (Lon)
Hughes, Gareth : *Trumpet* (NW)
Hughes, Gary : *Synthesiser* (Lon)
Hughes, Glenn : *Pianoforte* (Mid)
Hughes, Ian : *Composer* (Lon)
Hughes, Jack : *Saxophones* (NE)
Hughes, James : *Violin* (Mid)
Hughes, James : *Bass Guitar* (NW)
Hughes, Jeremy : *Cello* (E)
Hughes, Jill : *Flute* (NE)
Hughes, Jim : *Harmonica (Inc Bass)* (Mid)
Hughes, John : *Bass Guitar* (E)
Hughes, John : *Guitars* (NE)
Hughes, John : *Saxophones* (SW)
Hughes, Jonathan : *Pianoforte* (Mid)
Hughes, L : *Guitars* (SW)
Hughes, Laurence : *Guitars* (NW)
Hughes, Lionel : *Percussion* (Lon)
Hughes, Martin : *Percussion* (Lon)
Hughes, Martin : *Violin* (Sco)
Hughes, Natasha : *Double Bass* (SE)
Hughes, Nathan : *Saxophones* (Lon)

Hughes, Neville : *Violin* (Lon)
Hughes, Paul : *Guitars* (Lon)
Hughes, Peter : *Double Bass* (Lon)
Hughes, Peter : *Saxophones* (Lon)
Hughes, Phil : *Organ* (SE)
Hughes, Richard : *Bass Guitar* (Mid)
Hughes, Richard : *Percussion* (Sco)
Hughes, Robert : *Bass Trombone* (Lon)
Hughes, Robert : *Saxophones* (Lon)
Hughes, Robert : *Trombone* (Lon)
Hughes, Robin : *Guitars* (Mid)
Hughes, Rodger : *Keyboards* (Sco)
Hughes, Ronnie : *Trumpet* (Lon)
Hughes, Stevie : *Saxophones* (Lon)
Hughes, Ted : *Saxophones* (Lon)
Hughes, Ted : *Trombone* (Mid)
Hughes, Timothy : *Guitars* (Mid)
Hughes, Trevor : *Pianoforte* (E)
Hughes, Vanessa : *Violin* (Lon)
Hughes-Chamberlain, Ann : *Harp* (Lon)
Hughes-Jones, Catherine : *Viola* (SW)
Hugill, Andrew : *Harmonium* (Mid)
Hugo, Adam : *Saxophones* (SW)
Hugo, Peter : *Pianoforte* (SW)
Hugo, Tara : *Voice* (Lon)
Hugo, Vic : *Voice* (Lon)
Hulbert, Simon Leigh : *Keyboards* (Lon)
Hulett, Alistair : *Guitars* (Sco)
Hull, Arthur : *Saxophones* (NE)
Hull, Geoff : *Bass Guitar* (Mid)
Hull, Katie : *Violin* (Sco)
Hull, Peter : *Saxophones* (Lon)
Hulley, David : *Percussion* (Lon)
Hulme, Clifford : *Saxophones* (Mid)
Hulme, John D : *Trumpet* (NW)
Hulme, Kathy : *Saxophones* (Lon)
Hulse, Gareth : *Oboe* (Lon)
Hulston, David : *Guitars* (NW)
Hultmark, Carol : *Viola* (Lon)
Hultmark, Torbjorn : *Trumpet* (SE)
Humberstone, Clive : *Percussion* (NE)
Humberstone, Nigel : *Keyboards* (NE)
Humbey, Martin : *Viola* (Lon)
Humbles, Paul : *Percussion* (E)
Hume, Alastair : *Saxophones* (SE)
Hume, David : *Viola* (Lon)
Hume, Donald : *Pianoforte* (E)
Humm, Brena : *Percussion* (SW)
Humpage, John : *Violin* (NE)
Humphrey, Alan : *Violin* (E)
Humphrey, John : *Percussion* (Lon)
Humphrey, John : *Guitars* (SE)
Humphrey, Michael : *Violin* (Lon)
Humphrey, Simon : *Guitars* (Lon)
Humphreys, Alison : *Flute* (Mid)
Humphreys, Fenella : *Violin* (Lon)
Humphreys, John : *Trumpet* (E)
Humphreys, Kyra : *Violin* (Lon)
Humphreys, Mary : *Voice* (NW)
Humphreys, Pamela : *Voice* (SW)
Humphreys, Patricia : *Viola* (Lon)
Humphreys, Peter : *Guitars* (Lon)
Humphreys, Sydney : *Violin* (SE)
Humphries, Colin : *Saxophones* (Lon)
Humphries, Ian : *Violin* (Lon)
Humphries, Jamie : *Guitars* (SE)
Humphries, John : *Horn* (Lon)
Humphries, Mark : *Trumpet* (NE)
Humphries, Philip : *Trombone* (Lon)
Humphries, Roland : *Bass Guitar* (Lon)
Humphries, Ronald : *Trumpet* (Lon)
Humphries, Shaun : *Tuba* (SW)
Humphris, Caroline : *Music Director* (Lon)
Humphris, Ian : *Conductor* (Lon)
Humphris, Neil : *Bass Guitar* (SW)

Humphrys, Matthew : *Voice* (SE)
Huneke, Janna : *Flute* (Lon)
Hunka, Alison : *Violin* (Lon)
Hunka, Katherine : *Violin* (Lon)
Hunka, Nicholas : *Bassoon* (Lon)
Hunnisett, Bruce : *Saxophones* (NW)
Hunt : *Bass Guitar* (Lon)
Hunt, Alan : *Bass Guitar* (SW)
Hunt, Alison : *Violin* (NW)
Hunt, Andrew : *Guitars* (E)
Hunt, Angela : *Violin* (Lon)
Hunt, Annie : *Cello* (NW)
Hunt, Arthur : *Voice* (Mid)
Hunt, Barry : *Guitars* (Mid)
Hunt, Bill : *Keyboards* (Mid)
Hunt, Christopher : *Percussion* (Lon)
Hunt, Darryl : *Bass Guitar* (Lon)
Hunt, David : *Percussion* (Lon)
Hunt, Derek : *Trumpet* (Lon)
Hunt, Digby : *Trombone* (Lon)
Hunt, Donald : *Keyboards* (Lon)
Hunt, Frances : *Voice* (SE)
Hunt, Gerald : *Guitars* (Lon)
Hunt, Gordon : *Oboe* (Lon)
Hunt, James : *Saxophones* (Lon)
Hunt, James : *Saxophones* (Mid)
Hunt, James : *Oboe* (SE)
Hunt, Jayne : *Tympani* (NW)
Hunt, Jules : *Keyboards* (Mid)
Hunt, Margaret : *Viola* (Lon)
Hunt, Matthew : *Clarinet* (Lon)
Hunt, Max : *Keyboards* (SW)
Hunt, Peter : *Cello* (Sco)
Hunt, Richard : *Percussion* (E)
Hunt, Robert : *Saxophones* (Lon)
Hunt, Ronald : *Trumpet* (Lon)
Hunt, Roy : *Saxophones* (E)
Hunt, Royston : *Percussion* (SE)
Hunt, Simon : *Flute* (Lon)
Hunt, Steve : *Guitars* (SE)
Hunt, William : *Early Strings* (Lon)
Hunte, Owen : *Keyboards* (Lon)
Hunte, Rupert : *Saxophones* (Lon)
Hunter, Ailsa : *Violin* (Lon)
Hunter, Andrew : *Bassoon* (Sco)
Hunter, Colin : *Saxophones* (Sco)
Hunter, Craig : *Percussion* (Sco)
Hunter, Eanswyth : *Pianoforte* (NE)
Hunter, Garry : *Guitars* (Sco)
Hunter, Gerry : *Bandleader* (NE)
Hunter, Gillian : *Keyboards* (Sco)
Hunter, Graham : *Trumpet* (E)
Hunter, Jack : *Trumpet* (NE)
Hunter, James : *Violin* (NE)
Hunter, Jane : *Violin* (NW)
Hunter, Jennifer : *Percussion* (Sco)
Hunter, Joel : *Viola* (Sco)
Hunter, Jolyon : *Trumpet* (SE)
Hunter, Kieron : *Bass Guitar* (Lon)
Hunter, Larraine : *Pianoforte* (Mid)
Hunter, Len : *Arranger* (Lon)
Hunter, Mark : *Keyboards* (NW)
Hunter, Michael : *Pianoforte* (Sco)
Hunter, Neil : *Keyboards* (Mid)
Hunter, Nichola : *Flute* (NW)
Hunter, Robert : *Keyboards* (Lon)
Hunter, Ronnie : *Guitars* (Sco)
Hunter, Sean : *Double Bass* (Lon)
Hunter, Stephen : *Keyboards* (Sco)
Huntington, Peter : *Percussion* (Lon)
Huntley, Albert : *Keyboards* (SE)
Huntley, Rob : *Bass Guitar* (Lon)
Hurcombe, Eddie : *Double Bass* (SE)
Hurd, James : *Clarinet* (Lon)
Hurd, Tony : *Trumpet* (Mid)

Index of Members - Irwin

Irwin, Darren : *Trumpet* (NE)
Irwin, Raymond : *Saxophones* (Lon)
Isaac, Emily : *Cello* (Lon)
Isaac, Julie : *Keyboards* (Lon)
Isaac, Kathleen : *Violin* (SE)
Isaac, Michael : *Bass Guitar* (NW)
Isaac, Myfyr : *Guitars* (SW)
Isaacs, Brad : *Guitars* (Lon)
Isaacs, Carol : *Keyboards* (Lon)
Isaacs, Jonathan : *Mandolin* (Lon)
Isaacs, Maurice : *Violin* (Lon)
Isaacs, Peter : *Violin* (Sco)
Isaacson, Gerald : *Keyboards* (Lon)
Isaacson, Rhian : *Cello* (Lon)
Isherwood, Carol : *Voice* (Lon)
Isherwood, Cherry : *Harp* (Lon)
Isherwood, Martin : *Guitars* (NW)
Isherwood, Richard : *Guitars* (NW)
Ishmael, Clement : *Pianoforte* (Lon)
Isidore, Gus : *Guitars* (Lon)
Isley, Maxwell : *Trombone* (SW)
Islwyn, Sali : *Harp* (SW)
Ismail, Yashmin : *Voice* (Lon)
Israel-Wheeler, Samuel : *Voice* (Mid)
Isserlis, Annette : *Viola* (Lon)
Isserlis, Rachel : *Violin* (Lon)
Istance, Jennifer : *Cello* (SW)
Ital, Dave : *Guitars* (Lon)
Ites, Ras : *Guitars* (Lon)
Ites, Ras : *Keyboards* (Lon)
Itesman, Ras : *Latin American Percu* (NW)
Ive, Peter : *Percussion* (SE)
Ives, George : *Cello* (Lon)
Ives, Paul : *Cello* (Lon)
Ivitsky : *Bass Guitar* (Sco)
Ivory, Graham : *Horn* (Lon)
Ivory, Stewart : *DiDJeridu* (Lon)
Ivory, Stewart : *Trombone* (Lon)
Izaak, Ras : *Percussion* (Lon)
Izatt, Raymond : *Pianoforte* (NE)
Izod, Joseph : *Tuba* (Lon)
Izzett, Sarah : *Violin* (SW)

J

J, Stephen : *Organ* (NW)
J DJ Sweet : *Keyboards* (SE)
J., Michael : *Synthesiser* (E)
J., Ollie : *Keyboards* (Lon)
J.Jules, Shari : *Keyboards* (Lon)
J.M., Nick : *Percussion* (Lon)
J.S.M. : *Keyboards* (Mid)
Ja'Selle : *Voice* (Lon)
Jacas, Eileen : *Voice* (Lon)
Jack, Colin : *Guitars* (Sco)
Jack, Cy : *Bass Guitar* (Sco)
Jack, David : *Bass Guitar* (Sco)
Jack, Don : *Percussion* (NW)
Jack, Jonathan : *Guitars* (NE)
Jack, Nicki : *Keyboards* (Lon)
Jack, Robert : *Guitars* (SW)
Jack, Shanty : *Melodeon* (NE)
Jack, Tony : *Clarinet* (Mid)
Jackman, Andrew : *Recorders* (Lon)
Jackman, Bill : *Clarinet* (Lon)
Jackman, Diane : *Copyist* (E)
Jackman, Henry : *Keyboards* (Lon)
Jackman, James : *Keyboards* (Lon)
Jackman, Keith : *African Drums* (NE)
Jackman, Neil : *Bass Guitar* (E)
Jackman, Patrick : *Bass Trombone* (Lon)
Jackson, Adrian : *Music Director* (Mid)
Jackson, Alan : *Percussion* (Lon)
Jackson, Amanda : *Voice* (SE)
Jackson, Andrew : *Trumpet* (NE)
Jackson, Andrew : *Keyboards* (Sco)

Jackson, Art : *Pianoforte* (Lon)
Jackson, Bert : *Percussion* (SE)
Jackson, Bob : *Keyboards* (Lon)
Jackson, Bob : *Saxophones* (Mid)
Jackson, Bridie : *Voice* (NE)
Jackson, Carol : *Bass Guitar* (NW)
Jackson, Catherine : *Pianoforte* (Lon)
Jackson, Charles : *Oboe* (Sco)
Jackson, Christine : *Cello* (Lon)
Jackson, Colin : *Cello* (Lon)
Jackson, Daniel : *Pianoforte* (Lon)
Jackson, David : *Bass Guitar* (Lon)
Jackson, David : *Percussion* (Lon)
Jackson, Ellen : *Viola* (Lon)
Jackson, Ellis : *Trombone* (Lon)
Jackson, Garfield : *Viola* (Lon)
Jackson, Heather : *Tympani* (NE)
Jackson, Janine : *Voice* (Lon)
Jackson, Jeremy : *Violin* (SW)
Jackson, Jill : *Guitars* (Sco)
Jackson, John : *Percussion* (NE)
Jackson, Kenneth : *Percussion* (NW)
Jackson, Laurence : *Violin* (Lon)
Jackson, Leonard : *Percussion* (Mid)
Jackson, Mark : *Guitars* (NW)
Jackson, Mark N W : *Trumpet* (Mid)
Jackson, Michael : *Bass Guitar* (NE)
Jackson, Michael : *Pianoforte* (NE)
Jackson, Mike : *Guitars* (Lon)
Jackson, Nick : *Voice* (NW)
Jackson, Nick : *Voice* (SE)
Jackson, Paul : *Keyboards* (NW)
Jackson, Paul : *Pianoforte* (Lon)
Jackson, Peter : *Pianoforte* (NE)
Jackson, Rachel : *Violin* (Lon)
Jackson, Raymond : *Mandolin* (NE)
Jackson, Richard : *Saxophones* (Lon)
Jackson, Rob : *Guitars* (SE)
Jackson, Robert : *Percussion* (E)
Jackson, Roger : *Composer* (Lon)
Jackson, Ross : *Keyboards* (Sco)
Jackson, Ryan : *Voice* (Lon)
Jackson, Sally : *Bassoon* (Lon)
Jackson, Simon : *Violin* (Lon)
Jackson, Stephen : *Percussion* (Lon)
Jackson, Stephen : *Guitars* (Sco)
Jackson, Susan : *Percussion* (NW)
Jackson, Susan : *Keyboards* (SE)
Jackson, Thomas : *Violin* (NW)
Jackson, Tim : *Trumpet* (Lon)
Jackson, Tim : *Guitars* (SE)
Jackson, Timothy : *Horn* (NW)
Jackson, Tony : *Voice* (Lon)
Jackson, Trevor : *Percussion* (Mid)
Jackson, Wendy : *Guitars* (NW)
Jackson-Kane, Kit : *Voice* (NE)
Jacob, Huw : *Bass Guitar* (NW)
Jacob, Robert : *Guitars* (Lon)
Jacobs, George : *Trumpet* (Lon)
Jacobs, Howard : *Clarinet* (NW)
Jacobs, Jean : *Organ* (E)
Jacobs, Laurie : *Saxophones* (E)
Jacobs, Rachel : *Violin* (NW)
Jacobs, St Clair : *Songwriter* (Lon)
Jacobs, Susan : *Violin* (Mid)
Jacobsen, Peter : *Pianoforte* (Lon)
Jacoby, Elizabeth : *Oboe* (SW)
Jacques, Martyn : *Accordion* (Lon)
Jaeger, Lincoln : *Pianoforte* (Lon)
Jaeger, Penelope : *Trombone* (Mid)
Jaffa, Nina : *Saxophones* (Lon)
Jafrate, Keith : *Saxophones* (NE)
Jager, Alan : *Saxophones* (Mid)
Jagger, Mick : *Voice* (Lon)
Jagger, Peter : *Guitars* (Lon)

Jago, Cedric : *Keyboards* (SW)
Jago, Chris : *Percussion* (NW)
Jago, David : *Trombone* (E)
Jaimee : *Voice* (NE)
Jaimes, Mark : *Guitars* (Lon)
Jakins, Robert : *Bass Guitar* (E)
Jakob, Andrew : *Bassoon* (NE)
Jakszyk, Michael : *Guitars* (E)
Jallow, John : *Guitars* (Lon)
Jamac : *Songwriter* (NW)
James, Alan : *Guitars* (Lon)
James, Alexander : *Pianoforte* (NE)
James, Alexander : *Violin* (SW)
James, Andrew : *Percussion* (SE)
James, Aneurin : *Bass Trombone* (SW)
James, Barry : *Club DJ* (Lon)
James, Benedict : *Viola* (Lon)
James, Bob : *Trumpet* (Mid)
James, Brad : *Bass Guitar* (Lon)
James, Brad : *Percussion* (Lon)
James, Brian : *Keyboards* (Lon)
James, Carl : *Bass Guitar* (Lon)
James, Casey : *Voice* (Lon)
James, Cath : *Violin* (NE)
James, Chris : *Guitars* (Lon)
James, Daniel : *Trombone* (NE)
James, David : *Double Bass* (Lon)
James, David : *Percussion* (Lon)
James, Debbie : *Percussion* (NE)
James, Derek : *Trombone* (Lon)
James, Diane : *Violin* (Sco)
James, E : *Percussion* (SW)
James, Edward : *Guitars* (NW)
James, Gary : *Percussion* (Lon)
James, Haydn : *Conductor* (Lon)
James, Hilary : *Voice* (SE)
James, Ivor : *Guitars* (Mid)
James, J : *Cello* (SE)
James, Jayne : *Voice* (Lon)
James, John : *Voice* (Mid)
James, Leroy : *Voice* (Lon)
James, Luke : *Keyboards* (Lon)
James, Marcus : *Bass Guitar* (Lon)
James, Mark : *Oboe* (SE)
James, Martin : *Guitars* (NW)
James, Mary : *Oboe* (Sco)
James, Michael : *Voice* (Lon)
James, Michael : *Trombone* (Mid)
James, Mo : *Voice* (NE)
James, Natalie : *Oboe* (Lon)
James, Pat : *Viola* (Mid)
James, Pete : *Keyboards* (Sco)
James, Philip : *Violin* (SE)
James, Robert : *Guitars* (Mid)
James, Sian : *Pianoforte* (SW)
James, Spencer : *Guitars* (Mid)
James, Stanley : *Pianoforte* (SE)
James, Stew : *Guitars* (NW)
James, Stuart : *Violin* (Lon)
James, Sue : *Guitars* (NW)
James, Terence : *Saxophones* (NE)
James, Thomas : *Guitars* (Mid)
James, Timothy : *Guitars* (NW)
James, Tony : *Bass Guitar* (Lon)
James, Tony : *Keyboards* (NW)
James, Trevor : *Whistle* (E)
James (Aka Yorath), David : *Voice* (Lon)
James E : *Pianoforte* (Mid)
Jameson, Frederick : *Trumpet* (Lon)
Jameson-Vine, Zeben : *Keyboards* (Lon)
Jamieson, Gaby : *Pianoforte* (Lon)
Jamieson, James : *Pianoforte* (Lon)
Jamieson, John : *Guitars* (Lon)
Jamieson, Lindsay : *Percussion* (SE)
Jamieson, Michael : *Percussion* (Sco)

514

Index of Members - Johnson

Jamieson, Piero : *Guitars* (Sco)
Jamiroquai : *Voice* (Lon)
Jamison, Shelley : *Violin* (SW)
Jamma : *Steel Pan* (Mid)
Jamo : *Percussion* (Mid)
Janaway, Peter : *Guitars* (Lon)
Janes, Anders : *Double Bass* (Lon)
Janes, Eric : *Bandleader* (Lon)
Janes, Rachel : *Viola* (NW)
Janey : *Oboe* (Lon)
Jani, Maitreya : *Guitars* (Lon)
Jankiewicz, Thomas : *Keyboards* (SE)
Janobe : *Voice* (Lon)
Janse, Jennifer : *Cello* (Lon)
Jansen, Brigitte : *Guitars* (Lon)
Janssen, Volker : *Keyboards* (Lon)
Jansson, Bo : *Bass Trombone* (Lon)
Jardim, Luis : *Percussion* (Lon)
Jarlett, Dee : *Voice* (SW)
Jarman, Jill : *Keyboards* (E)
Jarman, Lynne : *Horn* (Lon)
Jarratt, Jeff : *Pianoforte* (Lon)
Jarratt-Knock, David : *Trumpet* (Mid)
Jarrett, Frank : *Percussion* (SE)
Jarvie, Marshall : *Pianoforte* (Sco)
Jarvis, Adrian : *Bass Trombone* (E)
Jarvis, Bill : *Pianoforte* (Sco)
Jarvis, Caleb : *Voice* (SW)
Jarvis, Christopher : *Pianoforte* (E)
Jarvis, Graham : *Guitars* (Lon)
Jarvis, Jonathan : *Bass Guitar* (Mid)
Jarvis, Margaret : *Percussion* (E)
Jarvis, Martin : *Tuba* (Lon)
Jarvis, Paul : *Guitars* (Lon)
Jarvis, Paul : *Violin* (NW)
Jarvis, Toby : *Composer* (Lon)
Jary, Catherine : *Cello* (Lon)
Jaskulski, Clive : *Trombone* (Lon)
Jasnoch, John : *Guitars* (NE)
Jasper, Lee : *Guitars* (Lon)
Jawal, Papa : *Organ* (Lon)
Jay : *Bass Guitar* (Lon)
Jay : *Keyboards* (SE)
Jay, Angelina : *Voice* (Mid)
Jay, Bee : *Keyboards* (Lon)
Jay, Cee : *Bass Guitar* (Lon)
Jay, Chad : *Voice* (SE)
Jay, Irving : *Pianoforte* (Lon)
Jay, Jenny : *Keyboards* (Mid)
Jay, Just : *Voice* (NE)
Jay, Justin : *Guitars* (E)
Jay, Martin : *Guitars* (Lon)
Jay, Nigel : *Violin* (NW)
Jay, Pamela : *Violin* (NW)
Jay, Steve : *Percussion* (SE)
Jay, Trevor : *Guitars* (E)
Jayasinha, Paul : *Trumpet* (Lon)
Jayasuriya, Arjuna : *Latin American Percu* (NW)
Jayes, Catherine : *Pianoforte* (Lon)
Jayes, Simon : *Percussion* (Lon)
Jaymson, Drew : *Voice* (Lon)
Jayne, Tara : *Voice* (Lon)
Jaz : *Bass Guitar* (Lon)
Jaz : *Voice* (Lon)
Jean-Marie, Lincoln : *Voice* (Lon)
Jean-Paul-Denis, Patrick : *Voice* (Lon)
Jeans, Clare : *Early Strings* (Lon)
Jeans, Michael : *Oboe* (Lon)
Jeavons, Colin : *Percussion* (Mid)
Jebbitt, Stuart : *Bass Guitar* (SE)
Jeffcutt, Francis : *Saxophones* (SW)
Jeffels, Joanne : *Guitars* (NE)
Jefferies, Edward : *Cello* (Lon)
Jefferis, Jennifer : *Keyboards* (SE)
Jefferis, Philip : *Guitars* (SW)

Jeffers, Rachel : *Flute* (Lon)
Jefferson, Geoff : *Percussion* (Mid)
Jefferson, Michael : *Keyboards* (SE)
Jeffery, Matthew : *Pianoforte* (NW)
Jefferys, Derek : *Voice* (SE)
Jeffes, Frank : *Guitars* (NW)
Jeffrey, Richard : *Percussion* (Lon)
Jeffrey, Robin : *Early Strings* (Lon)
Jeffries, Joanne : *Flute* (E)
Jeffries, Peter : *Keyboards* (Lon)
Jeffries, Richard : *Double Bass* (Lon)
Jeffs, Philip : *Keyboards* (E)
Jelitko, Patrick : *Saxophones* (SW)
Jellicoe, Laura : *Flute* (NW)
Jenking, Brian : *Bass Guitar* (Lon)
Jenkins, Albert : *Horn* (Lon)
Jenkins, Albert : *Trumpet* (SE)
Jenkins, Andrew : *Percussion* (SE)
Jenkins, Anthony : *Viola* (Lon)
Jenkins, Arthur : *Violin* (NW)
Jenkins, Billy : *Guitars* (Lon)
Jenkins, Brian : *Bass Guitar* (Mid)
Jenkins, Clive : *Keyboards* (SW)
Jenkins, Dan : *Trombone* (Lon)
Jenkins, Dave : *Keyboards* (Lon)
Jenkins, Huw : *Horn* (Lon)
Jenkins, Ian : *Saxophones* (NE)
Jenkins, Ian : *Keyboards* (NW)
Jenkins, John : *Tuba* (Lon)
Jenkins, John : *Double Bass* (SW)
Jenkins, Karl : *Composer* (Lon)
Jenkins, Keith : *Guitars* (Lon)
Jenkins, Lyle : *Saxophones* (Lon)
Jenkins, Nia : *Harp* (Lon)
Jenkins, Nigel : *Guitars* (Lon)
Jenkins, Peter : *Accordion* (Lon)
Jenkins, Peter : *Violin* (Lon)
Jenkins, Rae : *Conductor* (Lon)
Jenkins, Rhys : *Trumpet* (SW)
Jenkins, Richard : *Guitars* (SE)
Jenkins, Robert : *Clarinet* (SE)
Jenkins, Robert : *Organ* (SW)
Jenkins, Stuart : *Trumpet* (Lon)
Jenkins, Terry : *Percussion* (Lon)
Jenkins Jnr, Bob : *Percussion* (Lon)
Jenkinson, Andrew : *Guitars* (Mid)
Jenkinson, Derek : *Bass Guitar* (NW)
Jenkinson, James : *Percussion* (Mid)
Jenkinson, John : *Organ* (SE)
Jenkinson, Maeve : *Violin* (Lon)
Jenkinson, Michael : *Viola* (Mid)
Jenkinson, Richard : *Cello* (Lon)
Jenkinson, Wilfred : *Banjo* (NW)
Jenner, Anthony : *Guitars* (SW)
Jenner, Clive : *Percussion* (Lon)
Jenner, Derek : *Bandleader* (SE)
Jenner, Keith : *Guitars* (Sco)
Jenner, Robert : *Trumpet* (Lon)
Jenner, Stephen : *Trumpet* (Lon)
Jennings, Adrian : *Keyboards* (Mid)
Jennings, Andrew : *Trumpet* (Mid)
Jennings, Anne : *Viola* (NW)
Jennings, Anthony : *Clarinet* (Lon)
Jennings, Eric : *Trombone* (Lon)
Jennings, Garry : *Guitars* (NE)
Jennings, Ian : *Double Bass* (Lon)
Jennings, Jamie : *Electric Accordion* (SE)
Jennings, John : *Bass Guitar* (Lon)
Jennings, John : *Percussion* (NW)
Jennings, Lee : *Percussion* (Mid)
Jennings, Maurice : *Saxophones* (Lon)
Jennings, Neale : *Percussion* (Lon)
Jennings, Peter : *Guitars* (SE)
Jennings, Robert : *Violin* (Sco)
Jennings, Stephen : *Harmonica (Inc Bass)* (Mid)

Jensen, Andor : *Saxophones* (Lon)
Jensen, Mark : *Voice* (SE)
Jeremiah, Kevin : *Guitars* (SE)
Jerman, Joan : *Violin* (NW)
Jermy, John : *Trumpet* (E)
Jerome : *Pianoforte* (Lon)
Jervier, Paul : *Percussion* (Lon)
Jervis, Andy : *Percussion* (Mid)
Jesse, David : *Violin* (SW)
Jessop, Francesca : *Pianoforte* (Lon)
Jessop, Mary : *Viola* (Mid)
Jessop, Stephen : *Percussion* (NE)
Jessopp, Angela : *Violin* (Lon)
Jessup, William : *Saxophones* (NE)
Jewel, Dominic : *Violin* (SE)
Jewel, Ian : *Viola* (Lon)
Jewell, Jimmy : *Saxophones* (Lon)
Jewell, Ronald : *Organ* (E)
Jezard, John : *Viola* (Lon)
Jilly-B : *Saxophones* (Lon)
Jim : *Guitars* (E)
Jim : *Guitars* (SE)
Jimenez-Gomez, Alfonso : *Voice* (Lon)
Jinadu, Simon : *Voice* (Lon)
Jingles : *Bass Guitar* (Lon)
Jinski, Steve : *Clarinet* (NE)
Jnr, Geoff : *Keyboards* (NW)
Joachim, Ian : *Bass Guitar* (SW)
Job, Gillian : *Violin* (NE)
Jobson, David : *Guitars* (Lon)
Jobson, Jeremy : *Bass Guitar* (Lon)
Jobson, John : *Double Bass* (Lon)
Jobson, John : *Saxophones* (NW)
Jodelko, Rikki : *Guitars* (Lon)
Joe : *Bass Guitar* (Lon)
Joe, Smokey : *Keyboards* (Lon)
Joe-Adigwe, Ciozie : *Voice* (Sco)
Joebee : *Voice* (Lon)
Joel, Dr : *Pianoforte* (SW)
Johannesson, Chris : *Bass Guitar* (Lon)
Johannesson, Mikael : *Guitars* (Lon)
Johannsson, Johann : *Keyboards* (Lon)
Johansson, Glenn : *Guitars* (Lon)
John, Clive : *Guitars* (Mid)
John, Daniel : *Pianoforte* (Mid)
John, David : *Percussion* (Lon)
John, Delyth : *Viola* (Lon)
John, Elton : *Pianoforte* (Lon)
John, Ewan : *Guitars* (Sco)
John, Gareth : *Cello* (Sco)
John, Gwilym : *Saxophones* (SW)
John, Isabel : *Tympani* (Sco)
John, Jennifer : *Voice* (NW)
John, Karl : *Percussion* (NW)
John, Leee : *Voice* (Lon)
John, Malcolm : *Guitars* (Mid)
John, Martyn : *Percussion* (Lon)
John, Philip : *Keyboards* (SW)
John, Ronnie : *Percussion* (Mid)
John, Scott : *Keyboards* (SW)
John, Simon : *Bass Guitar* (SW)
John-Baptiste, Dave : *Voice* (SE)
John-Baptiste, Marcel : *Guitars* (E)
Johns, Antony : *Violin* (NE)
Johns, Graham : *Percussion* (NW)
Johns, Mark : *Keyboards* (E)
Johns, Mark : *Guitars* (Lon)
Johns, Terry : *Horn* (Sco)
Johnson, Adrian : *Keyboards* (Lon)
Johnson, Alan : *Cello* (NW)
Johnson, Alec : *Guitars* (NW)
Johnson, Alexandra : *Violin* (Lon)
Johnson, Alistair : *Pianoforte* (Lon)
Johnson, Amanda : *Violin* (NE)
Johnson, Benjamine : *Violin* (SE)

Index of Members - Larkey

Larkey, Glenn Edward : *Bass Guitar* (NW)
Larkin, Christopher : *Cow Horn* (Lon)
Larkin, Christopher : *Horn* (Lon)
Larkin, Ian : *Bass Guitar* (E)
Larkin, Michael : *Violin* (Sco)
Larkin, Paul : *Voice* (NE)
Larkin, Sally : *Voice* (SW)
Larn, Colin : *Percussion* (NW)
Larnie, Jane : *Voice* (Lon)
Larsen, Peter : *Guitars* (Lon)
Larsen, Philip : *Keyboards* (Lon)
Larsen, Rebecca : *Flute* (Lon)
Larsen, Victoria : *Voice* (SW)
Larsson, Janet : *Flute* (Lon)
Lascelles, James : *Keyboards* (Lon)
Lascelles, James : *Saxophones* (Lon)
Lasker, Anita : *Cello* (Lon)
Lasky, Simon : *Pianoforte* (SE)
Laslett, Phillip : *Percussion* (SE)
Lass, Ruth : *Cello* (SW)
Lasserson, David : *Violin* (Lon)
Latarche, Vanessa : *Pianoforte* (Lon)
Latchem, Barrington : *Trumpet* (SE)
Latchem, Malcolm : *Violin* (Lon)
Latham, Catherine : *Early Wind* (Lon)
Latham, Christopher : *Violin* (Sco)
Latham, Clive : *Keyboards* (Lon)
Latham, Dr John : *Clarinet* (SW)
Latham, Katy : *Violin* (SW)
Latham, Louise : *Violin* (NW)
Latham, Robert : *Music Director* (SW)
Latham, Sarah : *Trombone* (SW)
Latham, Warren : *Saxophones* (NW)
Lati : *Bass Guitar* (Lon)
Latimer, Andrew : *Guitars* (Lon)
Latimer, Colin : *Horn* (NE)
Latouche, Cleveland : *Voice* (Mid)
Lau Jong, On : *Viola* (Lon)
Laubrock, Ingrid : *Saxophones* (Lon)
Lauda, Pete : *Guitars* (NW)
Laugharne, David : *Pianoforte* (SW)
Laughlin, Philip : *Bass Guitar* (NE)
Laughlin, Richard : *Pianoforte* (NE)
Laula, Carol : *Voice* (Sco)
Laulund, Jorge : *Violin* (Lon)
Lauper, Cyndi : *Pianoforte* (Lon)
Laurence, Christopher : *Double Bass* (Lon)
Laurence, David : *Horn* (Lon)
Laurence, Graham : *Guitars* (SE)
Laurence, Grahame : *Pianoforte* (SE)
Laurence, Lesley : *Oboe* (Lon)
Laurence, Patrick : *Double Bass* (Lon)
Laurence, Stuart : *Percussion* (Lon)
Laurence, Zack : *Pianoforte* (Lon)
Laurens, Elizabeth : *Clarinet* (SW)
Laurenson, Graeme : *Guitars* (Sco)
Lauri, Stephen : *Guitars* (SE)
Lauricella, Remo : *Violin* (Lon)
Laurie, Cyril : *Clarinet* (Lon)
Laurie, Jill : *Flute* (Sco)
Laurie, Richard : *Clarinet* (Lon)
Lavelle, Caroline : *Cello* (Lon)
Lavelle, Tom : *Bass Guitar* (E)
Lavender, Mike : *Keyboards* (Mid)
Lavender, Peter : *Copyist* (Lon)
Laver, Keith : *Accordion* (SE)
Laverick, Samantha : *Cello* (Lon)
Lavigne, Berenice : *Violin* (Lon)
Law, Cheryl : *Viola* (Mid)
Law, Elizabeth : *Appalachian Dulcimer* (NE)
Law, James : *Trumpet* (Lon)
Law, Joanna : *Voice* (Lon)
Law, John : *Pianoforte* (Lon)
Law, John : *Double Bass* (SW)
Law, Mark : *Trumpet* (Lon)

Law, Michael : *Voice* (Lon)
Law, Simon : *Guitars* (Lon)
Law, Simon : *Percussion* (Lon)
Law, Tina : *Voice* (Mid)
Law, Tony : *Guitars* (E)
Lawal, Gasper : *African Drums* (Lon)
Lawes, John : *Trombone* (Lon)
Lawes, Peter : *Bass Guitar* (SE)
Lawes, Wayne : *Bass Guitar* (Lon)
Lawless, Jim : *Percussion* (Lon)
Lawley, John : *Oboe* (Lon)
Lawman, Derek : *Voice* (SW)
Lawn, George : *Percussion* (Lon)
Lawrance, Alison : *Cello* (Sco)
Lawrance, Nicholas : *Violin* (NE)
Lawrance, Aidan : *Bass Guitar* (NE)
Lawrence, Alan : *Composer* (Lon)
Lawrence, Alwin : *Violin* (Lon)
Lawrence, Anthony : *Pianoforte* (SE)
Lawrence, Arthur : *Tympani* (SE)
Lawrence, Bettina : *Cello* (Lon)
Lawrence, Betty : *Pianoforte* (SE)
Lawrence, Clive : *Guitars* (SE)
Lawrence, Daniel : *Guitars* (NW)
Lawrence, David : *Guitars* (E)
Lawrence, David : *Clarinet* (Lon)
Lawrence, David : *Percussion* (NE)
Lawrence, Della K : *Violin* (Mid)
Lawrence, Denise : *Voice* (SE)
Lawrence, Douglas : *Violin* (Sco)
Lawrence, Emma : *Voice* (Lon)
Lawrence, Henry : *Guitars* (SW)
Lawrence, James : *Guitars* (SW)
Lawrence, Jane : *Folk Fiddle* (NW)
Lawrence, Janette : *Mandolin* (Lon)
Lawrence, Jean : *Pianoforte* (E)
Lawrence, Jeff : *Pianoforte* (NW)
Lawrence, John : *Trumpet* (NW)
Lawrence, John : *Guitars* (SE)
Lawrence, John : *Saxophones* (SW)
Lawrence, Kenneth : *Violin* (Lon)
Lawrence, Martin : *Guitars* (Lon)
Lawrence, Martin : *Horn* (Lon)
Lawrence, Paul : *Tuba* (Lon)
Lawrence, Peter : *Guitars* (SW)
Lawrence, Phillip : *Trumpet* (Lon)
Lawrence, Quinny : *Percussion* (Lon)
Lawrence, Ralph : *Pianoforte* (SE)
Lawrence, Ruth : *Violin* (Mid)
Lawrence, Sandra : *Voice* (Lon)
Lawrence, Stephen : *Conductor* (E)
Lawrence, Stephen : *Guitars* (Lon)
Lawrence, Steve : *Bass Guitar* (Lon)
Lawrence, Steven : *Bouzouki* (Sco)
Lawrence, Stewart : *Guitars* (NW)
Lawrence, Susan : *Tympani* (SW)
Lawrence, Winston : *Percussion* (Lon)
Laws, Chris : *Percussion* (Lon)
Laws, Ian : *Guitars* (Lon)
Laws, Tim : *Guitars* (Lon)
Lawson, Chris : *Guitars* (Lon)
Lawson, Colin : *Clarinet* (Lon)
Lawson, Dave : *Synthesiser* (Lon)
Lawson, Don : *Percussion* (Lon)
Lawson, Douglas : *Flute* (Sco)
Lawson, Ellie : *Voice* (Lon)
Lawson, Ernest : *Horn* (Lon)
Lawson, Fraser : *Percussion* (SW)
Lawson, Margaret : *Violin* (Sco)
Lawson, Peter : *Pianoforte* (NW)
Lawson, Sarah : *Violin* (NE)
Lawson, Sarah A : *Clarinet* (NE)
Lawson, Stephen : *Percussion* (NW)
Lawther, Ian : *Bagpipes* (NE)
Lawton, Jack : *Pianoforte* (NW)

Lawty, F : *Trumpet* (NE)
Laxton, Elaine : *Pianoforte* (SE)
Lay, Pete : *Saxophones* (SE)
Lay, Peter : *Percussion* (SE)
Lay, Robert : *Cello* (Sco)
Lay, Robert : *Early Strings* (Sco)
Laycock, Gabriel : *Guitars* (SW)
Laycock, Ivor : *Trumpet* (Sco)
Laycock, Timothy : *Concertina (Inc Engl* (SW)
Layfield, Malcolm : *Violin* (NW)
Layton, Clive : *Keyboards* (Mid)
Layton, Elizabeth : *Violin* (E)
Layton, Paul : *Guitars* (Lon)
Layton, Richard : *Violin* (Lon)
Layton, Stephen : *Guitars* (Mid)
Layton, Teddy : *Clarinet* (SE)
Layton-Bennett, Marc : *Percussion* (Lon)
Layzell, Jim : *Organ* (SE)
Lazar, Natalie : *Voice* (Lon)
Lazaro, David : *Pianoforte* (Lon)
Lazell, Matthew : *Guitars* (SE)
Lazzari, Stephen : *Bass Guitar* (Mid)
Le Baigue, Paul : *Bass Guitar* (SE)
Le Feuvre, Gerard : *Cello* (Lon)
Le Feuvre, Phillipa : *Clarinet* (SW)
Le Foe, Ben : *Pianoforte* (SW)
Le Good, Rosemary : *Violin* (SE)
Le Goupil, Fiona : *Trumpet* (SW)
Le Grice, Ian : *Organ* (Lon)
Le Her, Thomas : *Bass Guitar* (E)
Le Messurier, James : *Percussion* (Lon)
Le Poer Power, Cecilia : *Voice* (Lon)
Le Sage, Bill : *Pianoforte* (Lon)
Le Serve, Valerie : *Voice* (SE)
Le Sueur, Jane : *Clarinet* (SW)
Le Vaillant, Tobye : *Double Bass* (SW)
Le-Grand, John : *Clarinet* (NE)
Le-Touzel, Jane : *Organ* (Lon)
Le Ferve, J : *Violin* (Lon)
Lea, Christopher : *Guitars* (Lon)
Lea, James : *Bass Guitar* (Lon)
Lea, Michael : *Double Bass* (Lon)
Lea, Robert : *Percussion* (NW)
Lea, Simon : *Percussion* (Lon)
Leach, Alan : *Percussion* (NE)
Leach, Christopher : *Bass Guitar* (NE)
Leach, Jeff : *Pianoforte* (Lon)
Leach, John : *Composer* (Lon)
Leach, John : *Trombone* (SW)
Leach, Karen : *Violin* (SE)
Leach, Kevin : *Organ* (NE)
Leach, Norman : *Electric Accordion* (Lon)
Leach, Peter : *Violin* (NW)
Leach, Richard : *Trombone* (E)
Leach, Rod : *Keyboards* (E)
Leach, Sarah : *Violin* (Mid)
Leadbeater, Ania : *Viola* (SW)
Leadbeater, David : *Trumpet* (NE)
Leadbeater, Michael : *Trombone* (NE)
Leadbeater, Sonia : *Cello* (Mid)
Leadbetter, Nicola : *Violin* (SE)
Leadbetter, Richard : *Pianoforte* (Mid)
Leadbetter, Susan : *Oboe* (SE)
Leader, Michael : *Guitars* (Lon)
Leader, Philip : *Organ* (SE)
Leaf, Helen : *Multi Instrumental* (Lon)
Leaf, Mary : *Violin* (Lon)
Leah, Philip : *Flute* (Mid)
Leahy, Terence : *Songwriter* (Lon)
Leake, Robert : *Saxophones* (Lon)
Leake, Steven : *Bass Guitar* (NE)
Leake, Tony : *Guitars* (Lon)
Lealman, Mike : *Guitars* (SE)
Lean, Laurence : *Guitars* (Sco)
Leaney, Tony : *Pianoforte* (Lon)

Index of Members - Lewin

Lewin, Giles : *Ethnic Strings* (Lon)
Lewin, Gordon : *Clarinet* (Lon)
Lewington, Ian : *Saxophones* (Lon)
Lewington, Martyn : *Trumpet* (Lon)
Lewington, Sarah : *Clarinet* (Lon)
Lewins, Stephen : *Double Bass* (E)
Lewinson, Peter : *Percussion* (Lon)
Lewinson, Steve : *Bass Guitar* (Lon)
Lewis, Alan : *Trumpet* (Lon)
Lewis, Alan : *Pianoforte* (SE)
Lewis, Alexander : *Trumpet* (NE)
Lewis, Amanda : *Voice* (Mid)
Lewis, Andrew : *Guitars* (Mid)
Lewis, Andy : *Bass Guitar* (Lon)
Lewis, Anthony : *Guitars* (E)
Lewis, Anthony : *Cello* (Lon)
Lewis, Anthony : *Bass Guitar* (SW)
Lewis, Anwen : *Composer* (NW)
Lewis, Arthur : *Pianoforte* (Lon)
Lewis, Bryn : *Harp* (Lon)
Lewis, Brynley : *Saxophones* (SE)
Lewis, Bunny : *Trumpet* (NW)
Lewis, Byron : *Keyboards* (Lon)
Lewis, Carl : *Violin* (Lon)
Lewis, Cass : *Bass Guitar* (Lon)
Lewis, Charles : *Keyboards* (Lon)
Lewis, Colin : *Bass Guitar* (SW)
Lewis, Dal : *Percussion* (Lon)
Lewis, David : *Saxophones* (Lon)
Lewis, David : *Violin* (Lon)
Lewis, David : *Bass Guitar* (NE)
Lewis, Dutch : *Saxophones* (Mid)
Lewis, Elizabeth : *Violin* (Mid)
Lewis, Eryl Bronwen : *Viola* (Lon)
Lewis, Gareth : *Organ* (SW)
Lewis, Gary : *Guitars* (Mid)
Lewis, Gary : *Guitars* (SW)
Lewis, Geoffrey : *Saxophones* (SE)
Lewis, Georgia : *Voice* (Lon)
Lewis, Graham : *Guitars* (SW)
Lewis, Gwyn : *Cornet* (SW)
Lewis, Hywel : *Trombone* (NW)
Lewis, Iorie : *Saxophones* (SW)
Lewis, Jackie : *Voice* (SE)
Lewis, Jak R : *Percussion* (NE)
Lewis, Jenny : *Voice* (Sco)
Lewis, John : *Trombone* (NW)
Lewis, Jonathan : *Saxophones* (SW)
Lewis, Juliet : *Oboe* (Lon)
Lewis, Keith : *Violin* (Lon)
Lewis, Keith : *Cello* (Mid)
Lewis, Kevin : *Bass Guitar* (SW)
Lewis, Laurie : *Violin* (Lon)
Lewis, Lee : *Guitars* (Lon)
Lewis, Lindel : *Keyboards* (Lon)
Lewis, Luke : *Ukelele* (Mid)
Lewis, Lurleen : *Voice* (Lon)
Lewis, Malcolm : *Clarinet* (SE)
Lewis, Matthew : *Guitars* (Lon)
Lewis, Melanie : *Voice* (Lon)
Lewis, Melanie : *Voice* (Mid)
Lewis, Oliver : *Violin* (Lon)
Lewis, Paul : *Violin* (Lon)
Lewis, Paul : *Voice* (Lon)
Lewis, Paul : *Voice* (Mid)
Lewis, Paul : *Bass Guitar* (SE)
Lewis, Peter : *Flute* (Lon)
Lewis, Peter : *Viola* (Lon)
Lewis, Peter : *Percussion* (SW)
Lewis, Philip : *Trombone* (Lon)
Lewis, Philip : *Violin* (Mid)
Lewis, Phyllis : *Violin* (SE)
Lewis, Ray : *Keyboards* (Lon)
Lewis, Richard : *Double Bass* (Lon)
Lewis, Richard : *Saxophones* (Lon)

Lewis, Roddy : *Trumpet* (SW)
Lewis, Roger : *Cello* (SW)
Lewis, Samuel : *Music Director* (Lon)
Lewis, Sharon : *Pianoforte* (SE)
Lewis, Sid : *Guitars* (Lon)
Lewis, Simon : *Violin* (Lon)
Lewis, Stephen : *Guitars* (NW)
Lewis, Steve : *Latin American Percu* (NW)
Lewis, Susan : *Oboe* (NW)
Lewis, Terry : *Double Bass* (Lon)
Lewis, Thomas : *Flute* (SW)
Lewis, Timothy : *Guitars* (NW)
Lewis, Vera : *Non Playing Member* (SW)
Lewis, Vic : *Conductor* (Lon)
Lewis, William : *Saxophones* (Sco)
Lewis-Jones, Christopher : *Pianoforte* (Mid)
Lewis-Lim, Claire : *Violin* (E)
Lewry, David : *Guitars* (SW)
Lewsley, Sebastian : *Keyboards* (Lon)
Lexicon, Laurie : *Keyboards* (NW)
Leyden, Patrick : *Guitars* (Lon)
Leyland, Ken : *Percussion* (NW)
Leyshon, Stephen : *Synthesiser* (SW)
Lez : *Percussion* (E)
Li, Simon : *Guitars* (Lon)
Liberson, Jack : *Violin* (Sco)
Lichtenstein, Babette : *Cello* (Lon)
Lichtenstern, Dorit : *Viola* (Lon)
Lid : *Voice* (NW)
Liddell, Clair : *Pianoforte* (Sco)
Liddell, David : *Trombone* (Lon)
Liddell, Nona : *Violin* (Lon)
Liddiard, Giles : *Trumpet* (Lon)
Liddington, Gethin : *Trumpet* (SW)
Liddle, Alison : *Keyboards* (Lon)
Liddle, Bob : *Trumpet* (NW)
Lidgey-Hutt, Fiona : *Latin American Percu* (E)
Lidyard, Geoffrey : *Guitars* (Lon)
Liebert, Vikki : *Voice* (Lon)
Liebmann, Helen : *Cello* (Lon)
Liepa, Janet : *Viola* (E)
Liesegang, William (Billy) : *Guitars* (Lon)
Liew, Sarah : *Violin* (Lon)
Liggins, Len : *Guitars* (NE)
Light, Amber : *Bandleader* (SE)
Light, John : *Organ* (Lon)
Light, Patrick : *Saxophones* (E)
Light, Sarah : *Oboe* (Lon)
Light, Tim : *Percussion* (SE)
Lightfoot, Leslie : *Percussion* (SE)
Lightfoot, Terry : *Clarinet* (E)
Lightman, Richard : *Guitars* (Lon)
Liken, Tim : *Keyboards* (Lon)
Liley, Bil : *Guitars* (SE)
Lill, Derek : *Guitars* (SE)
Lilley, Colin : *Flute* (Mid)
Lilley, George : *Violin* (SW)
Lilley, Janet : *Cello* (E)
Lilley, Mandy : *Voice* (Lon)
Lilley, Peter : *Violin* (SW)
Lilley, Terry : *Double Bass* (Mid)
Lilley, Tom : *Guitars* (E)
Lilleyman, Trevor : *Saxophones* (Mid)
Lillie, Paul : *Bass Guitar* (E)
Lillitos, Malachi : *Voice* (Lon)
Lilly, Rosemary : *Violin* (Lon)
Lillywhite, Stephen : *Bass Guitar* (Lon)
Lim, Barry : *Keyboards* (Mid)
Lim, David : *Uilleann* (NW)
Lim, Tze-Chian : *Viola* (E)
Limbrick, Alan : *Guitars* (Lon)
Limbrick, Simon : *Percussion* (Lon)
Limerick, Alison : *Voice* (Lon)
Lin, Malu R : *Violin* (Lon)
Linahan, Liz : *Guitars* (NE)

Linaker, Sonia : *Organ* (Mid)
Lince, Louis : *Banjo* (E)
Lincoln, Peter : *Guitars* (SE)
Lindahl, Mike : *Guitars* (Mid)
Lindemere, Peter : *Bass Guitar* (Lon)
Linder-Dewan, Kerstin : *Violin* (Lon)
Lindes, Hal : *Guitars* (Lon)
Lindley, John : *Bass Guitar* (E)
Lindley, Richard : *Double Bass* (NE)
Lindley, Steven : *Guitars* (NW)
Lindo, Sharon : *Early Strings* (Lon)
Lindridge, Nigel : *Guitars* (SW)
Lindsay, David : *Banjo* (Lon)
Lindsay, Douglas : *Violin* (Sco)
Lindsay, Fiona : *Voice* (Sco)
Lindsay, Geoffrey : *Saxophones* (NW)
Lindsay, James : *Trombone* (NW)
Lindsay, Michael : *Double Bass* (SW)
Lindsay, Nigel : *Organ* (Lon)
Lindsay, Patrick : *Saxophones* (Sco)
Lindsell, Robert : *Clarinet* (E)
Lindsell, Rosie : *Composer* (Lon)
Lindsey, James : *Accordion* (Sco)
Lindup, Michael : *Percussion* (Lon)
Lindvall, Helienne : *Voice* (Lon)
Lineham, Charlie : *Pan Pipes* (Lon)
Linell, Dorothy : *Early Strings* (Lon)
Lines, Ann : *Cello* (Lon)
Lines, Timothy : *Clarinet* (Lon)
Lines, Trevor : *Double Bass* (Mid)
Lines-Welchman, Helena : *Percussion* (Lon)
Linford, Anthony : *Trumpet* (SE)
Ling, Paul : *Saxophones* (NW)
Lingley, Joanne : *Saxophones* (E)
Lingwood, John : *Percussion* (NW)
Lingwood, Peter : *Pianoforte* (NW)
Linke, Paul : *Bass Guitar* (Lon)
Linklater, Andrew : *Violin* (Sco)
Linklater, William : *Cello* (Sco)
Linley, Elizabeth : *Oboe* (Lon)
Linley, Roger : *Double Bass* (Lon)
Linnard, Carl : *Guitars* (SW)
Linnemann, Henrik : *Flute* (NE)
Linscott, Jody : *Percussion* (Lon)
Linsen, Dave : *Keyboards* (SW)
Linskey, Michael : *Trumpet* (SW)
Linsley, Adam : *Trumpet* (Lon)
Linsley, Gary : *Saxophones* (NE)
Linter, Derek : *Percussion* (Lon)
Linton, Judith : *Violin* (Sco)
Linton, Simon : *Clarinet* (SW)
Lintott, Clare : *Horn* (Lon)
Lion, Margaret : *Pianoforte* (Lon)
Lipman, Amanda : *Violin* (Mid)
Lipman, Daniel : *Saxophones* (Lon)
Lipman, David : *Pianoforte* (Sco)
Lipman, Dominic : *Viola* (SW)
Lipscombe, William : *Voice* (Lon)
Lipson, Stephen : *Guitars* (Lon)
Lipton, Jonathan : *Horn* (Lon)
Lironi, Steve : *Percussion* (Sco)
Lishak, Bertha : *Violin* (Lon)
Lishak, Rosalyn : *Violin* (Lon)
Lisheen : *Bass Guitar* (SE)
Lishman, Anna : *Voice* (SE)
Lishman, Dave : *Organ* (NE)
Lisicki, Mark : *Guitars* (Lon)
Lisk, Alan : *Composer* (Lon)
Lismore, Jenifer : *Pianoforte* (Mid)
Lissauer, Peter : *Violin* (Lon)
Lister, Anne : *Guitars* (Lon)
Lister, Aynsley : *Guitars* (Mid)
Lister, Jane : *Harp* (Lon)
Lister, Martin : *Pianoforte* (Lon)
Litchfield, Mary : *Saxophones* (SE)

Litherland, James : *Guitars* (Lon)
Lithgow, Beverley : *Pianoforte* (Sco)
Little, Carlo : *Percussion* (Lon)
Little, David : *Bass Trombone* (NW)
Little, Derek : *Clarinet* (SE)
Little, Jamie : *Percussion* (Mid)
Little, Jeremy : *Tympani* (SW)
Little, Martin : *Saxophones* (Lon)
Little, Matt : *Pianoforte* (SE)
Little, Matthew : *Voice* (Lon)
Little, Owen : *Viola* (NW)
Little, Phil : *Percussion* (SE)
Littledyke, Sion : *Guitars* (Mid)
Littler, Corin : *Guitars* (NW)
Littlewood, Andrew : *Flute* (NE)
Littlewood, Graeme : *Violin* (Mid)
Littlewood, Martin : *Guitars* (NE)
Littlewood, Stanley : *Percussion* (NW)
Litton, Martin : *Pianoforte* (E)
Litvinoff, Adrian : *Double Bass* (Mid)
Lively, Josephine : *Oboe* (Lon)
Liverpool, Martin : *Keyboards* (NE)
Livesey, Chris : *Bass Guitar* (NW)
Livesey, Warne : *Bass Guitar* (Lon)
Livingston, David : *Synthesiser* (Sco)
Livingstone, Christine : *Cello* (Lon)
Livingstone, Gavin : *Guitars* (Sco)
Livingstone, James : *Saxophones* (Sco)
Livingstone, Nigel : *Percussion* (Sco)
Livy, Martyn : *Guitars* (SE)
Llewellyn, Aids : *Bass Guitar* (Mid)
Llewellyn, Gareth : *Trombone* (SE)
Llewellyn, John : *Bass Guitar* (Lon)
Llewellyn, Rhys : *Percussion* (NW)
Llewellyn, Steven : *Guitars* (Sco)
Llewellyn, Tim : *Guitars* (SW)
Llewellyn, Trevor : *Guitars* (SW)
Llewellyn, William : *Saxophones* (Mid)
Llewhellin, David : *Pianoforte* (Lon)
Llorenna, Kelly : *Voice* (NW)
Lloyd, Andrew : *Voice* (Mid)
Lloyd, Christopher : *Flute* (Lon)
Lloyd, Darren : *Trumpet* (Lon)
Lloyd, David : *Horn* (SW)
Lloyd, Derek : *Guitars* (SE)
Lloyd, Donald : *Bassoon* (SE)
Lloyd, Eddie : *Songwriter* (Lon)
Lloyd, Eddie : *Voice* (Lon)
Lloyd, Elizabeth : *Cello* (NE)
Lloyd, Frank : *Horn* (Lon)
Lloyd, Geoffrey : *Pianoforte* (SE)
Lloyd, Huw : *Guitars* (Lon)
Lloyd, Jacqueline : *Viola* (Lon)
Lloyd, Jeff : *Violin* (SW)
Lloyd, Joanna : *Saxophones* (Mid)
Lloyd, Kenneth : *Saxophones* (NW)
Lloyd, Maria : *Violin* (Mid)
Lloyd, Marie : *Clarinet* (Lon)
Lloyd, Mark : *Percussion* (Lon)
Lloyd, Mark : *Organ* (Mid)
Lloyd, Martyn : *Pianoforte* (NW)
Lloyd, Michael : *Viola* (Lon)
Lloyd, Nicholas : *Trombone* (Lon)
Lloyd, Philip : *Percussion* (NW)
Lloyd, Phillip : *Keyboards* (SW)
Lloyd, Rachel : *Voice* (NW)
Lloyd, Rebecca : *Oboe* (Lon)
Lloyd, Rick : *Music Director* (Lon)
Lloyd, Robert : *Trombone* (Lon)
Lloyd, Stephen : *Viola* (SW)
Lloyd, Thomas : *Organ* (SW)
Lloyd, Vin : *Guitars* (Mid)
Lloyd, William : *Pianoforte* (Lon)
Lloyd-Evans, Owen : *Double Bass* (NW)
Lloyd-Webber, Andrew : *Composer* (Lon)

Lloyd-Webber, Julian : *Cello* (Lon)
Lluna, Joan-Enric : *Clarinet* (Lon)
Lluna, Jose : *Horn* (Lon)
Loach, James : *Bass Tuba* (SE)
Loat, Alan : *Pianoforte* (NW)
Lobeck, Katharina : *Flute* (Lon)
Lobel, Ivor : *Guitars* (E)
Locantro, Tony : *Pianoforte* (Lon)
Lochbaum, Chloe : *Flute* (SE)
Lochner, David : *Guitars* (SE)
Lochrie, Jaz : *Bass Guitar* (Lon)
Lock, David : *Bassoon* (Lon)
Lock, Kate : *Clarinet* (SW)
Lock, Michael : *Trumpet* (SW)
Lock, Rosemary : *Flute* (Sco)
Lock, Simon : *Violin* (Lon)
Lock, Terence : *Pianoforte* (Mid)
Locke, David : *Percussion* (Lon)
Locke, Kathryn : *Cello* (E)
Locke, Martyn : *Percussion* (SW)
Locke, Peter : *Trombone* (SW)
Locke, Robert : *Bass Guitar* (SW)
Locke, Timothy : *Horn* (Lon)
Locker, Aileen : *Cello* (NE)
Locker, James : *Trombone* (NE)
Lockett, Dorian : *Double Bass* (SE)
Lockett, Julian : *Bassoon* (SE)
Lockett, Mark : *Keyboards* (Mid)
Lockett, Mornington : *Saxophones* (Lon)
Lockett, Peter : *Percussion* (Lon)
Lockey, Saskia : *Pianoforte* (Lon)
Lockhart, Robert : *Pianoforte* (Lon)
Lockhart, William : *Tympani* (Lon)
Lockheart, Mark : *Saxophones* (Lon)
Lockrane, Gareth : *Flute* (Lon)
Lockwood, Edward : *Horn* (Mid)
Lockwood, Nicholas : *Bass Guitar* (NE)
Lockwood, Ronald : *Violin* (SW)
Lockyer, Luke : *Horn* (SW)
Lockyer, Ronald : *Guitars* (SE)
Lockyer, Simon : *Cello* (SE)
Locock, Duke : *Saxophones* (SE)
Locock, Victoria : *Pianoforte* (Mid)
Lodder, Stephen : *Pianoforte* (Lon)
Lodge, Don : *Guitars* (NE)
Lodge, Gilly : *Saxophones* (Lon)
Lodge, John : *Bass Guitar* (Lon)
Lodge, William : *Saxophones* (Lon)
Lodwick, Wynfoed : *Clarinet* (SW)
Loehry, Adrienne : *Voice* (SE)
Loeser, Brigitte : *Cello* (Lon)
Loewenthal, Martin : *Copyist* (Lon)
Loewenthal, Sara : *Double Bass* (Lon)
Lofthouse, Chris : *Guitars* (Lon)
Lofthouse, Francis : *Saxophones* (NW)
Loftin, Fred : *Pianoforte* (Lon)
Loftin, John : *Double Bass* (Lon)
Lofts, Geoff : *Percussion* (Lon)
Loftus, David : *Tuba* (Lon)
Lofty, James : *Bass Guitar* (NE)
Logan, Alistair : *Clarinet* (Lon)
Logan, Doug : *Trombone* (Lon)
Logan, John : *Horn* (Sco)
Logan, Kirstie : *Cor Anglais* (Sco)
Logan, Kirstie : *Early Wind* (Sco)
Logan, Kirstie : *Oboe* (Sco)
Logie, Nicholas : *Viola* (Lon)
Lole, Peter : *Music Director* (Lon)
Lomas, Adrian : *Percussion* (NW)
Lomas, Michael : *Trombone* (SW)
Lomas, Trevor : *Pianoforte* (SE)
Lomax, Oliver (Pka Shogun) : *Composer* (E)
Lomax, Raymond : *Conductor* (NW)
Lomax, Raymond : *Tympani* (NW)
Lombard, Freddy : *Violin* (Mid)

Lone, Johnny : *Voice* (NE)
Lonergan, Dick : *Percussion* (SE)
Lonergan, Terence : *Cello* (SW)
Loney, Cyril : *Percussion* (SW)
Loney, Rebecca : *Voice* (SW)
Long, Andrew : *Violin* (NW)
Long, Craig : *Percussion* (Lon)
Long, Jim : *Clarinet* (SE)
Long, Linda : *Voice* (SW)
Long, Martin : *Guitars* (SE)
Long, Naomi : *Pianoforte* (SE)
Long, Paul : *Trumpet* (NE)
Long, Pete : *Banjo* (SW)
Long, Peter : *Saxophones* (Lon)
Long, Richard : *Percussion* (E)
Long, Stephen : *Percussion* (Lon)
Long, Stephen : *Keyboards* (SE)
Long, Wendy : *Pianoforte* (Lon)
Long, William : *Percussion* (E)
Longcroft, Roger : *Trombone* (SE)
Longden, Anthony : *Bass Guitar* (Lon)
Longden, Lee P : *Music Director* (NW)
Longden, Pamela : *Harpsichord* (Mid)
Longford, Tina : *Violin* (Lon)
Longhurst, Cliff : *Percussion* (Lon)
Longhurst, Victoria : *Harp* (Lon)
Longley, Chick : *Pianoforte* (SE)
Longmore, Ken : *Percussion* (SE)
Longmore, Scott : *Percussion* (Lon)
Longstaff, Danny : *Trombone* (Mid)
Longster, George : *Percussion* (NE)
Longworth, Deborah : *Percussion* (Lon)
Longworth, James : *Guitars* (Lon)
Lopez Valle, Omar : *Trumpet* (Lon)
Lopez-Real, Carlos : *Saxophones* (Lon)
Loraine, Josey : *Guitars* (Mid)
Lord, Clare : *Guitars* (Mid)
Lord, Didge : *DiDJeridu* (SE)
Lord, Julie : *Horn* (Lon)
Lord, Michael : *Rapper* (Lon)
Lord, Roger : *Oboe* (Lon)
Lord, Stan : *Saxophones* (Lon)
Lord, Timothy : *Guitars* (SW)
Lord, Victoria : *Voice* (Lon)
Lordan, Erin : *Voice* (Lon)
Lorelei : *Voice* (Lon)
Loren : *Voice* (Lon)
Lorenz, Gordon : *Trumpet* (E)
Lorenz, V : *Voice* (Lon)
Lorenzo, Jimmy : *Bass Guitar* (NW)
Lorimer, Roddy : *Trumpet* (Lon)
Loring, Keith : *Guitars* (SW)
Lorkin, Eddie : *Trombone* (Lon)
Lorriman, Christine : *Flute* (NW)
Losi, Marco : *Pianoforte* (Lon)
Loston, Dale : *Violin* (Lon)
Lothian, Eric : *Voice* (Sco)
Loughran, Anne : *Pianoforte* (Mid)
Loughrey, Michelle : *Recorders* (SE)
Louis, Leslie : *Pianoforte* (Lon)
Louise, Janel : *Percussion* (E)
Louise, Joanna : *Flute* (SE)
Loukes, Robert : *Guitars* (Lon)
Lovatt, Michael : *Trumpet* (Lon)
Love : *Voice* (Lon)
Love, Aidan : *Keyboards* (Lon)
Love, Danny : *Voice* (Lon)
Love, Fiona : *Violin* (NE)
Love, Kate : *Percussion* (E)
Love, Wendy : *Harmonica (Inc Bass)* (Sco)
Love, William : *Organ* (NW)
Loveday, Alan : *Violin* (Lon)
Loveday, Bob : *Violin* (Lon)
Loveday, Martin : *Cello* (Lon)
Loveday, Martin : *Violin* (Lon)

Index of Members - Lovegrove

Lovegrove, Adrian : *Guitars* (SE)
Lovejoy, Michael : *Violin* (Lon)
Loveless, Alex : *Pianoforte* (NW)
Lovell, Andy : *Saxophones* (NE)
Lovell, John : *Violin* (Lon)
Lovell, Jonathan : *Violin* (NE)
Lovell, Keith : *Viola* (Lon)
Lovell, Kolbrun : *Violin* (Lon)
Lovell, Maureen : *Cello* (Lon)
Lovell, Pat : *Violin* (Lon)
Lovell, Sara : *Cello* (NW)
Lovell, Sonny : *Guitars* (SE)
Lovell-Jones, Simon : *Conductor* (SW)
Lovelle, Laurie : *Double Bass* (Lon)
Lovelock, Andrew : *Percussion* (SE)
Lovelock, Michael : *Pianoforte* (Mid)
Lovemuscle, Johnny : *Voice* (SE)
Loverdidge, Dury : *Cello* (E)
Loveridge, Kitty : *Violin* (Lon)
Lovie, Louise : *Oboe* (Sco)
Lovini, Gary : *Violin* (Mid)
Low, Calum : *Accordion* (Sco)
Low, Patti : *Voice* (E)
Low, Rebecca : *Violin* (Lon)
Lowbury, Miriam : *Cello* (Lon)
Lowbury, Pauline : *Violin* (Lon)
Lowdell, Bob : *Copyist* (Lon)
Lowdell, John : *Cello* (Lon)
Lowe, Angela : *Cornet* (SW)
Lowe, Catherine : *Oboe* (NE)
Lowe, Charles : *Saxophones* (SE)
Lowe, Chris : *Pianoforte* (Lon)
Lowe, Chris : *Guitars* (SE)
Lowe, Christina : *Voice* (NW)
Lowe, Christopher : *Percussion* (NW)
Lowe, Christopher : *Trombone* (SE)
Lowe, David : *Percussion* (Lon)
Lowe, David : *Keyboards* (Mid)
Lowe, Frederick : *Clarinet* (Lon)
Lowe, Gary : *Bass Guitar* (NW)
Lowe, Jeremy : *Clarinet* (Lon)
Lowe, Jez : *Guitars* (NE)
Lowe, Jim : *Guitars* (NW)
Lowe, Kevin : *Saxophones* (Lon)
Lowe, Lindsey : *Trumpet* (Lon)
Lowe, Mark : *Tenor Horn* (NE)
Lowe, Martin : *Music Director* (Lon)
Lowe, Nick : *Bass Guitar* (Lon)
Lowe, Pearl : *Voice* (Lon)
Lowe, Peter : *Saxophones* (SE)
Lowe, Sidney : *Trombone* (NW)
Lowe, Steven : *Bass Guitar* (Lon)
Lowe, Thomas : *Trumpet* (Sco)
Lowe, Trevor : *Double Bass* (Lon)
Lowe, Veronica : *Guitars* (SW)
Lowe, Virginia : *Voice* (Lon)
Lowe, William : *Saxophones* (Mid)
Lowe-Watson, Andrew : *Pianoforte* (Lon)
Lowell, Timothy : *Guitars* (NW)
Lowes, Clare : *Cello* (SE)
Lowis, Nigel : *Guitars* (Lon)
Lowit, Peter : *Double Bass* (Sco)
Lowrey, Gregor : *Accordion* (Sco)
Lowrey, Ray : *Cello* (SE)
Lowrey, Robin : *Percussion* (SE)
Lowther, Graeme Eric (Brush) : *Percussion* (NE)
Lowther, Henry : *Trumpet* (Lon)
Lowther, Richard : *Guitars* (NE)
Loxam, Arnold : *Organ* (NE)
Loynes, Katherine : *Violin* (Lon)
Lubbock, Jeremy : *Pianoforte* (Lon)
Lucas, Adrian : *Organ* (Mid)
Lucas, Alison : *Viola* (Sco)
Lucas, Andrew : *Organ* (E)
Lucas, Antonia : *Voice* (Lon)

Lucas, Daniel : *Percussion* (Lon)
Lucas, David : *Guitars* (SW)
Lucas, Egly : *Guitars* (NE)
Lucas, Peter : *Guitars* (SW)
Lucas, Rob : *Bass Guitar* (Lon)
Lucas, Tony : *Tympani* (Lon)
Lucchesi, Dudley : *Violin* (SW)
Luce, Francine : *Voice* (Lon)
Luck, Brian : *Saxophones* (Lon)
Luck, Rupert : *Violin* (SW)
Luckhurst, Joanna : *Saxophones* (SE)
Lucy, Laura : *Clarinet* (Lon)
Lucy Live! : *Pianoforte* (E)
Ludford, Ian : *Cello* (Mid)
Ludford, Janet : *Cello* (Mid)
Ludlam, Bob : *Trumpet* (NE)
Ludlow, John : *Violin* (Lon)
Luff, Harold : *Trumpet* (Lon)
Lukas, Peter : *Saxophones* (Lon)
Luke, Dave : *Guitars* (Mid)
Lukeman, Jason : *Keyboards* (NE)
Lukoszevieze, Anton : *Cello* (Lon)
Lumb, Rachel : *Clarinet* (E)
Lumsdon, Des : *Saxophones* (Lon)
Lund, David : *Pianoforte* (Lon)
Lund, Eric : *Arranger* (Mid)
Lund, Richie : *Guitars* (Mid)
Lundberg, Rosemary : *Viola* (Lon)
Lundgren, Johan : *Guitars* (Lon)
Lundy, Mark : *Bass Guitar* (Lon)
Lunedei, Ezio : *Voice* (E)
Lunn, Michael : *Pianoforte* (NW)
Lunn, Philip : *Bass Guitar* (Mid)
Lunn, Roger : *Cello* (Lon)
Lunn, Simon : *Trumpet* (Mid)
Lunn, Tiffany : *Keyboards* (Mid)
Lunniss, Amanda : *Voice* (E)
Lunny, Manus : *Bouzouki* (Sco)
Lunt, Helen : *Cello* (SW)
Lunt, Nicholas : *Saxophones* (Lon)
Lunts, Michael : *Pianoforte* (NW)
Lupa : *Voice* (Lon)
Lupin, Mark : *Violin* (Lon)
Lupino, Angela : *Bass Guitar* (Lon)
Lupton, Karen : *Voice* (Lon)
Lurie, Robin : *Latin American Percu* (Lon)
Lusambo, Fiston : *Guitars* (Lon)
Luscombe, Stephen : *Composer* (Lon)
Lusher, David : *Trumpet* (Lon)
Lusher, Don : *Trombone* (Lon)
Lusher, Phil : *Bass Guitar* (Lon)
Lusher, Richmond : *Cello* (Sco)
Lusk, Susan : *Percussion* (E)
Luther, Paul : *Guitars* (SW)
Luton, Hamlet : *Bass Guitar* (NE)
Lux, Kitty : *Ukelele* (Lon)
Luxmoore, Kate : *Clarinet* (Mid)
Luyeyes, Jean : *Voice* (Lon)
Lyall, David : *Guitars* (E)
Lycett, David : *Violin* (Mid)
Lycett, Jonathan : *Clarinet* (Mid)
Lyddon, Rupert : *Guitars* (Lon)
Lydiatt, J : *Clarinet* (NW)
Lydon, Christopher : *Violin* (Lon)
Lydon, John : *Voice* (Lon)
Lyle, Andrew : *Clarinet* (Lon)
Lyle, George : *Double Bass* (Sco)
Lyle, Graham : *Guitars* (Lon)
Lyle, Teena : *Vibraphone* (Lon)
Lynall, Eleanor : *Saxophones* (SE)
Lynane, David : *Double Bass* (NW)
Lynch, Catharine : *Voice* (Lon)
Lynch, Curt : *Keyboards* (Lon)
Lynch, Dan : *Bass Guitar* (NW)
Lynch, Donald : *Keyboards* (Lon)

Lynch, Ged : *Percussion* (NW)
Lynch, James : *Trumpet* (Lon)
Lynch, Margaret : *Viola* (SW)
Lynch, Thomas : *Trombone* (Lon)
Lynch, Tom : *Guitars* (Lon)
Lynden, Patricia : *Flute* (Lon)
Lyndsey : *Voice* (E)
Lyne, David : *Pianoforte* (NW)
Lyness, Daniel : *Viola* (Lon)
Lynn, Alan : *Percussion* (Lon)
Lynn, Andrew : *Trumpet* (Sco)
Lynn, Brian : *Bass Trombone* (Lon)
Lynn, Eira : *Harp* (NW)
Lynn, Geoffrey : *Violin* (Lon)
Lynn, Ian : *Keyboards* (Lon)
Lynn, Warren : *Organ* (E)
Lynne, Deborah : *Violin* (Mid)
Lynwood, Andy : *Keyboards* (Lon)
Lyon, David : *Violin* (Lon)
Lyon, David : *Pianoforte* (SW)
Lyon, Jason : *Pianoforte* (Lon)
Lyons, Carol : *Percussion* (Sco)
Lyons, David : *Percussion* (Sco)
Lyons, Graham : *Bassoon* (NE)
Lyons, Harry : *Violin* (Lon)
Lyons, James : *Saxophones* (Mid)
Lyons, Lorna : *Clarinet* (E)
Lyons, Peter : *Saxophones* (NE)
Lyons, Rachel : *Flute* (NW)
Lyons, Roger : *Keyboards* (NW)
Lyons, Sean : *Guitars* (Lon)
Lyons, Shara : *Voice* (Lon)
Lyrical Lord Leo : *Accordion* (NW)
Lyrics, Leslie : *Voice* (Lon)
Lysander, Ebonard : *Pianoforte* (Lon)
Lysandrou, Andy : *Keyboards* (Lon)
Lyttelton, Humphrey : *Trumpet* (Lon)
Lytton, Tony : *Percussion* (Lon)

M

M, Johnny : *Voice* (Lon)
M87 : *Guitars* (SW)
Mabbett, Tony : *Trumpet* (Lon)
Mabbott, Gordon : *Pianoforte* (Sco)
Maby, Lewis : *Violin* (Lon)
Mac, Rob : *Guitars* (Lon)
Mac, Tony : *Percussion* (NW)
Macalan, Helen : *Voice* (Sco)
Macallister, Stephen : *Horn* (SW)
Macardle, Aileen : *Harp* (SE)
Macari, Amanda : *Oboe* (Sco)
Macarthur, Quee : *Bass Guitar* (Sco)
Macaskill, Paula : *Keyboards* (Sco)
Macaulay, Mary : *Pianoforte* (SW)
Macauley, Lorraine : *Keyboards* (NE)
Macauley, Valerie : *Keyboards* (NE)
Maccarthy, Ian : *Cello* (Mid)
Maccleaver, Grace : *Pianoforte* (Sco)
Maccoll, Calum : *Guitars* (E)
Maccoll, Kirsty : *Voice* (Lon)
Maccoll, Neill : *Guitars* (Lon)
Maccormack, Geoff : *Percussion* (Lon)
Macdominic, John : *Trumpet* (Lon)
Macdonald, Alan : *Trumpet* (Sco)
Macdonald, Allan : *Bagpipes* (Sco)
Macdonald, Allan : *Composer* (Sco)
Macdonald, Andrew : *Violin* (Lon)
Macdonald, Anne : *Oboe* (Lon)
Macdonald, Anne : *Violin* (Sco)
Macdonald, Calum : *Percussion* (Sco)
Macdonald, Donald : *Violin* (SE)
Macdonald, Edward : *Guitars* (Lon)
Macdonald, George : *Saxophones* (Sco)
Macdonald, Iain : *Highland Bagpipes* (Sco)
Macdonald, James : *Percussion* (Lon)

Macdonald, Janet : *Flute* (Lon)
Macdonald, Mac : *Banjo* (SW)
Macdonald, Neville : *Voice* (Lon)
Macdonald, Peter : *Percussion* (Lon)
Macdonald, Raymond : *Saxophones* (Sco)
Macdonald, Robert : *Pianoforte* (Lon)
Macdonald, Rory : *Bass Guitar* (Lon)
Macdonald, Stuart : *Saxophones* (NE)
Macdonnell, Tony : *Percussion* (Lon)
Macdougall, Donald : *Guitars* (Lon)
Mace, Charles : *Bass Guitar* (Lon)
Mace, Dawn : *Percussion* (NW)
Maceanruig, Heather : *Flute* (NW)
Macfadyen, Harry : *Guitars* (SW)
Macfarlane, Alison : *Melodeon* (E)
Macfarlane, Hugh : *Percussion* (Lon)
Macfarlane, Jane : *Cello* (Lon)
Macfarlane, Malcolm : *Guitars* (Lon)
Macgowan, Roger : *Trumpet* (SW)
Macgregor, Andy : *Guitars* (Sco)
Macha, Freddy : *Voice* (Lon)
Machin, Ben : *Voice* (Mid)
Machin, Timothy : *Songwriter* (Lon)
Machon, Paul : *Saxophones* (NE)
Macinnes, Alasdair : *Keyboards* (Sco)
Macinnes, Mairi : *Voice* (Sco)
Macintosh, Adrian : *Percussion* (Lon)
Macintosh, Felix : *Bass Guitar* (Lon)
Macintyre, Robert : *Keyboards* (Sco)
Mack, Arty : *Percussion* (NW)
Mack, Brian : *Viola* (Lon)
Mack, Charlie : *Percussion* (Lon)
Mack, Jimmy : *Voice* (E)
Mack, Pauline : *Viola* (Lon)
Mack, Robbie : *Keyboards* (NW)
Mack, Sharada : *Viola* (Lon)
Macka B : *Voice* (Mid)
Mackay, Callum : *Horn* (NE)
Mackay, David : *Pianoforte* (Lon)
Mackay, Gordon : *Violin* (Lon)
Mackay, Morag : *Voice* (Sco)
Mackay, Paul : *Composer* (NW)
Mackay, Sandra : *Oboe* (Lon)
Mackay, Sandra : *Voice* (Sco)
Mackay, Thomas : *Pianoforte* (Sco)
Mackelworth, Anna : *Voice* (Lon)
Mackendrick, Caroline : *Voice* (Lon)
Mackenzie, Andrew : *Guitars* (NW)
Mackenzie, Clen : *Guitars* (Sco)
Mackenzie, Hamish : *Pianoforte* (Sco)
Mackenzie, Henry : *Saxophones* (Lon)
Mackenzie, Jacqui : *Viola* (SE)
Mackenzie, John : *Clarinet* (NE)
Mackenzie, Kevin : *Guitars* (Sco)
Mackenzie, Lennox : *Violin* (Lon)
Mackenzie, Talitha : *Voice* (Sco)
Mackenzie, Wally : *Percussion* (NW)
Mackenzie, William : *Saxophones* (NW)
Mackerras, Sir Charles : *Conductor* (Lon)
Mackerron, Nick : *Guitars* (SW)
Mackey, Gina : *Harp* (Lon)
Mackey, Justin : *Pianoforte* (SE)
Mackey, Steven : *Bass Guitar* (NE)
Mackfall, Derek : *Trumpet* (NE)
Mackfall, Richard : *Organ* (NE)
Mackichan, Blair : *Pianoforte* (Lon)
Mackie, Alistair : *Trumpet* (Lon)
Mackie, David : *Pianoforte* (Lon)
Mackie, Douglas : *Violin* (Lon)
Mackie, George : *Mandolin* (Lon)
Mackie, James : *Keyboards* (Mid)
Mackie, Kevin : *Percussion* (Sco)
Mackie, Melbon : *Bassoon* (Lon)
Mackie, Neil : *Taiko Drums* (Sco)
Mackie, Ronnie : *Saxophones* (Lon)

Mackillop, Duncan : *Keyboards* (Lon)
Mackinder, Julia : *Harp* (Lon)
Mackinder, Michael : *Trombone* (NE)
Mackinder, Neville : *Bassoon* (Lon)
Mackinnon, Iain : *Violin* (Lon)
Mackinnon, Micheal : *Guitars* (Sco)
Mackintosh, Andy : *Saxophones* (Lon)
Mackintosh, Catherine : *Violin* (Lon)
Mackintosh, Gregor : *Guitars* (NE)
Mackintosh, Iain : *Banjo* (Sco)
Mackintosh, James : *Percussion* (Sco)
Mackintosh, Stewart : *Music Director* (Lon)
Mackison, Rachel : *Violin* (Sco)
Mackman, Richard : *Guitars* (E)
Mackmin, Norman : *Keyboards* (SE)
Mackrell, Elliet : *Violin* (Lon)
Mackrell, Kim : *Cello* (Lon)
Maclaren, Andrew : *Viola* (NW)
Maclaren, Barbara : *Horn* (Lon)
Maclaughlan, Glenn : *Percussion* (E)
Maclean, Alexander : *Bandleader* (E)
Maclean, Douglas : *Voice* (Sco)
Maclean, Gillian : *Viola* (Sco)
Maclean, Gordon : *Guitars* (Sco)
Maclean, Grahame : *Guitars* (E)
Maclean, Karen : *Keyboards* (Sco)
Maclean, Louise : *Horn* (Sco)
Maclean, Neil : *Pianoforte* (Lon)
Maclennan, Donald : *Keyboards* (Sco)
Macleod, Ali : *Guitars* (Sco)
Macleod, Donald : *Bagpipes* (Lon)
Macleod, Iain F : *Guitars* (Sco)
Macleod, James Andrew : *Guitars* (Mid)
Macleod, Kevin : *Banjo* (Sco)
Maclure, Andrew : *Percussion* (Lon)
Macmahon, Bree : *Voice* (Lon)
Macmahon, Graham : *Keyboards* (Lon)
Macmahon, Niall : *Guitars* (Lon)
Macmanus, Kieran : *Pianoforte* (Lon)
Macmanus, Liam : *Percussion* (Lon)
Macmanus, Ronan : *Voice* (Lon)
Macmanus, Ruairi : *Bass Guitar* (Lon)
Macmaster, Mary : *Harp* (Lon)
Macmurray, John : *Trumpet* (NW)
Macnaghten, Alex : *Bass Guitar* (NW)
Macnaghten, Anne : *Violin* (Lon)
Macnamara, Mandy : *Double Bass* (Lon)
Macneil, Michael : *Keyboards* (Sco)
Macnicol, John : *Trumpet* (Lon)
Macniven, Ronnie : *Trombone* (Sco)
Macniven, Tom : *Trumpet* (Sco)
Macnutt, Penny : *Flute* (Lon)
Macpherson, Cluny : *Bodhran* (NE)
Macpherson, Ian : *Arranger* (Lon)
Macpherson, Ian : *Pianoforte* (Sco)
Macpherson, Richard : *Trumpet* (Lon)
Macrae, Christina : *Cello* (Lon)
Macsherry, Fiona : *Pianoforte* (NE)
Mactavish, D Grant : *Electric Piano* (Sco)
Madden, David : *Trumpet* (Lon)
Madden, Dedi : *Guitars* (SE)
Madder, Louise : *Flute* (Mid)
Maddison, Damien : *Guitars* (NW)
Maddison, Karl : *Guitars* (NE)
Maddock, Malcolm : *Pianoforte* (Lon)
Maddocks, Gordon : *Percussion* (SW)
Maddocks, James : *Violin* (Lon)
Maddocks, John : *Clarinet* (SE)
Mader, Bill : *Saxophones* (SE)
Madgwick, Richard : *Pianoforte* (Lon)
Madigan, Brian : *Percussion* (SW)
Madilyn : *Voice* (Lon)
Madin, Richard : *Horn* (NE)
Mael, Ronald : *Guitars* (Lon)
Mael, Russell : *Guitars* (Lon)

Magee, Belinda : *Voice* (Lon)
Magee, Francis : *Tuba* (Sco)
Magee, Jenny : *Oboe* (Sco)
Magee, Michael : *Horn* (Lon)
Magee, Steven : *Bassoon* (NW)
Magee, William : *Percussion* (Lon)
Maggs, Haydon : *Voice* (SE)
Maggs, Hywel : *Guitars* (SW)
Maggs, John : *Pianoforte* (SW)
Magic, Mo : *Keyboards* (Lon)
Magnus, Ian : *Cello* (SE)
Magub, Maya : *Violin* (Lon)
Maguire, Caroline : *Double Bass* (Lon)
Maguire, Conor : *Flute* (Lon)
Maguire, Damian : *Percussion* (SE)
Maguire, Francis : *Double Bass* (Lon)
Maguire, Gordon : *Bass Guitar* (Mid)
Maguire, Hugh : *Violin* (Lon)
Maguire, Jack : *Violin* (SE)
Maguire, Paul : *Pianoforte* (Lon)
Maguire, Teresa : *Violin* (Lon)
Maguire, Tricia : *Viola* (E)
Maher, Joseph : *Violin* (SE)
Maher, Rachel : *Violin* (Lon)
Maher, Sean : *Guitars* (Lon)
Maher, Siobhan : *Voice* (NW)
Mahmoud, Mohammad : *Tabla* (Lon)
Mahoney, Linda : *Voice* (Sco)
Mahonney : *Voice* (Lon)
Mahony, Neil : *Guitars* (NW)
Maidman, Ian : *Bass Guitar* (Lon)
Mailey, Thomas : *Accordion* (Sco)
Main, Stephen : *Saxophones* (Lon)
Main-Ellen, Mark : *Percussion* (SE)
Mainard, Amanda : *Cello* (Mid)
Maine, Vicki : *Pianoforte* (Lon)
Maintenant, Fred : *Pianoforte* (SW)
Mainwaring, James : *Clarinet* (SW)
Mainwaring, Jonathan : *Trumpet* (SW)
Mainwaring, Peter : *Trumpet* (NW)
Mainwaring, Richard : *Violin* (SW)
Mair, Stephanie : *Voice* (Lon)
Mair, Stephen : *Double Bass* (Lon)
Maisey, Rachel : *Violin* (SW)
Maitland, Chris : *Percussion* (E)
Major, Lee : *Percussion* (E)
Major, Margaret : *Viola* (Lon)
Major, Willett : *Violin* (Mid)
Majumdar, Anna : *Pianoforte* (Lon)
Makhene, Josh Sello : *Percussion* (Mid)
Makinson, Alan : *Pianoforte* (NE)
Makos, Tony : *Bass Guitar* (Sco)
Makower, Will : *Pianoforte* (E)
Malabar, Clive : *Percussion* (Lon)
Malaki : *Guitars* (NE)
Malam, John : *Trumpet* (E)
Malarkey, Karen : *Voice* (Sco)
Malcolm, Austin : *Pianoforte* (Lon)
Malcomson, Hettie : *Composer* (SE)
Malcomson, Inge : *Saxophones* (SE)
Male, Don : *Non Playing Member* (SW)
Malik, Samia : *Voice* (E)
Malkinson, Chris : *Pianoforte* (E)
Mallalieu, Jonathan : *Pianoforte* (Lon)
Mallandaine, Jean : *Pianoforte* (Lon)
Mallen, Stuart : *Euphonium* (Mid)
Mallet, Arthur : *Violin* (SE)
Mallett, Gavin : *Trumpet* (Lon)
Mallett, John : *Recorders* (E)
Mallett, Lisa : *Flute* (Lon)
Mallett, Richard : *Keyboards* (SW)
Mallett, Timothy : *Bassoon* (Lon)
Mallett, Timothy : *Contra Bassoon* (Lon)
Mallinson, Gareth : *Keyboards* (NW)
Malloch, Stephen : *Guitars* (Sco)

Index of Members - Mathews

Mathews, Ray : *Guitars* (E)
Mathews, Stanley : *Pianoforte* (SE)
Mathieson, Eleanor : *Violin* (Lon)
Mathieson, Iain : *Percussion* (SW)
Mathieson, Ken : *Arranger* (Sco)
Mathieson, Ken : *Bandleader* (Sco)
Mathieson, Ken : *Percussion* (Sco)
Mathieson, Stephen : *Trombone* (Lon)
Mathis, Alan : *Bass Guitar* (Lon)
Mathison, Frank : *Bass Trombone* (NW)
Mathison, Peter : *Guitars* (Lon)
Mathunjwa, Julia : *Latin American Percu* (Lon)
Matley, Edward : *Violin* (NE)
Matt : *Keyboards* (E)
Mattacks, David : *Percussion* (Lon)
Matten, Douglas : *Arranger* (Lon)
Matthew, Howard : *Bass Guitar* (NW)
Matthew, Louise : *Flute* (Lon)
Matthews, Antony : *Keyboards* (SE)
Matthews, Benjamin : *Guitars* (Lon)
Matthews, Ceri : *Guitars* (SW)
Matthews, Charles : *Organ* (Mid)
Matthews, Colin : *Composer* (Lon)
Matthews, Colin : *Clarinet* (NE)
Matthews, Georgina : *Voice* (E)
Matthews, Glyn : *Percussion* (Lon)
Matthews, Graham : *Saxophones* (Mid)
Matthews, James : *Harmonica (Inc Bass* (SW)
Matthews, James : *Percussion* (SW)
Matthews, Janet : *Violin* (Lon)
Matthews, Jeremy : *Violin* (NE)
Matthews, John : *Saxophones* (Lon)
Matthews, John : *Voice* (Lon)
Matthews, Julie : *Pianoforte* (NW)
Matthews, Paul : *Saxophones* (Lon)
Matthews, Paul : *Bass Guitar* (SW)
Matthews, Peter : *Double Bass* (Lon)
Matthews, Peter : *Percussion* (NE)
Matthews, Phil : *Guitars* (Mid)
Matthews, Philip : *Tuba* (Mid)
Matthews, Roderick : *Guitars* (Lon)
Matthews, Sarah : *Violin* (Mid)
Matthews, Sean : *Latin American Percu* (Lon)
Matthews, Victoria : *Cello* (Lon)
Matthey, Clemence : *Cello* (Lon)
Matthias, John : *Violin* (SW)
Mattis, Audrey : *Voice* (NW)
Mattner, Audrey : *Violin* (Sco)
Mattos, Marcio : *Double Bass* (Lon)
Matts, Harry : *Pianoforte* (Mid)
Matts, Paul : *Guitars* (Mid)
Mattson, Daniel : *Voice* (Mid)
Mattu, Amit : *Percussion* (Mid)
Mattu, Jaspal : *Voice* (Mid)
Mattu, Satinder : *Club DJ* (Mid)
Matzdorf, David : *Voice* (Lon)
Maude, Tony : *Guitars* (Lon)
Maude-Roxby, Phyllida : *Viola* (SE)
Maughan, Karen : *Double Bass* (NE)
Maul, John : *Pianoforte* (E)
Mauldon, Robert : *Guitars* (SW)
Maule, Graham : *Voice* (Sco)
Maunder, Guera : *Violin* (Sco)
Maunder, Peter : *Clarinet* (Lon)
Maurel, Alain : *Percussion* (Lon)
Maurice, Brian : *Saxophones* (SE)
Maw, Stephen : *Bassoon* (Lon)
Mawdsley, Stephen : *Bass Guitar* (NW)
Mawson, Annie : *Clarsach* (NW)
Mawson, Jane : *Violin* (Sco)
Max, Paul : *Keyboards* (Lon)
Max, Robert : *Cello* (Lon)
Maxi : *Percussion* (NW)
Maxim, John : *Pianoforte* (Lon)
Maximen, Luvain : *Voice* (Lon)

Maxine : *Voice* (Lon)
Maxlove : *Voice* (Lon)
Maxted-Jones, Nicholas : *Violin* (Lon)
Maxwell, Edward : *Trumpet* (Lon)
Maxwell, Erik : *Saxophones* (NE)
Maxwell, Ian : *Guitars* (NE)
Maxwell, Melinda : *Oboe* (Lon)
Maxwell, Peter : *Guitars* (NE)
Maxwell, Vera : *Voice* (NE)
May, Andy : *Bodhran* (SW)
May, Brian : *Guitars* (Lon)
May, Charlotte : *Saxophones* (SW)
May, David : *Percussion* (Lon)
May, Dieselle : *Guitars* (Lon)
May, Elizabeth : *Flute* (SW)
May, Jack : *Pianoforte* (Lon)
May, Joanne : *Percussion* (Lon)
May, John : *Bass Guitar* (SE)
May, John : *Cello* (SW)
May, K : *Saxophones* (Lon)
May, Kaja : *Flute* (SW)
May, Kenneth : *Pianoforte* (SW)
May, Peter : *Percussion* (Lon)
May, Peter : *Accordion* (SE)
May, Rick : *Guitars* (Lon)
May, Simon : *Pianoforte* (Lon)
May, Steve : *Trumpet* (SW)
May, Tina : *Voice* (E)
Mayall, Arthur : *Pianoforte* (NE)
Mayall, Gaz : *Pianoforte* (Lon)
Maybank, Christopher : *Double Bass* (SE)
Maybey, Jon : *Guitars* (SW)
Maybury, Tess : *Bassoon* (Lon)
Maycock, Claire : *Flute* (Mid)
Maycock, Lee : *Keyboards* (SE)
Mayer, Gillian : *Violin* (Lon)
Mayer, John : *Violin* (Lon)
Mayer, Jonathan : *Sitar* (Lon)
Mayer, Michael : *Guitars* (Mid)
Mayer, Michael : *Clarinet* (SW)
Mayeras, Beatrice : *Percussion* (Lon)
Mayes, Jerry : *Accordion* (E)
Mayes, Joanna : *Pianoforte* (SW)
Mayes, Patricia : *Viola* (Lon)
Mayes, Paul : *Trumpet* (E)
Mayes, Paul : *Percussion* (Lon)
Mayes, Peter : *Violin* (Lon)
Mayes, Richard : *Guitars* (NW)
Mayfield, Big Al : *Voice* (Lon)
Mayger, Graham : *Flute* (Lon)
Mayger, Spencer : *Percussion* (Lon)
Mayhew, Judy : *Violin* (Lon)
Mayhew, Richard : *Trombone* (E)
Maynard, Andrew : *Banjo* (SE)
Maynard, Fergie : *Percussion* (Mid)
Maynard, Leslie : *Percussion* (SE)
Mayne, Caroline : *Percussion* (Lon)
Mayne, David Charles : *Percussion* (E)
Mayne, Helen : *Viola* (Mid)
Maynes, Malcolm : *Bass Guitar* (NE)
Mayo, Daren : *Guitars* (SE)
Mayo, Graham : *Conductor* (Mid)
Mayo, Graham : *Music Director* (Mid)
Mayo, Graham : *Pianoforte* (Mid)
Mayo, John : *Violin* (Lon)
Mayo, Sandra : *Pianoforte* (SW)
Mayor, Simon : *Violin* (SE)
Mays, Patsy : *Valve Trombone* (Lon)
Mays, Sally : *Pianoforte* (Lon)
Mayson, Jon : *Guitars* (NE)
Mazumder, Sonia : *Voice* (SE)
Mazzarini, Stefano : *Guitars* (Lon)
Mboob, Yusupha : *African Drums* (Mid)
Mc'Teagle : *Bass Guitar* (Lon)
MC, Suzy Q : *Voice* (Lon)

MC, Mc : *Rapper* (Lon)
MC Voyager : *Rapper* (Sco)
MC Weird : *Voice* (Lon)
McAlea, Kevin : *Keyboards* (Lon)
McAlindon, William : *Guitars* (Mid)
McAlister, Alison : *Violin* (NE)
McAllister, Andrew : *Percussion* (Sco)
McAllister, Colin : *Voice* (Sco)
McAllister, Kenneth : *Clarinet* (Lon)
McAllister, Kevin : *Trumpet* (E)
McAloon, Martin : *Guitars* (NE)
McAloon, Patrick : *Guitars* (NE)
McAlpine, Kenneth : *Keyboards* (Sco)
McAnaney, Tony : *Voice* (Lon)
McAndrew, Alex : *Bass Guitar* (Sco)
McAneney, Anne : *Trumpet* (Lon)
McArthur, Angus : *Guitars* (Lon)
McArthur, Gail : *Saxophones* (Sco)
McArthur, Neil : *Pianoforte* (Lon)
McArthur, Roy : *Percussion* (NE)
McAslan, Lorraine : *Violin* (Lon)
McAtominey, Aidan : *Tympani* (Lon)
McAuley, Brendan : *Pianoforte* (Lon)
McAuslan, Judith : *Violin* (Mid)
McB, Dan : *Saxophones* (Lon)
McBrain, Nicko : *Percussion* (Lon)
McBriarty, Jim : *Clarinet* (NE)
McBride, Prince : *Organ* (SE)
McBride, Sean : *Saxophones* (SW)
McCabe, Alec : *Guitars* (SE)
McCabe, Michelle : *Flute* (Sco)
McCabe, Raymond : *Percussion* (Sco)
McCafferty, Dan : *Voice* (Sco)
McCaffery, Lisa : *Keyboards* (Lon)
McCaffrey, Michael : *Guitars* (Lon)
McCague, Catherine : *Violin* (E)
McCalla, Subrina : *Voice* (Mid)
McCallum, David : *Trumpet* (Lon)
McCallum, Stuart : *Guitars* (NW)
McCammon, Cyril : *Pianoforte* (NE)
McCann, Ian : *Guitars* (Lon)
McCann, Ian : *Banjo* (NW)
McCann, Patrick : *Pianoforte* (Sco)
McCann, Phillip : *Cornet* (NE)
McCann, Thomas : *Tin Whistle* (Sco)
McCapra, Fiona : *Violin* (Lon)
McCarroll, Anthony : *Percussion* (NW)
McCarroll, Leonard : *Saxophones* (Lon)
McCarron, Monica : *Flute* (Lon)
McCarthy, Desmond : *Pianoforte* (SE)
McCarthy, Eileen : *Cello* (Lon)
McCarthy, Haydn : *Percussion* (SE)
McCarthy, Heather : *Pianoforte* (SW)
McCarthy, Jamie : *Recorders* (NW)
McCarthy, Juliet : *Cello* (Lon)
McCarthy, Ken : *Pianoforte* (Lon)
McCarthy, Kevin : *Synthesiser* (SE)
McCarthy, Martine : *Voice* (SW)
McCarthy, Patrick : *Trumpet* (Lon)
McCarthy, Patrick : *Guitars* (NE)
McCarthy, Paul : *Percussion* (Mid)
McCarthy, Peter : *Double Bass* (Lon)
McCarthy, Sinead : *Flute* (SE)
McCarthy, Susan : *Flute* (Lon)
McCaughern, Dan : *Guitars* (NE)
McCauley, Sean : *Pianoforte* (Sco)
McCauley, Shem : *Keyboards* (Lon)
McCausland, John : *Saxophones* (NW)
McCaw, John : *Clarinet* (Lon)
McCaw, Shirley : *Trombone* (Lon)
McChrystal, Gerard : *Saxophones* (Lon)
McClarnon, Elizabeth : *Voice* (NW)
McClean, James : *Guitars* (Mid)
McClean, Sidney : *Double Bass* (E)
McClenaghan, David : *Horn* (Sco)

McIntyre, W : *Violin* (NE)
McIver, Lesley : *Voice* (NW)
McIvor, Ian : *Guitars* (Sco)
McKay, Andrew : *Guitars* (NW)
McKay, Bob : *Saxophones* (Lon)
McKay, Elspeth : *Oboe* (Mid)
McKay, George : *Saxophones* (E)
McKay, James : *Trumpet* (Sco)
McKay, John : *Guitars* (Lon)
McKay, Patricia : *Clarinet* (Lon)
McKay, Paul : *Double Bass* (Sco)
McKean, Graeme : *Viola* (Lon)
McKean, Helen : *Oboe* (Lon)
McKee, David : *Bassoon* (E)
McKee, Eric : *Pianoforte* (Lon)
McKee, Susan : *Cello* (Lon)
McKell, Jane : *Voice* (SW)
McKelvay, David : *Viola* (SW)
McKelvie, Raymond : *Saxophones* (Sco)
McKendrick, Paul : *Voice* (NE)
McKenna, Hugh : *Oboe* (NW)
McKenna, Joe : *Saxophones* (E)
McKenna, Mae : *Voice* (Lon)
McKenna, Sophia : *Early Wind* (SW)
McKenzie, Adrian : *Percussion* (Lon)
McKenzie, Colin : *Horn* (Sco)
McKenzie, Derrick : *Percussion* (Lon)
McKenzie, Ian : *Percussion* (Lon)
McKenzie, James : *Accordion* (Sco)
McKenzie, Jock : *Trumpet* (SE)
McKenzie, Matthew : *Percussion* (E)
McKenzie, Mike : *Pianoforte* (Lon)
McKenzie, Owen : *Percussion* (SW)
McKenzie, Sheena : *Cello* (Lon)
McKenzie, Swanson : *Trumpet* (Sco)
McKeown, Bridget : *Violin* (NW)
McKerron, Charlie : *Folk Fiddle* (Sco)
McKew, Roger : *Guitars* (E)
McKibben, Ross : *Guitars* (Sco)
McKim, Stewart : *Double Bass* (SW)
McKinley, Sharon : *Cello* (Lon)
McKinley, Steven : *Keyboards* (NE)
McKinna, Iain : *Guitars* (Sco)
McKinna, Robert : *Bass Guitar* (Lon)
McKinney, Andrew : *Bass Guitar* (Lon)
McKinnon, Andrew : *Violin* (SW)
McKinnon, Bill : *Banjo* (SE)
McKone, Ernest : *Bass Guitar* (Lon)
McKreel, Andrew : *Tuba* (Sco)
McKrieth, Breeze : *Guitars* (Lon)
McKrieth, Jade : *Voice* (Lon)
McLaren, Andrew : *Percussion* (Lon)
McLaren, David : *Violin* (Lon)
McLaren, Jennifer : *Clarinet* (Lon)
McLaren, Julian : *Percussion* (Lon)
McLaren, Linda : *Violin* (Lon)
McLaren, Lorna : *Violin* (Sco)
McLaren, Malcolm : *Voice* (Lon)
McLaren, Neil : *Flute* (Lon)
McLaren, Nicol : *Accordion* (Sco)
McLaren, Nicol : *Bandleader* (Sco)
McLaren, Robert : *Bass Guitar* (SE)
McLarin, Lyn : *Flute* (SW)
McLaughlan, Anthony : *Bass Guitar* (E)
McLaughlin, Aileen : *Voice* (Lon)
McLaughlin, Dominic : *Guitars* (Sco)
McLaughlin, John : *James* (Guitars) (Sco)
McLaughlin, John : *Songwriter* (Sco)
McLaughlin, Larry : *Bass Guitar* (Lon)
McLaughlin, Mark : *Bass Trombone* (NW)
McLaughlin, Paul : *Voice* (Lon)
McLaughlin, William : *Bagpipes* (Sco)
McLay, Bruce : *Flute* (Lon)
McLean, Andy : *Saxophones* (Mid)
McLean, Benet : *Pianoforte* (Lon)

McLean, Beth : *Voice* (Lon)
McLean, Godfrey : *Percussion* (Lon)
McLean, Morris : *Arranger* (NW)
McLean, Pamela : *Voice* (Sco)
McLean, Philip : *Clarinet* (Sco)
McLean, Samuel : *Guitars* (Sco)
McLean, William : *Percussion* (Sco)
McLeish, Craig : *Conductor* (Lon)
McLellan, James : *Guitars* (Lon)
McLelland, George : *Saxophones* (Sco)
McLelland, Jock : *Guitars* (NE)
McLeod, Alex : *Guitars* (Mid)
McLeod, Callum : *Pianoforte* (Lon)
McLeod, David John : *Bass Guitar* (Lon)
McLeod, Iain : *Violin* (Lon)
McLeod, James : *Violin* (Lon)
McLeod, Mary : *Cello* (Lon)
McLeod, Rory : *Harmonica (Inc Bass* (Sco)
McLevy, Frank : *Percussion* (Sco)
McLevy, John : *Trumpet* (Lon)
McLocklan, Adam : *Bass Guitar* (NE)
McLoughlin, Diane : *Saxophones* (Lon)
McLoughlin, Rachel : *Horn* (Mid)
McLucas, James : *Highland Bagpipes* (Lon)
McMahon, Geraldine : *Voice* (E)
McMahon, John : *Saxophones* (Lon)
McMahon, Kevin : *Saxophones* (Lon)
McMahon, Martin : *Guitars* (NE)
McMahon, Robert : *Guitars* (Sco)
McMahon, Roy : *Guitars* (NW)
McMahon, Russell : *Oboe* (NW)
McManus, Christopher : *Pianoforte* (Lon)
McManus, John : *Bass Guitar* (Lon)
McManus, Steve : *Double Bass* (Lon)
McMaster, Bill : *Saxophones* (Sco)
McMaster, James : *Guitars* (Lon)
McMellon, Gregg : *Guitars* (Lon)
McMenemy, Michael : *Violin* (Lon)
McMillan, Alistair : *Voice* (Sco)
McMillan, Clare : *Oboe* (Lon)
McMillan, Ian : *Music Director* (Lon)
McMillan, Malcolm : *Clarinet* (Lon)
McMillan, Scott : *Keyboards* (Lon)
McMordie, Alistair : *Mandolin* (Sco)
McMurchie, Jacob : *Saxophones* (SW)
McMurdo, Craig : *Voice* (Sco)
McMurdo, Stewart : *Viola* (Sco)
McMurdo, Thomas : *Percussion* (Sco)
McMurray, Donald : *Percussion* (SE)
McMurtrie, Virginia : *Cello* (SE)
McNab, William : *Violin* (Sco)
McNally, James : *Whistle* (NE)
McNally, Jane : *Flute* (NW)
McNally, John : *Guitars* (NW)
McNamara, Rodney : *Percussion* (NE)
McNamee, Hugh : *Pianoforte* (Sco)
McNamee, John : *Bass Guitar* (SE)
McNamee-Healy, Cameron : *Percussion* (SE)
McNaught, Donald : *Violin* (SW)
McNaught, Paul : *Bass Guitar* (E)
McNaughton, D : *Saxophones* (Sco)
McNaughton, Duncan : *Trumpet* (Lon)
McNaughton, Elizabeth : *Voice* (SE)
McNaughton, Gavin : *Bassoon* (Lon)
McNeff, Stephen : *Composer* (Lon)
McNeice, Francis : *Bass Guitar* (NW)
McNeil, James : *Guitars* (Sco)
McNeil-Watson, Robert : *Keyboards* (E)
McNeill, Brian : *Violin* (Sco)
McNeill, David : *Keyboards* (E)
McNeish, Colin : *Bass Guitar* (Lon)
McNevin-Duff, Richard : *Guitars* (NW)
McNicholas, Steve : *Violin* (SE)
McNicol, Richard : *Flute* (Lon)
McNicoll, Keith : *Bass Trombone* (Lon)

McNicoll, Robert : *Pianoforte* (Lon)
McNiven, David : *Keyboards* (Sco)
McNulty, John : *Violin* (Mid)
McPhee, George : *Early Keyboards* (Sco)
McPhee, George : *Organ* (Sco)
McPherson, Andrew : *Guitars* (Sco)
McPherson, Caroline : *Voice* (Lon)
McPherson, John : *Bass Guitar* (Sco)
McPherson, Ken : *Bass Guitar* (NE)
McPherson, Kevin : *Pianoforte* (Lon)
McPike, Alan : *Keyboards* (Sco)
McQuaid, Stephen : *Guitars* (NE)
McQuater, Thomas : *Bass Guitar* (Lon)
McQuater, Thomas : *Trumpet* (Lon)
McQueen, David : *Bass Guitar* (NE)
McQueen, Helen : *Oboe* (Lon)
McQueen, Ross : *Trumpet* (Sco)
McQueen-Hunter, Douglas : *Voice* (Sco)
McRacken, Dave : *Keyboards* (Lon)
McRae, Colin : *Percussion* (Sco)
McRae, Ryan : *Guitars* (Sco)
McReynolds, Jacqueline : *Horn* (Lon)
McRiner, Raymond : *Guitars* (Lon)
McRobbie, Helen : *Voice* (SE)
McShane, Chris : *Tuba* (Lon)
McShee, Jacqui : *Voice* (SE)
McSweeney, Neil : *Guitars* (NE)
McSwiggan, Mark : *Guitars* (Sco)
McTell, Ralph : *Guitars* (Lon)
McTier, Duncan : *Double Bass* (Lon)
McTier, Ian : *Double Bass* (Sco)
Mculloch, Alan : *Percussion* (Lon)
McVay, Donald : *Viola* (Lon)
McVay, Ray : *Bandleader* (E)
McVeigh, Alice : *Cello* (Lon)
McVeigh, Simon : *Violin* (Lon)
McVey, Anthony : *Percussion* (Lon)
McVicar, Ewan : *Guitars* (Sco)
McVie, Ross : *Voice* (Sco)
McWhirter, Nicola : *Viola* (Sco)
McWilliam, Fiona : *Saxophones* (SW)
Meacham, John : *Bass Guitar* (SW)
Meacham, Kenneth : *Guitars* (SE)
Mead, Allan : *Horn* (SW)
Mead, David : *Guitars* (E)
Mead, Frank : *Saxophones* (Lon)
Mead, Jeff : *Guitars* (Lon)
Mead, Philip : *Pianoforte* (E)
Mead, Philip : *Pianoforte* (Lon)
Mead, Steve : *Guitars* (NW)
Mead, Steven : *Euphonium* (Mid)
Meade, Jenni : *Double Bass* (Sco)
Meade, Lennox : *Bass Guitar* (Lon)
Meade, Leonard : *Pianoforte* (Lon)
Meader, Rosemary : *Violin* (Lon)
Meadows, Alex : *Bass Guitar* (Lon)
Meadows, Anna : *Bassoon* (Lon)
Meadows, Colin : *Banjo* (Lon)
Meadows, Gabrielle : *Flute* (E)
Meadows, John : *Clarinet* (Mid)
Meakin, James : *Guitars* (NW)
Mealey, Maria : *Bassoon* (Mid)
Mealing, John : *Pianoforte* (Lon)
Meare, Annabelle : *Violin* (SW)
Mearns, Stella : *Pianoforte* (SE)
Mears, Andy : *Saxophones* (NE)
Measures, Ann : *Violin* (Lon)
Medboe, Haftor : *Guitars* (Sco)
Medcalf, Victoria : *Clarinet* (Lon)
Meddemmen, Brian : *Cello* (Lon)
Medford, Paul J : *Voice* (Lon)
Medhurst, Trevor : *Bass Guitar* (Lon)
Medland, Gerald : *Trombone* (SW)
Medlock, Colin : *Guitars* (E)
Medlock, Johnny : *Organ* (Mid)

Medrow, Alan : *Viola* (Lon)
Medrow, Elizabeth : *Javanese Gamelan* (Lon)
Medwin, Steven : *Bass Guitar* (Lon)
Mee : *Electric Violin* (Lon)
Mee, William : *Bass Trombone* (Lon)
Meecham, Jon : *Horn* (Lon)
Meehan, Jeremy : *Bass Guitar* (Lon)
Meehan, Paul : *Keyboards* (Lon)
Meek, Jessica : *Voice* (Mid)
Meek, John : *Viola* (Lon)
Meekums, Gary : *Percussion* (Lon)
Meggeson, David : *Guitars* (SW)
Meggido, Marc : *Double Bass* (Lon)
Mehta, Vikesh : *Synthesiser* (Lon)
Mei Ling, Fiesta : *Copyist* (Lon)
Meier, Patrizia : *Harp* (Lon)
Meiklejohn, Philip : *Horn* (NW)
Meinardi, Charles : *Violin* (Lon)
Meister, Martin : *Voice* (Lon)
Mekkaoui, Abdellatif : *Percussion* (NE)
Melbourne, Andrew : *Trombone* (SE)
Melbourne, Carrie : *Bass Guitar* (Lon)
Melbourne, John : *Percussion* (NW)
Meldrum, Raymond : *Guitars* (Sco)
Melhuish, Laura : *Violin* (Lon)
Melhus, Marianne : *Voice* (Lon)
Melia, Roland : *Conductor* (Lon)
Melius, Perry : *Percussion* (Lon)
Mellanby, Ian : *Bass Guitar* (Mid)
Melleck, Lydia : *Pianoforte* (Lon)
Meller, Mark : *Voice* (Lon)
Mellers, Neil : *Percussion* (SE)
Melliard, David : *Viola* (Lon)
Melling, Steve : *Pianoforte* (Lon)
Mellish, Margaret : *Accordion* (Sco)
Mellor, Brian : *Banjo* (Mid)
Mellor, Clare : *Flute* (Lon)
Mellor, David : *Music Director* (Lon)
Mellor, David : *Percussion* (Mid)
Mellor, Eric : *Double Bass* (SE)
Mellor, John : *Oboe* (NE)
Mellor, John : *Clarinet* (NW)
Mellor, Jon : *Bass Guitar* (Lon)
Mellor, Judith : *Flute* (NE)
Mellor, Martyn : *Guitars* (Mid)
Mellor, Nicholas : *Guitars* (NW)
Mellor, Steve : *Clarinet* (Mid)
Mellors, Katie : *Pianoforte* (SE)
Melly, Alan : *Saxophones* (SE)
Melly, George : *Voice* (Lon)
Melo.D : *Voice* (Lon)
Melody : *Keyboards* (Lon)
Melody, Mr. : *Voice* (Lon)
Melone : *Voice* (Lon)
Meloney, Sheron : *Violin* (NW)
Meloy, Laure : *Voice* (E)
Meloy, Stephen : *Keyboards* (Lon)
Melrose, Robert : *Guitars* (Lon)
Melrose, Thomas : *Percussion* (Lon)
Meltdown (Nick) : *Keyboards* (Lon)
Melville, Charles : *Pianoforte* (Lon)
Melville, Clarissa : *Flute* (Lon)
Melville, Elizabeth : *Violin* (Lon)
Melville, Thomas : *Saxophones* (NW)
Melvin, Rieke : *Pianoforte* (Lon)
Melvin, Rod : *Pianoforte* (Lon)
Menday, Rebecca : *Bassoon* (Lon)
Mendelssohn, Cecily : *Violin* (Lon)
Mendes, Galina : *Recorders* (SE)
Mendham, Tracey : *Saxophones* (Lon)
Mendonca, Maria : *Javanese Gamelan* (Lon)
Mendoza, Rod : *Pianoforte* (Lon)
Mendoza-Moreno, Alonso : *Percussion* (Lon)
Mennim, Robert : *Percussion* (SW)
Menter, Ian : *Saxophones* (SW)

Menter, Sam : *Keyboards* (SW)
Menzies, Laura : *Voice* (Sco)
Menzies, Stephen : *Voice* (NW)
Mepham, Rachel : *Clarinet* (Lon)
Mera, Nick : *Pianoforte* (E)
Meraviglia, Manfredo : *Composer* (Lon)
Mercel, Dave The Fly : *Percussion* (E)
Mercel, Robert : *Bass Guitar* (E)
Mercer, Frederick : *Bandleader* (Mid)
Mercer, Frederick : *Trombone* (Mid)
Mercer, James : *Bass Guitar* (Lon)
Mercer, Jean : *Trumpet* (Lon)
Mercer, Kas : *Guitars* (Lon)
Mercy, Philip : *Guitars* (SE)
Meredith, Allan : *Saxophones* (SW)
Meredith, Bill : *Pianoforte* (E)
Meredith, Daniel : *Clarinet* (Mid)
Meredith, David : *Pianoforte* (Mid)
Meredith, Martin : *Saxophones* (Mid)
Meredith, Nicholas : *Violin* (NE)
Meredith, Rachel : *Violin* (NE)
Meredith, Rod : *Guitars* (NE)
Meredith, Simon : *Saxophones* (Mid)
Merlo, Rinaldo : *Guitars* (Lon)
Mernick, Nick : *Violin* (Lon)
Merrell, Crispin : *Keyboards* (Lon)
Merrett, Peter : *Percussion* (SW)
Merrett, Steve : *Guitars* (NE)
Merrick, Alan : *Violin* (Lon)
Merrick, Linda : *Clarinet* (Lon)
Merrick, Stephen : *Accordion* (Lon)
Merritt, Albert : *Percussion* (Lon)
Merritt, George : *Percussion* (Sco)
Merry, Maurice : *Pianoforte* (Lon)
Merry, Michael : *Pianoforte* (Lon)
Merry, Peter : *Horn* (Lon)
Merry, Ronald : *Percussion* (Mid)
Merry, Simon : *Percussion* (Lon)
Merryweather, James : *Early Renaissance* (NE)
Merryweather, Michael : *Bassoon* (SW)
Merson, Stephen : *Violin* (Lon)
Mersonjones, Diane : *Violin* (Sco)
Merv : *Percussion* (Mid)
Messeder, Andre : *Double Bass* (Lon)
Messenger, Mark : *Violin* (E)
Messenger, Roger : *Trombone* (Lon)
Messent, Henry : *Flute* (Lon)
Messianist, Mashal : *Keyboards* (Lon)
Metcalfe, Bridget : *Voice* (Lon)
Metcalfe, Hugh : *Guitars* (Lon)
Metcalfe, Jane : *Viola* (Lon)
Metcalfe, Jeremy : *Violin* (Lon)
Metcalfe, John : *Viola* (NW)
Methven, David : *Bagpipes* (Sco)
Metliss, Jeremy : *Pianoforte* (Lon)
Metz, Dominique : *Percussion* (Lon)
Meuross, Reg : *Voice* (SW)
Mex, Paul : *Guitars* (E)
Meyer, Anne-Isabel : *Cello* (Lon)
Meyer, Daniel : *Violin* (Lon)
Meyer, Gloria : *Violin* (SE)
Meyer, Maurice : *Violin* (Lon)
Meyer, Richard : *Percussion* (NW)
Meylan, Pauline : *Voice* (SW)
Meynell, Anthony : *Guitars* (Lon)
Meyrick, Morfydd : *Viola* (SW)
Meyrick, Robert : *Guitars* (Mid)
Mezulis, Peter : *Percussion* (Mid)
Mhoireach, Anna : *Voice* (Sco)
Mian, David : *Trumpet* (Lon)
Micah, Paul : *Saxophones* (Lon)
Michael : *Voice* (Lon)
Michael, Darren : *Percussion* (Lon)
Michael, Donna : *Voice* (Lon)
Michael, Kelsey : *Voice* (Lon)

Michael, Philip : *Percussion* (SW)
Michaels, Christine : *Voice* (Lon)
Michaels, Mia : *Voice* (Lon)
Michaels, Shaun : *Voice* (SW)
Michaelson, Nicholas : *Guitars* (Lon)
Michalak, Kazimierz : *Early Strings* (Lon)
Michalisles, George : *Voice* (Lon)
Michel, Hilary : *Voice* (Lon)
Michell, Chris : *Flute* (SW)
Michelle-Jo : *Keyboards* (SW)
Michelmore, Guy : *Keyboards* (Lon)
Micklem, Henry : *Oboe* (Sco)
Middle East Music Org : *Oriental Drums* (Lon)
Middle East Music Org : *Percussion* (Lon)
Middleton, Brian : *Percussion* (Mid)
Middleton, John : *Composer* (Lon)
Middleton, Julia : *Saxophones* (SE)
Middleton, Kathleen : *Pianoforte* (Lon)
Middleton, Malcolm : *Guitars* (Sco)
Middleton, Max : *Pianoforte* (Lon)
Middleton, Nigel : *Violin* (NE)
Middleton, Paul : *Keyboards* (NE)
Middleton, Tracey : *Accordion* (Mid)
Middleton-Pollock, Marilyn : *Guitars* (NW)
Midgley, Cynthia : *Viola* (Sco)
Midgley, Robb : *Percussion* (Sco)
Midus : *Bass Guitar* (Lon)
Miekautsch, Dieter : *Pianoforte* (Lon)
Mighty Bijou : *Voice* (SW)
Mihajlovic, Dusan : *Guitars* (Lon)
Mike-E : *Guitars* (Lon)
Milan, Susan : *Flute* (Lon)
Milbourn, Gwenda : *Cello* (Lon)
Milburn, Douglas : *Double Bass* (NE)
Mildred, James : *Horn* (Sco)
Miles, Bethan : *Viola* (NW)
Miles, Claire : *Cello* (Lon)
Miles, David : *Bassoon* (Lon)
Miles, David : *Double Bass* (Lon)
Miles, Debbie : *Voice* (Mid)
Miles, George : *Accordion* (E)
Miles, Gillian : *Oboe* (E)
Miles, Jacqueline : *Violin* (Lon)
Miles, James : *Keyboards* (SW)
Miles, John : *Voice* (Lon)
Miles, John : *Pianoforte* (NW)
Miles, Kevin : *Bass Guitar* (Lon)
Miles, Matthew : *Double Bass* (NW)
Miles, Peter : *Voice* (Lon)
Miles, Raymond : *Pianoforte* (SE)
Miles, Rebecca : *Early Strings* (Lon)
Miles, Terry : *Pianoforte* (Lon)
Miles, Tom : *Pianoforte* (Lon)
Miletic, Dragan : *Accordion* (Lon)
Milford, Gareth : *Keyboards* (SW)
Milgate, Ken : *Voice* (NE)
Milholland, Joanna : *Cello* (Lon)
Mill, Gary : *Guitars* (Sco)
Mill, Sean : *Guitars* (NE)
Millar, Catherine : *Bassoon* (SE)
Millar, Cynthia : *Ondes Martenot* (Lon)
Millar, Deborah : *Guitars* (SE)
Millar, Duncan : *Pianoforte* (Lon)
Millar, Gus : *Percussion* (Sco)
Millar, Ian : *Saxophones* (Sco)
Millar, Jhalib : *Berimbau* (Lon)
Millar, Jhalib : *Djembe* (Lon)
Millar, Jhalib : *Indian Percussion* (Lon)
Millar, Jhalib : *Jaw's Harp* (Lon)
Millar, Jhalib : *Tabla* (Lon)
Millar, Phil : *Pianoforte* (NW)
Millar, Robin : *Guitars* (Lon)
Millar, Thomas : *Double Bass* (Mid)
Millar, Tom : *Keyboards* (Sco)
Millard, James : *Clarinet* (Lon)

Morgan, Paul : *Double Bass* (Lon)
Morgan, Pete : *Double Bass* (Lon)
Morgan, Peter : *Double Bass* (Lon)
Morgan, Peter : *Violin* (SE)
Morgan, Philippa : *Early Strings* (SW)
Morgan, Sarah : *Clarinet* (SE)
Morgan, Sian : *Bassoon* (SW)
Morgan, Simon : *Horn* (Lon)
Morgan, Steven : *Pianoforte* (Lon)
Morgan, Stewart : *Guitars* (Mid)
Morgan, Terry : *Double Bass* (SW)
Morgan, Thomas : *Pianoforte* (Lon)
Morgan, Tomas : *Violin* (Lon)
Morgan, Tudur : *Guitars* (NW)
Morgan, Veronica : *Horn* (NW)
Morgan-Williams, Ian : *Composer* (NW)
Morgans, Avril : *Clarinet* (Lon)
Morgans, Kathleen : *Violin* (NW)
Morgenstern, Julian : *Pianoforte* (Lon)
Moriah, Anthony : *Guitars* (Lon)
Moriarty, Dean : *Violin* (Lon)
Moriarty, James : *Pianoforte* (Lon)
Moris, Ed : *Organ* (Lon)
Morison, George : *Bass Guitar* (Sco)
Morland, Mig : *Percussion* (Lon)
Morley, Angela : *Composer* (Lon)
Morley, Christopher : *Horn* (NW)
Morley, Helen : *Voice* (SW)
Morley, Jeanette : *Pianoforte* (Mid)
Morley, Jeffrey : *Percussion* (SW)
Morley, Joanna : *Violin* (Lon)
Morley, John : *Guitars* (SE)
Morley, Joseph : *Pianoforte* (Lon)
Morley, Luke : *Guitars* (Lon)
Morley, Paul : *Guitars* (Mid)
Morley, Sarah : *Harp* (Lon)
Morley, Sarah : *Violin* (NW)
Morley, Wayne : *Copyist* (Lon)
Moroney, Helena : *Violin* (Sco)
Morph : *Guitars* (Sco)
Morphett, Catherine : *Clarinet* (Lon)
Morphew, Leonard : *Saxophones* (SE)
Morrell, Alfred : *Trombone* (Mid)
Morrell, Dane : *Percussion* (NE)
Morrell, Joanne : *Bassoon* (Lon)
Morrell, Kenneth : *Pianoforte* (NE)
Morrell, Rachael : *Voice* (Mid)
Morrell, Rebecca : *Pianoforte* (Mid)
Morrell, Tom : *Keyboards* (SE)
Morrice, Binky : *Percussion* (Lon)
Morrice, Dave : *Violin* (Sco)
Morrice, James : *Saxophones* (Sco)
Morris, Alan : *Violin* (SW)
Morris, Andrea : *Violin* (E)
Morris, Andrea : *Saxophones* (Lon)
Morris, Andrew : *Trumpet* (NW)
Morris, Andrew : *Violin* (Sco)
Morris, Andrew : *Saxophones* (SE)
Morris, Anne : *Cello* (NE)
Morris, Annette : *Voice* (NE)
Morris, Bension : *Organ* (Lon)
Morris, Brian : *Guitars* (Sco)
Morris, Catherine : *Viola* (NE)
Morris, Darren : *Pianoforte* (Lon)
Morris, David : *Percussion* (Lon)
Morris, David : *Guitars* (SE)
Morris, David : *Percussion* (SE)
Morris, David Lyle : *Voice* (Lon)
Morris, Edmund : *Double Bass* (Lon)
Morris, Edna : *Pianoforte* (NE)
Morris, Frank : *Double Bass* (SW)
Morris, Geoffrey : *Percussion* (Lon)
Morris, Gwyn : *Cello* (SW)
Morris, Hal : *Percussion* (SW)
Morris, Harvey : *Pianoforte* (NW)

Morris, Hayley : *Voice* (Lon)
Morris, Isobel : *Voice* (Lon)
Morris, James : *Sousaphone* (NW)
Morris, Jeremy : *Violin* (Lon)
Morris, John : *Keyboards* (NW)
Morris, John : *Pianoforte* (SE)
Morris, Keith : *Saxophones* (NE)
Morris, Lesley : *Voice* (SE)
Morris, Lucy : *Violin* (NW)
Morris, Manon : *Harp* (NW)
Morris, Margaret : *Pianoforte* (SW)
Morris, Martin : *Voice* (Lon)
Morris, Michael : *Double Bass* (SW)
Morris, Mo : *Electric Violin* (Lon)
Morris, Patricia : *Flute* (Lon)
Morris, Paulette : *Voice* (NE)
Morris, Pee Wee : *Percussion* (Lon)
Morris, Peter : *Double Bass* (E)
Morris, Peter : *Guitars* (Lon)
Morris, Peter : *Horn* (Mid)
Morris, Philip : *Trumpet* (SW)
Morris, Philip : *Trumpet* (SW)
Morris, Rex : *Saxophones* (Lon)
Morris, Ronald : *Saxophones* (SW)
Morris, Sarah : *Voice* (Lon)
Morris, Simon : *Cello* (Lon)
Morris, Sonny : *Trumpet* (Lon)
Morris, Stephen : *Violin* (Lon)
Morris, Stephen : *Percussion* (NW)
Morris, Steve : *Clarinet* (Lon)
Morris, Stewart : *Trumpet* (Mid)
Morris, Tim : *Percussion* (SE)
Morris, Victor : *Pianoforte* (Lon)
Morris-Jones, Catrin : *Harp* (Lon)
Morrish, Stephen : *Pianoforte* (SE)
Morrison, Aileen : *Viola* (Mid)
Morrison, Alan : *Trumpet* (NE)
Morrison, Anne : *Viola* (Lon)
Morrison, Arthur : *Trumpet* (NE)
Morrison, Barry : *Guitars* (Lon)
Morrison, Chas : *Percussion* (NW)
Morrison, Clifton : *Keyboards* (Lon)
Morrison, Daniel : *Guitars* (Mid)
Morrison, Dom : *Bass Guitar* (NW)
Morrison, Fergus : *Clarinet* (Lon)
Morrison, Fred : *Highland Bagpipes* (Sco)
Morrison, Gary : *Guitars* (Lon)
Morrison, Gavin : *Flute* (Lon)
Morrison, Ian : *Guitars* (Lon)
Morrison, James : *Violin* (Lon)
Morrison, James : *Guitars* (NW)
Morrison, Joan : *Horn* (Sco)
Morrison, Joe : *Violin* (Lon)
Morrison, John : *Trombone* (Mid)
Morrison, John : *Trumpet* (NE)
Morrison, Julie : *Voice* (Lon)
Morrison, Kirsten : *Violin* (Lon)
Morrison, Lynn : *Keyboards* (Sco)
Morrison, Rob : *Bass Guitar* (NW)
Morrison, Ronald : *Pianoforte* (Sco)
Morrison, Terrence : *Clarinet* (NE)
Morrison, Tom : *Voice* (NE)
Morrison, Van : *Guitars* (Lon)
Morrison, Will : *Percussion* (Lon)
Morriss, Peter : *Percussion* (Lon)
Morrissey, Clare : *Viola* (NW)
Morrissey, Dick : *Saxophones* (Lon)
Morrow, Alastair : *Percussion* (Lon)
Morrow, Chris : *Percussion* (Sco)
Morrow, Geoffrey : *Pianoforte* (Lon)
Morrow, Tony : *Guitars* (Lon)
Morse, Jane : *Violin* (SW)
Morsley, Austin : *Keyboards* (E)
Morson, Winston : *Guitars* (Lon)
Morter, Thomas : *Cello* (SE)

Mortimer, Anthony : *Pianoforte* (E)
Mortimer, Neville : *Violin* (NE)
Mortimer, Timothy : *Guitars* (Lon)
Mortimore, Bob : *Guitars* (Lon)
Mortimore, Cyril : *Pianoforte* (Mid)
Mortimore, Darren : *Percussion* (SW)
Mortimore, Malcolm : *Percussion* (SE)
Mortimore, Mick : *Double Bass* (Lon)
Morton, Adrian : *Trumpet* (SW)
Morton, Amanda : *Horn* (SW)
Morton, Charles : *Voice* (Lon)
Morton, Claire : *Cello* (Sco)
Morton, Clive : *Double Bass* (SW)
Morton, Greg : *Cello* (NW)
Morton, Ian : *Percussion* (Lon)
Morton, James : *Saxophones* (SW)
Morton, John : *Pianoforte* (Mid)
Morton, John : *Voice* (NE)
Morton, Jonathan : *Violin* (Lon)
Morton, Robin : *Concertina (Inc Engl* (Sco)
Morton, Simon : *Percussion* (Lon)
Morton, Simon : *Keyboards* (SW)
Morton, William : *Flute* (Lon)
Morton-Smith, Emma : *Voice* (NW)
Morwood, Michael : *Pianoforte* (Lon)
Morykit, Dmytro : *Composer* (Sco)
Morys, Melbourn : *Saxophones* (E)
Mosaic : *Voice* (Mid)
Mosby, Paul : *Oboe* (Lon)
Moscrop Young, Ann : *Cello* (NE)
Moseley, David : *Flute* (NE)
Moseley, Dexter : *Voice* (SE)
Moseley, Ian : *Trombone* (Mid)
Moseley, Margaret : *Violin* (NE)
Moser, Peter : *One Man Band* (NW)
Moses, David : *Double Bass* (Lon)
Moses, Jake : *Trombone* (Lon)
Moses, Jamie : *Guitars* (Lon)
Mosley, Anna : *Guitars* (NE)
Mosley, David : *Guitars* (NE)
Mosley, Janet : *Guitars* (SW)
Mosley, Kathryn : *Pianoforte* (Lon)
Mosley, Mark : *Trumpet* (NW)
Mosley, Paul : *Voice* (Lon)
Mosley, Raymond : *Violin* (Lon)
Mosonyi, Pierre : *Pianoforte* (Lon)
Mosquera, Luisito : *Voice* (Lon)
Moss, Dennis : *Guitars* (Lon)
Moss, John : *Voice* (Lon)
Moss, Martin : *Guitars* (SW)
Moss, Nicholas : *Saxophones* (Lon)
Moss, Paul : *Saxophones* (Lon)
Moss, Peter : *Guitars* (Lon)
Moss, Phil : *Trumpet* (NW)
Moss, Rachel : *Early Wind* (Lon)
Moss, Susan : *Clarinet* (SW)
Moss Tallon, Sally-Anne : *Voice* (SE)
Mossman, Jenny : *Clarinet* (Sco)
Mossop, Sue : *Mandolin* (Lon)
Motion, David : *Composer* (Lon)
Mottley, Susan : *Voice* (Lon)
Mottram, Julian : *Viola* (NW)
Mottram, Paul : *Composer* (Lon)
Mouat, W : *Bass Guitar* (Sco)
Mould, Cheryl : *Violin* (SE)
Mould, Kelvin : *Voice* (Mid)
Mould, Sidney : *Saxophones* (NE)
Moulding, Colin : *Bass Guitar* (SW)
Moulding, Kenneth : *Percussion* (E)
Moule, Frank : *Vibraphone* (Lon)
Moule, Graham : *Violin* (NE)
Moule, Sarah : *Voice* (Lon)
Moulsher, John : *Percussion* (Mid)
Moulton, Duncan : *Cello* (Lon)
Moulton, Sally : *Saxophones* (E)

Mount, Rodney : *Oboe* (Sco)
Mountain, January : *Viola* (SW)
Mountain, Paul : *Violin* (NE)
Mountain, Peter : *Violin* (NE)
Mounter, Michael : *Trumpet* (SE)
Mountford, John : *Percussion* (Mid)
Mourant, Paul : *Trumpet* (Lon)
Mousdale : *Percussion* (Sco)
Mouthfull, Mike : *Bass Guitar* (Lon)
Mowat, Andrew : *Keyboards* (Lon)
Mowat, Arthur : *Bandleader* (NE)
Mowat, Arthur : *Saxophones* (NE)
Mowat, Christopher : *Trombone* (Lon)
Mowat, David : *Trumpet* (SW)
Mowat, William : *Keyboards* (Lon)
Mowatt, Dennis : *Banjo* (Mid)
Mowatt, Roy : *Violin* (Lon)
Mower, Michael : *Saxophones* (Lon)
Mowlem, Matt : *Bass Guitar* (SE)
Moxham, David : *Guitars* (Lon)
Moxom, Nigel : *Pianoforte* (Lon)
Moxon, Andrew : *Horn* (Lon)
Moxon, Peter : *Trumpet* (Lon)
Moxon-Browne, Kicki : *Pianoforte* (Lon)
Moy, Kathleen : *Flute* (Lon)
Moy, Norman : *Saxophones* (Sco)
Moyes, Brian : *Violin* (Lon)
Moyes, Crawford : *Saxophones* (Lon)
Moyes, Darren : *Percussion* (Sco)
Moyet, Alison : *Voice* (Lon)
Moylan, Paul : *Double Bass* (Lon)
Moyo, Thomas : *Percussion* (Lon)
Moyse, Nigel : *Guitars* (Lon)
Moyse, Stephen : *Guitars* (Lon)
Mozart, Amadeus : *Keyboards* (Mid)
Mozzer : *Percussion* (Mid)
Mr D : *Pianoforte* (SE)
Mr Nutty : *Saxophones* (Lon)
Mr Talkative : *Voice* (NE)
Mtungwazi, Eska : *Voice* (Lon)
Mudeka, Anna : *Voice* (E)
Mudele, Joseph : *Double Bass* (Lon)
Mudge, Bill : *Pianoforte* (SE)
Muende, Paul : *Pianoforte* (Lon)
Muffett, Nicola : *Voice* (Lon)
Muggleton, Paul : *Guitars* (Lon)
Muir, Ian : *Accordion* (Sco)
Muir, James : *Pianoforte* (Sco)
Muir, Kenneth : *Guitars* (NE)
Muir, Peter : *Pianoforte* (Lon)
Muir, Susan : *Violin* (Sco)
Muirhead, Iain : *Trumpet* (Sco)
Muirhead, James : *Clarinet* (NW)
Mukherjee, Omith : *Guitars* (NE)
Mukherjee, Rudro : *Guitars* (NW)
Mulcahy, Beth : *Clarinet* (SW)
Mulcaster, Simon : *Guitars* (NW)
Mulder, Berend : *Viola* (Lon)
Muldoon, Joseph : *Guitars* (Mid)
Muldoon, Wilbur : *Guitars* (NE)
Muldoon, Zechariah : *Violin* (NE)
Mulford, Phillip : *Bass Guitar* (Lon)
Mulford, Robert : *Guitars* (Lon)
Mulhair, Paul : *Guitars* (Lon)
Mulhearn, Richard : *Saxophones* (NW)
Mulholland, Gregory : *Voice* (NW)
Mullan, Brian : *Cello* (Lon)
Mullarkey, Robin : *Guitars* (Lon)
Mullen, James : *Guitars* (Lon)
Mullen, Larry : *Percussion* (Lon)
Mullen, Mary : *Voice* (Lon)
Mullett, Cristobal : *Guitars* (Lon)
Mulley, Mark John : *Trombone* (Lon)
Mulligan, Hazel : *Violin* (Lon)
Mulligan, Steve : *Saxophones* (Lon)

Mullin, Daniel : *Violin* (Lon)
Mullin, Tim : *Percussion* (NW)
Mullineaux, Timothy : *Guitars* (Lon)
Mullings, Victor : *Pianoforte* (Mid)
Mullins, Andrew : *Pianoforte* (NE)
Mullins, Darrin : *Guitars* (Lon)
Mullon, Benjamin : *Guitars* (Lon)
Mulrain, Gordon : *Bass Guitar* (E)
Mulrine, Jonathan : *Bass Guitar* (Sco)
Mulvaney, Liam : *Guitars* (Lon)
Mulvey, St : *Bass Guitar* (Lon)
Muncey, Catherine : *Violin* (NW)
Muncey, Ian : *Trumpet* (E)
Muncey, Richard : *Viola* (NW)
Munday, David : *Guitars* (Lon)
Munday, Jason : *Clarinet* (Lon)
Munday, John : *Keyboards* (NE)
Munday, Ray : *Early Wind* (Sco)
Munday, Ray : *Trumpet* (Sco)
Munday, Terence : *Guitars* (Lon)
Munden, Dave : *Percussion* (Lon)
Munden, David : *Trumpet* (Lon)
Mundie, Gordon : *Trumpet* (Sco)
Mundy, Mary : *Cello* (Lon)
Munisamy, Nigel : *Horn* (SW)
Munks, Pamela : *Violin* (E)
Munn, Billy : *Music Director* (Lon)
Munn, Julia : *Clarinet* (Lon)
Munnery, Paul : *Trombone* (Mid)
Munns, Heather : *Voice* (SE)
Munns, Roger : *Keyboards* (Lon)
Munoz, Carlos : *Charango* (Mid)
Munoz, David : *Pianoforte* (NE)
Munoz, Fernando : *Charango* (Lon)
Munoz, Luis : *Keyboards* (E)
Munro, Anna Marie : *Pianoforte* (NW)
Munro, Charles : *Guitars* (Lon)
Munro, David : *Double Bass* (NE)
Munro, Donnie : *Guitars* (Sco)
Munro, Gavin : *Guitars* (Sco)
Munro, Julian : *Bassoon* (Sco)
Munro, Margaret : *Violin* (SW)
Munro, Stuart : *Percussion* (Sco)
Munsch, Melanie-Jane : *Clarinet* (SE)
Muntiz, Bae : *Guitars* (Lon)
Muotune, Jim : *Pianoforte* (Sco)
Muraldo, Caroline : *Voice* (Lon)
Muranyi, George : *Keyboards* (Lon)
Murcott, Dominic : *Percussion* (Lon)
Murden, Norman : *Organ* (NE)
Murdin, Geoffrey : *Cello* (NW)
Murdoch, Cameron : *Pianoforte* (Sco)
Murdoch, Donald : *Accordion* (Sco)
Murdoch, James : *Voice* (Sco)
Murdoch, Stuart : *Bass Guitar* (Sco)
Murfin, Muff : *Percussion* (Mid)
Murfin, Paul : *Percussion* (Mid)
Murgatroyd, John : *Voice* (Lon)
Muriel, Linda : *Voice* (Lon)
Murphy, Anthony : *Guitars* (Lon)
Murphy, Anthony : *Guitars* (NW)
Murphy, Arran : *Percussion* (Lon)
Murphy, Aubrey : *Violin* (Lon)
Murphy, Barrie : *Guitars* (SW)
Murphy, Dale : *Voice* (NW)
Murphy, David : *Viola* (E)
Murphy, Geoffrey : *Saxophones* (SW)
Murphy, Gerald : *Guitars* (NW)
Murphy, Gordon : *Saxophones* (Lon)
Murphy, Graham : *Keyboards* (Lon)
Murphy, Graham : *Guitars* (SE)
Murphy, Joe : *Accordion* (Lon)
Murphy, John : *Keyboards* (E)
Murphy, John : *Viola* (Lon)
Murphy, John : *Flute* (SE)

Murphy, Julie : *Voice* (SW)
Murphy, Kevin : *Clarinet* (Lon)
Murphy, Kim : *Bassoon* (Lon)
Murphy, Lisa : *Voice* (Lon)
Murphy, Malcolm : *Percussion* (Lon)
Murphy, Marianne : *Voice* (Sco)
Murphy, Maurice : *Trumpet* (Lon)
Murphy, Michael : *Pianoforte* (E)
Murphy, Michael : *Pianoforte* (Mid)
Murphy, Paul : *Guitars* (Mid)
Murphy, Richard : *Guitars* (NW)
Murphy, Robert : *Bagpipes* (Lon)
Murphy, Sarah : *Flute* (Lon)
Murphy, Thomas : *Violin* (Sco)
Murphy, Tracy : *Percussion* (NW)
Murphy, William : *Accordion* (Lon)
Murray, Andrew : *Pianoforte* (SW)
Murray, Andy : *Guitars* (Sco)
Murray, Ben : *Accordion* (NW)
Murray, David : *Guitars* (Lon)
Murray, David : *Pianoforte* (NE)
Murray, David : *Violin* (SW)
Murray, Donald : *Percussion* (NE)
Murray, Geraldine : *Banjo* (SW)
Murray, Gerry : *Trumpet* (Lon)
Murray, Gillian : *Viola* (Lon)
Murray, Glynn : *Bass Guitar* (Mid)
Murray, Holly : *Percussion* (SE)
Murray, Ian : *Mandolin* (Sco)
Murray, Ian : *Percussion* (Sco)
Murray, James : *Guitars* (Lon)
Murray, Jane : *Voice* (NW)
Murray, Jean : *Flute* (Sco)
Murray, John : *Saxophones* (E)
Murray, John : *Guitars* (NW)
Murray, John : *Voice* (Sco)
Murray, John : *Keyboards* (SW)
Murray, Kevin : *Guitars* (Sco)
Murray, Kieran : *Bass Guitar* (Sco)
Murray, Mark : *Bass Guitar* (Sco)
Murray, Michael : *Horn* (Lon)
Murray, Michael : *Clarinet* (SE)
Murray, Neil : *Bass Guitar* (Lon)
Murray, Neville : *Latin American Percu* (Lon)
Murray, Noel : *Saxophones* (Lon)
Murray, Paul : *Guitars* (NW)
Murray, Pete : *Guitars* (Lon)
Murray, Peter : *Bass Guitar* (Lon)
Murray, Peter : *Pianoforte* (Lon)
Murray, Peter : *Pianoforte* (Lon)
Murray, Rona : *Violin* (Lon)
Murray, Sarah : *Viola* (SW)
Murray, Simon : *Percussion* (Lon)
Murray, Simon J : *Music Director* (Lon)
Murray, Steven : *Bass Guitar* (SE)
Murrell, David : *Guitars* (SE)
Murrell, Trevor : *Percussion* (Lon)
Murricane, David : *Composer* (Sco)
Murrill, Jayne : *Trombone* (Lon)
Murrison, Jimmy : *Guitars* (Sco)
Murtagh, Andrew : *Pianoforte* (Mid)
Murthwaite, Carol : *Violin* (NE)
Musaji, Sabir : *Guitars* (NW)
Musgrave, Gerard : *Bass Guitar* (NE)
Musgrave, Jonathan : *Keyboards* (NW)
Mushroom : *Voice* (Lon)
Musikant, Jack : *Violin* (Lon)
Musk, David : *Natural Trumpet* (Lon)
Musker, Catherine : *Viola* (Lon)
Muskett, John : *Double Bass* (NW)
Muskett, Michael : *Clarinet* (SE)
Mussett, Andrew : *Tuba* (Lon)
Musson, Rachel Tara : *Flute* (SW)
Mustard, John M : *Cello* (Sco)
Musto, Chris : *Percussion* (Lon)

Newlands, Archie : *Trombone* (Lon)
Newman, Abigail : *Trombone* (Lon)
Newman, Adam : *Composer* (SE)
Newman, Al : *Saxophones* (Lon)
Newman, Andy (Thunderclap) : *Pianoforte* (Lon)
Newman, Anna : *Percussion* (SW)
Newman, Bob : *Guitars* (Mid)
Newman, Brian : *Horn* (Lon)
Newman, Caleb : *Guitars* (SW)
Newman, Chris : *Guitars* (NE)
Newman, Chris : *Pianoforte* (SE)
Newman, David : *Voice* (SE)
Newman, Del : *Arranger* (Lon)
Newman, Gareth : *Bassoon* (Lon)
Newman, Ian : *Bass Guitar* (E)
Newman, Jack : *Double Bass* (NE)
Newman, Jake : *Double Bass* (NW)
Newman, Michael : *Viola* (Lon)
Newman, Nili : *Flute* (Lon)
Newman, Paul : *Guitars* (SW)
Newman, Peter : *Violin* (Lon)
Newman, Peter : *Clarinet* (Mid)
Newman, Ruth : *Flute* (Lon)
Newman, Tim : *Trumpet* (SW)
Newman/T-Bone.Fretless, Eric : *Bass Guitar* (Lon)
Newmark, Andrew : *Percussion* (Lon)
Newnham, Alan : *Horn* (SE)
Newnham, Arnold : *Viola* (Lon)
Newnham, Arthur : *Guitars* (SE)
Newnham, Martin : *Guitars* (SE)
Newnham, Paul : *Bass Guitar* (Lon)
Newport, Christopher : *Horn* (Lon)
Newport, John : *Electric Piano* (SE)
Newport, Mark : *Pianoforte* (E)
Newport, Neil : *Pianoforte* (Mid)
Newsome, Roy : *Conductor* (NW)
Newson, Gerald : *Double Bass* (Lon)
Newton, Andrew : *Voice* (NW)
Newton, Brian : *Trombone* (Mid)
Newton, Christopher : *Music Director* (Lon)
Newton, David : *Double Bass* (Lon)
Newton, David : *Pianoforte* (Sco)
Newton, Edmund : *Pianoforte* (SW)
Newton, Eric : *Clarinet* (Mid)
Newton, Erica : *Cello* (Mid)
Newton, Gloria : *Pianoforte* (NW)
Newton, Ingrid : *Viola* (NW)
Newton, James : *Percussion* (SW)
Newton, Keechie : *Voice* (Lon)
Newton, Laura : *Viola* (NE)
Newton, Malcolm : *Pianoforte* (SE)
Newton, Pamela : *Viola* (NW)
Newton, Paul : *Trumpet* (Lon)
Newton, Peter : *Guitars* (NW)
Newton, Peter : *Double Bass* (SE)
Newton, Race : *Pianoforte* (NE)
Newton, Raymond : *Double Bass* (NE)
Newton, Raymond : *Double Bass* (SW)
Newton, Richard : *Voice* (SE)
Newton, Robert : *Bandleader* (Mid)
Newton, Robert : *Trombone* (Mid)
Newton, Rodney : *Percussion* (Lon)
Newton, Selwyn : *Clarinet* (Mid)
Newton, Thomas Jerome : *Keyboards* (SW)
Newton, Tony : *Bass Guitar* (Lon)
Newton, Tony : *Saxophones* (SE)
Newton, Victoria : *Voice* (Lon)
Newton, William : *Trumpet* (Lon)
Ng, Janine : *Flute* (Mid)
Ng, Nathan : *Guitars* (SW)
Ngwaba, Ike : *Percussion* (Lon)
Ni Chonaill, Niamh : *Viola* (Lon)
Ni'Chathasaigh, Maire : *Harp* (NE)
Niblett, Ben : *Pianoforte* (Mid)
Niblett, Christopher : *Bass Trombone* (SE)

Niblett, Zoe : *Voice* (Lon)
Niblock, Simon Mark : *Saxophones* (SE)
Nice, Andrew : *Cello* (Lon)
Nice, Colin : *Saxophones* (Mid)
Nice, Stephen : *Percussion* (Lon)
Nichol, Gordon : *Saxophones* (NW)
Nichol, Tom : *Percussion* (Lon)
Nicholas, Andy : *Guitars* (Lon)
Nicholas, Christopher : *Bass Guitar* (NW)
Nicholas, Dave : *Pianoforte* (NW)
Nicholas, Grant : *Guitars* (Lon)
Nicholas, Julian : *Saxophones* (SE)
Nicholas, Lee : *Percussion* (SW)
Nicholas, Nicholas : *Songwriter* (Lon)
Nicholas, Nick : *Pianoforte* (Lon)
Nicholas, Paul : *Guitars* (SW)
Nicholas, Philip : *Trumpet* (SW)
Nicholas, Robert : *Trumpet* (Lon)
Nicholl, Jason : *Guitars* (NW)
Nicholl, Phillip : *Voice* (Lon)
Nicholls, Al : *Saxophones* (Lon)
Nicholls, Alison : *Harp* (E)
Nicholls, Andy : *Saxophones* (Mid)
Nicholls, Barry : *Bass Guitar* (SE)
Nicholls, Benjamin : *Double Bass* (Lon)
Nicholls, Billy : *Guitars* (Lon)
Nicholls, Dave : *Bass Guitar* (Mid)
Nicholls, Geoff : *Keyboards* (Mid)
Nicholls, Geoffrey : *Percussion* (SE)
Nicholls, George : *Trombone* (SE)
Nicholls, Helen : *Voice* (Lon)
Nicholls, John : *Guitars* (Lon)
Nicholls, John : *Percussion* (Mid)
Nicholls, Jon : *Bass Guitar* (E)
Nicholls, Jonathan : *Composer* (SW)
Nicholls, Julianna : *Cello* (Sco)
Nicholls, Justin : *Guitars* (Lon)
Nicholls, Martin : *Bass Trombone* (Lon)
Nicholls, Matthew : *Guitars* (NW)
Nicholls, Simon : *Pianoforte* (Lon)
Nicholls, Victor : *Bass Guitar* (SE)
Nicholls-Bennett, John : *Trombone* (Lon)
Nichols, Alex : *Percussion* (Mid)
Nichols, Bernie : *Guitars* (E)
Nichols, Colin : *Saxophones* (Lon)
Nichols, David : *Violin* (SW)
Nichols, Ellie : *Voice* (E)
Nichols, Geoff : *Trumpet* (SW)
Nichols, Keith : *Pianoforte* (Lon)
Nichols, Michael : *Bass Guitar* (Lon)
Nichols, Peter : *Clarinet* (Lon)
Nichols, Thomas : *Keyboards* (Lon)
Nicholson, 'A Jay' : *Pianoforte* (Lon)
Nicholson, Patrick : *Keyboards* (Lon)
Nicholson, Paul : *Harpsichord* (Lon)
Nicholson, Pete : *Guitars* (SW)
Nicholson, Ralph : *Violin* (Lon)
Nicholson, Stuart : *Voice* (SE)
Nicholson, Timothy : *Horn* (NW)
Nicholson, Vanessa-Mae : *Violin* (Lon)
Nickel, Michael : *Trumpet* (Mid)
Nicklin, Celia : *Oboe* (Lon)
Nicklin, Christine : *Tympani* (Mid)
Nicklin, Edward : *Percussion* (E)
Nicklin, Gary : *Guitars* (E)
Nickols, Timothy : *Guitars* (SE)
Nickson, Jennifer : *Violin* (Lon)
Nicol, Andrew : *Pianoforte* (Sco)
Nicol, Kenneth : *Guitars* (NW)
Nicol, Michael : *Keyboards* (NW)
Nicol, Simon : *Guitars* (Lon)
Nicolaides, Kimon : *Violin* (Lon)
Nicolin, Bernadette : *Violin* (SW)
Nicoll, John : *Pianoforte* (SW)
Nicols, Maggie : *Voice* (Lon)

Nicolson, Alasdair : *Composer* (Lon)
Nicolson, Claire : *Voice* (Lon)
Nicolson, Nancy : *Melodeon* (Sco)
Niebla, Eduardo : *Guitars* (Lon)
Niel, David : *Trombone* (Sco)
Niel, Keith : *Trombone* (NW)
Nield, Richard : *Trombone* (Mid)
Nielinger, Carola : *Flute* (Lon)
Nielsen, Billy : *Guitars* (NE)
Nieman, Paul : *Trombone* (Lon)
Nieminski, Simon : *Organ* (Sco)
Niemira, Stephanie : *Violin* (Lon)
Nieper, Wendy : *Voice* (Mid)
Nieve, Steve : *Pianoforte* (Lon)
Nifton, Muriel : *Organ* (NE)
Nightingale, Mark : *Trombone* (Lon)
Nightingale, Trevor : *Pianoforte* (Lon)
Niles, Richard : *Guitars* (Lon)
Niles, Tessa : *Voice* (Lon)
Nilo, David : *Bass Guitar* (Mid)
Nina : *Voice* (Lon)
Nisbet, James : *Guitars* (Lon)
Nishihara, Mayumi : *Voice* (Lon)
Nishitani Gilliat, Catherine : *Voice* (Lon)
Nissen, David : *Balalaika* (Lon)
Nissen, David : *Bassoon* (Lon)
Nitu : *Voice* (Lon)
Nix, Zoe : *Voice* (Mid)
Nixon, Andy : *Percussion* (SW)
Nixon, Christopher : *Guitars* (SE)
Nixon, Doris : *Pianoforte* (NW)
Nixon, John : *Concertina (Inc Engl* (Mid)
Nixon, John : *Bass Guitar* (NE)
Nixon, Joyce : *Violin* (Lon)
Nixon, Patricia : *Flute* (Lon)
Nlewedim, Stella : *Voice* (Lon)
Noakes, Anna : *Flute* (Lon)
Noakes, Claire : *Violin* (NW)
Noakes, Rab : *Guitars* (Sco)
Nobes, Pauline : *Violin* (Lon)
Nobes, Roger : *Percussion* (E)
Noble, Austin : *Pianoforte* (Lon)
Noble, Bethan : *Violin* (Mid)
Noble, Brian : *Guitars* (SW)
Noble, Douglas : *Guitars* (Sco)
Noble, Duncan : *Bass Guitar* (Lon)
Noble, Geoffrey Charles : *Voice* (Mid)
Noble, John : *Pianoforte* (NE)
Noble, Joseph : *Keyboards* (Lon)
Noble, Liam : *Pianoforte* (Lon)
Noble, Louis : *Saxophones* (NW)
Nock, John : *Horn* (Mid)
Nock, John : *Pianoforte* (Mid)
Nockles, Bruce : *Trumpet* (Lon)
Noden, Paul : *Clarinet* (SW)
Noel, Lincoln : *Pianoforte* (Mid)
Nolan, Charles : *Violin* (Lon)
Nolan, Charles : *Violin* (Lon)
Nolan, David : *Violin* (Lon)
Nolan, Francis : *Flute* (Lon)
Nolan, Mike : *Pianoforte* (Lon)
Nolan, Robin : *Guitars* (Mid)
Nolan, Sean : *Guitars* (Lon)
Nolan, Sheila : *Percussion* (Lon)
Nolan, Tom : *Guitars* (Lon)
Noley : *Violin* (Lon)
Nolte, Thorsten : *Guitars* (Mid)
Noon, Graham : *Pianoforte* (SE)
Noot, Rebekah : *Trumpet* (NE)
Norden, Elizabeth : *Pianoforte* (Lon)
Norfolk, Simon : *Voice* (NW)
Norland, Brigitte : *Flute* (SW)
Norman, Andrew : *Horn* (SE)
Norman, Christopher : *Guitars* (NW)
Norman, Chuck : *Keyboards* (Lon)

Parnell, William : *Percussion* (Lon)
Parr, Colin : *Clarinet* (Mid)
Parr, John : *Guitars* (NE)
Parr, Jonny : *Guitars* (Sco)
Parr, Kenneth : *Saxophones* (SW)
Parratt, Tom : *Percussion* (Mid)
Parren, Chris : *Pianoforte* (Lon)
Parriah, Psilobye : *Voice* (Lon)
Parricelli, John : *Guitars* (Lon)
Parrington, Fred : *Violin* (Lon)
Parris, Bernard : *Saxophones* (Lon)
Parris, Janet : *Clarinet* (Lon)
Parrock, Tristan : *Pianoforte* (NE)
Parrot : *Keyboards* (NE)
Parrott, M : *Cello* (NW)
Parrott, Nigel : *Percussion* (NW)
Parry, Caroline : *Violin* (Sco)
Parry, Diane : *Saxophones* (Mid)
Parry, Dick : *Saxophones* (Lon)
Parry, Frederick : *Cello* (Sco)
Parry, Jane : *Flute* (Lon)
Parry, Kevin : *Trumpet* (NW)
Parry, Laurence : *Trumpet* (E)
Parry, Mark : *Voice* (NW)
Parry, Martin : *Flute* (Lon)
Parry, Ronald : *Percussion* (SE)
Parry, Russell : *Flute* (Mid)
Parsonage, Vincent : *Viola* (NE)
Parsons, Aneurin : *Double Bass* (Mid)
Parsons, Anthony : *Trombone* (Lon)
Parsons, Aubrey : *Voice* (SW)
Parsons, Bernard : *Bass Guitar* (SW)
Parsons, David : *Guitars* (Lon)
Parsons, David : *Violin* (SE)
Parsons, Jacqueline : *Bass Guitar* (Lon)
Parsons, Mike : *Cello* (Lon)
Parsons, Paul : *Voice* (Lon)
Parsons, Richard : *Pianoforte* (SW)
Parsons, Steve : *Guitars* (Lon)
Partington, Darren : *Keyboards* (NW)
Partington, Gitika : *Voice* (Lon)
Partington, Sydney : *Violin* (SW)
Partis, Lee : *Percussion* (SE)
Partridge, Andrew : *Guitars* (SW)
Partridge, Bernard : *Violin* (Lon)
Partridge, Christopher : *Viola* (NW)
Partridge, Elizabeth : *Violin* (Lon)
Partridge, Jennifer : *Pianoforte* (Lon)
Partridge, Jo : *Guitars* (Lon)
Partridge, John : *Contra Bassoon* (NW)
Partridge, Michael : *Percussion* (NW)
Partridge, Piers : *Guitars* (SW)
Parvez, Mohammed : *Percussion* (Mid)
Pascall, Neil : *Guitars* (NE)
Pascoe, Keith : *Violin* (Lon)
Pash, David : *Guitars* (Lon)
Pashley, Claire : *Recorders* (NE)
Pashley, Don : *Saxophones* (SE)
Pashley, John : *Trumpet* (NE)
Pashm, Max : *Voice* (SE)
Pask, Andrew : *Bass Guitar* (Lon)
Paske, Katy : *Violin* (E)
Passchier, Maja : *Cello* (E)
Passey, Francis : *Double Bass* (NE)
Passmore, Rhianon : *Clarinet* (SW)
Patches : *Guitars* (SW)
Pate, Donny : *Guitars* (Lon)
Patel, Bonky : *Latin American Percu* (Lon)
Pateman, Matthew : *Voice* (Lon)
Paterson, Andrew : *Horn* (Lon)
Paterson, Barbara : *Violin* (Sco)
Paterson, Don : *Guitars* (Sco)
Paterson, Foss : *Pianoforte* (Sco)
Paterson, Geo N : *Trumpet* (Lon)
Paterson, Helen : *Violin* (Lon)

Paterson, James : *Trombone* (Lon)
Paterson, Jean : *Violin* (Lon)
Paterson, Joseph : *Saxophones* (Mid)
Paterson, Kenny : *Voice* (Sco)
Paterson, Marc : *Percussion* (Sco)
Paterson, Nigel : *Guitars* (Lon)
Paterson, William : *Cello* (Sco)
Patience, Anthony Hewitt : *Guitars* (Lon)
Patience, Elaine : *Violin* (SE)
Paton, Adrian : *Pianoforte* (Lon)
Paton, David : *Bass Guitar* (Sco)
Paton, Kevin : *Guitars* (NW)
Paton, Philip : *Saxophones* (SE)
Paton, Reginald : *Trombone* (NW)
Paton, Rod : *Horn* (SE)
Paton, Roger : *Guitars* (E)
Patrick, Anne : *Viola* (SW)
Patrick, David : *Pianoforte* (Sco)
Patrick, John : *Arranger* (Mid)
Patrick, John : *Composer* (Mid)
Patrick, John : *Keyboards* (Mid)
Patrick, John : *Music Director* (Mid)
Patrick, John : *Pianoforte* (Mid)
Patrick, Mark : *Keyboards* (Mid)
Patrick, Maxwell : *Percussion* (NE)
Patrick, Nicholas : *Music Director* (Lon)
Patrick, Paul : *Percussion* (NW)
Patrucci, Bret : *Guitars* (Mid)
Patston, Edward : *Violin* (Lon)
Pattani, Hinal : *Keyboards* (Mid)
Pattemore, Gerald : *Guitars* (SW)
Pattenden, Jacqueline : *Viola* (SW)
Pattenden, Jacqueline : *Violin* (SW)
Patterson, Allan : *Percussion* (SW)
Patterson, Craig : *Trumpet* (NW)
Patterson, David : *Pianoforte* (NE)
Patterson, Drew : *Pianoforte* (Lon)
Patterson, Grant : *Percussion* (Mid)
Patterson, Jeff : *Voice* (Lon)
Patterson, John : *Guitars* (Mid)
Patterson, Mark : *Guitars* (NW)
Patterson, Martin : *Bass Guitar* (E)
Patterson, Nick : *Pianoforte* (SW)
Patterson, Patricia : *Voice* (Lon)
Patterson, Scott : *Trombone* (Lon)
Patterson, Shirley : *Percussion* (NE)
Patterson, Steven : *Percussion* (SE)
Pattinson, Andrew : *Guitars* (NE)
Pattinson, Iian : *Percussion* (Lon)
Pattinson, Susannah : *Violin* (Lon)
Pattison, Andrea : *Voice* (NE)
Pattison, Graham : *Guitars* (Lon)
Pattison, John : *Pianoforte* (NE)
Pattman, David : *Percussion* (Lon)
Patton, Joanna : *Clarinet* (NW)
Pattullo, Gordon : *Accordion* (Sco)
Paul, Alexandra : *Trombone* (Lon)
Paul, Daniel : *Cello* (NW)
Paul, Howard : *Voice* (Lon)
Paul, Jack : *Guitars* (Sco)
Paul, Michael : *Bass Guitar* (Lon)
Paul, Raymond : *Guitars* (SW)
Paul, Rod : *Mandolin* (Sco)
Paul, Ron : *Double Bass* (Lon)
Paul, Simon : *Guitars* (Lon)
Paul, Stevie : *Guitars* (E)
Pauley, John : *Electric Violin* (Sco)
Paveling, David : *Guitars* (SW)
Pavitt, Richard : *Guitars* (E)
Pavlou, Louis : *Percussion* (SE)
Pawlby, Arwood : *Trombone* (SW)
Pawley, Raymond : *Percussion* (E)
Pawluk, Ronnie : *Tuba* (Mid)
Pawson, Dan : *Trumpet* (Mid)
Paxman, Michael : *Guitars* (Lon)

Paxton, Edward : *Clarinet* (Sco)
Paxton, Timothy : *Cello* (Sco)
Pay, Antony : *Clarinet* (Lon)
Pay, Richard : *Percussion* (Lon)
Paye, Adrian : *Keyboards* (SE)
Payn, Nicholas : *Saxophones* (Lon)
Payne, Alan : *Saxophones* (Lon)
Payne, Bob : *Double Bass* (E)
Payne, Brian : *Pianoforte* (SW)
Payne, Ceri : *Guitars* (NE)
Payne, Cy : *Arranger* (Lon)
Payne, Donald : *Trumpet* (E)
Payne, Donald : *Trombone* (Mid)
Payne, Douglas : *Bass Guitar* (Lon)
Payne, Fiona : *Violin* (Sco)
Payne, Georgina : *Viola* (E)
Payne, Howard : *Percussion* (Lon)
Payne, Ian : *Guitars* (SE)
Payne, John : *Clarinet* (Lon)
Payne, Lars : *Cello* (Lon)
Payne, Laurence : *Keyboards* (Lon)
Payne, Lawrence : *Clarinet* (SE)
Payne, Leo : *Violin* (Lon)
Payne, Michael : *Bass Trombone* (NW)
Payne, Mike : *Bass Guitar* (E)
Payne, Nicholas : *Guitars* (Lon)
Payne, Nicola : *Horn* (Mid)
Payne, Ray : *Percussion* (NE)
Payne, Richard : *Keyboards* (Lon)
Payne, Richard : *Copyist* (Mid)
Payne, Robin : *Percussion* (Mid)
Payne, Stanley : *Trumpet* (SE)
Payne, Timothy : *Clarinet* (Lon)
Payton, Nik : *Saxophones* (Lon)
Peace, Dave : *Organ* (Mid)
Peace, Hazel : *Pianoforte* (SE)
Peach, Geraldine : *Oboe* (Lon)
Peach, Joss : *Pianoforte* (Lon)
Peachey, Derek : *Guitars* (E)
Peachey, Lynda : *Pianoforte* (Sco)
Peacock, Bob : *Pianoforte* (NE)
Peacock, Eddie : *Pianoforte* (NW)
Peacock, Joanna : *Bass Guitar* (Lon)
Peacock, Judith : *Harp* (Sco)
Peacock, Louise : *Violin* (NW)
Peacock, Mike : *Bass Guitar* (Lon)
Peacock, Nicholas : *Guitars* (SW)
Peacock, Stephen : *Cornet* (NE)
Peadar : *Tympani* (NW)
Peak, Edward : *Double Bass* (NW)
Peake, Alexandra : *Violin* (Sco)
Peake, Jacko : *Saxophones* (Lon)
Peake, Nicholas : *Keyboards* (NW)
Peake, Richard : *Violin* (Lon)
Peaker, Terry : *Bass Guitar* (Lon)
Pearce, Andrew : *Tuba* (Lon)
Pearce, Ben : *Trumpet* (SW)
Pearce, Bobby : *Pianoforte* (Lon)
Pearce, Butch : *Pianoforte* (SE)
Pearce, Chris : *Guitars* (SE)
Pearce, Christopher : *Viola* (Lon)
Pearce, Dave : *Percussion* (Lon)
Pearce, David : *Trombone* (Mid)
Pearce, Geoffrey : *Bass Guitar* (Mid)
Pearce, Gordon : *Double Bass* (Lon)
Pearce, Ian : *Percussion* (Lon)
Pearce, Irene : *Violin* (NW)
Pearce, John : *Pianoforte* (Lon)
Pearce, John : *Conductor* (NE)
Pearce, Kenneth : *Trombone* (SW)
Pearce, Lesley : *Violin* (E)
Pearce, Mary : *Voice* (Lon)
Pearce, Matt : *Guitars* (Lon)
Pearce, Michael : *Clarinet* (Lon)
Pearce, Montague : *Organ* (SW)

Index of Members - Pearce

Pearce, Richard : *Bass Guitar* (SE)
Pearce, Robert : *Trombone* (Lon)
Pearce, Roger : *Pianoforte* (SW)
Pearce, Roslyn : *Violin* (NE)
Pearce, Steve : *Bass Guitar* (Lon)
Pearce-Davies, Eileen : *Pianoforte* (NE)
Pearman, Mark : *Guitars* (NE)
Pearn, Jon : *Keyboards* (Lon)
Pearn, Matt : *Pianoforte* (Lon)
Pears, Les : *Bass Guitar* (Lon)
Pears, Michael : *Keyboards* (E)
Pears, Michael : *Pianoforte* (Mid)
Pearson, Adam : *Guitars* (NE)
Pearson, Andrew : *Voice* (E)
Pearson, Christopher : *Guitars* (Lon)
Pearson, Colin : *Trumpet* (NE)
Pearson, Dave : *Bandleader* (SE)
Pearson, Gary : *Voice* (NW)
Pearson, Geoff : *Double Bass* (Mid)
Pearson, Gill : *Violin* (NE)
Pearson, Graeme : *Guitars* (Sco)
Pearson, Guy : *Pianoforte* (Lon)
Pearson, Jack : *Percussion* (SW)
Pearson, John : *Guittarra Bahiana* (SE)
Pearson, Johnny : *Pianoforte* (Lon)
Pearson, Justin : *Cello* (Lon)
Pearson, Keith : *Guitars* (Lon)
Pearson, Ken : *Guitars* (NW)
Pearson, Leslie : *Pianoforte* (Lon)
Pearson, Mark : *Guitars* (Lon)
Pearson, Neil : *Guitars* (NE)
Pearson, Nicholas : *Guitars* (Lon)
Pearson, Nigel : *Bass Guitar* (SE)
Pearson, Robert : *Keyboards* (Mid)
Pearson, Roy : *Pianoforte* (E)
Pearson, Simon : *Percussion* (Lon)
Pearson-Thomas, Kathleen : *Voice* (Lon)
Pease, Mark : *Keyboards* (Lon)
Pease, Nigel : *Percussion* (NE)
Peat, Michael : *Guitars* (Mid)
Peate, Andrew : *Bandleader* (Mid)
Peate, Andrew : *Trumpet* (Mid)
Peberdy, Jack : *Arranger* (Lon)
Peberdy, Keith : *Bass Guitar* (NE)
Peck, Anne : *Percussion* (Lon)
Peck, Michael : *Pianoforte* (Lon)
Peckham, Geoffrey : *Bass Guitar* (SE)
Pedder, Arthur : *Trombone* (NW)
Pedder, John : *Bass Guitar* (NW)
Pedersen, Thomas : *Double Bass* (E)
Pedley, Chris : *Bass Guitar* (SE)
Pedro, Elohor : *Voice* (Lon)
Peel, John : *Early Percussion* (NE)
Peel, Jonathan : *Trumpet* (SE)
Peel, Ken : *Pianoforte* (SW)
Peel, Stanley Martin : *Guitars* (NW)
Peerless, Mary : *Viola* (Lon)
Peerman, Marina : *Keyboards* (SE)
Peet, Joe B : *Violin* (Lon)
Peet, Nigel : *Double Bass* (E)
Peffer, David : *Percussion* (Sco)
Pegg, Bev : *Guitars* (Mid)
Pegg, Dave : *Bass Guitar* (Mid)
Pegg, E : *Trumpet* (SW)
Pegg, Jon : *Guitars* (Mid)
Pegg, Kenneth : *Percussion* (NW)
Peggie, Andrew : *Composer* (Lon)
Pegna, Shirley : *Cello* (SW)
Peirce, Howard : *Double Bass* (Lon)
Peiro, Teddy : *Bandoneon* (Lon)
Pela, Suzy : *Pianoforte* (Lon)
Pelas, G : *Bouzouki* (Lon)
Pell, Robert : *Pianoforte* (NE)
Peller, David : *Double Bass* (Sco)
Peller, Helen : *Bassoon* (NW)

Pellett, Roy : *Clarinet* (SW)
Pelling, Kate : *Violin* (Mid)
Pellius, Everis : *Voice* (Lon)
Pellow, Marti : *Voice* (Sco)
Pells, Mary : *Cello* (E)
Pelly, Mysie : *Early Strings* (Sco)
Pelly, Mysie : *Viola* (Sco)
Peltier, Richard : *Steel Pan* (Lon)
Pemberton, Clare : *Voice* (Lon)
Pemberton, Mark : *Pianoforte* (Mid)
Penda, Hilaire : *Bass Guitar* (Lon)
Penders, Allan : *Guitars* (Sco)
Pendle : *Guitars* (Lon)
Pendlebury, Alan : *Bassoon* (NW)
Pendlebury, Karl : *Pianoforte* (Lon)
Pendlebury, Keith : *Pianoforte* (Mid)
Pendlebury, Marcia : *Voice* (Mid)
Pendlebury, Nicholas : *Viola* (Lon)
Pendlebury, Sally : *Cello* (NW)
Pendleton, Brian : *Pianoforte* (NW)
Pendrill, Christine : *Oboe* (Lon)
Pendry, Katherine : *Flute* (Lon)
Penfold : *Saxophones* (Lon)
Penfold, Emma : *Violin* (Lon)
Penfold, Gary : *Trombone* (SE)
Penfold, Jacqui : *Viola* (Sco)
Pengelly, Allan : *Percussion* (SE)
Penhorwood, Carole : *Pianoforte* (SW)
Peniston, George : *Double Bass* (Lon)
Penman, Alan : *Pianoforte* (Sco)
Penn, Alfred : *Bassoon* (Lon)
Penn, Matthew : *Guitars* (NW)
Pennant, Trevor : *Bass Guitar* (Lon)
Penneck, Anthony : *Bass Guitar* (SE)
Penney, Jonn : *Voice* (Mid)
Penney, Ken : *Organ* (Lon)
Penny, Mark : *Horn* (Mid)
Penny, Nick : *Paraguyan Harp* (E)
Penny, Robert : *Guitars* (Mid)
Penrose, Marcus : *Guitars* (SW)
Penrose, Richard : *Pianoforte* (SW)
Pentecost, Rickard : *Pianoforte* (SE)
Pentecost, Stephanie : *Voice* (SE)
Pentelow, Nicholas : *Saxophones* (Lon)
Pepler, Felix : *Keyboards* (SW)
Pepler, Mervyn : *Keyboards* (SW)
Peploe, Brian : *Saxophones* (SE)
Peppe, Daniel : *Bass Guitar* (Lon)
Pepper, Austin : *Horn* (SE)
Pepper, Len : *Trumpet* (Mid)
Pepper, Otis : *Keyboards* (Lon)
Pepperell, Alan : *Trombone* (NW)
Percival, Don : *Bass Guitar* (Lon)
Percival, Lynne : *Guitars* (NW)
Percival, Robert : *Bassoon* (Mid)
Percivall, Mabel : *Violin* (Lon)
Percy, Michael : *Bass Guitar* (NW)
Percy, Neil : *Tympani* (Lon)
Percy, Rebecca : *Viola* (SE)
Percy, Richard : *Clarinet* (Mid)
Percy, Roy : *Double Bass* (Sco)
Pereira, Clinton : *Voice* (SE)
Peres Da Costa, Neal : *Pianoforte* (Lon)
Peretti, Jacques : *Cello* (I.on)
Perez, Maria : *Voice* (Lon)
Perez Bennett, Maria : *Voice* (SE)
Perilli, Filiberto : *Keyboards* (Lon)
Perin, Bernard : *Trumpet* (Lon)
Perkes, Kate : *Violin* (Mid)
Perkin, Janet : *Viola* (Mid)
Perkins, Andrew : *Banjo* (SE)
Perkins, Brian : *Guitars* (Mid)
Perkins, David : *Double Bass* (NE)
Perkins, David : *Pianoforte* (Lon)
Perkins, Geoff : *Trombone* (Lon)

Perkins, Graeme : *Guitars* (Lon)
Perkins, Jeremy : *Viola* (Lon)
Perkins, John : *Sitar* (SW)
Perkins, Laurence : *Bassoon* (NW)
Perkins, Mark : *Percussion* (E)
Perkins, Roger : *Double Bass* (SE)
Perkins, Simon : *Voice* (Lon)
Perkins, Timothy : *Violin* (Mid)
Perkins, William : *Accordion* (SE)
Perks, David : *Cello* (Lon)
Perona-Wright, Hilary : *Voice* (Lon)
Perona-Wright, Nigel : *Flute* (Lon)
Perrett, Danielle : *Harp* (Lon)
Perrett, Rowan : *Violin* (Lon)
Perricone, Sarah : *Violin* (Sco)
Perridge, Joanna : *Flute* (Lon)
Perrin, Donald : *Trombone* (Mid)
Perrin, Glyn : *Pianoforte* (Lon)
Perrin, Ingrid : *Cello* (Lon)
Perrin, Roland : *Pianoforte* (Lon)
Perring, Giles : *Guitars* (Lon)
Perrins, Mark : *Guitars* (SE)
Perrins, Simon : *Percussion* (Mid)
Perrottet, Dave : *Valve Trombone* (Lon)
Perry, Adrian : *Violin* (Mid)
Perry, Aerron : *Keyboards* (NE)
Perry, Christian : *Bass Guitar* (SW)
Perry, David : *Saxophones* (SW)
Perry, Fraser : *Guitars* (SW)
Perry, Frederick : *Saxophones* (Lon)
Perry, John : *Voice* (Lon)
Perry, John : *Percussion* (NE)
Perry, Kenneth : *Trombone* (NW)
Perry, Kevin : *Guitars* (Lon)
Perry, Matthew : *Tympani* (Mid)
Perry, Nicholas : *Early Wind* (Lon)
Perry, Nina : *Voice* (Lon)
Perry, Ninian : *Double Bass* (Sco)
Perry, Peter : *Percussion* (Lon)
Perry, Ray : *Guitars* (NE)
Perry, Terence : *Saxophones* (NW)
Perry, Vicky : *Violin* (SE)
Persona : *Keyboards* (Sco)
Persson, Hans : *Percussion* (Lon)
Pert, Morris : *Percussion* (Lon)
Peskett, Elisabeth : *Viola* (Lon)
Peskett, John : *Horn* (Lon)
Peskett, Phillip : *Pianoforte* (Lon)
Petch, Christopher : *Trombone* (NW)
Peters, Aaron : *Flute* (Lon)
Peters, Alan : *Violin* (Lon)
Peters, Brian : *Melodeon* (NW)
Peters, Carolyne : *Recorders* (SW)
Peters, Charles : *Percussion* (SE)
Peters, Colin : *Pianoforte* (Lon)
Peters, Ian : *Clarinet* (SE)
Peters, Jane : *Saxophones* (NE)
Peters, Lynn : *Flute* (Lon)
Peters, Michael : *Guitars* (Lon)
Peters, Michael : *Guitars* (Lon)
Peters, Rob : *Percussion* (Mid)
Peters, Stephen : *Guitars* (Sco)
Peters, Steve : *Saxophones* (SW)
Petersen, Bjorn : *Violin* (NE)
Peterson, Soozy : *Clarinet* (Lon)
Pether, Margaret : *Flute* (SE)
Petit, Stephen : *Guitars* (Lon)
Petitclerc, Alain : *Violin* (Lon)
Petken, David : *Bass Trombone* (Lon)
Petri, David : *Cello* (NW)
Petrie, Jamie : *Keyboards* (Lon)
Petrie, Peter : *Bass Trombone* (Sco)
Pett, Andrew : *Guitars* (SW)
Pettengell, James : *Percussion* (SE)
Petter, Chris : *Trombone* (Lon)

Index of Members - Plumb

Plumb, Mary : *Clarinet* (NE)
Plumb, Stephen : *Percussion* (Lon)
Plume, Mo : *Keyboards* (NW)
Plumley, Gary : *Saxophones* (Lon)
Plummer, Craig : *Percussion* (Lon)
Plummer, James : *Guitars* (SW)
Plummer, Julian : *Horn* (NW)
Plummer, Sarah : *Violin* (SE)
Pluto : *Voice* (Lon)
Plytas, Nick : *Keyboards* (Lon)
Pockett, Kenneth : *Trombone* (SW)
Pocklington, Valerie : *Violin* (NW)
Pocock, Louis : *Percussion* (Lon)
Podger, Rachel : *Violin* (Lon)
Pointon, Mike : *Trombone* (Lon)
Poke, James : *Flute* (Lon)
Polack, Margaret : *Voice* (Mid)
Poleykett, Gary : *Keyboards* (SE)
Pollak, Crispin : *Guitars* (SE)
Pollani, Benedetto : *Viola* (Lon)
Pollard, Brian : *Keyboards* (SE)
Pollard, Clare : *Violin* (SE)
Pollard, Corinne : *Saxophones* (Lon)
Pollard, David : *Voice* (SE)
Pollard, Eric : *Saxophones* (NE)
Pollard, John : *Saxophones* (SE)
Pollard, Mark : *Bassoon* (NW)
Pollard, Rona : *Oboe* (Sco)
Polley, Deryck : *Saxophones* (E)
Pollitt, Jack : *Percussion* (Lon)
Pollitt, Samuel : *Saxophones* (NW)
Pollock, Andrew : *Violin* (Lon)
Pollock, Angie : *Pianoforte* (Lon)
Pollock, Margaret : *Bassoon* (Lon)
Pollock, Michael : *Pianoforte* (SW)
Pollock, Ronald : *Guitars* (Sco)
Polmear, Jeremy : *Oboe* (Lon)
Poloway, Harry : *Non Playing Member* (SW)
Polson, Michael : *Guitars* (Lon)
Pomeroy, Dennis : *Pianoforte* (SW)
Pomeroy, Lee : *Bass Guitar* (Lon)
Pond, Celia : *Cello* (Lon)
Ponder, Michael : *Viola* (Lon)
Ponsford, Raymond : *Violin* (NW)
Pontin, David : *Saxophones* (SE)
Ponton, Ben : *Keyboards* (NE)
Pontzen, Peter : *Pianoforte* (Lon)
Pook, Alan : *Violin* (Lon)
Pook, Andrew : *Percussion* (Lon)
Pook, Jocelyn : *Viola* (Lon)
Pool, Robert : *Violin* (Lon)
Poole, Adrian : *Bass Guitar* (Lon)
Poole, Andrew : *Keyboards* (NW)
Poole, Edward : *Bass Guitar* (E)
Poole, Glyn : *Keyboards* (NE)
Poole, Ian : *Percussion* (SW)
Poole, Julian : *Percussion* (Lon)
Poole, Ken : *Saxophones* (Lon)
Poole, Matthew : *Bass Guitar* (Lon)
Poole, Penelope : *Violin* (SE)
Poole, Peter : *Violin* (Lon)
Poole, Quentin : *Oboe* (Lon)
Poole, Ray : *Trumpet* (NE)
Poole, Ronald : *Bass Guitar* (NW)
Poole, Stan : *Saxophones* (Mid)
Poole, Steven : *Composer* (Lon)
Poole, Vanessa : *Bassoon* (NW)
Pooley, Alison : *Violin* (Lon)
Pooley, Anthony : *Violin* (Lon)
Pooley, Hilary : *Flute* (NW)
Pooley, Norman : *Percussion* (SW)
Pooley, Timothy : *Viola* (NW)
Poore, Jak : *Percussion* (NW)
Poore, Julian : *Trumpet* (Lon)
Poots, Alexander : *Trumpet* (Lon)

Pope, Anna : *Flute* (Lon)
Pope, Christopher : *Percussion* (SW)
Pope, Marcus : *Trumpet* (Sco)
Pope, Martin : *Early Strings* (Lon)
Pope, Martin : *Early Wind* (Lon)
Pope, Nicholas : *Pianoforte* (Lon)
Pope, Philip : *Composer* (Lon)
Pope, Sarah : *Viola* (Lon)
Pope, Victoria : *Pianoforte* (Lon)
Popescu, Eugen-Doreanu : *Viola* (Mid)
Popey, Martyn : *Guitars* (Lon)
Pople, Peter : *Violin* (Lon)
Pople, Ross : *Cello* (Lon)
Pople, T M : *Violin* (Lon)
Popo, Melissa : *Voice* (Lon)
Popov, David : *Composer* (Mid)
Popple, Terence : *Percussion* (Lon)
Popplewell, Andrew : *Keyboards* (NW)
Popplewell, Phil : *Guitars* (NW)
Popplewell, Richard : *Organ* (Lon)
Poppy, Andrew : *Pianoforte* (Lon)
Porcas, Jennifer : *Oboe* (Lon)
Porilo, Gregory : *Pianoforte* (Lon)
Portal, Kate : *Voice* (Lon)
Portas, Andrew : *Bass Guitar* (Mid)
Portas, Roger : *Keyboards* (Mid)
Portch, Kevin : *Bass Guitar* (Lon)
Porteous, Colin : *Guitars* (Lon)
Porteous, Diane : *Cello* (Lon)
Porteous, Guy : *Pianoforte* (NW)
Porteous, Rachel : *Violin* (NW)
Porter, Anthony : *Bass Guitar* (Lon)
Porter, Bob : *Bassoon* (Lon)
Porter, Brian : *Violin* (Lon)
Porter, Catherine : *Violin* (SW)
Porter, Colin : *Trombone* (SE)
Porter, Ian : *Bass Guitar* (SE)
Porter, John : *Bass Guitar* (Mid)
Porter, Joseph : *Percussion* (E)
Porter, Kevin : *Guitars* (SE)
Porter, Mark : *Voice* (SW)
Porter, Rachel : *Oboe* (SE)
Porter, Terence : *Saxophones* (Lon)
Porteus, Terry : *Violin* (SW)
Portman, Eugene : *Pianoforte* (NE)
Portman, Rachel : *Pianoforte* (Lon)
Portman, Tom : *Guitars* (SW)
Poskitt, Kjarton : *Pianoforte* (SE)
Posner, Michael : *Viola* (Lon)
Posnett, Martin : *Voice* (Lon)
Possible, Gilda : *Voice* (NW)
Postill, Isabelle : *Pianoforte* (Lon)
Poston, Alan : *Percussion* (E)
Potila, Tero : *Guitars* (Lon)
Potter, Alison : *Voice* (Lon)
Potter, Amanda : *Bassoon* (NW)
Potter, David : *Saxophones* (SE)
Potter, Gary : *Guitars* (NW)
Potter, James : *Cello* (Lon)
Potter, John : *Guitars* (Mid)
Potter, John : *Percussion* (SW)
Potter, Malcolm : *Percussion* (SE)
Potter, Roger : *Bass Guitar* (Lon)
Potter, Ruth : *Harp* (Lon)
Potter, Sally : *Saxophones* (Lon)
Potter, Sarah : *Pianoforte* (Lon)
Potter, Warwick : *Bassoon* (SE)
Potts, Andrew : *Saxophones* (Lon)
Potts, David : *Guitars* (NW)
Potts, Hugh : *Horn* (Sco)
Potts, John : *Trumpet* (Mid)
Potts, Mike : *Trumpet* (SW)
Potts, Raymond : *Guitars* (Mid)
Potts, Roy : *Trumpet* (NW)
Poulston, Wendy : *Violin* (E)

Poulter, John : *Tympani* (Sco)
Poulton, Geoffrey : *Trombone* (Mid)
Pound, Megan : *Violin* (Lon)
Povey, Bill : *Saxophones* (Lon)
Povey, Scott : *Saxophones* (Lon)
Powada, Neil : *Guitars* (Sco)
Powdrill, Joy : *Percussion* (Lon)
Powell, Andrew : *Composer* (Lon)
Powell, Anthony : *Keyboards* (Mid)
Powell, Clive : *Guitars* (Mid)
Powell, Dave : *Percussion* (Lon)
Powell, David : *Oboe* (Lon)
Powell, David : *Tuba* (Lon)
Powell, David : *Cello* (Mid)
Powell, David : *Keyboards* (SW)
Powell, Derek : *Violin* (SE)
Powell, Gary : *Guitars* (NW)
Powell, Glyn : *Guitars* (Lon)
Powell, Graham : *Organ* (NW)
Powell, Harriet : *Pianoforte* (Lon)
Powell, Heather : *Voice* (E)
Powell, Helen : *Oboe* (Lon)
Powell, James : *Percussion* (SW)
Powell, John : *Euphonium* (NW)
Powell, John : *Bass Trombone* (SW)
Powell, Kevin : *Bass Guitar* (Lon)
Powell, Margaret : *Cello* (Lon)
Powell, Nigel : *Percussion* (SE)
Powell, Owen : *Guitars* (SW)
Powell, Roy : *Pianoforte* (NW)
Powell, Samantha : *Pianoforte* (Lon)
Powell, Sian : *Voice* (SW)
Powell, Simon : *Trombone* (Lon)
Powell, Teresa : *Songwriter* (Lon)
Powell, Timothy : *Keyboards* (SE)
Powells, James : *Mandolin* (NE)
Power, Brendan : *Harmonica (Inc Bass* (Lon)
Power, David : *Percussion* (SW)
Power, James : *Clarinet* (NE)
Power, John : *Guitars* (NW)
Power, John : *Trombone* (Sco)
Power, Patrick : *Percussion* (SE)
Power, Paul : *Bass Guitar* (Lon)
Power, Roy : *Percussion* (NW)
Power, Shena : *Cello* (SW)
Power, Stephanie : *Guitars* (SW)
Power, Stephen : *Keyboards* (NW)
Power, Suzannah : *Pianoforte* (Lon)
Pownall, Colin : *Bass Clarinet* (NW)
Pownall, Gordon : *Keyboards* (E)
Pownceby, John : *Percussion* (NW)
Poyner, Jo : *Bassoon* (Mid)
Prager, Samuel : *Percussion* (SE)
Prange, Maria : *Voice* (NW)
Prangnell, Barnaby : *Clarinet* (SE)
Pratley, Alice : *Violin* (Lon)
Pratley, Susie : *Composer* (SE)
Pratt, Alan : *Trumpet* (NE)
Pratt, Guy : *Bass Guitar* (Lon)
Pratt, Maurice : *Trombone* (Lon)
Praze, Chris : *Guitars* (SW)
Precious : *Keyboards* (Lon)
Precious, Adam : *Double Bass* (Lon)
Predota, Christine : *Bassoon* (Mid)
Preece, Dane : *Pianoforte* (Mid)
Preece, Deborah : *Violin* (Lon)
Preece, George : *Violin* (SW)
Preece, Ian : *Guitars* (SE)
Preece, Oliver : *Trumpet* (Lon)
Preece, Pip : *Guitars* (Mid)
Preiss, Jonathan : *Guitars* (Lon)
Premru, Raymond : *Bass Trombone* (Lon)
Prendergast, Christopher : *Percussion* (NE)
Prendergast, Danny : *Guitars* (Lon)
Prentice, Brian : *Pianoforte* (Sco)

Ratcliffe, Edward : *Guitars* (NE)
Ratcliffe, Lynne : *Violin* (E)
Rathbone, Ian : *Viola* (Lon)
Rathbone, Joyce : *Pianoforte* (Lon)
Rathbone, Lucy : *Voice* (Lon)
Rathbone, Rosemary : *Flute* (Lon)
Rathmell, Walter : *Double Bass* (NE)
Rattee, Gina : *Keyboards* (Lon)
Rattenbury, Ken : *Trumpet* (Mid)
Rattigan, James : *Horn* (Lon)
Rattle, Ali : *Flute* (Lon)
Rattray, Catherine : *Horn* (Lon)
Rault, Odille : *Voice* (E)
Raval, Sandeep : *Tabla* (Lon)
Ravalico, Maurizio : *Latin American Percu* (Lon)
Ravel, Claire : *Voice* (Lon)
Raven, Clive : *Guitars* (Lon)
Raven, Daniel : *Bass Guitar* (Mid)
Raven, Mellie : *Voice* (Lon)
Ravenhill, Colin : *Percussion* (Lon)
Ravenor, Terence : *Bass Trombone* (SW)
Ravenscroft, Hermione : *Copyist* (SE)
Ravi (JP Freeman) : *Kora* (Lon)
Rawbone, Martyn : *Trombone* (Lon)
Rawbone, Nick : *Percussion* (Lon)
Rawe, Jackie : *Voice* (Lon)
Rawling, Dene : *Percussion* (NE)
Rawling, Michael : *Guitars* (SW)
Rawlings, Graham : *Pianoforte* (SW)
Rawlins, Peter : *Percussion* (Lon)
Rawson, Denis : *Pianoforte* (Lon)
Rawson, Irmeli : *Viola* (Lon)
Rawson, Paul : *Guitars* (SW)
Rawstron, Helen : *Oboe* (Lon)
Ray, Christopher : *Guitars* (Lon)
Ray, Clifford : *Saxophones* (SW)
Ray, Pennie : *Voice* (Lon)
Ray, Rita : *Club DJ* (Lon)
Raybould, Clare : *Violin* (Lon)
Raybould, Paul : *Flute* (Mid)
Raybould, Stephen : *Saxophones* (Mid)
Rayelle : *Voice* (Lon)
Rayfield, Harriet : *Violin* (Lon)
Raymond, P : *Voice* (E)
Raymond, Timothy : *Organ* (SW)
Raymonde, Monty : *Trumpet* (SE)
Rayner, Alison : *Bass Guitar* (Lon)
Rayner, Darryl : *Tuba* (NE)
Rayner, Harry : *Pianoforte* (Lon)
Rayner, Peter : *Scratcher* (E)
Rayner, Peter : *Cello* (Lon)
Rayner, Simon : *Horn* (Lon)
Raynes, Harry : *Saxophones* (NE)
Rayson : *Clarinet* (SE)
Rayson, John : *Viola* (Lon)
Razzell, Luke : *Pianoforte* (Lon)
Rea, Alistair : *Bass Guitar* (Mid)
Rea, Christopher : *Voice* (Lon)
Rea, Colin : *Pianoforte* (SW)
Rea, Jake : *Violin* (Lon)
Rea, Mark : *Percussion* (SE)
Read, Adrian : *Pianoforte* (NW)
Read, Alan : *Guitars* (Lon)
Read, Andrew : *Keyboards* (Lon)
Read, Bernard : *Organ* (E)
Read, Christine : *Violin* (Lon)
Read, Geoffrey : *Accordion* (Lon)
Read, John : *Bass Guitar* (Lon)
Read, Tom : *Bass Guitar* (NW)
Read, Tony : *Saxophones* (NE)
Readdy, William : *Pianoforte* (Lon)
Reader, Graham : *Tympani* (Lon)
Reader, James : *Pianoforte* (Lon)
Reader, Nicholas : *Bassoon* (Lon)
Reader, Philip : *Guitars* (Lon)

Reading, John : *Saxophones* (SE)
Readman, Peter : *Bass Guitar* (E)
Readman, Peter : *Pianoforte* (Mid)
Reagan, Samantha : *Violin* (Lon)
Reakes, Richard : *Oboe* (Mid)
Reaney, Andrew : *Guitars* (SE)
Rear, Michael : *Bassoon* (Lon)
Reardon, Stephen : *Guitars* (SE)
Reason, Jules : *Guitars* (SW)
Reason, Richard : *Pianoforte* (E)
Reay, Bryan : *Organ* (NE)
Reay, Jason : *Percussion* (SW)
Reay, Stephen : *Bassoon* (NE)
Rebbeck, Dave : *Double Bass* (SW)
Rebbeck, James : *Keyboards* (Lon)
Rebbeck, Janet : *Clarinet* (NW)
Rebel : *Voice* (Lon)
Rebello, Jason : *Pianoforte* (Lon)
Rebello, Simone : *Percussion* (Mid)
Rebelski, Martin : *Keyboards* (Mid)
Reca, Coqui (Koki) : *Guitars* (Lon)
Reckless, David : *Trombone* (Lon)
Recknell, James : *Pianoforte* (E)
Reckord, Rohan : *Voice* (Lon)
Redding, Philip : *Keyboards* (NE)
Reddington, Laurence : *Percussion* (SE)
Redfarn, Clare : *Harpsichord* (Lon)
Redfern, Jonathan : *Guitars* (NE)
Redfern, Tracey : *Trumpet* (Mid)
Redgate, Roger : *Violin* (Lon)
Redgrave, Constance : *Bass Guitar* (Lon)
Redgrave, Rose : *Viola* (NW)
Redman, Ben : *Percussion* (Sco)
Redmond, Andrew : *Saxophones* (Lon)
Redmond, Melanie : *Voice* (Lon)
Redmond, Patrick : *Pianoforte* (SE)
Redmonds, Duncan : *Voice* (Lon)
Redpath, Timothy : *Clarinet* (NW)
Redwood, Clifton : *Voice* (Lon)
Reece, Alf : *Tuba* (Lon)
Reece, Damon : *Percussion* (SW)
Reece, David : *Trombone* (Sco)
Reece, Eilen : *Viola* (Lon)
Reece, Gary : *Organ* (NW)
Reece, Robin : *Clarinet* (Lon)
Reed, Adrian : *Violin* (Lon)
Reed, Ashley : *Violin* (SE)
Reed, Christopher : *Guitars* (NE)
Reed, Elizabeth : *Violin* (SE)
Reed, Howard T : *Guitars* (NE)
Reed, Hugh : *Guitars* (Sco)
Reed, Janet : *Cello* (Lon)
Reed, Leslie : *Music Director* (SE)
Reed, Michael : *Conductor* (SW)
Reed, Oliver : *Saxophones* (SE)
Reed, Richard : *Keyboards* (E)
Reed, Roger : *Guitars* (Mid)
Reed, Stephen : *Keyboards* (SE)
Reed, Stewart : *Club DJ* (Lon)
Reed, Stuart : *Voice* (SE)
Reedie, Graeme : *Keyboards* (Sco)
Reekie, Alan : *Pianoforte* (Lon)
Reeman, Mike : *Bass Guitar* (Lon)
Rees, Alun : *Horn* (SW)
Rees, Calum : *Percussion* (Lon)
Rees, Carla : *Flute* (Lon)
Rees, Ceri : *Clarinet* (SW)
Rees, Charles : *Guitars* (Lon)
Rees, Elaine : *Keyboards* (Mid)
Rees, Emyr : *Tuba* (NW)
Rees, F : *Pianoforte* (SW)
Rees, Gareth : *Trumpet* (SW)
Rees, Howard : *Composer* (Lon)
Rees, Jonathan : *Violin* (Lon)
Rees, Jonathan : *Percussion* (SW)

Rees, Owen : *Trombone* (Lon)
Rees, Paul : *Percussion* (Lon)
Rees, Paul Rapsey : *Bass Guitar* (Lon)
Rees, Peter : *Oboe* (SW)
Rees, Stephanie : *Horn* (SE)
Rees, Stephen : *Violin* (SW)
Rees, Vaughan : *Percussion* (Lon)
Rees-Jones, Daniel : *Trumpet* (Lon)
Rees-Jones, John : *Double Bass* (Lon)
Rees-Williams, David : *Pianoforte* (SE)
Reesie : *Guitars* (E)
Reeve, Don : *Keyboards* (Lon)
Reeve, Eric : *Bass Guitar* (E)
Reeve, Julian : *Music Director* (E)
Reeve, Peter : *Trumpet* (Lon)
Reeves, Anthony : *Bass Guitar* (E)
Reeves, Barry : *Percussion* (Lon)
Reeves, Bernard : *Percussion* (Lon)
Reeves, Danielle : *Guitars* (Mid)
Reeves, Darren : *Pianoforte* (SE)
Reeves, Elizabeth : *Violin* (Sco)
Reeves, Helen : *Guitars* (Lon)
Reeves, Jeff : *Saxophones* (SE)
Reeves, John : *Pianoforte* (Mid)
Reeves, Kevin : *Voice* (Lon)
Reeves, Madeline : *Voice* (Lon)
Reeves, Marion : *Voice* (Mid)
Reeves, Paul : *Pianoforte* (Lon)
Reeves, Robert : *Pianoforte* (SE)
Refik, Samir : *Percussion* (Lon)
Regal, Gray : *Voice* (Lon)
Regan, Diane : *Voice* (Lon)
Regan, Valerie : *Violin* (NE)
Regis, Kaw : *Pianoforte* (Lon)
Regis, Preston : *Percussion* (Lon)
Regli, Claus : *Guitars* (Lon)
Rehmi, Jived : *Guitars* (Mid)
Reich, Max : *Pianoforte* (Lon)
Reid, Adrian : *Keyboards* (Lon)
Reid, Alan : *Synthesiser* (Sco)
Reid, Alexander : *Guitars* (Lon)
Reid, Allan : *Trumpet* (Lon)
Reid, Angela : *Voice* (Lon)
Reid, Beverley : *Voice* (Sco)
Reid, Caroline : *Violin* (Lon)
Reid, Colin : *Guitars* (NW)
Reid, Craig : *Voice* (Sco)
Reid, Dan : *Guitars* (Lon)
Reid, Donald : *Bassoon* (Lon)
Reid, Doug : *Violin* (NW)
Reid, Edmund : *Violin* (Lon)
Reid, Errol : *Keyboards* (Lon)
Reid, Gabriel : *Oboe* (NW)
Reid, Gavin : *Trumpet* (NW)
Reid, George : *Bagpipes* (Lon)
Reid, George : *Guitars* (Sco)
Reid, Grace : *Voice* (Lon)
Reid, Helen : *Flute* (SW)
Reid, Horace : *Keyboards* (Lon)
Reid, Ian J : *Percussion* (Lon)
Reid, James : *Guitars* (Lon)
Reid, Jane : *Violin* (Sco)
Reid, Joe : *Guitars* (Lon)
Reid, John : *Violin* (Mid)
Reid, Kenny : *Guitars* (Lon)
Reid, Linda : *Voice* (Sco)
Reid, Nan : *Viola* (Sco)
Reid, Neil : *Voice* (NW)
Reid, Nigel : *Voice* (Lon)
Reid, Patricia : *Trumpet* (Lon)
Reid, Paul : *Keyboards* (Lon)
Reid, Paul : *Trombone* (Mid)
Reid, Peter : *Trumpet* (Lon)
Reid, Raina : *Pianoforte* (Mid)
Reid, Reginald : *Trombone* (Mid)

Reid, Rickardo : *Keyboards* (Lon)
Reid, Roy : *Bass Guitar* (Lon)
Reid, Shelagh : *Violin* (Sco)
Reid, Sonia : *Voice* (Lon)
Reid, Steve : *Guitars* (Sco)
Reid, Symone : *Voice* (Lon)
Reid, Terry : *Guitars* (E)
Reid, William : *Guitars* (Lon)
Reid, William : *Violin* (Lon)
Reids : *Voice* (Lon)
Reidy, John : *Saxophones* (SE)
Reigate, Nigel : *Guitars* (E)
Reilly, Brian : *Violin* (NE)
Reilly, David : *Composer* (Lon)
Reilly, James : *Percussion* (Sco)
Reilly, Lorraine : *Guitars* (SW)
Reilly, Maggie : *Voice* (Lon)
Reilly, Peter : *Guitars* (SE)
Reilly, Peter : *Keyboards* (SW)
Reilly, Stanley : *Saxophones* (Sco)
Reilly, Steven : *Guitars* (Sco)
Reilly, Tommy : *Harmonica (Inc Bass* (Lon)
Reinhardt, Max : *Keyboards* (Lon)
Reinhardt, Thierry : *Saxophones* (Lon)
Reith, Angela : *Pianoforte* (Lon)
Relf, Jason : *Bass Guitar* (Lon)
Relton, John S : *Bass Guitar* (NW)
Remedee : *Voice* (Lon)
Remnant, Mary : *Violin* (Lon)
Renae, Louise : *Voice* (E)
Renaud, Norman : *Guitars* (Lon)
Renbourn, John : *Guitars* (Sco)
Rendell, Donald : *Saxophones* (Lon)
Rendell, Ernest : *Percussion* (SE)
Rendle, Calvin : *Guitars* (SE)
Rendle, Peter : *Oboe* (SE)
Renford, James : *Saxophones* (Mid)
Renhard, Jack : *Violin* (NE)
Renney, Tony : *Dobro* (NW)
Renney, Tony : *Guitars* (NW)
Rennie, Jane : *Bassoon* (SE)
Rennie, Jean : *Violin* (Sco)
Rennie, Michael : *Copyist* (Lon)
Rennie, Robert : *Percussion* (Sco)
Rennoldson, Philip : *Keyboards* (Lon)
Renshaw, Robin : *Organ* (NE)
Renshaw, Sophie : *Viola* (Lon)
Rentsch, Veronika : *Composer* (Lon)
Renvoize, Paul : *Guitars* (Lon)
Renvoize, Robert : *Trombone* (E)
Renwick, Charles : *Violin* (Lon)
Renwick, Clare : *Violin* (Lon)
Renwick, Tim : *Guitars* (Lon)
Requeda, Marc : *Guitars* (Lon)
Rest, Bernd : *Guitars* (Lon)
Retallick, Robert : *Violin* (Lon)
Rettig, Roger : *Guitars* (Lon)
Reuben, Cyril : *Saxophones* (Lon)
Reuben, Graham : *Saxophones* (NW)
Reveal, K M A : *Synthesiser* (Mid)
Revel, Cluness : *Pianoforte* (Sco)
Revell, Adrian : *Saxophones* (Lon)
Revell, Michael : *Horn* (Mid)
Revell, Patti : *Voice* (Lon)
Revens, Philip : *Trumpet* (Lon)
Revitt, Neil : *Percussion* (SE)
Rew, Angela : *Pianoforte* (Sco)
Rew, Kimberley : *Guitars* (E)
Reyesjunquera, Fernando : *Guitars* (Lon)
Reyland, Trevor : *Percussion* (E)
Reynish, Timothy : *Music Director* (NW)
Reynolds, Alison : *Oboe* (Mid)
Reynolds, Ambrose : *Bass Guitar* (NW)
Reynolds, Ashley : *Percussion* (Mid)
Reynolds, Basil : *Voice* (Lon)

Reynolds, Benjamin : *Keyboards* (SW)
Reynolds, Bruce : *Guitars* (Lon)
Reynolds, Carl : *Synthesiser* (Lon)
Reynolds, Clare : *Horn* (Lon)
Reynolds, Garry : *Guitars* (NW)
Reynolds, George : *Trumpet* (Lon)
Reynolds, Gerry : *Percussion* (NW)
Reynolds, Gillian : *Clarinet* (Mid)
Reynolds, Helen : *Cello* (SE)
Reynolds, Ian : *Flute* (Mid)
Reynolds, John : *Percussion* (Lon)
Reynolds, John : *Percussion* (Lon)
Reynolds, Julie : *Violin* (Sco)
Reynolds, Kevin : *Saxophones* (Lon)
Reynolds, Mandy : *Voice* (SE)
Reynolds, Marcus : *Trombone* (NE)
Reynolds, Michael : *Pianoforte* (NW)
Reynolds, Paul : *Trombone* (NW)
Reynolds, Peter : *Pianoforte* (Lon)
Reynolds, Peter : *Percussion* (SE)
Reynolds, Peter : *Composer* (SW)
Reynolds, Phil : *Double Bass* (Lon)
Reynolds, Robert : *Pianoforte* (Lon)
Reynolds, Samuel : *Pianoforte* (E)
Reynolds, Stanley : *Trumpet* (Lon)
Reynolds, Susan : *Voice* (Lon)
Reynolds, Thomas : *Trumpet* (SW)
Reynolds, Victor : *Saxophones* (Lon)
Rhead, David : *Guitars* (Mid)
Rhenius, Steve : *Guitars* (E)
Rhind, Gavin : *Violin* (Sco)
Rhind-Tutt, Mortimer : *Trumpet* (Lon)
Rhoden, Neil : *Music Director* (Lon)
Rhodes, Andrew : *Trumpet* (E)
Rhodes, Barbara : *Oboe* (Sco)
Rhodes, Burt : *Music Director* (Lon)
Rhodes, David : *Guitars* (SW)
Rhodes, Ian : *Violin* (Lon)
Rhodes, Linda : *Violin* (Mid)
Rhodes, Phil : *Trombone* (SE)
Rhodes, Sue : *Keyboards* (Lon)
Rhydderch, Lilo : *Harp* (NW)
Rhys, Christina : *Harp* (Lon)
Rhys-Jones, Merlin : *Guitars* (Lon)
Rialas, Costa : *Bouzouki* (Lon)
Ribbans, James : *Guitars* (Lon)
Riboulet, Marie : *Harp* (SW)
Ricardo, Peter : *Bandleader* (Lon)
Rice, Cecily : *Viola* (Mid)
Rice, Derek : *Organ* (Lon)
Rice, Ian : *Percussion* (E)
Rice, Leslie : *Guitars* (Sco)
Rice, Niall : *Guitars* (Lon)
Rice-Milton, Terence : *Voice* (E)
Rich, Gerald : *Viola* (Lon)
Rich, Harold : *Pianoforte* (Mid)
Rich, Jeffrey : *Percussion* (Lon)
Rich, Laura-Jane : *Pianoforte* (Lon)
Rich, Matthew : *Percussion* (Lon)
Rich T : *Keyboards* (SE)
Richard, Barrie : *Percussion* (NE)
Richard, Kelvin : *Keyboards* (Lon)
Richard, Nigel : *Guitars* (Sco)
Richard D : *Pianoforte* (NW)
Richards, Albert : *Percussion* (Mid)
Richards, Andrew : *Synthesiser* (Lon)
Richards, Ame : *Harpsichord* (SE)
Richards, Bill : *Guitars* (SE)
Richards, Bob : *Trumpet* (NE)
Richards, Carolyn : *Cello* (SW)
Richards, Cyrus : *Percussion* (Mid)
Richards, Delph : *Pianoforte* (NW)
Richards, Dewi John : *Bass Guitar* (NW)
Richards, Donald : *Trumpet* (SE)
Richards, Dylan : *Bass Guitar* (SW)

Richards, Eryl : *Pianoforte* (SW)
Richards, Frances : *Violin* (Lon)
Richards, Goff : *Music Director* (NW)
Richards, Jack : *Violin* (Lon)
Richards, Jack : *Percussion* (SE)
Richards, Jack : *Clarinet* (SW)
Richards, Jean : *Organ* (SW)
Richards, John : *Double Bass* (Lon)
Richards, John : *Guitars* (Lon)
Richards, John : *Guitars* (Mid)
Richards, Keith : *Guitars* (Lon)
Richards, Keith : *Guitars* (NE)
Richards, Margaret : *Cello* (Lon)
Richards, Nicole : *Voice* (Lon)
Richards, Paul : *Bass Guitar* (Mid)
Richards, Paul : *Clarinet* (NW)
Richards, Peter : *Guitars* (Mid)
Richards, Peter : *Horn* (NW)
Richards, Roger : *Pianoforte* (Lon)
Richards, Rosaline : *Voice* (NW)
Richards, Sharon : *Pianoforte* (SW)
Richards, Tim : *Pianoforte* (Lon)
Richards, Tony : *Percussion* (Mid)
Richards, Victor : *Percussion* (SE)
Richardson, Arthur : *Double Bass* (SE)
Richardson, Bill : *Trombone* (Mid)
Richardson, Christopher : *Synthesiser* (Lon)
Richardson, Clive : *Percussion* (E)
Richardson, Dave : *Mandolin* (Sco)
Richardson, Don : *Double Bass* (Lon)
Richardson, Elizabeth : *Violin* (SW)
Richardson, Eric : *Guitars* (SE)
Richardson, Gavin : *Percussion* (E)
Richardson, Geoffrey : *Viola* (Lon)
Richardson, Gerry : *Pianoforte* (NE)
Richardson, Ian : *Percussion* (Mid)
Richardson, Ian : *Early Renaissance* (NE)
Richardson, Ian : *Electric Accordion* (Sco)
Richardson, Jamie : *Percussion* (Mid)
Richardson, Janet : *Flute* (Sco)
Richardson, Jim : *Double Bass* (Lon)
Richardson, Joanna : *Violin* (NE)
Richardson, John : *Percussion* (Lon)
Richardson, John : *Banjo* (NE)
Richardson, Martin : *Violin* (NW)
Richardson, Nancy : *Violin* (NE)
Richardson, Paul : *Voice* (Mid)
Richardson, Robert : *Percussion* (Mid)
Richardson, Roger : *Pianoforte* (NE)
Richardson, Sally : *Oboe* (NW)
Richardson, Stephen : *Bass Guitar* (Lon)
Richardson, Stephen : *Guitars* (Lon)
Richardson, Stuart : *Guitars* (Sco)
Richardson, Susan : *Voice* (Lon)
Riches, Edgar : *Trumpet* (Lon)
Riches, Neil : *Pianoforte* (Mid)
Riches, Peter : *Keyboards* (Lon)
Richey, Angela : *Violin* (Mid)
Richman, Colin : *Keyboards* (Lon)
Richman, Reg : *Double Bass* (Lon)
Richmond, Dave : *Bass Guitar* (Lon)
Richmond, David : *Violin* (Lon)
Richmond, Edward : *Pianoforte* (Sco)
Richmond, Jim : *Saxophones* (Lon)
Richmond, Joe : *Trumpet* (Lon)
Richmond, Marcus : *Pianoforte* (Lon)
Richmond, Michael : *Guitars* (NE)
Richmond, Simon : *Latin American Percu* (Lon)
Richter, Mariette : *Violin* (Lon)
Rick : *Bass Guitar* (SW)
Rickarby, Barry : *Bass Guitar* (NE)
Rickard, Anthony : *Trumpet* (Lon)
Rickard, James : *Guitars* (SE)
Rickards, Adrian : *Keyboards* (SW)
Rickards, Charles : *Bass Guitar* (E)

Index of Members - Royle

Royle, Ian : *Trumpet* (NW)
Royle, Jeremy : *Clarinet* (Lon)
Royle, Roger : *Composer* (NW)
Roytunda, Fat Al : *Percussion* (Lon)
Rozsa, Suzanne : *Violin* (Lon)
Rubach, Keith : *Bassoon* (Mid)
Rubba : *Bass Guitar* (NW)
Ruberry, Mark : *Guitars* (SW)
Rubie, Michael : *Saxophones* (Lon)
Rubie, Steve : *Saxophones* (Lon)
Rubin, Ronald : *Pianoforte* (Lon)
Ruby : *Voice* (Lon)
Ruby, David : *Viola* (NW)
Rudall, Stephen : *Cello* (Lon)
Rudd, Hilary : *Voice* (Lon)
Rudd, Hilary : *Clarinet* (SE)
Rudd, Norman : *Pianoforte* (NE)
Ruddick, Joanna : *Pianoforte* (Mid)
Ruddick, John : *Trumpet* (Mid)
Ruddick, John : *Trumpet* (Mid)
Ruddock, Gerald : *Trumpet* (Lon)
Rudeforth, Peter : *Trumpet* (Lon)
Rudge, Eleanor : *Voice* (NW)
Rudland, Malcolm : *Music Director* (Lon)
Rudnick, Marius : *Saxophones* (Lon)
Ruff, Michael : *Accordion* (Lon)
Ruffelle, Louise : *Voice* (Lon)
Ruffer, Nancy : *Flute* (Lon)
Ruffy, Glen : *Percussion* (Lon)
Rugge-Price, James : *Multi Instrumental* (SE)
Ruhemann, Ileana : *Flute* (Lon)
Ruhm, Delia : *Flute* (Mid)
Rule-Minhinett, Ray : *Guitars* (E)
Rumbles, Kenny : *Percussion* (Lon)
Rumbol, Ronald : *Clarinet* (SE)
Rump, Avril : *Cello* (SW)
Rumsby, Tom : *Horn* (SE)
Rumsey, Michael : *Violin* (Lon)
Rumsey, Stephen : *Horn* (Lon)
Runchman, Mark : *Voice* (SE)
Runcorn, Simon : *Guitars* (Lon)
Rundall, Nick : *Guitars* (NW)
Rundell, Kevin : *Double Bass* (Lon)
Rundell, Lynn : *Oboe* (Sco)
Rundle, Anthony : *Guitars* (E)
Rundle, Timothy : *Oboe* (Mid)
Runswick, Daryl : *Composer* (Lon)
Ruocco, Joanne : *Percussion* (Lon)
Rupal, Sanjeve : *Bass Guitar* (Lon)
Rusby, Jack : *Trumpet* (Mid)
Rusby, Kate : *Voice* (NE)
Rusby, Stephen : *Banjo* (NE)
Rusdell, Vincent : *Guitars* (Lon)
Ruse, Kathleen : *Viola* (Lon)
Ruse, Michael : *Guitars* (SE)
Rush, Celeste : *Violin* (Lon)
Rush, Keith : *Keyboards* (SE)
Rush, Stuart : *Composer* (Lon)
Rushbrook, Simon : *Bass Guitar* (E)
Rushmore, Michael : *Percussion* (E)
Rushton, Gordon : *Trombone* (E)
Rushton, Mark : *Trombone* (Lon)
Rushton, Phillip : *Keyboards* (Mid)
Rushton, Stephen : *Percussion* (Lon)
Rushworth, Abigail : *Violin* (Lon)
Rushworth, Daniel : *Voice* (SE)
Rusmanis, Margot : *Violin* (Lon)
Ruso : *Voice* (Lon)
Russell, Alistair : *Guitars* (NE)
Russell, Bella : *Voice* (SW)
Russell, Dan : *Guitars* (Lon)
Russell, David : *Cello* (Mid)
Russell, Elizabeth : *Voice* (NW)
Russell, Graham : *Trumpet* (Lon)
Russell, Ian : *Percussion* (Mid)

Russell, Ian : *Horn* (SW)
Russell, James : *Guitars* (Sco)
Russell, Janet : *Guitars* (NE)
Russell, Jennifer : *Pianoforte* (Lon)
Russell, John : *Violin* (Lon)
Russell, Juliet : *Voice* (NW)
Russell, Lady : *Voice* (Sco)
Russell, Lloyd : *Pianoforte* (Lon)
Russell, Lucy : *Violin* (Lon)
Russell, Mark : *Keyboards* (Lon)
Russell, Mark : *Songwriter* (Lon)
Russell, Paul : *Percussion* (Mid)
Russell, Peter : *Percussion* (Lon)
Russell, Peter : *Pianoforte* (SE)
Russell, Ray : *Guitars* (Lon)
Russell, Richard : *Keyboards* (SE)
Russell, Sandi : *Voice* (NE)
Russell, Simon : *Bass Guitar* (Lon)
Russell, Simon : *Double Bass* (SE)
Russell, Steve : *Guitars* (Lon)
Russell-Smith, Colin : *Saxophones* (Mid)
Russell-Whitaker, Lynda : *Voice* (Lon)
Russo, Chuca : *Voice* (NW)
Russom, Paul : *Pianoforte* (Lon)
Rust, Tom : *Voice* (Lon)
Rutherford, Christian : *Horn* (Lon)
Rutherford, Jonathan : *Pianoforte* (Lon)
Rutherford, Maureen : *Pianoforte* (Sco)
Rutherford, Michael : *Bass Guitar* (Lon)
Rutherford, Paul : *Trombone* (Lon)
Rutherford, Richard : *Bass Guitar* (NE)
Rutherford, Samantha : *Flute* (Lon)
Rutherford, Walter : *Accordion* (Sco)
Rutkowski, Deirdre : *Voice* (Sco)
Rutland, Gillian : *Violin* (SW)
Rutland, Jennifer : *Percussion* (SW)
Rutland, Louis : *Violin* (Lon)
Ruttley, Edward : *Percussion* (E)
Ruttley, Rex : *Saxophones* (Lon)
Ryall, Imogen : *Pianoforte* (Lon)
Ryall, Nick : *Guitars* (E)
Ryall, Samuel : *Pianoforte* (E)
Ryan, Cliodhna : *Violin* (Lon)
Ryan, Colin : *Guitars* (Lon)
Ryan, Dave : *Voice* (Lon)
Ryan, Ellen : *Voice* (E)
Ryan, Eric : *Saxophones* (Lon)
Ryan, Jeffrey : *Double Bass* (SW)
Ryan, John : *Violin* (Lon)
Ryan, Joy : *Pianoforte* (E)
Ryan, Julie : *Trumpet* (Lon)
Ryan, Michael : *Guitars* (NW)
Ryan, Pat : *Percussion* (Lon)
Ryan, Paul : *Percussion* (NW)
Ryan, Petea : *Percussion* (SE)
Ryan, Timothy : *Bass Guitar* (NW)
Ryan, Vourneen : *Flute* (Lon)
Ryan-Carter, Adam : *Percussion* (NW)
Rycroft, Anne : *Viola* (Lon)
Rycroft, Frank : *Horn* (Lon)
Rycroft, Marjorie : *Cello* (Sco)
Rycroft, Marjorie : *Early Strings* (Sco)
Ryder, Allan : *Saxophones* (SE)
Ryder, Anna : *Multi Instrumental* (Lon)
Ryder, Katherine : *Pianoforte* (Lon)
Ryder, Keith : *Guitars* (Lon)
Ryder, Mark : *Pianoforte* (Lon)
Rye, Anthony : *Violin* (Lon)
Rye, Daniel : *Clarinet* (Lon)
Ryser, Terry : *Clarinet* (Lon)
Ryves, Martin : *Saxophones* (Lon)

S

Saadoun, Abdelkader : *Guitars* (Lon)
Saban, Justin : *Guitars* (SW)

Sabatini, Nicodemo : *Guitars* (Lon)
Sabedoria, Alison : *Voice* (Mid)
Saberton, Peter : *Pianoforte* (Lon)
Sabey, Richard : *Saxophones* (NE)
Sabijan, Drazen : *Guitars* (Lon)
Sabiu, Marco : *Keyboards* (Lon)
Sabo, Chuck : *Percussion* (Lon)
Sabri, G : *Tabla* (Mid)
Sacker, Judi : *Pianoforte* (NE)
Sacre, Stephen : *Voice* (SE)
Saddler, Alan : *Double Bass* (Sco)
Sadka, Ivan : *Pianoforte* (SW)
Sadler, Albert : *Banjo* (Lon)
Sadler, Chris : *Guitars* (E)
Sadler, Claire : *Double Bass* (NE)
Sadler, Gaynor : *Composer* (Lon)
Sadler, Jeremy : *Voice* (Lon)
Sadler, Jill : *Clarinet* (Lon)
Sadler, Mary : *Violin* (Lon)
Sadler, Ray : *Guitars* (NW)
Sadler, Richard : *Saxophones* (Lon)
Sadler, Sarah : *Viola* (Sco)
Sadler, Stephen : *Saxophones* (Lon)
Sadler, Tony : *Composer* (Lon)
Safri, Balwinder : *Voice* (Mid)
Sage, Matthew : *Guitars* (SW)
Sage, Norman : *Saxophones* (Lon)
Sager, Sidney : *Conductor* (SW)
Saggers, Donna : *Guitars* (Lon)
Saggese, Matteo : *Pianoforte* (Lon)
Sagi, Zoltan : *Clarinet* (Mid)
Sagoo, Bally : *Keyboards* (Mid)
Sagoo, Ranjit : *Clarinet* (Lon)
Sagov, Margo : *Guitars* (Lon)
Saich, John : *Guitars* (Sco)
Said, Jonathan : *Guitars* (Lon)
Said, Mario : *Bass Guitar* (Lon)
Sainsbury, Ian : *Keyboards* (E)
Sait, Ronald : *Percussion* (Lon)
Sajrawy, Michel : *Guitars* (Lon)
Salad, Mark : *Percussion* (SE)
Salaman, Clare : *Early Strings* (Lon)
Salavage, Neil : *Bassoon* (SE)
Saleem, Imaani : *Voice* (Lon)
Saleh, Morris : *Violin* (NW)
Sales, Dominic : *Percussion* (NE)
Salfield, Stephen : *Saxophones* (NE)
Salgado, Martha : *Guitars* (Lon)
Salinger, Anne : *Violin* (Lon)
Salisbury, Harold : *Saxophones* (NW)
Salisbury, Simon : *Bass Guitar* (NE)
Salkeld, Adam : *Guitars* (Lon)
Salkin, David : *Percussion* (Lon)
Sallis, Mark : *Guitars* (SE)
Sallis, Richard : *Percussion* (Mid)
Salliss, David : *Bass Guitar* (Lon)
Sallows, Gary : *Guitars* (E)
Salmins, Ralph : *Percussion* (Lon)
Salmon, Amanda : *Viola* (Mid)
Salmon, Colin : *Trumpet* (Lon)
Salmon, Derek : *Percussion* (SW)
Salmon, George : *Non Playing Member* (Mid)
Salmon, Godfrey : *Violin* (Lon)
Salmon, Jane : *Cello* (Lon)
Salmon, Murray : *Double Bass* (Lon)
Salmon, Peggy : *Pianoforte* (SW)
Salmons, Richard : *Bass Guitar* (Lon)
Salo, Satu : *Harp* (SE)
Salpeter, Max : *Violin* (Lon)
Salt, David : *Saxophones* (SW)
Salt, Jack : *Saxophones* (SE)
Salter, Graham : *Oboe* (Lon)
Salter, Lionel : *Conductor* (Lon)
Salter, Robert : *Violin* (Lon)
Salter, Susan : *Viola* (Lon)

Salter, Timothy : *Pianoforte* (Lon)
Salvage, Graham : *Bassoon* (NW)
Salvoni, Lou : *Percussion* (Lon)
Salway, Colin J : *Voice* (SE)
Salzedo, Leonard : *Composer* (Lon)
Sam Sam The Bongo Man : *Percussion* (Lon)
Sammes, Michael : *Voice* (Lon)
Sammons, Tony : *Accompanist* (Lon)
Sampson, Andy : *Keyboards* (Lon)
Sampson, Jeremy : *Violin* (Lon)
Sampson, John : *Trumpet* (Sco)
Sampson, Len : *Trombone* (SW)
Sampson, Mary : *Saxophones* (SW)
Sampson, Richard : *Voice* (Lon)
Sampson, Timothy : *Percussion* (Lon)
Sams, Alison : *Trumpet* (Lon)
Samuel, Jill : *Violin* (Lon)
Samuel, Mary : *Viola* (Lon)
Samuel, Robert : *Trumpet* (Lon)
Samuels, Elaine : *Guitars* (Lon)
Samuels, Jazante : *Voice* (Lon)
Samuels, Joyce : *Voice* (Lon)
Samuels, Neil : *Guitars* (Lon)
Samuels, Ray : *Double Bass* (Lon)
Samways, Gordon : *Trumpet* (SE)
Samy, Michella : *Voice* (Lon)
San Remo, Steevi : *Percussion* (E)
San Juan, Stefan : *Percussion* (Lon)
Sanchez, Michael : *Pianoforte* (Mid)
Sanchos : *Guitars* (NW)
Sandbach, Stanley : *Percussion* (NE)
Sandell, Ian : *Percussion* (SE)
Sandeman, David : *Flute* (Lon)
Sander, Adrian : *Clarinet* (NE)
Sander, Hilary : *Clarinet* (NE)
Sander, Peter : *Pianoforte* (Lon)
Sanders, Anthony : *Accordion* (SW)
Sanders, Bev : *Voice* (NW)
Sanders, Carl : *Trombone* (Mid)
Sanders, Daniel : *Keyboards* (NW)
Sanders, Diana : *Flute* (Mid)
Sanders, Geoffrey : *Pianoforte* (Lon)
Sanders, Jim : *Percussion* (SW)
Sanders, Joseph : *Oboe* (Lon)
Sanders, Mark : *Percussion* (Lon)
Sanders, Ric : *Violin* (Mid)
Sanders, Stephen : *Bass Guitar* (Lon)
Sanders, Timothy : *Saxophones* (Lon)
Sanderson, Derek : *Saxophones* (Sco)
Sanderson, Douglas : *Percussion* (NE)
Sanderson, Hayley : *Voice* (E)
Sanderson, John : *Saxophones* (Mid)
Sanderson, Nat : *Percussion* (Sco)
Sanderson, Nick : *Percussion* (Lon)
Sanderson, Richard : *Violin* (Mid)
Sanderson, Rosemary : *Viola* (Lon)
Sanderson, Sally : *Violin* (SE)
Sandford, Christopher : *Composer* (SE)
Sandhu, Surinder : *Sarangi* (Mid)
Sandilands, Iain : *Tympani* (Sco)
Sandira : *Latin American Percu* (Lon)
Sandland, Richard : *Tuba* (Mid)
Sandoe, Cliff : *Saxophones* (SE)
Sands, Ian : *Percussion* (Lon)
Sands, Ian Anthony : *Bass Guitar* (NE)
Sands, John : *Saxophones* (Lon)
Sands, Mick : *Voice* (Lon)
Sandwell, George : *Percussion* (SE)
Sandy : *Keyboards* (Lon)
Sandy : *Saxophones* (Lon)
Sanford, Don : *Guitars* (Lon)
Sanford, Gary : *Guitars* (Lon)
Sanger, Stephen : *Percussion* (Lon)
Sankey, Claire-Louise : *Violin* (Lon)
Sankey, Lee : *Harmonica (Inc Bass* (Lon)

Sansom, Claire : *Violin* (Lon)
Sansom, Marilyn : *Cello* (Lon)
Santana, Adriana : *Voice* (Lon)
Santilly, Bert : *Accordion* (E)
Santos, Ricardo : *Double Bass* (Lon)
Santry, Gary : *Percussion* (Mid)
Sappleton, David : *Percussion* (Lon)
Sapsed, Leonard : *Saxophones* (E)
Sapsford, Gordon : *Saxophones* (Lon)
Sapwell, Brian : *Trumpet* (E)
Sargeant, Benjamin : *Bass Guitar* (Lon)
Sargeant, Bob : *Keyboards* (Lon)
Sargeant, Derek : *Percussion* (SW)
Sargeant, Kim : *Tympani* (SW)
Sargeant, Michael : *Early Wind* (NE)
Sargeant, Paul : *Clarinet* (Lon)
Sargeant, Rex : *Bass Guitar* (Lon)
Sargent, Anthony : *Conductor* (Mid)
Sargent, Christopher : *Bass Guitar* (SE)
Sargent, Frederick : *Bass Guitar* (SE)
Sargent, Kevin : *Pianoforte* (Lon)
Sargent, Raymond : *Early Wind* (SE)
Sargon, Eric : *Viola* (Lon)
Sarici, Sedat : *Bass Guitar* (Lon)
Sarjantson, Douglas : *Organ* (NE)
Sarjeant, Derek : *Guitars* (Lon)
Sarko, Richard : *Bass Guitar* (NW)
Sarlin, Paula : *Voice* (Lon)
Sartin, Maurice : *Percussion* (SW)
Sartin, Paul : *Oboe* (SE)
Sarwar, Atif : *Voice* (E)
Sasha : *Voice* (E)
Sasha : *Keyboards* (Lon)
Sassoon, Jeremy : *Trumpet* (NW)
Sassoon, Julie : *Pianoforte* (NW)
Sassy : *Voice* (Mid)
Satterly, Christopher : *Pianoforte* (SE)
Satterthwaite, Chris : *Horn* (Lon)
Satterthwaite, Richard : *Guitars* (Mid)
Sauer, C : *Violin* (SW)
Saul, Peter : *Percussion* (SW)
Saul, Pinise : *Voice* (Lon)
Saul, T : *Keyboards* (Lon)
Saull, Maggie : *Violin* (Mid)
Sault, Russell : *Guitars* (Mid)
Saumarez, Victor : *Guitars* (Lon)
Saunders, Adam : *Composer* (Lon)
Saunders, Alan : *Keyboards* (NE)
Saunders, Andy : *Saxophones* (Lon)
Saunders, Antony : *Pianoforte* (Lon)
Saunders, Brian : *Pianoforte* (Lon)
Saunders, Camilla : *Pianoforte* (Lon)
Saunders, Cloe : *Pianoforte* (E)
Saunders, Duncan : *Bass Guitar* (E)
Saunders, Emily : *Clarinet* (Lon)
Saunders, Eve : *Oboe* (Lon)
Saunders, Francis : *Cello* (Lon)
Saunders, Francis : *Viola* (Mid)
Saunders, Gerald : *Percussion* (Lon)
Saunders, Harry : *Violin* (Lon)
Saunders, Helen : *Clarinet* (SW)
Saunders, James : *Pianoforte* (E)
Saunders, Jane : *Cor Anglais* (Mid)
Saunders, John : *Guitars* (Mid)
Saunders, John : *Trumpet* (Mid)
Saunders, Malcolm : *Keyboards* (Lon)
Saunders, Mark : *Percussion* (Lon)
Saunders, Nicolas : *Pianoforte* (SE)
Saunders, Patrick : *Clarinet* (Lon)
Saunders, Paul : *Clarinet* (Lon)
Saunders, Paul : *Bagpipes* (Mid)
Saunders, Penelope : *Violin* (Lon)
Saunders, Roger : *Guitars* (Lon)
Saunders, Stephen : *Percussion* (Lon)
Saunders, Steve : *Bass Trombone* (Lon)

Saunders, Sue : *Voice* (Lon)
Saunderson, Matthew : *Bass Guitar* (Lon)
Saunt, Lucy : *Violin* (SW)
Savage, Alan : *Percussion* (Lon)
Savage, Alan : *Percussion* (Mid)
Savage, Alastair : *Violin* (Sco)
Savage, David : *Keyboards* (SE)
Savage, Jimi : *Guitars* (NE)
Savage, Marcus : *Pianoforte* (Lon)
Savage, Nigel : *Percussion* (E)
Savage, Paul : *Percussion* (Sco)
Savage, Richard : *Bass Guitar* (Lon)
Savale, Steve Chandra : *Guitars* (Lon)
Savannah, Jonn : *Keyboards* (Lon)
Savcic, David : *Guitars* (Lon)
Savill, Martin : *Guitars* (SE)
Saville, Alex : *Keyboards* (Lon)
Saville, Deborah : *Cello* (NE)
Saville, Tommy : *Pianoforte* (Mid)
Saville, Vic : *Guitars* (Lon)
Sawbridge, Paul : *Horn* (Mid)
Sawers, Ingrid : *Pianoforte* (Sco)
Sawhney, Nitin : *Guitars* (Lon)
Sawtell, Paul : *Keyboards* (Mid)
Sawtell, Paul : *Music Director* (Mid)
Sawtell, Paul : *Pianoforte* (Mid)
Sawtell, Stephen : *Percussion* (Lon)
Sawyer, Helen : *Cello* (Lon)
Sawyer, Margaret : *Violin* (NE)
Sawyer, Phil : *Keyboards* (Lon)
Sawyers, Philip : *Violin* (Lon)
Sax, Sidney : *Violin* (Lon)
Saxby, Kate : *Double Bass* (Lon)
Saxby, Timothy : *Percussion* (Lon)
Saxl, Julian : *Violin* (Lon)
Saxton, Michael : *Clarinet* (SW)
Say, Michael : *Percussion* (Mid)
Sayer, Anthony : *Cello* (Sco)
Sayer, Eddy : *Percussion* (Lon)
Sayer, Raymond : *Saxophones* (SE)
Sayer, Ron James : *Bass Guitar* (E)
Sayers, Caroline : *Cello* (NW)
Sayers, Pete : *Guitars* (E)
Sayfritz, Mark : *Music Director* (Lon)
Scadding, James : *Bass Guitar* (SW)
Scahill, Alistair : *Viola* (Lon)
Scaife, James : *Percussion* (NW)
Scales, Rosemary : *Trumpet* (E)
Scally, Dennis : *Organ* (SW)
Scally, Michelle : *Flute* (NE)
Scandrett, Lindsay : *Pianoforte* (Lon)
Scannell, James : *Saxophones* (Lon)
Scantlebury, Anthony : *Percussion* (Lon)
Scarfe, Douglas : *Horn* (NE)
Scarfe, Stephen : *Keyboards* (NE)
Scarff, George : *Trumpet* (E)
Scarff, Richard : *Percussion* (Lon)
Scargill, Gary : *Keyboards* (NE)
Scarlett, Niara : *Pianoforte* (Lon)
Scarratt, Doug : *Guitars* (SE)
Scarth, Neil : *Guitars* (NE)
Sceptics Band : *Percussion* (SW)
Schaefer, Frank : *Cello* (Lon)
Schalom, Guy : *Percussion* (NW)
Schapper, Friedrich : *Guitars* (Lon)
Schatzberger, Lesley : *Clarinet* (Lon)
Schauerman, Julia : *Saxophones* (Lon)
Schay, Eva : *Violin* (Lon)
Schechter, Gregory : *Clarinet* (Lon)
Schelling, Laura : *Percussion* (Lon)
Schepens, Avril : *Viola* (NW)
Scheporat, Gudi : *Recorders* (SE)
Scheuer, Betty : *Violin* (Mid)
Schiele, Brian : *Viola* (Lon)
Schillace, Michele : *Percussion* (SW)

Schilsky, Erika : *Oboe* (Lon)
Schirmer, Beatrice : *Double Bass* (NW)
Schlaiffer, Don : *Violin* (SW)
Schlapp, Jan : *Viola* (Lon)
Schlenther, Deborah : *Violin* (Lon)
Schliffke, Joan : *Viola* (SW)
Schmeising, Evelyn : *Violin* (SE)
Schmid, Bettina : *Saxophones* (Lon)
Schmidt, Gerhard : *Violin* (E)
Schmool, Barak : *Saxophones* (Lon)
Schneider, Jonathan : *Keyboards* (Lon)
Schneider, Phil : *Bass Guitar* (Mid)
Schofield, Angela : *Double Bass* (Lon)
Schofield, Catherine : *Violin* (Lon)
Schofield, Linda : *Voice* (SE)
Schofield, Michael : *Viola* (Lon)
Schofield, Michael : *Saxophones* (NE)
Schofield, Paul : *Percussion* (NW)
Schofield, Phillippa : *Cello* (Lon)
Schofield, William : *Cello* (Lon)
Schogger, Daniel : *Pianoforte* (Lon)
Scholes, Philippa : *Pianoforte* (SW)
Scholes Corbett, Stuart : *Bass Guitar* (E)
Schooling, Tony : *Guitars* (Lon)
Schoonderwoerd, Peter : *Guitars* (Mid)
Schrecker, Patricia : *Viola* (SW)
Schrecker, Peter : *Violin* (SW)
Schreiber, Arianne : *Voice* (Lon)
Schroder, John : *Bassoon* (Mid)
Schroder, Julie : *Flute* (Mid)
Schroeder, Franziska : *Saxophones* (Sco)
Schuelein, Rainer : *Flute* (Lon)
Schueller, Michael : *Guitars* (E)
Schulman, Lorraine : *Clarinet* (Lon)
Schultzberg, Robert : *Percussion* (Lon)
Schunker, Adam : *Percussion* (SE)
Schunker, Dominic : *Keyboards* (SE)
Schurmann, Margaret : *Pianoforte* (Lon)
Schwarm, Christa : *Violin* (SE)
Schwartz, Curtis : *Guitars* (SE)
Schwarz, Martina : *Accordion* (Lon)
Schweinberger, Silvia : *Violin* (Lon)
Schwier, Peter : *Percussion* (Lon)
Schyffert, Pen : *Guitars* (Lon)
Scialla, Janelle : *Voice* (Lon)
Scoates, Richard : *Trombone* (Sco)
Scollay, Leonard : *Folk Fiddle* (Sco)
Scollen, Thomas : *Guitars* (SW)
Scooby : *Guitars* (E)
Scooby : *Guitars* (Sco)
Scooper, Nick : *Keyboards* (Lon)
Scordia, Geoffrey : *Cello* (Sco)
Scot, Dale : *Guitars* (E)
Scotcher, Terry : *Saxophones* (E)
Scott, Alison : *Voice* (SE)
Scott, Andrew : *Guitars* (Lon)
Scott, Andrew : *Saxophones* (NW)
Scott, Anthony : *Percussion* (E)
Scott, Bill : *Banjo* (Mid)
Scott, Brenda : *Voice* (Mid)
Scott, Bryan : *Double Bass* (Lon)
Scott, Carolyn : *Viola* (Lon)
Scott, Catherine : *Violin* (Mid)
Scott, Cedric : *Pianoforte* (Mid)
Scott, Christopher : *Keyboards* (NE)
Scott, Clive : *Keyboards* (Lon)
Scott, Clive : *Trumpet* (NW)
Scott, Damien : *Guitars* (SW)
Scott, Daniel : *Trombone* (Lon)
Scott, David : *Guitars* (Sco)
Scott, David : *Percussion* (Sco)
Scott, Derek : *Pianoforte* (Lon)
Scott, Donald : *Pianoforte* (NW)
Scott, Eileen : *Voice* (Lon)
Scott, Ernest : *Violin* (Mid)

Scott, Farran : *Violin* (Lon)
Scott, Fred : *Keyboards* (Lon)
Scott, Gavin : *Bass Guitar* (Lon)
Scott, Geoff : *Saxophones* (E)
Scott, Glenvin : *Pianoforte* (Lon)
Scott, Graeme : *Viola* (Lon)
Scott, Harry : *Pianoforte* (E)
Scott, Hector : *Violin* (Sco)
Scott, Iain : *Guitars* (Lon)
Scott, Iain : *Percussion* (Sco)
Scott, Ian : *Pianoforte* (E)
Scott, Ian : *Clarinet* (Lon)
Scott, Ian : *Viola* (Lon)
Scott, Irene : *Guitars* (Lon)
Scott, Jacky : *Guitars* (SE)
Scott, Jim : *Percussion* (SW)
Scott, Jim : *Percussion* (SW)
Scott, John : *Pianoforte* (Mid)
Scott, John : *Electric Accordion* (SW)
Scott, Johnathan : *Guitars* (NE)
Scott, Jon : *Trumpet* (Lon)
Scott, Jonathan : *Pianoforte* (SE)
Scott, Julian : *Percussion* (SW)
Scott, June : *Flute* (Lon)
Scott, Kevin : *Percussion* (SE)
Scott, Kirsteen : *Violin* (Mid)
Scott, Lauren : *Harp* (NW)
Scott, Malcolm : *Percussion* (Lon)
Scott, Mark : *Keyboards* (Lon)
Scott, Mark : *Keyboards* (SE)
Scott, Matthew : *Composer* (Lon)
Scott, Matthew : *Percussion* (Lon)
Scott, Michael : *Guitars* (Lon)
Scott, Michael J : *Keyboards* (NE)
Scott, Neil : *Harmonica (Inc Bass* (Sco)
Scott, Norman : *Organ* (Mid)
Scott, Paul : *Bass Guitar* (Lon)
Scott, Paul : *Oboe* (NE)
Scott, Philip : *Pianoforte* (SW)
Scott, Phoebe : *Cello* (Lon)
Scott, Rebbecca : *Violin* (Lon)
Scott, Richard : *Saxophones* (NE)
Scott, Richard : *Voice* (NE)
Scott, Robert : *Guitars* (Lon)
Scott, Robert : *Music Director* (Lon)
Scott, Robert : *Bass Guitar* (NE)
Scott, Robert : *Trombone* (NE)
Scott, Robert : *Guitars* (SE)
Scott, Robin : *Keyboards* (Lon)
Scott, Rupert : *Violin* (NE)
Scott, Russell : *Voice* (E)
Scott, Ruth : *Oboe* (Lon)
Scott, Sarah : *Violin* (Mid)
Scott, Sarnia : *Oboe* (Lon)
Scott, Shirley : *Violin* (Lon)
Scott, Simon : *Percussion* (Lon)
Scott, Stanley : *Percussion* (Lon)
Scott, Thomas : *Violin* (Sco)
Scott, Timothy : *Guitars* (NW)
Scott, Vyvyon : *Keyboards* (Lon)
Scott-Barrett, Dominic : *Percussion* (Lon)
Scott-Taylor, Ian : *Double Bass* (Lon)
Scott T : *Keyboards* (Mid)
Scourfield, Eluned : *Harp* (SW)
Scragg, Phil : *Bass Guitar* (Lon)
Scraggy : *Saxophones* (Mid)
Scrimgeour, David : *Saxophones* (Sco)
Scriven, Chris : *Guitars* (Lon)
Scriven, Graham : *Percussion* (SE)
Scriven, Lee : *Voice* (SE)
Scriven, Tony : *Percussion* (NE)
Scrivener, Andrew : *Violin* (NW)
Scrivener, Graham : *Clarinet* (Lon)
Scrivener, Matthew : *Violin* (Lon)
Scrivener, Paul : *Composer* (Lon)

Scrivens, Michael : *Bass Guitar* (Mid)
Scullion, John : *Violin* (Sco)
Scullion, Robert : *Keyboards* (Mid)
Scully, Mary : *Double Bass* (Lon)
Scurfield, Joseph : *Violin* (NE)
Scutt, Cyril : *Pianoforte* (SE)
Scutt, Martin : *Guitars* (NE)
Seabrook, Kathryn : *Flute* (Lon)
Seabrook, Ronnie : *Bass Guitar* (Lon)
Seabrook, Terence : *Pianoforte* (SE)
Seacome, Diggory : *Tympani* (SW)
Seago, Frank : *Trombone* (Lon)
Seago, Peter : *Clarinet* (Lon)
Seagrave Pearce, Susie : *Voice* (SE)
Seagroatt, Jon : *Saxophones* (SE)
Seal : *Voice* (Lon)
Seal, Michael : *Violin* (Mid)
Seal, Peter : *Guitars* (Lon)
Seale, Charlotte : *Harp* (Lon)
Sealy, Denice : *Voice* (Lon)
Sealy, Norman : *Percussion* (Lon)
Seaman, Caroline : *Voice* (Lon)
Seaman, David : *Conductor* (SW)
Seaman, John : *Double Bass* (SE)
Seaman, Nigel : *Tuba* (SW)
Seaman, Paul : *Keyboards* (NW)
Seaman, Robert : *Guitars* (Lon)
Sear, Andrew : *Percussion* (Lon)
Sear, Brian : *Bass Guitar* (Lon)
Sear, Gordon : *Percussion* (NW)
Sear, Natalie : *Pianoforte* (Mid)
Searchfield, Sheila : *Flute* (Lon)
Searle, Benjamin : *Trumpet* (Mid)
Searle, James : *Songwriter* (NW)
Searle-Barnes, Paul : *Pianoforte* (SE)
Sears, John : *Violin* (SW)
Seath, Ian : *Synthesiser* (Sco)
Seatle, Paul : *Guitars* (Lon)
Seaton, Alan : *Double Bass* (NE)
Seaton, Dennis : *Voice* (Mid)
Seaton, Ronald : *Pianoforte* (NE)
Seaton, Sylvia : *Violin* (Lon)
Seattle, Matt : *Cauld Wind Pipes* (Sco)
Seavor, Leslie : *Guitars* (NW)
Seaward, E : *Organ* (NE)
Sebastian, Frank : *Saxophones* (E)
Sebastian, Tania : *Keyboards* (Lon)
Sebunya, Charles : *Voice* (Lon)
Secker, John : *Bassoon* (SW)
Secluna, Clive : *Clarinet* (E)
Secret, Gillian : *Violin* (SE)
Secret, Robert : *Viola* (SE)
Seddon, Ambrose : *Guitars* (Lon)
Seddon, Colin : *Bass Guitar* (SW)
Seddon, Patsy : *Harp* (Sco)
Sedge, Charles : *Guitars* (E)
Sedge, James : *Percussion* (Lon)
Sedgwick, Prunella : *Violin* (Lon)
Sedgwick, Simon : *Bass Guitar* (Lon)
See, Janet : *Flute* (SE)
Seed, Christopher : *Pianoforte* (SE)
Seeger, Justin : *Bass Guitar* (Lon)
Seeger, Peggy : *Guitars* (Lon)
Seeley, Paul : *Pianoforte* (NE)
Seenan, Hugh : *Horn* (Lon)
Seewi, Assaf : *Percussion* (Lon)
Seezer, Maurice : *Pianoforte* (Lon)
Sefton, David : *Bass Guitar* (NW)
Segal, Emily : *Pianoforte* (Lon)
Segal, Jack : *Percussion* (Lon)
Segal, Joel : *Violin* (SW)
Segal, Lizzie : *Voice* (Lon)
Segal, Marianne : *Arranger* (Lon)
Segger, Jill : *Composer* (E)
Seggie, Peter : *Non Playing Member* (Mid)

Simmonds, John : *Saxophones* (Lon)
Simmonds, Maurice : *Pianoforte* (SE)
Simmonds, Mickey : *Keyboards* (Lon)
Simmonds, Ray : *Trumpet* (Lon)
Simmonds, Robert : *Trumpet* (Mid)
Simmonds, Ronald : *Bass Guitar* (E)
Simmons : *Composer* (Lon)
Simmons, Alan : *Double Bass* (Lon)
Simmons, Cathy : *Tuba* (SE)
Simmons, Daniel : *Percussion* (Lon)
Simmons, Ian : *Pianoforte* (Lon)
Simmons, Jacob : *Accordion* (SW)
Simmons, Mark : *Clarinet* (SW)
Simmons, Ray : *Trumpet* (Lon)
Simmons, Richard : *Pianoforte* (Lon)
Simmons, Robert : *Percussion* (Mid)
Simms, Andrew : *Saxophones* (E)
Simms, Dave : *Percussion* (SE)
Simms, Nicholas : *Percussion* (Lon)
Simms, Philip : *Double Bass* (Lon)
Simms, Rachel : *Bassoon* (Lon)
Simnett, Derek : *Voice* (Lon)
Simon, Daniel : *Keyboards* (Lon)
Simon, Paul : *Percussion* (Lon)
Simon, Richard : *Violin* (Lon)
Simon, Roy : *Guitars* (Lon)
Simon, Theo : *Percussion* (SW)
Simons, Andrew : *Guitars* (NE)
Simons, Gary : *Bass Guitar* (NE)
Simons, Harry : *Trombone* (NW)
Simons, Helen : *Bassoon* (Lon)
Simons, Jane : *Voice* (NE)
Simons, John : *Music Director* (Mid)
Simons, John : *Pianoforte* (Mid)
Simons, Les : *Saxophones* (Lon)
Simons, Martin : *Saxophones* (E)
Simons, Simone : *Voice* (Lon)
Simpson, Andrew : *Guitars* (Mid)
Simpson, Anne : *Violin* (Sco)
Simpson, Catherine : *Voice* (SE)
Simpson, Christopher : *Guitars* (NE)
Simpson, David : *Percussion* (Mid)
Simpson, David : *Bass Guitar* (Lon)
Simpson, Denis : *Percussion* (Mid)
Simpson, Derek : *Cello* (Lon)
Simpson, Erica : *Cello* (Lon)
Simpson, Georgina : *Clarinet* (Mid)
Simpson, Graham : *Pianoforte* (Mid)
Simpson, Herma : *Voice* (Mid)
Simpson, Iain : *Guitars* (Lon)
Simpson, Ian : *Bass Guitar* (SW)
Simpson, James : *Keyboards* (NE)
Simpson, Janet : *Pianoforte* (NW)
Simpson, Karen : *Flute* (NW)
Simpson, Kathleen : *Pianoforte* (NE)
Simpson, Lester : *Bagpipes* (Mid)
Simpson, Lilian : *Percussion* (Lon)
Simpson, Mark : *Guitars* (Lon)
Simpson, Michael : *Percussion* (Lon)
Simpson, Michael : *Percussion* (Mid)
Simpson, Michael : *Trumpet* (Mid)
Simpson, Olive : *Voice* (Lon)
Simpson, Paul : *Keyboards* (Mid)
Simpson, Peter : *Guitars* (NE)
Simpson, Peter : *Voice* (NE)
Simpson, Phil : *Saxophones* (Lon)
Simpson, Ray : *Voice* (Lon)
Simpson, Richard : *Oboe* (NW)
Simpson, Richard : *Guitars* (SW)
Simpson, Sally : *Pianoforte* (Lon)
Simpson, Steve : *Guitars* (Lon)
Simpson, Susan : *Violin* (Sco)
Sims, Ken : *Trumpet* (Lon)
Sims, Richard : *Trumpet* (NE)
Sims, Sam : *Banjo* (SW)

Sin, Jimmy : *Voice* (Lon)
Sinclair, Alan : *Bass Tuba* (Mid)
Sinclair, Alistair : *Bass Trombone* (Sco)
Sinclair, Bim : *Composer* (Lon)
Sinclair, Cameron Roy : *Percussion* (Lon)
Sinclair, Christine : *Violin* (Sco)
Sinclair, Dave : *Percussion* (Sco)
Sinclair, Douglas : *Guitars* (Sco)
Sinclair, Douglas : *Bass Guitar* (SE)
Sinclair, Eric : *Trombone* (Mid)
Sinclair, Fiona : *Viola* (NW)
Sinclair, George : *Bass Guitar* (Sco)
Sinclair, George : *Guitars* (Sco)
Sinclair, Jane : *Violin* (SW)
Sinclair, Ken : *Trumpet* (Lon)
Sinclair, Mark : *Pianoforte* (Sco)
Sinclair, Neil : *Accordion* (Sco)
Sinclair, Robert : *Bass Trombone* (Lon)
Sinclair, Roderick : *Guitars* (NE)
Sinden, Toby : *Percussion* (E)
Singer, Nicholas : *Banjo* (Lon)
Singer, Ray : *Percussion* (Lon)
Singh, Ajaib : *Keyboards* (Mid)
Singh, Bakhshish : *Songwriter* (Lon)
Singh, Dalvinder : *Keyboards* (NW)
Singh, Harjit : *Tabla* (Mid)
Singh, Malkit : *Tumbi* (Mid)
Singh, Manohar : *Voice* (Lon)
Singh, Mohinder : *Tabla* (Mid)
Singh, Samiera : *Voice* (Mid)
Singh, Sardara : *Voice* (Mid)
Singh, Satin El Indio : *Latin American Percu* (Lon)
Singhji, Oriol : *Saxophones* (E)
Singleton, Emlyn : *Violin* (Lon)
Singleton, John : *Trombone* (Lon)
Singleton, Julia : *Violin* (Lon)
Singleton, Leo : *Percussion* (SE)
Singleton, Philip : *Trumpet* (SE)
Singleton, Stephen : *Saxophones* (NE)
Sininerd, Owen : *Percussion* (SE)
Sinister : *Bass Guitar* (Lon)
Sinnott, Kevin : *Bass Guitar* (NW)
Sinton, John : *Double Bass* (Sco)
Sippings, Andrew : *Viola* (Lon)
Sired, Carole : *Flute* (Lon)
Siren, Steve : *Voice* (NW)
Siren, Sylvie : *Voice* (NW)
Sirett, John : *Double Bass* (Lon)
Siriwardena, Caroline : *Violin* (NE)
Sirota, Sophie : *Viola* (Lon)
Sisley, John : *Keyboards* (Lon)
Sisson, Richard : *Pianoforte* (E)
Sister Miriam : *Voice* (Lon)
Siswick, Julie : *Oboe* (SW)
Sivanesan, Sivanesan : *Veena* (Lon)
Sivier, William : *Percussion* (E)
Sivier, David : *Trombone* (Mid)
Siviter, Roger : *Trumpet* (Mid)
Skaith, Stephen : *Guitars* (Lon)
Skarbek, Charlie : *Keyboards* (Lon)
Skarbek, Sacha : *Keyboards* (Lon)
Skates, Anne : *Voice* (Lon)
Skates, Nicholas : *Guitars* (SE)
Skeaping, Emma : *Early Strings* (Lon)
Skeaping, Lucie : *Violin* (Lon)
Skeaping, Roderick : *Composer* (Lon)
Skeat, Leonard : *Double Bass* (Lon)
Skeat, Robert : *Bass Guitar* (Lon)
Sked, Malcolm : *Sousaphone* (Mid)
Skeet, Andrew : *Composer* (Lon)
Skeet, Christopher : *Guitars* (SE)
Skeete, Mark : *Pianoforte* (Lon)
Skelhorn, Gavin : *Guitars* (Lon)
Skelton, Matt : *Percussion* (Lon)
Skelton, Paul : *Percussion* (Lon)

Skempton, Howard : *Composer* (Mid)
Skene-Keating, Paul : *Pianoforte* (SE)
Skeoch, Fraser : *Music Director* (Lon)
Skewes, Hilary : *Violin* (Lon)
Ski : *Keyboards* (Lon)
Skidmore, Alan : *Saxophones* (Lon)
Skiffington, David : *Guitars* (Lon)
Skilbeck, Ben : *Percussion* (NE)
Skillen, Derrick : *Saxophones* (Sco)
Skillmaster : *Songwriter* (Mid)
Skinnard, Andrew : *Pianoforte* (SE)
Skinner, Ashley : *Guitars* (Mid)
Skinner, Colin : *Saxophones* (Lon)
Skinner, John : *Trumpet* (Lon)
Skinner, Katrina : *Oboe* (Lon)
Skinner, Michael : *Percussion* (Lon)
Skinner, Miriam : *Cello* (NW)
Skinner, Nigel : *Steel Pan* (SW)
Skinner, Peter : *Music Director* (NW)
Skinner, Richard : *Bassoon* (Lon)
Skinner, Stephen : *Clarinet* (Lon)
Skinner, Tom : *Percussion* (Lon)
Skinner, William : *Viola* (SW)
Skipper, Sandra : *Flute* (Lon)
Skipsey, Andrew : *Bass Guitar* (Lon)
Skivington, Peter : *Bass Guitar* (Lon)
Skuce, Peter : *Harpsichord* (Lon)
Skulski, Michael : *Guitars* (E)
Sky, Dr : *Guitars* (Lon)
Skye, Mel : *Voice* (Lon)
Skyrme, Martin : *Flute* (NW)
Slack, Frank : *Clarinet* (Lon)
Slack, Karen : *Clarinet* (Lon)
Slade, Andrew : *Violin* (NE)
Slade, Christopher : *Percussion* (SE)
Slade, Claire : *Double Bass* (Lon)
Slade, John : *Guitars* (E)
Slade, Julian : *Pianoforte* (Lon)
Slade, Justin : *Guitars* (Lon)
Slade, Owen : *Tuba* (Lon)
Slade, Roy : *Violin* (Lon)
Sladen, Matthew : *Pianoforte* (NE)
Slany, Sonia : *Violin* (Lon)
Slapper, Clifford : *Pianoforte* (Lon)
Slapper Dave : *Guitars* (NE)
Slater, Alan : *Bass Guitar* (NW)
Slater, Ashley : *Trombone* (Lon)
Slater, Carol : *Violin* (Lon)
Slater, Harry : *Bass Guitar* (Mid)
Slater, James : *Guitars* (NW)
Slater, John : *Percussion* (NW)
Slater, Judy : *Voice* (Sco)
Slater, Leon : *Saxophones* (Mid)
Slater, Matthew : *Composer* (Lon)
Slater, Nick : *Guitars* (E)
Slater, Rodney : *Saxophones* (E)
Slater, Rueben : *Percussion* (NW)
Slater, Ruth : *Violin* (Lon)
Slaughter, John : *Guitars* (E)
Slaven, Mick : *Guitars* (Sco)
Slaymark, Victor : *Clarinet* (Lon)
Sleath, Will : *Flute* (Lon)
Sledmere, Adrian : *Guitars* (Lon)
Slee, Nigel : *Double Bass* (NE)
Sleet, Nichole : *Voice* (Lon)
Sleigh, James : *Viola* (Lon)
Slide, Fred : *Trombone* (Lon)
Slide, Mark : *Guitars* (E)
Slim : *Accordion* (Lon)
Sloan, Alan : *Violin* (Lon)
Sloan, Bryan : *Keyboards* (Sco)
Sloan, John : *Percussion* (Lon)
Slocombe, Rob : *Trombone* (E)
Sloman, Carol : *Pianoforte* (SE)
Slowley, Paul : *Percussion* (Lon)

Stanley, Mike : *Music Director* (Lon)
Stanley, Sean : *Synthesiser* (Mid)
Stannard, Richard : *Keyboards* (Lon)
Stannard, Roy : *Pianoforte* (Lon)
Stannard, Tim : *Guitars* (Lon)
Stanton, Bernard : *Clarinet* (Lon)
Stanton, John : *Guitars* (NW)
Stanton, Stan : *Percussion* (E)
Stanton, Tony : *Copyist* (Lon)
Stanway, Peter : *Guitars* (Mid)
Stanway, Peter : *Guitars* (NW)
Staples, Andrew : *Viola* (Lon)
Staples, Andy : *Bass Guitar* (Lon)
Staples, Ann : *Cello* (SW)
Staples, I G : *Bass Guitar* (SE)
Staples, Julie : *Violin* (Lon)
Staples, Peter : *Percussion* (NW)
Stapleton, Cliff : *Hurdy-gurdy* (Lon)
Stapleton, Ian : *Percussion* (E)
Stapleton, John : *Pianoforte* (Lon)
Stapp, Petra : *Guitars* (Mid)
Starbuck, Simone : *Voice* (SE)
Stardust : *Percussion* (Lon)
Stares, Steve : *Bass Guitar* (SE)
Stark, Alan : *Percussion* (Sco)
Stark, Anthony : *Cello* (Lon)
Stark, John : *Trombone* (Sco)
Stark, Peter : *Conductor* (Lon)
Stark, Thomas : *Pianoforte* (SW)
Stark, Valerie : *Clarinet* (NW)
Starke, Gordon : *Violin* (Lon)
Starke, Jean : *Violin* (Lon)
Starkey, Jonathan : *Pianoforte* (NW)
Starkie, Gerard : *Voice* (NW)
Starks, Elliott : *Bass Guitar* (SW)
Starks, Gavin : *Synthesiser* (Lon)
Starlet, Charlotte : *Keyboards* (Sco)
Starr, Maxine : *Pianoforte* (Lon)
Start, Doug : *Bass Guitar* (E)
Startup, Benjamin : *Guitars* (SE)
Statham, David : *Horn* (Mid)
Statham, Paul : *Keyboards* (Lon)
Statham, Rob : *Bass Guitar* (Lon)
Statton, Alison : *Voice* (SW)
Staunton, Christopher : *Double Bass* (Mid)
Staveley, Colin : *Violin* (Lon)
Stavordale, John : *Percussion* (NW)
Stead, David : *Percussion* (Lon)
Stead, David : *Percussion* (NE)
Stead, Gillian : *Violin* (SE)
Stead, Sidney : *Cello* (NW)
Steadman, David : *Music Director* (Mid)
Steadman, Jack : *Violin* (Lon)
Stear, Geoff : *Bass Guitar* (SE)
Stear, Kate : *Violin* (SE)
Stearn, Christopher : *Bass Trombone* (Sco)
Steedman, David : *Horn* (NW)
Steedman, Heather : *Percussion* (Lon)
Steel, Barbara : *Violin* (SE)
Steel, Brian : *Double Bass* (Mid)
Steel, Brian D : *Keyboards* (SE)
Steel, Philip : *Pianoforte* (E)
Steel, Terry : *Saxophones* (E)
Steel, Trevor : *Guitars* (Lon)
Steele, Alexander : *Pianoforte* (SW)
Steele, Christopher : *Guitars* (NW)
Steele, Colin : *Trumpet* (Sco)
Steele, David : *Bass Guitar* (Mid)
Steele, David : *Bouzouki* (Sco)
Steele, Donald : *Trumpet* (Lon)
Steele, Jan : *Music Director* (Lon)
Steele, Jan : *Saxophones* (Lon)
Steele, John : *Saxophones* (NE)
Steele, Luke : *Bass Guitar* (SE)
Steele, Matthew : *Pianoforte* (NW)

Steele, Richard : *Synthesiser* (Lon)
Steele-Perkins, Crispian : *Trumpet* (Lon)
Steell, Robert : *Trombone* (Sco)
Steenkamp, Erica : *Guitars* (Lon)
Steer, Caroline : *Cello* (NW)
Steer, David : *Guitars* (Mid)
Steer, John : *Double Bass* (Lon)
Steer, Jonathan : *Cornet* (Lon)
Steer, Maxwell : *Composer* (SW)
Steer, Peter : *Voice* (Lon)
Steer, Richard : *Guitars* (SW)
Steers, Simon : *Guitars* (NE)
Stefano : *Pianoforte* (Lon)
Stefano : *Guitars* (NW)
Steggall, Richard : *Horn* (Lon)
Stehn, Leonard : *Cello* (Lon)
Stein, David : *Bass Guitar* (Lon)
Stein, John : *Violin* (SW)
Stein, Jonathan : *Pianoforte* (SW)
Stelling, Roy : *Accordion* (Mid)
Stelnicki, Craig : *Bass Guitar* (NW)
Stemp, Morris : *Violin* (NW)
Stenhouse, John : *Clarinet* (Lon)
Stenhouse, Linda : *Pianoforte* (NE)
Stenson, Tony : *Music Director* (Lon)
Stent, Keith : *Conductor* (Lon)
Stephen, Andrew : *Trumpet* (SW)
Stephen, Graham : *Guitars* (Sco)
Stephen, Ian Keith : *Banjo* (NE)
Stephen, Jack : *Percussion* (Lon)
Stephen, Rosahund : *Violin* (SW)
Stephens, Alison : *Mandolin* (Lon)
Stephens, Carla : *Voice* (SE)
Stephens, David : *Keyboards* (SE)
Stephens, James : *Guitars* (Lon)
Stephens, Kevin : *Trombone* (SW)
Stephens, Nicholas : *Double Bass* (Lon)
Stephens, Peter : *Violin* (NW)
Stephens, Stanley : *Trombone* (Mid)
Stephenson, Alfred : *Trumpet* (NE)
Stephenson, Anne : *Violin* (Lon)
Stephenson, Frederick : *Guitars* (Lon)
Stephenson, Gordon : *Trumpet* (SW)
Stephenson, Irene : *Violin* (NE)
Stephenson, James : *Oboe* (NE)
Stephenson, Karen : *Cello* (Mid)
Stephenson, Kate : *Voice* (Lon)
Stephenson, Lee : *Clarinet* (Lon)
Stephenson, Michael : *Guitars* (SE)
Stephenson, Robert : *Percussion* (NE)
Stephenson, Ronnie : *Percussion* (Sco)
Stephenson, Shawn : *Percussion* (Lon)
Stephenson, Steve : *Percussion* (E)
Steponitis, Bernie : *Pianoforte* (SE)
Steriopulos, Philip : *Double Bass* (Lon)
Sterling, Andrew : *Pianoforte* (E)
Stern, Christopher : *Voice* (E)
Sternefeld, Frank : *Harp* (NE)
Steven, Gary : *Percussion* (NW)
Steven, Yla : *Violin* (Sco)
Stevens, Ashley : *Violin* (Lon)
Stevens, Cat : *Guitars* (Lon)
Stevens, Cathy : *Viola* (SE)
Stevens, Dayle : *Violin* (Lon)
Stevens, Edmund : *Pianoforte* (Lon)
Stevens, Gary : *Cello* (SE)
Stevens, Gillian : *Cello* (SW)
Stevens, Jane : *Flute* (Lon)
Stevens, Jonathan : *Voice* (Lon)
Stevens, Laurie : *Percussion* (Mid)
Stevens, Mark : *Percussion* (Mid)
Stevens, Mark : *Keyboards* (NW)
Stevens, Mark : *Melodeon* (SE)
Stevens, Michael : *Saxophones* (SE)
Stevens, Nick : *Keyboards* (SW)

Stevens, Norman : *Pianoforte* (Lon)
Stevens, Paul : *Guitars* (E)
Stevens, Paul : *Folk Fiddle* (Lon)
Stevens, Paul : *Saxophones* (Lon)
Stevens, Peter : *Violin* (Lon)
Stevens, Rob : *Percussion* (Lon)
Stevens, Terry : *Voice* (Sco)
Stevens, Tony : *Bass Guitar* (E)
Stevenson, Andrew : *Guitars* (Mid)
Stevenson, Anna-Wendy : *Violin* (Sco)
Stevenson, Cath : *Pianoforte* (NE)
Stevenson, Daniel : *Guitars* (Lon)
Stevenson, Daniel : *Guitars* (Mid)
Stevenson, Douglas : *Guitars* (Sco)
Stevenson, Gary : *Guitars* (SE)
Stevenson, James : *Guitars* (Lon)
Stevenson, Jeremy : *Guitars* (E)
Stevenson, Kathleen : *Flute* (Lon)
Stevenson, Leslie : *Saxophones* (NW)
Stevenson, Nicholas : *Flute* (Lon)
Stevenson, Nicholas : *Trumpet* (SE)
Stevenson, Paul : *Guitars* (E)
Stevenson, Philip : *Guitars* (SE)
Stevenson, Savourna : *Harp* (Sco)
Stevenson, Thomas : *Trumpet* (Sco)
Stevenson, Tony : *Bass Guitar* (Lon)
Steward, Christopher : *Flute* (Mid)
Steward, Harold : *Pianoforte* (E)
Steward, Terry : *Saxophones* (Lon)
Stewart, Alex : *Bass Trombone* (Mid)
Stewart, Alexander : *Guitars* (Lon)
Stewart, Alistair : *Double Bass* (Sco)
Stewart, Bill : *Guitars* (Sco)
Stewart, Brian : *Flute* (NE)
Stewart, Christina : *Voice* (Sco)
Stewart, Claude : *Guitars* (Mid)
Stewart, Dan : *Bass Guitar* (Lon)
Stewart, Daniel : *Percussion* (NW)
Stewart, David : *Bass Trombone* (Lon)
Stewart, David : *Guitars* (Lon)
Stewart, David : *Percussion* (Sco)
Stewart, David : *Violin* (Sco)
Stewart, Diane : *Cello* (NW)
Stewart, Doug : *Guitars* (NE)
Stewart, Eva : *Flute* (NE)
Stewart, Ewan : *Percussion* (Lon)
Stewart, Godfrey : *Percussion* (Lon)
Stewart, Helena : *Voice* (Lon)
Stewart, Iain : *Bagpipes* (Lon)
Stewart, Ian : *Keyboards* (Lon)
Stewart, Jennifer : *Bassoon* (Sco)
Stewart, Jill : *Pianoforte* (Sco)
Stewart, Jimmy : *Bass Guitar* (Lon)
Stewart, Jo : *Pianoforte* (Lon)
Stewart, Joyce : *Violin* (Sco)
Stewart, Julia : *Violin* (Lon)
Stewart, Lois : *Violin* (Sco)
Stewart, M. : *Violin* (NW)
Stewart, Malc : *Synthesiser* (Mid)
Stewart, Mark : *Keyboards* (Lon)
Stewart, Michael : *Saxophones* (Sco)
Stewart, Robert : *Guitars* (Lon)
Stewart, Rod : *Voice* (Lon)
Stewart, Rodney : *Double Bass* (Lon)
Stewart, Roy : *Double Bass* (Lon)
Stewart, Roy : *Pianoforte* (Lon)
Stewart, Roy : *Violin* (Lon)
Stewart, Simon : *Guitars* (Lon)
Stewart, Simon : *Violin* (Lon)
Stewart, Stephen : *Trumpet* (Lon)
Stewart, Stephen : *Violin* (Lon)
Stewart, Tito : *Guitars* (Lon)
Stewart, Wendy : *Harp* (Sco)
Stewart, William : *Guitars* (Lon)
Stewart, William : *Guitars* (NE)

Thompson, Anthony David : *Trumpet* (Lon)
Thompson, Arthur : *Guitars* (Lon)
Thompson, Barbara : *Composer* (Lon)
Thompson, Barbara : *Saxophones* (Lon)
Thompson, Bernard : *Double Bass* (NE)
Thompson, Billy : *Violin* (SW)
Thompson, Bob : *Latin American Percu* (NW)
Thompson, Bunny : *Pianoforte* (Lon)
Thompson, Caroline : *Cello* (SE)
Thompson, Cathy : *Violin* (Lon)
Thompson, Charles : *Bass Guitar* (NW)
Thompson, Chris : *Percussion* (E)
Thompson, Chris : *Pianoforte* (Mid)
Thompson, Christie : *Pianoforte* (NE)
Thompson, Christopher : *Banjo* (Lon)
Thompson, Christopher : *Bass Guitar* (Lon)
Thompson, Christopher : *Voice* (Lon)
Thompson, Clare : *Violin* (Lon)
Thompson, Colin : *Guitars* (SW)
Thompson, Danny : *Double Bass* (Lon)
Thompson, David : *Guitars* (E)
Thompson, David : *Banjo* (NE)
Thompson, Doris : *Voice* (NW)
Thompson, Frank : *Saxophones* (Sco)
Thompson, Freddie : *Bass Guitar* (Lon)
Thompson, Gail : *Saxophones* (Lon)
Thompson, Gerald : *Saxophones* (NE)
Thompson, Harry : *Saxophones* (Mid)
Thompson, Hazel : *Violin* (NE)
Thompson, Jack : *Pianoforte* (Lon)
Thompson, James : *Saxophones* (Lon)
Thompson, Jason : *Keyboards* (Lon)
Thompson, Jeffrey : *Percussion* (NE)
Thompson, Joe : *Pianoforte* (Lon)
Thompson, John : *Bass Guitar* (Lon)
Thompson, John : *Bass Guitar* (Lon)
Thompson, John : *Trombone* (NE)
Thompson, Jonathan : *Bass Guitar* (NE)
Thompson, Julie : *Clarinet* (SW)
Thompson, Karen : *Violin* (Lon)
Thompson, Katie : *Saxophones* (E)
Thompson, Keith : *Guitars* (SW)
Thompson, Kevin : *Trombone* (Sco)
Thompson, Kevin J : *Organ* (Mid)
Thompson, Lawrence : *Pianoforte* (SW)
Thompson, Marcus : *Guitars* (Lon)
Thompson, Martin : *Guitars* (NW)
Thompson, Martyn : *Saxophones* (SE)
Thompson, Matt : *Latin American Percu* (SE)
Thompson, Michael : *Horn* (Lon)
Thompson, Michael : *Percussion* (Lon)
Thompson, Michael : *Violin* (NE)
Thompson, Naomi : *Voice* (Lon)
Thompson, Nicholas : *Guitars* (Lon)
Thompson, Nicholas : *Trumpet* (Lon)
Thompson, Nina : *Flute* (Lon)
Thompson, Paul : *Guitars* (Lon)
Thompson, Paul : *Percussion* (Lon)
Thompson, Penelope : *Viola* (Lon)
Thompson, Peter : *Clarinet* (Lon)
Thompson, R : *Violin* (NW)
Thompson, Rebecca : *Violin* (NW)
Thompson, Richard : *Guitars* (Lon)
Thompson, Rod : *Keyboards* (Lon)
Thompson, Rosalind : *Violin* (Lon)
Thompson, Rupert : *Percussion* (NW)
Thompson, Shaun : *Clarinet* (Lon)
Thompson, Sheik : *Saxophones* (Lon)
Thompson, Stanley : *Violin* (NW)
Thompson, Steve : *Guitars* (SE)
Thompson, Terence : *Clarinet* (Mid)
Thompson, Tommy : *Violin* (E)
Thompson, Wally : *Percussion* (SW)
Thompson, William : *Flugel Horn* (E)

Thompson, William : *Trumpet* (Lon)
Thompson, William : *Horn* (SE)
Thompson-Clarke, Robin : *Cello* (Lon)
Thompson-Smith, Mark : *Voice* (SE)
Thompson Sound, John : *Keyboards* (SE)
Thoms, Peter : *Trombone* (Lon)
Thomsett, Ian : *Flute* (SW)
Thomson, Allison : *Cornet* (Sco)
Thomson, Angie : *Flute* (Lon)
Thomson, Barbara E : *Pianoforte* (NW)
Thomson, Brian : *Trumpet* (Lon)
Thomson, Brian : *Bass Guitar* (Lon)
Thomson, Ellen : *Recorders* (Lon)
Thomson, Gary : *Trumpet* (Sco)
Thomson, Helen : *Harp* (Sco)
Thomson, Ian : *Bass Guitar* (NE)
Thomson, Inge : *Voice* (Sco)
Thomson, James : *Horn* (SE)
Thomson, Jimmy : *Saxophones* (NW)
Thomson, Katherine : *Harpsichord* (Mid)
Thomson, Kelvin : *Pianoforte* (Lon)
Thomson, Kenny : *Accordion* (Sco)
Thomson, Mark : *Guitars* (Lon)
Thomson, Murray : *Voice* (Mid)
Thomson, Nichol D : *Trombone* (Lon)
Thomson, Paul : *Guitars* (Lon)
Thomson, Paul : *Pianoforte* (Lon)
Thomson, Peter : *Trumpet* (NE)
Thomson, Rhuraidh : *Bass Guitar* (SE)
Thomson, Roderick : *Double Bass* (Lon)
Thomson, Shelagh : *Violin* (NW)
Thomson, Stuart : *Double Bass* (NW)
Thomson, Stuart : *Accordion* (Sco)
Thomson, Tobin : *Voice* (SE)
Thomson, Will : *Guitars* (SE)
Thomson, William : *Violin* (NW)
Thorborn, Ian : *Percussion* (E)
Thorburn, Andy : *Music Director* (Sco)
Thorby, George : *Bandleader* (E)
Thorby, Pamela : *Recorders* (Lon)
Thorgilson, Charles : *Violin* (SE)
Thorgilson, Janice : *Violin* (SE)
Thorley, Brent : *Guitars* (Lon)
Thorley, Peter : *Trombone* (Lon)
Thormahlen, Wiebke : *Violin* (Lon)
Thorn, Jennifer : *Violin* (Lon)
Thorn, Mike : *Bass Guitar* (Lon)
Thorn, Tracey : *Voice* (Lon)
Thornalley, Philip : *Bass Guitar* (Lon)
Thornber, Kraig : *Percussion* (Lon)
Thorndycraft, Ron : *Bassoon* (Lon)
Thorndycraft, Rosemary : *Early Strings* (Lon)
Thorne, Andrew : *Tuba* (SE)
Thorne, Christopher : *Pianoforte* (SE)
Thorne, David : *Organ* (SE)
Thorne, David : *Bass Guitar* (SW)
Thorne, Harry : *Guitars* (Lon)
Thorne, Louis : *Guitars* (E)
Thorne, Michael : *Synthesiser* (Lon)
Thorne, Mike : *Bass Guitar* (Lon)
Thorne, Mike : *Trombone* (SE)
Thorne, Philip : *Horn* (Lon)
Thorne, Phillip : *Guitars* (Sco)
Thorne, Richard : *Flute* (SE)
Thorne, Stephen : *Guitars* (SE)
Thorner, Madeleine : *Cello* (Lon)
Thornett, David : *Trombone* (Lon)
Thornhill, Leeroy : *Keyboards* (Lon)
Thornley, Steve : *Composer* (SE)
Thornton : *Voice* (E)
Thornton, Barrie : *Cello* (NE)
Thornton, Edward : *Trumpet* (Lon)
Thornton, Hilary : *Viola* (Sco)
Thornton, John : *Horn* (NW)
Thornton, Julia : *Harp* (E)

Thornton, Pat : *Keyboards* (SE)
Thornton, Paul : *Trumpet* (Lon)
Thornton, Sally : *Voice* (NW)
Thorogood, David : *Saxophones* (Lon)
Thorold, Rupert : *Percussion* (SE)
Thorp, Bernard : *Bass Guitar* (NE)
Thorp, Reginald : *Clarinet* (SE)
Thorp, William : *Violin* (Lon)
Thorpe, Anthony : *Guitars* (NW)
Thorpe, Bill : *Percussion* (Mid)
Thorpe, Colin : *Keyboards* (NW)
Thorpe, Mel : *Saxophones* (Mid)
Thorpe, Peter : *Percussion* (SW)
Thorpe, Raymond : *Percussion* (SE)
Thorpe, Simon : *Double Bass* (Lon)
Thoumire, Simon : *Concertina (Inc Engl)* (Sco)
Thow, Harry : *Percussion* (SE)
Threadgold, Helena : *Clarinet* (NE)
Throneycroft-Smith, Fraser : *Guitars* (SE)
Throup, Andrew G : *Pianoforte* (Lon)
Thrower, Harold : *Trumpet* (Lon)
Thulborn, Katherine : *Cello* (Lon)
Thurgood, Andrew : *Violin* (Lon)
Thurgood, John : *Clarinet* (E)
Thurgood, John : *Horn* (Lon)
Thurlbourn, Philip : *Trumpet* (E)
Thurlow, Sarah : *Clarinet* (Lon)
Thurlow, Tracey : *Clarinet* (Lon)
Thurman, Andrew : *Guitars* (NE)
Thurston, Jennifer : *Violin* (Lon)
Thwaites, Leonard : *Double Bass* (Mid)
Tibble, Howard : *Percussion* (Lon)
Tibbs, Gary : *Bass Guitar* (Lon)
Tibbs, Graham : *Percussion* (SE)
Tickell, Kathryn : *Northumbrian Pipes* (NE)
Tickle, David : *Percussion* (Lon)
Tidsey, Darrin : *Keyboards* (NW)
Tidswell, Irven : *Percussion* (NW)
Tiger, Brandy : *Voice* (Mid)
Tikaram, Ramon : *Voice* (SE)
Tilbrook, Adrian : *Percussion* (NE)
Tilbrook, Glenn : *Guitars* (Lon)
Tilbrook, Jonathan : *Conductor* (Lon)
Tilbrook, Lyn : *Voice* (NE)
Tilbury, John : *Pianoforte* (Lon)
Tilch, Karen : *Violin* (Lon)
Tildesley, Matthew : *Guitars* (Mid)
Tiler, Jeffrey : *Cello* (NE)
Tiller, Richard : *Double Bass* (NE)
Tilley, Edward : *Percussion* (Lon)
Tilley, Jennifer : *Clarinet* (SW)
Tilley, Louise : *Composer* (Lon)
Tilley, Sarah : *Violin* (Lon)
Tillotson, Liz : *Bass Guitar* (NE)
Tilsed, John : *Percussion* (NE)
Tilston, Alan : *Percussion* (Sco)
Tilston, Stephen : *Guitars* (SW)
Tilt, Marcus : *Pianoforte* (Lon)
Timberlake, Charles : *Pianoforte* (SE)
Timbler, John : *Pianoforte* (SE)
Timmins, Helen : *Guitars* (Mid)
Timms, Arthur : *Keyboards* (Lon)
Timms, Carole : *Flute* (SW)
Timms, David : *Pianoforte* (NE)
Timoney, Michael : *Synthesiser* (NW)
Timoney, Therese : *Violin* (Lon)
Timothy, Michael : *Keyboards* (Lon)
Tindale, Margaret : *Oboe* (Lon)
Tingay, Gillian : *Harp* (Lon)
Tingey, Giles : *Pianoforte* (Sco)
Tinker, Bob : *Trumpet* (SW)
Tinley, Stella : *Violin* (Mid)
Tiplady, Malcolm : *Clarinet* (Lon)
Tipper, Michael : *Guitars* (SE)
Tippett, Keith : *Pianoforte* (Lon)

Index of Members - Virji

Virji, Fayyaz : *Trombone* (Lon)
Virley, Keith : *Percussion* (E)
Virley, Nigel : *Pianoforte* (E)
Virtue, Michael : *Keyboards* (Mid)
Vishal : *Voice* (Lon)
Viskant, Joan : *Voice* (Lon)
Visser, Andy : *Saxophones* (Mid)
Vitali, Max : *Guitars* (NW)
Vitty, Keith : *Percussion* (SE)
Vivian, Robert : *Trumpet* (Mid)
Vizard, Jamie : *Keyboards* (NW)
Vocadlo, R Bernard : *Cello* (Lon)
Vochi.85, Hsm : *Voice* (NE)
Vogel, Dorothea : *Viola* (Lon)
Vogler, Andrea : *Percussion* (NW)
Vohralik, Julia : *Cello* (Lon)
Voigt, Sarah : *Violin* (Lon)
Volkard, Timothy : *Cello* (Lon)
Vollam, Helen : *Trombone* (Lon)
Volpiliere-Pierrot, Dan : *Latin American Percu* (SE)
Vom, Stephen : *Percussion* (Lon)
Von Gunten, Timothy : *Guitars* (E)
Vora, Anup : *Percussion* (Lon)
Vortex, Eddie : *Guitars* (SE)
Vorzanger, Edward : *Pianoforte* (Lon)
Vos, Josephine : *Violin* (SW)
Vosper, Al : *Guitars* (Lon)
Voss, James : *Guitars* (Lon)
Voss, Katrin : *Violin* (Lon)
Vousden, Edwin : *Banjo* (E)
Vowles, Iona : *Keyboards* (Lon)
Vowles, Thomas : *Cello* (Mid)
Voyager : *Percussion* (Lon)
Voysey, Susan : *Viola* (NW)
Vukotic, Bozidar : *Cello* (Lon)
Vye-Parminter, Arthur : *Arranger* (Lon)
Vyner, Edward : *Oboe* (NE)

W

Waaktaar-Savoy, Pal : *Guitars* (Lon)
Wachsmann, Philipp : *Violin* (Lon)
Wackett, Robert : *Percussion* (Lon)
Waddington, Frank : *Trumpet* (NW)
Waddington, Martin : *Keyboards* (Lon)
Waddington, Steven : *Guitars* (Lon)
Wade, Anne : *Pianoforte* (NE)
Wade, Anthony : *Pianoforte* (Lon)
Wade, Ashley : *Percussion* (NE)
Wade, Christine : *Keyboards* (Lon)
Wade, David : *Voice* (Lon)
Wade, Dick : *Saxophones* (E)
Wade, Michael : *Saxophones* (Lon)
Wade, Natalie : *Guitars* (E)
Wade, Nik : *Voice* (Lon)
Wade, Rebecca : *Viola* (Lon)
Wade, Rebecca : *Guitars* (NE)
Wade, Richard : *Violin* (Lon)
Wade, T : *Pianoforte* (Lon)
Wade, Timothy : *Trombone* (SE)
Wade, Vic : *Pianoforte* (Lon)
Wadey, Zoe : *Guitars* (NE)
Wadkin, Frank : *Trumpet* (Mid)
Wadman, Gregory : *Trumpet* (NE)
Wadsworth, Claire : *Bassoon* (Lon)
Wadsworth, Cyril : *Pianoforte* (NE)
Wadsworth, Della : *Flute* (NE)
Wadsworth, Derek : *Trombone* (Lon)
Wadsworth, Janus : *Horn* (NE)
Wadsworth, Paul : *Percussion* (SE)
Wadsworth, Sonya : *Violin* (NW)
Wag : *Guitars* (Lon)
Wager, Henrik : *Voice* (Lon)
Wager, Silas : *Composer* (Lon)
Waghorn, Ben : *Saxophones* (SW)

Wagland, James : *Percussion* (Lon)
Wagland, Simon : *Cello* (Lon)
Wagstaff, Anthony : *Percussion* (Lon)
Wagstaff, Nicholas : *Pianoforte* (SE)
Wagstaff, Stuart : *Bass Guitar* (SE)
Wain, Peter : *Pianoforte* (Mid)
Wain, Phil : *Bass Guitar* (Lon)
Wainwright, Anne : *Violin* (NW)
Wainwright, Richard : *Horn* (Lon)
Waissman, Brad : *Bass Guitar* (E)
Waite, Andrew : *Bass Guitar* (SW)
Waite, Bill : *Percussion* (E)
Waite, Brian : *Pianoforte* (Mid)
Waite, Nicola : *Clarinet* (Mid)
Waithe, Keith : *Flute* (Lon)
Waitt, Deryn : *Accordion* (NW)
Waitt, Robert : *Accordion* (NW)
Wake, Martin : *Percussion* (NE)
Wakefield, Audrey : *Violin* (Lon)
Wakefield, Graham : *Bass Guitar* (Lon)
Wakefield, Jeffrey : *Violin* (Lon)
Wakefield, Tony : *Arranger* (Lon)
Wakeford, Lucy : *Harp* (Lon)
Wakeford, Richard : *Horn* (Sco)
Wakeham, Daphne : *Violin* (Lon)
Wakelam, Susan : *Violin* (Lon)
Wakelin, John : *Voice* (SE)
Wakeling, David : *Guitars* (Mid)
Wakeman, Adam : *Keyboards* (SE)
Wakeman, Alan : *Saxophones* (Lon)
Wakeman, Rick : *Keyboards* (Lon)
Walch, Peter : *Pianoforte* (SE)
Walcott, Degiha : *Voice* (Mid)
Walcott, Mark : *Songwriter* (Lon)
Walcott-Gordon, Celestine : *Voice* (SW)
Walden, John : *Harmonica (Inc Bass* (Lon)
Walden, Peter : *Oboe* (Mid)
Walden, Suzanne : *Cello* (Mid)
Walden, Timothy : *Cello* (SW)
Waldie, Vernon : *Guitars* (E)
Waldmann, Adam : *Saxophones* (SE)
Waldmann, Alexander : *Percussion* (SE)
Waldock, Richard : *Double Bass* (NW)
Waldock, Wendy : *Cello* (Mid)
Waldron, Reginald : *Saxophones* (Lon)
Waldron, Tim : *Scratcher* (SW)
Wales, Eric : *Guitars* (Sco)
Wales, Jonathan : *Pianoforte* (Lon)
Walford, Tim : *Guitars* (NW)
Walkden, Eric : *Trumpet* (Mid)
Walkden, Michael : *Percussion* (E)
Walkden, Thomas : *Saxophones* (Mid)
Walker, Alistair : *Trumpet* (Lon)
Walker, Ann : *Clarinet* (NW)
Walker, Barry : *Violin* (NE)
Walker, Benjamin : *Pianoforte* (E)
Walker, Billy : *Percussion* (Mid)
Walker, Bo : *Bass Guitar* (Lon)
Walker, Chris : *Arranger* (Lon)
Walker, Christopher : *Guitars* (NE)
Walker, Christopher : *Clarinet* (SE)
Walker, Clare : *Bassoon* (SW)
Walker, Colin : *Cello* (Lon)
Walker, Crosby : *Keyboards* (E)
Walker, David : *Trumpet* (Lon)
Walker, David : *Voice* (Lon)
Walker, David : *Double Bass* (Mid)
Walker, David : *Pianoforte* (Mid)
Walker, Donald : *Double Bass* (Lon)
Walker, Edward : *Voice* (NE)
Walker, Elizabeth : *Flute* (Lon)
Walker, Frances : *Violin* (Lon)
Walker, Geoffrey : *Bassoon* (NE)
Walker, George : *Banjo* (SE)

Walker, Gordon : *Percussion* (Sco)
Walker, Graham : *Percussion* (Lon)
Walker, Helen : *Pianoforte* (NW)
Walker, Ian : *Banjo* (Sco)
Walker, Jake : *Viola* (Lon)
Walker, James : *Pianoforte* (Lon)
Walker, James : *Viola* (Lon)
Walker, James : *Percussion* (NE)
Walker, Jayne : *Violin* (E)
Walker, Jeffrey : *Bass Guitar* (Lon)
Walker, Joe : *Pianoforte* (Lon)
Walker, John : *Keyboards* (Mid)
Walker, Julia : *Cello* (Lon)
Walker, Julian : *Keyboards* (SW)
Walker, Kate : *Clarinet* (Lon)
Walker, Kathleen : *Cello* (Mid)
Walker, Kenneth : *Saxophones* (NE)
Walker, Kevin : *Bass Guitar* (NE)
Walker, Len : *Guitars* (Lon)
Walker, Lewis : *Double Bass* (NE)
Walker, Margaret : *Harp* (NW)
Walker, Mark : *Percussion* (Lon)
Walker, Mark : *Tympani* (SW)
Walker, Matthew : *Guitars* (NE)
Walker, Michael : *Organ* (Mid)
Walker, Michael : *Guitars* (NE)
Walker, Michael : *Percussion* (NW)
Walker, Nicholas : *Bass Guitar* (E)
Walker, Nicholas : *Saxophones* (E)
Walker, Nigel : *Guitars* (Lon)
Walker, Nina : *Pianoforte* (Lon)
Walker, Norman : *Brass* (NE)
Walker, Pamela : *Voice* (NW)
Walker, Patrick : *Guitars* (NE)
Walker, Phillip : *Horn* (Lon)
Walker, Rachael : *Viola* (SW)
Walker, Richard : *Guitars* (SE)
Walker, Robert : *Bass Guitar* (NW)
Walker, Robert : *Bassoon* (SE)
Walker, Sam : *Saxophones* (NE)
Walker, Sarah : *Pianoforte* (Lon)
Walker, Sarah : *Voice* (NW)
Walker, Shelley : *Guitars* (E)
Walker, Thomas : *Tuba* (Sco)
Walker, Timothy : *Guitars* (Lon)
Walker, Suzannah : *Horn* (E)
Walker, William : *Whistle* (NE)
Walker-Thom, Lydia : *Flute* (Sco)
Walkington, Julie : *Double Bass* (Lon)
Walklate, Mathew : *Voice* (NW)
Walklin, Leslie : *Clarinet* (Lon)
Walkom, Charles : *Double Bass* (NW)
Wall, Abby : *Early Strings* (E)
Wall, Andrew : *Bass Guitar* (SE)
Wall, Ashley : *Tuba* (Lon)
Wall, Charles : *Double Bass* (Mid)
Wall, Chris : *Pianoforte* (NW)
Wall, Jorgen : *Percussion* (Lon)
Wall, Nicholas : *Guitars* (Lon)
Wall, Philip : *Clarinet* (SW)
Wall, Richard : *Bass Trombone* (Lon)
Wall, Sharon : *Clarinet* (Mid)
Wall, Stephen : *Bass Guitar* (Mid)
Wallace, Andrew : *Pianoforte* (Lon)
Wallace, Barnaby : *Harmonica (Inc Bass* (Lon)
Wallace, Bridget : *Violin* (Lon)
Wallace, Darren : *DiDJeridu* (SW)
Wallace, David : *Pianoforte* (Lon)
Wallace, David : *Keyboards* (SE)
Wallace, Derek : *Violin* (Lon)
Wallace, Diane : *Voice* (Mid)
Wallace, E : *Cello* (NW)
Wallace, Graeme : *Pianoforte* (SE)
Wallace, Jimmy : *Saxophones* (SE)
Wallace, John : *Composer* (Lon)

Wallace, John : *Saxophones* (Lon)
Wallace, John : *Trumpet* (Lon)
Wallace, Keith : *Flute* (Sco)
Wallace, Liam Henry : *Guitars* (NW)
Wallace, Maria : *Keyboards* (Lon)
Wallace, Rachel : *Voice* (Lon)
Wallace, Richard : *Saxophones* (NE)
Wallace, Richard : *Viola* (NW)
Wallace, Robert : *Bagpipes* (Sco)
Wallace, Ronald : *Guitars* (NW)
Wallace, Simon : *Pianoforte* (Lon)
Wallace, Susan : *Voice* (NE)
Wallbank, Alfred : *Clarinet* (Lon)
Wallbank, Raymond : *Organ* (NW)
Wallen, Byron : *Trumpet* (Lon)
Waller, Alison : *Clarinet* (Sco)
Waller, Claire : *Flute* (NW)
Waller, Duncan : *Bass Guitar* (NE)
Waller, Garry : *Percussion* (SE)
Waller, George : *Clarinet* (Sco)
Waller, Norman : *Saxophones* (E)
Waller, Paul : *Percussion* (Lon)
Waller, Ronald : *Bassoon* (Lon)
Waller, Tony : *Trumpet* (SE)
Walley, Allen : *Double Bass* (Lon)
Walley, Brett : *Double Bass* (Mid)
Wallfisch, Benjamin : *Composer* (NW)
Wallfisch, Elizabeth : *Violin* (Lon)
Wallinger, Karl : *Keyboards* (Lon)
Wallington, Heather : *Viola* (NW)
Wallington, Martin : *Viola* (NW)
Wallington, Timothy : *Keyboards* (SE)
Wallis, Geoff : *Double Bass* (NW)
Wallis, George : *Percussion* (Mid)
Wallis, Matthew : *Keyboards* (SE)
Wallis, Walter J : *Voice* (E)
Wallman, Anthony : *Percussion* (Lon)
Wallwork, Terry : *Guitars* (SW)
Walmsley, John : *Guitars* (Mid)
Walmsley, Tony : *Guitars* (Lon)
Walpole, Steven : *Guitars* (NE)
Walpole, Victoria : *Oboe* (Lon)
Walpole-Brown, George : *Trombone* (SW)
Walsh, Bo : *Percussion* (NW)
Walsh, Brendan : *Pianoforte* (Lon)
Walsh, David : *Percussion* (NW)
Walsh, Francis : *Trumpet* (SE)
Walsh, Fred : *Flute* (Mid)
Walsh, Howard : *Violin* (Lon)
Walsh, Kate : *Flute* (Lon)
Walsh, Neil : *Bass Guitar* (NW)
Walsh, Patrick : *Percussion* (SE)
Walsh, Phil : *Bagpipes* (NW)
Walsh, Richard : *Percussion* (E)
Walsh, Sarah : *Clarinet* (Sco)
Walsh, Terry : *Guitars* (Lon)
Walsh, Tom : *Accordion* (NW)
Walshe, Katherine : *Voice* (E)
Walter, Dick : *Composer* (Lon)
Walter, John : *Pianoforte* (SW)
Walters, Art : *Pianoforte* (Lon)
Walters, Caroline : *Voice* (E)
Walters, David : *Percussion* (Lon)
Walters, David : *Pianoforte* (NW)
Walters, Geoffrey : *Keyboards* (SW)
Walters, Hannelore : *Voice* (Lon)
Walters, Hayley : *Oboe* (Lon)
Walters, Helena : *Violin* (Lon)
Walters, John : *Arranger* (Lon)
Walters, Julian : *Double Bass* (Mid)
Walters, Keith : *Double Bass* (Mid)
Walters, Louise : *Violin* (Lon)
Walters, Mark : *Trombone* (Lon)
Walters, Mark : *Flugel Horn* (NE)
Walters, Noel : *Voice* (NW)

Walters, Patrice : *Percussion* (Lon)
Walters, Rebecca : *Viola* (NW)
Walters, Simon : *Keyboards* (Lon)
Walters, Stephen : *Voice* (NE)
Walters, Tavis : *Trombone* (Mid)
Waltham, Rachel : *Cello* (Lon)
Walthew, John : *Clarinet* (SW)
Waltmann, Fabien : *Guitars* (Lon)
Walton, Andrew : *Violin* (Lon)
Walton, Anna : *Voice* (Lon)
Walton, Bob : *Trumpet* (Lon)
Walton, Dennis : *Saxophones* (Lon)
Walton, Harry : *Vibraphone* (Mid)
Walton, Ian : *Voice* (NE)
Walton, Jake : *Hurdy-gurdy* (SW)
Walton, Janis : *Violin* (Sco)
Walton, Lydia : *Voice* (SW)
Walton, Mark : *Violin* (Lon)
Walton, Michael : *Trumpet* (NE)
Walton, Michael : *Violin* (NE)
Walton, Paul : *Euphonium* (NW)
Walton, Pete : *Bass Guitar* (NW)
Walton, Peter : *Guitars* (Lon)
Walton, Robert : *Pianoforte* (Lon)
Walton, Sarah : *Violin* (Lon)
Walton, Simon : *Flute* (Lon)
Walton, Vincent : *Percussion* (NW)
Walwyn, David : *Voice* (Lon)
Wander, De'Jon : *Voice* (Lon)
Wands, Edna : *Pianoforte* (Sco)
Wang, Godfrey : *Composer* (Lon)
Wangford, Hank : *Voice* (Lon)
Wanklyn, Diana : *Double Bass* (NW)
Want, Judith : *Cello* (NE)
Warbeck, Stephen : *Composer* (Lon)
Warburton, Gareth : *Bass Guitar* (NW)
Warburton, James : *Horn* (Lon)
Warburton, Janine : *Trombone* (E)
Warburton, Jillian : *Violin* (Lon)
Warburton, Jonathan : *Bass Trombone* (Mid)
Warburton, Julian : *Percussion* (Lon)
Warburton, Paul : *Violin* (Mid)
Warburton, Stephen : *Bass Guitar* (NW)
Warburton, Stuart : *Harmonica (Inc Bass* (NW)
Warburton, Timothy : *Violin* (E)
Warburton, Val : *Pianoforte* (NE)
Warby, Frank : *Keyboards* (Lon)
Warchal, Wendy : *Voice* (Lon)
Ward, Arthur : *Percussion* (SE)
Ward, Ashley : *Percussion* (Lon)
Ward, Bob : *Trombone* (Lon)
Ward, Charles : *Saxophones* (NW)
Ward, Charlotte : *Cello* (Lon)
Ward, Chris : *Percussion* (NW)
Ward, Christopher : *Guitars* (Lon)
Ward, Christopher : *Saxophones* (NW)
Ward, Daniel : *Percussion* (NW)
Ward, David : *Keyboards* (Lon)
Ward, David : *Trumpet* (Lon)
Ward, Donald : *Bagpipes* (Mid)
Ward, Donald : *Percussion* (Mid)
Ward, Elizabeth : *Clarinet* (SE)
Ward, Gary : *Guitars* (NW)
Ward, Gavin : *Percussion* (SE)
Ward, George : *Pianoforte* (Lon)
Ward, George : *Trumpet* (SW)
Ward, Gill : *Voice* (E)
Ward, Graham : *Percussion* (Lon)
Ward, Helen : *Violin* (Lon)
Ward, Jeremy : *Bassoon* (Lon)
Ward, John : *Guitars* (E)
Ward, John : *Percussion* (NW)
Ward, John Matthew : *Guitars* (Lon)
Ward, Jonathan : *Percussion* (NE)

Ward, Justin : *Viola* (Lon)
Ward, Leila : *Oboe* (Lon)
Ward, Mark : *Organ* (SW)
Ward, Martin : *Guitars* (SW)
Ward, Matthew : *Violin* (Lon)
Ward, Michael : *Saxophones* (NE)
Ward, Nicholas : *Violin* (Lon)
Ward, Nicholas : *Percussion* (Mid)
Ward, Patrick : *Trombone* (NE)
Ward, Robert : *Flute* (NE)
Ward, Sally : *Viola* (Lon)
Ward, Simon : *Keyboards* (E)
Ward, Steven : *Bass Guitar* (SW)
Ward, Tamsin : *Saxophones* (SE)
Ward, Tim : *Percussion* (Mid)
Ward, Tony : *Cello* (Lon)
Ward, Winston : *Voice* (Lon)
Ward-Clarke, Jennifer : *Cello* (Lon)
Ward-Roden, Richard : *Cello* (Lon)
Ward-Webb, Andrew : *Guitars* (SE)
Wardale, Alf : *Guitars* (SW)
Wardale, Andrew : *Cello* (NW)
Wardally, Rikki : *Voice* (Lon)
Warde, Chris : *Guitars* (Mid)
Wardell, Joanna : *Cello* (SE)
Wardell, Tony : *Pianoforte* (SE)
Warden, Neil : *Guitars* (Sco)
Warden, Percy : *Pianoforte* (SE)
Wardman, Vicci : *Viola* (Lon)
Ware, Gareth : *Bass Guitar* (Mid)
Ware, Martin : *Keyboards* (Lon)
Ware, Peter : *Keyboards* (Lon)
Ware, Rebecca : *Electric Violin* (SE)
Ware, Rebecca : *Viola* (SE)
Ware, Zachary : *Guitars* (Sco)
Wareham, Donna : *Flute* (SE)
Wareham, Geoffrey : *Oboe* (Lon)
Wareham, Patricia : *Cello* (NE)
Wareham, Pete : *Saxophones* (Lon)
Wares, Alec : *Saxophones* (Mid)
Wargent, Richard : *Saxophones* (Lon)
Warham, Christine : *Cello* (NE)
Warham, Clive : *Bass Trombone* (NE)
Warhurst, Alan : *Bassoon* (Sco)
Warin, William : *Double Bass* (NE)
Waring, Silas : *Voice* (SE)
Warleigh, Raymond : *Saxophones* (Lon)
Warlow, Wayne : *Music Director* (SW)
Warman, Mark : *Music Director* (Lon)
Warne, Derek : *Music Director* (Lon)
Warner, Allen : *Guitars* (Lon)
Warner, Ernest : *Percussion* (SE)
Warner, Hilary : *Organ* (NW)
Warner, Kay : *Bassoon* (Lon)
Warner, Leon : *Percussion* (Lon)
Warner, Peter : *Saxophones* (Lon)
Warner, Richard : *Guitars* (Lon)
Warner, Stephen : *Double Bass* (Lon)
Warnes, Ann : *Horn* (Lon)
Warnock, Colin : *Keyboards* (Lon)
Warnock, Felix : *Bassoon* (Lon)
Warr, Noel : *Saxophones* (Mid)
Warr, Richard : *Guitars* (Mid)
Warr, Valerie : *Clarinet* (NW)
Warrack, Janet : *Viola* (Sco)
Warren, Antony : *Trombone* (NW)
Warren, Caroline : *Voice* (Sco)
Warren, David : *Guitars* (Lon)
Warren, Debbie : *Pianoforte* (Lon)
Warren, Deborah : *Saxophones* (E)
Warren, Edward : *Bassoon* (NW)
Warren, Ernest : *Trumpet* (SW)
Warren, Gareth : *Melodeon* (Mid)
Warren, Graham : *Horn* (Lon)
Warren, Jacqueline : *Voice* (SE)

Index of Members - Webb

Webb, Sarah : *Voice* (Lon)
Webb, Simon : *Guitars* (E)
Webb, Simon : *Cello* (SE)
Webb, Victoria : *Voice* (E)
Webb, William : *Keyboards* (NE)
Webb, William : *Violin* (NW)
Webb, William Grierson : *Conductor* (SE)
Webber, Beverly : *Flute* (NW)
Webber, David : *Voice* (E)
Webber, David : *Pianoforte* (SE)
Webber, Julie : *Violin* (Sco)
Webber, Kenneth : *Saxophones* (SW)
Webber, Martin : *Percussion* (SW)
Webber, Michael : *Vibraphone* (Mid)
Webber, Peter : *Guitars* (SW)
Webberley, Judith : *Viola* (Lon)
Webberley, Stephen : *Percussion* (Lon)
Weber, Alwin : *Violin* (Lon)
Webley, Warren : *Pianoforte* (Lon)
Webley, Yvonne : *Voice* (Lon)
Webster, Andrew : *Bass Clarinet* (Lon)
Webster, Andrew : *Saxophones* (NE)
Webster, Audrey : *Harp* (Lon)
Webster, Charles : *Keyboards* (Mid)
Webster, Claire : *Voice* (SE)
Webster, Darren : *Bass Guitar* (E)
Webster, Dave : *Percussion* (Lon)
Webster, Eric : *Banjo* (SE)
Webster, George : *Percussion* (Mid)
Webster, Jean : *Tympani* (NW)
Webster, Neil : *Pianoforte* (Lon)
Webster, Patience : *Mbira* (Lon)
Webster, Paul : *Pianoforte* (Lon)
Webster, Roger : *Cornet* (NW)
Weddle, Susan : *Bassoon* (Lon)
Wedell, Rebekka : *Voice* (Lon)
Wedge, James : *Trombone* (Mid)
Weedon, Bert : *Guitars* (Lon)
Weedon, Penelope : *Organ* (SW)
Weedon, Ralph : *Pianoforte* (Lon)
Weekes, Alan : *Guitars* (Lon)
Weekes, Desree : *Voice* (Lon)
Weekes, Donald : *Violin* (Lon)
Weeks, Geoffrey : *Trumpet* (NE)
Weeks, Sally-Ann : *Violin* (Lon)
Weigall, Richard : *Oboe* (Mid)
Weigand, George : *Early Strings* (Lon)
Weight, Alan : *Bass Guitar* (Lon)
Weightman, Dave : *Guitars* (Lon)
Weimar, Paul : *Saxophones* (Lon)
Weinberg, Anton : *Clarinet* (Lon)
Weinberg, Barry : *Pianoforte* (Lon)
Weinberg, Dan : *Guitars* (Lon)
Weinmann, Simon : *Violin* (SW)
Weir, Daniel : *Synthesiser* (SE)
Weir, Dominic : *Contra Bassoon* (Lon)
Weir, Hugh : *Trumpet* (Sco)
Weir, Keith : *Keyboards* (Lon)
Weiss, Catherine : *Violin* (Lon)
Weisz, Peter : *Keyboards* (Lon)
Weitz, Daniel : *Trumpet* (E)
Welch, Alison : *Viola* (NW)
Welch, Bruce : *Guitars* (Lon)
Welch, Colin : *Saxophones* (SE)
Welch, Edward : *Music Director* (SW)
Welch, Jennifer : *Flute* (Lon)
Welch, John : *Keyboards* (SW)
Welch, Jonathan : *Viola* (Lon)
Welch, Lizzy : *Voice* (Lon)
Welch, Nathan : *Guitars* (NW)
Welch, Timothy : *Viola* (Lon)
Welchman, Donna : *Violin* (Lon)
Welchman, Juliet : *Cello* (Lon)
Weldon, Nick : *Pianoforte* (Lon)
Weldon, Shelly : *Voice* (Lon)

Weldrake, Geoffrey : *Double Bass* (SW)
Welford, Steven : *Percussion* (NE)
Welham, John : *Voice* (E)
Wellard, Gordon : *Percussion* (Lon)
Weller, Andy : *Guitars* (E)
Weller, Charles : *Percussion* (Lon)
Weller, Don : *Saxophones* (Lon)
Weller, Karen : *Clarinet* (SE)
Weller, Martin : *Guitars* (Lon)
Weller, Paul : *Guitars* (Lon)
Weller, Sarah : *Voice* (Lon)
Weller, Tim : *Percussion* (SE)
Wellings, Clive : *Percussion* (SE)
Wellings, George : *Saxophones* (Lon)
Wellington, Canute : *Trumpet* (Lon)
Wellington, Christopher : *Viola* (Lon)
Wellington, Ian : *Guitars* (Lon)
Wellington, Julian : *Saxophones* (NE)
Wellington, Michael : *Keyboards* (NE)
Wellington, Sheena : *Voice* (Sco)
Wellins, Bobby : *Saxophones* (SW)
Wellman, Jim : *Saxophones* (Lon)
Wells, Billy : *Clarinet* (Lon)
Wells, Bobby : *Percussion* (SE)
Wells, Chris : *Composer* (Lon)
Wells, Colin : *Percussion* (Lon)
Wells, David Daniel : *Percussion* (NW)
Wells, Derek : *Trumpet* (Mid)
Wells, Fedd : *Voice* (Lon)
Wells, Frederick : *Percussion* (E)
Wells, Gary : *Bass Guitar* (NE)
Wells, Gavin : *Trumpet* (Mid)
Wells, Georgina : *Harp* (NE)
Wells, Graham : *Northumbrian Pipes* (Lon)
Wells, Ian : *Organ* (NW)
Wells, Jackie : *Cello* (NE)
Wells, Jane : *Composer* (E)
Wells, Jeremy : *Organ* (Lon)
Wells, John : *Music Director* (Mid)
Wells, John : *Pianoforte* (Mid)
Wells, Matthew : *Trumpet* (Lon)
Wells, Michael : *Trombone* (E)
Wells, Muriel : *Pianoforte* (Mid)
Wells, Richard : *Keyboards* (Lon)
Wells, Roger : *Percussion* (SW)
Wells, Ruth : *Guitars* (NE)
Wells, Timothy : *Double Bass* (Lon)
Wells, William : *Bass Guitar* (Sco)
Welmans, Nanette : *Voice* (Lon)
Welsford, Andrew : *Percussion* (Lon)
Welsh, Angela : *Cello* (Sco)
Welsh, Caroline J : *Flute* (Lon)
Welsh, David : *Trombone* (Sco)
Welsh, Joana : *Flute* (SE)
Welsh, Mark : *Percussion* (Lon)
Welsh, Matthew : *Percussion* (Sco)
Welsh, Moray : *Cello* (Lon)
Wendland, Peter : *Early Strings* (Lon)
Wernick, Lew : *Guitars* (Lon)
Wernick, Rebecca : *Voice* (E)
Werth, Howard : *Voice* (SE)
Wertheimer, Fay : *Viola* (NW)
Wescott, Christopher : *Double Bass* (Lon)
Wesley, Amos : *Saxophones* (NW)
Wesley, Peter : *Bassoon* (NW)
Wesling, David : *Cello* (NW)
Wesson, John : *Guitars* (Lon)
Wesson, Melvyn : *Keyboards* (Lon)
Wesson, Rees : *Accordion* (NW)
Wesson, Sebastian : *Guitars* (Lon)
West : *Guitars* (Mid)
West, Andrew : *Pianoforte* (Lon)
West, Angus : *Horn* (SW)
West, Christopher : *Double Bass* (Lon)
West, Colin : *Pianoforte* (SE)

West, David : *Keyboards* (SE)
West, Derek : *Violin* (Lon)
West, Helen : *Violin* (NE)
West, James : *Bass Guitar* (Mid)
West, Jeremy : *Early Wind* (Lon)
West, Joanna : *Violin* (Lon)
West, John : *Keyboards* (SW)
West, Julian : *Oboe* (Lon)
West, June : *Double Bass* (Lon)
West, Maureen : *Percussion* (SW)
West, Michael : *Guitars* (Mid)
West, Paul : *Clarinet* (SE)
West, Peter : *Guitars* (E)
West, Richard : *Clarinet* (Lon)
West, Richard : *Bass Guitar* (SW)
West, Ronald : *Percussion* (E)
West, Stephen : *Oboe* (Sco)
West, Tim : *Guitars* (SE)
West (McPherson), Fiona : *Viola* (Sco)
Westacott, Bronwen : *Pianoforte* (Mid)
Westaway, Robert : *Guitars* (Lon)
Westbrook, Kate : *Voice* (Lon)
Westbrook, Mike : *Pianoforte* (Lon)
Westbrook, Nicola : *Saxophones* (Mid)
Westcott, Geof : *Saxophones* (SW)
Westcott, Lois : *Violin* (SW)
Westcott, Stephen : *Bass Guitar* (Lon)
Westergaard, Michael : *Keyboards* (Lon)
Westerhoff, Gay-Yee : *Cello* (Lon)
Westerhout, Lisa : *Voice* (Lon)
Westerman, Martyn : *Trumpet* (SE)
Westley, Geoff : *Keyboards* (Lon)
Weston, Bryan : *Sousaphone* (Mid)
Weston, Clifford : *Pianoforte* (Mid)
Weston, Glenn : *Organ* (SE)
Weston, Harvey : *Double Bass* (E)
Weston, John : *Saxophones* (Lon)
Weston, Lee : *Guitars* (Mid)
Weston, Ray : *Percussion* (Lon)
Weston, Steve : *Bass Guitar* (NE)
Weston, Veryan : *Pianoforte* (E)
Westrop, Stephen : *Pianoforte* (Lon)
Westrup, Gunnar : *Viola* (SE)
Westrup, Raymond : *Percussion* (Mid)
Westwell, Paul : *Percussion* (SW)
Westwood, Jeremy : *Pianoforte* (Lon)
Westwood, Kenneth : *Percussion* (SW)
Westwood, Paul : *Bass Guitar* (Lon)
Westwood, Rowly : *Pianoforte* (NW)
Westwood, Tim : *Percussion* (Mid)
Wetherall, Richard : *Pianoforte* (NW)
Wetherell, Eric : *Pianoforte* (SW)
Wetters, Rosemary : *Cello* (Lon)
Wetton, John : *Guitars* (Lon)
Wexler, Elizabeth : *Violin* (Lon)
Wexler, Rebecca : *Viola* (Lon)
Whaley, Doug : *Trumpet* (NW)
Whaley, William : *Concertina (Inc Engl* (NE)
Whalley, Clare : *Pianoforte* (Lon)
Whalley, Tasmin : *Voice* (Lon)
Wharmby, Denise : *Voice* (Lon)
Wharmby, Tony : *Voice* (Lon)
Wharton, Terence : *Trumpet* (SE)
Whatley, Alison : *Oboe* (Mid)
Whatley, David : *Flute* (Mid)
Whatley, Kevin : *Voice* (SE)
Whatmore, Stuart : *Percussion* (SE)
Whealing, Ted : *Saxophones* (SE)
Wheater, Tim : *Flute* (Lon)
Wheatley, Adam : *Voice* (Lon)
Wheatley, Daniel : *Bass Guitar* (E)
Wheatley, George : *Double Bass* (Mid)
Wheatley, Jeremy : *Keyboards* (Lon)
Wheatley, Martin : *Guitars* (Lon)
Wheatley, Richard : *Pianoforte* (Mid)

Early music today

Britain's brightest early music news and listings magazine

TRY A SAMPLE SUBSCRIPTION

3 issues for £6.00

(**16% OFF** the cover price)

£2.40
Bi-monthly

MONEY BACK GUARANTEE
If the magazine fails to live up to your expectations, simply drop us a line and we will refund you for any unpublished issues.

Please send your cheque (payable to *Rhinegold Publishing Ltd*)
to: **Rhinegold Publishing Ltd (EMT Subs), FREEPOST, Gravesend, Kent DA12 3BR**

Fax: 01474 325557
Email: subscriptions@rhinegold.co.uk
Website: www.rhinegold.co.uk

CREDIT CARD HOTLINE: 01474 334500   (office hours)

Whitten, Chris : *Percussion* (Lon)
Whitter, James : *Guitars* (Mid)
Whitter, Winston : *Saxophones* (Lon)
Whitteridge, Janet : *Flute* (SW)
Whittick, Tim : *Bassoon* (NW)
Whittingham, Clive : *Trumpet* (SW)
Whittingham, Jill : *Banjo* (SW)
Whittingham, Marc Andrew : *Percussion* (SE)
Whittingham, Tom : *Trombone* (SW)
Whittington, Paul : *Pianoforte* (NE)
Whittle, Brian : *Saxophones* (NE)
Whittle, Mary : *Viola* (Lon)
Whittle, Sean : *Keyboards* (Lon)
Whittle, Tommy : *Saxophones* (Lon)
Whittle, Tony : *Guitars* (NE)
Whittow, Marion : *Oboe* (NW)
Whitwam, Barry : *Percussion* (NW)
Whitwell, Christopher : *Trumpet* (SE)
Whitworth, Gordon : *Trumpet* (Mid)
Whitworth, John : *Percussion* (NW)
Whitworth, Stanley : *Double Bass* (SE)
Whone, George : *Violin* (NE)
Whyatt, Peter : *Double Bass* (Lon)
Whymark, Robert John : *Guitars* (Mid)
Whyment, Martin : *Percussion* (NW)
Whyne, Janice : *Voice* (Lon)
Whyte, Alain : *Guitars* (Lon)
Whyte, David : *Keyboards* (Sco)
Whyte, Douglas : *Pianoforte* (Sco)
Whyte, Gordon : *Keyboards* (Sco)
Whyte, Jane : *Keyboards* (Sco)
Whyte, Jim : *Percussion* (Lon)
Whyte, Sharon : *Voice* (Mid)
Whytock, Richard : *Guitars* (Sco)
Whyton-Smith, Steve : *Latin American Percu* (Lon)
Wick, Denis : *Trombone* (Lon)
Wick, Stephen : *Cimbasso* (Lon)
Wick, Stephen : *Tuba* (Lon)
Wickens, Andrew : *Violin* (Lon)
Wickens, Barry : *Violin* (Lon)
Wickens, Derek : *Oboe* (Lon)
Wickens, Lee : *Percussion* (Lon)
Wickens (Wix), Paul : *Keyboards* (Lon)
Wicker, Simon : *Percussion* (E)
Wickes, Nicholas : *Voice* (Lon)
Wickham, Alan : *Trumpet* (Lon)
Wickham, Antonia : *Cello* (NE)
Wickham, Hazel : *Pianoforte* (SW)
Wickham, Hilary : *Flute* (SW)
Wickins, David : *Percussion* (Lon)
Wicks, Brian : *Saxophones* (Lon)
Wickson, Simon : *Percussion* (SE)
Widdowson, Jeffrey : *Bass Guitar* (Mid)
Widdup, Deborah : *Violin* (Lon)
Widdup, Vanessa : *Voice* (Lon)
Widger, Andrew : *Horn* (Lon)
Widgery, K Peter : *Horn* (Lon)
Wiegold, Richard : *Cello* (SW)
Wigby, Amanda : *Keyboards* (NW)
Wigens, Paul : *Percussion* (SW)
Wigfield, Leslie : *Saxophones* (Lon)
Wiggins, Gaye : *Violin* (Lon)
Wiggins, Martin : *Viola* (Sco)
Wiggins, Peter : *Oboe* (Lon)
Wiggs, Josephine : *Bass Guitar* (E)
Wiggy : *Guitars* (Lon)
Wigham, Carolyn : *Brass* (NE)
Wight, Gary : *Voice* (NE)
Wight, Patrick : *Guitars* (Lon)
Wightman, Brian : *Bassoon* (Lon)
Wightman, David : *Pianoforte* (SW)
Wigley, Hywel : *Guitars* (NW)
Wigley, Richard : *Bassoon* (NW)
Wignall, Oliver : *Guitars* (Mid)
Wijay-Wardener, Som : *Guitars* (Lon)

Wil : *Latin American Percu* (Lon)
Wilber, Bob : *Saxophones* (Lon)
Wilby, Rosie : *Voice* (Lon)
Wilce, Malcolm : *Organ* (SW)
Wilcock, Carol : *Cello* (NW)
Wilcock, Christopher : *Pianoforte* (NW)
Wilcock, Stephen : *Saxophones* (SE)
Wilcocks, Lizie : *Voice* (Lon)
Wilcox, Mike : *Saxophones* (Lon)
Wild, Bev : *Trumpet* (Mid)
Wild, Martin : *Percussion* (Mid)
Wild, Peter : *Guitars* (E)
Wildcat, Will : *Percussion* (Lon)
Wilde : *Guitars* (SW)
Wilde, Gail : *Clarinet* (NW)
Wilde, Libby : *Cello* (Lon)
Wilde, Peter : *Violin* (Lon)
Wilde, Peter : *Trumpet* (Mid)
Wilde, Richard : *Violin* (NW)
Wilde, Shane : *Voice* (Lon)
Wilde, William : *Percussion* (SW)
Wilding, Lucy : *Cello* (Lon)
Wildish, Valentino : *Percussion* (SE)
Wildman, Heather : *Voice* (E)
Wildy, Thomas : *Saxophones* (SW)
Wileman, Alan : *Viola* (Lon)
Wileman, Eric : *Viola* (Mid)
Wiles, Andrew : *Bass Guitar* (NE)
Wiles, Benjamin : *Pianoforte* (SW)
Wilford, Tim : *Violin* (Lon)
Wilgaus, Frank : *Guitars* (NE)
Wilkens, Ronald : *Guitars* (Lon)
Wilkes, Alan : *Guitars* (Mid)
Wilkes, David : *Percussion* (Mid)
Wilkes, Douglas : *Guitars* (Mid)
Wilkes, Fiona : *Voice* (Lon)
Wilkes, Judith : *Pianoforte* (Sco)
Wilkie, James : *Voice* (Sco)
Wilkie, Peter : *Trombone* (NE)
Wilkie, Steven James : *Violin* (NW)
Wilkin, Mark : *Percussion* (Lon)
Wilkins, Brian : *Percussion* (Sco)
Wilkins, Geoff : *Trumpet* (E)
Wilkins, George : *Keyboards* (SW)
Wilkins, Julian : *Horn* (E)
Wilkins, Lucy : *Violin* (Lon)
Wilkins, Michael : *Saxophones* (SW)
Wilkins, Neil : *Voice* (SE)
Wilkins, Peter : *Vibraphone* (Mid)
Wilkins, Richard : *Cello* (SW)
Wilkins, Wayne : *Pianoforte* (Lon)
Wilkins-Oppler, Nancy : *Violin* (Lon)
Wilkinson, Adrian : *Clarinet* (NW)
Wilkinson, Alan : *Saxophones* (Lon)
Wilkinson, Ann : *Violin* (SE)
Wilkinson, Bob : *Guitars* (SW)
Wilkinson, Clive : *Percussion* (NW)
Wilkinson, Collette : *Voice* (Lon)
Wilkinson, David : *Percussion* (NE)
Wilkinson, Derek : *Saxophones* (Mid)
Wilkinson, Dianne : *Guitars* (Lon)
Wilkinson, Eleanor : *Violin* (Lon)
Wilkinson, Jane : *Percussion* (NW)
Wilkinson, Jay : *Flute* (Lon)
Wilkinson, Jennifer : *Voice* (NE)
Wilkinson, Jeremy : *Pianoforte* (Lon)
Wilkinson, Jeremy : *Keyboards* (SE)
Wilkinson, Joan : *Viola* (NW)
Wilkinson, Katie : *Viola* (Lon)
Wilkinson, Keith : *Bass Guitar* (Lon)
Wilkinson, Ken : *Trumpet* (SW)
Wilkinson, Kenneth : *Saxophones* (NE)
Wilkinson, Kevin : *Percussion* (Lon)
Wilkinson, Mark : *Guitars* (NW)
Wilkinson, Mick : *Double Bass* (Lon)

Wilkinson, Neal : *Percussion* (Lon)
Wilkinson, Peter : *Trumpet* (SE)
Wilkinson, Peter : *Tuba* (SE)
Wilkinson, Roy : *Percussion* (Sco)
Wilkinson, Ruth : *Pianoforte* (Sco)
Wilkinson, Sly : *Keyboards* (Lon)
Wilkinson, Stuart : *Guitars* (Lon)
Wilks, Clive : *Keyboards* (NW)
Wilks, Diana : *Viola* (NE)
Wilks, Joe : *Percussion* (NE)
Wilks, Rachel : *Viola* (SW)
Wilks, Ralph : *Saxophones* (NW)
Willan, Eric : *Trumpet* (NW)
Willcock, Ian : *Composer* (Lon)
Willcocks, Jonathan : *Conductor* (SE)
Willcox, Gary : *Percussion* (Lon)
Wille, Tony : *Guitars* (Mid)
Willes, Dennis : *Percussion* (SW)
Willescroft, Simon : *Saxophones* (NW)
Willets, Colin : *Bandleader* (Mid)
Willets, Colin : *Vibraphone* (Mid)
Willets, Janice : *Percussion* (Mid)
Willets, Timothy : *Melodeon* (Mid)
Willett, Elisha : *Pianoforte* (Lon)
Willett, Marcus : *Double Bass* (SW)
Willett, Nobby : *Banjo* (SE)
Willetts, Annabelle : *Violin* (SE)
Willetts, Carey : *Bass Guitar* (Lon)
Willetts, Samuel : *Viola* (SE)
Willey, Norman : *Percussion* (Mid)
Willey, Patricia : *Harp* (Lon)
Willey, Paul : *Violin* (Lon)
Willey, Richard : *Sousaphone* (SW)
Willey, Roger : *Trombone* (Lon)
Williams, A : *Guitars* (E)
Williams, Alf : *Saxophones* (SW)
Williams, Alun J : *Horn* (SW)
Williams, Andrew : *Guitars* (Lon)
Williams, Andrew : *Guitars* (Lon)
Williams, Andrew : *Viola* (Lon)
Williams, Andrew : *Keyboards* (NW)
Williams, Andrew : *Bass Trombone* (SW)
Williams, Averill : *Flute* (Lon)
Williams, Barry : *Club DJ* (Lon)
Williams, Barry : *Saxophones* (Lon)
Williams, Barry : *Trumpet* (NE)
Williams, Ben : *Voice* (SW)
Williams, Bryan : *Trumpet* (Lon)
Williams, Carole : *Trombone* (NW)
Williams, Caroline : *Saxophones* (Lon)
Williams, Carsten : *Horn* (Lon)
Williams, Christoper : *Composer* (SW)
Williams, Christopher : *Guitars* (E)
Williams, Christopher : *Bass Guitar* (NW)
Williams, Christopher : *Saxophones* (NW)
Williams, Claire : *Voice* (NW)
Williams, Clare : *Pianoforte* (Lon)
Williams, Clifford : *Bass Guitar* (Lon)
Williams, Clifford : *Saxophones* (Mid)
Williams, Col : *Guitars* (SW)
Williams, Cuthbert : *Voice* (E)
Williams, Daniel : *Guitars* (NW)
Williams, Danny : *Bass Guitar* (Lon)
Williams, Daryl : *Trombone* (SW)
Williams, David : *Organ* (Lon)
Williams, David : *Keyboards* (Lon)
Williams, David : *Keyboards* (Lon)
Williams, David : *Voice* (Lon)
Williams, David : *Percussion* (Mid)
Williams, David : *Percussion* (Mid)
Williams, David : *Violin* (Mid)
Williams, David : *Guitars* (NW)
Williams, Dean : *Guitars* (Lon)
Williams, Donald : *Trombone* (SE)
Williams, Donna : *Voice* (Lon)

Index of Teachers

The following index of teachers is ordered by instrument and then alphabetically by name. This index should be used in conjunction with the National Directory of Members beginning on page 1. In cases where the teaching instrument differs from the main performing instrument, the main instrument is given alongside the index entry.

ACCORDION

Adamson, Deirdre (Sco)
Allen, Mark (SW)
Anderson, Billy (Sco)
Beautement, Wendy (NW)
Bradford, Colin (NE)
Brechin, Sandy (Sco)
Brogan, Shane (Sco)
Campbell, Brian (NE)
Campbell, James (Sco)
Coppard, Sue (SW)
Dumas, Andre (NW)
Dunn, Alan (Lon)
Fiondella, Gennard (SE)
Greig, Michael (Keyboards Sco)
Handle, Johnny (NE)
Harkin, Treasa (Sco)
Hawthorn, Heather (Mid)
Holt, Helen (Lon)
Hutcheon, Jim (Sco)
Leslie, John (Lon)
Letley, Roger (SE)
May, Peter (SE)
Mayes, Jerry (E)
Miles, George (E)
Oliver, David (NE)
Osborne, Jim (Mid)
Pachnine, Serguei (Lon)
Romero, John (E)
Rose, Saul (Lon)
Santilly, Bert (E)
Schwarz, Martina (Lon)
Socci, Antoine (Mid)
Trevani (Lon)
Tweed, Karen (Mid)
Vincent, Reuben (NW)
Willoughby, Robert (E)

AFRICAN DRUMS

Abiodun (NW)
Amu-Logotse, Gift (Sco)
Ayandosu (Lon)
Broderick, Ansell (Percussion NE)
Cruickshank, David Rowland (Sco)
Hughes, Allan (Sco)
Jackman, Keith (NE)
Jawal, Papa (Organ Lon)
Moon, Simon (SE)
Smalley, Christine (Latin American Perc. NW)
Susimi, Dele (Keyboards Lon)

ARRANGER

Bremner, Tony (Lon)
Chell, Peter (Keyboards Mid)
Day, Richard (Percussion Lon)
Elliott, John (Pianoforte SE)
Fahey, Brian (Music Director Sco)
Hawkins, John (Lon)
Jones, John (Saxophones SW)
Proletarski, Valery (Lon)
Stevenson, Leslie (Saxophones NW)

BAGPIPES

Campbell, Rory (Sco)
Carr, Terry (NW)
Caution, James (Lon)
Dunbar, Patrick (Highland Bagpipes SW)
Fagan, Kevin (SE)
Fleming, Ian (Lon)
Hay, Louise (Highland Bagpipes Sco)
Lawther, Ian (E)
Mor, Calum (SW)
Saunders, Paul (Mid)
Summers, Anne (NE)
Vaughan, Michael (Lon)

BALALAIKA

Ekkel, Bibs (Lon)
Peiro, Teddy (Lon)

BANJO

Bowers, Geoffrey (Mid)
Brown, John (Mid)
Dexter, Michael (NW)
Ineson, Richard (NE)
Jones, Stephen (E)
Kirk, Nicholas (NE)
Knight, Beverley (Sco)
Langham, Thomas (SW)
Meadows, Colin (Lon)
Napper, Tom (NE)
Sullivan, Anthony (NW)
Walton, Pete (NW)
Williams, Stuart (NW)

BASS CLARINET

Chamberlain, Ian (Lon)

BASS GUITAR

Abbott, Michael (SE)
Adams, David (SE)
Adshead, Christopher (Lon)
Allan, Simon (NE)
Anthony, David (SE)
Atkinson, Paul (SE)
Auker, Brian (Lon)
Ayre, Ian (Lon)
Baker, Dan (SE)
Balch, Colin (E)
Bamforth, Jon (E)
Banks, John (Guitars SE)
Barnett, Carl (NW)
Barr, James (SE)
Barton, Richard (NW)
Bass, Adrien (Lon)
Begg, Alistair (SE)
Benson, Phil (Lon)
Berry, David (Lon)
Blomberg, Philip Suen (Mid)
Boothby, Hannah (Mid)
Bown, Alison (Voice Mid)
Brooks, Michael (Lon)
Browne, Kevin (Lon)
Bruce, Paul (Lon)

Burrell, Alvin (Lon)
Canty, Laurence (Lon)
Carrera-Weatherley, David (SE)
Carroll, Colin (Lon)
Caulfield, John (SW)
Chalmers, Bryan (Sco)
Chippendale, Mick (NW)
Clark, Peter (Lon)
Clarke, Jimmi (Guitars E)
Clews, Karl (SE)
Clews, Martyn (Mid)
Clutterbuck, Carl (SW)
Cole, Jonathan (E)
Collen, James (SE)
Cook, John (E)
Cooper, Ray (Lon)
Corpe, David (Double Bass Lon)
Corpe, David (Lon)
Dale, Martin (Mid)
Davis, Gordon (Lon)
Davis, Peter (SE)
Day, John (NE)
Donnelly, John (Lon)
Downing, Paul (Lon)
Doyle, Andrew (SW)
Duncan, Pete (Lon)
Dyer, Billy (E)
Edmonds, Michael (Lon)
Elton, Mark (SE)
Elvin, Mark (Lon)
Evans, Glynn (Lon)
Evans, Neil (Lon)
Evans, Stephen (E)
Fairweather, Robert (Lon)
Felgate, Robert (Mid)
Field, Stephen (Lon)
Ford-Powell, Ken (Guitars E)
Fox, Adam (Guitars Lon)
Fox, Marcus (Lon)
France, Phil (NE)
Frangos, Marco (Lon)
Garside, Gus (Double Bass SE)
Gee, Steve (Lon)
Gibbon, Frank (NE)
Giles, Steve A (Mid)
Gilliam, Nick (Guitars NW)
Gisby, Steve (SE)
Glover, Dave (SE)
Goodier, David (SW)
Graham, Andrew (Lon)
Gray, Paul (SW)
Green, David (Lon)
Gregory, Michael (NE)
Gregory, Terrence (Lon)
Griffin, Dirk (Mid)
Gruner, Alan (Lon)
Gwizdala, Janek (Lon)
Halestrap, Lee (Guitars Lon)
Hamilton, Ian (NE)
Hamilton, Ross (Sco)
Hammond, Thomas (Trombone Lon)
Harries, Timothy (Double Bass Lon)
Harris, Sydney (SW)

TEACHERS - BASS GUITAR

Higgins, Andy (Lon)
Higgs, Lindsay (SE)
Hill, Anthony (Lon)
Hill, Matt (Sco)
Hillard, Ross (Mid)
Hills, John (Lon)
Howard, Nathan (Mid)
Hunter, Kieron (Lon)
Hylton, Francis (Lon)
Iles, Robert (SW)
Isaac, Michael (NW)
Ivitsky (Sco)
Jackman, Neil (E)
James, Carl (Lon)
Jarvis, Jonathan (Mid)
Joe (Lon)
Jolly, Warren (NE)
Jones, Alan (SE)
Jones, Dave (Lon)
Jones, Richard (Mid)
Jono (Lon)
Kay, Derek (Lon)
Keightley, Maryann (Horn Mid)
Keys, Ronnie (SW)
Khan, Kameel (Lon)
Kings, Michael (Lon)
Leese, Ian (NE)
Letman, Mark (Mid)
Lilley, Terry (Double Bass Mid)
Lindemere, Peter (Lon)
Linke, Paul (Lon)
Lochrie, Jaz (Lon)
Lucas, Rob (Lon)
Macarthur, Quee (Sco)
Makos, Tony (Sco)
Manington, David (Lon)
Mantovani, Davide (Lon)
Martin, Matthew (Mid)
Maynes, Malcolm (Lon)
McFarlane, Ed (Sco)
McHugh, Michael (Sco)
McKinney, Andrew (Lon)
McLeod, David John (Lon)
McLocklan, Adam (NE)
Milner, Robert A (SE)
Mitchell, Andy (Sco)
Moignard, Daniel (Voice Lon)
Moore, Jennifer (Mid)
Moore, Malcolm (Lon)
Morgan, Gareth (Lon)
Mulrine, Jonathan (Sco)
Mulvey, St (Lon)
Murray, Kieran (Sco)
Nichols, Michael (Lon)
Nunes, Wayne (Lon)
O'Lochlainn, Fionn (Lon)
O'Shea, Franc (SE)
O'Toole, Brian (Lon)
Odell, Rodney (Lon)
Orford, Lloyd (SE)
Osrin, Adrian David (Lon)
Palmer, Jeff (NE)
Parker, Peter (Lon)
Parkin, Matthew (Lon)
Peaker, Terry (Lon)
Peckham, Geoffrey (SE)
Pennant, Trevor (Lon)
Philpot, Rufus (Lon)
Pike, Tim (NW)
Poole, Adrian (Lon)
Portas, Andrew (Mid)
Porter, John (Mid)
Rayner, Alison (Lon)
Reeman, Mike (Lon)
Reeve, Eric (E)

Rickarby, Barry (NE)
Rickards, Charles (E)
Rollason, Mark (E)
Rosario, Rafeal (SE)
Rose, Philip (E)
Rosembert, Nixon (Lon)
Routcliffe, Kim (Lon)
Rutherford, Richard (NE)
Sanders, Stephen (Lon)
Sargeant, Benjamin (Lon)
Sarici, Sedat (Lon)
Sayer, Ron James (E)
Schneider, Phil (Mid)
Scott, Paul (Lon)
Selby, Philip (E)
Seraphico, Ricky (Guitars Lon)
Setchfield, David (Lon)
Sharkey, Grant (E)
Shorten, Daniel (Mid)
Spack, Ronald (Double Bass SE)
Spolia, Rajan (SE)
Staples, Andy (Lon)
Statham, Rob (Lon)
Stewart, Simon (Violin Lon)
Stock, Mike (Lon)
Sweeney, John (NW)
Swift, David (Lon)
Tate, George (SE)
Todd, Alan (Mid)
Tonge, Andrew (Mid)
Tunbridge, Grant (SE)
Two-Names (Mid)
Tyre, Grant (Sco)
Uwadiae, Owen (Double Bass Lon)
Vermont, Johnny (Guitars NW)
Wagstaff, Stuart (SE)
Walker, Kevin (NE)
Walton, Pete (NW)
Ward, Steven (SW)
Wells, Timothy (Double Bass Lon)
White, Devon (Lon)
White, Simon (Lon)
Whitfield, Andrew (NW)
Williams, Danny (Lon)
Williams, Gary (Guitars SE)
Williams, Philip (Lon)
Willmott, Peter (Double Bass NW)
Wilson, Neil (E)
Wilson, Peter (Lon)
Wong, Anthony (Lon)
Wright, Anthony (NE)

BASS TROMBONE

Ethridge, Stephen (NE)
Hall, Simon T (Mid)
Knight, Alison (Lon)
Lester, Andrew (Lon)
Little, David (NW)
McDonald, Lorna (Sco)
Stearn, Christopher (Sco)

BASS TUBA

Roberts, Simon (Tuba Mid)
Sinclair, Alan (Mid)

BASSOON

Barrett, Hazel (NW)
Bartholomew, Sally-Anne (SE)
Bassey, Andrew (Mid)
Bennett, Elizabeth (SE)
Bentley, Anne (Lon)
Betts, Robert (E)
Bishop, Ann (NE)
Blackwell, Susan (NE)

Bloxwich, Janet (Sco)
Brierley, Alison (Mid)
Brookes, Philip (Mid)
Bruce, Jo (SW)
Bryan, Fiona (Lon)
Buckland, David (SW)
Buckley, Ronald (Mid)
Burnell, Carol (NW)
Burnett, Sarah (Lon)
Butt, Eric (SE)
Calderbank, Merle (Mid)
Catchpole, Jackie (NE)
Chapple, Sara (Mid)
Codd, Robert (SW)
Cohen, Susanna (Lon)
Cookhorn, Margaret (Mid)
Dundas-Grant, Deirdre (Lon)
Elliott, Lizbeth (Lon)
Fairbank, Anne (Lon)
Farmery, Emma (Lon)
Fidler, Aoileann (SE)
Ford, Michael (Lon)
Foster, Dominic (SW)
Gilchrist, Neil (Lon)
Good, Michael (E)
Gourlay, Caireen (Sco)
Hadfield, Sarah (Lon)
Hague, Karen Michelle (Sco)
Hardwick, Sheila (NE)
Hardy, Martin (Conductor NW)
Harris, Paul (Lon)
Harrison, Peter (Lon)
Holland, Simon (Lon)
Hunter, Andrew (Sco)
Jackson, Sally (Lon)
Jakob, Andrew (NE)
Johnson, David (NE)
Judson, Paul (NE)
Kingslake, Clara (SW)
Lambourne, Philip (SE)
Lloyd, Donald (Lon)
Mason, Elizabeth (Lon)
Maybury, Tess (SE)
McKee, David (E)
Miles, David (Lon)
Millar, Catherine (SE)
Moore, Richard (Lon)
Morgan, Sian (SW)
Morrell, Joanne (Lon)
Murphy, Kim (Lon)
Neate, Michael (SW)
Nissen, David (Lon)
Pollard, Mark (NW)
Poole, Vanessa (NW)
Potter, Amanda (NW)
Potter, Warwick (SE)
Price, Jonathan (Lon)
Price, Sarah (Lon)
Rance, Jessica (SE)
Rowlinson, Tamsin (Lon)
Salvage, Graham (NW)
Schroder, John (Mid)
Shevlin, Zoe (Lon)
Simons, Helen (Lon)
Smith, Daniel (Lon)
Sneyd, Peter (SW)
Soulsby, Katherine (SW)
Summers, Isolde (SW)
Tate, Alison (E)
Theobald, Felicity (Mid)
Thorndycraft, Ron (NE)
Tumelty, Helen (Lon)
Turlington, Maurice (Mid)
Wadsworth, Claire (Lon)
Waller, Ronald (Lon)

Warner, Kay (Lon)
Waterhouse, William (Lon)
Waterston, Eileen (Sco)
Watson, Kathryn (Sco)
Way, Alan (Sco)
White, Eve (SE)
Wightman, Brian (Lon)
Williams, Glyn (Lon)
Wilson, Colin (SE)
Wilson, Lesley (Sco)
Wyver, Sheila (Contra Bassoon SE)

BODHRAN

Gladwell, Kevin (E)
Harris, David (Mid)
Lea, Robert (Percussion NW)
Macpherson, Cluny (NE)
Quinn, Peter (Keyboards Lon)
Savage, Nigel (E)
Shiner, Mark (Mandolin Mid)

BRASS

Alexander, Les (Cornet Sco)
Anderson, Dave (Trumpet Sco)
Anstee, Ian (Tuba NW)
Arthur, Edward (Trumpet Lon)
Banks, Ronald (Tuba Mid)
Barker, Stuart Christopher (Bagpipes Mid)
Barnes, Michael (Sco)
Bates, Mark (Bass Trombone NW)
Blair, Sandy (Tuba NW)
Blakemore, Karen (Trumpet Mid)
Boult, Geoffrey (Trumpet Sco)
Brackpool, Marion (Trombone Sco)
Breen, Ryan (Tuba NW)
Brocklesby, David (Trombone NE)
Broomhead, Richard (Bass Trombone Mid)
Bullas, Phillip (Trombone NE)
Bunce, Martin (Trumpet Lon)
Burden, John (Horn Lon)
Cadwallender, Muriel (Horn NE)
Chadd, Nicholas (Trombone SW)
Chaplin, Maggie (Mid)
Chatterton, Timothy (Trombone NW)
Chester, Ray (Bandleader NE)
Collinge, John (Trombone E)
Collins, Michael (Trumpet Lon)
Cooke, Matthew (Horn NW)
Cooper, Laurence (Trombone NW)
Cowieson, Lorne (Trumpet Sco)
Cranham, Christopher (Tuba SE)
Crompton, Andy (Trombone Lon)
Daniels, Gwyn (Trombone SW)
Darrington, Ian (Trumpet NW)
Deans, Brian (Trombone Sco)
Devereux, Frederick (Bass Trombone Mid)
Diprose, Michael (Trumpet Lon)
Douglas, Martin (Tuba Sco)
Edwards, David (Trumpet NW)
Ellsmore, Stuart (Trumpet SW)
England, Peter (Keyboards NW)
Fletcher, Paul (Trombone NE)
France, Adrian (Bass Trombone Lon)
Frere-Smith, Dennis (Trumpet Lon)
Friel, Alan (Trumpet Sco)
Frost, David (Trumpet SW)
Frost, Mark (Bass Trombone NW)
Gee, Darryl (Horn NE)
Glanfield, John (Saxophones SW)
Golightly, David Frederick (Tuba NW)
Goslyn, Roger (Trombone Lon)
Grenfell, Kevin (Trombone SW)
Hacon, Derek (Trumpet E)
Haggart, Alan (Trumpet Sco)

Hall, Matthew P (Tuba Mid)
Harper, Diane (Horn NW)
Harris, Christopher (Trumpet SW)
Harris, Martyn (Trumpet Mid)
Harrison, John (Cornet NE)
Harrison, Phillip (Trombone Mid)
Hartley-Bennett, Gordon (Horn Mid)
Hassan, Joseph (Tuba Lon)
Hawkes, Dennis (Euphonium Lon)
Hearnshaw, Colin (Trumpet NW)
Henderson, Diane (Trumpet Lon)
Hewitt, Miles (Horn Lon)
Hill, Colin (Trombone Lon)
Holdom, Colin (Trumpet E)
Hook, Heather (Sco)
Izod, Joseph (Tuba Lon)
Jenkins, Dan (Trombone Lon)
Jones, Andrew (Trumpet SW)
Jones, Karen (NW)
Jones, Martin (Trumpet NE)
Kaldor, Peter (Horn Lon)
Kampen, Paul (Horn NE)
Kearsey, Mike (Trombone Lon)
Kelsey, Xenophon (Conductor NE)
King, Alastair (Trombone Lon)
Lees, Tom (Trombone Lon)
Leeson, Mike (Trumpet NE)
Lewis, Hywel (Trombone NW)
Linford, Anthony (Trumpet SE)
Lowe, Angela (Cornet SW)
Ludlam, Bob (Trumpet NE)
Lyrical Lord Leo (Accordion NW)
Mallen, Stuart (Euphonium Mid)
Mann, Kenton (Trombone NW)
Martin, Robert (Bass Guitar SW)
McEwan, Gregon (Trumpet Mid)
Meiklejohn, Philip (Horn NW)
Melbourne, Andrew (Trombone SE)
Miller, Jeffrey (Tuba Lon)
Milne, John (Trombone Sco)
Minshall, Helen (Tuba NW)
Mitchell, Brian (Trumpet Sco)
Moore, Colin (Trumpet Lon)
Morgan, Veronica (Horn NW)
Morton, Adrian (Trumpet SW)
Moseley, Ian (Trombone Mid)
Nabb, Philippa (Trumpet SW)
Niblett, Christopher (Bass Trombone SE)
North, Chris (Flugel Horn SW)
Nurse, Gwyneth (Trombone NW)
O'Shannon, Terri (Saxophones Sco)
Ornsby, Glenn (Trumpet NE)
Pepper, Austin (Horn SE)
Petrie, Peter (Bass Trombone Sco)
Pickles, John (Trumpet Lon)
Prentice, David (Trumpet Sco)
Price, Jeremy (Trumpet Lon)
Price, Kevin (Trumpet Sco)
Rattray, Catherine (Horn Lon)
Rees, Emyr (Tuba NW)
Richards, Bob (Trumpet NE)
Richardson, Bill (Trombone Mid)
Roberts-Malpass, Edward (Trumpet Mid)
Royle, Ian (Trumpet NW)
Shepherd, Mark (Trumpet Mid)
Simons, Harry (Trombone NW)
Smith, Chris (Trombone Lon)
Stiff, Colin (Horn SW)
Storey, Leslie (Bass Trombone NW)
Swan, Malcolm (Trombone Lon)
Tatt, Mike (Bass Trombone Lon)
Taylor, David (Cornet Mid)
Tungay, T Paul (Trumpet SE)
Turner, John (Trombone Mid)
Van Der Walt, J Simon (Trumpet Sco)

Vaughan, Brian (Trumpet Lon)
Venn, Jimmy (Trumpet Mid)
Wadkin, Frank (Trumpet Mid)
Wasson, Barry (Bass Tuba NW)
Watt, William (Trombone SE)
Weatherley, Thomas (Trombone NE)
Weston, Bryan (Sousaphone Mid)
Whitehouse, David (Alto Trombone Lon)
Wigham, Carolyn (NE)
Willis, Simon (Euphonium NE)
Wilson, Paul (NE)
Winch, Matthew (Trumpet E)
Winterflood, John (Euphonium SW)
Woods, Gavin (Tuba NW)
Wrigley, Thomas (Trombone NW)
Young, Colin (SE)

CELLO

Adam, Stephen (Sco)
Adler, Stanley (Lon)
Aird, Liza Ellen (SW)
Aldersea, Rebecca (NW)
Ardagh-Walter, Catherine (Mid)
Armour, Lynn (Sco)
Ashby, Rhiannon (SE)
Ashforth, S (Bandleader NE)
Aslangul, Philip (Lon)
Attwood, Elspeth (Lon)
Bailey, Diana (Lon)
Bailey, Sarah (Lon)
Baines, Kathryn (E)
Baldwin, Kelly (Lon)
Balkwill, Maryan (Lon)
Banbury, James (Lon)
Banda, Pal (Lon)
Bates, Jasmine (Mid)
Baur, Jane (E)
Beall, David (NE)
Beamish, Dinah (Lon)
Bean, John (Mid)
Bean, Rebecca (Sco)
Bennet, Andrew (NW)
Bennett, Harriet (E)
Bersey, William (E)
Bevan, Catriona (SE)
Bingham, Ruth (NW)
Binney, Helena (Lon)
Binnie, Anne (Sco)
Birtchnell, Una (Lon)
Black, Catherine (Lon)
Blayden, Alastair (Lon)
Blomiley, Nigel (Lon)
Bolger, Lorraine (Mid)
Boole-Masterson, Naomi (Mid)
Bowell, Mary (NE)
Boyd, Marian (Sco)
Brewer, Emmeline (SW)
Bridger, Mary (Lon)
Brissenden, Elizabeth (NE)
Brook, Elaine (Sco)
Brown, Alison (Sco)
Brown, Gabrielle (Lon)
Brown, Graham (Mid)
Brown, Moira (Mid)
Bruce, William (Lon)
Brundan, Amanda (SE)
Brunner, Paul (Lon)
Bryan, John (Early Renaissance NE)
Bryan, Margaret (NE)
Bune, Margaret (SW)
Burgin, Judith (NE)
Burley, Imogen (Lon)
Burrowes, David (Lon)
Calverley, Anthony (Mid)
Carey, Jadie (Mid)

TEACHERS - CELLO

Cassidy, Claudine (SW)
Cawood, Elizabeth (NE)
Charlton, Neil (SE)
Chilcott, Polly (SE)
Child, Angela (SE)
Cleal, Carol (SE)
Clutton, Christine (Lon)
Cochrane, Ailsa J (Voice NW)
Coe, Jane (SE)
Coles, Janet (Lon)
Collarbone, Winifred (Mid)
Coote, Nicholas (Lon)
Corcos, Nadia (SW)
Cossack, Malka (Lon)
Cox, Joanne (E)
Cox, Paul (SE)
Cracknell, Robert (Mid)
Cranham, Lynden (SE)
Creaser, Sandra (SW)
Crouch, Janet (Lon)
Crump, Ursula (SW)
Cummings, Douglas (Lon)
Davidson, Anne (Sco)
Davidson, John (Sco)
Davies, Benjamin (Lon)
Davies, Huw (Lon)
Davis, Louise (E)
De Groote, Rudi (Sco)
Deacon, Lorraine (SE)
Deats, Gareth (Early Strings SE)
Del-Mar, Pauline (Lon)
Desbruslais, Julia (Lon)
Dickie, Charles (SW)
Dolton, Maria (Lon)
Donoghue, Laura (Lon)
Dorey, Sue (Lon)
Duncan, Helen (Sco)
Durham, Catherine (SW)
Edgar, Helen (Lon)
Eksteen, Charlotte (Lon)
Elliott, Deirdre (Lon)
Elliott, Rosemary (Lon)
Evans, Vicky (SW)
Fairhurst, Zoe (NW)
Farnon, Nicola (NE)
Few, Jonathan (Lon)
Findlay, Valerie (SE)
Fisher, Susannah (Lon)
Fitzgerald, David (Lon)
Fitzgerald, Josephine (Lon)
Fleet, Judith (Lon)
Ford, Rachel (Lon)
Fox, Margaret (NE)
Frost, Corinne (Mid)
Gardner, Thomas (Lon)
Geddes, Helen (Lon)
Gilde, Sean Karsten (Mid)
Gill, Timothy (E)
Gillett, Fiona (SE)
Gilliver, Rebecca (Lon)
Gledhill, Oliver (Lon)
Glossop, Keith (Lon)
Good (NW)
Goodborn, Olive (Mid)
Gow, Aline (Sco)
Graham, Mary-Louise (Lon)
Greensmith, Brian (NE)
Grimm, Nigel (NW)
Grunthal, Barbara (NW)
Gubbins, Jean (Mid)
Gwilt, Dawn (Mid)
Hale, Helen (Sco)
Harding, Kate (E)
Harmer, Marjorie (E)
Harper, Alison (Mid)

Harrington, Sarah (Sco)
Harris, Harold (Sco)
Harris, Kathryn (NW)
Harrison, James (Lon)
Havers, Angus (Lon)
Hawley, Joy (Lon)
Hayward, Valerie (NW)
Heinen, Elaine (Mid)
Henderson, Veronica (E)
Hess, Andrea (Lon)
Hess, Benjamin (Lon)
Hewitt, Keith (SW)
Heyes, Nicola (NE)
Heywood, Susan (E)
Hodges, Christopher (SW)
Holm, Jane (Lon)
Holt, Sian (Lon)
Hopgood, Andrea (E)
Hotton, Jean (NE)
Hoyle, Christopher (NW)
Hunt, Annie (NW)
Irvine, Benedict (NE)
Isaac, Emily (Lon)
Isaacson, Rhian (Lon)
Janse, Jennifer (Lon)
Jary, Catherine (Lon)
Jeans, Clare (Early Strings Lon)
Jenkinson, Richard (Lon)
John, Gareth (Sco)
Johnson, Jacqueline (SE)
Jones, Jenny (Lon)
Kaznowski, Michal (Lon)
Kears, Paul (Lon)
Kellett, Paul (Lon)
Kennaway, George (NE)
Kennedy, Laurien (SE)
Kerr, Felicity (Lon)
Kitchen, Jonathan (Lon)
Kristy, Nikki (Mid)
Lacey, Helen (SW)
Ladds, Roger (NE)
Ladds, Sally J (NE)
Langridge, Jennifer (NW)
Lannigan, Brendan (Lon)
Lass, Ruth (SW)
Laverick, Samantha (Lon)
Lay, Robert (Sco)
Le Feuvre, Gerard (Lon)
Leadbeater, Sonia (Mid)
Lebon, Christopher (Lon)
Leitch, John (Sco)
Lewis, Roger (SW)
Lilley, Janet (E)
Lines, Ann (Lon)
Linklater, William (Sco)
Livingstone, Christine (Lon)
Lloyd, Elizabeth (NE)
Loeser, Brigitte (Lon)
Loftin, John (Double Bass Lon)
Lovell, Maureen (Lon)
Lowes, Clare (SE)
Lowrey, Ray (SE)
Ludford, Ian (Mid)
Ludford, Janet (Mid)
Lukoszevieze, Anton (Lon)
Lunn, Roger (Lon)
Lunt, Helen (SW)
Macrae, Christina (Lon)
Mainard, Amanda (Mid)
Mandeville, Marion (SE)
Mansell, Christopher (Lon)
Marshall, Mark (NW)
Mason, Robin (Sco)
Matthey, Clemence (Lon)
May, John (SW)

McEwen, Kathryn (NE)
McGinnes, Maxine (Mid)
McIlwaine, Elizabeth (NW)
McKee, Susan (Lon)
McKenzie, Sheena (Lon)
McKinley, Sharon (Lon)
McLeod, Mary (Lon)
McMurtrie, Virginia (SE)
McVeigh, Alice (Lon)
Miles, Claire (Lon)
Millett, Sebastian (Lon)
Morgan, Philippa (Early Strings SW)
Morris, Simon (Lon)
Morton, Claire (Sco)
Mustard, John M (Sco)
Narvey, Mayda (Lon)
Nelson, Becca (NW)
Nice, Andrew (Lon)
Nicholls, Julianna (Sco)
Norman, David (Lon)
Norris, Robert (Lon)
Ogden, Nicola (E)
Pacey, Sara (Lon)
Parry, Frederick (Sco)
Passchier, Maja (E)
Pegna, Shirley (SW)
Pells, Mary (E)
Perrin, Ingrid (Lon)
Porteous, Diane (Lon)
Pressland, Ian (Lon)
Price, Jonathan (NW)
Quinn, Susan (NW)
Rayner, Peter (Lon)
Reed, Janet (Lon)
Richards, Carolyn (SW)
Richards, Margaret (Lon)
Riddell, Susanna (Lon)
Riley, Audrey (Lon)
Robb, Susan (Mid)
Roberts, Paul (NW)
Robinson, David (Lon)
Roper, Amaryllis (Lon)
Roulson, Michele (NE)
Routledge, William (Lon)
Routley, Priscilla (Sco)
Rowntree, Louise (Lon)
Roycroft, Miriam (NE)
Rudall, Stephen (Lon)
Sawyer, Helen (Lon)
Sayers, Caroline (NW)
Schofield, William (Lon)
Scott, Phoebe (Lon)
Shearman, Amanda (Sco)
Sheppard, Susan (Lon)
Shuttleworth, Anna (Lon)
Silver, Noreen (Sco)
Skeaping, Emma (Early Strings Lon)
Smart, Shirley (Mid)
Smith, Anne (NW)
Smith, Ursula (Lon)
Spear, Elizabeth (Mid)
Spencer, Kirstin (Lon)
Spencer-Smith, Clare (Mid)
Spooner, Joseph (Lon)
Staples, Ann (SW)
Stehn, Leonard (Lon)
Stephenson, Karen (Mid)
Stewart, Diane (NW)
Stocks, Linda (SW)
Strevens, Anita (Lon)
Stuart-Pennink, S (SE)
Tasker, John (NW)
Theo, Tatty (Early Strings Lon)
Thoday, Gillian (Lon)
Thompson-Clarke, Robin (Lon)

Thornton, Barrie (NE)
Threlfall, Stephen (NW)
Tiler, Jeffrey (NE)
Tomlinson, Juliet (SW)
Tucker, Kay (SE)
Turner, Rachel (Violin Lon)
Tustain, Sarah (Mid)
Tyler, Anne (SW)
Tyler, Jacqueline (Mid)
Tyler, Marianne (Lon)
Van Der Tang, Rachel (Lon)
Vella, Fiona (NW)
Vocadlo, R. Bernard (Lon)
Vukotic, Bozidar (Lon)
Walden, Suzanne (Mid)
Waldock, Wendy (Mid)
Wall, Abby (Early Strings E)
Waltham, Rachel (Lon)
Ward-Roden, Richard (Lon)
Wardale, Andrew (NW)
Warham, Christine (NE)
Watson, Andrea (Lon)
Weatherby, Wendy (Sco)
Weaver, Paul (Lon)
Webb, Simon (SE)
Welsh, Angela (Sco)
Wesling, David (NW)
Westerhoff, Gay-Yee (Lon)
Whettam, Rebeca (NW)
White, Peter (NW)
Whitehouse, Kathy (E)
Wickham, Antonia (NE)
Wiegold, Richard (SW)
Wilde, Libby (Lon)
Wilmers, Catherine (Lon)
Wilson, Sally (Lon)
Wilson, Spike (SE)
Wilson, Susanna (Lon)
Woodcock, Melanie (Lon)
Woollard, Anthony (Lon)
Worrall, Peter (NW)
Zagni, Ruth (SW)
Zoob, Naomi (Lon)

CELTIC HARP

Crook, Jennifer (SW)
Hidson, Jean (Mid)
Munoz, Fernando (Sco)

CITTERN

Coe, Pete (Bouzouki NE)

CLARINET

Allen, Frank (Mid)
Allen, Geraldine (Lon)
Allerton, Fred (Saxophones NE)
Allison, Christopher (Mid)
Anderson, Molly (NW)
Andrews, Alan (Lon)
Ashby, Duncan (Lon)
Atchinson, Mark (Saxophones SE)
Atkinson, Christopher (Lon)
Baigent, Nicola (Lon)
Banks, Kevin (SE)
Barber, Ron (Saxophones NE)
Barella, Timothy (Saxophones Sco)
Barlow, Caroline (SE)
Bartlett, Peter (NE)
Bateman, Marie (Mid)
Baughan, Claire (Lon)
Beaman, Julie (Lon)
Beckett, Seren (Sco)
Beever, J (Saxophones Lon)
Benn, Max (NW)

Bennett, Stephen (Lon)
Bishop, Susan (Lon)
Black, Ian (Pianoforte Sco)
Blackwood, William (Sco)
Blanken, Robert (SE)
Bomber, Ray (E)
Bondonno, Alessandro (Lon)
Boorer, Jeffrey (SW)
Booth, Jane (Lon)
Bowles, Thomas (Lon)
Bown, Edward (Saxophones NE)
Bowring, Sarah (Lon)
Boyd, Martin (Saxophones NE)
Brady, Gareth (Lon)
Bridgewater, Paul (SW)
Brimfield, Terence (SW)
Brinkley, Sarah (E)
Broadway, Grahame (Saxophones SE)
Brodie, Andy (Sco)
Brown, Suzanne (Voice SW)
Browne, Jacqueline (NW)
Bruce, Tony (Saxophones NE)
Brunton, Phillip D (Conductor E)
Bryant, Colin (Saxophones SE)
Bucknall, Juliet (Lon)
Burnell, Donald (SW)
Burvill, Mandy (Lon)
Butler, Verity (SW)
Butt, Raymond (SW)
Butterworth, Roy (SW)
Buxton, Ruth (Lon)
Cannon, Rachel (Lon)
Carter, David S (E)
Cartwright, Sally (SE)
Cartwright, Sarah (Mid)
Caruana, Nicholas (Mid)
Casey, Graham (Lon)
Cassidy, Carl (Lon)
Chamberlain, Sarah (Mid)
Cipolla, Sebastiano (Voice SW)
Clarke, Sarah (Lon)
Clement-Evans, Peryn (Lon)
Clennon, Ornette (Sco)
Cocks, Elaine (Lon)
Coles, Derren (Lon)
Collard, Esther (Lon)
Colville, Randolph (SE)
Condliffe, Jacqueline (Mid)
Conn, Harry (Saxophones Lon)
Cooper, Raymond (Saxophones NE)
Coote, Heather (SW)
Cornet, Victoria (SE)
Cowley, Guy (Lon)
Cox, Nicholas (NW)
Craven, Leslie (Lon)
Davies, Heidi (NW)
Davies, Noel (Saxophones SE)
De La Mothe, Peter (SE)
De La Rue, Richard (SW)
Dell, Peter (Lon)
Denford, Sharon (NE)
Denman, John (Lon)
Dexter-Mills, Suzanne (E)
Diakow, Tamara (Lon)
Dobree, Georgina (Lon)
Dolman, Sally (Saxophones Lon)
Dorr, Julie (NE)
Dowse, Edward (SE)
Drain, Pauline (Lon)
Ede, Terence (Saxophones Lon)
Edwards, Bryan (Lon)
Edwards, Felicity (Lon)
Edwards, Phillip (Lon)
Elkan, Geoffrey (Lon)
Elliott, Rosalynd (Lon)

Ellis, Ruth (Sco)
Entwistle, Eric (Saxophones Mid)
Estall, Joanna (Lon)
Fairbairn, Zoe (Lon)
Fairhurst, Lynne (NW)
Fairley, Douglas (Sco)
Farnham, Michael (Lon)
Ferer, Lionel (Lon)
Fielding, Peter (SW)
Fish, Rosalind (SE)
Foley, John (Sco)
Ford, Luan (Mid)
Foster, Nicholas (NW)
Fox, Derek (Saxophones SW)
Fox, Penelope (Viola NW)
Freeland, Joanne (Lon)
Fulcher, Harry (SW)
Fulker, Nicola (Lon)
Fussell, Angela (Lon)
Gale, David (Lon)
Galway, George (Flute NW)
Gibson, Daniel (NE)
Gibson, Tim (Copyist Lon)
Gilbert, Jack (Saxophones SE)
Gill, Susan (Lon)
Gittins, Kate (Lon)
Glasgow, Bill (Saxophones NW)
Godsell, Edward (Lon)
Goffin, Alison (NE)
Gould, Emily (NW)
Graham, Neville (Lon)
Green, Malcolm (Lon)
Greene, Philip (Sco)
Greenwood, Michael (SW)
Haggart, Alison (Sco)
Hallam, Norman (SE)
Hambleton, Hale (Lon)
Harlan, Ben (E)
Harrop, Sally (Mid)
Harvey, Paul (Lon)
Hastie, James (Clarinet Sco)
Hawkes, Claire (Alto Clarinet SE)
Hawkes, Gillian (Mid)
Haysted, Ian (Lon)
Hemmings, Diana (E)
Herson, Janet (Lon)
Heywood, David (NW)
Hibbert, Ian (Mid)
Hill, Lisa (SE)
Hill, Peter (NW)
Hill, Robert (Lon)
Hill, Steve (Lon)
Hirst, Willie (Saxophones NE)
Hodges, Valerie (SW)
Holdsworth, Gary (Lon)
Holman-Fox, Lynn (Lon)
Hood, Victoria (Mid)
Hopgood, Adrian (Saxophones E)
Hopkinson, Christopher (Mid)
Houghton, Anthony (NW)
Houghton, James (Lon)
Howes, Peter (Lon)
Hughes, Alison (SE)
Hurrell, Susan (NE)
Hyland, Julie (Lon)
Hyland, Terry (Lon)
Jager, Alan (Saxophones Mid)
Jenkins, Lyle (Saxophones Lon)
Johnston, Robert (Saxophones Sco)
Jones, Leslie (Lon)
Jones, Paula (SW)
Joseph, James (NE)
Joyce, Lucy (SE)
Joyce, Norman (Lon)
Kaye, Sally (Lon)

TEACHERS - CLARINET

Keenan, Andy (Lon)
Kempton, Karina (Lon)
Killoran, Ian (Lon)
King, Conrad (Bassoon Lon)
King, Stuart (Lon)
Kirby, David (Lon)
Kirby, Dawn (NW)
Kirkpatrick, Dennis (NW)
Laing, Gregor (Lon)
Laurens, Elizabeth (SW)
Lawson, Sarah A (NE)
Le-Grand, John (NE)
Leaver, Roger (Lon)
Ledingham, David (Lon)
Lewin, Gordon (Lon)
Lewington, Sarah (Lon)
Lewis, Malcolm (SE)
Light, Patrick (Saxophones E)
Lindsell, Robert (E)
Linton, Simon (SW)
Lluna, Joan-Enric (Lon)
Lock, Kate (SW)
Luxmoore, Kate (Mid)
Lyons, Lorna (E)
Mackenzie, John (NE)
Mainwaring, James (SW)
Marshall, Jeffrey (Saxophones NE)
Marshall, Roger (Lon)
Matthews, Paul (SW)
Maunder, Peter (Lon)
McAllister, Kenneth (Lon)
McDonald, George (NE)
McGovern, Clare (SE)
McKenna, Joe (Saxophones E)
McLaren, Jennifer (Lon)
Meadows, John (Mid)
Mendham, Tracey (Saxophones Lon)
Mepham, Rachel (Lon)
Merrick, Linda (SW)
Miller, David (NW)
Milner, Edward (NW)
Mitchell, Ian (Lon)
Mitchell, Timothy (Sco)
Mo, Chi-Yu (Lon)
Moore, Norman (NE)
Moore, Sarah (SE)
Moran, John (Mid)
Morgan, Bob (Composer Lon)
Morgan, Sarah (SE)
Morgans, Avril (Lon)
Morris, Steve (Lon)
Moss, Susan (Lon)
Mossman, Jenny (Sco)
Mould, Sidney (Saxophones NE)
Munday, Jason (Lon)
Munn, Julia (Lon)
Murphy, Kevin (Lon)
Muskett, Michael (SE)
Neale, Clive (E)
Nichols, Peter (Lon)
O'Brien, Mark (Mid)
Oades, Debbie (NE)
Oldland, Marie (Mid)
Passmore, Rhianon (SW)
Patton, Joanna (NW)
Payne, Lawrence (SE)
Percy, Richard (Mid)
Peters, Ian (SE)
Phillips, Jane (Lon)
Phillips, Nigel (Bandleader SW)
Pickering, Gillian (SE)
Plane, Robert (Lon)
Prosser, Grenville (Horn SW)
Purcell, Roger (NW)
Quilter, Graham (Lon)

Racz, Lynne (NW)
Rebbeck, Janet (NW)
Redpath, Timothy (NW)
Reilly, Stanley (Saxophones Sco)
Richards, Jack (SW)
Roberts, Anthony (SW)
Roberts, Christine (Lon)
Roberts, Hugh (SW)
Roberts, Kathryn (NE)
Roberts, Michael (NE)
Robinson, John (NE)
Robson, Barnaby (Lon)
Rogerson, Howard (NE)
Ross, Nicholas (Sco)
Rowe, Charles (Saxophones E)
Rudd, Hilary (SE)
Rye, Daniel (Lon)
Sagi, Zoltan (Mid)
Sander, Adrian (NE)
Sander, Hilary (NE)
Sandoe, Cliff (Saxophones SE)
Saunders, Paul (Lon)
Saxton, Michael (SW)
Schechter, Gregory (Lon)
Scrivener, Graham (Lon)
Segger, Jill (Composer E)
Sherlock, Howard (Saxophones SW)
Shilham, Brian (SE)
Shotton, Stephen (NW)
Simpson, Georgina (Mid)
Slack, Frank (Lon)
Slack, Karen (NW)
Slaymark, Victor (Lon)
Smith, George (Sco)
Sproston, Diane (Mid)
Stagg, Kathryn (Lon)
Storr, Josephine (SE)
Stowell, Christopher (Mid)
Stringle, Julian (Lon)
Sutton, Andrew (SE)
Sweeney, William (Sco)
Swindells, Duncan (Lon)
Tattersall, Elizabeth (E)
Tellick, Linda (SE)
Tempest, Roger (Saxophones Mid)
Tennant, Sarah (NW)
Thompson, Terence (Mid)
Thurlow, Tracey (Lon)
Todd, Liane (NE)
Tonks, Valerie (Saxophones Mid)
Trebble, Ceri (E)
Tromans, Mark (Lon)
Troughton, Harold (NW)
Tucker, Alison (Sco)
Turley, Pamela (Sco)
Turner, Karen (NW)
Underwood, James (Lon)
Vassallo, Antonino (Lon)
Vaughan, Caroline (NE)
Walker, Kate (Lon)
Wall, Sharon (Mid)
Waller, Norman (E)
Walsh, Sarah (Sco)
Walthew, John (SW)
Ward, Elizabeth (SE)
Warner, Leon (Percussion Lon)
Wasserman, Clare (Lon)
Watkinson, Peter (SW)
Watson, Ruth (Lon)
Watt, Ruth (SW)
Weinberg, Anton (Lon)
West, Paul (SE)
West, Richard (Lon)
Whelan, Larry (Lon)
Whennell, Tony (Lon)

Whight, Michael (Lon)
White, Brian (Saxophones SE)
Wilkinson, Adrian (NW)
Wilson, Roger (Saxophones Lon)
Wimhurst, Karen (Sco)
Wixey, Jayne (NE)
Woodhouse, Lynne (SW)
Woodland, Caroline (Mid)
Wyatt, Sally (Mid)

CLARSACH

Mawson, Annie (NW)
Wealleans, Michelle (Harp Sco)

COMPOSER

Adie, Nicholas (Guitars Lon)
Applegate, Simon J (Conductor SW)
Arden, Jeremy (Lon)
Burrell, Howard (Music Director E)
Burt, Nicholas (Mid)
Cawkwell, Roger (Saxophones Lon)
English, Virgil (Lon)
Flynn, Declan (Pianoforte Lon)
Fox, Matthew (Dulcimer Lon)
Francis, David (Music Director Lon)
Glandfield, Lou (Keyboards SE)
Goodall, David (Keyboards Sco)
Humphris, Ian (Conductor Lon)
Jordan, John (Lon)
Kriwaczek, Rohan (Clarinet SE)
Madigan, Brian (Percussion SW)
Mitchell, Andy (Guitars Mid)
Moser, Peter (One Man Band NW)
Nicholls, Jonathan (SW)
Painter, Christopher (SW)
Philips, Julian (E)
Powell, Roy (Pianoforte NW)
Pratley, Susie (SE)
Riley, Martin (Mid)
Sandy (Keyboards Lon)
Smith, Christopher (Trumpet NW)
Smith, Tommy (Saxophones Sco)
Stowell, David A (Conductor Mid)
Wells, Jane (E)
White, John (Pianoforte Lon)
Williams, Christoper (SW)
Willward, Frank (Keyboards SE)
Wilson, Jeffery (Lon)

CONCERTINA

Baynham, Frank (NW)
Harbron, Robert (Lon)
Oliver, Charlotte (SE)
Townsend, Dave (SE)

CONDUCTOR

Bowman, Aubrey (Lon)
Dewar, David (NE)
Hose, Anthony (SW)
Karar, Abdul (Bass Guitar SE)
Keane, James (Lon)
Stent, Keith (Lon)

CONTRA BASSOON

Cuthill, Ian (Bassoon Lon)

COR ANGLAIS

Bell, Morven (Sco)
Cowley, Francis (Trumpet SW)
Dawson, Stephen (Trumpet Lon)
Steer, Jonathan (Lon)
Thomas, Sylvia (Soprano Clarinet NW)
Webster, Roger (NW)
Williams, Wyn (Trumpet NW)

Winter, Martin (NW)

DHOLAK

Boparai, Harjinder (Keyboards Mid)
Mattu, Satinder (Club DJ Mid)

DIDJERIDU

Ashenashae (Percussion SE)
Bennun, Colin (Pianoforte SE)
Farrenden, Shaun (Lon)
Lord, Didge (SE)
Davies, Alicia (Lon)

DOUBLE BASS

Allan, Haydn (NE)
Allnatt, Michael (SW)
Anderson, Graham (NE)
Atkinson, Julian (Mid)
Ayre, David (Lon)
Bagshaw, David (NW)
Baker, Dawn (Lon)
Bargh, Andrew (Mid)
Bellatalla, Roberto (Lon)
Bersey, James (Composer Lon)
Black, Kenneth (Sco)
Blannin, Peter (E)
Boros, Gabor K (Lon)
Bosch, Leon (Lon)
Bougie (Lon)
Braime, Hilary (Mid)
Brian, BB (E)
Brocklehurst, Brian (Lon)
Brown, Lancelot (NE)
Bruggemeyer, Cecelia (Lon)
Burgess, John (SE)
Burgess, Samuel (Lon)
Calvert, Rebecca (Sco)
Canonici, Corrado (Lon)
Caribe, Mario (Sco)
Carrillo-Garcia, Roberto (NE)
Chilton, Roy (Lon)
Clow, Dionne (NE)
Coman, Matthew (Lon)
Condliffe, Mary (SW)
Constantinou, Stace (Pianoforte Mid)
Cook, Francesca (Lon)
Costello, Stephen (NW)
Crawford, Iain (Sco)
Croxon, Thomas (Lon)
Cruickshank, Andrew (Sco)
Curphey, Roger (Lon)
Dale, Julian (SW)
Dawes, Tim (Lon)
De-Lloyd, Rose-Marie (Cello SW)
Devlin, Peter (Lon)
Dougan, Anna (Sco)
Drever, Susan (Sco)
Dufty, Nigel (NW)
Dunning, Ronald (Lon)
Dupuy, Nicki (NW)
Eames, Roger (SW)
Eaton, Lynette (Lon)
Edwards, John (Lon)
Elliott, Catherine (Lon)
Falvey, Polly (SE)
Fell, Simon (Lon)
Fentimen, Rhiannon (Lon)
Ferguson, Alan (Sco)
Fernando, Imogen (SW)
Findley, David (NE)
Fitzgerald, Paul (E)
Fletcher, Clive (SE)
Friend, Alistair (Bass Guitar Lon)
Gee, Jon (Lon)

Glanville, David (Lon)
Glynn, Barry (SE)
Gordon, Jeremy (Lon)
Graham, Elizabeth (SE)
Graham-White, William (SW)
Gray, John (Mid)
Griffiths, Debbie (SE)
Grosse, Paul (Mid)
Halyburton, May (Sco)
Hames, Robin (Cello SW)
Hamilton, Armour (Sco)
Hamilton, Peter (Mid)
Harling, Keith (Lon)
Harper, Derek (Mid)
Haskins, Matthew (SW)
Hatrick, Thomas (Sco)
Haynes, Sarah (Lon)
Healey, Jane (Lon)
Heath, Lucy (Lon)
Hill, John (Lon)
Hill, Thomas Alan (Mid)
Hinde, Carl (NW)
Hodges, Peter (Lon)
Holgate, David (E)
Hosford, Liz (Lon)
Hoskins, John (Lon)
Hougham, Tony (Lon)
Hughes, Natasha (SE)
Hunter, Sean (Lon)
Hurcombe, Eddie (SE)
Jub (SE)
Keep, Andrew (SW)
Kenihan, David (SE)
Kershaw, 'Subbersive' Steve (SE)
Kilkenny, Anthony (SE)
Klute, Martin (Lon)
Knussen, Erik (Sco)
Large, Ronald (Mid)
Lloyd-Evans, Owen (NW)
Lowe, Trevor (Lon)
Maguire, Caroline (Lon)
Maguire, Francis (Lon)
Martin, Andrea (NW)
Matthews, Peter (Lon)
Maybank, Christopher (SE)
McGee, Billy (Lon)
McTier, Ian (Sco)
Meggido, Marc (Lon)
Miles, David (Lon)
Miller, Paul (NE)
Mizen, Valdon J (SE)
Moylan, Paul (Lon)
Mudele, Joseph (Lon)
Munro, David (NE)
Myers, Martin (Lon)
Nevison, George (Lon)
Newman, Jake (NW)
Newton, Raymond (NE)
Nwanoku, Chi-Chi (Lon)
Occleshaw, Bill (Contractor SW)
Osborn, Barbara (Mid)
Osborne, Tony (Lon)
Osman, Adrian (SE)
Pearce, Gordon (Lon)
Pedersen, Thomas (E)
Precious, Adam (Lon)
Presdee, John (Pianoforte SW)
Rankin, Dorothy (Sco)
Rees-Jones, John (Lon)
Richards, John (Lon)
Richardson, Jim (Lon)
Riley, Stuart F (NW)
Rivron, Dominic (NE)
Russell, Simon (SE)
Shaw, Lucy (Lon)

Shenton, John (Lon)
Shiels, Brian (Sco)
Shoulder, Michael (NE)
Smith, Ryan (Lon)
Somogyi, Arnold (Lon)
Storer, Daniel (NW)
Street, Carol (NW)
Stuart, Peter (NE)
Summerfield, John (Pianoforte SE)
Tattersdill, John (Mid)
Taylor, Michael (SW)
Thackeray, Jonathan (NW)
Thistlewood, Mark (Lon)
Thomson, Stuart (NW)
Waldock, Richard (NW)
Wall, Charles (Mid)
Wallis, Geoff (NW)
Waterworth, Andrew (Lon)
Watson, Ian (Lon)
Watson, Richard (Lon)
Watts, Steve (Lon)
West, Christopher (Lon)
Wheatley, George (Mid)
Whitford, David (Lon)
Williams, Gladys (NW)
Willis, Dave (Lon)
Wills, Margaret (Cello SW)
Woolf, Simon (Lon)
Worsley, Dominic (NW)
Wright, Brian (Mid)
Wright, Candy (Lon)
Wright, Mike (NW)
Wright, Russell (SE)
Wright, Sally Jane (E)
Young, Saffron (Lon)
Yule, Callum (Lon)
Zappulla, Fausto (Sco)

EARLY RENAISSANCE WIND

Richardson, Ian (NE)

EARLY STRINGS

Deller, Nicola (Lon)
Lindo, Sharon (Lon)
Michalak, Kazimierz (Lon)
Pinto, David (Lon)
Robinson, Dr Lucy (SW)
Salaman, Clare (Lon)
Shepherd, Martin (NW)
Wendland, Peter (Lon)
Yakeley, M (Lon)

ELECTRIC DOUBLE BASS

Goulding, Simon (NW)

EUPHONIUM

Childs, Robert (NE)
Down, Spencer (Lon)
Evans, Sarah (NE)
Mead, Steven (Mid)
Powell, John (NW)
Stark, John (Trombone Sco)
Walton, Paul (NW)

FLUTE

Abson, Joanne (NW)
Adams, Ann (Lon)
Adams, Fay (Lon)
Adams, Sally (SE)
Alexandra, Janet (Lon)
Allen, Anne (Lon)

TEACHERS - FLUTE

Allen, Sarah (Lon)
Anglim, Goretti (Lon)
Anson (Lon)
Ashe-Roy, Hilary (Mid)
Bailey, Owian (Lon)
Bailie, Laura (Sco)
Ball, Christopher (Lon)
Ballantyne, Ruth (SW)
Bamford, Jennifer (SW)
Barker, Naomi (NE)
Barley, Helen (Mid)
Barnard, Lianne (Lon)
Baster, Cheri (SE)
Bastin, Sarah (SW)
Baxter, Diane (SE)
Beatty, Frances (NE)
Bell, Kenneth (Lon)
Bentley, Clare (SE)
Bhattacharjee, Nicholas (NW)
Blewett, Suzanne (SW)
Body, Caroline (Lon)
Bookbinder, Laura (E)
Bourne, Sue (NE)
Bouvy, Yves (Lon)
Bowler, John (Lon)
Boylett, Lynda (NW)
Brewer, Mary (NW)
Bright, Helen (E)
Brown, Jacqueline (SW)
Buchanan, Mark Andrew (Saxophones Lon)
Bull, Sarah (NW)
Bunt, Felicity Jane (Lon)
Burgess, Jonathan (SW)
Burrows, Kathryn (Lon)
Buswell, John (SE)
Camerata, Trio (SW)
Camm, Howard (NE)
Canepa, Marco (Early Wind Lon)
Carr, Nikki (Lon)
Carter, Jillian (Lon)
Carter, Nick (NE)
Cartledge, Lucy (Sco)
Cartledge, Nicholas (SE)
Chambers, Colin (NW)
Chappell, Ruth (Lon)
Charlesworth, Clara (Mid)
Cheetham, Marguerite (NW)
Cheneour, Paul (SE)
Chisholm, Fiona (Sco)
Clark, Diane (Mid)
Clarke, Ian (Lon)
Cole, Susan (SW)
Core, Stephanie (Lon)
Coulcher, Jane (Lon)
Craig, Nicholas (Sco)
Croft, Nicola (NE)
Cupman, Beatrix (NE)
Cuthbertson, Caroline (Sco)
Da Costa, Doris (Lon)
Davies, Ros (Trombone Lon)
Davies, Sonja (Mid)
Davis, Deborah (Lon)
De Banzie, Helen (Lon)
De Lozey, Suzanne (NW)
Dennison, Alison (Mid)
Desorgher, Simon (Lon)
Di Prospero, Allessandra (Lon)
Dixon, Maurice (NE)
Doolan, Sarah (SW)
Dowton, Nicola (NW)
Drummond, Pippa (Mid)
Duckworth, Ruth (NW)
East, Carol (Mid)
Edwards, Nicola (NW)
Eke, Diane (NE)

Ellis, Samantha (Lon)
Evans, Karen (SE)
Evans, Susan (Sco)
Everett, Jenny (NW)
Ewins, Sally Ann (Lon)
Fairfield, Michael (SW)
Faja, Angelo (Conductor Lon)
Fenton, Judy (NW)
Filby, Anthony (Lon)
Filby, Brian (Saxophones Lon)
Finlayson, Donald (Sco)
Fitton, Judith (Lon)
Frampton, Pauline (NW)
Franklyn, Caroline (Lon)
Fraser, Lorraine (Sco)
Freeman, Sophia (Mid)
Fry, Pauline (Lon)
Gainham, Catherine (Lon)
Gallan, Anna (Mid)
Geldard, Lois (Lon)
Gennedy (NE)
Gent, Alison (Lon)
Gibley, Ruth (E)
Gibson, Rachel (SE)
Gillespie, Russell (NW)
Glover, Vanda (E)
Goetzee, Aidan (Lon)
Goodwin, Linda (Mid)
Gough, Geoff (Saxophones Mid)
Gould, David (Lon)
Grainger, Lindsay (NW)
Grealy, Siobhan (Lon)
Green, Christopher (Lon)
Greenwood, Ben (Saxophones Lon)
Gregory, Rachel (Lon)
Guild, Heather (Sco)
Hamilton, Rachel (Early Renaissance Lon)
Hanley, Francesca (Lon)
Harding, David (Saxophones SE)
Hargraves, Linda (NE)
Harris, Alison (SE)
Harris, Hayley (Lon)
Harris, Jane (Lon)
Hartley, Elaine (Sco)
Hayward, Ruth (Mid)
Helliwell, Donna (NE)
Hendrickse, Jan (Lon)
Higgins, Janet (SE)
Highton, Elizabeth (SW)
Hindle, Claire (SW)
Hodgson, Anne (Lon)
Hope, Carolyn (Lon)
Hughes, Enid (Lon)
Hughes, Jill (NE)
Hume, Alastair (Saxophones SE)
Humphreys, Alison (Mid)
Huneke, Janna (Lon)
Hunter, Nichola (NW)
Hurrell, Neslihan (Lon)
Hutchinson, Matthew (Saxophones NE)
Inglis, Jacqueline (Sco)
Jaffa, Nina (Saxophones Lon)
Jeffers, Rachel (Lon)
Jones, Belinda (Folk Fiddle NE)
Jones, Collette (NW)
Jones, Lois (Lon)
Joy, Susan/Susi (SE)
Judson, Ian (Lon)
Judson, Michael David (SE)
Kelbie, Catriona (Lon)
Kidman, Joanna (Lon)
King, Anne (E)
King, Zoe (SW)
Kingston, Jacqueline (E)
Kirkup, Sarah (Lon)

Koster, Jane (Lon)
Kutchmy, Irita (Pianoforte Lon)
Lacey, Christopher (Lon)
Larsen, Rebecca (Lon)
Larsson, Janet (Lon)
Lawson, Douglas (Sco)
Leah, Philip (Mid)
Lewis, Thomas (SW)
Linnemann, Henrik (NE)
Littlewood, Andrew (NE)
Lloyd, Christopher (Lon)
Lobeck, Katharina (Lon)
Lochbaum, Chloe (SE)
Lorriman, Christine (Lon)
Lyons, Rachel (NW)
Maceanruig, Heather (NW)
Macnutt, Penny (Lon)
Maguire, Conor (Lon)
Mallett, Lisa (Mid)
Malone, Jacqueline (NW)
Markland, Ben (Bass Guitar Mid)
Marsh, Elizabeth (Lon)
Marshall, Elizabeth (Lon)
Martin, Bruce (Lon)
Maycock, Claire (Mid)
McCabe, Michelle (Sco)
McCarron, Monica (Lon)
McCarthy, Sinead (SE)
McCarthy, Susan (Lon)
McDowall, Robert (Mid)
McHale, Jennifer (Lon)
McLarin, Lyn (SW)
McNally, Jane (NW)
Mellor, Clare (Lon)
Mellor, Judith (NE)
Melly, Alan (Saxophones SE)
Melville, Clarissa (Lon)
Michell, Chris (SW)
Mills, Betty (Lon)
Mills, Celia (NW)
Mills, Helen (Mid)
Milner, Jeanette (NW)
Mitcham, Sue (Lon)
Morfee, Susan (Lon)
Morgan, Dana (Mid)
Morgan, Jonathan (Trombone SW)
Morton, William (Lon)
Moy, Kathleen (Lon)
Murphy, John (SE)
Murphy, Sarah (Lon)
Murray, Jean (Sco)
Myles, Alison (Lon)
Nash, Jane (NW)
Nash, Julia (SE)
Negus, Annette (Mid)
Nelsen, Lisa (Lon)
New, Tim (NE)
Newman, Nili (Lon)
Ng, Janine (Mid)
Nielinger, Carola (Lon)
Nixon, Patricia (Lon)
Norland, Brigitte (SW)
Ogonovsky, Margaret (Lon)
Onissi, Marino (Saxophones Lon)
Orange, Evelyn (NE)
Ormiston, George (Sco)
Osmialowski, Lisa (Lon)
Owen, Stephen (NE)
Paice, Leonard (Lon)
Pailthorpe, Daniel (Lon)
Parfitt, Diane (SW)
Parker, Annie (Lon)
Parry, Russell (Mid)
Pendry, Katherine (Lon)
Perona-Wright, Nigel (Lon)

Peters, Aaron (Lon)
Pether, Margaret (SE)
Pinkerton, Alison (Sco)
Plaschkes, Roshana (Lon)
Plowman, Lynne (SW)
Pooley, Hilary (NW)
Pope, Anna (Lon)
Prior, John (NE)
Pyne, Anna (Lon)
Radley, Alison (E)
Rainer, Florica (NW)
Raybould, Paul (Mid)
Rees, Carla (Lon)
Reynolds, Ian (Mid)
Rivera, Stan (Lon)
Robb, Pete (Saxophones Mid)
Rochelle, Helen (Lon)
Roper, Judeth (Mid)
Rowson, Philip (Lon)
Russell-Smith, Colin (Saxophones Mid)
Rutherford, Samantha (Lon)
Sanders, Diana (Mid)
Schroder, Julie (Mid)
Scialla, Janelle (Voice Lon)
Searchfield, Sheila (Lon)
See, Janet (SE)
Selvidge, Rachel (Lon)
Shackleton, Penelope (SE)
Sharman, Helen (Lon)
Sharp, Paul (Lon)
Sheldon, Hannah (NW)
Shrubshall, Peter (Lon)
Shuttleworth, Jack (NE)
Silverman, Susie (Lon)
Simpson, Karen (NW)
Skipper, Sandra (Lon)
Skyrme, Martin (NW)
Sleath, Will (Lon)
Smith, Denise (SE)
Smith, Dominic (SE)
Smith, Edwina (NE)
Smith, Grace (SW)
Smith, Trudi (Lon)
Spratt, Kirsten (Lon)
Steele, Jan (Saxophones Lon)
Stevens, Jane (Lon)
Stevenson, Nicholas (Lon)
Stewart, Eva (NE)
Stinton, Jennifer (Lon)
Stockmann, Caroline (Lon)
Strevens, Nancy (Lon)
Summers, William (Lon)
Sutherland, Rowland (Lon)
Suttee, Teresa (SE)
Sykes, Branwen (SW)
Taggart, Hilary (Lon)
Taggart, Patrick (Lon)
Tate, Gavin (Lon)
Taylor, Debra (Lon)
Taylor, Richard (Lon)
Taylorson, Timothy (Lon)
Tebby, Kate (Mid)
Temple, Claire (Lon)
Thomas, Kathryn (Lon)
Thomas, Matthew (SW)
Thompson, Nina (Lon)
Thomsett, Ian (SW)
Thorne, Richard (SE)
Timms, Carole (SW)
Tonkins, Tracey (Lon)
Treggor, Judith (Lon)
Tribble, Fay (Lon)
Tullberg, Matilda (Lon)
Tulloch, Nicola (NE)
Tunstall, Sarah (Lon)

Turner, Nicola (Lon)
Underwood, Mark (Lon)
Underwood, Ruth (Lon)
Uttley, Michelle (NW)
Vann, Esther (Mid)
Viola, Lucia (Lon)
Wadsworth, Della (NE)
Walker, Elizabeth (Lon)
Walker, Geoffrey (Bassoon NE)
Walker-Thom, Lydia (Sco)
Wallace, Keith (Sco)
Waller, Claire (NW)
Walsh, Kate (Lon)
Walton, Simon (Lon)
Wareham, Donna (SE)
Warrington, Nicola (NE)
Way, Janet (SE)
Welch, Jennifer (Lon)
Welsh, Joana (SE)
White, Brian (SE)
Whitteridge, Janet (SW)
Wickham, Hilary (SW)
Wilkins, Michael (Saxophones SW)
Willis, Maxine (Lon)
Willy, Jennifer (SW)
Wilson, Fiona (SE)
Winn, Robert (Lon)
Woods, Janet (E)
Wright, Joanna (SE)
Wyver, Andrew (Alto Flute Lon)

FOLK FIDDLE

Anglim, Carlene (Mid)
Back, Shaun (NW)
Barfield, Kate (Violin Mid)
Bartram, Chris (SW)
Berthoud, Mahrey (SE)
Berthoud, Philip (SE)
Collier, Daniel (Violin Lon)
Cooper, Pete (Violin Lon)
Driver, Fiona (Sco)
Fairbairn, Hazel (E)
Francis, Carolyn (NW)
Geddes, Amy (Sco)
Hardie, Ian (Sco)
James, Cath (Violin NE)
Langlois, Yves (SE)
Mann, Dave (NW)
Marriott, Beryl (Pianoforte E)
McCulloch, Alistair (Violin Sco)
Moody, Helen (SW)
Shotliff, Jennifer (NW)
Sneyd, Will (Violin Lon)
Spencer, Nick (Sco)
Stevenson, Anna-Wendy (Violin Sco)
Stout, Christopher (Violin Sco)
Sullivan, Edel (Accompanist Lon)
Trundle, Anthony (Violin NW)
Wilson, Roger (Mid)
Wrigley, Jennifer (Sco)

GUITAR

Adams, Dean (Lon)
Aime-Aziza (Lon)
Aldridge, Graham (Lon)
Alexander, Charles (Lon)
Aliwell, Rick (NE)
Allen, Benjamin (Lon)
Allen, Mark (SE)
Andersen, Jens (Sco)
Anderson, Greg (NE)
Andrew, Nick (Lon)
Andrews, Matthew (Lon)
Anzalone, Maurizio (Lon)

Appleton, Richard (NE)
Argondizza, Peter (Sco)
Armer, Derek (SE)
Armstrong, Kevin (SE)
Arrowsmith, David (Lon)
Arrowsmith, David (Mid)
Artaud, Austin (SE)
Arthurs, Richard (NE)
Ashcroft, Keith John (NW)
Ashton, Stephen (NW)
Ashworth, David (NE)
Ashworth, Dominic (Lon)
Atherton, Paul (NW)
Austen, Ed (SE)
Austin, Lee (Mid)
Avery, Steve (Lon)
Bailey, Chris (SE)
Baker, Andy (Lon)
Baker, Jo (E)
Baker, Peter (Lon)
Balch, Gareth (SE)
Bannerman, Kari (Lon)
Barclay, John (Sco)
Barlow, Stephen (NW)
Barnowski, Alan (SE)
Bass, David (Sco)
Batchelar, Peter (NW)
Bates, Phil (Mid)
Bautista, Manuel (Lon)
Beardsmore, Andrew (Lon)
Behrens, Adam (Lon)
Beining, Elmar (Saxophones Lon)
Bellingham, Matthew (NW)
Benbow, Steve (Lon)
Benham, Patrick (SW)
Benie, Noel (Lon)
Bennett, Roy (NE)
Bentham, John (Lon)
Bentley, Richard (SE)
Berdichevsky, Daniel (Lon)
Berry, Ronnie (Sco)
Berryman, Peter (SW)
Betts, Kevin (E)
Bick, Mark (SW)
Billingham, Edward (SE)
Birrane, James (NW)
Blackham, Robert (Lon)
Blackman, Daniel (E)
Blackman, Robert (Lon)
Blackwell, John (Lon)
Blake, Adam (Lon)
Blake, Richard (Lon)
Bluglass, Charles (NW)
Bolam, Frank (Sco)
Bold, David (Lon)
Bolton, Richard (Lon)
Bond, Paul (Lon)
Booga (E)
Boreham, Daniel (SE)
Borjanic, Dusan (Lon)
Boyd, Stuart (NW)
Boyde, Hugh (E)
Brady, John (Lon)
Brailsford, Murray (Mid)
Bramson, Susanne (Lon)
Brewin, Simon (SE)
Broad, John (SW)
Broadley, Robert (Composer Lon)
Brockett, David (Sco)
Brooks, Jon (NE)
Broughton, Ben (Bass Guitar NW)
Brown, Daniel (SW)
Brown, Leslie (SE)
Brown, Martin (NE)
Brown, Noel (Lon)

TEACHERS - GUITAR

Brown, Paul (NW)
Brown, Sarah (Voice Lon)
Browne, Andrew (Voice Mid)
Bryden, Paul (NW)
Bukic, Mirsad (Lon)
Burden, David (E)
Burley, Raymond (SE)
Burns, Gill (NW)
Burrell, Richard (Lon)
Burt, Peter (SE)
Burton, Tigger (Bass Guitar Lon)
Butcher, Kevin (E)
Callard, Peter (Lon)
Calvo, Robbie (Lon)
Campbell, Neil (Sco)
Capone, Philip (Lon)
Carless, Timothy (Lon)
Carleton, Iain (Sco)
Carr, Michael (SW)
Carroll, David (Mid)
Carter, Dean (Lon)
Carter, Peter (E)
Carter, Vince (Lon)
Cartwright, Danny (Mid)
Cartwright, David (E)
Cartwright, Deirdre (Lon)
Caruso, Tony (Lon)
Cashmore, Catherine (Mid)
Catley, Marc (NW)
Cebula, Andy (Mid)
Cesarz, Stan (Keyboards SE)
Chambers, Jeff (NE)
Chapman, Michael (Lon)
Chapman, Richard (Lon)
Chenhall, Nicholas (Mid)
Cherry, John (E)
Christie, Simon (NE)
Christie, Steven (Pianoforte SE)
Christopher, Jeremy (SE)
Clark, Paul (SW)
Clark, Piers (SE)
Clarke, Anthony (NW)
Clarke, David (Lon)
Clarke, Sean (NE)
Clayton, Anthony (Lon)
Clews, Paul (SW)
Coady, Alan (Sco)
Coates, Simon (Lon)
Cole, BJ (Lon)
Coles, Andrew (Lon)
Collett, Andrew (Mid)
Collins, Gerald (SE)
Collumbine, Syd (NE)
Colman, Anthony (Voice Lon)
Colquhoun, David (Lon)
Coltham, Mike (Voice SE)
Connell-Hinkes, John (SE)
Contogeorge, Peter (Lon)
Conway, David (Lon)
Cook, Alec (NW)
Coombs, Dominic (Mid)
Coombs, Mike (E)
Cooper, Ian (Double Bass SW)
Cooper, Neville (Mid)
Coote, Anthony (Lon)
Corbould, Graham (Lon)
Corello, Paul (Lon)
Cornwell, Brian (SE)
Couch, Paul (NW)
Court, John (SW)
Coutts, Stephen (Sco)
Cox, David (Lon)
Cox, Julian (Double Bass Lon)
Cox, Mark (SE)
Crampton, Tim (SW)

Cranenburgh, Ernie (Lon)
Crehan, Derek (Mid)
Crozier-Cole, Jerry (SW)
Curran, James (Sco)
Curtis, Adrian (Lon)
Curtis, Steve (Lon)
Curzon, Phil (NW)
Dack, John (Lon)
Dale, Dave (Mid)
Dallaway, Paul (Lon)
Danae, Pascal (Lon)
Dangerfield, Christopher (Mid)
Davies, Ben (NE)
Davies, Jack (Mandolin Lon)
Davies, Neol (Mid)
Davies, Philip (SE)
Davies, Simon (E)
Davis, Keith (SW)
Davis, Stan (Mid)
Dawson, Jim (Lon)
Dawson, Martin (NE)
Dawson, Phil (Lon)
De Oliveira, Paulo (Lon)
De Pearle, Merlin (SE)
Dean, James (SE)
Dean, Neville (E)
Dee, Barrie (SE)
Delgardo, Sandie (Mid)
Dennis, Garry (Lon)
Dennison, Jeffery (Mid)
Derrig, Sean (Mid)
Dillett, Ross (Mid)
Dixon, Jolyon (SW)
Dixon, Peter (Lon)
Domay, Michael (Bass Guitar SE)
Donald, Martin (Lon)
Done, Steve (Lon)
Donnelly, Paul (NE)
Dooley, Joseph (Lon)
Dougall, Jama (Sco)
Douglas, Sarah (Lon)
Dowlen, Olly (Double Bass E)
Downs, Stephen (Mid)
Drake, Adam (Lon)
Duffy, Melvin (Lon)
Dunstan, Dunstan (SE)
Durrant, Richard (SE)
Duvoisin, Michel (Song Writer Lon)
Dye, Patrick (NE)
Dyson, Katherine (NW)
Dzierzanowski, Udo (SE)
Eales, Ben (Lon)
Ealovega, Benjamin (Lon)
Eardley, Ian (Mid)
Earl Bass Guitar (Lon)
Earl, Rhoderick (SW)
Easto, Dave (SW)
Edmondes, William (Lon)
Edwards, Steven (Lon)
Elder, Jose (Lon)
Ellis, Clark (SW)
Ellis, Simon (SE)
Evans, Claudette (Percussion SE)
Evans, David (Lon)
Evans, Mark (Lon)
Evans, Simon (E)
Eyre, Lee (Lon)
Eyres, David (Mid)
Fallon Jnr, Bob (SE)
Farrel, Conor (NW)
Farrugia, Peter (Lon)
Fentimen, Philip (Lon)
Finney, David (Voice Lon)
Fioramonti, Javier (Lon)
Fisher, Martin (Lon)

Fisher, Stephen (Bass Guitar Lon)
Fitzmaurice, Tristan (NE)
Flanagan, Lin (SE)
Flynn, Christopher (NW)
Foad, Paul (Mid)
Fogg, Rod (Lon)
Foley, Steven (Lon)
Forcione, Antonio (Lon)
Forman, Emma (Voice Sco)
Fornachon, Peter (SE)
Forster, John (NW)
Fox, Allie (Sco)
Frampton, Peter (NW)
Francis, Mark (Lon)
Francis, Nic (SE)
Franks, Jeremy (NE)
Freeman, Bill (NW)
Frost, Eleanor (NE)
Fullarton, Andy (Sco)
Furness, Clive (Lon)
Fyfe, James (Voice Lon)
G, Damian (NW)
Gallo, Ray (Lon)
Gammon, Vic (Melodeon NE)
Garcia, Gerald (SE)
Garcia, Nestor (Lon)
Gardiner, Paula (Double Bass SW)
Gareh, Daniel (Lon)
Garner, Tyrone (Mid)
Gibb, Steve (Sco)
Gilkes, Max (Mid)
Gilligan, Stephen (NW)
Gilmour, John (Sco)
Gittens, Allister (Mid)
Gleave, Jane (NW)
Goddard, Jonathan (Composer E)
Godfrey, Jonathan (Mid)
Goldberg, Ivor (Lon)
Goldman, David (Lon)
Goldsmith, Anthony (Lon)
Goodall, Peter (SW)
Goodman, M J (Lon)
Gordon, Stan (Lon)
Granger, Greta (Voice Lon)
Grant, Jacqueline (Lon)
Gray, Andy (Lon)
Gray, Thomas (Lon)
Green, Mick (Lon)
Griffiths, Alan (Mid)
Griffiths, Anthony (NW)
Grigue, Stephan Perez (Lon)
Grove, Ben (SE)
Guirey, Sagat (Lon)
Gustavina, Mark (Lon)
Haddock, Glynn (E)
Hall, Richard (Mid)
Hambleton-Smith, Sandra (Lon)
Hammond, Paul (SE)
Hands, David (E)
Harding, Elizabeth (Lon)
Hares, Paul (NE)
Harris, Derrick (NE)
Harris, Klaus (SE)
Harrison, Julian (Mid)
Harrop, Steven (NE)
Harrup, Guy (SW)
Hart, Daniel (Lon)
Haslett, Matt (Lon)
Hatto, David (SE)
Hayward, Jonathan (Lon)
Haywood, Mark (SW)
Haywood, Tony (E)
Heggarty, Leigh (Lon)
Hemming, Paul (SE)
Henderson, Martin (Lon)

Henderson, Paul (Sco)
Hendry, Robert (Lon)
Henning, Martin (Bass Guitar SW)
Hennings, Stephen (Lon)
Hepbir, Jonathan (SE)
Highley, David (NE)
Hill, Alan (Lon)
Hill, Francis (Lon)
Hill, Richard (SE)
Hill, Shane (SE)
Hill, Steve (SW)
Hinchliffe, Keith (NE)
Hoban, Peter (Lon)
Hobson, Gregory (E)
Hodge, Al (SW)
Hodgkins, Tim (Mid)
Hodgson, Lee (E)
Hogg, John (NE)
Holland, Bernie (Lon)
Hollinshead, Anji (Mid)
Holme, Mark (Lon)
Hooper, Chris (Mid)
Hope, Harvey (Lon)
Hornsby, James (NW)
Hough, Colm (SE)
Houlston, Robert (E)
Howe, Julian (Bass Guitar SW)
Hudson, Phillip (Lon)
Hughes, Timothy (Mid)
Humphreys, Peter (Lon)
Humphries, Jamie (SE)
Hunt, Gerald (Lon)
Hunter, Ronnie (Sco)
Hutchinson, Benjamin (E)
Hutchinson, Mark (Mid)
Hyett, Keith (SW)
Hyland, Colin (Mid)
Hyland, Victor (SE)
Hynes, Michael (SE)
Illes, Robert (Lon)
Inglis, Katherine (NW)
Isherwood, Richard (NW)
Jack, Jonathan (NE)
Jack, Robert (SW)
Jackson, Andrew (Trumpet NE)
Jackson, Wendy (NW)
James, Thomas (Mid)
Jani, Maitreya (Lon)
Jay, Justin (E)
Jeffels, Joanne (NE)
Jenkins, Billy (Lon)
Jenkins, Rhys (Trumpet SW)
Jenkinson, Andrew (Mid)
Jenner, Keith (Sco)
Jeremiah, Kevin (SE)
Jim (E)
Jobson, David (Lon)
Johannesson, Mikael (Lon)
John, Clive (Mid)
John, Malcolm (Mid)
John-Baptiste, Marcel (E)
Johnson, Colin (E)
Johnson, Laurie (E)
Johnson, Norman (NE)
Johnson, Ronnie (SE)
Johnston, Dawn (Lon)
Jolly, Aidan (NW)
Jones, Gary (NW)
Jones, Mazlyn (SW)
Jones, Philip (SE)
Jones, Trevor (Lon)
Judge, Paul (NE)
Kane, Reuben (SE)
Kay, Dylan (Lon)
Kearns, Paul (Mid)

Keating, Kevin (Lon)
Kelly, Richard (SW)
Kendler, Eran (Lon)
Kenney, Gordon (Voice Lon)
Kent, Andrew (Mid)
Khan, Adam (SW)
Khwaja, Darius (Voice Lon)
Kiddie, Alexander (NE)
Kiernan, Michael (NW)
King, Dave (NW)
Kirkley, Lisa (Mid)
Knight, Jon (Voice Mid)
Knight, Michael (Lon)
Korsah, Daniel (Lon)
Kotarac, Dragan (Lon)
Lacey, Duncan (SW)
Lakeman, Sean Nicholas (SW)
Lambert, Dave (SE)
Laming, Stephen (SE)
Lamprell, Adam (Lon)
Langmead, Mark (Lon)
Lauda, Pete (NW)
Lawman, Derek (Voice SW)
Lawrence, David (E)
Lawrence, James (SW)
Lawrence, Peter (SW)
Lazell, Matthew (SE)
Leckerman, Wendy (Sco)
Lee, Leslie (Lon)
Lee, Nicholas (E)
Lees, Simon (Mid)
Leggett, Jeremy (SE)
Leventhal, Alex (Mid)
Lewis, Matthew (Lon)
Lewis, Timothy (NW)
Limbrick, Alan (Lon)
Linahan, Liz (NE)
Lindahl, Mike (Mid)
Littlewood, Martin (NE)
Lofthouse, Chris (Lon)
Longworth, James (Lon)
Loring, Keith (SW)
Lovegrove, Adrian (SE)
Lowe, Veronica (SW)
Lowell, Timothy (NW)
Lowther, Richard (NE)
Lusambo, Fiston (Lon)
M87 (SW)
Mackay, Paul (Composer NW)
Mackenzie, Kevin (Sco)
Mackman, Richard (E)
Macleod, James Andrew (Mid)
Malaki (NE)
Mann, John (Lon)
Mann, Terry (Multi Instrumental Lon)
Mannion, Peter (SW)
Manzangi, Safro (Lon)
Marlow, Andrew (Lon)
Marples, David (Mid)
Marshall, Alastair (Lon)
Marshall, Jamie (Lon)
Marshall, Nick (Lon)
Martin, Eddie (SW)
Martin, Keith (E)
Martin, Manolo (Lon)
Martin, Peter (SE)
Martyr, David (Lon)
Mason, Alan (Mid)
Masters, Christopher (NW)
May, Rick (Lon)
Mayson, Jon (NE)
Mazzarini, Stefano (Lon)
McCarthy, Patrick (NE)
McCaughern, Dan (NE)
McDermott, Patrick (Lon)

McGillivray, Bill (Lon)
McLeish, Craig (Conductor Lon)
McMahon, Martin (NE)
McNeish, Colin (Bass Guitar Lon)
McQueen-Hunter, Douglas (Voice Sco)
Mead, David (E)
Medboe, Haftor (Sco)
Meldrum, Raymond (Sco)
Melrose, Robert (Lon)
Merrett, Steve (NE)
Michalises, George (Voice Lon)
Miller, Adrian (Lon)
Miller, Glynn (NW)
Milligan, Ross (Lon)
Milligan, Max (E)
Mills, John (SW)
Mills, Timothy (SW)
Milner, Pascha (E)
Mitchell, Carl (NW)
Mitchell, David (Pianoforte Sco)
Mitchell, John (Lon)
Moloney, Fergus (Lon)
Mona, Pete (Lon)
Monk, Peter (NE)
Monks, Barry (E)
Montgomery, Doc (SW)
Moody, Doog (E)
Moody, John (Lon)
Moore, Chris (NW)
Moore, Jamie Woods (Lon)
Moran, Mike (NW)
Moreton, Chris (SW)
Morgan, Andrew (SW)
Morph (Sco)
Morris, Brian (Sco)
Morson, Winston (Lon)
Mosley, Janet (SW)
Moyse, Nigel (Lon)
Mulcaster, Simon (NW)
Mulford, Robert (Lon)
Mullett, Cristobal (Lon)
Munro, Gavin (Sco)
Murphy, Anthony (Lon)
Murray, Kevin (Sco)
Murray, Paul (NW)
Murray, Pete (Lon)
Mutimanwa, Kawele (Lon)
Myhill, John (SE)
Nailon, Alex (Lon)
Naish, Simon (SE)
Naylor, Patrick (Lon)
Neep, Paul (NW)
Neill, Kevin (NW)
Nelis, William (NW)
Nelson, James (Mid)
Nelson, Stephen (Sco)
Newland, Christoper (Lon)
Nicholas, Paul (SW)
Niebla, Eduardo (Lon)
Nixon, Christopher (SE)
Noble, Douglas (Sco)
Nolan, Sean (Lon)
O'Donovan, Michael (Voice Lon)
O'Hagan, Tree (NW)
Ogden, Craig (Lon)
Oldale, Luke (Lon)
Oneill, Shane (Lon)
Ongley, Marc (Lon)
Orchin, Mark (SE)
Osborne, Andrew (Mid)
Othen, Simon (Mid)
Ouvry, Peter (Lon)
Overon, Geoff (Mid)
Oxley, Colin (Lon)
Pagan, Simon (NE)

TEACHERS - GUITAR

Paice, Sally (SE)
Pailthorpe, Michael (SE)
Pallett, Ian (SW)
Pallett, Nicholas (SW)
Parfitt (SW)
Parker, Brian (SE)
Parkin, Andrew (Lon)
Parkinson, Brian (NW)
Pate, Donny (Lon)
Paton, Kevin (NW)
Payne, Ceri (NE)
Peacock, Nicholas (SW)
Pearce, Chris (SE)
Pearson, Graeme (Sco)
Pearson, John (Guittara Bahiana SE)
Pearson, Ken (NW)
Peel, Stanley Martin (NW)
Penn, Matthew (NW)
Penrose, Marcus (SW)
Perkins, Brian (Mid)
Perry, John (Voice Lon)
Phillips, Jonathan (Lon)
Phillips, Keith (NW)
Phillips, Norman (NE)
Pickford, David (SE)
Picton, Simon (Lon)
Piha, Sam (Lon)
Pilcher, Jonathan (Lon)
Pincott, Colin (Lon)
Pitman, Toby (SE)
Popey, Martyn (Lon)
Porter, Kevin (SE)
Portman, Tom (SW)
Potts, Raymond (Mid)
Powell, Gary (NW)
Powell, Glyn (Lon)
Preiss, Jonathan (Lon)
Preston, Mark (Lon)
Price, David (Lon)
Price, Ian (Mid)
Prior, Matt (E)
Pusey, Chris (SE)
Pusey, James (Lon)
Pyatt, Andrew (NW)
Pym, Alexander (Lon)
Quinteiro, Elisio (Theorbo Lon)
Qunta, Tony (Lon)
Radcliffe, Nicholas (Lon)
Rademacker, Kalle (Lon)
Ray, Christopher (Lon)
Reason, Jules (SW)
Reca, Coqui (Koki) (Lon)
Reed, Roger (Mid)
Rees, Paul Rapsey (Bass Guitar Lon)
Reid, Colin (NW)
Reid, Dan (Lon)
Reid, Kenny (Lon)
Renney, Tony (NW)
Rest, Bernd (Lon)
Rice, Niall (Lon)
Rickard, James (SE)
Rippon, Nigel (SE)
Roberts, Derek (Mid)
Roberts, Graham (Lon)
Roberts, Sarah (NE)
Robertson, Alan C (NE)
Robinson, David (Mid)
Robinson, Douglas (Pianoforte NE)
Robinson, Keith (Voice NE)
Robinson, Peter (Mid)
Robinson, Roy (Mid)
Roche, Eric (Lon)
Rodriguez-Duran, Cesar (Bass Guitar Lon)
Rogers, Neil (Lon)
Rood, Mark (SE)

Rose, Adrian (Mid)
Ross, Andy (NW)
Ross, Filipe (Lon)
Ross, Malcolm (Lon)
Ruberry, Mark (SW)
Runcorn, Simon (Lon)
Rusdell, Vincent (Lon)
Russell, Steve (Lon)
Ryall, Nick (E)
Ryan, Joy (Pianoforte E)
Sabatini, Nicodemo (Lon)
Sabijan, Drazen (Lon)
Sadler, Chris (E)
Sajrawy, Michel (Lon)
Samuels, Elaine (Lon)
Sanchos (NW)
Sanford, Gary (Lon)
Savage, Jimi (NE)
Savcic, David (Lon)
Savill, Martin (SE)
Scarratt, Doug (SE)
Schapper, Friedrich (Lon)
Scholes Corbett, Stuart (Bass Guitar E)
Schoonderwoerd, Peter (Mid)
Scott, Iain (Lon)
Scott, Johnathan (NE)
Scott, Timothy (NW)
Seal, Peter (Lon)
Searle, James (Bass Guitar SW)
Segal, Marianne (Arranger Lon)
Sellars, Dale (E)
Selwyn, Esmond (Lon)
Senior, Henry (Lon)
Serci, Giorgio (Lon)
Sergeant (Mid)
Settle, Ray (NW)
Sexton, Mark (SE)
Shaffer, Mark (Lon)
Sharman, David (Lon)
Sheridan, Mark (Voice NE)
Shipton, Russ (Lon)
Si (Mid)
Sidwell, Jason (Mid)
Simons, Andrew (NE)
Simpson, Peter (NE)
Skates, Nicholas (SE)
Skeet, Christopher (SE)
Skulski, Michael (E)
Siedmere, Adrian (Lon)
Slide, Mark (E)
Smith, Andy (NW)
Smith, Benjamin (E)
Smith, Brian (Lon)
Smith, Graham (Mid)
Smith, Isabel (Viola Lon)
Smith, Jamie (Bass Guitar Mid)
Smith, John (Mid)
Smith, Martin (NE)
Smith, Neil (NW)
Smith, Peter (NE)
Smith, Richard (Mid)
Smith, Roger (Lon)
Smith, Stevie (Voice NW)
Smith, Timothy (E)
Solly, Daniel (Lon)
Sparks, Jeremy (Lon)
Spearman, Michael (E)
Speight, Colin (SW)
Spencer, David (NE)
Squire, Simon (Mid)
Stacey, Neil (E)
Stevenson, Daniel (Lon)
Stevenson, Daniel (Mid)
Stevenson, Paul (E)
Stokes, Peter (NE)

Stokes, Peter (SW)
Stoloff, Paul (Bass Guitar NW)
Stone, Bob (Lon)
Stone, Tim (Lon)
Stonehill, Lou (SE)
Stopes, Ian (NW)
Stoppard, Jon (Accordion NE)
Storry, Richard (Lon)
Stoysin, Branco (Lon)
Strang, James (Lon)
Strange, Michael (SW)
Styles, Nobby (SE)
Summerfield, Saffron (Voice Lon)
Summers, Al (SW)
Summers, Gerry (SW)
Sutherland, Roy (Lon)
Sweet, Paul (SE)
Swift, Jeffrey (NE)
Taylor, Max (Lon)
Taylor, Richard (SE)
Teague, Nik (NE)
Temple, Howard (Lon)
Thomas, Daniel (Lon)
Thomas, Paul (Lon)
Thompson, Colin (SW)
Thompson, Marcus (Lon)
Thompson, Steve (SE)
Thorne, Louis (E)
Throneycroft-Smith, Fraser (SE)
Tommis, Colin (NW)
Tompkins, Nial (Lon)
Townsend, Neil (SE)
Toye, Dave (SE)
Trepekunas, Sauliius (SE)
Trilby, Dave (SE)
Truong, Jack (Lon)
Tugwell, Paul (Lon)
Tym, Robert (E)
Utting, William (E)
Veitch, Roland (Lon)
Vellacott, Stephen (E)
Venemore, Drew (NE)
Vincent, Martin (SE)
Wadey, Zoe (NE)
Walker, Christopher (NE)
Walker, Crosby (Keyboards E)
Wall, Nicholas (Lon)
Walpole, Steven (NE)
Wardale, Alf (SW)
Warden, Neil (Sco)
Warner, Stephen (Double Bass Lon)
Warren, David (Lon)
Waterhouse, Michael (E)
Waters, Stephen (Lon)
Watkins, Paul (SW)
Watson, Andy (Lon)
Watson, Richard (SE)
Weaver, James (E)
Webb, Andrew (E)
Webb, Christopher (Lon)
Webb, Craig (Mid)
Webber, Peter (SW)
Weekes, Alan (Lon)
Welch, Nathan (NW)
Weller, Andy (E)
Wesson, Sebastian (Lon)
West (Mid)
Whitaker, Maxwell (SW)
White, Eddie (Lon)
White, Stephen (Lon)
Whitehead, Paul (NW)
Wignall, Oliver (Mid)
Wild, Peter (E)
Wilkinson, Stuart (Lon)
Wille, Tony (Mid)

Williams, David (NW)
Williams, J Owen (Lon)
Williams, Tony (SW)
Williams, Trevor (SE)
Willis, Michael (SW)
Willis, Tommy (NW)
Wilson, David (NE)
Wilson, John (NE)
Wilson, Miles (Mid)
Winter, Dominic (Mid)
Winton, Neil (Sco)
Witchell, Robbie (NE)
Wong, Chris (E)
Wood, Dave (SW)
Wood, James (NW)
Wood, Kenneth (Lon)
Woods, Michael (NE)
Woollven, David (Sco)
Woolway, Ian (Lon)
Wotton, Christopher (SW)
Wright, Eric (SE)
Wrigley, Stephen (SE)
Wroth, Michael (SW)
Wyness, James (Sco)
Wynn, Dylan (SW)
Young, David (SE)
Zala, Nick (Lon)
Zolotuhin, Adrian (Lon)

HAMMER DULCIMER

Dove Dulcimers (SW)
Smith, Geoff (Percussion SE)

HARMONICA

Armer, Eddie (Lon)
Arnhold, Gerd (SE)
B., Roy (Saxophones E)
Black, Donald (Sco)
Griffiths, Matt (Lon)
Hewlett, Ben (SW)
Hughes, Jim (Mid)
Kilduff, Vinnie (Whistle Lon)
Lamb, Paul (Lon)
Neville, Glen (Lon)
Oneill, Con (SE)
Power, Brendan (Lon)
Shahadah, Owen (Pianoforte Lon)
Tate, Douglas (E)
Toussaint, David (Lon)
Wallace, Barnaby (Lon)

HARMONIUM

Markanday, Sheila (Sitar Lon)
Sima (Lon)
Singh, Manohar (Voice Lon)

HARMONY

Frayling-Kelly, Frederick (Violin Sco)
Maintenant, Fred (Pianoforte SW)
Thorpe, Simon (Double Bass Lon)
Wilson, Herman (Composer Lon)

HARP

Aldrich-Smith, V.J. (SW)
Arnold, Helen (Lon)
Askew, Sophie (Sco)
Aslin, Anita (NE)
Barford, Imogen (Lon)
Bass, Rowena (Mid)
Bell, Jean (NW)
Bennett, Janet (NE)
Bevis, Suzanne (SE)
Boden, Daphne (Lon)
Bromberg, Sheila (Lon)

Broome, Jenny (SE)
Christensen, Anna (NW)
Clifton-Welker, Fiona (Lon)
Davies, Rhodri (Lon)
Davis, Brian (Lon)
Deere-Jones, Sarah (SE)
Duggan, Louisa (Lon)
Edwards, Morfen (Lon)
Finnemore, Audrey (SE)
Gilbertson, Dorothy (NE)
Gostick, Bethan (Lon)
Granger, Emma (Lon)
Hamilton, Claire (SW)
Hayward, Jack (Lon)
Herrmann, Jill (Mid)
Hewat, Corrina Dawn (Sco)
Jenkins, Nia (Lon)
Jones, Dafydd (NW)
Jones, Jennifer (SW)
Jones, Mair (NW)
Lister, Jane (Lon)
Lynn, Eira (NW)
Macardle, Aileen (SE)
Marshall, Triona (E)
Marshalsay, Karen (Sco)
Meier, Patrizia (Lon)
Molin, Maxine Isabella (NW)
Monger, Eileen (Celtic Harp E)
Morley, Sarah (Lon)
Morris, Manon (Lon)
Morris-Jones, Catrin (Lon)
Ovett, Luisa-Maria (SE)
Peacock, Judith (Sco)
Perrett, Danielle (Lon)
Ramsdale, Emma (Lon)
Rhydderch, Llio (NW)
Rhys, Christina (Lon)
Roberts, Bethan (SW)
Rogers, Natalia (SE)
Salo, Satu (SE)
Scott, Lauren (NW)
Scourfield, Eluned (SW)
Seale, Charlotte (Lon)
Smith, Joy (Lon)
Spero, Patricia (Lon)
Sternefeld, Frank (NE)
Swain, Carys (SW)
Swift, Kay Sheehan (SE)
Thomas, Sian Morgan (SW)
Thornton, Julia (E)
Trentham, Alice (Lon)
Webb, Hugh (Lon)
Willison, Suzanne (Lon)

HARPSICHORD

Brown, Helena (Lon)
Cave, Penelope (SE)
Chapman, Jane (Lon)
Cole, Maggie (Lon)
Cuckston, Alan (NE)
Cummings, Laurence (Lon)
Francis, David (NW)
Glen, Karen (Lon)
Hellyer Jones, Jonathan (Lon)
Knight, Stephen (SW)
Richards, Arne (SE)

HIGHLAND BAGPIPES

Kelly, Jack (NE)
Macdonald, Iain (Sco)
McGrath, Helen (Lon)
McLucas, James (Lon)
Morrison, Fred (Sco)

Piper 2000, (SE)
Winstanley, Colin (NW)

HORN

Abbott, Kevin (Lon)
Amos, Roberta (SW)
Antcliff, Andrew (Lon)
Ashworth, Robert (NE)
Atkins, Lorraine (SE)
Avery, Karyn (SW)
Ball, Tim (NW)
Bates, Marcus (Lon)
Baxendale, Sue (Sco)
Bentley, David (Lon)
Bird, Gillian (Lon)
Blackwood, Kenneth (Sco)
Bunyan, Rachel (Lon)
Caldicott, Stephen (SE)
Carlton, Dennis (Lon)
Carr, Gordon (Lon)
Clack, David (Lon)
Cowling, Steven (Sco)
Davies, Chris (Lon)
Davies, Ieuan (SE)
Davies, Vivian (Lon)
De Jong Cleyndert, Christina (E)
Diack, Jim (Lon)
Dimiceli, Lilla (Mid)
Disney, Stella (Mid)
Dodson, Peter (NE)
Ferguson, Sian (Mid)
Finney, Nigel (Mid)
Fisher, Ian (SW)
Foggin, Ellen (Lon)
Frost, Emma (SW)
Fuller, Adrian (NW)
Gladstone, Anthony (Lon)
Grainger, Martin (Lon)
Gray, David (E)
Gray, David (Mid)
Green, Oliver (Lon)
Griffiths, Simon (SW)
Guerrier, John (Sco)
Hall, Ralph (Mid)
Harrison-Preiss, Dagmara (SE)
Hassan, Jonathan (Lon)
Hayward, Russell (NW)
Hellen, Marian (E)
Hill, Timothy (Mid)
Hipwell, Naomi (Lon)
Holliday, Claire (NW)
Hopkins, Shirley (Lon)
Hortin, Christopher (SW)
Howe, Tom (NW)
Hutchings, Clare (Lon)
Johns, Terry (Sco)
Jones, John (SW)
Kane, Mark (SE)
Keddie, Iain (Lon)
Kennedy, Richard (Lon)
Klein, Paul (Sco)
Langley, Michael (SW)
Langrish, Anthony (Lon)
Latimer, Colin (NE)
Laurence, David (Lon)
Lipton, Jonathan (Lon)
Lockyer, Luke (SW)
Macallister, Stephen (SW)
Magee, Michael (Lon)
McLoughlin, Rachel (Mid)
McReynolds, Jacqueline (Lon)
Meecham, Jon (Lon)
Molcher, Robert (SW)
Morcombe, Jonathan (Lon)
Morris, Peter (Mid)

Morton, Amanda (SW)
Moxon, Andrew (Lon)
Newman, Brian (Lon)
Nock, John (Mid)
Norris, Adrian (Lon)
Parker, Robert (Mid)
Paton, Rod (SE)
Penny, Mark (Mid)
Peskett, John (Lon)
Reynolds, Clare (Lon)
Roberts, Emma (Lon)
Rogers, Laurence (NW)
Ronayne, Pamela (Lon)
Sawbridge, Paul (Mid)
Sharp, John D (Sco)
Sheppard, Laura (Lon)
Shillaw, David (SW)
Shillito, Martin (NE)
Silsby, Lynn (SE)
Snook, John (E)
Stoker, Lindsey (NW)
Stott, Ian (Lon)
Strevens, Patrick (Lon)
Sugars, Marion (Lon)
Sutton, Andrew (SE)
Taggart, Martin (NW)
Tellick, Keith (Trumpet SE)
Thomas, Elinor (NE)
Thomson, James (SE)
Thorne, Philip (Lon)
Truman, Paul (Mid)
Wainwright, Richard (Lon)
Waller, Colin (E)
Warburton, James (Lon)
Way, Aileen (Sco)
Wheeler, David (Lon)
Widgery, K.Peter (Lon)
Wilkinson, Ruth (Pianoforte Sco)
Williams, Alun J (SW)
Wilson, W (Lon)
Wood, James (NE)
Woodcock, George (Lon)
Wythe, David (Lon)
Yeowell, Ronald (Lon)

HURDY-GURDY

Attfield, Raymond (Lon)
Eaton, Nigel (Lon)
Heape, Emma (SE)

IMPROVISATION

Batson, Ray (Trumpet E)
Dickson, John (Trumpet Lon)
Fleckney, Clive (Pianoforte E)
Furnish, Pete (Double Bass SW)
Harvey, Eddie (Trombone E)
Hession, Paul (Percussion NE)
Hignell, Lauren (Saxophones Lon)
Hudson, Robert (Pianoforte Mid)
Jafrate, Keith (Saxophones NE)
Parker, Eddie (Flute Lon)
Quinn, Paul (Pianoforte SW)
Roden, David (Pianoforte SW)
Wain, Phil (Bass Guitar Lon)
Walker, Sam (Saxophones NE)
Watts, Trevor (Saxophones SE)

IRISH PIPES

Burton, Alan (Lon)
Hannigan, Steafan (Lon)

JAVANESE GAMELAN

Channing, Andrew (Lon)
Dally, Nikhil (Pianoforte Lon)
Mendonca, Maria (Lon)

KEYBOARD

Aralepo, Anthony (Lon)
Arnold, Simon (Mid)
Barnes, Gregg (Sco)
Barnes, Lester (Saxophones Lon)
Beale, Mike (Organ SW)
Bellwood, Derek (NE)
Benbow, Richard (Lon)
Bridger, Raymond (Guitars Lon)
Browne, Colin (Mid)
Burholt, Stephen (Lon)
Burke, David (Pianoforte NW)
Burrows, Stephen (Pianoforte NW)
Callingham, Robin (Vibraphone Lon)
Campbell, Francis (Pianoforte Lon)
Case (E)
Chapman, Margaret (Pianoforte Mid)
Chiney.T (Rapper Lon)
Claxton, Andrew (Composer Lon)
Cook, John (Lon)
Corbett, David (SE)
Cox, Mitchell (Pianoforte E)
Crew, Paul (Lon)
Czerwik, Jonathan (NE)
Daley, Peter (Mid)
Daniel, Charles (SW)
Davis, Peter (Lon)
Douglas-Stewart, Jim (SW)
Dutton, Owen (Mid)
England, Peter (NW)
Garman, Julian (Lon)
Green, Martyn (Saxophones NW)
Guild, Duncan (Sco)
Hampson, Phillip (SE)
Harris, Anthony (SW)
Hastings, George (NE)
Hawkes, Adam (Double Bass Lon)
Hawkes, Andy (Mid)
Hern, Martyn (SW)
Hillman, George (SE)
Hobbs, Jason (Organ NE)
Hunter, Gillian (Sco)
Jones, Ean (Sco)
Jozefowicz-Bukowska, Suzanne (Pianoforte Lon)
Larder, Jez (SE)
Layton, Clive (Mid)
Lemer, Peter (Synthesiser Lon)
Macaskill, Paula (Sco)
Maloney, Sheila (Composer Lon)
McNeil-Watson, Robert (E)
Michelle-Jo (SW)
Millar, Phil (Pianoforte NW)
Miller, Paul (Lon)
Mr D, (Pianoforte SE)
Musgrave, Jonathan (NW)
Parkes, Steve (Lon)
Peacock, Bob (Pianoforte NE)
Pearce, John (Conductor NE)
Puddick, John (E)
Questel-Lewis, Keith (NW)
Redding, Philip (NE)
Rees, Elaine (Mid)
Rhodes, Sue (Lon)
Roberts, Martin (SE)
Roberts, Sheaw (Percussion Lon)
Rose, David (Mid)
Satterthwaite, Richard (Guitars Mid)
Scargill, Gary (NE)
Sherriff, Steve (Mid)

Short-Pullman, Darren (Lon)
Smith, Jennifer (E)
Stamp, Peter (E)
Steele, Richard (Synthesiser Lon)
Stubbings, Richard (SW)
Taylor, David (Organ Mid)
Thakrar, Kiran (Lon)
Thompson, Jason (Lon)
Tolley, Alison (Organ Mid)
Vizard, Jamie (NW)
Watson, Neil (Lon)
Watts, Steve (Lon)
Wells, Jeremy (Organ Lon)
White, Graham (Mid)
Wilcock, Christopher (Pianoforte NW)
Wilkinson, Jeremy (SE)
Williams, David (Lon)
Young, Tony (E)

KOTO

Yanagisawa, Rie (Lon)

LATIN AMERICAN PERCUSSION

Bell, Sam (NE)
Bongo Billy (Lon)
Burton, Patrick (Banjo NE)
Clare, Steven (Mid)
Crawford, Paul (Lon)
Cummings, Andrew (NE)
Douriet, Leonel (Percussion Lon)
Earley, Kevin (Percussion Lon)
Fletcher, Chris (Lon)
Gonzalez, Jorge (Lon)
Hickson, Andrew (NW)
Huggins, Christopher (Sco)
Jayasuriya, Arjuna (NW)
Kari-Kari, Kofi (Lon)
Le Messurier, James (Percussion Lon)
Lidgey-Hutt, Fiona (E)
Mathunjwa, Julia (Lon)
McGuire, Edward (Mid)
Nuzzoli, Gabriele (Lon)
Oliver, Rowan (Bass Guitar Lon)
Orr, Hamish (Lon)
Ravalico, Maurizio (Lon)
Rivera, Paco (NE)
Seddon, Colin (Bass Guitar SW)
Stignac, Bobby (Lon)
Vora, Anup (Percussion Lon)
Winckless, Geoffrey (NE)

MANDOLIN

Harris, Ian (SE)
Isaacs, Jonathan (Lon)
Paul, Rod (Sco)
Robinson, John (Sco)
Stephens, Alison (Lon)
Thomas, David (Lon)

MELODEON

Adamson, Richard (Pianoforte NE)
Aldis, Kathryn (E)
Cutting, Andy (Mid)
Holloway, Keith (SE)
Peters, Brian (NW)
Smith, Ian (Mid)
Turner, Gareth (Mid)
Van Eyken, Tim (SW)

MULTI INSTRUMENTAL

Frost, Susan (Voice Lon)

MUSIC DIRECTOR

Burnett, Sandy (Lon)
Clark, Andrew (Horn Lon)
Woodward, Adrian (Trumpet Lon)

NORTHUMBRIAN PIPES

Cato, Pauline (NE)
Higgs, Paul (SE)

OBOE

Abbott, Juliet (NW)
Aldis, Maddy (NW)
Armstrong, Warwick (NW)
Ashton, Laura (Sco)
Austen, Susan (NW)
Bailey, Helen (Lon)
Baldwin, Janet (SW)
Bell, Morven (Sco)
Bessell, John (Lon)
Blewett, Lorna (SW)
Brawn, Victoria (Lon)
Britton, Vanessa (SE)
Broadbent, Rachel (Lon)
Browne, Geoffrey (Lon)
Burden, Rachel (E)
Caldicott, Louise (Lon)
Carlson, Neil (E)
Carter, Gillian (SE)
Coates, Tamara (Lon)
Codd, Jean Marsden (SW)
Cole, Andrew (NE)
Cooper, Anna (NW)
Davey, Thomas (NW)
Davies, Maxine (Lon)
Dewis (SW)
Dickinson, Stella (Lon)
Dillon, Shaun (Sco)
Downer, Jane (Early Wind Lon)
Draper, Matthew (Lon)
Dyer, Graham (SW)
Eastaway, James (Lon)
Eaton, Tim (Lon)
Elias, Ruth (SE)
Emanuel, Jane (NW)
Evans, Jane (Lon)
Fallows, Jacqueline (Sco)
Ferran, Marcia (Lon)
Fisher, Fay (SW)
Forbes, Cherry (E)
Freedman, Sara (Lon)
Freer, Anthony (Lon)
Frost, Susan (Lon)
Fyfe, Elizabeth (Lon)
Galloway, Jennifer (NW)
Geer, Christine (Lon)
Gerrard, Gillian (E)
Glover, Anne (Lon)
Goodey, Paul (Lon)
Gosby, Jennifer (Lon)
Graeme, Peter (Lon)
Green, Helen (Mid)
Greene, Ann (Lon)
Grint[Wharton], Sara (Lon)
Gripton, Sue (Mid)
Hamilton, Ian (NE)
Harvey-Brown, Stacey (Mid)
Hennessy, Gail (Lon)
Herd, Judith (Sco)

Holbrow, Pauline (Saxophones Lon)
Howard, Jackie (NW)
Hunt, James (SE)
Ifeka, Althea (Lon)
Ing, Hazel (NW)
Jackson, Charles (Sco)
Jacoby, Elizabeth (SW)
James, Mark (SE)
Janey (Lon)
Johnson, Clare (Sco)
Keeble, Kim (Lon)
Keech, Diana (NE)
Kellett, Colin (NE)
Kelly, Dominic (Lon)
King, Andrew (SW)
King, Carolyn (SE)
Kirk, Julian Robert (Lon)
Kirk, Tanya (Lon)
Kitt, Derek (SW)
Knight, Janice (Lon)
Laurence, Lesley (Lon)
Leadbetter, Susan (SE)
Lepage, Katharine (SE)
Lewis, Susan (NW)
Light, Sarah (Lon)
Lively, Josephine (Lon)
Lovie, Louise (Sco)
Macdonald, Anne (Lon)
Magee, Jenny (Sco)
Manning, Laura (Lon)
McCracken, Stella (Sco)
McDonald, John (Early Wind Lon)
McKean, Helen (Lon)
McMahon, Russell (NW)
Miles, Gillian (E)
Miller, Tess (Lon)
Milton, Simon (Sco)
Mogridge, Jessica (Mid)
Montagu, Moyra (Lon)
Moore, Patricia (Mid)
Mount, Rodney (Sco)
Oldfield, Judith E (NW)
Oliver, Victoria (E)
Palmer, Carole (NE)
Powell, Helen (Lon)
Proctor, Judy (Lon)
Radcliffe, Mark (Lon)
Ragge, Melanie (Lon)
Rawstron, Helen (Lon)
Rees, Peter (SW)
Reid, Gabriel (NW)
Rendle, Peter (SE)
Reynolds, Alison (Mid)
Rhodes, Barbara (Sco)
Richardson, Sally (NW)
Ringrose, Emma (NW)
Rolles, Annie (SE)
Rousseau, Judith (NE)
Rundell, Lynn (Sco)
Saunders, Eve (Lon)
Saunders, Jane (Cor Anglais Mid)
Schilsky, Erika (Lon)
Scott, Ruth (Lon)
Scott, Sarnia (Lon)
Shephard, Jo (Lon)
Siswick, Julie (SW)
Skinner, Katrina (Lon)
Small, Jonathan (NW)
Smart, David (Lon)
Smith, Wendy (NW)
Storer, Hilary (Lon)
Stretton, Jane (NE)
Stringer, John (NE)
Swain, Christine (NW)
Swan, Nicola (Mid)

Tanner, Catherine (SW)
Taylor, Lara (Lon)
Theobald, Ruth (Mid)
Thomas, David (Mid)
Thomas, Sylvia (Mid)
Todd, Hazel (Lon)
Walpole, Victoria (Lon)
Weale, Judith (E)
West, Stephen (Sco)
White, Penny (Lon)
Whittow, Marion (Lon)
Willits, Lucinda (SE)
Wilson, David (Lon)

ORGAN

Addey, Douglas (Keyboards NE)
Akehurst, Anthony (Pianoforte SE)
Allen, Ronald (Mid)
Bailey, Leonard (SE)
Barlow, Ken (NW)
Beesley, John (NW)
Bellwood, Derek (NE)
Bergin, Johnny (SE)
Bevan, Sydney (Pianoforte SE)
Bishop, Sharon (NE)
Borthwick, Morgan (NW)
Bortoft, Tim (NE)
Brookshaw, David (Pianoforte Mid)
Byram-Wigfield, Timothy (Sco)
Corbett, David (SE)
Court, Robert (SW)
Craig, Paul (Mid)
Dobson, John (Keyboards NE)
Ellis, Sharon (Mid)
Evans, Ray (Keyboards NW)
Fletcher-Campbell, Christopher (SE)
Fowke, Jon (Pianoforte Lon)
Gilmore-James, Terence (SW)
Gormley, John (Sco)
Gresch, David (Vibraphone NW)
Gutteridge, Simon (Lon)
Hall, Martin (SE)
Hammond, Mark (Lon)
Harper, Cloff (Synthesiser Lon)
Harper, Norman (Lon)
Harris, Michael (SE)
Heighway, John (SE)
Hetherington, George (NE)
Hine, Keith (Guitars Mid)
Horsey, Alan (NE)
Jupp, Bridget (SE)
Kelly, Julian (Pianoforte Lon)
Kenyon, Brian (NW)
Loxam, Arnold (NE)
Mackfall, Richard (NE)
Martez, Tony (Keyboards NE)
Martine, Ray (SE)
Mason, Margaret (Pianoforte Lon)
Parmley, Andrew (Music Director Lon)
Rice, Derek (Lon)
Rigler, Sue (SW)
Rose, Barry (SW)
Rudland, Malcolm (Music Director Lon)
Sharpe, Donald (Mid)
Sisley, John (Keyboards Lon)
Smaller, Frank (NE)
Smitton, Charles (NW)
Sparks, Michael (NW)
Stacey, Robert (SE)
Stuart, Peter (NW)
Trentham, Tony (Accordion Mid)
Wallbank, Raymond (NW)
Warby, Frank (Keyboards Lon)
Weedon, Penelope (SW)
Wells, Ian (NW)

TEACHERS - ORGAN

Whittaker, Anthony (Mid)
Worth, Chris (NE)

OUD

Alsaady, Ahmed (Lon)

PERCUSSION

Adams, Dawne (Lon)
Adams, Ian (Lon)
Adams, Ken (Mid)
Aitchison, Jacqueline (Sco)
Albrighton, Che (Lon)
Aldridge, Luke (Lon)
Aldridge, Mark (Mid)
Alexander, Tommas (Lon)
Allardyce, Patricia (Lon)
Allatson, Lee (Mid)
Allcock, Garry (Mid)
Allen, Simon (Lon)
Allen, Simon (NE)
Andrews, Lea (Voice Lon)
Anstice-Brown, Sam (SW)
Appleby, Colin (NW)
Archer, Mitchell (Mid)
Arnott, William (Sco)
Ashby, Charles (NE)
Atkins, Matthew (Lon)
Aubertin, Mark (Mid)
Ayres, Frank (NE)
Bacon, Simon (Lon)
Badejo, Peter (Lon)
Baines, Andy (Composer NW)
Baker, Bernard (SW)
Ballantine, Ian (Vibraphone Lon)
Bamford, Richard (Sco)
Bancroft, Thomas (Sco)
Banks, Stephen (Lon)
Banks, Tristan (SE)
Barchild, Teresa (Lon)
Barclay, Graeme (Sco)
Barrett, Nicholas (NE)
Barron, Christine Angela (Mid)
Bartlett, Keith (Lon)
Barwell, Steven (Mid)
Batting, Roger (E)
Beane, Norman (NE)
Beard, Richard (Lon)
Beecham, Ian (NW)
Bellingham, David (Keyboards SE)
Bengry, Peter (NW)
Benham, Trevor (SE)
Benjafield, Richard (SE)
Bernardin, Jim (NW)
Berthon, Darell (Sco)
Bianco, Anthony (Lon)
Biggs, Brett (NE)
Black, Barry (NE)
Blackstock, Kenneth (NW)
Blanchard, Richard (NE)
Bonett, Kevin (SE)
Bool, Helen P (Mid)
Booroff, Stephane (SE)
Booth, Brian (Tympani Lon)
Borenius, Louis (SE)
Boucher, Alex (E)
Bouzida, Nasser (SE)
Bowden, Graham (Mid)
Bowden, James (Lon)
Boyle, Tommy (Sco)
Bradley, Graham (SW)
Brady, Colin (E)
Bratt, Andrew (Lon)
Breslaw, Joshua (Lon)
Brian, Robert (SW)

Bright, Martin (E)
Brocklehurst, Neil (Lon)
Brodie, Emma (NW)
Brooker, Chris (Music Director Lon)
Brooker, Jonathan (Lon)
Brown, Alan (Lon)
Brown, Bill (SE)
Brown, Geoff (Lon)
Brown, Kevin (Mid)
Brown, Leo (NW)
Brown, Paul (Lon)
Bruce, Deborah (Lon)
Bryant, Terl (Lon)
Budge, William (E)
Bullock, Neil (Mid)
Burgess, Chris (Lon)
Burgess, Timothy (SE)
Burns, Keith W (Sco)
Burville, Eric (SE)
Bushell, Adam (Lon)
Butler, Matthew (NE)
Butlin, Matthew (SW)
Butterly, Kevin (Mid)
Byng, Frank (Lon)
Caddy, Joe (SE)
Caldas, John (Lon)
Callow, Haydn (Lon)
Cannelli, Tony (NE)
Cargill, Suzy (Sco)
Carpena, Francesco (Lon)
Carroll, Johnny (Mid)
Cattanach, Davy (Sco)
Cattermole, Nicholas (Lon)
Cavanagh, Damien (SW)
Cecil, Marc (E)
Chapman, Jon (NE)
Chappell, Jonathan (SE)
Charles, Richard (NW)
Cheetham, Maurice (NW)
Child, Glen (SE)
Church, Daniel (Lon)
Clark, Benedict (Lon)
Claydon, Mark (Lon)
Clayton, Eddy (E)
Cleall, Robert (SE)
Clements, Mat (Sco)
Coccia, Dominic (Lon)
Collis, Bill (Lon)
Cook, Andrew (NE)
Cooper, Albert (SE)
Cooper, David (NE)
Cooper, Douglas (SW)
Cooper, Freddie (SW)
Cooper, Geoffrey (Lon)
Cooper, Joe (Lon)
Corbett, Heather (Sco)
Cormell, Alastair (Mid)
Cornwall, Lindel (Voice Lon)
Corradi, Max (Lon)
Cottee, Andrew (SE)
Coulter, Ian (Sco)
Coulthard, Paul (NW)
Cox, Allan (Lon)
Craner, Robert (Mid)
Creese, Stephen (Lon)
Crockford, Barny (Lon)
Crompton, Don (NW)
Cross, Malcolm (Lon)
Crossen, Steven (SW)
Cubberley, Gary (SE)
Culham, Graeme (E)
Cumber, Peter (Lon)
Cummings, George (Mid)
Dangerfield, Nicholas (Mid)
Dare, Graham (Lon)

Das, Aniruddha (Bass Guitar Lon)
Davies, Martin (NE)
Davies, Martin (SW)
Davis, Andrew (SW)
Davison, Brian (SW)
Day, Ann (SE)
Debnam, Alex (SE)
Dennis, Kelvin (NE)
Devers, Peter (Guitars Sco)
Diamond, Ross (Lon)
Dibbs, Martin (Sco)
Dick, Malcolm (NE)
Dick, Norman (NE)
Doe, Terry (Lon)
Double, George (Lon)
Dow, Pamela (Sco)
Dowdall, Graham (Lon)
Dransfield, Mark (NE)
Drees, Michele (Lon)
Dyer, Julie (Lon)
Dyson, Lewis (Mid)
Edgoose, Simon (Lon)
Elliott, Jon (NW)
Ellmer, John (SE)
Emney, Brian (Lon)
Eoghain (Sco)
Etherington, Mark (SW)
Evans, Christophe (E)
Evans, Guy (Lon)
Evans, Peter (Tympani Sco)
Fairclough, Peter (NE)
Fall, David (Lon)
Fallowell, Peter (SE)
Farnell, Thomas (Mid)
Faulkner, Janet (SE)
Feast, Les (SE)
Fennell, Tony (SW)
Ferrera, Stephen (Lon)
Ferris, Jim (SW)
Finch, Greg (NW)
Finlay, Rick (Lon)
Fishwick, Mathew (Lon)
Fitzgibbon, Martin (SW)
Flaherty, Daniel (Sco)
Fleeman, Jim (Lon)
Fletcher, Mark (Lon)
Fletcher, Stephen (NE)
Forbes, Ian (NE)
Forgrieve, Ian (Tympani NW)
Foster, Neil (Lon)
Fox, The (Mid)
Francis, Paul (E)
Francis, Paul (NE)
Frankish, Paul (NE)
Fry, Alan (NW)
Fullbrook, Charles (Lon)
Fullbrook, Richard (Sco)
Fulton, Janet (Tympani NE)
Gale, Derek (Lon)
Gallais, Lydie (Lon)
Gammon, Aaron (NE)
Gammons, Rod (Lon)
Garner, Tim (Lon)
Garrett, Malcolm (Mid)
George, Dave (SE)
Giddings, John (SW)
Gilchrist, Stephen (Lon)
Gillings, Gerry (E)
Giovannini, Davide (Lon)
Girling, Chris (SW)
Gleadhill, Andrew (Lon)
Goddard, James (SE)
Goodill, Tim (NE)
Goodman, Ronnie (Sco)
Goodman, Toby (E)

Goodwin, James (NW)
Gordon, Cameron (Lon)
Gordon, Tom (Lon)
Gorelick, Simon (SE)
Graham, John (SE)
Grange, Pierson (Lon)
Grant, Simon (NE)
Green, Mark (SE)
Green, Steve (Lon)
Greenhouse, Philip (Mid)
Greenwood, Alexander (NE)
Greeve, Micky (Lon)
Griffiths, Andrew (SW)
Griffiths, Benjamin (Mid)
Griffiths, David (SW)
Griffiths, Matthew (SW)
Grigg, Michael (Lon)
Grossart, James (Sco)
Guegan, Neil (Lon)
H, David (Lon)
Hackney, Alan (Mid)
Hague, Ian (Lon)
Halfyard, Paul (NE)
Hall, Laurence (SE)
Hamilton, Ross (SW)
Hanson-Usher, Moira (NW)
Harding, Wendy (Sco)
Harfield, Ross (SW)
Harper, Michael (NW)
Harper, Phillip (Lon)
Harries, Alun (Lon)
Harris, Ian (SE)
Harris, Stephen (SW)
Harris, Steve (SE)
Harris, Steven (Lon)
Harrison, Ian (Saxophones E)
Harrison, Kerry (NE)
Harrison, Anthony (NW)
Hassell, David (NW)
Hastings, Sophie (NW)
Hattee, David (Lon)
Hawkes, Jodie (Lon)
Hawley, Russell (Mid)
Hearn, Martin (Lon)
Hedgecock, John Bernard (SE)
Hegan, Patrick (NW)
Henderson, Albert (NE)
Henshaw, Elliott (NW)
Herbert, Andrew (Mid)
Heywood, David (NW)
Hicks, Robert (SW)
Hickson, Andrew (NW)
Hiley, Paul (SW)
Hill, Gary Oliver (Mid)
Hiscock, Stephen (Lon)
Hlela, Betty (African Drums Lon)
Hogan, Neil (Lon)
Hoggarth, Craig (NW)
Hogger, John (E)
Holden, Timothy (NW)
Holland, Steve (Lon)
Holland-Hanbury, Nigel (Mid)
Hooper, Jon (Lon)
Horwood, Jack (SE)
Hose, Paul (Mid)
Howard, Terence (SW)
Howell, Peter (Lon)
Howells, Jonathan (Lon)
Howland, Peter (Lon)
Hubbard, Richard (E)
Hudson, Paul (NE)
Huggett, Roy (SE)
Hunt, Jayne (Tympani NW)
Hunter, Craig (Sco)
Hurren, Jim (Mid)

Hutchinson, Ben (Lon)
Hyde, Gary (Lon)
Hyder, Ken (Lon)
I'Anson, Chris (Sco)
Illingworth, Patrick (NW)
Ingham, Alan (NE)
Jackson, David (Lon)
Jackson, Susan (NW)
Jago, Chris (NW)
James, Andrew (SE)
James, Debbie (NE)
Jamieson, Michael (Sco)
Jenkinson, James (Mid)
Jenner, Clive (Lon)
Jennings, Lee (Mid)
Jennings, Neale (Lon)
Jimenez-Gomez, Alfonso (Voice Lon)
Johnson, Brian (Lon)
Jones, Derek (SW)
Jones, Michael (Tympani SW)
Kaplan, Stuart (NE)
Karno, Gilbey (Lon)
Keel, John (SW)
Kendell, Robert (Lon)
Kendle, Jackie (Lon)
Kennell, David (SE)
Kerr, Roger (Lon)
Keyte, Jason (Mid)
Kimber, Christopher (Lon)
King, Gareth (SE)
King, Jeff (SE)
Knight, Bob (Lon)
Kodish, Paul (Lon)
Kohut, Steven (NE)
Larcombe, David (E)
Lawrence, David (NE)
Lawson, Stephen (NW)
Lea, Simon (Lon)
Lee, Crissy (Lon)
Lee, John (NE)
Lee, Jonathan (Lon)
Lee, Ric (NW)
Lewis, Jak R (NE)
Lewis, Steve (Latin American Perc. NW)
Limbrick, Simon (Lon)
Little, Phil (SE)
Littlewood, Stanley (NW)
Locke, Martyn (SW)
Long, Stephen (Lon)
Louise, Janel (E)
Love, Kate (E)
Lowe, Christopher (NW)
Lyons, Carol (Sco)
Macdonald, James (Lon)
Macdonald, Peter (Lon)
Maguire, Damian (SE)
Maitland, Chris (E)
Manoilovich, Vancho (Lon)
Mantero, Francesco (Lon)
Manuel, Robert (SW)
Marriott, Ian (Lon)
Marshall, Gary (SE)
Marshall, Jim (SE)
Mason, Darren (Lon)
Mathews, Merlin (E)
Mathieson, Iain (SW)
Matthews, Glyn (Lon)
Maurel, Alain (Lon)
May, Joanne (Lon)
McArthur, Roy (NE)
McAtominey, Aidan (Tympani Lon)
McCarthy, Paul (Mid)
McDonough, Matthew (Lon)
McFarlane, Philip (Lon)
McFarlane, Philip (Mid)

McGovern, Bernard (NE)
McGuire, Gerard (Mid)
McUlloch, Alan (Lon)
McVey, Anthony (Lon)
Melius, Perry (Lon)
Metz, Dominique (Lon)
Mezulis, Peter (Mid)
Miller, Dusty (SW)
Millest, Simon (Mid)
Mills, Andrew (SE)
Mills, Des (SE)
Missingham, Andrew (Lon)
Mitchell, John (SW)
Monomania (Mid)
Monson, Darren (Lon)
Moore, Simon (NW)
Morena, Mick (Lon)
Morgan, Greg (NW)
Morrison, Will (Lon)
Moyes, Darren (Sco)
Mullin, Tim (NW)
Murcott, Dominic (Lon)
Myers, Geoff (NE)
Naish, Sarah (Tympani Sco)
Natkanski, Michael (Lon)
Nettleton, David (NE)
Nicholls, John (Mid)
Nicklin, Edward (E)
Nolan, Sheila (Lon)
O'Callaghan, Cion (Lon)
O'Neill, Kevin (NE)
Odell, Roger (Lon)
Oliver, Matthew (Lon)
Orrell, Tony (SW)
Osborn, Michael (Lon)
Palin, Jessica (Latin American Perc Lon)
Palmer, Steve (Mid)
Pamphille, Ishmael (Bass Guitar Lon)
Panda, George (Lon)
Papageorgiou, Nicolaos (Lon)
Park, John (Lon)
Parker, Norman (Tympani Mid)
Parratt, Tom (Mid)
Parry, Ronald (SE)
Patterson, Jeff (Voice Lon)
Pattinson, Iian (Lon)
Payne, Ray (NE)
Payne, Robin (Mid)
Pearce, Ian (Lon)
Peck, Anne (Lon)
Perrins, Simon (Mid)
Phillips, Barry (Lon)
Pickering, Michael (Lon)
Plummer, Craig (Lon)
Pollitt, Jack (Lon)
Poore, Jak (NW)
Power, Patrick (SE)
Prichard, George (Non Playing Member Mid)
Proctor, Martin (Lon)
Purse, Robert (Sco)
Quammie, Quinton (SW)
Rae, John (Sco)
Randle, Alan (Lon)
Rankin, Alasdair (Sco)
Ravenhill, Colin (Lon)
Rawbone, Nick (Lon)
Reay, Jason (SW)
Redman, Ben (Sco)
Reyland, Trevor (E)
Rich, Matthew (Lon)
Richards, Jack (SE)
Richards, Tony (Mid)
Richardson, Clive (E)
Richardson, Robert (Mid)
Riley, Michael (Lon)

MUSIC EDUCATION YEARBOOK

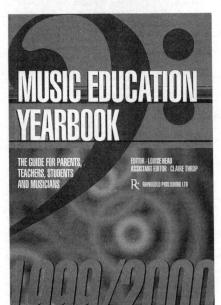

The Guide for Parents, Teachers, Students and Musicians

Provides contact information, course details, scholarship policy and entry requirements for all independent schools, conservatoires, colleges and universities nationwide. Plus world music, local authorities, music and book publishers, information technology, youth orchestras and choirs, teacher resources, summer schools and more.

Published each May
700 pages

HOW TO ORDER

Please send a cheque for **£18.00** (inc. p&p) payable to *Rhinegold Publishing Ltd* to: **MEYB Sales, Rhinegold Publishing, FREEPOST, London WC2H 8BR.**

TELEPHONE: **0171 333 1721** (or 020 7333 1721 after 22 Apr 2000)
FAX: **0171 333 1769** (or 020 7333 1769 after 22 Apr 2000)
EMAIL: **sales@rhinegold.co.uk**
WEBSITE: **www.rhinegold.co.uk**

Ritchie, Fiona (Lon)
Roberts, Dylan (Lon)
Roberts, Eryl (Lon)
Roberts, Mark (Lon)
Roberts, Penny (E)
Robinson, Ian (NW)
Robinson, Stephen (E)
Robinson, Tim (SW)
Rodwell, Brian (Mid)
Roman, Adam (Lon)
Roscoe, John (NW)
Roth, Stephen (SW)
Rouleau, Franck (Lon)
Roy, Jimmy (Lon)
Ruttley, Edward (E)
Saadoun, Abdelkader (Guitars Lon)
Sales, Dominic (NE)
Salmon, Derek (SW)
Sam, Papa (Guitars Lon)
Sam Sam The Bongo Man (Lon)
San Juan, Stefan (Lon)
San Remo, Steevi (E)
Sanders, Mark (Lon)
Santry, Gary (Mid)
Saxby, Timothy (Lon)
Scantlebury, Anthony (Lon)
Scarff, Richard (Lon)
Schalom, Guy (NW)
Scott, Jim (SW)
Sheehan, Ashley (Mid)
Shefford, Justin (SE)
Sheinman, Charles (Mid)
Sherman, Ted (Lon)
Simpson, David (Mid)
Simpson, Michael (Lon)
Sivier, William (E)
Skelton, Matt (Lon)
Smith, Alex (Lon)
Smith, Caroline (NW)
Smith, Geoff (SE)
Smith, Jason (SE)
Smith, Jeremy (Mid)
Smith, Martin (SE)
Smith, Paul (NE)
Smith, Paul (NE)
Smith, Philip (Lon)
Smith, Robert (Mid)
Sneddon, Montgomery (Sco)
Snooden, Matthew (SE)
Snow, John (Lon)
Soan, Ashley (Lon)
Socci, Stephen (Mid)
Solomon, Philip (SE)
Somerville, Robert (E)
Sparkes, Anne (E)
Sparrow, Edwin (Lon)
Sproxton, Andrew (NW)
Stams, Erik (Lon)
Stancliffe, Fred (Lon)
Stephenson, Robert (NE)
Stephenson, Ronnie (Sco)
Stevens, Rob (Lon)
Stone, Brian (Mid)
Street, Steve (Mid)
Stuart, Paul (NW)
Sturgis, Mike (SE)
Sugden, Benjamin (E)
Sullivan, Terence (SE)
Sutton, Mike (NW)
Sveinsson, Agust (NW)
Swanson, David (Sco)
Sykes, Christopher (NE)
Tagford, James (SE)
Tams, Cedric (Mid)
Taylor, James (Sco)

Taylor, Steve (Lon)
Taylor-Holmes, B (Mid)
Temple, David (Lon)
Tharp, Ian (Lon)
Thew, Graeme (SE)
Thomas, Bryan (NW)
Thomas, Neil (NE)
Thorne, Mike (Trombone SE)
Thornley, Steve (Composer SE)
Thow, Harry (SE)
Tilbrook, Adrian (NE)
Tolansky, Jonathan (Tympani Lon)
Tomkins, Trevor (Lon)
Toms, Elliot (Lon)
Tracey, Scott (SW)
Treacey, Andrew (NW)
Tring, Lisa (Mid)
Trower, Terence (Lon)
Tuup (Lon)
Twyford, Benjamin (Lon)
Twyman, Nick (Lon)
Ughi, Federico (Lon)
Vear, Anthony (Lon)
Vernon, Howard (NW)
Vincent, Raymond (SE)
Vintner, Steven (Lon)
Vogler, Andrea (NW)
Walker, Gordon (Sco)
Walker, Michael (NW)
Warburton, Julian (Lon)
Ward, Arthur (SE)
Ward, Donald (Mid)
Ward, Jonathan (NE)
Waterman, Kevin, (Mid)
Watson, Edward (SW)
Watt, Anthony (Pianoforte NW)
Watton, Gary (NE)
Webber, Martin (SW)
Webster, Dave (Lon)
White, David (SE)
Whyte, Jim (Lon)
Wickens, Lee (Lon)
Wicker, Simon (E)
Wilkin, Mark (Lon)
Willcox, Gary (Lon)
Williams, David (Mid)
Williams, David (Mid)
Williams, Paul (SE)
Wilshere, Brian (Lon)
Wilson, Anthony (NE)
Wilson, Derek (Lon)
Wilson-Dickson, Sovra (Violin Lon)
Wimpress, Daniel (Lon)
Winston, Giselle (Lon)
Wolf, Robert (Lon)
Woodward, Justin (Lon)
Woodward, Malcolm (NE)
Woolway, Colin (Lon)
Wortley, Barry (E)
Wraight, Andrew (SW)
Wren, Isobel (NW)
Wright, Anthony (SE)
Wright, Chris (SE)
Wright, Douglas (Mid)
Wright, Jack (SW)
Wright, Tim (Lon)
York, Keith (Mid)
Young, Ian (SE)
Young, Richard (NW)
Youssef, My (Lon)
Zara (Guitars Mid)

PIANOFORTE

Abbey, Francis (Lon)
Abdey, Eric (Organ SE)

Adams, Elin (Oboe SW)
Adcock, Michael (Accordion E)
Adele, Maia (SW)
Alexander, Mike (Mid)
Alexander-Max, Susan (Lon)
Allan, Dorothy (Keyboards Lon)
Alldis, Dominic (Lon)
Allen, Keith (NW)
Allsopp, Peter (NE)
Alston, Pauline (NW)
Anderson, April Joy (Voice Lon)
Anderson, Ewan (Conductor NW)
Angell, Frances (Lon)
Anstiss, Hayley (Lon)
Ap Sion, Pwyll (Keyboards NW)
Appleton, David (Lon)
Apsley, Richard (Conductor Lon)
Arlidge, Victoria (Composer Lon)
Armatage, Justine (Lon)
Arnold, Benedict (Saxophones Lon)
Arnold, Peter (SE)
Ash, Jacqueline (SW)
Asher, John (Lon)
Atkinson, Alistair (Keyboards NE)
Atkinson, Cliff (Lon)
Atkinson, Georgina (Lon)
Atkinson, Richard (Lon)
Austin, Dean (Lon)
Axtell, Daniel (Lon)
Baggott, John (SW)
Bailey, Gavin (NE)
Bailey, Sarah-Jane (Violin SE)
Bailey, Terence (Mid)
Baines, Colin (Double Bass Mid)
Baker, James (Mid)
Baker, Jonathan (Horn Lon)
Baker, Kathleen (NE)
Ball, Patricia (SE)
Bamford, Gary (SW)
Banel, Mark (Sco)
Banks, Jon (Dulcimer E)
Barclay, Kenneth (Lon)
Barker, Angela (Lon)
Barnard, Keith (Composer Lon)
Barnes, Brian (Mid)
Barnes, Mary (Sco)
Barnwell, Edward (NW)
Baron, Michael (SW)
Barrand, Roderick (NW)
Barrett, Trevor (Mid)
Batchellor, Heather (Keyboards Lon)
Batsford, Richard (Voice Mid)
Beadle, Richard (Lon)
Beale, Charles (Keyboards Lon)
Bean, Alison (Double Bass Mid)
Beard, Paul (Lon)
Beddows, Stanley (Conductor SW)
Bedford, Andrew (NE)
Beebee, David (Lon)
Bell, Katie (NE)
Bennett, Patrick (NE)
Bentley, Ed (Organ Lon)
Berry, Alan (Mid)
Berry, Alison (Lon)
Beswick, John (Conductor SW)
Birch, Catherine (E)
Bishop, Chiz (Organ SE)
Blackwood, Peter (SW)
Blake, Wayne (Mid)
Bleasdale, John (NW)
Blomfield, Jim (SW)
Blunn, Nick (Mid)
Bolingbroke, Paula (SE)
Boltz, Michael (E)
Booth, Donald (Keyboards SW)

TEACHERS - PIANOFORTE

Borzymowska, Izabela (SE)
Bottrill, Andrew (SE)
Bousie, Mark (Accordion Lon)
Bown, Eileen (NE)
Bradley, Kate (Voice Lon)
Bradley, Sarah (Viola Lon)
Bramwell, Jonathan (NW)
Branson, Peter (SE)
Bratkowski, Cheryl (NE)
Breese, Emma (SW)
Breingan, Stan (Sco)
Brereton, Charles (Lon)
Briscoe, Anthony (Lon)
Broadbent, Don (NE)
Broderick, Golda (Lon)
Bromilow, W (NW)
Brookes, Ritchie (SW)
Brown, Alan (Double Bass Lon)
Brown, Alison (Sco)
Brown, Anne (SW)
Brown, David-Joseph (Lon)
Brown, Paul (SW)
Brown, Simon (E)
Brown, Tanya (Lon)
Buckberry, Ivan (Mid)
Buckle, Ian (NW)
Bunkell, David (Lon)
Burbidge, Victor (Lon)
Burden, Elizabeth (SE)
Burke, Nicola (Trumpet Lon)
Burley, Elizabeth (Lon)
Burman, David (Lon)
Burnham, Catherine (SW)
Burrell, Paul (Lon)
Burrows, Georgina (Voice Lon)
Burrows, Helen (E)
Burtenshaw, Leslie (NE)
Burton, Cathy (Guitars SE)
Button, Jean (SE)
Calnan, Anthony (Lon)
Calvert, Gillian (NE)
Cameron, Hilary (Lon)
Campbell, Adam (Lon)
Campbell, Joel (Keyboards Lon)
Capocci, Nicholas (SE)
Carey, Timothy (Lon)
Carr, Carlina (Lon)
Carr, Jennifer (Lon)
Carroll, Richard (Lon)
Carsan, Paul (Composer Lon)
Carter, Margot (SE)
Cartmell, Tom (NE)
Casey, Richard (NW)
Castle, Geoff (Keyboards Lon)
Cawley, Tom (Lon)
Cepeda, Jose (Lon)
Chadwick, Graham (NW)
Chambers, Rebecca (NW)
Chapman, Greg (Lon)
Chase, Elizabeth (Lon)
Cheer, John (SW)
Chester, Craig (Lon)
Chisnall, Leslie (Mid)
Clarke, Jane (SE)
Clarke, Jonathan (Mid)
Clarke, Miranda (Lon)
Clarke, Oliver (Mid)
Clarke, Owain (Celtic Harp SE)
Clewlow, Alf (Keyboards E)
Cliff, Tony (Composer SW)
Clouts, Philip (Lon)
Coates, Richard (Lon)
Cochrane, Lynda (Sco)
Cockerill, Craig (NE)
Cohen, Leon (Lon)

Colchester, Sheila (SE)
Coleman, John (Mid)
Collis, Christopher (Mid)
Collisson, Stephen (Mid)
Condon, Matthew (Keyboards Lon)
Connell, Patrick (NW)
Cook Berendina, Jill (SE)
Cooper, Sally (Lon)
Coppard, Tessa (Lon)
Corbet, Alan (Mid)
Corbett, David (SE)
Cordiner, A. (Sco)
Corley, Stephen (Lon)
Corrick, Gordon (NE)
Cosgrove, Declan (NW)
Cosmas, Genie (Lon)
Cottis, Nicholas (SW)
Cowan, Anne F (Sco)
Cox (Mid)
Cozens, Spencer (Keyboards Lon)
Cranville, Patricia (NW)
Crawford, John (Sco)
Cremona, Robert (Composer SE)
Critchinson, John (Lon)
Croft, Philip (NE)
Croker, Joanne (Voice Lon)
Cropper, Sarah (Lon)
Cunnison, Belinda (Sco)
Curran, Sara (Lon)
Davey, Colin (Organ Lon)
Davidson-Kelly, Kirsteen (Lon)
Davies, Austin (SW)
Davies, Harvey (NW)
Davies, Helen (NW)
Davies, Peter (Lon)
Davis, Jeremy (Lon)
Davison, Roger (Lon)
Dawkins, Rita (Violin Mid)
Dawkins, Tanera (Cello Lon)
Dawney, Michael (SE)
Dawson, Mark (SW)
Dawson, Nick (Lon)
Day, Stuart (NE)
Day, Tony (Keyboards SE)
De Jong, Ronald (Lon)
Dean, Alan (Mid)
Dearnley, Dorothy (NW)
Death, Stewart (NW)
Defferd, Trevor (SE)
Dibdin, Daniel (Lon)
Dignam, Kate (Lon)
Djudurovic, Dragan (Lon)
Dockrell-Tyler, Elizabeth (Lon)
Don, Nigel (Sco)
Donovan, John (Lon)
Dourado, Timothy (Lon)
Dowie, Christopher (Organ SE)
Draisey, James (SW)
Dressler, Andrew (NE)
Drinkwater, Neil (Lon)
Du Valle, Cecil (SW)
Duari, Meena Louise (NW)
Duffy, Gerald (NW)
Duke, Henry (SE)
Duncan, Robert (Sco)
Dunn, Christopher (Lon)
Dunstall, Clive (Lon)
Dunstan, James (Mid)
Dutton, Richard (SE)
Eames, Tudur (Harp Lon)
Ecclestone, Daniel (Lon)
Edmunds, Chris (SW)
Edwards, Andrew (Lon)
Edwards, Mark (SE)
Edwards, Pamela (Harpsichord Lon)

Elliott, Kevin (SE)
Ellsbury, Brian (Lon)
Emery, Helen (SE)
Etherington, Matthew (NE)
Evans, Andrew (Lon)
Evans, Kat (Electric Violin Lon)
Eveleigh, Deborah (Voice SE)
Faint, Peter (NW)
Farrelly, Gerard (Keyboards Lon)
Fawcett, Caleb (Lon)
Feeney, Eric (Mid)
Fenn-Smith, Jeremy (Lon)
Fergusson-Nicol, Avni (Voice NW)
Field, Beatrice (SE)
Fielder, Robert (SE)
Fielding, Mark (Lon)
Finch, Matthew (SW)
Fisher, Roger (Organ Mid)
Fitness, Julia (Voice SE)
Fleischer, Marion (Mid)
Fletcher, Paul (NW)
Flinders, John (Lon)
Forbes, Jerry (SW)
Ford, Andrew (Mid)
Ford, Gillian (Lon)
Foster, Ben (Music Director Lon)
Foulcer, Alexander (Voice Lon)
Fowkes, Edwin (Tympani Mid)
Fowler, Karen (Mid)
Fowler, Michael (Mid)
Fox, Nigel (Lon)
Fox, Sylvia (Mid)
Foxley, Simon (Lon)
Franklin, Harry (Mid)
Franklin, Maxine (Lon)
Franklin, Nikki (SE)
Friesner, Andrew (Music Director Lon)
Fryer, Ruth (SW)
Fuller, Gareth (Mid)
Furnish, Alfred (Mid)
Fyles, Kenneth (NW)
Gabriel, Ella (SE)
Gadian, Wendy (NW)
Gard, John-Paul (SW)
Garden, Stuart (NE)
Garland, Miranda (SW)
Garrick, Michael (Lon)
Gatti, Luca (Lon)
Gibbin, Hilary (SW)
Gibbons, John (SW)
Gibbs, Louise (Voice Lon)
Glasser, Adam (Harmonica Lon)
Glavey, Radina (Lon)
Glavin, Helen (Lon)
Goggins, Mark (NW)
Goldsmith, Tracey (Accordion Lon)
Goldstein, Martin (Lon)
Goodger, Derek (Harpsichord SE)
Goodhand, Francis (NW)
Gordon, Marilyn (Music Director Lon)
Goss, Luke (SW)
Gough, John (NW)
Gould, Peter (SE)
Gray, Catherine (Mid)
Gray, Ian (Organ NW)
Gray, Simon (Conductor SE)
Greaves, Jack (NE)
Greenlee, Martin (SW)
Greenshields, Lynne (SE)
Greenway, Mike (Keyboards Lon)
Gregory, John Brandon (NE)
Gregory, Sean (Composer Lon)
Griffiths, Gareth (NW)
Grigelis, Alexander (Keyboards Sco)
Grosvenor, David (Tuba NE)

Grove, Peter (SW)
Gulliford, Jonathan (SW)
Guppy, Eileen (NW)
Gutman, Stephen (Lon)
Gwinnell-Lee, Joanne (Voice Lon)
Hadley, Colin (NW)
Hadley, Nicola (Accordion Lon)
Hague, Chistopher (NW)
Hall, Ambrose Edison (E)
Hall, Garth (SE)
Hall, John (Mid)
Haney, Janet Elizabeth (Lon)
Hara, Yumi Voice (Lon)
Harding, Timothy (Music Director Mid)
Hardy, Robert (Keyboards E)
Harris, Keith (SE)
Harris, Richard (Lon)
Harris, Tris (Lon)
Harrison, Frank (E)
Harrod, Andrew Kear (Double Bass Lon)
Harvey, Simon (E)
Harwood, Juliet (SW)
Haslam, Dominic (Lon)
Hatton, Janet (Lon)
Hawkes, Brian (SE)
Hawkins, Mary (SW)
Hay, Victoria (usic Director Lon)
Haydock, Neil (SE)
Hayston, Nicola (Early Strings Lon)
Hayward, Peter (SE)
Head, Raymond (Lon)
Heaviside, Colin (E)
Heawood, Marian (E)
Heckel, Stefan (Lon)
Heeley, Roger (Mid)
Henderson, Allie (Lon)
Herman, Marilyn (Voice Lon)
Hester, Kate (Mid)
Heywood, Sandra (SE)
Hill, Kathrine (Mid)
Hill, Stephen (SE)
Hilton, Andrew (NE)
Hodges, Maurice (Recorders E)
Hogger, Alan (NW)
Holder, Michael (Lon)
Holler, Felix (Lon)
Holloway, Yvonne (Lon)
Holmes, Alison (NW)
Hooper, Tony (Mid)
Hopper, Jennifer (SE)
Hopson, Yvonne (NE)
Hora, Johanna (Mid)
Horobin, Liz (SW)
Horton, Christine (NW)
Horton, Ronald (Mid)
Hughes, Catherine (SE)
Hughes, Trevor (E)
Hugo, Peter (SW)
Humphris, Caroline (Music Director Lon)
Hunt, Max (Keyboards SW)
Hunter, Eanswyth (NE)
Hunter, Larraine (Mid)
Hunter, Neil (Keyboards Mid)
Hurden, Sammy (SW)
Hutchins, Adam (NW)
Hyatt, Michael (Lon)
Hyde, Jill (Tympani NW)
Hyland, Wyn (Lon)
Ibbett, Jane (Mid)
Incledon, Rosalind (SW)
Ingle, Anthony (Lon)
Ingleby, Mark (Lon)
Jackson, Catherine (Lon)
Jaeger, Lincoln (Lon)
James, Alexander (NE)

Jamieson, Gaby (Lon)
Jenkins, John (Double Bass SW)
Johnson, Alistair (Lon)
Johnson, Griff (Keyboards Lon)
Johnson, Stuart (Conductor Mid)
Johnston, David (Lon)
Jones, Benjamin (Keyboards SE)
Jones, David (Keyboards E)
Jones, David (NW)
Jones, David (SW)
Jones, Dyfan (SW)
Jones, Ian (Lon)
Jones, Ian (Mid)
Jones, Ilid Anne (NW)
Jones, Mark (SE)
Jones, Rona (NW)
Jones, Roy (Keyboards SW)
Jones, Tryphena (Mid)
Jubinsky, Julian (SW)
Kavanavich, Kerrie (E)
Keir, Andrew (NW)
Kenward, Elaine (Lon)
Kimberley, Carol (Mid)
Kirkman, Dorothy (SE)
Kirkpatrick, Elizabeth (E)
Koller, Hans (Lon)
Kristy, Andrew (Synthesiser Mid)
Kuermayr, Gunther (Lon)
Lambert, Edward (Composer Lon)
Lambert, Michael (Mid)
Lane, Annie (Voice SE)
Langfield, Valerie (NW)
Latarche, Vanessa (Lon)
Law, John (Lon)
Lawson, Peter (NW)
Laxton, Elaine (SE)
Leach, Jeff (Lon)
Lee, Kat (Voice Lon)
Lee, Michael (Viola NE)
Lee, Patrick (NE)
Leek, Andrew (Mid)
Leitch, Hazel (Sco)
Lelong, Chad (Lon)
Lenton, Suzanne (NE)
Leport, Jeannette (SE)
Lester, Harold (Lon)
Lewis, Alan (SE)
Lewis, Gareth (Organ SW)
Liddell, Clair (Sco)
Light, John (Organ Lon)
Lingwood, Peter (NW)
Lismore, Jenifer (Mid)
Lithgow, Beverley (Sco)
Little, Matt (SE)
Lloyd, Martyn (NW)
Loat, Alan (NW)
Lockett, Mark (Keyboards Mid)
Locock, Victoria (Mid)
Lole, Peter (Music Director Lon)
Loughran, Anne (Mid)
Love, William (Organ NW)
Lovell-Jones, Simon (Conductor SW)
Lundberg, George (NE)
Lysander, Ebonard (Lon)
Macaulay, Mary (SW)
Maggs, John (SW)
Malkinson, Chris (E)
Mallalieu, Jonathan (Lon)
Manley, Joyce (SW)
Manners, Kim (NE)
Maramis, Dimitris (SW)
March, Sylvia (Mid)
Marquez, Marina (Lon)
Marsden, Robin (Lon)
Marshall, Bridget (Organ E)

Martin, Marcus (SE)
Mason, Janette (Lon)
Massey, Andrew (Lon)
Maul, John (E)
Maxim, John (Lon)
Mayo, Graham (Mid)
McCarthy, Heather (SW)
McCarthy, Kevin (Synthesiser SE)
McCaw, Shirley (Trombone Lon)
McDonald, David (Sco)
McFarlane, Frank (Lon)
McIntyre, Paul (Lon)
Mead, Philip (E)
Mead, Philip (Lon)
Melleck, Lydia (Lon)
Mellor, David (Music Director Lon)
Metliss, Jeremy (Lon)
Michel, Hilary (Voice Lon)
Miles, Tom (Lon)
Miller, Judith (SE)
Miller, Steven (Lon)
Milne, Ian (Sco)
Milner, Michael (NW)
Milverton, Craig (SW)
Mitchell, Christopher (Lon)
Mitchell, Steven (Mid)
Mobbs, Kenneth (SW)
Mollison, Deborah (Composer Lon)
Monteith-Mathie, Ian (Music Director Sco)
Moore, Gary (SE)
Moran, Paul (Keyboards Lon)
Morgan, Basil (SW)
Morgan, Beverly (Mid)
Morgan, Kevin (Organ NW)
Morley, Jeanette (Mid)
Morrell, Kenneth (NE)
Morrell, Tom (Keyboards SE)
Morris, Darren (Lon)
Morris, Edna (NE)
Morris, Harvey (NW)
Morrish, Stephen (SE)
Mortimer, Anthony (E)
Morton, Simon (Keyboards SW)
Mosonyi, Pierre (Lon)
Moxon-Browne, Kicki (Lon)
Muir, Peter (Lon)
Murdoch, Cameron (Sco)
Murray, David (NE)
Murray, Simon J (Music Director Lon)
Murtagh, Andrew (Mid)
Nair, Dhevdhas (SW)
Nankivell, Hugh (NE)
Napier, Marie Louise (Clarsach Sco)
Neiger, Rachel (Lon)
Nelson, Andrew (NE)
Nembhard, Carl (Mid)
Newport, Mark (E)
Newport, Neil (Mid)
Newton, Race (NE)
Nicol, Andrew (Sco)
Nicoll, John (SW)
Nieminski, Simon (Organ Sco)
Nieve, Steve (Lon)
Nobes, Roger (Percussion E)
Noble, Austin (Lon)
Nock, John (Mid)
Noel, Lincoln (Mid)
Nolan, Mike (Sco)
Norden, Elizabeth (Lon)
Norton, Jamie (Lon)
O'Dwyer, Eamonn (Guitars Lon)
O'Keefe, Peggy (Sco)
O'Regan, Matthew (Lon)
Oakman, Steven Mark (Lon)
Ockendon, Hugh (Lon)

TEACHERS - PIANOFORTE

Offer, Andrew (Lon)
Ogden, Ron (Keyboards NW)
Ohara, Leigh (Lon)
Oliver, Anthony (Lon)
Orford, Martin (Keyboards SE)
Ormiston, Susan (SE)
Osborne, Kelly (SW)
Overman, Arlette (Voice E)
Owens, Stephen (Mid)
Palmer, Greg (Lon)
Palmer, Kristian J (SW)
Palmer, Philip (SE)
Papworth, Peter (SE)
Parker, Veronica (Lon)
Patrick, David (Sco)
Patterson, David (NE)
Patterson, Drew (Lon)
Peach, Geraldine (Oboe Lon)
Pearce-Davies, Eileen (NE)
Pell, Robert (NE)
Pendlebury, Karl (Lon)
Penrose, Richard (SW)
Peres Da Costa, Neal (Lon)
Pharoah, Kenneth (SE)
Piatti, Polo (Lon)
Pickett, Martin (SE)
Piga, Daniele (SE)
Pilkington, Stephen (Music Director NW)
Piper, Sheila (NE)
Pipkin, Dominic (Lon)
Pistol, Julia (Lon)
Plank, Kathleen (SW)
Pledge, Andrew (Lon)
Plowright, Dennis (Lon)
Pope, Nicholas (Lon)
Porilo, Gregory (Lon)
Postill, Isabelle (Lon)
Potter, Sarah (Lon)
Preece, Dane (Mid)
Prentice, Brian (Sco)
Presland, Carole (Lon)
Price, David (SW)
Priest, John (Lon)
Priestley, Brian (Lon)
Pringle, Ben (E)
Protts, Patrick J (Composer Lon)
Puckette, Muriel Waters (Lon)
Pulman, Mark (NE)
Purcell, Simon (Lon)
Pywell, Jim (Composer NE)
Quirk, Wendy (Violin Mid)
Randall, Mark (Organ SW)
Rapps, Andrew (Music Director Lon)
Rastoptchina, Anna (Sco)
Rawson, Irmeli (Viola Lon)
Razzell, Luke (Lon)
Rea, Colin (SW)
Readman, Peter (Mid)
Rebello, Jason (Lon)
Redfarn, Clare (Harpsichord Lon)
Rees-Williams, David (SE)
Reeves, Darren (SE)
Reeves, Paul (Lon)
Rennie, Jane (Bassoon SE)
Richard D, (NW)
Richards, Delph (Mid)
Richards, Eryl (SW)
Richards, Tim (Lon)
Richardson, Gerry (NE)
Richardson, Neil (Lon)
Riddell, Don (SW)
Riley, Ian (Mid)
Riley, Lewis (SW)
Rixen, Nicholas (Lon)
Robb, Marion (Sco)

Roberts, Keith (Copyist Lon)
Roberts, Shirley (Mid)
Roberts, Stephanie (Mid)
Roberts, Steven (Conductor NE)
Robinson, Peter (SE)
Roden, Margaret (SW)
Rogers, Cathy (Keyboards SE)
Rooney, Joe (NW)
Rosser, Pete (SW)
Rossi, Denis (SW)
Round, Michael (Lon)
Round-Turner, Charlie (E)
Rouse, Helen (SE)
Roussou, Eugenia (NE)
Rowden-Martin, Amanda Jane (Violin NE)
Rowe, John (NE)
Rowlands, Maxim (Lon)
Rudd, Hilary (Voice Lon)
Ruddick, Joanna (Mid)
Rush, Keith (Keyboards SE)
Russell, Jennifer (Lon)
Russell, Lloyd (Lon)
Ryall, Samuel (E)
Saberton, Peter (Lon)
Saggese, Matteo (Lon)
Salmon, Peggy (SW)
Sander, Peter (Lon)
Sanders, Geoffrey (Lon)
Sassoon, Julie (NW)
Saunders, Camilla (Lon)
Saunders, Malcolm (Keyboards Lon)
Saunders, Nicolas (SE)
Scott, Ian (E)
Scott, John (Mid)
Scott, Robin (Keyboards Lon)
Seabrook, Terence (SE)
Sear, Natalie (Mid)
Seed, Christopher (SE)
Seeley, Paul (NE)
Segal, Emily (Lon)
Selwyn, Peter (Lon)
Sharp, Tim (Lon)
Shaw, Claire (Lon)
Shaw, Francis (Composer Lon)
Shaw, Hazel (Violin SW)
Shepherd, John (Mid)
Shepherd, Neil (Organ SW)
Sheriff, Naadia (Lon)
Sherrah-Davies, Helen (Violin SE)
Shrubsole, David (Music Director Lon)
Shutt, Karen (Mid)
Siddol, Simon (Mid)
Sidgwick, Arthur (SW)
Silk, Richard (Harpsichord Mid)
Silkoff, David (Lon)
Simmons, Richard (Lon)
Simons, Jane (Voice NE)
Simpson, Sally (Lon)
Skene-Keating, Paul (SE)
Slapper, Clifford (Lon)
Sly, Marcus (NW)
Smith, Andrew (Lon)
Smith, Caroline (Lon)
Smith, Clorinda (Keyboards E)
Smith, Daniel (Mid)
Smith, Gerry (Mid)
Smith, Penelope (Sco)
Smith, Philip (SW)
Smith, Timothy (Lon)
Snelson, John (Music Director Lon)
Spellar, Judith (Lon)
Spencer, Grant (NE)
Spoors, Barry (NE)
Squires, Chris (Lon)
Staniforth, Thomas (Mid)

Stanley, Matthew (Lon)
Stark, Thomas (SW)
Steel, Philip (E)
Steele, Alexander (SW)
Steer, Maxwell (Composer SW)
Stein, Jonathan (SW)
Stenhouse, Linda (NE)
Steponitis, Bernie (SE)
Sterling, Andrew (E)
Stevenson, Cath (NE)
Stirling, Jesus (Keyboards Lon)
Stirling, Penelope (NW)
Stirling-Buick, Njal (E)
Stokes, Russell (Lon)
Stone, Colin (Lon)
Stott, Katharine (Mid)
Strachan, Martyn (Organ Sco)
Strevett, Keith (Lon)
Stuckey, Robert (Lon)
Sudlow, Paul (Viola Mid)
Summers, Sarah (SW)
Swan, Kelly (Lon)
Swan, Richard (Lon)
Symcox, Benedicte (Lon)
Sziklafi, Joseph (Music Director Lon)
2 True Records (Keyboards Lon)
Tate, Ian (NW)
Taws, Johnny (NE)
Taylor, Christopher (Lon)
Taylor, Harold (Mid)
Taylor, Holly Oboe (Lon)
Taylor, Jonathan (SW)
Taylor, Margaret (Sco)
Teers, Stephen (Lon)
Thomas, James (Keyboards Lon)
Thomas, John (Lon)
Thomas-Bosovskaya, Olga (Lon)
Thompson, Christie (NE)
Thompson, Joe (Lon)
Thomson, Barbara E (NW)
Thorburn, Andy (Music Director Sco)
Thornton, Peter Campbell (NW)
Throup, Andrew G (Lon)
Tilley, Louise (Composer Lon)
Tilt, Marcus (Lon)
Tite, Martyn (Mid)
Tomalin, Nicholas (Lon)
Tong, Daniel (Lon)
Topping, Sylvia (Mid)
Trew, Jennifer (Lon)
Treweek, James (Lon)
Tribble, James (Lon)
Tuffin, Donald (Mid)
Turner, Stephen (E)
Twiselton, Simon (SE)
Underwood, Sue (Mid)
Van Hellenberg Hubar, Theresia (Harp Lon)
Vause, David (NE)
Venn, Paul (Mid)
Vere, Penny (Mid)
Verma, Shan (Lon)
Veulens, Marietta (Lon)
Vicary, Andrea (Lon)
Vincent, Amanda (Keyboards Lon)
Wade, Anne (NE)
Wade, Vic (Lon)
Wakeley, Tom (Voice Lon)
Walker, Sarah (Lon)
Wallace, David (Lon)
Walter, John (SW)
Warner, Hilary (Organ NW)
Warren, Debbie (Lon)
Warren, Paula (Lon)
Waterman, Mark (Keyboards Lon)
Watson, Neil (Lon)

Wayne, Philip (Mid)
Webb, Margaret (Viola NW)
Webber, David (SE)
West, Colin (SE)
Westacott, Bronwen (Mid)
Wetherall, Richard (NW)
Whalley, Clare (Lon)
Wheeler, Shula (Viola NE)
White, Gillian (SW)
White, Gregory (SE)
White, Ian (SE)
White, Joel (NE)
White, Meredith (Lon)
White, P (Mid)
Whitehead, Nicolas (Lon)
Whitfield, Steve (NE)
Whittaker, Anthony (NW)
Whittamore, Monica (SE)
Whittell, Adrian (SE)
Whittington, Paul (NE)
Whyte, Jane (Keyboards Sco)
Wickham, Hazel (SW)
Widdup, Vanessa (Voice Lon)
Wilkes, Judith (Sco)
Wilkinson, Jeremy (Lon)
Williams, Clare (Lon)
Williams, Gareth (Lon)
Williams, Gillian (NW)
Williams, Russell (E)
Williams, Shiu-Ju (Lon)
Williams, Susan (Lon)
Willie, Anne (NW)
Wilson, Jen (SW)
Wiltshire, Christopher (NE)
Wood, Lesley (NW)
Wood, Matthew (Keyboards NW)
Wood, Trevor (Organ NW)
Wood Aed, James (SE)
Woods, Huntley (NE)
Woodward, Julia (NE)
Woolcock, Rebecca (Lon)
Wright, Henry (NW)
Wrigley, Hazel (Guitars Sco)
Wyatt, Roger (Mid)
Wyse, Josephine (NW)
Young, Valerie (SW)
Young, Jennifer (NW)
Zehm, Norbert (NW)

PICCOLO

Spiers, Jane (Flute Lon)

RAPPER

Jay, Just (Voice NE)
Lord, Michael (Lon)

RECORDERS

Beckett, Rachel (Lon)
Burgess, Paul (SW)
Camlin, David (Guitars NW)
Clements, Antony (Lon)
Dale, Alison (Mid)
Greenway, Rhiannon (Lon)
Gulland, Brian (Composer Lon)
Hill-Ahmad, Jennifer (Sco)
Keeler, Emily (Lon)
Kershaw, Caroline (Early Wind Lon)
Klein, Susan (Lon)
Loughrey, Michelle (SE)
McCreery, Jean (Lon)
Mendes, Galina (SE)
Moss, Rachel (Early Wind Lon)
Page, Elizabeth (Lon)
Pashley, Claire (NE)

Peters, Carolyne (SW)
Robbins, Zoe (Mid)
Scheporat, Gudi (SE)
Shaw, Marian (Lon)
Smyth, Carol (Mid)
Solomon, Ashley (Lon)
Thomson, Ellen (Lon)
Thorby, Pamela (Lon)
Wastie, Heather (Mid)
Westlake, Margaret (Early Strings E)
Wheelock, Emma (SW)

REPETITEUR

Gibbs, Margaret (Pianoforte Lon)
Smith, Pamela (Pianoforte Lon)

SANTOOR

Deoora, Kiranpal Singh (Lon)
Sandhu, Surinder (Mid)

SAXOPHONES

Aagre, Froy (Mid)
Aaron, Dave (Lon)
Adams, Alyson (Lon)
Airth, Graeme (Lon)
Ajao, Steve (Mid)
Albu, Ben (Lon)
Alderson, Geoffrey (SE)
Aldridge, Chris (Mid)
Anderson, Jamie (Lon)
Andrade, Marcelo (Lon)
Andrews, Victoria (SE)
Annesley, Luke (Lon)
Anselm, John (SW)
Armstrong, Sarah (NE)
Ashley, Ceri (Mid)
Austin, Michael (SE)
B, Stevie (Mid)
Bak, Nik (NW)
Baker, David (Lon)
Banks, Solomon (Sco)
Barnes, Dee (E)
Barratt, Elisabeth (Lon)
Bartlett, Rachel (Lon)
Beauvoisin, Allon (Sco)
Beck, Christian (Lon)
Benson, Jeffrey (Lon)
Bill, Douglas (Mid)
Bitelli, David (Lon)
Black, David (NE)
Blackmore, David (Lon)
Boddy, Suzi (E)
Booth, Paul (SE)
Boston, Bill (Lon)
Bowles, Geoffrey (SW)
Braggins, Belinda (Lon)
Brawley, Michael (Sco)
Bray, Ned (Lon)
Brewer, Christian (Lon)
Bridge, Derek (NE)
Briggs, Simon (Lon)
Broadley, Gerald (Lon)
Brooker, Scott (Lon)
Brooks, Anna (Mid)
Brown, Graeme (E)
Brown, Jimmie (Violin Lon)
Brown, Katherine (Lon)
Brown, Katherine (SE)
Browning, Peter (Lon)
Brush, Andy (E)
Budd, Graeme (SW)
Budgen, Adrian (E)
Bullers, Adrian (Mid)
Bulley, Alan (Lon)

Burch, Paul (Lon)
Burgess, Nancy (Mid)
Burke, Vicki (SW)
Burney, Mike (Mid)
Butterworth, Derek (SE)
Bywater, Kay (Lon)
Caffrey, Jason (Lon)
Caines, Ronald (SE)
Caldwell, Christopher (Lon)
Cameron, Bruce (E)
Cardew, Horace (Lon)
Carter, Paul (SW)
Carter, Peter (NE)
Castle, Ben (Lon)
Chard, David (Mid)
Charman, Colin (Lon)
Chilkes, Jack (Lon)
Clark, Dugald (SE)
Clynes, Kenneth (Mid)
Coates, Michael (Lon)
Cook, Peter (Lon)
Covey, Rachael (Lon)
Cowles, Colin (Bassoon SW)
Cox, David (SE)
Cox Snr, Gary (NW)
Crabb, Colin (Mid)
Crawford, Adrian (Lon)
Crawford, Neill (SE)
Crowther, Brian (NW)
Culmer, Tony (E)
Curtis, George (Clarinet Lon)
Dales, Raymond (NE)
Dampier, Allan (Mid)
Darby, Ruth (NW)
Davidson, Doug (NW)
Davies, Michael (Mid)
Dean, Elton (Lon)
Dean, Julian (Lon)
Deller, Neil (E)
Devere, Andrea (NE)
Devonshire, Paul (E)
Dickaty, Raymond (Lon)
Dolton, Aaron (Mid)
Donnelly, Donal (NE)
Donnison, Glyn (E)
Dorfman, Dave (SW)
Dovey, Norman (Mid)
Dowlaszewicz, Ewa (Lon)
Downs, Nicholas (Bassoon SE)
Draycott, Ian (E)
Drouet, Ben (Mid)
Dudzik, Bogdan (SE)
Duff, Jack (Sco)
Dyson, John (NW)
Edwards, Owen (Mid)
Edwards, Ricky B (Lon)
Elboz, John (Lon)
Elliott, Bill (Lon)
Elliott, Louise (Lon)
Ellis, Ian (Lon)
Ellison, John (NW)
Emeny, Trevor (Mid)
Evans, Iestyn (Sco)
Evans, Phil (Lon)
Farrington, John (E)
Fawcett, Andrew (Mid)
Fawcus, Paul (E)
Ferri, Manny (Sco)
Fifield, Fraser (Sco)
Figes, Kevin (SW)
Fish, Kate (SE)
Forbes, Stewart (Sco)
Forsyth, Alexander (SE)
Fowler, Robert (SE)
France, Timothy (NW)

TEACHERS - SAXOPHONES

Francis, Chris (Lon)
Francis, Joe (Lon)
Frank, Samuel (Lon)
Frost, Norman (NW)
Gamlen, Amy (Lon)
Garofalo, Enrico (NW)
Gee, Paul (SE)
Gilby, Simon (Lon)
Gill, Michael (Lon)
Gilligan, Craig (Mid)
Glasson, Charlotte (SE)
Goldstein, Lloyd (Lon)
Goodliffe, Ivor (SW)
Gordon, Jeff (Lon)
Grant, Bradley (Lon)
Gray, Mike (Mid)
Green, Alby (Lon)
Gregory, Alfred (Mid)
Gregory, Steve (Lon)
Griffin, John (Lon)
Griffith, Frank (Lon)
Grimster, Alan (SE)
Gumbley, Chris (Mid)
Guttridge, Derek (Lon)
Guy, Chris (Lon)
Hacker, Jane (Lon)
Hall, Mike (NW)
Hamer, Dick (SW)
Hammond, Ruth (Lon)
Harris, Jamie (Mid)
Harris, Syd (Lon)
Harrison, David (SE)
Haselip, John (SE)
Haslam, George (SE)
Hathaway, Tina (Lon)
Hatherill, Robert (Lon)
Haw, Dave (Sco)
Heathorn, Ron (SE)
Heckstall-Smith, Dick (Lon)
Helliwell, John (NW)
Henry, Simon (Lon)
Herbert, Paul (SW)
Heritage, Tom (NE)
Herniman, Tim (Lon)
Higgins, Suzanne (NW)
Hind, Matthew (Pianoforte NE)
Hingston, Michael (E)
Hoban, Lynne (Lon)
Hollingsworth, Catherine (Mid)
Hollis, Paul (Mid)
Holmes, Alan (Lon)
Holmes, Alexandra (NE)
Hopkins, David (Clarinet NW)
Hopkins, Mike (SE)
Hornby, Edward (NW)
Horton, Hannah (E)
Horton, Tildi (Mid)
Howe, Ronald (SE)
Howison, Julian (NW)
Hoyle, Minnie (Lon)
Hughes, Robert (Lon)
Hull, Peter (Lon)
Hulme, Clifford (Mid)
Hunnisett, Bruce (NW)
Hunt, James (Mid)
Hunt, Roy (E)
Hunter, Colin (Sco)
Ingham, David (E)
Jackson, Bob (Mid)
Jackson, Richard (Lon)
Jennings, Maurice (Lon)
Jensen, Andor (Lon)
Johnson, Leonard (Mid)
Johnson, Stuart (NE)
Jolly, Paul (E)

Kane, Christopher (Lon)
Karuzas, Jason (Lon)
Kavanagh, Richard (NE)
Kean, Bret (Clarinet Lon)
Kershaw, Martin (Sco)
Kiddier, Kenneth (Lon)
Knight, James (Lon)
Kraabel, Caroline (Lon)
Lambrou, Evangelos (Lon)
Lammin, Dennis (Lon)
Lascelles, James (Lon)
Laubrock, Ingrid (Lon)
Lewis, Brynley (SE)
Lewis, Geoffrey (SE)
Lightfoot, Terry (Clarinet E)
Ling, Paul (NW)
Lipman, Daniel (Lon)
Little, Martin (Lon)
Lockheart, Mark (Lon)
Lodge, Gilly (Lon)
Lyons, Graham (Bassoon NE)
Lyons, Peter (NE)
Macdonald, Raymond (Sco)
Machon, Paul (NE)
Mackintosh, Andy (Lon)
Manzin, Roberto (Lon)
Marks, Robert (Lon)
Marsden, Roger (NW)
Marshall, Terry (SE)
Martin, Benjamin (Mid)
Martin, Bob (Lon)
Martin, Jeremy (E)
Martinelli, Gary (NW)
Massey, Jack (SE)
Matthews, Graham (Mid)
Matthews, Paul (Bass Guitar Lon)
McChrystal, Gerard (Lon)
McGarry, Pat (NE)
McGill, Howard (Lon)
McGirr, Priscilla (SE)
McKelvie, Raymond (Sco)
McMahon, Kevin (Lon)
McMurchie, Jacob (Lon)
McWilliam, Fiona (SW)
Mears, Andy (NE)
Meredith, Martin (Mid)
Middleton, Julia (SE)
Millen, Penny (E)
Miller, Morris (Lon)
Mitchell, Alexander (Lon)
Monks, Gil (Mid)
Moore, Keith (Clarinet Lon)
Moore, Ollie (SW)
Moore, Sarha (Lon)
Moran, Tom (NE)
Morrice, James (Sco)
Morris, Andrea (Lon)
Moss, Paul (Lon)
Mowat, Arthur (NE)
Moy, Norman (Sco)
Mulhearn, Richard (NW)
Murphy, Geoffrey (SW)
Nash, Nigel (Lon)
Neighbour, Peter (Clarinet Lon)
Nice, Colin (Mid)
Nicholls, Andy (Mid)
O'Loughlin, William (Mid)
O'Neill, John (Lon)
Oates, Niall (Lon)
Ormiston, David (NE)
Orton, Kenneth (Mid)
Osborn, Sarah (Lon)
Owen, Lyndon (NE)
Packham, Kit (Lon)
Pardy, Richard (Lon)

Park, Benjamin (Lon)
Parlett, Michael (Lon)
Parry, Diane (Mid)
Pashley, Don (SE)
Paton, Philip (SE)
Peake, Jacko (Lon)
Perry, Terence (NW)
Peters, Jane (NE)
Petter, Jonathon (Clarinet Lon)
Phillips, Jim (E)
Phillips, Norman (Mid)
Pickering, Brian (Lon)
Pickering, Michelle (Mid)
Pillinger, Helen (NW)
Place, Adrian (SW)
Plumley, Gary (Lon)
Pollard, John (SE)
Poole, Stan (Mid)
Potts, Andrew (Lon)
Pretty, Adam (Lon)
Price, Ian (Lon)
Pullin, David (E)
Purnell, Joel (NW)
Purves, Ross (Lon)
Pyne, Christopher (E)
Quayle, Chrissy (Lon)
Radford, Tony (E)
Ramsden, Mark (Lon)
Read, Tony (NE)
Redmond, Andrew (Lon)
Reed, Oliver (SE)
Rendell, Donald (Lon)
Reynolds, Kevin (Lon)
Ridding, Neale (Lon)
Ridout, Beverley (SE)
Riley, Barry (Lon)
Ripper, John (E)
Roach, Paul (Lon)
Robb, Damon (Mid)
Robert, Peter (SW)
Robinson, George (NE)
Robson, Kim (NE)
Rose, Simon (Guitars Lon)
Rose, Tim (SW)
Ross, Andrew (Lon)
Rossetti-Bonell, Adrian (Lon)
Rowland, Trevor (E)
Rubie, Steve (Lon)
Rudnick, Marius (Lon)
Ryder, Allan (SE)
Salisbury, Harold (NW)
Sampson, Mary (SW)
Scannell, James (Lon)
Schauerman, Julia (Lon)
Schroeder, Franziska (Sco)
Seagroatt, Jon (SE)
Shackleton, Geraldine (Lon)
Shakespeare, Colin (NE)
Sharp, Karen (E)
Sheehan, Peter (Lon)
Sheldon, Camilla (Lon)
Sherman, Pete (NW)
Shoham, Jeremy (Lon)
Shrubshall, Catherine (Lon)
Shutler, Stella (Mid)
Simmonds, John (Lon)
Simons, Martin (E)
Simpson, Phil (Lon)
Smethurst-Evans, Hilary (SE)
Smith, Bill (NE)
Smith, George (Sco)
Smith, Harrison (Lon)
Smith, Ian (Mid)
Smith, Nicholas (Lon)
Smith, Robert (SW)

Smith, Rodney (Lon)
Sneddon, William (NE)
Spall, Hubert (Lon)
Spanglecock, Zack (SE)
Speake, Martin (Lon)
Spiers, Stuart (Mid)
Stabbins, Larry (SW)
Steele, John (NE)
Stevens, Paul (Lon)
Stokes, David (Mid)
Street, Karen (Lon)
Stuart, Donald (Lon)
Summerbell, Fred (Lon)
Summers, Paul (Lon)
Swan, Leon (Sco)
Swingler, Val (Lon)
Swope, Brad (NE)
Taylor, Jonathan (NE)
Taylor, Mat (Mid)
Tayton, Steve (Mid)
Telford, Jake (Lon)
Theodoulou, Nathan (Mid)
Thomas, Owen (Lon)
Thomas, Peter (Lon)
Thompson, Chris (Pianoforte Mid)
Thompson, Katie (E)
Thompson, Sheik (Lon)
Thorpe, Mel (Mid)
Tobias, Sarah (Lon)
Todd, William (SE)
Tomkins, Peter (SW)
Tomlinson, Jim (Lon)
Tompson, Mike (Lon)
Toomey, Mark (NE)
Toussaint, Jean (Lon)
Towndrow, Paul (Sco)
Townsend, Rob (Lon)
Travis, Theodore (Lon)
Ulitzka, Ivan (Lon)
Vallance, Dave (NE)
Van Den Berg, Russell (Lon)
Visser, Andy (Mid)
Wakeman, Alan (Lon)
Walker, Nicholas (E)
Wallace, Jimmy (SE)
Ward, Tamsin (SE)
Wareham, Pete (Lon)
Wares, Alec (Mid)
Warleigh, Raymond (Lon)
Wearne, Sarah (Lon)
Westbrook, Nicola (Mid)
White, Brian (SE)
White, Frank (Lon)
White, Robert (E)
Whittle, Brian (NE)
Wigfield, Leslie (Lon)
Wilkinson, Kenneth (NE)
Williams, Caroline (Lon)
Williams, Clifford (Mid)
Williams, Elaine (SE)
Williams, Michael (Lon)
Williams, Paul (SE)
Williamson, Andrew (SW)
Wilson, Graeme (Sco)
Wishart, Bobby (Flute Sco)
Withers, Alan (Mid)
Wood, Paul (Mid)
Woodhouse, John (NW)
Woodin, Paul (Clarinet Lon)
Woods, Anthony (Lon)
Woodthorpe, Arthur (NE)
Woolgar, Richard (NE)
Wright, Don (SE)
Wyver, Nicolas (SE)
York, Clive (Lon)

SCRATCHER

Craig, Munro (Voice NE)
De Salvo, Joe (Mid)
Farrell, Gerard (Lon)
Perkins, John (SW)
Romain, Ricky (SW)

SONGWRITER

Black, Matthew (Guitars Mid)
Chastanet, Maxine (Percussion Lon)
Crippin, Dick (Bass Guitar Lon)
Evans, Andrew (Double Bass Lon)
Germain, Roberto L (Guitars SE)
Lawrence, Henry (Guitars SW)

STEEL PANS

Bravo, Bravo (Lon)
Campbell, Hilary (Percussion SW)
Edwards, David John (NE)
Jamma (Mid)
Peltier, Richard (Lon)
Trotman, Gary (Lon)

STRINGS

Lovell, Jonathan (Violin NE)

SYNTHESISER

Blake, Tim (Lon)
Latham, Clive (Keyboards Lon)
Khan, Yousef (Lon)
Mahmoud, Mohammad (Lon)
Millar, Jhalib (Lon)
Nathekar, Abdul (Lon)
Raval, Sandeep (Lon)
Sheikh, Esmail (Lon)
Singh, Harjit (Mid)

TAIKO DRUMS

Barrow, James (SE)
Kurumaya, Masaaki (Sco)

TENOR HORN

Bathgate, Melvyn (NE)
Barham, John (Arranger Lon)
Brodrick, Dean (Keyboards Lon)
Brownlie, John (Guitars E)
Chapman, Philip (Conductor NE)
Collier, Graham (Composer Lon)
Dalton, Paul (Voice NE)
Davis, John (Conductor Mid)
Esdaile, Sarah (Arranger Sco)
Evans, Keith (Guitars Mid)
Evans, Russ (Pianoforte Sco)
Faggioni, Valerio (Pianoforte Lon)
Harkcom, Clive (Conductor Lon)
Hughes, Robert (Trombone Lon)
Jones, Stuart (Pianoforte Mid)
Lester, Mark (Keyboards Lon)
Longden, Lee P (Music Director NW)
May, Kaja (Flute SW)
McGuigan, Shane (Guitars Lon)
Pattenden, Jacqueline (SW)
Raymond, Timothy (Organ SW)
Rebbeck, Dave (Double Bass SW)
Rosselson, Daniela (Voice Lon)
Schmool, Barak (Saxophones Lon)
Stowell, Robin (Violin SW)
Wallace, Liam Henry (Guitars NW)
Whitbread, Adam (Guitars Lon)

TIN WHISTLE

Knorr, Rebecca (Flute Sco)

TROMBONE

Adams, Ian (Mid)
Adlam, Michael (Lon)
Austin, Garfield (SW)
Austin, Gary (SE)
Barker, Andrew (Sco)
Barnby, Stuart (SE)
Bean, Bernard (Bass Trombone Lon)
Belshaw, Warren (Lon)
Bennett, Bob (Mid)
Berry, John (SW)
Berryman, Andrew (NW)
Bone, David (Bass Trombone Sco)
Bowen, Colin (Bass Trombone Sco)
Bowen, Glyn (SW)
Brand, Gail (Lon)
Brierley, Eric (NW)
Brookes, Arthur (Bass Trombone Lon)
Brookes, Martha (Mid)
Browning, Stephen (Bass Trombone Lon)
Bunker, Andrew (Lon)
Burgess, Rob (Bass Trombone Lon)
Campbell, Gordon (Lon)
Campbell, Murray (Early Wind Sco)
Cannell, Helen (Voice SE)
Care, Melvyn (Lon)
Cole, David (E)
Colman, Matthew (Lon)
Cooper, Albert (Sco)
Cronin, Robert (Lon)
Cunningham, David (Mid)
Davies, Rosalyn (NW)
Davis, Michael (SE)
Davis, Paul (NW)
Daykin, Barry (NW)
Dearness, Magnus (Lon)
Dickinson, Barnaby (Lon)
Douglas, Arthur (Mid)
Douglas, Bruce (Bass Trombone Lon)
Dowse, Matt (Lon)
Duerden, Quentin (Mid)
Dungey, Peter (SE)
Edney, John (Lon)
Enright, Jonathan (Lon)
Evans, Gary (SW)
Fairley, Don (NE)
Farley, Paul (NE)
Flack, John (Lon)
Fletcher, Carl (Mid)
Flood, John (NE)
Forte, Remo (NE)
Fowles, Michael (Mid)
Franklin, Jasper (SE)
Fraser, Andrew (Sco)
Fullbrook, Mark (SE)
Glover, Jason (Lon)
Golding, Ian (Lon)
Gray, Stuart (NE)
Green, Alwyn (Bass Trombone Mid)
Green, Lance (Sco)
Greenfield, Alexander (Bass Trombone NE)
Guy, Christopher (Lon)
Hairsine, William (Bass Trombone NE)
Hall, Caroline (Lon)
Hambleton, Robert (NW)
Hankin, David (Sco)
Haworth, Matthew (NW)
Hayes, Stephen (SE)
Hemmings, John (E)
Hendy, John (SW)
Hewson, Daniel (SE)

TEACHERS - TROMBONE

Hissey, David (Lon)
Holding, Christopher (Bass Trombone E)
Holliday, Robert P (NW)
Holt, David (Lon)
Horsley, Rob (NE)
Horton, Ashley (Mid)
Howe, Anthony (Lon)
Hunt, Digby (Lon)
Hyde, Paul (Bandleader SE)
Incledon, Chris (SW)
Innes, Michael (Lon)
Ivory, Stewart (Lon)
Johnson, Simon (NW)
Jones, Cliff (Lon)
Jones, Marcus (Lon)
Jones, Nick (NW)
Lacey, Peter (Mid)
Latham, Sarah (SW)
Leach, John (SW)
Legge, Steven (SW)
Liddell, David (Lon)
Llewellyn, Gareth (SE)
Lomas, Michael (SW)
Lynn, Brian (Bass Trombone Lon)
Mackinder, Michael (NE)
Mansfield, Peter (SE)
Mansfield, Simon (Bass Trombone NW)
Mathieson, Stephen (Lon)
McGovern, Edward (Sco)
McGregor, Kenneth (Lon)
Mee, William (Bass Trombone Lon)
Mercer, Frederick (Mid)
Miller, Amos (Lon)
Miller, Helen (Mid)
Mires, Trevor (Lon)
Mulley, Mark John (Lon)
Murrill, Jayne (Lon)
Nell, Philip (Lon)
Nicholls-Bennett, John (Lon)
Norris, Keith (NE)
Parker, Brian (NE)
Parker, Stuart (Lon)
Pepperell, Alan (NW)
Petch, Christopher (NW)
Phillips, William (Sco)
Pippen, Jonathan (SW)
Power, John (Sco)
Price, David (SW)
Prior, James (Lon)
Pritchard, David (Bass Trombone NE)
Pugsley, Simon (NE)
Rae, Ian (Mid)
Rae, Roger (Mid)
Ravenor, Terence (Bass Trombone SW)
Rawbone, Martyn (Lon)
Reece, David (Sco)
Rees, Owen (Lon)
Reid, Paul (Mid)
Reid, Reginald (Mid)
Robinson, Timothy (Bass Trombone NW)
Robson, James (Lon)
Rutherford, Paul (Lon)
Sanders, Carl (Mid)
Sharman, Dave (Lon)
Shiner, Colin (SW)
Sigouin, Toby (Sco)
Smith, Malcolm (Lon)
Snell, Andrew Bass (Trombone NE)
Stroud, Martyn (SE)
Stubbings, Richard (Bass Trombone Lon)
Sunners, Derek (NE)
Sykes, Paul (SE)
Taylor, Leon (Lon)
Tearnan, Gregory (Bass Trombone Mid)
Thompson, John (NE)

Townend, Mark (Lon)
Turnbull, Allan (Mid)
Walker, Norman (Brass NE)
Walters, Tavis (Mid)
Warburton, Janine (E)
Warham, Clive Bass (Trombone NE)
Warren, Antony (NW)
Watson, Nicholas (Bass Trombone E)
Wheldon, Philip (Sco)
White, Ian (Lon)
White, Philip (SE)
Wilkie, Peter (NE)
Williams, Carole (NW)
Williams, Daryl (SW)
Wise, Denis (SE)
Wittmann, Neil (NE)
Wood, Andrew (Lon)
York, Norton (SE)

TRUMPET

Abbott, Gary (NW)
Adcroft, Hylton (SE)
Addinell, Roy (Mid)
Alan, Barbara (Lon)
Alemany, Jesus (SE)
Alexander, Ian (SE)
Allen, Bryan (Mid)
Allison, Mark Blair (Mid)
Andre, Denis (Lon)
Anthony, Phil (Bandleader E)
Appleyard, David (Lon)
Armstrong, Mark (Lon)
Atkins, Andrew (Music Director Lon)
Austin, John (SW)
Avery, Clement (Bass Guitar NE)
Bailey, Deborah (Mid)
Bailey, Michael (SW)
Bailey, Phillip (Mid)
Bailey, Stephen (Mid)
Baker, David (SE)
Baker, Nicholas (Lon)
Baker, Richard (SE)
Ball, Brendan (Lon)
Ball, Mick (Lon)
Banks, John (Lon)
Barker, John (NE)
Barnes, Dylan (Lon)
Bateman, Donald (Lon)
Beavis, Peter (Lon)
Bell, Bob (Lon)
Bennett, Paul (Mid)
Bennett, Robert (Mid)
Benson, Hedley (NE)
Betley, Peter (SW)
Bickerdike, John (Mid)
Birch, Michael (SE)
Blackadder, David (Mid)
Boa, David (Lon)
Bolton, David (E)
Bond, Gary (Mid)
Bonney, Alex (Lon)
Booth, Matthew (Lon)
Breeze, Nicholas (SE)
Brewer, Edwin (SE)
Brinkley, David (SW)
Brook, David (Lon)
Broughall, Sharon (Lon)
Brown, Annette Sox (Lon)
Brown, Graham (SE)
Brown, John (NW)
Browning, David (NW)
Buckenham, Gemma (Lon)
Burgess, Norman (Lon)
Butcher, Raymond (Mid)
Cadman , Mark (Mid)

Callard, Andrew (Lon)
Campbell, Duncan (Lon)
Catt, Arthur (Lon)
Chapple, Michael (SE)
Charlton, Kay (Lon)
Chatfield, Wally (SW)
Cheney, Simon (Lon)
Chislett, Stephen (SE)
Clancy, Edmund (Sco)
Clark, Christopher (SE)
Coleman, Jamie (Lon)
Coles, Toby (Lon)
Collins, Henry (Lon)
Corbett, Bryan (Mid)
Corbett, Jon (E)
Cornell, Andrew (NW)
Coull, Christopher (NW)
Cox, Philip (E)
Craft, Colin (Lon)
Cumberland, Mark (Lon)
Cutler, David (Lon)
Cutting, Robert (E)
Dallimore, Andrew (NW)
Davies, Ivor (SW)
Davies, Lawrence (SW)
Davies, Nigel (NE)
Davy, Kevin (NW)
Deacon, Andrew (SE)
Deacon, Christopher (SE)
Diagram, Andy (Lon)
Dipple, Laura (NW)
Doherty, James (Tuba Lon)
Douglas, Anthony (Lon)
Douthwaite, Aileen (Horn Sco)
Downey, Alan (Lon)
Durrant, John (Lon)
Dvorak, James (Lon)
Edwards, Benjamin (Lon)
Edwards, Denis (Lon)
Edwards, Marc (SE)
Ellis, Stephen (Cornet SW)
Elms, Simon (Lon)
Else, Duncan (NE)
England, James (NW)
Eno, Jonathan (Mid)
Fairweather, Digby (Lon)
Field, Dennis (Cornet E)
Field, Dominic (Lon)
Field, Sarah (Lon)
Findon, Julia (SE)
Fish, Nigel (SE)
Fishwick, Steven (Lon)
Ford, Robert (NW)
France, Leonard (NW)
Frohlick, Ashley (NW)
Fulker, Martin (Lon)
Fullick, Teddy (Mid)
Gallagher, Steven (SE)
Garvey, Edward (NE)
Gasson, Chris (Mid)
Ghigi, James (Lon)
Gibbon, Nigel (Mid)
Gibson, Stephen (NW)
Gifford, Katherine (Lon)
Gill, Raymond (NE)
Gillies, Gary (Sco)
Gosden, Malcolm (Lon)
Goulden, Mick (Lon)
Gray, Malcolm (NE)
Greig, Murray (NE)
Gumpert, Alice (Lon)
Haggart, Kevin (Music Director Sco)
Hague, Andrew (SW)
Haines, Cliff (Lon)
Haines, Cris (SW)

Hall, Malcolm (Lon)
Hamer, Ian (Lon)
Hammerton, Dan (NE)
Handy, Allen (Composer Lon)
Hanson, Dick (Lon)
Harpin, J W (SW)
Harries, Martyn (SW)
Harrison, Michael (Lon)
Harrold, Shaun (Natural Trumpet Sco)
Hart, Arden (Lon)
Hartley, Mark (SE)
Hawkins, Tony (SE)
Hayward, Cecil (Mid)
Hayward, Tim (Lon)
Henderson, Stuart (SE)
Higham, Mark (Mid)
Hinton, Michael (Lon)
Holland, Matt (Lon)
Hollingsworth, Paul (SE)
Hooke, Shaun (Mid)
Hopkins, Peter (Mid)
Horn, Adrian (NE)
Hornett, Michael (Lon)
Hoskins, Andrew (Lon)
Hoskins, Mark (Lon)
Huggett, Jeremy (Saxophones SW)
Hulme, John D (NW)
Humphries, Mark (NE)
Hurrell, Martin (Lon)
Hutchinson, Simon (Lon)
Huxham, Anthony (SW)
Ings, Martin (SE)
Jackson, Tim (Lon)
Jenner, Robert (SW)
Jennings, Andrew (Mid)
Jones, Kris (NW)
Jones, Simon (Mid)
Jones, Stephen (Lon)
Jones, William (SW)
Jordan, Marc (Lon)
Joseph, Max (SW)
Kavanagh, Gary (SE)
Keller, Lesley (Lon)
Kelly, Dorian (SE)
Kelly, Lance (Lon)
Kerby, Philip (Lon)
Kitchen, Steven (SE)
Klubben, Kristine (Lon)
Lake, Andrew (SE)
Langley, Noel (Lon)
Latchem, Barrington (SE)
Law, Mark (Lon)
Lawrence, Phillip (Lon)
Lee, Linda (SW)
Lenton, Simon (Mid)
Leon, Andreas (Lon)
Lewington, Martyn (Lon)
Lewis, Alexander (NE)
Lewis, Roddy (SW)
Linsley, Adam (Lon)
Lowe, Thomas (Sco)
Macdonald, Alan (Sco)
Malam, John (E)
Marks, Paul (NW)
Marsden, Karl (Lon)
Marsh, Anne (SW)
Martin, Raymond (E)
Maxwell, Edward (Lon)
Mayes, Paul (E)
McCarthy, Patrick (Lon)
McComb, James (Sco)
McDevitt, Chas (Cornet Lon)
McKenzie, Jock (SE)
McNaughton, Duncan (Lon)
McQueen, Ross (Sco)

Miller, Geoff (Lon)
Mitchell, Reginald (SW)
Moffat, George (Lon)
Moisey, Avelia (Lon)
Moore, Kate (Lon)
Morris, Philip (SW)
Morrison, Arthur (NE)
Morrison, John (NE)
Mourant, Paul (Lon)
Moxon, Peter (Lon)
Muirhead, Iain (Sco)
Munday, Ray (Sco)
Narbeth, Cyril (Mid)
Nevins, Angela (Mid)
Nevins, Paul (Mid)
Newton, Paul (Lon)
Nicholas, Philip (SW)
Nicholas, Robert (Lon)
Noot, Rebekah (NE)
Norman, Andrew (Horn SE)
O'Connell, Pat (SE)
Ornsby, Clifford (NE)
Osborne, Robert (Lon)
Owen, Donald (Mid)
Owen, William (Sco)
Palmer, Neil (Lon)
Parker, Kevin (Mid)
Parry, Kevin (NW)
Patterson, Craig (NW)
Payne, Stanley (SE)
Pearson, Colin (NE)
Pickering, Philip (Lon)
Pockett, Kenneth (Trombone SW)
Poole, Ray (NE)
Price, David (Lon)
Prosser, Stewart (Lon)
Quirk, Jonathan (Mid)
Rattenbury, Ken (Mid)
Rees, Gareth (SW)
Reid, Gavin (NW)
Reynolds, George (Lon)
Rhind-Tutt, Mortimer (Lon)
Riches, Edgar (Lon)
Ritson, Gary (NE)
Rolinson, Peter (Mid)
Ruddick, John (Mid)
Rudeforth, Peter (Lon)
Samuel, Robert (Lon)
Scales, Rosemary (E)
Scott, Clive (NW)
Sharp, Paul (Sco)
Shaw, Martin (Lon)
Shaw, Michael (Lon)
Shead, David (SW)
Sidwell, Richard (Lon)
Simmonds, Robert (Mid)
Singleton, Philip (SE)
Siviter, Roger (Mid)
Smets, Andrew (SE)
Smith, David (Mid)
Smith, John (Lon)
Smith, Lucy (SE)
Smith, Malcolm (Lon)
Smith, Ronnie (SE)
Snowdon, Jonathan (NE)
Speed, Paul (Lon)
Spencer, Stephen (SE)
Stephen, Andrew (SW)
Stephenson, Alfred (NE)
Storey, Benjamin (NW)
Storr, Christopher (Mid)
Stretton, Jim (NE)
Summers, Mike (Lon)
Sutton, Richard (Mid)
Tannock, Fraser (SE)

Taylor, Bob (NW)
Taylor, Paul (E)
Tearle, Roderick (Lon)
The Bass Man, (SE)
Thomas, Richard (Lon)
Thompson, Anthony David (Lon)
Thomson, Brian (Lon)
Tinker, Bob (SW)
Titchener, Stephen (E)
Tomlinson, Alan (NW)
Towse, John (NE)
Trigg, Stephen (SW)
Turner, Joanne (Lon)
Twelftree, Paul (Lon)
Urquhart, Andrew (SE)
Vivian, Robert (Mid)
Waddington, Frank (NW)
Walkden, Eric (Mid)
Wallen, Byron (Lon)
Waller, Tony (SE)
Walsh, Francis (SE)
Walton, Michael (NE)
Watkeys, John (SW)
Watson, William (Bandleader NE)
Webb, Mark (NE)
Weeks, Geoffrey (NE)
Weitz, Daniel (E)
Wellington, Canute (Lon)
Wells, Derek (Mid)
Wells, Gavin (Mid)
Wells, Matthew (Lon)
Westerman, Martyn (SE)
Wharton, Terence (SE)
Whelan, Angela (Mid)
White, Barbara (Lon)
White, Peter H (SE)
White, Simon (SE)
Williams, Barry (NE)
Williams, Bryan (Lon)
Williams, Stephen (SW)
Wilson, Ruari (Sco)
Winckless, Richard (NE)
Wood, Joanna (Lon)
Woon, Andrew (SE)
Wright, Dean (Lon)
Wyndham, Janet (E)
Wynette, Al (Lon)
Wynter, Max (Lon)
Yates, Joanna (NE)
Yates, Jon (SE)
Zawada, Jan (SE)

TUBA

Brown, Franklin (Valve Trombone Lon)
Cattanach, Andrew (NW)
Cleary, Neil (Music Director E)
Daniel, Mike (Lon)
Davies, Ian (Bass Trombone SW)
Farr, Paul (Lon)
Fox, Richard (Lon)
Gordon-Shute, David (Lon)
Grappy, Andy (Bass Tuba Lon)
Halliday, Richard (Lon)
Hore, Philip (Sco)
Hudson, David (SW)
Irvine, Nigel (Lon)
Jarvis, Martin (Lon)
Johnson, Michael (NW)
Jones, David (Music Director SE)
Jones, Huw (Lon)
Kornhauser, David (NW)
Lammin, Lee (SW)
Marshall, Oren (Lon)
McShane, Chris (Sco)
Moore, Geoffrey (SE)

TEACHERS - TUBA

Morgan, Kevin (Lon)
Mutter, David (SE)
Norman, Robin (E)
Pawluk, Ronnie (Mid)
Shaw, Norman (NE)
Stear, Geoff (Bass Guitar SE)
Thorne, Andrew (SE)
Warriner, Andrew (NE)
Wilkinson, Peter (SE)
Birkby, Peter (Percussion NW)
Bixley, Susan (Percussion Lon)
Bradley, Christopher (NE)
Bywater, Scott (Lon)
Colburt, Peter (Percussion SE)
Davis, Mary (Mid)
Fowler, Harry (SW)
Gibson, Martin (Sco)
Gunnee, Dorothy (Sco)
Harrison, Giles (SW)
Heeley, Brian (Percussion SE)
Hockings, David (Lon)
Hood, Ian (NW)
Hood, James (Mid)
Horne, Richard (Lon)
Innes, Lorna (Percussion Sco)
Jackson, Heather (NE)
John, Isabel (Sco)
Keszei, Janos (Lon)
Kindleysides, Judy (NE)
Little, Jeremy (SW)
Moate, John (NW)
Palmer, Timothy (Percussion SE)
Peadar (NW)
Philbert, Paul (Lon)
Poulter, John (Sco)
Rigby, Gordon (Sco)
Roach, Simon (Sco)
Sandilands, Iain (Sco)
Seacome, Diggory (SW)
Sinclair, Cameron Roy (Percussion Lon)
Vallis, Paul (Lon)
Whettam, Andrew (Percussion NW)
Williams, Timothy (NW)

UILLEANN

Lim, David (NW)
O'Grady, James (E)

UKELELE

Crofts, David (SE)
Kerr, Anthony (Lon)
Pyne, Martin (E)

VIOLA

Anstey, Kathryn (NW)
Appel, Susan (E)
Atkins, Jane (Lon)
Bateman, Anthony (NW)
Bell, Elizabeth (Lon)
Benjamin, Rachel (Lon)
Bennett, Christina (SW)
Bicknell, Susan (Lon)
Blew, Douglas (SE)
Bonetti, Angela (Lon)
Borthwick, Sophia (Lon)
Bradley, Karen (Lon)
Brien, Juliet (E)
Brooker, David (Lon)
Brown, Harvey (Lon)
Brown, Sally A (SE)
Bucknall, Joan (Lon)
Bull, Christine (SW)
Busbridge, Judith (Lon)
Carlile, Brian (NW)

Carney, Adele (Lon)
Cashin, Janice (NW)
Cassells, Linda (Sco)
Chamberlain, Ian (Mid)
Chapman, Andrea (Mid)
Child, Ann (Lon)
Clarke, Robert (SW)
Cochrane, Christopher (Lon)
Cohen, Ross (SW)
Cohen, Ruth (Lon)
Compton, Matthew (NW)
Constable, Caitlin (NW)
Cooper, Veronica (Sco)
Cornford, Daniel (Lon)
Coyle, Jayne (NW)
Crabtree, Richard (Violin SW)
Crane, Alice (Mid)
Cross, Charles (Lon)
Cumming, Oonagh (SE)
Del Mar, Antonia (Lon)
Demmel, Karen (Lon)
Dickinson, Scott (Lon)
Dike, Giovanna (NE)
Edwards, Genene (Composer Lon)
Else, Pam (NE)
Emanuel, Elizabeth (Lon)
Fairhurst, Naomi (Lon)
Ferreira (NW)
Fraser, Nicolette (E)
Frith, Emily (Lon)
Fuse, Kenji (Lon)
Gaffney, Naomi (SW)
Galbraith, Joanna (Sco)
Gale, Jacoba (SE)
Gillett, Andrew (SW)
Green, Stuart (SE)
Greswell, John (E)
Griffin, Elizabeth (SE)
Hadfield, Verity (SW)
Hall, Diana (NE)
Hall, Yvonne (Sco)
Hamilton, Joanna (Sco)
Harrison, Sheila (NE)
Heartfield, Sarah (NE)
Heather, Elizabeth (Mid)
Hebbron, Celia (NW)
Hiscox, Pamela (Mid)
Hodges, Laura (Lon)
Howson, Nicholas (Lon)
Hume, David (Lon)
Jenkinson, Micheal (Mid)
Jessop, Mary (Mid)
Jones, Sara (Lon)
Jones, Wendy (Lon)
Jopling, Juliet (Lon)
Keiller, Pearl (Lon)
Kelly, Matthew (Lon)
Ketteringham, Charles (Sco)
King, Leon (Lon)
Liepa, Janet (E)
Lim, Tze-Chian (E)
Lovell, Keith (Lon)
Mack, Sharada (Lon)
Mackenzie, Jacqui (SE)
Maclean, Gillian (Sco)
Manning, Gerald (Lon)
Masters, Brian (Lon)
Masters, Sally (SE)
Mayne, Helen (Mid)
McColl, Elizabeth (Sco)
McMurdo, Stewart (Sco)
McWhirter, Nicola (Sco)
Miles, Bethan (NW)
Morris, Catherine (NE)
Morrissey, Clare (NW)

Mountain, January (SW)
Newton, Laura (NE)
Newton, Pamela (NW)
Norman, Heather (Sco)
Norris, Susan (Lon)
Parfitt, Sarah (Lon)
Parsonage, Vincent (NE)
Pattenden, Jacqueline (SW)
Pelly, Mysie (Viola Sco)
Percy, Rebecca (SE)
Perkin, Janet (Mid)
Prentice, Thomas (Lon)
Prescott, Cordelia (NE)
Pridgeon-Heller, Tanya (SE)
Pullman, James (Lon)
Reece, Eilen (Lon)
Renshaw, Sophie (Lon)
Rice, Cecily (NW)
Robertson, Fiona (Sco)
Robinson, Anne (NE)
Rogers, John (Lon)
Rose, Peter (Mid)
Sanderson, Rosemary (Lon)
Seymour, Marion (Lon)
Shaw, Linda (NW)
Shorrocks, Robert (NE)
Sidgreaves, Joan (SW)
Smith, Andrew (Lon)
Snowdon, Andrea (NE)
Soni, Jean (NW)
Soothill, Fiona (NW)
Sweet, Fay (Lon)
Taylor, Peter (SW)
Theo, Lucy (Lon)
Thomas, Linda (SW)
Valdimarsdottir, Asdis (Lon)
Van-Weede, Benedict (SW)
Varlow, Elizabeth (Lon)
Vogel, Dorothea (Lon)
Walker, Jake (Lon)
Wallington, Heather (NW)
Wardman, Vicci (Lon)
Ware, Rebecca (SE)
Warrilow, Kenneth (NW)
Watson, Joy (Mid)
Welch, Alison (NW)
Wellington, Christopher (Lon)
White, Bruce (Lon)
Wiggins, Martin (Sco)
Wilks, Rachel (SW)
Williams, Dorothy (NW)
Williams, Paul (E)
Williamson, Felicity (Lon)
Williamson, Malcolm (Lon)
Wilson, Rona (NE)
Woods, Jacquelyn (Lon)
Worthington, Judith (Sco)
Wren, Katherine (Sco)
Wyly, Elizabeth (NE)
Yendole, Lucy (Lon)
Young, Keith (SW)
Zarb, Nikos (Lon)

VIOLIN

Acton, Jonathan (Lon)
Aitchison, Duncan (Sco)
Akroyd, Karen (E)
Alburger, Mary (Viola Sco)
Alderton, Stuart (Lon)
Alexander, James (Sco)
Allen, Susanna (Saxophones Lon)
Allen-Smith, Catherine (Mid)
Allin, Ralph (Mid)
Allison, Malcolm (Lon)
Allison, Susan (NE)

Alzapiedi, Dania (NW)
Archard, Joanna (Lon)
Armitage, Shahla (NW)
Arsenault, Terry (SE)
Askew, Katy (Mid)
Aston, Susan (Mid)
Atkinson, Julia (Lon)
Auty, Karen (NW)
Avery, Dennis (Mid)
Azulek, Celi (Viola Lon)
Baddeley, Jonathan (Mid)
Baddeley, Raymond (Mid)
Baden, Barbara (NW)
Bailie, Kathryn (Sco)
Baker, Robert (SW)
Ballara, Carlo (Lon)
Ballard, Philippa (Lon)
Banks, Anthony (NW)
Bannister, Julius (Viola Lon)
Barker, Kaye (Lon)
Barnes, Charles (NW)
Barry, Edward (Lon)
Bartel-Brown, Justin (Lon)
Bass, Elizabeth (NW)
Bayley, Paulette (NW)
Beales, Jon (Sco)
Beaman, David (Lon)
Belton, Catherine (Lon)
Benham, Bill (Lon)
Bennet, John (NE)
Bennett, Bob (SW)
Bennett, Frances (SW)
Beresford, Peter (Vibraphone Lon)
Bergersen, Elisa (E)
Berry, Gillian (SW)
Betteridge, Lisa (SW)
Bevan, Louise (Lon)
Bezkorvany, Sergei (Lon)
Bickel, Maya (Lon)
Biddle, Georgina (NE)
Binks, Elizabeth (Lon)
Birchall, Kate (Lon)
Birks, Heather (Viola Lon)
Bishop, Sean (Viola Lon)
Biss, Hannah (Lon)
Bithel, Karen (NE)
Black, Catherine (SW)
Black, Julia (Early Strings NW)
Bladen, Anthony (SW)
Blinkhorn, Anna (NW)
Blunt, Alison (Lon)
Blythe, Astrid (Sco)
Bolton, Malcolm (Sco)
Bome, Helen (E)
Booth, Trevor (NE)
Boothroyd, Edward (NW)
Bowles, Tina (Lon)
Bowran, Susan (Lon)
Boyfield, Rachel (NE)
Boyle, Rebecca (Lon)
Brackley Jones, Helen (NE)
Bradley, Anna (Lon)
Bradley, Jeremy (NW)
Bradley, Martin (Mid)
Bradshaw, Heather (Mid)
Brandon, John (Lon)
Bridges, Helen (NW)
Britten, John (Mid)
Britton, Amanda (NW)
Brocklehurst, Julia (Lon)
Brooks, Vyvyan (Mid)
Broome, Marcus (Lon)
Broome, Noel (NE)
Brown, Abigail (Lon)
Brown, Brian (Music Director E)

Brown, Christine (NE)
Bruce, Arthur (Sco)
Bryant, Toni (Lon)
Bryce, Morven (Lon)
Buckley, Sylvia (Mid)
Bulcock, Maritza (Viola Lon)
Bull, Geoffrey (Mid)
Bultz, Jane (SE)
Burchell, Judith (Lon)
Burgess, Jane (Mid)
Burns, Catriona (Mid)
Burns, Edward (SW)
Burrage, Martin (NW)
Butler, Holly (Viola Lon)
Butler, Lucy (NW)
Butt, Edmund (Lon)
Button, Philip (Sco)
Button, Sarah (Lon)
Byron, Freda (Viola NE)
Caesar, Angela (Lon)
Cairney, Alan (Double Bass Sco)
Caldi, Claudia (Lon)
Calthorpe, Emer (Lon)
Calvert, Robin (Sco)
Campbell, Clare (NE)
Campbell, Stephen (Guitars NE)
Campbell-Kelly, Peter (Sco)
Campton, Rosemary (Lon)
Cantoni, Michele (Lon)
Cantrill, Lucy (Lon)
Carey, Louise (Mid)
Carpenter, Elizabeth (Lon)
Carpenter, Julia (Sco)
Carter, Lara (SE)
Carvell, Susan (Lon)
Chalk, Simon (Mid)
Challoner, Peter (NE)
Chambers, Catherine (NE)
Chambers, Stephanie (Viola Lon)
Chandru (Lon)
Chappell, Clare (SW)
Charlesworth, Adrian (Lon)
Chasey, Vivien (NW)
Chater, Jennifer (Mid)
Chatterton, Josephine (NE)
Chisholm, Barbara (NE)
Chivers, Mark (Viola NW)
Churchill, Caroline (Lon)
Clark, Graham (NW)
Clark, Peter (NE)
Clarke, Barbara (E)
Clarke, David (Mid)
Clegg, Philip (NE)
Clement-Smith, Helen (E)
Clements, Heather (SE)
Cleveland, Anthony (Lon)
Clissold, Helen (Lon)
Coates, Emily (Lon)
Coates, Thomas (NE)
Cochrane, Helen (Lon)
Cockroft, Anna (SW)
Cohen, Mary (Mid)
Cole, Dennis (SW)
Coleman, Rebecca (Lon)
Coles, James (Lon)
Collier, Susan (Lon)
Collinge-Hill, Lucy (Mid)
Colyer, Ronald (SE)
Concannon Hodges, Nicholas (Lon)
Connors, Clare (Lon)
Constable, Jennifer (SW)
Constantine, Benjamin (Lon)
Cooke, Eleanor (Mid)
Cooley, Catherine (NE)
Cooper, David (NE)

Cooper, John (NE)
Corcoran, Tony (NE)
Cormican, Karen (Lon)
Couldridge, Richard (Lon)
Coultas, Michael (SW)
Course, Gail (SE)
Cowan, Lucy (Sco)
Cowdy, Judith (NW)
Crabb, Elizabeth (Mid)
Crafer, Rachel (Lon)
Crawford, Janet (SW)
Crooke, Elizabeth (E)
Crooks, Margaret (SW)
Cucchiara, Antonio (Lon)
Curiel, Jennifer (E)
Currie, Leslie (Sco)
Curteis, Jason (Viola NW)
Curteis, Patricia (Viola NW)
Cutter, Michael (SE)
D'Almeida, Dale (SW)
D'Souza, Fiona (Mid)
Dalgleish, David James (Sco)
Dally, Angela (Lon)
Dalton, Christine (Lon)
Daly, Declan (Lon)
Damerell, Benjamin (Lon)
David, Vanessa (Lon)
Davidson, Ian (Mid)
Davies, Adrian (SE)
Davies, Angharad (SW)
Davies, Carolyn (Viola Lon)
Davies, Diane (NE)
Davies, Gareth (NW)
Davies, John (NW)
Davies, John (SW)
Davies, John J (Lon)
De Jesus, Elena (Mid)
De La Mare, Calina (Lon)
De Saulles, Teresa (Lon)
Dean, Joan (Mid)
Della-Verde, Guy (SE)
Dewar, Hilary (Viola NE)
Dinwoodie, Stephen (Lon)
Djachenko, Yuri (Lon)
Dodd, Mairi (Mid)
Doherty, Gerard (Sco)
Drane, Jacqueline (Lon)
Driscoll, Kim (SW)
Drury, Sarah (Lon)
Du Feu, Elizabeth (SW)
Duffin, Lesley (Sco)
Duffy, Gerald (NW)
Duffy, Margaret (NW)
Duggan, Geoffrey (Viola Mid)
Duncan, Mary J (Sco)
Dunn, Lawrence (Sco)
Dytor, Sarah (SE)
Eales, Adrian (SW)
Eaton, Sarah (NW)
Eaton, Susan (NE)
Ede, Stephanie (Lon)
Edwards, Helen (NE)
Edwards, Julie (NE)
Edwards, Juliet (Lon)
Edwards, Nigel (Lon)
Eke, Jonathan (NE)
Elder, Morag-Anne (Sco)
Elderton, Ann (Lon)
Eldridge, Kathryn (SW)
Emslie, Susan (Sco)
Eraut, Cynthia (SE)
Estruch-Lorain, Ernesto (Lon)
Evans, Elizabeth (Lon)
Faelber, Kathleen (E)
Fallowfield, Nicholas (Mid)

TEACHERS - VIOLIN

Faulkner, Jane (Lon)
Fell, Carolyn (E)
Ferguson, Jane (Sco)
Field, Patricia (Viola Sco)
Field, Thomas (NW)
Fisher, Joshua (Lon)
Fleetcroft, Martin (Viola NE)
Fleming, Charles (NE)
Fleming, Robert (Lon)
Flint, John (Mid)
Foley, Edward (Sco)
Fordyce, Emily (SE)
Forester, Helen (Viola SE)
Foster, Claire (Lon)
Foster, Jill (NE)
Francis, David (Lon)
Franz, Beth (Lon)
Fraser, Rosemary (SE)
French, Rita (SE)
Froomes, Janet (SE)
Fuchs, Antonia (Lon)
Funnell, Ruth (Lon)
Gaby (Lon)
Gallagher, Charlotte (SE)
Gandy, Judith (Mid)
Garrick, Christian (Lon)
Geradine, Kay (E)
Gibbs, Robert Whysall (Lon)
Gibson, Jerre (Sco)
Gibson, Philip (Lon)
Giddey, Anna (Lon)
Gilchrist, Eleonor (Lon)
Giles, David (Lon)
Giles, Stephen (Viola Lon)
Gillett, Tania (Mid)
Gillies, Archibald (Sco)
Gleeson, Jane (NW)
Goddard, Caroline (Viola NE)
Godrich, Vic (Lon)
Godson, Daphne (Sco)
Goldberg, Rachelle (Lon)
Goldstein, Jennie (Lon)
Gomersall, Barry (NE)
Gomm, Jane (Lon)
Gott, Howard (Lon)
Gould, Christopher (E)
Gould, Edna (Sco)
Grajner, Erica (Lon)
Grant, Barbara (Lon)
Grant, Miriam (Lon)
Grattan, Louise (Lon)
Graudina, Anete (Lon)
Gray, Hebbie (Sco)
Gray, Michael Antony (Lon)
Green, Jan (Viola Sco)
Greenwood, Beverley (NW)
Griffiths, Dominic (Lon)
Groves, Rosalyn (Lon)
Grun, Gundula (Lon)
Guest, Elizabeth (Lon)
Gwynn, Ceredig (NW)
Hadwen, David (Mid)
Hadwen, Richard (Mid)
Hale, Brian (Sco)
Hall, Susan (NW)
Hall, Sylvia (SE)
Halstead, Christian (Lon)
Hamerton, Susan (Lon)
Hamilton, Annemauraide (NW)
Hamilton, Claire (Viola Sco)
Hamlin, Julian (Lon)
Hardie, Alastair (Sco)
Harding, Rachel (NE)
Hargreaves, Brenda (NW)
Harkess, Lynda (Sco)

Harper, Elizabeth (Viola Lon)
Harper, Villia (Mid)
Harris, Amelia (Viola Lon)
Hart, Catherine (Lon)
Hatrick, Sara (Sco)
Hawkins, Clare (NW)
Haxworth, Jessica (SE)
Hayes, Victor (NW)
Heacock, Richard (SE)
Head, Philip (Mid)
Head, Rosemary (E)
Heald, Sarah (NW)
Heanue, Teresa (Lon)
Heath, Juliette (Lon)
Hebbron, Celia (NW)
Hemming, Katherine (E)
Henbest, Rosemary (Lon)
Hennessey, Andrew (Electric Violin Sco)
Hess, Rachel (Lon)
Hewitt, Michael (SE)
Heyman, Paul (Electric Violin Lon)
Hickman, Victor (NE)
Hicks, Janet (Lon)
Hill, Jackie (Mid)
Hillier, Marion (NE)
Hilton, Christopher (NE)
Hodges, Laura (Lon)
Holding, Sian (NW)
Holmes, Jill (Viola NW)
Holmes, Sophia (SW)
Honore, Philippe (Lon)
Hooley, Ann (Lon)
Hooper, Barbara (SE)
Horne, Gabrielle (NW)
Hounam, John-Lawrence (Lon)
Howard, Francis (SW)
Howes, Charlotte (NE)
Howitt, Tricia (Viola NW)
Huber, Colin (Lon)
Huby, Mary (NE)
Huggett-Ling, Fiona (Lon)
Hughes, James (Mid)
Hughes, Martin (Sco)
Hunter, Jane (NW)
Hussey, Stephen (Lon)
Hutchings, Nicola (Lon)
Hutton, James (NW)
Ingram, Michael (NE)
Ingram, Sheila (NE)
Ings, Elizabeth (SE)
Innes, Grahame (Lon)
Ions, Hilary (NE)
Isaac, Kathleen (SE)
Isaacs, Maurice (Lon)
Izzett, Sarah (SW)
Jackson, Rachel (Lon)
Jacobs, Rachel (NW)
Jessopp, Angela (Lon)
Johnson, Amanda (NE)
Johnson, David (Percussion Lon)
Johnson, Simon (Viola Sco)
Johnson, Tom (SW)
Jones, Derek (SE)
Jones, Elizabeth (Sco)
Jones, Frances (Viola Mid)
Jones, Justin (Lon)
Jones, Lesley (Mid)
Jones, Mary (Lon)
Jones, Rebecca (Lon)
Jordan, Susanna (NW)
Jorysz, Walter (NE)
Joyce, David (Mid)
Jutton, Maureen (SW)
Kavina, Vabiz (Lon)
Keir, Douglas (Sco)

Kellett, Michael (SE)
Kelly, Wendi (Viola Lon)
Kemp, Thomas (Lon)
Kerr, Elaine (Sco)
Kerr, Emma (E)
Kerr, Harry (Lon)
Kershaw, Elizabeth (SW)
Khoo, Christine (Cello SW)
King, Barbara (SE)
King, Bridget (NE)
King, Diane (NE)
King, Jenny (Lon)
Kirby, Anne-Marie (Lon)
Kirby, Susan (NW)
Kitchen, Robert (E)
Knight, Mark (Lon)
Koco, Raimonda (NE)
Kok, Darrell (Lon)
Kramer-Gabriel, Miriam (Lon)
Kuo, Nicolette (Lon)
Kurosinski, Margaret (NE)
Kyriakou, Maria (Mid)
Lambert, Chris (Mid)
Langford, Lynda (NW)
Langford, Oliver (Lon)
Lansom, Mark (NW)
Larkin, Michael (Sco)
Latham, Christopher (Sco)
Latham, Katy (SW)
Laulund, Jorge (Lon)
Lavigne, Berenice (Lon)
Lawrance, Nicholas (NE)
Lawrence, Della K (Mid)
Lawrence, Douglas (Sco)
Leach, Sarah (Mid)
Leary, Valerie (NE)
Leary, William (NE)
Leaver, Richard (Lon)
Lee, Hai (NW)
Lefaux, Georgina (NE)
Leighton, Lindsay (Lon)
Leighton-Jones, Juliet (Lon)
Leitch, Lorna (Sco)
Levitas, Diana (E)
Levy, Mark (SE)
Levy, Nicholas (Lon)
Lewis, David (Lon)
Lewis, Paul (Lon)
Lewis-Lim, Claire (E)
Lichtenstern, Dorit (Viola Lon)
Lilly, Rosemary (Lon)
Linklater, Andrew (Sco)
Lishak, Bertha (Lon)
Little, Owen (Viola NW)
Littlewood, Graeme (Mid)
Lloyd, Jeff (SW)
Lloyd, Maria (Mid)
Lock, Simon (Lon)
Long, Andrew (NW)
Loston, Dale (Lon)
Loynes, Katherine (Lon)
Lucchesi, Dudley (SW)
Ludlow, John (Lon)
Lundberg, Rosemary (Viola Lon)
Lycett, David (Mid)
Lynn, Geoffrey (Lon)
Lyons, Harry (Lon)
Lyons, Shara (Voice Lon)
Macdonald, Anne (Sco)
Mackay, Gordon (Lon)
Mackison, Rachel (Sco)
Maguire, Jack (SE)
Maguire, Teresa (Lon)
Maher, Rachel (Lon)
Mainwaring, Richard (SW)

Major, Willett (Mid)
Mallock, Sarah (Lon)
Mann, Jeanne (Lon)
Manning, Judy (Viola Lon)
Maplestone, Trevor (SW)
Margeson, Jane (Lon)
Marjoram, Elizabeth (Mid)
Marleyn, Denise (Lon)
Marsden, Harvey (NE)
Martin, Mary (Lon)
Martin, Paul (Viola Lon)
Marx, Julian (Viola Sco)
Masarachi, Robert (Lon)
Mason, Frances (Lon)
Mathieson, Eleanor (Lon)
Matley, Edward (NE)
Matthews, Sarah (Mid)
Mattner, Audrey (Sco)
Maunder, Guera (Sco)
Maxwell, Vera (SW)
McCague, Catherine (E)
McConkey, Elizabeth (Lon)
McConnell, Arthur (SE)
McCool, Annamaria (NE)
McCusker, Kelly (Mid)
McFarlane, Clare (NW)
McGarva, Andrew (Sco)
McInally, Sian (NW)
McIntosh, Rosalind (Lon)
McKinnon, Andrew (SW)
McLaren, Linda (Lon)
McNab, William (Sco)
McNulty, John (Mid)
Meare, Annabelle (SW)
Measures, Ann (Lon)
Medrow, Alan (Viola Lon)
Melhuish, Laura (Lon)
Melville, Elizabeth (Lon)
Meyer, Daniel (Lon)
Meyer, Maurice (Lon)
Miller, Marisa (SE)
Milne, Julia (Lon)
Mitchell, Emma (SE)
Monnington, Ann (Lon)
Monument, Julie (Lon)
Moore, Andrew (Mid)
Morgan, Annette (Viola SW)
Morgan, Peter (SE)
Moroney, Helena (Sco)
Morris, Alan (SW)
Morris, Andrea (E)
Morris, Stephen (Lon)
Morrison, Anne (Viola Lon)
Morrison, Kirsten (Lon)
Morse, Jane (SW)
Moseley, Margaret (NE)
Mould, Cheryl (SE)
Mountain, Paul (NE)
Muir, Susan (Sco)
Mullin, Daniel (Lon)
Muncey, Catherine (NW)
Munks, Pamela (E)
Murphy, Aubrey (Lon)
Murphy, David (Viola E)
Murthwaite, Carol (NE)
Myerscough, Nadia (Lon)
Nagle, Susan (Mid)
Neil, Renee (Sco)
Neller, Dawn (Lon)
Newcombe, Karin (Lon)
Newman, Peter (Lon)
Newton, Ingrid (Viola NW)
Noakes, Claire (NW)
Nobes, Pauline (Lon)
Noble, Bethan (Mid)

Noley (Lon)
Norman, Helen (Lon)
Norton, Fiona (NE)
Nunn, Patrick (Composer Lon)
O'Connor, Mary (Lon)
O'Riordan, Colin (Sco)
Oliver, Robert (NE)
Olyver, Marianne (Lon)
Osahn, Prabjote (Lon)
Ovenden, Elizabeth (Lon)
Owen, Martin (Lon)
Pacey, Fiona (Viola NE)
Pagulatos, Antonia (Lon)
Palmer, Rebecca (Lon)
Pantin, Rachel (Lon)
Parfitt, Claire (Lon)
Parham, Barbara (Viola NE)
Parish, Byron (Mid)
Parkin, Claire (Lon)
Paske, Katy (E)
Patience, Elaine (SE)
Patrick, Anne (Viola SW)
Pattenden, Jacqueline (SW)
Pattinson, Susannah (Lon)
Peacock, Louise (NW)
Peake, Alexandra (Sco)
Pearce, Andrew (Tuba Lon)
Pearson, Gill (NE)
Peet, Joe B (Lon)
Pelling, Kate (Mid)
Pelly, Mysie (Sco)
Percivall, Mabel (Lon)
Perkins, Simon (Lon)
Perry, Vicky (SE)
Phillips, Sian (SW)
Pigott, Raymond (NE)
Pigott, Sheila (NE)
Pitchford, Clare (Mid)
Pollard, Clare (SE)
Poole, Penelope (SE)
Pooley, Alison (Lon)
Powell, Derek (SE)
Pratley, Alice (Lon)
Prescott, Raymond (Lon)
Preston, Joyce (SW)
Price, Helina (SW)
Pryce, Melody (SE)
Quillen, Jean (Viola SE)
Rafferty, Mary (NE)
Raybould, Clare (Lon)
Rea, Jake (Lon)
Reagan, Samantha (Lon)
Reed, Ashley (SE)
Reid, Caroline (Lon)
Reid, Edmund (Lon)
Reid, Jane (Sco)
Reid, Nan (Viola Sco)
Reid, Shelagh (Sco)
Reilly, Brian (NE)
Renhard, Jack (NE)
Renwick, Charles (Lon)
Rhodes, Linda (Mid)
Richardson, Joanna (NE)
Richardson, Martin (NW)
Richey, Angela (Mid)
Richter, Mariette (Lon)
Ridley, Anthony (NW)
Riley, David (NE)
Roberts, Rosemary (Lon)
Robertson, Kirstie (SE)
Robertson, Mhairi (Sco)
Robinson, John (Sco)
Robinson, William (Lon)
Roby, Peter (E)
Rochester, Percy (Saxophones NE)

Rodden, Andrew (Sco)
Rodgers, Simon (Guitars SE)
Rogers, Elen (NW)
Rollin, Lisa Voice (Lon)
Rossi, Davide (SW)
Rossi, Liz (NW)
Rowe, Elizabeth (Lon)
Rowe, Janet (E)
Rushworth, Abigail (Lon)
Ryan, Cliodhna (Lon)
Ryan, John (Lon)
Rye, Anthony (Lon)
Salinger, Anne (Lon)
Sanderson, Sally (SE)
Sankey, Claire-Louise (Lon)
Saunt, Lucy (SW)
Savage, Alastair (Sco)
Sawyer, Margaret (NE)
Sawyers, Philip (Lon)
Saxl, Julian (Lon)
Scheuer, Betty (Mid)
Schlaiffer, Don (SW)
Schmeising, Evelyn (SE)
Schofield, Catherine (Lon)
Schrecker, Peter (SW)
Schweinberger, Silvia (Lon)
Scott, Catherine (Mid)
Scott, Farran (Lon)
Scott, Hector (Sco)
Scott, Kirsteen (Mid)
Seal, Michael (Mid)
Sears, John (SW)
Seldis, Francesca (SW)
Sephton, Eileen (SE)
Sewart, Charles (Lon)
Shackelton, Louise (Lon)
Sharp, Louise (Mid)
Sharpe, Nigel (Lon)
Sharples, Joyce (NW)
Shave, Katherine (Viola Lon)
Shaw, Michael (Mid)
Shaw, Ronald (Sco)
Sheldon, Glen (Lon)
Silverbrooke, Ceinwen (Mid)
Silverston, Anita (SW)
Simans, Kathleen (Sco)
Simpson, Susan (Sco)
Sinclair, Christine (Sco)
Skeaping, Roderick (Composer Lon)
Slade, Andrew (NE)
Smith, Abigail (Mid)
Smith, Andrew James Thomas (Lon)
Smith, Graham (SW)
Smith, Ian (SE)
Smith, Keith (SE)
Smith, Martin (E)
Smith, Maureen (Lon)
Smith, Roger (Lon)
Smith, Simon (Lon)
Smyth, Hilary (Sco)
Smyth, Julia (SW)
Snape, Richard (Mid)
Snow, Ursula (Lon)
Solarek, Marina (Lon)
Sonneveld, Martin (SE)
Spencer, Eileen (NE)
Spurrell, Jill (Mid)
Stacey, Brenda (SW)
Stait, Anya (SW)
Stait, Brien (SE)
Stanbury, Rosemary (SW)
Stanley, Helen B (Lon)
Staveley, Colin (Lon)
Stear, Kate (SE)
Stephen, Rosahund (SW)

Stephenson, Anne (Lon)
Stevens, Ashley (Lon)
Stewart, Julia (Lon)
Stewart, Lois (Sco)
Stokes, Helen (NW)
Stott, Rachel (Early Strings Lon)
Strachan, Andrew (Sco)
Strachan, Johanna (Electric Violin SE)
Stratton, Craig (Lon)
Strike, Sarah (SW)
Strong, Rae (Recorders NE)
Strong, Roger (Mid)
Stubbs, Christine (NE)
Sturt, Hilary (Lon)
Stutzer, Ernestine (Viola Lon)
Sutherland, Rhona (Sco)
Sutton, Sylvia (NE)
Swarbrick, Simon (SW)
Symons, Tamsin (NE)
Tann, Elsie (Mid)
Tarlton, Gillian (Lon)
Tattersdill, Rona (Viola Mid)
Taylor, Esther (Viola NW)
Taylor, Imogen (Lon)
Taylor, Sheila (NW)
Taylor, Susan (SE)
Tendler, Ronald (SE)
Tennant, Sophia (Lon)
Teo-Wa (Lon)
Terry, Diane (E)
Thoday, Janet (Mid)
Thomas, Alun (Lon)
Thomas, Clive (Sco)
Thomas, George (SW)
Thomas, Kenneth (Lon)
Thomas, Vivian (SW)
Thompson, Billy (SW)
Thompson, Michael (NE)
Thompson, Rebecca (NW)
Thormahlen, Wiebke (Lon)
Thorn, Jennifer (Lon)
Tilley, Sarah (Lon)
Tir, Kayleigh (Viola Lon)
Toms, Thomas (Lon)
Toney, Elizabeth (Mid)
Tonson-Ward, Maxwell (NE)
Topping, John (SE)
Tordoff, Helen (NE)
Townsend, Joe (Lon)
Trentham, Julie (Lon)
Turnbull, Kate (SE)
Turnlund, Martin (Lon)
Underhill, Jennifer (Lon)
Underwood, Brian (Lon)
Underwood, James (SE)
Van Ments, Elizabeth (Lon)
Van-Ingen, Judith (NW)
Vance, Simon (NW)
Vaughan, Kerry (Lon)
Vince, Carina (Lon)
Voigt, Sarah (Lon)
Wadsworth, Sonya (NW)
Walker, Jayne (E)
Wallace, Bridget (Lon)
Walters, Louise (Lon)
Warburton, Jillian (Lon)
Waterhouse, Celia (Lon)
Waterworth, Kate (Lon)
Watkinson, Andrew (NE)
Watmough, Katherine (NE)
Watson, George (SE)
Watson, Kitty (Sco)
Weale, Stephen (E)
Wearne, Amelia (Viola SE)
Weeks, Sally-Ann (Lon)

West, Helen (NE)
West, Joanna (Lon)
Wheeler, Geoffrey (Mid)
White, Alison (SE)
White, Janice (Lon)
White, Nicola (Lon)
White, Rosemary (Mid)
White, Sarah (Lon)
Whitehead, Elaine (Lon)
Whitfield, Lawrence (Lon)
Whitford, Dorothy (NE)
Wilde, Richard (NW)
Wileman, Eric (Viola Mid)
Wilkinson, Ann (SE)
Williams, Robin (Lon)
Williams, Rosemary (SW)
Williamson, Heather (SE)
Willoughby, Brenda (SW)
Wilson, Brian Lloyd (Lon)
Wilson, Katherine (Lon)
Wilson, Marina (Lon)
Winfield, Catriona (Sco)
Winter, Philip (Lon)
Witkowsky, Mario (Lon)
Wolstonholme, Edward (NE)
Wood, Beverley (SE)
Wood, Catherine (Lon)
Woodburn, Veronica (SW)
Woodsford, Patricia (SW)
Worsley, Len (Lon)
Wright, Brian (Lon)
Wright, Janet (NE)
Wright, Lucy (NW)
Wright, Mary (Viola Lon)
Wyburn, Carla (Lon)
Yates, Catherine (NW)
Youcheng (SE)
Young, Isabel (NW)
Young, Marsha (Lon)
Young, Sara (Lon)
Young, Wendy (Viola Lon)

VOICE

Ade (Lon)
Allard, Marie-Louise (Mid)
Amata, Karl (Keyboards Lon)
Anderson, Birgitte (NW)
Arden-Griffith, Paul (Lon)
Askew, Rebecca (Lon)
Auty, Rachel (Lon)
Babington, Susan (NE)
Baker, Lois (NW)
Bancroft, Sophie (Sco)
Barnes, Derek (Music Director Lon)
Barr, Stuart (Conductor Lon)
Barrett, Annette (Mid)
Barstad, Ingeborg (Lon)
Beard, Alison (Lon)
Beard, Susan (Lon)
Bennett, Rachel (Lon)
Boyland, Stephen (NW)
Braithwaite, Tracey (Sco)
Brebner, Alexander (Sco)
Brooks, Lorna (Sco)
Brown, Lisa (Lon)
Brown, Rosanna (NE)
Brydon-Phillips, Mary (Lon)
Burrowes, Margaret (Lon)
Buttolph, Katharine (Mid)
Caine, Angela (SE)
Callan, Margaret (Sco)
Canale, Donna (Lon)
Carmel, Heather (Lon)
Carter, Elinor (SE)
Cartney, Jane (SE)

Cassell, Debbie (Lon)
Catterall, Deborah (NW)
Chiotis, Zoe (Mid)
Clarke, Maurice (Lon)
Clutson, Steven (SW)
Collins, Jo (Lon)
Colman, Sara (Mid)
Constantine, Helen (Lon)
Cooper, Dorothy (SE)
Cotterill, Marianne (Lon)
Cragg, Eileen (Lon)
Daisical, Laka (Lon)
Dale, Josie (Lon)
Danzig, Karen (Lon)
Darennth, Suzanne (Lon)
Davies, Claire (Lon)
Davies, Kimberley (NW)
Davies, Mary (SW)
Dawe, Judi (Lon)
De La Poer, Petra (Mid)
De Peyer, Lorrayn (Lon)
Dell (Lon)
Denis, Carol (Lon)
Depass, Michele (Lon)
Dewey, Clare (NW)
Dickov, Caroline (Sco)
Dietrich, Simone (Lon)
Dinning, Judy (NE)
Dobie, Allyson (E)
Douglas, Stacey-Jane (Lon)
Dovaston, Isabella (Sco)
Duncan, Fionna (Sco)
Dunn, Julie (Lon)
Easton, Lydia (SE)
Edwards, Carlton (Pianoforte Lon)
Edwards, Janet (Lon)
Edwards, Nicola (Composer SW)
Evans, Dan (Guitars SE)
Evans, Peter (SE)
Evans, Stephanie (SW)
Evelyn, Alison (Song Writer Lon)
Everitt, Craig (NE)
Exley, Heather (Lon)
Fardell, Sandra (SW)
Fenton, Paula (E)
Fergusson, Harriet (Lon)
Fletcher, Liz (Lon)
Franklin, Ben (Lon)
Frayling-Kelly, Nigel (Sco)
Freeman, Sue-Lee (NE)
French, Sally (NE)
Gair, Robin (SW)
Gayle, Godfrey (Mid)
Geneves, Jean-Jacques (Guitars Lon)
Gibson, Lee (Lon)
Goldsmith, Sally (Mandolin NE)
Goll, Achemedes (Lon)
Gray, Suzanne (Lon)
Hamilton, Timothy (SE)
Harding-Chestney, Kaytie (SE)
Harkin, Holly (NE)
Harley, Dan (Mid)
Harris, Wendy (SE)
Harvey-Piper, Penelope (Pianoforte Lon)
Henderson, Gareth (Lon)
Herail, Caroline (Lon)
Higgins, Elaine (Lon)
Higgs, Jessica (Lon)
Higham, Cynthia (SE)
Hodgkin, Keyy (E)
Hubbard, Christine (SE)
Hyatt, Marianne (Lon)
Ifan, Gareth (SW)
Jean-Paul-Denis, Patrick (Lon)
John, Jennifer (NW)

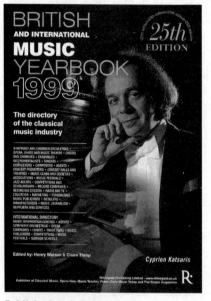

Jones, Delyth (Mid)
Jones, Sianed (E)
Joshi, Divya (Lon)
Karian, Karin (SE)
Katie Accordion (E)
Kay, Sandra (Lon)
Kelly, Juliet (Lon)
Kelman, Laura (Sco)
Kelsey, Lisa (Guitars Mid)
Kenyon, Sam (Lon)
Kerr, Sandra (Concertina NE)
Kerr-Elliott, Nancy (Folk Fiddle NE)
Khoda, Nichelle (Mid)
Kokot, Estelle (Lon)
Kully (Mid)
Kydd, Christine (Sco)
L'Estrange, Alexander (Lon)
Labbett, Julia (SE)
Laird, Jonathan (Pianoforte Mid)
Lani (Lon)
Laraway, Simone (SE)
Latham, Robert (Music Director SW)
Lawson, Ellie (Lon)
Leaf, Helen (Multi Instrumental Lon)
Lillitos, Malachi (Lon)
Lishman, Anna (SE)
Love, Danny (Lon)
Luce, Francine (Lon)
Macha, Freddy (Lon)
Mackenzie, Talitha (Sco)
Mackintosh, Stewart (Music Director Lon)
Malik, Samia (E)
Mardi, Dee (E)
Marshall, Steve (SW)
Mason, Myriam (Lon)
Mattis, Audrey (NW)
Mattu, Jaspal (Mid)
May, Tina (E)
Mayo, Sandra (Pianoforte SW)
McLaughlin, Paul (Sco)
McLellan, James (Guitars Sco)
McMahon, Geraldine (E)
McNaughton, Elizabeth (SE)
McPherson, Caroline (Lon)
Meloy, Laure (E)
Miller, Todd (Lon)
Miller, Yvonne (Lon)
Mitchell, Andrew (Lon)

Mobbs, Charlotte (Sco)
Morris, Lesley (SE)
Morris, Paulette (NE)
Morton, John (NE)
Moss Tallon, Sally-Anne (SE)
Mudeka, Anna (E)
Myers, John (Lon)
Neumayr, Elisabeth (Lon)
Nieper, Wendy (Mid)
O'Neill, Shelagh (Pianoforte NW)
O'Sullivan, Eileen (Lon)
Ogston, Bruce (Lon)
Otter-Barry, Lisa (SW)
Owen, Johathan (Lon)
Pace, Julie (Pianoforte Mid)
Page, Felicity (Lon)
Pandit, Vishwa (Lon)
Partington, Gitika (Lon)
Pattison, Andrea (NE)
Pellius, Everis (Lon)
Perry, Nina (Lon)
Polack, Margaret (Mid)
Pownall, Gordon (Keyboards E)
Proudlove, Kate (Mid)
Quin, Sue (NW)
Quinlan, Kevin (Pianoforte Lon)
Randell, Andrew (Mid)
Reeves, Kevin (Lon)
Richardson, Susan (Lon)
Rix, Delrae (Lon)
Romeo, Jennifer (Lon)
Rosato, Tania (E)
Rowley, Jacqueline (Pianoforte Mid)
Russell, Juliet (NW)
Russell-Cowan, Lynne (SW)
Rust, Tom (Lon)
Ryall, Imogen (Pianoforte Lon)
Sabedoria, Alison (Mid)
Sanders, Bev (NW)
Shaw, Teresa (SE)
Shea, Elizabeth (SE)
Sheppard, Helen (SE)
Shin (Mid)
Smith, Marilyn (Sco)
Smith, Maureen (Lon)
South, Zoe (Lon)
Spilling, James (Lon)
Sproston, Trevor (Mid)

Stratton, Cindy (SW)
Swallow, Deborah (Lon)
Swan, Karen (SW)
Sylvi-D (SE)
Tanjy (SW)
Tayus (Lon)
Thomas, Annemarie (Pianoforte Lon)
Thompson, Caroline (Cello SE)
Tobin, Christine (Lon)
Tormann, John (Lon)
Tozer, Cathy (Lon)
Tyndall, Debby (SE)
Wade, Anthony (Pianoforte Lon)
Wade, David (Lon)
Wager, Henrik (Lon)
Walwyn, David (Lon)
Ward, Gill (E)
Webb, Bruce (Composer E)
Webb, Helen (Lon)
Webster, Patience (Mbira Lon)
Wedell, Rebekka (Lon)
Westerhout, Lisa (Lon)
Wilby, Rosie (Lon)
Wilkinson, Jennifer (NE)
Williams, Rob (Lon)
Williamson, Nick (Pianoforte Lon)
Wocker, Sebastian (Lon)
Woods, John (Pianoforte NW)
Woodvine-West, Joyce (Mid)
Wootton, Douglas (Early Strings Lon)
Wright, Stewart (Percussion Lon)
Yogeswaran, Manickam (Lon)

WEST AFRICAN PERCUSSION

Vickers, Diane (Percussion NW)

WOODWIND

Bidder, Helena (Oboe NW)
Deans, Robert (Saxophones Sco)
Fenn, Michelle (Oboe Sco)
Hurst, Eileen (Flute NW)
Moore, Malcolm (Clarinet NE)
Stone, Tony (Saxophones SW)
Tanner, Stephen (Flute SE)
Yates, Simeon (Clarinet NE)

Advertising Index

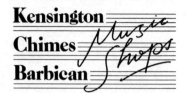

British Performing Arts Yearbook

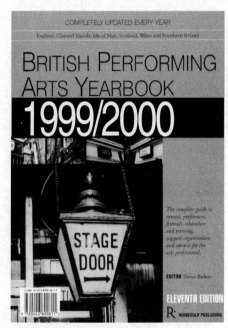

The complete guide to venues, performers, festivals, education and training, support organisations and services for the arts professional

Provides information on companies and solo performers; orchestras; jazz and light music; arts festivals; suppliers and services; plus over 1,200 venues detailing everything from stage dimensions and lighting rig to the artistic policy, booking terms and the distance to the nearest railway station.

Published each June
600 pages

HOW TO ORDER

Please send a cheque for **£27.45** (inc. p&p) payable to *Rhinegold Publishing Ltd* to: **BPAY Sales, Rhinegold Publishing, FREEPOST, London WC2H 8BR.**

TELEPHONE:	**0171 333 1721** (or 020 7333 1721 after 22 Apr 2000)
FAX:	**0171 333 1769** (or 020 7333 1769 after 22 Apr 2000)
EMAIL:	**sales@rhinegold.co.uk**
WEBSITE:	**www.rhinegold.co.uk**